DIRECTORY OF AMERICAN FIRMS OPERATING IN FOREIGN COUNTRIES

17th Edition

VOLUME 2

Alphabetical Listing of American Corporations with Foreign Operations by Country (continued)

Denmark to Macau

Pages: 1381-2752

UNIWORLD BUSINESS PUBLICATIONS, INC.
257 Central Park West, Suite 10A
New York, NY 10024-4110
Tel: (212) 496-2448
Fax: (212) 769-0413
uniworldbp@aol.com
www.uniworldbp.com

First Edition	1954
Second Edition	1957
Third Edition	1959
Fourth Edition	1961
Fifth Edition	1964
Sixth Edition	1966
Seventh Edition	1969
Eighth Edition	1975
Ninth Edition	1979
Tenth Edition	1984
Eleventh Edition	1987
Twelfth Edition	1991
Thirteenth Edition	1994
Fourteenth Edition	1996
Fifteenth Edition	1999
Sixteenth Edition	2001
Seventeenth Edition	2003

Copyright © 2003 by
Uniworld Business Publications, Inc.
257 Central Park West
New York, New York 10024
uniworldbp@aol.com
www.uniworldbp.com
ISBN: 0-8360-0047-1

Printed in the United States of America

Introduction

Since it was first published in 1955, *Directory of American Firms Operating in Foreign Countries* has been an authoritative source of information on American firms, which have branches, subsidiaries, or affiliates outside the United States. Designed to aid anyone interested in American business activities abroad, it is the only reference work of its kind. The directory has been used by public, university, business, government and special libraries, banks, accounting, brokerage and investment firms, manufacturers, transportation companies, advertising and personnel agencies, researchers, embassies and many governmental agencies dealing with commerce, trade and foreign relations.

The 17th edition contains over 3,000 U.S. firms with nearly 36,500 branches, subsidiaries and affiliates in 187 countries.

The Directory consists of three volumes

Volume 1 - Part One: lists, in alphabetical order, American firms that have operations abroad. Each entry contains the company's U.S. address, telephone/fax, NAICS (North American Industrial Codes System) and description of principal product/service, and lists the foreign countries in which it has a branch, subsidiary, or affiliate. Some key personnel are noted, when provided: Chief Executive Officer (CEO), International Operations or Foreign Operations Officer (IO), and Human Resources Director (HR). These titles are meant to be generic and are assigned to the names given to us as the Chief Executive, the person in charge of International Operations and the senior Human Resources officer. Also the web site address, annual revenue and number of employees are included, when available.

Volume 1 - Part Two, and **Volumes 2** and **3:** contain listings by country from Albania to Zimbabwe of the American firms' foreign operations. Each country listing includes, alphabetically, the name of the U.S. parent firm, address, telephone, fax, web site address, NAICS principal product/service, and the name and address of its branch, subsidiary, or affiliates in that country.

U.S. Direct Investment Abroad

The overseas companies in this specialized listing are those in which American Firms have a substantial direct capital investment and which have been identified by the parent as a wholly or partially owned subsidiary, affiliate or branch. Franchises, representatives and non-commercial enterprises or institutions, such as hospitals, schools, etc., financed or operated by American philanthropic or religious organizations, are not included.

U.S. direct dollar investment in foreign countries continued to increase by 6% for 2001, down from the average 11.3% increase reported for the years 1999-2001. The number of U.S. companies with foreign operations captured by our research has increased nearly 20% to over 3,000; however, the number of foreign subsidiaries, branches and affiliates of those U.S. companies has grown from 18,000 in our 14th edition (1996) to 36,500 in this edition. Europe remains the lead region for Direct U.S. Investments, with the UK the lead country, followed by Canada and The Netherlands.

U.S. Direct Investment Abroad - Top Countries
(Historical-cost basis in $ Billions)
U.S. Bureau of Economic Analysis, 2001

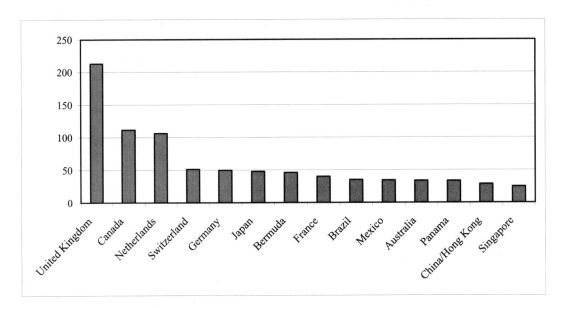

U.S. Direct Investment Abroad - by Region
(Historical-cost basis in $ Billions)
U.S. Bureau of Economic Analysis, 2001

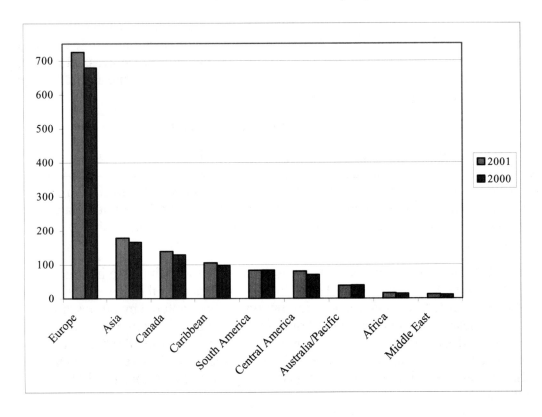

North American Industry Classification System (NAICS)

For the first time we have included a numeric industrial classification. We have chosen the North American Industry Classification System (NAICS), which has replaced the U.S. Standard Industrial Classification (SIC). The official U.S. Census Bureau listing of all NAICS is available at **www.census.gov/epcd/naics02/.**

Source and Accuracy of Listings

In preparing the 2003 - 17th edition, 800 new companies have been added, and over 300 firms which were dissolved, no longer maintain operations abroad or were acquired, have been deleted. The primary sources of information were U.S. parent company, annual reports, press releases and other public and private publications. Direct telephone and fax contact was used extensively for verification and clarification.

The aim of this listing is to provide accurate, up-to-date listings. However, the Editor and Publisher cannot guarantee that the information received from a company or other source as the basis for an entry is correct. In addition, the designations and listings are not to be considered definitive as to legal status or the relationship between the American and the foreign firms.

As extensive as this compilation may be it does not claim to be all-inclusive. It contains only what has been disclosed to us. Also in a directory of this scope some inaccuracies are inevitable. It would be appreciated if the reader noting such would inform us so corrections can be made in future editions.

Acknowledgments

Our sincere appreciation is extended to all company representatives who cooperated so generously in providing information for this directory, and to everyone who assisted in its preparation: Associate Editor Lynn Sherwood, Associate Publisher Debra Lipian, and Book Designer David Bornstein.

Barbara D. Fiorito, Editor
Uniworld Business Publications, Inc.

Company Designations

Abbreviation	Term	Country
AB	Aktiebolag	Sweden
AG	Aktiengesellschaft	Austria, Germany, Switzerland
AS	Anonim Sirketi	Turkey
A/S	Aktieselskab	Denmark
	Aksjeselskap	Norway
BV	Beslotene Vennootschap	Netherlands
CA	Compania Anonima	Venezuela
CIE	Compagnie	Belgium, France
CO/Co.	Company	Canada, England, U.S.
CORP/Corp.	Corporation	England, U.S.
GmbH	Gesellschaft mit beschrankter Haftung	Austria, Germany
INC/Inc.	Incorporated	Canada, England, U.S.
KG	Kommanditgesellschaft	Germany
KK	Kabushiki Kaisha	Japan
LTD/Ltd.	Limited	Canada, England, U.S.
MIJ	Maatschappij	Netherlands
NV	Naamloze Vennoostchap	Belgium, Netherlands
OY	Osakeyhtio	Finland
P/L	Proprietary Limited	Australia
PLC	Public Limited Company	England, Scotland
PT	Perusahaan Terbatas	Indonesia
SA	Sociedad Anonima	Argentina, Brazil, Colombia, Spain, Venezuela
	Societe Anonyme	Belgium, France, Switzerland
SARL	Societe Anonoyme a Responsabilite Limitee	Belgium, France, Switzerland
SPA	Societa per Azioni	Italy
Sp z o.o	Spolka Odpowiedzialnoscia	Poland
SPRL	Societe de Personnes a Responsabilite Limitee	Belgium
SRL	Societa a Responsabilita Limitata	Italy

Abbreviations Used in This Report

A/C	Air Conditioning
Access	Accessories
Adv	Advertising
Affil	Affiliate(d)
Agcy	Agent/Agency
Agric	Agriculture
Apt	Apartment
Arch	Architect(ural)
Assur	Assurance
Auto	Automotive
Aux	Auxiliary
Av/Ave	Avenida/Avenue
Bil	Billion
Bldg	Building
Blvd	Boulevard
Bus	Business
CEO	Chief Executive Officer
Chem	Chemical
Chmn	Chairman
Cir	Circulation
Co	Company
Col	Colonia
Com	Components
Coml	Commercial
Commun	Communications
Conslt	Consultant/Consulting
Constr	Construction
Corp	Corporate/Corporation
Cust	Customer
Dept	Department
Devel	Development
Diag	Diagnostic
Dir.	Director
Dist	District
Distr	Distributor/Distribution
Div	Division
Divers	Diversified
Dom	Domestic
Econ	Economics
Educ	Education
Elec	Electric(al)
Electr	Electronic(s)
Emp	Employee(s)
Eng	Engineer(ing)
Envi	Environmental
Equip	Equipment
EVP	Executive Vice President
Exch	Exchange
Exec	Executive
Exp	Export(er)
Explor	Exploration
Fax	Facsimile
Fin	Financial/Finance
Fl	Floor
FO	Foreign Operation(s) Officer
For	Foreign
Frt	Freight
Furn	Furniture
Fwdg	Forwarding
Gds	Goods
Gen	General
Hdqtrs/HQ	Headquarters
Hdwe	Hardware
Hwy	Highway
Hos	Hospital
HR	Human Resources Officer
Hydr	Hydraulic(s)
Imp	Import(er)
Inc	Incorporated
Ind	Industrial/Industry
Inf	Information
Ins	Insurance
Inspc	Inspect(ion)
Instru	Instrument
Intl	International
Invest	Investment
JV	Joint Venture
Lab	Laboratory
Liq	Liquid
Ltd	Limited
Mach	Machine(ry)
Maint	Maintenance
Mat	Material
Mdse	Merchandise
Mdsng	Merchandising
Meas	Measurement
Med	Medical
Mfg	Manufacturing
Mfr	Manufacture(r)
Mgmt	Management
Mgn	Managing
Mgr.	Manager
Mil	Million
Mkt	Market
Mktg	Marketing
Mng Dir	Managing Director

Mng Ptrn	Managing Partner	Rep	Representative
Mng.	Managing	Ret	Retail(er)
Nat	Natural	Rfg	Refining
NE	Northeast	Ry	Railway
No/N	North	Sci	Scientific
NW	Northwest	SE	Southeast
Oper	Operation	Serv	Service(s)
Orgn	Organization(al)	So/S	South
Pass	Passenger	Spec	Special(ty)/Specialized
Petrol	Petroleum	St/Str	Street
Pharm	Pharmaceutical(s)	Sta	Station
Plt	Plant	Ste	Suite
Prdt	Product(s)	Str	Strasse
Pres	President	Sub	Subsidiary
Prin	Principal	Super	Supervision
Print	Printing	Svce	Service(s)
Proc	Process(ing)	SVP	Senior Vice President
Prod	Production	SW	Southwest
Prog	Programming	Sys	System
Pte/Prt.	Private	Tech	Technical/Technology
Ptnr	Partner	Tel	Telephone
Pty	Proprietary	Telecom	Telecommunications
Pub	Publisher/Publishing	Temp	Temperature
R&D	Research & Development	Trans	Transmission
Rd	Road	Transp	Transport(ation)
Recre	Recreation(al)	TV	Television
Refrig	Refrigeration	VP	Vice President
Reg	Regional	Whl	Wholesale(r)
Reins	Reinsurance	Whse	Warehouse
Rel	Relations		

Notes on Alphabetizing

Alphabetizing in this directory is by computer sort which places numerals before letters; and, among names, places special characters before numbers and letters in the following order: blanks, ampersands, plus signs, dashes, periods and slashes. For example, 3Z Co. precedes A Z Co., which precedes, in the following order, A&Z Co., A+Z Co., A-Z Co., AZ Co., A/Z Co., A1Z Co. and AZ Co.

Names such as The Jones Corp., Charles Jones Inc., and L.M. Jones & Co., are alphabetized conventionally: all will be found under J. Names that consist of initials only (e.g., LFM Co.) are in strict alphabetical order : Lewis., LFM Co., Lintz Inc.

While the custom in most countries is to place company designations (Co., Inc., etc.) at the end of the firm's name, that is not always the case. For example, Finland's "Oy" and +Sweden's "AB" sometimes appear at the end and sometimes at the beginning of the company's name; in this directory they have been disregarded in alphabetizing. The reader is advised to check more than one location when looking for a firm whose listing might be affected by the company designation.

Table of Contents – Volume 2

Alphabetical Listing of American Corporations with Foreign Operations by Country (continued):

Publisher's Notes...*Related Publications*

Denmark

24 HOUR FITNESS WORLDWIDE INC.

5020 Franklin Drive, Pleasanton, CA, 94588

Tel: (925) 416-3100   Fax: (925) 416-3146   www.24hourfitness.com

Owns and manages fitness centers.

Form & Fitness Herning, Vestergade 24-26, DK-7400 Herning, Denmark

24/7 REAL MEDIA, INC.

1250 Broadway, New York, NY, 10001-3701

Tel: (212) 231-7100   Fax: (212) 760-1774   www.247media.com

Provides global online advertising, sponsorships, e-commerce and direct marketing solutions to advertisers and Web publishers.

24/7 Media Denmark, Ny Kongensgade 11, DK-1472 København K, Denmark

Tel: 45-70-247-247

3COM CORPORATION

5400 Bayfront Plaza, Santa Clara, CA, 95052-8145

Tel: (408) 326-5000   Fax: (408) 326-5001   www.3com.com

Engaged in the development and manufacture of computer networking products and systems.

3Com Nordic AB, Gydevang 39-41, DK-3450 Allerød, Denmark

Tel: 45-39-27-8500 Fax: 45-39-27-0844

3M (MINNESOTA MINING & MFG.)

3M Center, St. Paul, MN, 55144-1000

Tel: (651) 733-1110   Fax: (651) 733-9973   www.mmm.com

Mfr. diversified products for industry, consumer, health care, imaging, communications, transport, safety, etc.

3M Denmark A/S, Fabriksparken 15, DK-2600 Glostrup, Denmark

Tel: 45-43-48-0100 Fax: 45-43-96-8596

ABBOTT LABORATORIES

100 Abbott Park Rd., Abbott Park, IL, 60064

Tel: (847) 937-6100   Fax: (847) 937-1511   www.abbott.com

Development, manufacture and sale of diversified health care products and services.

Abbott Laboratories A/S, Smakkendalen 6, DK-2820 Gentofte, Denmark

Tel: 45-39-77-0000

ABS (AMERICAN BUREAU OF SHIPPING)

ABS Plaza, 16855 Northchase Drive, Houston, TX, 77060

Tel: (281) 877-6000   Fax: (281) 877-6344   www.eagle.org

Classification and certification of ships and offshore structures, development and technical assistance.

ABS Europe Ltd., St. Kongens Gade 92, DK-1264 Copenhagen K, Denmark

ACCENTURE LTD.

1345 Avenue of the Americas, New York, NY, 10105

Tel: (917) 452-4400   Fax: (917) 527-9915   www.accenture.com

Provides management and technology consulting services.

Accenture, Oslo Plads 1, DK-2100 Copenhagen Ø, Denmark

Tel: 45-33-42-2000 Fax: 45-33-42-7100

ADAC LABORATORIES, INC.

540 Alder Drive, Milpitas, CA, 95035

Tel: (408) 321-9100   Fax: (408) 321-9536   www.adaclabs.com

Mfr. cameras and equipment for nuclear medicine.

ADAC Laboratories A/S, Vandmanden 16b, DK-9200 Aalborg, Denmark

Tel: 45-98-18-3661

ADOBE SYSTEMS INCORPORATED

345 Park Avenue, San Jose, CA, 95110

Tel: (408) 536-6000   Fax: (408) 537-6000   www.adobe.com

Engaged in print technology and distributor of Acrobat Reader.

Adobe Systems Denmark A/S, Gydevang 39-41, DK-3450 Allerød København, Denmark

ADVENT SOFTWARE, INC.

301 Brannan Street, San Francisco, CA, 94107

Tel: (415) 543-7696   Fax: (415) 543-5070   www.advent.com

Mfr. portfolio software.

Advent Denmark AS, Studiestraede 30A, DK-1455 Copenhagen, Denmark

Tel: 45-33-37-6000

AIG AMERICAN INTERNATIONAL GROUP INC.

70 Pine Street, New York, NY, 10270

Tel: (212) 770-7000   Fax: (212) 509-9705   www.aig.com

Worldwide insurance and financial services.

AIG Europe S.A., Nyropsgade 47, DK-1602 Copenhagen, Denmark

AIRBORNE INC.

3101 Western Ave., PO Box 662, Seattle, WA, 98121

Tel: (206) 285-4600   Fax: (206) 281-1444   www.airborne.com

Air transport services.

Airborne Express Denmark A/S, Amager landevej 149a, DK-2770 Kastrup, Denmark

Tel: 45-702707027   Fax: 45-7027-7066

ALLEN-BRADLEY COMPANY, INC.

1201 South Second Street, Milwaukee, WI, 53204

Tel: (414) 382-2000   Fax: (414) 382-4444   www.ab.com

Mfr. electrical controls and information devices.

Allen-Bradley A/S, Herstedostervej 27-29, DK-2620 Albertslund, Denmark

AMCOL INTERNATIONAL CORPORATION

1500 West Shure Drive, Ste. 500, Arlington Heights, IL, 60004

Tel: (847) 394-8730   Fax: (847) 506-6199   www.amcol.com

Mfr. specialty chemicals and environmental bentonite products.

CETCO Europe, Ellebjergvej 39, DK-2450 Coperhagen, Denmark

AMERADA HESS CORPORATION

1185 Avenue of the Americas, New York, NY, 10036

Tel: (212) 997-8500   Fax: (212) 536-8390   www.hess.com

Crude oil and natural gas.

Amerada Hess A/S, Ostergade 26B, DK-1100 Copenhagen K, Denmark

AMETEK INC.

37 N. Valley Road, PO Box 1764, Paoli, PA, 19301-0801

Tel: (610) 647-2121   Fax: (610) 296-3412   www.ametek.com

Mfr. instruments, electric motors and engineered materials.

AMETEK A/S, Gydevang 32-34, PO Box 30, DK-3450 Allerød, Denmark

Tel: 45-48-16-8000   Fax: 45-48-16-8080

ANALOGIC CORPORATION

8 Centennial Drive, Peabody, MA, 01960

Tel: (978) 977-3000   Fax: (978) 977-6811   www.analogic.com

Design/mfr. precision measure, signal processing and imaging equipment for medical, scientific, industry and communications.

B&K Medical A/S, Sandtoften 9, DK-2820 Gentofte, Denmark

ANC RENTAL CORPORATION

200 S. Andrews Ave., Ft. Lauderdale, FL, 33301

Tel: (954) 320-4000   Fax: (954) 320-4077   www.ancrental.com

Engaged in car rental services, including National Car Rental and Alamo Rent A Car.

National Car Rental, Gammel Kongevej 70, DK-1850 Copenhagen V, Denmark

ANDERSEN

33 West Monroe Street, Chicago, IL, 60603

Tel: (312) 580-0033   Fax: (312) 507-6748   www.andersen.com

*Accounting and audit, tax and management consulting services. **Firm under worldwide reorganization; new data unavailable for this edition.*

Andersen Worldwide, Midtermolen 1, PO Box 2662, DK-2100 Copenhagen 0, Denmark

Tel: 45-35-25-2525

Andersen Worldwide, H.H. Seedorffs Straede 3-5, DK-8000 Aarhus C, Denmark

Tel: 45-86-19-5555

ANIXTER INTERNATIONAL INC..

4711 Golf Road, Skokie, IL, 60076

Tel: (847) 677-2600   Fax: (847) 677-8557   www.anixter.com

Distributor wiring systems/products for voice, video, data and power applications.

Anixter Denmark, Ringager 4C, DK-2605 Brondby, Denmark

Tel: 45-7010-8800 Fax: 45-71010-8801

AON CORPORATION

200 East Randolph, Chicago, IL, 60601

Tel: (312) 381-1000   Fax: (312) 381-6032   www.aon.com

Insurance brokers worldwide; underwrites accident and health insurance, specialty and professional insurance; and provides risk management consultation.

AON Denmark A/S, Skanderborgvej 234, DK-8260 Viby J Aarhus, Denmark

Tel: 45-86-28-8811 Fax: 45-86-28-8822 Contact: Lars Grunnet

APOGENT TECHNOLOGIES INC.

48 Congress Street, Portsmouth, NH, 03801

Tel: (603) 433-6131   Fax: (603) 431-0860   www.apogent.com

Design, mfr. & sell products for laboratories, clinical research, industrial markets & analytical products.

Nunc A/S, PO Box 280, DK-4000 Roskilde, Denmark

APPLERA CORPORATION

301 Merritt 7, Norwalk, CT, 06851

Tel: (203) 840-2000   Fax: (203) 840-2312   www.applera.com

Leading supplier of systems for life science research and related applications.

Applied Biosystems, Linde Alle 7B, DK-2850 Naerun, Denmark

Tel: 45-45-58-6000

APW, INC.

N22 W23685 Ridgeview Parkway West, Waukesha, WI, 53188-1013

Tel: (262) 523-7600   Fax: (262) 523-7624   www.apw1.com

Mfr. hi-pressure tools, vibration control products, consumables, technical furniture and enclosures.

APW Power Supply, Smedevaenget, 1-9, DK- 5560 Aarup, Denmark

ARROW ELECTRONICS INC.

25 Hub Drive, Melville, NY, 11747

Tel: (516) 391-1300   Fax: (516) 391-1640   www.arrow.com

Distributor of electronic components and computer products.

Arrow Denmark, Smedeholm 13A, DK-2730 Herlev, Denmark

Microtronica Denmark A/S, Mileparken 20E, DK-274 Skovlunde, Denmark

Tel: 45-44-50-8100   Fax: 45-44-50-8110

ASHLAND OIL INC.

50 E. RiverCenter Blvd., Box 391, Covington, KY, 41012-0391

Tel: (859) 815-3333   Fax: (859) 815-5053   www.ashland.com

Petroleum exploration, refining and transportation; mfr. chemicals, oils and lubricants.

Valvoline Nordisk Biltjeneste ApS, Vejiegardegej 45-47, Vallensbaek Strand, DK-2665 Copenhagen, Denmark

ASSOCIATED MERCHANDISING CORPORATION

500 Seventh Ave., 2nd Fl., New York, NY, 10018

Tel: (212) 819-6600   Fax: (212) 819-6701   www.theamc.com

Retail service organization; apparel, shoes and accessories.

Associated Merchandising Corp., Tornsangerveg 5, DK-3600 Frederikssund, Denmark

ASSOCIATED PRESS INC.

50 Rockefeller Plaza, New York, NY, 10020-1605

Tel: (212) 621-1500   Fax: (212) 621-5447   www.ap.com

News gathering agency.

The Associated Press A/S, Bremerholm 1-3, DK-1069 Copenhagen, Denmark

Tel: 45-33-11-1504

ATMEL CORPORATION

2325 Orchard Pkwy., San Jose, CA, 95131

Tel: (408) 441-0311   Fax: (408) 436-4200   www.atmel.com

Design, manufacture and marketing of advanced semiconductors.

Atmel Denmark, Telefonvej 8, DK-2860 Søborg, Denmark

Tel: 45-3957-7333   Fax: 45-3957-7335

Atmel Denmark, Naverland 2, DK-1600 Glostrup, Denmark

Tel: 45-43-430-801   Fax: 45-43-430-861

ATTACHMATE CORPORATION

3617 131st Avenue SE, Bellevue, WA, 98006-1332

Tel: (425) 644-4010   Fax: (425) 747-9924   www.attachmate.com

Mfr. connectivity software.

Attachmate Denmark, Damholme 14-16, DK-3660 Stenlose, Denmark

Tel: 45-42-17-1000   Fax: 45-42-17-2223

AVERY DENNISON CORPORATION

150 N. Orange Grove Blvd., Pasadena, CA, 91103

Tel: (626) 304-2000   Fax: (626) 792-7312   www.averydennison.com

Mfr. pressure-sensitive adhesives and materials, office products, labels, tags, retail systems, Carter's Ink and specialty chemicals.

Avery Dennison A/S, Industrivej 59, DK-4683 Ronnede, Denmark

Tel: 45-70-10-1800   Fax: 45-70-10-1833

R. Ancker Jorgensen A/S, 18 Topstykket, DK-3460 Birkerød, Denmark

AVID TECHNOLOGY, INC.

1 Park West, Tewksbury, MA, 01876

Tel: (978) 640-6789   Fax: (978) 640-1366   www.avid.com

Mfr. animation design software and digital and audio systems.

Avid DK, Gladsaxevej 382, DK-2860 Søborg, Denmark

Tel: 45-39-55-9999   Fax: 45-39-55-9990

AVNET INC.

2211 South 47th Street, Phoenix, AZ, 85034

Tel: (480) 643-2000   Fax: (480) 643-4670   www.avnet.com

Distributor electronic components, computers and peripherals.

Avnet Nortec A/S, Transformervej 17, DK-2730 Herlev, Denmark

Tel: 45-4488-0800   Fax: 45-4488-0888

BAKER HUGHES INCORPORATED

3900 Essex Lane, Ste. 1200, Houston, TX, 77027

Tel: (713) 439-8600   Fax: (713) 439-8699   www.bakerhughes.com

Develop and apply technology to drill, complete and produce oil and natural gas wells; provide separation systems to petroleum, municipal, continuous process and mining industries.

Baker Hughes de Mexico, S. de R.L. de C.V., Haandvaerkervej 2-4, DK-6710 Esbjerg, Denmark

Tel: 45-75-15-3866   Fax: 45-75-15-4976

BALTEK CORPORATION

10 Fairway Court, PO Box 195, Northvale, NJ, 07647

Tel: (201) 767-1400   Fax: (201) 387-6631   www.baltek.com

Mfr. light lumber, balsa wood and PVC foam.

Baltek Scandinavia, Hvolgarden 6, V. Hasslng, DK-9310 Hasslng, Denmark

C. R. BARD, INC.

730 Central Ave., Murray Hill, NJ, 07974

Tel: (908) 277-8000   Fax: (908) 277-8078   www.crbard.com

Mfr. health care products.

Bard Medical Systems Denmark AB, PO Box 14, DK-3000 Helsinger, Denmark

BATES WORLDWIDE INC.

498 Seventh Avenue, New York, NY, 10018

Tel: (212) 297-7000   Fax: (212) 986-0270   www.batesww.com

Advertising, marketing, public relations and media consulting.

Bates A/S, Landemaarket 29, DK-1119 Copenhagen K, Denmark

Tel: 45-33-13-7913   Fax: 45-33-15-7126   Contact: H. U. Longhi, CEO

Leise & Company, Landemaeket 19, DK-1119 Copenhagan K, Denmark

Tel: 45-33-33-0077   Fax: 45-33-33-9998   Contact: S. Leise, Dir.

Norgard Mikkelsen Reklamebureau A/S, Vandeveerksvel 18, DK-5100 Odanse C, Denmark

Tel: 45-66-14-1480   Contact: Erik Laumand, Dir.

BAX GLOBAL INC.

16808 Armstrong Ave., PO Box 19571, Irvine, CA, 92623

Tel: (949) 752-4000   Fax: (949) 260-3182   www.baxworld.com

Air freight forwarder.

BAX Global A/S - Denmark, Kirstinehoj 47, DK-2770 Copenhagen, Denmark

Tel: 45-32-51-3366   Fax: 45-32-51-2116

BAXTER INTERNATIONAL INC.

One Baxter Parkway, Deerfield, IL, 60015

Tel: (847) 948-2000   Fax: (847) 948-3948   www.baxter.com

Mfr. products and provide services in the field of the administration of medication and bioscience.

Baxter A/S, Gydevang 30, DK-3450 Allerød, Denmark

BBDO WORLDWIDE

1285 Ave. of the Americas, New York, NY, 10019

Tel: (212) 459-5000   Fax: (212) 459-6645   www.bbdo.com

Multinational group of advertising agencies.

BBDO Denmark, Copenhagen, Denmark

BDO SEIDMAN, LLP   BELGIUM

130 East Randolph Street, Chicago, IL, 60601

Tel: (312) 856-9100   Fax: (312) 856-1379   www.bdo.com

International accounting and financial consulting firm.

BDP Scanrevision Aktieselskab, Strandgade 12, DK-1401 Copenhagen K, Denmark

Tel: 45-32-96-1100   Fax: 45-32-96-1101   Contact: Jens Rye

BEA SYSTEMS, INC.

2315 North First Street, St. Jose, CA, 95131

Tel: (408) 570-8000   Fax: (408) 570-8091   www.beasys.com

Develops communications management software and provider of software consulting services.

BEA Systems, Datavej 62, DK-3460 Birkerød, Denmark

BELLSOUTH CORPORATION LATIN AMERICA

1155 Peachtree Street NE, Ste. 400, Atlanta, GA, 30367

Tel: (404) 249-4800   Fax: (404) 249-4880   www.bellsouth.com

Mobile communications, telecommunications network systems.

Sonofon Holding A/S, Lyngse Alee 3, DK-2070 Hersholm, Denmark

Tel: 45-38-18-6000   Fax: 45-38-18-6060

BEST WESTERN INTERNATIONAL

6201 North 24th Place, Phoenix, AZ, 85106

Tel: (602) 957-4200   Fax: (602) 957-5740   www.bestwestern.com

International hotel chain.

Hellerup Parkhotel, DK-2900 Hellerup, Denmark

Neptun Hotel, DK-1250 Copenhagen K, Denmark

BIOGEN, INC.

14 Cambridge Center, Cambridge, MA, 02142

Tel: (617) 679-2000   Fax: (617) 679-2617   www.biogen.com

Engaged in medical research and development of autoimmune diseases.

Biogen (Denmark A/S), Lyngbyvej 28, DK-2100 Copenhagen, Denmark

Tel: 45-39-16-91-91

BIO-RAD LABORATORIES INC.

1000 Alfred Nobel Drive, Hercules, CA, 94547

Tel: (510) 724-7000   Fax: (510) 724-3167   www.bio-rad.com

Mfr. life science research products, clinical diagnostics, analytical instruments.

Bio-Rad Laboratories, Generatorvej 8C, DK-2730 Herlev, Denmark

BIOWHITTAKER INC.

8830 Biggs Ford Road, Walkersville, MD, 21793

Tel: (301) 898-7025   Fax: (301) 845-6099   www.biowhittaker.com

Mfr. cell culture products, endotoxin detection assays.

BioWhittaker, Risingevej 1, DK-2665 Vallensbaek Strand, Denmark

Tel: 45-4356-7400

BLACK & DECKER CORPORATION

701 E. Joppa Road, Towson, MD, 21286

Tel: (410) 716-3900   Fax: (410) 716-2933   www.blackanddecker.com

Mfr. power tools and accessories, security hardware, small appliances, fasteners, information systems and services.

Black & Decker Denmark, Attn: Denmark Office, 701 East Joppa Road, Towson, MD, 21286

BLUE OCEAN SOFTWARE, INC.

15310 Amberly Drive, Ste. 370, Tampa, FL, 33647

Tel: (813) 977-4553   Fax: (813) 979-4447   www.blueocean.com

Mfr. software.

Blue Ocean Software, Jules Verneweg 113, DK-5015 BJ Tilburg, Denmark

BMC SOFTWARE, INC.

2101 City West Blvd., Houston, TX, 77042-2827

Tel: (713) 918-8800   Fax: (713) 918-8000   www.bmc.com

Engaged in mainframe-related utilities software and services.

BMC Software, Borupvang 2D, DK-2750 Ballerup, Denmark

BOSE CORPORATION

The Mountain, Framingham, MA, 01701-9168

Tel: (508) 879-7330   Fax: (508) 766-7543   www.bose.com

Mfr. quality audio equipment and speakers.

BOSEA/S, Industrivej 7, DK-2605 Brondby, Denmark

BOSTON SCIENTIFIC CORPORATION (BSC)

One Scientific Place, Natick, MA, 01760-1537

Tel: (508) 650-8000   Fax: (508) 650-8923   www.bostonscientific.com

Developer, manufacturer and marketer of medical devices.

Meadox Surgimed A/S, Gymnasievej 5, DK-3660 Stenlose, Denmark

Tel: 45-42-17-3990 Fax: 45-42-17-1955

BOWNE & COMPANY, INC.

345 Hudson Street, New York, NY, 10014

Tel: (212) 924-5500   Fax: (212) 229-3420   www.bowne.com

Financial printing and foreign language translation, localization (software), internet design and maintenance and facilities management.

Bowne Global Solutions, Købmagergade 19, DK-1150 Copenhagen K, Denmark

Tel: 45-33-7490-00 Fax: 45-33-7490-01

BOYDEN CONSULTING CORPORATION

364 Elwood Ave., Hawthorne, NY, 10502

Tel: (914) 747-0093   Fax: (914) 980-6147   www.boyden.com

International executive search firm.

Boyden Associates Ltd., Store Kongensgade 92, DK-1264 Copenhagen K, Denmark

Tel: 45-33-129988

BOZELL GROUP

40 West 23rd Street, New York, NY, 10010

Tel: (212) 727-5000   Fax: (212) 645-9173   www.bozell.com

Advertising, marketing, public relations and media consulting.

En Vision Copenhagen, Amager Torv 14, 4, Post Office 2233, DK-1160 Copenhagen, Denmark

Tel: 45-33-30-1355 Fax: 45-33-30-1334   Contact: Soren Parup, Dir.

En Vision Grafisk (Arhus) Tegnestue A/S, Copenhagen 261, Christiansgade 30, DK-8100 Aarhus C, Denmark

Tel: 45-86-19-4455 Fax: 45-86-18-4767   Contact: Bent Christensen, Mgr.

BRANSON ULTRASONICS CORPORATION

41 Eagle Road, Danbury, CT, 06813-1961

Tel: (203) 796-0400   Fax: (203) 796-2285   www.branson-plasticsjoin.com

Engaged in design, development, manufacture and marketing of plastics joining, precision cleaning and processing equipment.

Branson Ultrasonics-Scandinavia, Lojtegardsvej 155, DK-2770 Kastrup, Denmark

Tel: 45-32-513-233 Fax: 45-32-515-139

BRISTOL-MYERS SQUIBB COMPANY

345 Park Ave., New York, NY, 10154-0037

Tel: (212) 546-4000   Fax: (212) 546-4020   www.bms.com

Pharmaceutical and food preparations, medical and surgical instruments.

Bristol-Myers Squibb A/B, Wilder Plads, Byning V, DK-1404 Copenhagen, Denmark

ConvaTec, 3/4 Gersborgvej 64-65, DK-2800 Lyngby, Denmark

ConvaTec Denmark, Jaegersborgvej 65-66, DK-2800 Lyngby, Denmark

BROADVISION, INC.

585 Broadway, Redwood City, CA, 94063

Tel: (650) 261-5100   Fax: (650) 261-5900   www.broadvision.com

Develops and delivers an integrated suite of packaged applications for personalized enterprise portals.

BroadVision Denmark, Lyngsoe Allé 3, DK-2970 Hørsholm, Denmark

Tel: 45-45-17-9900

BUDGET GROUP, INC.

125 Basin St., Ste. 210, Daytona Beach, FL, 32114

Tel: (904) 238-7035   Fax: (904) 238-7461   www.budgetrentacar.com

Car and truck rental system.

Budget Rent A Car, Kastrup International Airport, DK-2770 Copenhagen, Denmark

Tel: 45-32-52-3900   Fax: 45-32-52-5218

LEO BURNETT, DIV. B-COM 3 GROUP

35 West Wacker Drive, Chicago, IL, 60601

Tel: (312) 220-5959   Fax: (312) 220-6533   www.leoburnett.com

Engaged in advertising, marketing, media buying and planning, and public relations.

Leo Burnett Denmark, Vesterbrogade 2B, DK-1620 Copenhagen V, Denmark

BURSON-MARSTELLER

230 Park Avenue South, New York, NY, 10003-1566

Tel: (212) 614-4000   Fax: (212) 614-4262   www.bm.com

Public relations/public affairs consultants.

Burson-Marsteller/Public Affairs Group A/S, Blegdamsvej 104, DK-2100 Copenhagen, Denmark

Tel: 45-35-43-7375   Fax: 45-35-43-7377

CABLE DESIGN TECHNOLOGIES CORPORATION

661 Andersen Drive, Plaza 7, Pittsburgh, PA, 15220

Tel: (412) 937-2300   Fax: (412) 937-9690   www.cdtc.com

Mfr. computer connector copper, fiber optic and composite cables.

CEKAN/CDT, Videhojvej 4, DK-8883 Gjern, Denmark

Tel: 45-86-87-5299

CAMBREX CORPORATION

1 Meadowlands Plaza, East Rutherford, NJ, 07063

Tel: (201) 804-3000   Fax: (201) 804-9852   www.cambrex.com

human health, animal health/agriculture and Mfr. biotechnology products and produce specialty chemicals.

Nordic Synthesis, Geo Svane - Maltegardsvej 18C, DK-2810 Gentofte, Denmark

CANBERRA INDUSTRIES, INC.

800 Research Parkway, Meriden, CT, 06450

Tel: (203) 238-2351   Fax: (203) 235-1347   www.canberra.com

Mfr. instruments for nuclear research.

Canberra Packard, Greveager 7, DK-2670 Greve, Denmark

Tel: 45-43-909023   Fax: 45-43-906741

CANDLE CORPORATION

201 N. Douglas Street, El Segundo, CA, 90245

Tel: (310) 535-3600   Fax: (310) 727-4287   www.candle.com

Mfr. management software.

Candle Service Ltd., Lyngso Alle 3, DK-2970 Copenhagen, Denmark

CARGILL, INC.

15407 McGinty Road West, Minnetonka, MN, 55440-5625

Tel: (612) 742-7575   Fax: (612) 742-7393   www.cargill.com

Food products, feeds, animal products.

Cargill Scandinavia A/S, Nikolaj Plads 34, DK-1067 Copenhagen K, Denmark

Tel: 45-33-32-3436

CARLISLE COMPANIES INC.

13925 Ballantyne Corporate Place, Ste. 400, Charlotte, NC, 28277

Tel: (704) 501-1100   Fax: (704) 501-1190   www.carlisle.com

Engaged in rubber, plastics and friction technologies.

Icopal A/S, Mileparken 38, DK-2730 Herlev, Denmark

Tel: 45-44-88-5500

CARPENTER COMPANY

5016 Monument Avenue, Richmond, VA, 23220

Tel: (904) 359-0800   Fax: (804) 353-0694   www.carpenter.com

Mfr. polyurethane foam and chemicals.

Carpenter APS, PO Box 79, Holmensvej 9, DK 3600 Frederikssund, Denmark

CATERPILLAR INC.

100 NE Adams Street, Peoria, IL, 61629-6105

Tel: (309) 675-1000   Fax: (309) 675-1182   www.cat.com

Mfr. earth/material-handling and construction machinery and equipment and engines.

Caterpillar, Inc., Copenhagen, Denmark

CB RICHARD ELLIS SERVICES

200 N. Sepulveda Blvd., Ste. 300, El Segundo, CA, 90245-4380

Tel: (310) 563-8600   Fax: (310) 563-8670   www.cbrichardellis.com

Commercial real estate services.

CB Richard Ellis, Sundtoldvej 8E, DK-3000 Helsingor, Denmark

CENTRA SOFTWARE, INC.

430 Bedford Street, Lexington, MA, 02421

Tel: (781) 861-7000   Fax: (781) 863-7288   www.centra.com

Mfr. on-line learning software.

Centra Software Nordic, Naverland 2, DK-2600 Glostrup, Denmark

CHECKPOINT SYSTEMS, INC.

101 Wolf Drive, Thorofare, NJ, 08086

Tel: (856) 848-1800   Fax: (856) 848-0937   www.checkpointsystems.com

Mfr. test, measurement and closed-circuit television systems.

Checkpoint Systems Danmark Aps., Banemarksvej 50, DK-2605 Brondby, Denmark

Tel: 45-4329-3838   Fax: 45-4329-3800

THE CHERRY CORPORATION

3600 Sunset Ave., PO Box 718, Waukegan, IL, 60087

Tel: (847) 662-9200   Fax: (847) 662-2990   www.cherrycorp.com

Mfr. electrical switches, electronic keyboards, controls and displays.

ACTE Denmark, Telefonvej 8, DK-2860 Søborg, Denmark

CHESTERTON BLUMENAUER BINSWANGER

Two Logan Square, 4th Floor, Philadelphia, PA, 19103-2759

Tel: (215) 448-6000   Fax: (215) 448-6238   www.cbbi.com

Real estate and related services.

CBB Denmark, 10, Ved Stranden, DK-1061 Copenhagen K, Denmark

Contact: Steen Winther-Petersen

THE CHUBB CORPORATION

15 Mountain View Road, Warren, NJ, 07061-1615

Tel: (908) 580-2000   Fax: (908) 580-3606   www.chubb.com

Holding company for property and casualty insurance and liability insurance for corporate executives.

Chubb Insurance Co. of Europe, SA, Marina Park, Sundkrogsgade 4, DK-2100 Copenhagen, Denmark

Tel: 45-39-17-5000   Fax: 45-39-17-5970

CIGNA COMPANIES

One Liberty Place, Philadelphia, PA, 19192

Tel: (215) 761-1000   Fax: (215) 761-5511   www.cigna.com

Insurance, invest, health care and other financial services.

CIGNA Insurance Co. of Europe SA/NV, Amargeriorv 24, DK-1160 Copenhagen K, Denmark

Insurance Co. of North America, c/o PFA Skade, Marina Park, Sundkrogsgade 4, DK-2100 Copenhagen 0, Denmark

CINCINNATI INCORPORATED

PO Box 11111, Cincinnati, OH, 45211

Tel: (513) 367-7100   Fax: (513) 367-7552   www.e-ci.com

Mfr. metal fabricating equipment.

Herstad & Piper A/S, Jernholmen 48C, Hvidovre, Denmark

Tel: 45-36-77-4000   Fax: 45-36-77-7740

CINCOM SYSTEMS INC.

55 Merchant Street, Cincinnati, OH, 45446

Tel: (513) 612-2300   Fax: (513) 481-8332   www.cincom.com

Develop/distributor computer software.

Cincom Systems Inc., Copenhagen, Denmark

CISCO SYSTEMS, INC.

170 West Tasman Drive, San Jose, CA, 95134-1706

Tel: (408) 526-4000   Fax: (408) 526-4100   www.cisco.com

Develop/mfr./market computer hardware and software networking systems.

Cisco Systems, Vesterbrogade 149, DK-1620 Copenhagen, Denmark

Tel: 45-33-26-5900   Fax: 45-33-26-5901

CITIGROUP, INC.

399 Park Avenue, New York, NY, 10022

Tel: (212) 559-1000   Fax: (212) 559-3646   www.citigroup.com

Provides insurance and financial services worldwide.

Citigroup, Copenhagen, Denmark

Contact: Ineke Bussemaker

CITRIX SYSTEMS, INC.

6400 NW 6th Way, Fort Lauderdale, FL, 33309

Tel: (954) 267-3000   Fax: (954) 267-9319   www.citrix.com

Developer of computer software.

Citrix Systems Nordic, Kalkbrænderiløbskaj 4, DK-2100 Copenhagen, Denmark

Tel: 45-39193400   Fax: 45-39193401

CLEAR CHANNEL COMMUNICATIONS

200 East Basse Road, San Antonio, TX, 78209

Tel: (210) 822-2828   Fax: (210) 822-2299   www.clearchannel.com

Owns, manages, promotes and produces concerts and shows; programs and sells airtime for radio stations, owns and places outdoor advertising displays and provides agent services to athletes and broadcasters.

More Group, Gerdasgade 35, 1. Sal, DK-2500 Valby, Denmark

Tel: 45-36-4-0244   Fax: 45-26-44-1850   Contact: Henrik Sorensen, Mgr.

CNA FINANCIAL CORPORATION

CNA Plaza, Chicago, IL, 60685

Tel: (312) 822-5000   Fax: (312) 822-6419   www.cna.com

Commercial property/casualty insurance policies.

CNA Insurance Company (Europe) Limited (CIE), Copenhagen, Denmark

THE COCA-COLA COMPANY

1 Coca Cola Plaza, Atlanta, GA, 30313

Tel: (404) 676-2121 Fax: (404) 676-6792 www.coca-cola.com

Mfr./marketing/distributor soft drinks, syrups and concentrates, juice and juice-drink products.

Coca-Cola Nordic Beverages (CCNB), Strandvejen #60, 5, DK-2900 Hellerup, Copenhagen, Denmark

COLFAX CORPORATION

9211 Forest Hill Avenue, Ste. 109, Richmond, VA, 23235

Tel: (804) 560-4070 Fax: (804) 560-4076 www.colfaxcorp.com

Mfr. industrial clutches and brakes and motion control products and components.

Alfa Laval A/S, Krondalvej 7, DK-2610 Rodovre, Denmark

COLGATE-PALMOLIVE COMPANY

300 Park Ave., New York, NY, 10022

Tel: (212) 310-2000 Fax: (212) 310-2919 www.colgate.com

Mfr. pharmaceuticals, cosmetics, toiletries and detergents.

Colgate-Palmolive A/S, Smedeland 9, DK-2600 Glostrup, Denmark

COLLIERS INTERNATIONAL PROPERTY CONSULTANTS INC.

84 State Street, 3rd Fl., Boston, MA, 02109

Tel: (617) 722-0221 Fax: (617) 722-0224 www.colliers.com

Engaged in commercial real estate.

Colliers International, Nyopsgade 17, DK-1602 Copenhagen, Denmark

COMMERCE ONE, INC.

4440 Rosewood Dr., Pleasanton, CA, 94588-3050

Tel: (925) 520-6000 Fax: (925) 520-6060 www.commerceone.com

Provides software and services.

Commerce One Denmark, Larsbjoernsstrade 3, DK-1454 Copenhagen, Denmark

COMPUTER ASSOCIATES INTERNATIONAL INC.

One Computer Associates Plaza, Islandia, NY, 11788

Tel: (516) 342-5224 Fax: (516) 342-5329 www.cai.com

Integrated business software for enterprise computing and information management, application development, manufacturing, financial applications and professional services.

Computer Associates Scandinavia A/S, Ryttermarken 10, DK-3520 Farum, Denmark

COMPUTER SCIENCES CORPORATION

2100 East Grand Ave., El Segundo, CA, 90245

Tel: (310) 615-0311 Fax: (310) 322-9768 www.csc.com

Information technology services, management consulting, systems integration, outsourcing.

CSC Computer Sciences AB - Scandinavian Division, Copenhagen, Denmark

Contact: Denis Hocking, Pres.

COMPUWARE CORPORATION

31440 Northwestern Hwy., Farmington Hills, MI, 48334-2564

Tel: (248) 737-7300 Fax: (248) 737-7108 www.compuware.com

Develop and market software for enterprise and e-commerce solutions.

Compuware Denmark, Telegrafvej 5, DK-2750 Ballerup, Denmark

Tel: 45-44-68-0122

COMVERSE, INC.

100 Quannapowitt Parkway, Wakefield, MA, 01880

Tel: (781) 246-9000 Fax: (781) 224-8143 www.comverse.com

Provides communications solutions.

Comverse Denmark, Helsignforsgade 27, DK-8200 Aarhus N, Denmark

CONAGRA FOODS, INC.

One ConAgra Drive, Omaha, NE, 68102-5001

Tel: (402) 595-4000   Fax: (402) 595-4707   www.conagra.com

Prepared/frozen foods, grains, flour, animal feeds, agro chemicals, poultry, meat, dairy products, including Healthy Choice, Butterball and Hunt's.

ConAgra Inc., Copenhagen, Denmark

COOPER BUSSMANN

PO Box 14460, St. Louis, MO, 63178-4460

Tel: (636) 394-2877   Fax: (636) 527-1405   www.bussmann.com

Mfr. and markets circuit protection products for the electrical, electronic, and automotive industries.

Bussmann Industries, 5 Literbuen, DK-2740 Skovlunde Copenhagen, Denmark

Tel: 45-44-85-0900   Fax: 45-44-85-0901

COOPER INDUSTRIES INC.

6600 Travis Street, Ste. 5800, Houston, TX, 77002

Tel: (713) 209-8400   Fax: (713) 209-8995   www.cooperindustries.com

Mfr./distributor electrical products, tools, hardware and automotive products, fuses and accessories for electronic applications and circuit boards.

Bussmann, Div. Cooper Industries, 5 Literbuen, DK-2740 Skovlunde Copenhagen, Denmark

Tel: 45-44-85-0900   Fax: 45-44-85-0901

CORDIS CORPORATION

PO Box 25700, Miami, FL, 33102-5700

Tel: (305) 824-2000   Fax: (305) 824-2747   www.cordis.com

Mfr. medical devices and systems.

Cordis Denmark, Blokken 39, DK-3460 Birkerød, Denmark

CROMPTON CORPORATION

One American Lane, Greenwich, CT, 06831

Tel: (203) 552-2000   Fax: (203) 552-2870   www.cromptoncorp.com

Mfr. dyes, colors, flavors, fragrances, specialty chemicals and industrial products.

Crompton GmbH, Rundforbivej 2, DK-2950 Vedbaek, Denmark

CROWN CORK & SEAL COMPANY, INC.

One Crown Way, Philadelphia, PA, 19154-4599

Tel: (215) 698-5100   Fax: (215) 698-5201   www.crowncork.com

Mfr. metal and plastic packaging, including steel and aluminum cans for food, beverage and household products.

Crown Cork Co. A/S, Hoerskaetten 13, DK-2630 Taastrup, Denmark

CTS CORPORATION

905 Northwest Boulevard, Elkhart, IN, 46514

Tel: (219) 293-7511   Fax: (219) 293-6146   www.ctscorp.com

Mfr. designs, produces and sells passive, electro-mechanical, hybrid and interconnect components for OEMs.

J.D. Friderichsen A/S, DK-2800 Lyngby, Denmark

CUBIC CORPORATION

9333 Balboa Ave., PO Box 85587, San Diego, CA, 92123

Tel: (858) 277-6780   Fax: (858) 277-1878   www.cubic.com

Automatic fare collection equipment, training systems.

Scanpoint Technology A/S, Vibeholms Alle 22, DK-2605 Brondby, Denmark

Tel: 45-43-43-3999 Fax: 45-43-43-3940   Contact: George Nora, Mng. Dir.

CURTISS-WRIGHT CORPORATION

1200 Wall Street West, Lyndhurst, NJ, 07071-0635

Tel: (201) 896-8400   Fax: (201) 438-5680   www.curtisswright.com

Mfr. precision components and systems, engineered services to aerospace, flow control and marine industry.

Curtiss-Wright Accessory Services, PO Box 51, DK-7470 Karup, Denmark

Tel: 45-9710-0555   Fax: 45-9710-0558

D&B (DUN & BRADSTREET CORPORATION))

1 Diamond Hill Road, Murray Hill, NJ, 07974

Tel: (908) 665-5000   Fax: (908) 665-5524   www.dnb.com

Provides corporate credit, marketing and accounts-receivable management services and publishes financial information.

D&B Denmark, Egegaardsvej 39, DK 2610 Rodovre, Denmark

Tel: 45-36-70-5566

DANIEL INDUSTRIES INC.

9753 Pine Lake Drive, PO Box 55435, Houston, TX, 77224

Tel: (713) 467-6000   Fax: (713) 827-3889   www.danielind.com

Fluid measurement, flow control, actuation and analytical products, services and integrated solutions primarily for natural gas and oil producers, transporters and refiners worldwide.

Daniel Industries/Emerson Process Management, Hejrevang 11, DK 3450 Allerød, Denmark

DANZAS AEI, INC.

120 Tokeneke Road, PO Box 1231, Darien, CT, 06820

Tel: (203) 655-7900   Fax: (203) 655-5779   www.aeilogistics.com

International air freight forwarder.

Danzas AEI, Mineralvej 29, DK-9220 Aalborg, Denmark

D'ARCY MASIUS BENTON & BOWLES INC. (DMB&B)

1675 Broadway, New York, NY, 10019

Tel: (212) 468-3622   Fax: (212) 468-2987   www.darcyww.com

Full service international advertising and communications group.

DMB&B Europe, Sankt Knudsvej 41, DK-1903 Frederiksberg C, Denmark

DMB&B Europe, Brostes Gaard, Ovengaden Oven Vandet 10, DK-1415 Copenhagen K, Denmark

DDB WORLDWIDE COMMUNICATIONS GROUP

437 Madison Ave., New York, NY, 10022

Tel: (212) 415-2000   Fax: (212) 415-3417   www.ddbn.com

Advertising agency.

DDB Worldwide, Shellhuset, Kampmannsgade 2, DK-1604 Copenhagen, Denmark

Tel: 45-3346-3000

DELL COMPUTER CORPORATION

One Dell Way, Round Rock, TX, 78682-2222

Tel: (512) 338-4400   Fax: (512) 728-3653   www.dell.com

Direct marketer and supplier of computer systems.

Dell Denmark, Slossmarkren 11, Dk-2970 Hørsholm, Denmark

Tel: 45-45-17-0100   Fax: 45-45-17-0117   Contact: Ulf Sandmark, Mng. Dir.

DELOITTE TOUCHE TOHMATSU INTERNATIONAL

1633 Broadway, New York, NY, 10019

Tel: (212) 492-4000   Fax: (212) 392-4154   www.deloitte.com

Accounting, audit, tax and management consulting services.

Deloitte & Touche, H.C. Andersens Blvd. 2, DK-1780 Copenhagen V, Denmark

DHL WORLDWIDE EXPRESS

50 California Avenue, San Francisco, CA, 94111

Tel: (415) 677-6100   Fax: (415) 824-9700   www.dhl.com

Worldwide air express carrier.

DHL Worldwide Express, Jydekrogen 14, DK-2625 Vallensbaek, Denmark

Tel: 45-70-13-1131

DIAGNOSTIC PRODUCTS CORPORATION

5700 West 96th Street, Los Angeles, CA, 90045

Tel: (310) 645-8200   Fax: (310) 645-9999   www.dpcweb.com

Mfr. diagnostic products.

DPC Scandinavia, Sandvadsvej 1, DK-4600 Køge, Denmark

Tel: 45-70-20-0145   Fax: 45-70-20-0146

DIGI INTERNATIONAL INC.

11001 Bren Road East, Minnetonka, MN, 55343

Tel: (952) 912-3444   Fax: (952) 912-4952   www.digi.com

Mfr. computer hardware.

Digi International Denmark, Hejreskowej, 18C, 1.9.8, DK-3490 Kvistgaard, Denmark

Tel: 45-49-17-70-90   Fax: 45-49-17-70-91

DIONEX CORPORATION

1228 Titan Way, PO Box 3603, Sunnyvale, CA, 94086-3603

Tel: (408) 737-0700   Fax: (408) 730-9403   www.dionex.com

Develop/mfr./market chromatography systems and related products.

Radiometer Danmark A/S, Egegaardsvej 41-st, DK-2610 Rodovre, Denmark

WALT DISNEY COMPANY

500 South Buena Vista Street, Burbank, CA, 91521

Tel: (818) 560-1000   Fax: (818) 560-1930   www.disney.com

Film/TV production, theme parks, resorts, publishing, recording and retail stores.

Walt Disney Productions A/S, Ostergade 24B, DK-1100 Copenhagen, Denmark

DIVINE

1301 N. Elston Ave., Chicago, IL, 60622

Tel: (773) 394-6600   Fax: (773) 394-6601   www.divine.com

Software and services provider.

Divine, Inc., Parallellvej 10, DK-2800 Lyngby, Denmark

DOUBLECLICK, INC.

450 West 33rd Street, New York, NY, 10001

Tel: (212) 683-0001   Fax: (212) 889-0062   www.doubleclick.net

Engaged in online advertising and e-mail marketing.

Doubleclick, Ltd., Vester Voldgade 83, DK-1552 Copenhagen V, Denmark

THE DOW CHEMICAL COMPANY

2030 Dow Center, Midland, MI, 48674

Tel: (989) 636-1000   Fax: (989) 636-3228   www.dow.com

Mfr. chemicals, plastics, pharmaceuticals, agricultural products, consumer products.

Dow Chemical A/S, Strandvejen 171, DK-2900 Hellerup, Denmark

DRAKE BEAM MORIN INC.

100 Park Avenue, 11th Fl., New York, NY, 10017

Tel: (212) 692-7700   Fax: (212) 297-0426   www.dbm.com

Human resource management consulting and training.

DBM International, Copenhagen Europe Ctr., Vesterbrogade 149, DK-1620 Copenhagen V, Denmark

Tel: 45-33-79-0803   Fax: 45-75-72-3855

EASTMAN CHEMICAL COMPANY

100 North Eastman Road, Kingsport, TN, 37662-5075

Tel: (423) 229-2000   Fax: (423) 229-1351   www.eastman.com

Mfr. plastics, chemicals, fibers.

Eastman Chemical B.V., Naverland 2, 11th Fl., DK-2600 Glostrup, Denmark

Tel: 45-77-31-7760   Fax: 45-77-31-7761   Contact: Jens Michael Poulsen

EASTMAN KODAK COMPANY

343 State Street, Rochester, NY, 14650

Tel: (716) 724-4000   Fax: (716) 724-1089   www.kodak.com

Develop/mfr. photo and chemicals products, information management/video/copier systems, fibers/plastics for various industry.

Eastman Chemical Intl. AG - Kodak A/S, Dybendal Alle 10, DK-2630 Taastrup, Denmark

ECOLAB INC.

370 N. Wabasha Street, St. Paul, MN, 55102

Tel: (651) 293-2233   Fax: (651) 293-2379   www.ecolab.com

Develop/mfr. premium cleaning, sanitizing and maintenance products and services for the hospitality, institutional, and residential markets.

Ecolab Ltd., Copenhagen, Denmark

Tel: 45-36-15-8585

EG&G INC.

900 Clopper Road, Ste. 200, Gaithersburg, MD, 20878

Tel: (301) 840-3000   Fax: (301) 590-0502   www.egginc.com

Diversified R/D, mfr. and services.

Wallac Danmark A/S, Gydevang 21, DK-3450 Allerød, Denmark

EGL INC. (EAGLE GLOBAL LOGISTICS)

15350 Vickery Drive, Houston, TX, 77032

Tel: (281) 618-3100   Fax: (281) 618-3223   www.eagleusa.com

Ocean/air freight forwarding, customs brokerage, packing and wholesale, logistics management and insurance.

EGL Eagle Global Logistics, H. C. Tvenges VEJ 3-5, DK-8100 Aarhus C, Denmark

Tel: 45-86-13-4400   Fax: 45-86-13-6251

EGL Eagle Global Logistics, Lufthavnsvej 27 D, DK-7190 Billund, Denmark

Tel: 45-75-33-1233   Fax: 45-75-33-2763

EGL Eagle Global Logistics, Amager Landevej 149, PO Box 110, DK-2770 Kastrup, Denmark

Tel: 45-32-501-322   Fax: 45-32-501-979

ELANCO ANIMAL HEALTH

500 East 96th Street, Ste. 125, Indianapolis, IN, 46240

Tel: (317) 276-3000   Fax: (317) 276-6116   www.elanco.com

Antibiotics and fine chemicals.

Elanco Animal Health, Thoravej 4, DK-2400 Copenhagen NV, Denmark

ELECTRONIC DATA SYSTEMS, INC. (EDS)

5400 Legacy Dr., Plano, TX, 75024

Tel: (972) 604-6000   Fax: (972) 605-2643   www.eds.com

Engaged in systems integration, network and systems operations and management consulting.

EDS Denmark A/S, Stoberigade 14, DK-2450 DK-2450, Denmark

ELECTRONICS FOR IMAGING, INC. (EFI)

303 Velocity Way, Foster City, CA, 94404

Tel: (650) 357-3500   Fax: (650) 357-3907   www.efi.com

Design/mfr. computer software and hardware for color desktop publishing.

EFI Denmark, Regus House, Larsbjømsstræde 3, DK-1454 Copenhagen, Denmark

Tel: 45 33-37-7240

EMC CORPORATION

35 Parkwood Drive, Hopkinton, MA, 01748-9103

Tel: (508) 435-1000   Fax: (508) 435-8884   www.emc.com

Designs/supplies intelligent enterprise storage and retrieval technology for open systems, mainframes and midrange environments.

EMC Computer Systems, Meterbuer 15 A, DK-2740 Skovlunde Meterbuer, Denmark

Tel: 45-70-10-6878

EMERSON PROCESS MANAGEMENT

8301Cameron Road, Austin, TX, 78754

Tel: (512) 834-7689   Fax: (512) 832-3232   www.frco.com

Mfr. industrial process control equipment.

Emerson Process Management, Hejrevang 11, DK-3450 Allerød, Denmark

EMERY FORWARDING

One Lagoon Drive, Ste. 400, Redwood City, CA, 94065

Tel: (650) 596-9600   Fax: (650) 596-7901   www.emeryworld.com

Freight transport, global logistics and air cargo.

Emery Forwarding, Fuglebaekvej 4A, DK-2770 Kastrup Copenhagen, Denmark

ENERGIZER HOLDINGS, INC.

533 Maryville University Dr., St. Louis, MO, 63141

Tel: (314) 985-2000   Fax: (214) 985-2205   www.energizer.com

Mfr. Eveready and Energizer brand batteries and lighting products.

Energizer Nordic A/S, Farum Gydevej 63, DK-3520 Farum Copenhagen, Denmark

Tel: 45-44-990088   Fax: 45-44-990022

ENGELHARD CORPORATION

101 Wood Avenue South, Iselin, NJ, 08830

Tel: (732) 205-5000   Fax: (732) 632-9253   www.engelhard.com

Mfr. pigments, additives, catalysts, chemicals, engineered materials.

Engelhard-Clal Denmark, Hoffdingsvej 36, DK-2500 Valby, Denmark

Tel: 45-36-14-0000   Fax: 45-36-14-0001

ERNST & YOUNG INTERNATIONAL

5 Times Square, New York, NY, 10036

Tel: (212) 773-3000   Fax: (212) 773-6350   www.eyi.com

Engaged in assurance and advisory business services, tax, law and corporate finance.

Ernst & Young International, Tagensvej 86, DK-2200 Copenhagen N, Denmark

Tel: 45-35-82-4848   Fax: 45-35-82-4710   Contact: Per Lundbaek Christensen

ESTEE LAUDER COMPANIES INC.

767 Fifth Ave., New York, NY, 10153

Tel: (212) 572-4200   Fax: (212) 572-3941   www.esteelauder.com

Cosmetics, perfumes and Aveda hair care products.

Estee Lauder Cosmetics A/S, Norregade 7-A, DK-1165 Copenhagen K, Denmark

EURO RSCG WORLDWIDE

350 Hudson Street, New York, NY, 10014

Tel: (212) 886-2000   Fax: (212) 886-2016   www.eurorscg.com

International advertising agency group.

EURO RSCG Copenhagen, Vangehusvej 19, Copenhagen OE, Denmark

EXXON MOBIL CORPORATION

5959 Las Colinas Blvd., Irving, TX, 75039-2298

Tel: (972) 444-1000   Fax: (972) 444-1882   www.exxonmobil.com

Petroleum exploration, production, refining; mfr. petroleum and chemicals products; coal and minerals.

Exxon Mobil, Inc., Frederiksberggade 24, DK-1459 Copenhagen, Denmark

Tel: 45-33-69-1710

FERRO CORPORATION

1000 Lakeside Ave., Cleveland, OH, 44114-7000

Tel: (216) 641-8580   Fax: (216) 696-5784   www.ferro.com

Mfr. Specialty chemicals, coatings, plastics, colors, refractories.

Ferro B.V., Industrivej 10, Vassingerod, DK-3540 Lynge, Denmark

Tel: 45-42-18-8222   Fax: 45-42-18-7634   Contact: P. Nielson, Off. Mgr.

FKI LOGISTEX
1500 Lebanon Road, Danville, KY, 40422

Tel: (877) 935-4564   Fax: (877) 935-4564   www.fkilogistex.com

Mfr. integrated material handling solutions for distribution, baggage handling, freight, parcel, and manufacturing applications.

FKI Logistex Europe, PO Pedersens Vej 10, DK-8200 Aarhus, Denmark

Tel: 45-87-414141

FLOWSERVE CORPORATION
222 W. Los Colinas Blvd., Irving, TX, 75039

Tel: (972) 443-6500   Fax: (972) 443-6858   www.flowserve.com

Mfr. chemicals equipment, pumps, valves, filters, fans and heat exchangers.

Flowserve, Hejrevang 6, DK-3450 Allerød, Denmark

Contact: Preben Cipikoff

FMC CORPORATION
1735 Market St., Philadelphia, PA, 19103

Tel: (215) 299-6000   Fax: (215) 299-6618   www.fmc.com

Mfr. specialty chemicals, including alginate, carrageenan and microcrystalline cellulose.

FMC Denmark, Risingevej 1, 2665 Vallensbaek Strand, Copenhagen, Denmark

FORD MOTOR COMPANY
One American Road, Dearborn, MI, 48126

Tel: (313) 322-3000   Fax: (313) 322-9600   www.ford.com

Mfr./sales motor vehicles.

Ford Motor Co. A/S, Sluseholmen 1, DK-2450 Copenhagen SV, Denmark

FORMICA CORPORATION
10155 Reading Road, Cincinnati, OH, 45241-4805

Tel: (513) 786-3400   Fax: (513) 786-3082   www.formica.com

Mfr. decorative laminate, adhesives and solvents.

Formica Danmark, Peder Nielsens Vej 8, DK-8600 Silkeborg, Denmark

FRITZ COMPANIES, INC., DIV. UPS
706 Mission Street, Ste. 900, San Francisco, CA, 94103

Tel: (415) 904-8360   Fax: (415) 904-8661   www.fritz.com

Integrated transportation, sourcing, distribution and customs brokerage services.

Fritz Companies Inc., DK-9200 Aalborg, Denmark

GE BETZ, DIV. GE SPECIALTY MATERIALS
4636 Somerton Road, PO Box 3002, Trevose, PA, 19053-6783

Tel: (215) 355-3300   Fax: (215) 953-5524   www.gebetz.com

Engaged in engineered chemical treatment of water and process systems in industrial, commercial and institutional facilities

GE Betz, Div. GE Specialty Materials, Skt. Pauls Gade 42, DK-8000 Aarhus C, Denmark

GEN RE INTERMEDIARIES CORPORATION
PO Box 10216, Stamford, CT, 06904-2216

Tel: (203) 357-8883   Fax: (203) 328-6408   www.genre.com

Provides reinsurance services worldwide.

General Re Europe Scandinavia, Chr. IX's Gade 10, 3rd Fl., DK-1111 Copenhagen K, Denmark

Tel: 45-33-33-7878 Fax: 45-33-33-7475   Contact: Hans-Kristian Jacobsen

Kölnische Norden A/S, Chr. IX's Cade 10, 3rd Fl., DK-1111 Copenhagen K, Denmark

Tel: 45-33-33-7878 Fax: 45-33-33-7475   Contact: Hans-Kristian Jacobsen, Gen. Mgr.

GENERAL ELECTRIC CAPITAL CORPORATION

260 Long Ridge Road, Stamford, CT, 06927

Tel: (203) 357-4000   Fax: (203) 357-6489   www.gecapital.com

Financial, property, casualty insurance, computer sales and trailer leasing services.

GE Capital Equipment Finance AB, Grønningen 25, Gronningen 25, DK-1270 Copenhagen, Denmark

Tel: 45-33-97-9593   Fax: 45-33-97-9441

GENERAL ELECTRIC COMPANY

3135 Easton Turnpike, Fairfield, CT, 06431

Tel: (203) 373-2211   Fax: (203) 373-3131   www.ge.com

Diversified manufacturing, technology and services.

GE Capital Info Technology GE Information Services Inc., Groenningen 25, DK-1270 Copenhagen, Denmark

GE Capital Info Technology Solutions AS, Blokken 11-15, DK-3460 Birkerød, Denmark

Tel: 45-45-945353

GE Capital Info Technology Solutions AS, Sindahisvej 37, DK-8240 Risskov, Denmark

Tel: 45-86-219453

GE Lighting A/S, SDR-Ringvej 45, DK-2605 Brandby, Denmark

GE Medical Systems Europe, Fabriksparken 20, DK-2600 Glostrup, Denmark

Tel: 45-43-485000

GE SeaCo Scandinavia, Vesterbrogade 149, Fabriksparken 20, DK-1620 Copenhagen, Denmark

Tel: 45-3386-2000

GENERAL MOTORS ACCEPTANCE CORPORATION

3044 W. Grand Blvd., Detroit, MI, 48202

Tel: (313) 556-5000   Fax: (313) 556-5108   www.gmac.com

Automobile financing.

GMAC Finansiering A/S, Klampenborgvej 232, DK-2800 Lyngby, Denmark

GENERAL MOTORS CORPORATION

300 Renaissance Center, Detroit, MI, 48285

Tel: (313) 556-5000   Fax: (313) 556-5108   www.gm.com

Mfr. full line vehicles, automotive electronics, commercial technologies, telecommunications, space, finance.

General Motors Denmark A/S, Tobaksvejen 22, DK-2860 Søborg, Denmark

GENUITY, INC.

225 Presidential Way, Woburn, MA, 01801

Tel: (781) 865-2000   Fax: (781) 865-3936   www.genuity.com

R/D computer, communications, acoustics technologies and internetworking services.

Genuity Denmark, Lyngbyvej 32 F, DK-2100 Copenhagen, Denmark

GERBER SCIENTIFIC, INC.

83 Gerber Road West, South Windsor, CT, 06074

Tel: (860) 644-1551   Fax: (860) 644-5547   www.gerberscientific.com

Mfr. computer-based automated manufacturing and design systems for signs and graphics.

Gerber Technology A/S, Niebuhr Division, Navervej 10-12, DK-7430 Ikast, Denmark

THE GILLETTE COMPANY

Prudential Tower Building, Boston, MA, 02199

Tel: (617) 421-7000   Fax: (617) 421-7123   www.gillette.com

Develop/mfr. personal care/use products: blades and razors, toiletries, cosmetics, stationery.

Braun Denmark A/S, Søborg, Denmark

Gillette A/S, Teglholm Alle 15, DK-2450 Copenhagen, Denmark

GILSON INC.

3000 W. Beltline Hwy, PO Box 620027, Middleton, WI, 53562-0027

Tel: (608) 836-1551   Fax: (608) 831-4451   www.gilson.com

Mfr. analytical/biomedical instruments.

Biolab, A.S., Sindalsvej 29, DK-240 Risskov, Denmark

GLEASON CORPORATION

1000 University Ave., Rochester, NY, 14692

Tel: (716) 473-1000   Fax: (716) 461-4348   www.gleasoncorp.com

Mfr. gear making machine tools; tooling and services.

T. Lundsteen A/S, Nordholmen 4, Postboks 1929, DK-2650 Hividovre, Denmark

Tel: 45-36-49-8611   Fax: 45-36-49-1717

W. R. GRACE & COMPANY

7500 Grace Drive, Columbia, MD, 21044

Tel: (410) 531-4000   Fax: (410) 531-4367   www.grace.com

Mfr. specialty chemicals and materials: packaging, health care, catalysts, construction, water treatment/process.

W.R. Grace, Generatorvej 8D, DK-2730 Herlev, Denmark

GRANITE SYSTEMS, INC.

1228 Elm Street, Manchester, NH, 03101

Tel: (603) 625-0100   Fax: (603) 625-4812   www.granitesystems.com

Mfr. service resource management software.

Granite Systems, Inc., Regus House, Iarsbjomsstraede 3, DK-1454 Copenhagen, Denmark

Tel: 45-333-77250

GRANT THORNTON INTERNATIONAL

800 One Prudential Plaza, 130 E. Randolph Drive, Chicago, IL, 60601-6050

Tel: (312) 856-0001   Fax: (312) 616-7052   www.grantthornton.com

Accounting, audit, tax and management consulting services.

Grothen & Perregaard, Stockholmsgade 45, DK-2100 Copenhagen Ø, Denmark

Tel: 45-35-27-1100   Contact: J. Frank Jakobsen

GREY GLOBAL GROUP

777 Third Ave., New York, NY, 10017

Tel: (212) 546-2000   Fax: (212) 546-1495   www.grey.com

International advertising agency.

Grey Communications Group, Sankt Peders Straede 49A, DK-1453 Copenhagen K, Denmark

GUIDANT CORPORATION

111 Monument Circle, 29th Fl., Indianapolis, IN, 46204

Tel: (317) 971-2000   Fax: (317) 971-2040   www.guidant.com

Mfr. cardiovascular therapeutic devices.

Guidant Denmark A/S, Lygten 2C 4, DK-2400 Copenhagen NV, Denmark

HALLIBURTON COMPANY

500 North Akard Street, Ste. 3600, Dallas, TX, 75201-3391

Tel: (214) 978-2600   Fax: (214) 978-2685   www.halliburton.com

Engaged in diversified energy services, engineering and construction.

Halliburton Ltd., PO Box 4060, DK-6715 Esbjerg, Denmark

Tel: 45-79-14-5400   Fax: 45-79-14-5410

HANDY & HARMAN

555 Theodore Fremd Ave., Rye, NY, 10580

Tel: (914) 921-5200   Fax: (914) 925-4496   www.handyha

Precious and specialty metals for industry, refining, scrap metal; diversified industrial mfr.

Indiana Tube Denmark A/S, Kokbjerg 25, DK-6000 Kolding, Denmark

HARMAN INTERNATIONAL INDUSTRIES, INC.

1101 Pennsylvania Ave. NW, Ste. 1010, Washington, DC, 20004

Tel: (202) 393-1101   Fax: (202) 393-3064   www.harman.com

Mfr. audio and video equipment, loudspeakers and sound reinforcement equipment.

Harman Denmark, Birkeroed Kongevej 194B, DK-3460 Birkerød, Denmark

HARRIS CORPORATION

1025 West NASA Blvd., Melbourne, FL, 32919

Tel: (407) 727-9100   Fax: (407) 727-9344   www.harris.com

Mfr. communications and information-handling equipment, including copying and fax systems.

Independent Elcronic Components, Bernhard Bangs Alle 39, DK-2000 Frederiksberg, Denmark

Tel: 45-38-10-2925   Fax: 45-38-10-2926

HEIDRICK & STRUGGLES INTERNATIONAL, INC.

233 South Wacker Drive, Chicago, IL, 60606

Tel: (312) 496-1200   Fax: (312) 496-1290   www.heidrick.com

Executive search firm.

Heidrick & Struggles Intl. Inc., Hammerensgade 1, DK-1267 Copenhagen K, Denmark

Tel: 45-35-43-7044   Fax: 45-35-43-7045

HELLER FINANCIAL INC.

500 West Monroe Street, Chicago, IL, 60661

Tel: (312) 441-7000   Fax: (312) 441-7367   www.hellerfin.com

Financial services.

Nordisk Factoring A/S, Teknikerbyen 21, DK-2830 Virum, Denmark

HERCULES INC.

Hercules Plaza, 1313 N. Market Street, Wilmington, DE, 19894-0001

Tel: (302) 594-5000   Fax: (302) 594-5400   www.herc.com

Mfr. specialty chemicals, plastics, film and fibers, coatings, resins and food ingredients.

A/S Kobenhavns Pektinfabrik, Ved Banen 16, DK-4623 Lille Skensved, Denmark

HEWLETT-PACKARD COMPANY

3000 Hanover Street, Palo Alto, CA, 94304-1185

Tel: (650) 857-1501   Fax: (650) 857-5518   www.hp.com

Mfr. computing, communications and measurement products and services.

Hewlett-Packard A/S, Kongevejen 25, DK-3460 Birkerød, Denmark

HONEYWELL INTERNATIONAL INC.

Honeywell Plaza, Minneapolis, MN, 55408

Tel: (612) 951-1000   Fax: (612) 951-8537   www.honeywell.com

Develop/mfr. controls for home and building, industry, space and aviation, burglar and fire alarm systems.

Honeywell A/S, Automatikvej 1, DK-2860 Søborg, Denmark

Tel: 45-39-55=5555   Fax: 45-39-55=5551

HORWATH INTERNATIONAL ASSOCIATION

420 Lexington Avenue, Suite 526, New York, NY, 10170-0526

Tel: (212) 808-2000   Fax: (212) 808-2020   www.horwath.com

Public accountants and auditors.

Horwath, Revisorerne Strandvejen 58, Strandvejen 58, DK-2900 Hellerup, Denmark

Tel: 45-3929-2500

HOUGHTON INTERNATIONAL INC.

PO Box 930, Madison & Van Buren Avenues, Valley Forge, PA, 19482-0930

Tel: (610) 666-4000   Fax: (610) 666-1376   www.houghtonintl.com

Mfr. specialty chemicals, hydraulic fluids and lubricants.

Houghton Danmark A/S, Skodsborgvej 48A, DK-2830 Virum, Denmark

Tel: 45-45-85-23-00

HOWMEDICA OSTEONICS, INC.

59 Route 17 South, Allendale, NJ, 07401

Tel: (201) 507-7300   Fax: (201) 935-4873   www.howmedica.com

Mfr. of maxillofacial products (orthopedic implants).

Howmedica Denmark, Copenhagen, Denmark

Tel: 45-33-93-6099

J.M. HUBER CORPORATION

333 Thornall Street, Edison, NJ, 08818

Tel: (732) 549-8600   Fax: (732) 549-2239   www.huber.com

Diversified, multinational supplier of engineered materials, natural resources and technology-based services to customers spanning many industries, from paper and energy to plastics and construction.

Huber Engineered Materials, Copenhagen, Denmark

HYPERION SOLUTIONS CORPORATION

1344 Crossman Avenue, Sunnyvale, CA, 94089

Tel: (408) 744-9500   Fax: (408) 744-0400   www.hyperion.com

Mfr. data analysis software tools.

Hyperion Denmark, Fredericiagade 16, DK-1310 Copenhagen K, Denmark

Tel: 45-33-74-3300 Fax: 45-33-74-3301

i2 TECHNOLOGIES, INC.

11701 Luna Road, Dallas, TX, 75234

Tel: (214) 860-6106   Fax: (214) 860-6060   www.i2.com

Engaged in supply chain management; solutions to help companies collaborate on decision-making processes.

i2 Technologies A/S, Hovedgaden 8, DK-3460 Birkerød, Denmark

IBM CORPORATION

1133 Westchester Avenue, White Plains, NY, 10604

Tel: (914) 765-1900   Fax: (914) 765-7382   www.ibm.com

Information products, technology and services.

IBM Nordic Information Centre A/S, Nymollevej 85, Lyngby, DK-2800 Aarhus, Denmark

Tel: 45-45-23-3000 Fax: 45-45-93-2420

IDEX CORPORATION

630 Dundee Road, Ste. 400, Northbrook, IL, 60062

Tel: (847) 498-7070   Fax: (847) 498-3940   www.idexcorp.com

Mfr. industrial pumps, lubrication systems, metal fabrication equipment, bending and clamping devices.

Viking Pump (Europe) Limited, Syrenvej 1, DK-4920 Sollested K, Denmark

IFR SYSTEMS, INC.

10200 West York Street, Wichita, KS, 67215-8999

Tel: (316) 522-4981   Fax: (316) 524-2623   www.ifrsys.com

Mfr. electronic test and measurement equipment.

IFR Sysems, Inc., Oesertorv 12d, DK-7800 Skive, Denmark

Tel: 45-9614-0045

IKON OFFICE SOLUTIONS

70 Valley Stream Parkway, Malvern, PA, 19355

Tel: (610) 296-8000   Fax: (610) 408-7022   www.ikon.com

Sales of office equipment, including fax machines, copiers and printers.

IKON Office Solutions, Vallensbaekvej 44, DK-2625 Vallensbaek, Denmark

Tel: 45-43-666768 Fax: 45-43-666969 Contact: Henning Rudbech

IMI NORGREN GROUP

5400 South Delaware Street, Littleton, CO, 80120-1663

Tel: (303) 794-2611   Fax: (303) 795-9487   www.usa.norgren.com

Mfr. pneumatic filters, regulators, lubricators, valves, automation systems, dryers, push-in fittings.

IMI Norgren AS, Vesterlundvej 18, DK-2730 Herlev, Denmark

Tel: 45-44-91-4166 Fax: 45-44-91-1560

INFONET SERVICES CORPORATION

2160 East Grand Ave., El Segundo, CA, 90245-1022

Tel: (310) 335-2600   Fax: (310) 335-4507   www.infonet.com

Provider of Internet services and electronic messaging services.

Infonet Denmark, Lautruphoej 2-6, DK-2750 Ballerup, Denmark

Tel: 45-44-80-1111   Fax: 45-44-80-4228

INGRAM MICRO INC.

1600 E. St. Andrew Place, Santa Ana, CA, 92799

Tel: (714) 566-1000   Fax: (714) 566-7940   www.ingrammicro.com

Engaged in wholesale distribution of microcomputer products.

Ingram Micro A/S, Slotsmarken 16, DK-2970 Hørsholm, Denmark

INTEL CORPORATION

2200 Mission College Blvd., Santa Clara, CA, 95052-8119

Tel: (408) 765-8080   Fax: (408) 765-1739   www.intel.com

Mfr. semiconductor, microprocessor and micro-communications components and systems.

Giga Intel (Denmark) Ltd., Mileparken 22, DK-2740 Skovlunde, Denmark

Emp: 146

INTELLIGROUP, INC.

499 Thornall Street, Edison, NJ, 08837

Tel: (732) 590-1600   Fax: (732) 362-2100   www.intelligroup.com

Provides systems integration, customer software and Internet application development.

Intelligroup Nordic A/S, Slotsgade 18, DK-5000 Odense C, Denmark

Tel: 45-70-25-1020   Contact: Martin Dupont

INTERGRAPH CORPORATION

One Madison Industrial Park, Huntsville, AL, 35894-0001

Tel: (256) 730-2000   Fax: (256) 730-7898   www.intergraph.com

Develop/mfr. interactive computer graphic systems.

Intergraph CAD/CAM (Denmark) A/S, Roskildevej 39, DK-2000 Frederiksberg, Denmark

Tel: 45-36-44-5888   Fax: 45-36-44-2070

INTERMEC TECHNOLOGIES CORPORATION

6001 36th Avenue West, PO Box 4280, Everett, WA, 98203-9280

Tel: (425) 348-2600   Fax: (425) 355-9551   www.intermec.com

Mfr. and distributor automated data collection systems.

Intermec Technologies A/S, Gydevang 21A, DK-3450 Allerød, Denmark

Tel: 45-48-16-6166   Fax: 45-18-16-6167

INTERNATIONAL PAPER COMPANY

400 Atlantic Street, Stamford, CT, 06921

Tel: (203) 541-8000   Fax: (203) 358-6444   www.ipaper.com

Mfr./distributor container board, paper and wood products.

Horsell Enk A/S, Valjoejs Alle 155, DK-2610 Roedovre, Denmark

Ilford Photo A/S, Gadelandet 18, DK-2700 Bronshoj, Denmark

INTERNATIONAL RECTIFIER CORPORATION

233 Kansas Street, El Segundo, CA, 90245

Tel: (310) 322-3331   Fax: (310) 322-3332   www.irf.com

Mfr. power semiconductor components.

International Rectifier Corp., PO Box 88, Teelfonvej 8, DK-2860 Søborg, Denmark

Tel: 45-39-57-7150   Fax: 45-39-57-7152

INVITROGEN CORPORATION

1600 Faraday Avenue, Carlsbad, CA, 92008

Tel: (760) 603-7200   Fax: (760) 602-6500   www.invitrogen.com

Mfr. products and kits for gene analysis.

Invitrogen A/S, Testrupgerdsvej 8-10, DK-26300 Taastrup, Denmark

J. WALTER THOMPSON COMPANY

466 Lexington Ave., New York, NY, 10017

Tel: (212) 210-7000   Fax: (212) 210-6944   www.jwt.com

International advertising and marketing services.

J. Walter Thompson Co., Copenhagen, Denmark

JOHNSON & JOHNSON

One Johnson & Johnson Plaza, New Brunswick, NJ, 08933

Tel: (732) 524-0400   Fax: (732) 214-0334   www.jnj.com

Mfr./distributor/R&D pharmaceutical, health care and cosmetic products.

Janssen-Cilag, PO Box 149, DK-3460 Birkerød, Denmark

SC JOHNSON

1525 Howe St., Racine, WI, 53403

Tel: (262) 260-2000   Fax: (262) 260-2133   www.scjohnsonwax.com

Home, auto, commercial and personal care products and specialty chemicals.

SC Johnson, Midtager 18, DK-2600 Glostrup, Denmark

JUKI UNION SPECIAL CORPORATION

8500 N.W. 17th St., Miami, FL, 33126

Tel: (305) 594-0059   Fax: (305) 594-0720   www.unionspecial.com

Mfr. sewing machines.

Rothenborg International, Neptunvej 10-12, DK-7430 Ikast, Denmark

A.T. KEARNEY INC.

5400 Legacy Dr., Plano, TX, 75201

Tel: (972) 604-4600   Fax: (972) 543-7680   www.atkearney.com

Management consultants and executive search.

A. T. Kearney A/S, Amaliegade 12, DK-1256 Copenhagen K, Denmark

Tel: 45-33-69-3000

KELLOGG COMPANY

One Kellogg Square, PO Box 3599, Battle Creek, MI, 49016-3599

Tel: (616) 961-2000   Fax: (616) 961-2871   www.kelloggs.com

Mfr. ready-to-eat cereals and convenience foods.

Nordisk Kellogg's A/S, Attn: Denmark Office, One Kellogg Square, PO Box 3599, Battle Creek, MI, 49016-3599

KELLY SERVICES, INC.

999 W. Big Beaver Road, Troy, MI, 48084

Tel: (248) 362-4444   Fax: (248) 244-4154   www.kellyservices.com

Temporary help placement.

Kelly Services of Denmark, Inc., Amagertorv 11, DK-1160 Copenhagen K, Denmark

Tel: 45-33-11-7070   Fax: 45--33-11-5122

KENNAMETAL INC.

1600 Technology Way, PO Box 231, Latrobe, PA, 15650

Tel: (724) 539-5000   Fax: (724) 539-4710   www.kennametal.com

Tools, hard carbide and tungsten alloys for metalworking industry.

Granaths Hardmetal A/S, DK-7000 Fredericia, Denmark

Tel: 45-75-94-2122   Fax: 45-75-94-1975

KINETIC CONCEPTS, INC.

8023 Vantage Drive, San Antonio, TX, 78230-4728

Tel: (210) 524-9000   Fax: (210) 255-4524   www.KCI1.com

Mfr. specialized medical beds.

KCI Medical, Strandvejen 343, DK-2930 Klampenborg, Denmark

Tel: 45-3990-0180

KOPPERS INDUSTRIES INC.

436 Seventh Ave., Pittsburgh, PA, 15219-1800

Tel: (412) 227-2000   Fax: (412) 227-2333   www.koppers.com

Construction materials and services; chemicals and building products.

Koppers Denmark A/S, Avernakke, DK-5800 Nyborg, Denmark

Tel: 45-6331-31-00

KORN/FERRY INTERNATIONAL

1800 Century Park East, Los Angeles, CA, 90067

Tel: (310) 843-4100   Fax: (310) 553-6452   www.kornferry.com

Engaged in executive search and management consulting.

Korn/Ferry International, Copenhagen, Denmark

Tel: 45-35-25-0090   Fax: 45-35-25-0099

KPMG CONSULTING INC.

1676 International Dr., McLean, VA, 22102

Tel: (703) 747-3000   Fax: (703) 747-8500   www.kpmg.com

Accounting and audit, tax and management consulting services.

KPMG International, Borups All, Copenhagen, Denmark

Tel: 45-38-18-3000   Fax: 45-38-18-3045   Contact: Finn L. Meyer, Sr. Ptnr.

KPMG International, Vestre Havnepromenade 1, DK-9000 Aalborg, Denmark

KPMG International, Torret 10, DK-5800 Nyborg, Denmark

KPMG International, Burstenbindervej 6, DK-5230 Odense, Denmark

KPMG International, Sundsmarkvej 12, DK-6400 Søoderborg, Denmark

LAMSON & SESSIONS COMPANY

25701 Science Park Drive, Cleveland, OH, 44122

Tel: (216) 464-3400   Fax: (216) 464-1455   www.lamson-sessions.com

Mfr. thermoplastic enclosures, fittings, conduit and pipe, and wiring devices for the electrical, telecommunications, consumer, power and waste water markets.

Lamson & Sessions APS, Rojrupveg 15, DK-5550 Langeskov, Denmark

LANIER WORLDWIDE, INC.

2300 Parklake Drive, N.E., Atlanta, GA, 30345

Tel: (770) 496-9500   Fax: (770) 938-1020   www.lanier.com

Specialize in digital copiers and multi-functional systems.

Lanier Denmark A/S, Markaervej 5, DK-2630 Taastrup, Denmark

Tel: 45-43-71-0200   Fax: 45-43-71-0221

LECROY CORPORATION

700 Chestnut Ridge Road, Chestnut Ridge, NY, 10977

Tel: (845) 425-2000   Fax: (845) 425-8967   www.lecroy.com

Mfr. signal analyzers and electronic measurement systems.

Metric A/S, Markaervej 7, Postboks 6, DK-2630 Taastrup, Denmark

Tel: 45-43-71-6444   Fax: 45-43-71-6433

LEVI STRAUSS & COMPANY

1155 Battery St., San Francisco, CA, 94111-1230

Tel: (415) 544-6000   Fax: (415) 501-3939   www.levistrauss.com

Mfr. and distributor of casual wearing apparel, including jeans and sportswear.

Levi Strauss Denmark, Kattesundet 4, DK-1458 Copenhagen K, Denmark

Tel: 45-33-15-5800   Fax: 45-22-15-6539

LEVOLOR/HARDWARE GROUP, DIV. NEWELL RUBBERMAID

29 East Stephenson Street, Freeport, IL, 61032

Tel: (815) 235-4171   Fax: (815) 235-4171   www.americantool.com

Mfr. hand tools, cutting tools and power tool accessories.

ATC, Div. Levolor Hardware Group, Industriholmen 15A, DK-2650 Hvidovre, Denmark

Tel: 45-36-88-3588   Fax: 45-36-88-3599

LEXMARK INTERNATIONAL

740 W. New Circle Rd., Lexington, KY, 40550

Tel: (859) 232-2000   Fax: (859) 232-1886   www.lexmark.com

Develop, manufacture, supply of printing solutions and products, including laser, inkjet, and dot matrix printers.

Lexmark Nordic LLC, Bregnerødvej 96, DK-3460 Birkerød, Denmark

Tel: 45-99-88-88

ELI LILLY & COMPANY

Lilly Corporate Center, Indianapolis, IN, 46285

Tel: (317) 276-2000   Fax: (317) 277-6579   www.lilly.com

Mfr. pharmaceuticals and animal health products.

Eli Lilly Denmark A/S, Thoravej 4, DK-2400 Copenhagen, Denmark

Tel: 45-38-16-8600   Fax: 45-38-88-1733

LOCKHEED MARTIN CORPORATION

6801 Rockledge Drive, Bethesda, MD, 20817

Tel: (301) 897-6000   Fax: (301) 897-6652   www.imco.com

Design/mfr./management systems in fields of space, defense, energy, electronics and technical services.

Lockheed International, LRO NEA Lindberg, DK-2250 Ballerup, Denmark

Tel: 45-44-97-1311   Fax: 45-44-97-1311

LSI LOGIC CORPORATION

1551 McCarthy Blvd., Milpitas, CA, 95035

Tel: (408) 433-8000   Fax: (408) 954-3220   www.lsilogic.com

Develop and manufacture semiconductors.

LSI Logic Development Center Ballerup, Lautrupuang 2B, DK-2750 Ballerup, Denmark

Tel: 45-44-86-5555   Fax: 45-44-86-5556

MANPOWER INTERNATIONAL INC.

5301 N. Ironwood Rd., PO Box 2053, Milwaukee, WI, 53201-2053

Tel: (414) 961-1000   Fax: (414) 961-7081   www.manpower.com

Temporary help, contract service, training and testing.

Manpower A/S, Norre Voldgade 19, DK-1358 Copenhagen K, Denmark

Tel: 45-33-69-8000   Fax: 45-33-69-8080

MARSH & McLENNAN COS INC.

1166 Ave. of the Americas, New York, NY, 10036-2774

Tel: (212) 345-5000   Fax: (212) 345-4808   www.marshmac.com

Insurance agents/brokers, pension and investment management consulting services.

Bonnor Marsh & McLennan A/S, Teknikerbyen 3, DK-2830 Virum, Denmark

Tel: 45-45-95-9595   Fax: 45-45-95-9500   Contact: John Bonnon

MASCO CORPORATION

21001 Van Born Road, Taylor, MI, 48180

Tel: (313) 274-7400   Fax: (313) 374-6666   www.masco.com

Mfr. faucets, cabinets, locks and numerous home improvement, building and home furnishings products.

Damixa A/S, Ostibirkvej 2, Postbox 50, DK-5240 Odense NO, Denmark

Tel: 45-66-10-9700

MAXON CORPORATION

201 East 18th Street, Muncie, IN, 47302

Tel: (765) 284-3304   Fax: (765) 286-8394   www.maxoncorp.com

Industry combustion equipment and valves.

Maxon Combustion Systems A/S, Centervej 2, DK-6000 Kolding, Denmark

Tel: 45-70-27-0999

McCANN-ERICKSON WORLDGROUP

750 Third Ave., New York, NY, 10017

Tel: (212) 697-6000   Fax: (212) 984-3575   www.mccann.com

International advertising and marketing services.

McCann-Erickson A/S, Kalkbrænderihavnsgade 4, DK-12100 Copenhagen K, Denmark

McDONALD'S CORPORATION

McDonald's Plaza, Oak Brook, IL, 60523

Tel: (630) 623-3000   Fax: (630) 623-7409   www.mcdonalds.com

Fast food chain stores.

McDonald's Corp., Denmark

Contact: Jesper Gad Andresen, Mgr.

McKINSEY & COMPANY

55 East 52nd Street, New York, NY, 10022

Tel: (212) 446-7000   Fax: (212) 446-8575   www.mckinsey.com

Management and business consulting services.

McKinsey & Company, Ved Stranden 14, DK-1061 Copenhagen, Denmark

Tel: 45-33-93-3030   Fax: 45-33-93-1621

MEMOREX CORPORATION

10100 Pioneer Blvd., Ste. 110, Santa Fe Springs, CA, 90670

Tel: (562) 906-2800   Fax: (562) 906-2848   www.memorex.com

Magnetic recording tapes, etc.

MRX A/S, Vallensbaekvej 25, DK-2600 Glostrup, Denmark

MENTOR GRAPHICS

8005 SW Boeckman Road, Wilsonville, OR, 97070-7777

Tel: (503) 685-7000   Fax: (503) 685-1202   www.mentorg.com

Develop/mfr. software tools for embedded systems market.

Mentor Graphics, Naverland 2, DK-2600 Glostrup, Denmark

Tel: 45-70-207566

MERCK & COMPANY, INC.

One Merck Drive, PO Box 100, Whitehouse Station, NJ, 08889-0100

Tel: (908) 423-1000   Fax: (908) 423-2592   www.merck.com

Pharmaceuticals, chemicals and biologicals.

MSD Denmark, Smedeland 8, DK-2600 Glostrup, Denmark

Tel: 45-43-28-7766

MERCURY INTERACTIVE CORPORATION

1325 Borregas Ave., Sunnyvale, CA, 94089

Tel: (408) 822-5200   Fax: (408) 822-5300   www.merc-int.com

Mfr. computer software to decipher and eliminate "bugs" from systems.

Mercury Interactive, Borupvang 2B, 2 sal, tv, DK-2750 Ballerup, Denmark

MICROSOFT CORPORATION

One Microsoft Way, Redmond, WA, 98052-6399

Tel: (425) 882-8080   Fax: (425) 936-7329   www.microsoft.com

Computer software, peripherals and services.

Microsoft Danmark APS, Lautruphoj 1-3, DK-2750 Ballerup, Denmark

Tel: 45-44-89-0100   Fax: 45-44-68-5510

MILACRON INC.

2090 Florence Ave., Cincinnati, OH, 45206

Tel: (513) 487-5000   Fax: (513) 487-5057   www.milacron.com

Metalworking and plastics technologies.

Ferromatik Milacron A/S, Hesselager 14, DK-2605 Brøndby, Denmark

Tel: 45-43-43-1600 Fax: 45-43-43-1699   Contact: Jörgen Juul-Andersen

MILLIPORE CORPORATION

80 Ashby Road, PO Box 9125, Bedford, MA, 01730

Tel: (781) 533-6000   Fax: (781) 533-3110   www.millipore.com

Mfr. flow and pressure measurement and control components; precision filters, hi-performance liquid chromatography instruments.

Millipore A/S, Baldersbven 46, DK-2640 Hedehusene, Denmark

MODINE MANUFACTURING COMPANY

1500 DeKoven Ave., Racine, WI, 53403

Tel: (262) 636-1200   Fax: (262) 636-1424   www.modine.com

Mfr. heat-transfer products.

Modine Manufacturing Co., Horsens, Denmark

MOLEX INC.

2222 Wellington Court, Lisle, IL, 60532

Tel: (630) 969-4550   Fax: (630) 969-1352   www.molex.com

Mfr. electronic, electrical and fiber optic interconnection products and systems, switches, application tooling.

Molex G. Østervig A/S, Paul Bergsoes Vej 16, DK-2600 Glostrup, Denmark

MONSANTO

800 N. Lindbergh Boulevard, St. Louis, MO, 63167

Tel: (314) 694-1000   Fax: (314) 694-7625   www.monsanto.com

Life sciences company focusing on agriculture, nutrition, pharmaceuticals, health and wellness and sustainable development.

Monsanto Denmark, Smedeland 6, DK-2600 Glostrup, Denmark

Tel: 45-434-57-799   Fax: 45-434-59-472

MOOG INC.

300 Jamison Road, East Aurora, NY, 14052-0018

Tel: (716) 652-2000   Fax: (716) 687-4471   www.moog.com

Mfr. precision control components and systems.

Moog Buhl Automotson, Topstykkat 24, DK-3460 Birkerød, Denmark

J. P. MORGAN CHASE & CO. INC.

270 Park Ave., New York, NY, 10017

Tel: (212) 270-6000   Fax: (212) 622-9030   www.jpmorganchase.com

Provides integrated financial solutions for institutions and individuals worldwide, including asset management, investment banking and commercial banking.

J. P. Morgan Chase & Co., Vognmagergade 10, DK-1120 Copenhagen, Denmark

MOTOROLA, INC.

1303 East Algonquin Road, Schaumburg, IL, 60196

Tel: (847) 576-5000   Fax: (847) 538-5191   www.motorola.com

Mfr. communications equipment, semiconductors and cellular phones.

Motorola Storno A/S, Midtager 20, DK-2605 Broendby, Denmark

Tel: 45-43-45-5544   Fax: 45-43-43-4358

NATIONAL STARCH AND CHEMICAL COMPANY
10 Finderne Ave., Bridgewater, NJ, 08807-3300

Tel: (908) 685-5000   Fax: (908) 685-5005   www.nationalstarch.com

Mfr. adhesives and sealants, resins and specialty chemicals, electronic materials and adhesives, food products, industry starch.

National Starch and Chemical, Bogballevej 9, DK-7171 Uldum, Denmark

NCH CORPORATION
2727 Chemsearch Blvd., Irving, TX, 75062

Tel: (972) 438-0211   Fax: (972) 438-0707   www.nch.com

Engaged in manufacturing and specialty chemicals.

National Chemsearch, Industribuen 7E, DK-2635 Ishoj, Denmark

NETIQ CORPORATION
3553 North First Street, San Jose, CA, 95134

Tel: (408) 856-3000   Fax: (408) 273-0578   www.netiq.com

Mfr. performance management software.

NetIQ Denmark Aps, Parallelvej 10, DK-2800 Lyngby, Denmark

NETWORK ASSOCIATES, INC.
3965 Freedom Circle, Santa Clara, CA, 95054

Tel: (408) 988-3832   Fax: (408) 970-9727   www.networkassociates.com

Designs and produces network security and network management software and hardware.

Network Associates, Lautruphoej 1-3, DK-2750 Ballerup, Denmark
Tel: 45-70-277-277   Fax: 45-44-209-910

NEW HAMPSHIRE BALL BEARINGS INC. (NHBB)
9700 Independence Ave., Chatsworth, CA, 91311-4323

Tel: (818) 407-9300   Fax: (818) 407-9300   www.nhbb.com

Mfr. bearings and bearing assemblies.

NHBB, c/o Coboc, Solvaenget 15, Denmark

AC NIELSEN COMPANY
177 Broad Street, Stamford, CT, 06901

Tel: (203) 961-3000   Fax: (203) 961-3190   www.acnielsen.com

Engaged in market and consumer research.

ACNielsen, Strandboulevarden 89, DK-2100 Copenhagen, Denmark

NL INDUSTRIES, INC.
16825 Northchase Drive, Ste. 1200, Houston, TX, 77060-2544

Tel: (281) 423-3300   Fax: (281) 423-3236   www.nl-ind.com

Producer of titanium dioxide pigments.

Kronos Marketing, Div. NL Industries, Hanne Nielsens Vej 10, DK-2840 Holte, Denmark

NORDSON CORPORATION
28601 Clemens Road, Westlake, OH, 44145-4551

Tel: (440) 892-1580   Fax: (440) 892-9507   www.nordson.com

Mfr. industry application equipment, sealants and packaging machinery.

Nordson Danmark A/S, Laehegnet 75, DK-2620 Albertslund, Denmark
Tel: 45-43-64-8500   Fax: 45-43-64-1101

NORTON ABRASIVES COMPANY
1 New Bond Street, Worcester, MA, 01606

Tel: (508) 795-5000   Fax: (508) 795-5741   www.nortonabrasives.com

Mfr. abrasives for industrial manufacturing.

Norton BV Holland, Fynsvej 73, DK-6000 Kolding, Denmark

NOVELL WORLDWIDE

1800 S. Novell Place, Provo, UT, 84606

Tel: (801) 861-7000   Fax: (801) 861-5555   www.novell.com

Develop/mfr. networking software and related equipment.

Novell Danmark, Slotsmarken 12, DK-2970 Hørsholm, Denmark

NU SKIN ENTERPRISES, INC.

75 West Center St., Provo, UT, 84601

Tel: (801) 345-6100   Fax: (801) 345-5999   www.nuskin.com

Develops and distributes premium-quality personal care and nutritional products.

NuSkin Denmark, Rosenkaeret 13A, Søborg, Denmark

ORACLE CORPORATION

500 Oracle Parkway, Redwood Shores, CA, 94065

Tel: (650) 506-7000   Fax: (650) 506-7200   www.oracle.com

Develop/manufacture software.

Oracle Denmark, Copenhagen, Denmark

OSMONICS INC.

5951 Clearwater Drive, Minnetonka, MN, 55343-8995

Tel: (952) 933-2277   Fax: (952) 933-0141   www.osmonics.com

Mfr. equipment, controls and components for the filtration and water-treatment industries.

Osmonics, Copenhagen, Denmark

OTIS ELEVATOR COMPANY

One Farm Springs Road, Farmington, CT, 06032

Tel: (860) 676-6000   Fax: (860) 676-5111   www.otis.com

Mfr. elevators and escalators.

Otis A/S, Ellekaer 9A, DK-2730 Herlev, Denmark

OWENS-CORNING CORPORATION

One Owens Corning Pkwy., Toledo, OH, 43659

Tel: (419) 248-8000   Fax: (419) 248-8445   www.owenscorning.com

Mfr. building materials systems and composites systems.

Dansk-Svensk Glasfiber A/S (Denmark), Denmark

PANAMETRICS

221 Crescent Street, Waltham, MA, 02154

Tel: (781) 899-2719   Fax: (781) 899-1552   www.panametrics.com

Engaged in manufacture and distribution of ultrasonic testing equipment and process control instrumentation.

Houlberg (Panametrics), Myrestien 7, DK-2670 Greve Strand, Denmark

Tel: 45-43-90-3181 Fax: 45-43-90-3133

PANDUIT CORPORATION

17301 Ridgeland Ave., Tinley Park, IL, 60477-0981

Tel: (708) 532-1800   Fax: (708) 532-1811   www.panduit.com

Mfr. of network connectivity and electrical products.

Panduit Denmark, Gydevang 39-41, DK-3450 Allerød, Denmark

PARAMETRIC TECHNOLOGY CORPORATION

140 Kendrick St., Needham, MA, 02494

Tel: (781) 370-5000   Fax: (781) 370-6000   www.ptc.com

Supplier of mechanical design automation and product data management software and services.

Parametric Technology Denmark, Skovbrynet 1, DK-6000 Kolding, Denmark

Tel: 45-75-50-0258 Fax: 45-75-50-0259

Parametric Technology Denmark A/S, Stationsparken 24, DK-2600 Glostrup, Denmark

Tel: 45-73-27-0600 Fax: 45-43-43-9099

PARKER HANNIFIN CORPORATION

6035 Parkland Blvd., Cleveland, OH, 44124-4141

Tel: (216) 896-3000   Fax: (216) 896-4000   www.parker.com

Mfr. motion-control products.

Parker Hannifin Danmark A/S, Industribuen 8, Industrigrenen 11, DK-2635 Ishoj, Denmark

Polar Seals ApS, PTFE-Packing Mfg. Operation, Hellebaekvej 57, DK-3000 Helsingor, Denmark

PEREGRINE SYSTEMS, INC.

3611 Valley Centre Drive, San Diego, CA, 92130

Tel: (858) 481-5000   Fax: (858) 481-1751   www.peregrine.com

Mfr. resource planning software.

Peregrine Systems A/S, Bernstorffsvej 154, DK-2900 Hellerup, Denmark

PFIZER INC.

235 East 42nd Street, New York, NY, 10017-5755

Tel: (212) 573-2323   Fax: (212) 573-7851   www.pfizer.com

Research-based, global health care company.

Pfizer A/S, Laubrupvag 8, DK-2750 Ballerup, Denmark

Tel: 45-44-20-1100   Fax: 45-44-20-1101

PHARMACIA CORPORATION

100 Route 206 North, Peapack, NJ, 07977

Tel: (908) 901-8000   Fax: (908) 901-8379   www.pharmacia.com

Mfr. pharmaceuticals, agricultural products, industry chemicals.

Pharmacia AS, Overgaden Neden Vandet 7, DK-1414 Copenhagen K, Denmark

Tel: 45-32-965200   Fax: 45-32-967040

PHILLIPS PETROLEUM COMPANY

Phillips Building, 411 S. Keeler Ave., Bartlesville, OK, 74004

Tel: (918) 661-6600   Fax: (918) 661-7636   www.phillips66.com

Crude oil, natural gas, liquefied petroleum gas, gasoline and petro-chemicals.

Phillips Industri & Handel, PO Box 1919, DK-2300 Copenhagen, Denmark

PIC GROUP

2929 Seventh Avenue, Ste. 130, Berkeley, CA, 94710

Tel: (510) 848-8266   Fax: (510) 848-0324   www.pic.com

Engaged in biotechnology.

PIC Denmark, Postboks 7021, DK-9200 Aalborg, Denmark

POLYONE CORPORATION

200 Public Square, Cleveland, OH, 44114-2304

Tel: (216) 589-4000   Fax: (216) 589-4077   www.polyone.com

Mfr. custom made compounded plastics, including polymer, elastomer, colorant and additive products.

PolyOne Denmark, Naverland 16, DK-2600 Glostrup, Denmark

POWERWARE CORPORATION

8609 Six Forks Road, Raleigh, NC, 27615

Tel: (919) 870-3020   Fax: (919) 870-3100   www.powerware.com

Mfr./services uninterruptible power supplies and related equipment.

Powerware Electronics AB, Hammerholmen 39 L-M, DK-2650 Hvidovre, Denmark

Tel: 45-36-77-7910   Fax: 45-36-77-7921

PRICEWATERHOUSECOOPERS LLP

1301 Ave. of the Americas, New York, NY, 10019

Tel: (212) 596-7000   Fax: (212) 259-1301   www.pwcglobal.com

Accounting and auditing, tax and management, and human resource consulting services.

PriceWaterhouseCoopers, Tuborg Blvd. 1, PO Box 129, DK-2900 Hellerup, Denmark

Tel: 45-39-47-0000   Fax: 45-39-47-0010

PriceWaterhouseCoopers, Aboulevarden 70, DK-8000 Aarhus C, Denmark
Tel: 45-89-32-0000   Fax: 45-89-32-0010

PRIMIX SOLUTIONS INC.

311 Arsenal Street, Watertown, MA, 02472

Tel: (617) 923-6500   Fax: (617) 923-6565   www.primix.com

Provides technology consulting and systems integration services.

Primix Solutions Denmark, 9 Kongensgade 9, DK-1472 Copenhagen K, Denmark
Tel: 45-33-63-0510

PROCTER & GAMBLE COMPANY

One Procter & Gamble Plaza, Cincinnati, OH, 45202

Tel: (513) 983-1100   Fax: (513) 562-4500   www.pg.com

Personal care, food, laundry, cleaning and industry products.

Procter & Gamble, Paludan Mullersvej 82, DK-8200 Aarhus N, Denmark
Procter & Gamble, Postboks 1459, DK-7500 Holstebro, Denmark
Tel: 45-70-12-3839
Procter & Gamble Nordic, Postboks 1459, Hostrupsvej 9, DK-7500 Holstebro, Denmark

THE QUAKER OATS COMPANY

Quaker Tower, 321 North Clark Street, Chicago, IL, 60610-4714

Tel: (312) 222-7111   Fax: (312) 222-8323   www.quakeroats.com

Mfr. foods and beverages.

OTA A/S, Islands Brygge 39, DK-2300 Copenhagen S, Denmark

QUARK, INC.

1800 Grant Street, Denver, CO, 80203

Tel: (303) 894-8888   Fax: (303) 894-3398   www.quark.com

Mfr. and sales of desktop publishing software.

Quark Scandinavia, Byvolden 25 A+B, DK-4000 Roskilde, Denmark

QUINTILES TRANSNATIONAL CORPORATION

4709 Creekstone Dr., Durham, NC, 27703

Tel: (919) 998-2000   Fax: (919) 998-9113   www.quintiles.com

Mfr. pharmaceuticals.

Quintiles AB, Global House, Kvæsthusgade 4, DK-1251 Copenhagen K, Denmark

QWEST COMMUNICATIONS INTERNATIONAL INC.

1801 California Street, Ste. 5200, Denver, CO, 80202

Tel: (303) 896-2020   Fax: (303) 793-6654   www.uswest.com

Tele-communications provider; integrated communications services.

KPNQwest (JV), Copenhagen, Denmark

RADISSON HOTELS INTERNATIONAL

Carlson Pkwy., PO Box 59159, Minneapolis, MN, 55459-8204

Tel: (612) 540-5526   Fax: (612) 449-3400   www.radisson.com

Operates, manages and franchises full-service hotels and resorts worldwide.

Radisson SAS Royal Hotel Copenhagen, Hammerichsgade 1, DK-1611 Copenhagen V, Denmark
Tel: 45-33-42-6000   Fax: 45-33-42-6100

RAY & BERNDTSON, INC.

301 Commerce, Ste. 2300, Fort Worth, TX, 76102

Tel: (817) 334-0500   Fax: (817) 334-0779   www.prb.com

Executive search, management audit and management consulting firm.

Ray & Berndtson, Nyhavn 63 C, DK-1051 Copenhagen K, Denmark
Tel: 45-33-14=3636   Fax: 45-33-32=4332   Contact: Kurt Brusgaard, Mng. Ptnr.

READER'S DIGEST ASSOCIATION, INC.

Reader's Digest Rd., Pleasantville, NY, 10570

Tel: (914) 238-1000   Fax: (914) 238-4559   www.readersdigest.com

Publisher of magazines and books and direct mail marketer.

Forlaget Det Bedste A/S, Jagtvej 169B, PO Box 810, DK-2100 Copenhagen, Denmark

REEBOK INTERNATIONAL LTD.

1895 J. W. Foster Blvd., Canton, MA, 02021

Tel: (781) 401-5000   Fax: (781) 401-7402   www.reebok.com

Mfr. athletic shoes including casual, dress golf and walking shoes.

Reebok Denmark, Herstedvang 4, DK-2620 Albertslund, Denmark

REFLEXITE TECHNOLOGY

120 Darling Drive, Avon, CT, 06001

Tel: (860) 676-7100   Fax: (860) 676-7199   www.reflexite.com

Mfr. plastic film, sheet, materials and shapes, optical lenses.

Reflexite Europe A/S, Lyngsø Alle 3, DK-2970 Hørsholm, Denmark

Tel: 45-45-76-1122   Fax: 45-45-76-1102   Contact: Lars Thomsen, Mgr.

REPLOGLE GLOBES INC.

2801 South 25th Ave., Broadview, IL, 60153-4589

Tel: (708) 343-0900   Fax: (708) 343-0923   www.rephogleglobes.com

Mfr. geographical world globes.

Scanglobe A/S, 23 Ulvevej, DK-4622 Havdrup, Denmark

Tel: 45-46-18-5400   Fax: 45-46-18-5270   Contact: Per Lund-Hansen

REXNORD CORPORATION

4701 West Greenfield Ave., Milwaukee, WI, 53214

Tel: (414) 643-3000   Fax: (414) 643-3078   www.rexnord.com

Mfr. power transmission and conveying components.

Rexnord Marbett-MCC, Moerkhoejvej 138 2.H., DK-2730 Herlev, Denmark

RF MICRO DEVICES, INC.

7628 Thorndike Road, Greensboro, NC, 27409-9421

Tel: (336) 664-1233   Fax: (336) 931-7454   www.rfmd.com

Mfr. amplifiers and modulators for wireless communications devices.

RF Micro Devices, Inc., Klokkestobervej 2, DK9490 Pandrup, Denmark

Tel: 45-96730441   Fax: 45-96730446

RICHARDSON ELECTRONICS, LTD.

40 W 267 Keslinger Road, LaFox, IL, 60147-0393

Tel: (630) 208-2200   Fax: (630) 208-2550   www.rell.com

Mfr. and distribution of electron tubes and related equipment.

Richardson Electronics, Baldersbuen 15H, DK-2640 Hedehusene, Denmark

ROCKWELL AUTOMATION, INC.

777 East Wisconsin Ave., Ste. 1400, Milwaukee, WI, 53202

Tel: (414) 212-5200   Fax: (414) 212-5201   www.rockwellautomation.com

Products and service for aerospace and defense, automotive, electronics, graphics and automation industry.

Rockwell Automation A/S, Herstedoestervej 27-29, DK-2620 Albertslund, Denmark

Tel: 45-43-46-6000   Fax: 45-43-46-6001

ROHM AND HAAS COMPANY

100 Independence Mall West, Philadelphia, PA, 19106

Tel: (215) 592-3000   Fax: (215) 592-3377   www.rohmhaas.com

Mfr. specialty chemicals.

Rohm and Haas European Holding ApS, Vester Farimagsgade 6, 1/F, DK-1606 Copenhagen V, Denmark

Tel: 45-3393-3318

RUSSELL REYNOLDS ASSOCIATES INC.

200 Park Avenue, New York, NY, 10166-0002

Tel: (212) 351-2000   Fax: (212) 370-0896   www.russreyn.com

Executive recruiting services.

Russell Reynolds Associates Inc., Østergade 1, First Fl., DK-1100 Copenhagen K, Denmark

Tel: 45-33-69-2320   Fax: 45-33-69-2349   Contact: Kai Hammerich

SAS INSTITUTE INC.

SAS Campus Drive, Cary, NC, 27513

Tel: (919) 677-8000   Fax: (919) 677-4444   www.sas.com

Mfr. and distribution of decision support software.

SAS Institute (Denmark) Inc., Kroyer Kielbergs Vej 3, DK-8660 Skanderborg, Denmark

Tel: 45-33-96-9898   Fax: 45-33-96-9991

SBC COMMUNICATIONS INC.

175 East Houston, San Antonio, TX, 78205

Tel: (210) 821-4105   Fax: (210) 351-5034   www.sbc.com

Engaged in telecommunications.

Tele Danmark A/S, Knnikeegde 16, DK-8000 Aarhus C, Denmark

Contact: Knud Heinesen, Chmn..

SCHENKER USA INC.

150 Albany Ave., Freeport, NY, 11520

Tel: (516) 403-5416   Fax: (516) 377-3092   www.schenkerusa.com

Freight forwarders.

Schenker Albert Nielsen A.S, Park AIIU 350, Copenhagen Brondby, DK-2605 Copenhagen, Denmark

Tel: 45-43-63-5544   Fax: 45-43-63-1808

SCHERING-PLOUGH CORPORATION

One Giralda Farms, Madison, NJ, 07940-1000

Tel: (973) 822-7000   Fax: (973) 822-7048   www.sch-plough.com

Proprietary drug and cosmetic products.

Schering-Plough Animal Health, Postbox 297, Hvedemarken 12, DK-3520 Farum, Denmark

SCIENTIFIC-ATLANTA, INC.

5030 Sugarloaf Pkwy., Lawrenceville, GA, 30044

Tel: (770) 903-5000   Fax: (770) 236-6777   www.sciatl.com

Mfr. cable set-top boxes, modems, transmission and distribution equipment.

Arcodan A/S, Sub. of Scientific-Atlanta, Augustenborg Landevej 7, DK-6400 Søoderborg, Denmark

Tel: 45-74-42-2150   Fax: 45-74-42-3907

G.D. SEARLE & COMPANY

5200 Old Orchard Road, Skokie, IL, 60077

Tel: (847) 982-7000   Fax: (847) 470-1480   www.searlehealthnet.com

Mfr. pharmaceuticals, health care, optical products and specialty chemicals.

Searle Scandinavia, Division of Monsanto Danmark A.S., Skelbaekgade, DK-1717 Copenhagen V, Denmark

Tel: 45-31-241533   Fax: 45-31-243120

THE SERVICEMASTER COMPANY

2300 Warrenville Road, Downers Grove, IL, 60515-1700

Tel: (630) 271-1300   Fax: (630) 271-2710   www.svm.com

Provides residential consumer services, including lawn care and landscape maintenance, termite and pest control, plumbing, heating and air conditioning maintenance and repair.

Merry Maids, Copenhagen, Denmark

SIEBEL SYSTEMS, INC.

2207 Bridgepointe Pkwy., San Mateo, CA, 94404

Tel: (650) 295-5000   Fax: (650) 295-5111   www.siebel.com

Provider of e-Business applications software.

Siebel Systems Danmark ApS, Parallelvej 10, DK-2800 Lyngby, Denmark

SILICON GRAPHICS INC.

1600 Amphitheatre Pkwy., Mountain View, CA, 94043-1351

Tel: (650) 960-1980   Fax: (650) 932-0661   www.sgi.com

Design/mfr. special-effects computer graphic systems and software.

Silicon Graphics A/S, Stationsparken 25, DK-2600 Glostrup, Denmark

Tel: 45-43-43-8600   Fax: 45-43-43-8606

SKYWORKS SOLUTIONS, INC.

20 Sylvan Road, Woburn, MA, 01801

Tel: (781) 935-5150   Fax: (781) 824-4579   www.skyworksinc.com

Mfr. electronic and microwave components.

Skyworks Solutions, Parallelvej 10, Lyngby, DK-2800 Copenhagen, Denmark

Contact: Jan Thoning

SOTHEBY'S HOLDINGS, INC.

1334 York Avenue, New York, NY, 10021

Tel: (212) 606-7000   Fax: (212) 606-7027   www.sothebys.com

Auction house specializing in fine art and jewelry.

Sotheby's Holdings, Inc., Bredgade 6, DK-1260 Copenhagen, Denmark

Tel: 45-33-135-556   Fax: 45-33-930-119   Contact: Baroness Hanne Wedell-Wedellsborg

SPERRY-SUN DRILLING SERVICES

PO Box 60070, Houston, TX, 77205

Tel: (281) 871-5100   Fax: (281) 871-5742   www.sperry-sun.com

Provides drilling services to the oil and gas drilling industry.

Sperry-Sun, Inc., Strandvejen 188 J, DK-2920 Charlottenlund Copenhagen, Denmark

SPSS INC.

233 S. Wacker Dr., 11th Fl., Chicago, IL, 60606

Tel: (312) 651-6000   Fax: (312) 329-3668   www.spss.com

Mfr. statistical software.

SPSS Danmark A/S, Rojelskaer 11, DK-2840 Holte, Denmark

THE ST. PAUL COMPANIES, INC.

385 Washington Street, St. Paul, MN, 55102

Tel: (651) 310-7911   Fax: (651) 310-8294   www.stpaul.com

Provides investment, insurance and reinsurance services.

Topdanmark Forsikring A.S, Borupvang 4, DK-2750 Ballerup, Denmark

STANDARD COMMERCIAL CORPORATION

2201 Miller Rd., PO Box 450, Wilson, NC, 27894

Tel: (252) 291-5507   Fax: (252) 237-1109   www.sccgroup.com

Leaf tobacco dealers and processors and wool processors.

Leafco A/S, Tordenskjoldsjade 24, DK-1055 Copenhagen, Denmark

THE STANLEY WORKS

1000 Stanley Drive, PO Box 7000, New Britain, CT, 06053

Tel: (860) 225-5111   Fax: (860) 827-3987   www.stanleyworks.com

Mfr. hand tools and hardware.

Stanley Tools, Norde Standvej 119 B, DK-3150 Hellenbaek, Denmark

STARWOOD HOTELS & RESORTS WORLDWIDE

777 Westchester Avenue, White Plains, NY, 10604

Tel: (914) 640-8100   Fax: (914) 640-8316   www.starwoodhotels.com

Hotel operations including Sheraton, Westin, St. Regis, Four Points and Caesars.

Sheraton Copenhagen Hotel, Vester Sogade 6, DK-1601 Copenhagen V, Denmark

STATE STREET CORPORATION

225 Franklin Street, Boston, MA, 02101

Tel: (617) 786-3000   Fax: (617) 654-3386   www.statestreet.com

Engaged in investment management and institutional investor services.

State Street Bank & Trust, Larsbjoernstraede 3, DK-1454 Copenhagen K, Denmark

STORAGE TECHNOLOGY CORPORATION

One Storagetech Dr., Louisville, CO, 80028-4377

Tel: (303) 673-5151   Fax: (303) 673-5019   www.stortek.com

Mfr., market, service information, storage and retrieval systems.

StorageTek A/S, Hassellunden 11 A, Smoerum, DK 2765 Copenhagen, Denmark

Tel: 45-44-83-61-11   Fax: 45-44-83-61-12   Contact: Soren Nielsen

SYBASE, INC.

5000 Hacienda Dr., Dublin, CA, 94568

Tel: (925) 236-5000   Fax: (925) 236-4321   www.sybase.com

Design/mfg/distribution of database management systems, software development tools, connectivity products, consulting and technical support services..

Sybase Denmark A/S, Lyngbyvej 20, DK-2100 Copenhagen, Denmark

Tel: 45-39-27-7913   Fax: 45-39-27-7912

SYLVAN LEARNING SYSTEMS, INC.

1001 Fleet St., Baltimore, MD, 21202

Tel: (410) 843-8000   Fax: (410) 843-8057   www.sylvan.net

Engaged in private education, tutoring, computerized testing services and English classes for overseas executives.

Jürgen Gratze & Martin Mohr GmbH, De-la-Chevallerie-Straße 42, DK-45894 Gelsenkirchen-Buer, Denmark

SYMBOL TECHNOLOGIES, INC.

One Symbol Plaza, Holtsville, NY, 11742-1300

Tel: (631) 738-2400   Fax: (631) 738-5990   www.symbol.com

Mfr. Bar code-driven data management systems, wireless LAN's, and Portable Shopping System™.

Symbol Technologies Denmark A/S, Gydevange 2, DK-3450 Allerød, Denmark

Tel: 45-70-20-1718   Fax: 45-70-20-1716

SYNOPSYS, INC.

700 East Middlefield Road, Mountain View, CA, 94043

Tel: (650) 962-5000   Fax: (650) 965-8637   www.synopsys.com

Mfr. electronic design automation software.

Synopsys Denmark, Vesterbrogade 13, 2, DK-1620 Copenhagen V, Denmark

Tel: 45-70-212-222   Fax: 45-70-212-220

TBWA WORLDWIDE

488 Madison Avenue, 6th Floor, New York, NY, 10022

Tel: (212) 804-1000   Fax: (212) 804-1200   www.tbwachiat.com

International full service advertising agency.

TBWA Reklamebureau, Copenhagen, Denmark

TECA CORPORATION (THERMO ELECTRIC COOLING AMERICA

4048 West Schubert, Chicago, IL, 60639

Tel: (773) 342-4900   Fax: (773) 342-0191   www.thermoelectric.com

Mfr. solid state cooling products, including air-conditioners, cold plates and liquid chillers.

Telemetric Instruments, Gl. Hovedgade 10E, DK-2970 Hørsholm, Denmark

TECH/OPS SEVCON INC.

40 North Avenue, Burlington, MA, 01803

Tel: (781) 229-7896   Fax: (781) 229-8603   www.sevcon.com

Design, manufacture, and marketing of microprocessor based control systems for battery powered vehicles.

BC Trading ApS., Travegaardsvej 20, DK-3320 Meloese, Denmark

Tel: 45-4821-0575   Fax: 45-4821-0574

TEKTRONIX INC.

14200 SW Karl Braun Dr., PO Box 500, Beaverton, OR, 97077

Tel: (503) 627-7111   Fax: (503) 627-2406   www.tek.com

Mfr. test and measure, visual systems/color printing and communications/video and networking products.

Tektronix A/S, Tonsbakken 16-18, DK-2740 Skovlunde, Denmark

Tel: 45-44-85-0700   Fax: 45-44-85-0701

TELEFLEX INC.

630 W. Germantown Pike, Ste. 450, Plymouth Meeting, PA, 19462

Tel: (610) 834-6301   Fax: (610) 834-8307   www.teleflex.com

Design, manufacture and marketing of mechanical and electro-mechanical systems, control systems and surgical devices.

Rüsch Danmark ApS Teleflex, Islandsvej 3, DK-4681 Herfolge, Denmark

TELLABS INC.

1415 W. Diehl Rd., Naperville, IL, 60563

Tel: (630) 378-8800   Fax: (630) 852-7346   www.tellabs.com

Design/mfr./service voice/data transport and network access systems.

Tellabs Denmark, Lautrupbjerg 7-11, DK–2750 Ballerup, Denmark

TENNECO AUTOMOTIVE INC.

500 North Field Drive, Lake Forest, IL, 60045

Tel: (847) 482-5241   Fax: (847) 482-5295   www.tenneco-automotive.com

Mfr. automotive parts, exhaust systems and service equipment.

Walker Denmark A/S, Falstervej 11, DK-5500 Middelfart, Denmark

Tel: 45-64-41-4545   Fax: 45-64-41-6529   Contact: Aksel Pedersen, Mgr.

TERADATA

1700 South Patterson Blvd., Dayton, OH, 45479

Tel: (937) 445-5000   Fax: (937) 445-1682   www.teradata.com

Mfr. software to store information.

Teradata Div., NCR, Vibevej 20, DK-24 Copenhagen NV, Denmark

TEXAS INSTRUMENTS INC.

12500 TI Blvd., Dallas, TX, 75266

Tel: (972) 995-3773   Fax: (972) 995-4360   www.ti.com

Mfr. semiconductor devices, electronic electro-mechanical systems, instruments and controls.

Texas Instruments, Copenhagen, Denmark

THE MARMON GROUP, INC.

200 West Adams, Ste. 2211, Chicago, IL, 60606

Tel: (312) 372-9500   Fax: (312) 845-5305   www.marmon.com

Holding company for diversified manufacturing and service firms.

PBN Medicals Denmark A/S, Knud Bro Alle 3, DK-3660 Stenlose, Denmark

TITANIUM METALS CORPORATION (TIMET)

1999 Broadway, Suite 4300, Denver, CO, 80202

Tel: (303) 296-5600   Fax: (303) 296-5650   www.timet.com

Produce light weight titanium sponge (metal) for aerospace and auto industries.

Gronbech & Sonner, Scandiagade 25, DK 2450 Kobenhavn SV, Denmark

TMP WORLDWIDE, INC.

622 Third Ave., New York, NY, 10017

Tel: (212) 351-7000   Fax: (212) 658-0540   www.tmpw.com

#1 Yellow Pages agency and a leader in the recruitment and interactive advertising fields.

TMP Worldwide Advertising & Communications, Strandvejen 140, Hellerup, DK-2900 Copenhagen, Denmark

TOKHEIM CORPORATION

PO Box 360, 10501 Corporate Drive, Fort Wayne, IN, 46845

Tel: (219) 470-4600   Fax: (219) 482-2677   www.tokheim.com

Engaged in design, manufacture and service of electronic and mechanical petroleum marketing systems.

Tokheim Denmark, Hejrevang 10, DK-3450 Allerf, Denmark

TRANSOCEAN INC.

4 Greenway Plaza, Houston, TX, 77046

Tel: (713) 232-7500   Fax: (713) 232-7027   www.deepwater.com

Engaged in oil and gas offshore drilling.

Transocean Inc., Amerikavej 1, DK-6700 Esbjerg, Denmark

TRANTER PHE, INC.

PO Box 2289, Wichita Falls, TX, 76306

Tel: (940) 723-7125   Fax: (940) 723-1131   www.tranter.com

Mfr. heat exchangers.

SWEP Danmark A/S, Sofienlystvej 7, Postbox 20, DK-8340 Malling, Denmark

Tel: 45-86-93-3633   Fax: 45-86-93-3895

TTI, INC.

2441 Northeast Pkwy., Fort Worth, TX, 76106-1896

Tel: (817) 740-9000   Fax: (817) 740-9898   www.ttiinc.com

Distribution of resistors and capacitors, including cables and sockets.

TTI, Inc., Engager 2-4, DK-2605 Brondby, Denmark

UNISYS CORPORATION.

PO Box 500, Union Meeting Road, Blue Bell, PA, 19424

Tel: (215) 986-4011   Fax: (215) 986-6850   www.unisys.com

Mfr./marketing/servicing electronic information systems.

Unisys A/S, Biegdamsvej 56, DK-2100 Copenhagen, Denmark

UNITED PARCEL SERVICE, INC.

55 Glenlake Parkway, NE, Atlanta, GA, 30328

Tel: (404) 828-6000   Fax: (404) 828-6593   www.ups.com

International package-delivery service.

UPS Danmark A/S - Head Office, Naverland 7, DK-2600 Glostrup, Denmark

Tel: 45-43-23-8888   Fax: 45-43-23-8800

UNITED TECHNOLOGIES CORPORATION

One Financial Plaza, Hartford, CT, 06103

Tel: (860) 728-7000   Fax: (860) 728-7979   www.utc.com

Mfr. aircraft engines, elevators, A/C, auto equipment, space and military electronic and rocket propulsion systems. Products include Pratt and Whitney, Otis elevators, Carrier heating and air conditioning and Sikorsky helicopters.

Nielson-Otis Elevator A/S, Hoerkaer 7-9, DK-2730 Harlev, Denmark

UNIVERSAL SECURITY INSTRUMENTS, INC.

PO Box 825, Binghamton, NY, 13902-0825

Tel: (607) 779-7689   Fax: (607) 779-7301   www.uic.com

Provider of innovative electronic circuit assembly technology and equipment, integrated system solutions, and process expertise.

PC Trading A/S, Lystrup, Denmark

Tel: 45-86-741233   Fax: 45-86-741755

Sincotron A/S, Risskov, Denmark

Tel: 45-86-21-7744   Fax: 45-86-21-7766

URSCHEL LABORATORIES INC.

2503 Calumet Ave., PO Box 2200, Valparaiso, IN, 46384-2200

Tel: (219) 464-4811   Fax: (219) 462-3879   www.urschel.com

Design/mfr. precision food processing equipment.

Urschel Intl. Ltd., Pilevej 24, Taulov, Fredericia, Denmark

UUNET

22001 Loudoun County Pkwy., Ashburn, VA, 20147

Tel: (703) 206-5600   Fax: (703) 206-5601   www.uu.net

World's largest Internet service provider; World Wide Web hosting services, security products and consulting services to businesses, professionals, and on-line service providers.

UUNET Denmark, Roholmsvej 19, DK-2620 Albertslund, Denmark

VALSPAR CORPORATION

1101 South Third Street, Minneapolis, MN, 55415-1259

Tel: (612) 332-7371   Fax: (612) 375-7723   www.valspar.com

Mfr. paints and coatings.

Valspar (Norway) Corporation AS, Meterbuen 3-5, DK 2740 Skovlunde, Denmark

VARIAN MEDICAL SYSTEMS, INC.

3050 Hansen Way, Palo Alto, CA, 94304-100

Tel: (650) 493-4000   Fax: (650) 424-5358   www.varian.com

Mfr. microwave tubes and devices, analytical instruments, semiconductor process and medical equipment, vacuum systems.

Varian Semiconductor, Lyskaer 9, DK-2730 Herlev, Denmark

VERITAS SOFTWARE INC.

350 Ellis Street, Mountain View, CA, 94043

Tel: (650) 527-8000   Fax: (650) 527-8050   www.veritas.com

Mfr. of storage management software for data protection, application availability, and disaster recovery.

VERITAS Software, Inc., Lyngbyvej 20, Copenhagen, Denmark

VIEWSONIC CORPORATION

381 Brea Canyon Road, Walnut, CA, 91789

Tel: (909) 444-8888   Fax: (909) 869-7958   www.viewsonic.com

Mfr. displays.

ViewSonic Denmark, Lyngbyvei 20, DK-2100 Copenhagen, Denmark

Tel: 45-70-221171   Fax: 45-70-221181

WALBRO ENGINE MANAGEMENT

7400 N. Oracle Road, Ste. 310, Tucson, AZ, 85704

Tel: (520) 877-3000   Fax: (520) 877-3006   www.walbro.com

Mfr. motor vehicle accessories and parts, automotive fluid carrying systems.

TI Group Automotive Systems/Bundy Refrig, Romersvej 7-9, DK-7430 Ikast, Denmark

WASTE MANAGEMENT, INC.

1001 Fannin Street, Ste. 4000, Houston, TX, 77002

Tel: (713) 512-6200   Fax: (713) 512-6299   www.wastemanagement.com

Environmental services and disposal company; collection, processing, transfer and disposal facilities.

Waste Management Danmark Miljøservice A/S, Ørnegärdsvej 19, DK-2820 Gentofte, Denmark

Waste Management Denmark/Renovadan, Islevdalvej 110, DK-2610 Rodovre, Denmark

WATERS CORPORATION

34 Maple Street, Milford, MA, 01757

Tel: (508) 478-2000   Fax: (508) 872-1990   www.waters.com

Mfr./distribute liquid chromatographic instruments and test and measurement equipment.

Waters Denmark, Baldersbuen 46, DK-2640 Hedehusene, Denmark

WEATHERFORD INTERNATIONAL, INC.

515 Post Oak Blvd. Ste. 600, Houston, TX, 77027-3415

Tel: (713) 287-8400   Fax: (713) 963-9785   www.weatherford.com

Oilfield services, products and equipment; mfr. marine cranes for oil and gas industry.

Weatherford Intl., c/o Dogis Aps, Made Engvej 7, DK-6701 Esbjerg, Denmark

WEBER MARKING SYSTEMS INC.

711 West Algonquin Road, Arlington Heights, IL, 60005-4457

Tel: (847) 364-8500   Fax: (847) 364-8575   www.webermarking.com

Mfr. label printing systems and custom labels.

Weber Marking Systems A/S, Nordkrogen 7, DK-7300 Jelling, Denmark

WEST PHARMACEUTICAL SERVICES, INC.

101 Gordon Drive, Lionville, PA, 19341-0645

Tel: (610) 594-2900   Fax: (610) 594-3000   www.westpharma.com

Mfr. packaging and plastic components for health care and consumer products.

West Pharmaceutical Services, Fuglevangsvej 51, DK-8700 Horsens, Denmark

WESTAFF SERVICES, INC.

301 Lennon Lane, Walnut Creek, CA, 94598-2453

Tel: (925) 930-5300   Fax: (925) 934-5489   www.westaff.com

Secretarial and clerical temporary service.

Western Service A/S, PO Box 2088, DK-1013 Copenhagen K, Denmark

WHX CORPORATION

110 East 59th St., New York, NY, 10022

Tel: (212) 355-5200   Fax: (212) 355-5336   www.handyharman.com

Mfr. flat-rolled steel and associated metal products.

Indiana Tube, Div. Handy & Harman, Kokbjerg 25, DK-6000 Kolding, Denmark
Tel: 45-75-51-7222 Fax: 45-75-51-7224

WORLD COURIER INC.

45 Southfield Avenue, Ste. 3450, Stamford, CT, 06902-7210

Tel: (203) 975-9333   Fax: (203) 316-9455   www.worldcourier.com

International courier service.

World Courier Copenhagen, Fuzlebaekvej 3, DK-2770 Kastrup, Denmark

WORLD FUEL SERVICES CORPORATION

700 S. Royal Poinciana Blvd., Ste. 800, Miami Springs, FL, 33166

Tel: (305) 883-8554   Fax: (305) 887-2642   www.wfscorp.com

Provides airport services to aircraft.

Trans-Tec Services (UK) Ltd., Gammelbyvej 2, DK-4653 Karise, Denmark

WYETH PHARMACEUTICALS

555 E. Lancaster Ave., Wayne, PA, 19087-5109

Tel: (610) 971-5400   Fax: (610) 995-4668   www.wyeth.com

Mfr. antibiotics and pharmaceutical products.

Wyeth-Lederle Denmark, Produktionsvej 24, DK-2600 Glostrup, Denmark
Tel: 45-44-88-8805

XEROX CORPORATION

800 Long Ridge Road, PO Box 1600, Stamford, CT, 06904

Tel: (203) 968-3000   Fax: (203) 968-4312   www.xerox.com

Mfr. document processing equipment, systems and supplies.

Rank Xerox A/S, Borupvang 5C, DK-2750 Ballerup, Denmark
Tel: 45-44-65-4444 Fax: 45-44-65-4813

YAHOO! INC.

701 First Avenue, Sunnyvale, CA, 94089

Tel: (408) 439-3300   Fax: (408) 439-3301   www.yahoo-inc.com

Internet media company providing specialized content, free electronic mail and community offerings and commerce.

Yahoo! Inc., Denmark

YELLOW CORPORATION

10990 Roe Ave., PO Box 7270, Overland Park, KS, 66207

Tel: (913) 696-6100   Fax: (913) 696-6116   www.yellowcorp.com

Commodity transportation.

Frans Maas Danmark A/S, Naverland 8, DK-2600 Glostrup, Denmark

Frans Maas Danmark A/S, Solbaken 22, Hammeleve PO Box 149, DK-6500 Vojens, Denmark

YORK INTERNATIONAL CORPORATION

631 South Richland Ave., York, PA, 17403

Tel: (717) 771-7890   Fax: (717) 771-6212   www.york.com

Mfr. heating, ventilating, air conditioning and refrigeration equipment.

Gram Refrigeration, Aage Grams Vej 1, DK-6500 Vojens, Denmark

YOUNG & RUBICAM INC.

285 Madison Ave., New York, NY, 10017

Tel: (212) 210-3000   Fax: (212) 370-3796   www.yr.com

Advertising, public relations, direct marketing and sales promotion, corporate and product ID management.

Young & Rubicam Copenhagen, Enhjornvagens Bastion, Langebrogade 6V, DK-1411 Copenhagen K, Denmark

ZEBRA TECHNOLOGIES CORPORATION

333 Corporate Woods Pkwy., Vernon Hills, IL, 60061-3109

Tel: (847) 634-6700   Fax: (847) 913-8766   www.zebracorporation.com

Mfr. bar code systems.

Zebra Technologies Europe Limited, Lautruphøj 1-3, DK-2750 Ballerup, Denmark

Tel: 45-4420-9929   Contact: Bo Simon Larsen

ZIMMER HOLDINGS, INC.

345 East Main St., Warsaw, IN, 46580

Tel: (574) 267-6131   Fax: (574) 372-4988   www.zimmer.com

Engaged in design and manufacture of orthopedic products.

Zimmer Denmark, Ringager 2, DK-2605 Broendby, Denmark

Tel: 45-43-63-64-60   Fax: 45-43-63-64-61

Djibouti

DHL WORLDWIDE EXPRESS

50 California Avenue, San Francisco, CA, 94111

Tel: (415) 677-6100   Fax: (415) 824-9700   www.dhl.com

Worldwide air express carrier.

DHL Worldwide Express, rue de Geneve, PO Box 81, Djibouti

Tel: 253-35-0642

ERNST & YOUNG INTERNATIONAL

5 Times Square, New York, NY, 10036

Tel: (212) 773-3000   Fax: (212) 773-6350   www.eyi.com

Engaged in assurance and advisory business services, tax, law and corporate finance.

Ernst & Young International, Boite Poste 2593, Djibouti

Tel: 253-2-725625   Fax: 253-2-716271   Contact: Coutts Otolo

STARWOOD HOTELS & RESORTS WORLDWIDE

777 Westchester Avenue, White Plains, NY, 10604

Tel: (914) 640-8100   Fax: (914) 640-8316   www.starwoodhotels.com

Hotel operations including Sheraton, Westin, St. Regis, Four Points and Caesars.

Djibouti Sheraton Hotel, Plateau de Serpent, BP 1924, Djibouti

Tel: 253-350405   Fax: 253-355892

XEROX CORPORATION

800 Long Ridge Road, PO Box 1600, Stamford, CT, 06904

Tel: (203) 968-3000   Fax: (203) 968-4312   www.xerox.com

Mfr. document processing equipment, systems and supplies.

Dcp La Source Information, rue d'Athenes, BP 2537, Djibouti

Tel: 253-354-347

Dominican Republic

3M (MINNESOTA MINING & MFG.)

3M Center, St. Paul, MN, 55144-1000

Tel: (651) 733-1110   Fax: (651) 733-9973   www.mmm.com

Mfr. diversified products for industry, consumer, health care, imaging, communications, transport, safety, etc.

3M Dominicana SA, Ave. Luperon, Zona Industrial de Herrera, Santo Domingo, Dominican Republic

Tel: 809-530-6560   Fax: 809-537-2344

ABBOTT LABORATORIES

100 Abbott Park Rd., Abbott Park, IL, 60064

Tel: (847) 937-6100   Fax: (847) 937-1511   www.abbott.com

Development, manufacture and sale of diversified health care products and services.

Abbott Laboratories International, Ave. Charles Summer, 15 Los Prados, Santo Domingo, Dominican Republic

AMERICAN COMMERCIAL LINES LLC

1701 East Market Street, Jeffersonville, IN, 47130

Tel: (812) 288-0100   Fax: (812) 288-1664   www.aclines.com

Engaged in cargo transportation and river terminals.

ACL International, Carretera Melia Km. 10, Muelles Cementos Nacionies, San Pedro de Macoris, Dominican Republic

Tel: 809-246-0842   Contact: Enrique Gil

AMERICAN STANDARD COMPANIES, INC.

One Centennial Avenue, Piscataway, NJ, 08855-6820

Tel: (732) 980-3000   Fax: (732) 980-6118   www.americanstandard.com

Mfr. automotive, plumbing, heating, air conditioning products and medical diagnostics systems.

Sanitarios Dominicanos SA, Aptdo. 910, Santiago de Los Caballeros, Dominican Republic

AMR CORPORATION (AMERICAN AIRLINES)

4333 Amon Carter Boulevard, Ft. Worth, TX, 76155

Tel: (817) 963-1234   Fax: (817) 967-9641   www.amrcorp.com

Air transport services.

American Airlines Inc., Aptdo. 1295, El Conde #401, Edif. Copello, Santo Domingo, Dominican Republic

ANC RENTAL CORPORATION

200 S. Andrews Ave., Ft. Lauderdale, FL, 33301

Tel: (954) 320-4000   Fax: (954) 320-4077   www.ancrental.com

Engaged in car rental services, including National Car Rental and Alamo Rent A Car.

National Car Rental, A. Lincoln 1056, Aptdo. 800, Santo Domingo, Dominican Republic

ANTILLAS AIR CARGO CARRIER

JFK International Airport, Cargo Building 68, Jamaica, NY, 11430

Tel: (718) 917-6855   Fax: (718) 244-0764   www.antillasair.com

Provides air cargo services.

Antillas Air Cargo Services, Aeropuerto Int'l Las Americas, Edificio #14, Santiago de los Caballeros, Dominican Republic

Tel: 809-549-0114   Fax: 809-549-0187   Contact: Harold Olivares

Antillas Air Cargo Services, Warehouse No. 1, No. 120-B2, Puerto Plata Int'l Airport, Puerto Plata, Dominican Republic

AON CORPORATION

200 East Randolph, Chicago, IL, 60601

Tel: (312) 381-1000   Fax: (312) 381-6032   www.aon.com

Insurance brokers worldwide; underwrites accident and health insurance, specialty and professional insurance; and provides risk management consultation.

AON Worldwide / Redondo Llenas SG, S.A., Plazar El Alcazar Calle Manuel de Jesus, Santo Domingo, Dominican Republic

Tel: 809-567-7178   Fax: 809-541-9333   Contact: M.R. Redondo

AVON PRODUCTS, INC.

1345 Avenue of the Americas, New York, NY, 10105-0196

Tel: (212) 282-5000   Fax: (212) 282-6049   www.avon.com

Mfr. direct seller of cosmetics and beauty-related items.

Productos Avon, S.A., Apartado Postal 21727, Santo Domingo, Dominican Republic

Tel: 809-567-5586   Fax: 809-566-9082   Contact: Ada Mena, Sales Mgr.

R.G. BARRY CORPORATION

13405 Yarmouth Road NW, Pickerington, OH, 43147

Tel: (614) 864-6400   Fax: (614) 866-9787   www.rgbarry.com

Mfr. slippers and footwear.

Barry de Republica Dominica, Zona Franca San Isidro S.A., Carr. San Isidro Km 17, Santo Domingo, Dominican Republic

Tel: 809-476-1790   Fax: 809-476-1794

BATES WORLDWIDE INC.

498 Seventh Avenue, New York, NY, 10018

Tel: (212) 297-7000   Fax: (212) 986-0270   www.batesww.com

Advertising, marketing, public relations and media consulting.

EPI Bates, H. Nunez #41, Urb. Fernandez, Santo Domingo, Dominican Republic

Tel: 809-567-7888   Fax: 809-567-8905   Contact: A.Guerrero, Pres.

BAXTER INTERNATIONAL INC.

One Baxter Parkway, Deerfield, IL, 60015

Tel: (847) 948-2000   Fax: (847) 948-3948   www.baxter.com

Mfr. products and provide services in the field of the administration of medication and bioscience.

Baxter Laboratorios SA, Aptdo. Postal 21426, Parque Industrial Itabo, Haina, Dominican Republic

BRISTOL-MYERS SQUIBB COMPANY

345 Park Ave., New York, NY, 10154-0037

Tel: (212) 546-4000   Fax: (212) 546-4020   www.bms.com

Pharmaceutical and food preparations, medical and surgical instruments.

Bristol-Myers Squibb - Dominican Republic, Apartado 1167, Santo Domingo, Dominican Republic

ConvaTec, Div. Bristol-Myers Dominicana, Auto 30 de May Km. 13 1/2, Santo Domingo, Dominican Republic

BUDGET GROUP, INC.

125 Basin St., Ste. 210, Daytona Beach, FL, 32114

Tel: (904) 238-7035   Fax: (904) 238-7461   www.budgetrentacar.com

Car and truck rental system.

Budget Rent A Car, Las Americas International Airport, Santo Domingo, Dominican Republic

Tel: 809-567-0175

LEO BURNETT, DIV. B-COM 3 GROUP

35 West Wacker Drive, Chicago, IL, 60601

Tel: (312) 220-5959   Fax: (312) 220-6533   www.leoburnett.com

Engaged in advertising, marketing, media buying and planning, and public relations.

Leo Burnett Inc., Prolongacion Arabia 13, Arroyo Hondo, Santo Domingo, Dominican Republic

CALMAQUIP ENGINEERING CORPORATION

7240 N.W. 12th Street, Miami, FL, 33121

Tel: (305) 592-4510   Fax: (305) 593-9618   www.calmaquip.com

Engineering project management

Calmest SA, Abraham Lincoln, Esquina Modesto Diaz, Aptdo. 1693, Santo Domingo, Dominican Republic

CENTENNIAL COMMUNICATIONS CORPORATION

3349 Route 138, Bldg. A, Wall, NJ, 07753

Tel: (732) 556-2200   Fax: (732) 556-2200   www.centennialcom.com

Engaged in wireless telecommunications services.

All American Cables & Radio ITT, Santo Domingo, Dominican Republic

CHECKPOINT SYSTEMS, INC.

101 Wolf Drive, Thorofare, NJ, 08086

Tel: (856) 848-1800   Fax: (856) 848-0937   www.checkpointsystems.com

Mfr. test, measurement and closed-circuit television systems.

ASMI, Checkpoint Dominicana, Ave. John F. Kennedy Esq. W Churchill, Edif. Plaza Compostela, Suite 2-A, Santo Domingo, Dominican Republic

Tel: 809-541-0200   Fax: 809-566-4556   Contact: Sadik Yabra P.

CIGNA COMPANIES

One Liberty Place, Philadelphia, PA, 19192

Tel: (215) 761-1000   Fax: (215) 761-5511   www.cigna.com

Insurance, invest, health care and other financial services.

Insurance Co. of North America, Edif. Torre BHD 2 piso, Av. Winston Churchill/Esq. 27 de Feb., Santo Domingo, Dominican Republic

CITIGROUP, INC.

399 Park Avenue, New York, NY, 10022

Tel: (212) 559-1000   Fax: (212) 559-3646   www.citigroup.com

Provides insurance and financial services worldwide.

Citigroup, John F. Kennedy 1 piso 4, Apartado Postal 1492, Santo Domingo, Dominican Republic

Tel: 809-566-5611   Fax: 809-567-2255   Contact: Henry Comber

THE CLOROX COMPANY

1221 Broadway, PO Box 24305, Oakland, CA, 94623-1305

Tel: (510) 271-7000   Fax: (510) 832-1463   www.clorox.com

Mfr. soap and detergents, and domestic consumer packaged products.

Producter del Holgar C por A, Santo Domingo, Dominican Republic

CONTINENTAL AIRLINES INC.

1600 Smith St., Houston, TX, 77002

Tel: (713) 324-5000   Fax: (713) 324-2637   www.continental.com

International airline carrier.

Continental Airlines Inc., Dominican Republic

CSX CORPORATION

901 East Cary Street, Richmond, VA, 23860

Tel: (804) 782-1400   Fax: (804) 782-6747   www.csx.com

Provides freight delivery and contract logistics services.

Rio Haina Terminal/CSX, Puerto de Haina Occidental, Haina, Dominican Republic

Tel: 809-542-2591   Fax: 809-542-2882

D'ARCY MASIUS BENTON & BOWLES INC. (DMB&B)

1675 Broadway, New York, NY, 10019

Tel: (212) 468-3622   Fax: (212) 468-2987   www.darcyww.com

Full service international advertising and communications group.

Staff/DMB&B, Edif. Concordia Ste. 211, C/Jose A. Soler, Esq. A. Lincoln, Santo Domingo, Dominican Republic

Tel: 809-563-1212   Fax: 809-563-7784   Contact: Jose Rivera, Pres.

DELOITTE TOUCHE TOHMATSU INTERNATIONAL

1633 Broadway, New York, NY, 10019

Tel: (212) 492-4000   Fax: (212) 392-4154   www.deloitte.com

Accounting, audit, tax and management consulting services.

Deloitte & Touche, Gomez, Santos. Gonzalez & Asociados, Scotiabank Bldg., Av. J.F.Kennedy, Esq. Lope de Vega, Santo Domingo, Dominican Republic

DETROIT DIESEL CORPORATION

13400 Outer Drive West, Detroit, MI, 48239

Tel: (313) 592-5000   Fax: (313) 592-5058   www.detroitdiesel.com

Mfr. diesel and aircraft engines and heavy-duty transmissions.

Equipos Diesel S.A., PO Box 800, H. Lopez-Penha ESQ F Gerardino, Santo Domingo, Dominican Republic
Tel: 809-540-3800   Fax: 809-563-7400

DHL WORLDWIDE EXPRESS

50 California Avenue, San Francisco, CA, 94111

Tel: (415) 677-6100   Fax: (415) 824-9700   www.dhl.com

Worldwide air express carrier.

DHL Worldwide Express, Av. Sarasota 26, Santo Domingo, Dominican Republic
Tel: 809-534-7888

DOVER CORPORATION

280 Park Ave., New York, NY, 10017-1292

Tel: (212) 922-1640   Fax: (212) 922-1656   www.dovercorporation.com

Holding company for varied industries; assembly and testing equipment, oil-well gear and other industrial products.

Dalsan C. Por A, Apartado de Correos 751, Ave. Lopez de Vega, Santo Domingo, Dominican Republic
Tel: 809-565-4431   Fax: 809-541-7313

EASTMAN KODAK COMPANY

343 State Street, Rochester, NY, 14650

Tel: (716) 724-4000   Fax: (716) 724-1089   www.kodak.com

Develop/mfr. photo and chemicals products, information management/video/copier systems, fibers/plastics for various industry.

Kodak Dominicana, Av. Charles Sumner 17, Santo Domingo, Dominican Republic

EDWARDS LIFESCIENCES CORPORATION

1 Edwards Way, Irvine, CA, 92614

Tel: (949) 250-2500   Fax: (949) 250-2525   www.edwards.com

Mfr. instruments for cardiovascular patients.

Edwards Lifesciences, Zona France Industrial de Haina, Haina, San Cristobal, Dominican Republic

EGL INC. (EAGLE GLOBAL LOGISTICS)

15350 Vickery Drive, Houston, TX, 77032

Tel: (281) 618-3100   Fax: (281) 618-3223   www.eagleusa.com

Ocean/air freight forwarding, customs brokerage, packing and wholesale, logistics management and insurance.

EGL Eagle Global Logistics, Ave. George Washington 353, PO Box 852, Santo Domingo, Dominican Republic
Tel: 809-221-6111   Fax: 809-689-2177

ENRON CORPORATION

1400 Smith Street, Houston, TX, 77002-7369

Tel: (713) 853-6161   Fax: (713) 853-3129   www.enron.com

Exploration, production, transportation and distribution of integrated natural gas and electricity. ****Corporation under worldwide reorganization; new data unavailable for this edition.**

Smith/Enron, Ave Winston Churchill #1100, Edi La Universal de Seguros, Piso 4to, Santo Domingo, Dominican Republic

ERNST & YOUNG INTERNATIONAL

5 Times Square, New York, NY, 10036

Tel: (212) 773-3000   Fax: (212) 773-6350   www.eyi.com

Engaged in assurance and advisory business services, tax, law and corporate finance.

Francisco & Asociados, Aptdo 140, Santo Domingo, Dominican Republic

Tel: 809-565-5831   Fax: 809-541-3883   Contact: Ramon Francisco

ETHAN ALLEN INTERIORS INC.

Ethan Allen Drive, Danbury, CT, 06811

Tel: (203) 743-8000   Fax: (203) 743-8298   www.ethanallen.com

Mfr. and sale of premium-priced furniture and home furnishings.

Ethan Allen Home Interiors, Gustavo Mejia Ricart 124A, Santo Domingo, Dominican Republic

Tel: 809-540-3846   Fax: 809-542-3807

FEDERAL-MOGUL CORPORATION

26555 Northwestern Highway, PO Box 1966, Southfield, MI, 48034

Tel: (248) 354-7700   Fax: (248) 354-8983   www.federal-mogul.com

Mfr./distributor precision parts for automobiles, trucks, farm and construction vehicles.

Federal-Mogul Dominicana SA, Dominican Republic

FRITZ COMPANIES, INC., DIV. UPS

706 Mission Street, Ste. 900, San Francisco, CA, 94103

Tel: (415) 904-8360   Fax: (415) 904-8661   www.fritz.com

Integrated transportation, sourcing, distribution and customs brokerage services.

Fritz Companies Inc., Santo Domingo, Dominican Republic

H.B. FULLER COMPANY

1200 Willow Lake Blvd., Vadnais Heights, MN, 55110

Tel: (651) 236-5900   Fax: (651) 236-5898   www.hbfuller.com

Mfr./distributor adhesives, sealants, coatings, paints, waxes, sanitation chemicals.

H.B. Fuller Dominicana, S.A., Apartado No.004, Piedra Bianca, Haina, San Cristobal, Dominican Republic

Tel: 809-542-2902   Fax: 809-542-2585

THE GILLETTE COMPANY

Prudential Tower Building, Boston, MA, 02199

Tel: (617) 421-7000   Fax: (617) 421-7123   www.gillette.com

Develop/mfr. personal care/use products: blades and razors, toiletries, cosmetics, stationery.

Gillette Dominicana SA, Santo Domingo, Dominican Republic

GIW INDUSTRIES, INC.

5000 Wrightsboro Rd., Grovetown, GA, 30813

Tel: (706) 863-1011   Fax: (706) 860-5897   www.giwindustries.com

Mfr. slurry pumps.

Tritublock, Luis F. Thomas #10, Santo Domingo, Dominican Republic

GOYA FOODS, INC.

100 Seaview Dr., Secaucus, NJ, 07096

Tel: (201) 348-4900   Fax: (201) 348-6609   www.goyafoods.com

Produces canned and packaged Hispanic food products, fruit juices and frozen entrees.

Goya Foods, Inc., Avenida José Ortega & Gasset No. 201, Dominican Republic

Tel: 809-541-4900   Fax: 809-567-9657

GREY GLOBAL GROUP

777 Third Ave., New York, NY, 10017

Tel: (212) 546-2000   Fax: (212) 546-1495   www.grey.com

International advertising agency.

El Taller Creativo, Santo Domingo, Dominican Republic

HEWITT ASSOCIATES LLC

100 Half Day Road, Lincolnshire, IL, 60069

Tel: (847) 295-5000   Fax: (847) 295-7634   www.hewitt.com

Employee benefits consulting firm.

Hewitt Associates, Plaza Naco, Suite 2-46, Santo Domingo, Dominican Republic

Tel: 809-227-9444

HOLIDAY INN (BASS RESORTS) WORLDWIDE, INC.

3 Ravinia Drive, Ste. 2900, Atlanta, GA, 30346-2149

Tel: (770) 604-2000   Fax: (770) 604-5403   www.holidayinn.com

Hotels, restaurants and casinos.

Holiday Inn, Av. Anacaona, Santo Domingo, Dominican Republic

HORWATH INTERNATIONAL ASSOCIATION

420 Lexington Avenue, Suite 526, New York, NY, 10170-0526

Tel: (212) 808-2000   Fax: (212) 808-2020   www.horwath.com

Public accountants and auditors.

Sotero Peralta y Associados, Aptdo. 355-2, Av. Winston Churchill, Edif. Lama, Santo Domingo, Dominican Republic

INFONET SERVICES CORPORATION

2160 East Grand Ave., El Segundo, CA, 90245-1022

Tel: (310) 335-2600   Fax: (310) 335-4507   www.infonet.com

Provider of Internet services and electronic messaging services.

Infonet Dominican Republic, Abraham Lincoln 953, Santo Domingo, Dominican Republic

Tel: 809-220-5114   Fax: 809-220-5286

INTER-CONTINENTAL HOTELS

3 Ravinia Drive, Suite 2900, Atlanta, GA, 30346-2149

Tel: (770) 604-2000   Fax: (770) 604-5403   www.interconti.com

Worldwide hotel and resort accommodations.

V Centerario Inter-Continental Santo Domingo, Av. George Washington 218, PO Box 2890, Santo Domingo, Dominican Republic

Tel: 809-221-0000   Fax: 809-221-2020

INTERNATIONAL PAPER COMPANY

400 Atlantic Street, Stamford, CT, 06921

Tel: (203) 541-8000   Fax: (203) 358-6444   www.ipaper.com

Mfr./distributor container board, paper and wood products.

Impresora del Yaque C por A, Autopista Santiago Navarrete Km 2.5, Santiago/Navarrete, Dominican Republic

J. WALTER THOMPSON COMPANY

466 Lexington Ave., New York, NY, 10017

Tel: (212) 210-7000   Fax: (212) 210-6944   www.jwt.com

International advertising and marketing services.

Thompson AIFE MFP, Santo Domingo, Dominican Republic

JOHNSON & JOHNSON

One Johnson & Johnson Plaza, New Brunswick, NJ, 08933

Tel: (732) 524-0400   Fax: (732) 214-0334   www.jnj.com

Mfr./distributor/R&D pharmaceutical, health care and cosmetic products.

Johnson & Johnson (Dominicana) C por A, Aptdo. Postal 2252, Santo Domingo, Dominican Republic

SC JOHNSON

1525 Howe St., Racine, WI, 53403

Tel: (262) 260-2000   Fax: (262) 260-2133   www.scjohnsonwax.com

Home, auto, commercial and personal care products and specialty chemicals.

SC Johnson, Av. San Martin 296, Santo Domingo, Dominican Republic

KPMG CONSULTING INC.

1676 International Dr., McLean, VA, 22102

Tel: (703) 747-3000   Fax: (703) 747-8500   www.kpmg.com

Accounting and audit, tax and management consulting services.

KPMG International, Edif. Hache East Entrance, 1 piso, 4th Level, JFK Ave., Santo Domingo, Dominican Republic
Tel: 809-566-9161   Fax: 809-566-3468   Contact: Juan R. Herrera, Sr. Ptnr.

KPMG International, Apartado Postal 1519, Santiago, Dominican Republic

KPMG International, J. F. Kennedy Ave., Santo Domingo, Dominican Republic

LANIER WORLDWIDE, INC.

2300 Parklake Drive, N.E., Atlanta, GA, 30345

Tel: (770) 496-9500   Fax: (770) 938-1020   www.lanier.com

Specialize in digital copiers and multi-functional systems.

Lanier Dominicana, S.A., Av. 27 de Febrero, Esquina Calle H, Zona Ind. De Hererra, Santo Domingo, Dominican Republic
Tel: 809-537-7779   Fax: 809-537-8590

MAIDENFORM WORLDWIDE INC.

154 Avenue E, Bayonne, NJ, 07002

Tel: (201) 436-9200   Fax: (201) 436-9009   www.maidenform.com

Mfr. intimate apparel.

Elizabeth Needle Craft Inc., Zona Franca de la Romana, La Romana, Dominican Republic

Nicholas Needlecraft Inc., Apdo. Postal 150, Higuey, Dominican Republic

MARSH & McLENNAN COS INC.

1166 Ave. of the Americas, New York, NY, 10036-2774

Tel: (212) 345-5000   Fax: (212) 345-4808   www.marshmac.com

Insurance agents/brokers, pension and investment management consulting services.

Ros & Asociados S.A., Ave. Winston Churchill, Esq. Jose Brea, Pena Santo Domingo, Dominican Republic
Tel: 809-567-1021   Fax: 809-562-4764

MAXXIM MEDICAL, INC.

950 Winer Street, Ste. 2900, Waltham, MA, 02451

Tel: (781) 906-0700   Fax: (781) 906-0710   www.maxximmedical.com

Mfr. latex and non-latex medical gloves.

Fabritek La Romana, Zona Franca Industrial, La Romana, DR, Dominican Republic
Tel: 809-556-2140   Fax: 809-556-4373

McCANN-ERICKSON WORLDGROUP

750 Third Ave., New York, NY, 10017

Tel: (212) 697-6000   Fax: (212) 984-3575   www.mccann.com

International advertising and marketing services.

McCann-Erickson Dominicana SA, Moises Garcia 17, Gazque, Santo Domingo, Dominican Republic

J. P. MORGAN CHASE & CO. INC.

270 Park Ave., New York, NY, 10017

Tel: (212) 270-6000   Fax: (212) 622-9030   www.jpmorganchase.com

Provides integrated financial solutions for institutions and individuals worldwide, including asset management, investment banking and commercial banking.

J. P. Morgan Chase & Co., Av. John F. Kennedy y Tiradentes, Aptdo. 1408, Santo Domingo, Dominican Republic

OGILVY & MATHER WORLDWIDE

309 West 49th Street, New York, NY, 10017-7399

Tel: (212) 237-4000   Fax: (212) 237-5123   www.ogilvypr.com

Engaged in public relations and communications.

Ogilvy Public Relations Worldwide, Santo Domingo, Dominican Republic

PAN-AMERICAN LIFE INSURANCE COMPANY

Pan American Life Center, 601 Poydras St., New Orleans, LA, 70130-0219

Tel: (504) 566-1300   Fax: (504) 566-3600   www.panamericanlife.com

Insurance services.

Cia de Seguros PALIC SA, Abraham Lincoln esq. Jose Amado Soler, Santo Domingo, Dominican Republic

Tel: 809-562-1271   Fax: 809-562-1825   Contact: Eduardo Tolentino, VP & Gen. Mgr.   Emp: 70

PENETONE CORPORATION

74 Hudson Avenue, Tenafly, NJ, 07670

Tel: (201) 567-3000   Fax: (201) 569-5340   www.west-penetone.com

Sanitary equipment and supplies.

West Chemical Products, Aptdo. 428, Santo Domingo, Dominican Republic

PERKIN ELMER, INC.

45 William Street, Wellesley, MA, 02481

Tel: (781) 237-5100   Fax: (781) 431-4255   www.perkinelmer.com

Mfr. equipment and devices to detect explosives and bombs on airline carriers.

Inversiones Tecnicas Dominicanas S.A., Luisa Ozema Pellerano #7 Altos, Zona 2 Gazcue, Santo Domingo, Dominican Republic

Tel: 809-688-4927   Fax: 809-682-9506

PINNACLE WORLDWIDE, INC.

1201 Marquette Ave., Ste. 300, Minneapolis, MN, 55403

Tel: (612) 338-2215   Fax: (612) 338-2572   www.pinnacleww.com

International network of independent public relations firms.

Medios Del Caribe, S.A., Calle Nicolas de Bari #8, La Esperilla, Dominican Republic

POWER-ONE, INC.

740 Calle Plano, Camarillo, CA, 93012

Tel: (805) 987-8741   Fax: (805) 388-0476   www.power-one.com

Mfr. converters and voltage power switchers for electronic equipment.

Power-One Ltd., Zona Franca Las Americas, Autopista Las Americas KM22, Santo Dominigo, Dominican Republic

PRICEWATERHOUSECOOPERS LLP

1301 Ave. of the Americas, New York, NY, 10019

Tel: (212) 596-7000   Fax: (212) 259-1301   www.pwcglobal.com

Accounting and auditing, tax and management, and human resource consulting services.

PriceWaterhouseCoopers, Edif. Bank of Nova Scotia, Av. J F Kennedy, Esq.de Av. Lope de Vega, POB 1286, Santo Domingo, Dominican Republic

Tel: 809-567-7741   Fax: 809-541-1210

RAYOVAC CORPORATION

601 Rayovac Drive, Madison, WI, 53711-2497

Tel: (608) 275-3340   Fax: (608) 275-4577   www.rayovac.com

Mfr. batteries and lighting devices.

Rayovac Dominican Republic, S.A., Prolongación Ave. Rómulo Betancourt, Zona Industrial de Herrera, Santo Domingo, Dominican Republic

RENAISSANCE HOTELS AND RESORTS

10400 Fernwood Road, Bethesda, MD, 20817

Tel: (301) 380-3000   Fax: (301) 380-5181   www.renaissancehotels.com

upscale, full-service hotel and resort chain under Marriott International, Inc.

Renaissance Jaragua Hotel and Casino, Santo Domingo, Dominican Republic

Tel: 809-221-2222

RUDDICK CORPORATION

301 S. Tryon St., Ste. 1800, Charlotte, NC, 28202

Tel: (704) 372-5404   Fax: (704) 372-6409   www.amefird.com

Mfr. industrial sewing thread for worldwide industrial and consumer markets.

Hilos A&E Dominicana SA, Zona Franca, Santiago, Dominican Republic

RUSSIN & VECCHI L.L.P.

815 Connecticut Ave. NW, Ste. 650, Washington, DC, 20006

Tel: (202) 822-6100   Fax: (202) 822-6101   www.rvhb.com

Engaged in international law.

Russin & Vecchi, LLP, Plaza Turisol, Local 11-A, Puerto Plata, Dominican Republic

Tel: 809-586-5535   Fax: 809-586-5861   Contact: Luis Heredia Bonetti

Russin & Vecchi, LLP, Apartado 425, Calle El Recodo # 2, Edificio Monte Mirador, 3/F, Santo Domingo, Dominican Republic

Tel: 809-535-9511   Fax: 809-535-6649   Contact: Luis Heredia Bonetti

THE SERVICEMASTER COMPANY

2300 Warrenville Road, Downers Grove, IL, 60515-1700

Tel: (630) 271-1300   Fax: (630) 271-2710   www.svm.com

Provides residential consumer services, including lawn care and landscape maintenance, termite and pest control, plumbing, heating and air conditioning maintenance and repair.

Terminix, Santo Domingo, Dominican Republic

SKYTEL COMMUNICATIONS, INC.

515 E. Amite St., Jackson, MS, 39201

Tel: (601) 944-1300   Fax: (601) 944-3900   www.skytel.com

Provides wireless messaging services, radio paging services and systems implementation.

TeleCentral Teletrim, Santo Domingo, Dominican Republic

STARWOOD HOTELS & RESORTS WORLDWIDE

777 Westchester Avenue, White Plains, NY, 10604

Tel: (914) 640-8100   Fax: (914) 640-8316   www.starwoodhotels.com

Hotel operations including Sheraton, Westin, St. Regis, Four Points and Caesars.

Santo Domingo Sheraton Hotel & Casino, Av. George Washington 365, Aptdo. 1493, Santo Domingo, Dominican Republic

UNITED PARCEL SERVICE, INC.

55 Glenlake Parkway, NE, Atlanta, GA, 30328

Tel: (404) 828-6000   Fax: (404) 828-6593   www.ups.com

International package-delivery service.

UPS / Dominican Parcel Service, S.A., Calle Jose Amado Soler, Esq. Abrahan Lincoln, Edif. Progresus, Santo Domingo, Dominican Republic

Tel: 809-563-5639   Fax: 809-565-9561

THE WACKENHUT CORPORATION

4200 Wackenhut Dr., Ste. 100, Palm Beach Gardens, FL, 33410

Tel: (561) 622-5656   Fax: (561) 691-6736   www.wackenhut.com

Security systems and services.

Wackenhut Dominicana S.A., Paseo de los Locutores 36, Ensanche Piantini, Aptdo. 1677, Zona 1, Santo Domingo, Dominican Republic

Tel: 809-544-3333   Fax: 809-567-4767

THE WARNACO GROUP INC.

90 Park Ave., New York, NY, 10016

Tel: (212) 661-1300   Fax: (212) 687-0480   www.warnaco.com

Mfr./sales intimate apparel and men's and women's sportswear.

Warnaco, Santo Domingo, Dominican Republic

WENDY'S INTERNATIONAL, INC.

4288 West Dublin Granville Roads, Dublin, OH, 43017-0256

Tel: (614) 764-3100   Fax: (614) 764-3459   www.wendysintl.com

Fast food restaurant chain.

Wendy's International, Dominican Republic

WOMETCO ENTERPRISES INC.

3195 Ponce de Leon Blvd., Coral Gables, FL, 33134

Tel: (305) 529-1400   Fax: (305) 529-1499

Television broadcasting, film distribution, bottling, vending machines and proprietor of Miami Seaquarium.

Operadora Filmica SA, Aptdo. 1396, Av. Bolivar 453, Zona 2, Santo Domingo, Dominican Republic

XEROX CORPORATION

800 Long Ridge Road, PO Box 1600, Stamford, CT, 06904

Tel: (203) 968-3000   Fax: (203) 968-4312   www.xerox.com

Mfr. document processing equipment, systems and supplies.

Xerox Dominicana C.POR.A., Apartado #40, Ave. Bolivar 1004, Ens. LaJulia, Santo Domingo, Dominican Republic

Fax: 809-541-2762

YOUNG & RUBICAM INC.

285 Madison Ave., New York, NY, 10017

Tel: (212) 210-3000   Fax: (212) 370-3796   www.yr.com

Advertising, public relations, direct marketing and sales promotion, corporate and product ID management.

Young & Rubicam Damaris C por A, Av. de Los Proceres, Esq. Camino del Oeste, Arroya Hondo, Santo Domingo, Dominican Republic

Ecuador

3M (MINNESOTA MINING & MFG.)

3M Center, St. Paul, MN, 55144-1000

Tel: (651) 733-1110   Fax: (651) 733-9973   www.mmm.com

Mfr. diversified products for industry, consumer, health care, imaging, communications, transport, safety, etc.

3M Ecuador CA, Km.1.5 Via Duran, Tambo, Guayaquil, Ecuador

Tel: 593-4-800-777   Fax: 593-4-802-254

ABBOTT LABORATORIES

100 Abbott Park Rd., Abbott Park, IL, 60064

Tel: (847) 937-6100   Fax: (847) 937-1511   www.abbott.com

Development, manufacture and sale of diversified health care products and services.

Abbott Laboratories del Ecuador, S.A., Primero De Mayo, 610 Y Mascote, Guayaquil, Ecuador

Tel: 593-4-80-0808

ABS (AMERICAN BUREAU OF SHIPPING)

ABS Plaza, 16855 Northchase Drive, Houston, TX, 77060

Tel: (281) 877-6000   Fax: (281) 877-6344   www.eagle.org

Classification and certification of ships and offshore structures, development and technical assistance.

ABS Ecuador, Nueva Kennedy, Ciudadela Sagrada Familia, Manzana "B" Villa "4", Guayaquil, Ecuador

ABS Europe, Nueva Kennedy, Ciudadela Sagrada Familia, Manzana "B" Villa "4", Guayaquil, Ecuador

Tel: 593-4-228-1811

AIG AMERICAN INTERNATIONAL GROUP INC.

70 Pine Street, New York, NY, 10270

Tel: (212) 770-7000   Fax: (212) 509-9705   www.aig.com

Worldwide insurance and financial services.

AIG S.A., Ave. Brasil No. 293, Quito, Ecuador

ABC, INC.

77 West 66th Street, 13th Fl., New York, NY, 10023

Tel: (212) 456-7777   Fax: (212) 456-6384   www.abc.com

Radio/TV production and broadcasting.

Primera Television Ecuatoriana SA, Calle Padre Aguirre y Nueva Tola, Casilla 70, Quito, Ecuador

Primera Television Ecuatoriana SA, 9 de Octubre 1200, Casilla 5063, Guayaquil, Ecuador

Telesistema del Ecuador SA, Palacio Municipal, Casilla 400, Cuenca, Ecuador

ANC RENTAL CORPORATION

200 S. Andrews Ave., Ft. Lauderdale, FL, 33301

Tel: (954) 320-4000   Fax: (954) 320-4077   www.ancrental.com

Engaged in car rental services, including National Car Rental and Alamo Rent A Car.

National Car Rental, Madrid 1471 y 12 de Octubre, Quito, Ecuador

ANDERSEN

33 West Monroe Street, Chicago, IL, 60603

Tel: (312) 580-0033   Fax: (312) 507-6748   www.andersen.com

Accounting and audit, tax and management consulting services. **Firm under worldwide reorganization; new data unavailable for this edition.

Andersen Worldwide, Av. Diego de Almagro #1550 y, PO Box 17-11-06465, Quito, Ecuador

Tel: 593-2-545-624

AON CORPORATION

200 East Randolph, Chicago, IL, 60601

Tel: (312) 381-1000   Fax: (312) 381-6032   www.aon.com

Insurance brokers worldwide; underwrites accident and health insurance, specialty and professional insurance; and provides risk management consultation.

AON Worldwide / Uniseguros CA, Calle 8, Conominio 2.001 Ciudadela Kennedy, Guayaquil, Ecuador

Tel: 593-4-287144 Fax: 593-4-282952   Contact: Robert E. Cackett

APPLERA CORPORATION

301 Merritt 7, Norwalk, CT, 06851

Tel: (203) 840-2000   Fax: (203) 840-2312   www.applera.com

Leading supplier of systems for life science research and related applications.

Distecnica Ltda., Avenida Los Shyris N34-368, Quito, Ecuador

ARMOR HOLDINGS, INC.

1400 Marsh Landing Parkway, Ste. 112, Jacksonville, FL, 32250

Tel: (904) 741-5400   Fax: (904) 741-5403   www.armorholdings.com

Holding company engaged in security products and services.

Defense Sysems Ecuador SA, Av. Gonzalez Suarez No. 32-341, Y Corona, Edi. Banco Del Pinchincha, Primer Piso Sur, Quito, Ecuador

Tel: 593-2-902-236 Fax: 593-2-902-237   Contact: Luis Gabela

AVIS GROUP HOLDINGS, INC.

6 Sylvan Way, Parsippany, NJ, 07054

Tel: (973) 222-3000   Fax: (973) 222-4381   www.avis.com

Car rental services.

Avis Group Holdings Ltd., P. Icaza 425 y Cordova, Guayaquil, Ecuador

AVON PRODUCTS, INC.

1345 Avenue of the Americas, New York, NY, 10105-0196

Tel: (212) 282-5000   Fax: (212) 282-6049   www.avon.com

Mfr. direct seller of cosmetics and beauty-related items.

Productos Avon Ecuador S.A., El Batan #405 y Av. 6 de Diciembre, Frente al Colegio, Benalcazar, Ecuador

Tel: 593-2-259791 Fax: 593-2-259792   Contact: Gladys de Len, Sales Mgr.

BAKER HUGHES INCORPORATED

3900 Essex Lane, Ste. 1200, Houston, TX, 77027

Tel: (713) 439-8600   Fax: (713) 439-8699   www.bakerhughes.com

Develop and apply technology to drill, complete and produce oil and natural gas wells; provide separation systems to petroleum, municipal, continuous process and mining industries.

Baker Transworld Inc., Av. Amazonas 477 Y Roca, piso 7, Of. 720, Quito, Ecuador

Tel: 593-2-554356   Fax: 593-2-564881

BAKER PETROLITE CORPORATION

3900 Essex Lane, Houston, TX, 77027

Tel: (713) 599-7400   Fax: (713) 599-7592   www.bakerhughes.com

Mfr. specialty chemical treating programs, performance-enhancing additives and related equipment and services.

Ecuatoriana de Petroquimicos Petrolite SA, Edif. Albatros, Av. de los Shyris 1240 y Portugal, Casilla 11026, Quito, Ecuador

BATES WORLDWIDE INC.

498 Seventh Avenue, New York, NY, 10018

Tel: (212) 297-7000   Fax: (212) 986-0270   www.batesww.com

Advertising, marketing, public relations and media consulting.

VIP Bates Ecuador, Whimper 777, Casilla 4558-A, Quito, Ecuador

Tel: 593-2-502-024 Fax: 593-2-563-901   Contact: G. Vallejo, Pres.

BDO SEIDMAN, LLP   BELGIUM

130 East Randolph Street, Chicago, IL, 60601

Tel: (312) 856-9100   Fax: (312) 856-1379   www.bdo.com

International accounting and financial consulting firm.

BDO Stern, Av. Amazonas 540 y Carrión, Edif. Londres 6, deg; piso, Quito, Ecuador

Tel: 593-2-566-915   Fax: 593-2-504-477   Contact: Rolf Stern

BELCO OIL & GAS CORPORATION

767 Fifth Ave., 46th Fl., New York, NY, 10153

Tel: (212) 644-2200   Fax: (212) 644-2230   www.belcooil-gas.com

Exploration and production of crude oil and natural gas.

Belco Petroleum Ecuador Inc., Cordova 808 y V.M. Rendon, Edif. Torres de la Merced, Guayaquil, Ecuador

BELLSOUTH CORPORATION LATIN AMERICA

1155 Peachtree Street NE, Ste. 400, Atlanta, GA, 30367

Tel: (404) 249-4800   Fax: (404) 249-4880   www.bellsouth.com

Mobile communications, telecommunications network systems.

BellSouth Ecuador, Edif. BellSouth, Av. Republica Y La Pradera, Esquina, Quito, Ecuador

Tel: 593-2-227-700   Fax: 593-2-227-597

BEST WESTERN INTERNATIONAL

6201 North 24th Place, Phoenix, AZ, 85106

Tel: (602) 957-4200   Fax: (602) 957-5740   www.bestwestern.com

International hotel chain.

Best Western Quito, Gonzalez Suarez 2500, Box 2201, Quito, Ecuador

BOZELL GROUP

40 West 23rd Street, New York, NY, 10010

Tel: (212) 727-5000   Fax: (212) 645-9173   www.bozell.com

Advertising, marketing, public relations and media consulting.

Bozell Ecuador, Ave. Miguel H. Alcivar, MZ 3V, #3, Guayaquil, Ecuador

Tel: 593-4-395-855   Fax: 593-4-395-865   Contact: Adriana R. de Hernandez, Mng. Dir.

BRISTOL-MYERS SQUIBB COMPANY

345 Park Ave., New York, NY, 10154-0037

Tel: (212) 546-4000   Fax: (212) 546-4020   www.bms.com

Pharmaceutical and food preparations, medical and surgical instruments.

Bristol-Myers Squibb Company - Ecuador, Juan Diguja, No. 198 Yvos Andes, Esquina Quito, Ecuador

Bristol-Myers Squibb Company - Ecuador, Mecanos, 3ER piso, Guayaquil, Ecuador

ConvaTec, Div. Bristol-Myers Squibb CO., Av. Las Americas, Edif. Mecanos, Piso 3, Guayaquil, Ecuador

BUDGET GROUP, INC.

125 Basin St., Ste. 210, Daytona Beach, FL, 32114

Tel: (904) 238-7035   Fax: (904) 238-7461   www.budgetrentacar.com

Car and truck rental system.

Budget Rent A Car De Quito, 1408 Y Colon Esquina Ave Amazo, Guayaquil, Ecuador

LEO BURNETT, DIV. B-COM 3 GROUP

35 West Wacker Drive, Chicago, IL, 60601

Tel: (312) 220-5959   Fax: (312) 220-6533   www.leoburnett.com

Engaged in advertising, marketing, media buying and planning, and public relations.

Valencia y Asociados Publicidad, Quito, Ecuador

CALMAQUIP ENGINEERING CORPORATION

7240 N.W. 12th Street, Miami, FL, 33121

Tel: (305) 592-4510   Fax: (305) 593-9618   www.calmaquip.com

Engineering project management

Calmaquip Engineering del Ecuador SA, Casilla 56, Edif. Torres de Colon, Av. Colon 1346, Quito, Ecuador

CARBOLINE COMPANY

350 Hanley Industrial Court, St. Louis, MO, 63144

Tel: (314) 644-1000   Fax: (314) 644-4617   www.carboline.com

Mfr. coatings and sealants.

Pinturas Condor SA, 763 Ruiz de Castill, Quito, Ecuador

CHESTERTON BLUMENAUER BINSWANGER

Two Logan Square, 4th Floor, Philadelphia, PA, 19103-2759

Tel: (215) 448-6000   Fax: (215) 448-6238   www.cbbi.com

Real estate and related services.

Binswanger Ecuador, Av. Al Parque y Alonso Torres, Edif. Centrum El Bosque, Oficina No. 206, Quito, Ecuador

Contact: Cristina Moshenek

CHEVRON TEXACO CORPORATION

575 Market Street, San Francisco, CA, 94105-2856

Tel: (415) 894-7700   Fax: (415) 894-2248   www.chevrontexaco.com

Oil exploration, production and petroleum products.

ChevronTexaco Ecador, LYTECA, Mons. Doming Comin, Casilla 6071, Guayaquil, Ecuador

CHIQUITA BRANDS INTERNATIONAL INC.

250 East Fifth Street, Cincinnati, OH, 45202

Tel: (513) 784-8000   Fax: (513) 784-8030   www.chiquita.com

Sale and distribution of bananas, fresh fruits and processed foods.

Compania Agricola del Guayas, Aptdo. Aereo 09-01-4245, Guayaquil, Ecuador

CIGNA COMPANIES

One Liberty Place, Philadelphia, PA, 19192

Tel: (215) 761-1000   Fax: (215) 761-5511   www.cigna.com

Insurance, invest, health care and other financial services.

CIGNA Worldwide Insurance Co., Edif. Antisana, 4 piso, Av. Amazonas 3655, Catalina Herrera, Quito, Ecuador

Indi Servicios C Ltda., Av. Eloy Alfaro 939 y Amazonas, Quito, Ecuador

CITIGROUP, INC.

399 Park Avenue, New York, NY, 10022

Tel: (212) 559-1000   Fax: (212) 559-3646   www.citigroup.com

Provides insurance and financial services worldwide.

Citigroup, Juan Leon Mera 130 y Ave. Patria, Edif. CFN, Quito, Ecuador

Tel: 593-2-563-300   Fax: 593-2-566-893   Contact: Sebastian Paredes

CMS ENERGY CORPORATION

330 Town Center Dr., Ste. 1100, Dearborn, MI, 48126

Tel: (313) 436-9200   Fax: (313) 436-9225   www.cmsenergy.com

Independent power plant operator.

CMS Nomeco/Samedan Oil, Quito, Ecuador

CONE MILLS CORPORATION

3101 N. Elm Street, PO Box 26540, Greensboro, NC, 27415-6540

Tel: (336) 379-6220   Fax: (336) 379-6287   www.cone.com

Mfr. denims, flannels, chamois and other fabrics.

I.D. Tex. Cia, Ltda. (Miguel Brito), Panamericana Norte Km. 6.5, C/ Hernando Diaz y Antonio Flor Esq., Quito, Ecuador

CONTINENTAL AIRLINES INC.

1600 Smith St., Houston, TX, 77002

Tel: (713) 324-5000   Fax: (713) 324-2637   www.continental.com

International airline carrier.

Continental Airlines Inc., Ecuador

CORN PRODUCTS INTERNATIONAL, INC.

6500 South Archer Ave., Bedford Park, IL, 60501-1933

Tel: (708) 563-2400   Fax: (708) 563-6852   www.cornproducts.com

Produces corn products for ingredients corn starch corn oil and corn syrups.

Poliquimicos del Ecuador S.A./Indumaiz del Ecuador, S.A., Km 61/2 Via a Daule, PO Box 09-06-214, Guayaquil, Ecuador

Tel: 593-4-254700   Fax: 593-4-254483

CROMPTON CORPORATION

One American Lane, Greenwich, CT, 06831

Tel: (203) 552-2000   Fax: (203) 552-2870   www.cromptoncorp.com

Mfr. dyes, colors, flavors, fragrances, specialty chemicals and industrial products.

Crompton Ecuador SA, Autopista Manual Cordova Galarza, Km. 10.5, Apartado Postal 1703557, Quito, Ecuador

CROWN CORK & SEAL COMPANY, INC.

One Crown Way, Philadelphia, PA, 19154-4599

Tel: (215) 698-5100   Fax: (215) 698-5201   www.crowncork.com

Mfr. metal and plastic packaging, including steel and aluminum cans for food, beverage and household products.

Crown Cork del Ecuador CA, Casilla 5401 & 8888, Guayaquil, Ecuador

DANZAS AEI, INC.

120 Tokeneke Road, PO Box 1231, Darien, CT, 06820

Tel: (203) 655-7900   Fax: (203) 655-5779   www.aeilogistics.com

International air freight forwarder.

Danzas AEI, Avda. Shyris 1900 y, Diario el Zuriago, 3cr y 4to piso, Quito, Ecuador

Tel: 593-2-463-356

D'ARCY MASIUS BENTON & BOWLES INC. (DMB&B)

1675 Broadway, New York, NY, 10019

Tel: (212) 468-3622   Fax: (212) 468-2987   www.darcyww.com

Full service international advertising and communications group.

Creacional/DMB&B, Costanera 611 Y Las Monjas, Guayaquil, Ecuador

Tel: 593-4-38-0132   Fax: 593-4-88-5692   Contact: Miguel Loret De Mola, Gen. Mgr.

DELOITTE TOUCHE TOHMATSU INTERNATIONAL

1633 Broadway, New York, NY, 10019

Tel: (212) 492-4000   Fax: (212) 392-4154   www.deloitte.com

Accounting, audit, tax and management consulting services.

Deloitte & Touche, Edif. Contemporaneo, Noveno piso, Tulcan 803 y Av. 9 de Octubre, Guayaquil, Ecuador

Deloitte & Touche, Edif. Xerox Septimo piso, Av. Amazonas 3617 Y Pablo Sanz, Quito, Ecuador

DHL WORLDWIDE EXPRESS

50 California Avenue, San Francisco, CA, 94111

Tel: (415) 677-6100   Fax: (415) 824-9700   www.dhl.com

Worldwide air express carrier.

DHL Worldwide Express, Av. Republica 396 y Diego de Alamgro, Quito, Ecuador

Tel: 593-2-565059

DOLE FOOD COMPANY, INC.

One Dole Drive, Westlake Village, CA, 91362

Tel: (818) 874-4000   Fax: (818) 879-6615   www.dole.com

Produces/distributes fresh fruits and vegetables and canned juices and fruits.

Dole Food Company, Ecuador

DOVER CORPORATION

280 Park Ave., New York, NY, 10017-1292

Tel: (212) 922-1640   Fax: (212) 922-1656   www.dovercorporation.com

Holding company for varied industries; assembly and testing equipment, oil-well gear and other industrial products.

Celco Cia Ltd., Cordova 10004 Y.P. Ycaza, Guayaquil, Ecuador

Tel: 593-4-431-2987   Fax: 593-4-313-324

THE DOW CHEMICAL COMPANY

2030 Dow Center, Midland, MI, 48674

Tel: (989) 636-1000   Fax: (989) 636-3228   www.dow.com

Mfr. chemicals, plastics, pharmaceuticals, agricultural products, consumer products.

Dow Chemical Intl. Inc., Circunvalacion Calle 6a., Urdesa, Casilla 6560, Guayaquil, Ecuador

LIFE (Laboratorios Industriales Faramceuticos Ecuatorianos), Edif. LIFE, Av. Zumaco y de la Prensa, Casilla 458, Quito, Ecuador

LIFE (Laboratorios Industriales Faramceuticos Ecuatorianos), V.M. Rendon 408, Casilla 3783, Guayaquil, Ecuador

J.D. EDWARDS & COMPANY

One Technology Way, Denver, CO, 80237

Tel: (303) 334-4000   Fax: (303) 334-4970   www.jdedwards.com

Computer software products.

E.D.P. ECU, Calle Rumipamba #706 Y Av. Republica, Edif. Borja Paez P-3 Ofs. 32-33, Quito, Ecuador

Tel: 593-2-263-036   Fax: 593-2-263-037

EFCO

1800 NE Broadway Ave., Des Moines, IA, 50316-0386

Tel: (515) 266-1141   Fax: (515) 266-7970   www.efco-usa.com

Mfr. systems for concrete construction.

EFCO, Shyris 2678 y Garpar Villarroel, Edif. El Tablon, piso 60, Casilla 17-15-181-C, Quito, Ecuador

EGL INC. (EAGLE GLOBAL LOGISTICS)

15350 Vickery Drive, Houston, TX, 77032

Tel: (281) 618-3100   Fax: (281) 618-3223   www.eagleusa.com

Ocean/air freight forwarding, customs brokerage, packing and wholesale, logistics management and insurance.

EGL Eagle Global Logistics, Robles 653 Y Amazonas, piso 4TO, Of. 411, Quito, Ecuador

Tel: 593-2-236-440   Fax: 593-2-221-946

EGL Eagle Global Logistics, CLDA Kennedy Norte, MZ 103 Atras de Llantera Oso, Guayaquil, Ecuador

Tel: 593-4-281-416   Fax: 593-4-281-818

ENTRIX

5252 Westchester, Suite 250, Houston, TX, 77005

Tel: (713) 666-6223   Fax: (713) 666-5227   www.entrix.com

Consulting services firm specializing in environmental sciences, geosciences, and environmental engineering.

ENTRIX Ecuador, Teresa de Cepeda, N34-225 y Av. Republica, Quito, Ecuador

Tel: 593-2-2251-422   Fax: 593-2-2251-422

ERNST & YOUNG INTERNATIONAL

5 Times Square, New York, NY, 10036

Tel: (212) 773-3000   Fax: (212) 773-6350   www.eyi.com

Engaged in assurance and advisory business services, tax, law and corporate finance.

Ernst & Young International, PO Box 09-01-9094, Guayaquil, Ecuador

Tel: 593-4-560-655   Fax: 593-4-562-199   Contact: Cesar R. Holguin

Ernst & Young International, Attn: Quito Office, PO Box 09-01-9094, Guayaquil, Ecuador

Tel: 593-2-439-383   Fax: 593-2-439-375

EXPEDITORS INTERNATIONAL OF WASHINGTON INC.

1015 Third Avenue, 12th Fl., Seattle, WA, 98104-1182

Tel: (206) 674-3400   Fax: (206) 682-9777   www.expd.com

Air/ocean freight forwarding, customs brokerage, international logistics solutions.

Leidasa SAC, Av. Juan Tanca Marengo Km. 1.5, Edif. Sumelec, Primer piso, Ofic. 01, Guayaquil, Ecuador

Leidasa SAC, Faustino Sarmiento 158 y Portete, Quito, Ecuador

FEDERAL-MOGUL CORPORATION

26555 Northwestern Highway, PO Box 1966, Southfield, MI, 48034

Tel: (248) 354-7700   Fax: (248) 354-8983   www.federal-mogul.com

Mfr./distributor precision parts for automobiles, trucks, farm and construction vehicles.

Federal-Mogul del Ecuador SA, Quito, Ecuador

FERRO CORPORATION

1000 Lakeside Ave., Cleveland, OH, 44114-7000

Tel: (216) 641-8580   Fax: (216) 696-5784   www.ferro.com

Mfr. Specialty chemicals, coatings, plastics, colors, refractories.

Ferro Ecuadoriana SA, PO Box 01-01-1188, Cuenca, Ecuador

Tel: 593-7-801288   Fax: 593-7-807042   Contact: Braulio Fernandez, Mng. Dir.

FLINT INK CORPORATION

4600 Arrowhead Drive, Ann Arbor, MI, 48105

Tel: (734) 622-6000   Fax: (734) 622-6060   www.flintink.com

Manufacturer of printing inks and pigments.

Flink Ink Corporation, Guayaquil, Ecuador

FRITZ COMPANIES, INC., DIV. UPS

706 Mission Street, Ste. 900, San Francisco, CA, 94103

Tel: (415) 904-8360   Fax: (415) 904-8661   www.fritz.com

Integrated transportation, sourcing, distribution and customs brokerage services.

Fritz Companies Inc., Guayaquil, Ecuador

H.B. FULLER COMPANY

1200 Willow Lake Blvd., Vadnais Heights, MN, 55110

Tel: (651) 236-5900   Fax: (651) 236-5898   www.hbfuller.com

Mfr./distributor adhesives, sealants, coatings, paints, waxes, sanitation chemicals.

Glidden Ecuador, Quito Sales Office, Av. America 4034 y Lallemet, Casilla Postal 01-17-3545, Quito, Ecuador

Tel: 593-2-259418   Fax: 593-2-435545

H.B. Fuller Ecuador SA, Casilla 7441, Guayaquil, Ecuador

Tel: 593-4-25-0588   Fax: 593-4-25-0901

GE BETZ, DIV. GE SPECIALTY MATERIALS

4636 Somerton Road, PO Box 3002, Trevose, PA, 19053-6783

Tel: (215) 355-3300   Fax: (215) 953-5524   www.gebetz.com

Engaged in engineered chemical treatment of water and process systems in industrial, commercial and institutional facilities

GE Betz, Div. GE Specialty Materials, Calle Luiz de Gongora, Casa no. 0152, Cjidaleda Oscus Ambato, Ecuador

GENERAL MOTORS CORPORATION

300 Renaissance Center, Detroit, MI, 48285

Tel: (313) 556-5000   Fax: (313) 556-5108   www.gm.com

Mfr. full line vehicles, automotive electronics, commercial technologies, telecommunications, space, finance.

Autos y Maquinas del Ecuador SA, Quito, Ecuador

Omnibus BB Transportes SA, Quito, Ecuador

THE GILLETTE COMPANY

Prudential Tower Building, Boston, MA, 02199

Tel: (617) 421-7000   Fax: (617) 421-7123   www.gillette.com

Develop/mfr. personal care/use products: blades and razors, toiletries, cosmetics, stationery.

Gillette del Ecuador SA, KM 6.5 Via a Daule, Guayaquil, Ecuador

GLOBAL SILVERHAWK INTERNATIONAL MOVING

1000 Burnett Avenue, Concord, CA, 94520

Tel: (510) 609-7080   Fax: (510) 609-7081   www.globalsilverhawk.com

International moving and forwarding.

Global Transportes Ltda., Bartolome Sanchez #N 71-69, Y J. Guerrero, Quito, Ecuador

Tel: 593-9-457-742   Contact: Pablo Calero, Gen. Mgr.

GRANT THORNTON INTERNATIONAL

800 One Prudential Plaza, 130 E. Randolph Drive, Chicago, IL, 60601-6050

Tel: (312) 856-0001   Fax: (312) 616-7052   www.grantthornton.com

Accounting, audit, tax and management consulting services.

Grant Thornton Alvarado Schaffer Y Asociados, Avda Las Lomas 306, PO Box 09-01-5601, Guayaquil, Ecuador

Contact: Manuel Alvarado

GREY GLOBAL GROUP

777 Third Ave., New York, NY, 10017

Tel: (212) 546-2000   Fax: (212) 546-1495   www.grey.com

International advertising agency.

DeMaruri, Guayaquil, Ecuador

HAEMONETICS CORPORATION

400 Wood Road, Braintree, MA, 02184-9114

Tel: (781) 848-7100   Fax: (781) 848-5106   www.haemonetics.com

Mfr. automated blood processing systems and blood products.

Comercial Mersal S.A., Calle Italia 344, Quito, Ecuador

Contact: Hector Merino S., Pres.

HALLIBURTON COMPANY

500 North Akard Street, Ste. 3600, Dallas, TX, 75201-3391

Tel: (214) 978-2600   Fax: (214) 978-2685   www.halliburton.com

Engaged in diversified energy services, engineering and construction.

Halliburton Ltd., Calle Japon 123 y Av. Amazonas, Edif. Ferlosant, Quito, Ecuador

Tel: 593-6-830-447   Fax: 593-6-830-235

H.J. HEINZ COMPANY

600 Grant Street, Pittsburgh, PA, 15219

Tel: (412) 456-5700   Fax: (412) 456-6128   www.heinz.com

Processed food products and nutritional services.

Star-Kist Foods Inc., Guayaquil, Ecuador

HELMERICH & PAYNE INC.

Utica at Twenty-First, Tulsa, OK, 74114-1398

Tel: (918) 742-5531   Fax: (918) 743-2671   www.hpinc.com

Engaged in contract drilling and oil and gas exploration and production.

Helmerich & Payne del Ecuador, Av. Republica 1650 y Azuay, Quito, Ecuador

HORWATH INTERNATIONAL ASSOCIATION

420 Lexington Avenue, Suite 526, New York, NY, 10170-0526

Tel: (212) 808-2000   Fax: (212) 808-2020   www.horwath.com

Public accountants and auditors.

Willi Bamberger & Asociados C.Ltda, Av. 10 de Agosto 1792 (2do y 4to pisos), Edificio Santa Rosa, Quito, Ecuador

Tel: 593-2-2224-181

IBM CORPORATION

1133 Westchester Avenue, White Plains, NY, 10604

Tel: (914) 765-1900   Fax: (914) 765-7382   www.ibm.com

Information products, technology and services.

IBM del Ecuador C.A., Diego de Almagro 2054 y Whimper, Quito, Ecuador

Tel: 593-2-565100   Fax: 593-2-565145

IMATION CORPORATION

One Imation Place, Oakdale, MN, 55128

Tel: (612) 704-4000   Fax: (612) 704-3444   www.imation.com

Dry laser-imaging film systems.

Imation Ecuador, S.A., Edificio Torres del Norte, Av. Miguel H. Alcivar, Mz 506, Torre B, Primer Piso, Ofic.03, Guayaquil, Ecuador

INFONET SERVICES CORPORATION

2160 East Grand Ave., El Segundo, CA, 90245-1022

Tel: (310) 335-2600   Fax: (310) 335-4507   www.infonet.com

Provider of Internet services and electronic messaging services.

Infonet Ecuador, Av. America 3576 y Atahualpa, PO Box 1703398, Quito, Ecuador

Tel: 593-2-444-965   Fax: 593-2-444-966

INGRAM MICRO INC.

1600 E. St. Andrew Place, Santa Ana, CA, 92799

Tel: (714) 566-1000   Fax: (714) 566-7940   www.ingrammicro.com

Engaged in wholesale distribution of microcomputer products.

Ingram Micro Inc., Bulgaria 146 y Diego de Almagro, #11 Mezzanine, Quito, Ecuador

Tel: 593-2-222-2044   Fax: 593-2-222-3163

INSTRON CORPORATION

100 Royal Street, Canton, MA, 02021-1089

Tel: (781) 575-5000   Fax: (781) 575-5751   www.instron.com

Mfr., markets and services materials testing instruments, systems and accessories.

Protecto Coasin S.A., Ecuador

IRRIDELCO INTERNATIONAL CORPORATION

440 Sylvan Ave., Englewood Cliffs, NJ, 07632

Tel: (201) 569-3030   Fax: (201) 569-9237   www.irridelco.com

Mfr. and distributor of the most comprehensive lines of mechanical and micro irrigation; pumps and irrigation systems.

IDC Ecuador, 1 ro de Mayo 1006 y Tulcan, 7mo piso, Guayaquil, Ecuador

Tel: 593-428-1010   Fax: 593-428-1256   Contact: Cristobal Ripalda

J. WALTER THOMPSON COMPANY

466 Lexington Ave., New York, NY, 10017

Tel: (212) 210-7000   Fax: (212) 210-6944   www.jwt.com

International advertising and marketing services.

Norlop Thompson Asociados, Guayaquil, Ecuador

JOHNSON & JOHNSON

One Johnson & Johnson Plaza, New Brunswick, NJ, 08933

Tel: (732) 524-0400   Fax: (732) 214-0334   www.jnj.com

Mfr./distributor/R&D pharmaceutical, health care and cosmetic products.

Johnson & Johnson del Ecuador SA, Casilla 09-01-7206, Guayaquil, Ecuador

SC JOHNSON

1525 Howe St., Racine, WI, 53403

Tel: (262) 260-2000   Fax: (262) 260-2133   www.scjohnsonwax.com

Home, auto, commercial and personal care products and specialty chemicals.

SC Johnson, PO Box 09-01-874, Guayaquil, Ecuador

KPMG CONSULTING INC.

1676 International Dr., McLean, VA, 22102

Tel: (703) 747-3000   Fax: (703) 747-8500   www.kpmg.com

Accounting and audit, tax and management consulting services.

KPMG International, Av. Amazonas 1188 y Cordero, Edif. FLOPEC, 6to.piso, Quito, Ecuador

KPMG International, Cdla. Kennedy Norte, Av. Miguel Alcivar, Mz. 302, Solar 7 y 8, Guayaquil, Ecuador

Tel: 593-4-290697   Fax: 593-4-288774   Contact: Leonidas Sánchez, Jr., Sr. Ptnr.

THE LUBRIZOL CORPORATION

29400 Lakeland Blvd., Wickliffe, OH, 44092-2298

Tel: (440) 943-4200   Fax: (440) 943-5337   www.lubrizol.com

Mfr. chemicals additives for lubricants and fuels.

Lubrizol de Ecuador, Guayaquil, Ecuador

Tel: 593-4-288-538

MANPOWER INTERNATIONAL INC.

5301 N. Ironwood Rd., PO Box 2053, Milwaukee, WI, 53201-2053

Tel: (414) 961-1000   Fax: (414) 961-7081   www.manpower.com

Temporary help, contract service, training and testing.

Manpower - Quito, Jorge Washington 570 y Juan Leon Mera, Quito, Ecuador

Tel: 593-2-504-867   Fax: 5932--509-517

MARRIOTT INTERNATIONAL INC.

10400 Fernwood Rd., Bethesda, MD, 20817

Tel: (301) 380-3000   Fax: (301) 380-5181   www.marriott.com

Hotel services.

Quito Marriott Hotel, Quito, Ecuador

Tel: 593-2-506-366

MARSH & McLENNAN COS INC.

1166 Ave. of the Americas, New York, NY, 10036-2774

Tel: (212) 345-5000   Fax: (212) 345-4808   www.marshmac.com

Insurance agents/brokers, pension and investment management consulting services.

Tecniseguros Cia. Ltda., Whimper 1210, Casilla 17-21-0433, Quito, Ecuador

Tel: 593-2-250-5655   Fax: 593-2-256-4773   Contact: Francisco Proano-Salvador

Tecniseguros Cia. Ltda., Edif. Tecniseguros Kennedy Norte, Calle San Rogue y Av. Francisco de Orellana, Guayaquil, Ecuador

Tel: 593-4-468-0700   Fax: 593-4-468-0822   Contact: Pedro Hallon

McCANN-ERICKSON WORLDGROUP

750 Third Ave., New York, NY, 10017

Tel: (212) 697-6000   Fax: (212) 984-3575   www.mccann.com

International advertising and marketing services.

McCann Erickson Publicidad SA, Leonidas Plaza 150, 18 de Septiembre, Casilla 3491, Quito, Ecuador

McCann Erickson Publicidad SA, Malecon 1401, Casilla 5809, Guayaquil, Ecuador

MERCK & COMPANY, INC.

One Merck Drive, PO Box 100, Whitehouse Station, NJ, 08889-0100

Tel: (908) 423-1000   Fax: (908) 423-2592   www.merck.com

Pharmaceuticals, chemicals and biologicals.

Merck, Sharp & Dohme Intl., Carretera al Tingo, Guayaquil, Ecuador

M-I

PO Box 48242, Houston, TX, 77242-2842

Tel: (713) 739-0222   Fax: (713) 308-9503   www.midf.com

Developer, manufacturer and marketer of drilling and completion fluids and services.

MIOL Swaco, Republica del Salvador No. 500 e Irlanda, Edificio Siglo XXI, Piso 1W, Quito, Ecuador

Tel: 593-2-269381   Fax: 593-2-261701

MICROSOFT CORPORATION

One Microsoft Way, Redmond, WA, 98052-6399

Tel: (425) 882-8080   Fax: (425) 936-7329   www.microsoft.com

Computer software, peripherals and services.

Microsoft Del Ecuador S.A., Av. Naciones Unidas 1014 y, Av .Amazonas (esquina), Edif. La Previsora, Torre A, Officina 1001, Quito, Ecuador

Tel: 593-2-463-090   Fax: 593-2-463-093

J. P. MORGAN CHASE & CO. INC.

270 Park Ave., New York, NY, 10017

Tel: (212) 270-6000   Fax: (212) 622-9030   www.jpmorganchase.com

Provides integrated financial solutions for institutions and individuals worldwide, including asset management, investment banking and commercial banking.

J. P. Morgan Chase & Co., 18 de Septiembre 332 y Juan Leon Mera, piso 7, Casilla 9439, Sucursal 7, Quito, Ecuador

NATURE'S SUNSHINE PRODUCTS, INC.

75 East 1700 South, Provo, UT, 84605

Tel: (801) 342-4300   Fax: (801) 342-4305   www.naturessunshine.com

Mfr. and sales of holistic health products.

Nature's Sunshine Products, Ave el Batan 405, y 6 de Diciembre, Quito, Ecuador

AC NIELSEN COMPANY

177 Broad Street, Stamford, CT, 06901

Tel: (203) 961-3000   Fax: (203) 961-3190   www.acnielsen.com

Engaged in market and consumer research.

ACNielsen, Av. Amazonas 3655 y Juan Pablo Sanz., Edi. Antisana I., Piso 8, Off 801, Quito, Ecuador

NORDSON CORPORATION

28601 Clemens Road, Westlake, OH, 44145-4551

Tel: (440) 892-1580   Fax: (440) 892-9507   www.nordson.com

Mfr. industry application equipment, sealants and packaging machinery.

Industrial de Servicios, Cia. Ltda., Fray Bartolome de las Casas, 745 (Interior) y Carvajal, Apdo. Postal 17-08-8095, Quito, Ecuador

OCCIDENTAL PETROLEUM CORPORATION

10889 Wilshire Blvd., Los Angeles, CA, 90024

Tel: (310) 208-8800   Fax: (310) 443-6690   www.oxy.com

Petroleum and petroleum products, chemicals, plastics.

Occidental of Ecuador Inc., Ecuador

OWENS-ILLINOIS, INC.

One SeaGate, PO Box 1035, Toledo, OH, 43666

Tel: (419) 247-5000   Fax: (419) 247-2839   www.o-i.com

Mfr. glass containers and packaging products.

Cristaleria del Ecuador, S.A., 22.5 Km Via Perimetral, PO Box 09-01-5684, Guayaquil, Ecuador

Tel: 593-489-3032

PAN-AMERICAN LIFE INSURANCE COMPANY

Pan American Life Center, 601 Poydras St., New Orleans, LA, 70130-0219

Tel: (504) 566-1300   Fax: (504) 566-3600   www.panamericanlife.com

Insurance services.

Pan-American Life Insurance Co., Av. Republica del Salvador 10-81, y Naciones Unidas, Torre Londres, pisos 10 y 11, Quito, Ecuador

Tel: 593-2-253-490   Fax: 593-2-252-502   Contact: Juan Mario Bustamante   Emp: 54

PARKER DRILLING COMPANY

1401 Enclave Pkwy., Ste. 600, Houston, TX, 77077

Tel: (281) 406-2000   Fax: (281) 406-2001   www.parkerdrilling.com

Provides land contract drilling services to firms in the oil and gas industry.

Parker Drilling Co. of South America, Calle Brasil 293 y, Jacinto de la Cueva, Edi IACA Piso 2, Quito, Ecuador

PERKIN ELMER, INC.

45 William Street, Wellesley, MA, 02481

Tel: (781) 237-5100   Fax: (781) 431-4255   www.perkinelmer.com

Mfr. equipment and devices to detect explosives and bombs on airline carriers.

Proinstra S.A., Rumipampa E2-64 y Republica, Edificio Alex, OF 102, Quito, Ecuador

Tel: 593-2-444-363   Fax: 593-2-351-502

PETROLEUM HELICOPTERS, INC.

2001 SE Evangeline Thwy., Lafayette, LA, 70508

Tel: (337) 235-2452   Fax: (337) 232-6537   www.phihelico.com

Aerial transportation and helicopter charter.

Ecuavia-Oriente SA, Av. 6 de Diciembre 3805 y Noruega, Quito, Ecuador

PFIZER INC.

235 East 42nd Street, New York, NY, 10017-5755

Tel: (212) 573-2323   Fax: (212) 573-7851   www.pfizer.com

Research-based, global health care company.

Pfizer CA, Ecuador

PHARMACIA CORPORATION

100 Route 206 North, Peapack, NJ, 07977

Tel: (908) 901-8000   Fax: (908) 901-8379   www.pharmacia.com

Mfr. pharmaceuticals, agricultural products, industry chemicals.

Pharmacia & Upjohn Inter-American Corp., Ave. Naciones Unidas E2-49 e Omaquito, Quito, Ecuador

Tel: 593-2-265313   Fax: 593-2-459066

PHELPS DODGE CORPORATION

2600 North Central Ave., Phoenix, AZ, 85004-3089

Tel: (602) 234-8100   Fax: (602) 234-8337   www.phelpsdodge.com

Copper, minerals, metals and special engineered products for transportation and electrical markets.

Cables Electricos Ecuatorianos CA (CABLEC), Casilla 1701, 02730 Quito, Ecuador

PRAXAIR, INC.

39 Old Ridgebury Road, Danbury, CT, 06810-5113

Tel: (203) 837-2000   Fax: (203) 837-2450   www.praxair.com

Produces and distributes industrial and specialty gases.

Praxair Ecuador S.A., Km 2.5, Via Duran Tambo, Via a la Feria, Guayaquil, Ecuador

Tel: 593-4-480-3710   Fax: 593-4-486-2990

PRICEWATERHOUSECOOPERS LLP

1301 Ave. of the Americas, New York, NY, 10019

Tel: (212) 596-7000   Fax: (212) 259-1301   www.pwcglobal.com

Accounting and auditing, tax and management, and human resource consulting services.

PriceWaterhouseCoopers, Av. 12 de Octubre 394, 1-6 piso, Casilla 17-21227, Quito, Ecuador

Tel: 593-2-562288   Fax: 593-2-567096

PriceWaterhouseCoopers, Carchi 702, piso 2, Casilla 5820, Guayaquil, Ecuador

Tel: 593-4-280-757   Fax: 593-4-284-153

SKYTEL COMMUNICATIONS, INC.

515 E. Amite St., Jackson, MS, 39201

Tel: (601) 944-1300   Fax: (601) 944-3900   www.skytel.com

Provides wireless messaging services, radio paging services and systems implementation.

Buscapersona Ecuador, Quito, Ecuador

THE ST. PAUL COMPANIES, INC.

385 Washington Street, St. Paul, MN, 55102

Tel: (651) 310-7911   Fax: (651) 310-8294   www.stpaul.com

Provides investment, insurance and reinsurance services.

Compania de Seguros Ecuatoriano - Sujiza S.A., Av. 9 de Octubre, PO Box Casilla 397, Guayaquil, Ecuador

THE STANLEY WORKS

1000 Stanley Drive, PO Box 7000, New Britain, CT, 06053

Tel: (860) 225-5111　　　　Fax: (860) 827-3987　　　　www.stanleyworks.com

Mfr. hand tools and hardware.

Stanley Latin America, Piso 5, Officina 5, Eloy Alfaro y Cuenca, Guayaquil, Ecuador

SYBASE, INC.

5000 Hacienda Dr., Dublin, CA, 94568

Tel: (925) 236-5000　　　　Fax: (925) 236-4321　　　　www.sybase.com

Design/mfg/distribution of database management systems, software development tools, connectivity products, consulting and technical support services..

InfoPower, S.A., Alpallana 289, Diego de Alnagro, Quito, Ecuador

Tel: 593-2-508-593　Fax: 593-2-500-806

UNION CARBIDE CORPORATION

39 Old Ridgebury Road, Danbury, CT, 06817

Tel: (203) 794-2000　　　　Fax: (203) 794-6269　　　　www.unioncarbide.com

Mfr. industrial chemicals, plastics and resins.

UCAR Polimeros y Quimicos CA SA de CV, Casilla 09-01-5322, Guayaquil, Ecuador

UNITED PARCEL SERVICE, INC.

55 Glenlake Parkway, NE, Atlanta, GA, 30328

Tel: (404) 828-6000　　　　Fax: (404) 828-6593　　　　www.ups.com

International package-delivery service.

UPS / Ecuador, Nuñez de Vela 470 e Ignacio San Maria, Edificio Metropoli, Planta Baja Quito, Ecuador

Tel: 593-2-460-598　Fax: 593-2-258-270

VERITAS DGC INC.

10300 Town Park Drive, Houston, TX, 77072

Tel: (832) 351-8300　　　　Fax: (832) 351-8701　　　　www.veritasdgc.com

Provides integrated geophysical services designed to manage exploration risk and enhance drilling and production success.

Veritas GeoServices Ltd., Rumipamba #706 ente Republica y Amazons, Edificio Borja-Paez, Piso 7, Quito, Ecuador

THE WACKENHUT CORPORATION

4200 Wackenhut Dr., Ste. 100, Palm Beach Gardens, FL, 33410

Tel: (561) 622-5656　　　　Fax: (561) 691-6736　　　　www.wackenhut.com

Security systems and services.

Wackenhut del Ecuador SA, Valladolid 936 y Cordero, Casilla 17-11-04791, Quito, Ecuador

Tel: 593-2-224-664　Fax: 593-2-225-109

WATERS CORPORATION

34 Maple Street, Milford, MA, 01757

Tel: (508) 478-2000　　　　Fax: (508) 872-1990　　　　www.waters.com

Mfr./distribute liquid chromatographic instruments and test and measurement equipment.

Purifluidos Cia Ltda., Calle Ultimas Noticias, 461 (N38 - 29) y el Telegrafo, Quito, Ecuador

Contact: Luis Miguel Ortega

WORLD COURIER INC.

45 Southfield Avenue, Ste. 3450, Stamford, CT, 06902-7210

Tel: (203) 975-9333　　　　Fax: (203) 316-9455　　　　www.worldcourier.com

International courier service.

World Courier de Ecuador, Robles 653 y Amazonas, Quito, Ecuador

World Courier de Ecuador, Elizalde 1194 Pichincha, Of. 404, Guayaquil, Ecuador

WYETH PHARMACEUTICALS

555 E. Lancaster Ave., Wayne, PA, 19087-5109

Tel: (610) 971-5400   Fax: (610) 995-4668   www.wyeth.com

Mfr. antibiotics and pharmaceutical products.

Wyeth-Ayerst-Lederle International, Inglaterra 200 y Av. Eloy, Alfaro Quito, Ecuador

Tel: 593-2-226-502

XEROX CORPORATION

800 Long Ridge Road, PO Box 1600, Stamford, CT, 06904

Tel: (203) 968-3000   Fax: (203) 968-4312   www.xerox.com

Mfr. document processing equipment, systems and supplies.

Xerox del Ecuador, S.A., Ave. Amazonas 3623 Y Juan Pablo Sanz, Apt. Postal 17-03-174, Quito, Ecuador

Tel: 593-2-439-952   Fax: 593-1-430-994

YORK INTERNATIONAL CORPORATION

631 South Richland Ave., York, PA, 17403

Tel: (717) 771-7890   Fax: (717) 771-6212   www.york.com

Mfr. heating, ventilating, air conditioning and refrigeration equipment.

York Ecuador, Parque Comercial California, Via Daule Km. 11.5, Guayaquil, Ecuador

Egypt

3COM CORPORATION

5400 Bayfront Plaza, Santa Clara, CA, 95052-8145

Tel: (408) 326-5000   Fax: (408) 326-5001   www.3com.com

Engaged in the development and manufacture of computer networking products and systems.

3Com Egypt, 7 Soliman Abza Street, Office No. 1, Dokki, Cairo, Egypt

3M (MINNESOTA MINING & MFG.)

3M Center, St. Paul, MN, 55144-1000

Tel: (651) 733-1110   Fax: (651) 733-9973   www.mmm.com

Mfr. diversified products for industry, consumer, health care, imaging, communications, transport, safety, etc.

3M Egypt Ltd., Sofitel Towers 19th Fl., Corniche El-Nil Street, Maadi, Cairo, Egypt

Tel: 202-417-6559   Fax: 202-417-6558

ABBOTT LABORATORIES

100 Abbott Park Rd., Abbott Park, IL, 60064

Tel: (847) 937-6100   Fax: (847) 937-1511   www.abbott.com

Development, manufacture and sale of diversified health care products and services.

Abbott Diagnostics Division, 4 Africa Street, Nasr City Cairo, Egypt

Tel: 20-2-271-6306

Abbott Laboratories, S.A., PO Box 2678, Horreya, Heliopolis Cairo 11361, Egypt

Tel: 20-2-245-4963

ABS (AMERICAN BUREAU OF SHIPPING)

ABS Plaza, 16855 Northchase Drive, Houston, TX, 77060

Tel: (281) 877-6000   Fax: (281) 877-6344   www.eagle.org

Classification and certification of ships and offshore structures, development and technical assistance.

ABS Europe, 23 Saad Zaghlool Street, Ekonomakis Bldg., Flat No. 10, Suez 43511, Egypt

AGRA BAYMONT, INC.

14100 58th St. North, Clearwater, FL, 33760-3796

Tel: (727) 578-0100   Fax: (727) 577-6946   www.baymont.com

Provides data conversion, maintenance, and implementation services for utility, public, and commercial industries and offers services in photogram metric mapping, remote sensing, imagery analysis, and resource mapping.

Geonex Corp., 21 Adnan Omar Sidqy St., Ex Qambis St., Dokki Cairo, Egypt

ALLERGAN INC.

2525 Dupont Drive, Irvine, CA, 92612

Tel: (714) 246-4500   Fax: (714) 246-6987   www.allergan.com

Mfr. therapeutic eye care products and skin care pharmaceuticals.

Allergan Scientific, 51 Abbas El Akkad, Nasr City, Cairo, Egypt

Tel: 20-2-404-0273   Fax: 20-2-261-0620

AMERICAN EXPRESS COMPANY

90 Hudson Street, Jersey City, NJ, 07302

Tel: (212) 640-2000   Fax: (212) 619-9802   www.americanexpress.com

Engaged in travel, travelers cheques, charge card and financial services.

American Express Foreign Exchange Services, Cornish El Nil Street, Aswan, Egypt

ANC RENTAL CORPORATION

200 S. Andrews Ave., Ft. Lauderdale, FL, 33301

Tel: (954) 320-4000   Fax: (954) 320-4077   www.ancrental.com

Engaged in car rental services, including National Car Rental and Alamo Rent A Car.

National Car Rental, Hotel Indiana, 16 Saraya St., Dokki, Cairo, Egypt

ANDERSEN

33 West Monroe Street, Chicago, IL, 60603

Tel: (312) 580-0033   Fax: (312) 507-6748   www.andersen.com

Accounting and audit, tax and management consulting services. **Firm under worldwide reorganization; new data unavailable for this edition.

Andersen Egypt/Allied Accountants, Mobica Tower 37, El Ahrar St., PO Box 97, Dokki Cairo, Egypt

Tel: 20-2-336-2000

Arthur Andersen Egypt/Allied Accountants, PO Box 97, Dokki, Giza, Egypt

Tel: 20-3-850-227

APACHE CORPORATION

2000 Post Oak Blvd., Ste. 100, Houston, TX, 77056-4400

Tel: (713) 296-6000   Fax: (713) 296-6496   www.apachecorp.com

Engaged in independent oil and gas exploration and production.

Apache Egypt Companies, 8 Street No. 281, New Maadi, Cairo, Egypt

Contact: Rodney J. Eichler

ARBOR ACRES FARM INC.

439 Marlborough Road, Glastonbury, CT, 06033

Tel: (860) 633-4681   Fax: (860) 633-2433   www.aaf.com

Producers of male and female broiler breeders, commercial egg layers.

Misr Poultry, 15-A Radwan Ebn El Tabib Street, PO Box 125, Giza, Cairo, Egypt

ASSOCIATED PRESS INC.

50 Rockefeller Plaza, New York, NY, 10020-1605

Tel: (212) 621-1500   Fax: (212) 621-5447   www.ap.com

News gathering agency.

The Associated Press, 113 Karr Eo Mil, Cairo, Egypt

Tel: 20-2-578-4091

AT&T CORPORATION

295 N. Maple Ave., Basking Ridge, NJ, 07920-1002

Tel: (908) 221-2000   Fax: (908) 221-2528   www.att.com

Engaged in long distance telecommunications.

AT&T Egypt, El Nasr Bldg., Nite St., Cairo, Egypt

BAKER & McKENZIE

130 East Randolph Drive, Ste. 2500, Chicago, IL, 60601

Tel: (312) 861-8000   Fax: (312) 861-2899   www.bakerinfo.com

International legal services.

Helmy & Hamza, World Trade Ctr., 1191 Cornich El Nil, 18th Fl., Cairo, Egypt

Tel: 20-2-579-1801   Fax: 20-2-579-1808

BAKER HUGHES INCORPORATED

3900 Essex Lane, Ste. 1200, Houston, TX, 77027

Tel: (713) 439-8600   Fax: (713) 439-8699   www.bakerhughes.com

Develop and apply technology to drill, complete and produce oil and natural gas wells; provide separation systems to petroleum, municipal, continuous process and mining industries.

Baker Eastern, S.A., 21 Rd. 263 Corner 281, Third Secor, New Maadi Cairo, Egypt

Tel: 20-2-3521651   Fax: 20-2-3533638

Milchem Intl. Ltd., 8 Rd. 279, Villa El Baraka, New Maadi Cairo, Egypt

THE BANK OF NEW YORK
One Wall Street, New York, NY, 10286

Tel: (212) 495-1784   Fax: (212) 495-2546   www.bankofny.com

Banking services.

The Bank of New York, 9 Abdelmounim Riyad St., Dokki Giza 12311, Egypt

Tel: 20-2-336-5818

BATES WORLDWIDE INC.
498 Seventh Avenue, New York, NY, 10018

Tel: (212) 297-7000   Fax: (212) 986-0270   www.batesww.com

Advertising, marketing, public relations and media consulting.

Bates Egypt, 19 Soliman Abaza St., Mahandesseen, Cairo, Egypt

Tel: 20-2-713-203   Fax: 20-2-361-3616   Contact: Mike Chamberlain, Dir.

BBDO WORLDWIDE
1285 Ave. of the Americas, New York, NY, 10019

Tel: (212) 459-5000   Fax: (212) 459-6645   www.bbdo.com

Multinational group of advertising agencies.

Impact Advertising, Cairo, Egypt

BDO SEIDMAN, LLP   BELGIUM
130 East Randolph Street, Chicago, IL, 60601

Tel: (312) 856-9100   Fax: (312) 856-1379   www.bdo.com

International accounting and financial consulting firm.

Saleh, Barsoum & Abdel Aziz, 95C Mirgany St., Cairo 11341, Egypt

Tel: 20-2-417-2756   Fax: 20-2-290-4038   Contact: Magdy K. Saleh

BECHTEL GROUP INC.
50 Beale Street, PO Box 3965, San Francisco, CA, 94105-1895

Tel: (415) 768-1234   Fax: (415) 768-9038   www.bechtel.com

General contractors in engineering, construction and project management.

Bechtel International Corp., World Trade Ctr., 1191 Cornich El Nil St. Breaulac, Cairo, Egypt

Tel: 20-2-574-7801   Fax: 20-2-574-8893

BENTLY NEVADA CORPORATION
1631 Bently Parkway South, Minden, NV, 89423

Tel: (775) 782-3611   Fax: (775) 782-9259   www.bently.com

Provides hardware, software, and services for machinery information and management systems.

Petroleum & Industrial Consultants, 4 Maarouf Street, PO Box 1232, Cairo, Egypt

LOUIS BERGER INTERNATIONAL INC.
100 Halsted Street, East Orange, NJ, 07019

Tel: (201) 678-1960   Fax: (201) 672-4284   www.louisberger.com

Consulting engineers, engaged in architecture, environmental and advisory services.

Louis Berger International Inc. & Pacer Consultants, Drainage Research Institute, PO Box 15621/5, Delta Barrage Cairo, Egypt

Tel: 20-2-218-9383   Fax: 20-2-218-9153

Louis Berger International Inc.(MKE/LBII), Fum El Ismailia Khalfawi, Post No.1161, Shoubra El Mexilat Cairo, Egypt

BEST WESTERN INTERNATIONAL
6201 North 24th Place, Phoenix, AZ, 85106

Tel: (602) 957-4200   Fax: (602) 957-5740   www.bestwestern.com

International hotel chain.

Pyramids Hotel, Kingfaisal Rd., Giza, Egypt

BLACK & VEATCH LLP

8400 Ward Pkwy., PO Box 8405, Kansas City, MO, 64114

Tel: (816) 339-2000   Fax: (816) 339-2934   www.bv.com

Engaged in engineering, construction and consulting, specializing in infrastructure development in the fields of energy, water and information.

Black & Veatch International, 722 Al-Horria Ave., Victoria Alexandria, Egypt

Tel: 20-3-587-5824 Fax: 20-3-587-1284 Contact: David C. Howe

Black & Veatch International, 35 Abdel Moneim Riad St., Mohandeseen, Cairo, Egypt

Tel: 20-2-335-0232 Fax: 20-2-361-5039 Contact: David C. Howe

BVI/MWA, 96 Ammar Ibn Yasser St., Nozha Heliopolis, Cairo, Egypt

BOZELL GROUP

40 West 23rd Street, New York, NY, 10010

Tel: (212) 727-5000   Fax: (212) 645-9173   www.bozell.com

Advertising, marketing, public relations and media consulting.

Animation Advertising Agency, 28 Lebanon St., Mohandeseen, Cairo, Egypt

Tel: 20-2-344-0958 Fax: 20-2-303-1420 Contact: Ihab Gohar, Gen. Mgr.

BRISTOL-MYERS SQUIBB COMPANY

345 Park Ave., New York, NY, 10154-0037

Tel: (212) 546-4000   Fax: (212) 546-4020   www.bms.com

Pharmaceutical and food preparations, medical and surgical instruments.

Bristol-Myer Squibb - Middle East, Studio Misr Str 17, Giza Pyramids, Cairo, Egypt

Bristol-Myers Squibb - Mid East Reg. Office/Cairo, El Nasr Square, 1 Wadi El Nil Str, Mohandessen, Egypt

ConvaTec Egypt, 372 Pyramids St., Giza, Egypt

ConvaTec Middle East, PO Box 223, Giza Cairo 12211, Egypt

BUDGET GROUP, INC.

125 Basin St., Ste. 210, Daytona Beach, FL, 32114

Tel: (904) 238-7035   Fax: (904) 238-7461   www.budgetrentacar.com

Car and truck rental system.

Budget Rent A Car, Cairo International Airport, Cairo, Egypt

Tel: 20-2-443-775

LEO BURNETT, DIV. B-COM 3 GROUP

35 West Wacker Drive, Chicago, IL, 60601

Tel: (312) 220-5959   Fax: (312) 220-6533   www.leoburnett.com

Engaged in advertising, marketing, media buying and planning, and public relations.

AMA Leo Burnett, 21 Ahmed Orabi Street, El Nahda Tower, El Sahafeyeinn, Giza Cairo, Egypt

CALTEX CORPORATION

PO Box 619500, Dallas, TX, 75261-9500

Tel: (972) 830-1000   Fax: (972) 830-1081   www.caltex.com

Petroleum products.

Caltex (Egypt) SAE, 7 Lazoghli St., Garden City Cairo, Egypt

CARANA CORPORATION

4350 N. Fairfax Drive, Ste. 500, Arlington, VA, 22203

Tel: (703) 243-1700   Fax: (703) 243-0471   www.carana.com

Foreign trade consulting.

CARANA Corp., 20 Aisha El Taymouriya Street, 1/F, Ste. 2, Garden City Cairo, Egypt

CARBOLINE COMPANY

350 Hanley Industrial Court, St. Louis, MO, 63144

Tel: (314) 644-1000   Fax: (314) 644-4617   www.carboline.com

Mfr. coatings and sealants.

Dr. Mohy Sallaly, 3 El Nasser St., Heliopolis Cairo, Egypt

CARGILL, INC.

15407 McGinty Road West, Minnetonka, MN, 55440-5625

Tel: (612) 742-7575   Fax: (612) 742-7393   www.cargill.com

Food products, feeds, animal products.

Cargill Limited Egypt, Cairo, Egypt

CARRIER CORPORATION

One Carrier Place, Farmington, CT, 06034-4015

Tel: (860) 674-3000   Fax: (860) 679-3010   www.carrier.com

Mfr./distributor/services A/C, heating and refrigeration equipment.

ABAC Air Conditioning Co. (Adel Bishara & Co.), Cairo, Egypt

Carrier Air Conditioning Egypt Ltd., Cairo, Egypt

Tel: 20-2-348-3369   Fax: 20-2-349-8124

CDM INTERNATIONAL INC.

50 Hampshire Street, Cambridge, MA, 02139

Tel: (617) 452-6000   Fax: (617) 452-8000   www.cdm.com

Consulting engineers.

CDM Egypt, 1 El Mahata Square, Maadi Palace Bldg., #503, Maadi Cairo, Egypt

Tel: 20-2-380-1702

CH2M HILL INC.

6060 South Willow Drive, Greenwood Village, CO, 80111

Tel: (303) 771-0900   Fax: (303) 770-2616   www.ch2m.com

Consulting engineers, planners, economists and scientists.

CH2M Hill, 4, Road 203, Maadi Cairo, Egypt

Tel: 20-2-761-529

CITIGROUP, INC.

399 Park Avenue, New York, NY, 10022

Tel: (212) 559-1000   Fax: (212) 559-3646   www.citigroup.com

Provides insurance and financial services worldwide.

Citigroup, 4 Ahmed Pasha St., PO Box 188, Garden City Cairo 11511, Egypt

Contact: Shayne C. Elliott

THE CLOROX COMPANY

1221 Broadway, PO Box 24305, Oakland, CA, 94623-1305

Tel: (510) 271-7000   Fax: (510) 832-1463   www.clorox.com

Mfr. soap and detergents, and domestic consumer packaged products.

Household Cleaning Products Co. of Egypt, Cairo, Egypt

THE COCA-COLA COMPANY

1 Coca Cola Plaza, Atlanta, GA, 30313

Tel: (404) 676-2121   Fax: (404) 676-6792   www.coca-cola.com

Mfr./marketing/distributor soft drinks, syrups and concentrates, juice and juice-drink products.

Coca-Cola Bottling Companies of Egypt, Cairo, Egypt

CONOCO INC.

600 N. Dairy Ashford, Houston, TX, 77252

Tel: (281) 293-1000   Fax: (281) 293-1440   www.conoco.com

Oil, gas, coal, chemicals and minerals.

Continental Mid Delta Petroleum Co., PO Box 16, 51-A Old Cairo-Helwan Rd., Maadi Cairo, Egypt

COOPER CAMERON CORPORATION

515 Post Oak Blvd., Ste.1200, Houston, TX, 77027

Tel: (713) 513-3300   Fax: (713) 513-3355   www.coopercameron.com

Mfr. oil and gas industry equipment.

Cooper Cameron Egypt, Villa El Baraka, No. 8 Road 279, New Maadi Cairo, Egypt

CORE LABORATORIES

6316 Windfern, Houston, TX, 77040

Tel: (713) 328-2673   Fax: (713) 328-2150   www.corelab.com

Petroleum testing and analysis, analytical chemicals, laboratory and octane analysis instrumentation.

Core Laboratories, PO Box 45, Maadi Cairo 11431, Egypt

CUTLER-HAMMER, DIV. EATON CORP.

173 Heatherdown Drive, Westerville, OH, 43082

Tel: (614) 882-3282   Fax: (614) 895-7111   www.cutlerhammer.com

Mfr. electrical control products and power distribution equipment.

Cutler-Hammer, 9 Shehab St., #11, Mohandeseen, Cairo, Egypt

DANZAS AEI, INC.

120 Tokeneke Road, PO Box 1231, Darien, CT, 06820

Tel: (203) 655-7900   Fax: (203) 655-5779   www.aeilogistics.com

International air freight forwarder.

Danzas AEI Intercontinental Egypt, 36, Delivrande Street, Heliopolis, Cairo, Egypt

Tel: 20-2-2907-838   Fax: 20-2-2910-616

D'ARCY MASIUS BENTON & BOWLES INC. (DMB&B)

1675 Broadway, New York, NY, 10019

Tel: (212) 468-3622   Fax: (212) 468-2987   www.darcyww.com

Full service international advertising and communications group.

DMB&B Cairo, 52 Ahmed Orbai Street, Mohandessen, Cairo, Egypt

DATASCOPE CORPORATION

14 Phillips Pkwy., Montvale, NJ, 07645

Tel: (201) 391-8100   Fax: (201) 307-5400   www.datascope.com

Mfr. medical devices.

Datascope Middle East, 37 Ahmed El-Sawy Street, Area No. 6, Nasr City Cairo, Egypt

DDB WORLDWIDE COMMUNICATIONS GROUP

437 Madison Ave., New York, NY, 10022

Tel: (212) 415-2000   Fax: (212) 415-3417   www.ddbn.com

Advertising agency.

TN Communications Group, Giza, Egypt

DELOITTE TOUCHE TOHMATSU INTERNATIONAL

1633 Broadway, New York, NY, 10019

Tel: (212) 492-4000   Fax: (212) 392-4154   www.deloitte.com

Accounting, audit, tax and management consulting services.

Shawki & Company, PO Box 154, 78 Abd Al Salam Areef St., Borg El Sallam Glym Sidi Gaber, Alexandria 21411, Egypt

Shawki & Company, PO Box 2095, Banque Misr Tower, 153 Mohamed Farid St., Cairo 11511, Egypt

DHL WORLDWIDE EXPRESS

50 California Avenue, San Francisco, CA, 94111

Tel: (415) 677-6100   Fax: (415) 824-9700   www.dhl.com

Worldwide air express carrier.

DHL Worldwide Express, El Mona Towers, 16 Lebanon St., Mohandessin Cairo, Egypt

Tel: 20-2-302-9801

DIONEX CORPORATION

1228 Titan Way, PO Box 3603, Sunnyvale, CA, 94086-3603

Tel: (408) 737-0700   Fax: (408) 730-9403   www.dionex.com

Develop/mfr./market chromatography systems and related products.

Beta Electronics, 6 Sennar Street, Madint El-Talaba-Giza 12411, Egypt

EASTMAN KODAK COMPANY

343 State Street, Rochester, NY, 14650

Tel: (716) 724-4000   Fax: (716) 724-1089   www.kodak.com

Develop/mfr. photo and chemicals products, information management/video/copier systems, fibers/plastics for various industry.

Kodak SA, PO Box 527, 20 Adley St., Cairo, Egypt

J.D. EDWARDS & COMPANY

One Technology Way, Denver, CO, 80237

Tel: (303) 334-4000   Fax: (303) 334-4970   www.jdedwards.com

Computer software products.

CITE, Cairo Info. Tech. & Engineering, 68 Kasr El Aini St., Garden City Cairo, Egypt

Tel: 20-2-356-0531   Fax: 20-2-3551063

EG&G INC.

900 Clopper Road, Ste. 200, Gaithersburg, MD, 20878

Tel: (301) 840-3000   Fax: (301) 590-0502   www.egginc.com

Diversified R/D, mfr. and services.

EG&G Sealol, PO Box 151 M. Farid, 139 Mogamah El Masaneh St., Cairo, Egypt

EGL INC. (EAGLE GLOBAL LOGISTICS)

15350 Vickery Drive, Houston, TX, 77032

Tel: (281) 618-3100   Fax: (281) 618-3223   www.eagleusa.com

Ocean/air freight forwarding, customs brokerage, packing and wholesale, logistics management and insurance.

EGL Eagle Global Logistics, 21, El Khalifa El Maamoun St., Roxy Tower, Ste. 105, Heliopolis Cairo, Egypt

Tel: 20-2-418-3323   Fax: 20-2-291-1866

EGL Eagle Global Logistics, 2 Champollion Str, Azarita, Alexandria, Egypt

Tel: 20-3-483-8307   Fax: 20-3-483-8307

ERNST & YOUNG INTERNATIONAL

5 Times Square, New York, NY, 10036

Tel: (212) 773-3000   Fax: (212) 773-6350   www.eyi.com

Engaged in assurance and advisory business services, tax, law and corporate finance.

Associates of Ernst & Young/Zarrouk, Khaled & Co., PO Box 110/12655, Mohandessin Cairo, Egypt

Tel: 20-2-303-2229   Fax: 20-2-303-2228   Contact: Taha M. Khaled

ETHAN ALLEN INTERIORS INC.

Ethan Allen Drive, Danbury, CT, 06811

Tel: (203) 743-8000   Fax: (203) 743-8298   www.ethanallen.com

Mfr. and sale of premium-priced furniture and home furnishings.

Ethan Allen Home Interiors, 2 Abdel Aziz El Hawary Street, Heliopolis Cairo, Egypt

Tel: 20-2-414-9622

EXPEDITORS INTERNATIONAL OF WASHINGTON INC.

1015 Third Avenue, 12th Fl., Seattle, WA, 98104-1182

Tel: (206) 674-3400   Fax: (206) 682-9777   www.expd.com

Air/ocean freight forwarding, customs brokerage, international logistics solutions.

Expeditors Sarah International, 8 South Eastern Sheraton Area,, Flat #1 2 and 4, Heliopolis Cairo, Egypt

Tel: 20-2-267-0604   Fax: 20-2-267-0603

EXXON MOBIL CORPORATION

5959 Las Colinas Blvd., Irving, TX, 75039-2298

Tel: (972) 444-1000   Fax: (972) 444-1882   www.exxonmobil.com

Petroleum exploration, production, refining; mfr. petroleum and chemicals products; coal and minerals.

Exxon Mobil, Inc., Egypt

FERRO CORPORATION

1000 Lakeside Ave., Cleveland, OH, 44114-7000

Tel: (216) 641-8580   Fax: (216) 696-5784   www.ferro.com

Mfr. Specialty chemicals, coatings, plastics, colors, refractories.

Ferro B.V., PO Box 274, Cairo, Egypt

Fax: 20-2-575-9094   Contact: L.E. Tuema

FISHER SCIENTIFIC INTERNATIONAL INC.

1 Liberty Lane, Hampton, NH, 03842

Tel: (603) 929-5911   Fax: (603) 929-0222   www.fisherscientific.com

Mfr. and distribution of science equipment, instruments, and supplies.

Fisher Scientific Middle East and Africa, Mohey El Din St Abou El Ezz St, Dokki, Giza, Egypt

Tel: 20-2-336-7880   Fax: 20-2-361-3211

FMC TECHNOLOGIES, INC.

200 E. Randolph Dr., Chicago, IL, 60601

Tel: (312) 861-6000   Fax: (312) 861-6176   www.fmctechnologies.com

Mfr. bulk material handling and automation equipment and cargo loaders.

FMC Surface Wellhead Equipment, 1 Road 293, New Maadi, Cairo, Egypt

FRITZ COMPANIES, INC., DIV. UPS

706 Mission Street, Ste. 900, San Francisco, CA, 94103

Tel: (415) 904-8360   Fax: (415) 904-8661   www.fritz.com

Integrated transportation, sourcing, distribution and customs brokerage services.

Fritz Companies Inc., Alexandria, Egypt

GENERAL DYNAMICS CORPORATION

3190 Fairview Park Drive, Falls Church, VA, 22042-4523

Tel: (703) 876-3000   Fax: (703) 876-3125   www.gendyn.com

Mfr. aerospace equipment, submarines, strategic systems, armored vehicles, defense support systems.

General Dynamics Intl., 39 Beirut St., Heliopolis, Cairo, Egypt

GENERAL ELECTRIC COMPANY

3135 Easton Turnpike, Fairfield, CT, 06431

Tel: (203) 373-2211   Fax: (203) 373-3131   www.ge.com

Diversified manufacturing, technology and services.

GE International, 1085 Corniche El-Nil, Garden City Cairo, Egypt

Tel: 20-2-357-1917   Fax: 20-2-355-7816

GE/Nuovo Pignone, 2 Wadl El Nil Strasse, Cairo, Egypt

Tel: 20-2-346-1191   Fax: 20-2-348-4532

GENERAL MOTORS CORPORATION

300 Renaissance Center, Detroit, MI, 48285

Tel: (313) 556-5000   Fax: (313) 556-5108   www.gm.com

Mfr. full line vehicles, automotive electronics, commercial technologies, telecommunications, space, finance.

General Motors Egypt SAE, Cairo, Egypt

THE GILLETTE COMPANY

Prudential Tower Building, Boston, MA, 02199

Tel: (617) 421-7000   Fax: (617) 421-7123   www.gillette.com

Develop/mfr. personal care/use products: blades and razors, toiletries, cosmetics, stationery.

Gillette Egypt SAE, Cairo, Egypt

GLEASON CORPORATION

1000 University Ave., Rochester, NY, 14692

Tel: (716) 473-1000   Fax: (716) 461-4348   www.gleasoncorp.com

Mfr. gear making machine tools; tooling and services.

Emeco, 56 Hegaz Street, Heliopolis/Cairo, Egypt

Tel: 20-2-240-2461   Fax: 20-2-246-5573

GLOBAL SILVERHAWK INTERNATIONAL MOVING

1000 Burnett Avenue, Concord, CA, 94520

Tel: (510) 609-7080 Fax: (510) 609-7081 www.globalsilverhawk.com

International moving and forwarding.

Global Silverhawk, 54 Nazih Khalfa St., Heliopolis Cairo, Egypt

Tel: 20-2-258-7509 Contact: Ivan Pearce, Gen. Mgr.

GOLDEN STATE FOODS

18301 Von Karman Avenue, Ste. 1100, Irvine, CA, 92612

Tel: (949) 252-2000 Fax: (949) 252-2080 www.goldenstatefoods.com

Engaged in food processing and distribution.

Golden State Foods, First Industrial Zone, Lot 321, Sixth of October City, Egypt

GRANT THORNTON INTERNATIONAL

800 One Prudential Plaza, 130 E. Randolph Drive, Chicago, IL, 60601-6050

Tel: (312) 856-0001 Fax: (312) 616-7052 www.grantthornton.com

Accounting, audit, tax and management consulting services.

Mohamed Hilal & Co, 87 Ramsis Street, Cairo, Egypt

Tel: 20-2-574-8410

HALLIBURTON COMPANY

500 North Akard Street, Ste. 3600, Dallas, TX, 75201-3391

Tel: (214) 978-2600 Fax: (214) 978-2685 www.halliburton.com

Engaged in diversified energy services, engineering and construction.

Halliburton Equipment Company S.A.E, PO Box 323, Maadi Cairo 11431, Egypt

Tel: 20-2-352-9622 Fax: 20-2-352-0677

H.J. HEINZ COMPANY

600 Grant Street, Pittsburgh, PA, 15219

Tel: (412) 456-5700 Fax: (412) 456-6128 www.heinz.com

Processed food products and nutritional services.

Cairo Foods Industries SAE, Cairo, Egypt

HILTON HOTELS CORPORATION

9336 Civic Center Drive, Beverly Hills, CA, 90210

Tel: (310) 278-4321 Fax: (310) 205-7880 www.hiltonhotels.com

International hotel chain: Hilton International, Vista Hotels and Hilton National Hotels.

Cairo Nile Hilton, Tahrir Square, Cairo, Egypt

Cairo Ramses Hilton, 1115 Corniche El Nil, Cairo, Egypt

Hurghada Hilton Resort, Main St. Hurghada Safaga, Hurghada, Egypt

Nuweiba Hilton Coral Resort, c/o Nile Hilton Annex, Office No. 8, Tahrir Square, Cairo, Egypt

HOLIDAY INN (BASS RESORTS) WORLDWIDE, INC.

3 Ravinia Drive, Ste. 2900, Atlanta, GA, 30346-2149

Tel: (770) 604-2000 Fax: (770) 604-5403 www.holidayinn.com

Hotels, restaurants and casinos.

Holiday Inn, Guiza-Pyramids, PO Box 25, Cairo Intl. Airport, Cairo, Egypt

HONEYWELL INTERNATIONAL INC.

Honeywell Plaza, Minneapolis, MN, 55408

Tel: (612) 951-1000 Fax: (612) 951-8537 www.honeywell.com

Develop/mfr. controls for home and building, industry, space and aviation, burglar and fire alarm systems.

Honeywell Ltd., 33 Nabeli El Wakad St., Heliopolis West, Cairo, Egypt

Tel: 20-2-417-6150 Fax: 20-2-290-0294

HORWATH INTERNATIONAL ASSOCIATION

420 Lexington Avenue, Suite 526, New York, NY, 10170-0526

Tel: (212) 808-2000   Fax: (212) 808-2020   www.horwath.com

Public accountants and auditors.

Youssef Nabih & Co., 22 Kasr El Nil St., Cairo, Egypt

IBM CORPORATION

1133 Westchester Avenue, White Plains, NY, 10604

Tel: (914) 765-1900   Fax: (914) 765-7382   www.ibm.com

Information products, technology and services.

IBM World Trade Corporation Egypt, 56 Gamiette El-Dowal El-Arabia, Mohandessen Giza, Egypt

Tel: 20-2-349-2533   Fax: 20-2-360-1227

IDEX CORPORATION

630 Dundee Road, Ste. 400, Northbrook, IL, 60062

Tel: (847) 498-7070   Fax: (847) 498-3940   www.idexcorp.com

Mfr. industrial pumps, lubrication systems, metal fabrication equipment, bending and clamping devices.

Selim International, 32 Salah Salem St., Elsafa Tower, Obour Gardens, Cairo, Egypt

Selim International, 539 M Horria Avenue, Gleem, Alexandria, Egypt

INFONET SERVICES CORPORATION

2160 East Grand Ave., El Segundo, CA, 90245-1022

Tel: (310) 335-2600   Fax: (310) 335-4507   www.infonet.com

Provider of Internet services and electronic messaging services.

Infonet Egypt, PO Box 2742 Hurrya, Cairo 11361, Egypt

Tel: 20-2-337-6407   Fax: 20-2-337-6480

INTEL CORPORATION

2200 Mission College Blvd., Santa Clara, CA, 95052-8119

Tel: (408) 765-8080   Fax: (408) 765-1739   www.intel.com

Mfr. semiconductor, microprocessor and micro-communications components and systems.

Intel Corporation, Aradia Mall, Regus Office, Cairo, Egypt

Tel: 202-580-6656

INTER-CONTINENTAL HOTELS

3 Ravinia Drive, Suite 2900, Atlanta, GA, 30346-2149

Tel: (770) 604-2000   Fax: (770) 604-5403   www.interconti.com

Worldwide hotel and resort accommodations.

Hurghada Inter-Continental Resort & Casino, PO Box 36, Hurghada, Red Sea, Egypt

Tel: 20-65-446911   Fax: 20-65-446910

INTERGEN (INTERNATIONAL GENERATING CO., LTD.)

15 Wayside Road, Burlington, MA, 01803-4609

Tel: (781) 933-3000   Fax: (781) 933-3001   www.intergen.com

Global power and fuel asset development company; develops, owns and operates electric power plants and related distribution facilities.

InterGen Sidi Krir Generating Co., 14 Refaa Street, Dokki, Giza, Egypt

INTERGRAPH CORPORATION

One Madison Industrial Park, Huntsville, AL, 35894-0001

Tel: (256) 730-2000   Fax: (256) 730-7898   www.intergraph.com

Develop/mfr. interactive computer graphic systems.

Intergraph Egypt, 35-36 Mammar Soor Nadi El-Zamalek, Cairo, Egypt

Tel: 20-2-305-2702   Fax: 20-2-30-52701

INTERNATIONAL FLAVORS & FRAGRANCES INC.

521 West 57th Street, New York, NY, 10019-2960

Tel: (212) 765-5500   Fax: (212) 708-7132   www.iff.com

Design/mfr. flavors, fragrances and aroma chemicals.

International Flavors & Fragrances, 6 October City, St. 79 - First Industrial Area, Box 114 Al Haram, Cairo 12556, Egypt

ITT-GOULDS PUMPS INC.

2881 East Bayard Street, Seneca Falls, NY, 13148

Tel: (315) 568-2811   Fax: (315) 568-7651   www.gouldspumps.com

Mfr. industrial and water systems pumps.

Goulds Pumps, 8 Ahmed El Shediak Ard El Golf Heliopolis, Cairo, Egypt

JOHNSON & JOHNSON

One Johnson & Johnson Plaza, New Brunswick, NJ, 08933

Tel: (732) 524-0400   Fax: (732) 214-0334   www.jnj.com

Mfr./distributor/R&D pharmaceutical, health care and cosmetic products.

Johnson & Johnson (Egypt) S.A.E., 24 El Shaheed, Abdel Moneim Hafez Street, Nozha Heliopolis, Cairo, Egypt

SC JOHNSON

1525 Howe St., Racine, WI, 53403

Tel: (262) 260-2000   Fax: (262) 260-2133   www.scjohnsonwax.com

Home, auto, commercial and personal care products and specialty chemicals.

SC Johnson, 44 El Teyaran, Nafr City, Egypt

JOSLYN HI-VOLTAGE CORPORATION

4000 East 116th Street, Cleveland, OH, 44105

Tel: (216) 271-6600   Fax: (216) 341-3615   www.joslynhivoltage.com

Mfr. power transmission and distribution equipment for electric utilities including reclosers, sectionalizers, capacitor switches and controls.

ETO Joslyn Hi-Voltage Corp., 6 Abd El Kawy Ahmed Street, El Mohandseen, Cairo 12411, Egypt

KELLOGG BROWN & ROOT INC.

PO Box 4557, Houston, TX, 77210-4557

Tel: (713) 676-3011   Fax: (713) 676-8695   www.halliburton.com

Engaged in technology-based engineering and construction.

Kellogg Brown & Root, 10 Kamei Mohamed St., Zamalek Cairo, Egypt

Kellogg Brown & Root, 5 Hafez Ramadan St., Nasr City - Cairo, Egypt

KPMG CONSULTING INC.

1676 International Dr., McLean, VA, 22102

Tel: (703) 747-3000   Fax: (703) 747-8500   www.kpmg.com

Accounting and audit, tax and management consulting services.

KPMG Hazem Hassan, 72 Mohi Eldin Abul Ezz St., Mohandeseen, Cairo, Egypt

Tel: 20-2-336-9094   Fax: 20-2-349-7224   Contact: Hazem Hssan, Sr. Ptnr.

KPMG Hazem Hassan, 1 Gamal El-Din Yassein St., Ramleh Station, Alexandria, Egypt

LANCER CORPORATION

6655 Lancer Blvd., San Antonio, TX, 78219

Tel: (210) 310-7000   Fax: (210) 310-7252   www.lancercorp.com

Mfr. beverage dispensing equipment.

Lancer Corporation, 7 Mubarak Street, East Ain Shams, Cairo 11311, Egypt

ELI LILLY & COMPANY

Lilly Corporate Center, Indianapolis, IN, 46285

Tel: (317) 276-2000   Fax: (317) 277-6579   www.lilly.com

Mfr. pharmaceuticals and animal health products.

Eli Lilly Egypt S.A.E., 1097 Cornich El-Nil St., 3rd Fl., Garden City Cairo, Egypt

Tel: 20-2-355-9487   Fax: 20-2-354-2034

LOCKHEED MARTIN CORPORATION

6801 Rockledge Drive, Bethesda, MD, 20817

Tel: (301) 897-6000   Fax: (301) 897-6652   www.imco.com

Design/mfr./management systems in fields of space, defense, energy, electronics and technical services.

Lockheed Martin International S.A., 19 El-Shahid Helmy, El Masry Street, Almaza Cairo, Egypt

Tel: 20-2-418-5420 Fax: 20-2-415-3825 Contact: Robert G. Atcheson, VP

Lockheed Martin Intl. SA, PO Box 2648 Horreya, El Maza-Heliopolis, Almaza Cairo, Egypt

Tel: 20-2-418-5420 Fax: 20-2-291-7493 Contact: R. Lawrence, Pres. Middle East & Africa

THE LUBRIZOL CORPORATION

29400 Lakeland Blvd., Wickliffe, OH, 44092-2298

Tel: (440) 943-4200   Fax: (440) 943-5337   www.lubrizol.com

Mfr. chemicals additives for lubricants and fuels.

Lubrizol Egypt, Cairo, Egypt

Tel: 20-2-335-3375

LUCENT TECHNOLOGIES, INC.

600 Mountain Ave., Murray Hill, NJ, 07974-0636

Tel: (908) 582-3000   Fax: (908) 582-2576   www.lucent.com

Design/mfr. wide range of public and private networks, communication systems and software, data networking systems, business telephone systems and microelectronics components.

Lucent Technologies International, 13 Road, #250, Salah Salem Square- Degla, El Maadi 11742, Egypt

MARATHON LE TOURNEAU COMPANY

PO Box 2307, Longview, TX, 75606

Tel: (903) 237-7000   Fax: (903) 236-6533   www.letourneau-inc.com

Mfr. heavy construction and mining machinery equipment.

Sitco, 18 Abdel Moncion Riyad St., El Mohandessin, Cairo, Egypt

MARATHON OIL COMPANY

5555 San Felipe Road, Houston, TX, 77056

Tel: (713) 629-6600   Fax: (713) 296-2952   www.marathon.com

Oil and gas exploration.

Marathon Petroleum Egypt Ltd., PO Box 52, Maadi Cairo, Egypt

MARRIOTT INTERNATIONAL INC.

10400 Fernwood Rd., Bethesda, MD, 20817

Tel: (301) 380-3000   Fax: (301) 380-5181   www.marriott.com

Hotel services.

Cairo Marriott Hotel, Cairo, Egypt

Tel: 20-2-340-8888

Hurghada Marriott Beach Resort, Hurghada, Egypt

Tel: 20-65-600-190

Sharm El Sheikh Marriott Beach Resort, Sharm El Sheikh, Egypt

Tel: 20-62-600-190

MARSH & McLENNAN COS INC.

1166 Ave. of the Americas, New York, NY, 10036-2774

Tel: (212) 345-5000   Fax: (212) 345-4808   www.marshmac.com

Insurance agents/brokers, pension and investment management consulting services.

J&H Marsh & McLennan (Middle East) Ltd., 30 Lebanon St., Ste. #703, Mohandessin, Cairo, Egypt

Tel: 20-2-305-3881 Fax: 20-2-305-3883 Contact: Roger E. Powell

McDERMOTT INTERNATIONAL INC.

1450 Poydras Street, PO Box 60035, New Orleans, LA, 70160-0035

Tel: (504) 587-5400   Fax: (504) 587-6153   www.mcdermott.com

Provides energy, engineering and construction services for industrial, utility, and hydrocarbon processing facilities, and to the offshore oil and natural gas industries.

Babcock & Wilcox Egypt, S.A.E., PO Box 1626, Manial Shiga, Giza, Cairo, Egypt

Tel: 20-2-572-7491   Fax: 20-2-572-8376

McDONALD'S CORPORATION

McDonald's Plaza, Oak Brook, IL, 60523

Tel: (630) 623-3000   Fax: (630) 623-7409   www.mcdonalds.com

Fast food chain stores.

McDonald's Corp., Cairo, Egypt

MECHANICAL DYNAMICS, INC.

2300 Traverwood Drive, Ann Arbor, MI, 48105

Tel: (734) 994-3800   Fax: (734) 994-6418   www.adams.com

Mfr. Adams prototyping software for functional virtual prototyping solutions.

TriTECH, 25 Mossadak Street, Giza, Egypt

Tel: 20-2-336-8140

MENTOR GRAPHICS

8005 SW Boeckman Road, Wilsonville, OR, 97070-7777

Tel: (503) 685-7000   Fax: (503) 685-1202   www.mentorg.com

Develop/mfr. software tools for embedded systems market.

Microtec Egypt, Cairo, Egypt

METCALF & EDDY INTERNATIONAL INC.

30 Harvard Mill Square, Wakefield, MA, 01880

Tel: (781) 246-5200   Fax: (781) 245-6293   www.m-e.com

Provides water, wastewater, and hazardous waste system design and design/build services to industry and government clients.

Metcalf & Eddy International, 35 El Sheikh Abdel Hamid Awad, Nasr City, Cairo, Egypt

WWCG, PO Box 2351, Alexandria, Egypt

M-I

PO Box 48242, Houston, TX, 77242-2842

Tel: (713) 739-0222   Fax: (713) 308-9503   www.midf.com

Developer, manufacturer and marketer of drilling and completion fluids and services.

MIOL Egypt, 4 El Saha El Shabia Street, Maadi Cairo, Egypt

Tel: 20-2-3508463   Fax: 20-2-3505944

MICROSOFT CORPORATION

One Microsoft Way, Redmond, WA, 98052-6399

Tel: (425) 882-8080   Fax: (425) 936-7329   www.microsoft.com

Computer software, peripherals and services.

Microsoft Egypt, 2 Abdel Kader Hamza Street, Garden City Cairo Center, 4/F, Cairo, Egypt

Tel: 20-2-594-2445   Fax: 20-2-594-2194

J. P. MORGAN CHASE & CO. INC.

270 Park Ave., New York, NY, 10017

Tel: (212) 270-6000   Fax: (212) 622-9030   www.jpmorganchase.com

Provides integrated financial solutions for institutions and individuals worldwide, including asset management, investment banking and commercial banking.

J. P. Morgan Chase & Co., PO Box 1962, 3 Ahmed Nessim St., Giza Cairo, Egypt

Tel: 20-2-361-0393   Fax: 20-2-361-0496

J. P. Morgan Chase & Co., PO Box 781, 9 Gamal E.A. Mahassen St., Garden City Cairo, Egypt

J. P. Morgan Chase & Co., PO Box 2430, 12 El Birgas St., Garden City Cairo, Egypt

MOTOROLA, INC.

1303 East Algonquin Road, Schaumburg, IL, 60196

Tel: (847) 576-5000   Fax: (847) 538-5191   www.motorola.com

Mfr. communications equipment, semiconductors and cellular phones.

Motorola Egypt, Abu El Feda Building, 3 Abu El Feda St., Zamalek Cairo, Egypt

Tel: 20-2-341-5783 Fax: 20-2-341-5790

NEW HORIZONS WORLDWIDE, INC.

1900 S. State College Blvd., Anaheim, CA, 92806-6135

Tel: (714) 940-8000   Fax: www.newhorizons.com

Provides customer-focused computer training choices, through computer training centers.

New Horizons Worldwide, 6 Hussein Ahmed Rashad Street, Dokki, Giza, Cairo, Egypt

Tel: 202-338-9756

AC NIELSEN COMPANY

177 Broad Street, Stamford, CT, 06901

Tel: (203) 961-3000   Fax: (203) 961-3190   www.acnielsen.com

Engaged in market and consumer research.

ACNielsen, 8, Abdul Salam Zaki Street, Al Oroba Heliopolis, 4/5F, Cairo, Egypt

NORDSON CORPORATION

28601 Clemens Road, Westlake, OH, 44145-4551

Tel: (440) 892-1580   Fax: (440) 892-9507   www.nordson.com

Mfr. industry application equipment, sealants and packaging machinery.

IDC Company, 17, Ez El-Dien Taha St.,, Nasr City, Cairo 11371, Egypt

NOVELL WORLDWIDE

1800 S. Novell Place, Provo, UT, 84606

Tel: (801) 861-7000   Fax: (801) 861-5555   www.novell.com

Develop/mfr. networking software and related equipment.

Novell Egypt, 1 Degla Street, Mohandessin, Cairo, Egypt

OCEANEERING INTERNATIONAL INC.

11911 FM 529, Houston, TX, 77041

Tel: (713) 329-4500   Fax: (713) 329-4951   www.oceaneering.com

Transportation equipment, underwater service to offshore oil and gas industry.

Solus Ocean Systems, PO Box 380, 99A Misr Helwan Road, 2/F, Maadi Cairo, Egypt

OTIS ELEVATOR COMPANY

One Farm Springs Road, Farmington, CT, 06032

Tel: (860) 676-6000   Fax: (860) 676-5111   www.otis.com

Mfr. elevators and escalators.

Otis Elevator Co. SAE, 11 Dr. M. Mandour St., Nasr City District 1, Cairo, Egypt

PARKER HANNIFIN CORPORATION

6035 Parkland Blvd., Cleveland, OH, 44124-4141

Tel: (216) 896-3000   Fax: (216) 896-4000   www.parker.com

Mfr. motion-control products.

Parker Hannifin, 8B Zahraa Maadi, Region 17F, Cairo, Egypt

PARSONS BRINCKERHOFF INC.

One Penn Plaza, New York, NY, 10119-0061

Tel: (212) 465-5000   Fax: (212) 465-5096   www.pbworld.com

Provides planning, engineering, construction management and operations and maintenance services.

GCMC Egypt, 35 Abdel Moniem Raid Street, Mohandiseen, Dokki, Cairo, Egypt

Tel: 20-2-335-0232   Fax: 20-2-361-5039

PFIZER INC.

235 East 42nd Street, New York, NY, 10017-5755

Tel: (212) 573-2323   Fax: (212) 573-7851   www.pfizer.com

Research-based, global health care company.

Pfizer Egypt SAE, Egypt

PHARMACIA CORPORATION

100 Route 206 North, Peapack, NJ, 07977

Tel: (908) 901-8000   Fax: (908) 901-8379   www.pharmacia.com

Mfr. pharmaceuticals, agricultural products, industry chemicals.

Pharmacia & Upjohn Scientific Office, 259 Pyramid Street, 2nd floor, apt. #10, Giza-Cairo, Egypt

Tel: 20-2-531-9745   Fax: 20-2-585-3087

PHILLIPS PETROLEUM COMPANY

Phillips Building, 411 S. Keeler Ave., Bartlesville, OK, 74004

Tel: (918) 661-6600   Fax: (918) 661-7636   www.phillips66.com

Crude oil, natural gas, liquefied petroleum gas, gasoline and petro-chemicals.

Phillips Petroleum Co., PO Box 63, 32 Lumumba St., Alexandria, Egypt

PINNACLE WORLDWIDE, INC.

1201 Marquette Ave., Ste. 300, Minneapolis, MN, 55403

Tel: (612) 338-2215   Fax: (612) 338-2572   www.pinnacleww.com

International network of independent public relations firms.

RadaResearch & Public Relations, 1 Mostafa El Wakil St., Heliopolis Cairo, Egypt

Tel: 20-2-291-7956   Contact: Loula Zaklama

PIONEER HI-BRED INTERNATIONAL INC.

400 Locust Street, Ste. 800, Des Moines, IA, 50309

Tel: (515) 248-4800   Fax: (515) 248-4999   www.pioneer.com

Agricultural chemicals, farm supplies, biological products, research.

Misr Pioneer Seed Co., 98 Army Forces Bldgs., Nasr City Cairo 1371, Egypt

PRICEWATERHOUSECOOPERS LLP

1301 Ave. of the Americas, New York, NY, 10019

Tel: (212) 596-7000   Fax: (212) 259-1301   www.pwcglobal.com

Accounting and auditing, tax and management, and human resource consulting services.

PriceWaterhouseCoopers, 4 Road 261, New Maadi, Cairo, Egypt

Tel: 20-2-353-0914   Fax: 20-2-353-0915

PROCTER & GAMBLE COMPANY

One Procter & Gamble Plaza, Cincinnati, OH, 45202

Tel: (513) 983-1100   Fax: (513) 562-4500   www.pg.com

Personal care, food, laundry, cleaning and industry products.

Procter & Gamble Egypt, 1191 Corniche El-Nil Street, Boulaque, Cairo, Egypt

Procter & Gamble Egypt, 1191 Corniche El-Nil St. Boulaque, World Trade Center Building, Cairo, Egypt

RADISSON HOTELS INTERNATIONAL

Carlson Pkwy., PO Box 59159, Minneapolis, MN, 55459-8204

Tel: (612) 540-5526   Fax: (612) 449-3400   www.radisson.com

Operates, manages and franchises full-service hotels and resorts worldwide.

Radisson Hotels Intl., Attn: Egyptian Office, Carlson Parkway, PO Box 59159, Minneapolis, MN, 55459-8204

RAYTHEON COMPANY

141 Spring Street, Lexington, MA, 02173

Tel: (781) 862-6600   Fax: (781) 860-2172   www.raytheon.com

Mfr. diversified electronics, appliances, energy and environmental products; publishing, industry and construction services.

Raytheon International, Cairo, Egypt

Tel: 20-2-516-7248   Fax: 20-2-516-7248   Contact: Daniel Burnham, Pres.

RENAISSANCE HOTELS AND RESORTS

10400 Fernwood Road, Bethesda, MD, 20817

Tel: (301) 380-3000   Fax: (301) 380-5181   www.renaissancehotels.com

upscale, full-service hotel and resort chain under Marriott International, Inc.

Renaissance Alexandria Hotel, Alexandria, Egypt

Tel: 20-3-548-3977

SCHENKER USA INC.

150 Albany Ave., Freeport, NY, 11520

Tel: (516) 403-5416   Fax: (516) 377-3092   www.schenkerusa.com

Freight forwarders.

Quick Cargo Door to Door, 5 Tehran St., POB Box 415, Dokki Cairo, Egypt

Tel: 20-2-349-2948   Fax: 20-2-360-5838

SCHERING-PLOUGH CORPORATION

One Giralda Farms, Madison, NJ, 07940-1000

Tel: (973) 822-7000   Fax: (973) 822-7048   www.sch-plough.com

Proprietary drug and cosmetic products.

Essex Animal Health Chemie A.G., 1 Gamal Ezz El Din Salama Street, Heliopolis Cairo, Egypt

SONESTA INTERNATIONAL HOTELS CORPORATION

200 Clarendon Street, Boston, MA, 02116

Tel: (617) 421-5400   Fax: (617) 421-5402   www.sonesta.com

Own/manage hotels, resorts, and Nile cruises.

Sonesta Hotel Cairo, 4 El Tayaran St., Nasr City Cairo, Egypt

SPERRY-SUN DRILLING SERVICES

PO Box 60070, Houston, TX, 77205

Tel: (281) 871-5100   Fax: (281) 871-5742   www.sperry-sun.com

Provides drilling services to the oil and gas drilling industry.

Sperry-Sun, Inc., 15 Road 150 Maadi, Cairo, Egypt

Tel: 20-2-376-81-70

STANLEY CONSULTANTS, INC.

Stanley Building, 225 Iowa Ave., Muscatine, IA, 52761-3764

Tel: (563) 264-6600   Fax: (563) 264-6658   www.stanleygroup.com

Engaged in engineering, architectural, planning and management services.

Stanley Consultants, Inc., Alexandria Project Office Gate No., AGOSD East Wastewater Treatment Plant, Agricultural Road,
Smouha Alexandria, Egypt

Tel: 20-3-426-4280   Fax: 20-3-426-4281

STARWOOD HOTELS & RESORTS WORLDWIDE

777 Westchester Avenue, White Plains, NY, 10604

Tel: (914) 640-8100   Fax: (914) 640-8316   www.starwoodhotels.com

Hotel operations including Sheraton, Westin, St. Regis, Four Points and Caesars.

Cairo Sheraton Hotel & Casino, PO Box 11, Galae Sq., Giza, Egypt

Montazah Sheraton Hotel, Corniche Rd., Montazah, Alexandria, Egypt

Sheraton Heliopolis Hotel & Towers, Uruba Street, Cairo, Egypt

Tel: 20-2-267-7730

Sheraton Miramar Resort El Gouna, Red Sea, El Gouna, Egypt

Tel: 20-65-545606   Fax: 20-65-545608

STIEFEL LABORATORIES INC.

255 Alhambra Circle, Ste. 1000, Coral Gables, FL, 33134

Tel: (305) 443-3807   Fax: (305) 443-3467   www.stiefel.com

Mfr. pharmaceuticals, dermatological specialties.

Stiefel Laboratories Egypt, 21 El Khaliefa El Mamoun St., #504, Heliopolis Cairo, Egypt

THE TRANE COMPANY

3600 Pammel Creek Road, La Crosse, WI, 54601

Tel: (608) 787-2000   Fax: (608) 787-4990   www.trane.com

Mfr. distribution and service of A/C systems and equipment.

Trane Cairo, 34A El Hegaz St., Heliopolis Cairo, Egypt

TRANSOCEAN INC.

4 Greenway Plaza, Houston, TX, 77046

Tel: (713) 232-7500   Fax: (713) 232-7027   www.deepwater.com

Engaged in oil and gas offshore drilling.

Transocean Inc., PO Box 352, Maadi, Cairo, Egypt

U.S. WHEAT ASSOCIATES

1620 "I" Street NW, Ste. 801, Washington, DC, 20006-4005

Tel: (202) 463-0999   Fax: (202) 785-1052   www.uswheat.org

Market development for wheat products.

U.S. Wheat Associates Inc., 12 Midam El-Sheikh Youssel, Barclays Bank Bldg., Garden City Cairo, Egypt

UNION CARBIDE CORPORATION

39 Old Ridgebury Road, Danbury, CT, 06817

Tel: (203) 794-2000   Fax: (203) 794-6269   www.unioncarbide.com

Mfr. industrial chemicals, plastics and resins.

Union Carbide Middle East Ltd., 6 Ibn El Nabih St., #3, 1st Floor, Zamalek, Cairo, Egypt

UNITED PARCEL SERVICE, INC.

55 Glenlake Parkway, NE, Atlanta, GA, 30328

Tel: (404) 828-6000   Fax: (404) 828-6593   www.ups.com

International package-delivery service.

United Parcel Service Egypt, 19A Adly St., Cairo, Egypt

Tel: 20-2-391-9028   Fax: 20-2-393-0911

UNIVERSAL SECURITY INSTRUMENTS, INC.

PO Box 825, Binghamton, NY, 13902-0825

Tel: (607) 779-7689   Fax: (607) 779-7301   www.uic.com

Provider of innovative electronic circuit assembly technology and equipment, integrated system solutions, and process expertise.

EPIC, Heliopolis Cairo, Egypt

Tel: 20-2-417-4812   Fax: 20-2-418-2516

EPIC Advanced Mfr. Systems, S.A.E., Heliopolis, Cairo, Egypt

Tel: 20-2-417-4812   Fax: 20-2-418-2516

VERIZON WIRELESS, INC.

180 Washington Valley Rd., Bedminster, NJ, 07921

Tel: (908) 306-7000   Fax: (908) 306-6927   www.verizonwireless.com

Engaged in mobile phone operations.

Vodafone Egypt, 7A Courniche El Nile, Maadi Cairo, Egypt

WASHINGTON GROUP INTERNATIONAL, INC.

720 Park Blvd., PO Box 73, Boise, ID, 83729

Tel: (208) 386-5000   Fax: (208) 386-7186   www.wgint.com

Engaged in engineering and construction.

Washington Group International, Inc., 28 Road 7, Apt. #4, Maadi Cairo, Egypt

Tel: 20-2-378-1958   Fax: 20-2-378-1914

WEATHERFORD INTERNATIONAL, INC.

515 Post Oak Blvd. Ste. 600, Houston, TX, 77027-3415

Tel: (713) 287-8400   Fax: (713) 963-9785   www.weatherford.com

Oilfield services, products and equipment; mfr. marine cranes for oil and gas industry.

Weatherford Oil Tool, PO Box 128, 8 Aswan Sq., Mohandessin Giza, Cairo, Egypt

Tel: 20-2-3755-906   Fax: 20-2-375-0090

W-H ENERGY SERVICES, INC.

10370 Richmond Avenue, Ste. 990, Houston, TX, 77042

Tel: (713) 974-9071   Fax: (713) 974-7029   www.whes.com

Engaged in diversified oil field services.

PathFinder Energy, 1 Saudi Co. Bldgs., Nozha Street, Nasr City Cairo, Egypt

WYETH PHARMACEUTICALS

555 E. Lancaster Ave., Wayne, PA, 19087-5109

Tel: (610) 971-5400   Fax: (610) 995-4668   www.wyeth.com

Mfr. antibiotics and pharmaceutical products.

Wyeth-Ayerst International Inc., Villa No. 2 Street, No. 161, Maadi Cairo, Egypt

Tel: 20-2-525-3290

XEROX CORPORATION

800 Long Ridge Road, PO Box 1600, Stamford, CT, 06904

Tel: (203) 968-3000   Fax: (203) 968-4312   www.xerox.com

Mfr. document processing equipment, systems and supplies.

Xerox Egypt S.A.E., 2 Lebanon St., Mohandessin, El Giza Cairo, Egypt

Tel: 20-2-344-4918   Fax: 20-2-303-3888

YORK INTERNATIONAL CORPORATION

631 South Richland Ave., York, PA, 17403

Tel: (717) 771-7890   Fax: (717) 771-6212   www.york.com

Mfr. heating, ventilating, air conditioning and refrigeration equipment.

MIRACO, 48 El Batal Ahmed Abdel, Aziz St., Dokki, Giza, Egypt

York Air Conditioning and Refrigeration, Inc., 10 El Kamel Mohamed Street, 10/F, Flat 3, Cairo, Egypt

Tel: 20-2-340-8306   Fax: 20-2-341-0840

El Salvador

3M (MINNESOTA MINING & MFG.)

3M Center, St. Paul, MN, 55144-1000

Tel: (651) 733-1110   Fax: (651) 733-9973   www.mmm.com

Mfr. diversified products for industry, consumer, health care, imaging, communications, transport, safety, etc.

3M El Salvador SA de CV, Calle Chaporrastique 11, Urban. Industrial Santa Elena, Antiguo Cuzcatlan, La Liberdad, El Salvador

Tel: 503-278-3344   Fax: 503-278-3313

AIG AMERICAN INTERNATIONAL GROUP INC.

70 Pine Street, New York, NY, 10270

Tel: (212) 770-7000   Fax: (212) 509-9705   www.aig.com

Worldwide insurance and financial services.

AIG S.A., Calle Loma Linda 265, Col. San Benito, San Salvador, El Salvador

ANC RENTAL CORPORATION

200 S. Andrews Ave., Ft. Lauderdale, FL, 33301

Tel: (954) 320-4000   Fax: (954) 320-4077   www.ancrental.com

Engaged in car rental services, including National Car Rental and Alamo Rent A Car.

National Car Rental, Centro Profesional Edif., Mena 1, Centro de Gobierno, San Salvador, El Salvador

ANTILLAS AIR CARGO CARRIER

JFK International Airport, Cargo Building 68, Jamaica, NY, 11430

Tel: (718) 917-6855   Fax: (718) 244-0764   www.antillasair.com

Provides air cargo services.

Antillas Air Cargo Services, Aeropuerto Int'l de Camalapa, San Salvador, El Salvador

Tel: 503-339-9725   Fax: 506-339-9708   Contact: Gustavo Flores

AON CORPORATION

200 East Randolph, Chicago, IL, 60601

Tel: (312) 381-1000   Fax: (312) 381-6032   www.aon.com

Insurance brokers worldwide; underwrites accident and health insurance, specialty and professional insurance; and provides risk management consultation.

AON Worldwide / Auditores de Riesgos Internacionales, Calle La Reforma y Av., San Salvador, El Salvador

Tel: 503-223-7475   Fax: 503-298-4126   Contact: Guillermo Rovera- Paloma

APPLERA CORPORATION

301 Merritt 7, Norwalk, CT, 06851

Tel: (203) 840-2000   Fax: (203) 840-2312   www.applera.com

Leading supplier of systems for life science research and related applications.

Coresa S.A., Ave. Izalco, Bloque 6, No. 40, San Salvador, El Salvador

AVON PRODUCTS, INC.

1345 Avenue of the Americas, New York, NY, 10105-0196

Tel: (212) 282-5000   Fax: (212) 282-6049   www.avon.com

Mfr. direct seller of cosmetics and beauty-related items.

Productos Avon S.A., 15-1/2 Carretera al Puerto de la Libertad, Departamento de la Liberlad, San Salvador, El Salvador

Tel: 503-288-9511   Fax: 503-288-3952   Contact: Maribel de Campos, Sales Mgr.

AVX CORPORATION

801 17th Ave. South, Myrtle Beach, SC, 29577

Tel: (843) 448-9411   Fax: (843) 448-7139   www.avxcorp.com

Mfr. multilayer ceramic capacitors.

AVX Industries, Apdto. Postal 1, Ilopango Calle Cajutepoque 4-2, Zona Franca, San Bartole San Salvador, El Salvador

BALDOR ELECTRIC COMPANY

5711 R.S. Boreham Jr. Street, Fort Smith, AR, 72908

Tel: (501) 646-4711   Fax: (501) 648-5792   www.baldor.com

Mfr. electric motors.

Baldor Central America, Res. Pinares de Sulza, Pol. 15 #44, Nva. San Salvador, El Salvador

Tel: 50-3-288-1519

BATES WORLDWIDE INC.

498 Seventh Avenue, New York, NY, 10018

Tel: (212) 297-7000   Fax: (212) 986-0270   www.batesww.com

Advertising, marketing, public relations and media consulting.

ANLE Publicidad, Corresponsal Bates, Av. La Capilla #331, Col. San Benito, El Salvador

Tel: 503-289-1045   Fax: 503-289-1712   Contact: Luis Sanchez, Dir.

LOUIS BERGER INTERNATIONAL INC.

100 Halsted Street, East Orange, NJ, 07019

Tel: (201) 678-1960   Fax: (201) 672-4284   www.louisberger.com

Consulting engineers, engaged in architecture, environmental and advisory services.

Louis Berger International Inc., Av. 81 Norte y 9A, Calle Poniente Col. Escalon, San Salvador, El Salvador

Tel: 503-263-3025   Fax: 503-263-3663

BEST WESTERN INTERNATIONAL

6201 North 24th Place, Phoenix, AZ, 85106

Tel: (602) 957-4200   Fax: (602) 957-5740   www.bestwestern.com

International hotel chain.

BW Siesta, Blvd. Los Proceres 01217, San Salvador, El Salvador

Tel: 503-243-0377

BRISTOL-MYERS SQUIBB COMPANY

345 Park Ave., New York, NY, 10154-0037

Tel: (212) 546-4000   Fax: (212) 546-4020   www.bms.com

Pharmaceutical and food preparations, medical and surgical instruments.

Bristol-Myers Squibb, Ave. Olimpica 3765, Col. Escalon, San Salvador, El Salvador

Compania Bristol-Myers de Centro America, Col. Roma, Blvd Venezuela, Edif. Industrias, San Salvador, El Salvador

LEO BURNETT, DIV. B-COM 3 GROUP

35 West Wacker Drive, Chicago, IL, 60601

Tel: (312) 220-5959   Fax: (312) 220-6533   www.leoburnett.com

Engaged in advertising, marketing, media buying and planning, and public relations.

Publicidad Diaz, S.A. de C.V., 67 Avenida Norte #120, Colonia Escalon, San Salvador, El Salvador

CITIGROUP, INC.

399 Park Avenue, New York, NY, 10022

Tel: (212) 559-1000   Fax: (212) 559-3646   www.citigroup.com

Provides insurance and financial services worldwide.

Citigroup, Alameda Dr. Manuel Enrique Araujo 3530, Km. 4, Edif. B, San Salvador, El Salvador

Tel: 503-245-3011   Fax: 503-245-1842   Contact: Steven J. Puig

COLGATE-PALMOLIVE COMPANY

300 Park Ave., New York, NY, 10022

Tel: (212) 310-2000   Fax: (212) 310-2919   www.colgate.com

Mfr. pharmaceuticals, cosmetics, toiletries and detergents.

Colgate-Palmolive (Central America) Inc., Km 9.5 Carretera Al Puerto la Libertad, San Salvador, El Salvador

COMMERCE GROUP CORPORATION

6001 N. 91st Street, Milwaukee, WI, 53225-1795

Tel: (414) 462-5310   Fax: (414) 462-5312   www.commercegroupcorp.com

Gold mining.

Commerce/Sanseb Joint Venture, 6 Calle Poniente 208, San Miguel, El Salvador

Tel: 503-660-1671   Fax: 503-661-6568   Contact: Luis A. Limay, Mgr.   Emp: 320

CONTINENTAL AIRLINES INC.

1600 Smith St., Houston, TX, 77002

Tel: (713) 324-5000   Fax: (713) 324-2637   www.continental.com

International airline carrier.

Continental Airlines Inc., San Salvador, El Salvador

CRAWFORD & COMPANY

5620 Glenridge Drive NE, Atlanta, GA, 30342

Tel: (404) 256-0830   Fax: (404) 847-4025   www.crawfordandcompany.com

Provides international insurance services engaged in risk management and claims adjustment.

Rudy Solares SA, Div. Crawford, 79 Ave. norte, No. 507-2, San Salvador, El Salvador

D'ARCY MASIUS BENTON & BOWLES INC. (DMB&B)

1675 Broadway, New York, NY, 10019

Tel: (212) 468-3622   Fax: (212) 468-2987   www.darcyww.com

Full service international advertising and communications group.

Cronos/DMB&B, 75 Av. Norte 620, Col. Escalon, San Salvador, El Salvador

Tel: 503-223-139   Fax: 503-279-2840

DDB WORLDWIDE COMMUNICATIONS GROUP

437 Madison Ave., New York, NY, 10022

Tel: (212) 415-2000   Fax: (212) 415-3417   www.ddbn.com

Advertising agency.

RCM DDB Needham, San Salvador, El Salvador

DHL WORLDWIDE EXPRESS

50 California Avenue, San Francisco, CA, 94111

Tel: (415) 677-6100   Fax: (415) 824-9700   www.dhl.com

Worldwide air express carrier.

DHL Worldwide Express, 47 Av. Norte #104, San Salvador, El Salvador

Tel: 503-2-790411

DIONEX CORPORATION

1228 Titan Way, PO Box 3603, Sunnyvale, CA, 94086-3603

Tel: (408) 737-0700   Fax: (408) 730-9403   www.dionex.com

Develop/mfr./market chromatography systems and related products.

Analitica Salvadorena, S.A. de C.V., Avenida Washington. No. 104, Colonia Libertad, San Salvador, El Salvador

DOVER CORPORATION

280 Park Ave., New York, NY, 10017-1292

Tel: (212) 922-1640   Fax: (212) 922-1656   www.dovercorporation.com

Holding company for varied industries; assembly and testing equipment, oil-well gear and other industrial products.

Distribuidora Yale, S.A. De C.V., 39 Av. Sur #540, Col. Flor Blanca, San Salvador, El Salvador

Tel: 503-222-4817   Fax: 503-222-4850

THE DOW CHEMICAL COMPANY

2030 Dow Center, Midland, MI, 48674

Tel: (989) 636-1000   Fax: (989) 636-3228   www.dow.com

Mfr. chemicals, plastics, pharmaceuticals, agricultural products, consumer products.

Laboratorios Life de El Salvador SA, San Salvador, El Salvador

EGL INC. (EAGLE GLOBAL LOGISTICS)

15350 Vickery Drive, Houston, TX, 77032

Tel: (281) 618-3100   Fax: (281) 618-3223   www.eagleusa.com

Ocean/air freight forwarding, customs brokerage, packing and wholesale, logistics management and insurance.

EGL Eagle Global Logistics, 3A. Calle Oriente #226, Edif. Kury, San Salvador, El Salvador

Tel: 503-2-221-415   Fax: 503-2-790-363

EXXON MOBIL CORPORATION

5959 Las Colinas Blvd., Irving, TX, 75039-2298

Tel: (972) 444-1000   Fax: (972) 444-1882   www.exxonmobil.com

Petroleum exploration, production, refining; mfr. petroleum and chemicals products; coal and minerals.

Exxon Mobil, Inc., San Salvador, El Salvador

FRITZ COMPANIES, INC., DIV. UPS

706 Mission Street, Ste. 900, San Francisco, CA, 94103

Tel: (415) 904-8360   Fax: (415) 904-8661   www.fritz.com

Integrated transportation, sourcing, distribution and customs brokerage services.

Fritz Companies Inc., San Salvador, El Salvador

H.B. FULLER COMPANY

1200 Willow Lake Blvd., Vadnais Heights, MN, 55110

Tel: (651) 236-5900   Fax: (651) 236-5898   www.hbfuller.com

Mfr./distributor adhesives, sealants, coatings, paints, waxes, sanitation chemicals.

H.B. Fuller El Salvador, S.A. de C.V., Parque Industrial de Desarrollo, Km. 7 1/2 Antigua Carretera Panamericana, Soyapango 1213, San Salvador, El Salvador

Tel: 503-294-1933   Fax: 503-294-1910

Kativo Industrial, 23 Ave. Sur Entre 12 y 14, Calle Ponientel 1389, San Salvador, El Salvador

Tel: 503-221-1466   Fax: 503-222-3263

GARAN, INC.

350 Fifth Avenue, New York, NY, 10118

Tel: (212) 563-2000   Fax: (212) 971-2250

Designs, manufactures and markets apparel for men, women and children.

Garan de El Salvador, San Salvador, El Salvador

THE GILLETTE COMPANY

Prudential Tower Building, Boston, MA, 02199

Tel: (617) 421-7000   Fax: (617) 421-7123   www.gillette.com

Develop/mfr. personal care/use products: blades and razors, toiletries, cosmetics, stationery.

Gillette de El Salvador SA, San Salvador, El Salvador

GRANT THORNTON INTERNATIONAL

800 One Prudential Plaza, 130 E. Randolph Drive, Chicago, IL, 60601-6050

Tel: (312) 856-0001   Fax: (312) 616-7052   www.grantthornton.com

Accounting, audit, tax and management consulting services.

Grant Thornton, Castellanos Campos & Cia, 71 Av. Norte, 346 Colonia Escalon, San Salvador, El Salvador

Contact: Jose Atilio Campos

GREY GLOBAL GROUP

777 Third Ave., New York, NY, 10017

Tel: (212) 546-2000   Fax: (212) 546-1495   www.grey.com

International advertising agency.

J.M. Creativos, San Salvador, El Salvador

GRIFFITH LABORATORIES INC.

One Griffith Center, Alsip, IL, 60658

Tel: (708) 371-0900   Fax: (708) 597-3294   www.griffithlabs.com

Mfr. industrial food ingredients and equipment.

Griffith Labs Inc., San Salvador, El Salvador

Tel: 503-223-7575   Fax: 503-223-0398

INTER-CONTINENTAL HOTELS

3 Ravinia Drive, Suite 2900, Atlanta, GA, 30346-2149

Tel: (770) 604-2000   Fax: (770) 604-5403   www.interconti.com

Worldwide hotel and resort accommodations.

Camino Real Inter-Continental San Salvador, Blvd. de Los Heroes y Ave. Sisimiles, San Salvador, El Salvador

Tel: 503-260-1333   Fax: 503-260-5660

J. WALTER THOMPSON COMPANY

466 Lexington Ave., New York, NY, 10017

Tel: (212) 210-7000   Fax: (212) 210-6944   www.jwt.com

International advertising and marketing services.

APCU-Thompson, San Salvador, El Salvador

KENNAMETAL INC.

1600 Technology Way, PO Box 231, Latrobe, PA, 15650

Tel: (724) 539-5000   Fax: (724) 539-4710   www.kennametal.com

Tools, hard carbide and tungsten alloys for metalworking industry.

Prometca, S.A. de C.V., 41 Av. Sur y Calle Colon No. 2143, Col. 3 de Mayo., San Salvador, El Salvador

Tel: 503-245-4163   Fax: 503-223-3219

KIMBERLY-CLARK CORPORATION

351 Phelps Drive, Irving, TX, 75038

Tel: (972) 281-1200   Fax: (972) 281-1435   www.kimberly-clark.com

Mfr./sales/distribution of consumer tissue, household and personal care products.

Kimberly-Clark de Centro America SA, Sitio del Niño, El Salvador

KPMG CONSULTING INC.

1676 International Dr., McLean, VA, 22102

Tel: (703) 747-3000   Fax: (703) 747-8500   www.kpmg.com

Accounting and audit, tax and management consulting services.

KPMG International, Av. Olimpica 3324 y 3330, San Salvador, El Salvador

Tel: 503-224-1351   Fax: 503-298-3354   Contact: Hector R. Figueroa, Sr. Ptnr.

LANIER WORLDWIDE, INC.

2300 Parklake Drive, N.E., Atlanta, GA, 30345

Tel: (770) 496-9500   Fax: (770) 938-1020   www.lanier.com

Specialize in digital copiers and multi-functional systems.

Lanier de El Salvador, S.A., Calle El Progreso No. 3114, Col. Avila, San Salvador, El Salvador

Tel: 503-298-0944   Fax: 503-2452-429

LEUCADIA NATIONAL CORPORATION

315 Park Avenue South, New York, NY, 10010

Tel: (212) 460-1900   Fax: (212) 598-4869

Holding company: real estate, banking, insurance, equipment leasing, mfr. plastics, cable, sinks and cabinets.

Cia. de Alumbrado Electrico de San Salvador SA, Apartado 186, San Salvador, El Salvador

LIZ CLAIBORNE INC.

1441 Broadway, 22nd Fl., New York, NY, 10018

Tel: (212) 354-4900   Fax: (212) 626-1800   www.lizclaiborne.com

Apparel manufacturer.

Liz Claiborne De El Salvador, S.A, El Salvador

MARRIOTT INTERNATIONAL INC.

10400 Fernwood Rd., Bethesda, MD, 20817

Tel: (301) 380-3000   Fax: (301) 380-5181   www.marriott.com

Hotel services.

San Salvador Marriott Hotel, San Salvador, El Salvador

Tel: 503-298-1433

MARSH & McLENNAN COS INC.

1166 Ave. of the Americas, New York, NY, 10036-2774

Tel: (212) 345-5000   Fax: (212) 345-4808   www.marshmac.com

Insurance agents/brokers, pension and investment management consulting services.

Consultores de Seguros S.A., Condominio Centro Roosevelt, Edif. C, #34, 55 A.S. #221 y Alameda Roosevelt, San Salvador, El Salvador

Tel: 503-246-691   Fax: 503-241-247

Servicios Y Asesorias S.A., 57 Av. Norte, #201, San Salvador, El Salvador

Tel: 503-260-5521   Fax: 503-260-5523   Contact: Carlos Iraheta

MARY KAY COSMETICS INC.

16251 No. Dallas Pkwy, Dallas, TX, 75248

Tel: (972) 687-6300   Fax: (972) 687-1609   www.marykay-cosmetic.com

Mfr. and direct sales of cosmetics and toiletries.

Masdel Mary Kay El Salvador, Centro Comerical Villas Espanolas, Local D-21 Y D-22, Paseo General Escalon, San Salvador, El Salvador

McCANN-ERICKSON WORLDGROUP

750 Third Ave., New York, NY, 10017

Tel: (212) 697-6000   Fax: (212) 984-3575   www.mccann.com

International advertising and marketing services.

McCann-Erickson Centroamericana (EI Salvador) SA, Metrocentro Nivel 2, Aptdo. 1170, San Salvador, El Salvador

McCORMICK & COMPANY, INC.

18 Loveton Circle, Sparks, MD, 21152-6000

Tel: (410) 771-7301   Fax: (410) 527-8289   www.mccormick.com

Manufactures, markets and distributes spices, seasonings, flavors and other specialty food products.

McCormick de Centro America, S.A. de C.V., Apartado Postal (01) 189, San Salvador, El Salvador

Tel: 503-243-0122   Fax: 503-243-0735

MYERS INTERNATIONAL INC.

1293 South Main Street, Akron, OH, 44301

Tel: (330) 253-5592   Fax: (330) 253-0035   www.myerstiresupply.com

Mfr. tire retreading and maintenance equipment and supplies.

Myers De El Salvador, 4 ta Calle Poniente 2212, Colonia Flor Blanca, San Salvador, El Salvador

Tel: 503-260-7636   Fax: 503-260-7176

NATURE'S SUNSHINE PRODUCTS, INC.

75 East 1700 South, Provo, UT, 84605

Tel: (801) 342-4300   Fax: (801) 342-4305   www.naturessunshine.com

Mfr. and sales of holistic health products.

Nature's Sunshine Products, 9a Calle Poniente 3952, Colonia Escalon, San Salvadore, El Salvador

OGILVY & MATHER WORLDWIDE

309 West 49th Street, New York, NY, 10017-7399

Tel: (212) 237-4000   Fax: (212) 237-5123   www.ogilvypr.com

Engaged in public relations and communications.

Ogilvy Public Relations Worldwide, San Salvador, El Salvador

PAN-AMERICAN LIFE INSURANCE COMPANY

Pan American Life Center, 601 Poydras St., New Orleans, LA, 70130-0219

Tel: (504) 566-1300   Fax: (504) 566-3600   www.panamericanlife.com

Insurance services.

Pan-American Life Insurance Co., Condominio Torre Roble, piso 10, Metrocentro, San Salvador, El Salvador

Tel: 503-2-60-8899   Fax: 503-2-60-3340   Contact: Mario Hector Salazar   Emp: 72

PARSONS CORPORATION

100 West Walnut Street, Pasadena, CA, 91124

Tel: (626) 440-2000   Fax: (626) 440-4919   www.parsons.com

Engaged in engineering, procurement, and construction management services.

Parsons El Salvador, Consorcia De Leuw, Cather, Consulta S.A. de C.V., Calle Los Almendros #20-A, San Miguel, El Salvador

PERKIN ELMER, INC.

45 William Street, Wellesley, MA, 02481

Tel: (781) 237-5100   Fax: (781) 431-4255   www.perkinelmer.com

Mfr. equipment and devices to detect explosives and bombs on airline carriers.

Coresa, Residencial San Luis, Av. Lincoln, Block 6, #40, San Salvador, El Salvador

PHELPS DODGE CORPORATION

2600 North Central Ave., Phoenix, AZ, 85004-3089

Tel: (602) 234-8100   Fax: (602) 234-8337   www.phelpsdodge.com

Copper, minerals, metals and special engineered products for transportation and electrical markets.

Conductores Electricos de Centro America SA (CONELCA), Aptdo. 283, San Salvador, El Salvador

PPL GLOBAL CORPORATION

2 N. 9th St, Allentown, PA, 18101

Tel: (610) 774-5151   Fax: (610) 774-4198   www.pplweb.com

Energy holding company engaged in electric.

Distribuidora de Electricidad del Sur S.A., San Salvador, El Salvador

PRICEWATERHOUSECOOPERS LLP

1301 Ave. of the Americas, New York, NY, 10019

Tel: (212) 596-7000   Fax: (212) 259-1301   www.pwcglobal.com

Accounting and auditing, tax and management, and human resource consulting services.

PriceWaterhouseCoopers, Ct. Prof. Presidente, Av. La Revolucion y Calle, Circunvalacion AP 695, San Salvador, El Salvador

Tel: 503-279-0745   Fax: 503-279-0751

PROCTER & GAMBLE COMPANY

One Procter & Gamble Plaza, Cincinnati, OH, 45202

Tel: (513) 983-1100   Fax: (513) 562-4500   www.pg.com

Personal care, food, laundry, cleaning and industry products.

Procter & Gamble, 35 Av. Notre y Prolongacion Calle Arce, #131 Col. Flor Blanca, San Salvador, El Salvador

RAYOVAC CORPORATION

601 Rayovac Drive, Madison, WI, 53711-2497

Tel: (608) 275-3340   Fax: (608) 275-4577   www.rayovac.com

Mfr. batteries and lighting devices.

Rayovac El Salvador S.A. de C.V., Boulevard Merliot Jardines de la Libertad, Apartado Postal 2079, Ciudad Merliot, Santa Tecla, El Salvador

RENA WARE DISTRIBUTORS INC.

PO Box 97050, Redmond, WA, 98073-9750

Tel: (425) 881-6171   Fax: (425) 882-7500   www.renaware.com

Mfr. stainless steel cookware and water filtration products.

Distribuidores Rena Ware, S.A. de C.V., 1ra. Calle Poniente y 45 Avenida Norte, San Salvador, El Salvador

RUDDICK CORPORATION

301 S. Tryon St., Ste. 1800, Charlotte, NC, 28202

Tel: (704) 372-5404   Fax: (704) 372-6409   www.amefird.com

Mfr. industrial sewing thread for worldwide industrial and consumer markets.

Hilos A&E De El Salvador, Edificio D Kilometro 36, Carretera Panamericana A Santa Ana, San Salvador, El Salvador

UAL CORPORATION

1200 E. Algonquin Rd., Chicago, IL, 60007

Tel: (847) 700-4000   Fax: (847) 700-4081   www.ual.com

Air transportation, passenger and freight services.

United Airlines, San Salvador, El Salvador

UNITED PARCEL SERVICE, INC.

55 Glenlake Parkway, NE, Atlanta, GA, 30328

Tel: (404) 828-6000   Fax: (404) 828-6593   www.ups.com

International package-delivery service.

UPS / Courier Internacional S.A., Calle El Progreso No. 3139, Col. Roma, San Salvador, El Salvador
Tel: 503-279-0934   Fax: 503-279-0936

THE WACKENHUT CORPORATION

4200 Wackenhut Dr., Ste. 100, Palm Beach Gardens, FL, 33410

Tel: (561) 622-5656   Fax: (561) 691-6736   www.wackenhut.com

Security systems and services.

Wackenhut de El Salvador SA de CV, Calle Loma Linda 327, Col. San Benito, San Salvador, El Salvador
Tel: 503-298-6285   Fax: 503-298-6592

WENDY'S INTERNATIONAL, INC.

4288 West Dublin Granville Roads, Dublin, OH, 43017-0256

Tel: (614) 764-3100   Fax: (614) 764-3459   www.wendysintl.com

Fast food restaurant chain.

Wendy's International, San Salvador, El Salvador

XEROX CORPORATION

800 Long Ridge Road, PO Box 1600, Stamford, CT, 06904

Tel: (203) 968-3000   Fax: (203) 968-4312   www.xerox.com

Mfr. document processing equipment, systems and supplies.

Xerox de El Salvador S.A., Final Blvd. Santa Elena Y, Urban. Santa Elena, Edif. Xerox, San Salvador, El Salvador
Tel: 503-278-8000   Fax: 503-278-8686

YOUNG & RUBICAM INC.

285 Madison Ave., New York, NY, 10017

Tel: (212) 210-3000   Fax: (212) 370-3796   www.yr.com

Advertising, public relations, direct marketing and sales promotion, corporate and product ID management.

Lemisimun Publicidad, San Salvador, El Salvador

England, U.K.

24/7 REAL MEDIA, INC.

1250 Broadway, New York, NY, 10001-3701

Tel: (212) 231-7100   Fax: (212) 760-1774   www.247media.com

Provides global online advertising, sponsorships, e-commerce and direct marketing solutions to advertisers and Web publishers.

24/7 Media UK Ltd., Egyptian House, 170-173 Picadilly, London W1J 9EJ, UK

Tel: 44-207-355-3223

3COM CORPORATION

5400 Bayfront Plaza, Santa Clara, CA, 95052-8145

Tel: (408) 326-5000   Fax: (408) 326-5001   www.3com.com

Engaged in the development and manufacture of computer networking products and systems.

3Com UK Ltd., Boundary Way, Maylands Park South, Hemel Hempstead HP2 7YU, UK

Tel: 44-1442-438000   Fax: 44-1442-438333

3D LABS INC., LTD.

480 Potrero Avenue, Sunnyvale, CA, 94086

Tel: (408) 530-4700   Fax: (408) 530-4701   www.3dlabs.com

Produces 3D graphics accelerators chips for the PC computer platform.

3D Labs Ltd., Meadlake Place, Thorpe Lea Rd., Egham Surrey TW20 8HE, UK

Tel: 44-178-447-0555   Fax: 44-178-447-0699

3D SYSTEMS CORPORATION

26081 Avenue Hall, Valencia, CA, 91355

Tel: (805) 295-5600   Fax: (805) 294-8406   www.3dsystems.com

Mfr. computer lasers.

3D Systems Europe Ltd, Mark House, Mark Road, Hemel Hempstead, Herts HP2 7UA, UK

3D/INTERNATIONAL INC.

1900 West Loop South, Ste. 400, Houston, TX, 77027

Tel: (713) 871-7000   Fax: (713) 871-7456   www.3di.com

Engaged in design, management and environmental services.

3D/I-London, London, UK

THE 3DO COMPANY

100 Cardinal Way, Ste. 425, Redwood City, CA, 94063

Tel: (650) 385-3000   Fax: (650) 385-3184   www.3do.com

Mfr. entertainment software.

3DO UK Ltd., Vantage House, 1 Weir Road, London SW198UX, UK

Tel: 44-207-761-9300

3M (MINNESOTA MINING & MFG.)

3M Center, St. Paul, MN, 55144-1000

Tel: (651) 733-1110   Fax: (651) 733-9973   www.mmm.com

Mfr. diversified products for industry, consumer, health care, imaging, communications, transport, safety, etc.

3M United Kingdom PLC, 3M House, Market Place, PO Box 1, Bracknell Berkshire RG12 1JU, UK

Tel: 44-1344-858-000   Fax: 44-1344-858-306   Contact: Wayne W. Brown

3M TOUCH SYSTEMS, INC.

300 Griffin Brook Park Drive, Methuen, MA, 01844

Tel: (978) 659-9000   Fax: (978) 659-9100   www.microtouch.com

Mfr. Touchscreen Sensors, Touch Monitors, and Industrial Computer Products.

3M Touch Systems, Ltd., 163 Milton Park, Abingdon, Oxon OX14 4SD, UK

Tel: 44-1235-444400 Fax: 44-1235-861603

A. B. DICK COMPANY

7400 Caldwell Avenue, Niles, IL, 60714-3806

Tel: (847) 779-1900   Fax: (847) 779-1900   www.abdick.com

Mfr./sales automation systems.

A. B. Dick Limited, 983 Great West Road, Brentford, Middlesex TW8 9DN, UK

Tel: 44-181-568-9297 Fax: 44-181-847-0779

AAF INTERNATIONAL (AMERICAN AIR FILTER)

10300 Ormsby Park Place, Ste. 600, Louisville, KY, 40232-5690

Tel: (502) 637-0011   Fax: (502) 637-0321   www.aafintl.com

Mfr. air filtration and pollution control and noise control equipment.

AAF Ltd., Bassington Lane, Cramlington, Northumberland NE23 8AF, UK

Tel: 44-1670-713477 Fax: 44-1670-714370

AAR CORPORATION

1100 North Wood Dale Road, Wood Dale, IL, 60191

Tel: (630) 227-2000   Fax: (630) 227-2019   www.aarcorp.com

Provides aviation repair and supply provisioning; aircraft sales and leasing.

AAR Allen Group International, 35 Willow Lane, Mitcham, Surrey CR4 4UQ, UK

Tel: 44-181-640-2225 Fax: 44-181-685-9247   Contact: Alex Vlielander

AAR Allen Group International, Cardinal Point Newall Road, Hounslow, Middlesex TW6 2BP, UK

Tel: 44-181-759-4022   Fax: 44-181-897-9005   Contact: Jon Clark

AAVID THERMAL TECHNOLOGIES, INC.

1 Eagle Square, Ste. 509, Concord, NH, 03301

Tel: (603) 224-1117   Fax: (603) 224-6673   www.aatt.com

Mfr. fluid dynamics software.

Aavid Thermalloy Ltd., Cheney Manor, Swindon Wiltshire SN2 2QN, UK

Tel: 44-01-793-401400

ABBOTT LABORATORIES

100 Abbott Park Rd., Abbott Park, IL, 60064

Tel: (847) 937-6100   Fax: (847) 937-1511   www.abbott.com

Development, manufacture and sale of diversified health care products and services.

Abbott Laboratories Ltd., Norden Road, Maidenhead Berkshire SL6 4XL, UK

Abbott Laboratories Ltd., Abbott House Norden Road, Maidenhead, Berkshire SL6 4XE, UK

ABRASIVE TECHNOLOGY INC.

8400 Green Meadows Drive, Lewis Center, OH, 43035

Tel: (740) 548-4100   Fax: (740) 548-7617   www.abrasive-tech.com

Mfr. diamond and CBN tooling: bits, blades, drills, wheels, belts, discs.

Habit Diamond Ltd., Blackmarsh Road, Mochdre Business Park, Colwyn Bay LL28 5HA, UK

Tel: 44-1492-542-400 Fax: 44-1492-542-401

Habit Diamond Ltd., Greenhough Road, Lichfield, Staffordshire WS13 7AU, UK

Tel: 44-1543-441-000   Fax: 44-1543-441-001

Habit Diamond Ltd., Long Acre, Saltash Parkway Industrial Estate, Saltash, Cornwall PL12 6LZ, UK

Tel: 44-1752-677-360   Fax: 44-1752-677-361

Habit Diamond Ltd., Roxby Place, Fulham, London SW6 1RT, UK

Tel: 44-20-7471-0200   Fax: 44-20-7471-0202

ABS (AMERICAN BUREAU OF SHIPPING)

ABS Plaza, 16855 Northchase Drive, Houston, TX, 77060

Tel: (281) 877-6000   Fax: (281) 877-6344   www.eagle.org

Classification and certification of ships and offshore structures, development and technical assistance.

ABS Europe, ABS House, 1 Frying Pan Alley, London E1 7HR, UK

Tel: 44-207-247 3255

ACAMBIS INC.

38 Sidney Street, Cambridge, MA, 02139

Tel: (617) 494-1339   Fax: (617) 494-1741   www.acambis.com

Engaged in biotechnology and the development of vaccines (JV with Baxter Healthcare).

Acambis PLC, 100 Fulbourn Road, Cambridge CB1 9PT, UK

Tel: 44-1223-275-300

ACCENTURE LTD.

1345 Avenue of the Americas, New York, NY, 10105

Tel: (917) 452-4400   Fax: (917) 527-9915   www.accenture.com

Provides management and technology consulting services.

Accenture, 2 Arundel St., London WC2R 3LT, UK

Tel: 44-207-438-5000   Fax: 44-207-831-1133

Accenture, Kingsley Hall, 20 Bailey Lane, Manchester Airport, Manchester M90 4AN, UK

Tel: 44-161-435-5000   Fax: 44-161-435-5050

Accenture, Riverside House, Riverside Walk, Windsor, Berkshire SL4 1NA, UK

Tel: 44-1753-605-000   Fax: 44-1753-605-050

ACCLAIM ENTERTAINMENT, INC.

One Acclaim Plaza, Glen Cove, NY, 11542

Tel: (516) 656-5000   Fax: (516) 656-2040   www.acclaim.com

Mfr. video games.

Acclaim Entertainment, Ltd., 112-120 Brompton Road, Knightsbridge London SW3 1JJ, UK

Tel: 44-207-344-5000

Acclaim Studios London, Ltd., Knolly's House, 1st Fl, 17 Addiscombe Road, Croydon Surrey CRO 6SR, UK

Acclaim Studios Teeside, Ltd., Dunedin House Riverside Quay, Stockton-on-Tees, Cleveland TS17-6BJ, UK

ACCO WORLD CORPORATION

300 Tower Parkway, Lincolnshire, IL, 60069

Tel: (847) 541-9500   Fax: (847) 541-5750   www.accobrands.com

Provides services in the office and computer markets and manufactures paper fasteners, clips, metal fasteners, binders and staplers.

ACCO Europe, The Lodge, Harmonsworth Lane, Harmonsworth, West Drayto, Middlesex UB 7 2LQ, UK

ACCO Europe Plc, Gatehouse Road, Aylesbury, Bucks HP 19 3DT, UK

Tel: 44-1296-394833   Fax: 44-1296-483512   Contact: Steve Keen

ACCOUNTANTS ON CALL

Park 80 West, Plaza 2, 9th Fl., Saddle Brook, NJ, 07663

Tel: (201) 843-0006   Fax: (201) 843-4936   www.aocnet.com

Full-service staffing and executive search firm specializing in accounting and financial personnel.

Accountants on Call, Portland Tower, 3/F, Portland Street, Manchester M1 3LD, UK

Tel: 44-161-236-6866   Fax: 44-161-236-2053

Accountants on Call, 36 Park Row, Leeds LS1 5JL, UK

Tel: 44-113-245-6145   Fax: 44-113-244-0023

Accountants on Call, 33 Regent Street, 5/F, London SW1Y 4NB, UK

Tel: 44-207-440-3670   Fax: 44-207-440-3680

Accountants on Call, 38/40 The Maltings, St. Albans AL1 3HA, UK

Tel: 44-727-848482   Fax: 44-727-834151

Accountants on Call, 38/40 The Maltings, St. Albans, Hertfordshire AL1 3HA, UK

Accountants on Call, 1 High Street, Chelmsford Essex CM1 1BE, UK

Accountants on Call, 13-15 Blagrave Street, Reading RG1-1PJ, UK

Accountants on Call, 11 Sheen Rd., Richmond TW9 1AD, UK

Tel: 44-181-332-1888   Fax: 44-181-332-0777

Accountants on Call, Anglo City House, 1/F, 2-6 Shirley Road, Southhampton, Hampshire SO15 3EU, UK

Tel: 44-117-930-8600

ACCURIDE INTERNATIONAL, INC.

12311 Shoemaker Ave., Santa Fe Springs, CA, 90670-4721

Tel: (562) 903-0200   Fax: (562) 903-0208   www.accuride.com

Mfr. drawer slides.

Accuride International, Liliput Rd., Brackmills Industrial Estate, Northampton NN4 7AS, UK

Contact: Jim Armstrong, VP

ACE CONTROLS INC.

23435 Industrial Park Drive, Farmington Hills, MI, 48024

Tel: (248) 476-0213   Fax: (248) 276-2470   www.acecontrols.com

Industry hydraulic shock absorbers, cylinders, valves and automation controls.

ACE Controls Intl., Belvedere Road, Newton-Le-Willows, Merseyside WA12 0JJ, UK

Tel: 44-1925-227171   Fax: 44-1925-229323

ACHESON COLLOIDS INDUSTRIES, INC.

1600 Washington Avenue, Port Huron, MI, 48060

Tel: (810) 984-5581   Fax: (810) 984-1446   www.nationalstarch.com

Chemicals, chemical preparations, paints and lubricating oils.

Acheson Colloids Company, Prince Rock, Plymouth PL4 0SP, UK

Tel: 44-1752-207120   Fax: 44-1752-207133

Acheson Industries Ltd., Sun Life House, 85 Queens Road, Reading Berkshire RG1 4PT, UK

Tel: 44-118-958-8844   Fax: 44-118-957-4897

ACME UNITED CORPORATION

1931 Black Rock Turnpike, Fairfield, CT, 06432

Tel: (203) 332-7330   Fax: (203) 576-0007   www.acmeunited.com

Mfr. mathematics tools, including rulers, protractors, compasses and scissors.

Acme United Limited, Surmanco Div., Unit 5, Manor Park Estate, Kettlebridge Road, Sheffield S9 3AJ, UK

Tel: 44-114-564000   Fax: 44-114-564001

ACT MANUFACTURING, INC.

2 Cabot Road, Hudson, MA, 01749

Tel: (978) 567-4000   Fax: (978) 568-1904   www.actmfg.com

Mfr. printed circuit boards.

ACT Manufacturing, Meridian Business Park, Meridian East, Leicester LE3 2WZ, UK

Tel: 44-1162-822888   Fax: 44-1162-822889

ACTEL CORPORATION

955 East Arquest Avenue, Sunnyvale, CA, 94086-4533

Tel: (408) 739-1010   Fax: (408) 739-1540   www.actel.com

Mfr. integrated circuits.

Actel Europe Ltd., Maxfli Court, Riverside Way, Camberley, Surrey GU15 3YL, UK

Tel: 44-1276-401-450

ACTION INSTRUMENTS INC.

8601 Aero Drive, San Diego, CA, 92123

Tel: (619) 279-5726   Fax: (619) 279-6290   www.actionio.com

Mfr. electronic instruments and industrial measurements computers.

Action Instruments Ltd., Dominion Way, Worthing West Sussex BN14 8QL, UK

Tel: 44-1-903-205-222   Fax: 44-1-903-203-767   Contact: Alan Boot

Action Instruments UK, Faraday Close, Durrington, Worthing, West Sussex N13 3PL, UK

Tel: 44-1-903-268-500   Fax: 44--713-501-216

ACTIONPOINT, INC.

1299 Parkmoor Avenue, San Jose, CA, 95126

Tel: (408) 325-3800 Fax: (408) 325-3985 www.actionpoint.com

Develops software for e-commerce.

ActionPoint UK, Hanover House, Cross Lanes, Buildford GU1 1UG, UK

Tel: 44-1483-460500 Fax: 44-1483-460600

ACTIVISION

3100 Ocean Park Boulevard, Santa Monica, CA, 90405

Tel: (310) 255-2000 Fax: (310) 255-2100 www.activision.com

Development and manufacture of entertainment software and video games.

Activision UK Ltd., Bemini House, 133 High St., Ylewsley West Drayton, Middlesex UB7 7QL, UK

Tel: 44-1895-456-7 Fax: 44-1895-456-709 Emp: 128

ACTUATE CORPORATION

701 Gateway Boulevard, South San Francisco, CA, 94080

Tel: (650) 837-2000 Fax: (650) 827-1560 www.actuate.com

Develops software.

Actuate UK Ltd., No. 1 The Arena, Downshire Way, Bracknell Berkshire RG12 1PU, UK

Tel: 44-1344-316040 Fax: 44-1344-316001

ACUITY BRANDS, INC.

1420 Peachtree Street NE, Atlanta, GA, 30309-3002

Tel: (404) 853-1000 Fax: (404) 853-1015 www.acuitybrands.com

Mfr. lighting fixtures and chemical cleaning products.

Holophane Europe, Bond Avenue, Milton Keynes MK1 1JG, UK

ACXIOM CORPORATION

1 Information Way, Little Rock, AR, 72203-8180

Tel: (501) 342-1000 Fax: (501) 336-3919 www.acxiom.com

Data warehouse, database manager, and other marketing information services.

Acxiom Limited, Counting House, 53 Tooley Street, London SE1 2QN, UK

Tel: 44-207-526-5100 Fax: 44-207-526-5200

ADAC LABORATORIES, INC.

540 Alder Drive, Milpitas, CA, 95035

Tel: (408) 321-9100 Fax: (408) 321-9536 www.adaclabs.com

Mfr. cameras and equipment for nuclear medicine.

ADAC Laboratories UK, 3/4 Reycote Lane, Milton Common, Oxford OX9 2NP, UK

Tel: 44-18-4427-8011

ADAMS RITE MANUFACTURING COMPANY

260 West Santa Fe Street, Pomona, CA, 91767-2116

Tel: (909) 632-2300 Fax: (909) 632-3267 www.adamsrite.com

Mfr. architectural door hardware.

Adams Rite (Europe) Ltd., Unit 6, Moreton Industrial Estate, London Rd., Swanley, Kent BR8 8TZ, UK

Tel: 44-1322-669211 Fax: 44-1322-613230 Contact: Mr. I. Mackay

ADAYTUM, INC.

2051 Killebrew Drive, Ste. 40, Bloomington, MN, 55425-1820

Tel: (952) 858-8585 Fax: (952) 858-8881 www.adaytum.com

Mfr. enterprise software.

Adaytum Ltd., Hythe House, 200 Shepherds Bush Road, London W6 7NL, UK

Tel: 44-207-471-9000 Fax: 44-207-603-3363

Adaytum Ltd., Castlegate Tower Hill, Bristol BS2 OJA, UK

Tel: 44-117-921-5555

ADC TELECOMMUNICATIONS INC.

13625 Technology Drive, Eden Prairie, MN, 55344

Tel: (952) 938-8080   Fax: (952) 946-3292   www.adc.com

Mfr. telecommunications equipment.

ADC Europe, Unit 4, Beacontree Plaza, Gillette Way, Reading RG2 OBS, UK

Tel: 44-11-89-879-200 Fax: 44-11-89-314-388

ADE CORPORATION

80 Wilson Way, Westwood, MA, 02090

Tel: (781) 467-3500   Fax: (781) 467-0500   www.ade.com

Mfr. semiconductor wafers and computer disks.

ADE International, 10/11 Shenley Pavilions, Milton Keynes MK5 6LB, UK

Tel: 44-1908-507799 Fax: 44-1908-503366

ADEMCO INTERNATIONAL

1769 N.W. 79th Avenue, Miami, FL, 33126

Tel: (305) 477-5204   Fax: (305) 477-5404   www.ademcoint.com

Mfr. security, fire and burglary systems and products.

ADEMCO Marketing, 12 The Paddock, Hambridge Rd., Newbury Berkshire RG14 5TQ, UK

ADOBE SYSTEMS INCORPORATED

345 Park Avenue, San Jose, CA, 95110

Tel: (408) 536-6000   Fax: (408) 537-6000   www.adobe.com

Engaged in print technology and distributor of Acrobat Reader.

Adobe Systems UK, Waterview House, 1 Roundwood Avenue, Stockley Park Uxbridge, Middlesex UB11 9AE, UK

Tel: 44-208-606-4000

ADVANCE PUBLICATIONS, INC.

950 Fingerboard Road, Staten Island, NY, 10305

Tel: (718) 981-1234   Fax: (718) 981-1415   www.advance.net

Publishing company (Glamour, Vogue, GQ, Architectural Digest) and cable TV operations.

Advance Publications, Inc., London, UK

ADVANCED BRAIN TECHNOLOGIES (ABT)

PO Box 1088, Ogden, UT, 84402

Tel: (801) 622-5676   Fax: (801) 622-5676   www.advancedbrain.com

Engaged in research to create products, programs, and services that enhance health, learning and productivity.

Advanced Brain Technologies (ABT), Oak Tree Cottage, 30 Gardyn Croft, Taverham, Norwich, Norfolk NR8 6UZ, UK

ADVANCED DIGITAL INFORMATION CORPORATION

11431 Willows Rd. NE, PO Box 97057, Redmond, WA, 98073

Tel: (425) 881-8004   Fax: (425) 881-2296   www.adic.com

Mfr. computer storage systems.

ADIC UK, 115 Wharfedale Road, Winnersh, Berkshire RG41 5RB, UK

ADVANCED ENERGY INDUSTRIES, INC.

1625 Sharp Point Drive, Fort Collins, CO, 80525

Tel: (970) 221-4670   Fax: (970) 221-5583   www.advanced-energy.com

Mfr. semiconductors.

Advanced Energy Aera Products, Units 1&2, Bliston Glen Enterprise Centre, 1 Dryden Road, Edinburgh EH20 9LZ, UK

ADVANCED MICRO DEVICES INC.

1 AMD Place, Sunnyvale, CA, 94086

Tel: (408) 732-2400   Fax: (408) 982-6164   www.amd.com

Mfr. integrated circuits for communications and computation industry.

Advanced Micro Devices UK Ltd., 11 The Parks, Haydock, Newton le Willows, Merseyside WA12 OJQ, UK

Tel: 44-1942-272-888 Fax: 44-1942-272-797

Advanced Micro Devices UK Ltd., AMD House, Frimley Business Park, Camberley, Surrey GU16 5SL, UK

Tel: 44-1276-803100   Fax: 44-1276-803227

ADVANCED MP TECHNOLOGY, INC.

1010 Calle Sombra, San Clemente, CA, 92673-6480

Tel: (949) 492-3113   Fax: (949) 492-5068   www.advancedmp.com

Engaged in distribution of electronic components.

Advanced MP Technology Ltd., 1 Down Place Hammersmith, London W6 9JH, UK

ADVANCED PRODUCTS COMPANY

33 Defco Park Road, North Haven, CT, 06473

Tel: (203) 239-3341   Fax: (203) 234-7233   www.advpro.com

Mfr. metallic and PTFE seals and gaskets.

Advanced Products (Seals & Gaskets) Ltd., Unit 25A, 1 Industrial Estate, Consett Durham DH8 6SR, UK

Contact: Helge De Vriendt

ADVANSTAR COMMUNICATIONS INC.

545 Boylston Steet, Boston, MA, 02116

Tel: (617) 267-6500   Fax: (617) 267-6900   www.advanstar.com

Provides business to business marketing services.

Advanstar Communications, Advanstar House, Park West Sealand Road, Chester CH1 4RN, UK

Tel: 44-1244-378888

Advanstar Communications, Unit C, 1/F, Lamb House, Church Street, Chiswick, London W4 2PD, UK

Tel: 44-208-987-0900   Fax: 44-208-987-0901

ADVENT SOFTWARE, INC.

301 Brannan Street, San Francisco, CA, 94107

Tel: (415) 543-7696   Fax: (415) 543-5070   www.advent.com

Mfr. portfolio software.

Advent Europe Ltd., Berkeley Square House, 2/F, 2 Berkeley Square, London W1Z 6EA, UK

Tel: 44-20-7887-6021

ADVERTISING.COM, INC.

1010 Hull Street, 2nd. Fl., Baltimore, MD, 21230

Tel: (410) 244-1370   Fax: (410) 244-1699   www.advertising.com

Engaged web-based advertising.

Advertising.com Inc., 9 Hatton Street, 3/F, London NW8 8PL, UK

Tel: 44-207-563-0500   Contact: Nicholas Green

AEARO CORPORATION

5457 West 79th Street, Indianapolis, IN, 46268

Tel: (317) 692-6666   Fax: (317) 692-6772   www.aearo.co

Mfr. personal protection equipment, including hart hats and safety clothing.

Aearo UK, Acumen Centre, First Avenue, Poynton, Stockport Cheshire SK12 1FJ, UK

AECOM TECHNOLOGY CORPORATION

555 S. Flower, Los Angeles, CA, 90071

Tel: (213) 593-8000   Fax: (213) 593-8729   www.aecom.com

Develops, designs, builds, and maintains facilities for public and private facilities.

FaberMaunsell, 160 Croydon Road, Beckenham, BR3 4DE, UK

Contact: Chris Kimberley

AERO SYSTEMS ENGINEERING, INC.

358 E. Fillmore Ave., St. Paul, MN, 55107

Tel: (651) 227-7515   Fax: (651) 227-0519   www.aerosysengr.com

Engaged in wind tunnel and jet engine testing and engineering. (JV of Celsius Inc.)

Aero Systems Aviation Corp, 24 Sussex Rd., Haynards Heath, Sussex RH16 4FA, UK

AEROGLIDE CORPORATION

PO Box 29505, Raleigh, NC, 27626-0505

Tel: (919) 851-2000   Fax: (919) 851-6029   www.aeroglide.com

Mfr. rotary dryers, dehydrators, roasters, grain and coffee dryers.

Aeroglide Corporation UK, 22-23 Scotgate, Stamford Lincs PE9 2Q, UK

Tel: 44-1780-767-007   Fax: 44-1780-767-008

AEROMARITIME, INC.

4115 Pleasant Valley Drive, Chantilly, VA, 22021

Tel: (703) 631-3111   Fax: (703) 631-3144   www.aeromarusa.com

Military electronics, turbine engines and shafts.

Aeromaritime Ltd., The Conifers, Maiden Street, Maiden Street, Weston, Herts SG47AA, UK

Tel: 44-1462-790062   Fax: 44-1462-790063

AEROVOX INC.

167 John Vertente Boulevard, New Bedford, MA, 02745

Tel: (508) 994-9661   Fax: (508) 995-3000   www.aerovox.com

Manufacturer of capacitors for electrical and electronic applications.

BHC Aerovox Ltd., 20-21 Cumberland Dr., Granby Industrial Estate, Weymouth, Dorset DT4 9TE, UK

Tel: 44-1305-782-871   Fax: 44-1305-760-670   Contact: Graham Yates, Mng. Dir.

THE AES CORPORATION

1001 North 19th Street, Arlington, VA, 22209

Tel: (703) 522-1315   Fax: (703) 528-4510   www.aesc.com

Gas and electric utility.

AES UK, Burleigh House, 18 Parkshot, Richmond TW9 2RG, UK

Tel: 44-208-334-5300 Fax: 44-208-940-1170   Contact: Mark Fitzpatrick, Mgr.

AETHER SYSTEMS, INC.

11460 Cronridge Drive, Owings Mills, MD, 21117

Tel: (410) 654-6400   Fax: (410) 654-6554   www.aethersystems.com

Engaged in wireless technology and applications.

Aether Systems, 200 Brooke Drive, Ste. 135, Green Park, Reading, Berkshire RG2 6UB, UK

Tel: 44-118-949-7019

AFFILIATED MANAGERS GROUP, INC.

2 International Place, 23rd Fl., Boston, MA, 02110

Tel: (617) 747-3300   Fax: (617) 747-3380   www.amg.com

Engaged in asset management.

First Quadrant UK, 86 Jermyn Street, 5/F, London SW1Y 6JD, UK

Tel: 44-207-973-0972   Fax: 44-207-973-8109   Contact: Robert H. Brown, Mng. Dir.

AFFYMETRIX, INC.

3380 Central Expressway, Santa Clara, CA, 95051

Tel: (408) 721-5000   Fax: (408) 481-0422   www.affymetrix.com

Engaged in development and manufacture of gene chip systems for research and treatments of infectious diseases.

Affymetrix UK Ltd., Voyager Mercury Park, Wycombe Lane, Wooburn Green, High Wycombe HP10 0HH, UK

Tel: 44-1628-552550   Fax: 44-1628-552585

AGCO CORPORATION

4205 River Green Parkway, Duluth, GA, 30096-2568

Tel: (770) 813-9200   Fax: (770) 813-6038   www.agcocorp.com

Mfr. farm equipment and machinery.

AGCO Limited, PO Box 62, Banner Lane, Coventry CV4 9GF, UK

Tel: 44-24-76-694400   Fax: 44-24-76-852495

AGENCY.COM LTD.

20 Exchange Place, 15th Fl, New York, NY, 10005

Tel: (212) 358-2600   Fax: (212) 358-2604   www.agency.com

Engaged in Website design and technology integration.

Agency.Com, 8 Crinan Street, Battlebridge Basin, London N1 95Q, UK

Tel: 44-207-964-8200

AGERE SYSTEMS

555 Union Boulevard, Allentown, PA, 18109-3286

Tel: (610) 712-4323   Fax: (610) 712-4106   www.agere.com

Mfr. of communications chips.

Agere Systems Marketpoint, Ltd., Unit 6, The Western Centre, Western Road, Bracknell, Berkshire RG12 1RW, UK

Tel: 44-7000-624624

AGILE SOFTWARE CORPORATION

1 Almaden Blvd., San Jose, CA, 95113-2253

Tel: (408) 975-3900   Fax: (408) 271-4862   www.agilesoft.com

Mfr. software for supply chain management.

Agile Software Ltd., 3000 Hillswood Drive, Hillswood Business Park, Chertsey Surrey KT16 ORS, UK

AGILENT TECHNOLOGIES, INC.

395 Page Mill Road, PO Box 10395, Palo Alto, CA, 94303

Tel: (650) 752-5000   Fax: (650) 752-5633   www.agilent.com

Mfr. communications components.

Agilent Technologies Ltd., Amen Corner, Cain Road, Bracknell Berkshire RG12 1HN, UK

AGRA BAYMONT, INC.

14100 58th St. North, Clearwater, FL, 33760-3796

Tel: (727) 578-0100   Fax: (727) 577-6946   www.baymont.com

Provides data conversion, maintenance, and implementation services for utility, public, and commercial industries and offers services in photogram metric mapping, remote sensing, imagery analysis, and resource mapping.

Geonex Corp., Barwell Business Ctr., Unit 7, Arthur St., Barwell, Leicestershire LE9 8GZ, UK

AIG AMERICAN INTERNATIONAL GROUP INC.

70 Pine Street, New York, NY, 10270

Tel: (212) 770-7000   Fax: (212) 509-9705   www.aig.com

Worldwide insurance and financial services.

AIG Europe, 120 Fenchurch Street, London EC3M 5 BP, UK

American Life Ins. Co., 55 Mark Lane, London EC3R 7NE, UK

AIR PRODUCTS AND CHEMICALS, INC.

7201 Hamilton Boulevard, Allentown, PA, 18195-1501

Tel: (610) 481-4911   Fax: (610) 481-5900   www.airproducts.com

Mfr. industry gases and related equipment, specialty chemicals, environmental/energy systems.

Air Products PLC, Hershan Place, Molesey Rd., Walton-on-Thames, Surrey KT12 4RZ, UK

AIRSEA PACKING

40-35 22nd Street, Long Island City, NY, 11101

Tel: (718) 937-6800   Fax: (718) 937-9646   www.airseapacking.com

Air and sea freight.

AirSea Packing Group Inc., Air Sea House, Third Cross Road, Twickenham Middlesex TW4 5EB, UK

Tel: 44-20-8893-3303   Fax: 44-20-8893-3068   Contact: Lloyd Brammer

AJAX MAGNETHERMIC CORPORATION

1745 Overland Ave. NE, PO Box 991, Warren, OH, 44482

Tel: (330) 372-8511   Fax: (330) 372-8644   www.ajaxcan.com

Mfr. induction heating and melting equipment.

Ajax Magnethermic Europe Ltd., Holland Rd., Ajax Park, Oxsted, Surrey RH8 9BA, UK

AKAMAI TECHNOLOGIES, INC.

500 Technology Square, Cambridge, MA, 02139

Tel: (617) 250-3000   Fax: (617) 250-3001   www.akamai.com

Develops routing technologies for websites.

Akamai Technologies UK, Bldg. A, Trinity Court, Wokingham Road, Bracknell Berkshire RG42 1PL, UK

Tel: 44-13-4466-8023   Fax: 44-13-4466-8200

AKIN, GUMP, STRAUSS, HAUER & FELD LLP

1333 New Hampshire Ave., N.W., Washington, DC, 20036

Tel: (202) 877-4000   Fax: (202) 887-4288   www.akingump.com

Engaged in international law.

Akin Gump, Strauss, Hauer & Feld LLP, One Angel Court, London EC2R 7HJ, UK

Tel: 44-207-796-9600   Fax: 44-207-796-9610

ALADDIN INDUSTRIES INC.

703 Murfreesboro Road, Nashville, TN, 37210

Tel: (615) 748-3000   Fax: (615) 748-3070   www.aladdinindustries.com

Mfr. vacuum insulated products, insulated food containers and servers.

Aladdin Industries Ltd., 6 Grovelands Business Center, Hemel Hempstead, Hertfordshire HP2 7TE, UK

Tel: 44-1442-235-585   Fax: 44-1442-235-760

ALBANY INTERNATIONAL CORPORATION

1373 Broadway, Albany, NY, 12204

Tel: (518) 445-2200   Fax: (518) 445-2265   www.albint.com

Mfr. broadwoven and engineered fabrics, plastic products, filtration media.

Albany Engineered Systems Europe Ltd., 2 Buckingham Ave., Trading Estate, Slough, Berkshire SL1 4NB, UK

J.K. Industrial Fabrics, Roach Bank Mill, PO Box 28, Pimhole Rd., Bury, Lancashire BL9 7HA, UK

James Kenyon & Son (PMC), Pilsworth Mill, PO Box 35, Bury, Lancashire BL9 8QE, UK

ALBERTO-CULVER COMPANY

2525 Armitage Ave., Melrose Park, IL, 60160

Tel: (708) 450-3000   Fax: (708) 450-3354   www.alberto.com

Mfr./marketing personal care and household brand products.

Alberto-Culver Co. (UK) Ltd., Lime Tree Way, Hampshire Business Park, Basingstoke Hampshire RG24 8WH, UK

Tel: 44-1256-705000   Fax: 44-1256-705001

Ogee Ltd., Unit 4, Area 10, Headley Park Ind. Estate, Headley Rd., Woodley nr. Reading, Berkshire RG5 4SW, UK

ALCOA INC.

Alcoa Center, 201 Isabella Street at 7th Street Bridge, Pittsburgh, PA, 15212-5858

Tel: (412) 553-4545   Fax: (412) 553-4498   www.alcoa.com

World's leading producer of aluminum and alumina; mining, refining, smelting, fabricating and recycling.

Alcoa Extruded Products (UK) Ltd., Swansea, UK

Alcoa Manufacturing (G.B.) Ltd., Swansea, UK

Alcoa Systems (UK) Ltd., Stratford-on-Avon, UK

ALCOA FUJIKURA LTD.

800 Crescent Centre Drive, Ste. 600, Franklin, TN, 37067

Tel: (615) 778-6000   Fax: (615) 778-5927   www.alcoa-fujikura.com

Mfr. optical ground wire, tube cable, fiber optic connectors and automotive wiring harnesses. (JV of Alcoa USA).

AFL Telecommunications, Newcombe Drive, Hawksworth, Swindon SN2 1DZ, UK

Tel: 44-1793-647200 Fax: 44-1793-513198   Contact: Frank M. Larence

ALCONE MARKETING GROUP

4 Studebaker, Irvine, CA, 92618

Tel: (949) 770-4400   Fax: (949) 770-2957   www.alconemarketing.com

Engaged in sales promotion and marketing services.

Alcone Marketing Group, 239 Old Marylebone Road, London NW1 5QT, UK

Tel: 44-20-7298-7001 Fax: 44-20-7298-7075   Contact: Ian Jacob

ALLEGHENY LUDLUM CORPORATION

1000 Six PPG Place, Pittsburgh, PA, 15222

Tel: (412) 394-2805   Fax: (412) 394-2800   www.alleghenyludlum.com

Mfr. steel and alloys.

Allegheny Ludlum UK, Sheffield, UK

Tel: 44-114-2720-081   Fax: 44-114-2731-637

ALLEGHENY TECHNOLOGIES INC.

1000 Six PPG Place, Pittsburgh, PA, 15222

Tel: (412) 394-2800   Fax: (412) 394-2805   www.alleghenytechnologies.com

Diversified mfr. aviation and electronics, specialty metals, industrial and consumer products.

Allegheny Technologies, The Harlequin Centre, Southall Lane, Southall, London UB2 5NH, UK

Allvac Ltd., Atlas House, Attercliffe Road, Sheffield S4 7UY, UK

Titanium International Ltd., Keys House, Granby Avenue, Garrett Green, Birmingham B33 0SP, UK

ALLEGIANCE HEALTHCARE CORPORATION

1430 Waukegan Road, McGaw Park, IL, 60085

Tel: (847) 689-8410   Fax: (847) 578-4437   www.allegiance.net

Manufactures and distributes medical, surgical, respiratory therapy and laboratory products.

Allegiance Healthcare Ltd., Frankland Road, Blagrove Swindon, Wiltshire SN5 8RU, UK

ALLEGIS CORPORATION

1550 Bryant Street, 2nd Fl., San Francisco, CA, 94103

Tel: (415) 551-0600   Fax: (415) 551-0601   www.allegis.com

Mfr. management software.

Allegis Corporation UK, 33 St. James's Square, London SW1Y 4JS, UK

Tel: 44-207-661-9336

ALLEGIS GROUP INC.

6992 Columbia Gateway Dr., Bldg. D, Columbia, MD, 21046

Tel: (410) 540-7000   Fax: (410) 540-7099   www.aerotek.com

Recruitment and placement services.

Allegis Group, Therese House, 2/F, 29-30 Glasshouse Yard, London EC1A 4JN, UK

Allegis Group, 223 Berwick Avenue, Slough Berkshire SL1 4QT, UK

Tel: 44-1753-775566

Allegis Group, 15 Castle Street, High Wycombe, Bucks HP13 6RU, UK

Tel: 44-149-451-2222

ALLEN TELECOM

25101 Chagrin Boulevard, Beachwood, OH, 44122-5619

Tel: (216) 765-5818   Fax: (216) 765-0410   www.allentele.com

Mfr. communications equipment, automotive bodies and parts, electronic components.

Allen Telecom Ltd., 9 Cheapside, London EC2V 6AD, UK

Forem U.K. Ltd, Unit D, Castle Industrial Parkway, Pear Tree Lane, Newbury, Berkshire RG14 2EZ, UK

Tel: 44-163-556-9695   Fax: 44-163-556-9463

ALLEN-BRADLEY COMPANY, INC.

1201 South Second Street, Milwaukee, WI, 53204

Tel: (414) 382-2000   Fax: (414) 382-4444   www.ab.com

Mfr. electrical controls and information devices.

Allen-Bradley Applied Systems, Denbigh Rd., Bletchley, Milton Keynes MK1 1EP, UK

Allen-Bradley Industrial Automation Products, Pitfield, Kiln Farm, Milton Keynes MK11 3DR, UK

OSAI A-B Ltd., Allen-Bradley Motion Control Div., 2 Hatchpond Rd., Poole, Dorset BH17 7LQ, UK

ALLERGAN INC.

2525 Dupont Drive, Irvine, CA, 92612

Tel: (714) 246-4500   Fax: (714) 246-6987   www.allergan.com

Mfr. therapeutic eye care products and skin care pharmaceuticals.

Allergan Ltd., Crown Centre, Coronation Road, High Wycombe, Bucks HP 12 3SH, UK

Tel: 44-1494-444722   Fax: 44-1494-473593

ALLIANCE CAPITAL MANAGEMENT HOLDING LP

1345 Ave. of the Americas, New York, NY, 10105

Tel: (212) 969-1000   Fax: (212) 969-2229   www.alliancecapital.com

Engaged in fund management for large corporations.

Alliance Capital Limited, 1 Mayfair Place, London WIX 6JJ, UK

Tel: 44-20-7470-0100

Sanford C. Bernstein Limited, Div. Alliance Capital, 99 Gresham Street, London EC2V 7NG, UK

Tel: 44-20-7367-7300

ALLIANCE SEMICONDUCTOR CORPORATION

2675 Augustine Drive, Santa Clara, CA, 95054

Tel: (408) 855-4900   Fax: (408) 855-4999   www.alsc.com

Mfr. semi-conductors and related chips.

Alliance Semiconductor European Hdqrts., Bldg. A, Trinity Court, Wokingham Road, Bracknell Berkshire RG42 1PL, UK

Tel: 44-1344-668031   Fax: 44-1344-668250

ALLIED INDUSTRIES WASTE, INC.

15880 N. Greenway-Hayden Loop, Ste. 100, Scottsdale, AZ, 85260

Tel: (480) 627-2700   Fax: (480) 627-2701   www.alliedwaste.com

Engaged in residential, commercial, and industrial waste management.

Allied Waste Ltd., Unit 10B, Mallusk Park, Industrial Estate, Newtownabbey BT36 4FS, UK

ALLTEL CORPORATION

1 Allied Drive, Little Rock, AR, 72202

Tel: (501) 905-8000   Fax: (501) 905-6444   www.alltel.com

Full range outsourcing services.

ALLTEL Systems Ltd., London, UK

ALPHA WIRE COMPANY

711 Lidgerwood Ave., Elizabeth, NJ, 07207

Tel: (908) 925-8000   Fax: (908) 925-6923   www.alphawire.com

Mfr. wire, cable and tubing products.

Alpha Wire International, Sudbury International Business Ctr., Brooklands Close, Windmill Rd., Sunbury-on-Thames Middlesex TW16 7DX, UK

Tel: 44-1932-772-422 Fax: 44-1932-772-433   Contact: Evan Jarrell, Sales Mgr.   Emp: 5

ALTERA CORPORATION

101 Innovation Drive, San Jose, CA, 95134

Tel: (408) 544-7000   Fax: (408) 544-8303   www.altera.com

Mfr. high-density programmable chips for semi-conductor industry.

Altera UK Limited, Holmers Farm Way, High Wycombe, Buckinghamshire HP12 4XF, UK

Tel: 44-1-494-602-000

ALTHEIMER & GRAY

10 South Wacker Drive, Ste. 4000, Chicago, IL, 60606-7482

Tel: (312) 715-4000   Fax: (312) 715-4800   www.altheimer.com

Engaged in international law.

Altheimer & Gray, 7 Bishopsgate, London EC2N 3AR, UK

Tel: 44-20-7786-5700   Fax: 44-20-7786-0000   Contact: Robert C. Bata

ALTIRIS, INC.

588 West 400 South, Lindon, UT, 84042

Tel: (801) 226-8500　　　Fax: (801) 226-8506　　　www.altiris.com

Mfr. IT systems management software.

Altiris Ltd., Grove House Lutyens Close, Chineham Court, Basingstoke RG24 8AG, UK

ALZA CORPORATION

1900 Charleston Road, Mountain View, CA, 94039

Tel: (650) 564-5000　　　Fax: (650) 564-5121　　　www.alza.com

Pharmaceutical firm engaged in drugs transmitted through the skin, including skin patches.

ALZA Limited UK, Cambridge, UK

AMAZON.COM, INC.

1200 12th Ave. South, Ste. 1200, Seattle, WA, 98144-2734

Tel: (206) 266-1000　　　Fax: (206) 266-4206　　　www.amazon.com

Computer site that offers books, CDs, DVDS, videos, toys, tools, and electronics.

Amazon.Com UK, 1-9 The Grove, Slough Berkshire SL1 QP, UK

AMBAC FINANCIAL GROUP

One State Street Plaza, New York, NY, 10004

Tel: (212) 668-0340　　　Fax: (212) 509-9109　　　www.ambac.com

Reinsurance company.

Ambac Insurance UK Ltd., St. Helen's, One Undershaft, London EC3A 8JL, UK

Tel: 44-207-444-7200　　Fax: 44-207-444-7227　　Contact: David Wallis, First VP

AMCOL INTERNATIONAL CORPORATION

1500 West Shure Drive, Ste. 500, Arlington Heights, IL, 60004

Tel: (847) 394-8730　　　Fax: (847) 506-6199　　　www.amcol.com

Mfr. specialty chemicals and environmental bentonite products.

CETCO Europe Ltd., Birch House, Scott Quays, Birkenhead, Merseyside L41 1FB, UK

Tel: 44-151-606-5900　　Fax: 44-151-606-5963　　Contact: Mike Lapinski, Mng. Dir.　　Emp: 64

Chemdal Ltd., East St., Birkenhead L41 1FG, UK

Tel: 44-151-630-5299　　Fax: 44-151-638-5312　　Contact: Gary Castagna, Mng. Dir.　　Emp: 155

Volclay Ltd., Birkenhead Road, Wallasey Merseyside CH44 7BU, UK

Tel: 44-151-638-0967　　Fax: 44-151-638-7000　　Contact: Peter Thorpe, Mng. Dir.　　Emp: 100

AMDOCS LIMITED

1390 Timberlake Manor Pkwy., Chesterfield, MO, 63017

Tel: (314) 212-7000　　　Fax: (314) 212-7500　　　www.amdocs.com

Mfr. telecommunications software.

Amdocs UK, Fleetway house, 25 Farringdon Street, London EC4A 4EP, UK

Tel: 44-207-343-2500

AMERADA HESS CORPORATION

1185 Avenue of the Americas, New York, NY, 10036

Tel: (212) 997-8500　　　Fax: (212) 536-8390　　　www.hess.com

Crude oil and natural gas.

Amerada Hess Ltd., 33 Grosvenor Place, London SW1X 7HY, UK

AMEREX ENERGY

One Sugar Creek Center Blvd., Suite 700, Sugar Land, TX, 77478

Tel: (281) 340-5200　　　Fax: (281) 634-8883　　　www.amerexenergy.com

energy broker, providing voice brokerage, market liquidity, price discovery and data services.

Amerex Petroleum (UK) Ltd., 1 Albemarle Street, London W1X 3HF, UK

Tel: 44-171-629-6668

AMERICAN APPRAISAL ASSOCIATES INC.

411 E. Wisconsin Ave., Ste. 1900, Milwaukee, WI, 53202

Tel: (414) 271-7240   Fax: (414) 271-1041   www.american-appraisal.com

Valuation consulting services.

American Appraisal (UK) Ltd., 65-66 Queen Street, London EC4R 1 EB, UK

Tel: 44-20-7329-1776   Fax: 44-20-7248-1453   Contact: Ian Gough

AMERICAN AXLE & MANUFACTURING HOLDINGS, INC.

1840 Holbrook Ave., Detroit, MI, 48212

Tel: (313) 974-2000   Fax: (313) 974-3090   www.aam.com

Mfr. axles, propeller shafts and chassis components.

Albion Automotive, Lancashire Enterprises Business Park, Centruion Way, Leyland Preston PR5 1TZ, UK

Contact: Michael D. Straney, VP Europe

Farington Components Limited, Div. AAM, Farington Components Ltd., Golden Hill Lane, Leyland, Preston PR5 1UA, UK

Contact: Michael D. Straney, VP Europe

AMERICAN COMPUTER & TELEPHONE, INC.

1603 SE 19th Street, Ste. 112, Edmond, OK, 73013

Tel: (405) 216-8080   Fax: (405) 216-8080   www.amcat.com

Mfr. software.

AMCAT UK, 212 Piccadilly, London W1V 9LD, UK

Tel: 44-207-830-9610

AMERICAN ELECTRIC POWER COMPANY, INC.

1 Riverside Plaza, Columbus, OH, 43215-2373

Tel: (614) 223-1000   Fax: (614) 223-1823   www.aep.com

Electric utility holding company.

CitiPower Services, Forest Gate, Brighton Road, Crawley West Sussex RH11 9 BH, UK

Tel: 44-1293-565888   Fax: 44-1293-657327

AMERICAN EXPRESS COMPANY

90 Hudson Street, Jersey City, NJ, 07302

Tel: (212) 640-2000   Fax: (212) 619-9802   www.americanexpress.com

Engaged in travel, travelers cheques, charge card and financial services.

American Express, 111 Cheapside, London EC2V 6DT, UK

Tel: 44-207-3670101

American Express Foreign Exchange Service, 4 Queen Street, Oxford OX1 1EJ, UK

Tel: 44-1865-207-101

American Express Services Europe Ltd., 78 Brompton Rd., Knightsbridge, London, UK, UKSW3 1ER

Tel: 44-207-584-6482

AMERICAN GREETINGS CORPORATION

One American Road, Cleveland, OH, 44144-2398

Tel: (216) 252-7300   Fax: (216) 252-6777   www.amgreetings.com

Mfr./distributor greeting cards (American Greetings Forget Me Not and Gibson), gift wrappings, tags, seals, ribbons and party goods.

Carlton Cards Ltd., Mill St East, Dewsbury, W. Yorkshire WF12 9AW, UK

U.K. Greetings Ltd., London, UK

AMERICAN LOCKER GROUP INC.

608 Allen Street, Jamestown, NY, 14701-3966

Tel: (716) 664-9600   Fax: (716) 483-2822   www.americanlocker.com

Mfr. coin-operated locks and office furniture.

W.B. Bawn & Co. Ltd., Northern Way, Mildenhall Road, Bury St. Edmunds, Suffolk IP32 6NH, UK

Tel: 44-1-284-727617

AMERICAN MANAGEMENT SYSTEMS, INC. (AMS)

4050 Legato Road, 10th Fl., Fairfax, VA, 22033

Tel: (703) 267-8000   Fax: (703) 267-5073   www.amsinc.com

Provides integrated IT solutions, outsourcing, and transformation services.

AMS Management Systems UK Ltd., 51-55 Gresham St., 2nd Fl., London EC2V 7JH, UK

Tel: 44-207-710-6600   Fax: 44-207-710-6700   Contact: David Ogram, Mng. Dir.   Emp: 240

AMERICAN MEDICAL SYSTEMS HOLDING, INC.

10700 Bren Road West, Minnetonka, MN, 55343

Tel: (952) 933-4666   Fax: (952) 930-6157   www.visitams.com

Mfr. urological devices.

American Medical Systems U.K., 9 Ironbridge House, 2-4 Windmill Lane, Hanwell, Middlesex UB2 4NJ, UK

Tel: 44-208-606-9955   Contact: Caroline Willis

AMERICAN METER COMPANY

300 Welsh Road, Bldg. 1, Horsham, PA, 19044-2234

Tel: (215) 830-1800   Fax: (215) 830-1890   www.americanmeter.com

Mfr. measure and control services for natural gas industry.

Intl. Gas Apparatus Ltd., Glebeland Rd., Yorktown Industrial Estate, Camberley, Surrey GU1 53X, UK

AMERICAN OPTICAL LENS CO.

PO Box 8020, Southbridge, MA, 01550

Tel: (508) 764-5000   Fax: (508) 764-5010   www.alolens.com

Mfr. ophthalmic lenses and frames, custom molded products, specialty lenses.

UK Optical Ltd., 76-77 Capitol Industrial Park, Capitol Way, London NW9 0EW, UK

AMERICAN RE-INSURANCE COMPANY

555 College Road East, Princeton, NJ, 08543

Tel: (609) 243-4200   Fax: (609) 243-4257   www.amre.com

Reinsurance.

American Re-Insurance Co. (UK) Ltd., 52/54 Grace Church St., London EC3V 0EH, UK

AMERICAN SAFETY RAZOR COMPANY

240 Cedar Knolls Rd., Ste. 401, Cedar Knolls, NJ, 07927

Tel: (973) 753-3000   Fax: (973) 326-9004   www.asrco.com

Mfr. private-label and branded shaving razors and blades and cotton swabs.

Personna International UK Ltd., Unite 11, Ratcher Wa, Crown Farm Ind. Estate, Forest Town Mansfield, Nottinghamshire NG19 OFS, UK

AMERICAN SOFTWARE, INC.

470 East Paces Ferry Road, NE, Atlanta, GA, 30305

Tel: (404) 261-4381   Fax: (404) 264-5514   www.amsoftware.com

Mfr./sales of financial control software and systems.

American Software, St. Georges Business Centre, Locke King Road, Weybridge Surry KY13 OTS, UK

Tel: 44-19-328-55554   Fax: 44-19-328-54563

AMERICAN STANDARD COMPANIES, INC.

One Centennial Avenue, Piscataway, NJ, 08855-6820

Tel: (732) 980-3000   Fax: (732) 980-6118   www.americanstandard.com

Mfr. automotive, plumbing, heating, air conditioning products and medical diagnostics systems.

DiaSorin Ltd., Charles House, Toutley Road, Wokingham Berkshire RG41 1QN, UK

Ideal Standard Ltd., PO Box 60, National Ave., Hull HU5 4JE, UK

AMERICAN TECHNICAL CERAMICS CORPORATION

17 Stepar Place, Huntington Station, NY, 11746

Tel: (631) 622-4700   Fax: (631) 622-4748   www.alceramics.com

Mfr. ceramic porcelain capacitors and ceramic-based electronic products.

Phase Components Ltd., Unit 5, Genesis Centre Redkiln Way, Horsham, Sussex RH13 5QH, UK

Tel: 44-1403-241862   Fax: 44-1403-241858

AMERICAN VANGUARD CORPORATION

4695 MacArthur Ct., Newport Beach, CA, 92660

Tel: (949) 260-1200   Fax: (949) 260-1201   www.amvao-chemical.com

Mfr. specialty chemicals.

Amvac Chemical UK Limited, Surrey Technology Centre, 40 Occam Road, Guildford, Surrey GU2 5YG, UK

Tel: 44-1483-295-780   Fax: 44-1483-573-704

AMERINDO INVESTMENT ADVISORS INC.

1 Embarcadero Center, Ste. 2300, San Francisco, CA, 94111

Tel: (415) 362-0292   Fax: (415) 362-0533   www.amerindo.com

Engaged in fund management.

Amerindo International, 43 Upper Grosvenor Street, London WIX 9PG, UK

Tel: 44-207-629-2349

AMES TEXTILE CORPORATION

710 Chelmsford Street, Lowell, MA, 01851

Tel: (978) 458-3321   Fax: (978) 441-9808   www.amestextile.com

Mfr. textile products.

Ames Mills Victoria Mill, Church St., Westhoughton, Bolton, Lancaster BL5 3QP, UK

AMETEK INC.

37 N. Valley Road, PO Box 1764, Paoli, PA, 19301-0801

Tel: (610) 647-2121   Fax: (610) 296-3412   www.ametek.com

Mfr. instruments, electric motors and engineered materials.

AMETEK Precision Instruments (UK) Ltd., 12 Barnes Wallis Road, Segensworth East, Fareham Hampshire P015 5TT, UK

Tel: 44-1489-574221   Fax: 44-1489-885118

AMETEK Precision Instruments (UK) Ltd., Unit 20 Ridgeway, Donibristle Industrial Estate, Dunfermline, Fife PO15 5TT, UK

Tel: 44-1383-825-630   Fax: 44-1383-825-715

AMETEK POWER INSTRUMENTS, INC.

255 North Union Street, Rochester, NY, 14605

Tel: (716) 263-7700   Fax: (716) 262-4777   www.rochester.com

Mfr. transient recorders, microprocessor-based relays, calibrators, annunciators, and signal conditioners.

AMETEK Power Instruments, 64 Appledore Avenue, Bexleyheath, Kent DA7 6QH, UK

Contact: Sean Gardener

AMTEK Power Instruments, 9 Laurel Close, Corfe Mullen, Wimborne, Dorset BH21 3TD, UK

Tel: 44-1202-698833   Contact: Brian Lincoln

AMGEN INC.

One Amgen Center Drive, Thousand Oaks, CA, 91320-1799

Tel: (805) 447-1000   Fax: (805) 499-2694   www.amgen.com

Biotechnology research and pharmaceuticals.

Amgen Limited, 240 Cambridge Science Park, Milton Road, Cambridge CB4 4WD, UK

Tel: 44-1223-420-305

AMPCO METAL, INC.

1745 S. 38th Street, PO Box 2004, Milwaukee, WI, 53201

Tel: (414) 645-3750   Fax: (414) 645-3225   www.ampcometal.com

Mfr./distributor/sale cast and wrought copper-based alloys.

Ampco Metal Ltd., 17 Binns Close off Torington Ave., Coventry CV4 9TB, UK

AMPEX CORPORATION

1228 Douglas Avenue, Redwood City, CA, 94063-3199

Tel: (650) 367-2011   Fax: (650) 367-4669   www.ampex.com

Mfr. extremely high-performance digital data storage, data retrieval and image processing systems for a broad range of corporate scientific and government applications.

Ampex Great Britain Ltd., Ampex House Beechwood, Chineham Business Park, Chineham, Basingstoke RG24 8WA, UK

Tel: 44-1256-814410   Fax: 44-1256-814456   Contact: Chris Fitton   Emp: 15

AMPHENOL CORPORATION

358 Hall Ave., Wallingford, CT, 06492-7530

Tel: (203) 265-8900   Fax: (203) 265-8793   www.amphenol.com

Mfr. electronic interconnect penetrate systems and assemblies.

Amphenol Ltd., Thanet Way, Whitstable, Kent CT5 3JF, UK

Tel: 44-1227-773-200

AMR CORPORATION (AMERICAN AIRLINES)

4333 Amon Carter Boulevard, Ft. Worth, TX, 76155

Tel: (817) 963-1234   Fax: (817) 967-9641   www.amrcorp.com

Air transport services.

American Airlines Inc., 7 Albemarle St., London W1X 3AF, UK

American Airlines Inc., Rm. 6, Level 7, Manchester Airport, Cheshire M22 5PA, UK

AMSTED INDUSTRIES INC.

205 North Michigan Ave., Chicago, IL, 60601

Tel: (312) 645-1700   Fax: (312) 819-8523   www.amsted.com

Privately-held, diversified manufacturer of products for the construction and building markets, general industry and the railroads.

Baltimore Aircoil Ltd., Princewood Rd., Earlstrees Industrial Estate, Corby Northants NN17-4AP, UK

Tel: 44-1536-200-312   Fax: 44-1536-265-793   Contact: Robert I. Macleod-Smith, Mng. Dir.   Emp: 100

AMTROL INC.

1400 Division Road, West Warwick, RI, 02893

Tel: (401) 884-6300   Fax: (401) 885-2567   www.amtrol.com

Mfr. water heaters and controls.

AMX UK Ltd., Auster Road, Clifton Moor, York, North Yorkshire YO30 4GD, UK

Tel: 44-1904-343100   Contact: Rupert Powell

AMWAY CORPORATION

7575 Fulton Street East, Ada, MI, 49355-0001

Tel: (616) 787-6000   Fax: (616) 787-6177   www.amway.com

Mfr./sale home care, personal care, nutrition and houseware products.

Amway (Europe) Ltd., Bank House, 171 Midsummer Blvd., Central Milton Keynes MK9 1ED, UK

Amway (UK) Ltd., Snowdon Dr., Winterhill, Milton Keynes MK6 1AR, UK

ANACOMP INC.

12365 Crosthwaite Circle, Poway, CA, 92064

Tel: (858) 679-9797   Fax: (858) 748-9482   www.anacomp.com

Engaged in electronic information management services and products.

Anacomp Ltd., Mulberry Business Park, Fishponds Road, Wokingham, Berkshire RG41 2GY, UK

ANADARKO PETROLEUM CORPORATION

17001 Northchase Drive, Houston, TX, 77060

Tel: (281) 875-1101   Fax: (281) 874-3316   www.anadarko.com

Exploration, development, production and marketing of oil and gas.

Anadarko Petroleum Corp., PO Box 576, 1 Harefield Road, Uxbridge Middlesex, London UB8 1YH, UK

Tel: 44-1895-209-400   Fax: 44-1895-209-444

ANADIGICS, INC.

35 Technology Drive, Warren, NJ, 07059

Tel: (908) 668-5000   Fax: (908) 668-5068   www.anadigics.com

Mfr. radio-frequency, integrated circuits for wireless and fiber optic communications.

ANADIGICS UK Limited, Dimon Place, Riverside Way, Camberley Surrey GU15 3YF, UK

Tel: 44-1276-63167

ANALOG DEVICES INC.

1 Technology Way, Norwood, MA, 02062

Tel: (781) 329-4700   Fax: (781) 326-8703   www.analog.com

Mfr. integrated circuits and related devices.

Analog Devices, 30 Tower View King's Hill, West Malling, Kent ME19 4AD, UK

Analog Devices Ltd., Station Ave., Walton-on-Thames, Surrey KT12 1PF, UK

Analog Devices Ltd., Rothwell House, Pembroke Road, Newbury RG14 1BX, England

ANALOGIC CORPORATION

8 Centennial Drive, Peabody, MA, 01960

Tel: (978) 977-3000   Fax: (978) 977-6811   www.analogic.com

Design/mfr. precision measure, signal processing and imaging equipment for medical, scientific, industry and communications.

Analogic Ltd., Ascot House, Doncastle Rd., Bracknell, Berkshire RG12 4PE, UK

SKY Computers Ltd., Div. Analogic, Ascot House, Doncastle Rd., Bracknell, Berkshire RG12 4PE, UK

ANALYSTS INTERNATIONAL CORPORATION

3601 West 76th Street, Minneapolis, MN, 55435

Tel: (612) 835-5900   Fax: (612) 897-4555   www.analysts.com

Provides computer software-related services, including systems analysis, design and programming.

Analysts International Corporation, Lincoln House The Paddocks, Cherry Hinton Road, Cambridge CB1 8DH, UK

Tel: 44-1223-500055   Fax: 44-1223-576646

ANAREN MICROWAVE INC.

6635 Kirkville Road, East Syracuse, NY, 13057

Tel: (315) 432-8909   Fax: (315) 432-9121   www.anaren.com

Mfr./services microwave components.

Anaren Microwave (Europe) Inc., 12 Somerset House, Suite 16 & 17, Hussar Court, Waterlooville, Hampshire PO7 7SG, UK

Tel: 44-2392-232392   Fax: 44-2392-251369   Contact: Rob Orford

ANC RENTAL CORPORATION

200 S. Andrews Ave., Ft. Lauderdale, FL, 33301

Tel: (954) 320-4000   Fax: (954) 320-4077   www.ancrental.com

Engaged in car rental services, including National Car Rental and Alamo Rent A Car.

National Car Rental, Davis House, Wilton Rd., London SWI, UK

ANCHOR HOCKING CORPORATION

519 Pierce Ave., PO Box 600, Lancaster, OH, 43130-0600

Tel: (740) 687-2111   Fax: (740) 687-2543   www.anchorhocking.com

Mfr. glassware and dinnerware plastic products.

Anchor Hocking Corp. UK, 271 High St., Berkhamsted, Hertfordshire HP4 1AA, UK

ANDERSEN

33 West Monroe Street, Chicago, IL, 60603

Tel: (312) 580-0033   Fax: (312) 507-6748   www.andersen.com

*Accounting and audit, tax and management consulting services. **Firm under worldwide reorganization; new data unavailable for this edition.*

Andersen Worldwide, One Victoria Square, Birmingham B1 1BD, UK

Tel: 44-121-233-2101   Fax: 44-121-233-2954

Andersen Worldwide, Broad Quay House, Broad Quay, Bristol BS1 4DJ, UK

Tel: 44-117-927-7436   Fax: 44-117-927-7507

Andersen Worldwide, Betjeman House, 104 Hills Rd., Cambridge CB2 1LH, UK
Tel: 44-1223-353906   Fax: 44-1223-366287

Andersen Worldwide, Pearl Assurance House, 7 New Bridge St., Newcastle-upon-Tyne NE1 8BQ, UK
Tel: 44-191-261-2481

Andersen Worldwide, One City Square, Leeds LS1 2AL, UK
Tel: 44-113-207-7000   Fax: 44-113-245-9240

Andersen Worldwide, Fothergill House, 16 King St., Nottingham NG1 2AS, UK
Tel: 44-115-935-3900   Fax: 44-115-935-3949

Andersen/Binder Hamlyn, Bank House, 9 Charlotte St., London EC4M 7BH, UK
Tel: 44-161-224-2121   Fax: 44-161-228-1421

Andersen/Garretts, 1 Surrey St., London WC2R 2PS, UK
Tel: 44-207-438-3000

Binder Hamlyn, Bank House, 9 Charlotte St., Manchester M1 4EU, UK

Garrett & Co., Abbots House, Abbey St., Reading Berkshire RG1 3BD, UK

ANDREW CORPORATION

10500 West 153rd Street, Orland Park, IL, 60462
Tel: (708) 349-3300   Fax: (708) 349-5410   www.andrew.com

Designer, manufacturer, and supplier of communications equipment, services, and systems.

Andrew Ltd., Ilex Bldg., Mulberry Business Park, Fishponds Rd., Wokingham Berkshire RG41 2GY, UK
Tel: 44-118-977-6886   Fax: 44-118-979-4005

ANDREWS & KURTH LLP

600 Travis Street, Ste. 4200, Houston, TX, 77002
Tel: (713) 220-4200   Fax: (713) 220-4285   www.andrewskurth.com

Engaged in international law.

Andrews & Kurth LLP, Level 16, City Tower, 40 Basinghall Street, London EC2V 5DE, UK
Tel: 44-207-382-0550   Fax: 44-207-614-0012

ANGELICA CORPORATION

424 South Woods Mill Road, Ste. 300, Chesterfield, MO, 63017-3406
Tel: (314) 854-3800   Fax: (314) 854-3890   www.angelica-corp.com

Mfr. marketing and sales of uniforms.

Angelica Intl. Ltd., Ashton Rd., Golborne, Warrington WA3 3UL, UK

ANH REFRACTORIES COMPANY

Cherrington Corporate Center, 400 Fairway Drive, Moon Township, PA, 15108
Tel: (412) 375-6600   Fax: (412) 375-6421   www.hwr.com

Mfr. refractory products and services to the iron and steel, cement and lime, energy, chemicals, nonferrous metals and environmental technology industries.

Harbison Walker Refractories Ltd., Dock Rd. South, Bromborough, Wirral, Merseyside L62 4SP, UK

ANHEUSER-BUSCH INTERNATIONAL INC.

One Busch Place, St. Louis, MO, 63118-1852
Tel: (314) 577-2000   Fax: (314) 577-2900   www.anheuser-busch.com

Malt production, aluminum beverage containers, rice milling, real estate development, metalized and paper label printing, railcar repair and theme-park facilities.

Anheuser-Busch Europe Inc., Radgemore House, Henley-on-Thames, Oxon RG9 4NP, UK

Anheuser-Bush European Trade Ltd., London, UK

Stag Brewery, West London, UK

ANIXTER INTERNATIONAL INC..

4711 Golf Road, Skokie, IL, 60076
Tel: (847) 677-2600   Fax: (847) 677-8557   www.anixter.com

Distributor wiring systems/products for voice, video, data and power applications.

Anixter Europe, 1 York Road, Uxbridge-Middlesex UR8 1RN, UK
Tel: 44-1895-818181

Anixter U.K., Veritas House, 125 Finsbury Pavement, London EC2A 1NQ, UK
Tel: 44-207-638-6380   Fax: 44-207-638-6387

Anixter U.K., Howmoss Drive, Kirkhill Ind Est., Dyce Aberdeen AB21 OGL, UK
Tel: 44-121-472-2255   Fax: 44-122-472-2290

Anixter U.K., 26 The Office Village, 3rd Fl., Exchange Quay Salford, Manchester M5 3EQ, UK

Anixter U.K., Concourse House, Ste 31, Dewsbury Road, Leeds LS11 7DF, UK

Anixter U.K., Saltley Trading Estate, Unit 119, Saltley Birmingham, West Midlands B8 1BL, UK

ANSELL HEALTHCARE INCORPORATED
200 Schulz Drive, Red Bank, NJ, 07701
Tel: (732) 345-5400   Fax: (732) 219-5114   www.ansellhealthcare.com
Mfr. industrial gloves, rubber and plastic products, protective clothing.

Ansell Healthcare UK, Ansell House, 119 Ewell Road, Surbiton Surrey KT6 6AL, UK
Tel: 44-181-481-1800

ANSWERTHINK, INC.
1001 Brickell Bay Drive, Ste. 3000, Miami, FL, 33131
Tel: (305) 375-8005   Fax: (305) 379-8810   www.answerthink.com
Engaged in e-commerce strategies.

Answerthink, Inc., Condor House, 5/F, 5-12 St. Paul's Churchyard, London EC4M 8BE, UK

ANSYS TECHNOLOGIES, INC.
25200 Commercentre Drive, Lake Forest, CA, 92630-8810
Tel: (949) 770-9381   Fax: (949) 770-0863   www.ansysinc.com
Develops, manufactures, and markets leading edge technology disposable medical diagnostic products.

ANSYS Technologies, Ltd., Old Court, 311A Chase Road, Southgate N14 6JS,, UK

ANSYS, INC.
275 Technology Drive, Canonsburg, PA, 15317
Tel: (724) 746-3304   Fax: (724) 514-9494   www.ansys.com
Mfr. CAD and CAE software.

ANSYS Ltd., Waterloo House, 1/F, Riseley Business Park, Riseley BER RG7 1QE, UK
Tel: 44-118-9881-456   Contact: David Brooks

ANTEON INTERNATIONAL CORPORATION
3211 Jermantown Road, Ste. 700, Fairfax, VA, 22030-2801
Tel: (703) 246-0200   Fax: (703) 246-0294   www.anteon.com
Engaged in information technology systems engineering.

Anteon International Corporation, Anteon House, Newark Road, Peterborough Cambs PE1 5FL, UK
Tel: 44-1733-296866

AOL TIME WARNER
75 Rockefeller Plaza, New York, NY, 10019
Tel: (212) 484-8000   Fax: (212) 275-3046   www.aoltimewarner.com
Engaged in media and communications; provides internet services, communications, publishing and entertainment.

MacDonald & Co. (Publishers) Ltd., Greater London House, Hampstead Rd., London NW1 7QX, UK

Time Warner Books UK, Brettenham House, Lancaster Place, London WC2E 7EN, UK
Contact: David Young

Time-Life International Ltd., Time & Life Bldg., New Bond St., London, UK

AON CORPORATION
200 East Randolph, Chicago, IL, 60601
Tel: (312) 381-1000   Fax: (312) 381-6032   www.aon.com
Insurance brokers worldwide; underwrites accident and health insurance, specialty and professional insurance; and provides risk management consultation.

AON Risk Services Ltd. - Head UK Office, Lloyds Chambers 1, Portsoken St., London E1 8DF, UK
Tel: 44-207-680-4000   Fax: 44-207-601-4007   Contact: Nick Maher

APAR INFOTECH CORPORATION

160 Technology Drive, Canonsburg, PA, 15317

Tel: (724) 745-7100   Fax: (724) 745-6494   www.apar.com

Provides software development.

Apar Infotech Limited, Berkshire House 11/F, Queen's Street, Maidenhead SL6 1NF, UK

Tel: 44-16288-17000   Fax: 44-16288-17001

API MOTION INC.

45 Hazelwood Dr., Amherst, NY, 14228

Tel: (716) 691-9100   Fax: (716) 691-9181   www.apimotion.com

Engaged in motion control solutions using motors and drives, motor gear heads, resolver and encoder feedback devices.

API Motion UK Ltd., Headlands Bus. Park, Salisbury Rd., Ringwood, Hampshire BH24 3PB, UK

APL LOGISTICS

1111 Broadway, Oakland, CA, 94607

Tel: (510) 272-8000   Fax: (510) 272-7421   www.apllogistics.com

Provides ocean container shipping and logistics services.

APL UK, Eagle Court, 9 Vine Street, Uxbridge Middlesex UB8 1QE, UK

Tel: 44-1895-202600   Fax: 44-1895-202606   Contact: Thomas Poulsen,

APOGENT TECHNOLOGIES INC.

48 Congress Street, Portsmouth, NH, 03801

Tel: (603) 433-6131   Fax: (603) 431-0860   www.apogent.com

Design, mfr. & sell products for laboratories, clinical research, industrial markets & analytical products.

Electrothermal Engineering Ltd., 419 Sutton Road, Southend-onSea, Essex SS2 5PH, UK

Tel: 44-12702-612211   Fax: 44-1702-619888

Genevac Limited, Ipswich, UK

Kerr UK Ltd., 27 Coningsby Rd., Bretton, Peterborough, Cambridgeshire PE3 8SB, UK

Nalge (UK) Ltd., Foxwood Ct., Rotherwas Industrial Estate, Hereford HR2 6JQ, UK

APPLE COMPUTER, INC.

One Infinite Loop, Cupertino, CA, 95014

Tel: (408) 996-1010   Fax: (408) 974-2113   www.apple.com

Personal computers, peripherals and software.

Apple Computer (UK) Ltd., Eastman Way, Helem, Hempstead, Hertfordshire HP2 7HQ, UK

APPLERA CORPORATION

301 Merritt 7, Norwalk, CT, 06851

Tel: (203) 840-2000   Fax: (203) 840-2312   www.applera.com

Leading supplier of systems for life science research and related applications.

Applied Biosystems UK, 7 Kingsland Grange, Woolston Warrington, Cheshire WA1 7SR, UK

Tel: 44-1925-825-650

APPLIED MATERIALS, INC.

3050 Bowers Ave., Santa Clara, CA, 95054-3299

Tel: (408) 727-5555   Fax: (408) 727-9943   www.appliedmaterials.com

Supplies manufacturing systems and services to the semiconductor industry.

Applied Materials UK Ltd., European Technical Centre, Coble Dene Rd., Royal Quays North Shields, Tyne & Wear NE29 6AZ, UK

Tel: 44-191-293-6000   Fax: 44-191-293-6024

Applied Materials, Ltd., Implant Division, Foundry Lane, Horsham, West Sussex RH13 5PY, UK

Tel: 44-1403-222345   Fax: 44-1403-222353

APPLIX, INC.

289 Turnpike Rd., Westboro, MA, 01581

Tel: (508) 870-0300   Fax: (508) 366-4873   www.applix.com

Engaged in business productivity application software.

APPLIX, Inc., 48 Leicester Square, London WC2H 7LT, UK

Tel: 44-207-968-4300

APRISMA MANAGEMENT TECHNOLOGIES, INC.

273 Corporate Drive, Portsmouth, NH, 03801

Tel: (603) 334-2100   Fax: (603) 334-2784   www.aprisma.com

Mfr. software.

Aprisma EMEA Headquarters, Newbury Business Park, London Road, Newbury, Berkshire RG14 2PZ, UK

APW, INC.

N22 W23685 Ridgeview Parkway West, Waukesha, WI, 53188-1013

Tel: (262) 523-7600   Fax: (262) 523-7624   www.apw1.com

Mfr. hi-pressure tools, vibration control products, consumables, technical furniture and enclosures.

APW UK, Flanders Road, Hedge End, Southampton Hampshire SO30 2LG, UK

APW-WRIGHT LINE INC.

160 Gold Star Blvd., Worcester, MA, 01606

Tel: (508) 852-4300   Fax: (508) 853-8904   www.wrightline.com

Provides technical environment solutions for productive, space-effective, and reconfigurable work environments.

APW-Wright Line Inc., Ashley Road, Uxbridge, Middlesex UB8 2SQ, UK

AQUENT

711 Boylston Street, Boston, MA, 02116

Tel: (617) 535-5000   Fax: (617) 535-6001   www.aquent.com

Engaged in temporary, specialized employment.

AQUENT, Oxford Street, 3/F, Manchester M1 5JE, UK

AQUENT, 1 Bedford Street, London WC2E 9HD, UK

Contact: Steve Hutson

ARAMARK CORPORATION

1101 Market Street, Philadelphia, PA, 19107-2988

Tel: (215) 238-3000   Fax: (215) 238-3333   www.aramark.com

Provides managed services for food, work and safety clothing, education, recreation and facilities.

ARAMARK UK Ltd., Aramark House, Honey End Lane, Tilehurst Reading, Berkshire RG3 RQ1, UK

Tel: 44-118-9596-761   Fax: 44-118-9580-039   Contact: William McCall, Mng. Dir.

ARAMARK UK Ltd., Millbank Tower, 21-24 Millbank, London SW1P 4QP, UK

Tel: 44-20-7963-0000   Fax: 44-20-7963-0500

ARBORTEXT, INC.

1000 Victors Way, Ann Arbor, MI, 48108

Tel: (734) 997-0200   Fax: (734) 997-0201   www.arbortext.com

Mfr. publishing software.

Arbortext UK, 72 Hammersmith Road, London W14 8TH, UK

Tel: 44-207-559-3475   Contact: Nathan Birtle

ARCHER DANIELS MIDLAND COMPANY (ADM)

4666 Faries Parkway, Decatur, IL, 62526

Tel: (217) 424-5200   Fax: (217) 424-6196   www.admworld.com

Grain processing: flours, grains, oils and flax fiber.

British Arkady Co. Ltd., Old Trafford, Manchester M16 ONJ, UK

ARIBA, INC.

1565 Charleston Rd., Mountain View, CA, 94043

Tel: (650) 930-6200   Fax: (650) 930-6300   www.ariba.com

Mfr. software.

Ariba UK Ltd., 5 New Square, Bedfont Lakes Feltham, Middlesex TW14 H8A, UK

Tel: 44-20-8751-6700

ARMOR HOLDINGS, INC.

1400 Marsh Landing Parkway, Ste. 112, Jacksonville, FL, 32250

Tel: (904) 741-5400   Fax: (904) 741-5403   www.armorholdings.com

Holding company engaged in security products and services.

Armor Group UK, 25 Buckingham Gate, London SW1E 6LD, UK

Tel: 44-20-7808-5800

ARMSTRONG HOLDINGS, INC.

2500 Columbia Avenue, Lancaster, PA, 17604-3001

Tel: (717) 397-0611   Fax: (717) 396-2787   www.armstrong.com

Mfr. and marketing interior furnishings and specialty products for building, auto and textile industry.

Armstrong World Industries Ltd., Fleck Way, Teesside Industrial Estate Thornaby, Stockton-on-Tees, Cleveland TS17 9JT, UK

Tel: 44-1642-760679

ARNOLD & PORTER

555 12th Street, N.W., Washington, DC, 20004-1202

Tel: (202) 942-5000   Fax: (202) 942-5999   www.arnoldporter.com

International law firm.

Arnold & Porter, Tower 42, 25 Buclersbury, London EC4NV BDA, UK

Tel: 44-207-329-4329   Fax: 44-207-653-9829   Contact: James D. Dinnage

ARQULE, INC.

19 Presidential Way, Woburn, MA, 01801-5140

Tel: (781) 994-0300   Fax: (781) 376-6019   www.arqule.com

Engaged in drug development.

Arqule UK Ltd., 127 Cambridge Science Park, Milton Road, Cambridge CB4 0GD, UK

Tel: 44-1223-424-825

ARRIS GROUP, INC.

11450 Technology Circle, Duluth, GA, 30097

Tel: (678) 473-2000   Fax: (678) 473-8182   www.arrisi.com

Mfr. communications equipment.

ARRIS International, PO Box 336, Feltham, Middlesex TW13 6WJ, UK

ARROW ELECTRONICS INC.

25 Hub Drive, Melville, NY, 11747

Tel: (516) 391-1300   Fax: (516) 391-1640   www.arrow.com

Distributor of electronic components and computer products.

Arrow Alliance, St. Martins Business Centre, Cambridge Road, Bedford MK41 OLF, UK

Arrow Electronics (UK) Ltd., St. Martins Way, Cambridge Rd., Bedford MK4 2LF, UK

Tel: 44-1234-791-444   Fax: 44-1234-791-491   Contact: Harriet Green, Mng. Dir.

ART TECHNOLOGY GROUP, INC.

25 First Street, Cambridge, MA, 02141

Tel: (617) 386-1000   Fax: (617) 386-1111   www.atg.com

Mfr. application service software.

Art Technology Group Europe, Apex Plaza, Forbury Road, Reading RG1 1AX, UK

Tel: 44-118-956-5000

ARVIN MERITOR INC

2135 W. Maple Rd., Troy, MI, 48084-7186

Tel: (248) 435-1000   Fax: (248) 435-1393   www.arvinmeritor.com

Mfr. of automotive exhaust systems and ride control products, axles and power-steering pumps.

ArvinMeritor Commercial Vehicle Systems, Unit 21, Suttons Park Avenue, Suttons Business, Reading Berkshire RG6 1LA, UK

Tel: 44-118-935-9126   Fax: 44-118-935-9138   Contact: James Randall

ASCENTIAL SOFTWARE CORPORATION

50 Washington Street, Westboro, MA, 01581

Tel: (508) 366-3888   Fax: (508) 366-3669   www.ascentialsoftware.com

Mfr. software.

Ascential Software, 7 New Square, Bedfont lakes, Feltham Middlesex TW14 8HA, UK

Tel: 44-208-818-0700

ASERA INC.

600 Clipper Drive, Ste. 100, Belmont, CA, 94002

Tel: (650) 769-1200   Fax: (650) 769-1234   www.asera.com

Engaged in eBusiness solutions.

Asera Limited, Brook House, 229/243 Shepherd's Bush Road, Hammersmith, London W6 7AN, UK

Tel: 44-208-237-6350

ASG (ALLEN SYSTEMS GROUP)

1333 Third Avenue South, Naples, FL, 34102

Tel: (941) 435-2200   Fax: (941) 263-3692   www.asg.com

Mainframe computer software, specializing in OnMark 2000 software.

ASG UK, Ziggurat Grosvenor Road, St. Albans L1 3HW, UK

Tel: 44-1727-736-300

ASHLAND OIL INC.

50 E. RiverCenter Blvd., Box 391, Covington, KY, 41012-0391

Tel: (859) 815-3333   Fax: (859) 815-5053   www.ashland.com

Petroleum exploration, refining and transportation; mfr. chemicals, oils and lubricants.

Ashland International Ltd., 110 Jermyn Street, London SW1Y 6EE, UK

Tel: 44-171-930-1040

Droitwich Ashland UK, Vale Industrial Estate, Kidderminster, Kidderminster, Worcestershire DY11 7QP, UK

Contact: Mike Woodward

ASHWORTH BROTHERS INC.

450 Armour Dale, Winchester, VA, 22601

Tel: (540) 662-3494   Fax: (540) 662-3150   www.ashworth.com

Mfr. of metal, plastic and hybrid process conveyor belting, engineering services and conveyor systems.

Ashworth Europe Ltd., Bldg. 19, First Ave., The Pensnett Estate, Kingswinford, West Midlands DY6 7TR, UK

Tel: 44-1384-355000

ASPECT COMMUNICATIONS CORPORATION

1310 Ridder Park Dr., San Jose, CA, 95131-2312

Tel: (408) 325-2200   Fax: (408) 325-2260   www.aspect.com

Mfr. software and related equipment.

Aspect UK, 2 The Square, Stockley Park, Uxbridge Middlesex UB11 1AD, UK

Tel: 44-20-8589-1000

Aspect UK, 11 The Parks, Haydock, Newton-Le Willows Merseyside WA12 OJQ, UK

ASPEN TECHNOLOGY, INC.

10 Canal Park, Cambridge, MA, 02141

Tel: (617) 949-1000   Fax: (617) 949-1030   www.aspentec.com

Mfr. software for chemists and refineries.

AspenTech UK Ltd., 4 Churchgates, The Wilderness, Berkhamsted Herts HP4 2UB, UK

AspenTech UK Ltd., Waterway House, The Ham, Brentford Middlesex, UK

ASPEON, INC.

17891 Cartwright Road, Irvine, CA, 92514-6216

Tel: (949) 440-8000   Fax: (949) 440-8087   www.aspeon.com

Mfr. restaurant, point-of-sale computers.

Aspeon Europe, Javelin House, Clayton Road, Birchwood, Warrington Cheshire WA3 6RP, UK

ASSET ALLIANCE CORPORATION

800 Third Avenue, New York, NY, 10022

Tel: (212) 207-8786   Fax: (212) 207-8785   www.assetalliance.com

Holding company engaged in investment management firms.

Asset Alliance UK, 16 Charles Street, Mayfair, London W13 5DS, UK

Tel: 44-207-659-2900   Fax: 44-207-659-2901   Contact: Michael W. Azien

ASSOCIATED MERCHANDISING CORPORATION

500 Seventh Ave., 2nd Fl., New York, NY, 10018

Tel: (212) 819-6600   Fax: (212) 819-6701   www.theamc.com

Retail service organization; apparel, shoes and accessories.

Associated Merchandising Corp., 32 Wigmore St., London W1H 0DB, UK

ASSOCIATED PRESS INC.

50 Rockefeller Plaza, New York, NY, 10020-1605

Tel: (212) 621-1500   Fax: (212) 621-5447   www.ap.com

News gathering agency.

The Associated Press Ltd., 12 Norwich St., London EC4A 1BP, UK

Tel: 44-207-353-1515

ASTEA INTERNATIONAL, INC.

455 Business Center Drive, Horsham, PA, 19044

Tel: (215) 682-2500   Fax: (215) 682-2515   www.astea.com

Produces computer software that assists to automate and manage field service, sales and customer support operations.

Astea International Inc., Trent House, University Way, The Technology Park, Cranfield, Bedfordshire MK43 0AN, UK

Tel: 44-1234-756-700

ASTRONAUTICS CORPORATION OF AMERICA

4115 N. Teutonia Ave., Milwaukee, WI, 53209-6731

Tel: (414) 447-8200   Fax: (414) 447-8231   www.astronautics.com

Design/development/mfr. aircraft instruments, avionics, electronics systems, vehicle electronics and computer maintenance service.

Astronautics UK, 28 Tekels Ave., Camberley, Surrey, UK

ASYST TECHNOLOGIES, INC.

48761 Kato Road, Fremont, CA, 94538

Tel: (510) 661-5000   Fax: (510) 661-5166   www.asyst.com

Produces wafer handling equipment.

Asyst Technologies European Hdqrts., Shaw House, Pegler Way, Crawley W. Sussex R11 1AF, UK

Tel: 44-1293-763016   Fax: 44-1293-763188

AT&T BROADBAND, LLC

188 Inverness Dr. West, Englewood, CO, 80112

Tel: (303) 875-5500   Fax: (303) 875-4984   www.broadband.att.com

Provides broadband technology services; digital TV, digital telephone and high-speed cable internet services.

One 2 One, London, UK

TeleWest, London, UK

AT&T CORPORATION

295 N. Maple Ave., Basking Ridge, NJ, 07920-1002

Tel: (908) 221-2000   Fax: (908) 221-2528   www.att.com

Engaged in long distance telecommunications.

AT&T (UK) Ltd., Norfolk House, 31 St. James Sq., London SW1Y 4JR, UK

ATLANTIC MUTUAL COMPANIES

140 Broadway, New York, NY, 10005

Tel: (212) 943-1800   Fax: (212) 428-6566   www.atlanticmutual.com

Engaged in insurance.

Atlantic Mutual International, Ltd, 150 Minories, London EC3N 1LS, UK

Tel: 44-270-709-9991   Contact: Michael Walton

ATLAS AIR WORLDWIDE HOLDINGS

2000 Westchester Avenue, Purchase, NY, 10577-2543

Tel: (914) 701-8000   Fax: (914) 701-8001   www.atlasair.com

Air cargo carrier.

Atlas Air UK, Heathrow Airport, London, UK

Tel: 44-1784-266212   Fax: 44-1784-266219

ATMEL CORPORATION

2325 Orchard Pkwy., San Jose, CA, 95131

Tel: (408) 441-0311   Fax: (408) 436-4200   www.atmel.com

Design, manufacture and marketing of advanced semiconductors.

Atmel UK Ltd., Coliseum Business Centre, Riverside Way, Camberly Surrey GU15 3YL, UK

Tel: 44-1276-686-677

ATTACHMATE CORPORATION

3617 131st Avenue SE, Bellevue, WA, 98006-1332

Tel: (425) 644-4010   Fax: (425) 747-9924   www.attachmate.com

Mfr. connectivity software.

Attachmate International UK Ltd., Styal Road, Manchester, UK

Tel: 44-161-490-8111   Fax: 44-161-49-8222

AUDIO VISUAL SERVICES CORPORATION

111 West Ocean Blvd, Ste., Long Beach, CA, 90802

Tel: (562) 366-0620   Fax: (562) 366-0628   www.avservicecorp.com

Plans and produces meetings, events, and media campaigns: creates film/video presentations; supports in-house communications and training programs: and supplies audio-visual equipment.

Audio Visual Services, 191 The Vale, Acton, London W3 7QS, UK

Tel: 44-181-735-2000   Fax: 44-181-735-2020

Audio Visual Services, 4 Buckingham Gate, London SW1E 6JP, UK

Tel: 44-207-393-4950   Fax: 44-207-393-4951

AUTHORIA, INC.

300 Fifth Avenue, Waltham, MA, 02451

Tel: (781) 530-2000   Fax: (781) 530-2001   www.authoria.com

Mfr. benefit plans software.

Authoria Inc., Trinity House Cambridge Business Park, Cowley Road, Cambridge CB4 OW2, UK

Tel: 44-1223-393505   Fax: 44-1223-393501

AUTODESK INC.

111 McInnis Parkway, San Rafael, CA, 94903

Tel: (415) 507-5000   Fax: (415) 507-6112   www.autodesk.com

Develop/marketing/support computer-aided design, engineering, scientific and multimedia software products.

Autodesk Ltd., Cross Lanes, Guildford, Surrey GU1 1UK, UK

Tel: 44-1483-303-322   Fax: 44-1483-304-556

AUTOMATIC DATA PROCESSING INC.

One ADP Blvd., Roseland, NJ, 07068

Tel: (973) 994-5000   Fax: (973) 994-5387   www.adp.com

Data processing services.

ADP Network Services Ltd., ADP House, 2 Pine Trees Chertsey Lane, Staines, Surrey TW18 3DS, UK

Tel: 44-1784-429000   Fax: 44-1784-429010   Contact: Karen Burton

AUTOMATIC SWITCH CO. (ASCO)

50-60 Hanover Rd., Florham Park, NJ, 07932

Tel: (973) 966-2000   Fax: (973) 966-2628   www.asco.com

Mfr. solenoid valves, emergency power controls, pressure and temperature switches.

ASCO Power Technologies, Fourth Avenue, Globe Park, Marlow, Buckinghamshire SL7 1YG, UK

Tel: 44-1628-403-873   Fax: 44-1628-403-867

AUTOSPLICE INC.

10121 Barnes Canyon Road, San Diego, CA, 92121

Tel: (858) 535-0077   Fax: (858) 535-0130   www.autosplice.com

Mfr. electronic components.

Autosplice UK Ltd., 6 Brockles Mead, Harlow Essex CM19 4PS, UK

Tel: 44-1279-635-896   Fax: 44-1279-635-904   Contact: Ged Bushnell

AUTO-TROL TECHNOLOGY CORPORATION

12500 North Washington Street, Denver, CO, 80241-2400

Tel: (303) 452-4919   Fax: (303) 252-2249   www.auto-trol.com

Develops, markets and integrates computer-based solutions for industrial companies and government agencies worldwide.

Centra Technology Ltd., The Technology Centre, Wolverhampton Science Park, Wolverhampton WV10 9RU, UK

Tel: 44-1902-824282   Emp: 6

AVERY DENNISON CORPORATION

150 N. Orange Grove Blvd., Pasadena, CA, 91103

Tel: (626) 304-2000   Fax: (626) 792-7312   www.averydennison.com

Mfr. pressure-sensitive adhesives and materials, office products, labels, tags, retail systems, Carter's Ink and specialty chemicals.

Avery Intl. Adhesive Products Ltd., 48 West St., Marlow, Buckinghamshire SL7 2NB, UK

Avery Label Systems Ltd., Gardener Rd., Maidenhead, Berkshire SL6 7PU, UK

Dennison PLC, Merchant Drive, Indus Est Mead Hertf, Nord, Hert SG13 7AY, UK

Dennison Transoceanic Corp., Elvaco House, High St., Engham, Surrey TW20 9DN, UK

Fasson UK Ltd., Eastman Way, Hemel Hempstead, Hampstead HP2 7HE, UK

AVICI SYSTEMS INC.

101 Billerica Avenue, Bldg. 2, North Billerica, MA, 01862

Tel: (978) 964-2000   Fax: (978) 955-2100   www.avici.com

Engaged in telecommunications.

Avici Systems International, 10 Stratton Street, Mayfair, London W1J 8LG, UK

Tel: 44-207-546-8638

AVID TECHNOLOGY, INC.

1 Park West, Tewksbury, MA, 01876

Tel: (978) 640-6789   Fax: (978) 640-1366   www.avid.com

Mfr. animation design software and digital and audio systems.

Avid Technology Europe Ltd., Pinewood Studios, Pinewood Road, Iver Heath, Bucks SL0 0NH, UK

Tel: 44-175-365-5999   Fax: 44-175-365-4999

AVMARK INC.

1925 North Lynn Street, Arlington, VA, 22209-1707

Tel: (703) 528-5610   Fax: (703) 528-3689   www.avmark.com

Aviation consult, aircraft appraisal, aviation related publications.

Avmark International Ltd., 26 Eccleston Square, London SW1V 1NS, UK

Contact: Danile Solon

AVNET INC.

2211 South 47th Street, Phoenix, AZ, 85034

Tel: (480) 643-2000   Fax: (480) 643-4670   www.avnet.com

Distributor electronic components, computers and peripherals.

Avnet EMG Ltd., Avnet House, Rutherford Close, Meadway Stevenage Hertfordshire SG1 2EF, UK

Tel: 44-1438-788500   Fax: 44-1438-788250

BFI Ibexsa Electronics Ltd., BFI-IBEXSA House, Burnt Ash Road, Quarry Wood Ind. Estate, Aylesford Kent ME20 7NA, UK

Tel: 44-1622-882-467   Fax: 44-1622-882-469

AVON PRODUCTS, INC.

1345 Avenue of the Americas, New York, NY, 10105-0196

Tel: (212) 282-5000   Fax: (212) 282-6049   www.avon.com

Mfr. direct seller of cosmetics and beauty-related items.

Avon Cosmetics Ltd., Earlstrees Rd., Corby Northants NN17 4AZ, UK

Tel: 44-845-60-50-400   Fax: 44-1536-402493   Contact: Peter Nicholls

AVX CORPORATION

801 17th Ave. South, Myrtle Beach, SC, 29577

Tel: (843) 448-9411   Fax: (843) 448-7139   www.avxcorp.com

Mfr. multilayer ceramic capacitors.

AVX Ltd., Stafford House, Station Rd., Aldershot, Hants GU11 1BA, UK

AXEDA SYSTEMS INC.

257 Great Valley Pkwy., Malvern, PA, 19355

Tel: (610) 251-9999   Fax: (610) 695-2592   www.axeda.com

Mfr. software.

Axeda Systems, Burlington House, 369 Wellingborough Road, Northampton NN14 EU, UK

AXXCELERA BROADBAND WIRELESS

111 Castilian Drive, Santa Barbara, CA, 93117

Tel: (805) 968-9621   Fax: (805) 968-0791   www.axxcelera.com

Provider of wireless broadband solutions for Internet service providers.

AXXCELERA Broadband UK, The Westbrook Centre, Milton Road, Cambridge CB4 1YQ, UK

Tel: 44-1223-713713   Contact: Philip Rushton

BAIN & COMPANY, INC.

Two Copley Place, Boston, MA, 02116

Tel: (617) 572-2000   Fax: (617) 572-2427   www.bain.com

Strategic management consulting services.

Bain & Co. Inc. United Kingdom, 40 Strand, London WC2N 5HZ, UK

Tel: 44-207-969-6000   Fax: 44-207-969-6666

ROBERT W. BAIRD & CO. INCORPORATED

PO Box 672, Milwaukee, WI, 53201

Tel: (414) 765-3500   Fax: (414) 765-3600   www.rwbaird.com

Engaged in investment banking, serving individuals, corporations, municipalities and institutional investors.

Granville Baird, Mint House, 77 Mansell Street, London E1 8AF, UK

Tel: 44-20-7488-1212   Contact: Michael Proudlock

Granville Baird, Aimtree House, 1 York Place, Leeds LD1 2DR, UK

Tel: 44-113-280-3500   Fax: 44-113-280-3501   Contact: David Williamson

Granville Baird, Cheshire House, 18-20 Booth Street, Manchester M2 4AN, UK
Tel: 44-161-236-6600 Fax: 44-161-236-6650
Granville Baird Capital Partners, Waisingham House, 35 Seething Lane, London EC3N 4AH, UK
Contact: John Martin
Granville Baird Capital Partners, Brazennose House, Brazennose Street, 5/F, Manchester M2 5BP, U.K.
Contact: Roy Farmer

BAKER & McKENZIE
130 East Randolph Drive, Ste. 2500, Chicago, IL, 60601
Tel: (312) 861-8000   Fax: (312) 861-2899   www.bakerinfo.com
International legal services.
Baker & McKenzie, 100 New Bridge St., London EC4V 6JA, UK
Tel: 44-207-919-1000 Fax: 44-207-919-1999

BAKER BOTTS LLP
910 Louisiana Street, Ste. 3000, Houston, TX, 77002-4995
Tel: (713) 229-1234   Fax: (713) 229-1522   www.bakerbotts.com
International law firm.
Baker Botts LLP, 45 Ludgate Hill, London EC4M 7JU, UK
Tel: 44-207-778-1400 Contact: Jay T. Kolb, Mng. Ptnr.

MICHAEL BAKER CORPORATION
420 Rouser Road, Bldg. 3, Coraopolis, PA, 15108
Tel: (412) 269-6300   Fax: (412) 269-6097   www.mbakercorp.com
Engineering and construction operations and technical services.
Overseas Technical Service (Harrow) Ltd., 104 College Rd., 1st Fl., Harrow, Middlesex HA1 1BQ, UK
Tel: 44-20-8861-0100 Fax: 44-20-8861-3101

BAKER HUGHES INCORPORATED
3900 Essex Lane, Ste. 1200, Houston, TX, 77027
Tel: (713) 439-8600   Fax: (713) 439-8699   www.bakerhughes.com
Develop and apply technology to drill, complete and produce oil and natural gas wells; provide separation systems to petroleum, municipal, continuous process and mining industries.
Baker Hughes INTEQ, Eastern Hemisphere Business Unit, Hammersley House, 2nd Floor, 5/8 Warwick St., London W2R 6JE, UK
Tel: 44-207-544-8100 Fax: 44-207-544-8101
Baker Hughes Process, Swift House, Cosford Lane, Rugby Warwickshire CV21 1QN, UK
Tel: 44-1788-555667
Baker Hughes Process Syatems, Swift House, Cosford Lane, Rugby Warwickshire CV21 1QN, UK
Tel: 44-1788-534100 Fax: 44-1788-534101
Baker Oil Tools (UK) Ltd., Eurocentre, North River Rd., Great Yarmouth Norfolk NR30 1TE, UK
Tel: 44-1493-332212 Fax: 44-1493-852294
Milchem Drilling Fluids, East Quay, S. Denes Rd., Great Yarmouth Norfolk, UK

BAKER PETROLITE CORPORATION
3900 Essex Lane, Houston, TX, 77027
Tel: (713) 599-7400   Fax: (713) 599-7592   www.bakerhughes.com
Mfr. specialty chemical treating programs, performance-enhancing additives and related equipment and services.
Petrolite Ltd., Kirkby Bank Rd., Knowsley Industrial Park North, Liverpool L33 7SY, UK

BALDOR ELECTRIC COMPANY
5711 R.S. Boreham Jr. Street, Fort Smith, AR, 72908
Tel: (501) 646-4711   Fax: (501) 648-5792   www.baldor.com
Mfr. electric motors.
Baldor UK Ltd., Mint Motion Centre, 6, Bristol Distribution Park, Hawkley Drive, Bristol BS32 0BF, UK
Tel: 44-1454-850000

BALDWIN TECHNOLOGY COMPANY, INC.

12 Commerce Drive, Shelton, CT, 06484

Tel: (203) 402-1000 Fax: (203) 402-5500 www.baldwintech.com

Mfr./services material handling, accessories, control and prepress equipment for print industry.

Baldwin (UK) Ltd., Unit 13, Apex Business Centre, Boscombe Rd., Dunstable, Bedfordshire LU5 4SB, UK

Tel: 44-1-582-477499 Fax: 44-1-582-478510 Contact: John S. Chapman, Mng. Dir.

BALTEK CORPORATION

10 Fairway Court, PO Box 195, Northvale, NJ, 07647

Tel: (201) 767-1400 Fax: (201) 387-6631 www.baltek.com

Mfr. light lumber, balsa wood and PVC foam.

Baltek Ltd., 64 High Street, Croydon CR0 9XN, UK

Tel: 44-181-688-4398

BALTIMORE AIRCOIL CO., INC.

PO Box 7322, Baltimore, MD, 21227

Tel: (410) 799-6200 Fax: (410) 799-6416 www.baltimoreaircoil.com

Mfr. evaporative heat transfer and ice thermal storage products.

Baltimore Aircoil Ltd., Princewood Rd., Earlstress Ind. Est., Corby Northants NN17 2AP, UK

BAND-IT IDEX CORPORATION

4799 Dahlia Street, Denver, CO, 80216

Tel: (303) 320-4555 Fax: (303) 333-6549 www.band-it-idex.com

Mfr. industrial pressure clamps.

BAND-It Co. Ltd., Speedwell Industrial Estate, Staveley Chesterfield S43 3PF, UK

BANK OF AMERICA CORPORATION

Bank of America Corporate Center, Charlotte, NC, 28255

Tel: (415) 622-3530 Fax: (704) 386-6699 www.bankofamerica.com

Financial services.

Bank of America Intl. Ltd., 1 Alie St., PO Box 407, London E1 8DE, UK

Tel: 44-207-634-4402 Fax: 44-207-634-4707 Contact: Clive P. Adamson, SVP

THE BANK OF NEW YORK

One Wall Street, New York, NY, 10286

Tel: (212) 495-1784 Fax: (212) 495-2546 www.bankofny.com

Banking services.

The Bank of New York, One Canada Square, London E14 5AL, UK

Tel: 44-207-322-6098 Fax: 44-207-322-6023

The Bank of New York Capital Markets Ltd., 46 Berkeley Street, London W1X 6AA, UK

Tel: 44-207-499-1234 Fax: 44-207-322-6030

BANK ONE CORPORATION

One Bank One Plaza, Chicago, IL, 60670

Tel: (312) 732-4000 Fax: (312) 732-3366 www.fcnbd.com

Provides financial products and services.

Bank One, NA, One Triton Square, London NW1 3FN, UK

Tel: 44-207-388-3456 Fax: 44-207-388-4747 Contact: Pete B. McCarthy, Head of EMEA

C. R. BARD, INC.

730 Central Ave., Murray Hill, NJ, 07974

Tel: (908) 277-8000 Fax: (908) 277-8078 www.crbard.com

Mfr. health care products.

Bard Ltd., Forest House, Brighton Rd., Crawley West Sussex RH11 9BP, UK

BARNES GROUP INC.

123 Main Street, Bristol, CT, 06011-0489

Tel: (860) 583-7070   Fax: (860) 589-3507   www.barnesgroupinc.com

Mfr. produces precision mechanical and nitrogen gas springs for heavy machinery.

Associated Spring SPEC Ltd., Evesham, UK

Bowman Distribution Europe, Corsham, UK

Motalink & Bowman Systems UK, Corsham, UK

BARRA, INC.

2100 Milvia Street, Berkeley, CA, 94704

Tel: (510) 548-5442   Fax: (510) 548-4374   www.barra.com

Mfr. analytical software for private investors and portfolio managers.

BARRA International, Ltd., 75 King William Street, London EC4N 7BE, UK

Tel: 44-20-7283-2255   Fax: 44-20-7220-7555

BARRINGER TECHNOLOGIES INC.

30 Technology Drive, Warren, NJ, 07059

Tel: (908) 222-9100   Fax: (908) 222-1557   www.barringer.com

Provides advanced technology for security, law enforcement, including drug and explosive detectors.

Barringer Instruments UK Ltd., Unit 3, Lloyds Court Manor Royal, Crawley, West Sussex RH10 2QU, UK

Tel: 44-1293-433100   Fax: 44-1293-433200

BARRY CONTROLS INC.

40 Guest Street, PO Box 9105, Brighton, MA, 02135-9105

Tel: (617) 787-1555   Fax: (617) 254-7381   www.barrymounts.com

Mfr./sale vibration isolation mounting devices.

Barry Controls Europe, Molesey Rd. Hersham, Walton-on-Thames, Surrey KT12 3PQ, UK

Barry Controls Ltd., Molesey Road Hersham, Walton-on-Thames, Surrey KT12 3PQ, UK

Specialty Fasteners, Unit D, Seymour Wharf, Steamer Quay Road, Totnes Devon, UK

R.G. BARRY CORPORATION

13405 Yarmouth Road NW, Pickerington, OH, 43147

Tel: (614) 864-6400   Fax: (614) 866-9787   www.rgbarry.com

Mfr. slippers and footwear.

R. G. Barry International, Ste. 3/5-6, Harbour Yard Chelsea Harbour, London SW10 OXD, UK

Tel: 44-207-351-1322   Fax: 44-207-352-4068

BARRY-WEHMILLER COMPANIES, INC.

8020 Forsyth Boulevard, St. Louis, MO, 63105

Tel: (314) 862-8000   Fax: (314) 862-8858   www.barry-wehmillerco.com

Mfr. of packaging automation equipment for filling, closing, conveying, cartoning, shrink wrapping and case packing plus systems integration.

Barry-Wehmiller Europe, 1-5 Spring Valley Business Centre, Porters Wood, St. Albans, Herts AL3 6EN, UK

Tel: 44-1727-836101

Barry-Wehmiller Europe Ltd., 16 Roman Way, Thetford, Norfolk IP24 IXB, UK

Tel: 44-1842-754-171   Fax: 44-1842-755-318   Contact: David Clark   Emp: 20

BASE TEN SYSTEMS, INC.

528 Primrose Ct., Belle Mead, NJ, 08502

Tel: (908) 359-1867   Fax: (908) 359-1867   www.base10.com

Mfr. software for pharmaceutical companies.

Base Ten Systems Ltd., Pilgrim's Well, 429 London Road, Camberley Surrey GU15-3HZ, UK

BATES WORLDWIDE INC.

498 Seventh Avenue, New York, NY, 10018

Tel: (212) 297-7000   Fax: (212) 986-0270   www.batesww.com

Advertising, marketing, public relations and media consulting.

Bates Communications, 121-141 Westbourne Terrace, London W2 5JR, UK

Tel: 44-207-262-0708   Fax: 44-207-402-0020

Bates Interactive, 121-141 Westbourne Terrace, London W2 5JR, UK

Tel: 44-207-724-7228   Fax: 44-207-724-3075   Contact: M. Crossman, Mng. Dir.

Clarion Communications, Div. Cordiant, 121-141 Westbourne Terrace, London W2 6JR, UK

The Decision Shop, Westbourne House, 14-16 Westbourn Grove, London W1 RRH, UK

Tel: 44-207-229-6699   Fax: 44-207-229-0606   Contact: Bernard Walsh, Mng. Dir.

BATTELLE MEMORIAL INSTITUTE

505 King Ave., Columbus, OH, 43201-2693

Tel: (614) 424-6424   Fax: (614) 424-3260   www.battelle.org

Develops new technologies, commercializes products, and provides solutions for industry and government.

Battelle Institute Ltd., 15 Hanover Sq., London W1R 9AJ, UK

BAUSCH & LOMB INC.

One Bausch & Lomb Place, Rochester, NY, 14604-2701

Tel: (716) 338-6000   Fax: (716) 338-6007   www.bausch.com

Mfr. vision care products and accessories.

Bausch & Lomb U.K., Ltd., Bausch & Lomb House, 106-114 London Road, Kingston-Upon-Thames, Surrey KT2 6QJ, UK

BAX GLOBAL INC.

16808 Armstrong Ave., PO Box 19571, Irvine, CA, 92623

Tel: (949) 752-4000   Fax: (949) 260-3182   www.baxworld.com

Air freight forwarder.

BAX Global, Burlington House, 30-38 Church St., Staines Middlesex TW18 4EP, UK

Tel: 44-1784-877000   Fax: 44-1784-877003

BAX Global, Unitair Centre, Great South West Rd., Feltham, Middlesex TW14 8NT, UK

Tel: 44-181-899-3000   Fax: 44-181-899-3112

BAXTER INTERNATIONAL INC.

One Baxter Parkway, Deerfield, IL, 60015

Tel: (847) 948-2000   Fax: (847) 948-3948   www.baxter.com

Mfr. products and provide services in the field of the administration of medication and bioscience.

Baxter Healthcare Ltd., Wellington Business Park 31, Dukes Road Crowthorne, Berkshire RG45 6LS, UK

Tel: 44-1344-75-9300

Baxter Unicare, Cambridge Road, Harlow Essex CM20 2SG, UK

Tel: 44-1279-641-111

BBDO WORLDWIDE

1285 Ave. of the Americas, New York, NY, 10019

Tel: (212) 459-5000   Fax: (212) 459-6645   www.bbdo.com

Multinational group of advertising agencies.

Abbott Mead Vickers BBDO Ltd., 151 Marylebone Road, London NW1 5QE, UK

Tel: 44-207-7616-3500

BDO SEIDMAN, LLP   BELGIUM

130 East Randolph Street, Chicago, IL, 60601

Tel: (312) 856-9100   Fax: (312) 856-1379   www.bdo.com

International accounting and financial consulting firm.

BDO Stoy Hayward, 8 Baker St., London W1M 1DA, UK

Tel: 44-207-486-5888   Fax: 44-207-487-3686   Contact: Stephen P. Greene

BEA SYSTEMS, INC.

2315 North First Street, St. Jose, CA, 95131

Tel: (408) 570-8000   Fax: (408) 570-8091   www.beasys.com

Develops communications management software and provider of software consulting services.

BEA Systems Ltd., Windsor Court, Kingsmead Business Park, Frederick Place, High Wycombe Bucks HP11 1JU, UK

Tel: 44-1494-559500   Fax: 44-1494-452202

THE BEAR STEARNS & COMPANIES., INC.

245 Park Ave., New York, NY, 10167

Tel: (212) 272-2000   Fax: (212) 272-3092   www.bearstearns.com

Investment banking, securities broker/dealer and investment advisory services.

Bear Stearns International Ltd., One Canada Sq., London E14 5AD, UK

Tel: 44-207-516-6000   Fax: 44-207-516-6030

BECHTEL GROUP INC.

50 Beale Street, PO Box 3965, San Francisco, CA, 94105-1895

Tel: (415) 768-1234   Fax: (415) 768-9038   www.bechtel.com

General contractors in engineering, construction and project management.

Bechtel Great Britain, Bechtel House, PO Box 739, 245 Hammersmith Rd., London W6 8DP, UK

Tel: 44-181-846-5111   Fax: 44-181-846-6940

Bechtel Water, Chadwick House, Warrington Rd., Risley, Warrington WA3 6AE, UK

Tel: 44-192-585-7000   Fax: 44-192-585-7557

BECKMAN COULTER, INC.

4300 N. Harbor Boulevard, Fullerton, CA, 92834

Tel: (714) 871-4848   Fax: (714) 773-8898   www.beckmancoulter.com

Develop/mfr./marketing automated systems and supplies for biological analysis.

Beckman Coulter (U.K.) Limited, Oakley Court, Kingsmead Business Park, London Road, High Wycombe Buckinghamshire HP11 1JU, UK

Tel: 44-1494-441181

BELDEN, INC.

7701 Forsyth Blvd., Ste. 800, St. Louis, MO, 63015

Tel: (314) 854-8000   Fax: (314) 854-8001   www.belden.com

Mfr. electronic wire and cable products.

Belden UK Ltd., 10 Watergate Row, Watergate Street, Chester, Cheshire CH1 2LD, UK

BELKIN COMPONENTS

501 West Walnut Street, Compton, CA, 90220

Tel: (310) 898-1100   Fax: (310) 898-1111   www.belkin.com

Mfr. connectivity and power products.

Belkin Components, Ltd., Express Business Park, Shipton Way, Rushden NN10 6GL, UK

BELL MICROPRODUCTS INC.

1941 Ringwood Avenue, San Jose, CA, 95131

Tel: (408) 451-9400   Fax: (408) 451-1600   www.bellmicro.com

Distributes semiconductor and computer products from manufacturers.

Bell Microproducts Inc., Cox Lane Chessington, Suttry KT9 1SJ, UK

Tel: 44-20-8286-5000

BELLSOUTH CORPORATION LATIN AMERICA

1155 Peachtree Street NE, Ste. 400, Atlanta, GA, 30367

Tel: (404) 249-4800   Fax: (404) 249-4880   www.bellsouth.com

Mobile communications, telecommunications network systems.

Air Call Communications Ltd., Unit 6, Air Call Business Center, Colindeep Lane, Colindale London, UK

BEN & JERRY'S HOMEMADE INC.

30 Community Drive, South Burlington, VT, 05403-6828

Tel: (802) 651-9600   Fax: (802) 651-9647   www.benjerry.com

Mfr. premium ice cream.

Ben & Jerry's International, London, UK

BENTLY NEVADA CORPORATION

1631 Bently Parkway South, Minden, NV, 89423

Tel: (775) 782-3611   Fax: (775) 782-9259   www.bently.com

Provides hardware, software, and services for machinery information and management systems.

Bently Nevada (UK) Ltd, 2 Kelvin Close, Science Park N., Birchwood, Warrington, Cheshire WA3 7PB, UK

LOUIS BERGER INTERNATIONAL INC.

100 Halsted Street, East Orange, NJ, 07019

Tel: (201) 678-1960   Fax: (201) 672-4284   www.louisberger.com

Consulting engineers, engaged in architecture, environmental and advisory services.

Louis Berger International Inc., Britannia House, 1 Glenthorne Road, Hammersmith London W6 OLH, UK

Tel: 44-207-748-9898   Fax: 44-207-748-3880

BERLITZ CROSS-CULTURAL TRAINING INC.

400 Alexander Park, Princeton, NJ, 08540

Tel: (609) 514-9650   Fax: (609) 514-9689   www.berlitz.com

Consulting and management training services to bridge cultural gaps for international travelers as well as for business transferees and families.

Berlitz (U.K.) Limited, 321 Oxford Street, London W1A 3BZ, UK

Berlitz (U.K.) Limited, 9-13 Grosvenor St., London W1A 3BZ, UK

BERNARD HODES GROUP

555 Madison Ave., New York, NY, 10022

Tel: (212) 935-4000   Fax: (212) 755-7324   www.hodes.com

Provides recruitment communications and staffing solutions.

Bernard Hodes Group, 10 Regents Wharf All Saints Street, London N1 9RL, UK

MacMillan Bernard Hodes Group, Salisbury House, Bluecoats, Hertford SG14 1PU, UK

SANFORD C. BERNSTEIN & CO., LLC

1345 Avenue of the Americas, New York, NY, 10105

Tel: (212) 486-5800   Fax: (212) 756-4455   www.bernstein.com

Engaged in investment management and research.

Sanford C. Bernstein & Co., Div. ACL Private Group, 99 Gresham Street, London EC2V 7NG, UK

Tel: 44-20-7367-7300   Fax: 44-20-7367-7367   Contact: David Steyn, Mng. Dir.

BEST WESTERN INTERNATIONAL

6201 North 24th Place, Phoenix, AZ, 85106

Tel: (602) 957-4200   Fax: (602) 957-5740   www.bestwestern.com

International hotel chain.

Five Lake Hotel, Golf & Country Club, Colchester Rd., Essex, UK

Oatlands Park Hotel, Surrey KT13 9HB, UK

BHA GROUP HOLDINGS, INC.

8800 East 63rd Street, Kansas City, MO, 64133

Tel: (816) 356-8400   Fax: (816) 353-1873   www.bha.com

Mfr. air pollution control replacement parts.

BHA UK Ltd., Ste. 7, Cobham House, Shadsworth Gateway Estate, Haslingden Road, Blackburn BB1 2EE, UK

Tel: 44-1254-268900   Fax: 44-1254-268901

BICC GENERAL

4 Tesseneer Drive, Highland Heights, KY, 41076

Tel: (859) 572-8000   Fax: (859) 572-8444   www.generalcable.com

Mfr., marketing and distribution of copper, aluminum and fiber optic wire and cable products for the communications, energy and electrical markets.

BICC General, Hall Lane, Prescot, Merseyside L34 5TG, UK

BINGHAM McCUTCHEN LLP

150 Federal Street, Boston, MA, 02110

Tel: (617) 951-8000   Fax: (617) 951-8736   www.bingham.com

Engaged in international law.

Bingham McCutchen LLP, 8-10 Mansion House Place, London EC49 8LB, UK

Tel: 44-207-375-9770   Fax: 44-207-220-7431   Emp: 6

BINNEY & SMITH INC.

1100 Church Lane, PO Box 431, Easton, PA, 18044-0431

Tel: (610) 253-6271   Fax: (610) 250-5768   www.crayola.com

Mfr. crayons, art supplies and craft kits.

Binney & Smith Ltd., Ampthill Rd., Bedford MK42 9RS, UK

BIOGEN, INC.

14 Cambridge Center, Cambridge, MA, 02142

Tel: (617) 679-2000   Fax: (617) 679-2617   www.biogen.com

Engaged in medical research and development of autoimmune diseases.

Biogen Ltd., 5D Roxborough Way Foundation Park, Maidenhead Berkshire SL6 2UD, UK

Tel: 44-16-28-50-1000

BIO-RAD LABORATORIES INC.

1000 Alfred Nobel Drive, Hercules, CA, 94547

Tel: (510) 724-7000   Fax: (510) 724-3167   www.bio-rad.com

Mfr. life science research products, clinical diagnostics, analytical instruments.

Bio-Rad Laboratories Ltd., Bio-Rad House, Maylands Avenue, Hemel Hempstead, Herts HP2 7TD, UK

Tel: 44-1442-8328-2555

BIOWHITTAKER INC.

8830 Biggs Ford Road, Walkersville, MD, 21793

Tel: (301) 898-7025   Fax: (301) 845-6099   www.biowhittaker.com

Mfr. cell culture products, endotoxin detection assays.

BioWhittaker UK Ltd., BioWhittaker House, 1 Ashville Way, Wokingham Berkshire RG41 2PL, UK

Tel: 44-118-979-5234   Contact: David Guy

LumiTech UK, Nottingham Business Park, City Link, Nottingham NG2 4LA, UK

Tel: 44-115-848-4968   Fax: 44-115-848-4969

Seal Sands Chemicals Ltd., Seal Sands Road, Middlesbrough TS2 1UB, UK

Tel: 44-1642-546546   Fax: 44-1642-546068

BITSTREAM INC.

215 First Street, Cambridge, MA, 02142

Tel: (617) 497-6222   Fax: (617) 868-0784   www.bitstream.com

Mfr. typeface software.

Bitstream UK Ltd., 4 Churchill House, Churchill Road, Leckhampton, Cheltenham, Gloucestershire GL53 7EG, UK

Tel: 44-1242-227-377   Contact: Keith Gould

BLACK & DECKER CORPORATION

701 E. Joppa Road, Towson, MD, 21286

Tel: (410) 716-3900   Fax: (410) 716-2933   www.blackanddecker.com

Mfr. power tools and accessories, security hardware, small appliances, fasteners, information systems and services.

Black & Decker England, England Office, 701 East Joppa Road, Towson, MD, 21286

BLACK & VEATCH LLP

8400 Ward Pkwy., PO Box 8405, Kansas City, MO, 64114

Tel: (816) 339-2000   Fax: (816) 339-2934   www.bv.com

Engaged in engineering, construction and consulting, specializing in infrastructure development in the fields of energy, water and information.

Binnie Black & Veatch, c/o TW Utilities Engineering, Gainsboro/Blake House, Manor Farm Rd., Reading Berkshire RG2 0JN, UK

Tel: 44-118-923-6718   Fax: 44-118-923-6860   Contact: Stephen Beales, Div. Dir.

Binnie Black & Veatch, 25 Newgate St., Chester CH1 1DE, UK

Tel: 44-1244-317044   Fax: 44-1244-347256   Contact: Richard Coackley

Binnie Black & Veatch, Clifton Heights, Triangle West, Bristol BS8 1EJ, UK

Tel: 44-117-934-9896   Fax: 44-117-934-9897   Contact: Neil Bradley

Binnie Black & Veatch, Grosvenor House, 69 London Rd., Redhill Surrey RH1 1LQ, UK

Tel: 44-1737-774155   Fax: 44-1737-772767   Contact: Dave Still, EVP

BLACK BOX CORPORATION

1000 Park Dr., Lawrence, PA, 15055

Tel: (724) 746-5500   Fax: (724) 746-0746   www.blackbox.com

Direct marketer and technical service provider of communications, networking and related computer connectivity products.

Black Box Catalogue Ltd., 15 Cradock Rd., Reading, Berkshire RG2 0JT, UK

Tel: 44-118-965-5000   Fax: 44-118-965-5050   Contact: Roger Croft, Gen. Mgr.

H&R BLOCK, INC.

4400 Main Street, Kansas City, MO, 64111

Tel: (816) 753-6900   Fax: (816) 753-8628   www.hrblock.com

Tax preparation services and software, financial products and services and mortgage loans.

H&R Block UK Ltd., 2 The Courtyard, London Rd., Horsham, West Sussex RH12 1AT, UK

BLOOMBERG L.P.

499 Park Ave., New York, NY, 10022

Tel: (212) 318-2000   Fax: (212) 940-1954   www.bloomberg.com

Publishes magazines and provides TV, radio and newspaper wire services.

Bloomberg L.P., City Gate House, 39-45 Finsbury Square, London ECQA 1PQ, UK

BLOUNT INTERNATIONAL, INC

4520 Executive Park Dr., Montgomery, AL, 36116-1602

Tel: (334) 244-4000   Fax: (334) 271-8130   www.blount.com

Mfr. cutting chain and equipment, timber harvest and handling equipment and riding mowers.

Blount UK Ltd., 6 Station Dr., Bredon, Tewkesbury Gloucestershire GL20 7HQ, UK

Tel: 44-1684-772736   Fax: 44-1684-773154   Contact: Simon Pears, Branch Mgr.

BLUE OCEAN SOFTWARE, INC.

15310 Amberly Drive, Ste. 370, Tampa, FL, 33647

Tel: (813) 977-4553   Fax: (813) 979-4447   www.blueocean.com

Mfr. software.

Blue Ocean Software, 2239/2243 Coventry Road, Sheldon, Birmingham B26 3NW, UK

BLUE PUMPKIN SOFTWARE, INC.

884 Hermosa Court, Ste. 100, Sunnyvale, CA, 94085

Tel: (408) 830-5400   Fax: (408) 830-5411   www.bluepumpkin.com

Mfr. software.

Blue Pumpkin Software, 2 Manor Court, High Street, Harmondsworth, Middlesex UB7 OAQ, UK

BMC SOFTWARE, INC.

2101 City West Blvd., Houston, TX, 77042-2827

Tel: (713) 918-8800   Fax: (713) 918-8000   www.bmc.com

Engaged in mainframe-related utilities software and services.

BMC Software Ltd., Assurance House, Vicarage Road, Egham Surrey TW20 9JY, UK

BNS COMPANY

200 Frenchtown Rd., Ste. 2, North Kingstown, RI, 02852

Tel: (401) 886-7404   Fax: (410) 886-7407   www.bnsco.com

Engaged in the development of measurement software.

BNS Co. (PH) Ltd., 69 Strathmore Road, Teddington, Middlesex TW11 8UH, UK

Tel: 44-208-943-1214

THE BOEING COMPANY

100 N. Riverside Plaza, Chicago, IL, 60606

Tel: (312) 544-2000   Fax: (312) 544-2082   www.boeing.com.

World's largest aerospace company; mfr. military and commercial aircraft, missiles and satellite launch vehicles.

The Boeing Company, Heathrow Airport, London, UK

BOISE CASCADE CORPORATION

1111 West Jefferson Street, PO Box 50, Boise, ID, 83728-0001

Tel: (208) 384-6161   Fax: (208) 384-7189   www.bc.com

Mfr./distributor paper and paper products, building products, office products.

Boise Cascade Office Products, Ltd., Bolton, UK

Boise Cascade Office Products, Ltd., Doncaster, UK

Boise Cascade Sales Ltd., 7C Hill Ave., Amersham, Buckinghamshire HP6 5BD, UK

Tel: 44-149-443-4222   Fax: 44-149-443-1557   Contact: Kpjm Ramaer, Mng. Dir.

BOOZ-ALLEN & HAMILTON INC.

8283 Greensboro Drive, McLean, VA, 22102

Tel: (703) 902-5000   Fax: (703) 902-3333   www.bah.com

International management and technology consultants.

Booz, Allen & Hamilton Inc. Intl. (UK) Ltd., 7 Savoy Court, Strand, London WC2R 0EZ, UK

Tel: 44-207-393-3333   Fax: 44-207-393-0025

BORDEN CHEMICAL, INC.

180 East Broad Street, Columbus, OH, 43215

Tel: (614) 225-4000   Fax: www.bordenchem.com

Engaged in manufacture and sales of chemical products, including forest product and industrial resins, adhesives and UV coatings.

Borden Chemical, North West Industrial Estate, Peterlee County, Durham SR8 2HR, UK

Borden Chemical UK Ltd., Sully Plant, South Glamorgan CF64 5YU, UK

Tel: 44-1446-731266   Contact: Lee David

BORDERS GROUP, INC.

100 Phoenix Dr., Ann Arbor, MI, 48181

Tel: (734) 477-1100   Fax: (734) 477-1633   www.bordersgroup.com

Operates retail book stores, including music and videos, educational and entertainment products, in-store author appearances and casual espresso cafes.

Borders Books and Music, 203-207 Oxford Street, London W1R 1AH, UK

Tel: 44-207-292-1600   Fax: 44-207-292-1616

Borders Books and Music, Churchill Square Shopping Centre, Western Road, Brighton BN1 2EA, UK

Tel: 44-127-373-1122   Fax: 44-127-373-5566

BORLAND SOFTWARE CORPORATION

100 Enterprise Way, Scotts Valley, CA, 95066

Tel: (831) 431-1000   Fax: (831) 431-4141   www.borland.com

Mfr. development software.

Borland (UK) Ltd., 8 Pavilions, Ruscombe Business Park, Twyford Berkshire RG10 9NN, UK

Tel: 44-118-924-1400

BOSE CORPORATION

The Mountain, Framingham, MA, 01701-9168

Tel: (508) 879-7330   Fax: (508) 766-7543   www.bose.com

Mfr. quality audio equipment and speakers.

BOSE UK Ltd., PO Box 72, Exeter EX1 1ZG, UK

Tel: 44-1392-428366

THE BOSTON CONSULTING GROUP

Exchange Place, 31st Fl., Boston, MA, 02109

Tel: (617) 973-1200   Fax: (617) 973-1339   www.bcg.com

Management consulting company.

The Boston Consulting Group, Devonshire House, Mayfair Place, London WIX 5FH, UK

Tel: 44-207-753-5353

BOSTON SCIENTIFIC CORPORATION (BSC)

One Scientific Place, Natick, MA, 01760-1537

Tel: (508) 650-8000   Fax: (508) 650-8923   www.bostonscientific.com

Developer, manufacturer and marketer of medical devices.

Boston Scientific International, New England House, Sandridge Park, Porters Wood, St. Albans Herts AL3 6PH, UK

Tel: 44-1727-866633   Fax: 44-1727-865862

BOURNS INC.

1200 Columbia Avenue, Riverside, CA, 92507

Tel: (909) 781-5500   Fax: (909) 781-5006   www.bourns.com

Mfr. resistive components and networks, precision potentiometers, panel controls, switches, transducers and surge protectors..

Bourns Electronics Ltd., 90 Park St., Chamberley, Surrey GU15 3NY, UK

BOWNE & COMPANY, INC.

345 Hudson Street, New York, NY, 10014

Tel: (212) 924-5500   Fax: (212) 229-3420   www.bowne.com

Financial printing and foreign language translation, localization (software), internet design and maintenance and facilities management.

Bowne Business Solutions, 60 Queen Victoria Street, London EC4N 4TR, UK

Tel: 44-207-551-5000   Fax: 44-207-551-5151   Contact: Tim Walters, Mng. Dir.

Bowne Global Solutions, Center 3, Wilbury Way, Hitchin, Hertfordshire SG4 0TP, UK

BOXLIGHT CORPORATION

19332 Powder Hill Place, Poulsbo, WA, 98370

Tel: (360) 779-7901   Fax: (360) 779-3299   www.boxlight.com

Mfr./sales/rentals of LCD panels and overhead, computer-based projection/presentation systems.

Boxlight Ltd., 50 Churchill Square, Suite 10, Kings Hill, West Malling, UK

Tel: 44-1732-840-404   Fax: 44-1732-841-333

BOYDEN CONSULTING CORPORATION

364 Elwood Ave., Hawthorne, NY, 10502

Tel: (914) 747-0093   Fax: (914) 980-6147   www.boyden.com

International executive search firm.

Boyden Intl. Ltd., 24 Queen Anne's Gate, London SW1H 9AA, UK

Tel: 44-207-222-9033

BOZELL GROUP

40 West 23rd Street, New York, NY, 10010

Tel: (212) 727-5000   Fax: (212) 645-9173   www.bozell.com

Advertising, marketing, public relations and media consulting.

Bozell Worldwide - International Hdqtrs., 25 Wellington St., London WC2E 7DA, UK

Tel: 44-207-379-3474   Fax: 44-207-379-5926   Contact: Brian Tucker, Pres. Europe

Bray Leino Ltd., Filleigh, N. Devon EX32 ORX, UK

Tel: 44-1598-760700   Fax: 44-1598-760225   Contact: David Morgan, Chmn.

Delaney Fletcher Bozell, Ltd., 25 Wellington St., London WC2E 7DA, UK

Tel: 44-207-836-3474   Fax: 44-207-240-8739   Contact: Mark Lund, CEO

TN Media Inc., 25 Wellington St., London WC2E 7DA, UK

Tel: 44-207-836-3474   Fax: 44-207-240-0792   Contact: Dennis Lay, Mgr.

BRACEWELL & PATTERSON LLP

711 Louisiana Street, Ste. 2900, Houston, TX, 77002-2721

Tel: (713) 223-2900   Fax: (713) 223-2900   www.bracepatt.com

Engaged in international law.

Bracewell & Patterson LLP, 33 Davies Street, London W1Y 1FN, UK

BRADY CORPORATION

6555 W. Good Hope Road, Milwaukee, WI, 53223

Tel: (414) 358-6600   Fax: (414) 358-6600   www.whbrady.com

Mfr. industrial ID for wire marking, circuit boards; facility ID, signage, printing systems and software.

Brady Graphic Solutions Ltd., Summit House, Brooklands Close, Sunbury on Thames, Middlesex TW16 7EH, UK

Tel: 44-1932-789863   Fax: 44-1932-78-88-84

W.H. Brady Co., Ltd., Wildmere Industrial Estate, Banbury, Oxon OX16 7JU, UK

Tel: 44-1295-228200   Fax: 44-1295-228100   Contact: Peter Sephton, Mng. Dir.

BRANSON ULTRASONICS CORPORATION

41 Eagle Road, Danbury, CT, 06813-1961

Tel: (203) 796-0400   Fax: (203) 796-2285   www.branson-plasticsjoin.com

Engaged in design, development, manufacture and marketing of plastics joining, precision cleaning and processing equipment.

Branson Ultrasonics, The Fairview Estate, 27 Clayton Rd., Hayes Middlesex UB3 1AN, UK

Tel: 44-181-561-4422   Fax: 44-181-569-3788

BRIGGS & STRATTON CORPORATION

PO Box 702, Milwaukee, WI, 53201

Tel: (414) 259-5333   Fax: (414) 259-9594   www.briggesandstratton.com

Mfr. air-cooled gasoline engines for outdoor power equipment.

Briggs & Stratton U.K. Ltd., Attn: English Office, PO Box 72, Milwaukee, WI, 53201

BRINK'S INC.

Thorndal Circle, Darien, CT, 06820

Tel: (203) 662-7800   Fax: (203) 662-7968   www.brinks.com

Security transportation.

Brink's-Mat Ltd., London, UK

BRIO SOFTWARE, INC.

4980 Great America Pkwy., Santa Clara, CA, 95054

Tel: (408) 496-7400   Fax: (408) 496-7420   www.brio.com

Mfr. software.

Brio Software, 243 Brooklands Road, Weybridge, Surrey KT13 ORH, UK

BRISTOL BABCOCK INC.

1100 Buckingham Street, Watertown, CT, 06795

Tel: (203) 575-3000   Fax: (203) 575-3170   www.bristolbabcock.com

Mfr. process control instruments and SCADA systems.

Bristol Babcock Ltd., Vale Industrial Estate, Stourport Road, Kidderminster, Worcestershire DY11 7AU, UK

BRISTOL-MYERS SQUIBB COMPANY

345 Park Ave., New York, NY, 10154-0037

Tel: (212) 546-4000   Fax: (212) 546-4020   www.bms.com

Pharmaceutical and food preparations, medical and surgical instruments.

Bristol-Myers Squibb - Reg. HQ/London, 141-149 Staines Rd., Hounslow, Middlesex, UK

Bristol-Myers Squibb London, Swakeley House, Milton Rd., Ickenham, Uxbridge London, UK

C.V. Laboratories, Gordon House, Gordon Rd., Aldershot, UK

ConvaTec Ltd., Harrington House, Milton Road, Ickenham Uxbridge UB10 8PU, UK

Matrix UK, 114 St. Martins Lane, London WC2N 4AZ, UK

Zimmer, Ltd., Dunbeath Rd., Elgin Drive, Swindon Wiltshire, UK

BROADCOM CORPORATION INTERNATIONAL

16215 Alton Pkwy., Irvine, CA, 92619-7013

Tel: (949) 450-8700   Fax: (949) 450-8710   www.broadcom.com

Designs, develops and supplies integrated circuits and high density communication processors.

Broadcom Corporation, 36 London Street, Whitchurch, Hampshire RG28 7LQ, UK

Contact: Julian M. Wood

BROADVISION, INC.

585 Broadway, Redwood City, CA, 94063

Tel: (650) 261-5100   Fax: (650) 261-5900   www.broadvision.com

Develops and delivers an integrated suite of packaged applications for personalized enterprise portals.

BroadVision UK, 100 Longwater Avenue, Green Park, Reading RG2 6GP, UK

Tel: 44-118-920-7777

BROBECK PHLEGER & HARRISON LLP

Spear Street Tower, One Market St., San Francisco, CA, 94105

Tel: (415) 442-0900   Fax: (415) 442-1010   www.brobeck.com

Engaged in international law.

Brobeck Hale & Dorr International (JV), Alder Castle, 10 Noble Street, London EC2V 7QJ, UK

Tel: 44-20-7645-2400   Fax: 44-20-7645-2424   Contact: David A. Ayres, Mng. Prtn.

Brobeck Hale & Dorr International (JV), 25 Milton Park, Oxford OX14 4SH, UK

Tel: 44-1235-923-000   Fax: 44-1235-823-030   Contact: Kat Eavis

BROOKS-PRI AUTOMATION, INC.

15 Elizabeth Drive, Chelmsford, MA, 01824

Tel: (978) 262-2400   Fax: (978) 262-2500   www.brooks.com

Mfr. tool automation products.

Brooks Automation UK, Fairways Business Park, Unit 2, Deer Park Avenue, Livingston EH54 8AF, UK

Tel: 44-1506-449-000   Fax: 44-1506-449-001

Brooks Automation UK, 670 Eskdale Road, Winnersh Triangle, Wokingham RG41 5TS, UK

Tel: 44-118-921-5600   Fax: 44-118-921-5660

BROOKTROUT, INC.

250 First Avenue, Needham, MA, 02494

Tel: (781) 449-4100   Fax: (781) 449-9009   www.brooktroutinc.com

Mfr. hardware and software products.

Brooktrout Technology Europe, Unit 4, Enterprise Centre, Easthampstead Road, Bracknell Berkshire RG12 1YQ, UK

Tel: 44-1344-380280   Fax: 44-1344-380288   Contact: Richard Hamilton

Brooktrout Technology Europe, Stonebridge Street, Leatherhead, Surrey KT22 8BZ, UK

Tel: 44-1344-380280   Fax: 44-1372-379373

BROWN BROTHERS HARRIMAN & COMPANY

140 Broadway, New York, NY, 10005

Tel: (212) 483-1818   Fax: (212) 493-8526   www.bbh.com

Leading provider of mergers and acquisition advisory services and private equity capital to private and closely held public companies.

Brown Brothers Harriman Limited, Veritas House, 125 Finsbury Pavement, London EC2A 1PN, UK

BROWN RUDNICK BERLACK ISRAELS

One Financial Ctr., 745 Atlantic Avenue, Boston, MA, 02111

Tel: (617) 856-8200   Fax: (617) 856-8201   www.brownrudnick.com

Engaged in international law.

Brown Rudnick Berlack Israels, 8 Clifford Street, London W1S 2LQ, UK

Tel: 44-207-851-6000   Fax: 44-207-851-6100

BROWNING

1 Browning Place, Morgan, UT, 84050

Tel: (801) 876-2711   Fax: (801) 876-3331   www.browning.com

Sales and distribution of port firearms, fishing rods, etc.

Browning Sports UK, Lda., Milton Park 37D, Abingdon Oxon Milton 0X14 4RT, UK

BRUSH WELLMAN ENGINEERED MATERIALS INC.

17876 St. Clair Ave., Cleveland, OH, 44110

Tel: (216) 486-4200   Fax: (216) 383-4091   www.beminc.com

Mfr. beryllium, beryllium alloys and ceramics, specialty metal systems and precious metal products.

Brush Wellman Ltd., 2405 Ely Rd., Theale Commercial. Est., Theale Reading RG7 4BQ, UK

Tel: 44-118-930-3733   Fax: 44-181-930-3635

BRYAN CAVE LLP

211 North Broadway, St. Louis, MO, 63102

Tel: (314) 259-2000   Fax: (314) 259-2020   www.bryancave.com

International law firm.

Bryan Cave LLP, 33 Cannon Street, London EC4 M5TE, UK

Contact: Charles H. Attlee

BTU INTERNATIONAL

23 Esquire Rd., North Billerica, MA, 01862

Tel: (508) 667-4111   Fax: (508) 667-9068   www.btu.com

Mfr. of industrial furnaces.

BTU Engineering Ltd., 14-15 Armstrong Mall, Southwood Summit Centre, Farnborough, Hants. GU14 0NR, UK

BUCHANAN INGERSOLL PROFESSIONAL CORPORATION

301 Grant Street, Ste. 20, Pittsburgh, PA, 15219-1408

Tel: (412) 562-8800   Fax: (412) 562-1041   www.buchananingersoll.com

Engaged in international law.

Buchanan Ingersoll UK, International Financial Centre Tower 42, Old Broad Street, London EC2N 1HQ, UK

BUCK CONSULTANTS INC.

One Penn Plaza, New York, NY, 10119

Tel: (212) 330-1000   Fax: (212) 695-4184   www.buckconsultants.com

Employee benefit, actuarial and compensation consulting services.

Buck London, Old Broad Street, London EC2N 1HQ, UK

Tel: 44-20-7448-7000   Fax: 44-20-7448-7010   Contact: Eddie O'Hara

A. C. BUCKHORN INC.

55 West Techne Center Drive, Milford, OH, 45150

Tel: (513) 831-4402   Fax: (513) 831-5474   www.acbuckhorn.com

Mfr. of reusable plastic packaging systems, plastic containers and pallets and project management services.

Buckhorn Ltd., Unit 6-8, Industrial Estate, Stanton Harcourt, Oxon OX8 1SL, UK

Tel: 44-1865-88310   Fax: 44-1865-882792   Contact: Neville Jarvis, Gen. Mgr.   Emp: 6

BUCKMAN LABORATORIES INTERNATIONAL, INC.

1258 N. McLean Blvd., Memphis, TN, 38108-0308

Tel: (901) 278-0330   Fax: (901) 276-5343   www.buckman.com

Mfr. specialty chemicals.

Buckman Laboratories Ltd., Williams House Manchester Science Park, Lloyd Street North, Manchester M15 6SE, UK

BUCYRUS INTERNATIONAL, INC.

1100 Milwaukee Avenue, South Milwaukee, WI, 53172

Tel: (414) 768-4000   Fax: (414) 768-4474   www.bucyrus.com

Mfr. of surface mining equipment, primarily walking draglines, electric mining shovels and blast hole drills.

Bucyrus Europe Ltd., Becor House, Green Lane, Lincoln LN6 7DL, UK

Tel: 44-15-22513421   Fax: 44-15-22544438   Contact: David Lee, Mng. Dir.

BUDGET GROUP, INC.

125 Basin St., Ste. 210, Daytona Beach, FL, 32114

Tel: (904) 238-7035 Fax: (904) 238-7461 www.budgetrentacar.com

Car and truck rental system.

Budget Rent A Car International, 41 Marlows, Hemel Hempstead, Hertfordshire HP1 1XL, UK

Tel: 44-1442-276000 Fax: 44-1442-276000 Contact: Ron Norbut, VP & Mng. Dir.

BURLINGTON RESOURCES

5051 Westheimer, Ste. 1400, Houston, TX, 77056

Tel: (713) 624-9500 Fax: (713) 624-9555 www.br-inc.com

Engaged in the exploration, development, production and marketing of crude oil and natural gas.

Burlington Resources, 1 Canada Square, Canary Wharf, London E14 5AA, UK

Tel: 44-207-208-4646

LEO BURNETT, DIV. B-COM 3 GROUP

35 West Wacker Drive, Chicago, IL, 60601

Tel: (312) 220-5959 Fax: (312) 220-6533 www.leoburnett.com

Engaged in advertising, marketing, media buying and planning, and public relations.

Bartle Bogle Hegarty/Burnett, London, UK

Leo Burnett Company, London, UK

BURSON-MARSTELLER

230 Park Avenue South, New York, NY, 10003-1566

Tel: (212) 614-4000 Fax: (212) 614-4262 www.bm.com

Public relations/public affairs consultants.

Burson-Marsteller London, 24-28 Bloomsbury Way, London WC1A 2PX, UK

Tel: 44-207-831-6262- Fax: 44-207-430-1033 Emp: 160

Burson-Marsteller Ltd., 24-28 Bloomsbury Way, London WC1A 2PX, UK

Tel: 44-207-831-6262 Fax: 44-207-831-8138

BUSINESS WIRE

44 Montgomery Street, 39th Fl., San Francisco, CA, 94104

Tel: (415) 986-4422 Fax: (415) 788-5335 www.businesswire.com

Engaged in distribution of electronic news to worldwide news databases.

Business Wire UK, 117 Houndsditch, 1/F, London EC3A 7BT, UK

Tel: 44-207-626-1982 Fax: 44-207-626-1889

BUTLER INTERNATIONAL

110 Summit Ave., Montvale, NJ, 07645

Tel: (201) 573-8000 Fax: (201) 573-9723 www.butler.com

Leading supplier of skilled technical personnel.

Butler International, Kings Mill Lane, South Nutfield, Redhill, Surrey RH1 5NE, UK

Tel: 44-1737-822000 Fax: 44-1737-823031 Contact: David Leyshon

Butler International Executive Search, St. George's Business Centre, St. George's Square, Portsmouth, Hampshire PO1 3EZ, UK

Tel: 44-1705-819999 Fax: 44-1705-819990 Contact: Alex Rock, Dir.

Butler Rail Services, 5th Fl., West Wing City Cloisters, 188-196 Old St., London ECIV 9AY, UK

Tel: 44-207-251-4234 Fax: 44-207-251-4449 Contact: Tony Godfrey

Butler Services Group/Aerospace Services, Units D1, 2 & 3 Raylor Centre, James St., York Y01 3DW, UK

Tel: 44-1904-430233 Fax: 44-1904-430608 Contact: Dick Osguthorpe

BUTTERICK COMPANY, INC.

161 Avenue of the Americas, New York, NY, 10013

Tel: (212) 620-2500 Fax: (212) 620-2746 www.butterick.com

Prints sewing patterns and related magazines.

Butterick Fashion Marketing Ltd., New Lane, Havant, Hants. P09 2ND, UK

C&D TECHNOLOGIES

1400 Union Meeting Road, Blue Bell, PA, 19422

Tel: (215) 619-2700   Fax: (215) 619-7840   www.cdtechno.com

Mfr./produce electrical power storage and conversion products and industrial batteries.

C&D Technologies, Inc., 1 Tanners Drive, Blakelands North Milton Keynes, Buckinghamshire MK14 5BU, UK

Tel: 44-1908-615232

CABLE DESIGN TECHNOLOGIES CORPORATION

661 Andersen Drive, Plaza 7, Pittsburgh, PA, 15220

Tel: (412) 937-2300   Fax: (412) 937-9690   www.cdtc.com

Mfr. computer connector copper, fiber optic and composite cables.

Raydex/CDT, Gladden Place, West Gillibrands Skelmersdale, Lancashire WN8 9SX, UK

Tel: 44-1695-733-061

CABLETRON SYSTEMS, INC.

35 Industrial Way, PO Box 5005, Rochester, NH, 03866-5005

Tel: (603) 332-9400   Fax: (603) 337-3007   www.cabletron.com

Develop, manufacture and sales of support local and wide area network connectivity hardware and software.

Cabletron System, Network House, Newbury Business Park, London Rd., Newbury, Berkshire RG13 2PZ, UK

CABOT CORPORATION

2 Seaport Lane, Ste. 1300, Boston, MA, 02210-2019

Tel: (617) 345-0100   Fax: (617) 342-6103   www.cabot-corp.com

Mfr. carbon blacks, plastics; oil and gas, information systems.

BOCMIN Metals Ltd. (Cabot Mineral Resources), Broadway Chambers, Hammersmith Broadway, London W67 AF, UK

Cabot Alloys Europe (Engineered Products), Cabot House, William St., Windsor, Berkshire SL4 1BA, UK

Cabot Alloys UK Ltd. (HiTec Div.), Earlstrees Rd., Corby Northants NN17 2AZ, UK

Cabot Europe Ltd., Cabot Plastics Europe (Energy), Silk House, 6 Park Green, Macclesfield, Cheshire SK11 7NA, UK

Cabot Plastics Division (Energy), Gate St., Dukinfield, Cheshire SK14 4RZ, UK

Cabot Safety Ltd. (E-A-R), First Ave., Poynton, Stockport, Cheshire SK12 1YJ, UK

Deloro Stellite (WearTec Div.), Stratton St. Margaret, Swindon, Wiltshire SN3 4QA, UK

CABOT MICROELECTRONICS

870 Commons Drive, Aurora, IL, 60504

Tel: (630) 375-6631   Fax: (630) 375-5582   www.cabot-corp.com

Mfr. polishing compounds and polishing pads used in the manufacture of advanced semiconductors (chips) and rigid disks-critical components.

Cabot Microelectronics Europe, Sully Moors Road, Sully South Glamorgan, Glamorgan CF64 5RP, UK

Tel: 44-1446-736999

CACI INTERNATIONAL INC.

1100 North Glebe Road, Arlington, VA, 22201

Tel: (703) 841-7800   Fax: (703) 841-7882   www.caci.com

Provides simulation technology/software and designs factories, computer networks, and communications systems for military, electronic commerce digital document management, logistics and Y2K remediation.

CACI International, Inc., CACA House, Avonmore Rd., Kensington Village, London W14 8TS, UK

Tel: 44-207-602-6000

CADENCE DESIGN SYSTEMS, INC.

2655 Seely Ave., Bldg. 5, San Jose, CA, 95134

Tel: (408) 943-1234   Fax: (408) 943-0513   www.cadence.com

Mfr. electronic design automation software.

Cadence Design Systems UK, Bagshot Road, Bracknell, Berkshire RG12 0PH, UK

Tel: 44-1344-360333

Cadence Design Systems UK, St. John's Innovation Park, Cowley Road, Cambridge CB4 4WS, UK

Tel: 44-1223-421025

CADWALADER, WICKERSHAM & TAFT

100 Maiden Lane, New York, NY, 10038-4818

Tel: (212) 504-6000   Fax: (212) 504-6666   www.cadwalader.com

Engaged in international law.

Cadwalader, Wickersham & Taft, 55 Gracechurch St., London EC3V 0EE, UK

Tel: 44-207-456-8500 Fax: 44-207-456-8600

CALBIOCHEM-NOVABIOCHEM CORPORATION

10394 Pacific Center Court, San Diego, CA, 92121

Tel: (858) 450-9600   Fax: (858) 453-3552   www.calbiochem.com

Mfr. biochemicals, immunochemicals and reagents.

CN Biosciences Ltd., Boulevard Industrial Park, Padge Road, Beeston, Nottingham NG9 2JR, UK

CALDERA INTERNATIONAL

355 South 520 West, Ste. 100, Linden, UT, 84057

Tel: (801) 765-4999   Fax: (801) 765-1313   www.caldera.com

Provides integrated solutions for small-to-medium businesses, retail operations, telecommunications and other vertical markets.

Caldera Europe Limited, Croxley Business Park, Wingfield Court Hatters Lane, Watford WD18 8YN, UK

Tel: 44-1923-816344   Contact: Richard Perkins

CALGON CARBON CORPORATION

400 Calgon Carbon Drive, Pittsburgh, PA, 15230-0717

Tel: (412) 787-6700   Fax: (412) 787-4541   www.calgoncarbon.com

Mfr. activated carbon, related systems and services.

Charcoal Cloth International Ltd., High Tech House Commerce Way, Arena Business Park, Houghton Le Spring, Tyne & Wear DH4 5PP, UK

Chemviron Carbon Ltd., Number One Southlink, Oldham OL4 1DE, UK

CALIFORNIA CEDAR PRODUCTS COMPANY

400 Fresno Ave., Stockton, CA, 95201

Tel: (209) 944-5800   Fax: (209) 944-9072   www.calcedar.com

Mfr. Duraframe-brand matches and fireplace logs, and incense-cedar products.

California Cedar Products Co., 12 Goodwin's Court, St. Martin's Lane, London WC2N 4LL, UK

CALLAWAY GOLF COMPANY

2180 Rutherford Rd., Carlsbad, CA, 92008-8815

Tel: (760) 931-1771   Fax: (760) 931-8013   www.callawaygolf.com

Mfr. and sales of golf clubs.

Callaway Golf Europe Ltd., Barwell Business Park A-27, Leatherhead Road, Chessington Surrey KT9 2NY, UK

Tel: 44-20-8391-0111   Fax: 44-20-8391-9399

CALTEX CORPORATION

PO Box 619500, Dallas, TX, 75261-9500

Tel: (972) 830-1000   Fax: (972) 830-1081   www.caltex.com

Petroleum products.

Caltex Trading (UK) Ltd., Griffin House, 161 Hammersmith Rd., Hammersmith London W6 8B6, UK

CAMBREX CORPORATION

1 Meadowlands Plaza, East Rutherford, NJ, 07063

Tel: (201) 804-3000   Fax: (201) 804-9852   www.cambrex.com

human health, animal health/agriculture and Mfr. biotechnology products and produce specialty chemicals.

Cambrex Corp. Seal Sands Chemicals, Inc., Seal Sands Rd., Seal Sands, Middlesbrough TS2 1UB, UK

Tel: 44-1642-546546   Fax: 44-1642-546068

CAMINUS CORPORATION

825 Third Avenue, 28th Fl., New York, NY, 10022

Tel: (212) 515-3600   Fax: (212) 888-0691   www.caminus.com

Mfr. software.

Caminus Corporation, Castle Park, Cambridge CB3 ORA, UK

Tel: 44-1223-715-900

Caminus Corporation, Swan House, 33 Queen Street, London EC4R 1BR, UK

Tel: 44-207-332-4700

CAMITRO CORPORATION

4040 Campbell Avenue, Menlo Park, CA, 94025

Tel: (650) 614-7000   Fax: (650) 327-4639   www.camitro.com

Mfr. pharmaceuticals.

Camitro UK, 127 Cambridge Science Park, Milton Road, Cambridge CB4 OGD, UK

Tel: 44-1223-424-825   Contact: Teresa McCarthy, VP

CAMPBELL SOUP COMPANY

Campbell Place, Camden, NJ, 08103-1799

Tel: (856) 342-4800   Fax: (856) 342-3878   www.campbellsoup.com

Mfr. food products.

Campbell's UK Ltd., London, UK

CANBERRA INDUSTRIES, INC.

800 Research Parkway, Meriden, CT, 06450

Tel: (203) 238-2351   Fax: (203) 235-1347   www.canberra.com

Mfr. instruments for nuclear research.

Canberra Harwell, Ltd., 528.10 Unit 1, Harwell International Business Centre, Didcot, Oxfordshire OX11 0RA, UK

Tel: 44-1235-838333

CANDLE CORPORATION

201 N. Douglas Street, El Segundo, CA, 90245

Tel: (310) 535-3600   Fax: (310) 727-4287   www.candle.com

Mfr. management software.

Candle Service Ltd. UK, 1 Archipelago, Lyon Way Frimley, Camberley Surrey GU16 7ER, UK

CANNY BOWEN INC.

280 Park Avenue, 30th Fl., New York, NY, 10017

Tel: (212) 949-6611   Fax: (212) 949-5191   www.cannybowen.com

Executive search firm.

Canny, Bowen & Associates Ltd., 14 Queen Anne's Gate, St. James Park SW1 9A8, UK

CAPITAL CONTROLS COMPANY, INC.

3000 Advance Lane, PO Box 211, Colmar, PA, 18915-0211

Tel: (215) 997-4000   Fax: (215) 997-4062   www.capitalcontrols.com

Mfr./services water disinfecting products and systems.

Capital Controls Co. Ltd., Park Lane, Minworth Sutton Coldfield, West Midlands B76 9BL, UK

Tel: 44-121-313-2300

THE CAPITAL GROUP COS INC.

333 South Hope Street, Los Angeles, CA, 90071

Tel: (213) 486-9200   Fax: (213) 486-9557   www.capgroup.com

Investment management.

Capital International Ltd., 25 Bedford St., London WC2E 9HN, UK

CAPITAL ONE FINANCIAL CORPORATION

2980 Fairview Park Drive, Ste. 1300, Falls Church, VA, 22042-4525

Tel: (703) 205-1000   Fax: (703) 205-1090   www.capitalone.com

Holding company for credit card companies.

Capital One Bank, 18 Hanover Square, London W1R 9DA, UK

Tel: 44-207-543-2900   Fax: 44-207-543-2955   Contact: Rob Habgood

Capital One Services, Inc., Trent House, Station St., Nottingham NG2 3HX, UK

Tel: 44-115-843-3300   Fax: 44-115-843-3433   Contact: Rob Habgood

CAPTURA, INC.

6710 108th Avenue NE, Kirkland, WA, 98033

Tel: (425) 803-6000   Fax: (425) 803-6100   www.captura.com

Mfr. automated payment software.

Captura UK, Westacott Business Centre, Westacott Way, Maidenhead Berkshire SL6 3RT, UK

CARAUSTAR INDUSTRIES, INC.

3100 Joe Jerkins Blvd., Austell, GA, 30106

Tel: (770) 948-3101   Fax: (770) 732-3401   www.caraustar.com

Engaged in recycling of paper into paperboard.

Caraustar UK, 86 Bison Place, Leyland, Lancanshire PR 53QR, UK

CARAVAN TOURS INC.

401 North Michigan Ave., Chicago, IL, 60611

Tel: (312) 321-9800   Fax: (312) 321-9845   www.caravantours.com

Tour operator.

Caravan Tours Ltd., 59/65 Upper Ground, London SE1 9PQ, UK

CARBOLINE COMPANY

350 Hanley Industrial Court, St. Louis, MO, 63144

Tel: (314) 644-1000   Fax: (314) 644-4617   www.carboline.com

Mfr. coatings and sealants.

StonCor UK Ltd., Torrington Avenue, Coventry CV4 9TJ, UK

Tremco Ltd., 86-88 Bestobell Rd., Slough, Berks SL1 4SZ, UK

CARGILL COTTON USA

7101 Goodlett Farms Parkway, Cordova, TN, 38018

Tel: (901) 937-4500   Fax: (901) 937-4464   www.hohenberg.com

Mfr. cotton.

Cargill Cotton UK, Ralli House, Old Hall Street, Liverpool L3 9PP, UK

Tel: 44-151-242-7500   Fax: 44-151-242-7556

CARGILL, INC.

15407 McGinty Road West, Minnetonka, MN, 55440-5625

Tel: (612) 742-7575   Fax: (612) 742-7393   www.cargill.com

Food products, feeds, animal products.

Cargill PLC, Witham, St. Hughs, Lincoln LN6 9TN, UK

CARLISLE COMPANIES INC.

13925 Ballantyne Corporate Place, Ste. 400, Charlotte, NC, 28277

Tel: (704) 501-1100   Fax: (704) 501-1190   www.carlisle.com

Engaged in rubber, plastics and friction technologies.

Extract Technology Ltd., Bradley Junction Ind. Estate, Leeds Road, Huddersfield, West Yorkshire HD2 1UR, UK

Tel: 44-1484-432727   Fax: 44-1484-432659

CARLISLE SYNTEC SYSTEMS

PO Box 7000, Carlisle, PA, 17013

Tel: (717) 245-7000   Fax: (717) 245-9107   www.carlisle-syntec.com

Mfr. electrometric roofing and waterproofing systems.

Carlisle SynTec Systems UK, Unit 24, The Nursery, Sutton Courtenay, Abingdon Oxon OX14 4UA, UK

Tel: 44-1-235-848-000   Fax: 44-1-235-848-727

CARLSON COMPANIES, INC.

PO Box 59159, Minneapolis, MN, 55459

Tel: (612) 550-4520   Fax: (612) 550-4580   www.cmg.carlson.com

Marketing services agency.

Aegis Carlson, Aegis House, 42 New Street, Daventry NN11 4BU, UK

BBM Carlson, 220 Park Avenue, Aztec West Almondsbury, Bristol BS12 4SB, UK

Carlson Marketing Group, 116 Putney Bridge Road, London SW15 2NQ, UK

TFI Friday's Restaurant, 96/98 Bishops Bridge Road, Bayswater, London W2 5AA, UK

THE CARLYLE GROUP L.P.

1001 Pennsylvania Avenue, NW, Washington, DC, 20004-2505

Tel: (202) 347-2626   Fax: (202) 347-1818   www.thecarlylegroup.com

Global investor in defense contracts.

Carlyle London, 20 Berkeley Square, London W1X 6NB, UK

Tel: 44-207-894-1200   Fax: 44-207-894-1600

CARPENTER TECHNOLOGY CORPORATION

PO Box 14662, Reading, PA, 19612-4662

Tel: (610) 208-2000   Fax: (610) 208-3214   www.cartech.com

Mfr. specialty steels and structural ceramics for casting industrial.

Carpenter Technology (UK) Ltd., 6 Royal House, 11 Market Pl., Redditch Worcs. B98 8AA, UK

Cartech Intl. Ltd., 92C Bruneo Rd., Earlstrees Ind. Estate, Corby, Northants NN17 2JW, UK

CARREKER CORPORATION

4055 Valley View Lane, Ste. 1000, Dallas, TX, 75244

Tel: (972) 458-1981   Fax: (972) 701-0758   www.carreker.com

Mfr. banking software.

Carreker Corporation UK, Eastcheap Court, 5/F, 11 Philpot Lane, London EC3 M 8EA, UK

Tel: 44-207-469-1600   Fax: 44-207-283-5806

CARRIER CORPORATION

One Carrier Place, Farmington, CT, 06034-4015

Tel: (860) 674-3000   Fax: (860) 679-3010   www.carrier.com

Mfr./distributor/services A/C, heating and refrigeration equipment.

Carrier Distribution, Biggin Hill, UK

Tel: 44-1-959-5712   Fax: 44-1-959-570651

CARSEY-WERNER-MANDABACH LLC

4024 Radford Avenue, Studio City, CA, 91604

Tel: (818) 655-5598   Fax: (818) 655-5930   www.cwm.com

Owner of production studios and program distribution.

CW International Distribution, Chesham House, 150 Regent Street, London W1B 5SJ, UK

Tel: 44-207-432-0328

CASCADE CORPORATION

2201 NE 201st Ave., Fairview, OR, 97024-9718

Tel: (503) 669-6300   Fax: (503) 669-6321   www.cascor.com

Mfr. hydraulic forklift truck attachments.

Cascade (UK) Ltd., Bassington Industrial Estate, Cramlington New Town, Northumberland NE23 8AE, UK

Cascade Kenhar Products Ltd., Parkhouse Street Industrial Estate, Kelbrook Road, Openshaw Manchester M11 2DD, UK

Cascade Sheffield, 15 Orgreave Crescent, Dore House Industrial Estate, Handsworth, Sheffield S13 9NQ, UK

CAT PUMPS

1681 94th Lane NE, Minneapolis, MN, 55449-4324

Tel: (763) 780-5440   Fax: (763) 780-2958   www.catpumps.com

Mfr./distributor pumps.

Cat Pumps UK Ltd., Fleet Business Park, Sandy Lane, Church Crookham, Fleet Hampshire GU52 8BF, UK

Tel: 44-1252-622031   Contact: Lez Warren

CATALINA MARKETING CORPORATION

200 Carillon Pkwy., St. Petersburg, FL, 33716

Tel: (727) 579-5000   Fax: (727) 570-8507   www.catmktg.com

Engaged in supermarket couponing on-line.

Catalina Marketing UK Ltd., 1 Westminster Way, Oxford Oxfordshire OX2 0PZ, UK

Tel: 44-1865-200441

CATAPULT COMMUNICATIONS CORPORATION

160 South Whisman Road, Mountain View, CA, 94041

Tel: (650) 960-1025   Fax: (650) 960-1029   www.catapult.com

Mfr. test systems for telecommunications service providers.

Catapult Communications Corp., 1 Lansdowne Court, Bumpers Way, Chippenham, Wiltshire SN14 6RZ, UK

CATERPILLAR INC.

100 NE Adams Street, Peoria, IL, 61629-6105

Tel: (309) 675-1000   Fax: (309) 675-1182   www.cat.com

Mfr. earth/material-handling and construction machinery and equipment and engines.

Caterpillar Tractor Co. Ltd., Desford, Leicester LE9 9JT, UK

Tel: 44-1455-82-6826

CB RICHARD ELLIS SERVICES

200 N. Sepulveda Blvd., Ste. 300, El Segundo, CA, 90245-4380

Tel: (310) 563-8600   Fax: (310) 563-8670   www.cbrichardellis.com

Commercial real estate services.

CB Hillier Parker Ltd., Berkeley Square House, Berkeley Square, London W1X 6BB, UK

CB Hillier Parker Ltd., Berkeley Square House, Berkeley Square, London W1X 6AN, UK

Tel: 44-207-629-6699 Fax: 44-207-409-1476   Contact: Barry White, Co-Chair

CB Hillier Parker Ltd., Cheshire House, 18/20 Booth St., Manchester M2 4AN, UK

Tel: 44-161-455-7666

CBS TELEVISION NETWORK

51 West 52nd Street, New York, NY, 10019

Tel: (212) 975-4321   Fax: (212) 975-9387   www.cbs.com

TV/radio broadcasting, mfr. electronic systems for industry/defense, financial and environmental services.

Ottermill Ltd., Ottery St. Mary, Devon, Essex 11 1AG, UK

Westinghouse Electronics & Control Co., Haden House, Argyle Way, Stevenage, Hertfordshire SG1 2AH, UK

CCH INCORPORATED

2700 Lake Cook Road, Riverwoods, IL, 60015

Tel: (847) 267-7000   Fax: (800) 224-8299   www.cch.com

Provides tax and business law information and software for accounting, legal, human resources, securities and health care professionals.

CCH Editions Ltd., Telford Rd., Bicester, Oxon OX6 0XD, UK

CCITRIAD

804 Las Cimas Pkwy., Ste. 200, Austin, TX, 78746

Tel: (512) 328-2300   Fax: (512) 328-8209   www.cci-triad.com

Technology solutions for the automotive aftermarket and hardlines and lumber industries.

Tridex Systems Ltd., House Binley Business Park, Coventry, West Midlands CV3 2TQ, UK

Tel: 44-1203-636000 Fax: 44-1203-440049

CCS INTERNATIONAL LTD

145 Huguenot St. Suite 310, New Rochelle, NY, 10801

Tel: (914) 654-8700   Fax: (914) 654-1302   www.spyzone.com

Mfr. electronic security products.

CCS Counterspy Shop, 62 S. Audley Street, London W1Y 5DJ, UK

Tel: 44-207-408-0287   Fax: 44-207-629-9538

CDI CORPORATION

1717 Arch Street, 35th Fl., Philadelphia, PA, 19103

Tel: (215) 569-2200   Fax: (215) 569-1300   www.cdicorp.com

Engineering, technical and temporary personnel services.

Anders Elite, 69 Old Broad Street, London EC2M 1NQ, UK

Contact: Ray Shadforth

Anders Elite, Capital House, Houndwell Place, Southampton SO14 1HU, UK

Contact: Paul Scott

Anders Glaser Wills, 15 London Road, Twickenham London TW1 3ST, UK

Tel: 44-181-891-1144

Anders Glaser Wills, Clifton Heights, Triangle West, Bristol BS8 1EJ, UK

Tel: 44-117-922-1441

Anders Glaser Wills, 24 Bennetts Hill, Birmingham B2 5QP, UK

Tel: 44-121-643-5070

Anders Glaser Wills Ltd., 4 Maddison Ct., Maddison St., Southampton S01 0BU, UK

CDI International Ltd., Michael House, 55/57 Chase Side, Southgate London N14 5BU, UK

Harvard Associates, 10 Kingfisher Court, Farnham Road, Slough, Berkshire SL2 1JF, UK

Humana International Group, London, UK

Contact: Doug Bugie, Mng. Dir.

CEILCOTE AIR POLLUTION CONTROL

14955 Sprague Road, Strongsville, OH, 44136

Tel: (440) 243-0700   Fax: (440) 234-3486   www.ceilcoteapc.com

Mfr. corrosion-resistant material, air pollution control equipment, construction services.

Ceilcote UK Ltd., 70 Warwick Street, Birmingham B12 ONL, UK

Tel: 44-121-766-3022

CELL THERAPEUTICS, INC.

201 Elliott Avenue West, Ste. 400, Seattle, WA, 98119-4230

Tel: (206) 282-7100   Fax: (206) 272-4302   www.cticseattle.com

Mfr. pharmaceuticals for cancer treatment.

Cell Therapeutics UK Ltd., 1 Ropemaker Street, London EC2Y 9HT, UK

Tel: 44-208-895-4004   Fax: 44-208-895-4204

CELLSTAR CORPORATION

1730 Briercroft Ct., Carrollton, TX, 75006

Tel: (972) 466-5000   Fax: (972) 466-0288   www.cellstar.com

Provides wireless communications products.

CellStar UK, Unit 2000, Fifth Street Trafford Park, Manchester M17 1JX, UK

Tel: 44-161-888-8500   Fax: 44-161-888-8501

CENDANT CORPORATION

9 West 57th Street, New York, NY, 10019

Tel: (212) 413-1800   Fax: (212) 413-1918   www.cendant.com

Membership-based, direct marketer offering shopping/travel/insurance and dining discount programs

National Car Parks (NCP), Heathrow Airport, London, UK

CENTEX CORPORATION
2728 N. Harwood, Dallas, TX, 75201-1516

Tel: (214) 981-5000　　　Fax: (214) 981-6859　　　www.centex.com

Engaged in home building.

Centex International, London, UK

CENTRA SOFTWARE, INC.
430 Bedford Street, Lexington, MA, 02421

Tel: (781) 861-7000　　　Fax: (781) 863-7288　　　www.centra.com

Mfr. on-line learning software.

Centra Software, Siena Court, The Broadway, Maidenhead SL61NJ, UK

CENTRAL NATIONAL-GOTTESMAN INC.
3 Manhattanville Road, Purchase, NY, 10577-2110

Tel: (914) 696-9000　　　Fax: (914) 696-1066　　　www.cng-inc.com

Distribution of pulp and paper products.

Central National (UK) Ltd., The Pavillions, 1 Weston Rd., Kiln Lane, Epsom Surrey KT17 1JG, UK

Tel: 44-1-372-739-966　Fax: 44-1-372-748-152　Contact: Michael Hobday

CENTURY 21 REAL ESTATE CORPORATION
One Campus Drive, Parsippany, NJ, 07054-3826

Tel: (973) 496-5722　　　Fax: (973) 496-5527　　　www.century21.com

Engaged in real estate sales.

Century 21 United Kingdom, Ltd., Brosnan House, Darkes Lane, Potters Bar Hertfordshire EN6 1BW, UK

CEPHALON, INC.
145 Brandywine Pkwy., West Chester, PA, 19380

Tel: (610) 344-0200　　　Fax: (610) 344-0065　　　www.cephalon.com

Engaged in health science, research and development.

Cephalon UK Limited, 11/13 Frederick Sanger Road, Surrey Research Park, Guildord GU2 5YD, UK

Tel: 44-1-48-345-3360　Fax: 44-1-48-345-3324　Contact: Mark Watling

CERIDIAN CORPORATION
3311 E. Old Shakopee Road, Minneapolis, MN, 55425

Tel: (612) 853-8100　　　Fax: (612) 853-4068　　　www.ceridian.com

Provides diversified information services.

Ceridian Centrefile, 75 Leman St., London E1 8EX, UK

Tel: 44-207-335-3000　Contact: Ron Wood

Ceridian Centrefile, Continental Research, 132-140 Goswell Rd., London EC1V 7DP, UK

Tel: 44-207-490-5944

CERTEGY INC.
11720 Amber park Drive, Ste. 600, Alpharetta, GA, 30004

Tel: (678) 867-8000　　　Fax: (678) 867-8100　　　www.certegy.com

Provides credit, debit and merchant card processing, e-banking, check risk management and check cashing services to financial institutions and merchants worldwide.

Certegy Cheque Services, PO Box 88 Edgbaston, Birmingham B16 9DH, UK

Certegy UK, Radcliffe House, Blenheim Court, Solihull West Midlands B91 2AA, UK

Tel: 44-121-252-4700　Fax: 44-121-252-4882

CH2M HILL INC.
6060 South Willow Drive, Greenwood Village, CO, 80111

Tel: (303) 771-0900　　　Fax: (303) 770-2616　　　www.ch2m.com

Consulting engineers, planners, economists and scientists.

CH2M Hill, Avon House, Kensington Village, West Kensington, London W14 8TS, UK

Tel: 44-207-591-4600　Fax: 44-207-591-4660

CHADBOURNE & PARKE LLP

30 Rockefeller Plaza, New York, NY, 10112-0127

Tel: (212) 408-5100   Fax: (212) 541-5369   www.chadbourne.com

Engaged in international law.

Chadbourne & Parke, Regis House, 45 King William St., London EC4R 9AN, UK

Tel: 44-207-337-8000   Fax: 44-207-337-8001   Contact: Nancy Persechino, Adm. Prtn.

CHARLES RIVER ASSOCIATES INCORPORATED

200 Clarendon Street, Boston, MA, 02116-5092

Tel: (617) 425-3000   Fax: (617) 425-3132   www.crai.com

Provides business consulting services.

Charles River Associates, Berkeley Square House, Berkeley Square, London W1J 6BF, UK

Charles River Associates UK, 1 Undershaft, London EC3A 8EE, UK

Tel: 44-207-664-3700   Fax: 44-207-664-3998   Contact: Robert Laslett, VP

CHARLES RIVER LABORATORIES INTERNATIONAL, INC.

251 Ballardvale Street, Wilmington, MA, 01887-1000

Tel: (978) 658-6000   Fax: (978) 658-7132   www.criver.com

Engaged in sales of pathogen-free, fertilized chicken eggs for drug testing.

Charles River Endosafe, Inc., Manston Road, Margate Kent CT9 4LT, UK

Tel: 44-1843-82-2331

CHATTEM INC.

1715 West 38th Street, Chattanooga, TN, 37409

Tel: (423) 821-4571   Fax: (423) 821-6132   www.chattem.com

Mfr. health and beauty aids.

Chattem (UK) Ltd., Guerry House, Ringway Centre, Edison Rd., Basingstoke, Hampshire RG21 2YH, UK

CHECKFREE CORPORATION

4411 East Jones Bridge Road, Norcross, GA, 30082

Tel: (678) 375-3000   Fax: (678) 375-1477   www.checkfree.com

Engaged in electronic bill paying services.

Checkfree Corporation, 226 Berwick Avenue, 1/F, Slough Berkshire SL1 4QT, UK

Tel: 44-1753-567-896

CHECKPOINT SYSTEMS, INC.

101 Wolf Drive, Thorofare, NJ, 08086

Tel: (856) 848-1800   Fax: (856) 848-0937   www.checkpointsystems.com

Mfr. test, measurement and closed-circuit television systems.

Checkpoint Systems UK Ltd., Ash Industrial Estate, Unit 13, Flex Meadow, Pinnacles West, Harlow Essex CM19 5TJ, UK

Tel: 44-1279-452233   Fax: 44-1279-452884   Contact: Steve Midani, Mng. Dir.

CHEMETALL OAKITE

50 Valley Road, Berkeley Heights, NJ, 07922-2798

Tel: (908) 464-6900   Fax: (908) 464-7914   www.oakite.com

Mfr. chemical products for industry cleaning and metal treating.

Chemetall Speciality Chemicals Ltd., Denbigh Road, Bletchle Milton Keynes, UK

CHEMINEER INC.

PO Box 1123, Dayton, OH, 45401-1123

Tel: (937) 454-3200   Fax: (937) 454-3379   www.chemineer.com

Mfr. fluid agitators and static mixers for chemicals processing.

Chemineer Ltd., 7 Cranmer Rd., West Meadows, Derby DE2 6XT, UK

THE CHERRY CORPORATION

3600 Sunset Ave., PO Box 718, Waukegan, IL, 60087

Tel: (847) 662-9200   Fax: (847) 662-2990   www.cherrycorp.com

Mfr. electrical switches, electronic keyboards, controls and displays.

Cherry Electrical Products Ltd., Coldharbour Lane, Harpenden, Hertfordshire AL5 4UN, UK

Tel: 44-15-8276-3100   Fax: 44-15-8276-8883

CHESAPEAKE CORPORATION

1021 E. Cary St., Richmond, VA, 23218

Tel: (804) 697-1000   Fax: (804) 697-1199   www.cskcorp.com

Provides merchandising services and specialty packaging.

Field Group Plc., Misbourne House, Badminton Court, Old Amersham HP7 0DD, UK

Tel: 44-1494-720200

CHESTERTON BLUMENAUER BINSWANGER

Two Logan Square, 4th Floor, Philadelphia, PA, 19103-2759

Tel: (215) 448-6000   Fax: (215) 448-6238   www.cbbi.com

Real estate and related services.

Chesterton Blumenauer Binswanger, 54 Brook St., London W1A 2BU, UK

Tel: 90-312-2862323

Chesterton Blumenauer Binswanger, 22A The Ropewalk, Nottingham, London NG1 5DT, UK

Chesterton International plc, 30/34 Moorgate, London EC2R 6DN, UK

Chesterton International plc, Swan House, 37/39 High Holborn, London WC1V 6AA, UK

Chesterton International Plc, Minerva House East Parade, Leeds LS1 5PS, UK

CHEVRON PHILLIPS CHEMICAL COMPANY LP

1301 McKinney Street, Houston, TX, 77010

Tel: (713) 754-2000   Fax: (713) 754-2016   www.chevron.com

Mfr. petro chemicals.

Octel Associates, PO Box 17, Oil Sites Rd., Ellesmere Port, South Wirral L65 4HF, UK

The Associated Octel Co., PO Box 17, Oil Sites Rd., Ellesmere Port, South Wirral L65 4HF, UK

CHEVRON TEXACO CORPORATION

575 Market Street, San Francisco, CA, 94105-2856

Tel: (415) 894-7700   Fax: (415) 894-2248   www.chevrontexaco.com

Oil exploration, production and petroleum products.

ChevronTexaco, One Knightsbridge Green, London SWIX7QJ, UK

CHICAGO BRIDGE & IRON COMPANY (CBI)

10200 Grogan's Mill Road, Suite 300, The Woodlands, TX, 77380

Tel: (281) 774-2200   Fax: (281) 774-2202   www.chicago-bridge.com

Holding company: engaged in metal plate fabricating, construction and oil and gas drilling.

CBI Constructors, Ltd., Willowbank House, 97 Oxford Road, Uxbridge Middlesex UB8 1LU, UK

CHICAGO RAWHIDE INDUSTRIES (CRI)

735 Tollgate Road, Elgin, IL, 60123

Tel: (847) 742-7840   Fax: (847) 742-7845   www.chicago-rawhide.com

Mfr. shaft and face seals.

CR Industrial Prdts. Ltd., Elmdon Trading Estate, Unit 30, Bickenhill Lane, Marston Green, Birmingham B37 7HE, UK

CHIEF INDUSTRIES INC.

3942 West Old Highway 30, Grand Island, NE, 68802-2078

Tel: (308) 382-8820   Fax: (308) 381-7221   www.chiefind.com

Mfr. grain bins, steel buildings, grain handling and drying equipment, elevator legs and components.

Chief Industries UK Ltd., Bentall Industrial Estates, Maldon, Essex CM9 6JA, UK

Tel: 44-1621-868944   Fax: 44-1621-868955

CHIRON CORPORATION

4560 Horton Street, Emeryville, CA, 94608-2916

Tel: (510) 655-8730   Fax: (510) 655-9910   www.chiron.com

Engaged in biotechnology; biopharmaceuticals, blood testing and vaccines.

Chiron Diagnostics, Centaur House, Park Lane, Cranford Hounslow TW5 9RR, UK
Tel: 44-208-580-4000

CHOICE HOTELS INTERNATIONAL, INC.

10750 Columbia Pike, Silver Springs, MD, 20902

Tel: (301) 592-5000   Fax: (301) 592-6227   www.choicehotels.com

Hotel franchises, including Comfort Inn, Econo Lodge, Roadway Inn and Quality.

Choice Hotels International, Premier House, 1 Warwick Row, London SW1E 5ER, UK
Tel: 44-207-808-5656   Fax: 44-207-808-5657

THE CHRISTIAN SCIENCE PUBLISHING SOCIETY

1 Norway Street, Boston, MA, 02115

Tel: (617) 450-2000   Fax: (617) 450-7575   www.christianscience.com

Publishing company.

The Christian Science Monitor, 29 Chartfield Ave., London SW15 6HW, UK
Tel: 44-181-780-5931   Contact: Alexander MacLeod   Emp: 1

THE CHUBB CORPORATION

15 Mountain View Road, Warren, NJ, 07061-1615

Tel: (908) 580-2000   Fax: (908) 580-3606   www.chubb.com

Holding company for property and casualty insurance and liability insurance for corporate executives.

Chubb Insurance Company of Europe, S.A., 52-54 Leadenhall Street, London EC3A 2BJ, UK
Tel: 44-207-867-5555   Fax: 44-207-867-8687

Chubb Insurance Company of Europe, SA, 106 Fenchurch St., London EC3M 5JB, UK
Tel: 44-207-867-5555   Fax: 44-207-481-2256

Chubb Insurance Company of Europe, SA, 6th Fl., Cornwall Court, 19 Cornwall St., Birmingham B3 2DT, UK
Tel: 44-121-236-8803   Fax: 44-121-236-8994

Chubb Insurance Company of Europe, SA, 4/6 Abbey Gardens, Rading, Berkshire RG1 3BA, UK
Tel: 44-1734-510577   Fax: 44-1734-10505

Chubb Insurance Company of Europe, SA, 8th Fl., 82 King St., Manchester M1 4WQ, UK
Tel: 44-161-839-5624   Fax: 44-161-839-5625

Lloyds of London/Chubb Insurance Company of Europe, SA, Lloyds Bldg., 1 Lime St., London EC3M 7HA, UK
Tel: 44-207-867-555   Fax: 44-207-929-0166

CHURCH & DWIGHT COMPANY, INC.

469 North Harrison Street, Princeton, NJ, 08543

Tel: (609) 683-5900   Fax: (609) 497-7269   www.churchdwight.com

Specialty chemicals and consumer products.

Brotherton Specialty Products, Calder Vale Rd., Wakefield, West Yorkshire WF1 5PH, UK
Tel: 44-1924-371-919   Contact: Roger Perry, Mng. Dir.

CIENA CORPORATION

1201 Winterson Road, Linthicum, MD, 21090-2205

Tel: (410) 865-8500   Fax: (410) 694-5750   www.ciena.com

Mfr. optical network switching hardware.

CIENA Ltd., 43-51 Worship Street, London EC2A 2DX, UK
Tel: 44-207-125-5500   Fax: 44-207-125-5501

CIGNA COMPANIES

One Liberty Place, Philadelphia, PA, 19192

Tel: (215) 761-1000   Fax: (215) 761-5511   www.cigna.com

Insurance, invest, health care and other financial services.

CIGNA Insurance Co. of Europe SA/NV, Cigna House, 8 Lime St., London EC3M 7NA, UK

CIGNA Life Insurance Company of Europe S.A.-N.V., Tower House, 38 Trinity Square, London EC3N 4DJ, UK

Tel: 44-207-200-2005   Fax: 44-207-200-2004   Contact: Philippa Dickson

CIGNA Reinsurance Co. (UK) Ltd., Cigna House, 8 Lime St., London EC3M 7NA, UK

CIGNA Services UK Ltd., Cigna House, 8 Lime St., London EC3M 7NA, UK

CIGNA UK Holding Ltd., Cigna House, 8 Lime St., London EC3M 7NA, UK

CIGNA Unit Trust Managers Ltd., Crusader House, Reigate, Surrey RH2 8BL, UK

Crusader Managed Pension Funds Ltd., Crusader House, Reigate, Surrey RH2 8BL, UK

Crusader Staff Pension Investments Ltd., Crusader House, Reigate, Surrey RH2 8BL, UK

Ernest Linsdell Ltd., Commonwealth House, 1-19 New Oxford St., London WCIA 1NB, UK

Esis Intl. Inc., Chesterfield House, 26-28 Fenchurch St., London EC3M 3DH, UK

Growth Property Management Co. Ltd., Crusader House, Reigate, Surrey RH2 8BL, UK

Insurance Co. of North America, Cigna House, 8 Lime St., London EC3M 7NA, UK

Insurance Co. of North America (UK) Ltd., Cigna House, 8 Lime St., London EC3M 7NA, UK

Plough Investment Properties Ltd., Crusader House, Reigate, Surrey RH2 8BL, UK

CINCINNATI MACHINE INC.

4701 Marburg Ave., Cincinnati, OH, 45209

Tel: (513) 841-8100   Fax: (513) 841-8919   www.cinmach.com

Mfr. of CNC machine tools, such as turning centers, vertical machining centers and horizontal machining centers.

Cincinnati Machine, UK Ltd., Kingsbury Road, PO Box 505, Birmingham B24 0QU, UK

Tel: 44-121-351-3821

CINCOM SYSTEMS INC.

55 Merchant Street, Cincinnati, OH, 45446

Tel: (513) 612-2300   Fax: (513) 481-8332   www.cincom.com

Develop/distributor computer software.

Cincom Systems Inc., 3 Swan Street, Wilmslow, Cheshire SK9 1HF, UK

Cincom Systems Inc., 1 Grenfel Road, Maidenhead, Maidenhead SL6 1HN, UK

CINERGY CORPORATION

139 East Fourth Street, Cincinnati, OH, 45202

Tel: (513) 421-9500   Fax: (513) 287-3171   www.cinergy.com

Utility holding company - generates, transmits and distributes electricity and natural gas.

Midlands Electricity Plc., London, UK

CIRRUS LOGIC, INC.

4210 South industrial Drive, Austin, TX, 78744

Tel: (512) 445-7222   Fax: (512) 445-7581   www.cirrus.com

Engaged in manufacture of semiconductors and integrated circuits for entertainment devices.

Cirrus Logic UK, 4-5 Anglers Court, 33-44 Spittal Street, Marlow, Bucks SL7 1DB, UK

Tel: 44-1628-472-211

CISCO SYSTEMS, INC.

170 West Tasman Drive, San Jose, CA, 95134-1706

Tel: (408) 526-4000   Fax: (408) 526-4100   www.cisco.com

Develop/mfr./market computer hardware and software networking systems.

Cisco Systems, 3/F, Old Broad Street, London EC2 1HQ, UK

Tel: 44-207-496-3700   Fax: 44-207-496-3701

Cisco Systems, Eagle Court Concorde Business Park, Threapwood Road, Manchester M22 ORR, UK

Tel: 44-161-932-6270   Fax: 44-161-932-6333

Cisco Systems Ltd., 3 The Square, Stockley Park, Uxbridge Middlesex, UK

Tel: 44-181-756-8000   Fax: 44-181-756-8099

CITIGROUP, INC.

399 Park Avenue, New York, NY, 10022

Tel: (212) 559-1000   Fax: (212) 559-3646   www.citigroup.com

Provides insurance and financial services worldwide.

Citigroup, 332 Oxford Street, London W1N 9AA, UK

Citigroup, PO Box 200, Cottons Centre, Hay's Lane, London SE1 2QT, UK

Contact: Janet M. Allen, Mgr.

Citigroup, 65 Curzon St., London W1Y 7PE, UK

Tel: 44-207-355-4411   Contact: Tom Mulvihill, Mgr.

CITRIX SYSTEMS, INC.

6400 NW 6th Way, Fort Lauderdale, FL, 33309

Tel: (954) 267-3000   Fax: (954) 267-9319   www.citrix.com

Developer of computer software.

Citrix Systems UK Ltd., Buckingham Court, Kingsmead Business Park, London Road, High Wycombe Bucks HP11 1JU, UK

Tel: 44-1494-684900   Fax: 44-1494-684998

CLARCOR INC.

2323 Sixth Street, PO Box 7007, Rockford, IL, 61125

Tel: (815) 962-8867   Fax: (815) 962-0417   www.clarcor.com

Mfr. filtration products and consumer packaging products.

Baldwin Filters Ltd., Unit 2A, Daimler Close, Royal Oak Industrial Estate, Daventry NN11 5QJ, UK

Facet Industrial U.K. Ltd., Div. CLARCOR, Treforest Industrial Estate, G1&G4, Pontypridd Mid Glamorgan CF37 5YL, UK

CLARUS CORPORATION

3970 Johns Creek Court, Suwanee, GA, 30024

Tel: (770) 291-3900   Fax: (770) 291-8599   www.claruscorp.com

Mfr. procurement software.

Clarus EMEA, Clarus House Waltham Road, White Waltham, Maidenhead Berks SL6 3HY, UK

Tel: 44-1628-519900

CLAYTON INDUSTRIES

4213 N. Temple City Blvd., El Monte, CA, 91731

Tel: (626) 443-9381   Fax: (626) 442-1701   www.claytonindustries.com

Mfr. steam generators, dynamometers and water treatment chemicals.

Clayton Thermal Products, 3 Tatton Court, Kingsland Grange, Woolston, Warrington Cheshire WA I 4RW, UK

Tel: 44-1-925-823123   Fax: 44-1-925-817373

CLEAR CHANNEL COMMUNICATIONS

200 East Basse Road, San Antonio, TX, 78209

Tel: (210) 822-2828   Fax: (210) 822-2299   www.clearchannel.com

Owns, manages, promotes and produces concerts and shows; programs and sells airtime for radio stations, owns and places outdoor advertising displays and provides agent services to athletes and broadcasters.

More Group, 33 Golden Square, London W1R 3PA, UK

Tel: 44-207-287-6100   Fax: 44-20-287-9149

CLEARORBIT, INC.

6805 Capital of Texas Hwy., Ste. 370, Austin, TX, 78731

Tel: (512) 231-8191   Fax: (512) 231-0192   www.clearorbit.com

Mfr. software.

ClearOrbit UK, Glenfield Park 2, Blakewater Road, Blackburn Lancashire BB1 5QH, UK

CLEARY GOTTLIEB STEEN & HAMILTON

One Liberty Plaza, New York, NY, 10006

Tel: (212) 225-2000   Fax: (212) 225-3999   www.cgsh.com

Engaged in international law.

Cleary, Gottlieb, Steen & Hamilton, City Place House, 55 Basinghall St., London EC2V 5EH, UK

CLICK2LEARN.COM, INC.

110 110th Avenue NE, Bellevue, WA, 98004

Tel: (425) 462-0501   Fax: (425) 637-1504   www.click2learn.com

Provides software and services for developing on-line educational programs.

Click2learn.Com Ltd., 225 Marsh Wall, Docklands, London E14 9FW, UK

Tel: 44-20-7517-4200   Fax: 44-20-7517-4201

CLIFFORD CHANCE ROGERS & WELLS

200 Park Avenue, New York, NY, 10166-0153

Tel: (212) 878-8000   Fax: (212) 878-8375   www.cliffordchance.com

Engaged in international law.

Clifford Chance Rogers & Wells, 200 Aldersgate Street, London EC1A 4JJ, UK

Tel: 44-207-600-1000   Fax: 44-207-600-5555   Contact: Peter Charlton

CMGI, INC.

100 Brickstone Square, Andover, MA, 01810

Tel: (978) 684-3600   Fax: (978) 684-3814   www.cmgi.com

Holding company engaged in direct marketing and fulfillment and internet companies.

Flycast UK Limited, Berkeley Square House, 2/F, Mayfair London W1X 6EA, UK

CNA FINANCIAL CORPORATION

CNA Plaza, Chicago, IL, 60685

Tel: (312) 822-5000   Fax: (312) 822-6419   www.cna.com

Commercial property/casualty insurance policies.

CNA Insurance Company (Europe) Limited (CIE), London, UK

CNA/Marine Insurance Company, London, UK

CNH (CASE NEW HOLLAND) GLOBAL

100 South Saunders Road, Lake Forest, IL, 60045

Tel: (847) 955-3821   Fax: (847) 955-3961   www.casecorp.com

Mfr. and sale of agricultural and construction equipment.

Fermec Holdings Ltd., Barton Dock Rd., Stretford, Manchester M32 0YH, UK

Tel: 44-161-865-4400   Fax: 44-161-865-5427

Gem Sprayers Ltd., Station Rd., North Hykeham, Lincoln LN6 9AA, UK

Tel: 44-1522-500909   Fax: 44-1522-500662

J.I. Case Europe Ltd., Wheatley Hall Rd., Doncaster South Yorkshire DN2 4PG, UK

Tel: 44-1302-73-3200   Fax: 44-1302-76-1038   Contact: Felicia Howell, Gen. Mgr.

COACH LEATHERWEAR COMPANY

516 West 34th Street, New York, NY, 10001

Tel: (212) 594-1850   Fax: (212) 594-1682   www.coach.com

Mfr. and sales of high-quality leather products, including handbags, wallets and shoes.

The Coach Store, 8 Sloane Street, London SW1X 9LE, UK

THE COCA-COLA COMPANY

1 Coca Cola Plaza, Atlanta, GA, 30313

Tel: (404) 676-2121   Fax: (404) 676-6792   www.coca-cola.com

Mfr./marketing/distributor soft drinks, syrups and concentrates, juice and juice-drink products.

Coca-Cola Beverages plc, One Queen Caroline Street, London W6 9HQ, UK

Tel: 44-181-237-3000

Coca-Cola Great Britain, 1 Charter Place, Uxbridge, Middlesex UB8 1ST, UK

Coca-Cola Mid-East Ltd., Constitution House, 56 High St., Windsor Berkshire SL4 1JY, UK

Contact: A.R.C. Allan

Coca-Cola Northwest Europe, Pemberton House, 15 Wrights Lane, London W8 5SN, UK

Contact: John K. Sheppard

COGNEX CORPORATION

1 Vision Drive, Natick, MA, 01760

Tel: (508) 650-3000   Fax: (508) 650-3333   www.cognex.com

Mfr. machine vision systems.

Cognex Corporation Canada, Units 7-9, First Quarter, Blenheim Road, Epson Surrey KT19 9QN, UK

Tel: 44-1372-726150   Fax: 44-1372-726276

Cognex Corporation UK, Chancery House, 199 Silbury Boulevard, Milton Keynes MK9 1JL, UK

Tel: 44-1908-206000   Fax: 44-1908-392463

COGNITRONICS CORPORATION

3 Corporate Drive, Danbury, CT, 06810-4130

Tel: (203) 830-3400   Fax: (203) 830-3405   www.cognitronics.com

Mfr. telephone call processing products.

Dacon Electronics Plc., One Enterprise Way, Hemel Hempstead, Hertfordshire HP2 7YJ, UK

Tel: 44-1442-233222   Fax: 44-1442-219653   Contact: Roy Strutt, Mng. Dir.

COGNIZANT TECHNOLOGY SOLUTIONS CORPORATION

500 Glenpointe Centre West, Teaneck, NJ, 07666

Tel: (201) 801-0233   Fax: (201) 801-0243   www.cognizant.com

Provides software development , application management, computer date corrections, and currency conversion.

Cognizant Technology Solutions, 20 Orange Street, London WC2H 7ED, UK

COGSDILL TOOL PRODUCTS INC.

PO Box 7007, Camden, SC, 29020

Tel: (803) 438-4000   Fax: (803) 438-5263   www.cogsdill.com

Mfr. precision metalworking tools.

Cogsdill-Nuneaton Ltd., Tenlons Road, Nuneaton, UK

Tel: 44-120-338-3792

Cogsdill-Nuneaton Ltd., Holbrook Industrial Estate, Sheffield S19 5FR, UK

COHERENT INC.

5100 Patrick Henry Drive, PO Box 54980, Santa Clara, CA, 95056

Tel: (408) 764-4000   Fax: (408) 764-4800   www.cohr.com

Mfr. lasers for science, industrial and medical.

Coherent (UK) Ltd., Cambridge Science Park, Milton Rd., Cambridge CB4 4FR, UK

Coherent Optics (Europe) Ltd., 28-35 Ashville Way, Whetstone, Leicester LE8 6NU, UK

Tel: 44-1162-867-110

COIN ACCEPTORS INC. (COINCO)

300 Hunter Ave., St. Louis, MO, 63124

Tel: (314) 725-0100   Fax: (314) 725-1243   www.coinco.com

Coin mechanisms for vending machinery.

Coin Acceptors Europe Ltd., Coinco House, Imberhome Lane, East Grinstead, Sussex RH19 1QZ, UK

Tel: 44-1342-315724   Fax: 44-1342-313850

THE COLEMAN COMPANY, INC.

3600 N. Hydraulic, Wichita, KS, 67219

Tel: (316) 832-2700   Fax: (316) 832-2794   www.colemanoutdoors.com

Mfr. distributor and sales of camping and outdoor recreation products.

Coleman U.K. PLC, Gordano Gate Portishead, Bristol BS20 7GG, UK

COLFAX CORPORATION

9211 Forest Hill Avenue, Ste. 109, Richmond, VA, 23235

Tel: (804) 560-4070   Fax: (804) 560-4076   www.colfaxcorp.com

Mfr. industrial clutches and brakes and motion control products and components.

Warner Electric UK, St Helen Auckland, Bishop Auckland, County Durham DL14 9AA, UK

COLFAX PUMP GROUP, DIV. COLFAX INC.

1710 Airport Road, PO Box 5020, Monroe, NC, 28111-5020

Tel: (704) 289-6511   Fax: (704) 289-4839   www.colfaxpump.com

Mfr. rotary and centrifugal pumps.

IMO Industries (UK) Ltd., TransInstruments Div., Lennon Rd., Basingstoke, Hampshire RG22 4AW, UK

Morse Controls Ltd., Christopher Martin Rd., Basildon, Essex SS14 3ES, UK

COLGATE-PALMOLIVE COMPANY

300 Park Ave., New York, NY, 10022

Tel: (212) 310-2000   Fax: (212) 310-2919   www.colgate.com

Mfr. pharmaceuticals, cosmetics, toiletries and detergents.

Colgate-Palmolive Ltd., Guilford Business Park, Middleton Rd., Guilford Surrey, UK

COLLAGEN TECHNOLOGIES, INC.

2300 West Cornell Street, Milwaukee, WI, 53209

Tel: (414) 449-9267   Fax: www.cohensiontech.com

Mfr. prod for repair/replacement of damaged human tissue.

Collagen UK Ltd., The Business Centre, 6 Bertie Road, Thame, Oxfordshire OX9 3 FR, UK

COLLIERS INTERNATIONAL PROPERTY CONSULTANTS INC.

84 State Street, 3rd Fl., Boston, MA, 02109

Tel: (617) 722-0221   Fax: (617) 722-0224   www.colliers.com

Engaged in commercial real estate.

Colliers International, 14 Manchester, London W1U 3PP, UK

COMCAST CORPORATION

1500 Market St., Philadelphia, PA, 19102

Tel: (215) 665-1700   Fax: (215) 981-7790   www.comcast.com

Provides cable and broadband services and QVC electronic retailing.

QVC England, Marco Polo House, Chelsea Bridge, 346 Queenstown Road, London SW8 4NQ, UK

QVC England, South Boundary Road, Knowsley Industrial Park, Knowsley Liverpool L70 2QA, UK

COMDISCO HOLDING COMPANY

6111 N. River Road, Rosemont, IL, 60018

Tel: (847) 698-3000   Fax: (847) 518-5440   www.comdisco.com

Hi-tech asset and facility management and equipment leasing.

Comdisco United Kingdom, Ltd., Coventry, UK

COMERGENT TECHNOLOGIES, INC.

1201 Radio Road, Redwood City, CA, 94065

Tel: (650) 232-6000   Fax: (650) 232-6010   www.comergent.com

Mfr. sales software.

Comergent UK, 200 Brook Drive, Green Park, Reading, Berkshire RG2 6UB, UK
Tel: 44-118-949-7022

COMMERCE ONE, INC.

4440 Rosewood Dr., Pleasanton, CA, 94588-3050

Tel: (925) 520-6000   Fax: (925) 520-6060   www.commerceone.com

Provides software and services.

Commerce One UK Ltd., Minton Place, Victoria Street, Windsor Berkshire SL4 1EG, UK
Tel: 44-1753-483-000

COMMUNICATIONS SYSTEMS INC.

213 S. Main Street, Hector, MN, 55342

Tel: (320) 848-6231   Fax: (320) 848-2702   www.commsystems.com

Mfr. telecommunications equipment.

Austin Taylor Communications Ltd., Bethesda Gwynedd LL57 3BX, UK
Tel: 44-1248-600561   Contact: John Hudson   Emp: 150

COMMWORKS CORPORATION

3800 Golf Road, Rolling Meadows, IL, 60008

Tel: (847) 262-5000   Fax: (847) 262-0327   www.commworks.com

Provides Internet protocol-based network access software and equipment.

Commworks Europe, Boundary Way, Hemel Hempstead, Hertfordshire HP2 7YU, UK

Tel: 44-1442-432670

COMPUTER ASSOCIATES INTERNATIONAL INC.

One Computer Associates Plaza, Islandia, NY, 11788

Tel: (516) 342-5224   Fax: (516) 342-5329   www.cai.com

Integrated business software for enterprise computing and information management, application development, manufacturing, financial applications and professional services.

Computer Associates Plc, Computer Associates House, 183/187 Bath Rd., Slough, Berkshire SL1 4AA, UK

Tel: 44-1753-577-733

COMPUTER HORIZONS CORPORATION

49 Old Bloomfield Ave., Mountain Lakes, NJ, 07046-1495

Tel: (973) 299-4000   Fax: (973) 402-7988   www.computerhorizons.com

Engaged in software development.

Computer Horizons ISG, Berkshire House, Thames Side, Windsor Berkshire SL4 1QN, UK

Tel: 44-1753-753-123

COMPUTER NETWORK TECHNOLOGY CORPORATION

6000 Nathan Lane, Plymouth, MN, 55442

Tel: (763) 268-6000   Fax: (763) 268-6800   www.cnt.com

Engaged in the sale of storage networking products for creating and connecting storage area networks.

CNT UK, 2 Langley Quay, Waterside Drive, Langley Slough SL3 6EX, UK

COMPUTER SCIENCES CORPORATION

2100 East Grand Ave., El Segundo, CA, 90245

Tel: (310) 615-0311   Fax: (310) 322-9768   www.csc.com

Information technology services, management consulting, systems integration, outsourcing.

CSC Computer Sciences Ltd., 279 Farnborough Rd., Farnborough, Hampshire GU14 7LS, UK

Contact: Ronald W. Mackintosh, Group Pres.

COMPUTER TASK GROUP, INC.

800 Delaware Avenue, Buffalo, NY, 14209-2094

Tel: (716) 882-8000   Fax: (716) 887-7456   www.ctg.com

Provides data processing information through information technology.

Computer Task Group, Inc., 11 Beacontree Plaza, Gillette Way, Reading Berkshire RG2 OBS, UK

COMPUWARE CORPORATION

31440 Northwestern Hwy., Farmington Hills, MI, 48334-2564

Tel: (248) 737-7300   Fax: (248) 737-7108   www.compuware.com

Develop and market software for enterprise and e-commerce solutions.

Compuware Ltd., 163 Bath Road, Slough Berkshire SL1 4AA, UK

Tel: 44-1753-774-000   Fax: 44-1753-774-200

Compuware Ltd., Eagle Court, Concord Business Park, Threapwood Road, Manchester M22 0RR, UK

Tel: 44-161-932-6229

COMSHARE INC.

555 Briarwood Circle, Ste. 200, Ann Arbor, MI, 48108-3302

Tel: (734) 994-4800   Fax: (734) 994-5895   www.comshare.com

Managerial application software.

Comshare Ltd., 22 Chelsea Manor St., London SW3 5RL, UK

COMVERSE, INC.

100 Quannapowitt Parkway, Wakefield, MA, 01880

Tel: (781) 246-9000   Fax: (781) 224-8143   www.comverse.com

Provides communications solutions.

Comverse Infosys UK, Ltd., Hertford Place Denham Way, Maple Cross, Rickmansworth Hertfordshire WD3 2XF, UK

Tel: 44-1923-717-432   Fax: 44-1923-717-311

Loronix, Div. Comverse Infosys, Unit 1B, Intec 2, Wade Road, Basingstoke Hants RG24 8NE, UK

Tel: 44-12563-50711

CONAGRA FOODS, INC.

One ConAgra Drive, Omaha, NE, 68102-5001

Tel: (402) 595-4000   Fax: (402) 595-4707   www.conagra.com

Prepared/frozen foods, grains, flour, animal feeds, agro chemicals, poultry, meat, dairy products, including Healthy Choice, Butterball and Hunt's.

ConAgra Inc., UK

CONCERTO SOFTWARE

6 Technology Park Drive, Westford, MA, 01886

Tel: (978) 952-0200   Fax: (978) 952-0201   www.concerto.com

Mfr. call-center software for telephone operations.

Concerto UK Ltd., Elvian House, Nixey Close, Slough, Berkshire SL1 1ND, UK

Tel: 44-1753-756-700   Fax: 44-1753-756-701

THE CONCOURS GROUP, INC.

800 Rockmead Drive, Ste. 151, Kingwood, TX, 77339

Tel: (281) 359-3464   Fax: (281) 359-3443   www.concoursgroup.com

Provides e-business information technology.

Concours Group UK, 20 New Bond Street, London W1Y OAA, UK

Tel: 44-207-535-2800

CONCUR TECHNOLOGIES, INC.

6222 185th Avenue NE, Redmond, WA, 98052

Tel: (425) 702-8808   Fax: (425) 702-8828   www.concur.com

Mfr. software.

Concur UK, St. Mary's Court, The Broadway, Old Amersham, Buckinghamshire HP7 0UT, UK

CONCURRENT COMPUTER CORPORATION

4375 River Green Pkwy., Duluth, GA, 30096

Tel: (678) 258-4000   Fax: (678) 258-4300   www.ccur.com

Mfr. computer systems and software.

Concurrent Computer Corporation Ltd., Concurrent House, Railway Terrace, Slough Berkshire SL2 5BY, UK

Tel: 44-1-753-216800   Fax: 44-1-753-571661

CONDE NAST PUBLICATIONS INC.

1440 Broadway, 11th Fl., New York, NY, 10018

Tel: (212) 286-3700   Fax: (212) 286-5960   www.condenast.com

Publishing company.

Conde Nast Publications UK, Vogue House, Hanover Sq., London W1R 0AD, UK

CONEXANT SYSTEMS, INC.

4311 Jamboree Road, PO Box C, Newport Beach, CA, 92658-8902

Tel: (949) 483-4600   Fax: (949) 483-4078   www.conexant.com

Provides semiconductor products for communications electronics.

Conexant Systems UK Ltd., Berkshire Court, Western Road Bracknell, Berkshire RG12 1RE, UK

Tel: 44-1344-486-444   Fax: 44-1344-486-555

CONOCO INC.

600 N. Dairy Ashford, Houston, TX, 77252

Tel: (281) 293-1000   Fax: (281) 293-1440   www.conoco.com

Oil, gas, coal, chemicals and minerals.

Conch Methane Services Ltd., c/o Shell Intl. Gas Ltd., Shell Centre, London SE1 7NA, UK

Conoco (UK) Ltd., South Denes Rd., Great Yarmouth, Norfolk NR30 3QD, UK

Conoco Ltd., Park House, 116 Park St., London WIY 4NN, UK

Conoco Ltd., Conoco House, 230 Blackfriars Rd., London SE1 8NR, UK

Continental Oil Holdings Ltd., 103/105 Wigmore St., London W1H OEL, UK

Humber Refinery, South Killingholme, South Humberside DN40 3DW, UK

Vinatex Ltd., New Lane, Havant, Hampshire P09 2NQ, UK

CONSO INTERNATIONAL CORPORATION

513 North Duncan Bypass, Union, SC, 29379

Tel: (864) 427-9004   Fax: (864) 427-8820   www.conso.com

Mfr. of decorative trimming for home furnishings.

BT Products, Div. Conso International, PO Box 46, Coronation Street, Stockport, Cheshire SK5 7PJ, UK

CONSOLIDATED FREIGHTWAYS CORPORATION

16400 S.E. CF Way, Vancouver, WA, 98683

Tel: (360) 448-4000   Fax: (360) 448-4301   www.cf.com

Engaged in freight forwarding and logistics services.

Consolidated Freightways Corp., London, UK

CONSTELLATION BRANDS, INC.

300 Willowbrook Office Park, Fairport, NY, 14450

Tel: (716) 218-2169   Fax: (716) 218-6216   www.cbrands.com

Distributes wines and spirits.

Barton Intl. Ltd., 5th Fl., Sackville House, 40 Piccadilly, London W1V 9PA, UK

Matthew Clark Plc, Whitechurch Lane, Bristol BS14 0JZ, UK

Tel: 44-1275-830-345   Contact: Peter Aikens, CEO

CONSTRUCTION SPECIALTIES INC.

3 Werner Way, Lebanon, NJ, 08833

Tel: (908) 236-0800   Fax: (908) 236-0801   www.c-sgroup.com

Mfr. architectural building products.

Construction Specialties (UK) Ltd., Conspec House, St. Andrews Way Ind. Estate, Bicester Rd., Aylesbur Buckinghamshire HP19 3AF, UK

Tel: 44-1-2963-99700   Fax: 44-1-2963-99444   Contact: Robert Adams, Mng. Dir.

CONTINENTAL AIRLINES INC.

1600 Smith St., Houston, TX, 77002

Tel: (713) 324-5000   Fax: (713) 324-2637   www.continental.com

International airline carrier.

Continental Airlines Inc., Gatwick Airport, West Sussex, UK

CONVERGYS CORPORATION

201 E. 4th St., Cincinnati, OH, 45202

Tel: (513) 723-7000   Fax: (513) 421-8624   www.convergys.com

Engaged in data bill processing, telemarketing and customer services representation for major corporations.

Convergys Corporation, Baron House, Neville St., Newcastle NE1 5EA, UK

Tel: 44-191-233-3000

Convergys Corporation, 5 Bath Road, Slough, Berkshire SL1 3UA, UK

Tel: 44-1753-727700

COOPER BUSSMANN

PO Box 14460, St. Louis, MO, 63178-4460

Tel: (636) 394-2877   Fax: (636) 527-1405   www.bussmann.com

Mfr. and markets circuit protection products for the electrical, electronic, and automotive industries.

Bussmann UK Ltd., Burton-on-the-Wolds, Leicestershire LE12 5TH, UK

Tel: 44 1509 882737   Fax: 44 1509 882786

Cooper (UK) Ltd., Bussmann Division, Burton-on-the-Wolds, Leicestershire LE12 5TH, UK

Tel: 44-1509-882737

COOPER CAMERON CORPORATION

515 Post Oak Blvd., Ste.1200, Houston, TX, 77027

Tel: (713) 513-3300   Fax: (713) 513-3355   www.coopercameron.com

Mfr. oil and gas industry equipment.

Cooper Cameron UK, Unit 1-2, Boundary Rd., Harfrey's Ind. Est., Great Yarmouth Norfolk NR31 OLY, UK

Cooper Cameron UK, 5 Mondial Way Harlington, Hayes, London UB3 5AR, UK

Tel: 44-181-990-1800

THE COOPER COMPANIES, INC.

6140 Stoneridge Mall Rd., Ste. 590, Pleasanton, CA, 94588

Tel: (925) 460-3600   Fax: (925) 460-3649   www.coopercos.com

Mfr. contact lenses and gynecological instruments.

Cooper Vision UK Ltd., Hamble Hampshire, UK

COOPER INDUSTRIES INC.

6600 Travis Street, Ste. 5800, Houston, TX, 77002

Tel: (713) 209-8400   Fax: (713) 209-8995   www.cooperindustries.com

Mfr./distributor electrical products, tools, hardware and automotive products, fuses and accessories for electronic applications and circuit boards.

Cooper (UK) Ltd. Embray Contractors, Unit 5C, Clay Flatts, Industrial Estate, Wokingham Cumbria CA14 3YD, UK

Tel: 44-1900-970088   Fax: 44-1900-870099

Cooper (UK) Ltd., Bussmann Division, Burton-on-the-Wolds, Leicestershire LE12 5TH, UK

Tel: 44-1509-882737   Fax: 44-1509-882786

Cooper Automotive Europe - Champion Spark Plug Division, Arrowebrook Rd., Upton Wirral, Merseyside L49 0UQ, UK

Tel: 44-151-522-3000

Cooper Menvier, Southam Road, Banbury, Oxfordshire OX16 7RY, UK

Tel: 44-1295-256363

COOPER TIRE & RUBBER CO.

701 Lima Ave., Findlay, OH, 45840

Tel: (419) 423-1321   Fax: (419) 424-4108   www.coopertire.com

Mfr. and marketing of tires and automotive products.

Cooper Avon Tyres Ltd., Bath Road, Melksham, Wiltshire SN12 8AA, UK

Tel: 44-1225-703101   Fax: 44-1225-707880

COOPER TURBOCOMPRESSOR

3101 Broadway, PO Box 209, Buffalo, NY, 14225-0209

Tel: (716) 896-6600   Fax: (716) 896-1233   www.turbocompressor.com

Provides products and services for centrifugal air compression equipment for manufacturing and process air applications.

Cooper Turbocompressor UK, Cooper Cameron House, 5 Mondial Way, Middlesex UB35AR, UK

Tel: 44-181-990-1950   Fax: 44-181-990-1955

COOPERATIVE COMPUTING, INC.

804 Las Cimas Parkway, Ste. 200, Austin, TX, 78746

Tel: (512) 328-2300   Fax: (512) 326-6461   www.cci-triad.com

Mfr. information management software.

United Kingdom Tridex Systems, House Binley Business Park Coventry, West Midlands CV3 2TQ, UK

Tel: 44-247-663-6000

COOPER-STANDARD AUTOMOTIVE GROUP

2401 South Gulley Road, Dearborn, MI, 48124

Tel: (313) 561-1100   Fax: (313) 561-6526   www.cooperstandard.com

Mfr. molded and extruded rubber and plastic products for automotive and appliance industry, retread tire industry.

Cooper Standard Automotive, Dryden House, 1 St. Johns St., Huntingdon Cambs. PE18 6NU, UK

Tel: 44-1480-423000   Fax: 44-1480-423111

COPPERWELD

2200 Four Gateway Center, Pittsburgh, PA, 15222-1211

Tel: (412) 263-3200   Fax: (412) 263-6995   www.copperweld.com

Mfr. of high-quality steel tubing and tubing products.

Bimetallic Products UK, Div. Copperweld, Unit B1 Heslop, Halesfield 24, Telford, Shropshire, UK

CORBIS CORPORATION

15395 SE 30th Place, Ste. 300, Bellevue, WA, 98007

Tel: (425) 641-4505   Fax: (425) 643-9740   www.corbis.com

Provides digital photograph imagery to creative professionals in magazine, book and newspaper publishing, advertising and graphic design and Internet and new media publishing.

Corbin Corporation UK Ltd., 111 Salusbury Road, London NW6 6RG, UK

Tel: 44-207-644-7400   Fax: 44-207-644-7401

CORDIS CORPORATION

PO Box 25700, Miami, FL, 33102-5700

Tel: (305) 824-2000   Fax: (305) 824-2747   www.cordis.com

Mfr. medical devices and systems.

Cordis Div., J&J Medical, Coronation Road, South Ascot, Berkshire SL5 9EY, UK

CORECHANGE, INC.

260 Franklin Street, Ste. 1890, Boston, MA, 02110

Tel: (617) 204-3300   Fax: (617) 204-3333   www.corechange.com

Mfr. software.

Corechange UK Limited, 114 Power Road, London W4 5PY, UK

Tel: 44-208-996-3020   Contact: Nicky Wright

CORIXA CORPORATION

1124 Columbia St., Ste. 200, Seattle, WA, 98104

Tel: (206) 754-5711   Fax: (206) 754-5715   www.corixa.com

Mfr. blood analysis systems, flow cytometers, chemicals systems, scientific systems and reagents.

Biovation Limited (JV), Crombie Lodge, Aberdeen Science Park, Balgownie Drive, Aberdeen AB22 8GU, UK

Tel: 44-1224-707337

CORNING INC.

One Riverfront Plaza, Corning, NY, 14831-0001

Tel: (607) 974-9000   Fax: (607) 974-8091   www.corning.com

Mfr. glass and specialty materials, consumer products; communications, laboratory services.

Corning Communications Europe, 1 The Valley Centre, Gordon Road, High Wycombe, Buckingham HP13 6EQ, UK

Contact: Sandy Lyons

Corning Ltd., 1 The Valley Centre, Gordon Road, High Wycombe, Buckingham HP13 6EQ, UK

Tel: 44-1494-450589   Fax: 44-1494-450596

THE CORPORATE EXECUTIVE BOARD COMPANY

2000 Pennsylvania Avenue NW, Washington, DC, 20006

Tel: (202) 777-6000 Fax: (202) 777-5100 www.executiveboard.com

Provides business analysis and research services.

The Corporate Executive Board Company, 166 Piccadilly, London W1J 9EF, UK

Tel: 44-207-499-8700 Fax: 44-207-499-9700

CORPORATE SOFTWARE (CORPSOFT INC.)

2 Edgewater Drive, Norwood, MA, 02062

Tel: (781) 440-1000 Fax: (781) 440-7070 www.corpsoft.com

Mfr. asset management software.

Corporate Software, Mallard House, Peregrine Business Park, 11 Gomm Road, High Wycombe, Buckinghamshire HP13 7DL, UK

Tel: 44-870-577-1100 Fax: 44-870-577-1102

CORRPRO COMPANIES, INC.

1090 Enterprise Drive, Medina, OH, 44256

Tel: (330) 725-6681 Fax: (330) 723-0244 www.corrpro.com

Engaged in full-services corrosion engineering and cathodic protection.

Rohrback Cosasco Systems, Strawberry Hill, Fishers Lane, Cold Ash Newbury RG16 9NG, UK

Tel: 44-1635-202782 Fax: 44-1635-202582 Contact: Philip Large

Wilson Walton Europe, Adam St., Bowesfield Lane, Stockton-on-Tees, Cleveland TS18 3HQ, UK

Tel: 44-1642-614106 Fax: 44-1642-614100 Contact: John Chase and Mark Davies, Mgrs.

COSTCO WHOLESALE CORPORATION

999 Lake Dr., Issaquah, WA, 98027

Tel: (425) 313-8100 Fax: (425) 313-8103 www.costco.com

Operates wholesale, membership warehouse stores.

Costco Wholesale Corp., Leathley Road, Hunslet, Leeds LS10 1PX, UK

COUDERT BROTHERS LLP

1114 Ave. of the Americas, New York, NY, 10036-7794

Tel: (212) 626-4400 Fax: (212) 626-4120 www.coudert.com

Engaged in international law.

Coudert Brothers, 60 Cannon St., London EC4N 6JP, UK

Tel: 44-207-248-3000 Fax: 44-207-248-3001

COVANCE INC.

210 Carnegie Center, Princeton, NJ, 08540

Tel: (609) 452-4440 Fax: (609) 452-9375 www.covance.com

Pharmaceutical company engaged in research and clinical trials.

Covance Clinical Pathology Services (C.P.S.), Otley Road, Harrogate, North Yorkshire HG3 1PY, UK

Tel: 44-1423-500011

COVANTA ENERGY CORPORATION

40 Lane Road, Fairfield, NJ, 07004

Tel: (973) 882-9000 Fax: (973) 882-9121 www.covantenergy.com

Engaged in power generation.

Covanta Energy UK, London, UK

COVINGTON & BURLING

1201 Pennsylvania Ave., NW, Washington, DC, 20004-2401

Tel: (202) 662-6000 Fax: (202) 662-6291 www.cov.com

Engaged in international law.

Covington & Burling, 265 Strand, London WC2R 1BH, UK

Tel: 44-207-067-2000

SG COWEN SECURITIES

1221 Avenue of the America, New York, NY, 10020

Tel: (212) 495-6000   Fax: (212) 380-8212   www.cowen.com

Securities research, trading, broker/dealer services; investment banking and asset management.

Cowen Securities, Primrose Street, Exchange House, London EC2A 2DD, UK

Tel: 44-207-710-0900   Fax: 44-207-606-0289   Contact: Howard Dingley, Mgr.

CRAIN COMMUNICATIONS INC.

1155 Gratiot Avenue, Detroit, MI, 48207-2997

Tel: (313) 446-6000   Fax: (313) 446-6100   www.crain.com

Publishes business and trade journals.

Crain Communications Inc., New Garden House, 78 Hatton Garden, London EC1N 8LD, UK

Tel: 44-207-457-1400

CRANE & CO., INC.

30 South Street, Dalton, MA, 01226

Tel: (413) 684-2600   Fax: (413) 684-4278   www.crane.com

Mfr. fine cotton papers, currency paper for the U.S. Mint and high-performance battery separators.

CLD Stationery, Ltd, 7 Imperial Studios, Imperial Road, London SW6 2AG, UK

Tel: 44-20-7610-9292

SciMAT Limited, Dorcan 200, Murdock Road, Swindon SN3 5HY, UK

Tel: 44-1793-511160   Fax: 44-1793-533352

CRANE COMPANY

100 First Stamford Place, Stamford, CT, 06907

Tel: (203) 363-7300   Fax: (203) 363-7359   www.craneco.com

Diversified mfr. and distribution of engineered industrial products and the largest American distributor of doors, windows and millwork.

Crane Ltd., Audrey House, Ely Place, London EC1N 6SN, UK

UMC Industries Ltd., Dock Rd., Lytham, Lancshire FY8 5BD, UK

CRAVATH, SWAINE & MOORE

Worldwide Plaza, 825 Eighth Ave., New York, NY, 10019-7475

Tel: (212) 474-1000   Fax: (212) 474-3700   www.cravath.com

International law firm.

Cravath, Swaine & Moore, 10th Fl. 33 King William St., London EC4R 9DU, UK

Tel: 44-207-453-1000

CRAWFORD & COMPANY

5620 Glenridge Drive NE, Atlanta, GA, 30342

Tel: (404) 256-0830   Fax: (404) 847-4025   www.crawfordandcompany.com

Provides international insurance services engaged in risk management and claims adjustment.

Crawford & Company, Trinity Court, 42 Trinity Square, London EC3 N4TH, UK

Tel: 44-207-265-0611   Contact: Andy Homewood

CRC PRESS LLC

2000 NW Corporate Blvd., Boca Raton, FL, 33431

Tel: (561) 994-0555   Fax: (561) 997-0949   www.crcpress.com

Publishing: science, technical and medical books and journals.

CRC Press UK, 23-25 Blades Court, Deodar Road, London SW15 2NU, UK

Tel: 44-20-8875-4370   Fax: 44-20-8871-3443

CROMPTON CORPORATION

One American Lane, Greenwich, CT, 06831

Tel: (203) 552-2000   Fax: (203) 552-2870   www.cromptoncorp.com

Mfr. dyes, colors, flavors, fragrances, specialty chemicals and industrial products.

Crompton Europe Ltd., 4 Langley Quay, Waterside Drive, Slough Berkshire SL3 6EH, UK

Tel: 44-1753-603000

Davis-Standard Barrels and Screws, Unit 33, Hainge Road, Tividale, Oldbury, West Midlands B69 2NY, UK

THE CROSBY GROUP, INC.

PO Box 3128, 2801 Dawson Rd., Tulsa, OK, 74101-3128

Tel: (918) 834-4611   Fax: (918) 832-0940   www.thecrosbygroup.com

Mfr. machine tools, hardware, steel forgings.

Amdura Ltd., Euroway Blagrove Industrial Estate, D-6/7, Swindon, Wilts. SN5 8YL, UK

A.T. CROSS COMPANY

One Albion Road, Lincoln, RI, 02865

Tel: (401) 333-1200   Fax: (401) 334-2861   www.cross.com

Mfr. writing instruments, leads, erasers and ink refills.

A.T. Cross Ltd., Concorde House, Concorde St., Luton, Bedfordshire LU2 0JD, UK

Tel: 44-1582-422-793

CROWELL & MORING

1001 Pennsylvania Avenue, NW, Washington, DC, 20004-2595

Tel: (202) 624-2500   Fax: (202) 628-5116   www.crowellmoring.com

International law firm.

Crowell & Moring, 180 Fleet St., London EC4A 2HG, UK

Tel: 44-207-413-0011

CROWN CASTLE INTERNATIONAL, INC.

510 Bering Dr., Ste. 500, Houston, TX, 77057-1457

Tel: (713) 570-3000   Fax: (713) 570-3100   www.crowncomm.net

Digital audio and television broadcast transmission systems operations.

Crown Castle UK Limited, Warwick Technology Park, PO Box 98, Warwick CV34 6TN, UK

Tel: 44-1926-416000   Fax: 44-1926-416190   Contact: Bob Giles, Pres.

CROWN EQUIPMENT CORPORATION

40 South Washington Street, New Bremen, OH, 45869

Tel: (419) 629-2311   Fax: (419) 629-2900   www.crownlift.com

Mfr. and sales of forklift trucks and stackers.

Crown Lift Trucks Ltd., Fishponds Rd., Wokingham, Berkshire, UK

CRYOLIFE, INC.

1655 Roberts Blvd. North West, Kennesaw, GA, 30144

Tel: (770) 419-3355   Fax: (770) 426-0031   www.cryolife.com

Engaged in development of transplant organs and procedures.

CryoLife Europa, Ltd., Europa House Fareham Heights, Standard Way Fareham, Hampshire PO6 8XT, UK

Tel: 44-1329-229800   Fax: 44-1329-229801

DELTEK SYSTEMS, INC.

7887 East Belleview Avenue, Ste. 1000, Englewood, CO, 80111

Tel: (303) 796-2850   Fax: (303) 804-4088   www.csgsys.com

Mfr. customer service software.

CSG Systems UK, Northgate House, 1A Stoke Road, Slough Berkshire SL2 5AA, UK

Tel: 44-1753-745304

CUBIC CORPORATION

9333 Balboa Ave., PO Box 85587, San Diego, CA, 92123

Tel: (858) 277-6780   Fax: (858) 277-1878   www.cubic.com

Automatic fare collection equipment, training systems.

Cubic Tiltman Langley, 177 Nutfield Rd., Merstham Surrey RHI 3HH, UK

Thorn Transit Systems International Ltd., Wooley Hole Rd., Wells Somerset BA5 1AA, UK

Tel: 44-1749--670222   Fax: 44-1749-679363   Contact: Julian Slater, Mng. Dir.

CUBIST PHARMACEUTICALS, INC.

65 Hayden Avenue, Lexington, MA, 02421

Tel: (781) 860-8660   Fax: (781) 861-0556   www.cubist.com

Mfr. pharmaceuticals to fight infections.

Cubist Pharmaceuticals UK, 545 Ipswich Road, Slough Berkshire SL1 4EQ, UK

Tel: 44-1753-706-800   Fax: 44-1753-706-808

CULLIGAN INTERNATIONAL COMPANY

One Culligan Parkway, Northbrook, IL, 60062

Tel: (847) 205-6000   Fax: (847) 205-6030   www.culligan-man.com

Water treatment products and services.

Culligan Intl. Co., Blenheim Rd., Cressex Industrial Estate, High Wycombe HP12 3RS, UK

Tel: 44-1494-436484   Fax: 44-1494-523833

CUMMINS, INC.

500 Jackson Street, PO Box 3005, Columbus, IN, 47202-3005

Tel: (812) 377-5000   Fax: (812) 377-4937   www.cummins.com

Mfr. diesel engines.

Cummins Engine Co. Ltd., 46-50 Coombe Rd., New Malden, Surrey KT3 4QL, UK

Holset Engineering Company Ltd., Huddersfield, UK

CUNA MUTUAL BUSINESS SERVICES

5910 Mineral Point Rd., PO Box 391, Madison, WI, 53701

Tel: (608) 238-5851   Fax: (608) 238-0830   www.cunamutual.com

Insurance services.

ABCUL, Div. CUNA, Holyoake House Hanover Street, Manchester M60 0AS, UK

CUNO INCORPORATED

400 Research Pkwy., Meriden, CT, 06450

Tel: (203) 237-5541   Fax: (203) 238-8977   www.cuno.com

Mfr. water filtration products.

CUNO Ltd., Unit 21 Woking Business Park, Surrey GU21 5JY, UK

Tel: 44-1483735900

CURTIS, MALLET-PREVOST, COLT & MOSLE LLP

101 Park Ave., Ste 3500, New York, NY, 10178

Tel: (212) 696-6000   Fax: (212) 697-1559   www.cm-p.com

International law firm.

Curtis, Mallet-Prevost, Colt & Mosle LLP, Two Throgmorton Avenue, London EC2N 2DL, UK

Tel: 44-207-638-7957

CURTISS-WRIGHT CORPORATION

1200 Wall Street West, Lyndhurst, NJ, 07071-0635

Tel: (201) 896-8400   Fax: (201) 438-5680   www.curtisswright.com

Mfr. precision components and systems, engineered services to aerospace, flow control and marine industry.

Metal Improvement Co. (MIC), Ascot Drive, Derby DE2 8ST, UK

Metal Improvement Co. Ltd., Navigation House, Hambridge Lane, Newbury Berkshire RG14 5TU, UK

MIC, Div. Curtiss-Wright Corp., Pallion Industrial Estate, Unit 37, Sunderland,, Tyne and Wear SR4 6SN, UK

Tel: 44-191-514-1140

CUSHMAN & WAKEFIELD INC.

51 West 52nd Street, New York, NY, 10019

Tel: (212) 841-7500   Fax: (212) 841-7867   www.cushwake.com

Engaged in commercial real estate services.

Cushman & Wakefield Healey & Baker, 43-45 Portman Square, London W1H 0HE, UK

CUTLER-HAMMER, DIV. EATON CORP.

173 Heatherdown Drive, Westerville, OH, 43082

Tel: (614) 882-3282   Fax: (614) 895-7111   www.cutlerhammer.com

Mfr. electrical control products and power distribution equipment.

Cutler-Hammer Ltd., Mill Street, Ottery St. Mary, Devon EX11 1AG, UK

Tel: 44-1404-812131   Fax: 44-1404-815471

Cutler-Hammer Ltd., Carina - Sunrise Parkway, Linford Wood, Milton Keynes MK14 6NR, UK

Tel: 44-1908-541600   Fax: 44-1908-660527

CYBORG SYSTEMS, INC.

120 South Riverside Plaza, 17th Fl., Chicago, IL, 60606-0899

Tel: (312) 279-7000   Fax: (312) 454-0889   www.cyborg.com

Develop/mfr. human resources, payroll and time/attendance software.

CSI Product Group UK, Ltd., Central Court, Knoll Rise, Orpington Kent BR6 0JA, UK

Tel: 44-1-689-890220   Contact: David Stallion

CYLINK CORPORATION

3131 Jay Street, Santa Clara, CA, 95054

Tel: (408) 855-6000   Fax: (408) 855-6100   www.cyllink.com

Develop and manufactures encryption software.

Cylink UK, Ltd., Intec Business Park, Intec 4, Wade Road, Basingstoke Hants RG24 8NE, UK

Tel: 44-1256-345-900

CYPRESS SEMICONDUCTOR CORPORATION

3901 N. First Street, San Jose, CA, 95134-1599

Tel: (408) 943-2600   Fax: (408) 943-2796   www.cypress.com

Mfr. integrated circuits.

Cypress Semiconductor, Gate House, Fretherne Road, Welwyn Garden City, Hertfordshire AL8 6NS, UK

Tel: 44-1-707-37-87-00   Fax: 44-1-707-37-87-37

CYTEC INDUSTRIES, INC.

5 Garret Mountain Plaza, West Paterson, NJ, 07424

Tel: (973) 357-3100   Fax: (973) 357-3054   www.cytec.com

Mfr. specialty chemicals and materials.

Cytec Industries UK Ltd., Bowling Park Drive, Bradford, West Yorkshire BD4 7TT, UK

Tel: 44-1274-73-3891

D&B (DUN & BRADSTREET CORPORATION))

1 Diamond Hill Road, Murray Hill, NJ, 07974

Tel: (908) 665-5000   Fax: (908) 665-5524   www.dnb.com

Provides corporate credit, marketing and accounts-receivable management services and publishes financial information.

D&B UK, Office 801, Holmers Farm Way, High Wycombe, Bucks HP12 4UL, UK

Tel: 44-1494-422000

D&B UK Ltd., Holmers Farm Way, High Wycombe, Bucks HP12 4UL, UK

Tel: 44-1494-422000

DALLAS SEMICONDUCTOR CORPORATION

4401 South Beltway Parkway, Dallas, TX, 75244-3292

Tel: (972) 371-4000   Fax: (972) 371-4956   www.dalsemi.com

Design/mfr. computer chips and chip-based subsystems.

Dallas Semiconductor, Unit 27, West Midland Freeport, Birmingham B26 3QD, UK

Tel: 44-121-782-2959   Fax: 44-121-782-2156   Contact: Terry Andrews, Reg. Sales Mgr.

Dallas Semiconductor, 11 Medway Close, Wokingham, Berkshire RG41 3TP, UK

Tel: 44-121-782-2959   Fax: 44-121-782-2156   Contact: Terry Andrews, Reg. Sales Mgr.

DANA CORPORATION

4500 Dorr Street, Toledo, OH, 43615

Tel: (419) 535-4500   Fax: (419) 535-4643   www.dana.com

Mfr./sales of automotive, heavy truck, off-highway, fluid and mechanical power components and engine parts, filters and gaskets.

Dana Ltd./Dana Europe, Great Eastern House, Greenbridge Rd., Stratton St., Margaret Swindon, UK

Dana Spicer Europe Ltd., 31 Lyveden Road, Brackmills Northampton NN4 7ED, UK

Tel: 44-01-6046-75005

Spicer Europe, Electra Park, Electric Avenue, Witton B6 7DZ, UK

Spicer Off-Highway Axle Div., Abbey Road, Kirkstall Leeds LS5 3NF, UK

Tel: 44-113-258-4611

DANAHER CORPORATION

1250 24th St. NW, Ste. 800, Washington, DC, 20037

Tel: (202) 828-0850   Fax: (202) 828-0860   www.danaher.com

Mfr. hand tools and motion controls.

Aviation Services Europe, Pacific Scientific, 8 Boston Drive, Bourne End, Buckinghamshire SL8 5YS, UK

Contact: Robin Squires, VP

Danaher (UK) Ltd., 219 Kings Rd., Reading, Berkshire, UK

DANIEL INDUSTRIES INC.

9753 Pine Lake Drive, PO Box 55435, Houston, TX, 77224

Tel: (713) 467-6000   Fax: (713) 827-3889   www.danielind.com

Fluid measurement, flow control, actuation and analytical products, services and integrated solutions primarily for natural gas and oil producers, transporters and refiners worldwide.

Daniel International Ltd., Swinton Grange Malton, North Yorkshire Y017 0QR, UK

Tel: 44-1653-600425   Fax: 44-1653-600425

DANZAS AEI, INC.

120 Tokeneke Road, PO Box 1231, Darien, CT, 06820

Tel: (203) 655-7900   Fax: (203) 655-5779   www.aeilogistics.com

International air freight forwarder.

Danzas AEI, International Ave., Hounslow, Middlesex TW5 9JZ, UK

Tel: 44-181-754-5000   Fax: 44-181-754-5075

Danzas AEI, Century House, 100 Church St., Staines Middlesex TW18 4DQ, UK

Tel: 44-1784-871230   Fax: 44-1784-871240

D'ARCY MASIUS BENTON & BOWLES INC. (DMB&B)

1675 Broadway, New York, NY, 10019

Tel: (212) 468-3622   Fax: (212) 468-2987   www.darcyww.com

Full service international advertising and communications group.

DMB&B Europe, 76 Oxford St., London W1A 1DT, UK

DMB&B Europe, 2 St.James' Square, London SW1Y 4JN, UK

DATA TRANSLATION INC.

100 Locke Drive, Marlborough, MA, 01752-1192

Tel: (508) 481-3700   Fax: (508) 481-8620   www.datx.com

Mfr. peripheral boards for image and array processing micro-computers.

Data Translation Ltd., Unit 10, Plover House, Aviary Court Wade Road, Basingstoke Hants RG24 8PE, UK

Tel: 44-1256-333330

DATASCOPE CORPORATION

14 Phillips Pkwy., Montvale, NJ, 07645

Tel: (201) 391-8100   Fax: (201) 307-5400   www.datascope.com

Mfr. medical devices.

Datascope Medical Co. Ltd., Lakeview Court Spitfire Close, Ermine Business Park, Huntingdon Cambs PE18 6XR, UK

Tel: 44-1480-423600

DATASTREAM SYSTEMS, INC.

50 Datastream Plaza, Greenville, SC, 29605

Tel: (864) 422-5001   Fax: (864) 422-5000   www.datastream.net

Mfr. asset management software.

Datastream Systems UK ltd., 1210 Parkview, Arlington Business Park, Theale Berkshire RG7 4TY, UK

DATAWATCH CORPORATION

175 Cabot Street, Ste. 503, Lowell, MA, 01854

Tel: (978) 441-2200   Fax: (978) 275-8398   www.datawatch.com

Provider of business intelligence, enterprise reporting, data transformation and service management solutions.

Datawatch Europe Limited, The Software Centre, East Way, Lee Mill Industrial Estate, Ivybridge Devon PL21 9GE, UK

DAVIS POLK & WARDWELL

450 Lexington Ave., New York, NY, 10017

Tel: (212) 450-4000   Fax: (212) 450-4800   www.dpw.com

Engaged in international law.

Davis Polk & Wardwell, One Fredericks Place, London EC2R 8AB, UK

Tel: 44-141-418-1300   Fax: 44-151-418-1400

DAY RUNNER, INC.

2750 W. Moore Avenue, Fullerton, CA, 92833

Tel: (714) 680-3500   Fax: (714) 680-0538   www.dayrunner.com

Mfg./distribution of paper-based organizers.

Day Runner International Ltd., 2 Kings Hill Ave., Kings Hill, West Malling, Kent ME19 4TAQ, UK

Tel: 44-1732-842828   Fax: 44-1732-849030   Contact: D. Blake

DAYTON PROGRESS CORPORATION

500 Progress Road, Dayton, OH, 45449

Tel: (937) 859-5111   Fax: (937) 859-5353   www.daytonprogress.com

Engaged in the production of catalog and special punches, punch blanks and metal stamping tools.

Dayton Progress (UK) Ltd., G1, Holly Farm Business Park, Honiley Kenilworth, Warwickshire CV8 1NP, UK

DAZEL CORPORATION

301 Congress Ave., Ste. 1100, Austin, TX, 78701

Tel: (512) 494-7300   Fax: (512) 494-7394   www.dazel.com

Mfr. software for information delivery solutions on documents and reports.

Dazel UK, World Business Centre, Newall Road, London Heathrow Airport, Honslow TW6 2RJ, UK

Tel: 44-0208-263-2708

DDB WORLDWIDE COMMUNICATIONS GROUP

437 Madison Ave., New York, NY, 10022

Tel: (212) 415-2000   Fax: (212) 415-3417   www.ddbn.com

Advertising agency.

BMP DDB Needham Worldwide Ltd., 12 Bishop's Bridge Rd., London W2 6AA, UK

Griffin Bacal, London, UK

DDI CORPORATION

1220 Simon Circle, Anaheim, CA, 92806

Tel: (714) 688-7200   Fax: (714) 688-7400   www.ddiglobal.com

Engaged in software development tools contract manufacturing.

DDI Design Services, 214 Red Lion Road, Tolworth Surrey KT6 7RP, UK

DDI Design Services, John Tate Road, Foxholes Business Park, Hertford Hertfordshire SG13 7GB, UK

DDI Design Services, 32 Harris Road, Porte Marsh Industrial Estate, Calne, Wiltshire SN11 9PT, UK

Tel: 44-1249-814081

DEBEVOISE & PLIMPTON

919 Third Avenue, New York, NY, 10022

Tel: (212) 909-6000   Fax: (212) 909-6836   www.debevoise.com

Engaged in international law.

Debevoise & Plimpton, The International Financial Centre, Old Broad St., London EC4M 7AA, UK

Tel: 44-207-786-9000   Fax: 44-207-588-4180   Contact: James Kiernan, Mng. Prtn.   Emp: 22

DECHERT LLP

4000 Bell Atlantic Tower, 1717 Arch Street, Philadelphia, PA, 19103-2793

Tel: (215) 994-4000   Fax: (215) 994-2222   www.dechert.com

Engaged in international law.

Titmuss Sainer Dechert, 2 Sergeants Inn, London EC4Y 1LT, UK

Tel: 44-207-583-5353   Fax: 44-207-353-3683

DECISION STRATEGIES FAIRFAX INTERNATIONAL

33 East 33rd Street, New York, NY, 10016

Tel: (212) 935-4040   Fax: (212) 935-4046   www.dsfx.com

Provides discreet consulting, investigative, business intelligence and security services to corporations, financial and investment institutions, law firms and governments worldwide.

Decision Strategies UK Ltd., 31 Old Burlington Street, 2/F, London W1X 1LB, UK

Tel: 44-207-734-5361   Fax: 44-207-734-5378

DEERE & COMPANY

One John Deere Place, Moline, IL, 61265

Tel: (309) 765-8000   Fax: (309) 765-5772   www.deere.com

Mfr./sale agricultural, construction, utility, forestry and lawn, grounds care equipment.

John Deere Ltd., Harby Road, Langar, Nottingham NG13 9HT, UK

Tel: 44-1949-860491   Fax: 44-1949-860490

DELL COMPUTER CORPORATION

One Dell Way, Round Rock, TX, 78682-2222

Tel: (512) 338-4400   Fax: (512) 728-3653   www.dell.com

Direct marketer and supplier of computer systems.

Dell Computer Corporation, Dell Campus, Bracknell Berkshire RG12 1FA, UK

Tel: 44-1344-812-000   Fax: 44-1344-860-187   Contact: Adrian Weekes, Mng. Dir.

DELOITTE TOUCHE TOHMATSU INTERNATIONAL

1633 Broadway, New York, NY, 10019

Tel: (212) 492-4000   Fax: (212) 392-4154   www.deloitte.com

Accounting, audit, tax and management consulting services.

Braxton Associates, 90 Long Acre, London WC2E 9RA, UK

Deloitte & Touche, Stonecutter Court, 1 Stonecutter St., London EC4A 4TR, UK

Deloitte & Touche, 10-12 East Parade, Leeds LS1 2AJ, UK

DELPHAX TECHNOLOGIES

12500 Whitewater Drive, Minnetonka, MN, 55343-9420

Tel: (612) 939-9000   Fax: (612) 939-1151   www.delphax.com

Mfr. computer-controlled check coupon print systems.

Delphax Technologies, 3/4 Satellite Bus. Village, Fleming Way, Crawley, W. Sussex RH10 2NE, UK

DELTA AIR LINES INC.

Hartsfield International Airport, 1030 Delta Blvd., Atlanta, GA, 30320-6001

Tel: (404) 715-2600   Fax: (404) 715-5494   www.delta-air.com

Major worldwide airline; international air transport services.

Delta Air Lines Inc., Newcastle, UK

Delta Air Lines Inc., London-Gatwick, UK

Delta Air Lines Inc., Manchester, UK

DELTEK SYSTEMS, INC.

8280 Greensboro Drive, McLean, VA, 22102

Tel: (703) 734-8606   Fax: (703) 734-1146   www.deltec.com

Mfr. project management software.

Deltec UK, Hanover House, 3 Hanover Square, London W1S 1HD, UK

Tel: 44-207-518-5010   Fax: 44-207-518-5015

DELUXE CORPORATION

3680 Victoria Street North, Shoreview, MN, 55126-2966

Tel: (612) 483-7111   Fax: (612) 481-4163   www.deluxe.com

Leading U.S. check printer and provider of electronic payment services.

Deluxe Corporation, Nuffield Road, Unit 1, Harrowbrook Estates, Hinckley, Leicestershire LE10 3DG, UK

DENTSPLY INTERNATIONAL

570 West College Ave., PO Box 872, York, PA, 17405-0872

Tel: (717) 845-7511   Fax: (717) 843-6357   www.dentsply.com

Mfr. and distribution of dental supplies and equipment.

CMW Labs/Dentsply, Cornford Rd., Blackpool FY4 4QQ, UK

Dentsply AD Plastics, Clifton Rd., Marton, Blackpool FY4 4QF, UK

Tel: 44-1253-765024

Dentsply Ash Instruments, Pennycross Close, Beacon Park, Plymouth PL2 3NY, UK

Tel: 44-1752-709751

Dentsply Ceramco Ltd., Hamm Moor Lane, Addlestone, Weybridge Surrey KT15 2SE, UK

Tel: 44-1932-856240

Dentsply UK/Middle East/Africa, Hamm Moor Lane, Addlestone, Weybridge Surrey KT15 2SE, UK

Tel: 44-1932-853422

DEPUY INC.

700 Orthopaedic Drive, Warsaw, IN, 46581

Tel: (574) 267-8143   Fax: (574) 267-7196   www.depuy.com

Engaged in manufacture and sale of orthopedics.

DePuy International, St. Anthony's Road, Leeds LS11 8DT, UK

Tel: 44-113-2700-461

DETROIT DIESEL CORPORATION

13400 Outer Drive West, Detroit, MI, 48239

Tel: (313) 592-5000   Fax: (313) 592-5058   www.detroitdiesel.com

Mfr. diesel and aircraft engines and heavy-duty transmissions.

Mitchell Diesel Limited, Fulwood Road South, Sutton-IN-Ashfield, Nhps NG17 2JZ, UK

Tel: 44-16-2355-0550   Fax: 44-16-2355-1617

DEWEY BALLANTINE LLP

1301 Avenue of the Americas, New York, NY, 10019

Tel: (212) 259-8000   Fax: (212) 259-6333   www.deweyballantine.com

International law firm.

Dewey Ballantine LLP, 1 Undershaft, London EC3A 8LP, UK

Tel: 44-207-456-6000   Fax: 44-207-456-6001

DHL WORLDWIDE EXPRESS

50 California Avenue, San Francisco, CA, 94111

Tel: (415) 677-6100   Fax: (415) 824-9700   www.dhl.com

Worldwide air express carrier.

DHL Worldwide Express, Hillblom House, 1 Dukes, Green Ave., Feltham Middlesex TW14 0LR, UK

Tel: 44-181-831-5000   Fax: 44-181-831-5451

DHL Worldwide Express, Orbital Park, 178-188 Great South West Rd., Hounslow Middlesex TW4 6JS, UK

Tel: 44-181-818-8000   Fax: 44-181-818-8141

DIAGNOSTIC PRODUCTS CORPORATION
5700 West 96th Street, Los Angeles, CA, 90045

Tel: (310) 645-8200   Fax: (310) 645-9999   www.dpcweb.com

Mfr. diagnostic products.

Euro/DPC Ltd., Glyn Rhonwy, Llanberis Caernarfon, Gwynedd LL55 4EL, UK

Tel: 44-1286-871-871   Fax: 44-1286-871-802

DIAMOND CHAIN COMPANY
402 Kentucky Ave., Indianapolis, IN, 46225

Tel: (317) 638-6431   Fax: (317) 633-2243   www.diamondchain.com

Mfr. roller chains.

Diamond Chain UK, Blaydon Industrial Park, Units 7-9, Chainbridge Road, Blaydon-on-Tyne NE21 5AB, UK

DIAMOND POWER INTERNATIONAL, INC.
PO Box 415, Lancaster, OH, 43130

Tel: (740) 687-6500   Fax: (740) 687-7430   www.diamondpower.com

Mfg. boiler cleaning equipment and ash handling systems: soot blowers, controls, diagnostics systems, gauges, OEM parts, rebuilds and field service.

Diamond Power Site Services, Unit 5B, Heapham Road Industrial Estate, Gainsborough Lines DN21 1XP, UK

DIAMONDCLUSTER INTERNATIONAL, INC.
875 N. Michigan Avenue, Ste. 3000, Chicago, IL, 60611

Tel: (312) 255-5000   Fax: (312) 255-6000   www.diamondcluster.com

Engaged in electronic business development and support.

DiamondCluster International, Inc., Orion House 10/F, 5 Upper Street, Martin's Lane, London WC2H 9EA, UK

Tel: 44-20-7959-7700   Fax: 44-20-7959-7710

DICTAPHONE CORPORATION
3191 Broadbridge Ave., Stratford, CT, 06497-2559

Tel: (203) 381-7000   Fax: (203) 381-7100   www.dictaphone.com

Mfr./sale dictation, telephone answering and multi-channel voice communications recording systems.

Dictaphone Company Ltd., Chalk Hill Road, Hammersmith, London W6 8DW, UK

Tel: 44-207-878-5000

DIGI INTERNATIONAL INC.
11001 Bren Road East, Minnetonka, MN, 55343

Tel: (952) 912-3444   Fax: (952) 912-4952   www.digi.com

Mfr. computer hardware.

Digi International (UK) Ltd, Almondsbury Business Cente, Woodlands, Bradley Stoke, Bristol BS32 4QH, UK

Tel: 44-1454-643444   Fax: 44-1454-619048

DIMON INCORPORATED
512 Bridge Street, PO Box 681, Danville, VA, 24543-0681

Tel: (804) 792-7511   Fax: (804) 791-0377   www.dimon.com

One of world's largest importer and exporters of leaf tobacco.

DIMON International Services Limited, DIMON Place, Riverside Way, Camberley Surrey GU 15 3YF, UK

Tel: 44-1276-404-600   Fax: 44-1276-404-700

DIONEX CORPORATION
1228 Titan Way, PO Box 3603, Sunnyvale, CA, 94086-3603

Tel: (408) 737-0700   Fax: (408) 730-9403   www.dionex.com

Develop/mfr./market chromatography systems and related products.

Dionex (UK) Ltd., 4 Albany Court, Camberley Surrey GU15 2XA, UK

WALT DISNEY COMPANY
500 South Buena Vista Street, Burbank, CA, 91521

Tel: (818) 560-1000   Fax: (818) 560-1930   www.disney.com

Film/TV production, theme parks, resorts, publishing, recording and retail stores.

Walt Disney Productions Ltd., 68 Pall Mall, London SW1Y 5EX, UK

DIVINE

1301 N. Elston Ave., Chicago, IL, 60622

Tel: (773) 394-6600   Fax: (773) 394-6601   www.divine.com

Software and services provider.

Divine, Inc., 62-63 Queen Street, London EC4R 1AD, UK

DIXON TICONDEROGA COMPANY

195 International Parkway, Heathrow, FL, 32746

Tel: (407) 829-9000   Fax: (407) 829-2574   www.dixonticonderoga.com

Mfr. and sales writing instruments, drawing and art supplies and office products.

Dixon Europe, Ltd., 36 Stapledon Rd., Peterboro PE2 OTD, UK

DMC STRATEX NETWORKS, INC.

170 Rose Orchard Way, San Jose, CA, 95134

Tel: (408) 943-0777   Fax: (408) 944-1648   www.dmcstratexnetworks.com

Designs, manufactures, and markets advanced wireless solutions for wireless broadband access.

DMC Stratex Networks, Regus Central Boulevard, Blythe Valley Business Park, Solihull, West Midland B90 8AB, UK

Tel: 44-1564-711084   Fax: 44-1564-711335   Contact: Martyn Braime, VP

D-M-E COMPANY

29111 Stephenson Highway, Madison Heights, MI, 48071

Tel: (248) 398-6000   Fax: (248) 544-5705   www.dmeco.com

Manufacture and distribution of mold tooling, mold components, hot runner systems, and electronic controls for the plastics industry.

D-M-E UK, Div. Milacron UK Ltd., Halifax Road, Cressex Industrial Estate, High Wycombe Buckinghamshire HP12 3TN, UK

Tel: 44-494-559-300

DNA SCIENCES, INC.

6540 Kaiser Drive, Fremont, CA, 94555

Tel: (510) 494-4000   Fax: (510) 494-4010   www.dna.com

Engaged in diagnostic and drug development.

DNA Sciences Laboratories, Lockton House, Clarendon Road, Cambridge CB2 2BH, UK

DO ALL COMPANY

254 North Laurel Ave., Des Plaines, IL, 60016

Tel: (847) 803-7380   Fax: (847) 699-7524   www.doall.com

Distributors of machinery tools, metal cutting tools, instruments and industrial supplies for metalworking industry.

DoALL Company U.K., Ltd., Beldray Industrial Park, Unit 9, Mount Pleasant, Bilston, West Midlands WV14 7NH, UK

Tel: 44-1902-404842   Fax: 44-1902-354303

DOCUMENTUM, INC.

6801 Koll Center Pkwy., Pleasanton, CA, 94566

Tel: (925) 600-6800   Fax: (925) 600-6850   www.documentum.com

Mfr. content management software.

Documentum Software Europe Ltd, 5 Roundwood Avenue, Stockley Park, Uxbridge Middlesex UB11 1NZ, UK

DOLE FOOD COMPANY, INC.

One Dole Drive, Westlake Village, CA, 91362

Tel: (818) 874-4000   Fax: (818) 879-6615   www.dole.com

Produces/distributes fresh fruits and vegetables and canned juices and fruits.

Dole Food Company, London, UK

DONALDSON COMPANY, INC.

PO Box 1299, Minneapolis, MN, 55431

Tel: (952) 887-3131   Fax: (952) 887-3155   www.donaldson.com

Mfr. filtration systems and replacement parts.

Donaldson Filter Components Ltd., 65 Market St., Hednesford, Straffordshire WS12 5AD, UK

Tel: 44-1543-425-515   Fax: 44-1543-879-136

DONNA KARAN INTERNATIONAL INC.

550 Seventh Avenue, New York, NY, 10018

Tel: (212) 789-1500   Fax: (212) 921-3526   www.donnakaran.com

Design/manufacture/sale men's, women's, and children's clothes.

Donna Karan International (DKNY), 19 New Bond Street, London W1, UK

R.R. DONNELLEY & SONS COMPANY

77 West Wacker Drive, Chicago, IL, 60601-1696

Tel: (312) 326-8000   Fax: (312) 326-8543   www.rrdonnelley.com

Engaged in commercial printing and allied communication services.

R. R. Donnelley (UK) Ltd., Donnelley House, 25 Worship St., London EC2A 2DX, UK

Tel: 44-207-330-1690   Fax: 44-207-256-9133

R. R. Donnelley Ltd. - Pindar, 513 Browells Lane, Feltham, Middlesex TW13 7EQ, UK

Tel: 44-181-890-8933

R.R. Donnelley Ltd. York Division, Boroughbridge Rd., York YO2 5SS, UK

Tel: 44-190-479-8241

DOREMUS & COMPANY, INC.

200 Varick Street, New York, NY, 10271

Tel: (212) 366-3000   Fax: (212) 366-3629   www.doremus.com

Advertising and public relations.

Doremus & Co., 196 Tottenham Court Road, London W1P 9LD, UK

Tel: 44-207-419-4000   Fax: 44-207-419-4419   Contact: Garrett Lawrence

DORSEY & WHITNEY LLP

50 South Sixth Street, Ste. 1500, Minneapolis, MN, 55402

Tel: (612) 340-2600   Fax: (612) 340-2868   www.dorseylaw.com

International law firm.

Dorsey & Whitney LLP, 21 Wilson Street, London EC2M 2TD, UK

Tel: 44-20-7588-0800

DOUBLECLICK, INC.

450 West 33rd Street, New York, NY, 10001

Tel: (212) 683-0001   Fax: (212) 889-0062   www.doubleclick.net

Engaged in online advertising and e-mail marketing.

Doubleclick, Ltd., 204 Saint-Sacrement St., Ste. 303, Montreal PQ H2Y 1W8, UK

Doubleclick, Ltd. (Media), Cavendish House, 3/F, 128/134 Cleveland Street, London W1P 5DN, UK

Tel: 44-207-388-6565

DOVER CORPORATION

280 Park Ave., New York, NY, 10017-1292

Tel: (212) 922-1640   Fax: (212) 922-1656   www.dovercorporation.com

Holding company for varied industries; assembly and testing equipment, oil-well gear and other industrial products.

DEK Printing Machines Ltd., 11 Albany Road, Granby Ind Est, Weymouth DT4 9TH, UK

THE DOW CHEMICAL COMPANY

2030 Dow Center, Midland, MI, 48674

Tel: (989) 636-1000   Fax: (989) 636-3228   www.dow.com

Mfr. chemicals, plastics, pharmaceuticals, agricultural products, consumer products.

Dow Chemical Co. Ltd., Meadow Bank, Bath Rd., Hounslow TW5 9QY, UK

DOW JONES & COMPANY, INC.

200 Liberty Street, New York, NY, 10281

Tel: (212) 416-2000   Fax: (212) 416-4348   www.dj.com

Publishing and financial news services.

AP-Dow Jones, 76 Shoe Lane, London EC4A 3JB, UK

DRAFT WORLDWIDE

633 North St. Clair Street, Chicago, IL, 60611-3211

Tel: (312) 944-3500   Fax: (312) 944-3566   www.draftworldwide.com

Full service international advertising agency, engaged in brand building, direct and promotional marketing.

LVB DraftWorldwide (Lovell Vass Boddey), Worton Park, Cassington, Oxfordshire OX8 1EB, UK

Tel: 44-1865-88-4444   Fax: 44-1865-88-4488

DRAKE BEAM MORIN INC.

100 Park Avenue, 11th Fl., New York, NY, 10017

Tel: (212) 692-7700   Fax: (212) 297-0426   www.dbm.com

Human resource management consulting and training.

DBM UK, 5 Arlington St., St. James's, London SW1A 1RA, UK

Tel: 44-207-955-8200   Fax: 44-207-955-8201

DRESSER INSTRUMENT DIVISION

250 East Main Street, Stratford, CT, 06614-5145

Tel: (203) 378-8281   Fax: (203) 385-0357   www.dresserinstruments.com

Mfr. pressure gauges and temperature instruments.

Dresser Europe GmbH, East Gillibrands, Skelmersdale, Lancashire WN8 9TU, UK

Tel: 44-1695-52600 Fax: 44-1695-52693

Dresser Europe SA, 187 Knightsbridge, London SW7 1RJ, UK

Dresser Industries UK, East Gillibrands Skelmersdale, Lancashire WN8 9TU, UK

Tel: 44-1695-52600   Fax: 44-1695-52693

DRESSER-RAND COMPANY

PO Box 560, Paul Clark Drive, Olean, NY, 14760

Tel: (716) 375-3000   Fax: (716) 375-3178   www.dresser-rand.com

Mfr. generators, centrifugal compressors, turbines and control systems.

Dresser-Rand UK, C.I. Tower, St. Georges Square, High Street, New Malden, Surrey KT3 4DN, UK

Tel: 44-208-336-7300   Fax: 44-208-949-5606

DREVER COMPANY

PO Box 98, 380 Red Lion Road, Huntingdon, PA, 19006-0098

Tel: (215) 947-3400   Fax: (215) 947-7934   www.drever.com

Mfr. industrial furnaces and heat processing equipment.

Drever U.K., Astor House, 282 Lichfield Road, Sutton Coldfield, West Midlands B74 2UG, UK

Tel: 44-121-323-4994   Fax: 44-121-308-6336

DRIVER-HARRIS COMPANY

600 Essex St, Harrison, NJ, 07029

Tel: (973) 483-4802   Fax: (973) 483-4806   www.driver-harris.com

Mfr. non-ferrous alloys.

Kestrel Cables Distribution Ltd., Unit A2, Baird Court, Park Farm North Industrial Estate, Wellingborough, Northants NN8 6QJ, UK

Tel: 44-1933-402828   Fax: 44-1933-401832

Kingston Cable Dist. Ltd., Unit 4C/4D, Amsterdam Rd., Sutton Fields, Kingston-upon-Hull, UK

Tel: 44-1482-830367   Fax: 44-1482-830369

DRS TECHNOLOGIES, INC.

5 Dylvan Way, Parsippany, NJ, 07054

Tel: (973) 898-1500   Fax: (973) 898-4730   www.drs.com

Mfr. software and equipment for diagnostic and retrieval systems.

DRS Hadland Ltd., Harrow Yard, Akeman Street, Tring, Hertfordshire HP23 6AA, UK

DRS Rugged Systems (Europe) Ltd., Lynwood House, The Trading Estate, Farnham, Surrey GU9 9NN, UK

DST INNOVIS, INC.

1104 Investment Boulevard, El Dorado Hills, CA, 95762

Tel: (916) 878-2112   Fax: (916) 934-7054   www.dstinnovis.com

Provides innovative customer management and open billing solutions for the global video/broadband, telecommunications and utility industries.

DST Innovis Limited, Innovis House, 108 High Street, Crawley West Sussex RH10 1BB, UK

DST SYSTEMS, INC.

333 West 11th Street, Kansas City, MO, 64105

Tel: (816) 435-1000   Fax: (816) 435-8618   www.dstsystems.com

Mfr. financial software.

DST International, DST House, St. Mark's Hill, Surbiton, Surrey KT6 4QD, UK

DT INDUSTRIES, INC.

907 West 5th Street, Dayton, OH, 45407

Tel: (937) 586-5600   Fax: (937) 586-5601   www.dtindustries.com

Mfr automated production equipment and packaging systems for the pharmaceutical and food industries.

DT Industries UK, 3 Arden Road, Alcestec Warwickshire, UK

DT Indutries UK, Tingewick Road, Buckingham MK18 3EF, UK

DUANE MORRIS LLP

One Liberty Place, Philadelphia, PA, 19103-7396

Tel: (215) 979-1000   Fax: (215) 979-1020   www.duanemorris.com

Engaged in international law.

Duane Morris LLP, 4 Chiswell Street, 5/F, London EC1Y 4UP, UK

Tel: 44-207-786-2100   Fax: 44-207-786-2101

DUKE ENERGY CORPORATION

526 South Church Street, Charlotte, NC, 28202

Tel: (704) 594-6200   Fax: (704) 382-3814   www.duke-energy.com

Energy pipeline, oil and gas exploration and production.

Duke Energy Internatinoal, 5 Park Place, London SW1A 1LP, UK

Tel: 44-207-898-9006   Fax: 44-207-898-9261

Texas Eastern North Sea Inc., Berkeley Square House, Berkeley Sq., London W1X 5LE, UK

DUNHAM-BUSH INC.

101 Burgess Road, Harrisonburg, VA, 22801

Tel: (540) 574-6600   Fax: (540) 574-6618   www.dunham-bush.com

Provides innovative solutions for the heating, air conditioning and refrigeration segments.

Dunham-Bush Ltd., Fitzherbert Rd., Farlington, Portsmouth, UK

Dunham-Bush UK, Havant Hampshire, UK

DUO-FAST CORPORATION

2400 Galvin Dr., Elgin, IL, 60123

Tel: (847) 783-5500   Fax: (847) 669-7301   www.duofast.com

Mfr. staplers, tackers and nailers.

Duo-Fast UK, Northfield Drive, Northfield, Milton Keynes MK15 ODR, UK

E.I. DUPONT DE NEMOURS & COMPANY

1007 Market Street, Wilmington, DE, 19898

Tel: (302) 774-1000   Fax: (302) 774-7321   www.dupont.com

Mfr. and sales of diversified chemicals, plastics, specialty products and fibers.

Du Pont (UK) Ltd., Du Pont House, 18 Bream's Bldgs., Fetter Lane, London EC4A 1HT, UK

DuPont (U.K.) Limited, Ermin Street, Brockworth, Gloucester GL3 4HP, UK

Tel: 44-1452-633000   Fax: 44-1452-633251

DuPont Teijin Films U.K. Limited, PO Box 2002, Wilton, Middlesbrough TS90 8JF, UK

Tel: 44-1642-672000

DURACELL INTERNATIONAL INC.

8 Research Drive, Bethel, CT, 06801

Tel: (203) 796-4000   Fax: (203) 796-4745   www.duracell.com

Mfr. batteries.

Duracell Batteries Ltd., Mallory House, Hazelwick Ave., Three Bridges Crawley, West Sussex RH10 1FQ, UK

DVI, INC.

2500 york Road, Jamison, PA, 18929

Tel: (215) 488-5000   Fax: (215) 488-5010   www.dvifs.com

Engaged in financing of medical equipment.

DVI UK Ltd., 77 Cornhill, London EC3V 3QQ, UK

Tel: 44-207-648-2400

DYAX CORPORATION

300 Technology Square, Cambridge, MA, 02139

Tel: (617) 225-2500   Fax: (617) 225-2501   www.dyax.com

Engaged in the development o pharmaceutical products.

Biotage UK, 15 Hartforde Court, John Tate Road, Hertford SG13 7NW, UK

Tel: 44-01-992-501-535

DYNEGY INC.

1000 Louisiana, Ste. 5800, Houston, TX, 77002

Tel: (713) 507-6400   Fax: (713) 507-3871   www.dynegy.com

Holding company that transports and markets energy to local utilities and industrial businesses.

Dynegy U.K. Ltd., 1st Floor, 4 Grosvenor Place, London SW1Z 7HJ, UK

Tel: 44-207-591-6666   Fax: 44-207-591-6667   Contact: Gary Cardone, VP

EARTH TECH INC.

10 West Broadway, Ste. 240, Long Beach, CA, 90802-4443

Tel: (562) 951-2000   Fax: (562) 951-2100   www.earthtech.com

Engaged in environmental engineering.

Earth Tech Engineering Ltd., Wentworth Business Park, Tankersley, Barnsley, South Yorkshire S75 3DL, UK

EASTMAN & BEAUDINE INC.

5700 West Plano Parkway, Ste. 2800, Plano, TX, 75093

Tel: (972) 267-8891   Fax: (972) 267-8891   www.beaudine.com

Engaged in retained executive search and selection.

Eastman & Beaudine Inc., DeWalden Court, 85 New Cavendish St., London W1M 7RA, UK

EASTMAN CHEMICAL COMPANY

100 North Eastman Road, Kingsport, TN, 37662-5075

Tel: (423) 229-2000   Fax: (423) 229-1351   www.eastman.com

Mfr. plastics, chemicals, fibers.

Eastman Chemical Ectona Ltd., Siddick, Workington, Cumbria CA14 1LG, UK

Tel: 44-190-060-9236   Fax: 44-190-060-9279

Eastman Chemical Ectona Ltd., Hunter House Industrial Estate, Brenda Rd., Hartlepool, Cleveland TS25 2BE, UK

Tel: 44-1429-270084   Fax: 44-1429-222900

Eastman Chemical England Limited, Radcliffe Road, Bury, Lancashire BL9 9WW, UK

Tel: 44-161-763-3702   Fax: 44-161-763-4914   Contact: Anthony Flowers

Eastman Chemical European Technical Centre, Acornfield Rd., Knowsley Industrial Park North, Kirkby, Merseyside L33 7UT, UK

Tel: 44-151-548-5100   Fax: 44-151-547-2002   Contact: Paul McBride, Mgr.

Eastman Chemical Ltd., Brindley House, Corner Hall, Lawn Lane, Memel Hempstead, Hertfordshire HP3 9YT, UK

Tel: 44-144-224-1177   Fax: 44-144-224-1171   Contact: Frank Rescigno

Eastman Chemical Ltd., Peboc Div., Industrial Estate, Llangefni, Anglesey, Gwynedd LL77 7YQ, UK

Tel: 44-1248-723-890   Fax: 44-1248-750-724

EASTMAN KODAK COMPANY

343 State Street, Rochester, NY, 14650

Tel: (716) 724-4000   Fax: (716) 724-1089   www.kodak.com

Develop/mfr. photo and chemicals products, information management/video/copier systems, fibers/plastics for various industry.

Eastman Chemical (UK) Ltd., Brindley House, Corner Hall & Lawn Lane, Hemel Hempstead Herts. HP1 3HQ, UK

Eastman Kodak Co., 245 Hammersmith Rd., London W6 8PL, UK

Ectona Fibres Ltd., Siddick, Workington, Cumbria CA14 1LG, UK

Kodak Ltd., Kodak House, Box 66 Station Rd., Hemel Hempstead, Hertfordshire HP1 1JU, UK

T.J. Kenyon & Co., CES Training Centre, Caxton Way, Stevenage Herts. SG1 2DJ, UK

EATON CORPORATION

Eaton Center, 1111 Superior Ave., Cleveland, OH, 44114-2584

Tel: (216) 523-5000   Fax: (216) 479-7068   www.eaton.com

Advanced technical products for transportation and industrial markets.

Eaton Ltd., Eaton House, Staines Rd., Hounslow, Middlesex TW4 5DX, UK

ECOLAB INC.

370 N. Wabasha Street, St. Paul, MN, 55102

Tel: (651) 293-2233   Fax: (651) 293-2379   www.ecolab.com

Develop/mfr. premium cleaning, sanitizing and maintenance products and services for the hospitality, institutional, and residential markets.

Ecolab Ltd., London, UK

Tel: 44-1793-511221

ECOMETRY CORPORATION

1615 S. Congress Avenue, Delray Beach, FL, 33445-6368

Tel: (561) 265-2700   Fax: (561) 454-4803   www.ecometry.com

Mfr. distribution software.

Ecometry Ltd., Grove House, Huntingdon Road, Fenstanton, Huntingdon, Cambridgeshire PE18 9JG, UK

Tel: 44-1480-460-940

ECOWATER SYSTEMS INC.

PO Box 64420,1890 Woodlane Drive, St. Paul, MN, 55164-0420

Tel: (651) 739-5330   Fax: (651) 739-4547   www.ecowater.com

Mfr. water treatment and purification products.

EcoWater Systems, Ltd., #1 Independent Bus. Pk. Mill Rd., Stokenchurch, Buckinghampshire HP14 3TP, UK

Tel: 44-1-494-484000   Fax: 44-1-494-484396   Contact: Peter Marsh, Gen. Mgr.

EDDIE BAUER INC.

15010 NE 36th Street, Redmond, WA, 98073

Tel: (425) 882-6100   Fax: (425) 882-6383   www.eddiebauer.com

Clothing retailer and mail order catalog company.

Eddie Bauer Inc., London, UK

EDELMAN PUBLIC RELATIONS WORLDWIDE

200 East Randolph Drive, 62nd Fl., Chicago, IL, 60601

Tel: (312) 240-3000   Fax: (312) 240-0596   www.edelman.com

International independent public relations firm.

Edelman PR Worldwide, Haymarket House, 28/29 Haymarket, London SW1Y 4SP, UK

Tel: 44-207-344-1200   Fax: 44-207-344-1222   Contact: Tari Hibbitt, Mng. Dir.

EDISON INTERNATIONAL

2244 Walnut Grove Avenue, Rosemead, CA, 91770

Tel: (626) 302-2222   Fax: (626) 302-2517   www.edison.com

Utility holding company.

Edison Mission Energy, London, UK

J.D. EDWARDS & COMPANY

One Technology Way, Denver, CO, 80237

Tel: (303) 334-4000   Fax: (303) 334-4970   www.jdedwards.com

Computer software products.

J. D. Edwards, Colorado House, 300 Thames Valley Park Drive, Reading Berkshire RG6 1RD, UK

Tel: 44-118-9091-700   Fax: 44-118-909-1699

EFCO

1800 NE Broadway Ave., Des Moines, IA, 50316-0386

Tel: (515) 266-1141   Fax: (515) 266-7970   www.efco-usa.com

Mfr. systems for concrete construction.

EFCO UK Ltd., 22-28 Meadow Close, Ise Valley Ind. Estate, Wellingborough Northants NN8 4BH, UK

EG&G INC.

900 Clopper Road, Ste. 200, Gaithersburg, MD, 20878

Tel: (301) 840-3000   Fax: (301) 590-0502   www.egginc.com

Diversified R/D, mfr. and services.

EG&G Astrophysics Research Ltd., Coronation Rd., Cressex Business Park, High Wycombe, Buckinghamshire HP12 3TP, UK

EG&G Fiber Optics, Sorbus House, Mulberry Business Park, Wokingham, Berkshire RG41 2GY, UK

EG&G Ltd., Milton Keynes, 20 Vincent Ave., Crownhill Business Ctr., Crownhill, Milton Keynes MK8 0AB, UK

EG&G Reticon, 34/35 Market Pl., Wokingham, Berkshire RG40 1AT, UK

EG&G Sealol, Coronation Rd., Cressex Business Park, High Wycombe, Buckinghamshire HP12 3TP, UK

EGL INC. (EAGLE GLOBAL LOGISTICS)

15350 Vickery Drive, Houston, TX, 77032

Tel: (281) 618-3100   Fax: (281) 618-3223   www.eagleusa.com

Ocean/air freight forwarding, customs brokerage, packing and wholesale, logistics management and insurance.

EGL Eagle Global Logistics, Airport Freight Way, Freight Village, Newcastle Airport, Newcastle Upon Tyne NE13 8BU, UK

Tel: 44-191-271-2337   Fax: 44-191-271-4093

EGL Eagle Global Logistics, Bell Centre, Unit 11, Newton Rd., Crawley Sussex RH10 2FZ, UK

Tel: 44-1293-544-851   Fax: 44-1293-562-716

EGL Eagle Global Logistics, Bldg 301, Unit 5, World Freight Terminal, Manchester Airport, Manchester M90 5FY, UK

Tel: 44-161-436-4030   Fax: 44-161-437-8727

EGL Eagle Global Logistics, 81 Witham, Hull HU9 1AT, UK

Tel: 44-1482-226-464   Fax: 44-1482-225-054

EGL Eagle Global Logistics, Concourse House, Lime St., Liverpool LI1 1NY, UK

Tel: 44-151-708-6666   Fax: 44-151-708-7836

EGL Eagle Global Logistics, Batley Enterprise Centre, Unit 18 & 19, 513 Bradford Rd., Batley, West Yorkshire WF17 3JX, UK

Tel: 44-1924-470-730   Fax: 44-1924-470-787

EGL Eagle Global Logistics, 8 Willow Rd., Castle Donington, Derbyshire DE74 2NP, UK

Tel: 44-1332-850-111　　Fax: 44-1332-811-164

EGL Eagle Global Logistics, Parker Ave., Building 1, Felixstow, Suffolk 1P11 8HF, UK

Tel: 44-1394-676-488　　Fax: 44-1349-675-139

EGL Eagle Global Logistics, 2 Rubastic Rd., Southall, Middlesex UB2 5UP, UK

Tel: 44-181-843-9952　　Fax: 44-181-571-6031

EGL Eagle Global Logistics, 41 Barton Rd., Water Eaton Industrial Estate, Bletchely, Milton Keynes MK1 3EG, UK

Tel: 44-1908-371-541　　Fax: 44-1908-648-169

EGL Eagle Global Logistics, 40A Victoria Way, Charlton, London SE 7 7PS, UK

Tel: 44-181-293-4000　　Fax: 44-181-858-6143

EGL Eagle Global Logistics, Cargo Administration Bldg., Rooms 1-4A, Cargo Terminal, Stansted Airport South, Stansted Essex CM24 8QW, UK

Tel: 44-1279-680-366　　Fax: 44-1279-680-216

EGL Eagle Global Logistics, Luckyn Lane, Basildon, Essex SS14 3AX, UK

EGL Eagle Global Logistics, 2 Rubastic Rd., Southall, Middlesex UB2 5UP, UK

Tel: 44-181-843-9952　　Fax: 44-181-574-4196

EGL Eagle Global Logistics, Elmdon Trading Estate, Unit 17, Bickenhill Lane, Birmingham B37 7HE, UK

Tel: 44-121-782-5561　　Fax: 44-121-782-2623

EGL Eagle Global Logistics, Heywood Cargo Centre, Phoenix Close, Heywood Lancs OL10 1HJ, UK

Tel: 44-1706-624-245　　Fax: 44-1706-367-673

EL PASO ENERGY PARTNERS, LP

1001 Louisiana Street, Houston, TX, 77252-2511

Tel:　(713) 420-2131　　　　Fax:　(713) 420-4266　　　　www.epenergy.com

Energy and gas.

El Paso Energy International/Enfield Energy, Enfield, North London, UK

ELCOM INTERNATIONAL, INC.

10 Oceana Way, Norwood, MA, 02062

Tel:　(781) 440-3333　　　　Fax:　(781) 762-1540　　　　www.elcominternational.com

Mfr./sales PC products.

Elcom UK, Arrow Road North, Lakeside Redditch B98 8NN, UK

Tel: 44-1527-66800　Fax: 44-1527-61818

Elcom UK, 349 Edinburgh Avenue, Slough Berkshire SL1 4TU, UK

Tel: 44-1753-442-500

Elcom UK, Avocet House, Aviary Court, Wade Road, Basingstoke, Hampshire RG24 8PE, UK

Tel: 44-1256-697-222　Fax: 44-1256-697-100

ELECTRO SCIENTIFIC INDUSTRIES, INC.

13900 NW Science Park Drive, Portland, OR, 97229

Tel:　(503) 641-4141　　　　Fax:　(503) 643-4873　　　　www.esi.com

Mfg. production and testing equipment used in manufacture of electronic components in pagers and cellular communication devices.

Electro Scientific Industries Ltd., 6 Oak Court, Bretts Way, Crawley West Sussex RH10 2GB, UK

Tel: 44-1293-594005　Fax: 44-1293-594019　Contact: Peter Stamp

ELECTRONIC DATA SYSTEMS, INC. (EDS)

5400 Legacy Dr., Plano, TX, 75024

Tel:　(972) 604-6000　　　　Fax:　(972) 605-2643　　　　www.eds.com

Engaged in systems integration, network and systems operations and management consulting.

EDS UK Ltd., 4 Roundwood Avenue, Stockley Park, Stockley Park, Uxbridge UB11 1BQ, UK

Tel: 44-208-848-8989

ELECTRONICS FOR IMAGING, INC. (EFI)

303 Velocity Way, Foster City, CA, 94404

Tel: (650) 357-3500   Fax: (650) 357-3907   www.efi.com

Design/mfr. computer software and hardware for color desktop publishing.

EFI UK, Stonebridge House Padbury Oaks, Old Bath Road, Lomgford Middlesex UB7 0EW, UK

Tel: 44-181-476 7676

ELECTRO-SCIENCE LABORATORIES, INC.

416 East Church Road, King of Prussia, PA, 19406

Tel: (610) 272-8000   Fax: (610) 272-6759   www.electroscience.com

Mfr. advanced thick film materials for hybrid microcircuits and other electronic packaging and component applications.

ESL Agmet Ltd., 8 Commercial Road, Reading Berkshire RG2 0QZ, UK

Tel: 44-118-918-2400   Fax: 44-118-986-7331   Contact: John Whitmarsh

ELITE INFORMATION GROUP, INC.

5100 West Goldleaf Circle, Ste. 100, Los Angeles, CA, 90056-1271

Tel: (323) 642-5200   Fax: (323) 642-5400   www.eliteis.com

Mfr. software.

Elite Information Group Ltd., One Royal Exchange Avenue, Threadneedle Street, London EC3V 3LT, UK

Tel: 44-171-464-4148

EMBREX, INC.

1040 Swabia Court, Research Tri Park, NC, 27709-3989

Tel: (919) 941-5185   Fax: (919) 941-5186   www.embrex.com

Engaged in agricultural biotechnology.

Embrex Europe Ltd., 4 Lakes Industrial Park, Lower Chapel Hill, Braintree Essex CM7 3RU, UK

Tel: 44-1376-333111

EMC CORPORATION

35 Parkwood Drive, Hopkinton, MA, 01748-9103

Tel: (508) 435-1000   Fax: (508) 435-8884   www.emc.com

Designs/supplies intelligent enterprise storage and retrieval technology for open systems, mainframes and midrange environments.

EMC Computer Systems, Regents Park, Kingston Rd., Leatherhead Surrey KT22 7PY, UK

Tel: 44-1372-360000

EMC Computer Systems, The Old Vicarage, Market Place, Castle Donington Derbyshire DE74 2JB, UK

Tel: 44-1332-852809

EMC Computer Systems, Cobhan Gare, 34 Anyards Rd., Cogham Surrey KT11 2LA, UK

Tel: 44-1932-868333

EMC Computer Systems, 7 The Parks, Newton le Willows, Merseyside Haydock WA12 0JQ, UK

Tel: 44-1942-275514

EMC Computer Systems, Leigh Court, Abbotts Leigh, Bristol BS8 3RA, UK

Tel: 44-127-537-5054

EMCOR GROUP

101 Merritt Seven, 7th Fl., Norwalk, CT, 06851

Tel: (203) 849-7800   Fax: (203) 849-7870   www.emcorgroup.com

Engaged in specialty construction.

Delcommerce Contract Services Ltd., Stort Valley Industrial Estate, Stansted Road, Bishop's Stortford, Hertfordshire CM23 2TU, UK

EMCOR Drake & Scull Ltd., 51 Great North Road, Hatfield Hertfordshire AL9 5EN, UK

EMCOR Group, 1 Thameside Centre, Kew Bridge Road, Middlesex TW8 OHF, UK

Tel: 44-208-380-6700

EMERSON & CUMING COMPOSITE MATERIALS, INC.

59 Walpole Street, Canton, MA, 02021

Tel: (781) 821-4250　　　Fax: (781) 821-0737　　　www.emersoncuming.com

Mfr. high performance encapsulants, adhesives and coatings for the automotive, telecommunications and electronic industries.

Emerson & Cuming UK, Windsor Court, Kingsmead Business Park, London Road, High Wycombe Bucks HP11 1JU, UK

Tel: 44-1494-467-812

EMERSON ELECTRIC COMPANY

8000 W. Florissant Ave., PO Box 4100, St. Louis, MO, 63136

Tel: (314) 553-2000　　　Fax: (314) 553-3527　　　www.emersonelectric.com

Electrical and electronic products, industrial components and systems, consumer, government and defense products.

Emerson Europe, 40 Portman Square, London W1H 9FH, UK

Tel: 44-20-7-486-2755

EMERSON PROCESS MANAGEMENT

8301Cameron Road, Austin, TX, 78754

Tel: (512) 834-7689　　　Fax: (512) 832-3232　　　www.frco.com

Mfr. industrial process control equipment.

Emerson Process Management, Heath Place, Bognor Regis, West Sussex PO22 9SH, UK

Emerson Process Management, Horsfield Way, Bredbury SK 6 2SU, UK

Emerson Process Management, Medway House, Knight Rd., Strood Rochester, Kent ME2 2EZ, UK

Contact: Dave Renfrey

EMERY FORWARDING

One Lagoon Drive, Ste. 400, Redwood City, CA, 94065

Tel: (650) 596-9600　　　Fax: (650) 596-7901　　　www.emeryworld.com

Freight transport, global logistics and air cargo.

Emery Forwarding, Worldwide House, Unit 19, Airlinks Industrial Estate, Spitfire Way, Heston Middlesex T25 9NR, UK

Tel: 44-181-260-6000　　Fax: 44-181-260-6030

ENCAD, INC.

6059 Cornerstone Court West, San Diego, CA, 92121

Tel: (858) 452-0882　　　Fax: (858) 452-5618　　　www.encad.com

Mfr. large color printers for specialized graphics.

ENCAD Limited UK, Back Street, Wendover, Buckinghamshire HP22 6EB, UK

Tel: 44-12-9662-2222

ENCYCLOPAEDIA BRITANNICA INC.

310 S. Michigan Ave., Chicago, IL, 60604

Tel: (312) 427-9700　　　Fax: (312) 294-2176　　　www.eb.com

Publishing; books.

Encyclopaedia Britannica Intl. Ltd., Carew House, Station Approach, Wallington, Surrey SM6 0DA, UK

ENERGIZER HOLDINGS, INC.

533 Maryville University Dr., St. Louis, MO, 63141

Tel: (314) 985-2000　　　Fax: (214) 985-2205　　　www.energizer.com

Mfr. Eveready and Energizer brand batteries and lighting products.

Energizer UK, 93 Burleigh Gardens, Southgate London N14 5AQ, UK

Tel: 44-181-82-8918　　Fax: 44-181-882-8661

ENERPAC

6101 N. Baker Road, PO Box 3241, Milwaukee, WI, 53201-3241

Tel: (414) 781-6600　　　Fax: (414) 781-1049　　　www.enerpac.com

Mfr. hydraulic cylinders, pumps, valves, presses, tools, accessories and system components.

ENERPAC Ltd., Unit 3, Colemeadow Road, North Moons Moat, Redditch Worcester B98 9BP, UK

ENGELHARD CORPORATION

101 Wood Avenue South, Iselin, NJ, 08830

Tel: (732) 205-5000 Fax: (732) 632-9253 www.engelhard.com

Mfr. pigments, additives, catalysts, chemicals, engineered materials.

Engelhard-Clal UK, Valley Road, Cinderford GL14 2PB, UK

Tel: 44-1594-822181

Engelhard-Clal UK, 28 Hatton Garden, London EC1 N8DB, UK

Tel: 44-207-40-43100

Engelhard-Clal UK, West Midlands Freeport, Unit 22, Birmingham B26 3QD, UK

Tel: 44-12-1782-4381

Engelhard-Clal UK, Davis Road, Chessington Surrey KT9 1TD, UK

Tel: 44-181-974-3000

ENRON CORPORATION

1400 Smith Street, Houston, TX, 77002-7369

Tel: (713) 853-6161 Fax: (713) 853-3129 www.enron.com

Exploration, production, transportation and distribution of integrated natural gas and electricity. **Corporation under worldwide reorganization; new data unavailable for this edition.

Enron Direct, King Charles House, Park End Street, Oxford OX1 1JD, UK

Tel: 44-1865-202-545

Enron Engineering Services, Crofton House, Crofton Road, Portrack Lane, Stockton on Tees, Cleveland TS18 2QZ, UK

Enron Europe, Four Millbank, Westminster, London SW1P 3ET, UK

Enron Europe, 25 Victoria St., London SW1H OEX, UK

Tel: 44-207-316-5300 Contact: Mark Frevert, CEO

Enron Europe Ltd., 40 Grosvenor Place, London SW1X 7EN, UK

Tel: 44-20-7783-0000

Enron Power Operations Ltd., Enron House, Merchants Wharf, Westpoint Road, Stockton on Tees, UK

Enron Teeside Ltd., PO Box 54, Wilton Middlesborough, Cleveland TS90 8JA, UK

Sutton Bridge Power Station, Sutton Bridge, Spaulding, Lincolnshire PE12 9TF, UK

Teesside Gas Processing Plant, Seal Sands Road, Middlesborough Cleveland TS2 1UB, UK

ENTEGRITY SOLUTIONS CORPORATION

2077 Gateway Place, Ste. 200, San Jose, CA, 95110

Tel: (408) 487-8600 Fax: (408) 487-8610 www.entegrity.com

Mfr. security software.

Entegrity Solutions Ltd., Avis House, Park Road, Bracknell, Berkshire RG12 2BW, UK

Tel: 44-1344-782-950

EPICOR SOFTWARE CORPORATION

195 Technology Drive, Irvine, CA, 92618

Tel: (949) 585-4000 Fax: (949) 450-4419 www.epicor.com

Mfr. software for e-business.

Epicor Birmingham UK, 1 The Arena, Downshire Way, Bracknell Berks RG12 1PU, UK

Tel: 44-1344-468468

Epicor Birmingham UK, 2630 Kings Court, The Crescent Birmingham Business Park, Birmingham B37 7YE, UK

Tel: 44-121-779-1122

Epicor Birmingham UK, Cale Cross House, 5/F, 156 Pilgrim Street, Newcastle-Upon-Tyne NE1 6SU, UK

Tel: 44-191-230-2020

Epicor Manchester UK, Trafalgar House, 110 Manchester Road, Altrincham, Cheshire WA14 1NU, UK

Tel: 44-161-941-2727

EPRESENCE, INC.

120 Flanders Road, Westboro, MA, 01581

Tel: (508) 898-1000   Fax: (508) 898-1755   www.epresence.com

Provides electronic business services.

e-Presence UK Ltd., No. 1 Poultry, 2/F, London EC2R 8JR, UK

EQUIFAX INC.

1550 Peachtree St. NW, Atlanta, GA, 30309

Tel: (404) 885-8000   Fax: (404) 888-5452   www.equifax.com

Provides information and knowledge-based solutions on consumers and businesses around the world.

Equifax Europe (UK) Ltd., Capital House, 25 Chapel St., London NW1 5DS, UK

The Infocheck Group, Godmersham, Canterbury, UK

Transax PLC, Tricorn House, 51-53 Hagley Rd., Edgbaston, Birmingham B16 9DH, UK

UAPT-Infolink PLC, Capital House, 25 Chapel St., London NW1 5DS, UK

ERICO PRODUCTS INC.

34600 Solon Road, Cleveland, OH, 44139

Tel: (440) 248-0100   Fax: (440) 248-0723   www.erico.com

Mfr. electric welding apparatus and hardware, metal stampings, specialty fasteners.

Erico Europa (UK) Ltd., 52 Milford Road, Reading, Berkshire RG1 8LJ, UK

Tel: 44-118-958-8386

ERIEZ MAGNETICS

2200 Asbury Road, Erie, PA, 16506

Tel: (814) 835-6000   Fax: (814) 838-4960   www.eriez.com

Mfr. magnets, vibratory feeders, metal detectors, screeners/sizers, mining equipment, current separators.

Eriez Magnetics Europe Ltd., London, UK

Tel: 44-29-208-68501   Contact: Andy Lewis, Dir.

ERNST & YOUNG INTERNATIONAL

5 Times Square, New York, NY, 10036

Tel: (212) 773-3000   Fax: (212) 773-6350   www.eyi.com

Engaged in assurance and advisory business services, tax, law and corporate finance.

Ernst & Young International, One Colmore Row, Birmingham B3 2DB, UK

Ernst & Young International, PO Box 3, Lowgate House, Lowgate Hull HU1 1JJ, UK

Ernst & Young International, Broadwalk House, Southernhay West, Exeter EX1 1LF, UK

Ernst & Young International, Talbot Chambers, 2-6 North Church St., Sheffield S1 2DH, UK

Ernst & Young International, City Gate, Toll House Hill, Nottingham NG1 5FY, UK

Ernst & Young International, Cambridge House, 26 Tombland, Norwich NR3 1RH, UK

Ernst & Young International, Norham House, 12 New Bridge St. West, Newcastle upon Tyne NE1 8AD, UK

Ernst & Young International, Commercial Union House, Albert Square, Manchester M2 6LP, UK

Ernst & Young International, 400 Capability Green, Luton LU1 3LU, UK

Ernst & Young International, Compass House, 80 Newmarket Road, Cambridge CB5 8DZ, UK

Ernst & Young International, Rolls House, 7 Rolls Bldg. S, Fetter Lane, London EC4A 1NH, UK

Tel: 44-207-931-2587   Fax: 44-207-931-2504   Contact: Bill McHardy

Ernst & Young International, Becket House, 1 Lambeth Palace Rd., London SE1 7EU, UK

Ernst & Young International, Silkhouse Court, Tithebarn St., Liverpool L2 2LE, UK

Ernst & Young International, Provincial House, 37 New Walk, Leicester LE1 6TU, UK

Ernst & Young International, PO Box 61, Cloth Hall Court, 14 King Street, Leeds LS1 2JN, UK

Ernst & Young International, One Bridewell St., Bristol BS1 2AA, UK

Ernst & Young International, Wessex House, 19 Threefield Lane, Southampton SO14 3QB, UK

Ernst & Young International, Old Town Court, 10-14 High St., Swindon SN1 3EP, UK

Ernst & Young International, Apex Plaza, Reading RG1 1YE, UK

Ernst & Young International, Queens Hose, Queen St., Ipswich 1P1 1SW, UK

Ernst & Young International, New Priestgate House, 57 Priestgate, Peterborough PE1 1JX, UK

ESCO CORPORATION

2141 NW 25th Ave., Portland, OR, 97210

Tel: (503) 228-2141   Fax: (503) 778-6330   www.escocorp.com

Mfr. equipment for mining, construction and forestry industries.

ESCO Corp., Guisborough, UK

ESCO TECHNOLOGIES INC.

8888 Ladue Road, Ste. 200, St. Louis, MO, 63124-2090

Tel: (314) 213-7200   Fax: (314) 213-7250   www.escostl.com

Electronic subassemblies and components.

Ginsbury Electronic, Ltd., Div. ESCO, Ginsbury House, Sir Thomas Longley Road, Medway City Estate, Rochester, Kent ME2 4DU,, UK

Tel: 44-1634-290040   Contact: Neville Milward

PTI Technologies Ltd., Div. ESCO, Orgreave Lane, Handsworth, Sheffield S13 9NZ, UK

Tel: 44-114-2693999   Fax: 44-114-2691409

ESNI, INC.

35 Nutmeg Dr., Trumbull, CT, 06611

Tel: (203) 601-3000   Fax: (203) 601-3151   www.e-syncnet.com

Provider of managed enterprise services and solutions services.

Wiltek (UK) Ltd., 2 Apple Walk Kembrey Park, Swindon, Wiltshire SN2 6BL, UK

Tel: 44-1-793-41-4141   Fax: 44-1-793-41-4142

ESTERLINE TECHNOLOGIES

10800 NE 8th Street, Ste. 600, Bellevue, WA, 98004

Tel: (425) 453-9400   Fax: (425) 453-2916   www.esterline.com

Mfr. equipment and instruments for industrial automation, precision measure, data acquisition.

Excellon UK, Dominion Way, Rustington, Littlehampton, West Sussex BN16 3HQ, UK

Tel: 44-1903-858-000

International Precision Products BV, Station Yard, Thame Oxon OX9 3UH, UK

ETHYL CORPORATION

330 South 4th Street, PO Box 2189, Richmond, VA, 23219

Tel: (804) 788-5000   Fax: (804) 788-5688   www.ethyl.com

Provide additive chemistry solutions to enhance the performance of petroleum products.

Ethyl Petroleum Additives Ltd., London Rd., Bracknell, Berkshire RG12 2UW, UK

EURO RSCG WORLDWIDE

350 Hudson Street, New York, NY, 10014

Tel: (212) 886-2000   Fax: (212) 886-2016   www.eurorscg.com

International advertising agency group.

Biss Lancaster, 69 Monmouth Street, London, UK

EVELON, INC.

303 Second St., Marathon Plaza 3 N., San Francisco, CA, 94107

Tel: (415) 495-8811   Fax: (415) 957-1711   www.elevon.cc.com

Provider of premier financial software solutions for large and medium-size enterprises.

Arelon, Div. Evelon UK, The Gate House, Gatehouse Way, Aylesbury, Bucks HP19 8HG, UK

Tel: 44-1296-432951   Fax: 44-1296-398964

EVOLUTIONARY TECHNOLOGIES INTERNATIONAL, INC.

816 Congress Avenue, Ste. 1300, Austin, TX, 78701

Tel: (512) 383-3000   Fax: (512) 383-3300   www.eti.com

Mfr. data integration management software.

ETI, Inc., Denmark Court, 18 Market Place, Wokingham, Berkshire RG 40 1AL, UK

EVOLVE SOFTWARE, INC.

1400 65th Street, Ste. 100, Emeryville, CA, 94111-1808

Tel: (510) 428-6000   Fax: (510) 428-6999   www.evolve.com

Mfr. project management software.

Evolve Europe, Thames Court, 1 Victoria Street, Windsor Berkshire SL4 1YB, UK

Tel: 44-1753-752-474   Fax: 44-1753-752-475

EXCEL COMMUNICATIONS, INC.

8750 N. Central Expwy., Ste. 2000, Dallas, TX, 75231

Tel: (214) 863-8000   Fax: (214) 863-8843   www.excel.com

Long-distance telecommunications carrier.

Excel Communications, ETI Division, 137-143 Hammersmith Road, London W14 OQL, U.K.

EXCELERGY CORPORATION

181 Spring Street, Lexington, MA, 02421

Tel: (781) 372-5000   Fax: (781) 372-5297   www.excelergy.com

Mfr. billing system software.

Excelergy Europe, 1 Friary, Temple Quay, Bristol BS1 6EA, UK

Tel: 44-117-900-8440

EXCELLON AUTOMATION

24751 Crenshaw Boulevard, Torrance, CA, 90505

Tel: (310) 534-6300   Fax: (310) 534-6777   www.excellon.com

PCB drilling and routing machines; optical inspection equipment.

Excellon Intl., Dominion Way, Rustington, Littlehampton, W. Sussex BN16 3HQ, UK

Excellon UK, Dominion Way, Rustington, West Sussex BN16 3HQ, UK

Tel: 44-1-903-858000

EXCELON INC.

25 Mall Road, Burlington, MA, 01803

Tel: (781) 674-5000   Fax: (781) 674-5010   www.exceloncorp.com

Developer of object-oriented database management systems software.

eXcelon (UK) Limited, 1015 Arlington Business Park, Theale Reading Berkshire RG7 4SA, UK

Tel: 44-118-930-1200

eXcelon UK Ltd., 68 Lombard Street, London EC3V 9LJ, UK

Tel: 44-207-868-1710   Fax: 44-207-868-1810

EXE TECHNOLOGIES, INC.

8787 N. Stemmons Fwy., Dallas, TX, 75247-3702

Tel: (214) 775-6000   Fax: (214) 775-0911   www.exe.com

Provides a complete line of supply chain management execution software for WMS.

EXE Technologies, Inc. European Office, Ocean House, The Ring, Bracknell Berkshire RG12 1AH, UK

Tel: 44-1344-420144   Fax: 44-1344-41800

EXIDE TECHNOLOGIES

210 Carnegie Center, Ste. 500, Princeton, NJ, 08540

Tel: (609) 627-7200   Fax: (609) 627-7217   www.exideworld.com

Mfr. lead-acid automotive and industrial batteries.

Exide UK, Bolton, UK

EXPEDITORS INTERNATIONAL OF WASHINGTON INC.

1015 Third Avenue, 12th Fl., Seattle, WA, 98104-1182

Tel: (206) 674-3400   Fax: (206) 682-9777   www.expd.com

Air/ocean freight forwarding, customs brokerage, international logistics solutions.

Expeditors International (UK) Ltd., Unit 5, The Heston Centre, International Avenue, Southall Lane Heston Middlesex TW5 9NJ, UK

EXTENSITY, INC.

2200 Powell Street, Ste. 300, Emeryville, CA, 94608

Tel: (510) 594-5700   Fax: (510) 596-2676   www.extensity.com

Mfr. time management software.

Extensity Europe Ltd., Abbey House, Wellington Way, Weybridge Surrey KT13 OTT, UK

Tel: 44-1932-268-720

EXXON MOBIL CORPORATION

5959 Las Colinas Blvd., Irving, TX, 75039-2298

Tel: (972) 444-1000   Fax: (972) 444-1882   www.exxonmobil.com

Petroleum exploration, production, refining; mfr. petroleum and chemicals products; coal and minerals.

Exxon Mobil, Inc., Esso House, Victoria St., London SW1E 5JW, UK

Exxon Mobil, Inc., Cadland Rd., Hardley, Hythe, Southampton SO45 3NP, UK

Exxon Mobil, Inc., Arundel Towers, Portland Terrace, Fawley, Southampton SO9 2GW, UK

Exxon Mobil, Inc., 4600 Parkway, Whiteley Fareham, Hampshire PO15 7AP, UK

Tel: 44-1489-884400

E-Z-EM INC.

717 Main Street, Westbury, NY, 11590

Tel: (516) 333-8230   Fax: (516) 333-8278   www.ezem.com

Engaged in the design, manufacture and marketing of contrast media for gastrointestinal tract radiography.

E-Z-EM Ltd., 1230 High Rd., London N20 0LH, UK

Tel: 44-181-446-9714   Fax: 44-181-446-9810   Contact: Ginette Camps-Walsh, Gen. Mgr.   Emp: 14

FABREEKA INTERNATIONAL INC.

1023 Turnpike, PO Box 210, Stoughton, MA, 02072

Tel: (781) 341-3655   Fax: (781) 341-3983   www.fabreeka.com

Mfr. vibration isolation materials; consulting and engineering services.

Fabreeka Intl. Inc., 8-12 Jubilee Way, Thackley Old Rd., Shipley, W. Yorkshire BD18 1QS, UK

Tel: 44-1274-531333   Fax: 44-1274-531717

FACTSET RESEARCH SYSTEMS, INC.

1 Greenwich Plaza, Greenwich, CT, 06830

Tel: (203) 863-1599   Fax: (203) 863-1501   www.factset.com

Provides on-line investment research services to financial institutions.

FactSet Limited, One Angel Court, London EC2R 7HJ, UK

Tel: 44-207-606-0001

FAEGRE & BENSON LLP

2200 Norwest Center, 90 South Seventh Street, Minneapolis, MN, 55402-3901

Tel: (612) 336-3000   Fax: (612) 336-3026   www.faegre.com

International law firm.

Faegre Benson Hobson Audley, 7 Pilgrim St., London EC4V 6LB, UK

Tel: 44-207-450 4510   Fax: 44-20-7450-4544   Contact: Scott James, Ptnr.

FAIR, ISAAC AND COMPANY, INC.

200 Smith Ranch Road, San Rafael, CA, 94903

Tel: (415) 472-2211   Fax: (415) 492-5691   www.fairisaac.com

Mfr. automated systems for credit and loan approvals.

Fair, Isaac and Co., Concorde House, 2/F, Trinity Park, Birmingham B37 7ES, UK

Tel: 44-121-781-4500

FAIRCHILD PUBLICATIONS INC.

7 West 34th Street, New York, NY, 10001

Tel: (212) 630-4000   Fax: (212) 630-3563   www.fairchildpub.com

Magazine publishers: Women's Wear Daily, Supermarket News, Brand Marketing, Executive Technology, Footwear News, Salon News.

Fairchild Publications Inc., 20 Shorts Garden, London WC2H 9AU, UK

Tel: 44-207-240-0420   Fax: 44-207-240-0290

FAIRCHILD SEMICONDUCTOR INTERNATIONAL, INC.

82 Running Hill Road, South Portland, ME, 04106

Tel: (207) 775-8100   Fax: (207) 761-0392   www.fairchildsemi.com

Mfr. semiconductor chips.

Fairchild Semiconductor Ltd., 10 Interface Business Park, Binknoll Lane, Wootton Bassett, Swindon, Wiltshire 4SN 8SY, UK

Tel: 44-1793-856856   Fax: 44-1793-856857

THE FALK CORPORATION

3001 West Canal Street, PO Box 492,, Milwaukee, WI, 53208-4200

Tel: (414) 342-3131   Fax: (414) 937-4359   www.falkcorp.com

Designers and manufacturers of power transmission equipment including gears, geared reducers and drives, couplings.

Falk Corp UK, 8 Brunel Gate, 8 Brunel Industrial Estate, Harworth Doncaster DN11 8QB, UK

Falk Europe, Halifax HX3 5AX, UK

Tel: Dean Clough

FALLON WORLDWIDE

50 South Sixth Street, Minneapolis, MN, 55402

Tel: (612) 758-2345   Fax: (612) 758-2346   www.fallon.com

Advertising and marketing agency.

Fallon Worldwide UK, 67-69 Beak Street, London W1F 9SW, UK

Tel: 44-207-494-9120   Contact: Robert Senior

FARREL CORPORATION

25 Main Street, Ansonia, CT, 06401

Tel: (203) 736-5500   Fax: (203) 735-6267   www.farrel.com

Mfr. polymer processing equipment.

Farrel Ltd., Queensway, Castleton, PO Box 27, Rochdale, Lancashire OL11 2PF, UK

Tel: 44-01706-647434

FAXON COMPANY, INC.

15 Southwest Park, Westwood, MA, 02090

Tel: (781) 329-3350   Fax: (781) 329-9875   www.faxon.com

Library services; engaged in serials management and subscription services in the library marketplace.

RoweCom UK, Cannon House Folkestone, Kent CT19 5EE, UK

FEDDERS CORPORATION

505 Martinsville Road, Liberty Corner, NJ, 07938-0813

Tel: (908) 604-8686   Fax: (908) 604-0715   www.fedders.com

Mfr. room air conditioners, humidifiers and dehumidifiers.

Trion, Div. Fedders, Reith Way West Portway Industrial Estate, Andover Hampshire SP10 3TY, UK

Tel: 44-1264-364622   Contact: Peter Benn

FEDERAL-MOGUL CORPORATION

26555 Northwestern Highway, PO Box 1966, Southfield, MI, 48034

Tel: (248) 354-7700   Fax: (248) 354-8983   www.federal-mogul.com

Mfr./distributor precision parts for automobiles, trucks, farm and construction vehicles.

Federal-Mogul Aftermarket UK Ltd., Greyhound Drive, Bradford, West Yorkshire BD7 1NQ, UK

Tel: 44-1274-723481   Contact: Robin Shaw

Federal-Mogul Ltd., Neville Road, Bradford, West Yorkshire BD4 8TU, UK

Federal-Mogul Westwind Air Bearings Ltd., London, UK

FEDEX CORPORATION

942 South Shady Grove Rd., Memphis, TN, 38120

Tel: (901) 369-3600   Fax: (901) 395-2000   www.fdxcorp.com

Package express delivery service.

Federal Express (UK) Ltd., 1A Girling Way, Feltham, Middlesex TW14 0PH, UK

Tel: 44-800-123-800

Federal Express (UK) Ltd., 48-49 Westbrook Rd., Trafford Park, Manchester M17 1AY, UK

Tel: 44-800-123-800

FELLOWES, INC.

1789 Norwood Avenue, Itasca, IL, 60143-109

Tel: (630) 893-1600   Fax: (630) 893-1648   www.fellowes.com

Mfr. of office products and accessories.

Fellowes UK Ltd., Yorkshire Way, West Moor Park, Doncaster, South Yorkshire DN3 3FB, UK

Tel: 44-1302-836-800   Fax: 44-1302-836-899

FERGUSON COMPANY

11820 Lackland Road, St. Louis, MO, 63146-4281

Tel: (314) 567-3200   Fax: (314) 567-4701   www.ferguson-co.com

Mfr. indexing and transfer equipment, custom cams, parts handlers, rotary tables, link conveyors.

BSL Engineering Limited, Apex House, 19 Parkside Lane, Leeds LS11 5TD, UK

Tel: 44-113-276-2441   Contact: Richard Greenwood, Mgr.

FERREX INTERNATIONAL INC.

26 Broadway, 26th Fl., New York, NY, 10004

Tel: (212) 509-7030   Fax: (212) 344-4728   www.ferrex.com

Mfr. and distribution of road maintenance machinery, welding and industrial equipment and supplies.

Ferrex Europe, 51 Downsview Drive, Wivelsfield Green, NR. Haywards Heath, Sussex RH17 7RN, UK

Tel: 44-1-4444-71280   Fax: 44-1-4444-71073

FERRO CORPORATION

1000 Lakeside Ave., Cleveland, OH, 44114-7000

Tel: (216) 641-8580   Fax: (216) 696-5784   www.ferro.com

Mfr. Specialty chemicals, coatings, plastics, colors, refractories.

Ferro Ltd. Ceramic Division, Nile St., Burslem, Stoke-on-Tent ST6 2BQ, UK

Tel: 44-1782-824488   Fax: 44-1782-814238   Contact: Robert Latimer, Gen. Mgr.

Ferro Ltd. Colour & Enamel Divisions, Ounsdale Rd., Wombourne, Wolverhampton WV5 8DA, UK

Tel: 44-1902-324144   Fax: 44-1902-324265   Contact: Graham Rose, Mgr.

Ferro Ltd. Plastics & Drynamels Divisions, Westgate, Aldridge, West Midlands WS9 8YH, UK

Tel: 44-1922-58300   Fax: 44-1922-52986   Contact: David Ankrett, Gen. Mgr.

FERROTEC CORPORATION

40 Simon Street, Nashua, NH, 03061

Tel: (603) 883-9800   Fax: (603) 883-2308   www.ferrofluidics.com

Mfr. rotary feedthrough designs, emission seals, automated crystal-growing systems, bearings, ferrofluids.

Ferrotec (UK) Ltd., Talisman Business Centre, Bicester Oxon OX26 6HR, UK

Tel: 44-1869-363200

FIDUCIARY TRUST COMPANY INTERNATIONAL

175 Federal Street, Boston, MA, 02110

Tel: (617) 482-5270   Fax: (617) 482-5270   www.ftc.com

Banking services.

Fiduciary Trust (Intl.) SA, London, UK

FileNET CORPORATION

3565 Harbor Boulevard, Costa Mesa, CA, 92626

Tel: (714) 966-3400   Fax: (714) 966-3490   www.filenet.com

Provides integrated document management (IDM) software and services for internet and client server-based imaging, workflow, cold and electronic document management solutions.

FileNET Ltd., One The Square, Stockley Park, Uxbridge, Middlesex UB11 1FN, UK

Tel: 44-181-867-6363   Fax: 44-181-867-6365   Contact: Lou Valdini, Mgr.

FINANCIAL GUARANTY INSURANCE COMPANY

115 Broadway, New York, NY, 10006

Tel: (212) 312-3000   Fax: (212) 312-3093   www.fgic.com

Engaged in insuring debt securities and investment, operation, and information services to state and local governments

Financial Guaranty Insurance Co. (London), 20 St. James's St., London SW1A 1ES, UK

THE FINOVA GROUP, INC.

4800 N. Scottsdale Rd., Scottsdale, AZ, 85251-7623

Tel: (480) 636-4800   Fax: (480) 636-5726   www.finova.com

Provides commercial financing and asset-based loans to businesses.

FINOVA Group UK, 11 Albemarle Street, London W1X 3HE, UK

Tel: 44-207-493-5518   Contact: Robert Gordon

FIREPOND, INC.

890 Winter Stret, Waltham, MA, 02451

Tel: (781) 487-8400   Fax: (781) 487-8450   www.firepond.com

Mfr. enterprise software.

Firepond (UK) Ltd, Innovation House, Harvest Crescent, Ancells Business Park, Fleet Hampshire GU13 8UZ, UK

FIRESTONE POLYMERS

381 W. Wilbeth Road, Akron, OH, 44301

Tel: (330) 379-7864   Fax: (330) 379-7875   www.firesyn.com

Mfr. polymers; rubber, plastics and adhesives

Corrie Maccoll & Son, Ltd., New Loom House, 101 Backchurch Lane, London E1 1LU, UK

Tel: 44-207-481-1516   Fax: 44-207-702-4168   Contact: Andy Hurley

FIRST DATA CORPORATION

6200 S. Quebec Street, Greenwood Village, CO, 80111

Tel: (303) 488-8000   Fax: (303) 488-8000   www.firstdatacorp.com

Information and transaction processing services.

FDC (First Data), FDR House, Christopher Martin Rd., Basildon Essex S514 9AA, UK

Tel: 44-1268-296590   Contact: Gerald Hawkins

FIRST ENERGY CORP.

76 S. Main Street, Akron, OH, 44308-1890

Tel: (330) 384-3866   Fax: (330) 384-3866   www.firstenergycorp.com

Energy holding company.

Midlands Electricity plc, London, UK

FIRSTWAVE TECHNOLOGIES, INC.

2859 Paces Ferry Road, Ste. 1000, Atlanta, GA, 30339

Tel: (770) 431-1200   Fax: (770) 431-1201   www.firstwave.com

Mfr. CRM accounting and financial software.

Firstwave Technologies UK Ltd., The Pavilion, 1 Atwell Place, Thames Ditton, Surrey KT7 0NF, UK

Tel: 44-208-614-5300   Fax: 44-208-614-5310

FISERV INC.

PO Box 979, 255 Fiserv Drive, Brookfield, WI, 53008-0979

Tel: (414) 879-5000   Fax: (414) 879-5013   www.fiserv.com

Data processing products and services for the financial industry.

Catapult Technology Limited, Westgate House, 20 Wellcroft Road, Slough, Berkshire SL1 4AQ, UK

Tel: 44-1753-821148   Fax: 44-1753-825055   Contact: Keith Williams

Fiserv Europe Ltd., 5 Roundwood Ave., Stockley Pk., Uxbridge, Middlesex UB11 1AX, UK

FISHER DEVELOPMENT, INC.

1485 Bayshore Blvd., Ste. 152, San Francisco, CA, 94124-3002

Tel: (415) 486-1717   Fax: (415) 468-6241   www.fisherinc.com

General contractor for chain store developments.

Fisher Development UK, Berkeley Square House, 1/F, Berkeley Square, London W1J 6BS, UK

FISHER SCIENTIFIC INTERNATIONAL INC.

1 Liberty Lane, Hampton, NH, 03842

Tel: (603) 929-5911   Fax: (603) 929-0222   www.fisherscientific.com

Mfr. and distribution of science equipment, instruments, and supplies.

Fisher Scientific Clinical Services, Langhurstwood Road, Horsham, West Sussex RH12 4QD, UK

Fisher Scientific UK Ltd., Bishop Meadow Rd., Loughborough, Leicestershire LE11 5RG, UK

Tel: 44-1509-231166   Fax: 44-1509-231893

ORME Technologies, a division of Fisher Scientific UK Ltd., Whitbrook Way, Stakehill Industrial Park, Middleton, Manchester M24 2RH, UK

Tel: 44-161-653-4589   Fax: 44-161-655-3011

FITCH INC.

1 State Street Plaza, New York, NY, 10004

Tel: (212) 908-0500   Fax: (212) 480-4435   www.fitchibca.com

Supplies credit ratings.

Global Power & Energy, Div. Fitch, Eldon House, London EC2M 7UA, UK

FKI LOGISTEX

1500 Lebanon Road, Danville, KY, 40422

Tel: (877) 935-4564   Fax: (877) 935-4564   www.fkilogistex.com

Mfr. integrated material handling solutions for distribution, baggage handling, freight, parcel, and manufacturing applications.

Cleco Systems Limited, Riverside, Market Harborough, Leicestershire LE16 7PZ, UK

Tel: 44-1858-436200

FKI Plc, Lintas House, 15/19 New Fetter Lane, London EC4A 1LY, UK

Tel: 44--207-8320000

FLACK + KURTZ INC.

475 Fifth Ave., 8th Fl., New York, NY, 10017

Tel: (212) 532-9600   Fax: (212) 689-7489   www.flackandkurtz.com

Consulting engineers for building services, i.e.., HVAC, electrical, lighting, plumbing/hydraulics, life safety, fire protection and telecommunications.

Flack + Kurtz (UK) Inc., 143 Charing Cross Rd., London WC2H 0EE, UK

Tel: 44-207-494-2441 Fax: 44-207-494-2401   Contact: David Stillman   Emp: 35

C.B. FLEET COMPANY, INC.

4615 Murray Place, PO Box 11349, Lynchburg, VA, 24506

Tel: (804) 528-4000   Fax: (804) 847-4219   www.cbfleet.com

Mfr. pharmaceutical, health and beauty aids.

E.C. De Witt & Company Ltd., Tudor Road, Manor Park, Runcorn Cheshire WA7 ISZ, UK

Tel: 44-1-928-579-029   Fax: 44-1-928-579-712

FLEETBOSTON FINANCIAL CORPORATION

100 Federal Street, Boston, MA, 02110

Tel: (617) 434-2400   Fax: (617) 434-6943   www.fleet.com

Banking and insurance services.

FleetBoston - London, Bank Boston House, 39 Victoria St., PO Box 155, London SW1H OED, UK

Tel: 44-207-799-3333   Fax: 44-207-222-5649

FleetBoston Capital Ltd., Bank Boston House, 39 Victoria St., PO Box 155, London SW1H OED, UK

Tel: 44-207-732-9053   Fax: 44-207-932-9117

FLEXINTERNATIONAL SOFTWARE, INC.

2 Enterprise Drive, Shelton, CT, 06484

Tel: (203) 925-3040   Fax: (203) 925-3044   www.flexi.com

Mfr. financial analysis software.

Flexinternational Software UK, Tudor House, Kingsway Business Park, Oldfield Road, Hampston Middlesex TW111HD, UK

Tel: 44-108-939-5700   Fax: 44-208-939-5701

FLINT INK CORPORATION

4600 Arrowhead Drive, Ann Arbor, MI, 48105

Tel: (734) 622-6000   Fax: (734) 622-6060   www.flintink.com

Manufacturer of printing inks and pigments.

Flint Ink Europe, Stirling Rd. Industrial Estate, Dykehead Rd., Airdrie ML6 7UD, UK

Tel: 44-1236-761220   Fax: 44-1236-766126   Contact: Jim Mahony, Pres. Europe

Flint Ink Europe, Vauxhall Industrial Estate, Wrexham, Clwyd Ruabon LL14 6UH, UK

Tel: 44-1978-823456   Fax: 44-1978-823331   Contact: Jim Mahony, Pres. Europe

Flint Ink Europe, 3-4 Prospect Drive, Britannia Enterprise Park, Litchfield's, Staffordshire WS14 9UX, UK

Tel: 44-1543-414114   Fax: 4-1543-264489   Contact: Jim Mahony, Pres. Europe

Flint Ink Europe, PO Box 186, Old Heath Rd., Wolverhampton WV1 2RS, UK

Tel: 44-1902-871028   Fax: 44-1902-457461   Contact: Jim Mahony, Pres. Europe

Flint Ink Europe, 5/6 Marketside, Albert Rd., St. Phillip's, Bristol BS2 OXJ, UK

Tel: 44-207-9721181   Fax: 44-117-9710858   Contact: Jim Mahony, Pres. Europe

Flint Ink Europe, Willowyard Industrial Estate, Beith, Ayrshire K15 1LY, UK

Tel: 44-1505-504681   Fax: 44-1505-504202   Contact: Jim Mahony, Pres. Europe

FLIR SYSTEMS, INC.

16505 SW 72nd Ave., Portland, OR, 97224-1206

Tel: (503) 684-3731   Fax: (503) 684-5452   www.flir.com

Engaged in design and manufacture of imaging systems for aircraft, shipping, defense and environmental protection industries.

FLIR Systems International Ltd., 2 Kings Hill Ave., Kings Hill, West Malling, Kent ME19 4AQ, UK

Tel: 44-1732-220011   Fax: 44-1732-220014

FLOWSERVE CORPORATION

222 W. Los Colinas Blvd., Irving, TX, 75039

Tel: (972) 443-6500   Fax: (972) 443-6858   www.flowserve.com

Mfr. chemicals equipment, pumps, valves, filters, fans and heat exchangers.

Durametallic UK, Unit 13B, United Trading Estate, Old Trafford, Manchester M16 0RJ, UK

Flowserve UK, Dakota Avenue Salford, Manchester M5 2PU, UK

Contact: Steve Petter

FLUOR CORPORATION

One Enterprise Drive, Aliso Viejo, CA, 92656-2606

Tel: (949) 349-2000   Fax: (949) 349-5271   www.flour.com

Engineering and construction services.

Fluor Daniel International Ltd., 3 Shortlands, London W6 8DD, UK

Tel: 44-181-222-7000   Fax: 44-181-222-7050

Fluor Ltd., Fluor Daniel Centre, Watchmoor Park, Camberley, Surrey GU15 3YL, UK

FM GLOBAL INC.

1301 Atwood Avenue, Johnston, RI, 02919

Tel: (401) 275-3000   Fax: (401) 275-3029   www.fmglobal.com

Engaged in commercial and industrial property insurance and risk management, specializing in engineering-driven property protection.

FM Global, 1 Windsor Dials, Windsor, Berks SL4 1RS, UK

Tel: 44-175-375-0000   Fax: 44-175-386-8700

FM Insurance Co. Ltd., 105 Victoria St., London SW1E 6QT, UK

FMC CORPORATION

1735 Market St., Philadelphia, PA, 19103

Tel: (215) 299-6000   Fax: (215) 299-6618   www.fmc.com

Mfr. specialty chemicals, including alginate, carrageenan and microcrystalline cellulose.

FMC UK, Wirral International Business Park, Bromborough Wirral, Bromborough, UK

Tel: 44-15-482-7356

FMC TECHNOLOGIES, INC.

200 E. Randolph Dr., Chicago, IL, 60601

Tel: (312) 861-6000   Fax: (312) 861-6176   www.fmctechnologies.com

Mfr. bulk material handling and automation equipment and cargo loaders.

FMC Surface Wellhead Equipment, Balfour House, Churchfield Road, Walton-on-Thames Surrey KT12 2TD, UK

FMR (FIDELITY INVESTMENTS)

82 Devonshire Street, Boston, MA, 02109

Tel: (617) 563-7000   Fax: (617) 476-6105   www.fidelity.com

Diversified financial services company offering investment management, retirement, brokerage, and shareholder services directly to individuals and institutions and through financial intermediaries.

Fidelity InvestmentsLtd., Oakhill House, 130 Tonbridge Road, Hildenboroug Tonbridge, Kent TN11 9DZ, UK

FOOT LOCKER INC.

112 West 34th Street, New York, NY, 10020

Tel: (212) 720-3700   Fax: (212) 553-2042   www.venatorgroup.com

Mfr./sales shoes and sneakers.

Foot Locker International, 26 St. John's Rd., Clapham Junction, Clapham SW11 1PW, UK

Tel: 44-1717-7381286

Foot Locker International, Unit 43, The Pentagon Centre, Chatham ME4 4HP, UK

Tel: 44-1634-819112

Foot Locker International, The Galleries, Unit G, 37 Broadmead, Bristol BS1 3EU, UK

Tel: 44-117-9258132

Foot Locker International, 12 Palisades Shopping Centre, Birmingham B2 4XA, UK

Tel: 44-121-6325754

Foot Locker International, 52 Lakeside Centre, Thurrock RM16 1ZF, UK

Tel: 44-1708-891232

Foot Locker International, 19 Bull St., Birmingham B4 7AA, UK

Tel: 44-121-2330396

FORD MOTOR COMPANY

One American Road, Dearborn, MI, 48126

Tel: (313) 322-3000   Fax: (313) 322-9600   www.ford.com

Mfr./sales motor vehicles.

Aston Marton Ltd., Div. Ford, Lonsdale Place, Derby DE22 3LP, UK

Tel: 44-1332-371566   Fax: 44-1332-384600

Ford Motor Co. Ltd., Eagle Way, Brentwood, Essex CM13 3BW, UK

FOREST LABORATORIES INC.

909 Third Ave., 23rd Fl., New York, NY, 10022

Tel: (212) 421-7850   Fax: (212) 750-9152   www.frx.com

Mfr. name-brand and generic pharmaceutical products.

Pharmax Limited, 5 Bourne Rd., Bexley, Kent DA5 1NX, UK

Tel: 44-1-322-550-550

FORMICA CORPORATION

10155 Reading Road, Cincinnati, OH, 45241-4805

Tel: (513) 786-3400   Fax: (513) 786-3082   www.formica.com

Mfr. decorative laminate, adhesives and solvents.

Formica Limited, Coast Road, North Shields, Tyne & Wear NE29 8RE, UK

FORRESTER RESEARCH, INC.

400 Technology Square, Cambridge, MA, 02139

Tel: (617) 497-7090   Fax: (617) 868-0577   www.forrester.com

Provides clients an analysis of the effect of changing technologies on their operations.

Forrester Research UK, Charlotte House, 9-14 Windmill Street, London W1T 2JG, UK

Tel: 44-207-631-0202   Fax: 44-207-631-5252

FORTEL INC.

46832 Lakeview Blvd., Fremont, CA, 94538-6543

Tel: (510) 440-9600   Fax: (510) 440-9696   www.fortel.com

Mfr. e-business corporate software.

FORTEL Ltd., Fountain House, Cleeve Road, Leatherhead, Surrey KT22 7LX, UK

Tel: 44-1372-378-899   Fax: 44-1372-378-845

FOSSIL, INC.

2280 N. Greenville Avenue, Richardson, TX, 75082

Tel: (972) 234-2525   Fax: (972) 234-4669   www.fossil.com

Mfr. fashion watches

Fossil and Avia UK, PO Box 422, Redhill Surrey RH1 2PL, UK

Tel: 44-1737-788-703

Fossil UK, Covent Garden, 29 James Street, London WC2E 8PA, UK

Tel: 44-207-836-5400

L.B. FOSTER COMPANY

415 Holiday Drive, Pittsburgh, PA, 15220

Tel: (412) 928-3400   Fax: (412) 928-7891   www.lbfoster.com

Mfr. and sales of steel pipe, railroad rail, highway products and accessories.

L.B. Foster Co., European Div., 40 Charlwood Rd., Putney, London SW15, UK

FOSTER WHEELER LTD.

Perryville Corporate Park, Clinton, NJ, 08809-4000

Tel: (908) 730-4000   Fax: (908) 730-4100   www.fwc.com

Manufacturing, engineering and construction.

Foster Wheeler Energy Limited, High Force Road, Riverside Park, Middlesbrough Cleveland TS2 1RH, UK

Tel: 44-1642-230600   Fax: 44-1642-241097   Contact: Simon Schmuck

Foster Wheeler Lenergy Limited, Shinfield Park, Berkshire RG2 9FW, UK

Tel: 44-118-913-1234   Fax: 44-118-913-2333   Contact: Keith Batchelor

Foster Wheeler Management Operations Limited, Shinfield Park, Berkshire RG2 9FW, UK

Tel: 44-118-913-1234   Fax: 44-118-913-2333   Contact: John Oakey

Foster Wheeler Petroleum Development Limited, Shinfield Park, Berkshire RG2 9FW, UK

Tel: 44-118-913-1234   Fax: 44-118-913-2333   Contact: Don Harris, Mgr.

FOWLER, RODRIGUEZ, KINGSMILL, FLINT & GRAY

201 St. Charles Ave., 36th Fl., New Orleans, LA, 70170

Tel: (504) 523-2600   Fax: (504) 523-2705   www.fowlerrodriguez.com

Law firm specializing in maritime, insurance, int'l, environmental, oil/gas, transportation, bankruptcy and reorganization.

Fowler, Rodriguez, Kingsmill, Flint & Gray, Mitre House, 4th Fl., 12-14 Mitre St., London EC3A 5BU, UK

Tel: 44-207-929-4222   Fax: 44-207-929-0043

FRANK RUSSELL COMPANY

909 A Street, Tacoma, WA, 98402

Tel: (253) 572-9500   Fax: (253) 591-3495   www.russell.com

Investment management and asset strategy consulting.

Frank Russell Company Ltd., 12 Clifford St., London W1X 2FR, UK

Tel: 44-207-287-2858   Fax: 44-207-495-5447   Contact: Alison Ramsdale, Dir.   Emp: 10

Frank Russell Company Ltd., Rex House, 10 Regent Street, London SW1Y 4PE, UK

Tel: 44-207-287-2858   Fax: 44-207-414-0079   Contact: Johan Cras, Mng. Dir. UK   Emp: 100

FRANKLIN COVEY COMPANY

2200 W. Parkway Blvd., Salt Lake City, UT, 84119-2331

Tel: (801) 975-1776   Fax: (801) 977-1431   www.franklincovey.com

Provides productivity and time management products and seminars.

Franklin Covey U.K., Grimsbury Manor, Grimsbury Green, Banbury Oxfordshire OX16 3JQ, UK

Tel: 44-1295-274100   Fax: 44-1295-274101

Franklin Covey UK, PO Box 1000, Newcastle-upon-Tyne NE85 2BS, UK

THE FRANKLIN MINT

US Route 1, Media, PA, 19091-0001

Tel: (610) 459-6000   Fax: (610) 459-6880   www.franklinmint.com

Design/marketing collectibles and luxury items.

Franklin Mint Ltd., One South Quay Plaza, London E14 9WS, UK

FRANKLIN RESOURCES, INC.

1 Franklin Pkwy., Bldg. 970, 1st Fl., San Mateo, CA, 94404

Tel: (415) 312-2000   Fax: (415) 312-5606   www.frk.com

Global and domestic investment advisory and portfolio management.

Templeton Investment Management Ltd., London, UK

Tel: 44-131-469-4000   Fax: 44-131-228-4506

FREDRIKSON & BYRON, P.A.

1100 International Centre, Minneapolis, MN, 55402-3397

Tel: (612) 347-7000   Fax: (612) 347-7077   www.fredlaw.com

Engaged in international law.

Fredrikson & Byron, 16 Bedford Street, Convent Garden, London WC2E 9HF, UK

Tel: 44-207-395-3110

FRIED, FRANK, HARRIS, SHRIVER & JACOBSON

One New York Plaza, New York, NY, 10004-1980

Tel: (212) 859-8000   Fax: (212) 859-4000   www.ffhsj.com

International law firm.

Fried, Frank, Harris, Shriver & Jacobson, 99 City Road, London EC1Y 1AX, UK

Tel: 44-207-972-9600   Fax: 44-207-972-9602   Contact: Jerry Swirth, Ptnr.

FRITO-LAY COMPANY

7701 Legacy Drive, Plano, TX, 75024

Tel: (972) 334-7000   Fax: (972) 334-2019   www.fritolay.com

Mfr. snack food products.

Frito-Lay Holdings Ltd., London, UK

Walkers Smiths Snack Foods Ltd, London, UK

FRITZ COMPANIES, INC., DIV. UPS

706 Mission Street, Ste. 900, San Francisco, CA, 94103

Tel: (415) 904-8360   Fax: (415) 904-8661   www.fritz.com

Integrated transportation, sourcing, distribution and customs brokerage services.

Fritz Companies UK Ltd., Haslemere Heathrow Estate, Unit 1, Silver Jubilee Way, Cranford Middlesex TW4 6NF, UK

FRONTRANGE SOLUTIONS INC.

1125 Kelly Johnson Blvd., Colorado Springs, CO, 80820

Tel: (719) 531-5007   Fax: (719) 536-0620   www.frontrange.com

Mfr. customer support software.

FrontRange Solutions UK Ltd., 100 Longwater Avenue, Green Park Reading, Berks RG2 6GP, UK

Tel: 44-118-938-7300

FRONTSTEP, INC.

2800 Corporate Exchange Drive, Ste. 400, Columbus, OH, 43231

Tel: (614) 523-7000   Fax: (614) 895-2504   www.frontstep.com

Mfr. management software.

Frontstep UK Ltd., The Crescent, 2460 Regents Court, Birmingham B37 7YE, UK

FROST & SULLIVAN, INC.

7550 West Interstate 10, Ste. 910, San Antonio, TX, 78229

Tel: (210) 348-1000   Fax: (210) 348-1003   www.frost.com

Engaged in international marketing consulting and training.

Frost & Sullivan, 4 Grosvenor Road, SW1W ODH, UK

Tel: 44-207-730-3438

FSI INTERNATIONAL INC.

3455 Lyman Boulevard, Chaska, MN, 55318-3052

Tel: (952) 448-5440   Fax: (952) 448-2825   www.fsi-intl.com

Manufacturing equipment for computer silicon wafers.

Metron Technology Ltd., 6-7 Grafton Way, Basingstoke, Hampshire RG22 6HY, UK

Tel: 44-1256-792000   Fax: 44-1256-792033

FULBRIGHT & JAWORSKI LLP

1301 McKinney Street, Ste. 5100, Houston, TX, 77010

Tel: (713) 651-5151   Fax: (713) 651-5246   www.fulbright.com

Engaged in international law.

Fulbright & Jaworski, 2 St. Jane's Place, London SW1A 1NP, UK

Tel: 44-207-629-1207   Fax: 44-207-493-8259

H.B. FULLER COMPANY

1200 Willow Lake Blvd., Vadnais Heights, MN, 55110

Tel: (651) 236-5900   Fax: (651) 236-5898   www.hbfuller.com

Mfr./distributor adhesives, sealants, coatings, paints, waxes, sanitation chemicals.

H.B. Fuller Coatings, Ltd., 95 Aston Church Road, Nechells, Birmingham B7 5RQ, UK

Tel: 44-121-322-6900   Fax: 44-121-322-6901

H.B. Fuller U.K. Limited, Moor Road, Chesham, Buckinghamshire HP5 1SB, UK

H.B. Fuller U.K. Ltd., Amber Business Center, Greenhill Lane, Leabrooks Derbyshire DE55 4BR, UK

Tel: 44-1773-608877   Fax: 44-1773-528070

Linear Products, Ltd., 95 Aston Church Road, Nechells Birmingham B7 5RQ, UK

FULTON BOILER WORKS INC.

PO Box 257, Pulaski, NY, 13142-0257

Tel: (315) 298-5121   Fax: (315) 298-6390   www.fulton.com

Mfr. process heat transfer equipment, including steam and hot water boilers.

Fulton Boiler Works (GB) Ltd., Brislington Trading Estate, Broomhill Rd., Bristol BS4 TU, UK

Tel: 44-117-9723-322   Fax: 44-117-9723-358   Contact: Ian Davidson, Mng. Dir.   Emp: 50

FUNDTECH LTD.

30 Montgomery Street, Ste. 501, Jersey City, NJ, 07302

Tel: (201) 946-1100   Fax: (201) 946-1313   www.fundtech.com

Mfr. electronic funds transfer software.

Fundtech U.K. Ltd., 42 New Broad Street, London EC2M 1SB, UK

Tel: 44-207-588-1100   Fax: 44-207-588-1155

GA EXPRESS, INC.

17731 Mitchell North, Irvine, CA, 92614

Tel: (949) 250-4800   Fax: (949) 752-6772   www.gaexpress.com

Mfr. enterprise connectivity software.

GA eXpress, Ltd., 6 Albany Close, Bushey Heath, Hertshire WD2 3SG, UK

Contact: Bill Cotton

THE GAB ROBINS GROUP

Linden Plaza, 9 Campus Drive, Parsippany, NJ, 07054-4476

Tel: (973) 993-3400   Fax: (973) 993-9579   www.gabrobins.com

Engaged in insurance adjustments and claims.

Robins Davies Intl. (RDI), 35 Great St. Helen's, London EC3A 6HB, UK

Contact: Philippe Bès

GABELLI ASSET MANAGEMENT, INC.

1 Corporate Center, Rye, NY, 10580

Tel: (914) 921-3700   Fax: (914) 921-5392   www.gabelli.com

Engaged in fund management.

Gabelli Asset Management UK, 4/5 Princes Gate, London SW7, UK

Tel: 44-207-225-7922

GAFFNEY CLINE & ASSOCIATES INC.

PO Box 796309, Dallas, TX, 75379

Tel: (972) 733-1183   Fax: (972) 380-0180   www.gaffney-cline.com

Consultants to energy and mineral industrial.

Gaffney, Cline & Associates (GFA), Bentley Hall, Blacknest Alton, Hampshire GU34 4PU, UK

GALEY & LORD, INC.

980 Avenue of the Americas, New York, NY, 10018

Tel: (212) 465-3000   Fax: (212) 465-3025

Mfr. of denim, corduroy and blended cotton fabrics.

Klopman International, Div. Galey & Lord, 34 The Quadrant, Richmond-upon-Thames, Surrey TW9 1DN, UK

Tel: 44-208-334-5500   Contact: Giuseppe Rodino, Pres.

GALILEO INTERNATIONAL, INC.

1 Campus Dr., Parsippany, NJ, 07054

Tel: (973) 518-4000   Fax: (973) 518-4085   www.galileo.com

Operates computerized reservation systems (CRS) for travel.

Galileo Centre Europe, 2 Windsor Dials, Arthur Road, Windsor SL4 1RS, UK

Tel: 44-1-753-498-500   Fax: 44-1-753-498-501

ARTHUR J. GALLAGHER & CO.

2 Pierce Place, Itasca, IL, 60143-3141

Tel: (630) 773-3800   Fax: (630) 285-4000   www.ajg.com

Engaged in insurance brokerage and risk management services.

Arthur J. Gallagher UK Ltd., 9 Alie Street, London E1 8DE, UK

GALVESTON-HOUSTON COMPANY.

4900 Woodway, PO Box 2207, Houston, TX, 77056

Tel: (713) 966-2500   Fax: (713) 966-2575   www.hensleyind.com

Mfr. industrial equipment.

Bettis Actuators & Controls Ltd., Brunel Way, Fareham, Hantsford PO15 5SA, UK

GANNETT COMPANY, INC.

1100 Wilson Blvd., Arlington, VA, 22234

Tel: (703) 284-6000   Fax: (703) 364-0855   www.gannett.com

Newspaper publishing and broadcasting company.

Newsquest Bradford Ltd., Hall Ings, Bradford BD1 1JR, UK

Contact: Julie Wilson

USA Today Intl., 34-44 London Road, Morden Surrey SM4 5BR, UK

Tel: 44-20-8640-8989

THE GAP

2 Folsom St., San Francisco, CA, 94105

Tel: (650) 952-4400   Fax: (650) 952-5884   www.gap.com

Clothing store chain.

The Gap, London, UK

GARDNER-DENVER INC.

1800 Gardner Expressway, Quincy, IL, 62301

Tel: (217) 222-5400   Fax: (217) 228-8247   www.gardnerdenver.com

Mfr. portable air compressors and related drilling accessories.

Gardner Denver Limited, 51A Wycombe End, Beaconsfield, Bucks HP9 1LX, UK

Tel: 44-1494-680560

Gardner-Denver Ltd., Suite 3, Parkway Business Centre 2, Princess Road, Manchester M14 7LU, UK

Tel: 44-1612328986

GARLOCK SEALING TECHNOLOGIES

1666 Division Street, Palmyra, NY, 14522

Tel: (315) 597-4811   Fax: (315) 597-3216   www.garlock-inc.com

Mfr. of gaskets, packing, seals and expansion joints.

Garlock GB Ltd., Hambridge Rd., Newbury Berkshire RG14 5TG, UK

Tel: 44-1635-38509   Contact: David Willis, Mng. Dir.

GARTNER, INC.

56 Top Gallant Road, Stamford, CT, 06904-2212

Tel: (203) 316-1111   Fax: (203) 316-1100   www.gartner.com

Engaged in information technology consulting.

Gartner Group, Tamesis, The Glanty, Egham TW20 9AW, UK

Tel: 44-1784-431611

THE GATES RUBBER COMPANY

990 S. Broadway, PO Box 5887, Denver, CO, 80217-5887

Tel: (303) 744-1911   Fax: (303) 744-4000   www.gatesrubber.com

Mfr. automotive and industrial belts and hoses.

Gates Rubber Company, Edinburgh Road, Dumfries DG1 1QA, UK

GATEWAY INC.

4545 Towne Centre Ct., San Diego, CA, 92121

Tel: (858) 799-3401   Fax: (858) 779-3459   www.gateway.com

Computers manufacture, sales and services.

Gateway (UK) Ltd., 16 Kingfisher Ct., Hambridge Rd., Newbury, Berkshire RG14 5SJ, UK

GATX CORPORATION

500 West Monroe Street, Chicago, IL, 60661

Tel: (312) 621-6200   Fax: (312) 621-6648   www.gatxcapital.com

Lease and loan financing, residual guarantees.

GATX Asset Residual Management Plc., St. Andrew's House, West Street, Woking Surrey GU21 1EA, UK

Tel: 44-1483-747133   Fax: 44-1483-727679

GATX International Ltd., 25 Canada Square, 32/F, Canary Wharf, London E14 5LL, UK

Tel: 44-207-715-6600   Contact: Jeff Johnson

Lombard Network Services Ltd., Lombard House, Waterfront Business Park Elstree Road, Elstree Hertfordshire WD6 3BS, UK

Tel: 44-181-236-7800   Fax: 44-181-236-7899

GE BETZ, DIV. GE SPECIALTY MATERIALS

4636 Somerton Road, PO Box 3002, Trevose, PA, 19053-6783

Tel: (215) 355-3300   Fax: (215) 953-5524   www.gebetz.com

Engaged in engineered chemical treatment of water and process systems in industrial, commercial and institutional facilities

GE Betz, Div. GE Specialty Materials, Foundry Lane, Widnes, Cheshire WA8 8 UD, UK

GE CAPITAL FLEET SERVICES

3 Capital Drive, Eden Prairie, MN, 55344

Tel: (612) 828-1000   Fax: (612) 828-2010   www.gefleet.com

Corporate vehicle leasing and services.

GE Capital Fleet Services, Old Hall Road, Sale, Cheshire M33 2G7, UK

Tel: 44-870-444-9070

GE POLYMERSHAPES INC.

11515 Vanstory Drive, Huntersville, NC, 28078

Tel: (704) 205-3100   Fax: (704) 583-4715   www.gepolymershapes.com

Distributor of plastic sheet, rod, tube, and films.

GE Polymershapes, Rivermead Dr., Westlea, Swindon, Wittshire SN5 7YT, UK

Tel: 44-1763-648500

GEN RE INTERMEDIARIES CORPORATION

PO Box 10216, Stamford, CT, 06904-2216

Tel: (203) 357-8883   Fax: (203) 328-6408   www.genre.com

Provides reinsurance services worldwide.

General Re Europe Ltd. London, Corn Exchange, 55 Mark Lane, London EC3R 7NE, UK

Tel: 44-20-7426-6000   Fax: 44-20-7426-6001   Contact: Berto Sciolla, VP

General Re Europe Ltd. Manchester, 1 St. James Square, 5th Fl., Manchester M2 6DN, UK

Tel: 44-161-831-7555   Fax: 44-161-831-7700   Contact: Patricia A. Chandler, VP

General Re Financial Services Ltd. - London, Broadgate Court, 199 Bishopgate, London EC2M 3TY, UK

Tel: 44-207-448-4000   Fax: 44-207-448-4065

Hartford Re Europe, London Underwriting Centre, Suite 3, 5/F, 3 Minister Court, Mincing Lane, London EC3R 7DD, UK

Tel: 44-207-617-4400   Fax: 44-207-617-4422   Contact: John Daly, Gen. Mgr.

The Cologne Reinsurance Company Ltd., The Corn Exchange, 55 Mark Lane, London EC3R 7NE, UK

Tel: 44-207-426-1846   Fax: 44-207-426-1898   Contact: Alex Cowley, Gen. Mgr.

The Cologne Reinsurance Company Ltd., Cologne House, 13 Haydon St., London EC3N 1DB, UK

Tel: 44-207-481-1533   Fax: 44-207-480-6511   Contact: Brian Cragg, Mng. Dir.

GENCOR INDUSTRIES INC.

5201 N. Orange Blossom Trail, Orlando, FL, 32810

Tel: (407) 290-6000   Fax: (407) 578-0577   www.gencor.com

Mfr. heavy machinery for the production of highway construction materials, synthetic fuels and environmental control machinery and equipment.

CPM Europe, Ltd., West March, Daventry, Northants NN11 4SA, UK

Tel: 44-1327-70-4721   Fax: 44-1327-77-1831

Gencor Acp, Ltd., Wharf Way, Glen Parva, Leicester LE2 9TF, UK

Tel: 44-116-277-5555   Fax: 44-116-277-6563

GENEFORMATICS INCORPORATED

5830 Oberline Drive, Ste. 200, San Diego, CA, 92121

Tel: (858) 450-3331   Fax: (858) 450-1138   www.geneformatics.com

Engaged in drug research and development.

GeneFormatics UK, Boundary House, Boston Road, London W7 2QE, UK

Tel: 44-208-434-3533   Fax: 44-208-434-3534

GENERAL BINDING CORPORATION

One GBC Plaza, Northbrook, IL, 60062

Tel: (847) 272-3700   Fax: (847) 272-1369   www.gbc.com

Engaged in the design, manufacture and distribution of branded office equipment, related supplies and thermal laminating films.

GBC (United Kingdom) Limited, Rutherford Road, Basingstoke, Hampshire RG24 8PD, UK

GENERAL CABLE CORPORATION

4 Tesseneer Dr., Highland Heights, KY, 41076-9753

Tel: (859) 572-8000   Fax: (859) 572-8458   www.generalcable.com

Mfr. aluminum, copper and fiber optic wire and cable products.

General Cable, Hedgeley Road, Hebburn, Tyne and Wear NE31 1XR, UK

Tel: 44-191-483-2244

GENERAL DATACOMM INC.

6 Rubber Avenue, Naugatuck, CT, 06770

Tel: (203) 729-0271   Fax: (203) 729-2883   www.gdc.com

Mfr., sales and service of transportation equipment for communications networks.

General DataComm Ltd., Molly Millar Lane, Wokingham, Berkshire RG11 2QF, UK

Tel: 44-1734-774868

GENERAL DYNAMICS CORPORATION

3190 Fairview Park Drive, Falls Church, VA, 22042-4523

Tel: (703) 876-3000   Fax: (703) 876-3125   www.gendyn.com

Mfr. aerospace equipment, submarines, strategic systems, armored vehicles, defense support systems.

Computing Devices Company Ltd., Castleham Site, Castleham Rd., St. Leonards-On-Sea, East Sussex TN38 9NJ, UK

Tel: 44-1424-853-481   Fax: 44-1424-851-520   Contact: Sir Donald Spiers, Chmn.

Computing Devices Company Ltd., Highfield Business Park, Sidney Little Rd., St. Leonards-On-Sea, East Sussex TN38 9UB, UK

Tel: 44-1424-853-481   Fax: 44-1424-798-575   Contact: Sir Donald Spiers, Chmn.

GENERAL ELECTRIC CAPITAL CORPORATION

260 Long Ridge Road, Stamford, CT, 06927

Tel: (203) 357-4000   Fax: (203) 357-6489   www.gecapital.com

Financial, property, casualty insurance, computer sales and trailer leasing services.

GE Capital Equipment Finance Ltd, Capital House, Bond Street, Bristol BS1 3LA, UK

Tel: 44-117-929-8899

GE European Equipment Finance, Trinity Square, 23/59 Staines Road, Hounslow TW3 3HF, UK

Tel: 44-208-754-2100

GENERAL ELECTRIC COMPANY

3135 Easton Turnpike, Fairfield, CT, 06431

Tel: (203) 373-2211   Fax: (203) 373-3131   www.ge.com

Diversified manufacturing, technology and services.

GE Aircraft Engines, Unit C1, Main Avenue, Treforest Industrial Estate, Pontypridd Mid Clam CF37 5UR, UK

Tel: 44-1443-847-336   Fax: 44-1443-847-434

GE Appliances, 3 Shortlands, Hammersmith London W6 8BX, UK

Tel: 44-181-846-8645

GE FANUC Automation, Unit 1 Mill Square, Milton Keyes MK12 5BZ, UK

Tel: 44-190-884-4041   Fax: 44-190-884-4001

GE International, 3 Shortlands, Hammersmith, London W6 8BX, UK
Tel: 44-181-741-9900

GE SeaCo British Isles Ltd., Sea Containers House, 20 Upper Ground, London SE1 9PF, UK

GE/Nuovo Pignone, 25 Green St., London WIY 3FD, UK
Tel: 44-207-493-8211   Fax: 44-207-629-5684

International Wagon Services, Div. of GE Railcar, 3 Shortlands, Hammersmith, London W6 8BX, UK

GENERAL MOTORS ACCEPTANCE CORPORATION

3044 W. Grand Blvd., Detroit, MI, 48202
Tel: (313) 556-5000   Fax: (313) 556-5108   www.gmac.com
Automobile financing.

GMAC (UK) PLC, Metropolitan House, 1 Hagley Rd., Five Ways, Edgbaston Birmingham B16 8TG, UK

GMAC (UK) PLC, Kings House, Bond St., Bristol BS1 2AE, UK

GMAC (UK) PLC, Oakland House, Talbot Rd., Old Trafford, Manchester M16 OPQ, UK

GMAC (UK) PLC, Aire House, Swinegate, Leeds LS1 4AG, UK

GMAC (UK) PLC, Wesley House, 19 Chapel St., PO Box 11, Luton Beds LU1 2SE, UK

GENERAL MOTORS CORPORATION

300 Renaissance Center, Detroit, MI, 48285
Tel: (313) 556-5000   Fax: (313) 556-5108   www.gm.com
Mfr. full line vehicles, automotive electronics, commercial technologies, telecommunications, space, finance.

Delco Electronics Overseas Corp., Moorgate Rd., Kirkby, Liverpool L33 7XL, UK

Delco Products Overseas Corp., PO Box 4, High St. North, Dunstable LU6 1BQ, UK

General Motors Overseas Commercial Vehicle Corp., UK

Group Lotus PLC, Norwich Norfolk NR14 8E2, UK

Saginaw Overseas Corp., 1/8 Capitol Way, London NW9 OEH, UK

Vauxhall Motors Ltd., PO Box 3, Kimpton Rd., Luton LU2 0SY, UK

GENICOM CORPORATION

4500 Daly Drive, Ste. 100, Chantilly, VA, 20151
Tel: (703) 633-8700   Fax: (703) 222-7629   www.genicom.com
Supplier of network systems, service and printer solutions.

Genicom Limited, Armstrong Mall - Southwood, Farnborough, Hampshire GU14 ONR, UK
Tel: 44-1252-74-44-00

Genicom Ltd., Armstrong Mall Southwood, Farnborough, Hampshire GU14 ONR, UK
Contact: Tony Hammell

GENOMIC SOLUTIONS INC.

4355 Varsity Drive, Ste. E, Ann Arbor, MI, 48108
Tel: (734) 975-4800   Fax: (734) 975-4808   www.genomicsolutions.com
Mfr. software for gene research.

Genomic Solutions Ltd., 8 Blackstone Road, Huntingdon, Cambridgeshire PE29 6EF, UK
Tel: 44-1480-426-700   Fax: 44-1480-426-767

GENUITY, INC.

225 Presidential Way, Woburn, MA, 01801
Tel: (781) 865-2000   Fax: (781) 865-3936   www.genuity.com
R/D computer, communications, acoustics technologies and internetworking services.

Genuity UK, 1 Whitehall Road, Leeds LS1 4HR, UK

Genuity UK, 1 Transcentral, Bennet Road, Reading, Berkshire RG2 0QX, UK
Tel: 44-1344-668419   Contact: Louise Pearl

GENZYME CORPORATION

1 Kendall Square, Cambridge, MA, 02139-1562
Tel: (617) 252-7500   Fax: (617) 252-7600   www.genzyme.com
Mfr. healthcare products for enzyme deficient diseases.

GBL Genzyme SA, 50 Gibson Drive, Kings Hill West Malling, Kent ME19 4HG, UK

Genzyme Ltd., 37 Hollands Road, Haverhill Suffolk CB9 8PU, UK

Tel: 44-1440-703-522   Fax: 44-1440-707-783

GEO LOGISTICS CORPORATION

1521 E. Dyer Rd., Santa Ana, CA, 92705

Tel: (714) 513-3000   Fax: (714) 513-3120   www.geo-logistics.com

Engaged in freight forwarding, warehousing and distribution services, specializing in heavy cargo.

GeoLogistics Ltd., 117-120 Snargate Street, Dover Kent CT179EB, UK

Tel: 44-1304-240242   Fax: 44-1304-240325

GeoLogistics Ltd., Trafford Wharf Road, Trafford Park, Manchester M17 1EX, UK

Tel: 44-161-872-4022   Fax: 44-161-876-6045

GeoLogistics Ltd., Royal Court, 81 Tweedy Road, Bromley Kent BR1 1TW, UK

LEP Transport Ltd., Sunlight Wharf, Upper Thames Street, London EC4P 4AD, UK

GEOWORKS CORPORATION

960 Atlantic Avenue, Alameda, CA, 94501

Tel: (510) 614-1660   Fax: (510) 614-4250   www.geoworks.com

Mfr. operating system software.

Geoworks Ltd. UK, Beechfield House, Lyme Green Business Park, Macclesfield, Cheshire SK11 0JP, UK

Tel: 44-1625-503305   Contact: Ashley Griffiths

G-I HOLDINGS, INC.

1361 Alps Road, Wayne, NJ, 07470

Tel: (973) 628-3000   Fax: (973) 628-3326   www.gaf.com

Mfr. roofing and building materials.

G-I Holdings, Inc., Rythe House, 12 Littleworth Rd., Esher Surrey KT10 9PD, UK

G-I Holdings, Inc., Tilson Rd., Roundthorn, Wythenshawe, Manchester M23 9PH, UK

GIBSON, DUNN & CRUTCHER LLP

333 S. Grand Ave., Los Angeles, CA, 90071

Tel: (213) 229-7000   Fax: (213) 229-7520   www.gibsondunn.com

Engaged in international law.

Gibson, Dunn & Crutcher LLP, 30/35 Pall Mall, London SW1Y 5LP, UK

Tel: 44-207-925-0440   Fax: 44-207-925-2465

GIDDINGS & LEWIS INC.

142 Doty Street, PO Box 590, Fond du Lac, WI, 54936-0590

Tel: (920) 921-9400   Fax: (920) 929-4522   www.giddings.com

Mfr. machine tools, factory automation products and services.

Giddings & Lewis Cross Hüller, Randles Rd., Knowsley Industrial Park South, Prescot, Merseyside L34 9EZ, UK

Tel: 44-151-546-2010   Fax: 44-151-547-2801   Contact: Alan Ruddock, Mng. Dir.

GILEAD SCIENCES, INC.

333 Lakeside Dr, Foster City, CA, 94404

Tel: (650) 574-3000   Fax: (650) 578-9264   www.gilead.com

Engaged in healthcare research and development; biotech treatments for viruses.

NeXstar Pharmaceuticals, Ltd., Granta Park Abington, Cambridge CB1 6GT, UK

Tel: 44-122-357-1400   Fax: 44-122-357-1444

THE GILLETTE COMPANY

Prudential Tower Building, Boston, MA, 02199

Tel: (617) 421-7000   Fax: (617) 421-7123   www.gillette.com

Develop/mfr. personal care/use products: blades and razors, toiletries, cosmetics, stationery.

Braun (UK) Ltd., Sunbury-on-Thames, UK

Contact: Roger Murphy, Gen. Mgr.

Gillette Industries PLC, Isleworth Middlesex, UK

Contact: Roger Murphy, Gen. Mgr.

Gillette Personal Care Ltd., Isleworth Middlesex, UK

Contact: Roger Murphy, Gen. Mgr.

Gillette UK Ltd., Great West Road, Isleworth Middlesex TW7 5NP, UK

Contact: Roger Murphy, Gen. Mgr.

Jafra Cosmetics Intl. Ltd., Farnborough Hants., UK

Contact: Roger Murphy, Gen. Mgr.

Lidgate Intl. Ltd., Isleworth Middlesex, UK

Contact: Roger Murphy, Gen. Mgr.

Lustrasilk Intl. UK Ltd., Isleworth Middlesex, UK

Contact: Roger Murphy, Gen. Mgr.

Moorgate Industries Ltd., Isleworth Middlesex, UK

Contact: Roger Murphy, Gen. Mgr.

Nacet Co. Ltd., Isleworth Middlesex, UK

Contact: Roger Murphy, Gen. Mgr.

Oral-B Laboratories Dublin Inc., Aylesbury Buckinghamshire, UK

Contact: Roger Murphy, Gen. Mgr.

Oral-B Laboratories Intl. Ltd., Isleworth Middlesex, UK

Contact: Roger Murphy, Gen. Mgr.

Oral-B Laboratories Ltd., Aylesbury Buckinghamshire, UK

Contact: Roger Murphy, Gen. Mgr.

Oral-B Laboratories Newbridge Inc., Aylesbury Buckinghamshire, UK

Contact: Roger Murphy, Gen. Mgr.

Waterman Pens UK Ltd., Isleworth Middlesex, UK

Contact: Roger Murphy, Gen. Mgr.

GILSON INC.

3000 W. Beltline Hwy, PO Box 620027, Middleton, WI, 53562-0027

Tel: (608) 836-1551   Fax: (608) 831-4451   www.gilson.com

Mfr. analytical/biomedical instruments.

Anachem Ltd., Anachem House, Charles Street, Luton Bedfordshire LU2 OEB, UK

GLEASON CORPORATION

1000 University Ave., Rochester, NY, 14692

Tel: (716) 473-1000   Fax: (716) 461-4348   www.gleasoncorp.com

Mfr. gear making machine tools; tooling and services.

Gleason Works Ltd., 6B Derriford Business Park, Plymouth PL6 5QZ, UK

Tel: 44-1752-739661   Fax: 44-1752-724429

GLENAYRE ELECTRONICS LTD.

11360 Lakefield Drive, Duluth, GA, 30097

Tel: (770) 283-1000   Fax: (770) 497-3982   www.glenayre.com

Mfr. infrastructure components and pagers.

Glenayre Electronics (UK) Ltd., Challenge House 17-18a, Sherwood Drive Bletchley, Milton Keynes MK3 6JD, UK

Tel: 44-1908-644-642   Fax: 44-1908-644-643

GLOBAL PAYMENT TECHNOLOGIES, INC.

425B Oser Ave., Hauppauge, NY, 11788

Tel: (631) 231-1177   Fax: (631) 434-1771   www.gptx.com

Mfr. validators for authenticating currency.

Global Payment Technologies, Ltd., 29 Park Royal Metro Centre, Britannia Way, London NW10 7PA, UK

Tel: 44-20-8961-6116   Fax: 44-20-8961-6117

GLOBAL SANTA FE CORPORATION

777 North Eldridge Pkwy., Houston, TX, 77079

Tel: (281) 496-8000   Fax: (281) 531-1260   www.gsfdrill.com

Offshore contract drilling, turnkey drilling, oil and gas exploration and production.

Global SantaFe, London, UK

GLOBAL SILVERHAWK INTERNATIONAL MOVING

1000 Burnett Avenue, Concord, CA, 94520

Tel: (510) 609-7080   Fax: (510) 609-7081   www.globalsilverhawk.com

International moving and forwarding.

Global Silverhawk, 16 Perivale Ind. Park, Horsenden Lane S., Greenford Middlesex UB6 7RW, UK

Contact: Helen Brabbs, Gen. Mgr.

THE GOLDMAN SACHS GROUP

85 Broad Street, New York, NY, 10004

Tel: (212) 902-1000   Fax: (212) 902-3000   www.gs.com

Investment bankers; securities broker dealers.

Goldman Sachs Group, Peterborough Court, 133 Fleet St., London EC4A 2BB, UK

Tel: 44-207-774-1000

THE GOODYEAR TIRE & RUBBER COMPANY

1144 East Market Street, Akron, OH, 44316

Tel: (330) 796-2121   Fax: (330) 796-1817   www.goodyear.com

Mfr. tires, automotive belts and hose, conveyor belts, chemicals; oil pipeline transmission.

Goodyear Great Britain Ltd., Stafford Rd., Wolverhampton WV10 6D4, UK

GOSS INTERNATIONAL CORPORATION

700 Oakmont Lane, Westmont, IL, 60559-5546

Tel: (630) 850-5600   Fax: (630) 850-6310   www.gossgraphic.com

Engaged in the design and manufacture of advanced technology web offset press systems for the newspaper and commercial printing industries.

Goss Graphic Systems, Ltd., Greenbank Street, Preston, Lancashire PR1 7LA, UK

Tel: 44-1772-257571   Contact: Shane Lancaster, SVP & Gen. Mgr.

W. R. GRACE & COMPANY

7500 Grace Drive, Columbia, MD, 21044

Tel: (410) 531-4000   Fax: (410) 531-4367   www.grace.com

Mfr. specialty chemicals and materials: packaging, health care, catalysts, construction, water treatment/process.

W. R. Grace Ltd., 628 Ajax Avenue, Slough Berkshire SL1 4BH, UK

Tel: 44-1753-69-2929   Fax: 44-1753-63-7702

W. R. Grace Ltd., Clifton House, 1 Marston Rd., St. Neots Cambridgeshire PE19 2HN, UK

Tel: 44-1480-224-000   Fax: 44-1480-244-066

GRACO INC.

88 - 11th Avenue NE, PO Box 1441, Minneapolis, MN, 55440-1441

Tel: (612) 623-6000   Fax: (612) 623-6777   www.graco.com

Mfr. systems and equipment to service fluid handling systems and automotive equipment.

Graco UK, One Hovefield Ave., Burnt Mills B Industrial Estate, Basildon Essex SS13 1ND, UK

Tel: 870-9090-510   Fax: 870-9090-505

GRANITE SYSTEMS, INC.

1228 Elm Street, Manchester, NH, 03101

Tel: (603) 625-0100   Fax: (603) 625-4812   www.granitesystems.com

Mfr. service resource management software.

Granite Systems, Inc., 55-61 High Street, Frimley, Surrey GU16 5HJ, UK

Tel: 44-1276-515-515

GRANT THORNTON INTERNATIONAL

800 One Prudential Plaza, 130 E. Randolph Drive, Chicago, IL, 60601-6050

Tel: (312) 856-0001   Fax: (312) 616-7052   www.grantthornton.com

Accounting, audit, tax and management consulting services.

Grant Thornton, Heron House, Albert Square, Manchester M60 8GT, UK

Tel: 44-161-834-5414   Fax: 44-161-832-6042   Contact: Graema Whittaker

Grant Thornton, 18 Langton Place, Bury St. Edmunds, Suffolk IP33 1NE, UK

Tel: 44-1284-701271   Fax: 44-1284-762760   Contact: Graham Shorter

Grant Thornton, Kettering Pkwy., Kettering, Northants East Northampton NN15 6XR, UK

Tel: 44-1536-310000   Fax: 44-1536-315400   Contact: Aidan O'Rourke

Grant Thornton, 43 Queen Square, Bristol BS1 4QR, UK

Tel: 44-117-936-8901   Fax: 44-117-926-5458   Contact: Roger C. Zair

Grant Thornton International, Grant Thornton House, Melton Street, Euston Square, London NW1 2EP, UK

Tel: 44-207-383-5100   Fax: 44-207-728-2744   Contact: David C. McDonnell, Mgr.

Grant Thornton International, St John's Centre, 110 Albion Street, Leeds LS2 8LA, UK

Tel: 44-113-246-0211   Contact: David Naylor

GREAT LAKES CHEMICAL CORPORATION

500 East 96th Street, Ste. 500, Indianapolis, IN, 46240

Tel: (317) 715-3000   Fax: (317) 715-3050   www.greatlakeschem.com

Mfr. innovative specialty chemical solutions, including flame retardants and other polymer additives, water treatment chemicals, performance and fine chemicals, fire extinguishers.

Great Lakes Sales (UK) Ltd, Tenax Road, Trafford Park, Manchester M17 1WT, UK

Tel: 44-161-872-2323

GREAT PLAINS SOFTWARE, INC.

1 Long Tree Road, Fargo, ND, 58104

Tel: (701) 281-6500   Fax: (701) 281-6868   www.greatplains.com

Mfr. supply chain management software.

Great Plains Software UK, Culerdon House Abbots Way, Chertsey Surrey KT16 9JZ, UK

Tel: 44-1932-58100

GREENFIELD INDUSTRIES INC.

470 Old Evans Road, Evans, GA, 30809

Tel: (706) 863-7708   Fax: (706) 860-8559   www.gfi.com

Mfr. high-speed rotary cutting tools.

Cirbo Ltd. & RTW Ltd., 16 Normandy Way, Bodmin, Cornwall PL1 1EX, UK

GREY GLOBAL GROUP

777 Third Ave., New York, NY, 10017

Tel: (212) 546-2000   Fax: (212) 546-1495   www.grey.com

International advertising agency.

Grey Communications Group, 215-227 Great Portland St., London W1N 5HD, UK

Grey Europe, Wells Point, 79 Wells St., London W1P 3RE, UK

GREYHOUND LINES INC.

15110 N. Dallas Pkwy., Ste. 600, Dallas, TX, 75248

Tel: (972) 789-7000   Fax: (972) 789-7330   www.greyhound.com

Mfr. consumer products, transportation, consumer and financial services.

Greyhound Financial & Leasing Corp. AG, 11 Albemarle St., London W1X 3HE, UK

Greyhound Intl. Travel Inc., Sussex House, London Rd., East Grinstead, West Sussex RH19 1LD, UK

GRIFFITH LABORATORIES INC.

One Griffith Center, Alsip, IL, 60658

Tel: (708) 371-0900   Fax: (708) 597-3294   www.griffithlabs.com

Mfr. industrial food ingredients and equipment.

Griffith Laboratories (UK) Ltd., Cotes Park Estate, Somercotes, Derby DE5 4NN, UK

Tel: 44-1773-832-171   Fax: 44-1773-835-294

GROUP 1 SOFTWARE, INC.

4200 parliament Place, Ste. 600, Lanham, MD, 20706-1860

Tel: (301) 918-0400   Fax: (301) 918-0735   www.g1.com

Mfr. management software.

Group 1 Software Europe, Ltd., 2 Siskin House, Croxley Business Park, Hatter Lane, Watford, Hertfordshire WD18 8UE, UK

Tel: 44-1923-216-000

GROVE WORLDWIDE LLC

1565 Buchanon Trail East, Shady Grove, PA, 17256

Tel: (717) 597-8121   Fax: (717) 593-4062   www.groveworldwide.com

Mfr. cranes.

Grove Worldwide, 1 Emperor Way, Doxford Intl Business Park, Sunderland SR3 3XR, UK

Tel: 44-191-565-6281

GUEST SUPPLY INC.

4301 US Highway 1, PO Box 902, Monmouth Junction, NJ, 08852-0902

Tel: (609) 514-9696   Fax: (609) 514-2692   www.guestsupply.com

Mfr. personal care and housekeeping products.

Guest Intl. (England) Ltd., 4 Vulcan House, Calleva Park, Aldermaston, Berkshire RG7 4QW, UK

GUILFORD MILLS INC.

4925 West Market Street, PO Box 26969, Greensboro, NC, 27407

Tel: (336) 316-4000   Fax: (336) 316-4059   www.guilfordmills.com

Mfr. textiles.

Guilford Europe Ltd., Cotes Park, Somercotes, Derbyshire DE55 4NJ, UK

Tel: 44-1773-607-401

GULTON GRAPHIC INSTRUMENTS, INC.

212 Durham Ave., Metuchen, NJ, 08840

Tel: (732) 548-6500   Fax: (732) 548-6781   www.gulton.com

Mfr. electronic instruments, controls and communications equipment.

Gulton Graphic International, The Hyde, Brighton BN2 4JU, UK

GUPTA TECHNOLOGIES

975 Island Drive, Redwood Shores, CA, 94065

Tel: (650) 596-3400   Fax: (650) 596-4900   www.centurasoft.com

Mfr. software and database management tools

Gupta Technologies Ltd., Eagle House, The Ring, Bracknell, Berkshire RG12 1HB, UK

Tel: 44-1344-38-21-43   Fax: 44-1344-38-21-44

GUY CARPENTER & COMPANY, INC.

114 West 47th Street, New York, NY, 10036

Tel: (212) 323-1000   Fax: (212) 345-2494   www.guycarp.com

Engaged in global reinsurance and risk management.

Guy Carpenter & Company Ltd., 2 Clove Crescent, East India Dock, London E14 2BE, UK

Tel: 44-20-7357-1000   Fax: 44-20-7929-2705

Guy Carpenter & Company, Ltd., 33 Aldgate High Street, London EC3N 1AQ, UK

Tel: 44-207-357-1000   Fax: 44-207-357-1460

Resolutions International Ltd., Grove House Newland Street, Witham, Essex, London CM8 2UP, UK

Tel: 44-20-7338-2228   Fax: 44-20-7375-0361

THE GYMBOREE CORPORATION

700 Airport Boulevard, Ste. 200, Burlingame, CA, 94010-1912

Tel: (650) 579-0600   Fax: (650) 696-2920   www.gymboree.com

Mfr. and sales of children's apparel and on-site play programs.

Gymboree Corporation, 27 Queen Street, Oxford OX1 1ER, UK

HAEMONETICS CORPORATION

400 Wood Road, Braintree, MA, 02184-9114

Tel: (781) 848-7100   Fax: (781) 848-5106   www.haemonetics.com

Mfr. automated blood processing systems and blood products.

Haemonetics U.K. Ltd., Beechwood House, Elmete Lane, Roundhay Leeds LS8 2LQ, UK

Tel: 44-113-273-7711   Fax: 44-113-273-4055

HAGGAR CORPORATION

6113 Lemmon Avenue, Dallas, TX, 75209

Tel: (214) 352-8481   Fax: (214) 956-4367   www.haggarcorp.com

Mfr. apparel.

Haggar Apparel Ltd., 16-19 Eastcastle Street, London WIN 80B, UK

Tel: 44-20-7636-5255   Contact: Karen Ames

HAHT COMMERCE, INC.

400 Newton Road, Raleigh, NC, 27615

Tel: (919) 786-5100   Fax: (919) 786-5250   www.haht.com

Mfr. e-commerce software.

HAHT Commerce UK, 3000 Cathedral Hill, Guildford, Surrey GU2 7YB, UK

Tel: 44-1483-243539

HALE AND DORR LLP

60 State Street, Boston, MA, 02109

Tel: (617) 526-6000   Fax: (617) 526-5000   www.haledorr.com

Engaged in international law.

Brobeck Hale and Door International, Hasilwood House, 60 Bishopsgate, London EC2N 4AJ, UK

Tel: 44-207-638-6688   Fax: 44-207-638-5888   Contact: David M. Ayres

HALL, KINION & ASSOCIATES, INC.

2570 North First Street, Ste. 400, San Jose, CA, 95131

Tel: (408) 895-5200   Fax: (408) 383-0902   www.hallkinion.com

Engaged in placement of information technology professionals on a contract basis.

Hall Kinion Europe, Melita House, 124 Bridge Road, Chertsey Surrey KT16 8EX, UK

Tel: 44-1932-582800

HALLIBURTON COMPANY

500 North Akard Street, Ste. 3600, Dallas, TX, 75201-3391

Tel: (214) 978-2600   Fax: (214) 978-2685   www.halliburton.com

Engaged in diversified energy services, engineering and construction.

Halliburton Ltd., Hill Park Court, Springfield Drive, Leatherhead KT22 7NL, UK

Tel: 44-181-544-5000   Fax: 44-181-544-6655

Halliburton Ltd., Hill Park Court, Springfield Drive, Leatherhead Surrey KT22 7NL, UK

Tel: 44-1294-553-928   Fax: 44-1294-557-840

Halliburton Ltd., South Denes Rd., Great Yarmouth Norfolk NR30 3QF, UK

Tel: 44-1493-330300   Fax: 44-1493-330302

HALLMARK CARDS INC.

2501 McGee Street, Kansas City, MO, 64108

Tel: (816) 274-5100   Fax: (816) 274-5061   www.hallmark.com

Mfr. greeting cards and related products.

Hallmark Cards Ltd., Hallmark House, Station Rd., Henley-on-Thames, Oxfordshire RG9 1LQ, UK

Tel: 44-1491-578383

HA-LO INDUSTRIES, INC.

5800 West Touhy Avenue, Niles, IL, 60714

Tel: (847) 600-3000   Fax: (847) 600-4000   www.halo.com

Engaged in distribution of brand-awareness, promotional products.

HA-LO Marketing Ltd., Royal House 1/F, 1-4 Vine Street, Uxbridge UB8 1QE, UK

HAMILTON SUNSTRAND

One Hamilton Rd., Windsor Locks, CT, 06096-1010

Tel: (860) 654-6000   Fax: (860) 654-3469   www.hamiltonsunstrandcorp.com

Design/mfr. aerospace systems for commercial, regional, corporate and military aircraft.

Hamilton Sunstrand Corp., Wolverhampton, UK

HANDY & HARMAN

555 Theodore Fremd Ave., Rye, NY, 10580

Tel: (914) 921-5200   Fax: (914) 925-4496   www.handyha

Precious and specialty metals for industry, refining, scrap metal; diversified industrial mfr.

Lucas-Milhaupt - Europe, Gunnels Wood Park, Stevenage, Hertfordshire SG1 2BH, UK

Rigby Maryland (Stainless) Ltd., Crystal Works, Union Rd., Liversedge WF15 7JU, UK

HANOVER COMPRESSOR COMPANY

12001 N. Houston Rosslyn, Houston, TX, 77086

Tel: (281) 447-8787   Fax: (281) 447-8781   www.hanover-co.com

Engaged in natural gas compression services.

Hanover Compressor Company, 2 Park Street, Woburn, Milton Keynes MK17 9PG, UK

Tel: 44-1525-290-110

HARBORLITE CORPORATION

PO Box 100, Vicksburg, MI, 49097

Tel: (616) 649-1352   Fax: (616) 649-3707   www.worldminerals.com

Mining and process perlite filter media.

Harborlite UK Ltd., Livingston Rd., Hessle Hull, North Humberside HU13 0EG, UK

HARCOURT GENERAL, INC.

27 Boylston St., Chestnut Hill, MA, 02467

Tel: (617) 232-8200   Fax: (617) 739-1395   www.harcourt.com

Publisher of educational materials.

Harcourt General Ltd., Foortscray High St., Sidcup Kent DA14 5HP, UK

Tel: 44-181-300-3322   Fax: 44-181-309-0807

Harcourt General Publishers International, 24-28 Oval Rd., London NW1 7DX, UK

Tel: 44-207-424-4200   Fax: 44-207-482-2293

W.B. Saunders Co. Ltd., 24-28 Oval Rd., London NW1 7DX, UK

HARLEY-DAVIDSON INTERNATIONAL

3700 West Juneau Ave., Milwaukee, WI, 53201

Tel: (414) 342-4680   Fax: (414) 343-4621   www.harleydavidson.com

Mfr. motorcycles, recreational and commercial vehicles, parts and accessories.

Harley-Davidson U.K. Ltd., PO Box 27, Daventry, Northamptonshire NN11 5RW, UK

HARMAN INTERNATIONAL INDUSTRIES, INC.

1101 Pennsylvania Ave. NW, Ste. 1010, Washington, DC, 20004

Tel: (202) 393-1101   Fax: (202) 393-3064   www.harman.com

Mfr. audio and video equipment, loudspeakers and sound reinforcement equipment.

Harman UK Ltd., Unit 1B, Mill Street, Slough, Berkshire S12 5DD, UK

Harman/Becker Automotive Systems, No. 1 Friars Gate, 1011 Stratford Road, Shirley, West Midlands B90 4EB, UK

HARRIS CORPORATION

1025 West NASA Blvd., Melbourne, FL, 32919

Tel: (407) 727-9100   Fax: (407) 727-9344   www.harris.com

Mfr. communications and information-handling equipment, including copying and fax systems.

Harris Corporation, Eskdale Road, Winnersh Wokingham, Berkshire RG41 5TS, UK

Tel: 44-118-964-8000   Fax: 44-118-964-8001

Harris Semiconductor, Riverside Way, Watchmoor Park, Camberley Surrey GU15 3YQ, UK

Tel: 44-1276-686-886   Fax: 44-1276-682-323

HARSCO CORPORATION

PO Box 8888, 350 Poplar Church Rd., Camp Hill, PA, 17001-8888

Tel: (717) 763-7064   Fax: (717) 763-6424   www.harsco.com

Metal reclamation and mill services, infrastructure and construction and process industry products.

Heckett MultiServ, Div. Harsco, Harsco House Regent Park, 299 Kingston Road, Leatherhead, Surrey KT22 7SG, UK

Tel: 44-1372-381400

Sherwood Div., Harsco (UK) Ltd., Giltway, Giltbrook, Nottingham NG16 2GQ, UK

Taylor-Wharton Cryogenics (UK), Oxford St., Bilston, West Midlands WV14 7EG, UK

HARSCO TRACK TECHNOLOGIES

2401 Edmund Road, Box 20, Cayce-West Colombia, SC, 29171

Tel: (803) 822-9160   Fax: (803) 822-8710   www.harscotrack.com

Mfr./services railroad track maintenance-of-way equipment.

Harsco Track Technologies Limited, Chewton Street, Eastwood, NG16 3HB, UK

Tel: 44-1773-539480

HARTFORD STEAM BOILER INSPECTION & INSURANCE CO.)

One State Street, PO Box 5024, Hartford, CT, 06102-5024

Tel: (860) 722-1866   Fax: (860) 722-5770   www.hsb.com

Provides specialty insurance products and inspection services.

HSB Engineering Insurance Ltd., Aldgate House, 33 Aldgate High St., London EC3N 1AH, UK

Tel: 44-207-265-6600   Fax: 44-207-247-3529   Contact: Hans Schols, Pres.

HARVARD BIOSCIENCE, INC.

84 October Hill Road, Holliston, MA, 01746-1371

Tel: (508) 893-8999   Fax: (508) 429-5732   www.harvardbioscience.com

Mfr. tools for drug development.

Harvard Apparatus Ltd., Fircroft Way, Edenbridge, Kent TN8 6HE, UK

Tel: 44-1732-864001   Fax: 44-1732-863356

Scie-Plas ltd., Unit 3 Gainsborough Trading Estate, Old Road, Southam, Warwickshire CV33 OHP, UK

Tel: 44-1926-814093   Fax: 44-1926-813975

HASBRO INDUSTRIES INC.

1027 Newport Ave., Pawtucket, RI, 02861

Tel: (401) 725-8697   Fax: (401) 727-5099   www.hasbro.com

Mfr. toy products, including games and puzzles, dolls and plush products.

Europress, Div. Hasbro Interactive, Europe House Adlington Park, Macclesfield SK10 4NP, UK

Tel: 44-1625-855000

Hasbro Europe, 2 Roundwood Ave., Scockley Park Uxbridge, Middlesex UB11 18Z, UK

Tel: 44-181-569-1234   Fax: 44-181-569-1133

Wizards, Div. Hasbro Industries, 3/F, Nicholsons Walk, Maidenhead SL6 1LD, UK

Tel: 44-162-780-602

HAUPPAUGE DIGITAL, INC.

91 Cabot Court, Hauppauge, NY, 11788

Tel: (631) 434-1600   Fax: (631) 434-3198   www.hauppauge.com

Mfr. circuit boards.

Hauppauge Computer Works, Ltd., 6-10 Bank Chambers, Borough High Street, London SE1 9QQ, UK

Tel: 44-207-378-1997   Fax: 44-207-357-9171

HAYNES INTERNATIONAL INC.

1020 W. Park Ave., PO Box 9013, Kokomo, IN, 46904-9013

Tel: (765) 456-6000   Fax: (765) 456-6905   www.haynesintl.com

Development and manufacture of high-performance nickel and cobalt based alloys for service in severe corrosion and high-temperature applications.

Haynes International Ltd.., PO Box 10, Parkhouse St., Openshaw, Manchester M11 2ER, UK

Tel: 44-161-230-7777   Fax: 44-161-223-2412   Contact: P. L. Crawshaw, M.D.

HAYWARD INDUSTRIES, INC.

620 Division Street, Elizabeth, NJ, 07207

Tel: (908) 351-5400   Fax: (908) 351-7893   www.haywardnet.com

Mfr. industrial strainers.

Hayward Industries (UK) Ltd., Unit 2, Crowngate, Wyncolls Rd., Colchester, Essex CO4 4HT, UK

Tel: 44-1-206-854454   Fax: 44-1-206-851240

HCA, INC.

1 Park Plaza, Nashville, TN, 37203

Tel: (615) 344-9551   Fax: (615) 344-2266   www.hcaheathcare.com

Operates hospitals and surgery centers.

Harley Street Clinic, 35 Weymouth Street, London W1N 4BJ, UK

London Bridge Hospital, 27 Tooley Street, London SE1 2PR, UK

Portland Hospital, 209 Great Portland Street, London W1N 6AH, UK

The Lister Hospital, Chelsea Bridge Road, London SW1W 8RH, UK

The Princess Grace Hospital, 42-52 Nottingham Place, London W1U 5NY, UK

Wellington Private Hospital, Wellington Place, London NW8 9LE, UK

HEADWAY CORPORATE RESOURCES, INC.

317 Madison Avenue, New York, NY, 10017

Tel: (212) 672-6500   Fax: (212) 672-6699   www.headwaycorp.com

Engaged in operation of temporary staffing centers.

The Whitney Group, 17 Buckingham Gate, London SW1E 6LB, UK

Tel: 44-207-630-9255   Fax: 44-207-233-7915

HEALTHSOUTH CORPORATION

One HealthSouth Parkway, Birmingham, AL, 35243

Tel: (205) 967-7116   Fax: (205) 969-4740   www.healthsouth.com

Provider of comprehensive outpatient and rehabilitative healthcare services.

HealthSouth Diagnostic Center of Darlington, Hollyhurst Rd., Darlington, County Durham DL3 6UA, UK

Tel: 44-1325-3696   Fax: 44-1325-3617

HealthSouth Diagnostic Center of Guilford, Egerton Rd., Guilford, Surrey GU2 5R6, UK

Tel: 44-1483-3031   Fax: 44-1483-3046

HealthSouth Diagnostic Center of Hertfordshire, Campus QE2, Hospitals Howlands, Welwyn Garden City, Hertfordshire AL7 4HQ, UK

Tel: 44-1707-3909   Fax: 44-1707-3919

HealthSouth Diagnostic Center of Somerset, The Clinic Marsh Lane Huntworth, Gate N. Bridgewate, Somerset TA6 62Q, UK

Tel: 44-1278-4290   Fax: 44-1278-4458

HealthSouth Diagnostic Center of York, Sir Peter Shepherd Bldg., Wigginton Rd., York 403 9YU, UK

Tel: 44-1904-6422   Fax: 44-1904-6422

HEIDRICK & STRUGGLES INTERNATIONAL, INC.

233 South Wacker Drive, Chicago, IL, 60606

Tel: (312) 496-1200   Fax: (312) 496-1290   www.heidrick.com

Executive search firm.

Heidrick & Struggles Intl. Inc., 100 Picadilly, London W1V 9FN, UK

Tel: 44-207-491-3124   Fax: 44-207-734-9581

HEIL TRAILER INTERNATIONAL

PO Box 181100, Chattanooga, TN, 37414

Tel: (423) 855-6386   Fax: (423) 855-3459   www.heiltrailer.com

Mfr. and sales of AP and SS tank trailers for liquid, powder, chemicals, asphalt and aircraft refuelers and modular bulk containers.

Heil Trailer International, Ltd., Great Bridge Road, Bilston, West Midlands WV14 8NP, UK

Tel: 44-1902-353-141   Fax: 44-1902-405-509   Contact: Simon Morgan, Mng. Dir.

HEIN-WERNER CORPORATION

2110 A Pewaukee Rd., PO Box 1606, Waukesha, WI, 53188

Tel: (262) 542-6611   Fax: (262) 542-7890   www.blackhawk-kj.com

Mfr. auto body repair equipment, engine rebuilding and brake repair equipment, hydraulic cylinders.

Blackhawk Automotive Ltd., Brookfield Trading Estate, Leacon Road, Ashford, Kent TN23 4AU, UK

Contact: Bob Chaloner

H.J. HEINZ COMPANY

600 Grant Street, Pittsburgh, PA, 15219

Tel: (412) 456-5700   Fax: (412) 456-6128   www.heinz.com

Processed food products and nutritional services.

H.J. Heinz Central & Eastern Europe, Hayes Middlesex, UK

H.J. Heinz Co. Ltd., Hayes Middlesex, UK

Heinz Direct UK Ltd., London, UK

HELLER FINANCIAL INC.

500 West Monroe Street, Chicago, IL, 60661

Tel: (312) 441-7000   Fax: (312) 441-7367   www.hellerfin.com

Financial services.

NMB Heller Limited, St. Christopher House, Wellington Rd., South Stockport, Cheshire SK2 6UA, UK

NMB Heller Limited, 24 Bennetts Hill, Birmingham B2 5QP, UK

HENNINGSEN FOODS, INC.

2700 Westchester Avenue, Purchase, NY, 10577

Tel: (914) 701-4200   Fax: (914) 701-4050   www.henningsenfoods.com

Dehydrated egg, poultry and meat products.

Henningsen Foods Ltd., 168 Sloane St., London SW1, UK

HENRY SCHEIN, INC.

135 Duryea Rd., Melville, NY, 11747

Tel: (516) 843-5500   Fax: (516) 843-5658   www.henryschein.com

Mfr. and supply dental equipment.

Henry Schein Procare, 25-27 Merrick Road, Southall Middlesex UB2 4AU, UK

Tel: 44-181-235-5005

Inter-Dental Equipment Ltd., Unit 9, Langley Park, North Street, Langley Mill, Nottinghamshire NG16 4BS, UK

Tel: 44-1773-714-141

Zahn Dental Supplies Ltd., Unit 1E, South West Centre, 4 Anchor Road, Sheffield S8 0JR, UK

Tel: 44-1142-551-213

HERCULES INC.

Hercules Plaza, 1313 N. Market Street, Wilmington, DE, 19894-0001

Tel: (302) 594-5000   Fax: (302) 594-5400   www.herc.com

Mfr. specialty chemicals, plastics, film and fibers, coatings, resins and food ingredients.

Hercules Chemicals Ltd., 31 London Rd., Reigate, Surrey RH2 9YA, UK

Tel: 44-1737-242434   Fax: 44-1737-224287   Contact: Charles Murray

HERMAN MILLER INC.

855 East Main, Zeeland, MI, 49464

Tel: (616) 654-3000   Fax: (616) 654-5385   www.hermanmiller.com

Mfr. office furnishings.

Geiger Brickel / Herman Miller, 48/50 St. John Street, London EC1M 4DT, UK

Herman Miller Ltd., 149 Tottenham Court Road, London W1P 0JA, UK

Tel: 44-207-388-7331

Herman Miller Ltd., The Bond, 180-182 Fazeley Street, Birmingham B5 5SE, UK

Herman Miller Ltd., Bath Road, Chippenham SN14 0AT, UK

HEROIX

120 Wells Avenue, Newton, MA, 02459

Tel: (617) 527-1550   Fax: (617) 527-6132   www.heroix.com

Mfr. multiplatform, automated monitoring and management software.

Heroix Corporation, The Boulevard, Shire Park, Welwyn Garden City, Herts AL7 1EL, UK

Tel: 44-1707-336600

THE HERTZ CORPORATION

225 Brae Boulevard, Park Ridge, NJ, 07656-0713

Tel: (201) 307-2000   Fax: (201) 307-2644   www.hertz.com

Worldwide headquarters office for car rental, car leasing and equipment rental.

Hertz Rental Car, London, UK

HEWITT ASSOCIATES LLC

100 Half Day Road, Lincolnshire, IL, 60069

Tel: (847) 295-5000   Fax: (847) 295-7634   www.hewitt.com

Employee benefits consulting firm.

Hewitt Associates, Prospect House, Abbey View, St. Albans Hertfordshire AL1 2QU, UK

Tel: 44-1727-88-8200

HEWLETT-PACKARD COMPANY

3000 Hanover Street, Palo Alto, CA, 94304-1185

Tel: (650) 857-1501   Fax: (650) 857-5518   www.hp.com

Mfr. computing, communications and measurement products and services.

Hewlett-Packard Ltd., Amen Corner/Cain Rd., Bracknell, Berkshire RG12 1HN, UK

HEXCEL CORPORATION

281 Tresser Blvd., Stamford, CT, 06901

Tel: (203) 969-0666   Fax: (203) 358-3977   www.hexcel.com

Honeycomb core materials, specialty chemicals, resins and epoxies.

Hexcel UK, 31 Coope Green, Houghton, Preston, Lancashire PRS OUR, UK

HICKS, MUSE, TATE & FURST INC.

200 Crescent Court, Ste. 1600, Dallas, TX, 75201

Tel: (214) 740-7300   Fax: (214) 740-7313

Institutional investment services.

Hillsdown Holdings plc, Hillsdown House, 32 Hampstead High St., London NW3 1QD, UK

HIGH VOLTAGE ENGINEERING CORPORATION

401 Edgewater Place, Ste. 680, Wakefield, MA, 01880

Tel: (781) 224-1001   Fax: (781) 224-1011   www.highvolteng.com

Holding company: owner and operator of a diversified group of middle market industrial and technology-based manufacturing businesses.

Anacom Instruments Ltd., St. Peters Rd., Maidenhead SL6 7QA, UK

HIGHLANDS INSURANCE COMPANY

1000 Lenox Drive, Lawrenceville, NJ, 08648-0426

Tel: (609) 896-1921   Fax: (609) 219-9142   www.highlandsinsurance.com

Engaged in commercial property and casualty insurance.

Highlands Insurance Company (UK) Ltd., 117 Fenchurch Street, London EC3M 5EJ, UK

HILLENBRAND INDUSTRIES, INC.

700 State Route 46 East, Batesville, IN, 47006

Tel: (812) 934-7000   Fax: (812) 934-1963   www.hillenbrand.com

Holding company: mfr. hospital beds, incubators and caskets.

Hill-Rom Company Ltd., 89 Station Road, Ampthill Bedford MK45 2RE, UK

Tel: 44-1525-841-737   Contact: Bob Alexander

Hill-Rom Ltd., Clinitron House, Ashby de la Zouch, Leicestershire LE65 1JG, UK

Tel: 44-1530-411-000   Fax: 44-1530-411-555   Contact: Michael J. Clancy

HILLERICH & BRADSBY COMPANY INC

800 West Main St., PO Box 35700, Louisville, KY, 40202

Tel: (502) 585-5226   Fax: (502) 585-1179   www.slugger.com

Golf, baseball and softball equipment.

Hillerich & Bradsby Co. Ltd., Unit B4, Brookside Park, Middleton, Manchester M24 1GS, UK

Tel: 44-161-6548881   Fax: 44-161-6536864

HILTON HOTELS CORPORATION

9336 Civic Center Drive, Beverly Hills, CA, 90210

Tel: (310) 278-4321   Fax: (310) 205-7880   www.hiltonhotels.com

International hotel chain: Hilton International, Vista Hotels and Hilton National Hotels.

London Gatwick Airport Hilton, Gatwick Airport, Crawley, West Sussex RH6 OLL, UK

London Kensington Hilton, 7th Fl., 179-199 Holland Park Ave., London W11 4UH, UK

The Langham Hilton London, 1 Portland Place, Regent St., London W1N 4JA, UK

HNC SOFTWARE INC.

5930 Cornerstone Court West, San Diego, CA, 92121

Tel: (858) 546-8877   Fax: (858) 799-8006   www.hnc.com

Mfr. software to manage and detect fraud.

HNC Software UK Ltd., 1 Northumberland Avenue, Trafalgar Square, London WC2N 5BW, UK

Tel: 44-207-872-5526

HOCKMAN-LEWIS LTD.

200 Executive Drive, Ste. 320, West Orange, NJ, 07052

Tel: (973) 325-3838   Fax: (973) 325-7974   www.hockman-lewis.com

Engaged in petroleum industry export management.

Hockman UK Ltd., Unit 13, Eversley Way, Thorpe Industrial Estate, Egham TW20 8RG, UK

Tel: 44-1784-477022   Fax: 44-1784-477044

HOGAN & HARTSON LLP

555 13th Street NW, Washington, DC, 20004-1109

Tel: (202) 637-5600   Fax: (202) 637-5910   www.hhlaw.com

Engaged in international law.

Hogan & Hartson, One Angel Court, London EC2R 7HJ, UK

Tel: 44-107-367-0200

HOLLINGSWORTH & VOSE COMPANY

112 Washington Street, East Walpole, MA, 02032

Tel: (508) 668-0295   Fax: (508) 668-3557   www.hollingsworth-vose.com

Mfr. technical and industrial papers and non-woven fabrics.

Hollingsworth & Vose Air Filtration Limited, Waterford Bridge, Kentmere Cumbria LA8 9JJ, UK

Tel: 44-153-982-5200   Fax: 44-153-982-5201

HOLME ROBERTS & OWEN LLP

1700 Lincoln Street, Ste. 4100, Denver, CO, 80203

Tel: (303) 861-7000   Fax: (303) 866-0200   www.hro.com

Engaged in international law.

Holme Roberts & Owen, Heathcoat House, 3/F, 20 Saville Row, London W1S 3PR, UK

Tel: 44-207-494-5600   Fax: 44-207-287-9344   Contact: Paul G. Thompson

HOLOPHANE CORPORATION

214 Oakwood Ave., Newark, OH, 43055

Tel: (740) 349-4130   Fax: (740) 349-4426   www.holophane.com

Mfr. and marketer of premium quality, highly engineered, lighting systems targeted to the industrial, commercial and outdoor markets.

Holophane Europe Ltd., Box 36, Bond Ave., Bletchley, Milton Keynes MK1 1JG, UK

HOME PRODUCTS INTERNATIONAL, INC.

4501 W. 47th Street, Chicago, IL, 60632

Tel: (773) 890-1010   Fax: (773) 890-0523   www.hpii.com

Mfr. plastic household products.

HPI Ltd./Selfix, The Aldyrich House, London, UK

HONEYWELL INTERNATIONAL INC.

Honeywell Plaza, Minneapolis, MN, 55408

Tel: (612) 951-1000   Fax: (612) 951-8537   www.honeywell.com

Develop/mfr. controls for home and building, industry, space and aviation, burglar and fire alarm systems.

Honeywell Ltd., Arlington Business Park, Bracknell, Berkshire RG12 1EB, UK

Tel: 44-1344-656-000 Fax: 44-1344-656-240

HOOD SAILMAKERS INC.

23 Johnny Cake Hill, Middletown, RI, 02842

Tel: (401) 849-9400   Fax: (401) 849-9700   www.hood-sails.com

Mfr. furling genoas, jibs, easy stow mainsails, and spinnakers.

Hood Sailmakers Ltd., Bath Rd., Lymington, Hants. SO41 3RW, UK

HORWATH INTERNATIONAL ASSOCIATION

420 Lexington Avenue, Suite 526, New York, NY, 10170-0526

Tel: (212) 808-2000   Fax: (212) 808-2020   www.horwath.com

Public accountants and auditors.

Horwath Clark Whitehill, Queens House, 6/F, 2 Holly Road, Twickenham Middlesex TW1 4EG, UK

Horwath Consulting, 8 Baker St., London W1M 1DA, UK

Contact: James H.F.Gemmell

HOUGHTON INTERNATIONAL INC.

PO Box 930, Madison & Van Buren Avenues, Valley Forge, PA, 19482-0930

Tel: (610) 666-4000   Fax: (610) 666-1376   www.houghtonintl.com

Mfr. specialty chemicals, hydraulic fluids and lubricants.

Houghton Vaughan PLC, Beacon Road Ashburton, Trafford Park, Manchester MI7 IAF, UK

Tel: 44-161-872071

Houghton Vaughan PLC, Legge St., Birmingham B4 7EU, UK

Tel: 44-121-359-6100

HOUSEHOLD INTERNATIONAL INC.

2700 Sanders Road, Prospect Heights, IL, 60070

Tel: (847) 564-5000   Fax: (847) 205-7452   www.household.com

Consumer finance and credit card services.

Hamilton Direct Bank, North St., Winkfield, Windsor, Berkshire SL4 4TD, UK

Tel: 44-121-233-9100

HOWDEN BUFFALO COMPANY

2029 W. Dekalb St., Camden, SC, 29020

Tel: (803) 713-2200   Fax: (803) 713-2250   www.howdenbuffalo.com

Mfr. fans and air-handling units.

Howden Calidair, Nailsworth Mills Estate, Stroud, Gloucestershire GL6 OBS, UK

Tel: 44-1453-835900

HOWMEDICA OSTEONICS, INC.

59 Route 17 South, Allendale, NJ, 07401

Tel: (201) 507-7300   Fax: (201) 935-4873   www.howmedica.com

Mfr. of maxillofacial products (orthopedic implants).

Howmedica International Ltd., London, UK

Tel: 44-1784-444810

HOWMET CASTINGS

9 Old Kings Hwy. South, Darien, CT, 06820

Tel: (203) 857-3120   Fax: (203) 857-3158   www.howmet.com

Mfr. precision investment castings, alloys, engineering and refurbishment for jet aircraft and industrial gas turbine (IGT) engine components.

Exeter Alloy, Heron Road, Exeter, Devon EX2 7LL, UK

Tel: 44-1392-429700   Fax: 44-1392-429702   Contact: Don Thompson

Exeter Casting, Kestrel Way, Exeter, Devon EX2 7LG, UK

Tel: 44-1392-429700   Fax: 44-1392-429702   Contact: Greg Willis

HOWREY SIMON ARNOLD & WHITE LLP

1299 Pennsylvania Avenue NW, Washington, DC, 20004

Tel: (202) 783-0800   Fax: (202) 383-6610   www.howrey.com

Engaged in international law.

Howrey Simon Arnold & White, City Point, One Ropemaker Street, London EC2Y 9HS, UK

Tel: 44-207-628-3303   Contact: Jacobus C. Rasser

HQ GLOBAL WORKPLACES INC.

15305 Dallas Parkway, Ste. 1400, Addison, TX, 75001

Tel: (972) 361-8221   Fax: (972) 361-8221   www.hq.com

Provides office outsourcing, officing solutions, including internet access, telecommunications, meeting rooms, furnished offices and team rooms, state-of-the-art videoconferencing, and trained on-site administrative support teams -

HQ Global Workplaces, 33 St. James's Square, London SW1Y 4JS, UK

HQ Global Workplaces, 28 Grosvenor Street, London W1X 9FE, UK

HUBBARD ISA

PO Box 415, Walpole, NH, 03431

Tel: (603) 756-3311   Fax: (603) 756-9034   www.hubbard-isa.com

Poultry breeding R&D, poultry foundation breeding stock.

British United Turkeys Ltd., Warren Hall, Broughton Nr. Chester CH4 0EW, UK

Tel: 44-1244-661111   Fax: 44-1244-661105   Contact: Richard Hutchinson, Mgr.

HUBBELL INCORPORATED

584 Derby Milford Road, Orange, CT, 06477

Tel: (203) 799-4100   Fax: (203) 799-4208   www.hubbell.com

Electrical wiring components.

Hubbell Limited, Woburn Road Industrial Estate, Kempston Bedford MK42 7SH, UK

Tel: 44-1234-855444   Fax: 44-1234-854008

HUCK INTERNATIONAL INC.

3724 East Columbia Street, Tucson, AZ, 85714-3415

Tel: (520) 747-9898   Fax: (520) 750-7420   www.huck.com

Designer and manufacturer of high-performance, proprietary fasteners and fastener installation systems.

Huck International Ltd., Unit C, Stafford Park 7, Telford, Shropshire TF3 3BQ, UK

Tel: 44-1952-290011   Fax: 44-1952-290459

HUNKAR LABORATORIES INC.

7007 Valley Ave., Cincinnati, OH, 45244

Tel: (513) 272-1010   Fax: (513) 272-0013   www.hunkar.com

Process equipment for plastics industry and automated bar code data collection and printing solutions.

Hunkar UK Ltd., Royex House, Aldermanbury Sq., London EC2V 7LD, UK

HUNT CORPORATION

2005 Market Street, Philadelphia, PA, 19103

Tel: (215) 656-0300   Fax: (215) 656-3700   www.hunt-corp.com

Mfr. office, art and craft, and presentation products.

Hunt Europe Ltd., Chester Hall Lane, Basilton, Essex SS13 1ND, UK

HUNT OIL COMPANY

1445 Ross at Field, Dallas, TX, 75202

Tel: (214) 978-8000   Fax: (214) 978-8888   www.huntoil.com

Petroleum exploration and production.

Hunt Oil UK, London, UK

Tel: 44-1483-758-800   Contact: Larry Bottomley

HUNTON & WILLIAMS

951 East Byrd Street, East Tower, Richmond, VA, 23219-4074

Tel: (804) 788-8200   Fax: (804) 788-8218   www.hunton.com

Engaged in international law.

Hunton & Williams Ltd., 61/63 St. John Street, London EC1M 4AN, UK

Tel: 44-207-427-7850   Contact: Stephen J. Horvath III

HUNTSMAN CORPORATION

500 Huntsman Way, Salt Lake City, UT, 84108

Tel: (801) 532-5200   Fax: (801) 536-1581   www.huntsman.com

Mfr. and sales of specialty chemicals, industrial chemicals and petrochemicals.

Huntsman Polyurethanes, Hitchen Lane, Shepton Mallet, Somerset BA4 5TZ, UK

Tel: 44-1749-343061   Contact: R. Bonsmann

Huntsman Polyurethanes, PO Box 54, Middlesbrough TS90 8JA, UK

Tel: 44-1642-433498   Contact: B. Watson

Huntsman Tioxide, Tees Road, Hartlepool TS25 2DD, UK

Huntsman Tioxide, Moody Lane, Grimsby, N.E. Lincolnshire DN31 2SW, UK

Huntsman Tioxide, Haverton Hill Road, Billingham, Stockton-on-Tees TS23 1PS, UK

Tel: 44-1642-370300

Huntsman Tioxide, Lincoln House, 137-143 Hammersmith Road, London W14 0QL, UK

Tel: 44-207-3317777

HUSSMANN INTERNATIONAL

12999 St. Charles Rock Road, Bridgeton, MO, 63044

Tel: (314) 291-2000   Fax: (314) 291-5144   www.hussmann.com

Mfr. refrigeration and environmental control systems for food industrial.

Hussmann UK, Challenge House, Ste. 4, Sherwood Drive, Bletchley, Buckinghamshire MK3 6DP, UK

Tel: 44-1908-335100   Fax: 44-1908-335140

HYATT CORPORATION

200 West Madison Street, Chicago, IL, 60606

Tel: (312) 750-1234   Fax: (312) 750-8578   www.hyatt.com

International hotel management.

Hyatt Carlton Tower, Cadogan Place, London SW1Z 9PY, UK

Tel: 44-207-235-1234   Fax: 44-207-858-7085

Hyatt Regency Birmingham, 2 Bridge St., Birmingham B1 2JZ, UK

Tel: 44-121-643-1234   Fax: 44-121-616-2323

The Lowndes Hyatt, Lowndes St., London SW1X 9ES, UK

Tel: 44-207-823-1234   Fax: 44-207-235-1154

HYPERCOM CORPORATION

2851 West Kathleen Road, Phoenix, AZ, 85053

Tel: (602) 504-5000   Fax: (602) 504-4578   www.hypercom.com

Mfr. point-of-sale systems.

Hypercom EMEA Inc., Unit 2, Woking Eight, Forsyth Road, Woking, Surrey GU21 5SB, UK

Tel: 44-1483-718600   Fax: 44-1483-718601   Contact: Hugo Bolanos

Hypercom EMEA Inc., Unit 2, Woking Eight, Forsyth Road, Woking, Surrey GU21 5SB, UK

Tel: 44-1483-718600   Fax: 44-1483-718601   Contact: Hugo Bolanos

HYPERION SOLUTIONS CORPORATION

1344 Crossman Avenue, Sunnyvale, CA, 94089

Tel: (408) 744-9500   Fax: (408) 744-0400   www.hyperion.com

Mfr. data analysis software tools.

Hyperion UK, Hyperion House, Old Bracknell Lane West, Bracknell Berkshire RG12 7DD, UK

Tel: 44-1344-664-000   Fax: 44-1344-664-001

Hyperion UK, Axis Centre Hogarth Business Park, Burlington lane, London W4 2TH, UK

Tel: 44-20-8995-3631   Fax: 44-20-8995-3236

Hyperion UK, Enterprise House, Greencourts Business Park, 333 Styal Road, Manchester M22 5HY, UK

Tel: 44-161-498-2200   Fax: 44-161-498-2210

i2 TECHNOLOGIES, INC.

11701 Luna Road, Dallas, TX, 75234

Tel: (214) 860-6106   Fax: (214) 860-6060   www.i2.com

Engaged in supply chain management; solutions to help companies collaborate on decision-making processes.

i2 Technologies UK, Chineham Business Park, Basingstoke Hampshire RG24 8QY, UK

Tel: 44-1256-705-500

i2 Technologies UK, The Priory, Stomp Road Burnham, Berkshire SL1 7LL, UK

Tel: 44-1628-601-200

IBM CORPORATION

1133 Westchester Avenue, White Plains, NY, 10604

Tel: (914) 765-1900   Fax: (914) 765-7382   www.ibm.com

Information products, technology and services.

IBM United Kingdom Holdings Ltd., PO Box 41, North Harbour Portsmouth, Hampshire PO6 3AU, UK

Tel: 44-1705-482949   Fax: 44-1705-22114

IBP FOODS COMPANY INC.

PO Box 515, Dakota City, NE, 68731

Tel: (402) 494-2061   Fax: (402) 241-2068   www.ibpinc.com

Produce beef and pork, hides and associated products, animal feeds, pharmaceuticals.

IBP Inc., 5 Devonhurst Place, Heathfield Terrace, Chiswick, London W4 4JD, UK

Tel: 44-181-742-2888   Fax: 44-181-742-2484   Contact: Paul Garnham

ICC INDUSTRIES INC.

460 Park Ave., New York, NY, 10022

Tel: (212) 521-1700   Fax: (212) 521-1794   www.iccchem.com

Manufacturing and trading of chemicals, plastics and pharmaceuticals.

Durham Plastic Ltd., 22 Coatham Ave., Aycliffe Industrial Estate, Aycliffe County Durham DL5 6DB, UK

Tel: 44-1325-300-437   Fax: 44-1325-318-173   Contact: Amiram Talmon

Frutarom (UK) Ltd., Northbridge Rd., Berkhamsted Herts. HP4 1EF, UK

Tel: 44-1442-876-611   Fax: 44-1442-876-204   Contact: Brian Watts

ICC Chemicals (UK) Ltd., Northbridge Rd., Berkhamsted Hertfordshire HP4 1EF, UK

Tel: 44-1442-877-022   Fax: 44-1442-878-899   Contact: Michael Gaine

Pipe U.K. Ld., Aycliffe Industrial Estate, Newton Aycliffe County Durham DL5 6DB, UK

Tel: 44-1325-308-188   Fax: 44-1325-308-159   Contact: Amiran Talmon

ICF KAISER CONSULTING GROUP

9300 Lee Highway, Fairfax, VA, 22031

Tel: (703) 934-3000   Fax: (703) 934-3740   www.icfconsulting.com

Engaged in management, technology, and policy consulting services.

ICF Kaiser Consulting, Hamilton House, 3/F, Mabledon Place, Bloomsbury, London WC1H 9BB, UK

Tel: 44-207-554-8730

ICF KAISER INTERNATIONAL, INC.

9300 Lee Highway, Fairfax, VA, 22031

Tel: (703) 934-3600   Fax: (703) 934-9740   www.icfkaiser.com

Engaged in engineering, construction, program management, and consulting services.

ICF Kaiser International, Regal House, London Rd., Twickenham, Middlesex TW1 3QQ, UK

Tel: 44-181-892-4433

ICN PHARMACEUTICALS, INC.

3300 Hyland Ave., Costa Mesa, CA, 92626

Tel: (714) 545-0100   Fax: (714) 641-7268   www.icnpharm.com

Mfr. and distribution of pharmaceuticals.

ICN Pharmaceuticals, Inc., Cedarwood, Chineham Business Park, Crockford Lane, Basingstoke Hampshire RG24 8WD, UK

Tel: 44-125-670-7744

ICO, INC.

5333 Westheimer, Ste. 600, Houston, TX, 77056

Tel: (281) 351-4100   Fax: (281) 335-2201   www.icoinc.com

Engaged in processing petrochemicals and reconditioning oil well drilling equipment.

WEDCO Technology UK Ltd., Div. ICO, Sandars Rd., Heapham Rd. Ind. Estate, Gainsborough, Lincolnshire, UK

Tel: 44-1427-811401   Fax: 44-1427-811360   Contact: Stuart Grant, Mng. Dir.

ICORE INTERNATIONAL INC.

3780 Flightline Drive, Santa Rosa, CA, 95403-8227

Tel: (707) 535-2700   Fax: (707) 521-2524   www.icoreintl.com

Harness and conduit systems, battery connectors, etc.

Icore International Ltd, Leigh Road, Slough, Berkshire SC1 4BB, UK

Tel: 44-1753-574134

IDENTIX INCORPORATED

100 Cooper Ct., Los Gatos, CA, 95032

Tel: (408) 335-1400   Fax: (408) 395-8076   www.identix.com

Mfr. fingerprint verification systems.

Identix UK, Winton, Longmoor Lane, Mortimer Reading RG7 3RP, UK

Tel: 44-118-933-1456   Fax: 44-118-933-1117

IDEX CORPORATION

630 Dundee Road, Ste. 400, Northbrook, IL, 60062

Tel: (847) 498-7070   Fax: (847) 498-3940   www.idexcorp.com

Mfr. industrial pumps, lubrication systems, metal fabrication equipment, bending and clamping devices.

Band-It Co. Ltd., Speedwell Industrial Estate, Staveley, Chesterfield S43 3PF, UK

Johnson Pump (UK) Limited, Highfield Industrial Estate, Edison Road, Eastbourne, East Sussex BN23 6PT, UK

IDEXX LABORATORIES, INC.

1 IDEXX Dr., Westbrook, ME, 04092-2041

Tel: (207) 856-0300   Fax: (207) 856-0346   www.idexx.com

Mfr. and sales of veterinary products.

IDEXX Laboratories Ltd., Milton Court, Churchfield Road, Chalfont St. Peter, Buckinghamshire SL9 9EW, UK

Tel: 44-1-753-891-660

IDEXX Laboratories Ltd., Grange House, Sandbeck Way, Wetherby LS22 4DN, UK

Tel: 44-1937-581649

IDT CORPORATION

520 Broad Street, Newark, NJ, 07102

Tel: (973) 438-1000   Fax: (973) 438-4002   www.idt.net

Engaged in domestic and international long distance telecommunications.

IDT Europe, 69-77 Paul Street, London EC2A 4NQ, UK

Tel: 44-207-549-6000   Fax: 44-207-549-6001

IFR SYSTEMS, INC.

10200 West York Street, Wichita, KS, 67215-8999

Tel: (316) 522-4981   Fax: (316) 524-2623   www.ifrsys.com

Mfr. electronic test and measurement equipment.

IFR Systems UK, Units 14/15 Monks Brook Industrial Park, Chandlers Ford, Hampshire SO53 4RA, UK

IFR Systems, Inc., Longacres House, Six Hills Way, Stevenage SG1 2AN, UK

IGATE CORPORATION

680 Andersen Drive, Foster Plaza 10, Pittsburgh, PA, 15220

Tel: (412) 503-4450   Fax: (412) 503-4490   www.igatecorp.com

Provides IT services.

iGate, Mascot Systems Divison, Highway House, Norreys Drive, Maidenhead, Berkshire SL6 4BN, UK

Tel: 44-1628-589900   Fax: 44-1628-589901

IHS (INFORMATION HANDLING SERVICES GROUP

15 Inverness Way East, Englewood, CO, 80112

Tel: (303) 397-2300   Fax: (303) 397-2633   www.ihs.com

Leading provider of technical engineering information.

Technical Indexes Ltd., Willoughby Rd., Bracknell, Berkshire RG12 4DW, UK

II-VI INCORPORATED

375 Saxonburg Blvd., Saxonburg, PA, 16056

Tel: (724) 352-4455   Fax: (724) 352-4980   www.ii-vi.com

Mfr. lenses and mirrors.

II-VI U.K. Ltd., 1 Burley Road, Oakham, Leicestershire LE 15 6DH, UK

IKON OFFICE SOLUTIONS

70 Valley Stream Parkway, Malvern, PA, 19355

Tel: (610) 296-8000   Fax: (610) 408-7022   www.ikon.com

Sales of office equipment, including fax machines, copiers and printers.

IKON Office Solutions, 30 Cowcross St., London EC1M 6DQ, UK

Tel: 44-207-253-4545   Fax: 44-207-608-1538   Contact: David Mills

IKON Office Solutions, Ullswater Crescent, Coulsdon, Surrey CR5 2EQ, UK

Tel: 44-181-763-1010

IKOS SYSTEMS, INC.

79 Great Oaks Blvd., San Jose, CA, 95119

Tel: (408) 284-0400   Fax: (408) 284-0401   www.ikos.com

Mfr. hardware and software.

IKOS Systems, Inc., Stylus House, London Road, Bracknell Berkshire RG12 2UT, UK

Tel: 44-1-344-306-565

ILLINOIS TOOL WORKS (ITW)

3600 West Lake Ave., Glenview, IL, 60025-5811

Tel: (847) 724-7500   Fax: (847) 657-4268   www.itw.com

Mfr. gears, tools, fasteners, sealants, plastic and metal components for industrial, medical, etc.

ITW Hi-Cone, Cookham Road Bracknell, Berkshire RG12 1RB, UK

Tel: 44-1344-860-166   Fax: 44-1344-861-869   Contact: Barry Mitchell

ITW Hofmann, Div., Illinois Tool Works Company, 14, Sutton Park Avenue, Reading RG6 1AZ, UK

Tel: 44-118-966-9126   Fax: 44-118-926-6421

ITW Plexus UK, Unit 1, Bushacre Court, Garrard Way, Kettering Northants NN16 8TD, UK

Tel: 44-01536-314800   Fax: 44-01536-314801

IMANAGE, INC.

950 Tower Lane, Ste. 500, Foster City, CA, 94404

Tel: (650) 356-1166   Fax: (650) 627-8751   www.imanage.com

Mfr. Web-based management software.

iManage Ltd. UK, No. 1 Farnham Road, Guildford, Surrey GU2 4RG, UK

Tel: 44-1483-549040

IMI NORGREN GROUP

5400 South Delaware Street, Littleton, CO, 80120-1663

Tel: (303) 794-2611   Fax: (303) 795-9487   www.usa.norgren.com

Mfr. pneumatic filters, regulators, lubricators, valves, automation systems, dryers, push-in fittings.

IMI Norgren Ltd., PO Box 22, Eastern Ave., Lichfield, Staffordshire WS13 6SB, UK

Tel: 44-1543-414333   Fax: 44-1543-268052

IMPCO TECHNOLOGIES, INC.

16804 Gridley Place, Cerritos, CA, 90703

Tel: (562) 860-6666   Fax: (562) 809-1240   www.impco.ws

Mfr. fuel control processors.

IMPCO Industrial Engine Systems Division, 3 Dands Drive, Middleton Cheney, Banbury, Oxon OX17 2NN, UK

Tel: 44-1295-712196

IMPCO-BERU Technologies Ltd., West Wellow, Romsey, Hampshire SO51 6DB, UK

Tel: 44-1794-323-966   Fax: 44-1794-323-916

IMS HEALTH INCORPORATED

1499 Post Rd., Fairfield, CT, 06430

Tel: (203) 222-4200   Fax: (203) 222-4276   www.imshealth.com

Provides sales management reports and prescription tracking reports for pharmaceutical and health-care companies.

IMS Health UK, 7 Harewood Avenue, London NW1 6JB, UK

Tel: 44-20-7393-5888

INCYTE GENOMICS, INC.

3160 Porter Dr., Palo Alto, CA, 94304

Tel: (650) 855-0555   Fax: (650) 855-0572   www.incyte.com

Engaged in development of genetic information for drug development.

Incyte Genomics Botanic UK, 100 Hills Road, Cambridge CB2 1FF, UK

Tel: 44-1223-454-900

INDEL-DAVIS INC.

4401 S. Jackson Ave., Tulsa, OK, 74107

Tel: (918) 587-2151   Fax: (918) 446-1583   www.indel-davis.com

Engaged in web and graphic design and manufacture of toners and inks and oil field and seismic supplies.

Indel-Davis UK, Grafton Way Unit D3, Basingstoke, Hampshire RG22 6HY, UK

INDUCTOTHERM INDUSTRIES

10 Indel Ave., PO Box 157, Rancocas, NJ, 08073-0157

Tel: (609) 267-9000   Fax: (609) 267-5705   www.inductotherm.com

Mfr. induction melting furnaces, induction power supplies, charging and preheating systems, automatic pouring systems and computer control systems.

ADM Electrodes, Molly Millars lane, Wokingham Berks RG41 2PX, UK

Athena Controls, PO Box 176, Stockport SK3 OFL, UK

Guardscan Ltd., Unit 38 Drumhead Road, Chorley North Industrial Park, Chorley, Lancashire PR6 7BX, UK

Indoctoheat Banyard, 15 Factory Road, Upton Poole, Dorset BH16 5SN, UK

Inductotherm Europe, The Furlong, Berry Hill Industrial Estate, Droitwich, Worcestershire WR9 9AH, UK

Inductotherm Europe Ltd., The Furlong, Droitwich, Worcestershire WR9 9AH, UK

Tel: 44-1905-79-5100   Contact: Graham E. Hawkins

INDUS INTERNATIONAL, INC.

3301 Windy Ridge Pkwy., Atlanta, GA, 30339

Tel: (770) 952-8444   Fax: (770) 955-2977   www.indus.com

Mfr. asset management software.

Indus International Ltd., Britannia Wharf, Monument Road, Woking, Surrey GU21 5LW, UK

INDUSTRIAL ACOUSTICS COMPANY

1160 Commerce Ave., Bronx, NY, 10462

Tel: (718) 931-8000   Fax: (718) 863-1138   www.industrialacoustics.com

Design/mfr. acoustic structures for sound conditioning and noise control.

Industrial Acoustics Co. Ltd., Walton House, Central Trading Estate, Staines, Middlesex, UK

INFINIUM SOFTWARE, INC.

25 Communications Way, Hyannis, MA, 02601

Tel: (508) 778-2000   Fax: (508) 775-3764   www.infinium.com

Mfr. software.

Infinium Software UK, Crosby House, Meadowbank Furlong Road, Buckinghamshire SL8 5AJ, UK

INFOGRAMES, INC.

417 Fifth Avenue, New York, NY, 10016

Tel: (212) 726-6500   Fax: (212) 679-3224   www.infogrames.com

Mfr. video games.

Infogrames UK, Landmark House, Hammersmith Bridge Road, London W6 9DP, UK

Tel: 44-181-222-9700

Infogrames UK, 21 Castle Street, Castlefield Manchester M3 4SW, UK

INFONET SERVICES CORPORATION

2160 East Grand Ave., El Segundo, CA, 90245-1022

Tel: (310) 335-2600   Fax: (310) 335-4507   www.infonet.com

Provider of Internet services and electronic messaging services.

Infonet UK, Ltd., Heathcoat House, 20 Saville Row, London W1X 1AE, UK

Tel: 44-207-890-7500   Fax: 44-207-465-0453

INFORMATICA CORPORATION

2100 Seaport Blvd., Redwood City, CA, 94063

Tel: (650) 385-5000   Fax: (650) 385-5500   www.informatica.com

Mfr. computer software.

Informatica Software UK, 6 Waltham Park, Waltham Road, White Waltham, Maidenhead Berkshire SL6 3TN, UK

INFORMATION BUILDERS INC.

Two Penn Plaza, New York, NY, 10121-2898

Tel: (212) 736-4433   Fax: (212) 967-6406   www.ibi.com

Design and manufacture enterprise reporting software.

Information Builders (UK) Ltd., Station House, Harrow Rd., Wembley, Middlesex HA9 6DE, UK

Information Builders UK, Wembley Point, Harrow Road, Wembley Middlesex HA9 6DE, UK

Tel: 44-20-8982-4700

INFORMATION RESOURCES, INC. (IRI)

150 N. Clinton St., Chicago, IL, 60661

Tel: (312) 726-1221   Fax: (312) 726-0360   www.infores.com

Provides bar code scanner services for retail sales organizations; processes, analyzes and sells data from the huge database created from these services.

IRI InfoScan LTD., Eagle House, The Ring, Bracknell Berkshire RG12 1HB, UK

Tel: 44-1344-746000   Fax: 44-1344-746001

INFORMAX, INC.

7600 Wisconsin Avenue, Ste. 110, Bethesda, MD, 20814

Tel: (240) 747-4000   Fax: (240) 747-4010   www.informaxinc.com

Mfr. software to interpret DNA samples.

InforMax Inc., The Magdalen Centre, Robert Robinson Avenue, The Oxford Science Park, Oxford OX4 4GA, UK

Tel: 44-1865-784-580

INFOSPACE, INC.

601 108th Avenue, NE, Ste. 1200, Spokane, WA, 98004

Tel: (425) 201-6100   Fax: (425) 201-6163   www.infospace.com

Provides internet content syndications, including web information on Yellow and White Pages Directories, maps, etc.

TDL InfoSpace UK Ltd., 1 Farnham Road, Guildford, Surrey GU2 5RG, UK

Tel: 44-1483-549013   Fax: 44-1483-549133

INGERSOLL INTERNATIONAL INC.

707 Fulton Ave., Rockford, IL, 61103

Tel: (815) 987-6000   Fax: (815) 987-6725   www.ingersoll.com

Multinational supplier of special machine tools and services for the metalworking industries.

Ingersoll Milling Machines Ltd., Caxton Close, Drayton Fields, Daventry, Northants NN11 5RT, UK

Tel: 44-1327-313500

INGERSOLL-RAND COMPANY

200 Chestnut Ridge Road, Woodcliff Lake, NJ, 07675

Tel: (201) 573-0123   Fax: (201) 573-3172   www.irco.com

Leading innovation and solutions provider for the major global markets of Security and Safety, Climate Control, Industrial Solutions and Infrastructure.

Ingersoll-Dresser Pumps (UK) Ltd., Queens Way, Team Valley Trading Estate, Gateshead Tyne & Wear NE11, UK

Ingersoll-Rand Holdings Ltd., 2 Chorley New Rd., Bolton, Lancashire BL6 6JN, UK

Tel: 44-120-469-0690   Fax: 44-120-469-0388

Ingersoll-Rand Sales Co. Ltd., PO Box 23, Southmoor Rd., Wythenshawe, Manchester M23 9LN, UK

INGRAM MICRO INC.

1600 E. St. Andrew Place, Santa Ana, CA, 92799

Tel: (714) 566-1000   Fax: (714) 566-7940   www.ingrammicro.com

Engaged in wholesale distribution of microcomputer products.

Ingram Micro Inc., London, UK

INKTOMI CORPORATION

4100 East Third Avenue, Foster City, CA, 94404

Tel: (650) 653-2800   Fax: (650) 653-2801   www.iktomi.com

Mfr. software to boost speeds of computer networks.

Inktomi Corporation, Aldwych House, 81 Aldwych, London WC2B 4HN, UK

Tel: 44-207.430.5700

INNAPHASE CORPORATION

1700 Race Street, Philadelphia, PA, 19103

Tel: (215) 299-7400   Fax: (215) 299-1242   www.innaphase.com

Mfr. products for automation.

InnaPhase Limited, Deacon House St. Mary's Court, The Broadway, Amersham, Buckinghamshire HP7 OUT, UK

Tel: 44-1494-582-080

INNOVEX, INC.

5540 Pioneer Creek Drive, Maple Plain, MN, 55359-9003

Tel: (763) 479-5300   Fax: (763) 479-5395   www.innovexinc.com

Mfr. flexible circuits for hard disc drives.

Innovex Inc., Bedok House High Road, Ashton Keynes, Swindon SN6 6NX, UK

INPUT/OUTPUT, INC.

12300 Parc Crest Drive, Stafford, TX, 77477

Tel: (281) 933-3339   Fax: (281) 879-3626   www.I-o.com

Engaged in oil and gas exploration.

Input/Output, Leiden House, Delft Way, Norwich International Business Park, Norwich NR6 6BB, UK

Input/Output, Little Mead Industrial Estate, Cranleigh Surrey GU6 8ND, UK

INSESSION TECHNOLOGIES, INC.

218 South 108th Avenue, Omaha, NE, 68154

Tel: (402) 333-3322   Fax: (402) 333-9725   www.insession.com

Mfr. computer networking software.

Insession Technologies, 59 Clarendon Road, Watford Herts WD1 1LA, UK

INSIGHT ENTERPRISES, INC.

1305 West Auto Drive, Tempe, AZ, 85284

Tel: (480) 902-1001   Fax: (480) 902-1157   www.insight.com

Mfr. computers and software products.

Insight UK, Tech Bldgs., Highgrounds Way, Worksop S80 3AF, UK

Insight UK, Weston House, Westbar Green, Sheffield, South Yorkshire, UK

INSIGHTFUL CORPORATION

1700 Westlake Avenue North, Ste. 500, Seattle, WA, 98109-3044

Tel: (206) 283-8802   Fax: (206) 283-8691   www.insightful.com

Mfr. statistical analysis software.

Insightful UK, Knightway House 1/F, Park Street, Bagshot, Surrey GU19 5AQ, UK

INSTINET

875 Third Ave., New York, NY, 10022

Tel: (212) 310-9500   Fax: (212) 832-5183   www.instinet.com

Online investment brokerage.

LJR, Div. Instinet Europe Limited, Commodity Quay East Smithfield, London E1W 1AZ, UK

Tel: 44-207-680-3612   Fax: 44-207-481-4467

INSTRANET, INC.

60 West 35th Street, 8th Fl., New York, NY, 10001

Tel: (646) 473-0777   Fax: (877) 932-5826   www.instranet.com

Mfr. software.

InStranet Ltd., Centurion House, London Road, Staines Middlesex TW18 4AX, UK

INSTRON CORPORATION

100 Royal Street, Canton, MA, 02021-1089

Tel: (781) 575-5000   Fax: (781) 575-5751   www.instron.com

Mfr., markets and services materials testing instruments, systems and accessories.

Instron Ltd., Coronation Rd., High Wycombe, Buckinghamshire HP12 3SY, UK

Tel: 44-1494-464646

INSUL-8 CORPORATION

10102 F Street, Omaha, NE, 68127

Tel: (402) 339-9300   Fax: (402) 339-9627   www.insul-8.com

Mfr. mobile electrification products; conductor bar and festoon equipment.

Insul-8 Ltd., One Michigan Ave., Salford M5 2GL, UK

INTEGRAL VISION, INC.

700 Grand River Ave., Farmington Hills, MI, 48335-1563

Tel: (248) 471-2660   Fax: (248) 615-2971   www.iv-usa.com

Mfr. machine vision-based inspection systems.

Integral Vision Ltd., Unit 12, Railton Rd., Woburn Road Industrial Estate, Kempston, Bedford MK42 7PW, UK

INTEGRATED CIRCUIT SYSTEMS, INC. (ICS)

2435 Boulevard of the Generals, Norristown, PA, 19403

Tel: (610) 630-5300   Fax: (610) 630-5399   www.icst.com

Mfr. electronic timing devices.

ICS Europe, PO Box 38, Portslade BN42 4BL, UK

Tel: 44-1273-401301

INTEGRATED DEVICE TECHNOLOGY, INC. (IDT)

2975 Stender Way, Santa Clara, CA, 95054

Tel: (408) 727-6116   Fax: (408) 492-8674   www.idt.com

Mfr. high-performance semiconductors and modules.

Integrated Device Technology (IDT), Prime House, Barnett Wood Lane, Leatherhead, Surrey KT22 7DE, UK

Tel: 44-1372-363339   Fax: 44-1372-378851

INTEGRATED SILICON SOLUTION, INC.

2231 Lawson Lane, Santa Clara, CA, 95054-3311

Tel: (408) 588-0800   Fax: (408) 588-0805   www.issiusa.com

Mfr. high-speed memory chips and SRAMs.

Integrated Silicon Solution, Inc., Devon, UK

Tel: 44-1803--840-110

INTEL CORPORATION

2200 Mission College Blvd., Santa Clara, CA, 95052-8119

Tel: (408) 765-8080   Fax: (408) 765-1739   www.intel.com

Mfr. semiconductor, microprocessor and micro-communications components and systems.

Intel Corporation (UK) Ltd. (European Hdqtrs.), Pipers Way, Swindon SN3 1RJ, UK

Tel: 44-1793-403-000

INTELLIGROUP, INC.

499 Thornall Street, Edison, NJ, 08837

Tel: (732) 590-1600   Fax: (732) 362-2100   www.intelligroup.com

Provides systems integration, customer software and Internet application development.

Intelligroup Europe Ltd., The Manor House, Mount Street, Diss Norfolk IP22 4QQ, UK

Tel: 44-1379-650375   Contact: Peter Green

INTERACTIVE DATA CORPORATION

22 Crosby Drive, Bedford, MA, 01730

Tel: (781) 687-8500   Fax: (781) 687-8289   www.interactivedatacorp.com

Engaged in subscription services.

FT Interactive Data (UK), Fitzroy House 13-17, Epworth Street, London EC2A 4DL, UK

INTER-CONTINENTAL HOTELS

3 Ravinia Drive, Suite 2900, Atlanta, GA, 30346-2149

Tel: (770) 604-2000   Fax: (770) 604-5403   www.interconti.com

Worldwide hotel and resort accommodations.

Inter-Continental Hotels, The Thameside Centre, Kew Bridge Road, Brentford Middlesex TW8 OEB, UK

Tel: 44-181-847-3711   Fax: 44-181-569-9852

May Fair Inter-Continental London, Stratton St., London W1A 2AN, UK

Tel: 44-207-629-7777   Fax: 44-207-629-1459

INTERDEAN INTERCONEX, INC

55 Hunter Lane, Elmsford, NY, 10523-1317

Tel: (914) 347-6600   Fax: (914) 347-0129   www.interdean.com

Freight forwarding.

Interdean.Interconex, Central Way, Park Royal, London NW10 7XW, UK

Contact: Chris Baker

INTERFACE SOFTWARE, INC.

1420 Kensington Road, Ste. 320, Oak Brook, IL, 60523

Tel: (630) 572-1400   Fax: (630) 572-1818   www.interfacesoftware.com

Mfr. client relationship management software.

Interface Europe, 38 New Oxford Street, Ste. 204, London WC1A 1EP, UK

Tel: 44-207-379-6211

INTERFACE, INC.

2859 Paces Ferry Rd., Ste. 2000, Atlanta, GA, 30339

Tel: (770) 437-6800   Fax: (770) 803-6913   www.interfaceinc.com

Mfr. commercial broadloom carpet, textile, chemicals, architectural products and access flooring systems.

Interface Europe, Shelf Mills, Halifax, West Yorkshire HX3 7PA, UK

Tel: 44-1274-690690

Interface Fabrics Europe Ltd., Hopton Mills, Mirfield West Yorkshire, UK

Tel: 44-1924-491666

INTERGEN (INTERNATIONAL GENERATING CO., LTD.)

15 Wayside Road, Burlington, MA, 01803-4609

Tel: (781) 933-3000   Fax: (781) 933-3001   www.intergen.com

Global power and fuel asset development company; develops, owns and operates electric power plants and related distribution facilities.

InterGen (UK), Ltd., 20 St. James's St., London SW1A 1ES, UK

Tel: 44-207-543-3300   Fax: 44-207-839-0905

INTERGRAPH CORPORATION

One Madison Industrial Park, Huntsville, AL, 35894-0001

Tel: (256) 730-2000   Fax: (256) 730-7898   www.intergraph.com

Develop/mfr. interactive computer graphic systems.

Intergraph (UK) Ltd., Delta Business Park, Great Western Way, Swindon Wiltshire SN5 7XP, UK

Tel: 44-1793-619999   Fax: 44-1793-618508

INTERLIANT, INC.

Two Manhattanville Road, Purchase, NY, 10577-2118

Tel: (914) 640-9000   Fax: (914) 694-1190   www.interliant.com

Leading provider of managed infrastructure solutions, Provides cost-effective, secure solutions encompassing messaging, Web hosting, security, and professional consulting services.

Interliant UK, Burgoine House, 8 Lower Teddington Road, Hampton Wick, Kingston Upon Thames, UK

Tel: 44-208-939-8200

INTERMAGNETICS GENERAL CORPORATION

450 Old Niskayuna Road, PO Box 461, Latham, NY, 12110-0461

Tel: (518) 782-1122   Fax: (518) 783-2601   www.igc.com

Design and manufacture of super conductive magnets, magnetic systems and conductors, cryogenic products, refrigerants.

APD Cryogenics, 5 Jupiter House, Calleva Industrial Park, Aldermaston, Berkshire RG7 8NN, UK

Intermagnetics General (Europe) Ltd., PO Box 181, Oxford OX44 7AB, UK

INTERMEC TECHNOLOGIES CORPORATION

6001 36th Avenue West, PO Box 4280, Everett, WA, 98203-9280

Tel: (425) 348-2600   Fax: (425) 355-9551   www.intermec.com

Mfr. and distributor automated data collection systems.

Intermec International, Inc., European Headquarters, Sovereign House, Vastern Road, Reading RG1 8BY, UK

Tel: 44-118-987-9400   Fax: 44-118-987-9401

Intermec Technologies UK Ltd., 2 Bennet Court, Bennet Road, Reading Berkshire RG2 0QX, UK

Tel: 44-118-923-0800   Fax: 44-118-923-0801

INTERNAP NETWORK SERVICES CORPORATION

601 Union Street, Ste. 1000, Seattle, WA, 98101

Tel: (206) 441-8800   Fax: (206) 264-1833   www.internap.com

Mfr. software for data routing.

InterNap Network Services Corp. UK, Nations House, 103 Wigmore Street, London W1U 1QS, UK

Tel: 44-207-297-4800   Fax: 44-207-493-9302   Contact: Martin Burvill, VP

INTERNATIONAL COMPONENTS CORPORATION

420 N. May Street, Chicago, IL, 60622

Tel: (312) 829-2525   Fax: (312) 829-0213   www.icc-charge.com

Mfr. portable, rechargeable power, control and accessory products.

International Components Corp. (UK) Ltd., Kamone House, 63 St. Leonards Rd., Windsor Bray, Berkshire SL4 3BX, UK

INTERNATIONAL FLAVORS & FRAGRANCES INC.

521 West 57th Street, New York, NY, 10019-2960

Tel: (212) 765-5500   Fax: (212) 708-7132   www.iff.com

Design/mfr. flavors, fragrances and aroma chemicals.

International Flavors & Fragrances, Ltd., Commonwealth House, Hammersmith Intl. Centre, London W6 8DN, UK

Tel: 44-181-741-5771   Fax: 44-181-741-2566

INTERNATIONAL MANAGEMENT GROUP (IMG)

1360 East Ninth Street, Ste. 100, Cleveland, OH, 44114

Tel: (216) 522-1200   Fax: (216) 522-1145   www.imgworld.com

Manages athletes, sports academies and real estate facilities worldwide.

East Sussex National Golf Club, Little Horstead, Uckfield, East Sussex TN22 5ES, UK

Tel: 44-4522-766-777   Fax: 49-4522-766-717

European Golf Design, 75 Windsor Road, Chobham Surrey GU24 8LD, UK

Tel: 44-1276-855-955   Fax: 44-1276-856-190

IMG, Bentinck House, 3-8 Bolsover Street, London W1P 7HG, UK

Tel: 44-207-486-8011   Fax: 44-207-487-3116

IMG, Hogarth Business Park, Level 5, Burlington Lane, Chiswick London W4 2TH, UK

Tel: 44-208-233-5300   Fax: 44-208-233-5301

IMG, TWI House, 23 Eyot Gardens, Hammersmith, London W6 9TR, UK

Tel: 44-208-233-5400   Fax: 44-208-233-5801

IMG London, Pier House, Strand On The Green, Chiswick London W4 3NN, UK

Tel: 44-181-233-5000

Media House IMG Artists, Lovell House, 610 Chiswick High Road, London W4 5RX, UK

Tel: 44-208-233-5800   Fax: 44-208-233-5801

The Wynyard Club, Wellington Drive, Wynyard Park, Billingham TS22 5QJ, UK

Tel: 44-1-740-644-399   Fax: 44-1-740-644-599

INTERNATIONAL PAPER COMPANY

400 Atlantic Street, Stamford, CT, 06921

Tel: (203) 541-8000   Fax: (203) 358-6444   www.ipaper.com

Mfr./distributor container board, paper and wood products.

Anitec Image Ltd., 3&4 Suffolk Way, Drayton Rd., Abingdon-Oxon OX14 5JX, UK

Aussedat Rey Ltd., Hill House, McDonald Rd., Highgate Hill, London N19 SNA, UK

Bergvik Sales Ltd., Glen House, Stag Place, Victoria, London SW1E 5AG, UK

Boardcraft Ltd., Howard Rd., Eaton Socon, St. Neots, Huntingdon PE19 3ET, UK

Forest Lines Agencies Ltd., 14A Orwell House, Ferry Lane, Felixstowe, Suffolk IP11 8QL, UK

Horsell Graphic Industries, Howley Park Estate, Morley, Leeds LS27 0QT, UK

Horsell PLC, Nepshaw Lane S., Gildersome, Morley, Leeds LS27 7JQ, UK

Horsell Systems Ltd., Holt Court North, Aston Science Park, Birmingham B7 4AX, UK

Iford-Anitec, 14-22 Tottenham St., London W1P 0AH, UK

Ilford Ltd., Town Lane, Mobberley, Knutsford, Cheshire WA16 7HA, UK

International Paper Co. Ltd., 4/5 Grosvenor Pl., London SW1X 7HD, UK

Intl. Paper Cont., Road Three, Industrial Estate, Winsford, Cheshire CW7 3RJ, UK

IP Property Co. Ltd., Road Three, Industrial Estate, Winsford, Cheshire CW7 3RJ, UK

Masonite Co. Ltd., West Wing, Jason House, Kerry Hill, Horsforth, Leeds LS18 4JR, UK

Polyrey Ltd., Mattey House, 128-136 High St., Edgware, Middlesex HA8 7EL, UK

Strathmore-Beckett Intl. Ltd., 165 Dukes Ride, Crowthorne, Berkshire RG11 6DR, UK

Veratec Ltd., 4/5 Grosvenor Pl., London SW1X 7HD, UK

Veratec Ltd., First Field Lane, Braunton, N. Devon EX33 1ER, UK

INTERNATIONAL RECTIFIER CORPORATION

233 Kansas Street, El Segundo, CA, 90245

Tel: (310) 322-3331   Fax: (310) 322-3332   www.irf.com

Mfr. power semiconductor components.

International Rectifier Corp., Holland Rd., Hurst Green, Oxted, Surrey RH8 9BB, UK

Tel: 44-1883-732020   Fax: 44-1883-733410

INTERNATIONAL SPECIALTY PRODUCTS, INC.

1361 Alps Rd., Wayne, NJ, 07470

Tel: (973) 389-3083   Fax: (973) 628-4117   www.ispcorp.com

Mfr. specialty chemical products.

ISP (Great Britain) Co. Ltd., Tilson Road, Wythenshawe, Manchester M23 9PH, UK

Tel: 44-161-998-1122   Fax: 44-161-998-6218

ISP Europe, 40 Alan Turing Road, Surrey Research Park, Guilford Surrey, UK

Tel: 44-1483-407600   Fax: 44-1483-302175

INTER-TEL INC.

7300 W. Boston Street, Chandler, AZ, 85226

Tel: (480) 961-9000   Fax: (480) 961-1370   www.inter-tel.com

Design and manufacture of business communications systems related call processing software.

Inter-Tel Equipment UK Ltd., 9 Enterprise Ct., Newton Close Park Farm, Wellingborough, Northantshire NN8 3UX, UK

INTERVOICE-BRITE INC.

17811 Waterview Pkwy., Dallas, TX, 75206

Tel: (972) 454-8000   Fax: (972) 454-8707   www.intervoice.com

Mfr. telecom network hardware and software systems.

InterVoice-Brite Limited, Brite Court, Park Road, Gatley, Cheshire SK8 4HZ, UK

Tel: 44-161-495-1000   Fax: 44-161-495-1001

InterVoice-Brite Limited, Brannan House, 4 The Cambridge Business Park, Milton Road, Cambridge CB4 0WZ, UK

Tel: 44-1223-423-366   Fax: 44-1223-425-554

INTERWORLD CORPORATION

41 E. 11th St., 11th Fl., New York, NY, 10003

Tel: (212) 699-3630   Fax: (212) 699-3645   www.interworld.com

Mfr. commerce software.

InterWorld Corporation, 268 Bath Road, Berkshire SL1 4DX, UK

INTERWOVEN, INC.

803 11th Avenue, Sunnyvale, CA, 94089

Tel: (408) 774-2000   Fax: (408) 774-2002   www.interwoven.com

Mfr. web content management software.

Interwoven Europe (EMEA), Kingswood Kings Ride, Ascot Berkshire SL5 8AJ, UK

Tel: 44-1344-631900

INTRALOX INC.

Box 50699, New Orleans, LA, 70150-5307

Tel: (504) 733-0463   Fax: (504) 734-0063   www.intralox.com

Mfr. modular conveyor belts and accessories.

Intralox Ltd., Bldg. 90, Third Ave., Pensnett Trading Estate, Kingswinford, West Midlands DY6 7PP, UK

INTRUSION, INC.

1101 East Arapaho Road, Richardson, TX, 75081

Tel: (972) 234-6400   Fax: (972) 234-1467   www.intrusion.com

Mfr. security software.

Intrusion.Com, Ltd., Ancells Court Ancells Business Park, Fleet, Hants GU13 8UY, UK

INTUIT INC.

2535 Garcia Avenue, Mountain View, CA, 94043

Tel: (650) 944-6000   Fax: (650) 944-3699   www.intuit.com

Mfr. personal finance software.

Intuit UK Ltd., PO Box 2093, Swindon SN5 8TR, UK

Tel: 44-1793-699500

INVENTION SUBMISSION CORPORATION

217 Ninth Street, Pittsburgh, PA, 15222

Tel: (412) 288-1300   Fax: (412) 288-1354   www.isc-online.com

Inventor assistance services.

Invention Submission Corp., 50 New Bond St., London W1Y 9HA, UK

INVISION TECHNOLOGIES, INC.

7151 Gateway Blvd., Newark, CA, 94560

Tel: (510) 739-2400   Fax: (510) 739-6400   www.invision-tech.com

Mfr. detection systems to scan carry-on bags.

Invision Technologies UK, Silkin House, 5-7 Bath Road, Heathrow Hounslow TW6 2AA, UK

Tel: 44-208-754-9540   Fax: 44-208-754-9541

INVITROGEN CORPORATION

1600 Faraday Avenue, Carlsbad, CA, 92008

Tel: (760) 603-7200   Fax: (760) 602-6500   www.invitrogen.com

Mfr. products and kits for gene analysis.

Invitrogen Ltd., 3 Fountain Drive, Inchinnan Business Park, Paisley PA4 9RF, UK

Tel: 44-207-814-6100

IOMEGA CORPORATION

4435 Eastgate Mall, 3rd Fl., San Diego, CA, 92121

Tel: (858) 795-7000   Fax: (858) 795-7001   www.iomega.com

Mfr. data storage products.

Iomega, 7 Mt. Mews, High St., Hampton-on-Thames, Middlesex, UK

IONICS INC.

65 Grove Street, Watertown, MA, 02172

Tel: (617) 926-2500   Fax: (617) 926-4304   www.ionics.com

Mfr. desalination equipment.

Ionics UK Ltd., 16 Endeavour Way, London SW19 8UH, UK

IPSEN INDUSTRIES INC.

894 Ipsen Rd., Cherry Valley, IL, 61016

Tel: (815) 332-4941   Fax: (815) 332-7625   www.ipsen-intl.com

Heat treating equipment.

Ipsen UK Ltd., UNIT 1A, Nechlls Business Centre,, 31 Bollman St., Nechlls, Birmingham B7 4RP, UK

Tel: 44-121-359-5959   Fax: 44-121-359-5995   Contact: Rob Neale, Mgr.

IR FLUID PRODUCTS

PO Box 151, Bryan, OH, 43506

Tel: (419) 636-4242   Fax: (419) 633-1674   www.irco.com

Mfr. fluid control products, including pumps, valves, cylinders, logic controls and air line components.

IR Fluid Products (UK) Ltd., Walkers Rd., N. Moons Moat Industrial Park, Redditch, Worcestershire B98 9HE, UK

ITRON, INC.

2818 N. Sullivan Road, Spokane, WA, 99216-1897

Tel: (509) 924-9900   Fax: (509) 891-3355   www.itron.com

Mfr. wireless communication products.

Itron (UK) Ltd., Riverside Road, Gorleston, Great Yarmouth NR31 6PX, UK

Tel: 44-1493-601144   Contact: Andrew Stubbings

ITT INDUSTRIES, INC.

4 West Red Oak Lane, White Plains, NY, 10604

Tel: (914) 641-2000   Fax: (914) 696-2950   www.ittind.com

Mfr. pumps, systems and services to move and control water/fluids and produces connectors, switches, keypads and cabling used in computing, telecommunications, aerospace and industrial applications, as well as network services.

Jabsco (Marlow Pumps) UK, Thaxted Road, Saffron Walden Essex CB10 2UR, UK

Tel: 44-1799-513893   Fax: 44-1799-513902

Jabsco (UK), Bingley Road, Hoddesdon, Hertfordshire EN11, UK

Tel: 44-1992-450145   Fax: 44-1992-467132

Network Systems & Services/UK, Jays Close, Viables Estate, Hants Basingstoke RG22 4BA, UK

Tel: 44-1256-311750   Fax: 44-1256-364169

ITT-GOULDS PUMPS INC.

2881 East Bayard Street, Seneca Falls, NY, 13148

Tel: (315) 568-2811   Fax: (315) 568-7651   www.gouldspumps.com

Mfr. industrial and water systems pumps.

Chemquip Limited, High Peak Stockport, Cheshire SK23 6AR, UK

ITT Industries - Goulds Pumps, White Hart House, London Road, Blackwater Camberley, Surrey GU19 9AD, UK

Tel: 44-1276-600646

Jabsco (Marlow Pumps) UK, Thaxted Road, Saffron Walden Essex CB10 2UR, UK

Tel: 44-1799-513893   Fax: 44-1799-513902

Plenty Mirrlees Pumps Ltd., Hambridge Road, Newbury, Berkshire RG14 5TR, UK

Tel: 44-1635-42363

ITW DEVCON PLEXUS

30 Endicott Street, Danvers, MA, 01923

Tel: (978) 777-1100   Fax: (978) 774-0516   www.devcon-equip.com

Engaged in technology and products for OEM assembly, and maintenance/repair applications.

Devcon UK Ltd., Brunel Close, Park Farm Estate, Wellingborough, Northantshire, UK

Tel: 44-1-933-675299

ITW RANSBURG FINISHING SYSTEMS

320 Phillips Ave., Toledo, OH, 43612

Tel: (419) 470-2000   Fax: (419) 470-2112   www.itwransburg.com

Engaged in the design, manufacture and marketing of liquid electrostatic paint application equipment.

ITW Ransburg, Ringwood Rd., Bournemouth, Hants BH11 9LH, UK

ITW Switches, Norway Rd., Portsmouth PO3 5HT, UK

IVAX CORPORATION

4400 Biscayne Blvd., Miami, FL, 33137

Tel: (305) 575-6000   Fax: (305) 575-6055   www.ivax.com

Mfr. pharmaceuticals.

IVAX Pharmaceuticals UK, IVAX Quays, Albert Basin, Royal Docks, London E16 2QJ, UK

IVAX Runcom, Goddard Road, Astmoor, Runcorn Cheshire WA7 1QF, UK

IXYS CORPORATION

3540 Bassett Street, Santa Clara, CA, 95054

Tel: (408) 982-0700   Fax: (408) 748-9788   www.ixys.com

Mfr. semiconductors and modules.

IXYS Semiconductor, Providence House, Forest Road Binfield, Bracknell Berkshire RG12 5HP, UK

Tel: 44-1344-482820

J. WALTER THOMPSON COMPANY

466 Lexington Ave., New York, NY, 10017

Tel: (212) 210-7000   Fax: (212) 210-6944   www.jwt.com

International advertising and marketing services.

J. Walter Thompson Co., London, UK

JABIL CIRCUIT, INC.

10560 Ninth St. North, St. Petersburg, FL, 33716

Tel: (727) 557-9749   Fax: (727) 579-8529   www.jabil.com

Mfr. printed circuit boards, electronic components and systems.

Jabil Circuit, New Horizon Park, Cromwell Street, Coventry CV6 5FH, UK

Jabil Circuit UK, Edge Lane, Liverpool L7 9NW, UK

JACOBS ENGINEERING GROUP INC.

1111 S. Arroyo Parkway, Pasadena, CA, 91105

Tel: (626) 578-3500   Fax: (626) 578-6916   www.jacobs.com

Engineering, design and consulting; construction and construction management; process plant maintenance.

Jacobs Engineering Ltd., Knollys House, 17 Addiscombe Rd., Croydon, Surrey CR0 6SR, UK

Tel: 44-181-688-4477   Fax: 44-181-649-9213   Contact: Richard J. Slater, VP & Mng. Dir.   Emp: 184

Jacobs Engineering Ltd., UK

Tel: 44-161-80-4088   Fax: 44-161-474-7745   Contact: T. Michael Tate, Dir.   Emp: 256

JASON INCORPORATED

411 E. Wisconsin Ave., Ste 2100, Milwaukee, WI, 53202

Tel: (414) 277-9300   Fax: (414) 277-9445   www.jasoninc.com

Mfr. and sales auto trim and finishing products.

Milsco Manufacturing Company, Nuneaton, UK

JCI JONES CHEMICALS, INC.

808 Sarasota Quay, Sarasota, FL, 34236

Tel: (941) 330-1537   Fax: (941) 330-9657   www.jcichem.com

Repackager of chlorine and other chemicals used in water purification.

Jones Chemicals, Inc., London, UK

Tel: 44-20-7407-2212

JDA SOFTWARE GROUP, INC.

14400 N. 87th St., Scottsdale, AZ, 85260-3649

Tel: (480) 308-3000   Fax: (480) 308-3001   www.jda.com

Developer of information management software for retail, merchandising, distribution and store management.

JDA International, Ltd., 4-6 Churchill Court, Hortons Way, Westerham Kent TN16 BT1, UK

Tel: 44-1959-491-000   Fax: 44-1959-491-001

JDS UNIPHASE CORPORATION

210 Baypoint Pkwy., San Jose, CA, 95134

Tel: (408) 434-1800   Fax: (408) 954-0760   www.jdsunph.com

Mfr. advanced fiber optic products for the cable television and telecommunications industries.

JDS Uniphase Corporation, Bramingham Business Park, Enterprise Way Luton, Beds, LU3 4BU, UK

JDS Uniphase Ltd., 3-4 Waterside Business Park, Eastways, Witham Essex CM8 3YQ, UK

Tel: 44-1993-700800   Contact: Tim Greaves, VP

JDS Uniphase UK Limited, Broomhill Way, Torquay, Devon TQ2 7QL, UK

Tel: 44-1803-407807

JET-LUBE INC.

4849 Homestead, Ste. 200, Houston, TX, 77028

Tel: (713) 674-7617   Fax: (713) 678-4604   www.jetlube.com

Mfr. anti-seize compounds, thread sealants, lubricants, greases.

Ilex Lubricants Ltd., Reform Rd., Maidenhead, Berkshire SL6 8BY, UK

Tel: 44-16286-31913   Fax: 44-1628-773138

JLG INDUSTRIES INC.

One JLG Drive, McConnellsburg, PA, 17233-9533

Tel: (717) 485-5161   Fax: (717) 485-6417   www.jlg.com

Mfr. aerial work platforms and vertical personnel lifts.

JLG Industries UK, Unit 12, Southside, Bredbury Park Industrial Estate, Bredbury Stockport SK6 2SP, UK

Tel: 44-870-200-7700   Fax: 44-870-200-7711

JLG Industries UK, 7 Mount Mews, High Street Hampton TW12 2SH, UK

Tel: 44-208-213-5977   Fax: 44- 208-213-5976

JOHN HANCOCK FINANCIAL SERVICES, INC.

200 Clarendon Street, Boston, MA, 02117

Tel: (617) 572-6000   Fax: (617) 572-9799   www.johnhancock.com

Life insurance services.

Hancock International Private Equity Management, Ltd., 38 Trinity Sq., London, UK

JOHNS MANVILLE CORPORATION

717 17th Street, Denver, CO, 80202

Tel: (303) 978-2000   Fax: (303) 978-2318   www.jm.com

Mfr. fiberglass insulation, roofing products and systems, fiberglass material and reinforcements, filtration mats.

Johns Manville International, Canada House, 272 Field End Rd., Ruislip, Middlesex HA4 9NA, UK

JOHNSON & JOHNSON

One Johnson & Johnson Plaza, New Brunswick, NJ, 08933

Tel: (732) 524-0400   Fax: (732) 214-0334   www.jnj.com

Mfr./distributor/R&D pharmaceutical, health care and cosmetic products.

Janssen-Cilag Ltd., PO Box 79, Saunderton, High Wycombe HP14 4HJ, UK

Johnson & Johnson Ltd., Foundation Park, Roxborough Way, Maidenhead, Berkshire SL6 3UG, UK

Johnson & Johnson Medical Ltd., Coronation Rd., Ascot, Berkshire 5L5 9EY, UK

Johnson & Johnson Professional Products Ltd. (Europe), The Braccans, London Rd., Bracknell, Berkshire RG12 2AT, UK

LifeScan U.K., PO Box 79, Saunderton, High Wycombe HP14 4HJ, UK

Ortho-Clinical Diagnostics, Enterprise House, Station Rd., Loudwater, High Wycombe Bucks HP10 9UF, UK

Vistakon Europe, Bracknell, Berkshire RG12 2AT, UK

SC JOHNSON

1525 Howe St., Racine, WI, 53403

Tel: (262) 260-2000   Fax: (262) 260-2133   www.scjohnsonwax.com

Home, auto, commercial and personal care products and specialty chemicals.

SC Johnson Wax, Frimley Green Rd., Frimley, Surrey GU16 5AJ, UK

JOHNSON CONTROLS INC.

5757 N. Green Bay Ave., PO Box 591, Milwaukee, WI, 53201-0591

Tel: (414) 228-1200   Fax: (414) 228-2077   www.johnsoncontrols.com

Mfr. facility management and control systems and auto seating.

Johnson Control Systems Ltd., Convex House, Randall's Research Park, Leatherhead Surrey KT22 7TS, UK

Tel: 44-1-372-376111   Fax: 44-1-372-361413   Contact: Andrew J. Schlidt, Mng. Dir.

THE JOHNSON CORPORATION

805 Wood Street, Three Rivers, MI, 49093

Tel: (269) 278-1715   Fax: (269) 273-2230   www.joco.com

Mfr. rotary joints and siphon systems.

Johnson Corp (JOCO) Ltd., Little Lane, Ilkley, West Yorkshire LS29 8HY, UK

Tel: 44-1943-607550   Fax: 44-1943-609463

Johnson Systems International, Ilkey, UK

JOHNSON OUTDOORS, INC.

555 Main Street, Racine, WI, 53177

Tel: (262) 631-6600   Fax: (262) 631-6601   www.johnsonoutdoors.com

Mfr. diving, fishing, boating and camping sports equipment.

Scubapro U.K. Ltd., Vickers Business Centre, Ste. 10, Priestly Road, Basingstoke, Hampshire RG24 9NP, UK

Tel: 44-125-6812636   Fax: 44-125-6812646

JONES FINANCIAL COMPANIES, LP

12555 Manchester Road, Des Peres, MO, 63131

Tel: (314) 515-2000   Fax: (314) 515-2622   www.edwardjones.com

Engaged in investment securities.

Edward Jones Financial, 7 Westferry Circus, Canary Wharf, London E14 4HH, UK

JONES LANG LASALLE

153 East 53rd Street, New York, NY, 10022

Tel: (212) 812-5700   Fax: (212) 421-3544   www.am.joneslanglasalle.com

International marketing consultants, leasing agents and property management advisors.

Jones Lang Wootton, London, UK

JONES, DAY, REAVIS & POGUE

North Point, 901 Lakeside Ave., Cleveland, OH, 44114

Tel: (216) 586-3939   Fax: (216) 579-0212   www.jonesday.com

International law firm.

Jones, Day, Reavis & Pogue, Bucklersbury House, 3 Queen Victoria St., London EC4N 8NA, UK

Tel: 44-207-236-3939   Fax: 44-207-236-1113   Contact: Stephen E. Fiamma, Partner   Emp: 55

JOY GLOBAL

100 East Wisconsin Avenue Suite 2780, Milwaukee, WI, 53202

Tel: (414) 779-4500   Fax: (414) 779-4507   www.joyglobal.com

Mfr. of underground mining equipment.

Joy Global, Pinxton Service Centre, Kirkby Lane, Pinxton, Nottingham NG16 6HX, UK

Tel: 44-1773-515-200

JPMORGAN PRIVATE BANK

345 Park Avenue, New York, NY, 10154-1002

Tel: (212) 483-2323   Fax: (212) 464-1120   www.jpmorgan.com

Engaged in private banking services.

JPMorgan Private Bank, 125 London Wall, London EC2Y 5AJ, UK

JUKI UNION SPECIAL CORPORATION

8500 N.W. 17th St., Miami, FL, 33126

Tel: (305) 594-0059   Fax: (305) 594-0720   www.unionspecial.com

Mfr. sewing machines.

Union Special (UK) Ltd., 22 Mandervell Rd., Industrial Estate, Oadby Leicester LE2 5LQ, UK

Tel: 44-116-271-3292   Fax: 44-116-271-9239

JUNIPER NETWORKS, INC.

1194 North Mathilda Ave., Sunnyvale, CA, 94089

Tel: (408) 745-2000   Fax: (408) 745-2100   www.juniper.net

Engaged in the design and sales of Internet Protocol routers for access networks.

Juniper Networks UK, Juniper House, Guildford Road, Leatherhead Surrey KT22 9JH, UK

JUPITER MEDIA METRIX INC.

21 Astor Place, New York, NY, 10003

Tel: (212) 780-6060   Fax: (212) 780-6075   www.jmm.com

Engaged in research services to determine audience measurement.

Jupiter Media Metrix Inc., 32 Haymarket, Piccadilly, London SW1Y 4TP, UK

Tel: 44-207-747-0500

K-2, INC.

4900 South Eastern Ave., Los Angeles, CA, 90040

Tel: (323) 724-2800   Fax: (323) 724-8174   www.k2sports.com

Mfr. sporting goods, recreational and industrial products.

Shakespeare, Div. K2, PO Box 1, Broad Ground Road, Lakeside Redditch, GB Worcester B98 8NQ, UK

Tel: 44-1527-510-570

KADANT INC.

One Acton Place, Ste. 202, Acton, MA, 01720-3951

Tel: (978) 776-2000   Fax: (978) 635-1593   www.kandant.com

Mfr. paper recycling equipment.

Kadant UK, Clarence House, Clarence Place, 3/F, Newport, South Wales, UK

Kadant UK, Riverside Works/Woodhill Road, Post Office Box 6, Bury, Lancashire BL8 1DF, UK

Tel: 44-161-764-9111   Fax: 44-161-797-1496

KAMAN CORPORATION

1332 Blue Hills Ave., Bloomfield, CT, 06002

Tel: (860) 243-7100   Fax: (860) 243-6365   www.kaman.com

Mfr. aviation and aerospace products and services, musical instruments.

KMI Europe, Inc., London, UK

KAMDEN INTERNATIONAL SHIPPING INC.

179-02 150th Avenue, Jamaica, NY, 11434

Tel: (718) 553-8181   Fax: (718) 244-0030   www.kamden.com

Full service, international freight forwarder and customs broker.

Kamden Intl. Shipping Ltd., Kamden House, 673 Spur Road, North Feltham Trading Estate, Feltham Middlesex TW14 0SL, UK

Kamden Intl. Shipping Ltd., Unit 5, Lawnhurst Trading Estate, Ashurst Drive, Cheadle Heath Stockport, Cheshire SK3 0SD, UK

KAPPLER PROTECTIVE APPAREL & FABRICS

PO Box 218, 70 Grimes Drive, Guntersville, AL, 35976

Tel: (205) 505-4000   Fax: (205) 505-4004   www.kappler.com

Mfr. of protective apparel and fabrics.

Kappler Europe Ltd., Plot 1, Crown Farm Way, Mansfield, Nottinghamshire NG19 0FT, UK

Tel: 44-1623-416200   Contact: Thomas Mankert, Mng. Dir.   Emp: 120

KATY INDUSTRIES INC.

6300 South Syracuse Way, Ste. 300, Englewood, CO, 80111

Tel: (303) 290-9300   Fax: (303) 290-9344   www.katyindustries.com

Mfr. electronic and maintenance equipment for industrial and consumer markets.

Bach Simpson (UK) Ltd., Trenant Estate, Wadebridge, Cornwall PL27 6HD, UK

Darwins Alloy Castings Co. Ltd., Sheffield Rd., Tinsley, Sheffield S9 1RL, UK

LaBour Pump Co. Ltd., Denington Estate, Wellingborough, Northants NN8 2QL, UK

KAWNEER COMPANY, INC.

555 Guthridge Court, Norcross, GA, 30092

Tel: (770) 449-5555   Fax: (770) 734-1570   www.kawneer.com

Mfr. arch aluminum products for commercial construction.

Kawneer UK Ltd., Astmoor Industrial Estate, Astmoor, Runcorn, Cheshire WA7 1QQ, UK

KAYDON CORPORATION

315 E. Eisenhower Pkwy., Ste. 300, Ann Arbor, MI, 48108-3330

Tel: (734) 747-7025   Fax: (734) 747-6565   www.kaydon.com

Design/mfr. custom engineered products: bearings, rings, seals, etc.

Cooper Roller Bearings Co. Ltd., Wisbech, Kings Lynn, Norfolk PE30 5JX, UK

IDM Electronics Ltd., 30 Suttons Park Ave., Suttons Park Industrial Estate, Reading, Berkshire RG6 1AW, UK

KEANE, INC.

Ten City Square, Boston, MA, 02129

Tel: (617) 241-9200   Fax: (617) 241-9507   www.keane.com

Provides information technology services.

Keane UK, 53-55 New Bond Street, London W1Y 9DG, UK

Tel: 44-207-339-0000   Fax: 44-207-339-0001

Keane UK, Stonecourt, Siskin Drive, Coventry CV3 4FJ, UK

Tel: 44-1203-514400   Fax: 44-1203-514491

Keane UK, Lion House, Oscott Road, Wilton Birmingham B6 7UH, UK

Tel: 44-121-356-8383   Fax: 44-121-356-0463

A.T. KEARNEY INC.

5400 Legacy Dr., Plano, TX, 75201

Tel: (972) 604-4600   Fax: (972) 543-7680   www.atkearney.com

Management consultants and executive search.

A. T. Kearney Inc. Ltd., Lansdowne House, Berkeley Square, London W2X 5DH, UK

Tel: 44-207-468-8000

KEITHLEY INSTRUMENTS INC.

28775 Aurora Road, Cleveland, OH, 44139

Tel: (440) 248-0400   Fax: (440) 248-6168   www.keithley.com

Mfr. electronic test/measure instruments, PC-based data acquisition hardware/software.

Keithley Instruments Ltd., The Minister, 58 Portman Rd., Reading, Berks RG30 1EA, UK

KELLOGG BROWN & ROOT INC.

PO Box 4557, Houston, TX, 77210-4557

Tel: (713) 676-3011   Fax: (713) 676-8695   www.halliburton.com

Engaged in technology-based engineering and construction.

Kellogg Brown & Root, Kellogg Tower, KT 08A, Greenford Road, Greenford, Middlesex UB6 0JA, UK

Tel: 44-20-8872-7000   Fax: 44-20-8872-7272

Kellogg Brown & Root, Hill Park Court, Springfield Drive, Leatherhead Surrey KT22 7NL, UK

Tel: 44-181-544-5000   Fax: 44-181-544-4400   Contact: Roderick Kyle

Kellogg Brown & Root AOC, PO Box No. 8, ICI Acrylics, Cassel Works, New Road, Billingham TS23 1PR, UK

Kellogg Brown & Root Cardinal, Greenford Road, Greenford, London UB6 9AP, UK

Kellogg Brown & Root Civil, Churchgate House, 56 Oxford Street, Manchester M1 6EU, UK

Kellogg Brown & Root Civil, M65 Contract 1, Resident Engineers Office, Higher Stanworth Farm Bolton Road, Whithnell Chorley PR6 8PB, UK

Kellogg Brown & Root Ltd., Wessex House, Market St., Eastleigh Hants SO5 4FD, UK

Kellong Brown & Root Civil, Thorncroft Manor, Dorking Road, Leatherhead Surrey KT22 8JB, UK

KELLOGG COMPANY

One Kellogg Square, PO Box 3599, Battle Creek, MI, 49016-3599

Tel: (616) 961-2000   Fax: (616) 961-2871   www.kelloggs.com

Mfr. ready-to-eat cereals and convenience foods.

Kellogg Co. of Great Britain Ltd., Attn: English Office, One Kellogg Square, PO Box 3599, Battle Creek, MI, 49016-3599

KELLY SERVICES, INC.

999 W. Big Beaver Road, Troy, MI, 48084

Tel: (248) 362-4444   Fax: (248) 244-4154   www.kellyservices.com

Temporary help placement.

Kelly Services (UK) Ltd., Roswell House, 100 Middlesex St., London E1 7HD, UK

Tel: 44-207-247-4494 Fax: 44-207-247-2570

KEMLITE COMPANY, INC.

PO Box 2429, Joliet, IL, 60434

Tel: (815) 467-8600   Fax: (815) 467-8666   www.kemlite.com

Mfr. fiberglass reinforced plastic panels.

Kemlite Company, 25 Caker Stream Road, Alton, Hampshire GU34 2QF, UK

Tel: 44-151-650-0123 Fax: 44-151-650-0365

KENDA SYSTEMS INC.

One Stiles Road, Salem, NH, 03079

Tel: (603) 898-7884   Fax: (603) 898-3016   www.kenda.com

Computer programming services.

Kenda Systems Ltd., Regency House, 6b Queen St., Godalming, Surrey GU7 1BD, UK

Tel: 44-1483-418-191

Kenda Systems, Ltd., 1 Royal Exchange Avenue, London EC3V 3LT, UK

Tel: 44-20-7464-4070

THE KENDALL COMPANY TYCO HEALTHCARE

15 Hampshire Street, Mansfield, MA, 02048

Tel: (508) 261-8000   Fax: (508) 261-8542   www.kendallhq.com

Mfr. and markets a broad range of wound care, needles and syringes, electrodes, specialized paper, vascular therapy, urological care, incontinence care, and nursing care products.

The Kendall Co. (UK) Ltd., 154 Fareham Rd., Gosport, Hampshire PO13 0AS, UK

Tel: 44-1329-224-4114 Fax: 44-1329-224-4390

KENDLE INTERNATIONAL INC.

1200 Carew Tower, 441 Vine Street, Cincinnati, OH, 45202

Tel: (513) 381-5550   Fax: (513) 381-5870   www.kendle.com

Provides contract research and development services.

Kendle International, 24 Station Road, Ely, Cambridgeshire CB7 4BS, UK

Tel: 44-1353-669789 Fax: 44-1353-668473

Kendle International UK, 38 Wellington Business Park, Crowthorne, Berkshire RG45 6LS, UK

Tel: 44-1344-750-225   Fax: 44-1344-750-665

KENNAMETAL INC.

1600 Technology Way, PO Box 231, Latrobe, PA, 15650

Tel: (724) 539-5000   Fax: (724) 539-4710   www.kennametal.com

Tools, hard carbide and tungsten alloys for metalworking industry.

Kennametal Hertel U.K., The Pensnett Trading Estate, Kingswinford, W. Midlands, West Midland DY6 7NP, UK

Tel: 44-1384-408071   Fax: 44-1384-408015

KEPNER-TREGOE INC.

PO Box 704, Princeton, NJ, 08542-0740

Tel: (609) 921-2806   Fax: (609) 497-0130   www.kepner-tregoe.com

Management consulting; specializing in strategy formulation, problem solving, decision making, project management, and cost reduction.

Kepner-Tregor Ltd., 13-15 Victoria St., Windsor, Berkshire SL4 1HB, UK

Tel: 44-1753-856716   Fax: 44-1753-854929

KERR-McGEE CORPORATION

123 Robert S. Kerr Ave., Oklahoma City, OK, 73102

Tel: (405) 270-1313   Fax: (405) 270-3123   www.kerr-mcgee.com

Engaged in oil and gas exploration and manufacture of inorganic chemicals.

KG and Kerr-McGee Resources (U.K.) Limited, 75 Davies St., Mayfair, London W1Y 1FA, UK

KEYNOTE SYSTEMS, INC.

777 Mariners Island Blvd., San Mateo, CA, 94404

Tel: (650) 403-2400   Fax: (650) 403-5500   www.keynote.com

Provides Internet performance management services.

Keynote Europe, Berkeley Square House, 2/F, Berkeley Square, London W1J 6BD, UK

Tel: 44-207-887-4531   Fax: 44-207-887-4532

KIDDE-FENWAL, INC.

400 Main Street, Ashland, MA, 01721

Tel: (508) 881-2000   Fax: (508) 881-6729   www.kidde-fenwal.com

Mfr. temperature controls, ignition systems, fire and smoke detection and suppression systems.

Fenwal Intl., Lyons House, 2A Station Rd., Frimley, Camberley Surrey GU16 5HP, UK

KILPATRICK STOCKTON LLP

1100 Peachtree Street, NE, Ste. 2800, Atlanta, GA, 30309-4530

Tel: (404) 815-6500   Fax: (404) 815-6555   www.kilstock.com

Engaged in international law.

Kilpatrick Stockton, 68 Pall Mall, London SW1Y 5ES, UK

Tel: 44-207-321-0477   Fax: 44-207-930-9733

KIMBALL INTERNATIONAL INC.

1600 Royal Street, Jasper, IN, 47549

Tel: (812) 482-1600   Fax: (812) 482-8300   www.kimball.com

Mfr. office furniture and seating, pianos, wood veneers, plywood products.

Herrburger Brooks Ltd., Meadow Lane, Long Eaton, Nottingham NG10 2FG, UK

Kimball Europe Ltd., 21-27 Marylebone Lane, London W1M 5FG, UK

KIMBERLY-CLARK CORPORATION

351 Phelps Drive, Irving, TX, 75038

Tel: (972) 281-1200   Fax: (972) 281-1435   www.kimberly-clark.com

Mfr./sales/distribution of consumer tissue, household and personal care products.

Kimberly-Clark Ltd., Suite 211, K2 House, Heathfield Way, Dallington, Northampton NN5 7QP, UK

KINETIC CONCEPTS, INC.

8023 Vantage Drive, San Antonio, TX, 78230-4728

Tel: (210) 524-9000   Fax: (210) 255-4524   www.KCI1.com

Mfr. specialized medical beds.

KCI Medical, Two Rivers, Witney, Oxon OX8 6BH, UK

Tel: 44-1993-707-300   Contact: Les Lindsay

KINGSTON TECHNOLOGY COMPANY, INC.

17600 Newhope Street, Fountain Valley, CA, 92708

Tel: (714) 435-2600   Fax: (714) 435-2699   www.kingston.com

Mfr. memory modules.

Kingston Technology Europe, Ltd., Kingston Court, Brooklands Close, Sunbury-on-Thames, Middlesex TW16 7EP, UK

KINKO'S, INC.

255 W. Stanley Ave., Ventura, CA, 93002-8000

Tel: (805) 652-4000   Fax: (805) 652-4347   www.kinkos.com

Kinko's operates a 24-hour-a-day, global chain of photocopy stores.

Kinko's, 326 High Holburn St., London WC1V 7DD, UK

Tel: 44-207-539-2900   Fax: 44-207-539-2901

KIRKLAND & ELLIS

200 East Randolph Drive, Chicago, IL, 60601

Tel: (312) 861-2000   Fax: (312) 861-2200   www.kirkland.com

Engaged in international law.

Kirkland & Ellis, Tower 42, 25 Old Broad St., London EC2N 1HQ, UK

Tel: 44-207-816 8700   Fax: 44-207-816 8800   Contact: Samuel H. Hanbold, Ptnr.

KLA-TENCOR CORPORATION

160 Rio Robles, San Jose, CA, 95134

Tel: (408) 875-6000   Fax: (408) 875-3030   www.kia-tencor.ocm

Mfr. software and equipment.

KLA-Tencor UK, 19 Mulberry Business Park, Fishponds Road, Wokingham, Berkshire RG 412GY, UK

KNIGHT TRADING GROUP, INC.

525 Washington Blvd., Jersey City, NJ, 07310

Tel: (201) 222-9400   Fax: (201) 557-6853   www.knight-sec.com

Engaged in securities trading.

Knight Securities International Ltd., London Stock Exchange Bldg., 2 Throgmorton Street, London EC2N 1TE, UK

Tel: 44-207-997-1234   Fax: 44-207-997-7600   Contact: Walter F. Raquet, Chmn.

KNIGHT-RIDDER INC.

50 W. San Fernando Street, San Jose, CA, 95113

Tel: (408) 938-7700   Fax: (408) 938-7700   www.kri.com

Engaged in newspaper and Internet publishing.

Knight-Ridder Financial/Europe, KR House, 78 Fleet St., London EC4Y 1HY, UK

KNOLL, INC.

1235 Water Street, East Greenville, PA, 18041

Tel: (215) 679-7991   Fax: (215) 679-3904   www.knoll.com

Mfr. and sale of office furnishings.

Knoll International U.K. Ltd., Meridian House, Normanby Road, Scunthorpe, North Lincolnshire DN15 8QX, UK

Tel: 44-1724-281-555   Contact: Mark McCormack

KNOWLEDGEPLANET.COM, INC.

11490 Commerce Park Drive., Ste. 400, Reston, VA, 20191

Tel: (703) 262-6600   Fax: (703) 716-0237   www.knowledgeplanet.com

Mfr. software.

KnowledgePlanet Limited, 1 Liverpool Street, London EC2M 7QD, UK

Tel: 44-107-956-2036

KOCH INDUSTRIES INC.

4111 East 37th Street North, Wichita, KS, 67220-3203

Tel: (316) 828-5500   Fax: (316) 828-5950   www.kochind.com

Oil, financial services, agriculture and Purina Mills animal feed.

Koch Metals Trading Limited, 7 George Yard Lombard St., 7/F, London EC3V 9DH, UK

Tel: 44-207-648-6300   Fax: 44-20-7648-6301

KOCH-GLITSCH, INC.

4111 E. 37th Street North, Wichita, KS, 67220

Tel: (316) 828-5110   Fax: (316) 828-5263   www.koch-glitsch.com

Engaged in mass transfer, mist elimination, and motionless mixer technology.

Koch-Glitsch (UK) Ltd., King Street, Fenton, Stoke-on-Trent, Staffordshire, UK

Tel: 44-1782-744561   Fax: 44-1782-744330

KODAK POLYCHROME GRAPHICS

401 Merritt 7, Norwalk, CT, 06851

Tel: (203) 845-7000   Fax: (203) 845-7113   www.kodak.com

Metal offset plates, coating specialties, graphic arts films.

Kodak Polychrome Graphics, Axis 1, Rhodes Way, Watford, Hertfordshire WD24 4FD, UK

Tel: 44-1923-233-366   Fax: 44-1923-227-802   Contact: Peter U. Blum

THE KOHLER COMPANY

444 Highland Drive, Kohler, WI, 53044

Tel: (920) 457-4441   Fax: (920) 459-1274   www.kohlerco.com

Plumbing products, ceramic tile and stone, cabinetry, furniture, engines, generators, switch gear and hospitality.

Kohler Engines, J.H. Hancox Ltd., Alchester Rd., Portway, Birmingham B48 7JP, UK

Tel: 44-1564-824343   Fax: 44-1564-824073

Kohler Engines, Command House, Unit 1, Elder Way & Waterside Drive, Langley Slough Berkshire SL3 6EP, UK

Tel: 44-1753-580-771   Fax: 44-1753-580-036

Kohler Power Systems International, London, UK

KOHN PEDERSEN FOX ASSOCIATES PC

111 West 57th Street, New York, NY, 10019

Tel: (212) 977-6500   Fax: (212) 956-2526   www.kpf.com

Engaged in architectural design and planning.

Kohn Pedersen Fox Intl., 13 Langley St., London WC2H 9JG, UK

Tel: 44-207-836-6668   Contact: Jim Outen

KOPPERS INDUSTRIES INC.

436 Seventh Ave., Pittsburgh, PA, 15219-1800

Tel: (412) 227-2000   Fax: (412) 227-2333   www.koppers.com

Construction materials and services; chemicals and building products.

Koppers UK Ltd., Meridian House, Normanby Road, Scunthorpe, North Lincolnshire DN15 8QX, UK

Tel: 44-1724-281-555

KORN/FERRY INTERNATIONAL

1800 Century Park East, Los Angeles, CA, 90067

Tel: (310) 843-4100   Fax: (310) 553-6452   www.kornferry.com

Engaged in executive search and management consulting.

Korn/Ferry International Ltd., Regent Arcade House, 252 Regent St., London W1R 5DA, UK

Tel: 44-207-312-3100   Fax: 44-207-312-3130

KOSTER KEUNEN INC.

1021 Echo Lake Rd., Box 69, Watertown, CT, 06795-0069

Tel: (860) 945-3333   Fax: (860) 945-0330   www.kosterkeunen.com

Mfr. natural waxes, vegetable waxes and petroleum waxes for the cosmetic, pharmaceutical, food and candle industries.

Captiva Chemicals, 2 Priors Close, Bray Maidenhead Berkshire SL6 2ER, UK

Tel: 44-1-628-544540   Fax: 44-1-628-544541   Contact: Roy Clarkson

KPMG CONSULTING INC.

1676 International Dr., McLean, VA, 22102

Tel: (703) 747-3000   Fax: (703) 747-8500   www.kpmg.com

Accounting and audit, tax and management consulting services.

KPMG International, 1 Puddle Dock, Blackfriars, London EC4V 3PD, UK

KPMG International, Richmond park House, 15 Pembroke Rd., Clifton Bristol BS8 3BG, UK

KPMG International, 2 Cornwall St., Birmingham B3 2DL, UK

KPMG International, St. James' Square, Manchester M2 6DS, UK

KPMG International, 8 Salisbury Square, London EC4V 8BB, UK

Tel: 44-207-311-1000   Fax: 44-207-311-3311   Contact: Geoff R. Russell, Ptnr.

KPMG International, 110 The Quayside, Newcastle-upon-Tyne NE1 3DX, UK

KPMG International, Richmond House, 1 Rumford Place, Liverpool L3 9QY, UK

KPMG International, 37 Hills Rd., Cambridge CB2 1XL, UK

KRAFT FOODS INTERNATIONAL, INC., DIV. PHILIP MORRIS COS.

Three Lakes Drive, Northfield, IL, 60093

Tel: (847) 646-2000   Fax: (847) 646-6005   www.kraftfoods.com

Processor, distributor and manufacturer of food products.

Kraft Jacobs Suchard, St. Georges House, Bayshill Rd., Cheltenham GL 50 3AE, UK

KRISPY KREME DOUGHNUTS, INC.

370 Knollwood St., Ste. 500, Winston Salem, NC, 27103

Tel: (336) 725-2981   Fax: (336) 733-3791   www.krispykreme.com

Donut shop franchise.

Krispy Kreme Doughnuts, Inc., London, UK

KROLL INC.

9023 Columbine Road, Eden Prairie, MN, 55347

Tel: (952) 937-1107   Fax: (952) 937-5815   www.knollworldwide.com

Mfr. of software and engaged in data recovery services.

Kroll UK, 25 Savile Row, London W1S 2AL, UK
Tel: 44-207-396-0000   Fax: 44-207-396-9966

Kroll UK, 1 Oxford Court, Bishopsgate, Manchester M2 3WR, UK
Tel: 44-161-228-6622   Fax: 44-161-228-1199

KROLL ONTRACK, INC.

9023 Columbine Rd., Eden Prairie, MN, 55347

Tel: (612) 937-1107   Fax: (612) 937-5815   www.krollontrack.com

Computer data evidence services company, rescuing lost or corrupted data, and software sales.

Ontrack Data International, Inc., The Pavillions, One Weston Road, Kiln Lane, Epsom Surrey KT17 1JG, UK
Tel: 44-1372-741999   Fax: 44-1372-741441

KRONOS INCORPORATED

297 Billerica Road, Chelmsford, MA, 01824

Tel: (978) 250-9800   Fax: (978) 367-5900   www.kronos.com

Mfr. timekeeping systems software.

Kronos Systems Ltd., 2 Carey Road, Wokingham, Berkshire RG40 2NP, UK
Tel: 44-118-978-9784   Fax: 44-118-978-2214

Kronos Systems Ltd., Ten Pound Walk, Doncaster, South Yorkshire DN4 5HX, UK
Tel: 44-130-232-3880   Fax: 44-1302-32-8883

K-SWISS INC.

31248 Oak Crest Dr., Westlake Village, CA, 91361

Tel: (818) 706-5100   Fax: (818) 706-5390   www.k-swiss.com

Mfr. casual and athletic shoes, socks and leisure apparel.

K-Swiss (UK) Ltd., Tannery House, 4 Middle Leigh Street, Somerset BA16 OLA, UK
Tel: 44-145-844-5502

KULICKE & SOFFA INDUSTRIES INC.

2101 Blair Mill Road, Willow Grove, PA, 19090

Tel: (215) 784-6000   Fax: (215) 659-7588   www.kns.com

Semiconductor assembly systems and services.

IMPS Ltd., Unit 4, Apex Business Park, Diplocks Way Hailsham, East Sussex BN27 3JU, UK

THE KULJIAN CORPORATION

3700 Science Center, Philadelphia, PA, 19104

Tel: (215) 243-1900   Fax: (215) 243-1909

Studies, design, engineering, construction management and site supervision.

The Kuljian Corp., 500 Chesham House, 150 Regent St., London WIR 5FA, UK

KURT SALMON ASSOCIATES (KSA)

1355 Peachtree Street NE, Atlanta, GA, 30309

Tel: (404) 892-0321   Fax: (404) 898-9590   www.kurtsalmon.com

Management consulting: consumer products, retailing.

Kurt Salmon Associates, 14/15 Conduit Street, 4/F, London W1R 9TG, UK

Kurt Salmon Associates Ltd., Bruce Court, 25 Hale Rd., Altrincham WA14 2EY, UK

THE L. S. STARRETT COMPANY

121 Crescent Street, Athol, MA, 01331

Tel: (978) 249-3551   Fax: (978) 249-8495   www.starrett.com

Mfr. measuring tools and precision instruments.

Starrett Precision Optical, Snaygill Industrial Estate, Skipton North Yorkshire BD23 2QR, UK

L-3 COMMUNICATIONS HOLDINGS, INC.

600 Third Avenue, New York, NY, 10016

Tel: (212) 697-1111   Fax: (212) 490-0731   www.L-3com.com

Design and manufacture of high-tech communications systems, including specialized flight recorders.

L-3 Communications Holdings UK, The Spirella Building, Letchworth Garden City, Hertfordshire SG6 4ET, UK

Tel: 44-1462-476444

LADAS & PARRY

26 West 61st Street, New York, NY, 10023

Tel: (212) 708-1800   Fax: (212) 246-8959   www.ladasparry.com

International law firm.

Ladas & Parry, High Holborn House, 52-54 High Holborn, London WC1V 6RR, UK

Tel: 44-207-242-5566   Fax: 44-207-405-1908

LANCER CORPORATION

6655 Lancer Blvd., San Antonio, TX, 78219

Tel: (210) 310-7000   Fax: (210) 310-7252   www.lancercorp.com

Mfr. beverage dispensing equipment.

Lancer Corporation UK, 17 Bembridge Gardens, Ruislip Middlesex HA4 7ER, UK

Tel: 44-189-567-2667   Fax: 44-189-563-7537

LANDAUER INC.

2 Science Road, Glenwood, IL, 60425-1586

Tel: (708) 755-7000   Fax: (708) 755-7035   www.landauerinc.com

Provider of radiation dosimetry services to hospitals, medical and dental offices, university and national laboratories, nuclear power plants and other industries.

Landauer Inc., 12 North Oxford Business Centre, Lakesmere Close, Kidlington, Oxford OX5 1LG, UK

Tel: 44-1-86-537-3008   Contact: Dr. T. Finnigan, Dir. European Operations

LANDEGGER INDUSTRIES GROUP

150 East 52nd Street, New York, NY, 10022

Tel: (212) 916-8000   Fax: (212) 916-8057   www.ligroup.com

Paper and pulp mill machinery.

Black Clawson Intl. Ltd., 20/26 Wellesley Rd., Croydon, Surrey CR9 2BT, UK

LANDIS GARDNER

20 East Sixth Street, Waynesboro, PA, 17268-2050

Tel: (717) 762-2161   Fax: (717) 765-5143   www.landisgardner.com

Engaged in the design and manufacture of precision cylindrical and centerless grinders, and single and double-disc grinding machines.

Landis Lund Ltd., Cross Hills, Keighley, Yorkshire BD20 7SD, UK

Tel: 40-1-535-633-211   Fax: 40-1-535-635-493   Contact: Roger Coverdale

LANDOR ASSOCIATES

Klamath House, 1001 Front Street, San Francisco, CA, 94111-1424

Tel: (415) 955-1400   Fax: (415) 365-3190   www.landor.com

International marketing consulting firm, engaged in brand strategy, design, naming, digital branding, print literature design and research services.

Landor Associates, 18 Clerkenwell Green, London EC1R ODP, UK

Tel: 44-207-880-8000   Fax: 44-207-880-8001   Contact: Richard Ford, Dir. Europe

LANDS' END INC.

1 Lands' End Lane, Dodgeville, WI, 53595

Tel: (608) 935-9341   Fax: (608) 935-4260   www.landsend.com

Clothing, home furnishings and mail order catalog company.

Lands' End U.K., Pillings Rd., Oakham, Rutland LE15 6N4, UK

Tel: 44-1572-722-553   Fax: 44-1572-722-554   Contact: Steve Miles, Mng. Dir.   Emp: 400

LANGER, INC..

450 Commack Road, Deer Park, NY, 11729

Tel: (631) 667-1200   Fax: (631) 667-1203   www.langerbiomechanics.com

Mfr. prescription foot orthotics and gait-related products.

Langer, Inc., The Green, Stoke-on-Trent ST10 1RL, UK

Tel: 44-1538-755-861   Fax: 44-1538-755-862   Contact: Paul Barcroft

LANIER WORLDWIDE, INC.

2300 Parklake Drive, N.E., Atlanta, GA, 30345

Tel: (770) 496-9500   Fax: (770) 938-1020   www.lanier.com

Specialize in digital copiers and multi-functional systems.

Lanier United Kingdom Ltd., Kingmaker House, Station Rd., New Barnet Herts EN5 1NZ, UK

Tel: 44-181-447-1001   Fax: 44-181-364-8646

Lanier United Kingdom Ltd., Eskdale Rd., Winnershire, Wokingham Berkshire RG41 5TS, UK

Tel: 44-181-969-9500   Fax: 44-181-927-2771

Lanier United Kingdom Ltd., Faraday Court, Unit 1B, Faraday Road, Crawley West Sussex RH10 2PX, UK

Tel: 44-1293-516-804   Fax: 44-1293-516-807

Lanier United Kingdom Ltd., Renown House, Merchants Quay, Salford Quays, Manchester M5 255, UK

Tel: 44-161-848-0110   Fax: 44-161-848-0220

LATHAM & WATKINS

633 West 5th St., Ste. 4000, Los Angeles, CA, 90071-2007

Tel: (213) 485-1234   Fax: (213) 891-8763   www.lw.com

International law firm.

Latham & Watkins, One Angel Court, London EC2R 7HJ, UK

Tel: 44-141-374-4444   Fax: 44-207-374-4460

LATIN AMERICAN FINANCIAL PUBLICATIONS INC.

2121 Ponce de Leon Blvd., Ste. 1020, Coral Gables, FL, 33134

Tel: (305) 448-6593   Fax: (305) 448-0718   www.latinfinance.com

Latin America business magazine.

Latin Finance, London, UK

Tel: 44-181-579-4836   Fax: 44-181-579-5057   Contact: Robert Logan

LATTICE SEMICONDUCTOR CORPORATION

5555 NE Moore Court, Hillsboro, OR, 97124-6421

Tel: (503) 268-8000   Fax: (503) 268-8347   www.latticesemi.com

Mfr. programmable logic devices (PLDs).

Lattice Semiconductor UK, Hartham Park, Corsham, Wiltshire SN13 ORP, UK

Tel: 44-1249-700-888   Fax: 44-1249-700-880

LAWSON SOFTWARE, INC.

380 St. Peter Street, St. Paul, MN, 55102-1302

Tel: (651) 767-7000   Fax: (651) 767-7141   www.lawson.com

Mfr. enterprise resource planning software.

Lawson Software, 1000 Great West Road, Brentford Middlesex TW8 9HR, UK

LA-Z-BOY INCORPORATED

1284 N. Telegraph Rd., Monroe, MI, 48162

Tel: (734) 242-1444   Fax: (734) 241-4422   www.lazboy.com

Furniture gallery stores; upholstered furniture including chairs, sofas, reclining sofas, and modular seating groups.

Centurion Furniture PLC, Centurion Bldg., Lancashire Enterprises Business Park, Leyland, Lancashire PR5 3JW, UK

Tel: 44-1772-450111   Fax: 44-1772-453511

LEACH HOLDING CORPORATION

315 Post Road West, Westport, CT, 06880-4739

Tel: (203) 226-6577   Fax: (203) 226-6577   www.leachintl.com

Mfr. and design electrical switching and control devices for the aerospace and rail industries.

Leach International, 11 Westlinks, Tollgate Business Park, Chandlers Ford, Southampton Hampshire SO53 3TG, UK

Tel: 44-2380-653535

LEARNING TREE INTERNATIONAL, INC.

6053 West Century Blvd., Los Angeles, CA, 90045-0028

Tel: (310) 417-9700   Fax: (310) 417-8684   www.learningtree.com

Information technology training services.

Learning Tree International Ltd. (UK), Mole Business Park, Leatherhead, Surrey KT22 7AD, UK

Tel: 44-1372-364600   Fax: 44-1372-364611   Contact: Staffan Windrup, Mng. Dir.   Emp: 109

LeBOEUF, LAMB, GREENE & MacRAE LLP

125 West 55th Street, 12th Fl., New York, NY, 10019

Tel: (212) 424-8000   Fax: (212) 424-8500   www.llgm.com

International law firm.

LeBoeuf, Lamb, Greene & MacRae LLP, No.1 Minster Court, Mincing Lane, London EC3R 7AA, UK

Tel: 44-207-459-5000   Fax: 44-207-459-5099   Contact: Peter Sharp

LECG, INC.

2000 Powell Street, Emeryville, CA, 94608

Tel: (510) 653-9800   Fax: (510) 653-9898   www.lecg.com

Provides legal and economic consulting services.

LECG Ltd., 40-43 Chancery Lane, London WC2A 1JA, UK

Tel: 44-1070269-0500   Fax: 44-107-269-0515

LECROY CORPORATION

700 Chestnut Ridge Road, Chestnut Ridge, NY, 10977

Tel: (845) 425-2000   Fax: (845) 425-8967   www.lecroy.com

Mfr. signal analyzers and electronic measurement systems.

LeCroy Ltd., 27 Blacklands Way, Abingdon Business Park, Abingdon Oxon OX14 1DY, UK

Tel: 44-1235-536973

LEGATO SYSTEMS, INC.

2350 West El Camino Real, Mountain View, CA, 94040

Tel: (650) 210-7000   Fax: (650) 210-7032   www.legato.com

Mfr. storage management software.

Legato Systems Northern Europe, Legato House, Waltham Road, White Waltham, Maidenhead SL6 3TP, UK

Tel: 44-1628-511811

LEGG MASON, INC.

100 Light St., Baltimore, MD, 21202

Tel: (410) 539-0000   Fax: (410) 539-4175   www.leggmason.com

Financial services; securities brokerage and trading, investment management, institutional and individual clients, investment and commercial mortgage banking.

Legg Mason Wood Walker, London, UK

LEGGETT & PLATT, INC.

1 Leggett Road, Carthage, MO, 64836

Tel: (417) 358-8131   Fax: (417) 358-5840   www.leggett.com

Mfr. components for bedding and furniture.

Gateway Textiles Ltd., Nottinghamshire, UK

John Pring & Son Limited, Elworth Wire Mills, Sandbach, Cheshire CW11 3JQ, UK

Tel: 44-1270-763331   Fax: 44-1270-768279

LEHMAN BROTHERS HOLDINGS INC.

*101 Hudson Street, Jersey City, NJ, 07302

Tel: (201) 524-2000   Fax: (201) 524-2000   www.lehman.com

Financial services, securities and merchant banking services.

Lehman Brothers - European Hdqtrs., One Broadgate, London EC2M 7HA, UK

Tel: 44-207-601-0011   Fax: 44-207-260-3165

LENNOX INTERNATIONAL

2140 Lake Park Blvd., Richardson, TX, 75080

Tel: (972) 497-5000   Fax: (972) 497-5299   www.lennoxinternational.com

Mfr. air conditioning and gas heating products.

Lennox Industries Ltd., PO Box 174, Westgate Interchange, Northampton NN5 5AG, UK

LEVI STRAUSS & COMPANY

1155 Battery St., San Francisco, CA, 94111-1230

Tel: (415) 544-6000   Fax: (415) 501-3939   www.levistrauss.com

Mfr. and distributor of casual wearing apparel, including jeans and sportswear.

Levi Strauss (UK) Ltd., Levi's House, Moulton Park, Northampton NN3 1QAG, UK

Tel: 44-1604-790-436   Fax: 44-1604-790-400   Contact: , Pres. Europe

LEVOLOR/HARDWARE GROUP, DIV. NEWELL RUBBERMAID

29 East Stephenson Street, Freeport, IL, 61032

Tel: (815) 235-4171   Fax: (815) 235-4171   www.americantool.com

Mfr. hand tools, cutting tools and power tool accessories.

ATC, Div. Levolor Hardware Group, Parkway Works, Sheffield S9 3BL, UK

Tel: 44-114-244-9066   Fax: 44-114-256-1788

LEXMARK INTERNATIONAL

740 W. New Circle Rd., Lexington, KY, 40550

Tel: (859) 232-2000   Fax: (859) 232-1886   www.lexmark.com

Develop, manufacture, supply of printing solutions and products, including laser, inkjet, and dot matrix printers.

Lexmark International Ltd., Westhorpe House, Little Marlow Road, Marlow Buckinghamshire Sl7 3RQ, UK

Tel: 44-8704-44-0044   Fax: 44-8704-44-0033

LIBERTY LIVEWIRE CORPORATION

520 Broadway, 5th Fl., Santa Monica, CA, 90401

Tel: (310) 434-7000   Fax: (310) 434-7001   www.libertylivewire.com

Engaged in post production.

Liberty Livewire UK, 71 Dean Street, London W1D 3SF, UK

Tel: 44-207-468-8635   Contact: Mark Hewitt, Pres.

LIBERTY MUTUAL GROUP

175 Berkeley Street, Boston, MA, 02117

Tel: (617) 357-9500   Fax: (617) 350-7648   www.libertymutual. com

Provides workers' compensation insurance and operates physical rehabilitation centers and provides risk prevention management.

Liberty Mutual Insurance UK, One Minster Court, 4/F, Mincing Lane, London EC3R 7YE, UK

LIGHTBRIDGE, INC.

67 South Bedford Street, Burlington, MA, 01803

Tel: (781) 359-4000   Fax: (781) 359-4500   www.lightbridge.com

Engaged in consulting for telecom companies.

Lightbridge Technologies Ltd., Knyvett House, The Causeway, Staines, Middlesex TW18 3BA, UK

Tel: 44-1784-898-551   Fax: 44-1784-898-553

LIGHTNIN

135 Mt. Read Blvd., PO Box 1370, Rochester, NY, 14611

Tel: (716) 436-5550   Fax: (716) 436-5589   www.lightnin-mixers.com

Mfr., sale and services industrial mixing machinery and aerators.

LIGHTNIN Mixers Ltd., London Road South, Poynton, Stockport, Cheshire SK12 1LH, UK

Tel: 44-1625-87-6421

ELI LILLY & COMPANY

Lilly Corporate Center, Indianapolis, IN, 46285

Tel: (317) 276-2000   Fax: (317) 277-6579   www.lilly.com

Mfr. pharmaceuticals and animal health products.

Eli Lilly and Company Limited, Dextra Court Chapel Hill, Basingstoke Hampshire RG21 5SY, UK

Eli Lilly and Company Limited, Earl Wood Manor, Windlesham Surrey GU20 6PH, UK

Eli Lilly and Company Limited, Fleming Road, Speke, Liverpool L24 9LN, UK

Eli Lilly Intl. Corp., Lilly House 40-42, 13 Hanover Square, London W1R 0PA, UK

Tel: 44-207-409-4800   Fax: 44-207-409-4818   Contact: Gerhard N. Mayr, Pres. Intl.

LIMITORQUE

PO Box 11318, 5114 Woodall Road, Lynchburg, VA, 24506

Tel: (804) 528-4400   Fax: (804) 845-9736   www.limitorque.com

Mfr./marketing/services electric valve actuators.

Limitorque International, Trinity House Kennet Side, Newbury, Berkshire RG14 5EH, UK

Tel: 44-1-635-46999 Fax: 44-1-635-36034

LINCOLN ELECTRIC HOLDINGS

22801 St. Clair Ave., Cleveland, OH, 44117-1199

Tel: (216) 481-8100   Fax: (216) 486-8385   www.lincolnelectric.com

Mfr. arc welding and welding related products, oxy-fuel and thermal cutting equipment and integral AC motors.

Lincoln Electric (UK) Ltd., 6th Fifth Drive, Attercliffe Sheffield S4 7UT, UK

Tel: 44-114-249-3601   Fax: 44-114-249-3602   Contact: John Herold, Plant Mgr.

Lincoln Electric (UK) Ltd., Mansfield Road, Aston Sheffield S26 2BS, UK

Tel: 44-114-287-2401   Fax: 44-114-287-2582   Contact: Anthony Reid, Mng. Dir.

LINCOLN NATIONAL CORPORATION

1500 Market St., Ste. 3900, Philadelphia, PA, 19102-2112

Tel: (215) 448-1400   Fax: (215) 448-3962   www.lfg.com

Provides annuities, life insurance, 401(k) plans, life-health reinsurance, mutual funds, institutional investment management and financial planning and advisory services.

Lincoln Financial Group (LFG), Barnett Way, Barnwood, Gloucester GL4 3RZ, UK

Tel: 44-1452-374500

LINEAR TECHNOLOGY CORPORATION

1630 McCarthy Blvd., Milpitas, CA, 95035

Tel: (408) 432-1900   Fax: (408) 434-6441   www.linear-tech.com

Mfr. linear integrated circuit chips.

Linear Technology (UK) Ltd., The Coliseum Business Centre, Riverside Way, Camberley, Surrey GU15 3YL, UK

Tel: 44-1276-677676   Fax: 44-1276-64851

LINKAGE SOLUTIONS, INC.

1 Forbes Road, Lexington, MA, 02421

Tel: (781) 862-4030   Fax: (781) 862-2355   www.linkageinc.com

Engaged in human resources and training consulting services.

Linkage International, 16-20 The Causeway, Teddington Middlesex TW 11 OHE, UK

Tel: 44-208-977-9277

LIONBRIDGE TECHNOLOGIES, INC.

950 Winter St., Waltham, MA, 02451

Tel: (781) 434-6000   Fax: (781) 434-6034   www.lionbridge.com

Provides solutions for worldwide deployment of technology and content.

Lionbridge UK, 200 Brook Drive, Green Park, Reading Berkshire RG2 6UB, UK

VeriTest Cheshire, PO Box 13, The Heath, Runcorn, Cheshire WA7 4QF, UK

LITTELFUSE, INC.

800 East Northwest Hwy, Des Plains, IL, 60016

Tel: (847) 824-1188   Fax: (847) 391-0434   www.littelfuse.com

Mfr. fuses and circuit protectors.

Littelfuse UK Ltd., 3 Rutherford Road, Stephenson Industrial Estate, Washington Tyne and Wear NE37 3HX, UK

Tel: 44-191-415-8181

LIZ CLAIBORNE INC.

1441 Broadway, 22nd Fl., New York, NY, 10018

Tel: (212) 354-4900   Fax: (212) 626-1800   www.lizclaiborne.com

Apparel manufacturer.

Liz Claiborne Inc., Watford, UK

LNP ENGINEERING PLASTICS

475 Creamery Way, Exton, PA, 19341

Tel: (610) 363-4500   Fax: (610) 363-4749   www.geplastics.com

Mfr. thermoplastic composites.

General Electric Plastics, Old Hall Road Sale, Cheshire M33 2HG, UK

Tel: 44-161-905-5000

LOCKHEED MARTIN CORPORATION

6801 Rockledge Drive, Bethesda, MD, 20817

Tel: (301) 897-6000   Fax: (301) 897-6652   www.imco.com

Design/mfr./management systems in fields of space, defense, energy, electronics and technical services.

CalComp Europe Ltd., 176 Lutto Road, Chatham Kent ME4 5BP, UK

Tel: 44-1634-828385   Fax: 44-1634-828386

Lockheed Martin IMS, 20 Maltby Street, London SE1 3PG, UK

Tel: 44-207-252-1119   Fax: 44-207-252-1389

Lockheed Martin Intl. Ltd., 2 Castle End Farm Business Park, Castle End Road, Ruscomb Reading, Berkshire RG10 9XQ, UK

Tel: 44-207-344-0500   Fax: 44-207-734-341474

Lockheed Martin Intl. S.A., Communications Centre London, Alliance House, 29/30 High Holborn, London WC1V 6AZ, UK

Tel: 44-207-405-2969   Fax: 44-207-413-8120   Contact: K. Khambatta, Mgr.

Lockheed Martin Intl. S.A., 8th Fl., Berkeley Square House 9-14, Berkeley Square, London W1X 5LA, UK

Tel: 44-207-412-0555   Fax: 44-207-412-0547

Lockheed Martin UK Ltd., PO Box 41, North Harbour Portsmouth, Hampshire PO6 3AU, UK
Tel: 44-1-705-563406   Fax: 44-1-705-214889

MountainGate Data Systems UK Ltd., 20 Little Basing, PO Box 5064, Basingstoke Hants G24 8JA, UK
Tel: 44-1256-464-767   Fax: 44-1256-59748   Contact: M. D. Phillips, Mgr.

LORAL SPACE & COMMUNICATIONS LTD.
600 Third Ave., New York, NY, 10016
Tel: (212) 697-1105   Fax: (212) 338-5662   www.loral.com
Marketing coordination: defense electronics, communications systems.

Loral CyberStar, Pinewood Studios, Pinewood Road, Iver Buckinghamshire SLO ONH, UK

Loral Skynet, 9 Clifford Street, London W1X 1RB, UK
Tel: 44-207-534-7950   Fax: 44-207-534-7999

LORD CORPORATION
2000 West Grandview Blvd, Erie, PA, 16514
Tel: (814) 868-0924   Fax: (814) 486-4345   www.lordcorp.com
Mfg. adhesives, coatings, chemicals, film products.

Lord Corp., Ltd., Stretford Motorway Estate, Barton Dock Road, Stretford, Manchester M32 OZH, UK
Tel: 44-161-865-8048   Fax: 44-161-865-0096

Lord Corp., Ltd., Stretford Motorway Estate, Barton Dock Road, Stretford, Manchester M32 OZH, UK
Tel: 44-161-865-8048   Fax: 44-161-865-0096

Lord Corporation (Europe) Ltd., Coliseum Business Park, Ste. 14, Riverside Way, Watchmoor Park, Camberley Surrey GU15 3YL, UK
Tel: 44-1276-61776

Lord Corporation Birmingham Metals, Garrison Street, Birmingham B9 4BN, UK
Tel: 44-121-7666022   Fax: 44-121-667485

Lord Corporation Metech Europe Limited, Unit 2, Dunston Place, Dunston Road, Chesterfield, Derbyshire, England S41 8XA, UK
Tel: 44-1-246-260920   Fax: 44-1-246-260807

THE LOWE GROUP
One Dag Hammarskjold Plaza, New York, NY, 10017
Tel: (212) 605-8000   Fax: (212) 605-4705   www.interpublic.com
Full-service, integrated marketing communications company and advertising agency.

The Lowe Group, 4 Eaton Gate, London SW1W 9BJ, UK
Tel: 44-207-225-3434

LSI LOGIC CORPORATION
1551 McCarthy Blvd., Milpitas, CA, 95035
Tel: (408) 433-8000   Fax: (408) 954-3220   www.lsilogic.com
Develop and manufacture semiconductors.

LSI Logic Europe PLC, Greenwood House, London Road, Bracknell, Berkshire RE12 2UB, UK
Tel: 44-1-1344-426544   Fax: 44-1-1344-481039

LSI Logic Europe PLC, 2 Mount Pleasant, Cambridge CB3 OBL, UK

LTX CORPORATION
LTX Park, University Ave., Westwood, MA, 02090
Tel: (617) 461-1000   Fax: (617) 326-4883   www.ltx.com
Design/mfr. computer-controlled semiconductor test systems.

LTX (Europe) Ltd., Woking Business Park, Albert Dr., Woking Surrey GU21 5JY, UK

THE LUBRIZOL CORPORATION
29400 Lakeland Blvd., Wickliffe, OH, 44092-2298
Tel: (440) 943-4200   Fax: (440) 943-5337   www.lubrizol.com
Mfr. chemicals additives for lubricants and fuels.

Lubrizol (UK) Ltd., Palm Court, 4 Heron Sq., Richmond-upon-Thames, Surrey TW9 1EW, UK
Tel: 44-181-940-6060

Lubrizol Great Britain Ltd., Hampshire, UK

Tel: 44-1329-825-823

LUCENT TECHNOLOGIES, INC.

600 Mountain Ave., Murray Hill, NJ, 07974-0636

Tel: (908) 582-3000   Fax: (908) 582-2576   www.lucent.com

Design/mfr. wide range of public and private networks, communication systems and software, data networking systems, business telephone systems and microelectronics components.

Lucent Technologies - Network Systems, Swindon Rd., Malmesbury, Wiltshire SN16 9NA, UK

Tel: 44-1666-822-861   Fax: 44-1666-824-515   Contact: Sam Baxter, PR Mgr.

Lucent Technologies Bus. Communications Systems, Octel House, Ancells Road, Fleet Hampshire GU13, UK

Lucent Technologies Bus. Communications Systems Bell Labs, Northgate House, Staple Gardens, Winchester Hants S023 8SR, UK

Lucent Technologies Wireless Ltd., Greenways Business Park, Unit 7, Bellinger Close, Malmesbury Rd., Chippenham SN15 1BN, UK

Tel: 44-1666-832-740   Fax: 44-1666-832-181

Lucent Technologies/Bell Labs, Swindon Road, Malmesbury Wiltshire SN16 9NA, UK

Lucent Technologies/Bell Labs, Europe House, The Southwood Crescent, Farnborough Hants GU14 0NR, UK

Tel: 44-1252-391600   Fax: 44-1252-376966

Lucent Technologies/Bell Labs Global Commercial Markets, 101 Wigmore Street, 1/F, London W1H 9AB, UK

Tel: 44-207-647-8000

Microelectronics Europe, Microelectronics House, Kingswood Kings Ride, Ascot Berkshire SL5 8AD, UK

Network Systems, 101 Wedmore St., 2nd Fl., London WIH 9AB, UK

LYONDELL CHEMICAL COMPANY

1221 McKinney St., Houston, TX, 77010

Tel: (713) 652-7200   Fax: (713) 309-2074   www.lyondell.com

Mfr. polymers and petrochemicals.

Lyondell Chemical European Hdqrts., Lyondell House, Bridge Avenue, Maidenhead Berkshire SL6 1YP, UK

Tel: 44-1626-77-5000

M/A-COM INC.

1011 Pawtucket Boulevard, Lowell, MA, 01853-3295

Tel: (978) 442-5000   Fax: (978) 442-5354   www.macom.com

Mfr. radio frequency (RF) and microwave integrated circuits and IP Networks to the wireless telecommunications and defense-related industries.

M/A-COM Ltd., Div. Tyco, Centennial Court, Easthampstead Road, Bracknell Berkshire RG12 1YQ, UK

Tel: 44-1344-869595   Fax: 44-1344-300020

MacANDREWS & FORBES GROUP INC.

35 East 62nd St., New York, NY, 10021

Tel: (212) 688-9000   Fax: (212) 572-8400

Investment holding company.

MacAndrews & Forbes Co. Inc., Pembroke House, 44 Wellesley Rd., Croydon CR9 3QE, UK

MacDERMID INC.

245 Freight Street, Waterbury, CT, 06702-0671

Tel: (203) 575-5700   Fax: (203) 575-7900   www.macdermid.com

Chemicals processing for metal industrial, plastics, electronics cleaners, strippers.

MacDermid G.B. Ltd., Stafford Park, 18 Telford, Shropshire TF3 3BN, UK

Tel: 44-1952-290292   Fax: 44-1952-290375

MACROMEDIA, INC.

600 Townsend Street, San Francisco, CA, 94103-4945

Tel: (415) 252-2000   Fax: (415) 626-9603   www.macromedia.com

Engaged in web publishing.

Macromedia Europe (UK), Century Court, Millennium Way, Bracknell, Berkshire RG12 2XN, UK

Tel: 44-1344-458-600

MACROVISION CORPORATION

1341 Orleans Dr., Sunnyvale, CA, 94089

Tel: (408) 743-8600   Fax: (408) 743-8610   www.macrovision.com

Provider of digital rights management technologies for the home video, enterprise software and consumer interactive software markets.

GLOBEtrotter Europe Ltd., Vision House, Priory Court, Wellfield Road, Preston Brook, Cheshire WA7 3FR, UK

Tel: 44-1928-579-789   Fax: 44-1928-579-799   Contact: David Simmons

Macrovision Europe, Woodley House, Crockhamwell Road, Woodley, Reading, Berkshire RG5 3JP, UK

Tel: 44-118-969-1111   Fax: 44-118-969-1161   Contact: David Simmons

Macrovision UK Ltd., Charlwood House, The Runway, South Ruislip HA4 6SE, UK

Tel: 44-208-839-0400   Fax: 44-208-839-0409

MACTAC

4560 Darrow Road, Stow, OH, 44224

Tel: (330) 688-1111   Fax: (330) 688-2540   www.mactac.com

Mfr. pressure sensitive tapes, films and label materials.

MACtac U.K., The Britannia Trade Centre Units 4-6, Ryehill Close Lodge Farm, Northhampton NN5 7UA, UK

MADE2MANAGE SYSTEMS, INC.

9002 Purdue Road, Indianapolis, IN, 46268

Tel: (317) 532-7000   Fax: (317) 872-6454   www.made2manage.com

Mfr. enterprise resource planning software.

Made2Manage Systems Ltd., Knyvett House, The Causeway, Staine, Middlesex TW18 3BA, UK

MAGNETEK

10900 Wilshire Blvd., Suite 850, Los Angeles, CA, 90024

Tel: (310) 208-1980   Fax: (310) 208-6133   www.magnetek.com

Mfr. fractional horsepower electric motors.

MagneTek Universal Electric Ltd., PO Box 8, Peatham Rd., Gainsborough, Lincolnshire DN21 1XU, UK

MAGNETROL INTERNATIONAL

5300 Belmont Road, Downers Grove, IL, 60515-4499

Tel: (630) 969-4000   Fax: (630) 969-9489   www.magnetrol.com

Mfr. level and flow instrumentation.

Magnetrol International, Regent Business Centre, Jubilee Rd., Burgess Hill, W. Sussex RH15 9T1, UK

Tel: 44-1444-871-313   Fax: 44-1444-871-317   Contact: Paul Sayers, Gen. Mgr.

MAIL-WELL, INC.

8310 S. Valley Highway, Ste. 400, Englewood, CO, 80112-5806

Tel: (303) 790-8023   Fax: (303) 566-7466   www.mail-well.com

Engaged in commercial printing of custom envelopes and labels for direct mail, billing and catalogs.

Mail-Well Label, Bingswood Industrial Estate, Whaley Bridge, Stockport SK23 7SP, UK

Mail-Well Label, Unit 4, City Estates, Corngreaves Road, Cardley Heath, West Midlands B64 7EP, UK

Mail-Well Label, Victoria House, Victoria Road, Eccleshill Bradford, West Yorkshire BD2 2DD, UK

MALLINCKRODT BAKER, INC.

222 Red School Lane, Phillipsburg, NJ, 08865

Tel: (908) 859-2151   Fax: (908) 859-9318   www.mallbaker.com

Mfr. of high purity chemicals and related products and services.

Mallinckrodt Baker UK, 107/112 Leadenhall Street, London EC3A 4AH, UK

Tel: 44-1908-506000   Fax: 44-1908-503290

MALLINCKRODT PHARMACUTICALS, INC.

675 McDonnell Blvd., Hazelwood, MO, 63042

Tel: (314) 654-2000   Fax: (314) 654-5380   www.mallinckrodt.com

Mfr. products for respiratory care.

Mallinckrodt Northhampton, #11 North Portway Close, Round Spinney, Northhampton, UK

Tel: 44-1604-646132

Mallinckrodt UK Limited, 10 Talisman Business Centre, London Road, Bicester Oxfordshire OX6 0JX, UK
Tel: 44-1869-322700   Fax: 44-1869-321890

THE MANAGEMENT NETWORK GROUP, INC.
7300 College Blvd., Ste. 302, Overland Park, KS, 66210
Tel: (913) 345-9315   Fax: (913) 451-1845   www.tmng.com
Provides management consulting services.

TMNG Europe, Ltd., 90 Long Acre, Convent Garden, London WC2E 9RZ, UK
Tel: 44-207-283-3144

MANHATTAN ASSOCIATES, INC.
2300 Windy Ridge Pkwy., Ste. 700, Atlanta, GA, 30339
Tel: (770) 955-7070   Fax: (770) 955-0302   www.manh.com
Mfr. supply chain management software.

Manhattan Associates, Downshire Way, 2 The Arena, Bracknell, Berkshire RG12 1PU, UK
Tel: 44-1344-318000

THE MANITOWOC COMPANY, INC.
500 South 16th St., Manitowoc, WI, 54220
Tel: (920) 684-4410   Fax: (920) 683-8129   www.manitowoc.com
Mfr. cranes, ice-making machinery and contract products; ship repair and conversion.

Manitowoc Europe Ltd., St. James Mill Rd., Northampton NN5 5JW, UK

MANPOWER INTERNATIONAL INC.
5301 N. Ironwood Rd., PO Box 2053, Milwaukee, WI, 53201-2053
Tel: (414) 961-1000   Fax: (414) 961-7081   www.manpower.com
Temporary help, contract service, training and testing.

Manpower Plc. - International Hdqtrs., International House, 66 Chiltern St., London W1M 1PR, UK
Tel: 44-207-224-6688   Fax: 44-207-224-5253

MANUGISTICS INC.
2115 East Jefferson Street, Rockville, MD, 20852
Tel: (301) 984-5000   Fax: (301) 984-5094   www.manugistics.com
Computer software development services.

Manugistics International Ltd., Royal Albert House, Sheet St., Windsor, Berkshire SL4 1BE, UK

MAPICS, INC.
1000 Windward Concourse Pkwy., Alpharetta, GA, 30005
Tel: (678) 319-8000   Fax: (678) 319-8000   www.mapics.com
Mfr. software.

MAPICS UK, 6 Highlands Court, Cranmore Avenue, Solihull, West Midlands B90 4LE, UK

MARATHON LE TOURNEAU COMPANY
PO Box 2307, Longview, TX, 75606
Tel: (903) 237-7000   Fax: (903) 236-6533   www.letourneau-inc.com
Mfr. heavy construction and mining machinery equipment.

Le Tourneau Ltd., Blockwood-Hodge, Hunsbury, Hill Ave., Northampton NN4 9QT, UK

MARATHON OIL COMPANY
5555 San Felipe Road, Houston, TX, 77056
Tel: (713) 629-6600   Fax: (713) 296-2952   www.marathon.com
Oil and gas exploration.

Marathon Oil (UK) Ltd., Marathon House, 174 Marylebone Rd., London NW1 5AT, UK

MARCONI DATA SYSTEMS INC.
1500 Mittel Blvd., Wood Dale, IL, 60191
Tel: (630) 860-7300   Fax: (630) 616-3657   www.videojet.com
Mfr. computer peripherals and hardware, state-of-the-art industrial ink jet marking and coding products.

Videojet, Div. Marconi Data Systems, 153 Dixons Hill Road, Welham Green, Hertfordshire AL9 7JE, UK
Tel: 44-1707-275-844   Fax: 44-1707-272-492   Contact: Bill Eshmont

MARITZ INC.

1375 North Highway Drive, Fenton, MO, 63099

Tel: (636) 827-4000   Fax: (636) 827-3312   www.maritz.com

Engaged in travel and marketing services.

The Research Business International, Holford Mews, Cruikshank Street, London WC1X 9HW, UK

MARK IV INDUSTRIES INC.

501 John James Audubon Pkwy., PO Box 810, Amherst, NY, 14226-0810

Tel: (716) 689-4972   Fax: (716) 689-1529   www.mark-iv.com

Mfr. of engineered systems and components utilizing mechanical and fluid power transmission, fluid transfer, and power systems and components.

Dayco Europe Ltd., The Washington Centre, Halesowen Rd., Dudley West Midlands DY2 9RE, UK

Tel: 44-1384-245200   Fax: 44-1384-240222

MARKEL CORPORATION

4521 Highwoods Parkway, Glen Allen, VA, 23060-6148

Tel: (804) 747-0136   Fax: (804) 965-1600   www.markelcorp.com

Engaged in specialty insurance.

Markel International, The Markel Building, 49 Leadenhall Street, London EC3A 2EA, UK

Tel: 44-207-953-6000   Contact: Jeremy D. Cooke

MARKEM CORPORATION

150 Congress Street, Keene, NH, 03431

Tel: (603) 352-1130   Fax: (603) 357-1835   www.markem.com.

Mfr. and sales of industrial marking, print machinery and hot stamping foils.

Markem Systems Ltd., Astor Road & Eccles New Road, Salford Manchester M5 3DA, UK

Tel: 44-161-789-5500   Fax: 44-161-707-5566

Markem Systems, Ltd., Ladywell Trading Estate, Eccles Ne Rd., PO Box 3, Salford, Lancashire M5 2DA, UK

Tel: 44-161-789-5500   Fax: 44-161-707-5566

MARKET FACTS INC.

3040 Salt Creek Lane, Arlington Heights, IL, 60005

Tel: (847) 590-7000   Fax: (847) 590-7010   www.marketfacts.com

Market research services.

Market Facts, Inc., Parker Tower 43-49, Parker Street, London WC2B 5PS, UK

Tel: 44-207-430-6132   Contact: Virginia Weil

MARKETBRIDGE

4550 Montgomery Avenue, Bethesda, MD, 20814

Tel: (301) 907-3800   Fax: (301) 907-3282   www.market-bridge.com

Provides consulting services.

Marketbridge Ltd., 33 St. James's Square, London SW1Y 4SJ, UK

MARLEY COOLING TOWER COMPANY

7401 West 129th Street, Overland Park, KS, 66213

Tel: (913) 664-7400   Fax: (913) 664-7641   www.marleyct.com

Cooling and heating towers and waste treatment systems.

Marley Davenport Ltd., Gregory's Bank, Worcestershire WR3 8AB, UK

Tel: 44-1905-720-200   Fax: 44-1905-720-201

MARRIOTT INTERNATIONAL INC.

10400 Fernwood Rd., Bethesda, MD, 20817

Tel: (301) 380-3000   Fax: (301) 380-5181   www.marriott.com

Hotel services.

Marriott Courtyard Milton Keynes, London Rd., Newport Pagnell, Buckinghamshire, Milton Keynes MK16 0JA, UK

Tel: 44-1908-613688   Fax: 44-1908-617335

Marriott Courtyard Northampton, Bedford Road, Northampton NN4 7YF, UK

Tel: 44-1604-622777   Fax: 44-1604-635454

MARS INC.

6885 Elm Street, McLean, VA, 22101-3810

Tel: (703) 821-4900   Fax: (703) 448-9678   www.mars.com

Mfr. candy, snack foods, rice products and cat food.

Mars Ltd., Dundee Rd., Trading Estate, Slough, Buckinghamshire, UK

MARSH & McLENNAN COS INC.

1166 Ave. of the Americas, New York, NY, 10036-2774

Tel: (212) 345-5000   Fax: (212) 345-4808   www.marshmac.com

Insurance agents/brokers, pension and investment management consulting services.

Global Risk Management Consultancy, Aldgate House, 33 Aldgate High St., London EC3N 1AQ, UK

Tel: 44-207-945-7978   Fax: 44-207-945-7955

J&H Marsh & McLennan Ltd., Aldgate House, 33 Aldgate High St., London EC3N 1AQ, UK

Tel: 44-207-945-7700   Fax: 44-207-481-4277   Contact: Patrick Franklin-Adams

J&H Marsh & McLennan UK Ltd., The Bowring Bldg., Tower Place, London EC3P 3BE, UK

Tel: 44-207-357-1000   Fax: 44-207-929-2705   Contact: Dan Jones

Sedgwick Group, Sackville House, 143-152 Finchurch Street, London EC3N 6BN, UK

Tel: 44-207-377-3456   Fax: 44-207-377-3199   Contact: R. White-Cooper, CEO

William M. Mercer Fraser Ltd., Burwood House, 16 Caxton St., London SW1H 0QV, UK

MARSH BELLOFRAM

State Route 2, Box 305, Newell, WV, 26050

Tel: (304) 387-1200   Fax: (304) 387-1212   www.marshbellofram.com

Distributor of pressure gauges, valves and transmitters.

Bellofram Europe, 9 Castle Park, Queens Drive, Nottingham NG2 1AH, UK

Tel: 44-115-993-3300   Fax: 44-115-993-3301   Contact: Steve Clissold

MARY KAY COSMETICS INC.

16251 No. Dallas Pkwy, Dallas, TX, 75248

Tel: (972) 687-6300   Fax: (972) 687-1609   www.marykay-cosmetic.com

Mfr. and direct sales of cosmetics and toiletries.

Mary Kay Cosmetics (U.K.) Ltd., 28 Saville Row, London W1S 2EU, UK

Tel: 44-207-758-4900   Fax: 44-207-758-4909

MASCO CORPORATION

21001 Van Born Road, Taylor, MI, 48180

Tel: (313) 274-7400   Fax: (313) 374-6666   www.masco.com

Mfr. faucets, cabinets, locks and numerous home improvement, building and home furnishings products.

A&J Gummers, Birmingham, UK

Ametex UK Ltd., New England House, E. Riddlesden Bus. Park, Bradford Rd., Keighley W. Yorkshire BD20 5JH, UK

Avocet Hardware Plc, Brighton, UK

Berglen Group, Ltd., Waxford Business Park, Caxton Way, Watford Hertfordshire WD1 8ZF, UK

Tel: 44-1923-690100

Moore Group Ltd., Queen Mary House, Thorp Arch Trading Estate, Wetherby, West Yorkshire LS23 7BR, UK

Tel: 44-1937-842394

MASONITE CORPORATION

One South Wacker Drive, Chicago, IL, 60606

Tel: (312) 750-0900   Fax: (312) 750-0958   www.masonite.com

Mfr. hardboard, softboard and molded products.

Masonite Europe UK, Jason House Kerry Hill, Horseforth Leeds LS18 4JR, UK

Tel: 44-113-2587-689

MATRIXONE, INC.

210 Littleton Road, Westford, MA, 01886

Tel: (978) 589-4000　　　Fax: (978) 589-5700　　　www.matrixone.com

Mfr. software.

MatrixOne Limited, Oak House, Harry Weston Road, Binley Business Park, Coventry CV3 2UB, UK

MATTEL INC.

333 Continental Blvd., El Segundo, CA, 90245-5012

Tel: (310) 252-2000　　　Fax: (310) 252-2179　　　www.mattel.com

Mfr. toys, dolls, games, crafts and hobbies.

Fisher-Price Ltd., Fisher-Price House, Oaklands Park, Fishponds Rd., Wokingham RG11 2FD, UK

Kiddicraft Ltd., 13 Bridge Rd., Southall UB2 4AG, UK

Mattel United Kingdom Ltd., Meridian West, Leicester LE3 2WJ, UK

MAXIM INTEGRATED PRODUCTS, INC.

120 San Gabriel Drive, Sunnyvale, CA, 94086

Tel: (408) 737-7600　　　Fax: (460) 737-7194　　　www.maxim-ic.com

Mfr. analog and mixed signal integrated circuits.

Maxim Integrated Products UK Ltd., 3, Theale Technology Centre, Theale, Reading RG7 4XX, UK

MAXON CORPORATION

201 East 18th Street, Muncie, IN, 47302

Tel: (765) 284-3304　　　Fax: (765) 286-8394　　　www.maxoncorp.com

Industry combustion equipment and valves.

Maxon Combustion Systems Ltd., Chantry House, High Street, Coleshil B46 3BP, UK

Tel: 44-1675-464334　Fax: 44-1675-467285

MAXTOR CORPORATION

500 McCarthy Blvd., Milpitas, CA, 95035

Tel: (408) 894-5000　　　Fax: (408) 432-4510　　　www.maxtor.com

Mfr. develops and markets hard disk drives for desktop computer systems.

Maxtor Europe Ltd., Herts, UK

MAXXAM INC.

5847 San Felipe, Ste. 2600, Houston, TX, 77057

Tel: (713) 975-7600　　　Fax: (713) 267-3701

Holding company for aluminum and timber products and real estate industries.

MAXXAM Inc., UK

MAYER, BROWN, ROWE & MAW

190 S. LaSalle Street, Chicago, IL, 60603

Tel: (312) 782-0600　　　Fax: (312) 701-7711　　　www.mayerbrown.com

Engaged in international law.

Mayer, Brown & Platt, Bucklersbury House, 3 Queen Victoria St., London EC4N 8EL, UK

Tel: 44-207-246-6200　Fax: 44-207-329-4465

MAYFRAN INTERNATIONAL, INC.

PO Box 43038, Cleveland, OH, 44143

Tel: (440) 461-4100　　　Fax: (440) 461-5565　　　www.mayfran.com

Mfr. conveying systems, filtration equipment and separators that facilitate material handling and coolant recovery for automobile manufacturers and machine tool builders.

Mayfran UK Ltd, Orchard Court V, Binley Business Park, Harry Weston Road, Coventry CV3 2TQ, UK

MAYTAG CORPORATION

403 West Fourth Street North, Newton, IA, 50208

Tel: (515) 792-8000　　　Fax: (515) 787-8376　　　www.maytagcorp.com

Mfr./sales of large appliances, ovens, dishwashers, refrigerators and washing machines.

Maytag International, Hayes Gate House, 27 Uxbridge Rd., Middlesex UB4 OJN, UK

Tel: 44-181-569-3030

MBIA INC.

113 King Street, Armonk, NY, 10504

Tel: (914) 273-4545   Fax: (914) 765-3299   www.mbia.com

Provides investment and treasury management services and insurance for municipal bonds.

MBIA Insurance Corporation, 1 Great St. Helen's, 2/F, London EC3A 6HX, UK

Tel: 44-20-7920-6363   Contact: Jack Caouette

MBNA CORPORATION

1100 N. King Street, Wilmington, DE, 19801

Tel: (302) 453-9930   Fax: (302) 432-3614   www.mbna.com

Credit card issuer dealing primarily with VISA and MasterCard, home equity loans and property and casualty insurance.

MBNA Europe Bank Limited, Chester Business Park, Wrexham Road, Chester CH4 9FB, UK

McCANN-ERICKSON WORLDGROUP

750 Third Ave., New York, NY, 10017

Tel: (212) 697-6000   Fax: (212) 984-3575   www.mccann.com

International advertising and marketing services.

Magic Hat, Haddon House, 2-4 Fitzroy Street, London W1A 1AT, UK

McCann-Erickson, McCann-Erickson House, 7-11 Herbrand Street, London WC1N 1EX, UK

Tel: 44-207-837-3737

McCann-Erickson Manchester Ltd., PO Box 28, Bonis Hall, Prestbury, Macclesfield, Cheshire SK10 4EF, UK

McCann-Erickson Network Ltd., 6 King Street, Bristol BS 14EQ, UK

McCORMICK & COMPANY, INC.

18 Loveton Circle, Sparks, MD, 21152-6000

Tel: (410) 771-7301   Fax: (410) 527-8289   www.mccormick.com

Manufactures, markets and distributes spices, seasonings, flavors and other specialty food products.

McCormick U.K. PLC, Thame Rd., Haddenham, Aylesbury, Buckinghamshire HP 17 8LB, UK

McDERMOTT INTERNATIONAL INC.

1450 Poydras Street, PO Box 60035, New Orleans, LA, 70160-0035

Tel: (504) 587-5400   Fax: (504) 587-6153   www.mcdermott.com

Provides energy, engineering and construction services for industrial, utility, and hydrocarbon processing facilities, and to the offshore oil and natural gas industries.

J. Ray McDermott SA, One Albemarle St., London W1X 3HF, UK

McDERMOTT WILL & EMERY

227 W. Monroe Street, Chicago, IL, 60606-5096

Tel: (312) 372-2000   Fax: (312) 984-7700   www.mwe.com

Engaged in international law.

McDermott Will & Emery LLC, 7 Bishopsgate, London EC2N 3AQ, UK

Tel: 44-207-577-6900   Fax: 44-207-577-6950   Contact: John Reynolds

McDONALD'S CORPORATION

McDonald's Plaza, Oak Brook, IL, 60523

Tel: (630) 623-3000   Fax: (630) 623-7409   www.mcdonalds.com

Fast food chain stores.

McDonald's Corp., London, UK

THE McGRAW-HILL COMPANIES

1221 Avenue of the Americas, New York, NY, 10020

Tel: (212) 512-2000   Fax: (212) 512-2703   www.mccgraw-hill.com

Books, magazines, information systems, financial service, publishing and broadcast operations.

DRI Europe Ltd., Wimbledon Bridge House, 1 Hartfield Rd., Wimbledon SW19 3RU, UK

McGraw-Hill Book Co. UK Ltd., McG-H Intl. Training Systems, Shoppenhangers Rd., Maidenhead, Berkshire SL6 2Q1, UK

McGraw-Hill Intl. Publications Co. Ltd., Wimbledon Bridge House, 1 Hartfield Rd., Wimbledon SW19 3RU, UK

McKINSEY & COMPANY

55 East 52nd Street, New York, NY, 10022

Tel: (212) 446-7000   Fax: (212) 446-8575   www.mckinsey.com

Management and business consulting services.

McKinsey & Company, London - BTO, 1 Jermyn St., London SW1Y 4UH, UK

Tel: 44-207-839-8040   Fax: 44-207-873-9777

McKinsey & Company, One Jermyn St., London SW1Y 4UH, UK

Tel: 44-207-839-8040   Fax: 44-207-873-9777

MEASUREMENT SPECIALTIES, INC.

80 Little Falls Road, Fairfield, NJ, 07004

Tel: (973) 808-1819   Fax: (973) 808-1787   www.msiusa.com

Designer and manufacturer of sensors and sensor-based consumer products.

Measurement Specialties (UK) Ltd., 543 Ipswich Road, Slough Berkshire SL1 4EG, UK

Tel: 44-1753-53-7622

MECHANICAL DYNAMICS, INC.

2300 Traverwood Drive, Ann Arbor, MI, 48105

Tel: (734) 994-3800   Fax: (734) 994-6418   www.adams.com

Mfr. Adams prototyping software for functional virtual prototyping solutions.

Mechanical Dynamics International Ltd., 12 Clarendon Street, Warwickshire CV32 5ST, UK

Tel: 441-926-420-230

MEDEX ASSISTANCE CORPORATION

9515 Deereco Road, 4th Fl., Timonium, MD, 21093

Tel: (410) 453-6300   Fax: (410) 453-6301   www.medexassist.com

Medical and travel related assistance service.

Medex Assistance (Europe) PLC, Norwood House, 9 Dyke Rd., Brighton, East Sussex BN1 3FE, UK

MEDIA 100 INC.

450 Donald Lynch Blvd., Marlborough, MA, 01752

Tel: (508) 460-1600   Fax: (508) 481-8627   www.media100.com

Mfr. digital editing software and hardware.

Media 100 Ltd., 13 Westminster Ct., Hipley St., Old Woking, Surrey GU22 9LQ, UK

MEDIALINK WORLDWIDE INC.

708 Third Ave., New York, NY, 10017

Tel: (212) 682-8300   Fax: (212) 682-2370   www.medialink.com

Produces and distributes video and news releases for corporate and institutional clients worldwide, and public relations services.

Medialink Worldwide Inc., 7 Fitzroy Square, London W1P 5AL, UK

Tel: 44-207-554-2700   Fax: 44-207-554-2710   Contact: Jim Gold

THE MEDICINES COMPANY

1 Cambridge Center, Cambridge, MA, 02142

Tel: (617) 225-9099   Fax: (617) 225-2397   www.themedicinescompany.com

Engaged in the development of pharmaceuticals.

The Medicines Company, Buxton Court, 3 West Way, Botley, Oxford OX2 0SZ, UK

Tel: 44-1865-297-900

MEDICUS GROUP INTERNATIONAL

1675 Broadway, New York, NY, 10019

Tel: (212) 468-3100   Fax: (212) 468-3222   www.medicusgroup.com

Healthcare communications company engaged in professional advertising, sales promotion, global branding and launch planning.

Medicus UK London, 516 Wandsworth Road, London SW8 3JX, UK

MEDIWARE INFORMATION SYSTEMS, INC.

11711 West 79th Street, Lenexa, KS, 66214

Tel: (913) 307-1000   Fax: (913) 307-1111   www.mediware.com

Mfr. data management software.

Mediware Information Systems UK, 1 Repton Court, Basildon Essex SS13 1lN, UK

MEDTRONIC, INC.

7000 Central Ave. N.E., Minneapolis, MN, 55432-5604

Tel: (763) 514-4000   Fax: (763) 514-4879   www.medtronic.com

Mfr., sales and service of electrotherapeutic medical devices, specializing in implantable and invasive therapies.

Medtronic Ltd., Sherbourne House, Suite One, Croxley Business Centre, Watford WD1 8YE, UK

MELLON FINANCIAL CORPORATION

One Mellon Bank Center, Pittsburgh, PA, 15258-0001

Tel: (412) 234-5000   Fax: (412) 236-1662   www.mellon.com

Commercial and trade banking and foreign exchange.

Mellon Europe Ltd., Princess House, 1 Suffolk Lane, London EC4R 0AN, UK

Tel: 44-207-623-0800

Mellon London Branch, Princess House, 1 Suffolk Lane, London EC4R 0AN, UK

Newton Management Ltd., London, UK

Tel: 44-207-323-9000   Contact: Stewart W. Newton

Pareto Partners, 271 Regent St., London W1R 8PP, UK

Premier Administration Ltd., 5 Rayleigh Rd., Hutton, Brentwood, Essex CM13 1AA, UK

Tel: 44-127-722-7300

MEMC ELECTRONIC MATERIALS, INC.

501 Pearl Drive, St. Peters, MO, 63376

Tel: (636) 474-5500   Fax: (636) 474-5161   www.memc.com

Mfg. and distribution of silicon wafers.

MEMC Electronic Materials (UK) Ltd., Witan Court, 272 Witan Gate West, Central Milton Keynes, Buckinghamshire MK9 1EJ, UK

Tel: 44-1908-398500   Fax: 44-1908-398508

MEMOREX CORPORATION

10100 Pioneer Blvd., Ste. 110, Santa Fe Springs, CA, 90670

Tel: (562) 906-2800   Fax: (562) 906-2848   www.memorex.com

Magnetic recording tapes, etc.

Memorex UK Ltd., 96-102 Church St., Staines, Middlesex, UK

Memorex UK Ltd., Hounslow House, 730 London Rd., Hounslow Middlesex, UK

MENASHA CORPORATION

1645 Bergstrom Road, Neenah, WI, 54957-0367

Tel: (920) 751-1000   Fax: (920) 751-1236   www.menasha.com

Mfr. packaging and paperboard products.

Poly Hi Solidur UK, Sub. Menasha, Halifax Road, Todmorden, Lancashire OL14 5QQ, UK

MENTOR CORPORATION

201 Mentor Drive, Santa Barbara, CA, 93111

Tel: (805) 879-6000   Fax: (805) 967-7108   www.mentorcorp.com

Mfr. medical devices including breast implants.

Mentor Medical Systems Ltd., U.K., The Woolpack, Church Street, Wantage Oxon OX12 8BL, UK

Tel: 44-1235-768758

MENTOR GRAPHICS

8005 SW Boeckman Road, Wilsonville, OR, 97070-7777

Tel: (503) 685-7000   Fax: (503) 685-1202   www.mentorg.com

Develop/mfr. software tools for embedded systems market.

Mentor Graphics (UK) Ltd, Rivergate, Newbury Business Park, London Road, Basingstoke RG14 2QB, UK

Tel: 44-1635-811411

MERCER MANAGEMENT CONSULTING INC.

1166 Ave. of the Americas, New York, NY, 10036

Tel: (212) 345-3400   Fax: (212) 345-7414   www.mercermc.com

Provides clients with counsel in such areas as corporate and business strategy and growth planning, organizational development, and market and operations enhancement.

Mercer Management, 1-3 Grosvenor Place, London SW1X 7HJ, UK

MERCK & COMPANY, INC.

One Merck Drive, PO Box 100, Whitehouse Station, NJ, 08889-0100

Tel: (908) 423-1000   Fax: (908) 423-2592   www.merck.com

Pharmaceuticals, chemicals and biologicals.

Merck, Sharp & Dohme Ltd., Herford Rd., Hoddesdon Herts, Hertfordshire EN11 9BU, UK

MERCURY COMPUTER SYSTEMS, INC.

199 Riverneck Rd., Chelmsford, MA, 01824

Tel: (978) 256-1300   Fax: (978) 256-3599   www.mc.com

Mfr. digital signal processing systems for the defense and medical imaging markets.

Mercury Computer Systems Ltd., Bramley, UK

MERCURY INTERACTIVE CORPORATION

1325 Borregas Ave., Sunnyvale, CA, 94089

Tel: (408) 822-5200   Fax: (408) 822-5300   www.merc-int.com

Mfr. computer software to decipher and eliminate "bugs" from systems.

Mercury Interactive (UK) Ltd., 16 Coliseum Business Centre, Riverside Way, Watchmoor Park - Camberley, Surrey GU15 3YL, UK

Tel: 44-1276-808200   Fax: 44-1276-29134

MERRILL CORPORATION

1 Merrill Circle, St. Paul, MN, 55108

Tel: (651) 646-4501   Fax: (651) 646-5332   www.merrillcorp.com

Engaged in document management and data services.

Merrill UK, 101 Finsbury Pavement, London EC2A 1ER, UK

MERRILL LYNCH & COMPANY, INC.

World Financial Center, 250 Vesey Street, New York, NY, 10281-1332

Tel: (212) 236-1000   Fax: (212) 449-2892   www.ml.com

Security brokers and dealers, investment and business services.

Mercury Asset Management Co., London, UK

Merrill Lynch Europe, Lansdowne Building, 2 Lansdowne Road, Croydon CR0 2BX, UK

Merrill Lynch Europe, Quayside House, 3/F, 110 Quayside, Newcastle Upon Tyne NE1 3DX, UK

Merrill Lynch Europe PLC, Merrill Lynch Financial Centre, 2 King Edward Street, London EC1A 1HQ, UK

Tel: 44-207-628-1000

Merrill Lynch International, 20 Farringdon Rd., London EC1M 3NH, UK

Tel: 44-207-772-1000

Merrill Lynch International Bank, 33 Chester St., London SW1X 7XD, UK

Tel: 44-207-628-1000   Fax: 44-207-867-4040

META GROUP, INC.

208 Harbor Drive, PO Box 120061, Stamford, CT, 06912-0061

Tel: (203) 973-6700   Fax: (203) 359-8066   www.metagroup.com

Engaged in research and consulting, focusing on information technology and business transformation strategies.

META Group, META Group House, 2 King's Road, Hampshire GU51 3SZ, UK

Tel: 44-1252-819494   Fax: 44-1252-819595

METAL IMPROVEMENT COMPANY

10 Forest Ave., Paramus, NJ, 07652

Tel: (201) 843-7800   Fax: (201) 843-3460   www.metalimprovement.com

Mfr. shot peening.

Shot Peening, Div. Metal Improvement, Unit 37, Pallion Industrial Estate, Sunderland,Tyne and Wear SR4 6SN, UK

Shot Peening, Div. Metal Improvement, Ascot Drive, Derby DE24 8ST, UK

Shot Peening, Div. Metal Improvement, Hawarden Airport, Chester Road, Chester CH4 0BZ, UK

Shot Peening, Div. Metal Improvement, Hambridge Lane, Newbury, Berkshire RG14 5TU, UK

METASOLV, INC.

5560 Tennyson Pkwy., Plano, TX, 75024

Tel: (972) 403-8300   Fax: (972) 403-8333   www.metasolv.com

Mfr. software.

MetaSolv Software, Ltd., 90 Long Acre, Convent Garden, London WC2E 9R2, UK

METASTORM, INC.

836 Ritchie Hwy., Ste. 14, Severna Park, MD, 21146

Tel: (410) 647-9691   Fax: (410) 647-9717   www.metastorm.com

Mfr. business process management software.

Metastorm UK, Central House, 1 Alwyne Road, Wimbledon, London SW19, UK

METHODE ELECTRONICS INC.

7401 W. Wilson Ave., Chicago, IL, 60656

Tel: (708) 867-6777   Fax: (708) 867-6999   www.methode.com

Mfr. electronic components.

Methode Electronics Europe Ltd., 17 Bishop Street, Cherry Orchard, Shrewsbury Shropshire SY2 5HA, UK

Methode Electronics Europe Ltd., Vale of Leven Industrial Estate, Dumbarton G82 3PD, UK

METROLOGIC INSTRUMENTS, INC.

90 Coles Road, Blackwood, NJ, 08012

Tel: (856) 225-8100   Fax: (856) 228-6673   www.metrologic.com

Mfr. and sales of hologram based, bar code scanner systems.

Metrologic Instruments UK Limited, 58 Tempus Business Centre, Kingsclere Road, Basingstoke, Hampshire RG21 6XG, UK

METROMEDIA FIBER NETWORK, INC.

360 Hamilton Avenue, White Plains, NY, 10601

Tel: (914) 421-6700   Fax: (914) 421-6777   www.mfn.com

Mfr. urban fiber-optic networks for telecommunications providers.

Metromedia Fiber Network Inc., 7-11a Curtain Road, London EC2A 3LT, UK

Tel: 44-207-377-4700

METRON TECHNOLOGY

1350 Old Bayshore Highway, Ste. 210, Burlingame, CA, 94010

Tel: (650) 401-4600   Fax: (650) 373-1135   www.metrontech.com

Global provider of marketing, sales, service and support solutions to semiconductor materials and equipment suppliers and semiconductor manufacturers.

Metron Technology (United Kingdom) Ltd., 6 & 7 Grafton Way, Basingstoke, Hants RG22 6HY, UK

METROPOLITAN LIFE INSURANCE COMPANY

1 Madison Ave., New York, NY, 10010-3603

Tel: (212) 578-3818   Fax: (212) 252-7294   www.metlife.com

Insurance and retirement savings products and services.

Albany Life Assurance Co. Ltd., Metropolitain House, 3 Darkes Lane, Potters Bar Hertsford EN6 1AJ, UK

Tel: 44-852-2973-4000   Fax: 44-852-2826-9189   Contact: Joseph Yau, CEO & Mng. Dir.

GFM Intl. Investors Ltd., Orion House, 11th floor, 5 Upper St. Martin's Lane, London WC2H 9EA, UK

Tel: 44-207-957-9000   Fax: 44-207-957-9020   Contact: Ralph F. Verni, Chmn. & CEO

MICREL, INCORPORATED

2180Fortune Drive, San Jose, CA, 95131

Tel: (408) 944-0800   Fax: (408) 944-0510   www.micrel.com

Designer and mfr. of analog integrated circuits.

Micrel Europe, 21 Old Newtown Rd., Newbury RG14 7DP, UK

Tel: 44-1635-524455   Fax: 44-1635-524466

MICRO AGE, INC.

1330 West Southern Avenue, Tempe, AZ, 85282-1896

Tel: (480) 366-2000   Fax: (480) 966-7339   www.microage.com

Computer systems integrator, software products and telecommunications equipment.

MicroAge EMEA Regional Headquarters, Unit 7, Argent Centre, Silverdale Road, Haye, Middlesex UB3 3BS, UK

Tel: 44-181-587-3636   Fax: 44-181-587-3619

MICRO WAREHOUSE, INC.

535 Connecticut Ave., Norwalk, CT, 06854

Tel: (203) 899-4000   Fax: (203) 899-4203   www.warehouse.com

Catalog computer sales.

Micro Warehouse Ltd., Horizon One Studio Way, Borehamwood, Hertshire WD6 6WH, UK

Tel: 44-870-516-8674   Fax: 44-870-514-3338

MICROCHIP TECHNOLOGY INCORPORATED

2355 West Chandler Boulevard, Chandler, AZ, 85224

Tel: (602) 786-7200   Fax: (602) 899-9210   www.microchip.com

Mfr. electronic subassemblies and components.

AZ Microchip Technology Ltd., Microchip House, 505 Eskdale Rd., Wokingham, Berkshire RG41 5TU, UK

Tel: 44-118-921-5800   Fax: 44-118-921-5820

MICROMERITICS INSTRUMENT CORPORATION

One Micromeritics Drive, Norcross, GA, 30093-1877

Tel: (770) 662-3620   Fax: (770) 662-3696   www.micromeritics.com

Mfr. analytical instruments.

Micromeritics Ltd., Unit 2, Chestnut House, 178-182 High Street North, Dunstable Bedfordshire LU6 1AT, UK

Tel: 44-1582-475248

MICROMUSE INC.

139 Townsend Street, San Francisco, CA, 94107

Tel: (415) 538-9090   Fax: (415) 538-9091   www.micromuse.com

Mfr. software for information technology.

Micromuse Ltd., Disraeli House, 90 Putney Bridge Road, London SW18 1DA, UK

Tel: 44-208-875-9500

MICRON TECHNOLOGY, INC.

8000 S. Federal Way, Boise, ID, 83707-0006

Tel: (208) 368-4000   Fax: (208) 368-4435   www.micron.com

Mfr. random-access memory chips and semi-conductor memory components.

Micron Europe Limited, Micron House, Wellington Business Park, Dukes Ride, Crowthorne Berkshire RG45 6LS, UK

Tel: 44-1344-750750   Fax: 44-1344-750710

Micron Europe Ltd., UK Design Centre, Orchard Court, 1 Warfield Road, Bracknell Berkshire RG12 2XJ, UK
Tel: 44-1344-383-300   Fax: 44-1344-383-353

MICROSOFT CORPORATION
One Microsoft Way, Redmond, WA, 98052-6399

Tel: (425) 882-8080   Fax: (425) 936-7329   www.microsoft.com

Computer software, peripherals and services.

Microsoft United Kingdom Ltd., Microsoft Campus, Thames Valley Park, Reading RG6 1WG, UK
Tel: 44-870-601-0100   Fax: 44-870-602-0100

MICROSTRATEGY INCORPORATED
1861 International Drive, McLean, VA, 22102

Tel: (703) 848-8600   Fax: (703) 848-8610   www.microstrategy.com

Mfr. business intelligence software.

MicroStrategy Ltd., St. Martin's Place, 51 Bath Road, Slough Berkshire SL1 3UF, UK
Tel: 44-1753-826100

MIDAMERICAN ENERGY HOLDINGS
666 Grand Ave., Des Moines, IA, 50303

Tel: (515) 281-2900   Fax: (515) 281-2389   www.midamerican.com

Geothermal power; generates, transmits, and distributes electricity.

Northern and Yorkshire Electric, Carliol House Market Street, Newcastle upon Tyne NE1 6NE, UK

MILACRON INC.
2090 Florence Ave., Cincinnati, OH, 45206

Tel: (513) 487-5000   Fax: (513) 487-5057   www.milacron.com

Metalworking and plastics technologies.

Ferromatik Milacron (U.K.) Ltd., Carrwood Road, Chesterfield Trading Estate, Chesterfield Derbyshire S41 9QB, UK
Tel: 44-1246-260666 Fax: 44-1246-260474   Contact: David Lister

MILBANK, TWEED, HADLEY & McCLOY LLP
1 Chase Manhattan Plaza, New York, NY, 10005-1413

Tel: (212) 530-5000   Fax: (212) 530-5219   www.milbank.com

International law practice.

Milbank, Tweed, Hadley & McCloy, Dashwood House, 69 Old Brad St., London EC2M 1QS, UK
Tel: 44-207-448-3000 Fax: 44-207-448-3029

MILGO-TIMEPLEX, INC.
1619 N. Harrison Pkwy., Bldg. D, Sunrise, FL, 33323

Tel: (954) 846-6434   Fax: (954) 846-3275   www.milgo.com

Mfr. sale and services data communications equipment for network solutions.

Timeplex Ltd., 77 Boston Manor Rd., Brentford, Middlesex TW8 95W, UK

Timeplex Ltd., Timeplex House, North Parkway, Leeds LS14 6PX, UK

MILLENNIUM CHEMICALS INC.
PO Box 7015, 230 Half Mile Road, Red Bank, NJ, 07701-7015

Tel: (732) 933-5000   Fax: (732) 933-5200   www.millenniumchem.com

Mfr. specialty chemicals for paints, perfumes, and flavorings.

Millennium Chemicals Inc., PO Box 26, Grimsby, North East Lincolnshire DN40 2PR, UK

MILLENNIUM PHARMACEUTICALS, INC.
75 Sidney Street, Cambridge, MA, 02139

Tel: (617) 679-7000   Fax: (617) 374-7788   www.mlnm.com

Mfr. pharmaceuticals.

Millennium Pharmaceuticals UK, Granta Park, Great Abington, Cambridge CB1 6ET, UK
Tel: 44-1223-722404

MILLER ELECTRIC MFG. COMPANY

1635 W. Spencer Street, Appleton, WI, 54912-1079

Tel: (920) 734-9821   Fax: (920) 735-4125   www.millerwelds.com

Mfr. arc welding machines.

ITW Welding Products, Unit B1, Deakins Business Park, Blackburn Road, Egerton Bolton BL7 9RP, UK

Tel: 44-1204-593-493   Fax: 44-1204-598-066

MILLIMAN USA, INC.

1301 Fifth Avenue, Ste. 3800, Seattle, WA, 98101

Tel: (206) 624-7940   Fax: (206) 340-1380   www.milliman.com

Engaged in actuarial consulting services.

Milliman UK, Finsbury Tower, 103-105 Bunhill Row, London EC1Y 8LZ, UK

Tel: 44-207-847-6100

MILLIPORE CORPORATION

80 Ashby Road, PO Box 9125, Bedford, MA, 01730

Tel: (781) 533-6000   Fax: (781) 533-3110   www.millipore.com

Mfr. flow and pressure measurement and control components; precision filters, hi-performance liquid chromatography instruments.

Millipore (UK) Ltd., The Boulevard, Blackmoor Lane, Watford Hertshire WD1 8YW, UK

MILLWARD BROWN INTELLIQUEST

1250 South Capital, Bldg. 1, Ste. 600, Austin, TX, 78746-6464

Tel: (512) 329-0808   Fax: (512) 329-0888   www.intelliquest.com

Provides information-based services designed exclusively to help technology companies and Internet marketers.

Millward Brown IntelliQuest, Shand House, 14-20 Shand St., London SE1 2ES, UK

Tel: 44-207-357-9255   Fax: 44-207-403-1680

MILTON ROY COMPANY

201 Ivyland Road, Ivylan, PA, 18974

Tel: (215) 441-0800   Fax: (215) 293-0468   www.miltonroy.com

Mfr. medical and industry equipment and process control instruments.

Milton Roy UK Ltd., Oaklands Business Centre, Wokingham Berks RG41 2FD, UK

Tel: 44-11-89-77-10-66   Fax: 44-11-89-77-11-98   Contact: Martin Eagle

MINDSPEED TECHNOLOGIES

4000 MacArthur, Newport Beach, CA, 92660-3095

Tel: (949) 579-3000   Fax: (945) 579-3020   www.mindspeed.com

Mfr. integrated circuits.

Mindspeed Technologies, 100 Longwater Avenue, Green Park, Reading Berkshire RG2 6GP, UK

Tel: 44-118-920-9500

MINOLTA-QMS INC.

One Magnum Pass, PO Box 81250, Mobile, AL, 36618

Tel: (205) 633-4300   Fax: (205) 633-4866   www.qms.com

Mfr. of high-performance color and monochrome document printing solutions for office automation, electronic publishing, graphic design, and advanced imaging applications.

Minolta-QMS UK Ltd., Old Bridge House, The Hythe, Staines Middlesex TW18 3JF, UK

MINTEQ INTERNATIONAL INC.

395 Grove City Road, Slippery Rock, PA, 16057

Tel: (724) 794-3000   Fax: (724) 794-4455   www.mineralstech.com

Mfr./market specialty refractory and metallurgical products and application systems.

MINTEQ Ltd., Aldwarke Road, Rawmarsh, Rotherham, SouthYorkshire S65 3SR, UK

Tel: 44-1709-528-816   Fax: 44-1709-710-073   Contact: R. Brown, Mng. Dir.   Emp: 84

MISYS HEALTHCARE SYSTEMS

8529 Six Forks Road, Raleigh, NC, 27615

Tel: (919) 847-8102   Fax: (919) 846-1555   www.misyhealthcare.com

Mfr. practice management software.

Misys Healthcare UK, 67 Victoria Road, Burgess Hill, West Sussex RH15 9TR, UK

Tel: 44-1444-872628

MKS INSTRUMENTS INC.

6 Shattuck Road, Andover, MA, 01810-2449

Tel: (978) 975-2350   Fax: (978) 933-0750   www.astex.com

Provider of process infrastructure products and technologies that increase productivity in gas- and vacuum-based manufacturing.

ENI Europe, Highway House Norreys Drive, Maidenhead, Berks SL6 4BN, UK

Spectra SensorTech, Ltd, Cowley Way, Crewe, Cheshire CW1 6AG, UK

MOAI TECHNOLOGIES, INC.

260 Alpha Drive, Pittsburgh, PA, 15238

Tel: (412) 968-5490   Fax: (412) 968-5496   www.moai.com

Mfr. supply chain management software.

Moai Technologies UK, 8 Lincoln's Inn Fields, 3/F, London WC2A 3BP, UK

Tel: 44-207-841-1089

MODEM MEDIA, INC.

230 East Avenue, Norwalk, CT, 06855

Tel: (203) 299-7000   Fax: (230) 299-7060   www.modemmedia.com

Provides on-line marketing and consulting services.

Modem Media, Inc., 183 Eversholt Street, London NW1 1BU, UK

Tel: 44-20-7874-9400   Fax: 44-20-7874-9555   Contact: Tim Sexton, Mng. Dir.

MODINE MANUFACTURING COMPANY

1500 DeKoven Ave., Racine, WI, 53403

Tel: (262) 636-1200   Fax: (262) 636-1424   www.modine.com

Mfr. heat-transfer products.

Modine Intl. Sales Ltd., Raines House, Denby Dale Rd., Wakefield West Yorkshire WF1 1HR, UK

MODUS MEDIA, INC.

690 Canton Street, Westwood, MA, 02090

Tel: (781) 407-2000   Fax: (781) 407-3800   www.modusmedia.com

Engaged in outsourced manufacturing, fulfillment and distribution services.

Modus Media International Limited, 4-6 Grayshill Road, Westfield Industrial Estates, Cumbernauld G68 9HQ, UK

Tel: 44-1236-850300   Fax: 44-1236-850383

MOLECULAR DEVICES CORPORATION

1311 Orleans Drive, Sunnyvale, CA, 94089

Tel: (408) 747-1700   Fax: (408) 747-3601   www.moleculardevices.com

Engaged in the development and manufacture of pharmaceuticals.

Molecular Devices ltd., 135 Wharfedale Road, Winnersh Triagle, Winnersh, Wokingham RG41 5RB, UK

Tel: 44-118-944-8000

MOLEX INC.

2222 Wellington Court, Lisle, IL, 60532

Tel: (630) 969-4550   Fax: (630) 969-1352   www.molex.com

Mfr. electronic, electrical and fiber optic interconnection products and systems, switches, application tooling.

Molex Inc., Molex House, Millennium Centre, Farnham Surrey GU9 7XX, UK

MOLTECH POWER SYSTEMS

9062 South Rita Road, Tucson, AZ, 85747

Tel: (520) 799-7500 Fax: (520) 799-7501 www.moltechpower.com

Provides rechargeable battery solutions for industry applications.

Moltech Power Systems Ltd., Unit 20, Loomer Road, Chesterton Newcastle, Staffs ST5 7LB, UK

Tel: 44-1782-566688 Fax: 44-1782-565910

MONSANTO

800 N. Lindbergh Boulevard, St. Louis, MO, 63167

Tel: (314) 694-1000 Fax: (314) 694-7625 www.monsanto.com

Life sciences company focusing on agriculture, nutrition, pharmaceuticals, health and wellness and sustainable development.

Monsanto Co. Chemical Group, PO Box 53, Lane End Road, High Wycombe Bucks HP12 4HL, UK

PBI Cambridge Ltd., Maris Lane, Cambridge CB2 2LQ, UK

MOODY'S INVESTOR SERVICES, INC.

99 Church St., New York, NY, 10007

Tel: (212) 553-1658 Fax: (212) 553-0462 www.moodys.com

Publishes credit ratings.

Moody's Investors Service Ltd., 2 Minister Court, Mincing Lane, London EC3R 7XB, UK

Tel: 44-207-772 5370 Contact: Michael Foley

MOOG INC.

300 Jamison Road, East Aurora, NY, 14052-0018

Tel: (716) 652-2000 Fax: (716) 687-4471 www.moog.com

Mfr. precision control components and systems.

Moog Controls Ltd., Ashchurch, Tewkesbury, Gloucester GL20 8NA, UK

MORGAN ADVANCED MATERIALS AND TECHNOLOGY, INC.

441 Hall Ave., Saint Mary's, PA, 15857

Tel: (814) 781-1573 Fax: (814) 781-9262 www.mamat.com

Mfr. carbon graphite and silicon carbide components.

Morgan Advanced Materials and Technology, Quay Lane, Gosport, Hampshire PO12 4LJ, UK

J. P. MORGAN CHASE & CO. INC.

270 Park Ave., New York, NY, 10017

Tel: (212) 270-6000 Fax: (212) 622-9030 www.jpmorganchase.com

Provides integrated financial solutions for institutions and individuals worldwide, including asset management, investment banking and commercial banking.

J. P. Morgan Chase & Co., 125 London Wall, London EC2Y 5AJ, UK

J. P. Morgan Chase & Co., Woolgate House, Coleman St., London EC2P 2HD, UK

J. P. Morgan Chase & Co., Trinity Tower, 9 Thomas More St., London E1 9YT, UK

J. P. Morgan Chase & Co., 80 Coleman St., London EC2R 5BJL, UK

J. P. Morgan Chase & Co., Chaseside, Bournemouth, Dorset BH7 7DB, UK

J. P. Morgan Chase & Co., Colville House, 32 Curzon St., London W1Y 8AL, UK

J. P. Morgan Chase & Co., Chaseside, Bournemouth, Dorset BH7 7DB, UK

J. P. Morgan Chase & Co., 3 & 4th Fls., 68 Upper Thames St., London EC4V 3BJ, UK

J. P. Morgan Chase & Co., Colville House, 32 Curzon St., London W1Y 8AL, UK

MORGAN STANLEY DEAN WITTER & CO.

1585 Broadway, New York, NY, 10036

Tel: (212) 761-4000 Fax: (212) 761-0086 www.msdw.com

Securities and commodities brokerage, investment banking, money management, personal trusts.

Morgan Stanley & Co. International Ltd., 25 Cabot Square, Canary Wharf, London E14 4QA, UK

Morgan Stanley Dean Witter, 1 Appold St., 6th fl., Broadgate 5, London EC2A 2AA, UK

MORGAN, LEWIS & BOCKIUS LLP

1701 Market St., Philadelphia, PA, 19103-6993

Tel: (215) 963-5000   Fax: (215) 963-5299   www.morganlewis.com

International law firm.

Morgan, Lewis & Bockius LLP, 2 Gresham Street, London EC2V 7PE, UK

Tel: 44-207-710-5500   Fax: 44-207-710-5600   Contact: Thomas J. Benz, Mng. Ptnr.   Emp: 52

MORRISON & FOERSTER

425 Market Street, San Francisco, CA, 94105

Tel: (415) 268-7000   Fax: (415) 268-7522   www.mofo.com

Engaged in international law.

Morrison & Foerster, 21-26 Garlick Hill, London EC4V 2AU, UK

MOTIVE COMMUNICATIONS, INC.

12515 Research Blvd., Bldg., Austin, TX, 78759-2220

Tel: (512) 339-8335   Fax: (512) 339-9040   www.motive.com

Mfr. customer service software.

Motive Communications UK Ltd., 1 Northumberland Avenue, Trafalgar Square, London WC2N 5BW, UK

Tel: 44-208-986333

MOTOROLA, INC.

1303 East Algonquin Road, Schaumburg, IL, 60196

Tel: (847) 576-5000   Fax: (847) 538-5191   www.motorola.com

Mfr. communications equipment, semiconductors and cellular phones.

Motorola Information Systems, York Stream House, Suite 6, 2nd Fl., St. Ives Rd., Maidenhead Berkshire SL6 1RD, UK

Tel: 44-1628-586100   Fax: 44-1628-586101

Motorola Ltd., Taylors Rd., Stotfold, Hitchin Hertshire SG5 4AY, UK

Tel: 44-1462-831111   Fax: 44-1462-835879

Motorola Ltd. - European Research, Jays Close, Viables Industrial Estate, Basingstoke Hampshire RG22 4PD, UK

Tel: 44-1256-358211   Fax: 44-1256-469838

MP HOLDINGS INC., McCALL PATTERN

11 Penn Plaza, New York, NY, 10001

Tel: (212) 465-6800   Fax: (212) 465-6831   www.mccallpattern.com

Fashion patterns.

McCall Pattern Co., UK

MPS GROUP, INC. (MODIS PROFESSIONAL SERVICES)

1 Independent Dr., Jacksonville, FL, 32202-5060

Tel: (904) 360-2000   Fax: (904) 360-2814   www.modispro.com

Engaged in staffing for professional services and information technology.

Badenoch & Clark, 520-522 Elder Gate, Milton Keynes MK9 1LS, UK

Badenoch & Clark, 16-18 New Bridge Street, London EC4V 6AU, UK

Tel: 44-207-583-0073   Fax: 44-207-353-3908

Badenoch & Clark, 51-63 Dunsgate, Manchester M3 2BW, UK

Badenoch & Clark, 16-18 New Bridge Street, London EC4V 6AU, UK

Tel: 44-207-583-0073   Fax: 44-207-353-3908

Badenoch & Clark, 26 Albion Square, 2/F, Leeds LS1 6HX, UK

Tel: 44-113-231-4545   Fax: 44-113-231-4531

Badenoch & Clark, 16-18 Wellesley Road, Croyden CRO 2DD, UK

Tel: 44-181-686-6337

Badenoch & Clark, 14 Waterloo Street, Birmingham B2 STX, UK

Tel: 44-181-686-6337

Modis Solutions, 130 City Road, London EC1V 2NW, UK

Tel: 44-207-426-8300

Modis Solutions, 25-26 Brenkley Way, Newcastle NE13 6DS, UK

Modis Solutions, 24030 King Street, Watford WD1 8BP, UK

MPSI SYSTEMS INC.

4343 South 118 East Avenue, Tulsa, OK, 74146

Tel: (918) 877-6774   Fax: (918) 254-8764   www.mpsisys.com

Computer software, information system services.

MPSI Systems Ltd., Castlemead Lower Castle Street, Bristol BS1 3AG, UK

Tel: 44-117-917-5170   Fax: 44-117-917-5179

MQSOFTWARE, INC.

7575 Golden Valley Road, Ste. 140, Minneapolis, MN, 55427

Tel: (763) 546-9080   Fax: (763) 546-9083   www.mqsoftware.com

Mfr. enterprise application software.

MQSoftware Limited, Surrey Tech Centre, 40 Occam Road, Surrey Research Park, Guildford, Surrey GU2 7YG, UK

Tel: 44-1483-295400

MRO SOFTWARE, INC.

100 Crosby Drive, Bedford, MA, 01730

Tel: (781) 280-2000   Fax: (781) 280-0207   www.mrosoftware.com

Design/sales of enterprise asset maintenance software.

MRO Software, 88-100 Chertsey Road, Woking, Surrey GU2 15BJ, UK

Tel: 44-1-48-372-7000

MSC.SOFTWARE CORPORATION

2 MacArthur Place, Santa Ana, CA, 92707

Tel: (714) 540-8900   Fax: (714) 784-4056   www.mscsoftware.com

Develop finite element analysis software used in the field of computer-aided engineering.

MSC.Software Ltd., 11 Linford Forum, Rockingham Drive, Linford Wood, Milton Keynes MK 14 6LY, UK

MSC.Software Ltd., Cheshire Oaks Business Park, Lloyd Drive, South Wirral, Chester CH 65 9HQ, UK

MSC.Software Ltd., Unit 6, Bow Court, Fletchworth Gate, Coventry CV5 6SP, UK

MSC.Software Ltd., MSC House, Lyon Way, Frimley, Camberley, Surrey GU 16 5ER, UK

MTI TECHNOLOGY CORPORATION

4905 East LaPalma Avenue, Anaheim, CA, 92807

Tel: (714) 970-0300   Fax: (714) 693-2202   www.mti.com

Mfr. data storage systems software.

MTI Europe, Riverview House, Weyside Park, Catteshall Lane, Godalming GU7 1XE, UK

Tel: 44-1483-520-200   Fax: 44-1483-520-222

MTS SYSTEMS CORPORATION

14000 Technology Drive, Eden Prairie, MN, 55344-2290

Tel: (612) 937-4000   Fax: (612) 937-4515   www.mts.com

Develop/mfr. mechanical testing and simulation products and services, industry measure and automation instrumentation.

MTS Systems Ltd., Brook House, Somerford Court, Somerford House, Cirencester Glos GL7 1TW, UK

Tel: 44-1285-648800   Fax: 44-1285-658052   Contact: Mike Reeves

MTS, INCORPORATED

2500 Del Monte Street, West Sacramento, CA, 95691

Tel: (916) 373-2500   Fax: (916) 373-2535   www.towerrecords.com

Specialty retailer of music and video stores.

Tower Records, 1 Piccadilly Circus, London W13 0TR, UK

MUELLER INDUSTRIES, INC.

8285 Tournament Drive, Ste. 150, Memphis, TN, 38125

Tel: (901) 753-3200   Fax: (901) 753-3255   www.muellerindustries.com

Mfr. plumbing and heating products, refrigeration and A/C components, copper and copper alloy and metal forgings and extrusions.

Mueller Europe Ltd., Oxford Street Bilston, West Midlands WV14 7DS, UK

Tel: 44-1902-499-700   Fax: 44-1902-353-139

MULTEX.COM, INC.

100 Williams Street, 7th Fl., New York, NY, 10038

Tel: (212) 607-2500   Fax: (212) 607-2510   www.multex.com

Distributes financial information of corporations via the internet to professional investors.

Multex.com UK, 101 Finsbury Pavement, London EC2A 1RS, UK

Tel: 44-20-7871-8888   Fax: 44-20-7871-8800

MULTIGRAPHICS INC.

431 Lakeview Court, Mt. Prospect, IL, 60056

Tel: (847) 375-1700   Fax: (847) 375-1810   www.multigraphics.com

Mfr./sale/service printing and print prod equipment, mailroom/bindery systems, services and supplies for graphics industry.

Multi Graphics Intl. Inc., 2K Buckingham Ave., Slough, Berkshire SL1 4NA, UK

Multi Graphics Intl. Inc., PO Box 17, Maylands Ave., Hemel Hempstead, Hertfordshire HP2 7ET, UK

MURPHY OIL CORPORATION

PO Box 7000, 200 Peach St., El Dorado, AR, 71731-7000

Tel: (870) 862-6411   Fax: (870) 862-9057   www.murphyoilcorp.com

Crude oil, natural gas, mfr. petroleum products.

Murco Petroleum Ltd., Winston House, Dollis Park, Finchley, London N3 1HZ, UK

MUZAK LLC

3318 Lakemont Blvd., Fort Mill, SC, 29708

Tel: (803) 396-3000   Fax: (803) 396-3136   www.muzak.com

Engaged in music; sells and maintains sound systems and delivers music channels via satellite and broadcast transmission.

Muzak UK, Sheffield, UK

MWH GLOBAL, INC.

300 North Lake Avenue, Ste. 1200, Pasadena, CA, 91109

Tel: (626) 796-9141   Fax: (626) 568-6619   www.mw.com

Engaged in environmental engineering and construction services.

MWH Global, 201 Amersham Road, High Wycombe, Bucks HP13 5AJ, UK

Tel: 44-1494-526-240   Fax: 44-1494-522074

MYKROLIS CORPORATION

1 Patriots Park, Bedford, MA, 01730

Tel: (781) 695-7654   Fax: (781) 695-7639   www.mykrolis.com

Mfr. filtering equipment for gases and liquids.

Mykrolis (U.K.) Limited, Unit 19, Westmead Industrial Estate, Westlea, Swindon Wiltshire SN57YT, UK

Tel: 44-179-361-5808

NACCO INDUSTRIES INC.

5875 Landerbrook Drive, Mayfield Heights, OH, 44124

Tel: (440) 449-9600   Fax: (440) 449-9607   www.nacco.com

Holding company engaged in lift trucks, house wares and lignite coal mining.

Hyster Europe Ltd., Berk House, Basing View, Basingstoke, Hants RG21 2HQ, UK

THE NASH ENGINEERING COMPANY

9 Trefoil Drive, Trumbull, CT, 06611

Tel: (203) 459-3900   Fax: (203) 459-3511   www.nasheng.com

Mfr. air and gas compressors, vacuum pumps.

Nash Europe Ltd., Road One, Industrial Estate, Winsford, Cheshire CW7 3PL, UK

NATCO GROUP, INC.

2950 North Loop West, Houston, TX, 77092-8839

Tel: (713) 683-9292   Fax: (713) 683-6787   www.natcogroup.com

Mfr./sale/service oil and gas products.

NATCO (UK) Ltd., Fountain House, 1A Elm Park, Stanmore, Middlesex, London HA7 4AU, UK

Tel: 44-20-8420-7333   Fax: 44-20-8954-5886

NATIONAL FORGE COMPANY

One Front Street, Rt. No 6, Irvine, PA, 16329-1702

Tel: (814) 563-7522   Fax: (814) 563-9209   www.nationalforge.com

Mfr. forged and cast steel.

Mitchell, Shackleton & Co. Ltd., Green Lane, Patricroft, Manchester M30 8AD, UK

Tel: 44-161-789-2241

North West Forgemasters Ltd., Hyde Greater Manchester, UK

NATIONAL GYPSUM COMPANY

2001 Rexford Road, Charlotte, NC, 28211

Tel: (704) 365-7300   Fax: (704) 365-7276   www.national-gypsum.com

Mfr. building products and services.

The Austin Co. of U.K. Ltd., London, UK

NATIONAL INSTRUMENTS CORPORATION

11550 N. Mopac Expwy., Austin, TX, 78759-3504

Tel: (512) 338-9119   Fax: (512) 794-5794   www.ni.com

Mfr. hardware and graphical software.

National Instruments, Measurement House, Newbury Business Park, London Road, Newbury, Berkshire RG14 2PS, UK

NATIONAL MACHINERY COMPANY

161 Greenfield St., Tiffin, OH, 44883-2471

Tel: (419) 447-5211   Fax: (419) 447-5299   www.nationalmachinery.com

Mfr. high-speed metal parts forming machines.

National Machinery Company, Birmingham, UK

Tel: 44-0121-585-3072

NATIONAL STARCH AND CHEMICAL COMPANY

10 Finderne Ave., Bridgewater, NJ, 08807-3300

Tel: (908) 685-5000   Fax: (908) 685-5005   www.nationalstarch.com

Mfr. adhesives and sealants, resins and specialty chemicals, electronic materials and adhesives, food products, industry starch.

National Starch & Chemical, Dexter Works Barge Dock, Goole, Yorkshire DN14 5TG, UK

Tel: 44-1405-762641   Fax: 44-1405-768657

National Starch & Chemical Holdings Ltd. European Hdqrts., Windsor Court, Kingsmead Business Park, London Road, High Wycombe Bucks HP11 1JU, UK

Tel: 44-1494-467-500   Fax: 44-1494-467-560

National Starch & Chemical Ltd., Welton Rd., Braunston, Daventry, Northants NN11 7JL, UK

Tel: 44-1788-890248   Fax: 44-1788-891489

NATIONAL-OILWELL, INC.

PO Box 4638, Houston, TX, 77210-4638

Tel: (713) 960-5100   Fax: (713) 960-5428   www.natoil.com

Design, manufacture and sale of comprehensive systems and components used in oil and gas drilling and production.

National-Oilwell UK Ltd., South Gates Rd., Great Yarmouth, Norfolk, UK

Tel: 44-1493-856941   Fax: 44-1493-330039

National-Oilwell UK Ltd., Cheadle Heath, Stockport, Cheshire SK3 0SA, UK

Tel: 44-161-428-0755   Fax: 44-161-491-3733

NATIONAL-STANDARD COMPANY

1618 Terminal Road, Niles, MI, 49120

Tel: (616) 683-8100   Fax: (616) 683-6249   www.nationalstardard.com

Mfr. wire, wire related products, machinery and medical products.

National-Standard Co. Ltd., Heslop, Halesfield Industrial Estate, Telford, Shropshire, UK

National-Standard Co. Ltd., Stourport Rd., PO Box 23, Kidderminster, Worcestershire, UK

NATIONWIDE

One Nationwide Plaza, Columbus, OH, 43215-2220

Tel: (614) 249-7111   Fax: (614) 249-7705   www.nationwide.com

Insurance services.

Gartmore Investment Management PLC, 8 Fenchurch Place, London EC3M 4PH, UK

Contact: Jane Thornton

NAVIGANT CONSULTING, INC.

615 North Wabash Avenue, Chicago, IL, 60611

Tel: (312) 573-5600   Fax: (312) 573-5678   www.navigantconsulting.com

Provides management consulting services.

Peterson Consulting, 6 London Street, London EC3R 7LP, UK

Tel: 44-207-204-4000

NAVIGANT INTERNATIONAL, INC.

84 Inverness Circle East, Englewood, CO, 80112-5314

Tel: (303) 706-0800   Fax: (303) 706-0505   www.navigant.com

Engaged in corporate travel services.

Navigant International, Park Stables, Upton Lane, Upton, Northampton NN5 4UX, UK

Navigant UK, 6-8 Luke Street, London EC2A 4XY, UK

Tel: 44-207-950-2400

NAVIGATION TECHNOLOGIES CORPORATION

The Merchandise Mart, Ste. 900, Chicago, IL, 60654

Tel: (312) 894-7000   Fax: (312) 894-7050   www.navtech.com

Mfr. navigation systems for automobiles.

Navigation Technologies Ltd, Thamesbourne Lodge, Station Road, Bourne End, Buckinghamshire SL8 5QH, UK

NBTY, INC.

90 Orville Drive, Bohemia, NY, 11716

Tel: (631) 567-9500   Fax: (631) 567-7148   www.nbty.com

Mfr. and sale of vitamins through catalogs, on-line and retail stores.

Holland & Barrett, 6 Suffolk House, Banbury Road, Oxford, Oxfordshire OX2 7HN, UK

NCR (NATIONAL CASH REGISTER)

1700 South Patterson Blvd., Dayton, OH, 45479

Tel: (937) 445-5000   Fax: (937) 445-7042   www.ncr.com

Mfr. automated teller machines and high-performance stationary bar code scanners.

NCR Ltd., 206 Marylebone Rd., London NW1 6LY, UK

Tel: 44-207-725-8689 Fax: 44-207-725-8755 Contact: Andy Morss, VP

NCUBE CORPORATION

1825 NW 167th Place, Beaverton, OR, 97006

Tel: (503) 629-5088   Fax: (503) 645-1737   www.ncube.com

Mfr. computer servers.

nCUBE United Kingdom, The Atrium, The Grange, 18/21 Church Gate, Thatcham, Berkshire RG19 3PN, UK

NDCHEALTH CORPORATION

National Data Plaza, Atlanta, GA, 30329-2010

Tel: (404) 728-2000   Fax: (404) 728-2551   www.ndchealth.com

Mfr. billing management software.

NDCHealth Corporation, 1 Lacemaker Court, London Road, Amersham Buckinghamshire HP7 0HS, UK

Pharmacy Systems, NDC House, George Baylis Road, Droitwich Worcestershire WR9 9RB, UK

THE NDP GROUP, INC.

900 West Shore Road, Port Washington, NY, 11050

Tel: (516) 625-0700   Fax: (516) 625-2347   www.npd.com

Engaged in consumer buying research.

NDP Group, Rosemount House, Rosemount Avenue, West Byfleet, Surrey KT14 6LB, UK

NEON SYSTEMS, INC.

14100 Southwest Fwy., Ste. 500, Sugar Land, TX, 77478

Tel: (281) 491-4200   Fax: (281) 242-3880   www.neonsys.com

Mfr. security management software.

NEON Systems UK, No. 1 High Street, Windsor Berkshire SL4 1LD, UK

Tel: 44-1753-752800

NET PERCEPTIONS, INC.

7700 France Avenue South, Edina, MN, 55435

Tel: (952) 842-5000   Fax: (952) 842-5005   www.netperceptions.com

Mfr. software.

Net Perceptions, The Lodge at Oakley Court, Windsor, Berkshire SL4 5UF, UK

Tel: 44-1753-609992   Fax: 44-1753-609998

NETEGRITY, INC.

52 Second Avenue, Waltham, MA, 02154

Tel: (781) 890-1700   Fax: (781) 487-7791   www.netegrity.com

Mfr. security software.

Netegrity UK Ltd., Aston Court, Kingsmead Business Park, Frederick Place, High Wycombe HP 11, UK

Tel: 44-1494-616011   Fax: 44-1494-616192

NETIQ CORPORATION

3553 North First Street, San Jose, CA, 95134

Tel: (408) 856-3000   Fax: (408) 273-0578   www.netiq.com

Mfr. performance management software.

NetIQ Limited, Mallard Court, Market Square, Staines, Middlesex TW18 4RH, UK

Tel: 44-1784-454-500

NETMANAGE, INC.

10725 N. De Anza Blvd., Cupertino, CA, 95014

Tel: (408) 973-7171   Fax: (408) 257-6405   www.netmanage.com

Develop and manufacture computer software applications and tools.

NetManage UK, Ltd., Lyon Court, 2/F, Walsworth Rd., Hitchin Hertfordshire SG4 9SX, UK

Tel: 44-1462-775050   Fax: 44-1462-755055

NETWORK APPLIANCE, INC.

495 E. Java Drive, Sunnyvale, CA, 94089

Tel: (408) 822-6000   Fax: (408) 822-4501   www.netapp.com

Engaged in data storage market equipment.

Network Appliance, Waterview House
1 Roundwood Avenue, 1 Roundwood Avenue, Stockley Park, Uxbridge, Middlesex UB11 1EJ, UK

NETWORK ASSOCIATES, INC.

3965 Freedom Circle, Santa Clara, CA, 95054

Tel: (408) 988-3832   Fax: (408) 970-9727   www.networkassociates.com

Designs and produces network security and network management software and hardware.

Network Associates, 227 Bath Road, Slough, Berkshire SL1 5PP, UK

Tel: 44-1753-217500   Fax: 44-1753-217520

Network General UK Ltd., Alton House, Gatehouse Way, Buckinghamshire HP19 3XU, UK

Tel: 44-1296-318700   Fax: 44-1296-318777

NETWORK COMPUTING DEVICES, INC. (NCDI)

301 Ravendale Drive, Mountain View, CA, 94043

Tel: (650) 694-0650   Fax: (650) 961-7711   www.ncd.com

Provider of server- and web-based computing solutions

NCD UK, 20-22 Richfield Avenue, Reading Berkshire RG1 8LJ, UK

Tel: 44-845-4583710

NETWORK EQUIPMENT TECHNOLOGIES INC.

6500 Paseo Padre Pkwy., Freemont, CA, 94555

Tel: (510) 713-7300   Fax: (510) 574-4000   www.net.com

Mfr./service networking products to info-intensive organizations.

NET Ltd., Manor Court, Manor Royal, Crawley, West Sussex RH10 2PY, UK

NEUTROGENA CORPORATION

5760 West 96th Street, Los Angeles, CA, 90045

Tel: (310) 642-1150   Fax: (310) 337-5564   www.neutrogena.com

Mfr. facial cleansing, moisturizing products; body care, sun and hair care specialty products.

Neutrogena UK Ltd., Neutrogena House, Century Point, Halifax Rd., Cressex, High Wycombe HP12 3SL, UK

NEW BALANCE ATHLETIC SHOE, INC.

Brighton Landing, 20 Guest Street, Boston, MA, 02135-2088

Tel: (617) 783-4000   Fax: (617) 787-9355   www.newbalance.com

Mfr. men's and women's athletic shoes.

New Balance Athletic Shoes, 320 Firecrest Court, Centre Park, Warrington, Cheshire WA1 1RG, UK

NEW BRUNSWICK SCIENTIFIC COMPANY, INC.

44 Talmadge Road, Box 4005, Edison, NJ, 08818-4005

Tel: (732) 287-1200   Fax: (732) 287-4222   www.nbsc.com

Mfr. research and production equipment for life sciences.

New Brunswick Scientific (UK) Ltd., 163 Dixons Hill Rd., North Mymms, Hatfield AL9 75E, UK

Tel: 44-17072-75733   Fax: 41-17072-67859   Contact: Nick Vosper, Gen. Mgr.

NEW ENGLAND BUSINESS SERVICE, INC.

500 Main Street, Groton, MA, 01471

Tel: (978) 448-6111   Fax: (978) 449-3419   www.nebs.com

Provides mail order business forms.

NEBS Inc., Sovereign Way, Chester West Park, Chester CH1 4QU, UK

NEW HAMPSHIRE BALL BEARINGS INC. (NHBB)

9700 Independence Ave., Chatsworth, CA, 91311-4323

Tel: (818) 407-9300   Fax: (818) 407-9300   www.nhbb.com

Mfr. bearings and bearing assemblies.

NHBB, 1 Sterling Centre, Eastern Rd., Bracknell Berkshire RG12 2PW, UK

NEW HORIZONS WORLDWIDE, INC.

1900 S. State College Blvd., Anaheim, CA, 92806-6135

Tel: (714) 940-8000   Fax: www.newhorizons.com

Provides customer-focused computer training choices, through computer training centers.

New Horizons Worldwide, 85 Great Eastern Street, London EC2A 3HY, UK

Tel: 44-20-7684-2000

NEW YORK LIFE INSURANCE COMPANY

51 Madison Ave., New York, NY, 10010

Tel: (212) 576-7000   Fax: (212) 576-4291   www.newyorklife.com

Insurance services.

New York Life Insurance Co. UK, London, UK

THE NEW YORK TIMES COMPANY

229 West 43rd Street, New York, NY, 10036-3959

Tel: (212) 556-1234   Fax: (212) 556-7389   www.nytimes.com

Diversified media company including newspapers, magazines, television and radio stations, and electronic information and publishing.

International Herald Tribune (IHT), 40 Marsh Wall, London E14 9TP, UK

Tel: 44-207-510-5700

The New York Times London Bureau Ltd., 66 Burlingham Gate, London SW1E 64U, UK

NEWELL RUBBERMAID

29 East Stephenson Street, Freeport, IL, 61032-0943

Tel: (815) 235-4171   Fax: (815) 489-8212   www.newellco.com

Mfr. hardware, housewares, and office products.

McKechnie, Plc., Leighswood Rd., Aldridge Walsall, West Midlands WS9 8DS, UK

Tel: 44-192-274-3887   Fax: 44-192-245-1045

Newell Office Products of UK Inc., Unit 3, Clifton Rd., Shefford, Bedfordshire SG17 5AG, UK

NEWPORT CORPORATION

1791 Deere Ave., PO Box 19607, Irvine, CA, 92606

Tel: (949) 863-3144   Fax: (949) 253-1800   www.newport.com

Engaged in the design, manufacture and marketing of high-precision components, instruments and integrated systems to the fiber optic communications, semiconductor equipment and aerospace and research markets.

Newport Ltd., Newbury Business Park, 4320 First Avenue, London Road, Newbury, Berkshire RG14 2PZ, UK

Tel: 44-1635-521-757   Fax: 44-1635-521-348

NEXPRISE, INC.

701 Palomar Airport Road, Ste. 110, Carlsbad, CA, 92009

Tel: (760) 804-1333   Fax: (760) 804-1331   www.nexprise.com

Mfr. Internet software.

NexPrise Europe, Evenlode Court, Long Hanborough, Lxfordshire OX29 5SZ, UK

Tel: 44-1993-883-230

NICHOLAS CRITELLI ASSOCIATES, P.C.

Ste. 500, 317 Sixth Ave., Des Moines, IA, 50309-4128

Tel: (515) 243-3122   Fax: (515) 243-3121   www.critellilaw.com

International law firm.

Nicholas Critelli Associates, P.C., 9Stone Buildings, Lincoln's Inn, London WC2A 3TG, UK

Tel: 44-20-7404-5055   Fax: 44-20-7404-1551

NICOR INC.

1844 Ferry Road, Naperville, IL, 60563-9600

Tel: (630) 305-9500   Fax: (630) 983-9328   www.nicorinc.com

Engaged in distribution of natural gas.

Tropical Shipping Inc., Guiness Road, Unit 6, Trafford Park, Manchester M17 1SD, UK

Tropical Shipping, Inc., North Weald Airfield, North Weald, Essex CM16 6AA, UK

AC NIELSEN COMPANY

177 Broad Street, Stamford, CT, 06901

Tel: (203) 961-3000   Fax: (203) 961-3190   www.acnielsen.com

Engaged in market and consumer research.

ACNielsen, A.C.Nielsen House, London Road Headington, Oxford OX3 9RX, UK

NIKE INC.

One Bowerman Drive, Beaverton, OR, 97005

Tel: (503) 671-6453   Fax: (503) 671-6300   www.nike.com

Mfr. athletic footwear, equipment and apparel.

Nike United Kingdom Ltd., Dist. 4, Washington, Tyne & Wear NE38 7RN, UK

NIKU CORPORATION

305 Main Street, Redwood City, CA, 94063

Tel: (650) 298-4600   Fax: (650) 298-4601   www.niku.com

Mfr. software.

Niku Corporation Limited, Ziggurat, Grosvenor Road, St. Albans, Hertfordshire AL1 3DL, UK

NL INDUSTRIES, INC.
16825 Northchase Drive, Ste. 1200, Houston, TX, 77060-2544

Tel: (281) 423-3300   Fax: (281) 423-3236   www.nl-ind.com

Producer of titanium dioxide pigments.

Kronos Marketing, Div. NL Industries, Barons Court, Manchester Road, Wilmslow, Cheshire SK9 1BQ, UK

NORDSON CORPORATION
28601 Clemens Road, Westlake, OH, 44145-4551

Tel: (440) 892-1580   Fax: (440) 892-9507   www.nordson.com

Mfr. industry application equipment, sealants and packaging machinery.

Nordson U.K. Ltd., 816 Leigh Road, Slough, Berkshire SL1 4BD, UK

Tel: 44-1753-558000   Fax: 44-1753-558100

NORFOLK SOUTHERN CORPORATION
3 Commercial Place, Norfolk, VA, 23510-1291

Tel: (757) 629-2600   Fax: (757) 629-2798   www.nscorp.com

Holding company: transportation, including Conrail.

North American Van Lines Ltd., 15/16, Chestnut Way, Felthambrook Industrial Estate, Feltham, Middlesex TW13 7OP, UK

NORRISEAL CONTROLS
PO Box 40525, Houston, TX, 77240-0525

Tel: (713) 466-3552   Fax: (713) 896-7386   www.norriseal.com

Mfr. butterfly valves, fittings and plugs primarily for the oil and gas industries.

NF Technical Service Ltd., 4 Possil House, 23 Copse Hill, Wimbledon SW20 ONR, UK

Tel: 44-181-8793859   Fax: 44-181-8797374

NORTHERN TRUST CORPORATION
50 South LaSalle Street, Chicago, IL, 60675

Tel: (312) 630-6000   Fax: (312) 630-1512   www.ntrs.com

Engaged in banking and financial services.

Northern Trust Corp. - London Branch, 50 Bank Street, Canary Wharf, London E145NT, UK

Tel: 44-207-982-2000

NORTHROP GRUMMAN CORPORATION
1840 Century Park East, Los Angeles, CA, 90067-2199

Tel: (310) 553-6262   Fax: (310) 201-3023   www.northgrum.com

Advanced technology for aircraft, electronics, and technical support services.

Northrop Grumman IT Europe, Alpha House, Chilworth Science Park, Southampton SO16 7NS, UK

Tel: 44-23-8076-0484   Contact: Brian Luff

W.W. NORTON & COMPANY, INC.
500 Fifth Avenue, New York, NY, 10110

Tel: (212) 354-5500   Fax: (212) 869-0856   www.wwnorton.com

Publishers of professional and general interest books.

W. W. Norton & Company Ltd., Castle House, 75/76 Wells Street, London W1T 3QT, UK

Tel: 44-207-323-1579

NORTON ABRASIVES COMPANY
1 New Bond Street, Worcester, MA, 01606

Tel: (508) 795-5000   Fax: (508) 795-5741   www.nortonabrasives.com

Mfr. abrasives for industrial manufacturing.

Christensen Diamond Products (UK) Ltd., Govett Ave., Shepperton, Walton-on-Thames, Middlesex, UK

Clipper Mfr. Co., Thurmaston Blvd., Barkby Rd., Leicester LE4 7JB, UK

Norton Abrasives Ltd., Bridge Rd., East Welwyn Garden City, Hertfordshire AL 7HZ, UK

Norton Chemical Process Products Ltd., King St., Fenton, Stoke-on-Trent ST4 3LY, UK

Norton Intl., Cartwright House, 39/43 Monument Hill, Weybridge, Surrey KT13 8RN, UK

NOVELL WORLDWIDE

1800 S. Novell Place, Provo, UT, 84606

Tel: (801) 861-7000   Fax: (801) 861-5555   www.novell.com

Develop/mfr. networking software and related equipment.

Digital Research (UK) Ltd., Oxford House, Oxford St., Newbury, Berkshire RG13 1JB, UK

Novell (UK) Ltd., Sweetwell Rd., Bracknell, Berkshire RG12 1HH, UK

NOVELLUS SYSTEMS INC.

4000 North First Street, San Jose, CA, 95134

Tel: (408) 943-9700   Fax: (408) 943-3422   www.novellus.com

Mfr. chemical vapor deposition (CVD), physical vapor deposition (PVD) and copper electrofill systems.

Novellus Systems Ltd., Bishops Weald House, Unit 1EB, Albion Way, Horsham, West Sussex RH12 1AH, UK

Tel: 44-1403-265550 Fax: 44-1403-266554   Contact: David Avery, Pres.

NOVEON INTERNATIONAL

9911 Brecksville Road, Cleveland, OH, 44141-3427

Tel: (216) 447-5000   Fax: (216) 447-5669   www.noveoninc.com

Mfr. specialty chemicals.

Noveon UK Limited, Terminal House, Station Approach, Shepperton, Middlesex TW17 8AS, UK

NRG ENERGY, INC.

901 Marquette Avenue, Ste. 2300, Minneapolis, MN, 55402

Tel: (612) 373-5300   Fax: (612) 373-5466   www.nrgenergy.com

Electric power generation.

NRG Energy, Ltd., 54 St. James's Street, London SW1A 1JT, UK

Tel: 44-207-409-1025   Fax: 44-207-409-1074

NU SKIN ENTERPRISES, INC.

75 West Center St., Provo, UT, 84601

Tel: (801) 345-6100   Fax: (801) 345-5999   www.nuskin.com

Develops and distributes premium-quality personal care and nutritional products.

NuSkin Europe UK, Gomm Road, High Wycombe, Buckinghamshire HP13 7DL, UK

NUMATICS INC.

1450 North Milford Road, Highland, MI, 48357

Tel: (248) 887-4111   Fax: (248) 887-9190   www.numatics.com

Mfr. control valves and manifolds.

Numatics Ltd., PO Box 18, 23/24 Acacia Close, Cherrycourt Way, Leighton Buzzard, Beds. LU7 7DJ, UK

NVIDIA CORPORATION

2701 San Tomas Expressway, Santa Clara, CA, 95050

Tel: (408) 486-2000   Fax: (408) 486-2200   www.nvidia.com

Mfr. graphics chips for video gamers and graphics designers.

NVIDIA UK Ltd., Theale Court, 11-13 High Theale, Reading Berkshire 5AH, UK

NYPRO INC.

101 Union Street, Clinton, MA, 01510

Tel: (978) 365-9721   Fax: (978) 368-0236   www.nypro.com

Mfr. plastic parts for telecommunications industry.

Nypro UK, 70 Clywedog Road East, Wrexham Industrial Estate, Clwyd LL13 9UT, UK

OAK TECHNOLOGY, INC.

139 Kifer Court, Sunnyvale, CA, 94086

Tel: (408) 737-0888   Fax: (408) 737-3838   www.oaktech.com

Engaged in the design and manufacture of semiconductors.

Oak Technology, 8 Exchange Quay, 6/F, Salford Manchester M5 3EJ, UK

Tel: 44-161-932-1111   Fax: 44-161-932-1217

OAO TECHNOLOGY SOLUTIONS, INC.

7500 Greenway Center Drive, 16th Fl., Greenbelt, MD, 20770

Tel: (301) 486-0400   Fax: (301) 486-0415   www.oaot.com

Provides information technology services.

OAO Technology Solutions UK Ltd., Elta House Birmingham Road, Stratford-upon-Avon, Warwickshire CV37 0AQ, UK

THE O'BRIEN & GERE COMPANIES

5000 Brittonfield Parkway, Syracuse, NY, 13221

Tel: (315) 437-6100   Fax: (315) 463-7554   www.obg.com

Specializes in engineering, procurement and construction management of water/wastewater treatment facilities and provides specialized health and safety environmental advice to industry, commerce and government.

RMC Consultants Ltd., Abingdon, UK

Tel: 44-123-553-8616   Contact: John Gebrian   Emp: 60

OCCIDENTAL PETROLEUM CORPORATION

10889 Wilshire Blvd., Los Angeles, CA, 90024

Tel: (310) 208-8800   Fax: (310) 443-6690   www.oxy.com

Petroleum and petroleum products, chemicals, plastics.

Occidental Intl. Oil Inc., 16 Palace Street, London SW1 E5BQ, UK

OCEANEERING INTERNATIONAL INC.

11911 FM 529, Houston, TX, 77041

Tel: (713) 329-4500   Fax: (713) 329-4951   www.oceaneering.com

Transportation equipment, underwater service to offshore oil and gas industry.

Oceaneering UK, Cabbell Street, London NW 1 5BG, UK

OCTAGON WORLDWIDE

One Dag Hammarskjold Plaza, New York, NY, 10017

Tel: (212) 888-8847   Fax: (212) 403-7098   www.octagon.com

Engaged in sports and entertainment marketing.

Octagon Motorsports CSI (JV), 6 Eaton Gate, London SW1W 9BJ, UK

Tel: 44-207-881-8888   Fax: 44-20-7828-0887

ODETICS INC.

1515 South Manchester Ave., Anaheim, CA, 92802-2907

Tel: (714) 774-5000   Fax: (714) 780-7857   www.odetics.com

Design/mfr. digital data management products for mass data storage, communications and video security markets.

Odetics Europe Ltd., The Minster, 58 Portman, Reading Berkshire RG3 1EA, UK

C.M. OFFRAY & SON INC.

360 Rt. 24, Box 601, Chester, NJ, 07930-0601

Tel: (908) 879-4700   Fax: (908) 879-8588   www.offray.com

Mfr. ribbons and narrow fabrics.

C.M. Offray & Son Ltd., Fir Tree Pl., Church Rd., Ashford, Middlesex TW15 2PH, UK

OFFSHORE LOGISTICS, INC.

224 Rue de Jean, Lafayette, LA, 70505

Tel: (337) 233-1221   Fax: (337) 235-6678   www.olog.com

Engaged in helicopter transportation services for offshore oil and gas companies.

Bristow Helicopters Limited, Redhill Aerodrome, Redhill Surrey RH1 5JZ, UK

Bristow Helicopters Limited, North Denes Heliport, Caister Road, Great Yarmouth, Norfolk NR30 5TF, UK

THE O'GARA COMPANY

1250 24th Street, NW, Suite 300, Washington, DC, 20037

Tel: (202) 835-1680   Fax: (202) 835-1685   www.ogara.com

Security and consulting services and vehicles.

Kroll Associates UK Ltd., 25 Saville Row, London W1X 0AL, UK

Tel: 44-207-396-0000   Fax: 44-207-396-9966

O'Gara Satellite Networks, c/o Next Destination, Ltd, 25 The Claredon Centre, Salisbury Business Centre, Salisbury, Wiltshire SP1 2TJ, UK

Tel: 44-1722-410800   Fax: 44-1722-410777   Contact: Mark White

OGILVY & MATHER WORLDWIDE

309 West 49th Street, New York, NY, 10017-7399

Tel: (212) 237-4000   Fax: (212) 237-5123   www.ogilvypr.com

Engaged in public relations and communications.

Ogilvy Public Relations Worldwide, 10 Cabot Square, Canary Wharf, London E14 4QB, UK

Tel: 44-207-345-3000 Fax: 44-20-7345-6618   Contact: Donna Zurcher

OHAUS CORPORATION

PO Bpx 2033,19a Chapin Road, Pine Brook, NJ, 07058

Tel: (973) 377-9000   Fax: (973) 593-0359   www.ohaus.com

Mfr. balances and scales for laboratories, industry and education.

Ohaus UK Ltd., 64 Boston Road, Beaumont Leys, Leicester LE4 1AW, UK

Tel: 44-116-234-507   Fax: 44-116-235-9256

THE OHIO ART COMPANY

One Toy Street, PO Box 111, Bryan, OH, 43506

Tel: (419) 636-3141   Fax: (419) 636-7614   www.world-of-toys.com

Manufacture and distribution of toys; provides custom metal lithography and molded plastic products to other companies.

The Ohio Art Company (European Office), 74 Warren Rise, Frimley Camberly, Surrey GU16 5SW, UK

Tel: 44-1276-675-501   Fax: 44-1276-675-451

OIL STATES INDUSTRIES

7701 South Cooper Street, Arlington, TX, 76017

Tel: (817) 468-1400   Fax: (817) 468-6250   www.oilstates.com

Mfr. drilling and production machinery and supplies for oil and gas production.

Oil States Industries Ltd., PO Box 18192, London EC2A 4WB, UK

Oil States MCS, Ltd., Bouthwood Road, Sowerby Woods, Barrow-in-Furness, Cumbria LA14 4HB, UK

OIL-DRI CORPORATION OF AMERICA

410 North Michigan Ave., Ste. 400, Chicago, IL, 60611-4213

Tel: (312) 321-1515   Fax: (312) 321-1271   www.oil-dri.com

Developer, manufacturer and marketer of products for consumer, industrial and automotive, agricultural, sports fields and fluids purification markets and cat litter products.

Oil-Dri UK Ltd., c/o Consolidated Land Services, Humber Rd., South Killingsholme, Grimsby DN40 3DU, UK

THE OILGEAR COMPANY

2300 S. 51st Street, Milwaukee, WI, 53219

Tel: (414) 327-1700   Fax: (414) 327-0532   www.oilgear.com

Mfr. hydraulic power transmission machinery.

Oilgear Toweler Ltd., Oaklands Rd., Leeds LS13 1LG, UK

Oilgear Towler Ltd., Shuttleworth Rd., Goldington, Bedford Bedshire MK41 0EP, UK

OLAN MILLS, INC.

4325 Amnicola Hwy., Chattanooga, TN, 37422

Tel: (423) 622-5141   Fax: (423) 629-8128   www.olanmills.com

Portrait studios.

Olan Mills UK, Darby Close, Wellingborough, Northants NN8 6JU, UK

Tel: 44-1933-400200

OLIN CORPORATION

501 Merritt Seven, Norwalk, CT, 06856-4500

Tel: (203) 750-3000   Fax: (203) 750-3292   www.olin.com

Mfr. chemicals, metals, sporting ammunition and copper and copper alloy sheets.

Olin UK Ltd., Site 7, Kidderminster Rd., Cutnall Green, Droitwich, Worcestershire WR9 0NS, UK

O'MELVENY & MYERS LLP

400 South Hope Street, Ste. 1500, Los Angeles, CA, 90017-2801

Tel: (213) 430-6000   Fax: (213) 430-6407   www.omelveny.com

Engaged in international law.

O'Melveny & Myers, 3 Finsbury Square, London EC2A 1LA, UK

Tel: 44-207-256-8451   Contact: Adrian Harris

OMNICARE, INC.

100 E. River Center Blvd., Covington, KY, 41011

Tel: (859) 392-3300   Fax: (859) 392-3333   www.omnicare.com

Provides pharmaceutical and nursing home services.

Omnicare Clinical Packaging, Chippenham, UK

OMNICOM GROUP INC.

437 Madison Ave., New York, NY, 10022

Tel: (212) 415-3600   Fax: (212) 415-3530   www.omnicomgroup.com

International network of advertising, marketing, direct mail, public relations and consulting services.

BHWG Media, 191 Old Marylebone Road, London NW1 5DW, UK

GGT Group, 82 Dean St., London W1V 5AB, UK

Tel: 44-207-437-0434   Fax: 44-207-836-6626   Contact: Michael E. Greenlees, Chmn.   Emp: 3,082

OMNOVA SOLUTIONS INC.

175 Ghent Road, Fairlawn, OH, 44333

Tel: (330) 869-4200   Fax: (330) 869-4288   www.omnova.com

Mfr. wall coverings and decorative building products and specialty chemicals.

OMNOVA Decorative & Building Products, 74-78 Wood Lane End, Hemel Hempstead, Herfordshire HP2 4RF, UK

ON ASSIGNMENT, INC.

26651 West Agoura Road, Calabasas, CA, 91302

Tel: (818) 878-7900   Fax: (818) 878-7930   www.assignment.net

Temporary employment agency.

On Assignment UK Limited, Cambridge, UK

Tel: 44-1223-451-021

On Assignment UK Limited, Birmingham Midlands, UK

Tel: 44-121-224-5617

ONDEO NALCO COMPANY

Ondeo Nalco Center, 1601 W. Diehl Road, Naperville, IL, 60563-1198

Tel: (630) 305-1000   Fax: (630) 305-2900   www.ondeo-nalco.com

Mfr. specialty chemicals for water and waste water treatment, oil products and refining, industry processes; water and energy management service.

ONDEO Nalco, Aquazur Limited, Chapel House, Alma Road, Windsor SL4 3HD, UK

ONDEO Nalco Ltd., PO Box 11, Northwich, Cheshire CW8 4DX, UK

Tel: 44-1606-74488   Fax: 44-1606-79557

ONEIDA LTD.

163-181 Kenwood Avenue, Oneida, NY, 13421-2899

Tel: (315) 361-3000   Fax: (315) 361-3658   www.oneida.com

Mfr. stainless steel flatware, glassware, cookware and chine and plastic serving products.

Oneida Silversmiths Ltd., Elder Way, Waterside Drive, Langley Berkshire SL3 6EP, UK

Tel: 44-1753-212500   Fax: 44-1753-543476

ONESOURCE INFORMATION SERVICES, INC.

300 Baker Avenue, Concord, MA, 01742

Tel: (978) 318-4300   Fax: (978) 318-4690   www.onesource.com

Provides business information services on line.

One Source Information Services, 7/F, Block E, Dukes Court, Duke Street, Woking Surrey GU21 5BH, UK

Tel: 44-1483-241200   Fax: 44-1-1483-240007

ONYX SOFTWARE CORPORATION

3180 139th Avenue SE, Ste. 500, Bellevue, WA, 98005

Tel: (425) 451-8060   Fax: (425) 451-8277   www.onyx.com

Mfr. customer relationship management software.

Onyx Software UK, Trinity Court, Wokingham Road, Bracknell Berkshire RG42 1PL, UK

Tel: 44-1344-322-000

OPEN MARKET, INC.

1 Wayside Road, Burlington, MA, 01803

Tel: (781) 359-3000   Fax: (781) 359-8111   www.openmarket.com

Mfr. catalog management software.

Open Market UK Ltd., Arundell House, One Farm Yard, Windsor Berkshire SL4 1QL, UK

OPENWAVE SYSTEMS INC.

1400 Seaport Blvd., Redwood City, CA, 94063

Tel: (650) 480-8000   Fax: (650) 480-8100   www.openwave.com

Mfr. software for wireless telephones.

Openwave Systems, 23 Mark Road, Hemel Hempstead, Herts HP2 7DN, UK

Tel: 44-1442-458800   Fax: 44-1442-458899

Openwave Systems, Votec Centre, Hambridge Lane Units 1B and 6, Berkshire, Newbury RG14 5TN, UK

OPINION RESEARCH CORPORATION

23 Orchard Road, Skillman, NJ, 08558

Tel: (908) 281-5100   Fax: (908) 281-5103   www.opinionresearch.com

Engaged in market research.

Opinion Research UK, Angel Corner House, 1 Islington High St., London N19AH, UK

Tel: 44-207-675-1000

Opinion Research UK, 5th Floor City Point, 701 Chester Road, Stretford, Manchester M32 0RW, UK

Tel: 44-161-877-6781

OPTIO SOFTWARE, INC.

3015 Windward Plaza, Alpharetta, GA, 30005

Tel: (770) 576-3500   Fax: (770) 576-3699   www.optisosoftware.com

Mfr. information delivery software.

Optio Software UK Ltd., Enterprise Centre, Coventr yUniversity Technology, Puma Way, Coventry CV1 2PT, UK

Tel: 44-247-623-6336

ORACLE CORPORATION

500 Oracle Parkway, Redwood Shores, CA, 94065

Tel: (650) 506-7000   Fax: (650) 506-7200   www.oracle.com

Develop/manufacture software.

Oracle Corp., Oracle Park, Bittams Lane, Guilford Rd., Chertsey, Surrey KT16 9RG, UK

ORC MACRO INTERNATIONAL INC.

11785 Beltsville Dr., Calverton, MD, 20705-3119

Tel: (301) 572-0200   Fax: (301) 572-0999   www.macroint.com

Engaged in research and evaluation, training, consulting and information technology.

ORC Macro, Angel Corner House, 1 Islington High Street, London N19AH, UK

Tel: 44-20-7675-1000

ORCHID BIOSCIENCES, INC.

4390 US Route One North, Princeton, NJ, 08540

Tel: (609) 750-2200   Fax: (609) 750-6400   www.orchid.com

Engaged in genetic testing and drug development.

Orchid BioSciences Europe, Abingdon Business Park, 22 Blacklands Way, Abingdon, Oxfordshire OX14 1DY, UK

Tel: 44-1235-535-090

ORIEL INSTRUMENTS CORPORATION
150 Long Beach Boulevard, Stratford, CT, 06615
Tel: (203) 377-8282   Fax: (203) 378-2457   www.oriel.com
Mfr. optical goods.

L.O.T.-Oriel Ltd., 1 Mole Business Park, Leatherhead, Surrey KT22 7AU, UK
Tel: 44-1-372-378822   Fax: 44-1-372-375353

ORRICK, HERRINGTON & SUTCLIFFE LLP
400 ANSOME Street, San Francisco, CA, 94111-3143
Tel: (415) 392-1122   Fax: (415) 773-5759   www.orrick.com
Engaged in international law.

Orrick, Herrington & Sutcliffe LLP, 4 Broadgate, London EC2M 2DA, UK
Tel: 44-207-628-0078

OSI PHARMACEUTICALS, INC.
58 South Service Road, Melville, NY, 11747
Tel: (631) 962-2000   Fax: (631) 752-3880   www.osip.com
Engaged in pharmaceutical research.

OSI Pharmaceuticals, Inc., Aston Molecules Ltd., 10 Holt Court South, Aston Science Park, Birmingham B7 4EJ, UK
Tel: 44-131-359-1100

OSI Pharmaceuticals, Inc., Watlington Road, Oxford OX4 6LT, UK
Tel: 44-1865-780-800

OSMONICS INC.
5951 Clearwater Drive, Minnetonka, MN, 55343-8995
Tel: (952) 933-2277   Fax: (952) 933-0141   www.osmonics.com
Mfr. equipment, controls and components for the filtration and water-treatment industries.

Osmonics, Bristol, UK

OTIS ELEVATOR COMPANY
One Farm Springs Road, Farmington, CT, 06032
Tel: (860) 676-6000   Fax: (860) 676-5111   www.otis.com
Mfr. elevators and escalators.

Evans Lifts Ltd., Prospect Works, Abbey Lane, Leicester LE4 5QX, UK
Contact: Adel Eissa
Otis Elevator Co. UK, The Otis Bldg., 187 Twyford Abbey Road, London NW10 7DG, UK
Tel: 44-208-955-3000
Otis PLC, The Otis Bldg., 43/59 Clapham Rd., London SW9 OJZ, UK

OWENS-CORNING CORPORATION
One Owens Corning Pkwy., Toledo, OH, 43659
Tel: (419) 248-8000   Fax: (419) 248-8445   www.owenscorning.com
Mfr. building materials systems and composites systems.

Owens Corning Insulation UK, PO Box 10, Stafford Road, St. Helens WA10 3NS, UK

OWENS-ILLINOIS, INC.
One SeaGate, PO Box 1035, Toledo, OH, 43666
Tel: (419) 247-5000   Fax: (419) 247-2839   www.o-i.com
Mfr. glass containers and packaging products.

United Glass Ltd., Porters Wood, St. Albans, Hertfordshire AL3 6NY, UK

OXBOW CORPORATION
1601 Forum Place, Ste. 1400, West Palm Beach, FL, 33402
Tel: (561) 697-4300   Fax: (561) 640-8747   www.oxbow.com
Produces coal, carbon products and petroleum.

Oxbow Carbon, Phoenix Business Park, Ste. 4, Swansea West Wales SA7 9FB, UK

PACCAR INC.

777 106th Ave. NE, Bellevue, WA, 98004

Tel: (425) 468-7400   Fax: (425) 468-8216   www.pacar.com

Heavy duty dump trucks, military vehicles.

Leyland Trucks, Farington, UK

PACCAR International, Moss Lane, Sandbach, Cheshire CW11 9YW, UK

Tel: 44-1271-763244   Fax: 44-1270-767788

PACIFIC BELL TELEPHONE COMPANY

140 New Montgomery Street, San Francisco, CA, 94105

Tel: (415) 542-9000   Fax: (415) 543-7079   www.pacbell.com

Telecommunications and information systems.

One-to-One Ltd., Scorpio House, 102 Syndey St., London SW3 6NL, UK

PACIFIC MUTUAL HOLDING COMPANY

700 Newport Center Dr., Newport Beach, CA, 92660

Tel: (949) 640-3011   Fax: (949) 640-3483   www.pacificlife.com

Provides life and health insurance products, individual annuities and group employee benefits.

World-Wide Reassurance Company Limited, Windsor, UK

PACIFIC SCIENTIFIC COMPANY

4301 Kishwaukee Street, PO Box 106, Rockford, IL, 61105-0106

Tel: (815) 226-3100   Fax: (815) 226-3148   www.pacsci.com

Mfr. high performance motors and drives.

Pacific Scientific Ltd., Seven Centre, Bourne End, Buckinghamshire SL8 5YS, UK

PADCO INC.

1025 Thomas Jefferson Street NW, Ste. 170, Washington, DC, 20007-5209

Tel: (202) 337-2326   Fax: (202) 944-2350   www.padcoinc.com

Provides governments and private clients with comprehensive policy, planning, financial, environmental, geo-information management (GIS), privatization and training services for urban and regional development.

PADCO Europe Ltd., London, UK

PALL CORPORATION

2200 Northern Boulevard, East Hills, NY, 11548-1289

Tel: (516) 484-5400   Fax: (516) 484-5228   www.pall.com

Specialty materials and engineering; filters and related fluid clarification equipment.

Pall Europe Ltd., Europa House, Havant Street, Portsmouth P01 3PD, UK

Tel: 44-705-30-3303   Fax: 441-705-30-2506

Pall/Gelman Sciences Ltd., Brackmills Business Park, Caswell Road, Northampton NN4 7EZ, UK

Tel: 44-1604-70-4704   Fax: 44-1604-70-4724

PALM, INC.

5470 Great American Pkwy., Santa Clara, CA, 95054

Tel: (408) 878-9000   Fax: (408) 878-2750   www.palm.com

Mfr. handheld computers, Palm Pilot.

Palm Europe Ltd., 220 Wharfedale Road, Winnersh, Wokingham, Berkshire RG41 5TP, UK

PANAMETRICS

221 Crescent Street, Waltham, MA, 02154

Tel: (781) 899-2719   Fax: (781) 899-1552   www.panametrics.com

Engaged in manufacture and distribution of ultrasonic testing equipment and process control instrumentation.

Panametrics Ltd., Unit 2, Villiers Court, 40 Upper Mulgrave Rd., Cheam Surrey SM2 7AJ, UK

Tel: 44-181-643-5150   Fax: 44-181-643-4225   Contact: Arthur Berry

Panametrics NDT, Ltd., 12 Nightingale Close, Rotherham, South Yorkshire S60 2AB, UK

Tel: 44-1709-836115   Fax: 44-1709-8355177

PANDUIT CORPORATION

17301 Ridgeland Ave., Tinley Park, IL, 60477-0981

Tel: (708) 532-1800   Fax: (708) 532-1811   www.panduit.com

Mfr. of network connectivity and electrical products.

Panduit Europe Ltd., West World, Westgate, London W5 1XP, UK

Tel: 44-208-601-7200

PAPA JOHN'S INTERNATIONAL, INC.

2002 Papa John's Blvd., Louisville, KY, 40299-2334

Tel: (502) 266-5200   Fax: (502) 266-2925   www.papajohns.com

Retailer and pizza franchiser.

Papa John's International Inc., 56 Orsett Road, Grays, Essex RM17 5EH, UK

Tel: 44-1-375-382-828

PAPER CONVERTING MACHINE COMPANY

PO Box 19005, 2300 S. Ashland Ave., Green Bay, WI, 54307

Tel: (920) 494-5601   Fax: (920) 494-8865   www.pcmc.com

Mfr. converting machinery for the sanitary tissue, flexible packaging and disposables nonwovens industries.

Paper Converting Machine Co. Ltd., Southway Dr., Plymouth, Devon, UK

PARADYNE NETWORKS, INC.

8545 126 Ave. North, Largo, FL, 33773

Tel: (727) 530-2000   Fax: (727) 530-2875   www.paradyne.com

Engaged in data communications and high-speed network access solutions.

Paradyne Ltd., 225 Berwick Ave., Slough, Berkshire SL1 4QT, UK

PARAMETRIC TECHNOLOGY CORPORATION

140 Kendrick St., Needham, MA, 02494

Tel: (781) 370-5000   Fax: (781) 370-6000   www.ptc.com

Supplier of mechanical design automation and product data management software and services.

Parametric Technology (UK) Ltd., 20 Brindley Road, Unit 5, 1st Fl., Metropolitan House, Manchester M16 9HQ, UK

Tel: 44-161-877-6447   Fax: 44-161-877-6435

Parametric Technology (UK) Ltd., The Courtyard, Alban Park, Unit V Hatfield Road, St. Albans AL4 0LA, UK

Tel: 44-172-786-7577   Fax: 44-172-785-8314

Parametric Technology (UK) Ltd., 190 Aztec West, Park Avenue, Almondsbury, Bristol BS12 4TD, UK

Tel: 44-145-461-3201   Fax: 44-145-461-4522

Parametric Technology (UK) Ltd., Kings Hall, St. Ives Business Park, Parsons Green, St. Ives Huntingson, Cambridge PE17 4WY, UK

Tel: 44-148-046-1791   Fax: 44-148-046-1792

Parametric Technology (UK) Ltd., Argent Court, Sir William Lyons Road, Coventry CV4 7EZ, UK

Tel: 44-120-341-7718   Fax: 44-120-369-0924

Parametric Technology (UK) Ltd., Fifth Avenue Plaza, Block A, Queensway No., Team Valley Trading Estates, Gateshead Tyne & Wear NE11 0HF, UK

Tel: 44-191-491-5664   Fax: 44-191-491-4888

Parametric Technology (UK) Ltd., One Fleetwood Park, Barley Way, Fleet Hampshire GU13 8UT, UK

Tel: 44-125-281-7000   Fax: 44-125-280-0722

PAREXEL INTERNATIONAL CORPORATION

195 West Street, Waltham, MA, 02154

Tel: (781) 487-9900   Fax: (781) 487-0525   www.parexel.com

Provides contract medical, biotechnology, and pharmaceutical research and consulting services.

PAREXEL MMS Europe, Ltd., Wicker House, High St., Worthing, West Sussex BN11 1DJ, UK

Tel: 44-1903-205884   Fax: 44-1903-234862

PARK ELECTROCHEMICAL CORPORATION

5 Dakota Drive, Lake Success, NY, 11042

Tel: (516) 354-4100   Fax: (516) 354-4128   www.parkelectrochemical.com

Multi-layer laminate printed circuit materials, industry comps, plumbing hardware products.

New England Laminates (UK) Ltd., 1 Paddock Rd., W. Pimbo, Skelmersdale, Lancashire, UK

PARKER HANNIFIN CORPORATION

6035 Parkland Blvd., Cleveland, OH, 44124-4141

Tel: (216) 896-3000   Fax: (216) 896-4000   www.parker.com

Mfr. motion-control products.

Fluid Connector Products/Parker Hannifin PLC, Haydock Park Road, Derby DE2 8JA, UK

Hydraulic Filtration Div./Parker Hannifin PLC, Peel Street, Morley, Leeds LS27 8EL, UK

Instrumentation Products Div./Parker Hannifin PLC, Riverside Road, Barnstaple, Devon EX31 1NP, UK

Parker Digiplan Ltd., 21-22 Balena Close, Poole, Dorset BH17 7DX, UK

Parker Hannifin Corp., Parker House, 55 Maylands Avenue, Hemel Hempstead, Hertshire HP2 4SJ, UK

Parker Hannifin PLC, Barbados Way, Hellaby Industrial Estate, Hellaby Rotherham, South Yorkshire S66 8RX, UK

Parker Hannifin PLC, Cylinder Div., 6 Greycaine Road, Watford, Hertshire WD2 4QA, UK

Parker Hannifin PLC., Pneumatic Div., Walkmill Lane, Bridgtown Cannock, Staffordshire WS1 3LR, UK

Seal Products/Parker Hannifin PLC, Abbott House, Primrose Hill, Kings Langley, Hertshire WD4 8HY, UK

Seal Products/Parker Hannifin PLC/Chomerics Europe, Parkway, Globe Park, Marlow, Buckinghamshire SL7 1YB, UK

PARLEX CORPORATION

1 Parlex Place, Methuen, MA, 01844

Tel: (978) 685-4341   Fax: (978) 685-8809   www.parlex.com

Mfr. flexible interconnects for automotive, aerospace and telecommunications industries.

Parlex Corporation, Taylor Road, Newport Isle of Wright PO30 5LG, UK

Tel: 44-1983-526535

PARSONS BRINCKERHOFF INC.

One Penn Plaza, New York, NY, 10119-0061

Tel: (212) 465-5000   Fax: (212) 465-5096   www.pbworld.com

Provides planning, engineering, construction management and operations and maintenance services.

Parsons Brinckerhoff, 4 Roger Street, London WC1N 2JX, UK

Tel: 44-207-242-2898   Fax: 44-207-242-1981

Parsons Brinckerhoff, 4 New Street, York YO1 8RA, UK

Parsons Brinckerhoff, Poplar House Park West, Sealand Road, Chester CH1 4RN, UK

Tel: 44-1244-390690   Fax: 44-1244-398298

Parsons Brinckerhoff, Westbrook Mills, Godalming, Surrey GU7 2AZ, UK

Parsons Brinckerhoff, 44/45 Calthorpe Road, Edgbaston, Birmingham B15 1TH, UK

PARSONS CORPORATION

100 West Walnut Street, Pasadena, CA, 91124

Tel: (626) 440-2000   Fax: (626) 440-4919   www.parsons.com

Engaged in engineering, procurement, and construction management services.

Engineering Science Environmental Engineers, EMC Tower, Great West Road, Brentford Middlesex TW8 9AZ, UK

Parsons Engineering Science Inc., Newporte House, Low Moor Rd., Doddington Rd., Lincoln LN6 3JY, UK

PATNI COMPUTER SYSTEMS (PCS) DATA CONVERSION

238 Main Street, Cambridge, MA, 02142

Tel: (617) 354-7424   Fax: (617) 876-4711   www.patni.com

Software consulting and contract programming services.

Patni Computer Systems (UK) Ltd., Vistacentre, 50 Salisbury Road, Hounslow Middlesex TW4 6JQ, UK

Tel: 44-208-538-0120

PAUL, HASTINGS, JANOFSKY & WALKER LLP

555 South Flower Street, Los Angeles, CA, 90017-2371

Tel: (213) 683-6000   Fax: (213) 627-0705   www.phjw.com

Engaged in international employment law.

Paul, Hastings, Janofsky & Walker LLP, 25 Old Broad Street, Tower 42, London EC2N 1HQ, UK

Tel: 44-207-562-4000 Fax: 44-207-628-444

PAUL, WEISS, RIFKIND, WHARTON & GARRISON

1285 Ave. of the Americas, New York, NY, 10019-6064

Tel: (212) 373-3000   Fax: (212) 373-2268   www.paulweiss.com

Law firm engaged in American and international law practice.

Paul, Weiss, Rifkind, Wharton & Garrison, Alder Castle, 10 Noble Street, London EC2V 7JU, UK

Tel: 44-207-367-1600

PAYDEN & RYGEL

333 South Grand Avenue, Los Angeles, CA, 90071

Tel: (213) 625-1900   Fax: (213) 617-3110   www.payden.com

Engaged in financial and investment advisory services.

Payden & Rygel Global Ltd., 62 Cornhill, London EC3V 3NH, UK

Tel: 44-207-7621-3000

P-COM, INC.

3175 South Winchester Blvd., Campbell, CA, 95008

Tel: (408) 866-3666   Fax: (408) 866-3655   www.p-com.com

Mfr. microwave radio transmission equipment.

P-Com UK, Central Boulevard, Blythe Valley Business Park, Solihull, West Midlands B90 8AG, UK

Contact: Mark Emery

PEAVEY ELECTRONICS CORPORATION

711 A Street, Meridian, MS, 39301

Tel: (601) 483-5365   Fax: (601) 486-1278   www.peavey.com

Mfr. portable sound systems.

Peavey Electronics LTD, Great Folds Road, Oakley Hay Corby, Northants NN18 9ET, UK

PEDDINGHAUS CORPORATION

300 North Washington Avenue, Bradley, IL, 60915

Tel: (815) 937-3800   Fax: (815) 937-4003   www.peddinghaus.com

Mfr./distribute structure steel and plate-fabricating equipment.

Peddinghaus Corporation UK Ltd., Unit 6, Queensway Link Industrial Estate, Stafford Park 17, Talford Shropshire TF3 3DN, UK

Tel: 44-1952-200-377 Fax: 44-1952-292-877

PEGASYSTEMS INC.

101 Main Street, Cambridge, MA, 02142-1590

Tel: (617) 374-9600   Fax: (617) 374-9620   www.pegasystems.com

Mfr. customer service software.

Pegasystems UK, Apex Plaza, Reading Berkshire RG1 1AX, UK

Tel: 44-118-959-1150

PENN ENGINEERING

5190 Old Easton Road, Danboro, PA, 18916

Tel: (215) 766-8853   Fax: (215) 766-3633   www.penn-eng.com

Mfr. fasteners for the computer industry.

Penn Engineering UK, Kirk Sandall Industrial Estate, Doncaster, South Yorkshire DN3 1QR, UK

PENTAIR, INC.

1500 County Road, B2 West, St. Paul, MN, 55113-3105

Tel: (612) 636-7920   Fax: (612) 636-5508   www.pentair.com

Diversified manufacturer operating in electrical and electronic enclosures, professional tools/equipment and water products.

Pentair Enclosures, Maylands Avenue, Hemel Hempstead, Hertfordshire HP2 7DE, UK

PENTON MEDIA

1300 E. 9th St., Cleveland, OH, 44114

Tel: (216) 696-7000   Fax: (216) 696-7648   www.penton.com

Publisher of industrial/trade magazines.

Air Transport World, 34A West Street, Marlow, Buckinghamshire SL7 2NB, UK
Tel: 44-1628-477-775   Fax: 44-1628-481-111

Meko, Ltd., 134 Upper Chobham Road, Camberley, Surrey GU15 1EJ, UK
Tel: 44-1276-22677   Fax: 44-1276-64004

New Hope International Media, Brighton Media Center, Brighton, East Sussex BN1 1AL, UK
Tel: 44-1273-384-282   Fax: 44-1273-384-285

Penton Media Europe, Penton House, 288-290 Worton Road, Isleworth, Middlesex TW7 6EL, UK
Tel: 44-208-232-1600   Fax: 44-208-232-1650

Penton Media Europe, 288-290 Worton Road, Isleworth, Middlesex TW7 6EL, UK

Streaming Media, 45 Whitechapel Road, 3/F, London E1 1DU, UK
Tel: 44-20-7375-7500   Fax: 44-20-7375-7511

PENWEST PHARMACEUTICAL CO.

2981 Route 22, Patterson, NY, 12563-9970

Tel: (845) 878-3414   Fax: (845) 878-3484   www.penw.com

Engaged in the research, development and commercialization of novel drug delivery technologies.

Penwest Pharmaceuticals Ltd., Church House, 48 Church Street, Reigate Surrey RH2 OSN, UK
Tel: 44-1737-222323

PEOPLESOFT INC.

4460 Hacienda Drive, Pleasanton, CA, 94588-8618

Tel: (925) 225-3000   Fax: (925) 694-4444   www.peoplesoft.com

Mfr. applications to manage business operations across computer networks.

PeopleSoft UK, Apex Plaza, Reading, Berkshire GRG1 1AX, UK
Tel: 44-118-952-2000   Fax: 44-181-952-2001

PEPPERS AND ROGERS GROUP

20 Glover Avenue, Norwalk, CT, 06850

Tel: (203) 642-5121   Fax: (203) 642-5126   www.1to1.com

Engaged in technology consulting.

Peppers and Rogers, Hare Hatch Grange, Bath Road, Hare Hatch, Reading RG10 9SA, UK
Tel: 44-118-940-5800

PEPSiCO INC.

700 Anderson Hill Road, Purchase, NY, 10577-1444

Tel: (914) 253-2000   Fax: (914) 253-2070   www.pepsico.com

Beverages and snack foods.

Crispflow Ltd., London, UK

Frito-Lay Holdings Ltd., London, UK

PepsiCo Holdings Ltd., London, UK

PFI Agriculture Europe Ltd., London, UK

Walkers Smiths Snack Foods Ltd, London, UK

PEQUOT CAPITAL MANAGEMENT, INC.

500 Nyala Farms Road, Westport, CT, 06880

Tel: (203) 429-2200   Fax: (203) 429-2420   www.pequotcap.com

Engagement in investment and fund management.

Pequot Capital Management UK, 14 Berkeley Road, 2/F, London W1J 8DX, UK

Tel: 44-107-647-4300

PEREGRINE SYSTEMS, INC.

3611 Valley Centre Drive, San Diego, CA, 92130

Tel: (858) 481-5000   Fax: (858) 481-1751   www.peregrine.com

Mfr. resource planning software.

Peregrine Systems Ltd, Ambassador House, Paradise Road, Richmond, Surrey TW9 1SQ, UK

PERICOM SEMICONDUCTOR CORPORATION

2380 Bering Drive, San Jose, CA, 95131

Tel: (408) 435-0800   Fax: (408) 321-0933   wwwpericom.com

Mfr. electronic circuits.

Pericom Semiconductor, 1 Unit, A9 Plough Road Center, Great Bentley Essex CO7 8LG, UK

PERKIN ELMER, INC.

45 William Street, Wellesley, MA, 02481

Tel: (781) 237-5100   Fax: (781) 431-4255   www.perkinelmer.com

Mfr. equipment and devices to detect explosives and bombs on airline carriers.

PerkinElmer Life Sciences, Saxon Way Bar Hill, Cambridge CB3 8SL, UK

PerkinElmer Life Sciences, Mulberry Business Park, Wokingham Berks RG41 2GY, UK

Tel: 44-118-977-3493

PEROT SYSTEMS CORPORATION

12404 Park Central Drive, Dallas, TX, 75251

Tel: (972) 340-5000   Fax: (972) 455-4100   www.perotsystems.com

Provides technology and business solutions.

Perot Systems HPS Europe, Crown House 6/F, 1 Crown Square, Woking, Surrey GU21 6HR, UK

Tel: 44-1483-595400

PERRIGO COMPANY

515 Eastern Avenue, Allegan, MI, 49010

Tel: (616) 673-8451   Fax: (616) 673-9328   www.perrigo.com

Mfr. drugs and nutritional supplements.

Wrafton Laboratories Limited, Wrafton, Braunton, North Devon EX33 2DL, UK

PER-SE TECHNOLOGIES, INC.

2840 Mount Wilkinson Pkwy., Atlanta, GA, 30339

Tel: (770) 444-5300   Fax: (770) 444-4531   www.per-se.com

Engaged in medical practice management.

Per-Se Technologies, Homer House, Monson Street, Lincoln LN5 7RZ, UK

PERVASIVE SOFTWARE INC.

12365 Riata Trace Pkwy., Austin, TX, 78727

Tel: (512) 231-6000   Fax: (512) 231-6010   www.pervasive.com

Mfr. software.

Pervasive EMEAA, Regus House, Highbridge, Oxford Road, Uxbridge, Middlesex UB8 1HR, UK

PETERSON AMERICAN CORPORATION

21200 Telegraph Road, Southfield, MI, 48086-5059

Tel: (248) 799-5400   Fax: (248) 357-3176   www.pspring.com

Mfr. springs and wire products and metal stampings.

A-P Spring, Reddings Lane, Tyseley, Birmingham B11 3HA, UK

Tel: 44-121-706-2236

Heath Springs, Div. Peterson Spring UK, Hewell Road, Redditch, Worcestershire B97 6AY, UK

Tel: 44-527-61952   Fax: 44-527-591660   Contact: Edward Roberts

PFAUDLER, INC.

1000 West Ave., PO Box 23600, Rochester, NY, 14692-3600

Tel: (716) 235-1000   Fax: (716) 436-9644   www.pfaudler.com

Mfr. glass lined reactors, storage vessels and reglassing services.

Chemical Reactor Services Ltd., Bilston, UK

Tel: 44-1902-353-637   Fax: 44-1902-495-696

Chemical Reactor Services Ltd., Bolton, UK

PFIZER INC.

235 East 42nd Street, New York, NY, 10017-5755

Tel: (212) 573-2323   Fax: (212) 573-7851   www.pfizer.com

Research-based, global health care company.

Biomedical Sensors (Holdings) Ltd., London, UK

Biomedical Sensors Ltd., London, UK

Coty Ltd., London, UK

Feldene Ltd., London, UK

Invicta Pharmaceuticals Ltd., London, UK

Pfizer Group Ltd., PO Box 2, Ramsgate Road, Sandwich Kent CT13 9NJ, UK

Tel: 44-1304-616161

Pfizer Hospital Products Group Ltd., London, UK

Pfizer Hospital Products Group Pension Trustee Ltd., London, UK

Pfizer Hospital Products Inc., London, UK

Pfizer Ltd., London, UK

Pfizer Pension Trustees Ltd., London, UK

Richborough Pharmaceuticals Ltd., London, UK

Schick, Div. Pfizer, Sword House, Totteridge Road, High Wycombe, Bucks HP13 6EJ, UK

Tel: 44-1494-533300

Shiley Ltd., London, UK

TCP Ltd., London, UK

Unicliffe Ltd., London, UK

PRODUCTION GROUP INTERNATIONAL, INC.

2200 Wilson Blvd., Ste 200, Arlington, VA, 22201-3324

Tel: (703) 528-8484   Fax: (703) 528-1724   www.pgi.com

Provides major corporations with promotional events, planning and travel services, trade shows and exhibitions.

Spearhead Exhibitions, Ltd., Ocean St., Kingston Rd., New Malden, Surrey KT3 3L2, UK

Tel: 44-181-949-9222   Fax: 44-181-94-8186

PHARMACIA CORPORATION

100 Route 206 North, Peapack, NJ, 07977

Tel: (908) 901-8000   Fax: (908) 901-8379   www.pharmacia.com

Mfr. pharmaceuticals, agricultural products, industry chemicals.

Pharmacia & Upjohn, PO Box No. 8, Fleming Way, Crawley Sussex RH10 2LZ, UK

Pharmacia & Upjohn Ltd., Davy Avenue Knowhill, Milton Keynes MK5 8PH, UK

Tel: 44-1908-661101   Fax: 44-1908-690091

Upjohn Intl. Ltd., Fleming Way, Crawley, Sussex RH10 2NJ, UK

Upjohn Ltd., 23 Grosvenor Rd., St. Albans AL1 3AW, UK

PHARSIGHT CORPORATION

800 West ElCamino Real, Ste. 200, Mountain View, CA, 94040

Tel: (650) 314-3800   Fax: (650) 314-3810   www.pharsight.com

Engaged in drug development.

Pharsight Corporation, 2 Queen Caroline Argentum Center, Hammersmith London W6 9DX, UK

Tel: 44-208-323-8036

PHELPS DODGE CORPORATION

2600 North Central Ave., Phoenix, AZ, 85004-3089

Tel: (602) 234-8100   Fax: (602) 234-8337   www.phelpsdodge.com

Copper, minerals, metals and special engineered products for transportation and electrical markets.

Columbian Chemicals Co., London, UK

PHELPS DUNBAR, LLP

365 Canal Street, Ste. 2000, New Orleans, LA, 70130-6534

Tel: (504) 566-1311   Fax: (504) 568-9130   www.phelpsdunbar.com

Engaged in international law.

Phelps Dunbar, 1 Lime Street, Ste. 731, London EC3M 7DQ, UK

Tel: 44-207-929-0046

PHH ARVAL VEHICLE MANAGEMENT

307 International Circle, Hunt Valley, MD, 21030

Tel: (410) 771-3600   Fax: (410) 771-2841   www.phh.com

Provides fleet leasing and fleet management services to corporate and government clients with sales, service, delivery, executive or specialized trucks fleets.

PHH Vehicle Management Services, Oakland House, Talbot Rd., Old Tafford, Manchester M16 0PQ, UK

Tel: 44-1618-729571

PHH Vehicle Management Services, PHH Centre, Windmill Hill, Whitehall Way, Swindon Wiltshire SN5 6PE, UK

Tel: 44-1793-887000

PHILIP SERVICES CORP. INDUSTRIAL GROUP

9700 Higgins Road, Ste. 750, Rosemont, IL, 60018

Tel: (847) 685-9752   Fax: (847) 685-9775   www.philipinc.com

Trucking, refuse systems, staffing and numerous industrial-oriented services.

Ferrous Bath Reclamation Co., Ltd., Ironchurch Road, Off St. Andrews Road, Avonmouth Bristol BS11 9BP, UK

Tel: 44-117-982-6300 Fax: 44-117-938-1313   Contact: Phil Mumby

Ferrous Philip Metals (Europe) Ltd., Seven Brethren Bank, Industrial Estate, Barnstaple Devon, UK

Tel: 44-127-142-131   Fax: 44-127-142-669   Contact: Alec Heale

Industrial Services Philip Services (Europe), Thornley House, Carrington Business Park, Manchester M31 4SG, UK

Tel: 44-161-775-4488   Fax: 44-161-775-4407   Contact: Ralph Davies

Philip Services (Europe) Ltd., 44 Davies St., London W1Y ILD, UK

Tel: 44-207-518-0950   Fax: 44-207-518-0955   Contact: Ayman Gabarin, President

PHILIPP BROTHERS CHEMICALS INC.

1 Parker Plaza, 400 Kelby Street, Fort Lee, NJ, 07029

Tel: (201) 944-6020   Fax: (201) 944-7916   www.philipp-brothers.com

Mfr. industry and agricultural chemicals.

Wychem Ltd., Bury Road Stradishall-New Market, Suffolk CB8 8YN, UK

Tel: 44-1-440-820-338   Contact: Terry Robinson, Mng. Dir.

PHILLIPS PETROLEUM COMPANY

Phillips Building, 411 S. Keeler Ave., Bartlesville, OK, 74004

Tel: (918) 661-6600   Fax: (918) 661-7636   www.phillips66.com

Crude oil, natural gas, liquefied petroleum gas, gasoline and petro-chemicals.

Phillips Petroleum Co., Portland House, Stag Place, London SW1E 5DA, UK

PHILLIPS, DE PURY & LUXEMBOURG

3 West 57th Street, New York, NY, 10019

Tel: (212) 940-1200   Fax: (212) 688-1647   www.phillips-auctions.com

Auction house.

Phillips De Pury & Luxembourg, 49 Grosvenor Street, London W1K 3HP, UK

PHOTRONICS, INC.

1061 E. Indiantown Rd., Ste. 310, Jupiter, FL, 33477

Tel: (561) 745-1222   Fax: (561) 747-1432   www.photronics.com

Mfr. high-precision quartz photomasks for semiconductors.

Photronics, Inc., Trafford Wharf Road, Manchester M17 1PE, UK

Tel: 33-450-426-440   Fax: 33-450-426-494   Contact: Dominique Varloud

PIC GROUP

2929 Seventh Avenue, Ste. 130, Berkeley, CA, 94710

Tel: (510) 848-8266   Fax: (510) 848-0324   www.pic.com

Engaged in biotechnology.

PIC UK, Fyfield Wick, Abingdon, Oxfordshire OX13 5NA, UK

PIER 1 IMPORTS, INC.

301 Commerce St., Ste. 600, Fort Worth, TX, 76102

Tel: (817) 878-8000   Fax: (817) 252-8801   www.pier1.com

Specialty retailer of imported decorative home furnishings.

Pier 1 Imports, Inc., 91-95 King's Road, Chelsea SW3 4PA, UK

Tel: 44-270-351-7100

Pier 1 Imports, Inc., 200 Tottenham Court Road, WIP OAD, UK

Tel: 44-270-6377001

PILLAR INDUSTRIES INC.

21905 Gateway Road, Brookfield, WI, 53045

Tel: (262) 317-5300   Fax: (262) 317-5353   www.pillar.com

Mfr. induction heating and melting equipment.

Pillar Europe, Unit 9, Spring Rise, Falconer Road, Haverhill Suffolk CB9 7HJ, UK

PILLSBURY WINTHROP LLP

50 Fremont Street, San Francisco, CA, 94105

Tel: (415) 983-1000   Fax: (415) 983-1200   www.pillsburylaw.com

International law firm.

Pillsbury Winthrop LLP, 54 Lombard Street, London EC3V 9DH, UK

Tel: 44-207-648-9200

PINNACLE SYSTEMS

280 North Bernardo Ave., Mountain View, CA, 94043

Tel: (650) 526-1600   Fax: (650) 526-1601   www.pinnaclesys.com

Designs, manufactures, markets and supports a wide range of high-quality digital solutions that enable businesses and consumers to create, store, distribute and view video programs.

Pinnacle Systems Ltd., The Grand Union Office Park, Pinnacle Systems House, Packet Boat Lane, Middlesex, Uxbridge UB8 2GH, UK

Tel: 44-1895-442003

PINNACLE WORLDWIDE, INC.

1201 Marquette Ave., Ste. 300, Minneapolis, MN, 55403

Tel: (612) 338-2215   Fax: (612) 338-2572   www.pinnacleww.com

International network of independent public relations firms.

Barclay Stratton, Albert House, 27 Kelso Place, London W8 5QG, UK

Tel: 44-20-7544-6000   Fax: 44-20-7544-6290

PIONEER HI-BRED INTERNATIONAL INC.

400 Locust Street, Ste. 800, Des Moines, IA, 50309

Tel: (515) 248-4800   Fax: (515) 248-4999   www.pioneer.com

Agricultural chemicals, farm supplies, biological products, research.

Pioneer Hi-Bred Northern Europe GmbH, The Barn, Blisworth Hill Farm, Northampton Northants, Blisworth NN7 3DB, UK

Tel: 44-1604-858008

PIONEER-STANDARD ELECTRONICS, INC.

6065 Parkland Blvd., Cleveland, OH, 44124

Tel: (440) 720-8500 Fax: (440) 720-8501 www.pios.com

Mfr. and distribution of electronic parts for computers and networking equipment.

Eurodis Electron Plc., Reigate Hill House, Reigate, Surrey RH2 9NG, UK

Tel: 44-1737-242-464

Eurodis HB Electronics, Lever Street, Bolton, Lancashire BL3 6BJ, UK

Tel: 44-1204-555-000

PITNEY BOWES INC.

1 Elmcroft Road, Stamford, CT, 06926-0700

Tel: (203) 356-5000 Fax: (203) 351-6835 www.pitneybowes.com

Mfr. postage meters, mailroom equipment, copiers, bus supplies, bus services, facsimile systems and financial services.

Pitney Bowes Ltd., The Pinnacles, Harlow, Essex CM19 5BD, UK

Tel: 44-1279-426-731 Fax: 44-1279-449-275 Contact: Malachy Smith, Mng. Dir. Emp: 1,700

Pitney Bowes Management Services Ltd., New City Court, 20 St. Thomas Street, London SE1 9RS, UK

Tel: 44-207-962-1175

PLANAR SYSTEMS, INC.

1400 NW Compton Drive, Beaverton, OR, 97006

Tel: (503) 690-1100 Fax: (503) 690-1541 www.planar.com

Mfr. of flat panel displays and liquid crystal displays.

Planar Systems Ltd., Unit 2 Hampden House Monument Business Park, Monument Business Park Warpsgrove Lane, Chalgrove Oxon OX44 7RW, UK

Contact: Alan Liddle

PLANET HOLLYWOOD INTERNATIONAL, INC.

8669 Commodity Circle, Orlando, FL, 32819

Tel: (407) 363-7827 Fax: (407) 363-4862 www.planethollywood.com

Theme-dining restaurant chain and merchandise retail stores.

Planet Hollywood International, Inc., London, UK

PLANTRONICS

345 Encinal Street, Santa Cruz, CA, 95060

Tel: (831) 426-5858 Fax: (831) 425-5198 www.plantronics.com

Mfr. lightweight headsets and communications equipment and electrical and electronic appliances.

Plantronics MEEA Sales Region, 262 Regents Park Road, Wootton Bassett, Finchley SN3 3HN, UK

Tel: 44-1793-848999 Fax: 44-1793-848853 Contact: Howard Shenton

PLEXUS CORPORATION

55 Jewelers Park Drive, Neenah, WI, 54957-0677

Tel: (920) 722-3451 Fax: (920) 751-5395 www.plexus.com

Mfr. electronic products for companies in the telecommunications and computer markets.

Plexus Corporation, Quayside Park, Maldon, Essex CM9 5FA, UK

Tel: 44-1376-507-222 Fax: 44-1376-507-333

Plexux Corporation, Pinnacle Hill, Kelso, Roxburghshire TD5 8DW, UK

Tel: 44-1573-223-601 Fax: 44-1573-223-600

PLUMTREE SOFTWARE, INC.

500 Sansome Street, San Francisco, CA, 94111

Tel: (415) 263-8900 Fax: (415) 263-8991 www.plumtree.com

Mfr. organizational software.

Plumtree Software Ltd., 42-01 Suntec Tower 3, Siena Court, The Broadway, Maidenhead, Berks SN6 1NJ, UK

THE PMI GROUP, INC.

601 Montgomery Street, San Francisco, CA, 94111

Tel: (415) 788-7878   Fax: (415) 291-6191   www.pmigroup.com

Mortgage insurer.

PMI Mortgage Insurance Ltd., Essex Lodge, Station Road, London SW13 0LW, UK

PNY TECHNOLOGIES, INC.

299 Webro Road, Parsippany, NJ, 07054

Tel: (973) 515-9700   Fax: (973) 560-5281   www.pny.com

Mfr. computer memory chips.

PNY Technologies, Inc., Ringway House, Bell Road Daneshill, Basingstroke Hampshire RG24 8FB, UK

Tel: 44-1-256-338609   Fax: 44-1-256-338618

POLAROID CORPORATION

784 Memorial Drive, Cambridge, MA, 02139

Tel: (781) 386-2000   Fax: (781) 386-3924   www.polaroid.com

Photographic equipment and supplies, optical products.

Polaroid (UK) Ltd., Wheathampstead House, Codicote Road, Wheathampstead, Hertfordshire AL4 8SF, UK

Tel: 44-1582-632-000   Fax: 44-1582-632-001

R.L. POLK & COMPANY

26955 Northwestern Hwy., Southfield, MI, 48034

Tel: (248) 728-7111   Fax: (248) 393-2860   www.polk.com

Directories and direct mail advertising.

Polk (Europe) Ltd., Millfield, Ashwells Rd., Brentwood, Essex CM15 9ST, UK

Portica Ltd., Addison Rd., Chilton Industrial Estate, Sudbury, Suffolk CO10 6YJ, UK

The Ultimate Perspective Management Consultancy (TUP), Gladstone Place, 36-38 Upper Marlborough Rd., St. Albans, Hertfordshire AL1 3US, UK

POLO RALPH LAUREN CORPORATION

650 Madison Ave., New York, NY, 10022

Tel: (212) 318-7000   Fax: (212) 888-5780   www.poloralphlauren.com

Designs and markets clothing, bath and bedding and operates Polo Ralph Lauren and Polo Sport stores.

Ralph Lauren, Ltd., 143 New Bond St., London W1Y 9FD, UK

Tel: 44-207-493-4828   Contact: Sarah Manley, Mng. Dir.

POLYCOM, INC.

1565 Barber Lane, Milpitas, CA, 95035

Tel: (408) 526-9000   Fax: (408) 526-9100   www.polycom.com

Mfr. video conferencing systems, network bridging and multiplexing products, system peripherals.

Polycom, Inc., 270 Bath Rd., Slough, Berkshire SL1 4DX, UK

Tel: 44-1753-723000   Fax: 44-1753-723010

Polycom, Inc., St. James Court, Wilderspool Causeway, Warrington WA4 6PS, UK

Tel: 44-1925-633664   Fax: 44-1925-658878

PORTA SYSTEMS CORPORATION

575 Underhill Boulevard, Syosset, NY, 11791

Tel: (516) 364-9300   Fax: (516) 682-4636   www.portasystems.com

Design/mfr. products for the connection, protection, testing, administration and management of public and private telecommunications lines and networks.

Porta Systems Ltd., Royal Oak Way N., Royal Oak Ind. Est., Coventry NN1 15PQ, UK

PORTAL SOFTWARE, INC.

10200 S. De Anza Bolevard, Cupertino, CA, 95014

Tel: (408) 572-2000   Fax: (408) 572-2001   www.portal.com

Mfr. customer management and billing software.

Portal Software UK, Portal House, 7 Bath Road, Slough SL1 3UE, UK

Tel: 44-175-324-4000

PORTEC RAIL PRODUCTS INC.

900 Freeport Rd., Box 38250, Pittsburgh, PA, 15238-8250

Tel: (412) 782-6000   Fax: (412) 782-1037   www.portecrail.com

Provides rail freight and transit operators with innovative products, services and solutions.

Conveyors International, 43 Wenlock Way, Troon Industrial Area, Leicester LE4 9HU, UK

PORTER PRECISION PRODUCTS COMPANY

2734 Banning Road, PO Box 538706, Cincinnati, OH, 45239

Tel: (513) 923-3777   Fax: (513) 923-1111   www.porterpunch.com

Mfr. piercing punches and die supplies for metal stamping and tool/die industry.

Porter Precision Products Ltd., Masons Rd., Stratford-upon-Avon, Warwickshire CV37 9NF, UK

PORTERA SYSTEMS INC.

1715 Dell Avenue, Campbell, CA, 95008

Tel: (408) 364-3600   Fax: (408) 341-1830   www.portera.com

Mfr. computer software.

Portera EMEA, 3000 Cathedral Hill, Guildford Surrey GU 2 YB, UK

POTTERS INDUSTRIES INC.

PO Box 840, Valley Forge, PA, 19482-0840

Tel: (610) 651-4700   Fax: (610) 408-9724   www.pottersbeads.com

Mfr. glass spheres for road marking and industry applications.

Potters Ballotini Ltd., Bury St., Edmunds, UK

Tel: 44-1-284-715400

Potters-Ballotini Ltd., Pontefract Rd., Barnsley, South Yorkshire S71 1HJ, UK

POWELL, GOLDSTEIN, FRAZER & MURPHY

191 Peachtree Street NE, 16th Fl., Atlanta, GA, 30303-1740

Tel: (404) 572-6600   Fax: (404) 572-6999   www.pgfm.com

Engaged in international law.

Powell, Goldstein, Frazer & Murphy, 1 Lime Street, Ste. 731, London EC3M 7DQ, UK

Tel: 44-207-929-4765

POWER TECHNOLOGIES INC. (PTI)

1482 Erie Blvd., PO Box 1058, Schenectady, NY, 12301

Tel: (518) 395-5000   Fax: (518) 346-2777   www.pti-us.com

Power systems engineering, consulting, services and related control software; power quality hardware.

PTI Ltd., Cranford Court, King Street, Knutsford Cheshire WA16 8BW, UK

Tel: 44-1565-650388   Fax: 44-1565-750376

POWERQUEST CORPORATION

1359 North Research Way, Bldg. K, Box 1911, Orem, UT, 84059

Tel: (801) 437-8900   Fax: (801) 226-8941   www.powerquest.com

Provides storage lifecycle automation solutions.

PowerQuest UK, Ltd, Thames Tower, Station Approach, Reading RG1 1LX, UK

POWERWARE CORPORATION

8609 Six Forks Road, Raleigh, NC, 27615

Tel: (919) 870-3020   Fax: (919) 870-3100   www.powerware.com

Mfr./services uninterruptible power supplies and related equipment.

Powerware Electronics Ltd., 221 Dover Rd., Slough, Berkshire SL1 4RS, UK

Tel: 44-1753-608-700   Fax: 44-1753-608-995

PPG INDUSTRIES

One PPG Place, Pittsburgh, PA, 15272

Tel: (412) 434-3131   Fax: (412) 434-2190   www.ppg.com

Mfr. coatings, flat glass, fiber glass, chemicals.

PPG Indusries (UK) Ltd., Fiber Glass, PO Box 132, Leigh Rd., Wigam EN2 4XZ, UK

PPG Industries (UK) Ltd., Coatings, PO Box 359, Rotton Park St., Birmingham B16 0AD, UK

PPL GLOBAL CORPORATION

2 N. 9th St, Allentown, PA, 18101

Tel: (610) 774-5151   Fax: (610) 774-4198   www.pplweb.com

Energy holding company engaged in electric.

WPD Holdings UK, Avonbank, Feeder Road, Bristol BS2 0TB, UK

Tel: 44-117-933-2000   Fax: 44-117-933-2001   Contact: Robert Symons

PR NEWSWIRE ASSOCIATION INC.

810 Seventh Avenue, 35th Fl., New York, NY, 10019

Tel: (212) 596-1500   Fax: (212) 541-6114   www.prnewswire.com

Distribution of news releases and photos to media organizations.

PR Newswire Europe, Ludgate House, 245 Blackfriars Road, London SE1 9UY, UK

PRACTICEWORKS, INC.

1765 The Exchange, Atlanta, GA, 30339

Tel: (770) 850-5006   Fax: (770) 857-1300   www.practiceworks.com

Mfr. practice management software.

PracticeWorks UK Ltd., Elopak House, Rutherford Close, Meadway Technology Park, Stevenage Hertfordshire SG1 2 PR, UK

PracticeWorks UK Ltd., 123 Bath Row, Edgbaston Birmingham B15 1LS, UK

PRECISION VALVE & TRIM, INC.

11923 Cloverland Ave, Baton Rouge, LA, 70809

Tel: (225) 752-5600   Fax: (225) 752-5400   www.precisionvalve.com

Mfr. aerosol valves.

Precision Valve UK Ltd., Unit C, Newcombe Way, Orton Southgate, Peterborough, Cambs PE2 0SF, UK

PREFORMED LINE PRODUCTS COMPANY

600 Beta Drive, PO Box 91129, Mayfield, OH, 44101-3129

Tel: (440) 461-5200   Fax: (440) 442-8816   www.preformed.com

Mfr. pole line hardware for electrical transmission lines; splice closures and related products for telecommunications.

Preformed Line Products Ltd., East Portway, Andover, Hampshire SP10 3 LH, UK

Contact: David Hearnshaw

PREMIX INC.

PO Box 281, 3365 E. Center Street, North Kingsville, OH, 44068-0281

Tel: (440) 224-2181   Fax: (440) 224-2766   www.premix.com

Mfr. molded fiber glass, reinforced thermoset molding compounds and plastic parts.

Permali RP Ltd., 125 Bristol Rd., Gloucester GL1 5TT, UK

Tel: 44-1452-528-671   Fax: 44-1452-304-215   Contact: Mike Malloria, Mng. Dir   Emp: 104

PRESTOLITE ELECTRIC INC.

2311 Green Road, Ste. B, Ann Arbor, MI, 48105

Tel: (734) 913-6600   Fax: (734) 913-6656   www.prestolite.com

Mfr. alternators and starter motors.

Prestolite Electric Ltd., Larden Road, Acton, London W3 7RP, UK

Prestolite Electric Ltd., Cleveland Rd., Leyland PR5 1XB, UK

Tel: 44-1772-455515

PREVIO, INC.

12636 High Bluff Drive, 4th Fl., San Diego, CA, 92130

Tel: (858) 794-4300   Fax: (858) 794-4572   www.previo.com

Engaged in corporate electronic business support.

Previo Europe Limited, High View House Ste. 406, Charles Square, Bracknell Berkshire RG12 1DF, UK

Tel: 44-1344-397-593   Fax: 44-1377-397-617

PRG-SCHULTZ INTERNATIONAL INC.

2300 Windy Ridge Pkwy., Ste. 100 N, Atlanta, GA, 30339-8426

Tel: (770) 779-3900   Fax: (770) 898-2996   www.prgx.com

Engaged in comprehensive recovery auditing and process improvement services.

PRG UK, 950 Cabability Green, Luton LU1 3LU, UK

Tel: 44-1582-395-800

PRICEWATERHOUSECOOPERS LLP

1301 Ave. of the Americas, New York, NY, 10019

Tel: (212) 596-7000   Fax: (212) 259-1301   www.pwcglobal.com

Accounting and auditing, tax and management, and human resource consulting services.

PriceWaterhouseCoopers, 31 Great George St., Bristol BS1 5QD, UK

Tel: 44-117-929-1500   Fax: 44-117-929-0519

PriceWaterhouseCoopers, Southwark Towers, 32 London Bridge Street, London SE1 9SY, UK

Tel: 44-207-939-3000   Fax: 44-207-939-2526

PriceWaterhouseCoopers, Docklands Island Quay, 161 Marsh Wall, London E14 9SQ, UK

Tel: 44-207-939-3000   Fax: 44-207-538-5547

PriceWaterhouseCoopers, York House, York Street, Manchester M2 4WS, UK

Tel: 44-161-245-2000   Fax: 44-161-228-1429

PriceWaterhouseCoopers, The Quay, 30 Channel Way, Ocean Village Southampton, Hants SO14 3QG, UK

Tel: 44-1703-330077   Fax: 44-1703-223473

PriceWaterhouseCoopers, Cornwall Court, 19 Cornwall Street, Birmingham B3 2DT, UK

Tel: 44-121-200-3000   Fax: 44-121-200-2464

PRIMAVERA SYSTEMS, INC.

3 Bala Plaza West, Ste. 700, Bala Cynwyd, PA, 19004

Tel: (610) 667-8600   Fax: (610) 667-7894   www.primavera.com

Mfr. project management software.

Primavera Systems, Inc., Commonwealth House, 2/F, 2 Chalkhill Road, London W6 8DW, UK

Tel: 44-208-563-5533

PRIMUS KNOWLEDGE SOLUTIONS, INC.

1601 Fifth Avenue, Ste. 1900, Seattle, WA, 98101

Tel: (206) 834-8100   Fax: (206) 834-8125   www.primus.com

Mfr. management software.

Primus Knowledge Solutions UK Ltd., 268 Bath Road, Slough Berks SL1 4DX, UK

Tel: 44-1753-708411

PRINTCAFE SOFTWARE, INC.

40 24th Street, 5th Fl., Pittsburgh, PA, 15222

Tel: (412) 456-1141   Fax: (412) 456-1151   www.printcafe.com

Provides software and services.

Printcafe Europe Ltd., 281A St. Leonard's Road, Windsor Berkshire SL4 3DR, UK

Tel: 44-1753-622606   Fax: 44-1753-854339

PRINTRAK

1250 North Tustin Avenue, Anaheim, CA, 92807

Tel: (714) 238-2000   Fax: (714) 237-0018   www.printrakinternational.com

Mfr. enterprise software and related services for information management and decision support that ensures community safety and security, including sales of law enforcement tools, including fingerprint ID systems (AFIS).

Printrak Europe Middle East and Africa, No.1 Cobham Road, Ferndown Industrial Estate, Wimborne BH21 7PT, UK

Tel: 44-1202-862000

PRINTRONIX INC.

14600 Myford Road, Irvine, CA, 92606

Tel: (714) 368-2300   Fax: (714) 368-2600   www.printronix.com

Mfr. computer printers.

Printronix UK, Downmill Rd., Bracknell, Berkshire RG12 1QS, UK

Tel: 44-1344-869666   Fax: 44-1344-360967

Printronix UK, Loddon Vale House, Hurricane Way, Woodley, Berkshire RG5 4UX, UK

PROCTER & GAMBLE COMPANY

One Procter & Gamble Plaza, Cincinnati, OH, 45202

Tel: (513) 983-1100   Fax: (513) 562-4500   www.pg.com

Personal care, food, laundry, cleaning and industry products.

Procter & Gamble, St. Nicholas Ave., PO Box 1EL, Gosforth, Newcastle-upon-Tyne Tyne NE99 1EE, UK

Tel: 44-191-279-2000

PROCTER & GAMBLE PHARMACEUTICALS (P&GP)

17 Eaton Ave., Norwich, NY, 13815-1799

Tel: (607) 335-2111   Fax: (607) 335-2798   www.pg.com

Engaged in research dedicated to creating and delivering solutions that improve the health and well-being of people around the world.

Procter & Gamble Pharmaceuticals UK, Lovett House, Lovett Road, Staines, Middlesex TW18 3AZ, UK

PROGRESS SOFTWARE CORPORATION

14 Oak Park, Bedford, MA, 01730

Tel: (781) 280-4000   Fax: (781) 280-4095   www.progress.com

Mfr. software.

Progress Software, 210 Bath Road, Slough Berkshire SL 1 3XE, UK

PROQUEST COMPANY

300 N. Zeeb Road, Ann Arbor, MI, 48103

Tel: (734) 761-4700   Fax: (734) 997-4040   www.bellhowell.com

Engaged in information management services; publishers of electronic content for the academic, library, automotive and power sports industries.

ProQuest Information and Learning Company, The Quorum, Barnwell Road, Cambridge CB5 8SW, UK

ProQuest Information and Learning Company, The Quorum, Barnwell Road, Cambridge CB5 8SW, UK

PROVIDIAN FINANCIAL CORPORATION

201 Mission St., San Francisco, CA, 94105

Tel: (415) 543-0404   Fax: (415) 278-6028   www.providian.com

Provides standard and premium credit cards to consumers.

Providian Financial Corporation, Crawley, West Sussex, UK

Contact: James V. Elliott, Pres.

PROXIM CORPORATION

510 DeGuigne Drive, Sunnyvale, CA, 94089

Tel: (408) 731-2700   Fax: (408) 731-3675   www.proxim.com

Mfr. wireless modems.

Promix Corporation, PO Box 48, High Wycombe, Bucks HP14 4GA, UK

PRUDENTIAL FINANCIAL

751 Broad Street, Newark, NJ, 07102-3777

Tel: (973) 802-6000   Fax: (973) 802-2804   www.prudential.com

Sale of life insurance, financial services, asset management and brokerage.

Prudential-Bache International Bank Limited, 9 Devonshire Square, London EC2M 4HP, UK

Tel: 44-0207-548-5200   Fax: 44-020-7548-5252   Contact: Michael Walker

PSC INC.

111 SW Fifth Avenue, Ste. 4100, Portland, OR, 97204-3644

Tel: (503) 553-3920   Fax: (503) 553-3940   www.pscnet.com

Mfr. and sales of bar code scanners.

PSC Bar Code Ltd., Axis 3, Rhodes Way, Watford, Hertfordshire WD24 4TR, UK

Tel: 44-1923-809500   Fax: 44-1923-809505

PSI NET (PERFORMANCE SYSTEMS INTERNATIONAL INC.)

44983 Knoll Square, Ashburn, VA, 20147

Tel: (703) 726-4100   Fax: (703) 726-4200   www.psinet.com

Internet service provider.

PSINet UK Ltd., Brookmount Court, Units A & B, Kirkwood Road, Cambridge CB4 2QH, UK

Tel: 44-1-1223-577577   Fax: 44-1223-506577   Contact: Valerie Holt, VP & Mng. Dir.

PUBLIC SERVICE ENTERPRISE GROUP (PSEG)

80 Park Plaza, Newark, NJ, 07101

Tel: (973) 430-7000   Fax: (973) 623-5389   www.pseg.com

Electric and gas utility.

PSEG Global Ltd., 8 Bourdon Street, London W1X 9HX, UK

Tel: 44-207-744-0100   Fax: 44-207-744-0177   Contact: Matthew McGrath

PULSE ENGINEERING INC.

12220 World Trade Drive, PO 12235, San Diego, CA, 92112

Tel: (858) 674-8100   Fax: (858) 674-8262   www.pulseeng.com

Mfr. passive magnetic components and modules for use in Internet/broadband access, power, telecommunications and datacom applications.

Pulse Engineering UK, 1 & 2 Huxley Road, The Surrey Research Park, Guildford Surrey GU2 5RE, UK

PURE FISHING

1900 18th Street, Spirit Lake, IA, 51360

Tel: (712) 336-1520   Fax: (712) 336-4183   www.purefishing.com

Mfr. fishing rods, reels, lines and tackle, outdoor products, soft and hard baits.

Pure Fishing, Unit 5, Aston Way, Middlewich Motorway Estate, Middlewich Cheshire CW10 OHS, UK

Tel: 44-1606-836-921   Fax: 44-1606-836-411   Contact: Robbie Brightwell, Mng. Dir.   Emp: 17

PUTNAM INVESTMENTS

1 Post Office Square, Boston, MA, 02109

Tel: (617) 292-1000   Fax: (617) 292-1499   www.putnaminv.com

Money management; mutual funds, annuities and retirement plans.

Putnam Advisory Co. Ltd., Pollen House, 10-12 Cork St., London W1X 1PD, UK

QAD INC.

6450 Via Real, Carpinteria, CA, 93013

Tel: (805) 684-6614   Fax: (805) 566-4479   www.qad.com

Mfr. software.

QAD UK, Largotim House, Waterfront Business Park, Dudley Road Brierley Hill, West Midlands DY5 1LX, UK

QLOGIC CORPORATION

26600 Laguna Hills Drive, Aliso Veijo, CA, 92656

Tel: (949) 389-6000   Fax: (949) 389-6126   www.qlogic.com

Engaged in the design of management software.

Qlogic UK, Surrey Technology Centre, 40 Occam Road, Guildford GU2 5YG, UK

QRS CORPORATION

1400 Marina Way South, Richmond, CA, 94804

Tel: (510) 215-5000   Fax: (510) 215-3980   www.qrs.com

Provides business-to-business electronic data systems and services.

QRS Ltd., Royal Albert House, Sheet Street, Windsor, Berkshire SL4 1BE, UK

Tel: 44-1753-705185

QUAKER CHEMICAL CORPORATION

1 Quaker Park, 901 Hector St., Conshohocken, PA, 19428-0809

Tel: (610) 832-4000   Fax: (610) 832-8682   www.quakerchem.com

Mfr. developer, producer, and marketer of custom-formulated chemical specialty products.

Quaker Chemical Ltd., Bath Rd., Woodchester, Stroud, Gloucestershire, UK

Tel: 44-1453-874200   Contact: John H. Powell

THE QUAKER OATS COMPANY

Quaker Tower, 321 North Clark Street, Chicago, IL, 60610-4714

Tel: (312) 222-7111   Fax: (312) 222-8323   www.quakeroats.com

Mfr. foods and beverages.

Quaker Oats Ltd., PO Box 24, Bridge Rd., Southall Middlesex UB2 4AG, UK

Contact: George F. Sewell

QUALCOMM INC.

5775 Morehouse Dr., San Diego, CA, 92121-1714

Tel: (858) 587-1121   Fax: (858) 658-2100   www.qualcomm.com

Digital wireless telecommunications systems.

QUALCOMM UK, Block B, 2/F, Spectrum Point, Farnborough Road, Farnborough, UK

QUANTUM

500 McCarthy Blvd., Milpitas, CA, 95035

Tel: (408) 894-4000   Fax: (408) 894-3218   www.quantum.com

Mfr. computer peripherals.

Quantum Peripheral Products Ltd., 10 Bracknell Beeches, Bracknell, Berkshire RG12 7BW, UK

Tel: 44-1344-353510

QUARK, INC.

1800 Grant Street, Denver, CO, 80203

Tel: (303) 894-8888   Fax: (303) 894-3398   www.quark.com

Mfr. and sales of desktop publishing software.

Quark Systems ltd., Fulbrook Lane, Elstead GU8 6LG, UK

QUEXCO INCORPORATED

2777 N. Stemmons Fwy., Dallas, TX, 75207-2501

Tel: (214) 688-4000   Fax: (214) 630-5864

Engaged in recycling of scrapped lead acid batteries.

ECO-BAT Technologies, Cowley Lodge, Warren Carr, Matlock, Derbyshire DE4 2LE, UK

QUICK EAGLE NETWORKS INC.

217 Humboldt Court, Sunnyvale, CA, 94089

Tel: (408) 745-6200   Fax: (408) 745-6250   www.quickeagle.com

Mfr. digital multiplexers and network management software.

Quick Eagle Networks, Cardinal Point Park Road, Rickmansworth, Hertforshire WD3 1RE, UK

Tel: 44-1923-432708   Contact: Paul Shaw

QUINTILES TRANSNATIONAL CORPORATION

4709 Creekstone Dr., Durham, NC, 27703

Tel: (919) 998-2000   Fax: (919) 998-9113   www.quintiles.com

Mfr. pharmaceuticals.

G.D.R.U. Limited, 6 Newcomen Street, London SE1 1YR, UK

Medical Action Communications Ltd., Action International House, Crabtree Office Village, Eversley Way Thorpe Egham, Surrey TW20 8RY, UK

QWEST COMMUNICATIONS INTERNATIONAL INC.

1801 California Street, Ste. 5200, Denver, CO, 80202

Tel: (303) 896-2020   Fax: (303) 793-6654   www.uswest.com

Tele-communications provider; integrated communications services.

Telewest Broadband UK, London, UK

Tel: 44-207-333-8866   Fax: 44-207-333-8232

R. H. DONNELLY CORPORATION (RHD)

One Manhattanville Road, Purchase, NY, 10577

Tel: (914) 933-6400   Fax: (914) 933-6544   www.rhd.com

Publisher of Yellow Pages and telephone directories and provides direct mail and merchandising services.

Thomson Directories Ltd., 296 Farnborough Rd., Farnborough, Hants GU14 7NU, UK

RADIO SHACK CORPORATION

100 Throckmorton Street, Fort Worth, TX, 76102

Tel: (817) 390-3700   Fax: (817) 415-2647   www.tandy.com

Mfr. electronic and acoustic equipment; Radio Shack retail stores.

InterTAN, Inc., 2 Ascot Rd., Bedfont, Feltham, Middlesex TW14 8QH, UK

InterTAN, Inc., Tameway Tower, Bridge St., Walsallow WS1 1LA, UK

RADISSON HOTELS INTERNATIONAL

Carlson Pkwy., PO Box 59159, Minneapolis, MN, 55459-8204

Tel: (612) 540-5526   Fax: (612) 449-3400   www.radisson.com

Operates, manages and franchises full-service hotels and resorts worldwide.

Radisson Court Hotels, Attn: British Office, Carlson Parkway, PO Box 59159, Minneapolis, MN, 55459-8204

Tel: 44-207-589-2424   Fax: 44-207-225-2293

Radisson Savoy Court Hotel, Granville Place, London W1H OEH, UK

Tel: 44-207-408-0130   Fax: 44-207-493-2070

RADISYS CORPORATION

5445 NE Dawson Creek Drive, Hillsboro, OR, 97124

Tel: (503) 615-1100   Fax: (503) 615-1121   www.radisys.com

Mfr. embedded computer systems.

RadiSys UK, 10 Centech Park, N. Moons Moat, Fringe Meadow Road, Redditch, Worcestershire B98 9NR, UK

RAIN BIRD SPRINKLER MFG. CORPORATION

145 North Grand Ave., Glendora, CA, 91741-2469

Tel: (626) 963-9311   Fax: (626) 963-4287   www.rainbird.com

World's largest manufacturer of lawn sprinklers and irrigation systems equipment.

Rain Bird in UK, Riddens Lanes, Plimpton Green, Lewes, East Sussex BN7 3BJ, UK

Tel: 44-1273-891326   Fax: 44-1273-891327   Contact: Victor Jamieson

RAINBOW TECHNOLOGY INC.

50 Technology Dr., Irvine, CA, 92618

Tel: (949) 450-7300   Fax: (949) 450-7450   www.rainbow.com

Mfr. computer related security products.

Rainbow Technologies Ltd., 4 The Forum, Hanworth Lane, Chertsey, Surrey KT16 9JX, UK

RAND McNALLY & COMPANY

8255 North Central Park Ave., Skokie, IL, 60076-2970

Tel: (847) 329-8100   Fax: (847) 673-0539   www.randmcnally.com

Publishing, consumer software, information and retail.

De Agostini-Rand McNally, Griffin House, London, UK

RAPP COLLINS WORLDWIDE

437 Madison Ave., 3rd Fl., New York, NY, 10022

Tel: (212) 817-6800   Fax: (212) 686-7047   www.rappcollins.com

Engaged in direct marketing and advertising.

WWAV Rapp Collins Media Ltd., 1 Riverside, Manbre Road, London W6 9WA, UK

Tel: 44-208-735-7500   Fax: 44-208-735-8005   Contact: Peter Mitchell

WWAV Rapp Collins North, Mayesbrook House, Lawnswood Park, Redvers Close Leeds LS16 6QY, UK

Tel: 44-113-222-6300   Fax: 44-113-222-6363   Contact: Helen Simpson

WWAV Rapp Collins West, 40 Berkeley Square, Clifton, Bristol BS8 1HU, UK

Tel: 44-1179-041-243   Fax: 44-1179-041-145   Contact: Allan Freeman

RATIONAL SOFTWARE CORPORATION

18880 Homestead Road, Cupertino, CA, 95014-0721

Tel: (408) 863-9900   Fax: (408) 863-4120   www.rationale.com

Mfr. application development software.

Rational Software Ltd., Kingswood, Kings Ride, Ascot, Berkshire SL5 8AJ, UK

RAY & BERNDTSON, INC.

301 Commerce, Ste. 2300, Fort Worth, TX, 76102

Tel: (817) 334-0500   Fax: (817) 334-0779   www.prb.com

Executive search, management audit and management consulting firm.

Ray & Berndtson, 11 Hanover Square, London W1R 9HD, UK

Tel: 44-207-529-1111   Fax: 44-207-529-1000   Contact: Richard Boggis-Rolfe

RAYMOND JAMES FINANCIAL, INC.

880 Carillon Parkway, St. Petersburg, FL, 33716

Tel: (813) 573-3800   Fax: (813) 573-8244   www.rjf.com

Financial services; securities brokerage, asset management, and investment banking services.

Raymond James & Associates, Neptune House, 14 Finsbury Square, London EC2A 1BR, UK

Tel: 44-207-696-6150   Fax: 44-207-696-6197   Contact: E. Rowe

RAYONIER INC.

50 N. Laura Street, Jacksonville, FL, 32202

Tel: (904) 357-9100   Fax: (904) 357-9155   www.rayonier.com

Engaged in logging and manufacture of paper pulp, chemicals and cellulose.

Rayonier Industries Ltd., 17A Curson Street, London W1, UK

RAYOVAC CORPORATION

601 Rayovac Drive, Madison, WI, 53711-2497

Tel: (608) 275-3340   Fax: (608) 275-4577   www.rayovac.com

Mfr. batteries and lighting devices.

Rayovac Ltd., Galleon House King Street, Mainstone Kent ME14 1BG, UK

Tel: 441-622-676699

Rayovac Micro Power Ltd., Stephenson Estate, Dist. 12, Washington, Tyne & Wear NE37 3HW, UK

Rayovac Vidor Ltd., Beaumont Way, Aycliffe Industrial Estate, County Durham DL5 6SN, UK

RAYTHEON COMPANY

141 Spring Street, Lexington, MA, 02173

Tel: (781) 862-6600   Fax: (781) 860-2172   www.raytheon.com

Mfr. diversified electronics, appliances, energy and environmental products; publishing, industry and construction services.

Cosser Electronics Ltd., The Pinnacles, Elizabeth Way, Harlow Essex CM19 5BB, UK

Data Logic Ltd., The Pinnacles, Elizabeth Way, Harlow Essex CM19 5BB, UK

Electrical Installations Ltd., 65 Vincent Sq., Westminster, London SW1P 2NX, UK

Raytheon Aircraft Company, Eaton House Proctor Way, London (Luton) Airport, Bedfordshire LU2 9PE, UK

Contact: Keith Symes

Raytheon Aircraft Company/RAF Northolt, West End Road, Ruislip, Middlesex HA4 6NG, UK

Contact: Martin Nicholls

Raytheon Europe Ltd., Queens House, Greenhill Way, Harrow Middlesex HA1 1YR, UK

RAZORFISH, INC.

32 Mercer Street, New York, NY, 10013

Tel: (212) 966-5960   Fax: (212) 966-6915   www.razorfish.com

Engaged in consulting and web services.

Razorfish UK, 2 East Poultry Avenue, Smithfield London EC1A 9 PT, UK

Tel: 44-0207-549-4200

READER'S DIGEST ASSOCIATION, INC.

Reader's Digest Rd., Pleasantville, NY, 10570

Tel: (914) 238-1000   Fax: (914) 238-4559   www.readersdigest.com

Publisher of magazines and books and direct mail marketer.

Reader's Digest Association Ltd., 25 Berkeley Square, London W1X 6AB, UK

RECOTON CORPORATION

2950 Lake Emma Road, Lake Mary, FL, 32746

Tel: (407) 333-8900   Fax: (407) 333-8903   www.recoton.com

Mfr. electronic accessories and aftermarket products for computers and office equipment.

Recoton UK, Towngate Business Center, Lester Road, Walkden Manchester SN6 7UY, UK

Tel: 44-161-702-5000   Fax: 44-161-702-5001

RED HAT, INC.

1801 Varsity Drive, Raleigh, NC, 27606

Tel: (919) 754-3700   Fax: (919) 754-3701   www.redhat.com

Mfr. computer hardware and systems.

Red Hat UK Limited, 10 Alan Turing Road, Surrey Research Park, Guildford Surrey GU2 7YF, UK

RED WING SHOE COMPANY, INC.

314 Main Street, Red Wing, MN, 55066

Tel: (612) 388-8211   Fax: (612) 388-7415   www.redwingshoe.com

Leather tanning and finishing; mfr. footwear, retail shoe stores.

Red Wing Europe, Ltd., 26 Upper Tachbrook St., London SW1V 1SW, UK

Contact: Joseph Goggin, Pres.

REEBOK INTERNATIONAL LTD.

1895 J. W. Foster Blvd., Canton, MA, 02021

Tel: (781) 401-5000   Fax: (781) 401-7402   www.reebok.com

Mfr. athletic shoes including casual, dress golf and walking shoes.

Reebok Intl. Ltd., One The Square, Stockley Park, Uxbridge, Middlesex UB11 1DN, UK

Reebok United Kingdom, Moor Lane Mill, Lancaster LA1 1GF, UK

REED SMITH LLP

435 Sixth Avenue, Pittsburgh, PA, 15219

Tel: (412) 288-3131   Fax: (412) 288-3063   www.rssm.com

Engaged in international law.

Reed Smith LLP, Park House Station Square, Coventry CV1 2FL, UK

Tel: 44-24-7629-3000

Reed Smith Warner Cranston LLP, Pickfords Wharf, Clink Street, London SE1 9DG, UK

Tel: 44-207-403-2900

REFAC

115 River Rd., Edgewater, NJ, 07020-1099

Tel: (201) 943-4400   Fax: (201) 943-7400   www.refac.com

Consults to international technology transfer, foreign trade and power supplies firms for brand and trade marking licensing services..

REFAC, 175 Rivermead Ct., Ranelagh Gardens, London SW6 3SF, UK

Tel: 44-207-736-4909

REFCO GROUP LTD.

200 Liberty Street Tower A, New York, NY, 10281

Tel: (212) 693-7700   Fax: (212) 693-7856   www.refco.com

Commodity and security brokers engaged in the execution and clearing of futures and options and institutional asset management services.

Refco Futures Ltd., London, UK

Tel: 44-207-755-32914   Contact: John Steptoe

REFLEXITE TECHNOLOGY

120 Darling Drive, Avon, CT, 06001

Tel: (860) 676-7100   Fax: (860) 676-7199   www.reflexite.com

Mfr. plastic film, sheet, materials and shapes, optical lenses.

Reflexite UK Ltd., 4420 Nash Court, John Smith Drive, Oxford Business Park South Cowley, Oxford OX4 2RU, UK

Tel: 44-1865-396959   Fax: 44-1865-396960   Contact: Andrew McNeill

REGAL-BELOIT CORPORATION

200 State Street, Beloit, WI, 53512-0298

Tel: (608) 364-8800   Fax: (608) 364-8818   www.regal-beloit.com

Mfr. power transmission equipment, perishable cutting tools.

Marathon Electric-U.K., 6/F, Thistleton Sales Ind. Estate, Market Overton, Oakham Rutland LE15 7PP, UK

Tel: 44-1572-768206   Fax: 44-1572-768217

Opperman Mastergear, Ltd., Hambridge Road, Newbury Berkshire RG14 5TS, UK

Tel: 44-1635-811500   Fax: 44-1635-811501

RELIANCE GROUP HOLDINGS, INC.

55 East 52nd Street, New York, NY, 10055

Tel: (212) 909-1100   Fax: (212) 909-1864   www.rgh.com

Financial and insurance management services.

Reliance National Insurance Co. (Europe) Ltd., Reliance National House, 80 Leadenhall St., London EC3A 3DH, UK

Tel: 44-207-283-7110   Fax: 44-207-929-7453   Contact: Carl Bach, Mng. Dir.

RELIANT ENERGY, INC.

1111 Louisiana Street, Houston, TX, 77002

Tel: (713) 207-3000   Fax: (713) 207-0206   www.houind.com

Provides gas and electric services.

Reliant Energy Trading & Marketing, London, UK

REMINGTON PRODUCTS COMPANY, L.L.C.

60 Main Street, Bridgeport, CT, 06604

Tel: (203) 367-4400   Fax: (203) 332-4848   www.remington-products.com

Mfr. home appliances, electric shavers.

Remington Consumer Products Ltd., 116 High St., Egham, Surrey TW20 9HQ, UK

Tel: 44-1784-434343   Fax: 44-1784-437919   Contact: Geoffrey L. Hoddinott, VP & Gen. Mgr.

RENAISSANCE HOTELS AND RESORTS

10400 Fernwood Road, Bethesda, MD, 20817

Tel: (301) 380-3000   Fax: (301) 380-5181   www.renaissancehotels.com

upscale, full-service hotel and resort chain under Marriott International, Inc.

Renaissance London Hotel, Chancery Court, London, UK

Tel: 44-6196-4960

THE RENDON GROUP INC.

1875 Connecticut Ave., NE, Washington, DC, 20009

Tel: (202) 745-4900   Fax: (202) 745-0215   www.rendon.com

Public relations, print and video production, strategic communications.

TRG-UK, PO Box 698, Titchfield House, 69-85 Tabernacle St., London EC2A 4RR, UK

REQUISITE TECHNOLOGY, INC.

10955 Westmoor Drive, Ste. 100, Westminster, CO, 80021

Tel: (303) 474-2200   Fax: (303) 474-2211   www.requisite.com

Mfr. software.

Requisite Technology UK, Heathgate House 57, Colne Road, Twickenham, Middlesex TW2 6QA, UK

Tel: 44-208-755-7200   Fax: 44-208-755-7201

RESMED INC.

1440 Danielson Street, Poway, CA, 92064

Tel: (858) 746-2400   Fax: (858) 880-1618   www.resmed.com

Mfr. sleep apnea aids, including nasal masks and accessories.

ResMed UK Limited, 67B Milton Park, Abingdon Oxon OX14 4RS, UK

Tel: 44-1235-862-997   Fax: 44-1235-831-336

RESOURCES CONNECTION, INC.

695 Town Center Drive, Ste. 600, Costa Mesa, CA, 92626

Tel: (714) 430-6400   Fax: (714) 426-6090   www.resourcesconnection.com

Provides accounting and financial professional services.

Resources Connection UK, 117 Houndsditch, 2/F, London 3A 7BT, UK

Tel: 44-207-422-7780

RETEK INC.

950 Nicollet Mall, Minneapolis, MN, 55403

Tel: (612) 587-5000   Fax: (612) 587-5100   www.retek.com

Mfr. retail management software.

Retek Cambridge, Wellbrook Court, Unit 1, Block A, Girton Cambridgeshire CB3 ONA, UK

Tel: 44-1223-703-400   Fax: 44-1223-703-411

Retek UK, 110 Wigmore Street, London W1U 3RW, UK

Tel: 44-207-563-4610

REVLON INC.

625 Madison Ave., New York, NY, 10022

Tel: (212) 527-4000   Fax: (212) 527-4995   www.revlon.com

Mfr. cosmetics, fragrances, toiletries and beauty care products.

Revlon Intl. Corp. Ltd., 86 Brook St., London, UK

Contact: David Windeatt, Gen. Mgr.

REXNORD CORPORATION

4701 West Greenfield Ave., Milwaukee, WI, 53214

Tel: (414) 643-3000   Fax: (414) 643-3078   www.rexnord.com

Mfr. power transmission and conveying components.

Rexnord UK Ltd., Berkshire House, 252-256 Kings Rd., Reading Berkshire RG1 4HP, UK

RF MICRO DEVICES, INC.

7628 Thorndike Road, Greensboro, NC, 27409-9421

Tel: (336) 664-1233   Fax: (336) 931-7454   www.rfmd.com

Mfr. amplifiers and modulators for wireless communications devices.

RF Micro Devices, Inc., 100 Longwater Avenue, Suite #12, Reading RG2 6GP, UK

RHEOMETRIC SCIENTIFIC INC.

1 Possumtown Road, Piscataway, NJ, 08854

Tel: (732) 560-8550   Fax: (732) 560-7451   www.rheosci.com

Design/mfr. rheological instruments and systems.

Rheometric Scientific Ltd., Surrey Business Park, Weston Rd., Epsom, Surrey KT17 1JF, UK

RICH PRODUCTS CORPORATION

One Robert Rich Way, Buffalo, NY, 14213

Tel: (716) 878-8000 Fax: (716) 878-8765 www.richs.com

Mfr. non-dairy products and icings, fillings, dry cake mixes, baked goods and desserts, frozen seafood and specialty meat products.

Rich Products Ltd., Rough Farm, Atherstone-on-Stour, Stratford-upon-Avon, Warwickshire CV37 8DX, UK

Tel: 44-1789-450-030

RICHARDSON ELECTRONICS, LTD.

40 W 267 Keslinger Road, LaFox, IL, 60147-0393

Tel: (630) 208-2200 Fax: (630) 208-2550 www.rell.com

Mfr. and distribution of electron tubes and related equipment.

Richardson Electronics, Inspring House, Searby Road, Lincoln LN2 4DT, UK

RICHCO, INC.

5825 N. Tripp Ave., PO Box 804238, Chicago, IL, 60680

Tel: (773) 539-4060 Fax: (773) 539-6770 www.richco.com

Mfr. quality plastic fasteners, wire management devices, circuit board hardware, and custom components.

Richco Plastic UK, Richco House, Springhead Enterprise Park, Springhead Road, Gravesend Kent DA11 8HE, UK

Tel: 44-1474-327527

RIDGE TOOL COMPANY

400 Clark Street, Elyria, OH, 44035

Tel: (440) 323-5581 Fax: (440) 329-4853 www.ridgid.com

Mfr. hand and power tools for working pipe, drain cleaning equipment, etc.

Ridge Tool Ltd., Royston Rd., Baldock Herts, UK

RIGHT MANAGEMENT CONSULTANTS, INC.

1818 Market Street, 33rd Fl., Philadelphia, PA, 19103-3614

Tel: (215) 988-1588 Fax: (215) 988-9112 www.right.com

Out placement and human resources consulting services.

Right Management Consultants, Quay West Business Ctr., Trafford Wharf Rd., Manchester M17 1HH, UK

Tel: 44-161-877-7631

Right Management Consultants, Ouseburn Bldg., Albion Row, East Quayside, Newcastle-upon-Tyne, UK

Tel: 44-191-265-0555

Right Management Consultants, Dammas House, Dammas Lane, Swindon, Wiltshire SN1 3EJ, UK

Tel: 44-793-514660

Right Management Consultants, Prospect House, 32 Sovereign St., Leeds LS1 4BJ, UK

Tel: 44-532-425445

Right Management Consultants, Savannah House, 11-12, Charles II St., St. James's, London SW1Y 4QU, UK

Tel: 44-207-839-1001

THE RITZ-CARLTON HOTEL COMPANY, L.L.C.

3414 Peachtree Road NE, Ste. 300, Atlanta, GA, 30326

Tel: (404) 237-5500 Fax: (404) 365-9643 www.ritzcarlton.com

5-star hotel and restaurant chain.

The Ritz-Carlton Hotel Company, London, Bowater House West, 8th Floor, 114 Knightsbridge, London, UK

Tel: 44-207-581-4052

RIVIANA FOODS INC.

2777 Allen Parkway, 15th Fl., Houston, TX, 77019

Tel: (713) 529-3251 Fax: (713) 529-1661 www.rivianafoods.com

Process, market and distribute branded and private-label rice products.

Stevens & Brotherton Ltd., S&B House, 2 Vinson Close, Knoll Rise, Orpington, Kent BR6 0XG, UK

ROBERT HALF INTERNATIONAL INC.

2884 Sand Hill Road, Ste. 200, Menlo Park, CA, 94025

Tel:　(650) 234-6000　　　Fax:　(650) 234-6999　　　www.rhii.com

World leader in personnel and specialized staffing services.

Robert Half Intl. Inc., Walter House, 418 Strand, London WC2R 0PT, UK

Robert Half Intl. Inc., 63 Temple Row, Birmingham B2 5LS, UK

ROBERTS-GORDON INC.

1250 William Street, PO Box 44, Buffalo, NY, 14240-0044

Tel:　(716) 852-4400　　　Fax:　(716) 852-0854　　　www.roberts-gordon.com

Mfr. industry gas burners, industry space heaters, infrared radiant tube heaters.

Roberts-Gordon Europe Ltd., Oxford Street, Bilston, West Midlands WV14 7EG, UK

Tel: 44-1902-494425

C. H. ROBINSON WORLDWIDE, INC. (CHR)

8100 Mitchell Road, Eden Prairie, MN, 55344

Tel:　(612) 937-8500　　　Fax:　(612) 937-6714　　　www.chrobinson.com

Global door-to-door freight forwarding services, including flexible transportation solutions and global logistics.

C. H. Robinson (CHR), Albion Court, 68 Attleborough Road, Nuneaton Warcs CV11 4JJ, UK

Tel: 44-1817-548800

C. H. Robinson UK, Milton House, 27 Station Road, Egham Surrey TW20 9LD, UK

Tel: 44-1784-228550

ROCHESTER MIDLAND CORPORATION (RML)

PO Box 31515, 333 Hollenbeck St., Rochester, NY, 14603-1515

Tel:　(716) 336-2200　　　Fax:　(716) 467-4406　　　www.rochestermidland.com

Mfr. specialty chemicals for industry cleaning and maintenance, water treatment and personal hygiene.

Rochester Midland UK, London, UK

Tel: 44-1908-608088

ROCKWELL AUTOMATION, INC.

777 East Wisconsin Ave., Ste. 1400, Milwaukee, WI, 53202

Tel:　(414) 212-5200　　　Fax:　(414) 212-5201　　　www.rockwellautomation.com

Products and service for aerospace and defense, automotive, electronics, graphics and automation industry.

Rockwell (UK) Ltd., 21 Suttons Business Park, Earley, Reading, Berkshire RG6 1LA, UK

Tel: 44-118-926-111　Fax: 44-118-966-4016

Rockwell Automation Ltd., Rockwell House, Gateway, Crewe Cheshire CW1 6XN, UK

Tel: 44-1270-580-142　Fax: 44-1270-580-141

Rockwell Automation Ltd. Dodge UK, Hortonwood 10, Ste. A4, Telford, Shropshire TF1 4ES, UK

Tel: 44-1952-604-222　Fax: 44-1952-677-383

Rockwell Elecronic Eommerce, Rockwell House, Caldecotte Lake Business Park, Milton Keynes MK7 8LE, UK

Rockwell Electronic Commerce Ltd., Howes Percival House, 252 Upper Third St., Central Milton Keynes, Buckinghamshire MK9 1DZ, UK

Tel: 44-1908-200-200　Fax: 44-1908-609-124

Rockwell Semiconductor Systems Ltd., Spectrum Point, 279 Farnborough Rd., Farnborough, Hampshire GU14 7LS, UK

Tel: 44-1252-370-008　Fax: 44-1252-370-009

R.A. RODRIGUEZ, INC.

20 Seaview Boulevard, Port Washington, NY, 11050

Tel:　(516) 625-8080　　　Fax:　(516) 621-2424　　　www.rodriguez-usa.com

Distribution of ball and roller bearings, precision gears, mechanical systems and related products.

R. A. Rodriguez (UK) Ltd., 28 Campus Five, Letchworth Business Park, Letchworth, Hertfordshire SG6 2JF, UK

Tel: 44-1462-670044　Fax: 44-1462-670880　Contact: Derrick Elliott, Mng. Dir.

ROFIN-SINAR TECHNOLOGIES, INC.

45701 Mast St., Plymouth, MI, 48170

Tel: (734) 455-5400   Fax: (734) 455-2741   www.rofin-sinar.com

Mfr. industrial lasers.

ROFIN-SINAR UK Ltd., York Way Willerby, Kingston-Upon-Hill HU10 6HD, UK

Tel: 44-1482-650088   Fax: 44-1482-650022

ROHM AND HAAS COMPANY

100 Independence Mall West, Philadelphia, PA, 19106

Tel: (215) 592-3000   Fax: (215) 592-3377   www.rohmhaas.com

Mfr. specialty chemicals.

Morton International Limited, 18 Chesford Grange, Woolston, Warrington WA1 4RQ, UK

Morton International Ltd., Heckmondwike Road, Dewsbury Moore West Yorkshire EF13 3NG, UK

Rohm and Haas (UK) Limited, Tynesdie Works Ellison Street, Jarrow, Tyne and Wear NE32 3DJ, UK

Rohm and Haas (UK) Ltd., Lennig House, 2 Mason's Ave., Croydon, Surrey CR9 3NB, UK

Tel: 44-181-774-5300

Shipley Europe Ltd., Herald Way, Coventry CV3 2RQ, UK

Tel: 44-120-365-4400

Shipley Ronal, High Peak Laboratories, Ashbourne Road, Buxton Derbyshire SK17 9SS, UK

ROPER INDUSTRIES, INC.

160 Ben Burton Road, Bogart, GA, 30622

Tel: (706) 369-7170   Fax: (706) 353-6496   www.roperind.com

Mfr. analytical instruments.

Roper Scientific UK, PO Box 1192, Marlow Buckinghamshire SL7 1GB, UK

ROPES & GRAY

1 International Place, Boston, MA, 02110-2624

Tel: (617) 951-7000   Fax: (617) 951-7050   www.ropesgray.com

Engaged in international law.

Ropes & Gray UK, 12-14 Mitre Street, London EC3A 5BU, UK

Tel: 44-207-283-3367   Fax: 44-207-283-5195

ROSENBLUTH INTERNATIONAL

2401 Walnut Street, Philadelphia, PA, 19103-4390

Tel: (215) 977-4000   Fax: (215) 977-4028   www.rosenbluth.com

Provides corporate business travel services.

Rosenbluth International Alliance (RIA), Standard House, 16-22 Epworth Street, London EC2A 4DL, UK

Tel: 44-207-847-2600

ROSS SYSTEMS, INC.

2 Concourse Pkwy., Ste. 800, Atlanta, GA, 30328

Tel: (770) 351-9600   Fax: (770) 351-0036   www.rossinc.com

Mfr. supply chain management software.

Ross Systems UK, 7 Rushmills, Northhampton NN4 7YB, UK

Tel: 44-1604-630050

ROWAN COMPANIES INC.

2800 Post Oak Boulevard, Houston, TX, 77056-6196

Tel: (713) 621-7800   Fax: (713) 960-7560   www.rowancompanies.com

leading turnkey provider of large mobile equipment for forestry, intermodal, marine and mining markets, worldwide.

British American Offshore Ltd., 43 Upper Grosvenor Sq., London W1X 9P6, UK

ROWE INTERNATIONAL INC.

1500 Union Ave., S.E., Grand Rapids, MI, 49507

Tel: (616) 243-3633   Fax: (616) 243-9414   www.roweinternational.com

Vending machines, background music systems and jukeboxes; bill and coin changers.

Rowe (Europe) Ltd., Wickham Hall, Hadham Road., Bishop's Stortford, Hertsfordshire CM23 1JG, UK

Tel: 44-1279-757878   Fax: 44-1279-757545

T. ROWE PRICE ASSOCIATES, INC.

100 East Pratt Street, Baltimore, MD, 21202

Tel: (410) 345-2000   Fax: (410) 345-2394   www.troweprice.com

Investment and portfolio asset management.

Rowe Price-Fleming International, 25 Copthall Avenue, London, UK

ROWECOM, INC.

15 Southwest Park, Westwood, MA, 02090

Tel: (781) 410-3300   Fax: (781) 329-9875   www.rowe.com

On-line magazine and newspaper subscription services.

RoweCom UK, Cannon House Folkestone, Kent CT19 5EE, UK

Tel: 44-1202-850-101

ROYAL APPLIANCE MFG. COMPANY

7005 Cochran Rd., Glenwillow, OH, 44139

Tel: (440) 996-2000   Fax: (440) 996-2030   www.royalappliance.com

Mfr. vacuum cleaners.

J.A. Balch Ltd., Surrey House, 34 Eden St., Kingston-upon-Thames, Surrey KT1 1ER, UK

RPM INC.

PO Box 777, 2628 Pearl Road, Medina, OH, 44258

Tel: (330) 273-5090   Fax: (330) 225-8743   www.rpminc.com

Mfr. protective coatings and paints.

Nullifire Limited, Torrington Avenue, Coventry CV4 9TJ, UK

RSA SECURITY INC.

174 Middlesex Turnpike, Bedford, MA, 01730

Tel: (781) 515-5000   Fax: (781) 515-5010   www.rsasecurity.com

Mfr. software and hardware security products.

RSA Security UK, RSA House, Western Road, Bracknell Berks RG12 1RT, UK

Tel: 44-134-478-100   Fax: 44-134-478-1010

RTI INTERNATIONAL METALS, INC.

1000 Warren Avenue, Niles, OH, 44446

Tel: (330) 544-7700   Fax: (330) 544-7796   www.rmititanium.com

Mfr. milled titanium products.

RTI International UK, Riverside Estate, Fazeley Tamworth, Staffordshire B78 3RW, UK

RUDDICK CORPORATION

301 S. Tryon St., Ste. 1800, Charlotte, NC, 28202

Tel: (704) 372-5404   Fax: (704) 372-6409   www.amefird.com

Mfr. industrial sewing thread for worldwide industrial and consumer markets.

A&E Thread (GB) Ltd., Bankside Mills, Chapelfield, Radcliffe Manchester M26 9JF, UK

Tel: 44-161-766 1544   Fax: 44-161-766 9965

RUDER FINN INC.

301 East 57th Street, New York, NY, 10022

Tel: (212) 593-6400   Fax: (212) 593-6397   www.ruderfinn.com

Engaged in public relations service and broadcast communications.

Ruder Finn Complete Medical Communications Ltd., CMC House, Jordangate, Macclesfield, Cheshire SK10 1EW, UK

Ruder Finn U.K., 19 Chelsea Wharf, Lots Rd., London SW10 0QJ, UK

RUSS BERRIE AND COMPANY, INC.

111 Bauer Drive, Oakland, NJ, 07436

Tel: (201) 337-9000   Fax: (201) 405-7355   www.russberrie.com

Engaged in the design and sale of gift items, including stuffed animals and home décor items.

Russ Berrie UK Ltd., 40 Oriana Way, Nursling Industrial Estate, Southampton Hants SO16 0YU, UK

Tel: 44-1703-747-747

RUSSELL REYNOLDS ASSOCIATES INC.

200 Park Avenue, New York, NY, 10166-0002

Tel: (212) 351-2000   Fax: (212) 370-0896   www.russreyn.com

Executive recruiting services.

Russell Reynolds Associates Ltd., 24 St. James's Square, London SW1Y 4HZ, UK

Tel: 44-207-839-7788   Fax: 44-207-839-9395   Contact: Jane Kingsley/Simon Hearn

RVSI (ROBOTIC VISION SYSTEMS, INC.)

5 Shawmut Road, Canton, MA, 02021

Tel: (781) 821-0830   Fax: (781) 828-8942   www.rvsi.com

Mfr. machine visions systems; bar code scanners and data collection equipment.

RVSI Robotic Vision Systems, St. James' Ct., Bridgnorth Rd., Wollaston Stourbridge, West Midlands DY8 3QG, UK

RVSI UK, RVSI House, Claybrook Drive, Redditch Worcestershire B98 0FH, U.K.

RWD TECHNOLOGIES, INC.

10480 Little Paluxent Pkwy., Ste. 1200, Columbia, MD, 21044-3530

Tel: (410) 730-4377   Fax: (410) 964-0039   www.rwd.com

Mfr. software and services.

RWD Technologies, Stockley Park, 1/F, 3 Furzeground Way, Uxbridge UB11 1AJ, UK

RWD Technologies, 6250 Bishops Court, Solihull Pkwy., Birmingham Business Park, Birmingham B37 7YB, UK

S1 CORPORATION

3500 Lenox Road, Ste. 200, Atlanta, GA, 30326-1108

Tel: (404) 923-3500   Fax: (404) 923-6727   www.s1.com

Mfr. on-line banking software.

S1 Farnborough, B17/18 Armstrong Mall, Apolla Rise, Southwood, Farnborough GU14 0NR, UK

S1 London, Peninsular House, 8/F, 36, Monument St., London EC3R 8LJ, UK

SAATCHI & SAATCHI

375 Hudson St., New York, NY, 10014

Tel: (212) 463-2000   Fax: (212) 463-9855   www.saatchi-saatchi.com

Provides advertising and marketing services.

Saatchi & Saatchi, 80 Charlotte Street, London W1A 1AQ, UK

Contact: James Hall

SAFETY COMPONENTS INTERNATIONAL, INC.

41 Stevens Street, Greenville, SC, 29605

Tel: (864) 240-2600   Fax: (864) 240-2728   www.safetycomponents.com

Mfr. automobile airbag cushions and components..

Safety Components, Buckingham Court, 78 Buckingham Gate, London SW1E 6PE, UK

SAFETY-KLEEN CORPORATION

1301 Gervais Street, Columbia, SC, 29201

Tel: (803) 933-4200   Fax: (803) 933-4345   www.safety-kleen.com

Solvent based parts cleaning service; sludge/solvent recycling service.

Safety-Kleen Parts Washer Svce. Ltd., Box 14, Worton Hall, Worton Rd., Isleworth, Hounslow Middlesex, UK

SALANS HERTZFELD HEILBRONN CHRISTY & VIENER

620 Fifth Avenue, New York, NY, 10020-2457

Tel: (212) 632-5500   Fax: (212) 632-5555   www.salans.com

International law firm.

Salans Hertzfeld & Heilbronn HRK, Clements House, 14-18 Gresham Street, London EC2V 7NN, UK

SALOMON SMITH BARNEY HOLDINGS INC.

388 Greenwich Street, New York, NY, 10013

Tel: (212) 816-6000   Fax: (212) 816-8915   www.smithbarney.com

Securities dealers and underwriters.

Salomon Smith Barney Holdings, One Angel Ct., London EC2, UK

SALTON, INC.

1955 Field Court, Lake Forest, IL, 60045

Tel: (847) 803-4600   Fax: (847) 803-1211   www.saltoninc.com

Mfr. small appliances.

Salton Europe, Oldham Road A62 & Sisson Street, Manchester, UK

SANCHEZ COMPUTER ASSOCIATES, INC.

40 Valley Stream Pkwy, Malvern, PA, 19335

Tel: (610) 296-8877   Fax: (610) 296-7371   www.sanchez.com

Mfr. bank software.

Sanchez Computer, Murlain House, Union Street, Chester CH1 1QP, UK

Tel: 44-1244-347786   Fax: 44-1244-304377

SANDUSKY INTERNATIONAL

615 W. Market Street, PO Box 5012, Sandusky, OH, 44871-8012

Tel: (419) 626-5340   Fax: (419) 626-3339   www.sanduskyintl.com

Mfr. roll shells for paper machines, centrifugal tubular products.

Sandusky Walmsley Limited, Crompton Way, Bolton, Lancashire BL1 8UL, UK

Tel: 44-1204-396060

SANFORD CORPORATION

2711 Washington Boulevard, Bellwood, IL, 60104

Tel: (708) 547-6650   Fax: (708) 547-6719   www.sanfordcorp.com

Mfr. inks, writing, drawing and drafting instruments.

Sanford U.K., Oldmedow Road Kings Lynn, Norfolk PE 30 4JR, UK

SANGAMO BIOSCIENCES, INC.

501 Canal Blvd., Ste. 100A, Richmond, CA, 94804

Tel: (510) 970-6000   Fax: (510) 236-8951   www.sangamo.com

Engaged in drug research.

Sangamo BioSciences, Inc., 1-3 Burtonhole lane, London NW7 1AD, UK

Fax: 44-208-982-6748

SAPIENT CORPORATION

1 Memorial Drive, Cambridge, MA, 02142

Tel: (617) 621-0200   Fax: (617) 621-1300   www.sapient.com

Engaged in information technology and consulting services.

Sapient UK, 1 Bartholomew Lane, London EC2N 2AB, UK

Tel: 44-207-786-4500   Fax: 44-207-786-4600

SARA LEE CORPORATION

3 First National Plaza, Chicago, IL, 60602-4260

Tel: (312) 726-2600   Fax: (312) 558-4995   www.saralee.com

Mfr./distributor food and consumer packaged goods, intimate apparel and knitwear.

KOSL UK, Carnaby Industrial Estate, Bridlington, East Yorkshire YO15 3QY, UK

Pretty Polly Ltd., Unwin Rd., Sutton-in-Ashfield, Nottinghamshire NG17 4JJ, UK

SAS INSTITUTE INC.

SAS Campus Drive, Cary, NC, 27513

Tel: (919) 677-8000   Fax: (919) 677-4444   www.sas.com

Mfr. and distribution of decision support software.

SAS Institute, Exchange Quay, Manchester M5 3EJ, UK

SAS Institute (United Kingdon) Ltd., Henley Road, Medmenham, Marlow, Bucks SL7 2EB, UK

Tel: 44-16284-86933   Fax: 44-16284-83203

SATMETRIX SYSTEMS, INC.

100 View Street, Ste. 200, Mountain View, CA, 94041

Tel: (650) 314-2300   Fax: (650) 314-2301   www.satmetrix.com

Mfr. customer service software.

Satmetrix Ltd., Crown House, 72 Hammersmith Road, London W14 8TH, UK

Tel: 44-207-470-2440

SBC COMMUNICATIONS INC.

175 East Houston, San Antonio, TX, 78205

Tel: (210) 821-4105   Fax: (210) 351-5034   www.sbc.com

Engaged in telecommunications.

TeleWest, London, UK

SBS TECHNOLOGIES, INC.

2400 Louisiana Blvd. NE, Ste. 600, Albuquerque, NM, 87110

Tel: (505) 875-0600   Fax: (505) 875-0400   www.sbs.com

Mfr. high-tech computer components.

SBS Technologies UK, PO Box 14, Rochester ME3 9DJ, UK

SCANSOFT, INC.

9 Centennial Dr., Peabody, MA, 01960

Tel: (978) 977-2000   Fax: (978) 977-2436   www.scansoft.com

Mfr. digital imaging software for speech and language solutions.

ScanSoft, Inc., Reading, UK

Tel: 44-1189-668421

SCHENECTADY INTERNATIONAL INC.

PO Box 1046, Schenectady, NY, 12301

Tel: (518) 370-4200   Fax: (518) 382-8129   www.siigroup.com

Mfr. electrical insulating varnishes, enamels, phenolic resins, alkylphenols.

Schenectady Europe Ltd., Four Ashes, Wolverhampton WV10 7BT, UK

Tel: 44-1902-790-555   Fax: 44-1902-791-640   Contact: Geoffrey Harrison, Mng. Dir.

SCHENKER USA INC.

150 Albany Ave., Freeport, NY, 11520

Tel: (516) 403-5416   Fax: (516) 377-3092   www.schenkerusa.com

Freight forwarders.

Schenker International, 51-53 Hatton Garden, London EC1N 8QJ, UK

Tel: 44-207-242-3344   Fax: 44-207-242-0395

Schenker International, Newcastle Intl Airport, Freightway Woolsington, Newcastle upon Tyne NE13 8BH, UK

Tel: 44-191-214-0593   Fax: 44-191-214-0591

R. P. SCHERER CORPORATION

645 Martinsville Rd., Ste. 200, Basking Ridge, NJ, 07920

Tel: (908) 580-1500   Fax: (908) 580-9220   www.rpscherer.com

Mfr. pharmaceuticals; soft gelatin and two-piece hard shell capsules.

R.P. Scherer Ltd., Frankland Rd., Blagrove, Swindon Wilts. SN5 8YS, UK

Tel: 44-1793-488411   Fax: 44-1793-613394   Contact: Dr. Alan Raymond, Reg. VP   Emp: 346

R.P. Scherer UK, London, UK

SCHERING-PLOUGH CORPORATION

One Giralda Farms, Madison, NJ, 07940-1000

Tel: (973) 822-7000   Fax: (973) 822-7048   www.sch-plough.com

Proprietary drug and cosmetic products.

Schering Plough, 204 St. John St., London EC1P 1DH, UK

Schering-Plough Animal Health, Breakspear Road South, Harefield Uxbridge, Middlesex UB9 6LS, UK

SCHLEGEL SYSTEMS

1555 Jefferson Road, PO Box 23197, Rochester, NY, 14692-3197

Tel: (716) 427-7200   Fax: (716) 427-9993   www.schlegel.com

Mfr. engineered perimeter sealing systems for residential and commercial construction; fibers; rubber product.

Schlegel UK, Henlow Industrial Estate, Henlow Camp, Bedfordshire SG16 6DS, UK

SCHLUMBERGER LIMITED

153 East 53rd St., 57th Fl., New York, NY, 10022-4624

Tel: (212) 350-9400   Fax: (212) 350-9457   www.slb.com

Engaged in oil and gas services, metering and payment systems, and produces semiconductor testing equipment and smart cards.

Schlumberger Cambridge Research, High Cross Madingley Road, Cambridge CB3 0EL, UK

Tel: 44-1223-315576

Schlumberger Cards & Services, 1 Kingsway, London WC2B 6XH, UK

Schlumberger Ltd., Harfrey Road, Unit 9c, Harfrey Ind. Estate, Great Yarmouth Norfolk NR31 OLS, UK

SCHOLASTIC CORPORATION

555 Broadway, New York, NY, 10012

Tel: (212) 343-6100   Fax: (212) 343-6934   www.scholastic.com

Publishing/distribution educational and children's magazines, books, software.

Scholastic Ltd., Villiers House Clarendon Ave., Leamington Spa, Warwickshire CV32 5PR, UK

Tel: 44-1926-887799   Contact: David Kewley, Mng. Dir.

THE CHARLES SCHWAB CORPORATION

101 Montgomery Street, San Francisco, CA, 94104

Tel: (415) 627-7000   Fax: (415) 627-8840   www.schawb.com

Financial services; discount brokerage, retirement accounts.

Schwab International, Cannon House, 24 The Priory Queensway, Birmingham B4 6BS, UK

Schwab International., 38 Bishopgate, Crosby Court, London EC2N 4AJ, UK

Tel: 44-207-786-7102 Fax: 44-207-786-7172

SCIENCE APPLICATIONS INTL. CORPORATION (SAIC)

10260 Campus Point Dr., San Diego, CA, 92121

Tel: (858) 826-6000   Fax: (858) 535-7589   www.saic.com

Engaged in research and engineering.

SAIC Europe Ltd., 8/9 Stratton Street, London W1J 8, UK

SAIC UK Ltd., Castle Park, Cambridge CB3 O, UK

Tel: 44-1223-518790

SCIENT, INC.

79 Fifth Ave., 4th Fl., New York, NY, 10003

Tel: (212) 500-4900   Fax: (212) 500-5032   www.scient.com

Provides Internet and technology consulting services.

Scient UK Ltd., Elizabeth House, 39 York Road, London SE17NQ, UK

Tel: 44-20-7071-6300   Fax: 44-20-7071-6666

SCIENTIFIC GAMES INTERNATIONAL

750 Lexington Avenue, 25th Fl., New York, NY, 10022

Tel: (212) 754-2233   Fax: (212) 754-2372   www.scientificgames.com

Mfr. video gaming machines and computerized pari-mutuel wagering systems used at racetracks.

Scientific Games International, 81 Kirkstall Road, Leeds L53 1LH, UK

Tel: 44-113-204-5000   Fax: 44-113-204-5401

Scientific Games International, Unit 2, Phoenix Way, Bradford BD4 8JP, UK

Scientific Games International, George Mann Road, Leeds LS10 1DJ, UK

Tel: 44-113-385-5400   Fax: 44-113-385-5401

SCIENTIFIC-ATLANTA, INC.

5030 Sugarloaf Pkwy., Lawrenceville, GA, 30044

Tel: (770) 903-5000   Fax: (770) 236-6777   www.sciatl.com

Mfr. cable set-top boxes, modems, transmission and distribution equipment.

Scientific-Atlanta (UK) Ltd., Home Park Estate, Kings Langley, Hertshire WO4 8LZ, UK

Tel: 44-1923-266-133   Fax: 44-01923-269-018

SCM MICROSYSTEMS, INC.

47211 Bayside Pkwy., Fremont, CA, 94538

Tel: (510) 360-2300   Fax: (510) 360-0211   www.scmmicro.com

Mfr. computer hardware for digital cameras.

SCM Microsystems, UK, 10-11 Clock Tower Mews, Newmarket CB8 8LL, UK

Tel: 44-870-010-4889   Fax: 44-870-010-4868

THE SCOTTS COMPANY

14111 Scottslawn Rd., Marysville, OH, 43215

Tel: (937) 644-0011   Fax: (937) 644-7244   www.scottscompany.com

Leading U.S. maker of lawn and garden products.

Miracle Garden Care, London, UK

Scotts/Levington Horticulture Ltd., London, UK

SCP POOL CORPORATION

109 Northpark Blvd., Covington, LA, 70433-5001

Tel: (985) 892-5521   Fax: (985) 892-0517   www.scppool.com

Mfr. pool supplies.

SCP Pool Corporation, London, UK

SEACOR SMIT INC.

11200 Richmond Avenue, Ste. 400, Houston, TX, 77042

Tel: (713) 782-5990   Fax: (713) 782-5991   www.seacorsmit.com

Engaged in offshore marine services.

SEACOR Marine Limited, Columbus Buildings, Waveney Road, Lowestoft, Suffolk NR31 1BS, UK

SEAGATE TECHNOLOGY, INC.

920 Disc Dr., Scotts Valley, CA, 95066

Tel: (408) 438-6550   Fax: (408) 438-7205   www.seagate.com

Develop computer technology, software and hardware.

Seagate Software Ltd., 107 King St., Maidenhead, Berkshire SL6 1DP, UK

Tel: 44-1628-771-299   Fax: 44-1628-771-523

Seagate Technology, Inc., Seagate House, Globe Park, Fieldhouse Lane, Marlow Buckinghamshire SL5 1LW, UK

Tel: 44-1628-890366   Fax: 44-1628-890660   Contact: Brian Stanley, Dir.   Emp: 40

SEALED AIR CORPORATION

Park 80 East, Saddle Brook, NJ, 07663

Tel: (201) 791-7600   Fax: (201) 703-4205   www.sealedaircorp.com

Mfr. protective and specialty packaging solutions for industrial, food and consumer products.

Sealed Air (FPD) Ltd., Stafford Park 9, Telford, Shropshire TF3 3BZ, UK

Tel: 44-1-952-290471   Fax: 44-1-952-290950

Sealed Air Ltd., Telford Way, Kettering, Northants NN16 8UN, UK
Tel: 44-1536-315700   Fax: 44-1536-410576

Sealed Air Ltd., Saxton Way, Melbourne, Royston, Hertfordshire SG8 6DN, UK
Tel: 44-1763-261900   Fax: 44-1-763-261234

SEALY CORPORATION

Sealy Drive, One Office Pkwy., Trinity, NC, 27370
Tel: (336) 861-3500   Fax: (336) 861-3501   www.sealy.com
Mfr. bedding products, including box springs and mattresses.

Sealy UK, London, UK
Tel: 44-16973-20342

G.D. SEARLE & COMPANY

5200 Old Orchard Road, Skokie, IL, 60077
Tel: (847) 982-7000   Fax: (847) 470-1480   www.searlehealthnet.com
Mfr. pharmaceuticals, health care, optical products and specialty chemicals.

Searle & Co. Ltd., PO Box 53, Lane End Rd., High Wycombe, Buckinghamshire HP12 4HL, UK
Tel: 44-1494-521124   Fax: 44-1494-447872

Searle Pharmaceuticals, Whalton Rd., Morpeth, Northumberland NE61 3YA, UK
Tel: 44-1671-514311   Fax: 44-1670-517112

SECURE COMPUTING CORPORATION

4810 Harwood Rd., San Jose, CA, 95124
Tel: (408) 979-6000   Fax: (408) 979-6101   www.sctc.com
Mfr. software.

Secure Computing UK Ltd., 9 Shaftesbury Court, Chalvey Park, Slough Berkshire SL1 2ER, UK
Tel: 44-1753-826-000

SEDGWICK, DETERT, MORAN & ARNOLD

One Embarcadero Center, 16th Fl., San Francisco, CA, 94111
Tel: (415) 781-7900   Fax: (415) 781-2635   www.sdma.com
International law firm.

Sedgwick, Detert, Moran & Arnold, 5 Lloyds Avenue, London EC3N 3AE, UK
Tel: 44-207-929-1829   Fax: 44-207-929-1808

SEEBEYOND TECHNOLOGY CORPORATION

404 East Huntington Drive, Monrovia, CA, 91016
Tel: (626) 471-6000   Fax: (626) 471-6104   www.seebeyond.com
Mfr. business software.

SeeBeyond UK, 68 Lombard Street, London EC3V 9LJ, UK

SeeBeyond UK, Atrium Court, The Ring, Bracknell RG12 1BW, UK

SEECOMMERCE

3420 Hillview Avenue, Palo Alto, CA, 94304-1320
Tel: (650) 213-1800   Fax: (650) 812-3990   www.seecommerce.com
Mfr. supply chain management software.

SeeCommerce, Venture House, 2 Arlington Square, Downshire Way, Bracknell Berkshire RG12 1WA, UK

SEI INVESTMENTS COMPANY

1 Freedom Valley Drive, Oaks, PA, 19456-1100
Tel: (610) 676-1000   Fax: (610) 676-2995   www.seic.com
Accounting, evaluation and financial automated systems and services.

SEI Investments, 6-7 Queen St., London EC4N 1SP, UK

SEMITOOL, INC.

655 West Reserve Drive, Kalispell, MT, 59901

Tel: (406) 752-2107   Fax: (406) 752-5522   www.semitool.com

Mfr. semiconductor manufacturing equipment.

Semitool Europe, Ltd., 511 Coldhams Lane, Cambridge CB1 3JS, UK

Tel: 44-1223-505000

SEMTECH CORPORATION

200 Flynn Road, Camarillo, CA, 93012-8790

Tel: (805) 498-2111   Fax: (805) 498-3804   www.semtech.com

Mfr. silicon rectifiers, rectifier assemblies, capacitors, switching regulators, AC/DC converters.

Semtech Ltd., Units 2-3 Park Court, Premier Way, Romsey, Southampton S051 9AQ, UK

Tel: 44-1794-527-600   Fax: 44-1794-527-601

SENCO PRODUCTS INC.

8485 Broadwell Road, Cincinnati, OH, 45244

Tel: (513) 388-2000   Fax: (513) 388-2026   www.senco.com

Mfr. industry nailers, staplers, fasteners and accessories.

Senco Pneumatics (UK) Ltd., 211 Europa Blvd., Westbrook, Warrington, Cheshire WA5 5TN, UK

SENSIENT TECHNOLOGIES CORPORATION

777 E. Wisconsin Ave., Milwaukee, WI, 53202

Tel: (414) 271-6755   Fax: (414) 347-4783   www.sensient.com

Mfr. flavor applications for the beverage, bakery, confection, dairy, snack and savory markets.

Felton Worldwide Ltd., Castle Tower Works, Bilton Rd., Bletchley, Milton Keynes MK1 1HP, UK

SENSORMATIC ELECTRONICS CORPORATION

951 Yamato Road, Boca Raton, FL, 33431-0700

Tel: (561) 989-7000   Fax: (561) 989-7774   www.sensormatic.com

Electronic article surveillance equipment.

Sensormatic UK, Harefield Grove, Rickmansworth Road, Harefield Uxbridge, Middlesex UB9 6JY, UK

Tel: 44-1895-873-000   Fax: 44-1895-873-920   Contact: Mark Clark

SERVICE CORPORATION INTERNATIONAL

1929 Allen Parkway, Houston, TX, 77019

Tel: (713) 522-5141   Fax: (713) 525-5586   www.sci-corp.com

Operates funeral homes, cemeteries and crematoriums and sells caskets, burial vaults and cremation receptacles.

Great Southern Group plc, London, UK

Plantsbrook Group plc, London, UK

THE SERVICEMASTER COMPANY

2300 Warrenville Road, Downers Grove, IL, 60515-1700

Tel: (630) 271-1300   Fax: (630) 271-2710   www.svm.com

Provides residential consumer services, including lawn care and landscape maintenance, termite and pest control, plumbing, heating and air conditioning maintenance and repair.

ServiceMaster Ltd., 308 Melton Rd., Leicester LE4 7SL, UK

SHAKESPEARE FISHING TACKLE GROUP

3801 Westmore Drive, Columbia, SC, 29223

Tel: (803) 754-7000   Fax: (803) 754-7342   www.shakespeare-fishing.com

Mfr. fishing tackle.

Shakespeare Co. (UK), Broad Ground Rd., Lakeside, Redditch, Worcestershire B98 8NQ, UK

THE SHAW GROUP INC.

4171 Essen Lane, Baton Rouge, LA, 70809

Tel: (225) 932-2500   Fax: (225) 932-2661   www.shawgrp.com

Vertically-integrated provider of complete piping systems, and comprehensive engineering, procurement and construction services.

IT Group Infrastructure and Environmental Ltd., Embassy House 9/F, Queens Avenue, Clifton, Bristol BS8 1SB, UK

Tel: 44-117-930-4111   Fax: 44-117-930-4222

PTI Europe, Cranford Court King Street, Knutsford, Cheshire WA16 8BW, UK

Tel: 44-1565-650388   Fax: 44-1565-750376

Shaw Group U.K. Ltd., Stores Road, Derby DE21 4BG, UK

Contact: Neil Clark

Stone & Webster Ltd., 500 Elder Gate, Milton Keynes, Buckinghamshire MK9 1BA, UK

Tel: 44-1908-668-844   Fax: 44-1908-602-211

SHAW PITTMAN

2300 N Street, NW, Washington, DC, 20037

Tel: (202) 663-8000   Fax: (202) 663-8007   www.shawpittman.com

Engaged in international law.

Shaw Pittman UK, 25 Old Broad Street, Level 23, London EC2N 1HQ, UK

Tel: 44-207-847-9500   Contact: Robert Bishop

SHC, INC.

425 Meadow Street, Chicopee, MA, 01013

Tel: (413) 536-1200   Fax: (413) 322-2216   www.spalding.com

Mfr. athletic products, including golf balls, footballs, basketballs and volleyballs.

Spalding, Div. SHC, 16-19 Trafalgar Way, Bar Hill, Cambridge CB3 8SQ, UK

SHEAFFER PEN, INC.

301 Ave. H, Fort Madison, IA, 52627

Tel: (319) 372-3300   Fax: (319) 372-1263   www.sheaffer.com

Mfr. writing instruments.

Sheaffer Pen (UK) Ltd., Maylands Avenue, Hemel Hempstead, Hertfordshire HP2 7ER, UK

Tel: 44-1442-233411   Fax: 44-01442-233022

SHEARMAN & STERLING

599 Lexington Ave., New York, NY, 10022-6069

Tel: (212) 848-4000   Fax: (212) 848-7179   www.shearman.com

Law firm engaged in general American and international financial and commercial practice.

Shearman & Sterling, 199 Bishopsgate, 4th Fl., London EC2M 3TY, UK

Tel: 44-207-920-9000   Fax: 44-207-920-9020   Contact: Pamela M. Gibson, Mng. Ptnr.

THE SHERWIN-WILLIAMS COMPANY

101 Prospect Ave., N.W., Cleveland, OH, 44115-1075

Tel: (216) 566-2000   Fax: (216) 566-2947   www.sherwin-williams.com

Mfr. paint, wall coverings and related products.

FSW Ltd., Wharfedale Rd., Bradford, W. Yorks. BD4 6SE, UK

Lyons Technological Products Ltd., 26 New St. Square, London, UK

SHIPLEY COMPANY, LLC

455 Forest Street, Marlborough, MA, 01752

Tel: (508) 481-7950   Fax: (508) 485-9113   www.shipley.com

Supplier of materials and processes technology to the microelectronics and printed wiring board industries.

Shipley Europe Ltd., 18 Chesford Grange, Woolston, Warrington WA1 4RQ, UK

Tel: 44-1925-824105

Shipley Europe Ltd., Herald Way, Coventry CV3 2RQ, UK

Tel: 44-1203-654400   Fax: 44-1203-440331   Contact: R. Passmore, Pres. Euro. Group

Shipley Europe Ltd., 18 Chesford Grange Woolston, Warrington WA1 4RQ, UK

SHOOK, HARDY & BACON L.L.P.

1200 Main Street, Ste. 3100, Kansas City, MO, 64105-2118

Tel: (816) 474-6550   Fax: (816) 421-5547   www.shb.com

International law firm.

Shook, Hardy & Bacon, Manning House, 22 Carlisle Place, London SW1P 1JA, UK

SHOREWOOD PACKAGING CORPORATION

2 Manhattanville Rd., Purchase, NY, 10577-2196

Tel: (914) 397-1500   Fax: (914) 397-1596   www.shorepak.com

Mfr. packaging for video/music industry and consumer products.

Shorewood Packaging Co. Ltd., 36 Berwick St, London W1, UK

SHUTTS & BOWEN

201 Biscayne Boulevard, Miami, FL, 33131

Tel: (305) 358-6300   Fax: (305) 381-9982   www.shutts-law.com

International law firm.

Shutts & Bowen, 48 Mount St., London W1Y 5RE, UK

SIDLEY AUSTIN BROWN & WOOD, LLP

10 South Dearborn, Bank One Plaze, Chicago, IL, 60603

Tel: (312) 853-7000   Fax: (312) 853-7036   www.sidley.com

Engaged in international law.

Sidley Austin Brown & Wood LLP, One Threadneedle St., London EC2R 8AW, UK

Tel: 44-207-360-3600   Fax: 44-207-626-7937   Contact: Graeme C. Harrower, Ptnr.

SIEBEL SYSTEMS, INC.

2207 Bridgepointe Pkwy., San Mateo, CA, 94404

Tel: (650) 295-5000   Fax: (650) 295-5111   www.siebel.com

Provider of e-Business applications software.

Siebel Systems UK Ltd., Siebel Centre - The Glanty, Egham Surrey TW20 9DW, UK

Tel: 44-1784-494-900

SIG DOBOY INC.

869 South Knowles Ave., New Richmond, WI, 54017-1797

Tel: (715) 246-6511   Fax: (715) 246-6539   www.doboy.com

Mfr. packaging machinery.

SIG Plastic Technologies, Unit 15, Drakes Mews, Crownhill, MK8 0ER Milton Keynes Bucks, UK

SILICON GRAPHICS INC.

1600 Amphitheatre Pkwy., Mountain View, CA, 94043-1351

Tel: (650) 960-1980   Fax: (650) 932-0661   www.sgi.com

Design/mfr. special-effects computer graphic systems and software.

Silicon Graphics Ltd., Unit 9, Callendar Business Park, Callendar Rd., Falkirk FK1 1XR, UK

Tel: 44-1342-614-300   Fax: 44-1324-611-214

Silicon Graphics Ltd., 24 Chiswell St., London EC1Y 4TY, UK

Tel: 44-207-614-5900   Fax: 44-207-614-5905

Silicon Graphics Ltd., Forum 1, Station Rd., Theale, Reading RG7 4RA, UK

Tel: 44-118-930-7778   Fax: 44-118-930-7823

Silicon Graphics Ltd., 1530 Arlington Business Park, Theale, Reading RG7 4SB, UK

Tel: 44-118-925-7500   Fax: 44-118-925-7569

Silicon Graphics Ltd., Eagle Court, Concord Business Park, Threapwood Rd., Manchester M22 0RR, UK

Tel: 44-161-932-6000   Fax: 44-161-932-6001

Silicon Studio London, 20 Soho Square, London W1V 5FD, UK

Tel: 44-207-478-5000   Fax: 44-207-478-5001

SILICON STORAGE TECHNOLOGY, INC.

1171 Sonora Court, Sunnyvale, CA, 94086

Tel: (408) 735-9110   Fax: (408) 735-9036   www.ssti.com

Mfr./sale single power supply small ease-block flash memory components, and two-power supply MTP flash products.

Silicon Storage Technology Ltd., Terminal House, Station Approach, Shepperon, Middlesex TW17 8AS, UK

Tel: 44-1932-221212   Fax: 44-1932-230567   Contact: Richard Sawers

SIMON & SCHUSTER INC.

1230 Avenue of the Americas, New York, NY, 10020

Tel: (212) 698-7000   Fax: (212) 698-7007   www.simonandschuster.com

Publishes and distributes hardcover and paperback books, audiobooks and software.

Prentice-Hall Intl. (UK) Ltd., 66 Wood Lane End, Hemel Hempstead, Hertfordshire HP2 4RG, UK

Simon & Schuster Ltd., West Garden Pl., Kendal St., London W1 1AW, UK

SIMPLE TECH, INC.

3003 Daimler Street, Santa Ana, CA, 92705-5812

Tel: (949) 476-1180   Fax: (949) 476-1209   www.simpletech.com

Mfr. memory software.

Simple Tech Europe, Atantic House, Imperial Way, Reading RG2 0TD, UK

SIMPLEX GRINNELL

100 Simplex Dr., Westminster, MA, 01441

Tel: (978) 731-2500   Fax: (978) 731-7052   www.simplexgrinnell.com

Provides safety, fire detection, integrated security, communications, time and attendance and workforce management systems.

SimplexGrinnell International Pty. Ltd., Greville House, Hatton Road, Feltham, Middlesex TW14 9PX, UK

Tel: 44-20-8893-1333   Fax: 44-20-8893-1933

SimplexGrinnell International Pty. Ltd., 15 Harvard Court, Quay Business Centre, Winwick Quay, Warrington WA2 8LT, UK

Tel: 44-1925-234-959   Fax: 44-1925-243-221

SIMPLICITY PATTERN COMPANY, INC.

2 Park Avenue, 12th Fl., New York, NY, 10016

Tel: (212) 372-0500   Fax: (212) 372-0628   www.simplicity.com

Dress patterns.

Simplicity Patterns Ltd., Metropolis House, 39-45 Tottenham Court Rd., London W1P 9RD, UK

SIMPSON THACHER & BARTLETT

425 Lexington Ave., New York, NY, 10017

Tel: (212) 455-2000   Fax: (212) 455-2502   www.simpsonthacher.com

Engaged in international law.

Simpson Thacher & Bartlett, 99 Bishopsgate, London EC2M 3YH, UK

Tel: 44-207-422-4000   Fax: 44-207-422-4022   Contact: Walter A. Looney, Jr., Ptnr.

SITEL CORPORATION

111 South Calver Street, Ste. 1900, Baltimore, MD, 21202

Tel: (410) 246-1505   Fax: (410) 246-0200   www.sitel.com

Provides outsourced customer management services.

SITEL UK, Tolpits Lane, Moor Park, Rickmansworth Hertfordshire, UK

SKADDEN, ARPS, SLATE, MEAGHER & FLOM LLP

4 Times Square, New York, NY, 10036

Tel: (212) 735-3000   Fax: (212) 735-2000   www.sasmf.com

American/International law practice.

Skadden, Arps, Slate, Meagher & Flom LLP, One Canada Square, Canary Wharf, London E14 5DS, UK

Tel: 44-207-519-7000   Fax: 44-207-519-7070   Contact: Bruce M. Buck, Partner

SKIDMORE OWINGS & MERRILL LLP

224 S. Michigan Ave., Ste. 1000, Chicago, IL, 60604-2707

Tel: (312) 554-9090   Fax: (312) 360-4545   www.som.com

Engaged in architectural and engineering services.

SOM Inc., 46 Berkeley St., London W1X 6NT, UK

Tel: 44-207-930-9700   Fax: 44-207-930-9108

SKILLSOFT INC.

20 Industrial Park Drive, Nashua, NH, 03062

Tel: (603) 324-3000   Fax: (603) 324-3000   www.smartforce.com

Provides strategic learning solutions that help enterprises achieve tangible business results, such as increasing speed and effectiveness of business execution, driving revenues and reducing costs.

SkillSoft UK, The Lansbury Estate, Lower Guildford Road, Knaphill, Woking, Surrey GU21 2EP, UK

SKYWORKS SOLUTIONS, INC.

20 Sylvan Road, Woburn, MA, 01801

Tel: (781) 935-5150   Fax: (781) 824-4579   www.skyworksinc.com

Mfr. electronic and microwave components.

Skyworks Solutions, 100 Longwater Avenue, Green Park, Reading Berkshire RG2 6GP, UK

Contact: Steve Nugent

SLI, INC.

500 Chapman Street, Canton, MA, 02021

Tel: (781) 828-2948   Fax: (781) 828-2012   www.sli-lighting.com

Engaged in design, manufacture and sales of lighting systems, including lamps, fixtures and ballasts.

Concord Lighting Ltd., Avis Way, Newhaven, East Sussex BN9 0ED, UK

Tel: 44-1273-515811

WILBUR SMITH ASSOCIATES (WSA)

PO Box 92, Columbia, SC, 29202

Tel: (803) 758-4500   Fax: (803) 251-2064   www.wilbursmith.com

Consulting engineers.

Wilbur Smith Associates Inc. Intl., Linen Hall, 4/F, 162-168 Regent Street, London W1R 5TE, UK

Tel: 44-207-663-9706   Fax: 44-207-306-3166   Contact: Jamie Wheway

A.O. SMITH CORPORATION

11270 West Park Place, PO Box 23972, Milwaukee, WI, 53224

Tel: (414) 359-4000   Fax: (414) 359-4064   www.aosmith.com

Auto and truck frames, motors, water heaters, storage/handling systems, plastics, railroad products.

A. O. Smith, PO Box 8 Marshall Way, Gainsborough, Lincolnshire DN21 3ET, UK

Contact: David Dzimitrowicz

SMURFIT-STONE CONTAINER CORPORATION

150 N. Michigan Ave., Chicago, IL, 60601-7568

Tel: (312) 346-6600   Fax: (312) 580-3486   www.smurfit-stone.net

Mfr. paper and paper packaging.

Smurfit-Stone Container Corporation, Chesterfield, UK

SNAP-ON INCORPORATED

10801 Corporate Dr., Pleasant Prairie, WI, 53158-1603

Tel: (262) 656-5200   Fax: (262) 656-5577   www.snapon.com

Mfr. auto maintenance, diagnostic and emission testing equipment, hand tools, hydraulic lifts and tire changers.

Suntester (UK) Ltd., Oldmedow Rd., Hardwick Estate, King's Lynn, Norfolk PE30 4JW, UK

Tel: 44-1553-692422   Fax: 44-1553-691844   Contact: Michael Waldron, Mng. Dir.

SOFTWARE HOUSE INTERNATIONAL, INC.

2 Riverview Drive, Somerset, NJ, 08873

Tel: (732) 746-8888   Fax: (732) 764-8889   www.shi.com

Engaged in the distribution of software products.

SHI UK, CBS II West Wing, 382-390 Midsummer Blvd., Cental Milton Keynes MK9 2RG, UK

SOLA INTERNATIONAL INC.

10690 W. Ocean Air Drive, Ste. 300, San Diego, CA, 92130

Tel: (858) 509-9899   Fax: (858) 509-9898   www.sola.com

Mfr. and sales of plastic and glass eyeglasses.

SOLA Optical (UK) Ltd., PO Box 143, Holford Way, Holford, Birmingham B6 7UU, UK

Tel: 44-121-356-5595   Fax: 44-121-356-7678

SONOCO PRODUCTS COMPANY

North Second Street, PO Box 160, Hartsville, SC, 29550

Tel: (843) 383-7000   Fax: (843) 383-7008   www.sonoco.com

Mfr. packaging for consumer and industrial market and recycled paperboard.

Sonoco Capseals Liners, Greenock Rd., Trading Estate, Slough, Berkshire SL1 4QQ, UK

Tel: 44-1753-773000

Sonoco Consumer Packaging Europe, Stokes St., Clayton, Manchester M11 4QX, UK

Tel: 44-61-230-7000

Sonoco Engraph Label, Hedgehog House, 2 Michigan Ave., Broadway Salford, UK

Tel: 44-161-848-4800   Fax: 44-161-848-4830

Sonoco Engraph Label, Land of Green Ginger House, Anlaby, Hull HU10 6RN, UK

Tel: 44-1482-561166

Sonoco Europe Board Mills, Holywell Green, Stainland Halifax, West Yorkshire HX4 9PY, UK

Tel: 44-1422-374741

Sonoco Industrial Products, Tufthorne Ave., Cloeford, Gloucestershire GL16 8PP, UK

Tel: 44-1594-833272

Sonoco Industrial Products, Station Rd., Milnrow, Lancashire OL16 4HQ, UK

Tel: 44-1706-41661

SOTHEBY'S HOLDINGS, INC.

1334 York Avenue, New York, NY, 10021

Tel: (212) 606-7000   Fax: (212) 606-7027   www.sothebys.com

Auction house specializing in fine art and jewelry.

Sotheby's Holdings, Inc., Summers Place, Billingshurst, West Sussex RH14 9AD, UK

Tel: 44-1403-833-500   Fax: 44-1403-833-699   Contact: Timothy Wonnacott, Chmn.

Sotheby's Holdings, Inc., 34-35 New Bond Street, London W1A 2AA, UK

Tel: 44-20-7293-5000   Fax: 44-20-7293-5989

THE SOUTHERN COMPANY

270 Peachtree Street, N.W., Atlanta, GA, 30303

Tel: (404) 506-5000   Fax: (404) 506-0642   www.southernco.com

Electric utility.

Southern Energy-Europe, 31 Curzon St., London W147 7AE, UK

Tel: 44-207-491-1116   Fax: 44-207-491-1588   Contact: Barney Rush, Pres.

Southwestern Electricity, plc., 800 Park Ave., Aztec West, Almondsbury, Bristol B512 4SE, UK

Tel: 44-1454-201-101   Contact: Gale Klappa, Pres.

SPARKLER FILTERS INC.

PO Box 19, Conroe, TX, 77305-0019

Tel: (936) 756-4471   Fax: (936) 539-1165   www.sparklerfilters.com

Mfr. chemical process filtration industry.

Sparkler Filters Ltd., Palmcroy House, 387 London Road, West Croydon CRO 3PB, UK

Tel: 44-208-689-0863

SPECIAL METALS CORPORATION

4317 Middle Settlement Road, New Hartford, NY, 13413-5392

Tel: (315) 798-2900   Fax: (315) 798-6823   www.specialmetals.com

Mfr. alloys for aircraft engines.

Special Metals Wiggin Ltd., Holmer Road, Hereford HR4 9SL, UK

Tel: 44-1432-382-200

SPEEDFAM-IPEC INC.

305 N. 54th Street, Chandler, AZ, 85226-2416

Tel: (480) 961-1600   Fax: (480) 705-2793   www.sfamipec.com

Mfr. semiconductors.

SpeedFam-IPEC, Brindley Road, Dodwells Bridge, Industrial Estates, Hinckley Leicestershire LE 10 3BY, UK

Tel: 44-1-4556-31707   Fax: 44-1-4556-11360

SPENCER STUART MANAGEMENT CONSULTANTS

401 North Michigan Ave., Ste. 3400, Chicago, IL, 60611

Tel: (312) 822-0080   Fax: (312) 822-0116   www.spencerstuart.com

Executive recruitment firm.

Spencer Stuart & Associates Inc., 16 Connaught Place, London W2 2ED, UK

Tel: 44-207-298-3333   Fax: 44-207-298-3388   Contact: Lorna Parker

Spencer Stuart & Associates Inc., Gladstone House, Redvers Close, Lawnswood Park, Leeds LS16 6QY, UK

Tel: 44-113-230-7774   Fax: 44-113-230-7775   Contact: Michael Holford

SPERRY-SUN DRILLING SERVICES

PO Box 60070, Houston, TX, 77205

Tel: (281) 871-5100   Fax: (281) 871-5742   www.sperry-sun.com

Provides drilling services to the oil and gas drilling industry.

Sperry-Sun, Inc., Unit 4, Enterprise Way, Cheltenham Trade Park Arle Road, Cheltenham Gloucestershire GL51 8LZ, UK

Sperry-Sun, Inc., Morton Peto Road, Gapton Hall Ind. Estate, Great Yarmouth, Norfolk NR31 0LT, UK

SPHERION CORPORATION

2050 Spectrum Boulevard, Fort Lauderdale, FL, 33309

Tel: (954) 938-7600   Fax: (954) 938-7666   www.spherion.com

Provides temporary personnel placement and staffing.

Accountancy Additions, Hadleigh House, Guilford, UK

Tel: 44-148-345-0278

Interim Technology Consulting Group, Calthorpe House, Edgbaston, Birmingham, UK

Tel: 44-121-456-1020

Interim Technology Consulting Group, Nordic House, Purley, Surrey, UK

Tel: 44-181-660-1177

Michael Page Corporate Finance, 50 Cannon St., London EC4N 6JJ, UK

Tel: 44-207-269-1866

Michael Page Finance, Centurion House, St. Albans AL1 1SA, UK

Tel: 44-172-786-5813

Michael Page Finance, 29 St. Augustine's Parade, Bristol BS1 4UL, UK

Tel: 44-117-927-6509

Sales Recruitment Specialits, Aquis House, 6th Floor, Leeds LS1 5RU, UK

Tel: 44-113-242-7444

SPIROL INTERNATIONAL HOLDING CORPORATION

30 Rock Ave., Danielson, CT, 06239

Tel: (860) 774-8571   Fax: (860) 774-0487   www.spirol.com

Mfr. engineered fasteners, shims, automation equipment.

Spirol Ind. Ltd., Princewood Rd., Corby, Northantshire NN17 2ET, UK

Tel: 44-1536-267634   Fax: 44-1536-203415   Contact: Jon Fennell, Mng. Dir.   Emp: 38

SPRAYING SYSTEMS COMPANY

PO Box 7900, Wheaton, IL, 60189-7900

Tel: (630) 665-5000   Fax: (630) 260-0842   www.spray.com

Designs and manufactures industrial spray products.

Spraying Systems Limited, 4 Bourne Mill Industrial Estate, Guildford Road, Farnham Surrey GU9 9PS, UK

SPRINT CORPORATION

2330 Shawnee Mission Parkway, Westwood, KS, 66205

Tel: (913) 624-3000   Fax: (913) 624-3281   www.sprint.com

Telecommunications equipment and services.

Sprint Corporation, Rawdon House, Bond Close, Kingsland Business Park, Basingstoke Hampshire RG24 0PZ, UK

SPS TECHNOLOGIES INC.

165 Township Line Rd., Two Pitcairn Place, Jenkintown, PA, 19046

Tel: (215) 517-2000   Fax: (215) 517-2032   www.spstech.com

Mfr. aerospace and industry fasteners, tightening systems, magnetic materials, super alloys.

SPS Technologies Ltd., TJ Brooks Division, 191 Barkby Road, Troon Ind. Area, Leicester LE4 9HX, UK

Tel: 44-116-2768261   Fax: 44-116-2460523   Contact: Sean Barrett

SPS Technologies Ltd., PO Box 38, Burnaby Rd., Coventry CV6 4AE, UK

Unbrako UK/SPS Technologies Ltd, Cranford Street, Smethwick, West Midlands B66 2TA, UK

Tel: 44-121- 555 8855   Fax: 44-121-555 8866

SPSS INC.

233 S. Wacker Dr., 11th Fl., Chicago, IL, 60606

Tel: (312) 651-6000   Fax: (312) 329-3668   www.spss.com

Mfr. statistical software.

SPSS UK Ltd., SPSS House, St. Andrew's House 1/F, West Street, Woking GU21 1EB, UK

Contact: Martin Young

SPX CORPORATION

700 Terrace Point Drive, PO Box 3301, Muskegon, MI, 49443-3301

Tel: (231) 724-5000   Fax: (231) 724-5720   www.spx.com

Mfr. auto parts, special service tools, engine and drive-train parts.

Bear (UK) Ltd., Mercers Row, Cambridge CB5 8HY, UK

Kent-Moore UK & Euroline, 86 Wharfdale Rd., Tyseley, Birmingham B11 2DD, UK

Power Team UK, Unit 17E, Number One Industrial Estate, Co. Durham DH8 65Y, UK

Robinair UK, c/o Kent-Moore UK, 86 Wharfdale Rd., Tyseley, Birmingham B11 2DD, UK

SPX/Fenner Plc., Fenner Fluid Power Div., Yorkshire, UK

V.L. Churchill Ltd., PO Box 3, London Rd., Daventry, Northants NN11 4NF, UK

SQUIRE, SANDERS & DEMPSEY

4900 Key Tower, 127 Public Square, Cleveland, OH, 44114-1304

Tel: (216) 479-8500   Fax: (216) 479-8780   www.ssd.com

Engaged in international law.

Squire, Sanders & Dempsey, Royex House, Aldermanbury Square, London EC2V 7HR, UK

Tel: 44-207-776-5200   Fax: 44-207-776-5233   Contact: Joseph P. Markoski

SRI INTERNATIONAL

333 Ravenswood Ave., Menlo Park, CA, 94025-3493

Tel: (650) 859-2000   Fax: (650) 326-5512   www.sri.com

Engaged in international consulting and research.

Cambridge Computer Science Research Center, 23 Millers Yard, Mill Lane, Cambridge CB2 1RQ, UK

Tel: 44-1223-518234   Fax: 44-1223-517417

SRI Europe, Stanford House, 2 Manchester Square, London W1M 5RF, UK

SS&C TECHNOLOGIES, INC.

80 Lamberton Road, Windsor, CT, 06095

Tel: (860) 298-4500   Fax: (860) 298-4900   www.ssctech.com

Mfr. tracking software.

SS&C Ltd., 120 Cannon Street, 5th Fl., London EC4N 6AS, UK

SSA GLOBAL TECHNOLOGIES, INC.

500 W. Madison St., Ste. 3200, Chicago, IL, 60661

Tel: (312) 258-6000   Fax: (312) 474-7500   www.ssax.com

Mfr. computer software.

SSA Global, Frimley Business Park, Frimley, Cambeley, Surrey GU16 55G, UK

Tel: 44-1276-692-111   Fax: 4-1276-692-135

THE ST. PAUL COMPANIES, INC.

385 Washington Street, St. Paul, MN, 55102

Tel: (651) 310-7911   Fax: (651) 310-8294   www.stpaul.com

Provides investment, insurance and reinsurance services.

Ashley Palmer Ltd., 27 Leaden Hall St., London EC3A 1AA, UK

Tel: 44-207-488-0103   Fax: 44-207-481-4995

Camperdown UK Ltd., The St. Paul House, 23-27 Alie St., London E1 8DS, UK

Tel: 44-207-488-6321   Fax: 44-207-680-8903   Contact: Duncan Wilkinson, CEO

Cassidy Davis Underwriting Ltd., St. Helen's, 1 Undershaft, London EC3A 8JR, UK

Tel: 44-207-623-1026   Fax: 44-207-623-5225   Contact: Tony Cassidy

Eagle Star Insurance Company Ltd., London Commercial Centre, 82-84 Fenchurch St., London EC3M 4ES, UK

Gravett & Tilling Ltd., 61 St. Mary Avenue, 5th Floor, London EC3A 8AA, UK

Tel: 44-207-397-6800   Fax: 44-207-623-5718   Contact: John Tilling

St. Paul International Insurance Co. Ltd., 61-63 London Road, Redhill Surrey RH1 1N8, UK

Tel: 44-1737-787-787   Fax: 44-1737-787-172   Contact: Kent Urness, Pres. & CEO

St. Paul International Insurance Company Ltd., St. Paul House, 23-27 Alie St., London E1 8DS, UK

Tel: 44-207-488-6313   Fax: 44-207-488-6348

STANDARD COMMERCIAL CORPORATION

2201 Miller Rd., PO Box 450, Wilson, NC, 27894

Tel: (252) 291-5507   Fax: (252) 237-1109   www.sccgroup.com

Leaf tobacco dealers and processors and wool processors.

Standard Commercial Ltd., Standard House, Weyside Park, Godalming Surrey GU7 1XE, UK

Standard Wool (UK) Limited, Carlton Buildings, Clifton Street, Bradford BD8 7DB, UK

STANDARD MICROSYSTEMS CORPORATION

80 Arkay Drive, Hauppauge, NY, 11788

Tel: (631) 435-6000   Fax: (631) 273-5550   www.smsc.com

Telecommunications systems.

Insight MEMEC UK, Aylesbury, UK

Tel: 44-1296-330061

STANDEX INTERNATIONAL CORPORATION

6 Manor Parkway, Salem, NH, 03079

Tel: (603) 893-9701   Fax: (603) 893-7324   www.standex.com

Mfr. diversified graphics, institutional, industry, electronic and consumer products.

Barbeque King, 16 Richfield Ave., Reading Berkshire RG1 8PB, UK

Tel: 44-118-950-822   Fax: 44-118-959-1968   Contact: Stewart Greener, Mgr.

James Burn Binders, Stanton Harcourt Rd., Ensham Oxford OX8 1JE, UK

Tel: 44-1865-880-458   Fax: 44-1865-880-661   Contact: Mike Chapman

James Burn International, Douglas Rd., Esher, Surrey KT10 8BD, UK

Tel: 44-1372-466-801   Fax: 44-1372-469-422   Contact: David Baddaley, Mgr.

James Burn International, Cannon Way, Barugh Green, Barnsley South Yorkshire S75 1JU, UK

Tel: 44-1226-380-088   Fax: 44-1226-388-110   Contact: Clive Bromley, Mgr.

Standex Electronics UK Ltd., 40 Morley Rd., Tonbridge, Kent TN9 1RA, UK

Tel: 44-1732-771-023   Fax: 44-1732-770-122   Contact: John Hill, Mgr.

Standex Holdings Ltd., Stanton Harcourt Rd., Eynsham Oxfordshire OX8 1JE, UK

Tel: 44-1865-882-389   Fax: 44-1865-882-768   Contact: Mark Hampton, Mgr.

Standex International Ltd., Unit 6, Cromwell Road, Trading Estate, Bredbury Stockport, Cheshire SK6 2RF, UK

Tel: 44-161-430-6815   Fax: 44-161-494-5696   Contact: George Fryer, Mgr.

STANLEY BOSTITCH FASTENING SYSTEMS

815 Briggs Street, East Greenwich, RI, 02818

Tel: (401) 884-2500   Fax: (401) 885-6511   www.stanleybostich.com

Mfr. stapling machines, stapling supplies, fastening systems and wire.

Stanley Bostitch UK, Station Road, Edenbridge, Kent, UK

THE STANLEY WORKS

1000 Stanley Drive, PO Box 7000, New Britain, CT, 06053

Tel: (860) 225-5111   Fax: (860) 827-3987   www.stanleyworks.com

Mfr. hand tools and hardware.

MAC Tools, 10-12 Ravens Way, Northampton NN3 9UD, UK

Stanley Home Décor Mosley Stone, Ltd., Hollins Mill, Hollins Mill Lane, Sowerby Bridge, Halifax, West Yorkshire HX6 2RF, UK

Stanley Tools, Euroway Industrial Estate, Hellaby Lane, Hellaby Rotherham S66 8HN, UK

Stanley Tools, Gowerton Road, Brackmills, Northampton NN4 7BW, UK

Stanley UK, Woodside, Sheffield S3 9PD, UK

STAPLES, INC.

500 Staples Dr., Framingham, MA, 01702

Tel: (508) 253-3000   Fax: (508) 253-8989   www.staples.com

Superstore for office supplies and equipment.

Staples, UK, Westfields, London Rd., High Wycombe HP11 1HA, UK

Tel: 44-1494-474-990   Fax: 44-1494-474-194

STAR TELECOMMUNICATIONS, INC.

223 East De La Guerra Street, Santa Barbara, CA, 93101

Tel: (805) 899-1962   Fax: (805) 899-2972   www.startel.com

Provides long-distance telecommunications services.

Star Europe Ltd., Adelaide House, 626 Chiswick High Road, Level 3, London W4 5RY, UK

Tel: 44-208-580-5150

STARBUCKS CORPORATION

2401 Utah Ave. South, Seattle, WA, 98134

Tel: (206) 447-1575   Fax: (206) 447-0828   www.starbucks.com

Coffee bean retail store and coffee bars.

Starbucks Coffee Corp., London, UK

STARKEY LABORATORIES, INC.

6700 Washington Avenue South, Eden Prairie, MN, 55344

Tel: (952) 941-6401   Fax: (952) 947-4787   www.starkey.com

Mfr. custom in-the-ear hearing aids.

Starkey UK, WF Austin House, Bramhall Technology Park, Pepper Road, Hazel Grove, Stockport, SK7 5BX, UK

Tel: 44-161-483-2200

STARTEC GLOBAL COMMUNICATIONS CORPORATION

1151 Seven Locks Road, Potomac, MD, 20854

Tel: (301) 610-4300   Fax: (301) 610-4301   www.startec.com

Provides international phone service.

Startec UK, India House, 45 Curlew Street, London SE1 2ND, UK

STARTEK, INC.

100 Garfield St., Denver, CO, 80206

Tel: (303) 361-6000   Fax: (303) 388-9970   www.startek.com

Provides outsourcing solutions.

Startek Europe Ltd., Unit A, Sovereign Park, Brenda Road, Hartlepool TS25 1NN, UK

Tel: 44-1429-867711   Fax: 44-1429-233677

STARWOOD HOTELS & RESORTS WORLDWIDE

777 Westchester Avenue, White Plains, NY, 10604

Tel: (914) 640-8100   Fax: (914) 640-8316   www.starwoodhotels.com

Hotel operations including Sheraton, Westin, St. Regis, Four Points and Caesars.

Sheraton Sales Center, The Kiln House, 210 New Kings Rd., London SW6 4NZ, UK

STATE STREET CORPORATION

225 Franklin Street, Boston, MA, 02101

Tel: (617) 786-3000   Fax: (617) 654-3386   www.statestreet.com

Engaged in investment management and institutional investor services.

Rexiter Capital Management Limited, 21 Saint James Square, London SWIY 4SS, UK

State Street Bank & Trust, One Royal Exchange Steps, Royal Exchange, London EC3V 3LE, UK

State Street Fund Services, One Canada Square, Canary Wharf, London E14 5AF, UK

State Street Global Advisors, Almack House, 28 King St., London SW14 6QW, UK

State Street Global Advisors, 20 Saint James Square, London SWIY 4SS, UK

STEINER CORPORATION

505 E. South Temple, Salt Lake City, UT, 84102

Tel: (801) 328-8831   Fax: (801) 363-5680   www.alsco.com

Mfr. soap and towel dispensers and uniforms.

STEINERCO Ltd., Steiner House, Lake Lane, GB Barnham, West Sussex PO22 0AE, U.K.

STELLENT, INC.

7777 Golden Triangle Drive, Eden Prairie, MN, 55344

Tel: (952) 903-2000   Fax: (952) 829-5424   www.stellent.com

Mfr. Web-based software products.

Stellent UK, 339 High Street, Slough Berkshire S11 1TX, UK

STEMCO INC.

PO Box 1989, Longview, TX, 75606

Tel: (903) 758-9981   Fax: (903) 232-3508   www.stemco.com

Mfr. seals, hubcaps, hubodometers and locking nuts for heavy duty trucks, buses, trailers.

Garlock GB-STEMCO Products, Hambridge Rd., Newbury, Berkshire RG14 5TG, UK

Tel: 44-1635-38668   Fax: 44-1635-49586   Contact: Bob Bannister

STERIS CORPORATION

5960 Heisley Road, Mentor, OH, 44060

Tel: (440) 354-2600   Fax: (440) 639-4459   www.steris.com

Mfr. sterilization and infection control equipment, surgical tables, lighting systems for health, pharmaceutical and scientific industries.

Steris Corporation, 53 Church Rd., Ashford, Middlesex TW15 2TY, UK

STEWART ENTERPRISES, INC.

110 Veterans Memorial Blvd, Metairie, LA, 70005

Tel: (504) 837-5880   Fax: (504) 849-2307   www.stewartent.com

Provides funeral services.

Stewart Enterprises, 200-201 High Street, Exeter EX 4 3EB, UK

Tel: 44-1392-430792   Contact: Peter Ashby

STEWART INFORMATION SERVICES CORPORATION

1980 Post Oak Blvd., Ste. 800, Houston, TX, 77056

Tel: (713) 625-8100   Fax: (713) 552-9523   www.stewart.com

Engaged in title insurance services.

Stewart Information Services, 200-201 High Street, Exeter EX4 3EB, UK

Contact: Reta Coburn

STIEFEL LABORATORIES INC.

255 Alhambra Circle, Ste. 1000, Coral Gables, FL, 33134

Tel: (305) 443-3807   Fax: (305) 443-3467   www.stiefel.com

Mfr. pharmaceuticals, dermatological specialties.

Stiefel Laboratories Ltd., Whitebrook Park, 68 Lower Cookham Rd., Maidenhead, Berkshire SL6 8AL, UK

Stiefel Laboratories Ltd., Holtsur Lane, Woodburn Green, High Wycombe, Buckinghamshire HP10 0AU, UK

STILWELL FINANCIAL INC.

920 Main Street, Kansas City, MO, 64105

Tel: (816) 218-2400   Fax: (816) 218-2453   www.stilwellfinancial.com

Engaged in financial services.

Stilwell Financial, 9 Queen Anne Street, London W1G 9HW, UK

Stilwell Financial, 63 High Street, Chester CH3 8EE, UK

Stilwell Financial, The Rickyard, Newton Street Loe, Bath BA2 9BT, UK

STORAGE NETWORKS, INC.

255 Wyman Street, Waltham, MA, 02451

Tel: (781) 622-6700   Fax: (781) 622-6799   www.storagenetworks.com

Mfr. software to store and access data.

StorageNetworks, Inc., Knyvett House, The Causeway, Staines Middlesex TW18 3BA, UK

Tel: 44-1784-898-091   Fax: 44-1784-898-539

STORAGE TECHNOLOGY CORPORATION

One Storagetech Dr., Louisville, CO, 80028-4377

Tel: (303) 673-5151   Fax: (303) 673-5019   www.stortek.com

Mfr., market, service information, storage and retrieval systems.

StorageTek Holding Ltd., 6 Genesis Business Park, Albert Drive, Wokingham Surrey GU21 5RW, UK

Tel: 44-148-373-7654   Fax: 44-148-373-7655   Contact: Jeremy Fletcher

THE STRUCTURE TONE ORGANIZATION

15 East 26th Street, New York, NY, 10010-1589

Tel: (212) 481-6100   Fax: (212) 685-9267   www.structuretone.com

Provides general contracting and construction management.

Structure Tone Organization, Dexter House, 2 Royal Mint Court, London EC3N 4LA, UK

STRYKER CORPORATION

2725 Fairfield Rd., Kalamazoo, MI, 49002

Tel: (616) 385-2600   Fax: (616) 385-1062   www.strykercorp.com

Develops, manufactures and markets specialty surgical and medical products worldwide.

Stryker UK Ltd., Medway House, 5000 Newbury Business Park, Newbury Berkshire RG14 2ST, UK

Tel: 44-163-52-62400   Fax: 44-163-55-80606   Contact: Mark Reeves

SUDLER & HENNESSEY

230 Park Avenue South, New York, NY, 10003-1566

Tel: (212) 614-4100   Fax: (212) 598-6933   www.sudler.com

Engaged in healthcare products advertising.

Sudler & Hennessey Ltd., Greater London House, Hampstead Rd., London NW1 7QP, UK

Tel: 44-207-307-7800   Contact: Dr. Brian Kelly, Mng. Dir.

SULLAIR CORPORATION

3700 E. Michigan Blvd., Bldg. 1-2, Michigan City, IN, 46360

Tel: (219) 879-5451   Fax: (219) 874-1273   www.sullair.com

Mfr. high efficiency tandem compressors, vacuum systems, encapsulated compressors and air tools.

Sullair (UK) Ltd., 274 High St., Uxbridge, Middlesex UB8 ILQ, UK

SULLIVAN & CROMWELL

125 Broad Street, New York, NY, 10004-2498

Tel: (212) 558-4000   Fax: (212) 558-3588   www.sullcrom.com

Engaged in international law.

Sullivan & Cromwell, 1 New Fetter Lane, London EC4A 1AN, UK

Tel: 44-207-959-8900   Fax: 44-207-959-8950

SUN HEALTHCARE GROUP, INC.

101 Sun Avenue, N.E., Albuquerque, NM, 87109

Tel: (505) 821-3355   Fax: (505) 858-4735   www.sunh.com

Provides long-term and skilled nursing care.

Ashbourne PLC, St. George's Park School Street, St. George's Telford, Shropshire, UK

Contact: Elaine Farrall, Dir.

Sunscript U.K., London, UK

SUNGARD DATA SYSTEMS

1285 Drummers Lane, Wayne, PA, 19087

Tel: (610) 341-8700   Fax: (610) 341-8851   www.sungard.com

Provides ASP solutions to the buyside investment management market.

SunGard Data Systems, 33 St.. Mary Ave., Exchequer Court, London EC3A 8AA, UK

Tel: 44-20-7337-6000   Contact: Gavin Lavelle, Pres.

SunGard Data Systems, 10-16 North Street, Carshalton, Surrey SM5 2HU, UK

Tel: 44-181-669-5285   Contact: Norman Ireland, Pres.

SUNRISE MEDICAL INC.

7477 East Dry Creek Parkway, Longmont, CO, 80503

Tel: (303) 218-4500   Fax: (303) 218-4590   www.sunrisemedical.com

Designs, manufactures and markets rehabilitation products and assistive technology devices for people with disabilities, and patient care products used in nursing homes, hospitals and homecare settings.

Sunrise Medical Ltd., High Street Wollaston, Stourbridge West Midlands DY8 4PS, UK

Tel: 44-1384-44-6688

SUPERIOR GRAPHITE COMPANY

10 South Riverside Plaza, Chicago, IL, 60606

Tel: (312) 559-2999   Fax: (312) 559-9064   www.graphitesgc.com

Mfr. natural and synthetic graphites, electrodes, lubricants, suspensions, carbide and carbon.

Superior Graphite Co., 4th Fl., Knightsbridge, 197 Knightsbridge, London SW7 1RB, UK

Tel: 44-207-973-8866   Fax: 44-207-581-5413

SUPERIOR TUBE COMPANY

3900 Germantown Pike, Collegeville, PA, 19426

Tel: (610) 489-5200   Fax: (610) 489-5252   www.superiortube.com

Mfr. precision, seamless tubes for automotive, medical, aerospace and nuclear industries.

Fine Tubes Limited, Estober Works, Plymouth PL6 7LJ, UK

SUPRA PRODUCTS INC.

4001 Fairview Industrial Drive S.E., Salem, OR, 97302-1067

Tel: (503) 581-9101   Fax: (503) 364-1285   www.supra-products.com

Mfr. lockboxes and provides key and access management products.

Carl Bro Group, Mansion Gate Drive, Leeds LS7 4DN, UK

Contact: Ian Williams

Supra Europe, Unit 7, Cliffe Business Park, Bruntcliffe Road, Morley, Leeds LS27 OLQ, UK

Contact: Dean Brazenall

SVI SOLUTIONS, INC.

5607 Palmer Way, Carlsbad, CA, 92008

Tel: (760) 496-0280   Fax: (760) 496-0281   www.svisolutions.com

Mfr. software.

SVI Merchandise Management Systems, The Mill House, Royston Road, Wendens Ambo, Essex CB11 4JX, UK

Tel: 44-1799-542224   Fax: 44-1799-540205

SYBASE, INC.

5000 Hacienda Dr., Dublin, CA, 94568

Tel: (925) 236-5000   Fax: (925) 236-4321   www.sybase.com

Design/mfg/distribution of database management systems, software development tools, connectivity products, consulting and technical support services..

Sybase UK Ltd., Sybase Court, Crown Lane, Maidenhead, Berkshire SL6 8Q2, UK

Tel: 44-1628-597100   Fax: 44-1628-597000

SYBRON DENTAL SPECIALTIES, INC.

1717 West Collins, Orange, CA, 92867

Tel: (714) 516-7400   Fax: (714) 516-7904   www.sybrondental.com

Mfr. consumable dental products, light curing instruments and plastics for dental use.

Kerr International, Div. Sybron Dental1, Mallard Business Centre, Mallard Road, Bretton, Peterborough PE3 8YP, UK

Tel: 44-1733-260-998   Fax: 44-1733-262-096

SYMANTEC CORPORATION

20330 Stevens Creek Blvd., Cupertino, CA, 95014-2132

Tel: (408) 253-9600   Fax: (408) 253-3968   www.symantec.com

Designs and produces PC network security and network management software and hardware.

Symantec Ltd., St. Cloud's Gate, St. Cloud Way, Maidenhead, Berkshire SL6 8W, UK

Tel: 44-1628-59-2222   Fax: 44-1628-59-2393

SYMBOL TECHNOLOGIES, INC.

One Symbol Plaza, Holtsville, NY, 11742-1300

Tel: (631) 738-2400   Fax: (631) 738-5990   www.symbol.com

Mfr. Bar code-driven data management systems, wireless LAN's, and Portable Shopping System™.

Symbol Technologies Intl., Symbol Place, Winnersh Triangle, Berkshire RG41 5TP, UK

Tel: 44-118-945-7000   Fax: 44-118-945-7500

SYMMETRICOM, INC.

2300 Orchard Pkwy., San Jose, CA, 95131-1017

Tel: (408) 433-0910   Fax: (408) 428-7999   www.symmetricom.com

Mfr. synchronization and timing equipment for telephones and broadband networks.

Symmetricom Ltd., 150 Wharfedale Road, Winnersh Triangle, Berkshire RG41 5RB, UK

SYNAPTICS INCORPORATED

2381 Bering Drive, San Jose, CA, 95131

Tel: (408) 434-0110   Fax: (408) 434-9819   www.synaptics.com

Designs and sells interfaces for portable electronic devices.

Synaptics UK Ltd., 7340 Cambridge Research park, Ely Road, Waterbeach, Cambridge CB5 9TB, UK

SYNAVANT INC.

3445 Peachtree Road NE, Ste. 1400, Atlanta, GA, 30326

Tel: (404) 841-4000   Fax: (404) 841-4115   www.synavant.com

Mfr. support software for pharmaceutical industry.

Synavant UK, Swan House, 24 Bridge Street, Leatherhead Surrey KT22 8BZ, UK

Tel: 44-1372-389300

SYNCHRONICITY SOFTWARE, INC.

201 Forest Street, Marlboro, MA, 01752

Tel: (508) 485-4122 Fax: (508) 485-7514 www.synchronicity.com

Mfr. communications software.

Synchronicity Software UK, PO Box 5890, Newbury RG14 7XL, UK

SYNOPSYS, INC.

700 East Middlefield Road, Mountain View, CA, 94043

Tel: (650) 962-5000 Fax: (650) 965-8637 www.synopsys.com

Mfr. electronic design automation software.

Synopsys Europe, Imperium - Imperial Way, Worton Grange, Reading Berkshire RG2 0TD, UK

Tel: 44-118-931-3822 Fax: 44-118-975-0081

SYNPLICITY, INC.

935 Stewart Drive, Sunnyvale, CA, 94085

Tel: (408) 215-6000 Fax: (408) 990-0290 www.synplicity.com

Mfr. software.

Synplicity Europe, 100 The Ring, Bracknell, Berkshire RG12 1BW, UK

SYNQUEST, INC.

3500 Parkway Lane, Ste. 555, Norcross, GA, 30092

Tel: (770) 325-2000 Fax: (770) 325-2960 www.synquest.com

Provides supply chain management software.

Synquest UK, The Coach House, 163 Burwood Rd, Walton on Thames, Surrey KT12 4AT, UK

SYNTEGRA

4201 Lexington Avenue North, Arden Hills, MN, 55126-6198

Tel: (651) 415-2999 Fax: (651) 415-4891 www.cdc.com

Engaged in consulting and systems integration.

Syntegra Ltd., 3 Roundwood Ave., Stockley Park, Uxbridge Middlesex, London UB11 1AG, UK

Tel: 44-181-867-6000 Fax: 44-181-569-2511

SYNTELLECT INC.

16610 N. Black Canyon Hwy., Ste. 100, Phoenix, AZ, 85053

Tel: (602) 789-2800 Fax: (602) 789-2899 www.synellect.com

Mfr. telephone software.

Syntellect Ltd., The Courtyard Barns, Choke Lane, Maidenhead, Berkshire SL6 6PT, UK

SYSTEMAX INC.

22 Harbor Park Dr., Port Washington, NY, 11050

Tel: (516) 608-7000 Fax: (516) 608-7111 www.systemax.com

Direct marketer of computers and related products to businesses.

Misco Computer Supplies UK, Faraday Close, Park Farm Industrial Estate, Wellingborough, Northants NN8 6XH, UK

Tel: 44-1933-400-400

TAC WORLDWIDE COMPANIES

850 Washington Street, Dedham, MA, 02026

Tel: (781) 251-8000 Fax: (781) 251-8064 www.1tac.com

Engaged in temporary staffing.

TAC Europe, 55 Grosvenor Street, Mayfair, London W1K 3HY, UK

Tel: 44-207-659-9800 Fax: 44-207-659-9820

TAC Europe, The Pavilion, ViewPoint, Basing View, Basingstoke, Hampshire RG21 4RG, UK

Tel: 44-1256-365-700 Fax: 44-1256-365-717

TACONIC LTD.

PO Box 69, 136 Coon Brook Road, Petersburg, NY, 12138

Tel: (518) 658-3202   Fax: (518) 658-3204   www.4taconic.com

Mfr. Teflon/silicone-coated fiberglass fabrics, tapes and belts; specialty tapes and circuit board substrates.

Taconic UK, 15 Brunel Close, Drayton Fields Industrial Estate, Daventry, Northants NN11 5RB, UK

Tel: 44-1327-304500   Fax: 44-1327-304501

TALISMA CORPORATION

4600 Carillon Point, Kirkland, WA, 98033

Tel: (425) 897-2900   Fax: (425) 828-9587   www.talisma.com

Mfr. customer relationship management software.

Talisma UK Ltd., Siena Court, The Broadway, Maidenhead, Berkshire SL6 1NJ, UK

TALITY CORPORATION

555 River Oaks Pkwy., Bldg. 4, San Jose, CA, 95134

Tel: (408) 456-8200   Fax: (408) 456-8288   www.tality.com

Engaged in engineering design services.

Tality Ltd., One The Alba Campus, Livingston, West Lothian EH54 7HH, UK

Tality Ltd., St. John's Innovation Park, Cowley Road, Cambridge CB4 OWS, UK

TANGRAM ENTERPRISE SOLUTIONS, INC.

11000 Regency Pkwy. Ste. 401, Cary, NC, 27511

Tel: (919) 653-6000   Fax: (919) 653-6004   www.tesi.com

Mfr. enterprise solution software.

Tangram Enterprise Solutions, Albany House, Market Street, Maidenhead, Berkshire SL6 8BE, UK

Tel: 44-1628-421840   Fax: 44-1628-421501

TARANTELLA, INC.

425 Encinal Street, Santa Cruz, CA, 95060

Tel: (831) 425-7222   Fax: (831) 427-5400   www.tarantella.com

Mfr. server software.

Tarantella Ltd., Waterside House, Kirkstall Road, Leeds LS4 2QB, UK

Tarantella, Inc., 7 Britannia Court, West Drayton UB7 7PN, UK

Tel: 44-1895-456100

TATE ACCESS FLOORS INC.

7510 Montevideo Road, PO Box 278, Jessup, MD, 20794-0278

Tel: (410) 799-4200   Fax: (410) 799-4250   www.tateaccessfloors.com

Mfr. access floors for offices, equipment rooms, clean rooms and specialty applications.

Tate Access Limited, Cartbridge Lane South, Walsall, West Midlands WS4 1SD, UK

Tel: 44-1922-619-100

TBWA WORLDWIDE

488 Madison Avenue, 6th Floor, New York, NY, 10022

Tel: (212) 804-1000   Fax: (212) 804-1200   www.tbwachiat.com

International full service advertising agency.

TBWA UK, London, UK

TC INDUSTRIES

3703 South Route 31, Crystal Lake, IL, 60012-1312

Tel: (815) 459-2400   Fax: (815) 459-3303   www.tcindustries.com

Mfr./sales of fabricated metal products.

TC Industries of Europe Ltd., PO Box 2, Carlin How, Saltburn-by-the-Sea, Cleveland TS13 4EU, UK

THE TCW GROUP

865 S. Figueroa St., Ste. 1800, Los Angeles, CA, 90017

Tel: (213) 244-0000   Fax: (213) 244-0000   www.tcwgroup.com

Engaged in managing pension and profit sharing funds, retirement/health and welfare funds, insurance company funds, endowments and foundations.

TCW Group, London, UK

TEAM, INC.

Box 123, 200 Hermann Dr., Alvin, TX, 77511

Tel: (281) 331-6154   Fax: (281) 331-4107   www.teamindustrialservices.com

Consulting, engineering and rental services.

Team Environmental Services Ltd., MacAuley Rd., Unit 1, Huddersfield, W. Yorks. HD2 2US, UK

Tel: 44-1484-401900   Fax: 44-1484-401666

TECA CORPORATION (THERMO ELECTRIC COOLING AMERICA

4048 West Schubert, Chicago, IL, 60639

Tel: (773) 342-4900   Fax: (773) 342-0191   www.thermoelectric.com

Mfr. solid state cooling products, including air-conditioners, cold plates and liquid chillers.

Thermo Electric International, 17E Upper Field Rd., Dolphin Park, Eurolink, Sittingbourne Kent ME10 3UP, UK

TECH TEAM GLOBAL, INC.

27335 W. Eleven Mile Road, Southfield, MI, 48034

Tel: (248) 357-2866   Fax: (248) 357-2570   www.techteam.com

Provides help desk support and technical staffing.

Tech Team Europe Ltd., Criterion House, 40 Parkway, Chelmsford Essex CM2 7PN, UK

Tel: 44-1245-26-9100

TECH/OPS SEVCON INC.

40 North Avenue, Burlington, MA, 01803

Tel: (781) 229-7896   Fax: (781) 229-8603   www.sevcon.com

Design, manufacture, and marketing of microprocessor based control systems for battery powered vehicles.

Sevcon Ltd., Kingsway South, Gateshead NE11 OQA, UK

TECHNE CORPORATION

614 McKinley Place NE, Minneapolis, MN, 55413

Tel: (612) 379-8854   Fax: (612) 379-6580   www.techne-corp.com

Mfr. controls and instruments for blood analysis.

R&D Systems Europe Ltd. (RDSE), 19 Barton Lane, Abingdon Science Park, Abington OX 14 3NB, UK

TECHNITROL INC.

1210 Northbrook Drive, #385, Trevose, PA, 19053

Tel: (215) 355-2900   Fax: (215) 355-7397   www.technitrol

Mfr. of electronic components, electrical contacts, and other parts/materials.

Lloyd Instruments Ltd., Whittle Ave., Segensworth West, Fareham, Hants. PO15 5SH, UK

TECHNOLOGY SOLUTIONS COMPANY (TSC)

205 N. Michigan Ave., Ste. 1500, Chicago, IL, 60601

Tel: (312) 228-4500   Fax: (312) 228-4501   www.techsol.com

Designs computer information systems and strategic business and management consulting for major corporations.

TSC Europe, Regina House, 5 Queen Street, London EC4N 1SP, UK

Tel: 44-207-236-5000   Fax: 44-207-236-5001   Contact: Arthur Bird

TECUMSEH PRODUCTS COMPANY

100 E. Patterson Street, Tecumseh, MI, 49286-1899

Tel: (517) 423-8411   Fax: (517) 423-8526   www.tecumseh.com

Mfr. of hermetic compressors for air conditioning and refrigeration products, gasoline engines and power train components for lawn and garden applications, and pumps.

Tecnamotor (UK) Ltd., 152/154 Commercial Rd., Staines, Middlesex TW18 2QP, UK

TEKELEC

26580 West Agoura Road, Calabasas, CA, 91302

Tel: (818) 880-5656   Fax: (818) 880-6993   www.tekelec.com

Mfr. telecommunications testing equipment.

Tekelec UK, London, UK

Contact: David Colbeck

TEKTRONIX INC.

14200 SW Karl Braun Dr., PO Box 500, Beaverton, OR, 97077

Tel: (503) 627-7111   Fax: (503) 627-2406   www.tek.com

Mfr. test and measure, visual systems/color printing and communications/video and networking products.

Tektronix (UK) Ltd., Fourth Ave., Marlow London, Buckinghamshire SL7 1YD, UK

Tel: 44-1628-403300   Fax: 44-1628-403301

Tektronix UK Ltd, The Arena, Downshire Way, Bracknell Berkshire RG12 1PU, UK

Tel: 44-1344-392000   Fax: 44-1344-392001

TELCORDIA TECHNOLOGIES, INC.

445 South Street, Morristown, NJ, 07960-6438

Tel: (973) 829-2000   Fax: (973) 829-3172   www.telecordia.com

Mfr. telecom software.

Telcordia Technologies International, 8/9 Stratton Street, London W1J 8LF, UK

TELEFLEX INC.

630 W. Germantown Pike, Ste. 450, Plymouth Meeting, PA, 19462

Tel: (610) 834-6301   Fax: (610) 834-8307   www.teleflex.com

Design, manufacture and marketing of mechanical and electro-mechanical systems, control systems and surgical devices.

Astraflex Limited Euroflex Centre, Foxbridge Way, Normanton, West Yorkshire WF6 1TN, UK

Tel: 44-1924-228000

Cetrek Ltd. Teleflex Morse, 1 Factory Road, Upton, Poole, Dorset BH165SJ, UK

Rüsch UK Ltd., PO Box 138, Stirling Road Halifax Road, Cressex Business Park, High Wycombe, Buckinghamshire HP12 3ST, UK

Sermatech (UK) Limited, Lincoln, UK

Sermatech Repair Services Ltd., High Holborn Road, Codnor Ripley, Derbyshire, UK

Sermatech-Mal (UK), Dunnockshaw, UK

SermeTel (UK) Ltd., High Holborn Rd., Codner, Ripley, Derbyshire DE5 3NW, UK

Telair International, Unit 12, Space Way, North Feltham Trading Estate, Feltham TW14 OTH, UK

Tel: 44-208-890 0788   Fax: 020 8890 078

United Parts Driver Control Systems (UK) Ltd., Birmingham, UK

TELESCIENCES, INC.

2000 Midlantic Drive, Mt. Laurel, NJ, 08054-5476

Tel: (856) 866-1000   Fax: (856) 866-0185   www.telesciences.com

Mfr. and sales of traffic management software.

EDB 4Tel Ltd., 2 Queen Caroline Street, Argentum Hammersmith, London W69DX, UK

TELETECH HOLDINGS, INC.

9197 South Peoria Street, Englewood, CO, 80112-5833

Tel: (303) 397-8100   Fax: (303) 397-8668   www.teletech.com

Provider of teleservices.

TeleTech Holdings UK, Ground Floor, Benwell House, Green Street Sunbury-on-Thames, Middlesex TW16 6QT, UK

Tel: 44-193-275-3450   Fax: 44-193-275-3455

TELEX COMMUNICATIONS INC.

12000 Portland Ave. South, Burnsville, MN, 55337

Tel: (952) 884-4051   Fax: (952) 884-0043   www.telexcommunications.com

Mfr. communications, audio-visual and professional audio products.

Telex Communications (UK) Ltd., Premier Suites Exchange House, 494 Midsummer Blvd., Milton Keynes MK9 2EA, UK

Telex Communications (UK) Ltd., Viking House, Swallowdale Lane, Hemel Hempstead HP2 7HA, UK

TELLABS INC.

1415 W. Diehl Rd., Naperville, IL, 60563

Tel: (630) 378-8800   Fax: (630) 852-7346   www.tellabs.com

Design/mfr./service voice/data transport and network access systems.

Tellabs Coventry, 5 Ensign Business Center, Westwood Business Park, Westwood Way, Coventry CV4 8JA, UK
Contact: Heikki Hiltunen

Tellabs EMEA, Abbey Place, 24-28 Easton Street, High Wycombe Bucks HP11 1NT, UK
Contact: Heikki Hiltunen

Tellabs Oxfordshire, 29 The Quadrant, Abingdon Science Park, Barton Lane Abingdon, Oxfordshire OX14 3YS, UK

Tellabs UK Ltd., Eton Pl., 64 High St., Burnham, Buckinghamshire SL1 7J7, UK

TELLIUM, INC.

2 Crescent Place, Oceanport, NJ, 07757-0901

Tel: (732) 923-4100   Fax: (732) 923-9804   www.tellium.com

Mfr. optical switches for telecommunications networks.

Tellium UK, Golden Cross House, 8 Duncannon Street, London WC2N 4JF, UK
Tel: 44-207-484-5080   Fax: 44-207-484-5162

TELULAR CORPORATION

647 N. lakeview Pkwy., Vernon Hills, IL, 60061

Tel: (847) 247-9400   Fax: (847) 247-0021   www.telular.com

Mfr. and sales fixed wireless communications terminals.

Telular Corporation UK, Penchiney House, Ground Floor, Sough, Berkshire SL1 1QF, UK
Tel: 44-1753-486500   Fax: 44-1753-533174

TENNECO AUTOMOTIVE INC.

500 North Field Drive, Lake Forest, IL, 60045

Tel: (847) 482-5241   Fax: (847) 482-5295   www.tenneco-automotive.com

Mfr. automotive parts, exhaust systems and service equipment.

Monroe Europe (UK) Ltd., Manor Lane, Shipton Rd., York YO3 6UA, UK
Tel: 44-1904-659-833   Fax: 44-1904-623-159   Contact: Dave Westley, Mgr.   Emp: 554

Tenneco-Walker (UK) Ltd., Liverpool Rd., Burnley, Lancashire BB12 6HJ, UK
Tel: 44-1282-433-171   Fax: 44-1282-451-778   Contact: Ray Jenkins, Mgr.   Emp: 208

Walker UK Ltd., Wharfdale Rd., Tyseley, Birmingham B11 2DF, UK
Tel: 44-121-609-3001   Fax: 44-121-609-3049   Contact: Jeff Penny, Mgr.

TERADATA

1700 South Patterson Blvd., Dayton, OH, 45479

Tel: (937) 445-5000   Fax: (937) 445-1682   www.teradata.com

Mfr. software to store information.

Teradata Div., NCR, Alwyn House, 31 Windsor Street, Chertsey Surrey KT 16 8AT, UK

TERADYNE INC.

321 Harrison Ave., Boston, MA, 02118

Tel: (617) 482-2700   Fax: (617) 422-2910   www.teradyne.com

Mfr. electronic test equipment and blackplane connection systems.

Teradyne Ltd., The Western Centre, Units 4-5, Western Rd., Bracknell, Berkshire RG12 1RW, UK
Tel: 44-1344-426899   Contact: Jeff Corrigan, Reg. Mgr

TEREX CORPORATION

500 Post Road East, Ste. 320, Westport, CT, 06880

Tel: (203) 222-7170   Fax: (203) 222-7976   www.terex.com

Mfr. lifting and earthmoving equipment.

Benford Limited, The Cape, Warwick, Warwickshire CV34 5DR, UK

Tel: 44-1926-493466   Fax: 44-1926-490985   Contact: Tony Gardner

BL-Pegson ltd., Div. Terex, Mammoth Street, Coalville Leicestershire LE676 3GN, UK

Tel: 44-1530-518600

Powerscreen Equipment Ltd., Cheltonian House, Portsmouth Road, Esher Surrey KT10 9AA, UK

Tel: 44-1372-466-286   Fax: 44-1372-466-415

Powerscreen EquipmentUK, Portsmouth Road, Esher, Surrey KT10 9AA, UK

Powerscreen Ltd., 2 Sycamore Court, Birmingham Road, Allesley Coventry CV5 9BA, UK

Tel: 44-1203-405-100

Powerscreen Ltd., Appleton Thorn Trading Estate, Appleton Thorn Warrington, Cheshire WA4 4SN, UK

Tel: 44-1925-267-486

Powerscreen Midlands Ltd., 3 The Old Vicarage, Wardington Banbury, Oxfordshire OX17 1SA, UK

Tel: 44-1295-758-717

Powerscreen Southern Ltd., The Conifers, Filton Road, Hambrook Bristol BS16 1QG, UK

Tel: 44-1179-579017

Terex UK Limited, Watford Village, Northants NN6 YXN, UK

TERRA INDUSTRIES INC.

600 Fourth Street, PO Box 6000, Sioux City, IA, 51101-6000

Tel: (712) 277-1340   Fax: (712) 277-7364   www.terraindustries.com

Produces methanol and nitrogen fertilizers.

Terra Industries, PO Box 81, Billingham, Stockton-on-Tees TS23 1XT, UK

Tel: 44-164-255-0022

Terra Industries, Severnside, Hallen, Bristol BS10 7SJ, UK

Tel: 44-117-982-3601   Fax: 44-117-982-5750

TEXAS INSTRUMENTS INC.

12500 TI Blvd., Dallas, TX, 75266

Tel: (972) 995-3773   Fax: (972) 995-4360   www.ti.com

Mfr. semiconductor devices, electronic electro-mechanical systems, instruments and controls.

Texas Instruments, Manton Lane, Bedford MK41 7PA, UK

Texas Instruments, Northampton, UK

TEXTRON INC.

40 Westminster Street, Providence, RI, 02903

Tel: (401) 421-2800   Fax: (401) 421-2878   www.textron.com

Mfr. Aerospace (Bell Helicopter and Cessna Aircraft), industry and consumer products, fasteners and financial services.

Avdel Textron Ltd., Mundells, Welwyn Garden City, Hertfordshire AL7 1EZ, UK

Tel: 44-1707-668-668   Fax: 44-1707-338-828   Contact: Frank Gulden, Acting Pres.

Textron Automotive Co. Ltd., McCord Winn Div., Beech Lan, Derby Rd., Burton-on-Trent, Straffordshire, UK

Tel: 44-128-350-9409   Fax: 44-128-353-8605   Contact: J. R. Langridge

Textron Fastening Systems Limited, Mundells, Welwyn Garden City, Hertfordshire AL7 1EZ, UK

Tel: 44-1707-668668   Fax: 44-1707-338828

Textron Systems, Essex House, 141 Kings Rd., Brentwood, Essex CM14 4DT, UK

Tel: 44-1277-229-192   Fax: 44-1277-228-745   Contact: John Dunk, Dir. European Sales/Mktg.

THE MARMON GROUP, INC.

200 West Adams, Ste. 2211, Chicago, IL, 60606

Tel: (312) 372-9500   Fax: (312) 845-5305   www.marmon.com

Holding company for diversified manufacturing and service firms.

Getz Bros. & Co. Inc., 14 Queen Anne's Gate, St. James Park, London SW1 H9A, UK

Tel: 44-207-976-7701   Fax: 44-207-976-7265   Contact: Christopher Beale   Emp: 3

The Sloane Group, Booth Drive, Park Farm Estate, Wellingborough, Northants NN8 6GR, UK
Tel: 44-1933-401-555

The Sloane Group, 78 Buckingham Gate, London SW1E 6PE, UK
Tel: 44-20-7222-6040

The Sloane Group, Field Road, Mildenhall, Suffolk IP28 7PR, UK

THERMADYNE HOLDINGS CORPORATION

101 South Hanley Road, Suite 300, St. Louis, MO, 63105

Tel: (314) 746-2197   Fax: (314) 746-2349   www.thermadyne.com

Mfr. welding, cutting, and safety products.

Thermadyne UK, Chorley North Industrial Park, Europe Bldg., Chorley, Lancashire PR6 7BX, UK
Tel: 44-1257-261755

THERMA-TRU CORPORATION

1687 Woodlands Drive, Maumee, OH, 43537

Tel: (419) 891-7400   Fax: (419) 891-7411   www.thermatru.com

Mfr. fiberglass doors.

Therma-Tru International, GB-Hitchin, UK
Tel: 44-1462-484360   Fax: 44-1462-486470

THERMO ELECTRON CORPORATION

81 Wyman Street, Waltham, MA, 02454-9046

Tel: (781) 622-1000   Fax: (781) 622-1207   www.thermo.com

Develop, mfr., sale of process equipment &instruments for energy intensive and healthcare industries.

MicroPatent Europe, Div. Thermo Electron, 235 Southwark Bridge Road, London SE1 6LY, UK
Tel: 44-20-7450-5105

Nicolet Biomedical Ltd., Budbrooke Road, Warwick CV34 5XH, UK
Tel: 44-1926-490888

Thermo Electron Ltd., Woolborough Lane, Crawley, W. Sussex RH10 2AQ, UK

Winterburn Ltd., PO Box 6, Riverside Works, Woodhill Rd., Bury Lancashire BL8 1DF, UK

THERMO FINNIGAN CORPORATION

355 River Oaks Parkway, San Jose, CA, 95134-1991

Tel: (408) 433-4800   Fax: (408) 433-4823   www.thermo.com

Mfr. mass spectrometers.

Finnigan Hypersil Division, Chadwick Road, Astmoor Runcorn, Cheshire WA7 1PR, UK

Thermo Finnigan, Stafford House, Boundry Park, Hertfordshire, Hemel Hempstead HP2 7GE, UK

THERMO NICOLET CORPORATION

5225 Verona Road, Madison, WI, 53711-4495

Tel: (608) 276-6100   Fax: (608) 276-6222   www.nicolet.com

Mfr. infrared spectrometers and oscilloscopes and medical electro-diagnostic equipment.

Nicolet Instrument Ltd., Nicolet House, Budbrooke Road, Warwick CV34 5XH, UK

THERMO ORION, INC.

500 Cummings Court, Beverly, MA, 01915

Tel: (978) 922-4400   Fax: (978) 922-6015   www.thermoorion.com

Mfr. laboratory and industrial products, measure and display instruments.

Thermo Orion Europe, 12-16 Sedgeway Business Park, Witchford, Cambridgeshire CB6 2HY, UK
Tel: 44-1353-666111   Fax: 44-1353-666001

THERMO RAMSEY INC.

501 90th Avenue NW, Minneapolis, MN, 55433

Tel: (763) 783-2500   Fax: (763) 780-2525   www.thermoramsey.com

Mfr. of industrial control products.

Thermo Ramsey, Unit A2, Swift Park, Old Leicester Rd., Rugby, Warwickshire CV21 1DE, UK

THERMON MANUFACTURING COMPANY

100 Thermon Drive, PO Box 609, San Marcos, TX, 78667-0609

Tel: (512) 396-5801   Fax: (512) 396-3627   www.thermon.com

Mfr. steam and electric heat tracing systems, components and accessories.

Thermon (UK) Ltd., 18 Tower Rd., Glover West Trading Estate, District 11, Washington Tyne and Wear NE37 2SH, UK

THETFORD CORPORATION

7101 Jackson Road, PO Box 1285, Ann Arbor, MI, 48106

Tel: (734) 769-6000   Fax: (734) 769-2023   www.thetford.com

Mfr. sanitation products and chemicals.

Thetford Aqua Products Ltd., Centrovell Ind. Estate, Caldwell Rd., Nuneaton, Warwickshire CV11 4UD, UK

THOMAS & BETTS CORPORATION

8155 T&B Blvd., Memphis, TN, 38125

Tel: (901) 252-5000   Fax: (901) 685-1988   www.tnb.com

Mfr. elect/electronic connectors and accessories.

Thomas & Betts International, European Centre, Third Ave., Globe Park, Marlow Buckinghamshire SL7 1YF, UK

THOMAS INDUSTRIES INC.

4360 Brownsboro Road, Ste. 300, Louisville, KY, 40232

Tel: (502) 893-4600   Fax: (502) 893-4685   www.thomasind.com

Mfr. lighting fixtures and specialty pumps and compressors for global OEM applications.

ASF Thomas Limited, Unit 2, Alton Business Ctr., Omega Park, Alton, Hampshire GU34 2YU, UK

Tel: 44-1420-54-41-84 Fax: 44-1420-54-41-83   Contact: Warren Beese, Mng. Dir.

THOMAS TECHNOLOGY SOLUTIONS, INC.

One Progress Drive, Horsham, PA, 19044

Tel: (215) 643-5000   Fax: (215) 682-5381   www.reedtech.com

Provides custom solutions and services to help companies effectively create, manage, and publish information via multiple media.

Thomas Technology Solutions (UK) Ltd, Lee House, 1/F, 109 Hammersmith Road, London W14 0QH, UK

Tel: 44-207-070-7550   Fax: 44-207-070-7551   Contact: Peter Camilleri, Gen. Mgr.

THOMAS WEISEL PARTNERS LLC

1 Montgomery Street, San Francisco, CA, 94104

Tel: (415) 364-2500   Fax: (415) 364-2695   www.tweisel.com

Engaged in investment banking and institutional brokerage services.

Thomas Weisel Partners International, Princes House, 38 Jermyn Street, London SW1 Y6DN, UK

Tel: 44-207-7851-9500   Fax: 44-207-7851-9515

THORATEC CORPORATION

6035 Stoneridge Drive, Pleasanton, CA, 94588

Tel: (925) 847-8600   Fax: (925) 847-8574   www.thoratec.com

Mfr. artificial heart devices.

Thoratec Europe Ltd., 5 Brunel Court, Burrel Road, St. Ives Cambridgeshire PE27 3LW, UK

Tel: 44-7559-877901   Fax: 44-1480-461866

THQ, INC.

27001 Agoura Road, Ste. 325, Calabasas Hills, CA, 91301

Tel: (818) 871-5000   Fax: (818) 591-1615   www.thw.com

Engaged in publishing of video game titles.

THQ Entertainment UK, London, UK

THREE-FIVE SYSTEMS, INC.

1600 North Desert Drive, Tempe, AZ, 85281

Tel: (602) 389-8600   Fax: (602) 389-8989   www.threefive.com

Mfr. (LCDs) liquid crystal displays for electronics.

Three-Five Systems UK, Birch 12, Kembrey Business Park, Swindon SW2 8UX, UK

Tel: 44-1793-549-100   Fax: 44-1793-549-135

TIBCO SOFTWARE INC.

3165 Porter Drive, Palo Alto, CA, 94304

Tel: (650) 846-5000   Fax: (650) 846-1005   www.tibco.com

Mfr. software and provides e-commerce, consulting, and support services. (JV of Reuters UK)

TIBCO Software Inc., 35 New Bridge Street, London EC4V 6BW, UK

Tel: 44-0207-964-3700

TIDELAND SIGNAL CORPORATION

4310 Directors Row, PO Box 52430, Houston, TX, 77052-2430

Tel: (713) 681-6101   Fax: (713) 681-6233   www.tidelandsignal.com

Mfr./sale aids to marine navigation.

Tideland Signal Ltd., 15-19 Trowers Way, Redhill, Surrey RH1 2LH, UK

Tel: 44-1737-768-711   Fax: 44-1737-768-192   Contact: Roger Brown, Mng. Dir.

TIER TECHNOLOGIES, INC.

1350 Treat Blvd., Ste. 250, Walnut Creek, CA, 94596

Tel: (925) 937-3950   Fax: (925) 937-3752   www.tier.com

Provides business process reengineering outsourcing and consulting.

Tier Technologies, 19 Wellington Business Park, Dukes Ride, Crowthorne Berkshire RG45 6LS, UK

TIFFANY & COMPANY

727 Fifth Ave., New York, NY, 10022

Tel: (212) 755-8000   Fax: (212) 605-4465   www.tiffany.com

Mfr./retail fine jewelry, silverware, china, crystal, leather goods, etc.

Tiffany & Co.- Harrod's, Knightsbridge London SW1X 7XL, UK

Tel: 44-207-893-8503

Tiffany & Co. Ltd., 25 Old Bond St., London W1X 3AA, UK

Tel: 44-207-409-2790

THE TIMBERLAND COMPANY

200 Domain Drive, Stratham, NH, 03885

Tel: (603) 772-9500   Fax: (603) 773-1640   www.timberland.com

Design/mfr. footwear, apparel and accessories for men and women.

Timberland UK Ltd., River Park Ave., Staines, Middlesex TW18 3EN, UK

THE TIMKEN COMPANY

1835 Dueber Ave. SW, PO Box 6932, Canton, OH, 44706-0932

Tel: (330) 438-3000   Fax: (330) 471-4118   www.timken.com

Mfr. tapered roller bearings and quality alloy steels.

British Timken, Main Rd., Duston, Northampton NN5 6UL, UK

TIMKEN SUPER PRECISION

PO Box 547 Precision Park, Keene, NH, 03431-0547

Tel: (603) 352-0310   Fax: (603) 355-4553   www.timken.com

Mfr., sales and distribution of bearings, tape guides and systems for missiles, etc.

Timken Aerospace UK Ltd., PO Box 667, Upper Villiers Street, Wolverhampton, West Midlands WV2 4UH, UK

Tel: 44-1902-773300   Fax: 44-1902-771448

TITAN CORPORATION

3033 Science Park Rd., San Diego, CA, 92121

Tel: (858) 552-9500   Fax: (858) 552-9645   www.titan.com

Provides IT services, including computer and communication systems services and network security and systems engineering.

Titan Systems Corp, Camelot House, 76 Brompton Rd., London SW3, UK

TITANIUM METALS CORPORATION (TIMET)

1999 Broadway, Suite 4300, Denver, CO, 80202

Tel: (303) 296-5600   Fax: (303) 296-5650   www.timet.com

Produce light weight titanium sponge (metal) for aerospace and auto industries.

TIMET United Kingdom Ltd., Po Box 704 Witton, Birmingham B6 7UR, UK

TJX COMPANIES INC.

770 Cochituate Road, Framingham, MA, 01701

Tel: (508) 390-1000   Fax: (508) 390-2828   www.tjx.com

Retail stores, catalog and mail order houses.

T. J. Maxx, Edward Hyde Bldg., 38 Clarendon Rd., Watford Hertfershire WD1 1TX, UK

Tel: 44-1-92-347-5700

TMP WORLDWIDE, INC.

622 Third Ave., New York, NY, 10017

Tel: (212) 351-7000   Fax: (212) 658-0540   www.tmpw.com

#1 Yellow Pages agency and a leader in the recruitment and interactive advertising fields.

TMP Worldwide, 47 London Road, St. Albans, Hertfordshire AL1 1LJ, UK

TMP Worldwide, 15 Station Road, Reading, Berkshire RG1 1LG, UK

TMP Worldwide, Lilly House, 2/F, London W1R 9HD, UK

TMP Worldwide, Cardinal House, 39-40 Albemarie Street, London W1X 4ND, UK

Tel: 44-207-872-1500

TMP Worldwide eResourcing, 20 Soho Square, London W1V 5FD, UK

TODD-AO DVD CORPORATION

6601 Romaine Street, Hollywood, CA, 90038

Tel: (323) 962-5304   Fax: (323) 466-2327   www.todd-ao.com

Provides post-production and distribution services for TV and film production companies, including sound services and visual effects.

Todd-AO UK, 13 Hawley Crescent, London NW1 8NP, UK

Tel: 44-207-884-7900   Contact: Graham Hall, Mng. Dir.

TOGETHERSOFT CORPORATION

900 Main Campus Drive, Ste. 500, Raleigh, NC, 27606

Tel: (919) 833-5550   Fax: (919) 833-5533   www.togethersoft.com

Mfr. software.

TogetherSoft UK, Solent Business Park, 1460 Parkway, Whiteley Hampshire PO15 7AF, UK

Tel: 44-1489-866000

TOKHEIM CORPORATION

PO Box 360, 10501 Corporate Drive, Fort Wayne, IN, 46845

Tel: (219) 470-4600   Fax: (219) 482-2677   www.tokheim.com

Engaged in design, manufacture and service of electronic and mechanical petroleum marketing systems.

Tokheim UK Ltd., Unit 4, Cliveden Office Village, Lancaster Road, High Wycombe, Buckinghamshire HP12 3YZ, UK

TONIC SOFTWARE, INC.

9606 N. Mcpac Expwy., Ste. 900, Austin, TX, 78759

Tel: (512) 744-6400   Fax: (512) 744-6500   www.tonic.com

Mfr. application management software.

Tonic Software, Pinewood, Chineham Business Park, Basingstoke HANTS RG24 8AL, UK

Tel: 44-1256-698048   Fax: 44-1256-698584

THE TOPPS COMPANY, INC.

1 Whitehall Street, New York, NY, 10004-2108

Tel: (212) 376-0300   Fax: (212) 376-0573   www.topps.com

Mfr. entertainment products, principally collectible trading cards, confections, sticker collections, and comic books.

Topps (UK) Ltd., 18 Vincent Ave., Crownhill, Milton Keynes MK8 0AW, UK

Tel: 44-1908-800100 Fax: 44-1908-800200 Contact: Jeremy Charter

THE TORO COMPANY

8111 Lyndale Ave. South, Bloomington, MN, 55420

Tel: (952) 888-8801   Fax: (952) 887-8258   www.toro.com

Mfr. electric lawn and turf maintenance products and snow removal equipment.

Toro Wheelhorse UK, Unit 7, Heron Ind. Estate, Basingstoke Rd. Spencers Wood, Reading Berkshire, UK

TOTAL SYSTEM SERVICES, INC. (TSYS)

1600 First Avenue, Columbus, GA, 31901

Tel: (706) 649-6897   Fax: (706) 644-8065   www.totalsystem.com

Engaged in credit card processing.

TSYS Europe, York YO1 9QN, UK

Contact: Roger Van Scoy

TOTES ISOTONER CORPORATION

9655 International Blvd., PO Box 465658, Cincinnati, OH, 45246

Tel: (513) 682-8200   Fax: (513) 682-8602   www.totes.com

Mfr. rubber and plastic footwear, slippers, umbrellas.

Totes UK Limited, London, UK

TOWERS PERRIN

335 Madison Ave., New York, NY, 10017-4605

Tel: (212) 309-3400   Fax: (212) 309-0975   www.towers.com

Management consulting services.

Kinsley Lord, Towers, Perrin, 10 Picadilly Circus, London W1V OAE, UK

Tel: 44-207-379-4000 Fax: 44-207-806-6401

Tillinghast Towers Perrin, Verulam Point, Station Way, St. Albans, Hertfordshire AL1 5HE, UK

Tel: 44-172-784-6161 Fax: 44-17-278-48869

Tillinghast Towers Perrin, Lambourn Square, 2500 First Ave., Newbury Business Park, Newbury, Berkshire RG14 2PZ, UK

Tel: 44-163-555-0200 Fax: 44-163-541-322

Tillinghast Towers Perrin, Castlewood House, 77-91 New Oxford St., London WC1A 1PX, UK

Tel: 44-207-379-4411 Fax: 44-207-379-7478

TOYS R US INC.

461 From Road, Paramus, NJ, 07652

Tel: (201) 262-7800   Fax: (201) 845-0973   www.toysrus.com

Retail stores: toys and games, sporting goods, computer software, books, records.

Toys R Us Holdings PLC, Kenvon Dr., Forbury Ind. Estate, Reading, Berks RG1 3DH, UK

TRAMMELL CROW COMPANY

2200 Ross Ave., Ste. 3700, Dallas, TX, 75201

Tel: (214) 979-6100   Fax: (214) 979-6326   www.trammellcrow.com

Commercial real estate company providing brokerage, property management, development, construction and retail services.

Trammell Crow Savills (TCS), 36 Gervis Road, Bournemouth Dorset BH1 3EF, UK

Tel: 44-120-2314-151 Fax: 44-120-2214-181 Contact: Richard Buckley

Trammell Crow Savills (TCS), 20 Grosvenor Hill, Berkeley Square, London W1X 0HQ, UK

Tel: 44-207-4099-959 Fax: 44-207-4953-773 Contact: Edward Lyons, Pres. & CEO

THE TRANE COMPANY

3600 Pammel Creek Road, La Crosse, WI, 54601

Tel: (608) 787-2000   Fax: (608) 787-4990   www.trane.com

Mfr. distribution and service of A/C systems and equipment.

Trane (UK) Ltd., 60 Lenton Blvd., Nottingham N67 2EN, UK

Trane (UK) Ltd., 162 Windmill Rd. W., Sunbury-on-Thames, Middlesex TW16 7HB, UK

Trane (UK) Ltd., Howard House, 55 Marsh Lane, Hampton-in-Arden, Solihull B92 0AJ, UK

Trane (UK) Ltd., 218 Rothbury Terrace, Heaton, Newcastle-upon-Tyne NE6 5DF, UK

Trane (UK) Ltd., Enterprise Trading Estate, Guinness Rd., Trafford Park, Manchester MI7 1SD, UK

Trane (UK) Ltd., Centenary House, 205 New John St. W., Hockley Birmingham B19 3TZ, UK

Trane Central Africa, 1st Floor, Unit 3, Priory Court, Tuscan Way, Camberly, Surrey GU15 3YX, UK

TRANSACTION SYSTEMS ARCHITECTS, INC.

224 South 108th Avenue, Omaha, NE, 68154

Tel: (402) 334-5101   Fax: (402) 390-8077   www.tsainc.com

Mfr. software.

ACI UK, 59 Clarendon Road, Watford, Herts WD17 1FQ, UK

TRANSATLANTIC HOLDINGS, INC.

80 Pine Street, New York, NY, 10005

Tel: (212) 770-2000   Fax: (212) 289-6801   www.transre.com

Engaged in reinsurance.

TRC UK, Corn Exchange, 55 Mark Lane, London EC3R 4NE, UK

Tel: 44-207-204-8600   Fax: 44-207-480-5577   Contact: Paul Bonny

TRANSGENOMIC, INC.

12325 Emmet Street, Omaha, NE, 68184

Tel: (402) 452-5400   Fax: (402) 452-5401   www.transgenomic.com

Mfr. biotechnology software.

Transgenomic UK, The Quadrangle, Crewe Hall Weston Road, Crewe, Cheshire CW1 6UZ, UK

Tel: 44-1270-507-123

TRANSISTOR DEVICES, INC.

85 Horsehill Road, Cedar Knolls, NJ, 07927

Tel: (973) 267-1900   Fax: (973) 267-2047   www.tdipower.com

Mfr. electronic power supplies and equipment.

TDI Europe, Alder House, High Road, Rayleigh, Essex SS6 7SA, UK

Tel: 44-1266-779222

TRANTER PHE, INC.

PO Box 2289, Wichita Falls, TX, 76306

Tel: (940) 723-7125   Fax: (940) 723-1131   www.tranter.com

Mfr. heat exchangers.

SWEP Ltd., Chobham Ridges, The Maultway, Camberley, Surrey GU15 1QE, UK

Tel: 44-1276-64221   Fax: 44-1276-64344

SWEP Ltd., Hillgate Business Centre, Swallow St., Stockport SKI 3AU, UK

Tel: 44-161-476-6915   Fax: 44-161-476-6916

SWEP Ltd., Crossland Industrial Estate, Stockport Road West, Bredbury, Stockport SK6 2BR, UK

Tel: 44-161-406-9800   Fax: 44-161-406-9801

Tranter, Ltd., Monckton Road Industrial Estate, Unit 50, Wakefield WF27AL, UK

Tel: 44-1924-298-393   Fax: 44-1924-291-596

TREIBACHER SCHLEIFMITTEL CORPORATION

2000 College Ave., Niagara Falls, NY, 14305

Tel: (716) 286-1234   Fax: (716) 286-1224   www.treibacher-schleifm.com

Mfr. abrasives.

Treibacher Schleifmittel UK, 12/14 Claremont Road, West Byfleet, Surrey KT14 6DY, UK

TREMCO INC.

3735 Green Road, Beachwood, OH, 44122-5718

Tel: (216) 292-5000   Fax: (216) 292-5041   www.tremcoroofing.com

Mfr. protective coatings and sealants for building, maintenance and construction.

Tremco Limited, 88 Bestobell Rd., Slough, Berkshire SL1 4SZ, UK

Tel: 44-1753-691696   Contact: John Newens

TREMONT ADVISERS, INC.

555 Theodore Fremd Avenue, Rye, NY, 10580

Tel: (914) 925-1140   Fax: (914) 921-3499   www.tremontadvisers.com

Manages investment funds.

Tremont Advisors UK, 13-15 Carteret Street, London SW1H 9DJ, UK

Tel: 44-207-222-0099   Fax: 44-207-222-4499

TRENWICK GROUP LTD.

1 Canterbury Green, Stamford, CT, 06901

Tel: (203) 353-5500   Fax: (203) 353-5550   www.trenwick.com

Insurance holding group.

Trenwick International, No. 2 Minster Court, Mincing Lane, London EC3R 7FL, UK

Tel: 44-207-522-9393

TRIBUNE COMPANY

435 North Michigan Ave., Chicago, IL, 60611

Tel: (312) 222-9100   Fax: (312) 222-9100   www.tribune.com

Media company engaged in television and radio broadcasting, publishing and interactive.

TM/TribunePublishers Ltd., Lynton House, 7-12 Tavistock Sq., London WC1H 9LB, UK

TRICO MARINE SERVICES, INC.

250 North American Court, Houma, LA, 70363

Tel: (985) 851-3833   Fax: (985) 851-4321   www.tricomarine.com

Engaged in offshore transportation of construction equipment and rigs.

Trico Marine Services, 14 Albyn Terrace, Aberdeen AB 101 YAP, UK

TRICON GLOBAL RESTAURANTS INC.

1441 Gardner Lane, Louisville, KY, 40213

Tel: (502) 874-1000   Fax: (502) 874-8315   www.triconglobal.com

Owns and operates KFC, Taco Bell and Pizza Hut restaurant food chains.

Kentucky Fried Chicken (GB) Ltd., London, UK

Pizza Hut (UK) Ltd., London, UK

Pizza Hut Intl (England) Ltd., London, UK

Tricon Global, 32 Goldsworth Road, Working Surrey GU21 1JT, UK

TRIMBLE NAVIGATION LIMITED

645 N. Mary Ave., Sunnyvale, CA, 94086

Tel: (408) 481-8000   Fax: (408) 481-2000   www.trimble.com

Design/mfr. electronic geographic instrumentation.

Trimble Navigation Europe Ltd., Trimble House, Meridian Office Park, Osborne Way Hook, Hampshire RG27 9HX, UK

Tel: 44-1256-746   Fax: 44-1256-760-148

TRIPLE POINT TECHNOLOGY, INC.

301 Riverside Avenue, Westport, CT, 06880

Tel: (203) 291-7979   Fax: (203) 291-7977   www.tpt.com

Mfr. risk management software.

Triple Point Technology Limited, Prince Consort House, 109-111 Farringdon Road, London EC1R 3BW, UK

Tel: 44-207-841-7455

TRIPOINT GLOBAL COMMUNICATIONS

PO Box 368, Conover, NC, 28613

Tel: (828) 464-4141   Fax: (828) 464-4147   www.vertencomm.com

High-tech holding company; microwave components, amplifiers, converters, terminal network workstations, voice, video and data applications.

CSA Limited, Knight Road, Rochester, Kent ME2 2AX, UK

Tel: 44-1634-715-544   Fax: 44-1634-715-742   Contact: Ken Hayward, GM

TRIPOS, INC.

1699 S. Hanley Road, St. Louis, MO, 63144

Tel: (314) 647-1099   Fax: (314) 647-9241   www.tripos.com

Mfr. pharmaceutical software for research.

Tripos Receptor Research, Tamar Laboratory, Bude-Stratton Business Park, Bude, Cornwall EX23 8LY, UK

Tel: 44-1288-359-359   Fax: 44-1288-359-222

Tripos UK Ltd., Sunningdale House, Caldecotte Lake Drive, Milton Keynes MK7 8LF, UK

Tel: 44-1908-650-000

TRIUMPH GROUP, INC.

1255 Drummer Lane, Ste. 200, Wayne, PA, 19087

Tel: (610) 975-0420   Fax: (610) 975-0563   www.triumphgrp.com

Mfr. aircraft engines and parts.

Triumph Air Repair Limited, Church Lane, Lasham Hampshire GU34 4HL, UK

TROPICANA PRODUCTS, INC.

1001 13th Avenue East, Bradenton, FL, 34208

Tel: (941) 747-4461   Fax: (941) 665-5330   www.tropicana.com

Marketer and producer of branded juices, including Tropicana, Dole, Looza and Copella.

Copella Fruit Juices Ltd., Hill Farm Boxford Sudbury, Suffolk C010 5NY, UK

Tropicana U.K., Dorset House Regent Park, Leatherhead, Surrey KT22 7PL, UK

TROUTMAN SANDERS LLP

999 Peachtree Street NE, Atlanta, GA, 30309-3915

Tel: (404) 885-3651   Fax: (404) 885-3900   www.troutmansanders.com

International law firm.

Troutman Sanders LLP, 69 Old Broad Street, 10/F, London EC2M 1QS, UK

Tel: 44-207-65-2600   Contact: James H. Keaten

TRUSERV CORPORATION

8600 West Bryn Mawr, Chicago, IL, 60631-3505

Tel: (773) 695-5000   Fax: (773) 695-6541   www.truserv.com

Dealer-owned, independent, hardware store cooperative.

TruServ Corporation, London, UK

TRW INC.

1900 Richmond Road, Cleveland, OH, 44124-2760

Tel: (216) 291-7000   Fax: (216) 291-7932   www.trw.com

Electric and energy-related products, automotive and aerospace products, tools and fasteners.

British Pleuger Submersible Pumps Ltd., Station Rd., Coleshill Birmingham B46 1JH, UK

Cam Gears Ltd., 45 Wilbury Way, Hitchin, Hertfordshire SG4 OUT, UK

Hydrosteer, Arundel Rd., Luton, Bedfordshire, UK

Nelson Stud Welding Div. Carr Fastener Co. Ltd., Bessell Lane, Stapleford, Nottingham NG9 7BX, UK

TRW, 46 Park Street, London W1Y 4DJ, UK

Tel: 44-207-647-0610

TRW, Clevedon Plant, Kenn Rd., Clevedon Avon BS21 GL5, UK

TRW, Hitchin Plant, 45 Wilbury Way, Hitchin Hertfordshire SG4 0TO, UK

TRW Clifford Ltd., DuPont House, 101 Vaughan Way, Leicester LE1 4SA, UK

TRW Datacom Intl., Park House, 191 London Rd., Isleworth Middlesex TW7 5BQ, UK

TRW Mission Ltd., Berkeley Square House, Berkeley Square, London W1X 6JE, UK

TRW Reda, Div. TRW Mission Ltd., Ste. 8, Westminster Palace Gardens, 1/7 Artillery Row, London SW1, UK

TRW Spares, Furnace Rd., Likeston, Derbyshire DE7 5EP, UK

United-Carr Supplies Ltd., 112 Station Rd., Likeston, Derbyshire DE7 5LF, UK

Ventek Ltd., Station House, Harrow Rd., Wembley Middlesex HA9 6ER, UK

TTI, INC.

2441 Northeast Pkwy., Fort Worth, TX, 76106-1896

Tel: (817) 740-9000   Fax: (817) 740-9898   www.ttiinc.com

Distribution of resistors and capacitors, including cables and sockets.

TTI, Inc., 2 Cliveden Office Village, Lancaster Road, Cressex Business Park, High Wycombe Bucks HP12 3YZ, UK

TURNER INTERNATIONAL, DIV. THE TURNER CORPORATION

901 Main St., Ste. 4900, Dallas, TX, 75202

Tel: (214) 915-9600   Fax: (214) 915-9700   www.turnerconstruction.com

Engaged in general construction and construction management.

Turner Steiner International SA, London, UK

TUSCARORA INCORPORATED

800 Fifth Avenue, New Brighton, PA, 15066

Tel: (724) 843-8200   Fax: (724) 847-2140   www.tuscarora.com

Mfr. custom molded, foam plastic.

Tuscarora Limited UK, Cornhill Close, Lodge Farm Industrial Estate, Northampton NN5 7UB, UK

Tel: 44-1604-759543

Tuscarora Limited UK, 33 Stannary Street, London SE11 4AA, UK

Tel: 44-207-735-8848

Tuscarora Limited UK, Firth Road, Houstoun Industrial Estate, Livingston West Lothian EH54 5DJ, UK

Tel: 44-1506-434201

TW METALS INC.

760 Constitution Drive, Ste. 204, Exton, PA, 19341

Tel: (610) 458-1300   Fax: (610) 458-1399   www.twmetals.com

Engaged in metals distribution and processing.

Philip Cornes & Company Ltd., Lanner Building Clews Road, Redditch, Worcestershire B98 7ST, UK

TW Lye Technical Components, Folkes Road, Hayes Trading Estate, Lye, Stourbridge, West Midlands DY9 8RG, UK

Tel: 44-1384-898040

TW Metals UK, Majestic Road, Nursling Industrial Estate, Southampton SO16 0AF, UK

TXU (TEXAS UTILITIES)

1601 Bryan St., Dallas, TX, 75201

Tel: (214) 812-4600   Fax: (214) 812-7077   www.txu.com

Provides electric and natural gas services, energy trading, energy marketing and telecommunications.

TXU Europe, The Adelphi, 1-11 John Adams Street, London WC2N 6HT, UK

Tel: 44-207-879-8081   Fax: 44-207-879-8082

TYCO CAPITAL

1211 Avenue of the Americas, New York, NY, 10036

Tel: (212) 536-1390   Fax: (212) 536-1912   www.citgroup.com

Engaged in commercial finance.

ERF Finance, Ltd., Div. Tyco Capital, 7 Chantry Court, Forge Street, Crewe Cheshire CW1 2DU, UK

Newcourt, Div. Tyco Capital, Newcourt, 66 Buckingham Gate, London SW1E 6AU, UK

Newcourt, Div. Tyco Capital, 80 Stokes Croft, Bristol BS1 3QW, UK

U. S. INDUSTRIES, INC.

101 Wood Ave. South, Iselin, NJ, 08830

Tel: (732) 767-0700   Fax: (732) 767-2222   www.zurn.com

Mfr./sale of plumbing products and HVAC equipment; resource and fire sprinkler system construction.

Jacuzzi UK, Silverdale Road, Newcastle Under Lyme, Staffordshire ST56EL, UK

Jacuzzi UK Group PLC., PO Box 24, Batley, West Yorkshire WF17 9XD, UK

U.S. BANCORP PIPER JAFFRAY

800 Nicollet Mall, Ste. 800, Minneapolis, MN, 55402

Tel: (612) 303-6000   Fax: (612) 342-1040   www.piperjaffray.com

Provides investment solutions and services to businesses, institutions and individuals.

U.S. Bancorp Piper Jaffray, First Floor, Phoenix House, 18 King William Street, London EC4N 7US, UK

Tel: 44-20-7743-8700   Contact: B. Omlie & D. Lingafelter, VP & Mng. Dir.   Emp: 4

U.S. SAFETY

8101 Lenexa Drive, Lenexa, KS, 66214

Tel: (913) 599-5555   Fax: (913) 599-1703   www.ussafety.com

Design and manufacture of personal protection equipment, including goggles and face shields, air-purifying and disposable masks.

U. S. Safety, Div. Parmelee Ltd., Middlemore Lane W., Redhouse Industrial Estate, Aldridge, Walsall WS9 8DZ, UK

Contact: Gary Dawson

UAL CORPORATION

1200 E. Algonquin Rd., Chicago, IL, 60007

Tel: (847) 700-4000   Fax: (847) 700-4081   www.ual.com

Air transportation, passenger and freight services.

United Airlines, 718 Conduit St., London W1, UK

UBS PAINEWEBBER

1285 Ave. of the Americas, New York, NY, 10019

Tel: (212) 713-2000   Fax: (212) 713-4889   www.ubspainewebber.com

Engaged in stock brokerage and investment services.

UBS PaineWebber Intl. (UK) Ltd., One Finsbury Ave., London EC2M 2PA, UK

Tel: 44-207-422-2000

UNICA CORPORATION

55 Old Bedford Road, Lincoln, MA, 01773

Tel: (781) 259-5900   Fax: (781) 259-5901   www.unicacorp.com

Mfr. data mining software.

Unica Corporation UK, Aston Court, Kingsmead Business Park, Frederick Place, High Wycombe HP11 1LA, UK

Tel: 44-1494-616026   Fax: 44-1494-616001

UNIFI INC.

7201 West Friendly Ave., Greensboro, NC, 27410-6237

Tel: (336) 294-4410   Fax: (336) 316-5422   www.unifi-inc.com

Yarn spinning mills, throwing/winding mills.

Unifi Intl. Service Inc., St. Philipcourt Yard, Coleshill, Birmingham, W. Mids. B46 3AD, UK

UNION CARBIDE CORPORATION

39 Old Ridgebury Road, Danbury, CT, 06817

Tel: (203) 794-2000   Fax: (203) 794-6269   www.unioncarbide.com

Mfr. industrial chemicals, plastics and resins.

Union Carbide (UK) Ltd., 95 High St., Rickmansworth, Hertshire WD3 1RB, UK

UNIQUE BALANCE

2225 Kerper Blvd., Dubuque, IA, 52001

Tel: (563) 583-9776   Fax: (563) 583-5281   www.unique-balance.com

Mfr./sale of building hardware and sash balances.

Unique Balance, Div. Pomeroy Inc., Unit 5, Brookvale Estate, Brookvale Rd., Ulitton Birmingham B67 7AQ, UK

Tel: 44-121-344-7833   Fax: 44-121-344-7834   Contact: Tom Ryder

UNISYS CORPORATION.

PO Box 500, Union Meeting Road, Blue Bell, PA, 19424

Tel: (215) 986-4011   Fax: (215) 986-6850   www.unisys.com

Mfr./marketing/servicing electronic information systems.

Unisys Europe, Broad Quay House, Bristol BS14DJ, UK

Unisys Ltd., 31 Brentfield, Stonebridge Park, London NW10 8LS, UK

Unisys UK Ltd., 322 High Holborn, London WC1V7PW, UK

UNITED ASSET MANAGEMENT CORPORATION

One International Place, 44th Fl., Boston, MA, 02110

Tel: (617) 330-8900   Fax: (617) 330-1133   www.uam.com

Holding company for investment management services.

Old Mutual Fund Managers Limited, Div. UAM, Freepost 13488, London EC2B 2AN, UK

Tel: 44-207-332-7550

UNITED ELECTRIC CONTROLS COMPANY

PO Box 9143, Watertown, MA, 02172-9143

Tel: (617) 926-1000   Fax: (617) 926-4354   www.ueonline.com

Mfr./sale electro-mechanical and electronic controls and recorders.

United Electric Controls UK, Sulby House, North St., Sudbury Suffolk CO10 6RE, UK

UNITED PARCEL SERVICE, INC.

55 Glenlake Parkway, NE, Atlanta, GA, 30328

Tel: (404) 828-6000   Fax: (404) 828-6593   www.ups.com

International package-delivery service.

UPS Ltd. -Head Office, UPS House, Forest Rd., Feltham, Middlesex TW13 7DY, UK

Tel: 44-345-877-877

UNITED PRESS INTERNATIONAL (UPI)

1510 H Street NW, Washington, DC, 20005

Tel: (202) 898-8000   Fax: (202) 898-8057   www.upi.com

Collection and distributor of news, news pictures, financial data.

UPI International, 8 Bouverie St., London EC4Y 8BB, UK

UNITED STATES SURGICAL CORPORATION

150 Glover Ave., Norwalk, CT, 06856

Tel: (203) 845-1000   Fax: (203) 847-0635   www.ussurg.com

Mfr./development/market surgical staplers, laparoscopic instruments and sutures.

U.S. Surgical, Div. Tyco Healthcare UK, 154 Fareham Road, Gosport Hampshire PO13 OAS, UK

Tel: 44-1329-224-000

UNITED TECHNOLOGIES CORPORATION

One Financial Plaza, Hartford, CT, 06103

Tel: (860) 728-7000   Fax: (860) 728-7979   www.utc.com

Mfr. aircraft engines, elevators, A/C, auto equipment, space and military electronic and rocket propulsion systems.
Products include Pratt and Whitney, Otis elevators, Carrier heating and air conditioning and Sikorsky helicopters.

Caricor Ltd., Knightsbridge House, 197 Knightsbridge, London SW7 1RB, UK

Otis Elevator Co. Ltd., Otis Building, 43/59 Clapham Rd., London SW9 0JZ, UK

Porvair Ltd., Estuary Rd., Kings Lynn, Norfolk PE30 2HS, UK

UNIVERSAL CORPORATION

1501 N. Hamilton Street, Richmond, VA, 23230

Tel: (804) 359-9311   Fax: (804) 254-3582   www.universalcorp.com

Holding company for tobacco and commodities.

Universal Leaf (UK) Ltd., 25 Coombs Rd., Kingston-upon-Thames, Surrey KT2 7AB, UK

Universal Leaf Services Ltd., 2 Alric Ave., London SW3, UK

UNIVERSAL SECURITY INSTRUMENTS, INC.

PO Box 825, Binghamton, NY, 13902-0825

Tel: (607) 779-7689   Fax: (607) 779-7301   www.uic.com

Provider of innovative electronic circuit assembly technology and equipment, integrated system solutions, and process expertise.

Universal Instruments Electronics Ltd., Redhill Surrey, UK

Tel: 44-1737-77911   Fax: 44-1737-779710

UNIVERSAL WEATHER & AVIATION INC.

8787 Tallyho Road, Houston, TX, 77061

Tel: (713) 944-1622   Fax: (713) 943-4650   www.univ-wea.com

Provides service management, and worldwide weather and communications to the corporate aviation community.

Universal Aviation (UK) Ltd., Stansted Airport Bldg. 56D, Stansted, Essex CM24 1QH, UK

Tel: 44-1279-680-349   Fax: 44-1279-680-372

UNOCAL CORPORATION

2141 Rosecrans Ave., Ste. 4000, El Segundo, CA, 90245

Tel: (310) 726-7600   Fax: (310) 726-7817   www.unocal.com

Engaged in oil and gas exploration and production.

Unocal (UK) Ltd., 32 Cadbury Rd., Sunbury on Thames, Middlesex TW16 7LU, UK

UNOVA INC.

21900 Burbank Blvd., Woodland Hills, CA, 91367-7418

Tel: (818) 992-3000   Fax: (818) 992-2848   www.unova.com

Automated data collection, mobile computing and manufacturing systems.

Lamb Technicon UK, 22/23 Monkspath Business Park, Shirley, Solihull, Warwicks B90 4NZ, UK

Tel: 44-121-733-4235   Fax: 44-121-733-7061

Lamb UK, Hampstead Ave., Mildenhall, Suffolk IP28 7RE, UK

Tel: 44-1638-582200

Landis Lund, Div. UNOVA, Cross Hills, Keighley, West Yorkshire BD20 7SD, UK

Tel: 44-1535-633-211

UNUM PROVIDENT

2211 Congress Street, Portland, ME, 04122

Tel: (207) 770-2211   Fax: (207) 770-4510   www.unum.com

Disability and special risk insurance.

Unum Life Insurance Co. Ltd., Hamilton House, 1 Temple Avenue, Victoria Embankment, London EC4Y 0HA, UK

Tel: 44-1-306-887766   Fax: 44-1-306-887504   Contact: Martyn Field, Mng. Dir.

Unum Limited U.K., Milton Court, Dorking, Surrey RH4 3LZ, UK

Tel: 44-1-306-887766   Fax: 44-1-306-887504   Contact: Martyn Field, Mng. Dir.

Unum Limited UK, Swan House, 37/39 High Holborn, London WC1 V6A, UK

Unum UK Ltd., Airedale House, 77/85 Albion Street, Leeds LS15AJ, UK

UOP LLC

25 East Algonquin Road, Des Plaines, IL, 60017

Tel: (847) 391-2000   Fax: (847) 391-2253   www.uop.com

Engaged in developing and commercializing technology for license to the oil refining, petrochemical and gas processing industries.

UOP (UK) Ltd., Weedon Rd., Industrial Estate, Northampton, UK

UOP Ltd., 'Liongate' Ladymead, Guildford, Surrey GU1 1AT, UK

Tel: 44-1483-304-848   Fax: 44-1483-304-863

UPRIGHT INC.

1775 Park Street, Selma, CA, 93662

Tel: (209) 891-5200   Fax: (209) 896-9012   www.upright.com

Mfr. aerial work platforms and telescopic handlers.

UpRight UK Ltd., Telford, UK

URBAN OUTFITTERS, INC.

1809 Walnut St., Philadelphia, PA, 19103

Tel: (215) 564-2313   Fax: (215) 568-1549   www.urbanoutfitters.com

Retail stores for casual clothes, accessories, shoes, gifts and housewares.

Urban Outfitters, Inc., 36-38 Kensington High St., London, UK

Tel: 44-207-761-1001

UROPLASTY INC.

2718 Summer Street NE, Minneapolis, MN, 55413-2820

Tel: (612) 378-1180   Fax: (612) 378-2027   www.uroplasty.com

Mfr. urology products.

Bioplasty Ltd., Unit 3, Woodside Business Park, Whitley Wood Lane, Reading, Berkshire RG2 8LW, UK

URS CORPORATION

100 California Street, Ste. 500, San Francisco, CA, 94111

Tel: (415) 774-2700   Fax: (415) 398-1905   www.urscorp.com

Engineering, environmental and construction management services.

Ashact Ltd., Bridge House, Station Approach, Great Missenden, Buckinghamshire HP18 9AZ, UK

Dames & Moore, The Clifton Dispensary, 13 Dowry Sq., Bristol BS8 4SL, UK

Dames & Moore, 5/F, Blackfriar's House, St. Mary's Parsonage, Manchester M3 2JA, UK

Dames & Moore, 1/F, Booth House, 15-17 Church St., Twickenham TW1 3NJ, UK

Food & Agriculture Intl. Ltd., 1/F, Booth House, 15-17 Church St., Twickenham TW1 3NJ, UK

O'Brien-Kreitzberg, Artillery House, 7th fl., Artillery Row, London SW1P R1T, UK

URSCHEL LABORATORIES INC.

2503 Calumet Ave., PO Box 2200, Valparaiso, IN, 46384-2200

Tel: (219) 464-4811   Fax: (219) 462-3879   www.urschel.com

Design/mfr. precision food processing equipment.

Urschel Intl. Ltd., 6 Groby Trading Estate, Leicester LE6 0FH, UK

USA INTERACTIVE

152 W. 57th St., New York, NY, 10019

Tel: (212) 314-7300   Fax: (212) 314-7309   www.usainteractive.com

Owns and operates Ticketmaster, Home Shopping Network and on-line travel firm, Expedia.

Ticketmaster UK, Leicester Square, London WC2H 7LE, UK

USAA

9800 Fredericksburg Road, San Antonio, TX, 78288-3533

Tel: (210) 498-2211   Fax: (210) 498-9940   www.usaa.com

Provides financial services, life, property and casualty insurance and consumer sales services primarily to military and U.S. government personnel and their families.

USAA, London, UK

USF WORLDWIDE INC.

1100 Arlington Heights Road, Ste. 600, Itasca, IL, 60143

Tel: (630) 919-4800   Fax: (630) 773-9179   www.usfreightways.com

Provides shipping and transport support services.

USF Worldwide Logistics, Alpha Way, Thorpe Industrial Park, Egham, Egham Surrey TW20 8RZ, UK

Tel: 44-1784-480-100

USFILTER WALLACE & TIERNAN

1901 West Garden Road, Vineland, NJ, 08360

Tel: (609) 507-9000   Fax: (609) 507-4125   www.usfwt.com

Mfr. disinfections and chemical feed equipment.

USFilter Wallace & Tiernan Limited, Priory Works, Tonbridge, Kent TN11 0QL, UK

Tel: 44-732-771777   Fax: 44-732-771800

UTILICORP UNITED INC.

20 W. Ninth St., Kansas City, MO, 64105

Tel: (816) 421-6600   Fax: (816) 472-6281   www.utilicorp.com

Electric and gas utility.

United Gas Ltd., London, UK

UTILX CORPORATION

PO Box 97009, Kent, WA, 98064-9709

Tel: (253) 395-0200   Fax: (253) 395-1040   www.utilx.com

Mfr. utility construction machinery and guided boring systems and provides cable restoration services.

FlowMole Ltd., 33 Maylan Rd., Earlstrees Industrial Estate, Corby, Northamptonshire NN17 4DR, UK

Tel: 44-1536-400141 Fax: 44-1536-400142 Contact: Robert Bailey, Mng. Dir Emp: 25

UUNET

22001 Loudoun County Pkwy., Ashburn, VA, 20147

Tel: (703) 206-5600   Fax: (703) 206-5601   www.uu.net

World's largest Internet service provider; World Wide Web hosting services, security products and consulting services to businesses, professionals, and on-line service providers.

UUNET UK, Internet House, 332 Science Park, Cambridge CB4 0BZ, UK

UUNET UK, 332 Science Park, Milton Rd., Cambridge CB4 4BZ, UK

Tel: 44-1223 250100 Fax: 44-1223-2500335 Contact: Richard Keyes, Acting Mng. Dir. Emp: 400

VALHI INC.

5430 LBJ Freeway, Ste. 1700, Dallas, TX, 75240

Tel: (972) 233-1700   Fax: (972) 450-4278

Holding company engaged in the chemicals, component products, titanium metals and waste management industries.

Kronos UK Ltd., Winslow Cheshire, UK

VALSPAR CORPORATION

1101 South Third Street, Minneapolis, MN, 55415-1259

Tel: (612) 332-7371   Fax: (612) 375-7723   www.valspar.com

Mfr. paints and coatings.

Valspar Inc., London, UK

THE VALSPAR CORPORATION

4999 36th Street SE, PO Box 88010, Grand Rapids, MI, 49512

Tel: (616) 940-2900   Fax: (616) 285-7870   www.valspar.com

Mfr. custom industrial coatings, diversified consumer products.

Guardsman UK Ltd., 10 Blacklands Way, Abingdon Business Park, Abingdon, Oxfordshire OX14 1RD, UK

VANCE INTERNATIONAL, INC.

10467 White Granite Drive, Oakton, VA, 22124

Tel: (703) 685-6754   Fax: (703) 359-8456   www.vancesecurity.com

Engaged in security; executive protection and uniformed guards.

Vance International, 14 Montpelier Road, Ealing W5 2QP, UK

Tel: 44-208-810-5747 Contact: Stuart Page

VANTON PUMP & EQUIPMENT CORPORATION

201 Sweetland Ave., Hillside, NJ, 07205

Tel: (908) 688-4216   Fax: (908) 686-9314   www.vanton.com

Mfr. non-metallic rotary, horizontal and vertical pumps and accessories for corrosive, abrasive and chemically pure fluids.

Vanton Pumps Ltd., 26 Sandown Crescent, Unit 6, Radnor Industrial Estate, Congleton, Cheshire CW12 4XL, UK

Tel: 44-12602-77040 Fax: 44-12602-280605 Contact: Shaun Manley, CEO Emp: 15

VAPOR BUS INTERNATIONAL

6420 West Howard Street, Niles, IL, 60714-3395

Tel: (847) 967-8300   Fax: (847) 965-9874   www.vapordoors.com

Mfr. bus and rail transit automatic door systems, railcar/locomotive relays and contractors, vehicle ID systems.

Vapor Stone UK Ltd., 2nd Avenue Centrum 100, Burton on Trent, Staffordshire DE14 2WF, UK

Tel: 44-1283-743300   Fax: 44-1283-743333

Vapor UK, 28 Springdale Ct., Mickleover Derby, Derby DE3 5SW, UK

Tel: 44-1332-518788   Fax: 44-1332-519071   Contact: Anthony J. Walsh

VARCO INTERNATIONAL INC.

2000 W. Sam Houston Pkwy S., Ste. 1700, Houston, TX, 77042

Tel: (281) 953-2200   Fax: (281) 953-2400   www.varco.com

Mfr. oilfield and industry weight and measure systems.

Tuboscope (UK) Ltd., Unit 8, Bessemer Way, Harfreys Industrial Estate, Great Yarmouth, Norfolk NR 31 0LX, UK

VARIAN MEDICAL SYSTEMS, INC.

3050 Hansen Way, Palo Alto, CA, 94304-100

Tel: (650) 493-4000   Fax: (650) 424-5358   www.varian.com

Mfr. microwave tubes and devices, analytical instruments, semiconductor process and medical equipment, vacuum systems.

Varian Medical Systems, 28 Manor Rd., Walton-on-Thames, Surrey KT12 2QF, UK

Varian Medical Systems -TEM Limited, Gatwick Road, Crawley, West Sussex RH10 2RG, UK

Tel: 44-1293-601-272   Fax: 44-1293-534-570

VASTERA, INC.

45025 Aviation Drive, Ste. 300, Dulles, VA, 20166

Tel: (703) 661-9006   Fax: (703) 742-4580   www.vastera.com

Helps companies to define and deploy best business processes for trade and manages their global trade operations.

Vastera UK, Atlas House, 188 High Street, Egham Surrey TW209ED, UK

Tel: 44-1784-220400

Vastera UK, Ground Floor, Statham House, Talbot Road, Old Trafford, Manchester M32 OFP, UK

Tel: 44-161-8683410

VEECO INSTRUMENTS INC.

100 Sunnyside Blvd., Woodbury, NY, 11797

Tel: (516) 677-0200   Fax: (516) 677-9125   www.veeco.com

Mfr. surface profiler, atomic force microscopes, leak and plating thickness detectors and semiconductor products.

Veeco Instruments Ltd., Unit 8, Colne Way Court, Colne Way, Watford, Hertshire WD2 4NE, UK

Tel: 44-1923-210044   Fax: 44-1923-235130

VEEDER-ROOT COMPANY

125 Powder Forest Drive, PO Box 2003, Simsbury, CT, 06070-2003

Tel: (860) 651-2700   Fax: (860) 651-2704   www.veeder.com

Mfr. of automatic tank gauging systems.

Veeder-Root Europe, Hydrex House, Garden Road, Richmond TW9 4NR, UK

Tel: 44-208-392-1355   Fax: 44-208-878-6642   Contact: Steve Richards

VELCRO USA INC.

406 Brown Avenue, Manchester, NH, 03108

Tel: (603) 669-4892   Fax: (603) 669-9271   www.velcro.com

Mfr./sales of Velcro brand hook and loop fasteners, plastic buckles and metal hardware and cable control straps.

Velcro Limited, 1 Aston Way, Middlewich Industrial Estate, Middlewich Cheshire CW10 0HS, UK

Tel: 44-1606-738806

VELSICOL CHEMICAL CORPORATION

10400 West Higgins Road, Ste. 600, Rosemont, IL, 60018-3728

Tel: (847) 298-9000   Fax: (847) 298-9014   www.velsicol.com

Produces high performance specialty chemicals based on benzoic acid and cyclo pentadiene.

Velsicol Chemical Ltd., 8 Cedarwood, Chineham Business Park, Basingstoke, Hampshire RE24 8WD, UK

Tel: 44-1256-464649   Fax: 44-1256-817744   Contact: David Frederick, Exec. Mng. Dir.

VENTIV HEALTH, INC.

1114 Avenue of the Americas, 8th Fl., New York, NY, 10036

Tel: (212) 768-8000   Fax: (212) 768-7387   www.ventiv.com

Provides sales and marketing services for pharmaceutical companies.

Ventiv Health UK, Network House, Basing View, Basingstoke Hampshire RG21 4HG, UK

Tel: 44-1256-811-117

VERIFONE, INC.

4988 Great America Pkwy., Santa Clara, CA, 94054-1200

Tel: (408) 496-0444   Fax: (408) 919-5105   www.verifone.com

Mfr. electronic payment software and hardware.

VeriFone UK Ltd, Salamander Quay South, Park Lane, Harefield, Uxbridge, Middlesex UB9 6NY, UK

VERINT SYSTEMS INC.

234 Crossways Park Drive, Woodbury, NY, 11797

Tel: (516) 677-7300   Fax: (516) 677-7197   www.verintsystems.com

Mfr. and sales of analytic software.

Verint Systems UK, Hertford Place, Denham Way Maple Cross, Rickmansworth Hertfordshire WD3 2XF, UK

Tel: 44-1923-717-432   Fax: 44-1923-717-311

VERISIGN, INC.

1350 Charleston Rd., Mountain View, CA, 94043

Tel: (650) 961-7500   Fax: (650) 961-7300   www.verisign.com

Mfr. software.

BT Ignite, BT Centre, 81 Newgate Street, London EC1A 7AJ, UK

VERITAS SOFTWARE INC.

350 Ellis Street, Mountain View, CA, 94043

Tel: (650) 527-8000   Fax: (650) 527-8050   www.veritas.com

Mfr. of storage management software for data protection, application availability, and disaster recovery.

VERITAS Software UK, European Headquarters, Bittams Lane, Guildford Road, Chertsey, Surrey KT16 9RG, UK

VERITY, INC.

894 Ross Drive, Sunnyvale, CA, 94089

Tel: (408) 541-1500   Fax: (408) 541-1600   www.verity.com

Mfr. software to simplify management of information.

Verity UK Ltd., The Pavilions, Kiln Park Business Ctr., Kiln Lane, Epsom KT17 1JG, UK

Tel: 44-1372-74 70 76

VERIZON COMMUNICATIONS INC.

1095 Ave. of the Americas, New York, NY, 10036

Tel: (212) 395-2121   Fax: (212) 395-1285   www.verizon.com

Telecommunications.

Cable & Wireless Communications, London, UK

VERIZON WIRELESS, INC.

180 Washington Valley Rd., Bedminster, NJ, 07921

Tel: (908) 306-7000   Fax: (908) 306-6927   www.verizonwireless.com

Engaged in mobile phone operations.

Vodafone Group Plc, 2-4 London Road, Newbury Berkshire, UK

VERMEER MANUFACTURING COMPANY

PO Box 200, Pella, IA, 50219-0200

Tel: (515) 628-3141   Fax: (515) 621-7730   www.vermeer.com.

Mfr. agricultural and construction equipment.

B-Trac Equipment Ltd., 45-51 Rixon Road, Wellingborough, Northants NN8 4BA, UK

Tel: 44-1-933-274400   Fax: 44-1-933-274403   Contact: Martin Wright

VERSATA, INC.

300 Lakeside Drive, Ste. 1500, Oakland, CA, 94612

Tel: (510) 238-4100   Fax: (510) 238-4101   www.versata.com

Mfr. software.

Versata Europe Ltd., Parkshot House, 5 Kew Road, Richmond, Surrey TW9 2PR, UK

VERTEX INTERACTIVE, INC.

22 Audrey Place, Fairfield, NJ, 07004

Tel: (973) 777-3500   Fax: (973) 472-0814   www.vertexinteractive.com

Mfr. software.

Vertex Interactive, 20 Berkeley Square 7/F, London W1J 6HF, UK

Tel: 44-207-629-7008   Fax: 44-207-629-4534

Vertex Interactive (UK) Ltd., Unit B13 Armstrong Mall, Southwood, Farnborough Hampshire GU14 0NR, UK

Tel: 44-1252-522500

VERTEX PHARMACEUTICALS INC.

130 Weverly Street, Cambridge, MA, 02139-4242

Tel: (617) 444-6100   Fax: (617) 444-6680   www.vpharm.com

Research and development of pharmaceuticals.

Vertex Pharmaceuticals UK Ltd., 88 Milton Park, Abingdon, Oxfordshire OX14 4RY, UK

Tel: 44-1235-438-800

VIACOM INC.

1515 Broadway, 28th Fl., New York, NY, 10036-5794

Tel: (212) 258-6000   Fax: (212) 258-6358   www.viacom.com

Communications, publishing and entertainment.

Prentice Hall Intl. (UK) Ltd., 66 Wood Lane End, Hemel Hempstead, Hertfordshire HP2 4RG, UK

Viacom Intl. Ltd., 40 Conduit St., London W1R 9FB, UK

VIAD CORPORATION

1850 North Central Ave., Phoenix, AZ, 85077

Tel: (602) 207-4000   Fax: (602) 207-5900   www.viad.com

Provides convention, exhibit design and production services.

SDD Exhibitions, Div. Exhibitgroup/Giltspur, Marlborough House, Marlborough Road, Sheffield, UK

Contact: Charles J. Corsentino, Pres.

VIASYS HEALTHCARE INC.

227 Washington Street, Ste. 200, Conshohocken, PA, 19428

Tel: (610) 862-0800   Fax: (610) 862-0836   www.viasyshealthcare.com

Mfr. medical instruments and devices.

VIASYS Healthcare, Welton Road, Warwick CV34 5PZ, UK

Tel: 44-1926-490888   Contact: Dave Kelly

VIASYS Healthcare UK, Welton Road, Warwick CV34 5 PZ, UK

VIASYSTEMS GROUP, INC.

101 South Hanley Road, Ste. 40, St. Louis, MO, 63105

Tel: (314) 727-2087   Fax: (314) 719-2255   www.viasystems.com

Engaged in contract manufacturing of printed circuit boards.

Viasystems EMS, Antrim Road Ballynahinch, County Down BT24 8AN, UK

Viasystems EMS UK Ltd, Uxbridge Avenue, Coventry CV31RR, UK

VICON INDUSTRIES, INC.

89 Arkay Dr., Hauppauge, NY, 11788

Tel: (631) 952-2288   Fax: (631) 951-2288   www.vicon-cctv.com

Engaged in design, engineering and production of high quality video systems and equipment.

Vicon Industies (UK) Ltd., Brunel Way, Fareham, Hampshire PO15 5TX, UK

VICOR CORPORATION

25 Frontage Rd., Andover, MA, 01810-5413

Tel: (978) 470-2900   Fax: (978) 749-3536   www.vicr.com

Designs, manufactures, and markets modular power components and complete configurable and custom power systems.

Vicor UK, Coliseum Business Centre, Riverside Way, Camberley Surrey GU15 3YL, UK

Tel: 44-1276-678222

VIDEO DISPLAY CORPORATION

1868 Tucker Industrial Road, Tucker, GA, 30084

Tel: (770) 938-2080   Fax: (770) 493-3903   www.videodisplay.com

Mfr./rebuild/distribute video display components.

Video Display Europe, Ltd., 7 Arden Business Centre, Alcester Warkshire B49 6HW, UK

Tel: 44-1789-766664   Fax: 44-1789-764234

VIEWLOCITY, INC.

3475 Piedmont Road, Ste. 1700, Atlanta, GA, 30305

Tel: (404) 267-6400   Fax: (404) 267-6500   www.viewlocity.com

Mfr. supply chain management software.

Viewlocity UK, Sovereign Gate, 18-20 Kew Road, Richmond Surrey TW9 2NA, UK

Tel: 44-208-948-0200

VIEWSONIC CORPORATION

381 Brea Canyon Road, Walnut, CA, 91789

Tel: (909) 444-8888   Fax: (909) 869-7958   www.viewsonic.com

Mfr. displays.

ViewSonic Europe Ltd., ViewSonic House, Fleming Way, Crawley, West Sussex RH10 9GA, UK

VIGNETTE CORPORATION

1601 South Mopac Expwy., Bldg. 3, Austin, TX, 78746-5776

Tel: (512) 741-4300   Fax: (512) 741-4500   www.vignette.com

Mfr. software.

Vignette UK, 99 King Stret, Maidenhead, Berkshire SL6 1DP, UK

THE VIKING CORPORATION

210 N. Industrial Park Rd., Hastings, MI, 49058

Tel: (616) 945-9501   Fax: (616) 945-9599   www.vikingcorp.com

Mfr. fire extinguishing equipment.

Lansdale Viking Limited, Churchtown, Belton Doncaster, South Yorkshire DN9 1PB, UK

Tel: 44-1427 875999   Fax: 44-1427 875998

VIKING ELECTRONICS

1531 Industrial St., Hudson, WI, 54016

Tel: (715) 386-8861   Fax: (715) 386-4344   www.vikingelectronics.com

Mfr./sales of electronic interconnect systems.

Viking Connectors (UK) Ltd., Chatsworth House, Portland Close, Dunstable, Beds. LU5 4AW, UK

VINSON & ELKINS LLP

2300 First City Tower, 1001 Fannin, Houston, TX, 77002-6760

Tel: (713) 758-2222   Fax: (713) 758-2346   www.vinson-elkins.com

Engaged in international law.

Vinson & Elkins LP, 45 King William Street, London EC4R 9AN, UK

Tel: 44-20-7618-6000   Contact: Douglas B. Glass

VIRAGE LOGIC CORPORATION

46501 Landing Pkwy., Fremont, CA, 94538

Tel: (510) 360-8000   Fax: (510) 360-8099   www.viragelogic.com

Mfr. software.

Virage Logic Corporation, 3 Toomers Wharf, Canal Walk, Newbury, Berkshire RG14 1DY, UK

Tel: 44-1635-233100   Fax: 44-1635-233111

VIRAGE, INC.

411 Borel Avenue, Ste. 100 S, San Mateo, CA, 94402-3116

Tel: (650) 573-3210   Fax: (650) 573-3211   www.virage.com

Mfr. software.

Virage Europe, Ltd., Pinewood Studios, The Props Bldg., Pinewood Road, Iver Heath Buckinghamshire SLO ONH, UK

Tel: 44-1753-785-144

VISHAY INTERTECHNOLOGY INC.

63 Lincoln Hwy., Malvern, PA, 19355

Tel: (610) 644-1300   Fax: (610) 296-0657   www.vishay.com

Mfr. resistors, strain gages, capacitors, inductors, printed circuit boards.

Measurements Group UK Ltd., Stroudley Rd., Basingstoke RG24 0FW, UK

Vishay Components (UK) Ltd., Ayton Rd., Wymondham, Norfolk NR18 0RA, UK

Vishay Components (UK) Ltd., Pallion Industrial Estate, Sunderland SR4 6SU, UK

Tel: 44-191-514-4155

VISHAY VITRAMON INC.

PO Box 544, Bridgeport, CT, 06601

Tel: (203) 268-6261   Fax: (203) 261-4446   www.vitramon.com

Ceramic capacitors.

Vitramon Ltd., Wycombe Lane, Wooburn Green, Bucks, UK

VISION TEK, INC.

1175 Lakeside Drive, Gurnee, Il, 60013

Tel: (847) 360-7500   Fax: (847) 360-7144   www.visiontek.com

Mfr. computer memory.

Vision Tek, Argentum, 2 Queen Caroline Street, Hammersmith, London W6 9DX, UK

VITAL SIGNS, INC.

20 Campus Road, Totowa, NJ, 07512

Tel: (973) 790-1330   Fax: (973) 790-3307   www.vital-signs.com

Mfr. disposable medical products for critical care procedures.

BREAS Medical Ltd., Div. Vital Signs, 18, Lion & Lamb Yard, Farnham, Surrey GU9 7LL, UK

VIVITAR CORPORATION

1280 Rancho Conejo Blvd, Newbury Park, CA, 91320

Tel: (805) 498-7008   Fax: (805) 498-5086   www.vivitar.com

Mfr. photographic equipment, electronic supplies.

Vivitar UK Ltd., 22-23 Westmead, Swindon, Wiltshire SN5 7YT, UK

Tel: 44-01793-526211

VIZACOM INC.

3512 Veterans Memorical Hwy., Bohemia, NY, 11716

Tel: (631) 981-5500   Fax: (631) 981-0099   www.vizacom.com

Mfr. graphics applications software.

Vizy Interactive, London, UK

VOLT INFORMATION SCIENCES, INC.

560 Lexington Avenue, 16th Fl., New York, NY, 10022-6828

Tel: (212) 704-2400   Fax: (212) 704-2417   www.volt.com

Staffing services and telecommunication services.

Gatton Volt Computing Group, Gatton Place, St. Matthews Road, Redhill Surrey RH1 1TA, UK

Gatton Volt Computing Group, Artillery House, 11-19 Artillery Row, London SW1P 1RT, UK

Volt Autologic Ltd., Alban Park, Hatfield Rd., St. Albans, Hertfordshire AL4 0JJ, UK

Volt Management Corp. Technical Services, 150 Minories, London EC3N 1LS, UK

Tel: 44-1712-642246

VoltDelta Europe Ltd., Dolphin House, Windmill Rd., Sunbury on Thames, Middlesex TW16 7HT, UK

Tel: 44-1932-75555

VTEL PRODUCTS CORPORATION

108 Wild Basin Road, Austin, TX, 78746

Tel: (512) 314-2700   Fax: (512) 314-2792   www.vtel.com

Design, development, manufacture and sale of PC-based videoconferencing systems through reseller channels.

VTEL Europe Ltd., The Atrium Court, Apex Plaza, Reading RG1 1AX, UK

Tel: 44-118-955-3200

WACHOVIA CORPORATION

301 South College Street, Ste. 4000, Charlotte, NC, 28288-0013

Tel: (704) 374-6161   Fax: (704) 383-1240   www.wachovia.com

Engaged in commercial and retail banking services.

Wachovia Bank, 3 Bishopsgate, London EC2N 3AB, UK

THE WACKENHUT CORPORATION

4200 Wackenhut Dr., Ste. 100, Palm Beach Gardens, FL, 33410

Tel: (561) 622-5656   Fax: (561) 691-6736   www.wackenhut.com

Security systems and services.

Wackenhut UK Ltd. (WUK), 875 Sidcup Rd., New Etham, London SE9 3PP, UK

Tel: 44-181-850-4647   Fax: 44-181-850-0612

WAHL CLIPPER CORPORATION

2902 N. Locust Street, Sterling, IL, 61081

Tel: (815) 625-6525   Fax: (815) 625-1193   www.wahlclipper.com

Mfr. hair clippers, beard and mustache trimmers, shavers, pet clippers and soldering irons.

Wahl Europe Ltd., Herne Bay Trade Park, Sea St., Herne Bay, Kent CT6 8SZ, UK

WALBRO ENGINE MANAGEMENT

7400 N. Oracle Road, Ste. 310, Tucson, AZ, 85704

Tel: (520) 877-3000   Fax: (520) 877-3006   www.walbro.com

Mfr. motor vehicle accessories and parts, automotive fluid carrying systems.

TI Group Automotive Systems, Tenth Avenue, Deeside Industrial Park, Deeside Flintshire CH5 2UA, UK

WAL-MART STORES INC.

702 SW 8th Street, Bentonville, AR, 72716-8611

Tel: (501) 273-4000   Fax: (501) 273-1917   www.wal-mart.com

Retailer.

ASDA Group Limited, ASDA House, Southbank, Great Wilson St., Leeds LS11 5AD, UK

Tel: 44-113-243-5435   Fax: 44-113-241-8666   Contact: Allan L. Leighton, CEO

THE WARNACO GROUP INC.

90 Park Ave., New York, NY, 10016

Tel: (212) 661-1300   Fax: (212) 687-0480   www.warnaco.com

Mfr./sales intimate apparel and men's and women's sportswear.

Warner's (UK) Ltd., Blenheim Ind. Park., Dabell Ave., Nottingham NG6 8WA, UK

Warner's (UK) Ltd., Montague Row, Baker St., London W1H 1AB, UK

WARNER BROS.

4000 Warner Boulevard, Bldg.170, 3rd Fl., Burbank, CA, 91522

Tel: (818) 954-6000   Fax: (818) 977-4040   www.wbitv.com

Distributor TV programming and theatrical features.

Warner Bros., 135 Wardour St., London W1V 4AP, UK

Tel: 44-207-494-3710   Fax: 44-207-465-4207   Contact: John Berger, VP

WARNER ELECTRIC COMPANY

449 Gardner St., South Beloit, IL, 61080

Tel: (815) 389-3771   Fax: (815) 389-2582   www.warnernet.com

Global supplier of Power Transmission and Motion Control Solution Systems; automotive, industry brakes, and clutches.

Warner Electric, Div. Dana Ltd., St. Helen Aukland, Bishop Auckland, County Durham DL14 9AA, UK

Tel: 44-1388-45-8877

WARRANTECH CORPORATION

150 Westpark Way, Euless, TX, 76040

Tel: (817) 354-0095   Fax: (817) 436-6151   www.warrantech.com

Engaged in third party insurance in administering service warranties for manufacturers.

Warrantech UK Limited, London, UK

WASHINGTON GROUP INTERNATIONAL, INC.

720 Park Blvd., PO Box 73, Boise, ID, 83729

Tel: (208) 386-5000   Fax: (208) 386-7186   www.wgint.com

Engaged in engineering and construction.

Morrison Knudsen Limited, Spencer House, Unit 93, Dewhurst Road, Birchwood, Warrington Cheshire WA3 7PG, UK

Tel: 44-1925-854500   Fax: 44-1925-854599

Washington Group International, Inc., C.I. Tower, St. Georges Square, High Street, New Malden Surrey, UK

Tel: 44-20-8336-5100

THE WASHINGTON POST COMPANY

1150 15th St. NW, Washington, DC, 20071

Tel: (202) 334-6000   Fax: (202) 334-4536   www.washpostco.com

Engaged in magazine publishing, cable and television broadcasting, educational services and the Internet.

International Herald Tribune, 40 Marsh Wall, London E14 9TP, UK

Tel: 44-207-510-5700

Newsweek Inc., 25 Upper Brook St., London, UK

WASTE MANAGEMENT, INC.

1001 Fannin Street, Ste. 4000, Houston, TX, 77002

Tel: (713) 512-6200   Fax: (713) 512-6299   www.wastemanagement.com

Environmental services and disposal company; collection, processing, transfer and disposal facilities.

UK Waste Management Ltd., Gate House Castle Estate, Turnpike Rd., High Wycombe, Buckinghamshire HP12 3NR, UK

Waste Management Intl. PLC, 3 Shortlands, Hammersmith International Centre, London W6 8RX, UK

Tel: 44-181-563-7000   Fax: 44-181-563-6300   Contact: Bill Johnson, Pres.

WATERS CORPORATION

34 Maple Street, Milford, MA, 01757

Tel: (508) 478-2000   Fax: (508) 872-1990   www.waters.com

Mfr./distribute liquid chromatographic instruments and test and measurement equipment.

Waters (UK) Ltd., Millipore House, Abbey Rd., London NW10 7SP, UK

Waters (UK) Ltd., Millipore House, 11-15 Peterborough Rd., Harrow, Middlesex HA1 2YH, UK

Waters Associates Ltd., 324 Chester Rd., Hartford, Northwich, Cheshire CW8 2AH, UK

Waters UK, 730-740 Centennial Court, Centennial Park, Elstree, Hertsford WD6 3SZ, UK

Contact: Andre Ayache

WATLOW ELECTRIC MFG. COMPANY

12001 Lackland Rd., St. Louis, MO, 63146-4039

Tel: (314) 878-4600   Fax: (314) 434-1020   www.watlow.com

Mfr. electrical heating units, electronic controls, thermocouple wire, metal-sheathed cable, infrared sensors.

Watlow Ltd., Robey Close, Linby Industrial Estate, Linby Nottingham NG15 8AA, UK

Tel: 44-115-964-0777   Fax: 44-14-115-964-0071

WATSON PHARMACEUTICALS, INC.

311 Bonnie Circle, Corona, CA, 92880-2882

Tel: (909) 493-5300   Fax: (909) 493-5301   www.watsonpharm.com

Mfr. off-patent and branded pharmaceuticals.

Watson Pharmaceuticals, Gardener Place, Cnr. Howard Drive and Gardener Way, Pinelands 7405, UK

Watson Pharmaceuticals, Newbury, Berkshire RG20 8LU, UK

WATSON WYATT & COMPANY HOLDINGS

1717 H Street NW, Washington, DC, 20006-3807

Tel: (202) 715-7000   Fax: (202) 715-7700   www.watsonwyatt.com

Creates compensation and benefits programs for major corporations.

Watson Wyatt & Co., 21 Tothill Street, London SW1H 9LL, UK

Tel: 44-207-222-8033   Fax: 44-207-222-9182   Contact: Babloo Ramamurthy

WATTS INDUSTRIES, INC.

815 Chestnut Street, North Andover, MA, 01845-6098

Tel: (978) 688-1811   Fax: (978) 688-5841   www.wattsind.com

Designs/mfr./sales of industry valves and safety control products.

Watts UK Limited, St. Richards Road, Evesham, Worcestershire WR11 6XJ, UK

WD-40 COMPANY

1061 Cudahy Place, San Diego, CA, 92110-3998

Tel: (619) 275-1400   Fax: (619) 275-5823   www.wd40.com

Mfr. branded multiple-purpose lubrication, protection and general maintenance products.

WD-40 Company Ltd. (UK), PO Box 440, Brick Close, Kilm Farm, Milton Keynes MK11 3LJ, UK

Tel: 44-190-855-5400

WEATHERFORD INTERNATIONAL, INC.

515 Post Oak Blvd. Ste. 600, Houston, TX, 77027-3415

Tel: (713) 287-8400   Fax: (713) 963-9785   www.weatherford.com

Oilfield services, products and equipment; mfr. marine cranes for oil and gas industry.

Weatherford Intl. Inc., Harfreys Road, Harfreys Industrial Estate, Great Yarmouth, Norfolk NR31 0LS, UK

Tel: 44-1-493-657516   Fax: 44-1-493-653925

JERVIS B. WEBB COMPANY

34375 W.Twelve Mile Rd., Farmington Hills, MI, 48331

Tel: (248) 553-1220   Fax: (248) 553-1237   www.jervisbwebb.com

Mfr. integrators of material handling systems solutions.

Jervis B. Webb Co. Ltd., Dawson Rd., Mount Farm, Milton Keynes MK1 1QY, UK

WEBER-STEPHEN PRODUCTS COMPANY

200 East Daniels Road, Palatine, IL, 60067-6266

Tel: (847) 934-5700   Fax: (847) 934-0291   www.weberbq.com

Mfr./sales Weber cooking systems and barbeque and gas grills.

Erin Gardena/Weber-Stephen, U.K. Ltd., Astonia House, Baldock, Hertfordshire SG7 6UK, UK

Tel: 44-1462-89-6989   Fax: 44-1462-89-3598

WEBMETHODS, INC.

3930 Pender Drive, Fairfax, VA, 22030

Tel: (703) 460-2500   Fax: (703) 460-2599   www.webmethods.com

Mfr. automated business software.

WebMethods, Bowman House, 29 Wilson Street, London EC2M 2SJ, UK

WEBPLAN CORP.

100 Bayview Circle, Newport Beach, CA, 92660

Tel: (949) 509-2929   Fax: (949) 509-2922   www.webplan.com

Delivers software and services that combine supply chain planning and execution.

Webplan UK, Plexus Software, Burston House, Stafford, Staffordshire ST1 8ODS, UK

WEBRIDGE, INC.

1925 NW Amber Glen Pkwy., Ste. 400, Beaverton, OR, 97006

Tel: (503) 601-4000   Fax: (503) 601-4001   www.webridge.com

Mfr. software to manage online transactions.

Webridge European Headquarters, 10 Ironmonger Lane, London EC2V 8EY, UK

Tel: 44-207-606-1776

WEBSENSE, INC.

10240 Sorrento Valley Road, San Diego, CA, 92121

Tel: (858) 320-8000   Fax: (858) 458-2950   www.websense.com

Mfr. software.

Websense UK, 3000 Hillswood Drive, Hillswood Business park, Chertsey Surrey KT 16 0RS, UK

Tel: 44-1932-796001   Fax: 44-1932-796601

WEEDEN & CO. LP

145 Mason Street, Greenwich, CT, 06830

Tel: (203) 861-7600   Fax: (203) 861-7701   www.weedenco.com

Engaged in institutional equities trading.

Weeden International Ltd., 1 Liverpool Street, London EC2M 7QD, UK

WEIGHT WATCHERS INTERNATIONAL, INC.

175 Crossways Park Dr., Woodbury, NY, 11797

Tel: (516) 390-1400   Fax: (516) 390-1763   www.weightwatchers.com

Weight loss programs.

Weight Watchers (UK) Ltd, Kidwells Park House, Kidwells Park Drive, Maidenhead Berks SL6 8YT, UK

WEIL, GOTSHAL & MANGES LLP

767 Fifth Ave., New York, NY, 10153

Tel: (212) 310-8000   Fax: (212) 310-8007   www.weil.com

Engaged in international law.

Weil, Gotshal & Manges LLP, One South Place, London EC2M 2WG, UK

Tel: 44-207-903-1000   Fax: 44-207-903-0990   Contact: Erica L. Handling, Ptnr.

WELCH ALLYN INC.

4341 State Street Road, Skaneateles Falls, NY, 13153

Tel: (315) 685-4100   Fax: (315) 685-4091   www.welchallyn.com

Mfr. fiber optic products and medical diagnostic equipment.

CEL Instruments, Ltd., Div. Welch Allyn, 35-37 Bury Mead Road, Hitchin, Hertfordshire SG5 1RT, UK

Tel: 44-11-462-422411

HHP, Ltd., Div. Welch Allyn, Dallam Court Dallam Lane, Warrington, Cheshire WA2 7LT, UK

Tel: 44-1925-240055

Welch Allyn U.K. Ltd., Aston Abbotts, Buckinghamshire HP22 4ND, UK

Tel: 44-1-296-682140

WENDY'S INTERNATIONAL, INC.

4288 West Dublin Granville Roads, Dublin, OH, 43017-0256

Tel: (614) 764-3100   Fax: (614) 764-3459   www.wendysintl.com

Fast food restaurant chain.

Wendy's International, London, UK

WESCO INTERNATIONAL INC.

Four Station Square, Ste. 700, Pittsburgh, PA, 15219

Tel: (412) 454-2200   Fax: (412) 454-2505   www.wescodist.com

Mfr. electronic equipment and parts.

WESCO International, Knyvett House, The Causeway, Staines TW18 3BA, UK

Tel: 44-1784-898-641   Fax: 44-1784-898-305

WEST PHARMACEUTICAL SERVICES, INC.

101 Gordon Drive, Lionville, PA, 19341-0645

Tel: (610) 594-2900   Fax: (610) 594-3000   www.westpharma.com

Mfr. packaging and plastic components for health care and consumer products.

West Pharmaceutical Services, Bucklers Lane, Holmbush, St. Austell, Cornwall PL25 3JL, UK

West Pharmaceutical Services, Albert Einstein Center, Highfields Science Park, Nottingham NG7 2TN, UK

West Pharmaceutical Services, 18 Cliffe Industrial Estate Lewes, East Sussex BN8 6JL, UK

West Pharmaceutical Services, Cooksland Industrial Estate, Bodwin, Cornwall PL 31 2PZ, UK

WEST POINT STEVENS INC.

507 West 10th Street, PO Box 71, West Point, GA, 31833

Tel: (706) 645-4000   Fax: (706) 645-4121   www.westpointstevens.com

Mfr. household and apparel fabrics and bed and bath products.

West Point Stevens Inc., Berkhanstead, UK

West Point Stevens Inc., 4 Claridge Court, Lower Kings Road, Berkhamsted, Herts HP4 2AF, UK

WESTAFF SERVICES, INC.

301 Lennon Lane, Walnut Creek, CA, 94598-2453

Tel: (925) 930-5300   Fax: (925) 934-5489   www.westaff.com

Secretarial and clerical temporary service.

Western Temporary Services Ltd., 46/50 Southgate St., Gloucester GL1 2DR, UK

WESTERN DIGITAL CORPORATION

20511 Lake Forest Dr., Lake Forest, CA, 92630-7741

Tel: (949) 672-7000   Fax: (949) 672-5408   www.westerndigital.com

Mfr. hard disk drives, video graphics boards, VLSI.

Western Digital UK Ltd., Fairmount House, Bull Hill, Leatherhead, Surrey, UK

WESTERN GECO, INC.

PO Box 2469, Houston, TX, 77042-4299

Tel: (713) 789-9600   Fax: (713) 789-0172   www.bakerhughes.com

Provides comprehensive seismic services for oil and gas exploration, field development, and reservoir monitoring.

Western Geco UK, Schlumberger House, Buckingham Gate, Gatwick Airport, West Sussex RH6 0NZ, UK

Tel: 44-1293-556655   Contact: Gary Jones, Pres.

WESTERN UNION FINANCIAL SERVICES INC.

6200 South Quebec St., Ste. 320-A, Englewood, CO, 80111

Tel: (303) 488-8000   Fax: (303) 488-8705   www.westernunion.com

Engaged in financial and messaging service.

Londis Western Union, Londis 4-8, Mont Fort Place, Wimbledon, UK

Tel: 44-181-741-3639

Temple Fortune News, 11 Hallfwelle Parade, Finchley Rd., London, UK

WEYERHAEUSER COMPANY

33663 Weyerhaeuser Way South, Federal Way, WA, 98003

Tel: (253) 924-2345   Fax: (253) 924-2685   www.weyerhaeuser.com

Wood and wood fiber products.

Weyerhaeuser (UK) Ltd., 3 Curfew Yare Thames St., Windsor, Berkshire SL4 1SN, UK

WHIRLPOOL CORPORATION

2000 N. M-63, Benton Harbor, MI, 49022-2692

Tel: (616) 923-5000   Fax: (616) 923-5443   www.whirlpoolcorp.com

Mfr., market home appliances: Whirlpool, Roper, KitchenAid, Estate, and Inglis.

Whirlpool (UK) Ltd., 209 Purley Way, Croydon, Surrey CR9 4RY, UK

WHITE & CASE LLP

1155 Ave. of the Americas, New York, NY, 10036-2767

Tel: (212) 819-8200   Fax: (212) 354-8113   www.whitecase.com

Engaged in international law.

White & Case LLP, 7-11 Moorgate, London EC2R 6HH, UK

Tel: 44-207-726-6361   Fax: 44-207-726-8558   Contact: Peter D. Finlay

WHITTMAN-HART & USWEB/CKS

311 S. Wacker Drive, Ste. 3500, Chicago, IL, 60606-6621

Tel: (312) 922-9200   Fax: (312) 913-3020   www.uswebcks.com

Internet professional services firm; design and implementation services for multimedia marketing programs.

USWeb/CKS UK, 3 Shortlands, London W6 8DA, UK

Tel: 44-181-741-8999   Fax: 44-181-741-9413

WHX CORPORATION

110 East 59th St., New York, NY, 10022

Tel: (212) 355-5200   Fax: (212) 355-5336   www.handyharman.com

Mfr. flat-rolled steel and associated metal products.

Lucas-Milhaupt Europe, Div. Handy & Harman, 24-26 Boulton Road, Stevenage, Hertfordshire SG1 4QX, UK

Tel: 44-1438-750087   Fax: 44-1438-750098

Rigby-Maryland Ltd., Div. Handy & Harmon, Crystal Works, Union Road, Liversedge, West Yorkshire WF15 7JT, UK

Tel: 44-1924-407083   Fax: 44-1924-400071

WIDIA VALENITE INC

31700 Research Park Dr., Madison Heights, MI, 48071-4627

Tel: (248) 589-1000   Fax: (248) 597-4820   www.valenite.com

Cemented carbide, high speed steel, ceramic and diamond cutting tool products, etc.

Valenite-Modco (UK) Ltd., Unit 12, Alston Dr., Bradwell Abbey Industrial Estate, Milton Keynes MK13 9HA, UK

JOHN WILEY & SONS INC.

605 Third Ave., New York, NY, 10158-0012

Tel: (212) 850-6000   Fax: (212) 850-6088   www.wiley.com

Develops, publishes, and sells products in print and electronic media for the educational, professional, scientific, technical, medical, and consumer markets

John Wiley & Sons, Ltd, Baffins Lane, Chichester, West Sussex P019 IUD, UK

Tel: 44-1-243-779777   Fax: 44-1-243-775-878   Contact: John Jarvis, SVP

WILLAMETTE INDUSTRIES, INC.

1300 SW Fifth Ave., Ste. 3800, Portland, OR, 97201

Tel: (503) 227-5581   Fax: (503) 273-5603   www.wii.com

Mfr./sales and distribution of paper and wood products.

Willamette Europe Ltd., Maitland House, 10/F, Warrior Square, Southend-on-Sea, Essex SS1 2JY, UK

Tel: 44-1702-619044

WILLIAM MORRIS AGENCY INC.

One William Morris Place, Beverly Hills, CA, 90212

Tel: (310) 859-4000   Fax: (310) 859-4462   www.wma.com

Book, theatre, music, film, television and commercials agency.

William Morris Agency (UK) Ltd., 52/53 Poland Street, London W1F 7LX, UK

Tel: 44-207-534-6800   Fax: 44-207-534-6900

WILLIAMS MULLEN CLARK & DOBBINS

PO Box 1320, Richmond, VA, 23218-1320

Tel: (804) 643-1991   Fax: (804) 783-6507   www.wmcd.com

Engaged in international law.

Williams Mullen Clark & Dobbins, 2 Old Garden House, The Lanterns, Bridge Lane, London SW11 3AD, UK

Tel: 44-207-978-7748   Fax: 44-207-350-0156

T.D. WILLIAMSON INC.

6801 S. 65th West Avenue, Tulsa, OK, 74131-2444

Tel: (918) 447-5100   Fax: (918) 446-6327   www.tdwilliamson.com

Mfr. equipment and provide service for pipeline maintenance.

TDW, Ltd., Faraday Rd., Dorcan Way, Swindon Wiltshire SN3 5HF, UK

WILLKIE FARR & GALLAGHER

787 Seventh Avenue, New York, NY, 10019-6099

Tel: (212) 821-8000   Fax: (212) 821-8111   www.willkie.com

International law firm.

Willkie Farr & Gallagher, 35 Wilson St., London EC2M 2SJ, UK

Tel: 44-207-696-5454

WILMER, CUTLER & PICKERING (WCP)

2445 M Street, NW, Washington, DC, 20037-1420

Tel: (202) 663-6000   Fax: (202) 663-6363   www.wilmer.com

International law firm.

Wilmer, Cutler & Pickering, 4 Carlton Gardens, London SW1Y 5AA, UK

WILSON, ELSER, MOSKOWITZ, EDELMAN & DICKER LLP

150 East 42nd St., New York, NY, 10017

Tel: (212) 490-3000   Fax: (212) 490-3038   www.wemed.com

International law firm.

Wilson, Elser, Moskowitz, Edelman & Dicker, 65 Fenchurch St., London EC3M 4BE, UK

Tel: 44-20-7553-8383   Fax: 44-20-7553-8399   Contact: Thomas R. Cherry

WILTEL COMMUNICATIONS GROUP, INC.

One Technology Center, Tulsa, OK, 74103

Tel: (918) 547-6000   Fax: (918) 547-7134   www.wiltelcommunications.com

Engaged in carrier-focused fiber-optic networking and end-to-end integrated business communications solutions.

WilTel Europe, 60 Queen Victoria Street, 6th Fl., London EC4N 4SX, UK

A. WIMPFHEIMER & BRO., INC.

22 Bayview Ave., PO Box 472, Stonington, CT, 06378-1148

Tel: (860) 535-1050   Fax: (860) 535-4398   www.wimpvel.com

Mfr. of fine velvets, velveteens and corduroy.

Denholme Velvets Ltd., Halifax Road, Denholme, Bradford BD13 4EZ, UK

Tel: 44-1274-832185

WIND RIVER SYSTEMS, INC.

500 Wind River Way, Alameda, CA, 94501

Tel: (510) 748-4100   Fax: (510) 749-2010   www.isi.com

Develops and markets computer software products and services.

Wind River Systems UK, United 5 & 6 First Floor, Aston Science Park, Birmingham B7 4AZ, UK

Tel: 44-121-359-0999   Fax: 44-121-628-1889

WIRELESS FACILITIES, INC. (WFI).

4810 Eastgate Mall, San Diego, CA, 92121

Tel: (858) 228-2000   Fax: (858) 228-2001   www.wfinet.com

Engaged in the management of wireless networks.

WFI UK, 74 North Street, Guildford Surrey GU14AW, UK

WIREMOLD COMPANY INC.

PO Box 330639, West Hartford, CT, 06133-0639

Tel: (860) 233-6251   Fax: (860) 523-3699   www.wiremold.com

Mfr. noncurrent-carrying wiring devices.

Arena Cable Management, West Bromwich, UK

Davis International, Ltd., Salamandre plc, London, UK

Electrunk Ltd., London, UK

Walsall Cable Management, Ltd., West Midlands, UK

WIT SOUNDVIEW GROUP, INC.

826 Broadway, 6th Fl., New York, NY, 10003

Tel: (212) 253-4400   Fax: (212) 253-4428   www.witsoundview.com

Internet-based investment bank.

Wit Soundview Group Ltd., 120 Old Broad Street, London EC2 N1AR, UK

WITNESS SYSTEMS, INC.

300 Colonial Center Pkwy., Roswell, GA, 30076

Tel: (770) 754-1900   Fax: (707) 541-8888   www.witsys.com

Mfr. multimedia software.

Witness Systems, Eastheath Avenue, Wokingham, Berkshire RG4 12PR, UK

WJ COMMUNICATIONS INC.

401 River Oaks Pkwy., San Jose, CA, 95134

Tel: (408) 577-6200   Fax: (408) 577-6621   www.wj.com

Mfr. innovative broadband communications products for current and next generation fiber optic, broadband cable and wireless communications networks.

WJ Communications, Inc., Honeydew Cottage, Burton, Mere, Warminster BA12 6BR, UK

Tel: 44-1747-860187

WOODWARD GOVERNOR COMPANY

5001 N. Second Street, PO Box 7001, Rockford, IL, 61125-7001

Tel: (815) 877-7441   Fax: (815) 639-6033   www.woodward.com

Mfr./service speed control devices and systems for aircraft turbines, industrial engines and turbines.

Woodward Governor (UK) Ltd., 350 Basingstoke Rd., Reading, Berkshire RG2 0NY, UK

Tel: 44-118-975-2727   Fax: 44-118-975-1599   Contact: Tony Murphy   Emp: 165

WORLD COURIER INC.

45 Southfield Avenue, Ste. 3450, Stamford, CT, 06902-7210

Tel: (203) 975-9333   Fax: (203) 316-9455   www.worldcourier.com

International courier service.

World Courier (UK) Ltd., Faulkner House, Faulkner St., Manchester M1 4DU, UK

World Courier (UK) Ltd., 10-14 Bedford St., Covent Garden, London, UK

WORLD FUEL SERVICES CORPORATION

700 S. Royal Poinciana Blvd., Ste. 800, Miami Springs, FL, 33166

Tel: (305) 883-8554   Fax: (305) 887-2642   www.wfscorp.com

Provides airport services to aircraft.

Trans-Tec Services (UK) Ltd., 21/24 Millbank, London SW1 4QP, UK

WORLD MINERALS INC.

130 Castilian Drive, Santa Barbara, CA, 93117

Tel: (805) 562-0200   Fax: (805) 562-0298   www.worldminerals.com

Mfr. premium quality diatomite and perlite products.

World Minerals Ltd., Livingston Rd., Hessle Hull, North Humberside HU13 0EG, UK

WORLDCOM, INC.

500 Clinton Center Drive, Clinton, MS, 39060

Tel: (601) 360-8600   Fax: (601) 360-8616   www.wcom.com

*Telecommunications; serving local, long distance and Internet customers domestically and internationally. **Corporation under worldwide reorganization under Chapter 11 Bankruptcy; new data unavailable for this edition.*

WorldCom International, 14 Grays Inn Road, London WC1X 8HN, UK

WORLDXCHANGE COMMUNICATIONS

9999 Willow Creek Road, San Diego, CA, 92131

Tel: (858) 547-4933   Fax: (800) 995-4502   www.worldxchange.com

Provides international, long distance telecommunications services worldwide.

WorldxChange Communications, 626 Chiswick High Road, London W4 5RY, UK

Tel: 44-181-400-4400   Fax: 44-181-400-4444   Emp: 425

WORTHINGTON INDUSTRIES, INC.

1205 Dearborn Dr., Columbus, OH, 43085

Tel: (614) 438-3210   Fax: (614) 438-7948   www.worthingtonindustries.com

Mfr. flat-rolled steel.

Worthington Armstrong UK Ltd., Unit 401, Princes Way Central, Team Valley Trading Estate, Gateshead NE11 OUT, UK

Tel: 44-191-48-0606

WRIGHT MEDICAL GROUP, INC.

5677 Airline Road, Arlington, TN, 38002

Tel: (901) 867-9971   Fax: (901) 867-9534   www.wmt.com

Mfr. orthopedic reconstructive implants.

Wright Cremascoli UK, 17 Goldsworth Park Trading Estate, Woking Surrey GU21 3BA, UK

WM WRIGLEY JR. COMPANY

410 N. Michigan Ave., Chicago, IL, 60611-4287

Tel: (312) 644-2121   Fax: (312) 644-0353   www.wrigley.com

Mfr. chewing gum.

The Wrigley Company Ltd., Eastover, Plymouth, Devon PL6 7PR, UK

WRQ, INC.

1500 Dexter Avenue North, Seattle, WA, 98109

Tel: (206) 217-7100   Fax: (206) 217-7515   www.wrq.com

Mfr. software.

WRQ UK, 40 West Street Marlow, Buckinghamshire SL7 2NB, UK

WUNDERMAN

675 Avenue of the Americas, New York, NY, 10010

Tel: (212) 941-3000   Fax: (212) 941-2000   www.wunderman.com

Engaged in direct marketing.

Wunderman Ltd., Unit 3, Genesis Business Park, Albert Drive, Sheerwater, Woking Surrey GU21 5RW, UK
Wunderman UK Ltd., Greater London House, Hampstead Road, London NW17QP, UK

Tel: 44-20-7611-6666

WWF PAPER CORPORATION

Two Bala Plaza, 2nd Fl., Bala Cynwyd, PA, 19004

Tel: (610) 667-9210   Fax: (610) 667-2691   www.wwfpaper.com

Wholesale of fine papers.

WWF Paper Sales UK Ltd., Claire House, Bridge St., Leatherhead, Surrey KT22 8HY, UK

Tel: 44-1372-376133   Fax: 44-1372-374456   Contact: Roger Spikesman, Mng. Dir.

WYETH

5 Giralda Farms, Madison, NJ, 07940-0874

Tel: (973) 660-5000   Fax: (973) 660-7026   www.wyeth.com

Mfr. consumer healthcare products.

Wyeth Laboratories, Huntercombe Lane South, Taplow, Maidenhead, Berks SL6 OPH, UK

Tel: 44-1628-604-377   Fax: 44-1628-666-368

WYETH PHARMACEUTICALS

555 E. Lancaster Ave., Wayne, PA, 19087-5109

Tel: (610) 971-5400   Fax: (610) 995-4668   www.wyeth.com

Mfr. antibiotics and pharmaceutical products.

John Wyeth & Brother, Ltd., Huntercombe Lane South, Taplow Maidenhead, Berks SL6 OPH, UK

Tel: 44-1628-604-377

WYMAN-GORDON COMPANY

244 Worcester Street, North Grafton, MA, 01536-8001

Tel: (508) 839-4441   Fax: (508) 839-7500   www.wyman-gordon.com

Mfr. forging and investment casting components, composite airframe structures.

Wyman-Gordon Co., PO Box 590 Waterside North, Lincoln LN2 5XY, UK

Tel: 44-1522-525492   Fax: 44-1522-530276   Contact: David Waring

WYNN OIL COMPANY

1050 West Fifth Street, PO Box 9510, Azusa, CA, 91702-9510

Tel: (626) 334-0231   Fax: (626) 334-6463   www.wynnusa.com

Mfr. of specialty chemicals, equipment and related service programs for automotive and industrial markets.

Wynn Oil Co. (UK) Ltd., Thames Court, 2 Richfield Ave., Reading, Berkshire RG1 8EQ, UK

Tel: 44-118-950-4090   Fax: 44-118-950-4001   Contact: David Sussex, Gen. Mgr.   Emp: 12

WYSE TECHNOLOGY INC.

3471 North First Street, San Jose, CA, 95134

Tel: (408) 473-1200   Fax: (408) 473-2080   www.wyse.com

Mfr. computer network terminals.

Wyse Technology, 1 The Pavilions, Ruscombe Park, Twyford Berks RG10 9NN, UK

Tel: 44-118-934-2200   Fax: 44-118-934-0749

XANSER CORPORATION

2435 N. Central Expwy, 7th Fl., Richardson, TX, 75080

Tel: (972) 699-4000   Fax: (972) 699-4025   www.xanser.com

Engaged in information technology services.

Furmanite PLC, Furman House, Shap Road, Kendal, Cumbria LA9 6RU, UK

Contact: Peter Tetlow

XCEL ENERGY INC. (XEL)

414 Nicollet Mall, Minneapolis, MN, 55401

Tel: (612) 215-4559   Fax: (612) 215-4535   www.excelenergy.com

Electric and natural gas utility.

Yorkshire Electricity Group Plc. (XEL), Wetherby Road, Scarcroft Leeds LS14 3HS, UK

Tel: 44-11-289-2123

Yorkshire Electricity Group Plc. (XEL), 200 Clough Road, Hull HU5 1SN, UK

Tel: 44-345-413-356

XCHANGE APPLICATIONS, INC.

One Lincoln Plaza, 89 South Street, Boston, MA, 02111

Tel: (617) 737-2244   Fax: (617) 443-9143   www.xchange.com

Mfr. software.

Xchange Applications UK, 17 Great Cumberland Place, London W1H 7LA, UK

Tel: 44-207-298-0666

XELUS, INC.
290 Woodcliff Drive, Fairport, NY, 14450

Tel: (716) 248-9660   Fax: (716) 248-9199   www.xelus.com

Mfr. equipment and repair service software.

Xelus Software Limited, Parklands, Benham Valence, Newbury Berkshire RG20 8LU, UK

XEROX CORPORATION
800 Long Ridge Road, PO Box 1600, Stamford, CT, 06904

Tel: (203) 968-3000   Fax: (203) 968-4312   www.xerox.com

Mfr. document processing equipment, systems and supplies.

Xerox (UK) Ltd., 438 Midsummer Blvd., Central Milton Keynes, Milton Keynes MK9 2DZ, UK
Tel: 44-1908-692-444   Fax: 44-1908-609--225

Xerox (UK) Ltd., Bridge House, Uxbridge, Middlesex UB8 1HS, UK
Tel: 44-800-454-19   Fax: 44-1895-843-665

Xerox (UK) Ltd., Parkway, Marlow, Buckinghamshire SL7 1YL, UK

Xerox Research Centre Europe, 61 Regent Street, Cambridge CB2 1AB, UK

XILINX INC.
2100 Logic Drive, San Jose, CA, 95124-3400

Tel: (408) 559-7778   Fax: (408) 559-7114   www.xilinx.com

Programmable logic and related development systems software.

Xilinx Ltd., Benchmark House, 203 Brooklands Rd., Weybridge, Surrey KT13 ORH, UK
Tel: 44-1932-349401

XIRCOM, INC.
2300 Corporate Center Drive, Thousand Oaks, CA, 91320

Tel: (805) 376-9300   Fax: (805) 376-9311   www.xircom.com

Mfr. PC card network adapters and modems.

Xircom UK Limited, Worting House, Basingstoke, Hampshire RG23 8PY, UK
Tel: 44-1256-332-552

XL REINSURANCE AMERICA INC.
70 Seaview Ave., Stamford, CT, 06902-6040

Tel: (203) 964-5200   Fax: (203) 964-0763   www.xlcapital.com

Provides reinsurance products.

XL London Market Ltd., Fitzwilliam House, 10 St Mary Avenue, London EC3A 8NL, UK

XL Re Ltd., 12 Fenchurch Avenue, London EC3M 5BS, UK

X-RITE, INC.
3100 44th Street SW, Grandville, MI, 49418

Tel: (616) 534-7663   Fax: (616) 534-9215   www.xrite.com

Mfr. precision measurement devices, systems and processes that enhance the measurement of color, light and shape.

X-Rite Limited, The Acumen Centre, First Avenue, Poynton, Cheshire SK12 1FJ, UK
Tel: 44-1625-871100

XTRA CORPORATION
200 Nyala Farms Rd., Westport, CT, 06880

Tel: (203) 221-1005   Fax: (203) 221-9024   www.xtracorp.com

Holding company: leasing.

XTRA (UK) Leasing Ltd., Wilson's Corner, 1-5 Ingrave Rd., Bretwood, Essex CN15 8TB, UK
XTRA International, London, UK

YAHOO! INC.
701 First Avenue, Sunnyvale, CA, 94089

Tel: (408) 439-3300   Fax: (408) 439-3301   www.yahoo-inc.com

Internet media company providing specialized content, free electronic mail and community offerings and commerce.

Yahoo! UK Ltd., 80/81 St. Martin's Lane, London WC2N 4AA, UK
Tel: 44-207-664-0400   Fax: 44-207-664-0401   Contact: Fabiola Arredondo

YANTRA CORPORATION

1 Park West, Tewksbury, MA, 01876

Tel: (978) 513-6000 Fax: (978) 513-6006 www.yantra.com

Mfr. software providing supply chain solutions for the extended enterprise.

Yantra Technologies Ltd., Clivemont House, Clivemont Road, Maidenhead, Berkshire SL6 7BZ, UK

YELLOW CORPORATION

10990 Roe Ave., PO Box 7270, Overland Park, KS, 66207

Tel: (913) 696-6100 Fax: (913) 696-6116 www.yellowcorp.com

Commodity transportation.

Frans Maas (UK) Ltd., Link House, Tower Lane, Eastleigh, Hampshire S05 5NZ, UK

YORK INTERNATIONAL CORPORATION

631 South Richland Ave., York, PA, 17403

Tel: (717) 771-7890 Fax: (717) 771-6212 www.york.com

Mfr. heating, ventilating, air conditioning and refrigeration equipment.

York Intl. Ltd., Gardiners Lane S., Basildon, Essex SS14 3HE, UK

York U.K., Unit 17, Garonor Way, Royal Portbury, Bristol BS20 9XE, UK

Tel: 44-1275-375713

YOUNG & RUBICAM INC.

285 Madison Ave., New York, NY, 10017

Tel: (212) 210-3000 Fax: (212) 370-3796 www.yr.com

Advertising, public relations, direct marketing and sales promotion, corporate and product ID management.

Young & Rubicam Holdings Ltd. (European HQ), Greater London House, Hampstead Rd., London NW1 7QP, UK

Tel: 44-207-387-9366 Fax: 44-207-611-6570

YSI INC.

1700-1725 Brannum Lane, Yellow Springs, OH, 45387

Tel: (937) 767-7241 Fax: (937) 767-9353 www.ysi.com

Mfr. analyzers, measure instruments and electrical components.

YSI Ltd., Lynchford House, Lynchford Lane, Farnborough, Hampshire GU14 6LT, UK

Tel: 44-1252-514711

ZEBRA TECHNOLOGIES CORPORATION

333 Corporate Woods Pkwy., Vernon Hills, IL, 60061-3109

Tel: (847) 634-6700 Fax: (847) 913-8766 www.zebracorporation.com

Mfr. bar code systems.

Zebra Technologies Europe Limited, Pittman Way, Fulwood, Lancashire Preston PR2 9ZD, UK

Zebra Technologies Europe Limited, Zebra House, The Valley Centre, Gordon Road, High Wycombe, Buckinghamshire HP13 6EQ, UK

Tel: 44-1494-472872

ZEDTEC COMBUSTION SYSTEMS, INC.

3901 Washington Rd., Ste. 203, McMurray, PA, 15317

Tel: (724) 942-3408 Fax: (724) 942-4747 www.zedtec-usa.com

Mfr./sale/service combustion equipment for industrial furnaces in glass, forging heat treating, and aluminum industries.

Dyson/Hotwork, Bretton St., Saville Town Dewsbury, West Yorkshire WF12 9DB, UK

Tel: 44-724-942-3408 Fax: 44-724-942-4747 Contact: Dr. John Laming

ZIEBART INTERNATIONAL CORPORATION

1290 East Maple Road, Troy, MI, 48083

Tel: (248) 588-4100 Fax: (248) 588-0718 www.ziebart.com

Automotive aftermarket services.

Ziebart (EC) Ltd., PO Box 377, Eastbourne, East Sussex BN22 9QF, UK

ZIMMER HOLDINGS, INC.

345 East Main St., Warsaw, IN, 46580

Tel: (574) 267-6131   Fax: (574) 372-4988   www.zimmer.com

Engaged in design and manufacture of orthopedic products.

Zimmer Ltd., The Courtyard, Lancaster Place, South Marston Park, Swindon, Wiltshire SN3 4UQ, UK

Tel: 44-1793-58-4500

JOHN ZINK COMPANY

11920 East Apache, Tulsa, OK, 74121-1220

Tel: (918) 234-1800   Fax: (918) 234-2700   www.johnzink.com

Engaged in the development and manufacture of next-generation combustion products, technologies and clean-air solutions that power global industry.

John Zink Co. Ltd., High Common, 77 Woodside Rd., Amersham, Buckinghamshire HP6 6AA, UK

John Zink Co. Ltd., Dolphin House, 140 Windmill Road, Sunbury-on-Thames, Middlesex TW16 7HT, UK

ZOLL MEDICAL CORPORATION

32 Second Avenue, Burlington, MA, 01803

Tel: (781) 229-0020   Fax: (781) 272-5578   www.zoll.com

Mfr. electrical resuscitation devices and equipment.

ZOLL Medical UK Ltd., 49 Melford Court, Harwick Grange, Woolston, Warrington, Cheshire WAI 4RZ, UK

Tel: 44-1925-846-400

ZOOM TECHNOLOGIES, INC.

207 South Street, Boston, MA, 02111

Tel: (617) 423-1072   Fax: (617) 338-5015   www.zoomtel.com

Mfr. fax modems.

Hayes, Div. Zoom Telephonics, 430 Frimley Business Park, Frimley Camberley, Surrey GU16 5SG, UK

Tel: 44-870-720-0060   Fax: 44-870-720-0040

Estonia

AIG AMERICAN INTERNATIONAL GROUP INC.

70 Pine Street, New York, NY, 10270

Tel: (212) 770-7000   Fax: (212) 509-9705   www.aig.com

Worldwide insurance and financial services.

Seesam International Ins. Co., Vambota 6, EE-0001 Tallinn, Estonia

ANDERSEN

33 West Monroe Street, Chicago, IL, 60603

Tel: (312) 580-0033   Fax: (312) 507-6748   www.andersen.com

*Accounting and audit, tax and management consulting services. **Firm under worldwide reorganization; new data unavailable for this edition.*

Andersen Estonia AS, Parnu mnt. 21, EE-0001 Tallinn, Estonia

Tel: 372-6-266-466

AON CORPORATION

200 East Randolph, Chicago, IL, 60601

Tel: (312) 381-1000   Fax: (312) 381-6032   www.aon.com

Insurance brokers worldwide; underwrites accident and health insurance, specialty and professional insurance; and provides risk management consultation.

AON Eesti Kindlustusmaakler AS, Narva mnt. 9A, Tallinn 10117, Estonia

Contact: Kari Aitolehti

APPLERA CORPORATION

301 Merritt 7, Norwalk, CT, 06851

Tel: (203) 840-2000   Fax: (203) 840-2312   www.applera.com

Leading supplier of systems for life science research and related applications.

Applied Biosystems, Kreutzwaldi 1, EE-51014 Tartu, Estonia

AVNET INC.

2211 South 47th Street, Phoenix, AZ, 85034

Tel: (480) 643-2000   Fax: (480) 643-4670   www.avnet.com

Distributor electronic components, computers and peripherals.

Avnet Baltronic, Akadeemia tee 21F, EE-0026 Tallinn, Estonia

Tel: 372-639-7000   Fax: 372-639-7009

BATES WORLDWIDE INC.

498 Seventh Avenue, New York, NY, 10018

Tel: (212) 297-7000   Fax: (212) 986-0270   www.batesww.com

Advertising, marketing, public relations and media consulting.

Bates Estonia, Credo Reklaam AS, Aia 6, 80010 Pärnu, EE-10613 Tallinn, Estonia

Tel: 372-44-78555   Fax: 372-44-78555   Contact: R. Elsler, CEO

Bates Estonia Tallin, Endina 69, EE-006 Tallinn, Estonia

Tel: 372-6-105-800   Fax: 372-6-015-800   Contact: R. Vaga

BAX GLOBAL INC.

16808 Armstrong Ave., PO Box 19571, Irvine, CA, 92623

Tel: (949) 752-4000   Fax: (949) 260-3182   www.baxworld.com

Air freight forwarder.

Vim Agency Ltd., Lennujaama 2, Tee 2, EE-0011 Tallinn, Estonia

Tel: 372-6-388331   Fax: 372-6-388-332

BRISTOL-MYERS SQUIBB COMPANY

345 Park Ave., New York, NY, 10154-0037

Tel: (212) 546-4000   Fax: (212) 546-4020   www.bms.com

Pharmaceutical and food preparations, medical and surgical instruments.

BMS Estonia, Sepise 18, EE-11415 Tallinn, Estonia

Tel: 372-6401-1301

LEO BURNETT, DIV. B-COM 3 GROUP

35 West Wacker Drive, Chicago, IL, 60601

Tel: (312) 220-5959   Fax: (312) 220-6533   www.leoburnett.com

Engaged in advertising, marketing, media buying and planning, and public relations.

Kontuur - Leo Burnett, Tallinn, Estonia

DDB WORLDWIDE COMMUNICATIONS GROUP

437 Madison Ave., New York, NY, 10022

Tel: (212) 415-2000   Fax: (212) 415-3417   www.ddbn.com

Advertising agency.

Brand Sellers DDb Estonia, Tallinn, Estonia

DELOITTE TOUCHE TOHMATSU INTERNATIONAL

1633 Broadway, New York, NY, 10019

Tel: (212) 492-4000   Fax: (212) 392-4154   www.deloitte.com

Accounting, audit, tax and management consulting services.

Deloitte & Touche, Suur-Karja 21, EE-0001 Tallinn, Estonia

DHL WORLDWIDE EXPRESS

50 California Avenue, San Francisco, CA, 94111

Tel: (415) 677-6100   Fax: (415) 824-9700   www.dhl.com

Worldwide air express carrier.

DHL Worldwide Express, 5 Joe St., EE-0001 Tallinn, Estonia

Tel: 372-6-261083

DIAGNOSTIC PRODUCTS CORPORATION

5700 West 96th Street, Los Angeles, CA, 90045

Tel: (310) 645-8200   Fax: (310) 645-9999   www.dpcweb.com

Mfr. diagnostic products.

DPC Baltic OÜ, Pirita Tee 26B, EE-10127 Tallinn, Estonia

Tel: 372-627-93-44   Fax: 372-627-93-45

DRAKE BEAM MORIN INC.

100 Park Avenue, 11th Fl., New York, NY, 10017

Tel: (212) 692-7700   Fax: (212) 297-0426   www.dbm.com

Human resource management consulting and training.

DBM c/o MPS Mainor AS, 1 Kuhlbarsi St., EE-0001 Tallinn, Estonia

Tel: 372-620-7561   Fax: 372-620-7562

ERNST & YOUNG INTERNATIONAL

5 Times Square, New York, NY, 10036

Tel: (212) 773-3000   Fax: (212) 773-6350   www.eyi.com

Engaged in assurance and advisory business services, tax, law and corporate finance.

Ernst & Young Eesti AS, Tallinn Business Ctr., Harju St. 6, Ste. 510, EE-0001 Tallinn, Estonia

Tel: 372-6-310613   Fax: 372-6-310611   Contact: Kari Bjork

GREY GLOBAL GROUP

777 Third Ave., New York, NY, 10017

Tel: (212) 546-2000   Fax: (212) 546-1495   www.grey.com

International advertising agency.

Inorek Marketing, Tallinn, Estonia

IBM CORPORATION

1133 Westchester Avenue, White Plains, NY, 10604

Tel: (914) 765-1900   Fax: (914) 765-7382   www.ibm.com

Information products, technology and services.

IBM Estonia, Toompuiestee 33a, EE-10149 Tallinn, Estonia

JOHNSON & JOHNSON

One Johnson & Johnson Plaza, New Brunswick, NJ, 08933

Tel: (732) 524-0400   Fax: (732) 214-0334   www.jnj.com

Mfr./distributor/R&D pharmaceutical, health care and cosmetic products.

LifeScan Estonia, Paldiski mnt. 68, EST-10617 Tallinn, Estonia

JUKI UNION SPECIAL CORPORATION

8500 N.W. 17th St., Miami, FL, 33126

Tel: (305) 594-0059   Fax: (305) 594-0720   www.unionspecial.com

Mfr. sewing machines.

Pavel Ltd. Estonia, Liimi 3A, EE-0006 Tallinn, Estonia

KPMG CONSULTING INC.

1676 International Dr., McLean, VA, 22102

Tel: (703) 747-3000   Fax: (703) 747-8500   www.kpmg.com

Accounting and audit, tax and management consulting services.

KPMG International, Ahtri 10A, EE-0001 Tallinn, Estonia

Tel: 372-6-268700   Fax: 372-6-268777   Contact: Andres Root, Sr. Ptnr.

LECROY CORPORATION

700 Chestnut Ridge Road, Chestnut Ridge, NY, 10977

Tel: (845) 425-2000   Fax: (845) 425-8967   www.lecroy.com

Mfr. signal analyzers and electronic measurement systems.

LeCroy S.A., Estroonika Ou, Akadeemiatee 21 F, F101, EE-0016 Tallinn, Estonia

Tel: 372-654-2721

ELI LILLY & COMPANY

Lilly Corporate Center, Indianapolis, IN, 46285

Tel: (317) 276-2000   Fax: (317) 277-6579   www.lilly.com

Mfr. pharmaceuticals and animal health products.

Eli Lilly (Suisse) S.A., Roosikrantsi 10A-15, EE-0001 Tallinn, Estonia

Tel: 372-2-44-29-28   Fax: 372-2-44-29-28

McCANN-ERICKSON WORLDGROUP

750 Third Ave., New York, NY, 10017

Tel: (212) 697-6000   Fax: (212) 984-3575   www.mccann.com

International advertising and marketing services.

Division McCann-Erickson Tallinn, Tallinn, Estonia

McDONALD'S CORPORATION

McDonald's Plaza, Oak Brook, IL, 60523

Tel: (630) 623-3000   Fax: (630) 623-7409   www.mcdonalds.com

Fast food chain stores.

McDonald's Corp., Tallinn, Estonia

AC NIELSEN COMPANY

177 Broad Street, Stamford, CT, 06901

Tel: (203) 961-3000   Fax: (203) 961-3190   www.acnielsen.com

Engaged in market and consumer research.

ACNielsen, Narva mnt. 13a, EE-10151 Tallinn, Estonia

NRG ENERGY, INC.

901 Marquette Avenue, Ste. 2300, Minneapolis, MN, 55402

Tel: (612) 373-5300   Fax: (612) 373-5466   www.nrgenergy.com

Electric power generation.

NRGenerating International B.V., Muurivahe 41, 2/F, EE-0140 Tallinn, Estonia

Tel: 372-6-311-553   Fax: 372-6-311-554

OWENS-ILLINOIS, INC.

One SeaGate, PO Box 1035, Toledo, OH, 43666

Tel: (419) 247-5000   Fax: (419) 247-2839   www.o-i.com

Mfr. glass containers and packaging products.

A/S Jarvakandi Klaas, Tehaste 7, EE-79101 Jarvakandi, Estonia

Tel: 372-48-77285

PHARMACIA CORPORATION

100 Route 206 North, Peapack, NJ, 07977

Tel: (908) 901-8000   Fax: (908) 901-8379   www.pharmacia.com

Mfr. pharmaceuticals, agricultural products, industry chemicals.

Pharmacia & Upjohn S.A Estonia, Jalobsoni14, Kunderi 15, EE-10128 Tallinn, Estonia

Tel: 372-6-010-610   Fax: 372-6-010-611

PRICEWATERHOUSECOOPERS LLP

1301 Ave. of the Americas, New York, NY, 10019

Tel: (212) 596-7000   Fax: (212) 259-1301   www.pwcglobal.com

Accounting and auditing, tax and management, and human resource consulting services.

PriceWaterhouseCoopers, Narva mnt 9A, EE-0001 Tallinn, Estonia

Tel: 372-6-302-222   Fax: 372-6-302-220

PROCTER & GAMBLE COMPANY

One Procter & Gamble Plaza, Cincinnati, OH, 45202

Tel: (513) 983-1100   Fax: (513) 562-4500   www.pg.com

Personal care, food, laundry, cleaning and industry products.

Procter & Gamble, Peterburi tee 63, EE-0014 Tallinn, Estonia

Tel: 372-8-2-800-3000

SPSS INC.

233 S. Wacker Dr., 11th Fl., Chicago, IL, 60606

Tel: (312) 651-6000   Fax: (312) 329-3668   www.spss.com

Mfr. statistical software.

SPSS Estonia, Welzenbergl 20, EE-10150 Tallinn, Estonia

THE MARMON GROUP, INC.

200 West Adams, Ste. 2211, Chicago, IL, 60606

Tel: (312) 372-9500   Fax: (312) 845-5305   www.marmon.com

Holding company for diversified manufacturing and service firms.

Getz Estonia Ltd., 26 Ringtee St., Tartu, Estonia

Tel: 372-7-471531   Fax: 372-7-471853   Contact: Hanno Hansson

TRIPOINT GLOBAL COMMUNICATIONS

PO Box 368, Conover, NC, 28613

Tel: (828) 464-4141   Fax: (828) 464-4147   www.vertencomm.com

High-tech holding company; microwave components, amplifiers, converters, terminal network workstations, voice, video and data applications.

Tripoint Global, Forelli, 10, EE-10621 Tallinn, Estonia

Tel: 372-656-2937   Fax: 372-656-2932   Contact: Ulo Ambos, GM

UNITED PARCEL SERVICE, INC.

55 Glenlake Parkway, NE, Atlanta, GA, 30328

Tel: (404) 828-6000   Fax: (404) 828-6593   www.ups.com

International package-delivery service.

UPS Estonia - Head Office, 1 Nafta Str, EE-0001 Tallinn, Estonia

Tel: 372-6-419090

VELSICOL CHEMICAL CORPORATION

10400 West Higgins Road, Ste. 600, Rosemont, IL, 60018-3728

Tel: (847) 298-9000   Fax: (847) 298-9014   www.velsicol.com

Produces high performance specialty chemicals based on benzoic acid and cyclo pentadiene.

Velsicol Eesti, Parnu mnt. 16, Tuba 9, EE-001 Tallinn, Estonia

Tel: 372-6-314276   Fax: 372-6-314278   Contact: A. Nathan Scott, Mng. Dir.

WEIGHT WATCHERS INTERNATIONAL, INC.

175 Crossways Park Dr., Woodbury, NY, 11797

Tel: (516) 390-1400   Fax: (516) 390-1763   www.weightwatchers.com

Weight loss programs.

Weight Watchers Estonia, Forelli 12, 203, EE-10621 Tallinn, Estonia

WHIRLPOOL CORPORATION

2000 N. M-63, Benton Harbor, MI, 49022-2692

Tel: (616) 923-5000   Fax: (616) 923-5443   www.whirlpoolcorp.com

Mfr., market home appliances: Whirlpool, Roper, KitchenAid, Estate, and Inglis.

Whirlpool Eesti, Ehitajate tee 110, EE-12618 Tallinn, Estonia

YELLOW CORPORATION

10990 Roe Ave., PO Box 7270, Overland Park, KS, 66207

Tel: (913) 696-6100   Fax: (913) 696-6116   www.yellowcorp.com

Commodity transportation.

Frans Maas Expeditie B.V., Donker Duyvisweg 70, EE-3316 BL Dordrecht, Estonia

Tel: 31-78-6520-200

Ethiopia

LOUIS BERGER INTERNATIONAL INC.

100 Halsted Street, East Orange, NJ, 07019

Tel: (201) 678-1960   Fax: (201) 672-4284   www.louisberger.com

Consulting engineers, engaged in architecture, environmental and advisory services.

Louis Berger International Inc., Woreda 17, Kebele 20, PO Box 11880, Addis Ababa, Ethiopia

Tel: 251-1-183457   Fax: 251-1-615220

CROWN CORK & SEAL COMPANY, INC.

One Crown Way, Philadelphia, PA, 19154-4599

Tel: (215) 698-5100   Fax: (215) 698-5201   www.crowncork.com

Mfr. metal and plastic packaging, including steel and aluminum cans for food, beverage and household products.

Crown Cork & Can Mfr. Industries SC, PO Box 5501, Addis Ababa, Ethiopia

DANZAS AEI, INC.

120 Tokeneke Road, PO Box 1231, Darien, CT, 06820

Tel: (203) 655-7900   Fax: (203) 655-5779   www.aeilogistics.com

International air freight forwarder.

Danzas AEI/PanAfric Global p.l.c., Tsigie Marian Bldg., 2nd Fl., Churchill Ave., Addis Ababa, Ethiopia

Tel: 251-1-516-250   Fax: 251-1-612-766

DHL WORLDWIDE EXPRESS

50 California Avenue, San Francisco, CA, 94111

Tel: (415) 677-6100   Fax: (415) 824-9700   www.dhl.com

Worldwide air express carrier.

DHL Worldwide Express, Off Bole Rd., PO Box 40850, Addis Ababa, Ethiopia

Tel: 251-1-614281

HORWATH INTERNATIONAL ASSOCIATION

420 Lexington Avenue, Suite 526, New York, NY, 10170-0526

Tel: (212) 808-2000   Fax: (212) 808-2020   www.horwath.com

Public accountants and auditors.

Bocresion Haile & Co., PO Box 825, Addis Ababa, Ethiopia

IBM CORPORATION

1133 Westchester Avenue, White Plains, NY, 10604

Tel: (914) 765-1900   Fax: (914) 765-7382   www.ibm.com

Information products, technology and services.

IBM World Trade Corp., PO Box 3533, Addis Ababa, Ethiopia

LOCKHEED MARTIN CORPORATION

6801 Rockledge Drive, Bethesda, MD, 20817

Tel: (301) 897-6000   Fax: (301) 897-6652   www.imco.com

Design/mfr./management systems in fields of space, defense, energy, electronics and technical services.

Lockheed Martin Aeronautical Systems, PO Box 1755, Addis Ababa, Ethiopia

Contact: E. Cunningham, Rep.

McCANN-ERICKSON WORLDGROUP

750 Third Ave., New York, NY, 10017

Tel: (212) 697-6000   Fax: (212) 984-3575   www.mccann.com

International advertising and marketing services.

Lion McCann, Addis Ababa, Ethiopia

PIONEER HI-BRED INTERNATIONAL INC.

400 Locust Street, Ste. 800, Des Moines, IA, 50309

Tel: (515) 248-4800   Fax: (515) 248-4999   www.pioneer.com

Agricultural chemicals, farm supplies, biological products, research.

Pioneer Hi-Bred Seeds Inc., PO Box 1134, Addis Ababa, Ethiopia

SCHENKER USA INC.

150 Albany Ave., Freeport, NY, 11520

Tel: (516) 403-5416   Fax: (516) 377-3092   www.schenkerusa.com

Freight forwarders.

Shenkkor Ethiopia, Bole-Amce Rd., PO Box 3700, Addis Ababa, Ethiopia

Tel: 251-1-611-422   Fax: 251-1-611-392

STARWOOD HOTELS & RESORTS WORLDWIDE

777 Westchester Avenue, White Plains, NY, 10604

Tel: (914) 640-8100   Fax: (914) 640-8316   www.starwoodhotels.com

Hotel operations including Sheraton, Westin, St. Regis, Four Points and Caesars.

Sheraton Addis Ababa, Addis Ababa, Ethiopia

XEROX CORPORATION

800 Long Ridge Road, PO Box 1600, Stamford, CT, 06904

Tel: (203) 968-3000   Fax: (203) 968-4312   www.xerox.com

Mfr. document processing equipment, systems and supplies.

M&M Trans-Africa Trading Plc, PO Box 669, Addis Ababa, Ethiopia

Tel: 251-1-510-433

Fiji

3M (MINNESOTA MINING & MFG.)

3M Center, St. Paul, MN, 55144-1000

Tel: (651) 733-1110   Fax: (651) 733-9973   www.mmm.com

Mfr. diversified products for industry, consumer, health care, imaging, communications, transport, safety, etc.

3M Australia Pty. Ltd., PO Box 1121, Suva, Fiji

Tel: 67-9-30-4604

ANDERSEN

33 West Monroe Street, Chicago, IL, 60603

Tel: (312) 580-0033   Fax: (312) 507-6748   www.andersen.com

Accounting and audit, tax and management consulting services. **Firm under worldwide reorganization; new data unavailable for this edition.

Andersen Worldwide, Level 6, LICL House, Butt St., PO Box 855 GPO, Suva, Fiji

AON CORPORATION

200 East Randolph, Chicago, IL, 60601

Tel: (312) 381-1000   Fax: (312) 381-6032   www.aon.com

Insurance brokers worldwide; underwrites accident and health insurance, specialty and professional insurance; and provides risk management consultation.

AON Risk Services (Fiji) Ltd., 8th Fl., FNPF Place Victoria Parade, Suva, Fiji

Tel: 67-9-31-3177   Fax: 67-9-31-3373   Contact: Paul S. Dunk

BANK OF HAWAII CORPORATION

130 Merchant Street, Honolulu, HI, 96813

Tel: (808) 643-3888   Fax: (808) 537-8440   www.boh.com

Engaged in commercial and consumer banking services.

Bank of Hawaii Corporation, 15 Naviti Street, PO Box 6286, Lautoka, Fiji

BDO SEIDMAN, LLP   BELGIUM

130 East Randolph Street, Chicago, IL, 60601

Tel: (312) 856-9100   Fax: (312) 856-1379   www.bdo.com

International accounting and financial consulting firm.

BDO Zarin, Ali, PO Box 2475, Government Buildings, 8/F, Dominion House, Thompson St., Suva, Fiji

Tel: 67-9-31-4044   Fax: 67-9-30-2188   Contact: Nur Bano Ali

DANZAS AEI, INC.

120 Tokeneke Road, PO Box 1231, Darien, CT, 06820

Tel: (203) 655-7900   Fax: (203) 655-5779   www.aeilogistics.com

International air freight forwarder.

Danzas AEI, Unit 12, ATS Cargo Building, Nadi, Fiji

Tel: 67-9-72-0538   Fax: 67-9-72-0484

DELOITTE TOUCHE TOHMATSU INTERNATIONAL

1633 Broadway, New York, NY, 10019

Tel: (212) 492-4000   Fax: (212) 392-4154   www.deloitte.com

Accounting, audit, tax and management consulting services.

Vishnu Prasad & Company, PO Box 1396, Pacific House, Butt St., Suva, Fiji

DHL WORLDWIDE EXPRESS

50 California Avenue, San Francisco, CA, 94111

Tel: (415) 677-6100   Fax: (415) 824-9700   www.dhl.com

Worldwide air express carrier.

DHL Worldwide Express, 10 Holland St., Toorak, Box 13036, Suva, Fiji

Tel: 67-9-31-3166

EGL INC. (EAGLE GLOBAL LOGISTICS)

15350 Vickery Drive, Houston, TX, 77032

Tel: (281) 618-3100   Fax: (281) 618-3223   www.eagleusa.com

Ocean/air freight forwarding, customs brokerage, packing and wholesale, logistics management and insurance.

EGL Eagle Global Logistics, Office No. 125, CAAF Cargo Bldg., PO Box 9907, Nadi Airport, Fiji

Tel: 67-9-72-0333   Fax: 67-9-72-0306

ERNST & YOUNG INTERNATIONAL

5 Times Square, New York, NY, 10036

Tel: (212) 773-3000   Fax: (212) 773-6350   www.eyi.com

Engaged in assurance and advisory business services, tax, law and corporate finance.

Ernst & Young International, GPO Box 1359, Suva, Fiji

Tel: 67-9-30-2142   Fax: 67-9-30-0612   Contact: Francis Chung

FRITZ COMPANIES, INC., DIV. UPS

706 Mission Street, Ste. 900, San Francisco, CA, 94103

Tel: (415) 904-8360   Fax: (415) 904-8661   www.fritz.com

Integrated transportation, sourcing, distribution and customs brokerage services.

Fritz Companies Inc., Suva, Fiji

KOPPERS INDUSTRIES INC.

436 Seventh Ave., Pittsburgh, PA, 15219-1800

Tel: (412) 227-2000   Fax: (412) 227-2333   www.koppers.com

Construction materials and services; chemicals and building products.

Koppers-Hickson Timber, PO Box 4735, Lautoka, Fiji

KPMG CONSULTING INC.

1676 International Dr., McLean, VA, 22102

Tel: (703) 747-3000   Fax: (703) 747-8500   www.kpmg.com

Accounting and audit, tax and management consulting services.

KPMG International, Level 5, ANZ House, 25 Victoria Parade, Suva, Fiji

Tel: 67-9-30-1155   Fax: 67-9-30-1312   Contact: Brian J. Murphy, Sr. Ptnr.

KPMG International, 2nd Fl., Meghji Arjun Bldg., 157 Vitogo Parade, Lautoka, Fiji

MARSH & McLENNAN COS INC.

1166 Ave. of the Americas, New York, NY, 10036-2774

Tel: (212) 345-5000   Fax: (212) 345-4808   www.marshmac.com

Insurance agents/brokers, pension and investment management consulting services.

J&H Marsh & McLennan Ltd., 117 Vitogo Parade, Second Fl., Lautoka, Fiji

Tel: 67-9-66-2687   Fax: 67-9-66-1422   Contact: Paul Wilkins

J&H Marsh & McLennan Ltd., Level 5, Civic House, Victoria Parade, Suva, Fiji

Tel: 67-9-31-2799   Fax: 67-9-30-0737   Contact: Paul Wilkins

McDONALD'S CORPORATION

McDonald's Plaza, Oak Brook, IL, 60523

Tel: (630) 623-3000   Fax: (630) 623-7409   www.mcdonalds.com

Fast food chain stores.

McDonald's Corp., Suva, Fiji

PRICEWATERHOUSECOOPERS LLP

1301 Ave. of the Americas, New York, NY, 10019

Tel: (212) 596-7000   Fax: (212) 259-1301   www.pwcglobal.com

Accounting and auditing, tax and management, and human resource consulting services.

PriceWaterhouseCoopers, Dominion House, 6th Floor, Thomson Street, PO Box 156, Suva, Fiji

Tel: 67-9-31-3955   Fax: 67-9-30-0981

PriceWaterhouseCoopers, 131 Vitogo Parade, PO Box 514, Lautoka, Fiji

Tel: 67-9-66-1055   Fax: 67-9-66-4671

THE ST. PAUL COMPANIES, INC.

385 Washington Street, St. Paul, MN, 55102

Tel: (651) 310-7911   Fax: (651) 310-8294   www.stpaul.com

Provides investment, insurance and reinsurance services.

QBE Insurance (Fiji) Ltd., Queensland Insurance Centre, PO Box 101, Victoria Parade, Suva, Fiji

STARWOOD HOTELS & RESORTS WORLDWIDE

777 Westchester Avenue, White Plains, NY, 10604

Tel: (914) 640-8100   Fax: (914) 640-8316   www.starwoodhotels.com

Hotel operations including Sheraton, Westin, St. Regis, Four Points and Caesars.

Sheraton Fiji Resort, Denarau Beach, Nadi, Fiji

Tel: 67-9-75-0777   Fax: 679-750-818

1744

Finland

24/7 REAL MEDIA, INC.

1250 Broadway, New York, NY, 10001-3701

Tel: (212) 231-7100   Fax: (212) 760-1774   www.247media.com

Provides global online advertising, sponsorships, e-commerce and direct marketing solutions to advertisers and Web publishers.

24/7 Media Suomi, Bulevardi 13 A 9, FIN-00120 Helsinki, Finland

Tel: 358-9-540-7870

3COM CORPORATION

5400 Bayfront Plaza, Santa Clara, CA, 95052-8145

Tel: (408) 326-5000   Fax: (408) 326-5001   www.3com.com

Engaged in the development and manufacture of computer networking products and systems.

3Com Nordic, Postiosoite PL 116, FIN-01451 Vantaa, Finland

Tel: 358-9-2517-4050

3M (MINNESOTA MINING & MFG.)

3M Center, St. Paul, MN, 55144-1000

Tel: (651) 733-1110   Fax: (651) 733-9973   www.mmm.com

Mfr. diversified products for industry, consumer, health care, imaging, communications, transport, safety, etc.

3M Finland, Lars Sonckin Kaari 6, PO Box 26, FIN-02600 Espoo, Finland

Tel: 358-9-52521   Fax: 358-9-512944

AAF INTERNATIONAL (AMERICAN AIR FILTER)

10300 Ormsby Park Place, Ste. 600, Louisville, KY, 40232-5690

Tel: (502) 637-0011   Fax: (502) 637-0321   www.aafintl.com

Mfr. air filtration and pollution control and noise control equipment.

AAF Oy, Kutomotie 6B, FIN-00380 Helsinki, Finland

ABBOTT LABORATORIES

100 Abbott Park Rd., Abbott Park, IL, 60064

Tel: (847) 937-6100   Fax: (847) 937-1511   www.abbott.com

Development, manufacture and sale of diversified health care products and services.

Abbott Oyj, Pihatorma 1A, FIN-02240 Espoo, Finland

ACCENTURE LTD.

1345 Avenue of the Americas, New York, NY, 10105

Tel: (917) 452-4400   Fax: (917) 527-9915   www.accenture.com

Provides management and technology consulting services.

Accenture, Kansakoulukuja 1A, FIN-00100 Helsinki, Finland

Tel: 358-9-348-100   Fax: 358-9-693-633-50

ADVANCED MICRO DEVICES INC.

1 AMD Place, Sunnyvale, CA, 94086

Tel: (408) 732-2400   Fax: (408) 982-6164   www.amd.com

Mfr. integrated circuits for communications and computation industry.

Advanced Micro Devices AB, Pihatormae 1A, FIN-02240 Espoo, Finland

Tel: 358-9-881-3117   Fax: 358-9-804-1110

AGCO CORPORATION

4205 River Green Parkway, Duluth, GA, 30096-2568

Tel: (770) 813-9200   Fax: (770) 813-6038   www.agcocorp.com

Mfr. farm equipment and machinery.

OY Agrolux AB, Teollisuuskata 1B, PO Box 185, FIN-00511 Helsinki, Finland

AGILENT TECHNOLOGIES, INC.

395 Page Mill Road, PO Box 10395, Palo Alto, CA, 94303

Tel: (650) 752-5000   Fax: (650) 752-5633   www.agilent.com

Mfr. communications components.

Agilent Technologies Oy, Piispankalliontie 17, SF-02200 Espoo, Finland

AIG AMERICAN INTERNATIONAL GROUP INC.

70 Pine Street, New York, NY, 10270

Tel: (212) 770-7000   Fax: (212) 509-9705   www.aig.com

Worldwide insurance and financial services.

AIG Europe S.A., Unioninkatu 15, FIN-00130 Helsinki, Finland

ALBANY INTERNATIONAL CORPORATION

1373 Broadway, Albany, NY, 12204

Tel: (518) 445-2200   Fax: (518) 445-2265   www.albint.com

Mfr. broadwoven and engineered fabrics, plastic products, filtration media.

Fennofelt AB Oy, BVO Silantie 10, FIN-00390 Helsinki, Finland

ALTERA CORPORATION

101 Innovation Drive, San Jose, CA, 95134

Tel: (408) 544-7000   Fax: (408) 544-8303   www.altera.com

Mfr. high-density programmable chips for semi-conductor industry.

Altera Oy, Metsaneidonkuja 8, FIN-02130 Espoo, Finland
Tel: 358-9-43078216

AMGEN INC.

One Amgen Center Drive, Thousand Oaks, CA, 91320-1799

Tel: (805) 447-1000   Fax: (805) 499-2694   www.amgen.com

Biotechnology research and pharmaceuticals.

Amgen AB, Lukupurontie 2, PO Box 75, FIN-02201 Espoo, Finland
Tel: 358-9-549-00500   Fax: 358-9-549-00511

ANC RENTAL CORPORATION

200 S. Andrews Ave., Ft. Lauderdale, FL, 33301

Tel: (954) 320-4000   Fax: (954) 320-4077   www.ancrental.com

Engaged in car rental services, including National Car Rental and Alamo Rent A Car.

National Car Rental, Mariankatu 27, Helsinki, Finland

ANDERSEN

33 West Monroe Street, Chicago, IL, 60603

Tel: (312) 580-0033   Fax: (312) 507-6748   www.andersen.com

*Accounting and audit, tax and management consulting services. **Firm under worldwide reorganization; new data unavailable for this edition.*

Andersen Kihlman Oy, Kansakoulukuja 1 A, FIN-00100 Helsinki, Finland
Tel: 358-0-693-631

Andersen Kihlman Oy, Takojankatu 1, FIN-33540 Tampere, Finland

Arthur Andersen Kihlman Oy, Rautatienkatu 19, FIN-15110 Lahti, Finland
Tel: 358-18-752-1880

Arthur Andersen Oy, Takojankatu 1, FIN-33540 Tampere, Finland
Tel: 358-31-253-7700

Tilintarkastusosakeyhtio Soinio & Co., Veist "m"naukio 1-3, FIN-20100 Turku, Finland
Tel: 358-21-281-36816

ANDREW CORPORATION

10500 West 153rd Street, Orland Park, IL, 60462

Tel: (708) 349-3300   Fax: (708) 349-5410   www.andrew.com

Designer, manufacturer, and supplier of communications equipment, services, and systems.

Andrew Corp. Oy, Toni Tuppurainen, Urheilutie 9134, FIN-02700 Kauniainen, Finland

AON CORPORATION

200 East Randolph, Chicago, IL, 60601

Tel: (312) 381-1000   Fax: (312) 381-6032   www.aon.com

Insurance brokers worldwide; underwrites accident and health insurance, specialty and professional insurance; and provides risk management consultation.

AON Finland OY, Pohjantie 3, FIN-02100 Espoo, Finland

Tel: 358-201-266-490   Contact: Hannu Klemetti

APPLERA CORPORATION

301 Merritt 7, Norwalk, CT, 06851

Tel: (203) 840-2000   Fax: (203) 840-2312   www.applera.com

Leading supplier of systems for life science research and related applications.

Applied Biosystems, Metsanneidonkuja 8, FIN-02130 Espoo, Finland

APW, INC.

N22 W23685 Ridgeview Parkway West, Waukesha, WI, 53188-1013

Tel: (262) 523-7600   Fax: (262) 523-7624   www.apw1.com

Mfr. hi-pressure tools, vibration control products, consumables, technical furniture and enclosures.

APW Electronics, Puistotie 1, FIN-02760 Espoo, Finland

ARMSTRONG HOLDINGS, INC.

2500 Columbia Avenue, Lancaster, PA, 17604-3001

Tel: (717) 397-0611   Fax: (717) 396-2787   www.armstrong.com

Mfr. and marketing interior furnishings and specialty products for building, auto and textile industry.

Armstrong Floor Products Europe, Panimokatu IG, FIN-00580 Helsinki, Finland

Tel: 358-9-701-1511   Fax: 358-9-701-1744

ARROW ELECTRONICS INC.

25 Hub Drive, Melville, NY, 11747

Tel: (516) 391-1300   Fax: (516) 391-1640   www.arrow.com

Distributor of electronic components and computer products.

Arrow Finland, Tykistokatu 2B, FIN-20520 Turku, Finland

Arrow Northern Europe, Hankasuontie 3, FIN-00390 Helsinki, Finland

ATMEL CORPORATION

2325 Orchard Pkwy., San Jose, CA, 95131

Tel: (408) 441-0311   Fax: (408) 436-4200   www.atmel.com

Design, manufacture and marketing of advanced semiconductors.

Atmel Oy, Kappelitie 6B, FIN-02200 Espoo, Finland

Tel: 358-9-4520-820

AVERY DENNISON CORPORATION

150 N. Orange Grove Blvd., Pasadena, CA, 91103

Tel: (626) 304-2000   Fax: (626) 792-7312   www.averydennison.com

Mfr. pressure-sensitive adhesives and materials, office products, labels, tags, retail systems, Carter's Ink and specialty chemicals.

Fasson Tarra Oy, Box 217, FIN-02101 Espoo, Finland

Tel: 358-9-455-8233   Fax: 358-9-455-8501

AVID TECHNOLOGY, INC.

1 Park West, Tewksbury, MA, 01876

Tel: (978) 640-6789   Fax: (978) 640-1366   www.avid.com

Mfr. animation design software and digital and audio systems.

Avid Finland, Palkkatilankatu 1-3, FIN-00240 Helsinki, Finland

Fax: 358-9-2290-1620

AVNET INC.

2211 South 47th Street, Phoenix, AZ, 85034

Tel: (480) 643-2000   Fax: (480) 643-4670   www.avnet.com

Distributor electronic components, computers and peripherals.

Avnet Nortec OY, Italahdenkatua 18A, PL159, FIN-002111 Helsinki, Finland

Tel: 358-096-13181 Fax: 358-096-92326

AVON PRODUCTS, INC.

1345 Avenue of the Americas, New York, NY, 10105-0196

Tel: (212) 282-5000   Fax: (212) 282-6049   www.avon.com

Mfr. direct seller of cosmetics and beauty-related items.

A-Cosmetics Oy, Kutomotie 18, FIN-00380 Helsinki, Finland

Tel: 358-9-561-1510 Fax: 35-80-561-1615 Contact: Ismo Jarvinen

C. R. BARD, INC.

730 Central Ave., Murray Hill, NJ, 07974

Tel: (908) 277-8000   Fax: (908) 277-8078   www.crbard.com

Mfr. health care products.

Bard Medical Systems Oy, PL 25, FIN-00731 Helsinki, Finland

BATES WORLDWIDE INC.

498 Seventh Avenue, New York, NY, 10018

Tel: (212) 297-7000   Fax: (212) 986-0270   www.batesww.com

Advertising, marketing, public relations and media consulting.

Bates Helsinki Oy, Simonkaju 8, FIN-00100 Helsinki, Finland

Tel: 358-9-134431 Fax: 358-9-685-2446 Contact: Karl Koskinen, CEO

Bates Media, 141 Finland, Simonkatu 8, FIN-00100 Helsinki, Finland

Tel: 358-9-1344-344 Fax: 358-9-1344-3299 Contact: P. Ajanto, Dir.

BAXTER INTERNATIONAL INC.

One Baxter Parkway, Deerfield, IL, 60015

Tel: (847) 948-2000   Fax: (847) 948-3948   www.baxter.com

Mfr. products and provide services in the field of the administration of medication and bioscience.

Baxter Oy, Myyrmaentie 2 C 47, PO Box 46, FIN-01601 Vantaa, Finland

BBDO WORLDWIDE

1285 Ave. of the Americas, New York, NY, 10019

Tel: (212) 459-5000   Fax: (212) 459-6645   www.bbdo.com

Multinational group of advertising agencies.

BBDO Helsinki, Helsinki, Finland

BDO SEIDMAN, LLP   BELGIUM

130 East Randolph Street, Chicago, IL, 60601

Tel: (312) 856-9100   Fax: (312) 856-1379   www.bdo.com

International accounting and financial consulting firm.

BDO Finland OY, PL 166, Tukholmankatu 2, FIN-00251 Helsinki, Finland

Tel: 358-9-478-0812 Fax: 358-9-477-2521 Contact: Andre Kumlander

BEA SYSTEMS, INC.

2315 North First Street, St. Jose, CA, 95131

Tel: (408) 570-8000   Fax: (408) 570-8091   www.beasys.com

Develops communications management software and provider of software consulting services.

BEA Systems Oy, Westenintie 1, FIN-02160 Espoo, Finland

Tel: 358-9-502-4440   Fax: 358-9-502-44430

BEST WESTERN INTERNATIONAL

6201 North 24th Place, Phoenix, AZ, 85106

Tel: (602) 957-4200   Fax: (602) 957-5740   www.bestwestern.com

International hotel chain.

Seaside Hotel, FIN-00180 Helsinki, Finland

SAMUEL BINGHAM ENTERPRISES INC.

9529 South Main Street, Jonesboro, GA, 30236

Tel: (770) 477-7503   Fax: (770) 477-9532   www.binghamrollers.com

Mfr. rubber covered rolls, chemicals and supplies for the printing industry.

P.T. Bingham, PO Box 7, FIN-04261 Kerava 6, Finland

BIOGEN, INC.

14 Cambridge Center, Cambridge, MA, 02142

Tel: (617) 679-2000   Fax: (617) 679-2617   www.biogen.com

Engaged in medical research and development of autoimmune diseases.

Biogen Finland Oy, Pakkalankuja 6, FIN-01510 Vantaa, Finland

Tel: 358-9-77-43-7000   Fax: 358-9-77-43-7040

BLACK & DECKER CORPORATION

701 E. Joppa Road, Towson, MD, 21286

Tel: (410) 716-3900   Fax: (410) 716-2933   www.blackanddecker.com

Mfr. power tools and accessories, security hardware, small appliances, fasteners, information systems and services.

Black & Decker Finland, Attn: Finland Office, 701 East Joppa Road, Towson, MD, 21286

BMC SOFTWARE, INC.

2101 City West Blvd., Houston, TX, 77042-2827

Tel: (713) 918-8800   Fax: (713) 918-8000   www.bmc.com

Engaged in mainframe-related utilities software and services.

BMC Software, Lars Sonckin Kaari 10, FIN-02600 Espoo, Finland

BOOZ-ALLEN & HAMILTON INC.

8283 Greensboro Drive, McLean, VA, 22102

Tel: (703) 902-5000   Fax: (703) 902-3333   www.bah.com

International management and technology consultants.

Booz Allen & Hamilton, Alexandergatan 46 A, Helsinki, Finland

Tel: 358-9-61-54-600

THE BOSTON CONSULTING GROUP

Exchange Place, 31st Fl., Boston, MA, 02109

Tel: (617) 973-1200   Fax: (617) 973-1339   www.bcg.com

Management consulting company.

The Boston Consulting Group, Keskuskatu 1A, 4th Fl., FIN-00100 Helsinki, Finland

Tel: 358-9-228-661

BOWNE & COMPANY, INC.

345 Hudson Street, New York, NY, 10014

Tel: (212) 924-5500   Fax: (212) 229-3420   www.bowne.com

Financial printing and foreign language translation, localization (software), internet design and maintenance and facilities management.

Bowne Global Solutions, Piispanportti 5, FIN-00240 Espoo, Finland

Tel: 358-9-613-35-00   Fax: 358-9-613-35-390

BOYDEN CONSULTING CORPORATION

364 Elwood Ave., Hawthorne, NY, 10502

Tel: (914) 747-0093   Fax: (914) 980-6147   www.boyden.com

International executive search firm.

Boyden Associates Ltd., Etelaranta 4 B 10, FIN-00130 Helsinki, Finland

Tel: 358-9-6226-860

BOZELL GROUP

40 West 23rd Street, New York, NY, 10010

Tel: (212) 727-5000   Fax: (212) 645-9173   www.bozell.com

Advertising, marketing, public relations and media consulting.

Kauppaminos Bozell Oy, Etelaesplanadi 22A, FIN-00130 Helsinki, Finland

Tel: 358-9-478-200   Fax: 358-9-478-20400   Contact: Vesa-Pekka Leskinen, Mng. Dir.

BRANSON ULTRASONICS CORPORATION

41 Eagle Road, Danbury, CT, 06813-1961

Tel: (203) 796-0400   Fax: (203) 796-2285   www.branson-plasticsjoin.com

Engaged in design, development, manufacture and marketing of plastics joining, precision cleaning and processing equipment.

Oy Telko AB, PO Box 59, Hitsaanjankatu 9, FIN-00100 Helsinki, Finland

Tel: 358-9-615-500   Fax: 358-9-780-064

BRISTOL-MYERS SQUIBB COMPANY

345 Park Ave., New York, NY, 10154-0037

Tel: (212) 546-4000   Fax: (212) 546-4020   www.bms.com

Pharmaceutical and food preparations, medical and surgical instruments.

ConvaTec, Div. Bristol-Myers Squibb, Fredrikssgatan 33B, FIN-00120 Helsinki, Finland

Oriola Oy, PO Box 8, Oriontie 5, FIN-02101 Espoo, Finland

CADENCE DESIGN SYSTEMS, INC.

2655 Seely Ave., Bldg. 5, San Jose, CA, 95134

Tel: (408) 943-1234   Fax: (408) 943-0513   www.cadence.com

Mfr. electronic design automation software.

Cadence Design Systems, Äyritie 12 A, FIN-01510 Vantaa, Finland

Tel: 358-10-218-2200   Fax: 358-10-218-2222

CAMBREX CORPORATION

1 Meadowlands Plaza, East Rutherford, NJ, 07063

Tel: (201) 804-3000   Fax: (201) 804-9852   www.cambrex.com

human health, animal health/agriculture and Mfr. biotechnology products and produce specialty chemicals.

Timi H B Johansson Fima, Havsstrômmen 13, FIN-02320 Espoo, Finland

CANDLE CORPORATION

201 N. Douglas Street, El Segundo, CA, 90245

Tel: (310) 535-3600   Fax: (310) 727-4287   www.candle.com

Mfr. management software.

Candle Service Ltd., Aleksanterinkatu 17, FIN-00100 Helsinki, Finland

CARRIER CORPORATION

One Carrier Place, Farmington, CT, 06034-4015

Tel: (860) 674-3000   Fax: (860) 679-3010   www.carrier.com

Mfr./distributor/services A/C, heating and refrigeration equipment.

Carrier OY, Linnavourentie 28A, FIN-00950 Helsinki, Finland

Tel: 358-0-613-131   Fax: 358-0-613-13500

CASCADE CORPORATION

2201 NE 201st Ave., Fairview, OR, 97024-9718

Tel: (503) 669-6300   Fax: (503) 669-6321   www.cascor.com

Mfr. hydraulic forklift truck attachments.

Cascade Finland, Albert Petreliuksenkatu 3, FIN-01370 Vantaa, Finland

THE CHERRY CORPORATION

3600 Sunset Ave., PO Box 718, Waukegan, IL, 60087

Tel: (847) 662-9200   Fax: (847) 662-2990   www.cherrycorp.com

Mfr. electrical switches, electronic keyboards, controls and displays.

RepiComp OY, PO Box 36, FIN-00641 Helsinki, Finland

Tel: 358-9-75276650

CHESTERTON BLUMENAUER BINSWANGER

Two Logan Square, 4th Floor, Philadelphia, PA, 19103-2759

Tel: (215) 448-6000   Fax: (215) 448-6238   www.cbbi.com

Real estate and related services.

Blumenauer InterProperty International, Sateenkaari 3 A 26, FIN-02100 Helsinki, Finland

Contact: Peter Wellmann

CINCINNATI INCORPORATED

PO Box 11111, Cincinnati, OH, 45211

Tel: (513) 367-7100   Fax: (513) 367-7552   www.e-ci.com

Mfr. metal fabricating equipment.

OY Gronblom AB, PO Box 81, FIN-00811 Helsinki, Finland

Tel: 358-9-755-81   Fax: 358-9-780-715

CISCO SYSTEMS, INC.

170 West Tasman Drive, San Jose, CA, 95134-1706

Tel: (408) 526-4000   Fax: (408) 526-4100   www.cisco.com

Develop/mfr./market computer hardware and software networking systems.

Cisco Systems Finland, Jaakonkatu 2, FIN-01620 Vantaa, Finland

Tel: 358-9-878061   Fax: 358-9-5305-6775

CITIGROUP, INC.

399 Park Avenue, New York, NY, 10022

Tel: (212) 559-1000   Fax: (212) 559-3646   www.citigroup.com

Provides insurance and financial services worldwide.

Citigroup, Aleksanterinkatu 48A, PO Box 980, FIN-00101 Helsinki, Finland

Contact: Stephen L. Dwyre, Mgr.

CLEAR CHANNEL COMMUNICATIONS

200 East Basse Road, San Antonio, TX, 78209

Tel: (210) 822-2828   Fax: (210) 822-2299   www.clearchannel.com

Owns, manages, promotes and produces concerts and shows; programs and sells airtime for radio stations, owns and places outdoor advertising displays and provides agent services to athletes and broadcasters.

More Group, PO Box 23, FIN-00721 Helsinki, Finland

Tel: 358-9-8567-2700

COHERENT INC.

5100 Patrick Henry Drive, PO Box 54980, Santa Clara, CA, 95056

Tel: (408) 764-4000   Fax: (408) 764-4800   www.cohr.com

Mfr. lasers for science, industrial and medical.

Coherent Tutcore Ltd., Korkeakoulunkatu 52, POB 48, FIN-33721 Tampere, Finland

Tel: 358-3-357-1400   Fax: 358-3-318-4544

COMPUTER ASSOCIATES INTERNATIONAL INC.

One Computer Associates Plaza, Islandia, NY, 11788

Tel: (516) 342-5224   Fax: (516) 342-5329   www.cai.com

Integrated business software for enterprise computing and information management, application development, manufacturing, financial applications and professional services.

Computer Associates Finland OY, Italahdenkatu 15-17, FIN-00210 Helsinki, Finland

Tel: 358-9-34-8484

COMPUWARE CORPORATION

31440 Northwestern Hwy., Farmington Hills, MI, 48334-2564

Tel: (248) 737-7300   Fax: (248) 737-7108   www.compuware.com

Develop and market software for enterprise and e-commerce solutions.

Compuware Nordic, PO Box 38, Sornaisten Rantatie 23, FIN-00501 Helsinki, Finland

Tel: 358-9-5842-4040

CORDIS CORPORATION

PO Box 25700, Miami, FL, 33102-5700

Tel: (305) 824-2000   Fax: (305) 824-2747   www.cordis.com

Mfr. medical devices and systems.

Cordis Denmark, Metsänneidonkuja 8, FIN-02130 Espoo, Finland

CTS CORPORATION

905 Northwest Boulevard, Elkhart, IN, 46514

Tel: (219) 293-7511   Fax: (219) 293-6146   www.ctscorp.com

Mfr. designs, produces and sells passive, electro-mechanical, hybrid and interconnect components for OEMs.

CTS Wireless Components, Inc, Savilankatu 2 D 63, FIN-00250 Helsinki, Finland

CTS Wireless Components, Inc., Suonpaantie 11, FIN-21500 Piikkio, Finland

CYPRESS SEMICONDUCTOR CORPORATION

3901 N. First Street, San Jose, CA, 95134-1599

Tel: (408) 943-2600   Fax: (408) 943-2796   www.cypress.com

Mfr. integrated circuits.

Cypress Semiconductor, Unit 1606, Central Plaza, Lehdokkitie 2B, FIN-1300 Vantaa, Finland

Tel: 358-9-8511471   Fax: 358-98511482

D&B (DUN & BRADSTREET CORPORATION))

1 Diamond Hill Road, Murray Hill, NJ, 07974

Tel: (908) 665-5000   Fax: (908) 665-5524   www.dnb.com

Provides corporate credit, marketing and accounts-receivable management services and publishes financial information.

D&B, Sinimaentie 14C, Espoo, Finland

DANZAS AEI, INC.

120 Tokeneke Road, PO Box 1231, Darien, CT, 06820

Tel: (203) 655-7900   Fax: (203) 655-5779   www.aeilogistics.com

International air freight forwarder.

Danzas AEI, Koivuhaankuja 1A, FIN-01531 Vantaa, Finland

Tel: 358-9-825-4610   Fax: 358-9-825-46157

D'ARCY MASIUS BENTON & BOWLES INC. (DMB&B)

1675 Broadway, New York, NY, 10019

Tel: (212) 468-3622   Fax: (212) 468-2987   www.darcyww.com

Full service international advertising and communications group.

IMP Finland, Arkadiankatu 4C, FIN-00100 Helsinki, Finland

DDB WORLDWIDE COMMUNICATIONS GROUP

437 Madison Ave., New York, NY, 10022

Tel: (212) 415-2000   Fax: (212) 415-3417   www.ddbn.com

Advertising agency.

DDB Worldwide, Helsinki, Finland

DELOITTE TOUCHE TOHMATSU INTERNATIONAL

1633 Broadway, New York, NY, 10019

Tel: (212) 492-4000   Fax: (212) 392-4154   www.deloitte.com

Accounting, audit, tax and management consulting services.

Tuokko Deloitte & Touche Oy, PO Box 94, Munkkiniemen Puistotie 25, FIN-00330 Helsinki, Finland

DELTA AIR LINES INC.

Hartsfield International Airport, 1030 Delta Blvd., Atlanta, GA, 30320-6001

Tel: (404) 715-2600   Fax: (404) 715-5494   www.delta-air.com

Major worldwide airline; international air transport services.

Delta Air Lines Inc., Helsinki, Finland

DHL WORLDWIDE EXPRESS

50 California Avenue, San Francisco, CA, 94111

Tel: (415) 677-6100   Fax: (415) 824-9700   www.dhl.com

Worldwide air express carrier.

DHL Worldwide Express, Valimotie 7, FIN-01510 Vantaa, Finland

Tel: 358-9-777991

DIAGNOSTIC PRODUCTS CORPORATION

5700 West 96th Street, Los Angeles, CA, 90045

Tel: (310) 645-8200   Fax: (310) 645-9999   www.dpcweb.com

Mfr. diagnostic products.

DPC Finland O, Itäkatu 1-5 D 223, FIN-00930 Helsinki, Finland

Tel: 358-9-3434-960   Fax: 358-9-3434-9696

DIAMOND POWER INTERNATIONAL, INC.

PO Box 415, Lancaster, OH, 43130

Tel: (740) 687-6500   Fax: (740) 687-7430   www.diamondpower.com

Mfg. boiler cleaning equipment and ash handling systems: soot blowers, controls, diagnostics systems, gauges, OEM parts, rebuilds and field service.

Diamond Power Finland OY, PO Box 33, FIN-00701 Helsinki, Finland

Tel: 358-9-3508850   Fax: 358-9-3508850

DIONEX CORPORATION

1228 Titan Way, PO Box 3603, Sunnyvale, CA, 94086-3603

Tel: (408) 737-0700   Fax: (408) 730-9403   www.dionex.com

Develop/mfr./market chromatography systems and related products.

Oriola-Oy Prolab, PO Box 8, FIN-02101 Espoo, Finland

DOUBLECLICK, INC.

450 West 33rd Street, New York, NY, 10001

Tel: (212) 683-0001   Fax: (212) 889-0062   www.doubleclick.net

Engaged in online advertising and e-mail marketing.

Doubleclick, Ltd., Kalevankatu 30, 7 Krs, FIN-00100 Helsinki, Finland

THE DOW CHEMICAL COMPANY

2030 Dow Center, Midland, MI, 48674

Tel: (989) 636-1000   Fax: (989) 636-3228   www.dow.com

Mfr. chemicals, plastics, pharmaceuticals, agricultural products, consumer products.

Dow Suomi Oy, Palokankaantie 1, FIN-49460 Hamina, Finland

DRAFT WORLDWIDE

633 North St. Clair Street, Chicago, IL, 60611-3211

Tel: (312) 944-3500   Fax: (312) 944-3566   www.draftworldwide.com

Full service international advertising agency, engaged in brand building, direct and promotional marketing.

LAB Advertising Oy, Perameihenkatu 12E, FIN-00150 Helsinki, Finland

Tel: 358-9-622-635-20   Fax: 358-9-622-635-69

DRAKE BEAM MORIN INC.

100 Park Avenue, 11th Fl., New York, NY, 10017

Tel: (212) 692-7700   Fax: (212) 297-0426   www.dbm.com

Human resource management consulting and training.

DBM Outplacement Scandinavia Oy, Sarkiniementie 7, FIN-00210 Helsinki, Finland

Tel: 358-9-4300-0502   Fax: 358-9-4300-0301

E.I. DUPONT DE NEMOURS & COMPANY

1007 Market Street, Wilmington, DE, 19898

Tel: (302) 774-1000   Fax: (302) 774-7321   www.dupont.com

Mfr. and sales of diversified chemicals, plastics, specialty products and fibers.

DuPont Performance Coatings Scandinavia OY, Nihtisillankuja 3 A, FIN-02630 Espoo, Finland

Tel: 358-9-34-8811

EASTMAN KODAK COMPANY

343 State Street, Rochester, NY, 14650

Tel: (716) 724-4000   Fax: (716) 724-1089   www.kodak.com

Develop/mfr. photo and chemicals products, information management/video/copier systems, fibers/plastics for various industry.

Kodak Oy, PO Box 19, FIN-01511 Vantaa, Finland

ECOLAB INC.

370 N. Wabasha Street, St. Paul, MN, 55102

Tel: (651) 293-2233   Fax: (651) 293-2379   www.ecolab.com

Develop/mfr. premium cleaning, sanitizing and maintenance products and services for the hospitality, institutional, and residential markets.

Ecolab Ltd., Finland

Tel: 358-396-551

J.D. EDWARDS & COMPANY

One Technology Way, Denver, CO, 80237

Tel: (303) 334-4000   Fax: (303) 334-4970   www.jdedwards.com

Computer software products.

Major Blue Company, Vanhaistentie 1, FIN-00420 Helsinki, Finland

Tel: 358-530-531   Fax: 358-530-53300

EG&G INC.

900 Clopper Road, Ste. 200, Gaithersburg, MD, 20878

Tel: (301) 840-3000   Fax: (301) 590-0502   www.egginc.com

Diversified R/D, mfr. and services.

Wallac OY, Mustionkatu 6, PO Box 10, FIN-20101 Turku, Finland

EGL INC. (EAGLE GLOBAL LOGISTICS)

15350 Vickery Drive, Houston, TX, 77032

Tel: (281) 618-3100   Fax: (281) 618-3223   www.eagleusa.com

Ocean/air freight forwarding, customs brokerage, packing and wholesale, logistics management and insurance.

EGL Eagle Global Logistics, Siipitie 10, PO Box 15, FIN-01531 Vantaa, Finland

Tel: 358-826-133   Fax: 358-870-1482

EMC CORPORATION

35 Parkwood Drive, Hopkinton, MA, 01748-9103

Tel: (508) 435-1000   Fax: (508) 435-8884   www.emc.com

Designs/supplies intelligent enterprise storage and retrieval technology for open systems, mainframes and midrange environments.

EMC Computer-Systems Oy, Rauduntie 1, FIN-02130 Espoo, Finland

EMERSON PROCESS MANAGEMENT

8301Cameron Road, Austin, TX, 78754

Tel: (512) 834-7689   Fax: (512) 832-3232   www.frco.com

Mfr. industrial process control equipment.

Emerson Process Management, Pakkalankuja 6, FIN-01510 Vantaa, Finland

EMERY FORWARDING

One Lagoon Drive, Ste. 400, Redwood City, CA, 94065

Tel: (650) 596-9600   Fax: (650) 596-7901   www.emeryworld.com

Freight transport, global logistics and air cargo.

Emery Forwarding, Raissitie 6, FIN-O1510 Vantaa, Finland

ENGELHARD CORPORATION

101 Wood Avenue South, Iselin, NJ, 08830

Tel: (732) 205-5000   Fax: (732) 632-9253   www.engelhard.com

Mfr. pigments, additives, catalysts, chemicals, engineered materials.

Engelhard-Clal Finland, Teollisuuskatu 16, PO Box 22, FIN-20520 Turku, Finland

Tel: 358-82-23-75-648   Fax: 358-82-23-78-368

ENRON CORPORATION

1400 Smith Street, Houston, TX, 77002-7369

Tel: (713) 853-6161   Fax: (713) 853-3129   www.enron.com

Exploration, production, transportation and distribution of integrated natural gas and electricity. ****Corporation under worldwide reorganization; new data unavailable for this edition.**

Enron International Finland, Kasarmikatu 28A3, FIN-00130 Helsinki, Finland

Tel: 358-9-6815-7555

ERNST & YOUNG INTERNATIONAL

5 Times Square, New York, NY, 10036

Tel: (212) 773-3000   Fax: (212) 773-6350   www.eyi.com

Engaged in assurance and advisory business services, tax, law and corporate finance.

Tilintarkastajien Oy/Oy Ernst & Young Ab, Kaivokatu 8, FIN-00100 Helsinki, Finland

Tel: 358-0-1727-7406   Fax: 358-0-6221323   Contact: Tuula Helaniemi

ESCO TECHNOLOGIES INC.

8888 Ladue Road, Ste. 200, St. Louis, MO, 63124-2090

Tel: (314) 213-7200   Fax: (314) 213-7250   www.escostl.com

Electronic subassemblies and components.

ETS-Lindgren Ltd., Div. ESCO, Mekaanikontie 1, FIN - 27510 Eura, Finland

Tel: 358-2-8383 300

EURO RSCG WORLDWIDE

350 Hudson Street, New York, NY, 10014

Tel: (212) 886-2000   Fax: (212) 886-2016   www.eurorscg.com

International advertising agency group.

VPV EURO RSCG, Ruoholahdenkatu 26, Helsinki, Finland

EXPEDITORS INTERNATIONAL OF WASHINGTON INC.

1015 Third Avenue, 12th Fl., Seattle, WA, 98104-1182

Tel: (206) 674-3400   Fax: (206) 682-9777   www.expd.com

Air/ocean freight forwarding, customs brokerage, international logistics solutions.

Expeditors Finland Oy, Kuriiritie 15, FIN-01511 Vantaa, Finland

Tel: 358-9-870-1580   Fax: 358-9-870-1500

FORD MOTOR COMPANY

One American Road, Dearborn, MI, 48126

Tel: (313) 322-3000   Fax: (313) 322-9600   www.ford.com

Mfr./sales motor vehicles.

Oy Ford AB, Henry Fordin Katu 6, FIN-00101 Helsinki, Finland

FOSTER WHEELER LTD.

Perryville Corporate Park, Clinton, NJ, 08809-4000

Tel: (908) 730-4000   Fax: (908) 730-4100   www.fwc.com

Manufacturing, engineering and construction.

Foster Wheeler Energia Oy, Lautakunnankatu 6, PO Box 15, FIN-20781 Kaarina, Finland

Tel: 358-10-39311   Fax: 358-10-393-6300

Foster Wheeler Energia Oy, Varkaus Office, Relanderinkatua 2, PO Box 21, FIN-78201 Varkaus, Finland

Tel: 358-10-39311   Fax: 358-10-393-7689

Foster Wheeler Energia Oy, Sentnerikuja 2, PO Box 45, FIN-00441 Helsinki, Finland

Tel: 358-10-39311   Fax: 358-10-393-6199

Foster Wheeler Energia Oy, PO Box 66, FIN-48601 Karhula, Finland

Tel: 358-10-39311   Fax: 358-10-393-3309

Foster Wheeler Energia Oy, Relanderinkatua 2, PO Box 201, FIN-78201 Varkaus, Finland

Tel: 358-10-39311   Fax: 358-10-393-6162

Foster Wheeler Energia Oy, PO Box 6, FIN-45201 Kouvola, Finland

Tel: 358-10-39311   Fax: 358-10-393-3309

FRITZ COMPANIES, INC., DIV. UPS

706 Mission Street, Ste. 900, San Francisco, CA, 94103

Tel: (415) 904-8360   Fax: (415) 904-8661   www.fritz.com

Integrated transportation, sourcing, distribution and customs brokerage services.

Fritz Companies Inc., Helsinki, Finland

GARDNER-DENVER INC.

1800 Gardner Expressway, Quincy, IL, 62301

Tel: (217) 222-5400   Fax: (217) 228-8247   www.gardnerdenver.com

Mfr. portable air compressors and related drilling accessories.

Gardner Denver OY, Etu-Hankkionkatu 9, FIN-33700 Tampere, Finland

Tel: 358-205-44141

GE BETZ, DIV. GE SPECIALTY MATERIALS

4636 Somerton Road, PO Box 3002, Trevose, PA, 19053-6783

Tel: (215) 355-3300   Fax: (215) 953-5524   www.gebetz.com

Engaged in engineered chemical treatment of water and process systems in industrial, commercial and institutional facilities

GE Betz, Div. GE Specialty Materials, Tarmontie 6, FIN-15860 Hollola, Finland

GENERAL MOTORS ACCEPTANCE CORPORATION

3044 W. Grand Blvd., Detroit, MI, 48202

Tel: (313) 556-5000   Fax: (313) 556-5108   www.gmac.com

Automobile financing.

GMAC Rahoitus Oy, Kutojantie 8, FIN-02630 Espoo, Finland

GENERAL MOTORS CORPORATION

300 Renaissance Center, Detroit, MI, 48285

Tel: (313) 556-5000   Fax: (313) 556-5108   www.gm.com

Mfr. full line vehicles, automotive electronics, commercial technologies, telecommunications, space, finance.

Suomen General Motors Oy, Kutojantje 8, FIN-02630 Espoo, Finland

GEORGIA-PACIFIC GROUP

133 Peachtree Street NE, 41st Floor, Atlanta, GA, 30303

Tel: (404) 652-4000   Fax: (404) 230-7008   www.gp.com

Mfr. and distribution of tissue, pulp, paper and building products and related chemicals.

Georgia-Pacific Group, Espoo, Finland

THE GILLETTE COMPANY
Prudential Tower Building, Boston, MA, 02199

Tel: (617) 421-7000   Fax: (617) 421-7123   www.gillette.com

Develop/mfr. personal care/use products: blades and razors, toiletries, cosmetics, stationery.

Oy Gillette Finland AB, Nittykatu 8, FIN-02200 Espoo, Finland

GILSON INC.
3000 W. Beltline Hwy, PO Box 620027, Middleton, WI, 53562-0027

Tel: (608) 836-1551   Fax: (608) 831-4451   www.gilson.com

Mfr. analytical/biomedical instruments.

Norlab Oy, Vanhankyläntie 12/4, Hämeenkylän kartano, FIN-01630 Vantaa, Finland

GIW INDUSTRIES, INC.
5000 Wrightsboro Rd., Grovetown, GA, 30813

Tel: (706) 863-1011   Fax: (706) 860-5897   www.giwindustries.com

Mfr. slurry pumps.

Oy Mercantile-KSB AB, PO Box 129, Helsinki, Finland

GLEASON CORPORATION
1000 University Ave., Rochester, NY, 14692

Tel: (716) 473-1000   Fax: (716) 461-4348   www.gleasoncorp.com

Mfr. gear making machine tools; tooling and services.

Machinery Oy, Ansatie 5, FIN-01740 Vantaa, Finland

GREIF BROS. CORPORATION
425 Winer Road, Delaware, OH, 43015

Tel: (740) 549-6000   Fax: (740) 549-6100   www.greif.com

Mfr. shipping containers and containerboard products.

Van Leer Oyj, Lansituulentie 7, FIN-02100 Espoo, Finland

Tel: 358-9-6868-8361   Fax: 358-9-6868-81   Contact: Markku Pietinen

GREY GLOBAL GROUP
777 Third Ave., New York, NY, 10017

Tel: (212) 546-2000   Fax: (212) 546-1495   www.grey.com

International advertising agency.

AS & Grey, Annankatu 28, FIN-00100 Helsinki, Finland

Creator Grey, Eerikinkatu 28, FIN-00180 Helsinki, Finland

HEIDRICK & STRUGGLES INTERNATIONAL, INC.
233 South Wacker Drive, Chicago, IL, 60606

Tel: (312) 496-1200   Fax: (312) 496-1290   www.heidrick.com

Executive search firm.

Heidrick & Struggles Intl. Inc., Erottajankatu 9A, FIN-00130 Helsinki, Finland

Tel: 358-9-612-2130   Fax: 358-9-612-21340

HERCULES INC.
Hercules Plaza, 1313 N. Market Street, Wilmington, DE, 19894-0001

Tel: (302) 594-5000   Fax: (302) 594-5400   www.herc.com

Mfr. specialty chemicals, plastics, film and fibers, coatings, resins and food ingredients.

Hercules ChemicalsLtd., Tampere, Finland

Oy Hercules AB, Mannerheimintie 14A, FIN-00100 Helsinki, Finland

HEWLETT-PACKARD COMPANY
3000 Hanover Street, Palo Alto, CA, 94304-1185

Tel: (650) 857-1501   Fax: (650) 857-5518   www.hp.com

Mfr. computing, communications and measurement products and services.

Hewlett-Packard Oy, Piispankalliontie 17, FIN-02200 Espoo, Finland

Tel: 358-9-88-721

HONEYWELL INTERNATIONAL INC.

Honeywell Plaza, Minneapolis, MN, 55408

Tel: (612) 951-1000   Fax: (612) 951-8537   www.honeywell.com

Develop/mfr. controls for home and building, industry, space and aviation, burglar and fire alarm systems.

Honeywell OYJ, Ruukintie 8, FIN-02320 Espoo, Finland

Tel: 358-9-3480101   Fax: 358-9-348-01234

Honeywell Pulp & Paper, Varkaus Satakunnankatu 7, PL 168, FIN-78200 Varkaus, Finland

HORWATH INTERNATIONAL ASSOCIATION

420 Lexington Avenue, Suite 526, New York, NY, 10170-0526

Tel: (212) 808-2000   Fax: (212) 808-2020   www.horwath.com

Public accountants and auditors.

Horwath Oy Reivel, Juoksijantie 12, FIN-02580 Siuntio, Finland

Tel: 358-40-344-6000

HOUGHTON INTERNATIONAL INC.

PO Box 930, Madison & Van Buren Avenues, Valley Forge, PA, 19482-0930

Tel: (610) 666-4000   Fax: (610) 666-1376   www.houghtonintl.com

Mfr. specialty chemicals, hydraulic fluids and lubricants.

Teknoma Oy, PO Box 150, FIN-00211 Helsinki, Finland

Tel: 358-9-681021

HOWMEDICA OSTEONICS, INC.

59 Route 17 South, Allendale, NJ, 07401

Tel: (201) 507-7300   Fax: (201) 935-4873   www.howmedica.com

Mfr. of maxillofacial products (orthopedic implants).

Howmedica Finland, Helsinki, Finland

Tel: 358-9773-2277

J.M. HUBER CORPORATION

333 Thornall Street, Edison, NJ, 08818

Tel: (732) 549-8600   Fax: (732) 549-2239   www.huber.com

Diversified, multinational supplier of engineered materials, natural resources and technology-based services to customers spanning many industries, from paper and energy to plastics and construction.

Huber Engineered Materials, Hamina, Finland

HYPERION SOLUTIONS CORPORATION

1344 Crossman Avenue, Sunnyvale, CA, 94089

Tel: (408) 744-9500   Fax: (408) 744-0400   www.hyperion.com

Mfr. data analysis software tools.

Hyperion Finland, Westendintie 1-A, FIN-02160 Espoo, Finland

Tel: 358-9-439-20500

i2 TECHNOLOGIES, INC.

11701 Luna Road, Dallas, TX, 75234

Tel: (214) 860-6106   Fax: (214) 860-6060   www.i2.com

Engaged in supply chain management; solutions to help companies collaborate on decision-making processes.

i2 Technologies Finland, Eskolantie 1, FIN-00720 Helsinki, Finland

IBM CORPORATION

1133 Westchester Avenue, White Plains, NY, 10604

Tel: (914) 765-1900   Fax: (914) 765-7382   www.ibm.com

Information products, technology and services.

IBM Oy, IBM Nordic Information Center, PL 265, FIN-00101 Helsinki, Finland

Tel: 358-9-4591   Fax: 358-9-459-4442

IFR SYSTEMS, INC.

10200 West York Street, Wichita, KS, 67215-8999

Tel: (316) 522-4981   Fax: (316) 524-2623   www.ifrsys.com

Mfr. electronic test and measurement equipment.

IFR Systems, Inc., Pihatorma 1A, 3/F, FIN-02240 Espoo, Finland

INFONET SERVICES CORPORATION

2160 East Grand Ave., El Segundo, CA, 90245-1022

Tel: (310) 335-2600   Fax: (310) 335-4507   www.infonet.com

Provider of Internet services and electronic messaging services.

Oy Infonet Finland Ltd., Elimanenkatu 20, 1st Floor, FIN-00510 Helsinki, Finland

Tel: 358-2040-3737   Fax: 358-2040-3736

INGRAM MICRO INC.

1600 E. St. Andrew Place, Santa Ana, CA, 92799

Tel: (714) 566-1000   Fax: (714) 566-7940   www.ingrammicro.com

Engaged in wholesale distribution of microcomputer products.

Ingram Micro Oy, Vapaalantie 8, FIN-01650 Vantaa, Finland

INTEGRATED DEVICE TECHNOLOGY, INC. (IDT)

2975 Stender Way, Santa Clara, CA, 95054

Tel: (408) 727-6116   Fax: (408) 492-8674   www.idt.com

Mfr. high-performance semiconductors and modules.

Integrated Device Technology (IDT), Innopoli, Tekniikantie 12, FIN-02150 Espoo, Finland

Tel: 358-9-2517 3044   Fax: 358-9-2517 3045

INTER-CONTINENTAL HOTELS

3 Ravinia Drive, Suite 2900, Atlanta, GA, 30346-2149

Tel: (770) 604-2000   Fax: (770) 604-5403   www.interconti.com

Worldwide hotel and resort accommodations.

Strand Inter-Continental Helsinki, John Stenbergin Ranta 4, FIN-00530 Helsinki, Finland

Tel: 358-9-39-351   Fax: 358-9-393-5255

INTERGRAPH CORPORATION

One Madison Industrial Park, Huntsville, AL, 35894-0001

Tel: (256) 730-2000   Fax: (256) 730-7898   www.intergraph.com

Develop/mfr. interactive computer graphic systems.

Intergraph (Finland) OY, Kutojantie 11, FIN-02630 Espoo, Finland

Tel: 358-9-80-4641   Fax: 358-9-80-464333

INTERMEC TECHNOLOGIES CORPORATION

6001 36th Avenue West, PO Box 4280, Everett, WA, 98203-9280

Tel: (425) 348-2600   Fax: (425) 355-9551   www.intermec.com

Mfr. and distributor automated data collection systems.

Intermec Technologies OY, Valkjärventie 1, FIN-02130 Espoo, Finland

Tel: 358-9-523721   Fax: 358-9-529224

INTERNATIONAL PAPER COMPANY

400 Atlantic Street, Stamford, CT, 06921

Tel: (203) 541-8000   Fax: (203) 358-6444   www.ipaper.com

Mfr./distributor container board, paper and wood products.

Horsell Graafinen Oy, Rilhimietientie 4, FIN-01720 Vantaa, Finland

INTERNATIONAL RECTIFIER CORPORATION

233 Kansas Street, El Segundo, CA, 90245

Tel: (310) 322-3331   Fax: (310) 322-3332   www.irf.com

Mfr. power semiconductor components.

International Rectifier Corp., Mikkelankallio 3, FIN-02770 Espoo, Finland

Tel: 358-859-9155   Fax: 358-9-859-91560

ITT-GOULDS PUMPS INC.

2881 East Bayard Street, Seneca Falls, NY, 13148

Tel: (315) 568-2811   Fax: (315) 568-7651   www.gouldspumps.com

Mfr. industrial and water systems pumps.

Mäntän Pumppauspalvelu OY, Voimankatu 3, FIN-35820 Mänttä, Finland

Tel: 358-3-4748-136   Fax: 358-3-4748-135

J. WALTER THOMPSON COMPANY

466 Lexington Ave., New York, NY, 10017

Tel: (212) 210-7000   Fax: (212) 210-6944   www.jwt.com

International advertising and marketing services.

Thompson-Interplan, Helsinki, Finland

JUKI UNION SPECIAL CORPORATION

8500 N.W. 17th St., Miami, FL, 33126

Tel: (305) 594-0059   Fax: (305) 594-0720   www.unionspecial.com

Mfr. sewing machines.

Pavel Ltd. Finland, Melkonkatu 16B, FIN-00210 Helsinki, Finland

JUNIPER NETWORKS, INC.

1194 North Mathilda Ave., Sunnyvale, CA, 94089

Tel: (408) 745-2000   Fax: (408) 745-2100   www.juniper.net

Engaged in the design and sales of Internet Protocol routers for access networks.

Juniper Networks, Mannerheimintie 12B, FIN-00100 Helsinki, Finland

A.T. KEARNEY INC.

5400 Legacy Dr., Plano, TX, 75201

Tel: (972) 604-4600   Fax: (972) 543-7680   www.atkearney.com

Management consultants and executive search.

A. T. Kearney Oy, Metsanneidonkuja 10, PO Box 34, FIN-02131 Espoo, Finland

Tel: 358-9-751-7100

KELLOGG COMPANY

One Kellogg Square, PO Box 3599, Battle Creek, MI, 49016-3599

Tel: (616) 961-2000   Fax: (616) 961-2871   www.kelloggs.com

Mfr. ready-to-eat cereals and convenience foods.

Kellogg Finland, Attn: Finland Office, One Kellogg Square, PO Box 3599, Battle Creek, MI, 49016-3599

KENNAMETAL INC.

1600 Technology Way, PO Box 231, Latrobe, PA, 15650

Tel: (724) 539-5000   Fax: (724) 539-4710   www.kennametal.com

Tools, hard carbide and tungsten alloys for metalworking industry.

Hertek OY, FIN-05840 Hyvinkdd, Finland

Tel: 358-14-483050   Fax: 358-14-3053

KEPNER-TREGOE INC.

PO Box 704, Princeton, NJ, 08542-0740

Tel: (609) 921-2806   Fax: (609) 497-0130   www.kepner-tregoe.com

Management consulting; specializing in strategy formulation, problem solving, decision making, project management, and cost reduction.

Oy Rastor AB, Wavulinintie 3, FIN-00210 Helsinki, Finland

KIMBERLY-CLARK CORPORATION

351 Phelps Drive, Irving, TX, 75038

Tel: (972) 281-1200   Fax: (972) 281-1435   www.kimberly-clark.com

Mfr./sales/distribution of consumer tissue, household and personal care products.

Kimberly-Clark Corp., Helsinki, Finland

KORN/FERRY INTERNATIONAL

1800 Century Park East, Los Angeles, CA, 90067

Tel: (310) 843-4100   Fax: (310) 553-6452   www.kornferry.com

Engaged in executive search and management consulting.

Korn/Ferry International, Helsinki, Finland

Tel: 358-9-61-22-560   Fax: 358-9-61-22-5656

KPMG CONSULTING INC.

1676 International Dr., McLean, VA, 22102

Tel: (703) 747-3000   Fax: (703) 747-8500   www.kpmg.com

Accounting and audit, tax and management consulting services.

KPMG International, Kalcoankatu 3A, Helsinki, Finland

KPMG Wideri Oy Ab, Mannerheimintie 20 B, FIN-00100 Helsinki, Finland

Tel: 358-9-693931   Fax: 358-9-693-9399   Contact: Hannu Niilekselä, Ptnr.

KULICKE & SOFFA INDUSTRIES INC.

2101 Blair Mill Road, Willow Grove, PA, 19090

Tel: (215) 784-6000   Fax: (215) 659-7588   www.kns.com

Semiconductor assembly systems and services.

Sincotron Finland Oy, Lommilantie 1, FIN-02740 Espoo, Finland

LENNOX INTERNATIONAL

2140 Lake Park Blvd., Richardson, TX, 75080

Tel: (972) 497-5000   Fax: (972) 497-5299   www.lennoxinternational.com

Mfr. air conditioning and gas heating products.

Outokumpu Heatcraft J/V Outokumpu Oyj, Riihitontuntie 7 B, FIN-02201 Espoo, Finland

LEVI STRAUSS & COMPANY

1155 Battery St., San Francisco, CA, 94111-1230

Tel: (415) 544-6000   Fax: (415) 501-3939   www.levistrauss.com

Mfr. and distributor of casual wearing apparel, including jeans and sportswear.

Suomen Levi Strauss OY, Kaisaniemenkatu 3 B 25, FIN-00100 Helsinki, Finland

Tel: 358-962-5955   Fax: 358-962-4452

LEXMARK INTERNATIONAL

740 W. New Circle Rd., Lexington, KY, 40550

Tel: (859) 232-2000   Fax: (859) 232-1886   www.lexmark.com

Develop, manufacture, supply of printing solutions and products, including laser, inkjet, and dot matrix printers.

Lexmark Finland, Piispantilankuja 6, FIN-02240 Espoo, Finland

ELI LILLY & COMPANY

Lilly Corporate Center, Indianapolis, IN, 46285

Tel: (317) 276-2000   Fax: (317) 277-6579   www.lilly.com

Mfr. pharmaceuticals and animal health products.

Oy Eli Lilly Finland, Rajatorpantie 41C, 3rd Fl., FIN-01640 Vantaa, Finland

Tel: 358-9-854-5250   Fax: 358-9-854-2515

THE LUBRIZOL CORPORATION

29400 Lakeland Blvd., Wickliffe, OH, 44092-2298

Tel: (440) 943-4200   Fax: (440) 943-5337   www.lubrizol.com

Mfr. chemicals additives for lubricants and fuels.

Lubrizol Finland, Helsinki, Finland

Tel: 358-9-7001-7221

M/A-COM INC.

1011 Pawtucket Boulevard, Lowell, MA, 01853-3295

Tel: (978) 442-5000   Fax: (978) 442-5354   www.macom.com

Mfr. radio frequency (RF) and microwave integrated circuits and IP Networks to the wireless telecommunications and defense-related industries.

M/A-COM Ltd., Div. Tyco, Konalantie 47C, PO Box 100, FIN-00390 Helsinki, Finland

Tel: 358-9-5123-420   Fax: 3589-5123-4250

MALLINCKRODT PHARMACUTICALS, INC.

675 McDonnell Blvd., Hazelwood, MO, 63042

Tel: (314) 654-2000   Fax: (314) 654-5380   www.mallinckrodt.com

Mfr. products for respiratory care.

Mallinckrodt Finland, Kappelitie 8, FIN-02200 Espoo, Finland

Tel: 358-9-270-92900

MARK IV INDUSTRIES INC.

501 John James Audubon Pkwy., PO Box 810, Amherst, NY, 14226-0810

Tel: (716) 689-4972   Fax: (716) 689-1529   www.mark-iv.com

Mfr. of engineered systems and components utilizing mechanical and fluid power transmission, fluid transfer, and power systems and components.

M-Filter/Mark IV Automotive, PL 12, FIN-88601 Haapavesi, Finland

Tel: 358-8-452-232   Fax: 358-8-451-795

MARY KAY COSMETICS INC.

16251 No. Dallas Pkwy, Dallas, TX, 75248

Tel: (972) 687-6300   Fax: (972) 687-1609   www.marykay-cosmetic.com

Mfr. and direct sales of cosmetics and toiletries.

Mary Kay Lesley Cosmetics AB, Uggledalsvägen 21, FIN-427 40 Billdal, Finland

McCANN-ERICKSON WORLDGROUP

750 Third Ave., New York, NY, 10017

Tel: (212) 697-6000   Fax: (212) 984-3575   www.mccann.com

International advertising and marketing services.

Oy Liikemainonta-McCann AB, Keskuskatu 57, FIN-00100 Helsinki, Finland

Womena Oy, Yrjonkatu 29A, FIN-00100 Helsinki, Finland

McDONALD'S CORPORATION

McDonald's Plaza, Oak Brook, IL, 60523

Tel: (630) 623-3000   Fax: (630) 623-7409   www.mcdonalds.com

Fast food chain stores.

McDonald's Corp., Finland

McKINSEY & COMPANY

55 East 52nd Street, New York, NY, 10022

Tel: (212) 446-7000   Fax: (212) 446-8575   www.mckinsey.com

Management and business consulting services.

McKinsey & Company, Mannerheimintie 14 B, FIN-00100 Helsinki, Finland

Tel: 358-9-615-7100   Fax: 358-9-615-71200

MECHANICAL DYNAMICS, INC.

2300 Traverwood Drive, Ann Arbor, MI, 48105

Tel: (734) 994-3800   Fax: (734) 994-6418   www.adams.com

Mfr. Adams prototyping software for functional virtual prototyping solutions.

MBS Models Oy, Nihtisalontie 6, A1, FIN- 02630 Espoo, Finland

Tel: 358-9-43-926555   Fax: 358-9-43-926556

MEMOREX CORPORATION

10100 Pioneer Blvd., Ste. 110, Santa Fe Springs, CA, 90670

Tel: (562) 906-2800   Fax: (562) 906-2848   www.memorex.com

Magnetic recording tapes, etc.

Oy Memorex AB, Hopeatie 1B, PO Box 3, FIN-00400 Helsinki, Finland

MENTOR GRAPHICS

8005 SW Boeckman Road, Wilsonville, OR, 97070-7777

Tel: (503) 685-7000   Fax: (503) 685-1202   www.mentorg.com

Develop/mfr. software tools for embedded systems market.

Mentor Graphics, Metsänneidonkuja 6, FIN-02130 Espoo, Finland

MERCK & COMPANY, INC.

One Merck Drive, PO Box 100, Whitehouse Station, NJ, 08889-0100

Tel: (908) 423-1000   Fax: (908) 423-2592   www.merck.com

Pharmaceuticals, chemicals and biologicals.

Suomen MSD Oy, Maapallonkuja 1, FIN-02210 Espoo, Finland

MERCURY INTERACTIVE CORPORATION

1325 Borregas Ave., Sunnyvale, CA, 94089

Tel: (408) 822-5200   Fax: (408) 822-5300   www.merc-int.com

Mfr. computer software to decipher and eliminate "bugs" from systems.

Merury Interactive, Stella Luna, 6/F, Lars Sonckin Kaari 14, FIN-02600 Espoo, Finland

MICROSOFT CORPORATION

One Microsoft Way, Redmond, WA, 98052-6399

Tel: (425) 882-8080   Fax: (425) 936-7329   www.microsoft.com

Computer software, peripherals and services.

Microsoft Finland OY, Jaakonkatu 2, FIN-01620 Vantaa Suomi, Finland

Tel: 358-9-0525-501   Fax: 358-9-0878-8778

MILACRON INC.

2090 Florence Ave., Cincinnati, OH, 45206

Tel: (513) 487-5000   Fax: (513) 487-5057   www.milacron.com

Metalworking and plastics technologies.

Tresmeka Oy, PO Box 14, FIN-00371 Helsinki, Finland

Tel: 358-9-4764500   Fax: 358-9-4764525   Contact: Marcus Töttermann

MILLIPORE CORPORATION

80 Ashby Road, PO Box 9125, Bedford, MA, 01730

Tel: (781) 533-6000   Fax: (781) 533-3110   www.millipore.com

Mfr. flow and pressure measurement and control components; precision filters, hi-performance liquid chromatography instruments.

Millipore Oy, Ruukinkuja 1, FIN-02320 Espoo, Finland

MOLEX INC.

2222 Wellington Court, Lisle, IL, 60532

Tel: (630) 969-4550   Fax: (630) 969-1352   www.molex.com

Mfr. electronic, electrical and fiber optic interconnection products and systems, switches, application tooling.

Molex Finland, Lämmittäjänkatu 4, FIN-00810 Helsinki, Finland

MOOG INC.

300 Jamison Road, East Aurora, NY, 14052-0018

Tel: (716) 652-2000   Fax: (716) 687-4471   www.moog.com

Mfr. precision control components and systems.

Moog Finland, Tekniikanti 4, FIN-02150 Espoo, Finland

J. P. MORGAN CHASE & CO. INC.

270 Park Ave., New York, NY, 10017

Tel: (212) 270-6000   Fax: (212) 622-9030   www.jpmorganchase.com

Provides integrated financial solutions for institutions and individuals worldwide, including asset management, investment banking and commercial banking.

J. P. Morgan Chase & Co., PO Box 50, Kaivokatu 10A, FIN-00100 Helsinki, Finland

MOTOROLA, INC.

1303 East Algonquin Road, Schaumburg, IL, 60196

Tel: (847) 576-5000   Fax: (847) 538-5191   www.motorola.com

Mfr. communications equipment, semiconductors and cellular phones.

Motorola Finland AB, Hopeatie 2, FIN-00440 Helsinki, Finland

Tel: 358-9-6866-880   Fax: 358-9-676-287

NATIONAL INSTRUMENTS CORPORATION

11550 N. Mopac Expwy., Austin, TX, 78759-3504

Tel: (512) 338-9119   Fax: (512) 794-5794   www.ni.com

Mfr. hardware and graphical software.

National Instruments Finland Oy, PL 2, Sinikalliontie 9, FIN-02631 Espoo, Finland

NATIONAL STARCH AND CHEMICAL COMPANY

10 Finderne Ave., Bridgewater, NJ, 08807-3300

Tel: (908) 685-5000   Fax: (908) 685-5005   www.nationalstarch.com

Mfr. adhesives and sealants, resins and specialty chemicals, electronic materials and adhesives, food products, industry starch.

National Starch & Chemical AB, Pihatorma 1 A, FIN-02240 Espoo Helsinki, Finland

Tel: 358-9-2709-5436   Fax: 358-9-2709-5437

NETEGRITY, INC.

52 Second Avenue, Waltham, MA, 02154

Tel: (781) 890-1700   Fax: (781) 487-7791   www.netegrity.com

Mfr. security software.

Netegrity, Tilanhoitajankaari 22 C 51, FIN-00710 Helsinki, Finland

Tel: 358-9-3863890   Fax: 358-9-3863890

NETWORK ASSOCIATES, INC.

3965 Freedom Circle, Santa Clara, CA, 95054

Tel: (408) 988-3832   Fax: (408) 970-9727   www.networkassociates.com

Designs and produces network security and network management software and hardware.

Network Associates Oy, Mikonkatu 9, 5/F, FIN-00100 Helsinki, Finland

Tel: 358-9-527-070   Fax: 358-9-5270-7100

AC NIELSEN COMPANY

177 Broad Street, Stamford, CT, 06901

Tel: (203) 961-3000   Fax: (203) 961-3190   www.acnielsen.com

Engaged in market and consumer research.

ACNielsen, Tietajantie 14, FIN-02130 Espoo, Finland

NORDSON CORPORATION

28601 Clemens Road, Westlake, OH, 44145-4551

Tel: (440) 892-1580   Fax: (440) 892-9507   www.nordson.com

Mfr. industry application equipment, sealants and packaging machinery.

Nordson Finland Oy, Pihkatie 4, FIN-00410 Helsinki, Finland

Tel: 358-9-530-8080   Fax: 358-9-530-80850

NOVELL WORLDWIDE

1800 S. Novell Place, Provo, UT, 84606

Tel: (801) 861-7000   Fax: (801) 861-5555   www.novell.com

Develop/mfr. networking software and related equipment.

Novell Finland Oy, Lars Sockin kaari 14, FIN-02600 Espoo, Finland

OM GROUP, INC. (OMG)

3500 Terminal Tower, Cleveland, OH, 44113-2203

Tel: (216) 781-0083   Fax: (216) 781-0902   www.omgi.com

Producer and marketer of metal-based specialty chemicals.

Kokkola Chemicals Oy, Outokummuntie 6, FIN-67101 Kokkola, Finland

Tel: 358-6-8280 111

ONDEO NALCO COMPANY

Ondeo Nalco Center, 1601 W. Diehl Road, Naperville, IL, 60563-1198

Tel: (630) 305-1000   Fax: (630) 305-2900   www.ondeo-nalco.com

Mfr. specialty chemicals for water and waste water treatment, oil products and refining, industry processes; water and energy management service.

Suomen ONDEO Nalco Oy, Mikonkatu 8 A 9 KRS, FIN-00100 Helsinki, Finland

Tel: 358-9-4354-3360   Fax: 358-9-4354-3367

ORACLE CORPORATION

500 Oracle Parkway, Redwood Shores, CA, 94065

Tel: (650) 506-7000   Fax: (650) 506-7200   www.oracle.com

Develop/manufacture software.

Oracle Finland, Piispanportti 10, PO Box 47, FIN-02200 Espoo, Finland

OSMOSE INTERNATIONAL INC.

980 Ellicott Street, Buffalo, NY, 14209

Tel: (716) 882-5905   Fax: (716) 882-5139   www.osmose.com

Mfr. wood preservatives; maintenance and inspection utility poles, railroad track and marine piling.

Injecta Osmose A/S, PL 72, FIN-00131 Helsinki, Finland

Tel: 46-0-431-54766

OTIS ELEVATOR COMPANY

One Farm Springs Road, Farmington, CT, 06032

Tel: (860) 676-6000   Fax: (860) 676-5111   www.otis.com

Mfr. elevators and escalators.

Otis Oy, Vesimyllynkatu 3, PO Box 473, FIN-33310 Tampere, Finland

OWENS-ILLINOIS, INC.

One SeaGate, PO Box 1035, Toledo, OH, 43666

Tel: (419) 247-5000   Fax: (419) 247-2839   www.o-i.com

Mfr. glass containers and packaging products.

Karbulan Lasi Oy, PL 18, FIN-48601 Karhula, Finland

Tel: 358-5-224-2711   Fax: 358-5-224-2700

PANAMETRICS

221 Crescent Street, Waltham, MA, 02154

Tel: (781) 899-2719   Fax: (781) 899-1552   www.panametrics.com

Engaged in manufacture and distribution of ultrasonic testing equipment and process control instrumentation.

Orion Corporation, Ltd./Medion, Nilsiankatu 10-14, FIN-00510 Helsinki, Finland

Tel: 358-9-39371 Fax: 358-9-7018398   Contact: Ken Enberg

PARAMETRIC TECHNOLOGY CORPORATION

140 Kendrick St., Needham, MA, 02494

Tel: (781) 370-5000   Fax: (781) 370-6000   www.ptc.com

Supplier of mechanical design automation and product data management software and services.

Parametric Technology (Findland) Oy, Piispantilankuja 4, FIN-02240 Espoo, Finland

Tel: 358-9-8870-650   Fax: 358-9-8870-6525

PARKER HANNIFIN CORPORATION

6035 Parkland Blvd., Cleveland, OH, 44124-4141

Tel: (216) 896-3000   Fax: (216) 896-4000   www.parker.com

Mfr. motion-control products.

Oy Parker Hannifin (Finland), Ylastontie 16, FIN-01510 Vantaa, Finland
Parker Hannifin OY, Finn-Filter Div., FIN-31700 Urjala AS, Finland
Tel: 358-3-54100

PENWEST PHARMACEUTICAL CO.

2981 Route 22, Patterson, NY, 12563-9970

Tel: (845) 878-3414   Fax: (845) 878-3484   www.penw.com

Engaged in the research, development and commercialization of novel drug delivery technologies.

Penwest Pharmaceuticals Oy, Maitotie 4, FIN-15560 Nastola, Finland

PEREGRINE SYSTEMS, INC.

3611 Valley Centre Drive, San Diego, CA, 92130

Tel: (858) 481-5000   Fax: (858) 481-1751   www.peregrine.com

Mfr. resource planning software.

Peregrine Systems Oy, Metsänneidonkuja 8, FIN-02130 02130, Finland
Contact: Sinikka Semenoja

PERKIN ELMER, INC.

45 William Street, Wellesley, MA, 02481

Tel: (781) 237-5100   Fax: (781) 431-4255   www.perkinelmer.com

Mfr. equipment and devices to detect explosives and bombs on airline carriers.

PerkinElmer Life Sciences, PO Box 10, FIN-20101 Turku, Finland

PFIZER INC.

235 East 42nd Street, New York, NY, 10017-5755

Tel: (212) 573-2323   Fax: (212) 573-7851   www.pfizer.com

Research-based, global health care company.

Pfizer Oy, Tapiontori, Tapiola, Keskustorni, 3rd Fl, FIN-02100 Espoo, Finland

PHARMACIA CORPORATION

100 Route 206 North, Peapack, NJ, 07977

Tel: (908) 901-8000   Fax: (908) 901-8379   www.pharmacia.com

Mfr. pharmaceuticals, agricultural products, industry chemicals.

Pharmacia & Upjohn OY, Rajatorpantie 41C, 5th Floor, FIN-01640 Vantaa, Finland
Tel: 358-9-852-071   Fax: 358-9-852-1146

PITNEY BOWES INC.

1 Elmcroft Road, Stamford, CT, 06926-0700

Tel: (203) 356-5000   Fax: (203) 351-6835   www.pitneybowes.com

Mfr. postage meters, mailroom equipment, copiers, bus supplies, bus services, facsimile systems and financial services.

Pitney Bowes Oy, PL 109, FIN-00211 Helsinki, Finland
Tel: 358-0-692-5600   Fax: 358-0-692-6227   Contact: Kari Jantti, Mng. Dir.   Emp: 45

PLANAR SYSTEMS, INC.

1400 NW Compton Drive, Beaverton, OR, 97006

Tel: (503) 690-1100   Fax: (503) 690-1541   www.planar.com

Mfr. of flat panel displays and liquid crystal displays.

Planar Systems, Inc., European Hdqrts., Olarinluoma 9, PO Box 46, FIN-02201 Espoo, Finland
Tel: 358-9-4200-1   Fax: 358-9-4200-200

PLANET HOLLYWOOD INTERNATIONAL, INC.

8669 Commodity Circle, Orlando, FL, 32819

Tel: (407) 363-7827   Fax: (407) 363-4862   www.planethollywood.com

Theme-dining restaurant chain and merchandise retail stores.

Planet Hollywood International, Inc., Helsinki, Finland

POLAROID CORPORATION

784 Memorial Drive, Cambridge, MA, 02139

Tel: (781) 386-2000   Fax: (781) 386-3924   www.polaroid.com

Photographic equipment and supplies, optical products.

Polaroid Finland, Sinikalliontie 10, FIN-SF 02630 Espoo, Finland

POWERWARE CORPORATION

8609 Six Forks Road, Raleigh, NC, 27615

Tel: (919) 870-3020   Fax: (919) 870-3100   www.powerware.com

Mfr./services uninterruptible power supplies and related equipment.

Powerware Electronics Oy, Koskelontie 13, FIN-02920 Espoo, Finland

Tel: 358-9-452-661   Fax: 358-9-452-66568

PRICEWATERHOUSECOOPERS LLP

1301 Ave. of the Americas, New York, NY, 10019

Tel: (212) 596-7000   Fax: (212) 259-1301   www.pwcglobal.com

Accounting and auditing, tax and management, and human resource consulting services.

PriceWaterhouseCoopers, Vattuniemenranta 2, FIN-00210 Helsinki, Finland

Tel: 358-0-673-011   Fax: 358-0-674-118

PriceWaterhouseCoopers, Kehrasaari B, FIN-33200 Tampere, Finland

Tel: 358-31-242-8656   Fax: 358-31-2122-987

PROCTER & GAMBLE COMPANY

One Procter & Gamble Plaza, Cincinnati, OH, 45202

Tel: (513) 983-1100   Fax: (513) 562-4500   www.pg.com

Personal care, food, laundry, cleaning and industry products.

Procter & Gamble Nordic, Pl 173, Lars Sonckin Kaari 10, FIN-02601 Espoo, Finland

Procter & Gamble Oy, Kuluttajapalvelu Pl 73, FIN-00701 Helsinki, Finland

Tel: 358-9-203-25525

QUINTILES TRANSNATIONAL CORPORATION

4709 Creekstone Dr., Durham, NC, 27703

Tel: (919) 998-2000   Fax: (919) 998-9113   www.quintiles.com

Mfr. pharmaceuticals.

Quintiles OY, Tapiola Spektri Pilotti Building, 3F, ValkjSrventie 2, FIN-02130 Espoo, Finland

QWEST COMMUNICATIONS INTERNATIONAL INC.

1801 California Street, Ste. 5200, Denver, CO, 80202

Tel: (303) 896-2020   Fax: (303) 793-6654   www.uswest.com

Tele-communications provider; integrated communications services.

KPNQwest (JV), Helsinki, Finland

RADISSON HOTELS INTERNATIONAL

Carlson Pkwy., PO Box 59159, Minneapolis, MN, 55459-8204

Tel: (612) 540-5526   Fax: (612) 449-3400   www.radisson.com

Operates, manages and franchises full-service hotels and resorts worldwide.

Radisson SAS Royal Hotel Helsinki, Runeberginkatu 1, FIN-00100 Helsinki, Finland

Tel: 358-9-69-580   Fax: 358-9-69-587100

RATIONAL SOFTWARE CORPORATION

18880 Homestead Road, Cupertino, CA, 95014-0721

Tel: (408) 863-9900   Fax: (408) 863-4120   www.rationale.com

Mfr. application development software.

Rational Software Finland Oy, Stella Business Park, Lars Sonckin Kaari 16, FIN-02600 Espoo, Finland

RAY & BERNDTSON, INC.

301 Commerce, Ste. 2300, Fort Worth, TX, 76102

Tel: (817) 334-0500   Fax: (817) 334-0779   www.prb.com

Executive search, management audit and management consulting firm.

Ray & Berndtson, Bulevardi 5A, FIN-00120 Helsinki, Finland

Tel: 358-0-607300   Fax: 358-0-6801390   Contact: Finn Wardi, Mng. Ptnr.

RAZORFISH, INC.

32 Mercer Street, New York, NY, 10013

Tel: (212) 966-5960   Fax: (212) 966-6915   www.razorfish.com

Engaged in consulting and web services.

Razorfish Finland, Lapuankatu 4, FIN-00100 Helsinki, Finland

Tel: 358-9-41580800

READER'S DIGEST ASSOCIATION, INC.

Reader's Digest Rd., Pleasantville, NY, 10570

Tel: (914) 238-1000   Fax: (914) 238-4559   www.readersdigest.com

Publisher of magazines and books and direct mail marketer.

Reader's Digest AB Oy Valitut Palat, Sentnerikuja 5, FIN-00440 Helsinki, Finland

RICHCO, INC.

5825 N. Tripp Ave., PO Box 804238, Chicago, IL, 60680

Tel: (773) 539-4060   Fax: (773) 539-6770   www.richco.com

Mfr. quality plastic fasteners, wire management devices, circuit board hardware, and custom components.

Richco Finland, Riihltontuntle 2, FIN-02200 Espoo, Finland

Tel: 358-9-412-9170

SANMINA-SCI CORPORATION

2700 North First Street, San Jose, CA, 95134

Tel: (408) 964-3500   Fax: (408) 964-3799   www.sanmina-sci.com

Engaged in electronics contract manufacturing.

Sanmina Corporation, Teollisuuskatu 1, PO Box 60, FIN-44100 Aanckoski, Finland

Tel: 358-14-348-800   Fax: 358-14-348-8120

Sanmina-SCI Finland, Box 60, FIN 44101 Aanekoski, Finland

Tel: 46-6016-1100   Fax: 46-6016-1123

Sanmina-SCI Finland, Box 28, FIN-41161 Tikkakoski, Finland

Tel: 46-6016-1100   Fax: 46-6016-1123

SAS INSTITUTE INC.

SAS Campus Drive, Cary, NC, 27513

Tel: (919) 677-8000   Fax: (919) 677-4444   www.sas.com

Mfr. and distribution of decision support software.

SAS Institute (Finland) Ltd., Espoo, Finland

Tel: 358-9-5255-71   Fax: 358-9-5255-7200

SCHENKER USA INC.

150 Albany Ave., Freeport, NY, 11520

Tel: (516) 403-5416   Fax: (516) 377-3092   www.schenkerusa.com

Freight forwarders.

Schenker Kaukokiito Oy, Manttaalitie 7, PO Box 76, FIN-01530 Vantaa, Finland

Tel: 358-9-7561-1   Fax: 358-9-7561-425

SEALED AIR CORPORATION

Park 80 East, Saddle Brook, NJ, 07663

Tel: (201) 791-7600   Fax: (201) 703-4205   www.sealedaircorp.com

Mfr. protective and specialty packaging solutions for industrial, food and consumer products.

Sealed Air Oy, Kaavakuja 3, FIN-36220 Kangasala, Finland

Tel: 358-3-379-2510   Fax: 358-3-379-2508

G.D. SEARLE & COMPANY

5200 Old Orchard Road, Skokie, IL, 60077

Tel: (847) 982-7000   Fax: (847) 470-1480   www.searlehealthnet.com

Mfr. pharmaceuticals, health care, optical products and specialty chemicals.

Searle, UCB Pharma oy Finland, Maistraatinportti 2, FIN-00240 Helsinka, Finland

Tel: 358-0-1594-3040   Fax: 358-0-278-6828

THE SERVICEMASTER COMPANY

2300 Warrenville Road, Downers Grove, IL, 60515-1700

Tel: (630) 271-1300   Fax: (630) 271-2710   www.svm.com

Provides residential consumer services, including lawn care and landscape maintenance, termite and pest control, plumbing, heating and air conditioning maintenance and repair.

ServiceMaster, Helsinki, Finland

SKYWORKS SOLUTIONS, INC.

20 Sylvan Road, Woburn, MA, 01801

Tel: (781) 935-5150   Fax: (781) 824-4579   www.skyworksinc.com

Mfr. electronic and microwave components.

Skyworks Solutions, Regus Business Centre Kone Building,, Keilasatama 3, FIN-02150 Espoo, Finland

Contact: Pasi Ikonen

SOTHEBY'S HOLDINGS, INC.

1334 York Avenue, New York, NY, 10021

Tel: (212) 606-7000   Fax: (212) 606-7027   www.sothebys.com

Auction house specializing in fine art and jewelry.

Sotheby's Holdings, Inc., Bernhardinkatu 1B, FIN-00130 Helsinki, Finland

Tel: 358-962-21558   Contact: Claire Svartstrom

SPSS INC.

233 S. Wacker Dr., 11th Fl., Chicago, IL, 60606

Tel: (312) 651-6000   Fax: (312) 329-3668   www.spss.com

Mfr. statistical software.

SPSS Finland Oy, Sinikalliontie 12, FIN-02630 Espoo, Finland

SSA GLOBAL TECHNOLOGIES, INC.

500 W. Madison St., Ste. 3200, Chicago, IL, 60661

Tel: (312) 258-6000   Fax: (312) 474-7500   www.ssax.com

Mfr. computer software.

SSA Global, Helsinki, Finland

THE ST. PAUL COMPANIES, INC.

385 Washington Street, St. Paul, MN, 55102

Tel: (651) 310-7911   Fax: (651) 310-8294   www.stpaul.com

Provides investment, insurance and reinsurance services.

Enterprise Fennia Mutual Insurance Company, Asemamiehenkatu 3, FIN-00520 Helsinki, Finland

THE STANLEY WORKS

1000 Stanley Drive, PO Box 7000, New Britain, CT, 06053

Tel: (860) 225-5111   Fax: (860) 827-3987   www.stanleyworks.com

Mfr. hand tools and hardware.

Stanley Tools Suomen Stanley Oy, PL 186, FIN-01511 Vanta, Finland

STERIS CORPORATION

5960 Heisley Road, Mentor, OH, 44060

Tel: (440) 354-2600   Fax: (440) 639-4459   www.steris.com

Mfr. sterilization and infection control equipment, surgical tables, lighting systems for health, pharmaceutical and scientific industries.

Steris Corporation, Teollisuustie 2, FIN-04300 Tuusula, Finland

Steris Corporation, Tuusula, Finland

STORAGE TECHNOLOGY CORPORATION

One Storagetech Dr., Louisville, CO, 80028-4377

Tel: (303) 673-5151   Fax: (303) 673-5019   www.stortek.com

Mfr., market, service information, storage and retrieval systems.

StorageTek OY, Sinikalliontie 10, FIN-02630 Helsinki, Finland

Tel: 358-9-5259900 Fax: 358-9-52599040 Contact: Magnus Åström

STOWE WOODWARD MOUNT HOPE

One Technology Drive, Westborough, MA, 01581

Tel: (508) 616-9458   Fax: (508) 616-9479   www.stowewoodward.com

Mfr. roll covering and bowed roll technologies for the web handling industries.

Stowe Woodward Finland Oy, Box 7, FIN-04261 Kerava, Finland

SUN MICROSYSTEMS, INC.

901 San Antonio Road, Palo Alto, CA, 94303

Tel: (650) 960-1300   Fax: (650) 961-9131   www.sun.com

Computer peripherals and programming services.

Sun Microsystems Oy, Niittymaentie 9, FIN-02200 Espoo, Finland

SYBASE, INC.

5000 Hacienda Dr., Dublin, CA, 94568

Tel: (925) 236-5000   Fax: (925) 236-4321   www.sybase.com

Design/mfg/distribution of database management systems, software development tools, connectivity products, consulting and technical support services..

Sybase Finland OY, Jaakonkatu 2, FIN-01620 Vantaa, Finland

Tel: 358-9-7250-2200   Fax: 358-9-7250-2201

SYKES ENTERPRISES, INC.

100 N. Tampa Street, Ste. 3900, Tampa, FL, 33602

Tel: (813) 274-1000   Fax: (813) 273-0148   www.sykes.com

Provides information technology outsourcing services.

Sykes Enterprises, Mustionkatu 2, FIN-20750 Turku, Finland

SYMBOL TECHNOLOGIES, INC.

One Symbol Plaza, Holtsville, NY, 11742-1300

Tel: (631) 738-2400   Fax: (631) 738-5990   www.symbol.com

Mfr. Bar code-driven data management systems, wireless LAN's, and Portable Shopping System™.

Symbol Technologies Finland, Kaupintie 8A, Helsinki, Finland

Tel: 358-9-5407-580

SYNOPSYS, INC.

700 East Middlefield Road, Mountain View, CA, 94043

Tel: (650) 962-5000   Fax: (650) 965-8637   www.synopsys.com

Mfr. electronic design automation software.

Synopsys Oy, Lars Sonckin Kaari 14, FIN-02600 Espoo, Finland

Tel: 358-9-5406-4500   Fax: 358-9-5406-4519

TBWA WORLDWIDE

488 Madison Avenue, 6th Floor, New York, NY, 10022

Tel: (212) 804-1000   Fax: (212) 804-1200   www.tbwachiat.com

International full service advertising agency.

Paltemaa Huttunen Santala, Helsinki, Finland

TEKTRONIX INC.

14200 SW Karl Braun Dr., PO Box 500, Beaverton, OR, 97077

Tel: (503) 627-7111   Fax: (503) 627-2406   www.tek.com

Mfr. test and measure, visual systems/color printing and communications/video and networking products.

Tektronix Oy, Piispantilankuja 2, FIN-02240 Espoo Helsinki, Finland

Tel: 358-9-4783-400 Fax: 358-9-4783-4200

TELLABS INC.

1415 W. Diehl Rd., Naperville, IL, 60563

Tel: (630) 378-8800   Fax: (630) 852-7346   www.tellabs.com

Design/mfr./service voice/data transport and network access systems.

Tellabs Espoo, Sinikalliontie 7, FIN-02630 Espoo, Finland

TERADATA

1700 South Patterson Blvd., Dayton, OH, 45479

Tel: (937) 445-5000   Fax: (937) 445-1682   www.teradata.com

Mfr. software to store information.

Teradata Div., NCR, Valkjarventie 7A, FIN-02130 Espoo, Finland

Teradata Div., NCR, Valkjarventie 7A, FIN-02130 Espoo, Finland

TEXAS INSTRUMENTS INC.

12500 TI Blvd., Dallas, TX, 75266

Tel: (972) 995-3773   Fax: (972) 995-4360   www.ti.com

Mfr. semiconductor devices, electronic electro-mechanical systems, instruments and controls.

Texas Instruments, Helsinki, Finland

THE MARMON GROUP, INC.

200 West Adams, Ste. 2211, Chicago, IL, 60606

Tel: (312) 372-9500   Fax: (312) 845-5305   www.marmon.com

Holding company for diversified manufacturing and service firms.

Getz Bros. & Co. (Finland) Oy, FIN-15141 Lahti, Finland

Tel: 358-3-752-5182   Fax: 358-3-752-5192   Contact: N. Suti, Gen. Mgr.   Emp: 1

TOGETHERSOFT CORPORATION

900 Main Campus Drive, Ste. 500, Raleigh, NC, 27606

Tel: (919) 833-5550   Fax: (919) 833-5533   www.togethersoft.com

Mfr. software.

TogetherSoft Finland, Spektri Business Park, Metsanneldonkuja 10, FIN-02130 Espoo, Finland

TRANTER PHE, INC.

PO Box 2289, Wichita Falls, TX, 76306

Tel: (940) 723-7125   Fax: (940) 723-1131   www.tranter.com

Mfr. heat exchangers.

SWEP Energy Oy, Box 112, Veneentekijantie 1, FIN-00210 Helsinki, Finland

TXU (TEXAS UTILITIES)

1601 Bryan St., Dallas, TX, 75201

Tel: (214) 812-4600   Fax: (214) 812-7077   www.txu.com

Provides electric and natural gas services, energy trading, energy marketing and telecommunications.

Pohjolan Voima Oy, Töölönkatu 4, PO Box 40, FIN-00101 Helsinki, Finland

Tel: 358-9-693061   Fax: 358-9-69306335

UNISYS CORPORATION.

PO Box 500, Union Meeting Road, Blue Bell, PA, 19424

Tel: (215) 986-4011   Fax: (215) 986-6850   www.unisys.com

Mfr./marketing/servicing electronic information systems.

Unisys Oy, Niittijkatu 8, FIN-02201 Espoo, Finland

UNITED PARCEL SERVICE, INC.

55 Glenlake Parkway, NE, Atlanta, GA, 30328

Tel: (404) 828-6000   Fax: (404) 828-6593   www.ups.com

International package-delivery service.

UPS Finland Oy - Head Office, Valimotle 22, FIN-01510 Vantaa, Finland

Tel: 358-90-613-2477   Fax: 358-90-870-2267

UNIVERSAL SECURITY INSTRUMENTS, INC.

PO Box 825, Binghamton, NY, 13902-0825

Tel: (607) 779-7689   Fax: (607) 779-7301   www.uic.com

Provider of innovative electronic circuit assembly technology and equipment, integrated system solutions, and process expertise.

Lucatron Oy, Espoo, Finland
Tel: 358-0-9887-0610

UUNET

22001 Loudoun County Pkwy., Ashburn, VA, 20147

Tel: (703) 206-5600   Fax: (703) 206-5601   www.uu.net

World's largest Internet service provider; World Wide Web hosting services, security products and consulting services to businesses, professionals, and on-line service providers.

UUNET Finland Oy, Metsänneidonkuja 10, FIN-02130 Espoo, Finland

VIEWSONIC CORPORATION

381 Brea Canyon Road, Walnut, CA, 91789

Tel: (909) 444-8888   Fax: (909) 869-7958   www.viewsonic.com

Mfr. displays.

ViewSonic Finland, Lars Sonckin Kaari 14, FIN-02600 Espoo, Finland
Tel: 358-9-5406-4070   Fax: 358-9-5406-4075

THE VIKING CORPORATION

210 N. Industrial Park Rd., Hastings, MI, 49058

Tel: (616) 945-9501   Fax: (616) 945-9599   www.vikingcorp.com

Mfr. fire extinguishing equipment.

Viking Norhan AB, Meripuistotie 5/5, FIN-00210 Helsinki, Finland

WASTE MANAGEMENT, INC.

1001 Fannin Street, Ste. 4000, Houston, TX, 77002

Tel: (713) 512-6200   Fax: (713) 512-6299   www.wastemanagement.com

Environmental services and disposal company; collection, processing, transfer and disposal facilities.

Waste Management Ymparistopalvelut Oy, Valimotie 33, FIN-01510 Vantaa, Finland

WATERS CORPORATION

34 Maple Street, Milford, MA, 01757

Tel: (508) 478-2000   Fax: (508) 872-1990   www.waters.com

Mfr./distribute liquid chromatographic instruments and test and measurement equipment.

Waters Oy, Kuparitie 1, FIN-00440 Helsinki, Finland

WEIGHT WATCHERS INTERNATIONAL, INC.

175 Crossways Park Dr., Woodbury, NY, 11797

Tel: (516) 390-1400   Fax: (516) 390-1763   www.weightwatchers.com

Weight loss programs.

Weight Watchers International, Painonvartijat, Vattuniemenkatu 19, FIN-00210 Helsinki, Finland

WHITE & CASE LLP

1155 Ave. of the Americas, New York, NY, 10036-2767

Tel: (212) 819-8200   Fax: (212) 354-8113   www.whitecase.com

Engaged in international law.

Asianajotoimisto White & Case Oy, Eteläranta 14, FIN-00100 Helsinki, Finland
Tel: 358-9-228641 Fax: 358-9-22864-228   Contact: Petri Y.J. Haussila

WIND RIVER SYSTEMS, INC.

500 Wind River Way, Alameda, CA, 94501

Tel: (510) 748-4100   Fax: (510) 749-2010   www.isi.com

Develops and markets computer software products and services.

Wind River Systems AB, PO Box 120, FIN-01301 Vanta, Finland
Tel: 358-40-546-1469   Fax: 358-9-871-0405

WM WRIGLEY JR. COMPANY

410 N. Michigan Ave., Chicago, IL, 60611-4287

Tel: (312) 644-2121   Fax: (312) 644-0353   www.wrigley.com

Mfr. chewing gum.

Oy Wrigley Scandinavia AB, IL Poisvagen 9, FIN-20740 Abo, Finland

WUNDERMAN

675 Avenue of the Americas, New York, NY, 10010

Tel: (212) 941-3000   Fax: (212) 941-2000   www.wunderman.com

Engaged in direct marketing.

Wunderman, Snellmaninkatu 13, FIN-00170 Helsinki, Finland

XEROX CORPORATION

800 Long Ridge Road, PO Box 1600, Stamford, CT, 06904

Tel: (203) 968-3000   Fax: (203) 968-4312   www.xerox.com

Mfr. document processing equipment, systems and supplies.

Xerox OY, PL 5, FIN-02601 Espoo Helsinki, Finland

Tel: 358-9-887-0010   Fax: 358-9-0204 68599

YELLOW CORPORATION

10990 Roe Ave., PO Box 7270, Overland Park, KS, 66207

Tel: (913) 696-6100   Fax: (913) 696-6116   www.yellowcorp.com

Commodity transportation.

Frans Maas Finland Oy, Tyopajakatu 10B, PO Box 5, FIN-00501 Helsinki, Finland

YOUNG & RUBICAM INC.

285 Madison Ave., New York, NY, 10017

Tel: (212) 210-3000   Fax: (212) 370-3796   www.yr.com

Advertising, public relations, direct marketing and sales promotion, corporate and product ID management.

Young & Rubicam Inc., Helsinki, Finland

ZIMMER HOLDINGS, INC.

345 East Main St., Warsaw, IN, 46580

Tel: (574) 267-6131   Fax: (574) 372-4988   www.zimmer.com

Engaged in design and manufacture of orthopedic products.

Zimmer, Orionintie 5, PL 8, FIN-02101 Espoo, Finland

Fax: 358-9429-3117

France

24/7 REAL MEDIA, INC.

1250 Broadway, New York, NY, 10001-3701

Tel: (212) 231-7100   Fax: (212) 760-1774   www.247media.com

Provides global online advertising, sponsorships, e-commerce and direct marketing solutions to advertisers and Web publishers.

24/7 Media France, 20 rue Cambon, F-75001 Paris, France

Tel: 33-1-55-047-247

3COM CORPORATION

5400 Bayfront Plaza, Santa Clara, CA, 95052-8145

Tel: (408) 326-5000   Fax: (408) 326-5001   www.3com.com

Engaged in the development and manufacture of computer networking products and systems.

3Com France, Les Conqueraants, 1, Avenue de l'Atlantique, Boite postale 965 Les Ulis, F-91976 Courtaboeuf Cedex, France

Tel: 33-1-6986-6800   Fax: 33-1-6907-1154

3Com France, Centre D'Affaires Mercure, 445 Boulevard Gambetta, F-59976 Tourcoing Cedex, France

Tel: 33-3-2028-1707

3D SYSTEMS CORPORATION

26081 Avenue Hall, Valencia, CA, 91355

Tel: (805) 295-5600   Fax: (805) 294-8406   www.3dsystems.com

Mfr. computer lasers.

3D Systems, Parc Club Orsay Universite, 26 Rue Jean Rostand, F-91893 F-91893, France

THE 3DO COMPANY

100 Cardinal Way, Ste. 425, Redwood City, CA, 94063

Tel: (650) 385-3000   Fax: (650) 385-3184   www.3do.com

Mfr. entertainment software.

UBI Soft France, 28 Rue Armand Carrel, F-93108 Montreuil Sous Bois Cedex, France

3M (MINNESOTA MINING & MFG.)

3M Center, St. Paul, MN, 55144-1000

Tel: (651) 733-1110   Fax: (651) 733-9973   www.mmm.com

Mfr. diversified products for industry, consumer, health care, imaging, communications, transport, safety, etc.

3M France, Blvd. de L'Oise, F-95006 Cergy Pontoise Cedex, France

Tel: 33-1-3962-4485   Fax: 33-1-3031-7426   Contact: Stig G. Eriksson

3M TOUCH SYSTEMS, INC.

300 Griffin Brook Park Drive, Methuen, MA, 01844

Tel: (978) 659-9000   Fax: (978) 659-9100   www.microtouch.com

Mfr. Touchscreen Sensors, Touch Monitors, and Industrial Computer Products.

3M Touch Systems SARL, Europarc de Créteil, 19 rue Le Corbusier, F- 94042 Créteil Cedex, France

Tel: 33-1-4513-9030

AAF INTERNATIONAL (AMERICAN AIR FILTER)

10300 Ormsby Park Place, Ste. 600, Louisville, KY, 40232-5690

Tel: (502) 637-0011   Fax: (502) 637-0321   www.aafintl.com

Mfr. air filtration and pollution control and noise control equipment.

AAF SA, Rue William Dian, BP 3, F-27620 Gasny, France

Tel: 33-2-325-36060

AAF-SA, 42 rue Fortuny, F-75017 Paris, France

Tel: 33-1-44-29-9330

AAR CORPORATION

1100 North Wood Dale Road, Wood Dale, IL, 60191

Tel: (630) 227-2000   Fax: (630) 227-2019   www.aarcorp.com

Provides aviation repair and supply provisioning; aircraft sales and leasing.

AAR International, 112 rue de Paris, F-92110 Boulogne, France

Tel: 33-1-4604-2211   Fax: 33-1-4604-7015   Contact: Jean-Philippe Schumacher

AAVID THERMAL TECHNOLOGIES, INC.

1 Eagle Square, Ste. 509, Concord, NH, 03301

Tel: (603) 224-1117   Fax: (603) 224-6673   www.aatt.com

Mfr. fluid dynamics software.

Aavid Thermalloy Sarl, 10 Avenue Du Quebec, Villebon BP 116, F-91944 Courtaboeuf, France

Tel: 33-1-609-24126

ABBOTT LABORATORIES

100 Abbott Park Rd., Abbott Park, IL, 60064

Tel: (847) 937-6100   Fax: (847) 937-1511   www.abbott.com

Development, manufacture and sale of diversified health care products and services.

Abbott France S.A., 12 rue de la Couture, F-94518 Rungis Cedex, France

ABS (AMERICAN BUREAU OF SHIPPING)

ABS Plaza, 16855 Northchase Drive, Houston, TX, 77060

Tel: (281) 877-6000   Fax: (281) 877-6344   www.eagle.org

Classification and certification of ships and offshore structures, development and technical assistance.

ABS Europe Ltd., Les Docks - Atrium 10.3, 10, Place De La Joliette, F-13002 Marseille, France

ACCELRYS INC.

9685 Scranton Road, San Diego, CA, 92121-3752

Tel: (858) 799-5000   Fax: (858) 799-5100   www.accelrys.com

Mfr. software for drug research.

Accelrys France, Parc Club Orsay, Universite 20, Rue Jean Rostand, F-91898 Orsay Cedex, France

Tel: 33-1-6935-3232   Fax: 33-1-6941-9909

ACCENTURE LTD.

1345 Avenue of the Americas, New York, NY, 10105

Tel: (917) 452-4400   Fax: (917) 527-9915   www.accenture.com

Provides management and technology consulting services.

Accenture, Technology Park, Les Genêts, 449 route de Crêtes, F-06560 Sophia Antipolis, France

Tel: 33-4-92-94-6700   Fax: 33-4-92-94-6799

Accenture, 55 Ave. George V, F-75379 Paris Cédex 08, France

Tel: 33-1-53-23-5323   Fax: 33-1-53-23-5555

Accenture, Tour Crédit Lyonnais, 129 rue Servient, F-69431 Lyon Cédex 03, France

Tel: 33-4-78-63-7272   Fax: 33-4-78-95-37277

ACCLAIM ENTERTAINMENT, INC.

One Acclaim Plaza, Glen Cove, NY, 11542

Tel: (516) 656-5000   Fax: (516) 656-2040   www.acclaim.com

Mfr. video games.

Acclaim Entertainment SA, 67 rue de Courcelles, F-75008 Paris, France

Tel: 33-1-56-21-3100   Fax: 33-1-48-88-9494

ACCO WORLD CORPORATION

300 Tower Parkway, Lincolnshire, IL, 60069

Tel: (847) 541-9500   Fax: (847) 541-5750   www.accobrands.com

Provides services in the office and computer markets and manufactures paper fasteners, clips, metal fasteners, binders and staplers.

ACCO France SARL, Rue Ampere, BP 33, F-91430 Igny Zai, France

Tel: 33-1-6985-8906

ACCURIDE INTERNATIONAL, INC.

12311 Shoemaker Ave., Santa Fe Springs, CA, 90670-4721

Tel: (562) 903-0200   Fax: (562) 903-0208   www.accuride.com

Mfr. drawer slides.

Accuride International, 76 rue du Pontel, F-78100 Saint-Germain-en-Lave, France

Tel: 33-1-3973-0495

ACETO CORPORATION

One Hallow Lane, Ste. 201, Lake Success, NY, 11042-1215

Tel: (516) 627-6000   Fax: (516) 627-6093   www.aceto.com

Engaged in the distribution of chemicals.

Aceto France SA, 69 Boulevard des Canuts, F-69400 Lyon, France

Aceto France SAS, 57 Boulevard de Montmorency, F-75016 Paris, France

ACHESON COLLOIDS INDUSTRIES, INC.

1600 Washington Avenue, Port Huron, MI, 48060

Tel: (810) 984-5581   Fax: (810) 984-1446   www.nationalstarch.com

Chemicals, chemical preparations, paints and lubricating oils.

Acheson France S.A., Z.I. Ouest rue Georges Besse, BP 68, F-67152 Erstein Cedex, France

Tel: 33-3-88-59-0123   Fax: 33-3-88-59-0100

ACMI CORPORATION

136 Turnpike Road, Southborough, MA, 01772-2104

Tel: (508) 804-2600   Fax: (508) 804-2624   www.circoncorp.com

Mfr. and sales of medical and surgical endoscopes, instruments and video systems.

ACMI S.A., 7, avenue du General de Gaulle, F-91090 Lisses, France

Tel: 33-1-691-12150

ACT MANUFACTURING, INC.

2 Cabot Road, Hudson, MA, 01749

Tel: (978) 567-4000   Fax: (978) 568-1904   www.actmfg.com

Mfr. printed circuit boards.

ACT Manufacturing France, 34, rue du Nid de Pie, BP 428, F-90040 Angers Cedex 01, France

Tel: 241-736-000   Fax: 241-737-480

ACTEL CORPORATION

955 East Arquest Avenue, Sunnyvale, CA, 94086-4533

Tel: (408) 739-1010   Fax: (408) 739-1540   www.actel.com

Mfr. integrated circuits.

Actel Europe, 361 Avenue du General de Gaulle, F-92147 Clamart Cedex, France

ACTERNA CORPORATION

20400 Observation Drive, Germantown, MD, 20876

Tel: (301) 353-1550   Fax: (301) 353-1536   www.acterna.com

Develop, manufacture and market communications test instruments, systems, software and services.

Acterna Corporation, 46 bis, rue Pierre Curie PB 10, Z.I. Les Gatines, F- 78373 Plaisir Cedex,, France

ACTION INSTRUMENTS INC.

8601 Aero Drive, San Diego, CA, 92123

Tel: (619) 279-5726   Fax: (619) 279-6290   www.actionio.com

Mfr. electronic instruments and industrial measurements computers.

Action Instruments SA, 9 ave. du Canada, Parc Hightec, Les Ulis Cedex, France

Tel: 33-478-664-500   Fax: 33-478-352-490   Contact: Gerald Joner

ACTUATE CORPORATION

701 Gateway Boulevard, South San Francisco, CA, 94080

Tel: (650) 837-2000   Fax: (650) 827-1560   www.actuate.com

Develops software.

Actuate France, 27 rue du colonel Pierre Avia, F-75508 Paris 15, France

ACXIOM CORPORATION

1 Information Way, Little Rock, AR, 72203-8180

Tel: (501) 342-1000   Fax: (501) 336-3919   www.acxiom.com

Data warehouse, database manager, and other marketing information services.

Acxiom France, Le Pyramide, 36 Avenue Pierre Brosselette, F-92247 Malakoff Cedex, France

Tel: 33-1-46-57-0808

ADAC LABORATORIES, INC.

540 Alder Drive, Milpitas, CA, 95035

Tel: (408) 321-9100   Fax: (408) 321-9536   www.adaclabs.com

Mfr. cameras and equipment for nuclear medicine.

ADAC Laboratories SARL, 19 Avenue De Norvege, F-91953 Courtaboefuf Cedex, France

Tel: 33-16-092-0649

ADEPT TECHNOLOGY, INC.

150 Rose Orchard Way, San Jose, CA, 95134

Tel: (408) 432-0888   Fax: (408) 434-6267   www.adept.com

Mfr. robots for industries.

Adept Technology, Parc Du Moulin de Massy, 41, rue du Saule Trapu, F-91300 Massy, France

Tel: 33-1-6919-1616

ADOBE SYSTEMS INCORPORATED

345 Park Avenue, San Jose, CA, 95110

Tel: (408) 536-6000   Fax: (408) 537-6000   www.adobe.com

Engaged in print technology and distributor of Acrobat Reader.

Adobe Systems France EURL, Immeuble Atria, 2 rue du Centre, F-93885 Noisy-le-Grand Cédex, France

ADVANCE PUBLICATIONS, INC.

950 Fingerboard Road, Staten Island, NY, 10305

Tel: (718) 981-1234   Fax: (718) 981-1415   www.advance.net

Publishing company (Glamour, Vogue, GQ, Architectural Digest) and cable TV operations.

Advance Publications, Inc., Paris, France

ADVANCED DIGITAL INFORMATION CORPORATION

11431 Willows Rd. NE, PO Box 97057, Redmond, WA, 98073

Tel: (425) 881-8004   Fax: (425) 881-2296   www.adic.com

Mfr. computer storage systems.

ADIC France, ZAC des Basses Auges, 1 rue Alfred de Vigny, F-78112 Fourqueux, France

Tel: 33-1-3087-5300

ADVANCED ENERGY INDUSTRIES, INC.

1625 Sharp Point Drive, Fort Collins, CO, 80525

Tel: (970) 221-4670   Fax: (970) 221-5583   www.advanced-energy.com

Mfr. semiconductors.

Advanced Energy, 7, rue Claude Debussy, 94510 La Queue-En-Brie, France

ADVANCED FIBRE COMMUNICATIONS, INC.

1465 North McDowell Blvd., Petaluma, CA, 94954

Tel: (707) 794-7700   Fax: (707) 794-7777   www.fibre.com

Engaged in voice and data network access devices.

Advanced Fibre Communications, 54-56 Avenue Hoche, F-75008 Paris, France

Tel: 33-1-5660-5223 Fax: 33-1-5660-5558

ADVANCED MICRO DEVICES INC.

1 AMD Place, Sunnyvale, CA, 94086

Tel: (408) 732-2400   Fax: (408) 982-6164   www.amd.com

Mfr. integrated circuits for communications and computation industry.

Advanced Micro Devices SA, ZI Orlytech, 5, Allee du Cdt Mouchotte, F-91550 Paray Vielle Poste, France

ADVANCED PRODUCTS COMPANY

33 Defco Park Road, North Haven, CT, 06473

Tel: (203) 239-3341   Fax: (203) 234-7233   www.advpro.com

Mfr. metallic and PTFE seals and gaskets.

Advanced Products SARL, 8 Place de l'Eglise, F-78360 Montesson, France

ADVANSTAR COMMUNICATIONS INC.

545 Boylston Steet, Boston, MA, 02116

Tel: (617) 267-6500   Fax: (617) 267-6900   www.advanstar.com

Provides business to business marketing services.

MM Editions, 31/35 Rue Gambetta, F-92150 Suresnes, France

Tel: 33-1-41-18-86-18   Fax: 33-1-45-06-29-81

AERO SYSTEMS ENGINEERING, INC.

358 E. Fillmore Ave., St. Paul, MN, 55107

Tel: (651) 227-7515   Fax: (651) 227-0519   www.aerosysengr.com

Engaged in wind tunnel and jet engine testing and engineering. (JV of Celsius Inc.)

Aero Systems Aviation c/o M. Louis Casagrande, 278 rue des Bois Moissy, F-77530 Vaux LePenil Cedex, France

Tel: 33-1-6068-7637   Fax: 33-1-606-6435

AEROFLEX INCORPORATED

35 South Service Road, Plainview, NY, 11803

Tel: (516) 694-6700   Fax: (516) 694-4823   www.aeroflex.com

Mfr. aerospace and communications components.

Europtest SA, 5, place du General de Gaulle, F-78990 Elancourt, France

Tel: 33-1-3051-3399

AEROVOX INC.

167 John Vertente Boulevard, New Bedford, MA, 02745

Tel: (508) 994-9661   Fax: (508) 995-3000   www.aerovox.com

Manufacturer of capacitors for electrical and electronic applications.

BHC Aerovoc Ltd., 15 Rue de Londres, F-75009 Paris, France

Tel: 33-1-4285-4829   Fax: 33-1-4878-2680

AGENCY.COM LTD.

20 Exchange Place, 15th Fl, New York, NY, 10005

Tel: (212) 358-2600   Fax: (212) 358-2604   www.agency.com

Engaged in Website design and technology integration.

Agency.Com, 60-62 rue d'Hauteville, F-70510 Paris, France

AGILE SOFTWARE CORPORATION

1 Almaden Blvd., San Jose, CA, 95113-2253

Tel: (408) 975-3900   Fax: (408) 271-4862   www.agilesoft.com

Mfr. software for supply chain management.

Agile Software Corporation, 126, rue Gallieni, F-92643 Boulogne Billancourt Cedex, France

AGILENT TECHNOLOGIES, INC.

395 Page Mill Road, PO Box 10395, Palo Alto, CA, 94303

Tel: (650) 752-5000   Fax: (650) 752-5633   www.agilent.com

Mfr. communications components.

Agilent Technologies France, Z.A. de Courtaboeuf, 1 Avenue du Canada, F-91947 Les Ulis Cedex, France

Tel: 33-1-6982-6090

AIG AMERICAN INTERNATIONAL GROUP INC.

70 Pine Street, New York, NY, 10270

Tel: (212) 770-7000   Fax: (212) 509-9705   www.aig.com

Worldwide insurance and financial services.

AIG Europe France, S.A., Tour AIG, F-92079 Paris, France

AIR PRODUCTS AND CHEMICALS, INC.

7201 Hamilton Boulevard, Allentown, PA, 18195-1501

Tel: (610) 481-4911   Fax: (610) 481-5900   www.airproducts.com

Mfr. industry gases and related equipment, specialty chemicals, environmental/energy systems.

Air Products & Chemicals Inc., Tour Pleyel, Centre Paris, F-93521 Ste. Denis Cedex 01, France

AIRBORNE INC.

3101 Western Ave., PO Box 662, Seattle, WA, 98121

Tel: (206) 285-4600   Fax: (206) 281-1444   www.airborne.com

Air transport services.

Airborne Express, Aeroport Zone De Fret, F-59817 Lesquin, France

Tel: 33-3-20-879239   Fax: 33-3-20-879242

AIRSEA PACKING

40-35 22nd Street, Long Island City, NY, 11101

Tel: (718) 937-6800   Fax: (718) 937-9646   www.airseapacking.com

Air and sea freight.

AirSea Packing Group Limited, 14, rue de la Pointe, F-93130 Noisy le Sec, France

Tel: 33-1-4846-8142   Fax: 33-1-4846-0333   Contact: Mark Drasar

AKAMAI TECHNOLOGIES, INC.

500 Technology Square, Cambridge, MA, 02139

Tel: (617) 250-3000   Fax: (617) 250-3001   www.akamai.com

Develops routing technologies for websites.

Akamai Technologies France, 7 Avenue Georges Pompidou, F-92593 Levallois Peret Cedex, France

Tel: 33-1-4748-2218   Fax: 33-1-4748-2577

ALADDIN INDUSTRIES INC.

703 Murfreesboro Road, Nashville, TN, 37210

Tel: (615) 748-3000   Fax: (615) 748-3070   www.aladdinindustries.com

Mfr. vacuum insulated products, insulated food containers and servers.

Aladdin Industries SA, 5 rue de la Crois Martre, F-91120 Palaiseau, France

ALBANY INTERNATIONAL CORPORATION

1373 Broadway, Albany, NY, 12204

Tel: (518) 445-2200   Fax: (518) 445-2265   www.albint.com

Mfr. broadwoven and engineered fabrics, plastic products, filtration media.

Postillion SA, 6 rue Royale, F-77300 Fontainebleau, France

Postillion SA, F-24600 Riberac Dordogne, France

ALBERTO-CULVER COMPANY

2525 Armitage Ave., Melrose Park, IL, 60160

Tel: (708) 450-3000   Fax: (708) 450-3354   www.alberto.com

Mfr./marketing personal care and household brand products.

Indola SA, 54 rue de Paradis, F-75010 Paris, France

ALCOA INC.

Alcoa Center, 201 Isabella Street at 7th Street Bridge, Pittsburgh, PA, 15212-5858

Tel: (412) 553-4545   Fax: (412) 553-4498   www.alcoa.com

World's leading producer of aluminum and alumina; mining, refining, smelting, fabricating and recycling.

Kawneer France S.A., Lezat-sur-Leze, France

Z.I. Molina La Chazotte, rue de L'Avenir, B.P. 105, F-42003 Saint Etienne Cedex 1, France

ALLEGHENY LUDLUM CORPORATION

1000 Six PPG Place, Pittsburgh, PA, 15222

Tel: (412) 394-2805   Fax: (412) 394-2800   www.alleghenyludlum.com

Mfr. steel and alloys.

Allegheny Ludlum, Paris, France

Tel: 33-1-55-66-88-88   Fax: 33-6-07-54-25-13

ALLEGHENY TECHNOLOGIES INC.

1000 Six PPG Place, Pittsburgh, PA, 15222

Tel: (412) 394-2800 Fax: (412) 394-2805 www.alleghenytechnologies.com

Diversified mfr. aviation and electronics, specialty metals, industrial and consumer products.

Allegheny Technologies, L'Arche du Parc, 738 rue Yves Kerman, F-92658 Boulogne-Billancourt Cedex, France

Allvac Ltd., Div. de Stellram S.A., 111 Avenue Francois Arago, F-92003 Nanterre Cedex, France

Titanium Industries, Inc., ZAI Des Bruveres, Av JP Tibaud, F-78190 Trappes, France

ALLEGIANCE HEALTHCARE CORPORATION

1430 Waukegan Road, McGaw Park, IL, 60085

Tel: (847) 689-8410 Fax: (847) 578-4437 www.allegiance.net

Manufactures and distributes medical, surgical, respiratory therapy and laboratory products.

Allegiance Santé S.A., 6 Ave. Louis Pasteur, F-78311 Maurepas Cedex Paris, France

Tel: 33-1-34-61-5050 Fax: 33-1-34-61-5141 Contact: Alain Pernin, Dir. Mktg.

ALLEN TELECOM

25101 Chagrin Boulevard, Beachwood, OH, 44122-5619

Tel: (216) 765-5818 Fax: (216) 765-0410 www.allentele.com

Mfr. communications equipment, automotive bodies and parts, electronic components.

Forem France, Z.I. Des Ebisoires, Ferme des Ebisoires, F-78370 Plasir, France

Tel: 33-1-30-79-1530 Fax: 33-1-30-55-5537 Contact: Michel Laveille

Telia S.A., 46 Allee de Megevie, F-31170 Gradignan, France

Tel: 33-5-56-89-5619 Fax: 33-5-56-89-5344

ALLEN-BRADLEY COMPANY, INC.

1201 South Second Street, Milwaukee, WI, 53204

Tel: (414) 382-2000 Fax: (414) 382-4444 www.ab.com

Mfr. electrical controls and information devices.

Allen-Bradley Servovision SA, 36 ave. de l'Europe, F-78140 Velizy-Villacoublay, France

ALLERGAN INC.

2525 Dupont Drive, Irvine, CA, 92612

Tel: (714) 246-4500 Fax: (714) 246-6987 www.allergan.com

Mfr. therapeutic eye care products and skin care pharmaceuticals.

Allergan France, S.A., B.P. 442, F-06251 Mougins Cedex, France

Tel: 33-492-92-4400 Fax: 33-492-92-4410

ALLIANCE GAMING CORPORATION

6601 S. Bermuda Road, Las Vegas, NV, 89119

Tel: (702) 270-7600 Fax: (702) 263-5636 www.ally.com

Mfr. gaming machines.

Bally Gaming Systems, 54 Ave. Du Capitaine Glarner, F-93582 St. Ouen, France

ALPHARMA INC.

One Executive Drive, 4th Fl., Fort Lee, NJ, 07024

Tel: (201) 947-7774 Fax: (201) 947-4879 www.alpharma.com

Development/manufacture specialty human pharmaceuticals and animal health products.

Alpharma AS, Silic 411, 3 Impasse de la Noisette, F-91374 Verrieres le Buisson Cedex, France

Tel: 33-1-6953-4050 Fax: 33-1-6953-4051 Contact: Alain Richard, Mgr.

ALTIRIS, INC.

588 West 400 South, Lindon, UT, 84042

Tel: (801) 226-8500 Fax: (801) 226-8506 www.altiris.com

Mfr. IT systems management software.

Altiris France, 10, rue des Gaudines, F-78100 Saint Germain en Laye, France

AMAZON.COM, INC.
1200 12th Ave. South, Ste. 1200, Seattle, WA, 98144-2734

Tel: (206) 266-1000   Fax: (206) 266-4206   www.amazon.com

Computer site that offers books, CDs, DVDS, videos, toys, tools, and electronics.

Amazon.Com France, Paris, France

AMBAC FINANCIAL GROUP
One State Street Plaza, New York, NY, 10004

Tel: (212) 668-0340   Fax: (212) 509-9109   www.ambac.com

Reinsurance company.

MBIA Assurance S.A., Citicenter, 19, le Parvia, F-92073 Paris La Défense Cedex 37, France

Tel: 33-1-46-93-93   Contact: Manuel Chevalier, VP

AMC ENTERTAINMENT INC.
106 West 14th Street, Kansas City, MO, 64121-9615

Tel: (816) 221-4000   Fax: (816) 480-4617   www.amctheatres.com

Operates movie theater chains.

AMC Marine 20, Pole Marine, Rue des Fusiliers Marins, F-59140 Dunkerque, France

Tel: 33-3-2859-9290

AMCOL INTERNATIONAL CORPORATION
1500 West Shure Drive, Ste. 500, Arlington Heights, IL, 60004

Tel: (847) 394-8730   Fax: (847) 506-6199   www.amcol.com

Mfr. specialty chemicals and environmental bentonite products.

CETCO France, 17 Avenue General du De Gaulle, F-94220 Le Plessis Trevise, France

AMERICAN BANKNOTE CORPORATION
560 Sylvan Avenue, Englewood Cliffs, NJ, 07632

Tel: (201) 568-4400   Fax: (201) 568-4400   www.anbancor.com

Mfr. transaction cards and supplies electronic printing for corporate billing processes.

American Banknote Corp., Paris, France

ABC, INC.
77 West 66th Street, 13th Fl., New York, NY, 10023

Tel: (212) 456-7777   Fax: (212) 456-6384   www.abc.com

Radio/TV production and broadcasting.

ABC News, 22 ave. d'Eyleu, F-75116 Paris, France

AMERICAN EXPRESS COMPANY
90 Hudson Street, Jersey City, NJ, 07302

Tel: (212) 640-2000   Fax: (212) 619-9802   www.americanexpress.com

Engaged in travel, travelers cheques, charge card and financial services.

American Express Carte France SA, , 11 rue Scribe, F-75009 Paris, France

Tel: 33-1-47-77-7707

AMERICAN MANAGEMENT SYSTEMS, INC. (AMS)
4050 Legato Road, 10th Fl., Fairfax, VA, 22033

Tel: (703) 267-8000   Fax: (703) 267-5073   www.amsinc.com

Provides integrated IT solutions, outsourcing, and transformation services.

AMS Management Systems, 1, Place Boieldieu, F-75002 Paris, France

Tel: 33-1-4703-0548   Fax: 33-1-4703-0549

AMERICAN MEDICAL SYSTEMS HOLDING, INC.
10700 Bren Road West, Minnetonka, MN, 55343

Tel: (952) 933-4666   Fax: (952) 930-6157   www.visitams.com

Mfr. urological devices.

American Medical Systems, 19 bis avenue du Quebec, F-91951 Courtaboeuf Cedex, France

Contact: Daan Ruys

AMERICAN OPTICAL LENS CO.

PO Box 8020, Southbridge, MA, 01550

Tel: (508) 764-5000   Fax: (508) 764-5010   www.alolens.com

Mfr. ophthalmic lenses and frames, custom molded products, specialty lenses.

AO Ouest Optique, Rue Augustin Fresnel, Z.I. de la Guenaudiere, F-35304 Fougeres, France

Tel: 33-299-94-8474   Fax: 33-299-94-1890

AMERICAN SOFTWARE, INC.

470 East Paces Ferry Road, NE, Atlanta, GA, 30305

Tel: (404) 261-4381   Fax: (404) 264-5514   www.amsoftware.com

Mfr./sales of financial control software and systems.

American Software Tour Litwin, 10/10 bis rue Jean-Jaures, F-92807 Puteaux Ledex Paris, France

Tel: 33-1-4907-8555   Fax: 33-1-4907-8506

AMERICAN STANDARD COMPANIES, INC.

One Centennial Avenue, Piscataway, NJ, 08855-6820

Tel: (732) 980-3000   Fax: (732) 980-6118   www.americanstandard.com

Mfr. automotive, plumbing, heating, air conditioning products and medical diagnostics systems.

DiaSorin S.A., Parc De Haute Technologie, 11, rue Georges Besse, Bat 4, F-92160 Antony, France

Tel: 33-1-55-590422   Fax: 33-1-55-590440

International Unitary Products Société Trane, 1 rue des Ameriques, B.P. 6, F-88191 Golbey Cedex, France

Tel: 33-3-2931-7300

AMERON INTERNATIONAL CORPORATION

245 South Los Robles Ave., Pasadena, CA, 91109-7007

Tel: (626) 683-4000   Fax: (626) 683-4060   www.ameron.com

Mfr. steel pipe systems, concrete products, traffic and lighting poles, protective coatings.

Tubolining SA, BP 43, F-13367 Marseille Cedex 11, France

AMES TEXTILE CORPORATION

710 Chelmsford Street, Lowell, MA, 01851

Tel: (978) 458-3321   Fax: (978) 441-9808   www.amestextile.com

Mfr. textile products.

Ames France, 3 Chemin Departemental, Fallieres, St. Nabord, F-88200 Remiremont, France

AMETEK INC.

37 N. Valley Road, PO Box 1764, Paoli, PA, 19301-0801

Tel: (610) 647-2121   Fax: (610) 296-3412   www.ametek.com

Mfr. instruments, electric motors and engineered materials.

AMETEK Precision Instruments France SARL, 4 Rue Edouard Branly, F-78190 Trappes, France

Tel: 33-1-30-68-6920   Fax: 33-1-30-68-6929

AMGEN INC.

One Amgen Center Drive, Thousand Oaks, CA, 91320-1799

Tel: (805) 447-1000   Fax: (805) 499-2694   www.amgen.com

Biotechnology research and pharmaceuticals.

Amgen, S.A., c/o European Business Centre, 192 Avenue Charles de Gaulle, F-92523 Neuilly-sur-Seine Cedex, France

Tel: 33-1-408-82700

AMKOR TECHNOLOGY, INC.

1345 Enterprise Dr., West Chester, PA, 19380

Tel: (610) 431-9600   Fax: (610) 431-1988   www.amkor.com

Microchip technology engaged in semiconductor packaging and test services.

Amkor Technology S.A.R.L., BP 99, 13 Chemin du Levant, F-01210 Ferney-Voltaire, France

Tel: 33-4-50-40-9797

AMPCO METAL, INC.

1745 S. 38th Street, PO Box 2004, Milwaukee, WI, 53201

Tel: (414) 645-3750   Fax: (414) 645-3225   www.ampcometal.com

Mfr./distributor/sale cast and wrought copper-based alloys.

Ampco Metal SA, rue Claude Bernard, BP 22, F-78311 Maurepas Cedex, France

AMPEX CORPORATION

1228 Douglas Avenue, Redwood City, CA, 94063-3199

Tel: (650) 367-2011   Fax: (650) 367-4669   www.ampex.com

Mfr. extremely high-performance digital data storage, data retrieval and image processing systems for a broad range of corporate scientific and government applications.

Ampex SARL, Courcellor 1, 2 rue Curnonsky, F-75017 Paris, France

AMPHENOL CORPORATION

358 Hall Ave., Wallingford, CT, 06492-7530

Tel: (203) 265-8900   Fax: (203) 265-8793   www.amphenol.com

Mfr. electronic interconnect penetrate systems and assemblies.

Amphenol Automotive France, Immeuble Newton C, 7 Mail B, Thimonnier, F-77185 Lognes, France

Tel: 33-1-16462-7676

AMR CORPORATION (AMERICAN AIRLINES)

4333 Amon Carter Boulevard, Ft. Worth, TX, 76155

Tel: (817) 963-1234   Fax: (817) 967-9641   www.amrcorp.com

Air transport services.

American Airlines Inc., 82 ave. Marceau, F-75008 Paris, France

AMSTED INDUSTRIES INC.

205 North Michigan Ave., Chicago, IL, 60601

Tel: (312) 645-1700   Fax: (312) 819-8523   www.amsted.com

Privately-held, diversified manufacturer of products for the construction and building markets, general industry and the railroads.

Keystone Industries, Acieries De Ploermel, BP 103, F-56804 Ploermel, France

Tel: 33-2-97-73-2470

AMWAY CORPORATION

7575 Fulton Street East, Ada, MI, 49355-0001

Tel: (616) 787-6000   Fax: (616) 787-6177   www.amway.com

Mfr./sale home care, personal care, nutrition and houseware products.

Amway France, 14, Ave. Francois Sommer, BP 140, F-92185 Antony Cedex, France

ANACOMP INC.

12365 Crosthwaite Circle, Poway, CA, 92064

Tel: (858) 679-9797   Fax: (858) 748-9482   www.anacomp.com

Engaged in electronic information management services and products.

Anacomp SARL, 72-74 Quai de la Loire, F-75019 Paris, France

ANALOG DEVICES INC.

1 Technology Way, Norwood, MA, 02062

Tel: (781) 329-4700   Fax: (781) 326-8703   www.analog.com

Mfr. integrated circuits and related devices.

Analog Devices SA, 3, rue Georges Besse, F-92160 Antony, France

ANC RENTAL CORPORATION

200 S. Andrews Ave., Ft. Lauderdale, FL, 33301

Tel: (954) 320-4000   Fax: (954) 320-4077   www.ancrental.com

Engaged in car rental services, including National Car Rental and Alamo Rent A Car.

National Car Rental, 13, rue Sainte Catherine, Abbeville, France

National Car Rental, BP 212, Clamart Cedex, France

ANDERSEN

33 West Monroe Street, Chicago, IL, 60603

Tel: (312) 580-0033   Fax: (312) 507-6748   www.andersen.com

*Accounting and audit, tax and management consulting services. **Firm under worldwide reorganization; new data unavailable for this edition.*

Andersen Consulting, 129 rue Servient, F-69431 Lyon Cedex 03, France

Tel: 33-78-63-7400

Barbier Frinault & Associes, Tour Europe, 20 Place des Halles, F-67000 Strasbourg, France

Tel: 33-88-37-5930

Barbier Frinault & Associes, 129 rue Servient, F-69431 Lyon Cedex 03, France

Tel: 33-78-63-7200

S.G. Archibald/ Andersen Worldwide, Tour Gan, F-92082 Paris La Defense Cedex, France

Tel: 33-1-42-91-0700

ANDREW CORPORATION

10500 West 153rd Street, Orland Park, IL, 60462

Tel: (708) 349-3300   Fax: (708) 349-5410   www.andrew.com

Designer, manufacturer, and supplier of communications equipment, services, and systems.

Andrew SARL, 320 rue Helene Boucher, Z.I. Centre, F-78531 Buc Cedex, France

Tel: 33-1-39-24-1470   Fax: 33-1-39-56-5137

ANIXTER INTERNATIONAL INC..

4711 Golf Road, Skokie, IL, 60076

Tel: (847) 677-2600   Fax: (847) 677-8557   www.anixter.com

Distributor wiring systems/products for voice, video, data and power applications.

Anixter France, ZAC Paris Nord 2, BP 50008, 69 rue de la Belle Etoile, F-95945 Roissy Cedex, France

Anixter France, Z. I. Mi-Plaine BP, 9 rue Jean Rostand, F-69744 Lyon Genas Cedex, France

Tel: 33-4-78-90-0505   Fax: 33-4-78-40-6155

ANSELL HEALTHCARE INCORPORATED

200 Schulz Drive, Red Bank, NJ, 07701

Tel: (732) 345-5400   Fax: (732) 219-5114   www.ansellhealthcare.com

Mfr. industrial gloves, rubber and plastic products, protective clothing.

Ansell Healthcare S.A., 9 Chaussée Jules César, B.P. 238 Osny, F-95523 Cergy Pontoise Cedex, France

Tel: 33-1-34-24-5252

ANSYS, INC.

275 Technology Drive, Canonsburg, PA, 15317

Tel: (724) 746-3304   Fax: (724) 514-9494   www.ansys.com

Mfr. CAD and CAE software.

ANSYS Europe, Immeuble l'Orient, 10 Place Charles Beraudier, F-69428 Lyon, France

ANSYS France, Les Bureaux de Sevres, 2 rue Troyon, F-92316 Sevres, France

Contact: Eric Bienvenu

AOL TIME WARNER

75 Rockefeller Plaza, New York, NY, 10019

Tel: (212) 484-8000   Fax: (212) 275-3046   www.aoltimewarner.com

Engaged in media and communications; provides internet services, communications, publishing and entertainment.

AOL Time Warner France, 2 Place de La Défense, F-92053 Paris-La-Défense, France

Time-Life International SA, 17 ave. Matignon, F-75008 Paris, France

AON CORPORATION

200 East Randolph, Chicago, IL, 60601

Tel: (312) 381-1000   Fax: (312) 381-6032   www.aon.com

Insurance brokers worldwide; underwrites accident and health insurance, specialty and professional insurance; and provides risk management consultation.

AON France, 45, rue Kléber, F-92697 Levallois Perret Cedex, France

Tel: 33-1-58-757575   Fax: 33-1-58-757777   Contact: Daniel Souissi

API MOTION INC.

45 Hazelwood Dr., Amherst, NY, 14228

Tel: (716) 691-9100   Fax: (716) 691-9181   www.apimotion.com

Engaged in motion control solutions using motors and drives, motor gear heads, resolver and encoder feedback devices.

API Motion France SA, 2 rue Louis Pergaud, F-94706 Maisons Alfort Cedex, France

APL LOGISTICS

1111 Broadway, Oakland, CA, 94607

Tel: (510) 272-8000   Fax: (510) 272-7421   www.apllogistics.com

Provides ocean container shipping and logistics services.

APL France, 50, Boulevard du Colonel, F-94854 Ivry-Sur-Seine, France

APPLE COMPUTER, INC.

One Infinite Loop, Cupertino, CA, 95014

Tel: (408) 996-1010   Fax: (408) 974-2113   www.apple.com

Personal computers, peripherals and software.

Apple Computer France SARL, BP 131, ave. de l'Oceanie, Z.I. de Courtaboeuf, F-91944 Les Ulis, France

APPLERA CORPORATION

301 Merritt 7, Norwalk, CT, 06851

Tel: (203) 840-2000   Fax: (203) 840-2312   www.applera.com

Leading supplier of systems for life science research and related applications.

Applied Biosystems, 25, Av de la Baltique, BP 96, F-91943 Courtaboeuf Cedex, France

APPLIED MATERIALS, INC.

3050 Bowers Ave., Santa Clara, CA, 95054-3299

Tel: (408) 727-5555   Fax: (408) 727-9943   www.appliedmaterials.com

Supplies manufacturing systems and services to the semiconductor industry.

Applied Materials France S.A.R.L., Parc de la Julienne, Batiment E or F, F-91830 Le Coudray-Montceaux, France
Tel: 33-1-69-90-6100   Fax: 33-1-69-90-4045

APPLIX, INC.

289 Turnpike Rd., Westboro, MA, 01581

Tel: (508) 870-0300   Fax: (508) 366-4873   www.applix.com

Engaged in business productivity application software.

APPLIX, Inc., 22 rue Colbert, F-78885 Saint Quentin en Yvelines, France
Tel: 33-1-3064-7879   Fax: 33-1-3064-5435

APRISMA MANAGEMENT TECHNOLOGIES, INC.

273 Corporate Drive, Portsmouth, NH, 03801

Tel: (603) 334-2100   Fax: (603) 334-2784   www.aprisma.com

Mfr. software.

Aprisma EMEA, 68, rue Faidherbe, F-93100 Montreuil, France

APTAR GROUP, INC.

475 W. Terra Cotta Avenue, Ste. E, Crystal Lake, Il, 60014-9895

Tel: (815) 477-0424   Fax: (815) 477-0481   www.aptar.com

Mfr. soap and fragrance pump dispensers.

AptarGroup S.A., 147 rue du Président Roosevelt, B.P. 5232, F-78175 Saint Germain-en-Laye Cédex, France
Tel: 33-1-3087-1980   Fax: 33-1-30-87-0909

APW, INC.

N22 W23685 Ridgeview Parkway West, Waukesha, WI, 53188-1013

Tel: (262) 523-7600   Fax: (262) 523-7624   www.apw1.com

Mfr. hi-pressure tools, vibration control products, consumables, technical furniture and enclosures.

APW France, Rue de l'Industrie, B.P. 687, 60006, F-60006 Beauvais, France

AQUENT

711 Boylston Street, Boston, MA, 02116

Tel: (617) 535-5000   Fax: (617) 535-6001   www.aquent.com

Engaged in temporary, specialized employment.

AQUENT, 60 boulevard de Sébastopol, F-75003 Paris, France

ARBOR ACRES FARM INC.

439 Marlborough Road, Glastonbury, CT, 06033

Tel: (860) 633-4681   Fax: (860) 633-2433   www.aaf.com

Producers of male and female broiler breeders, commercial egg layers.

Arbor France SA, Favereau, F-33660 Saint Sauveur de Puynormand, France

Tel: 33-5-5769-6868   Contact: Alain Silvin, Pres.

ARBORTEXT, INC.

1000 Victors Way, Ann Arbor, MI, 48108

Tel: (734) 997-0200   Fax: (734) 997-0201   www.arbortext.com

Mfr. publishing software.

Arbortext France, 17 rue de la Baume, F-75008 Paris, France

ARIBA, INC.

1565 Charleston Rd., Mountain View, CA, 94043

Tel: (650) 930-6200   Fax: (650) 930-6300   www.ariba.com

Mfr. software.

Ariba France SARL, 23 rue Balzac, F-75008 Paris, France

ARMOR HOLDINGS, INC.

1400 Marsh Landing Parkway, Ste. 112, Jacksonville, FL, 32250

Tel: (904) 741-5400   Fax: (904) 741-5403   www.armorholdings.com

Holding company engaged in security products and services.

Defence Systems France SA, 34 Blvd. Haussman, F-75009 Paris, France

ARMSTRONG HOLDINGS, INC.

2500 Columbia Avenue, Lancaster, PA, 17604-3001

Tel: (717) 397-0611   Fax: (717) 396-2787   www.armstrong.com

Mfr. and marketing interior furnishings and specialty products for building, auto and textile industry.

Armstrong Floor Products Europe Sarl, Centre Atria, 58 Boulevard Carnot, F-62000 Arras, France

Tel: 33-3-21-13050

ARROW ELECTRONICS INC.

25 Hub Drive, Melville, NY, 11747

Tel: (516) 391-1300   Fax: (516) 391-1640   www.arrow.com

Distributor of electronic components and computer products.

Arrow Elecronique S.A.-Multicoposanta, Siege Socia, 73/79 rue des Solets, Silic 585, F-95\4663 Rungis Cedex, France

Arrow Electronique, 78-79 rue des Solets, Silic 585, F-94663 Rungis Cedex, France

Tel: 33-1-49-49-78   Fax: 33-1-46-86-7551   Contact: Philippe Djeddah, VP Mktg.

Arrow/CCI Elecronique, Siege Social, 12 alee de la Vierge, Silic 57, F-94653 Rungis Cedex, France

ARROW INTERNATIONAL, INC.

2400 Bernville Rd., Reading, PA, 19605

Tel: (610) 378-0131   Fax: (610) 374-5360   www.arrowintl.com

Develop, manufacture, and marketing of medical devices.

Arrow France S.A., Atlantic Parc Les Pyramides, 11, Route de Pitoys, P.A. de Maignon, F-64600 Anglet Cedex, France

Tel: 33-5-59-313490   Fax: 33-5-59-313491   Contact: Patrick Schall

ART TECHNOLOGY GROUP, INC.

25 First Street, Cambridge, MA, 02141

Tel: (617) 386-1000   Fax: (617) 386-1111   www.atg.com

Mfr. application service software.

Art Technology Group, 14 rue du 4 Septembre, F-75002 paris, France

ASG (ALLEN SYSTEMS GROUP)

1333 Third Avenue South, Naples, FL, 34102

Tel: (941) 435-2200   Fax: (941) 263-3692   www.asg.com

Mainframe computer software, specializing in OnMark 2000 software.

ASG France, Tour Manhattan, 6 Place de l'Iris, F-92095 Paris La Défense Cedex, France

Tel: 33-1-41-02-8585

ASHLAND OIL INC.

50 E. RiverCenter Blvd., Box 391, Covington, KY, 41012-0391

Tel: (859) 815-3333   Fax: (859) 815-5053   www.ashland.com

Petroleum exploration, refining and transportation; mfr. chemicals, oils and lubricants.

Ashland-Avebene SA, 136 ave. Gilbert de Voisins, F-78670 Villennes-sur-Seine, France

ASPECT COMMUNICATIONS CORPORATION

1310 Ridder Park Dr., San Jose, CA, 95131-2312

Tel: (408) 325-2200   Fax: (408) 325-2260   www.aspect.com

Mfr. software and related equipment.

Aspect France, Immeuble Le Carillion, 5 Esplanade Charles de Gaulle, F-92000 Nanterre Cedex, France

Tel: 33-1-5551-2100

ASPEN TECHNOLOGY, INC.

10 Canal Park, Cambridge, MA, 02141

Tel: (617) 949-1000   Fax: (617) 949-1030   www.aspentec.com

Mfr. software for chemists and refineries.

AspenTech Europe SA, 130 rue de Silly, F-2100 Boulogne, France

Tel: 33-1-4712-4772   Fax: 33-1-4712-4774

ASSOCIATED MERCHANDISING CORPORATION

500 Seventh Ave., 2nd Fl., New York, NY, 10018

Tel: (212) 819-6600   Fax: (212) 819-6701   www.theamc.com

Retail service organization; apparel, shoes and accessories.

Associated Merchandising Corp., 14 rue de Castiglione, F-75001 Paris, France

ASSOCIATED PRESS INC.

50 Rockefeller Plaza, New York, NY, 10020-1605

Tel: (212) 621-1500   Fax: (212) 621-5447   www.ap.com

News gathering agency.

The Associated Press, Paris, France

Tel: 33-1-43-59-8876

ASTEA INTERNATIONAL, INC.

455 Business Center Drive, Horsham, PA, 19044

Tel: (215) 682-2500   Fax: (215) 682-2515   www.astea.com

Produces computer software that assists to automate and manage field service, sales and customer support operations.

Astea France, 109 Chemin de Ronde, F-78290 Croissy sur Seine, France

Tel: 33-1-3015-4444

ATMEL CORPORATION

2325 Orchard Pkwy., San Jose, CA, 95131

Tel: (408) 441-0311   Fax: (408) 436-4200   www.atmel.com

Design, manufacture and marketing of advanced semiconductors.

Atmel Rousset, Zone Industrielle, F-13106 Rousset Cedex, France

Tel: 33-4-4253-6000

ATTACHMATE CORPORATION

3617 131st Avenue SE, Bellevue, WA, 98006-1332

Tel: (425) 644-4010   Fax: (425) 747-9924   www.attachmate.com

Mfr. connectivity software.

Attachmate Sales France, 62 bis Ave. Andre Morizet, F-92643 Boulogne-Billancourt Cedex, France

Tel: 33-1-46-04-1010   Fax: 33-1-49-09-0559

AUTODESK INC.

111 McInnis Parkway, San Rafael, CA, 94903

Tel: (415) 507-5000   Fax: (415) 507-6112   www.autodesk.com

Develop/marketing/support computer-aided design, engineering, scientific and multimedia software products.

Autodesk SARL, Batiment Les Ellipses 3/5, Ave. du Chemin de Presles, F-94410 Saint-Maurice, France

Tel: 33-1-45-11-5000   Fax: 33-1-45-11-5001

AUTOMATIC DATA PROCESSING INC.

One ADP Blvd., Roseland, NJ, 07068

Tel: (973) 994-5000   Fax: (973) 994-5387   www.adp.com

Data processing services.

ADP Europe, 148 rue Anatole France, F-92688 Levallois Perret Cedex Paris, France

Tel: 33-1-55-63-5027   Fax: 33-1-55-63-5079   Contact: Jenny Defaix

AUTOMATIC SWITCH CO. (ASCO)

50-60 Hanover Rd., Florham Park, NJ, 07932

Tel: (973) 966-2000   Fax: (973) 966-2628   www.asco.com

Mfr. solenoid valves, emergency power controls, pressure and temperature switches.

ASCO/Jouco, France, 32 ave. Albert 1er, BP 312, F-92506 Ruycil Malmaison, France

Tel: 33-1-47-14-3200   Fax: 33-1-47-14-3064   Contact: Pascal Lamonerie

AUTOSPLICE INC.

10121 Barnes Canyon Road, San Diego, CA, 92121

Tel: (858) 535-0077   Fax: (858) 535-0130   www.autosplice.com

Mfr. electronic components.

Autosplice France, 71 Boulevard Eugene Reguillon, F-69100 Villeurbonne, France

Tel: 33-4-7884-3939   Contact: Yvon Dussurget

AVERY DENNISON CORPORATION

150 N. Orange Grove Blvd., Pasadena, CA, 91103

Tel: (626) 304-2000   Fax: (626) 792-7312   www.averydennison.com

Mfr. pressure-sensitive adhesives and materials, office products, labels, tags, retail systems, Carter's Ink and specialty chemicals.

Avery Dennison, Immeuble La Panoramique, 5 Ave. de Verdun, F-94204 Irvy sur Siene Cedex, France

Tel: 33-1-45-215780   Fax: 33-1-45-215799

Doret SA, 8 rue Montgolfier, F-93115 Rosny-sous-Bois, France

Fasson France SARL, Champ-sur-Drac, F-38560 Jarrie, France

AVID TECHNOLOGY, INC.

1 Park West, Tewksbury, MA, 01876

Tel: (978) 640-6789   Fax: (978) 640-1366   www.avid.com

Mfr. animation design software and digital and audio systems.

Avid Technology SARL, 44 Avenue Georges Pompidou, F-92300 Levallois Perret, France

Fax: 33-1-4757-1527

AVNET INC.

2211 South 47th Street, Phoenix, AZ, 85034

Tel: (480) 643-2000   Fax: (480) 643-4670   www.avnet.com

Distributor electronic components, computers and peripherals.

Avnet CK Electronique, 31 Blvd. Pre Pommier, ZA du Champfleuri, F-38300 Bourgouin-Jallieu, France

Tel: 33-4744-38045   Fax: 33-47-4286911

Avnet EMG France SA, 79 rue Pierre-Semard, F-92322 Chatillon Cedex, France

Tel: 33-1-4965-2700   Fax: 33-1-5495-2769

BFI Ibexsa Electronique, 1 rue Lavoisier-ZI, F-91430 Igny, France

Tel: 33-169-337427   Fax: 33-169-337470

AVON PRODUCTS, INC.

1345 Avenue of the Americas, New York, NY, 10105-0196

Tel: (212) 282-5000   Fax: (212) 282-6049   www.avon.com

Mfr. direct seller of cosmetics and beauty-related items.

Avon SA, Chemin d'Uny, F-60290 Rantigny, France

Tel: 33-11-69-1400 Fax: 33-44-69-1750   Contact: Pierre Decroux, Sales Mgr.

AVX CORPORATION

801 17th Ave. South, Myrtle Beach, SC, 29577

Tel: (843) 448-9411   Fax: (843) 448-7139   www.avxcorp.com

Mfr. multilayer ceramic capacitors.

AVX SA, Chemin de la Poudiere, BP 287, F-76120 Grand Quevilly Rouen, France

AXCELIS TECHNOLOGIES, INC.

55 Cherry Hill Drive, Beverly, MA, 01915

Tel: (978) 787-4000   Fax: (978) 787-4200   www.axcelis.com

Mfr. implantation devices.

Axcelis Technologies SARL, 3 Avenue du Canada, LP 826, Batiment Gamma, F-91974 Les Ulis Cedex, France

AXEDA SYSTEMS INC.

257 Great Valley Pkwy., Malvern, PA, 19355

Tel: (610) 251-9999   Fax: (610) 695-2592   www.axeda.com

Mfr. software.

Axeda Systems, 129 Boulevard Pinel, F-69500 Bron, France

AZON CORPORATION

2204 Ravine Road, Kalamazoo, MI, 49004-3506

Tel: (616) 385-5942   Fax: (616) 385-5937   www.azonintl.com

Designs and manufactures special multi-component chemical metering, mixing and dispensing machines.

Azon FK&E France Ltd., 3 rue 6200, Compiegne, France

BAIN & COMPANY, INC.

Two Copley Place, Boston, MA, 02116

Tel: (617) 572-2000   Fax: (617) 572-2427   www.bain.com

Strategic management consulting services.

Bain & Compagnie, Snc., 21 blvd de la Madeleine, F-75001 Paris, France

Tel: 33-1-44-55-7575 Fax: 33-1-44-55-7600

ROBERT W. BAIRD & CO. INCORPORATED

PO Box 672, Milwaukee, WI, 53201

Tel: (414) 765-3500   Fax: (414) 765-3600   www.rwbaird.com

Engaged in investment banking, serving individuals, corporations, municipalities and institutional investors.

Granville Baird, 16 Avenue Hoehe, F-75008 Paris, France

Tel: 33-1-4076-0401   Fax: 33-1-4076-0402   Contact: Jacques Paquin

BAKER & McKENZIE

130 East Randolph Drive, Ste. 2500, Chicago, IL, 60601

Tel: (312) 861-8000   Fax: (312) 861-2899   www.bakerinfo.com

International legal services.

Baker & McKenzie, 32 Ave. Kleber, F-75116 Paris, France

Tel: 33-1-44-17-5300 Fax: 33-1-44-17-4575

BAKER HUGHES INCORPORATED

3900 Essex Lane, Ste. 1200, Houston, TX, 77027

Tel: (713) 439-8600   Fax: (713) 439-8699   www.bakerhughes.com

Develop and apply technology to drill, complete and produce oil and natural gas wells; provide separation systems to petroleum, municipal, continuous process and mining industries.

Baker Hughes International Ltd., Ave. Thimonnier, Zone Induspal, F- 64140 Lons, France

Baker Oil Tools S.A., Ave. Thimonier, Z.I. Lons, F-64143 Pau Billere Cedex, France

Tel: 33-5-59-32-8725   Fax: 33-5-59-62-3200

Milchem France SARL, 201 Bureaux de la Colline, F-92213 St. Cloud Paris, France

BAKER PETROLITE CORPORATION

3900 Essex Lane, Houston, TX, 77027

Tel: (713) 599-7400   Fax: (713) 599-7592   www.bakerhughes.com

Mfr. specialty chemical treating programs, performance-enhancing additives and related equipment and services.

Luzzatto & Figlio (France) SA, 10 ave. Percier, F-75008 Paris, France

Petrolite France SA, 10 ave. Percier, F-75008 Paris, France

BALDOR ELECTRIC COMPANY

5711 R.S. Boreham Jr. Street, Fort Smith, AR, 72908

Tel: (501) 646-4711   Fax: (501) 648-5792   www.baldor.com

Mfr. electric motors.

Baldor Automation, Groupe Jeambrun, ZI Athelia IV, Av. Du Mistral, F-13705 La Clotat Cedex, France

BALDWIN TECHNOLOGY COMPANY, INC.

12 Commerce Drive, Shelton, CT, 06484

Tel: (203) 402-1000   Fax: (203) 402-5500   www.baldwintech.com

Mfr./services material handling, accessories, control and prepress equipment for print industry.

Baldwin France Sarl, 20 Ave. de Bergoide, F-60550 Verneuil en Halatta, France

Tel: 33-3-42-50-681   Fax: 33-3-44-25-11640   Contact: Alain Fouque, Mng. Dir.

BALTEK CORPORATION

10 Fairway Court, PO Box 195, Northvale, NJ, 07647

Tel: (201) 767-1400   Fax: (201) 387-6631   www.baltek.com

Mfr. light lumber, balsa wood and PVC foam.

Baltek SA, 61 rue de La Fontaine, F-75016 Paris, France

Tel: 33-1-46-47-5850   Fax: 33-1-46-47-6658

BANK OF AMERICA CORPORATION

Bank of America Corporate Center, Charlotte, NC, 28255

Tel: (415) 622-3530   Fax: (704) 386-6699   www.bankofamerica.com

Financial services.

Bank of America NT & SA, 43-37 ave. de la Grande Armee, F-75782 Paris Cedex 16, France

Tel: 33-1-45-02-6800   Fax: 33-1-45-01-7789   Contact: Christian Bartholin, SVP

THE BANK OF NEW YORK

One Wall Street, New York, NY, 10286

Tel: (212) 495-1784   Fax: (212) 495-2546   www.bankofny.com

Banking services.

The Bank of New York, 13-15 Boulevard de la Madeleine, F-75001 Paris, France

Tel: 33-1-42-46-2625   Fax: 33-1-42-47-0236

C. R. BARD, INC.

730 Central Ave., Murray Hill, NJ, 07974

Tel: (908) 277-8000   Fax: (908) 277-8078   www.crbard.com

Mfr. health care products.

Laboratoires Bard SA, rue des Charmes, BP 145, F-78190 Trappes, France

BARNES GROUP INC.

123 Main Street, Bristol, CT, 06011-0489

Tel: (860) 583-7070   Fax: (860) 589-3507   www.barnesgroupinc.com

Mfr. produces precision mechanical and nitrogen gas springs for heavy machinery.

Associated Spring Ressorts SPEC, Montigny, France

Autoliaisons & LeSysteme Bowman, Voisins Le Bretonneux, France

Bowman Distribution France Sa, Elancourt, France

BARRINGER TECHNOLOGIES INC.

30 Technology Drive, Warren, NJ, 07059

Tel: (908) 222-9100   Fax: (908) 222-1557   www.barringer.com

Provides advanced technology for security, law enforcement, including drug and explosive detectors.

Barringer Europe, SARL, 4 rue Du Te, F-95724 Roissy Cedex, France

Tel: 33-1-48-62-5492   Fax: 33-1-48-62-5496

BARRY CONTROLS INC.

40 Guest Street, PO Box 9105, Brighton, MA, 02135-9105

Tel: (617) 787-1555   Fax: (617) 254-7381   www.barrymounts.com

Mfr./sale vibration isolation mounting devices.

Barry Controls Aerospace (European Service), Zone d'Aviation d'Affaires, Bat 41, F-31700 Toulouse, France

R.G. BARRY CORPORATION

13405 Yarmouth Road NW, Pickerington, OH, 43147

Tel: (614) 864-6400   Fax: (614) 866-9787   www.rgbarry.com

Mfr. slippers and footwear.

Fargeot et Cie SA, Route de Limoges, F-24800 Thiviers, France

Tel: 33-55-352-2486   Fax: 33-55-352-2649

R.G Barry Paris, 31 Square Saint Charles, F-75012 Paris, France

Tel: 33-14-468-8808   Fax: 33-14-307-3849

BATES WORLDWIDE INC.

498 Seventh Avenue, New York, NY, 10018

Tel: (212) 297-7000   Fax: (212) 986-0270   www.batesww.com

Advertising, marketing, public relations and media consulting.

Bates 141 France, 4 rue Sentou, F-92150 Sureenes, France

Tel: 33-1-41-38-9350   Fax: 33-1-41-38-9351   Contact: Patrick Geindre, Chmn.

Bates France, 11 rue Galvani, F-75838 Paris Cedex 17, France

Tel: 33-1-44-09-5959   Fax: 33-1-45-74-0806   Contact: Violaine Sanson-Tricard, CEO

BAUSCH & LOMB INC.

One Bausch & Lomb Place, Rochester, NY, 14604-2701

Tel: (716) 338-6000   Fax: (716) 338-6007   www.bausch.com

Mfr. vision care products and accessories.

Bausch & Lomb France SA, Route de Levis Saint No, F-78320 Le Mesnil St. Denis, France

BAX GLOBAL INC.

16808 Armstrong Ave., PO Box 19571, Irvine, CA, 92623

Tel: (949) 752-4000   Fax: (949) 260-3182   www.baxworld.com

Air freight forwarder.

BAX Global, rue des Deux Cedres, BP 10287, F-95704 Roissy Aeroport Cedex Paris, France

Tel: 33-1-48-64-6363   Fax: 33-1-48-62-7715

BAXTER INTERNATIONAL INC.

One Baxter Parkway, Deerfield, IL, 60015

Tel: (847) 948-2000   Fax: (847) 948-3948   www.baxter.com

Mfr. products and provide services in the field of the administration of medication and bioscience.

Baxter SA, Etaille, F-36400 La Chatre, France

BBDO WORLDWIDE

1285 Ave. of the Americas, New York, NY, 10019

Tel: (212) 459-5000   Fax: (212) 459-6645   www.bbdo.com

Multinational group of advertising agencies.

La Compagnie/BBDO, Issy-les-Moulineaux, France

BDO SEIDMAN, LLP   BELGIUM

130 East Randolph Street, Chicago, IL, 60601

Tel: (312) 856-9100   Fax: (312) 856-1379   www.bdo.com

International accounting and financial consulting firm.

BDO Gendrot, 25 Quai Carnot, F-92210 Paris-Saint-Cloud, France

Tel: 33-1-41-12-1314   Fax: 33-1-47-71-1700   Contact: Guy Gendrot

BEA SYSTEMS, INC.

2315 North First Street, St. Jose, CA, 95131

Tel: (408) 570-8000   Fax: (408) 570-8091   www.beasys.com

Develops communications management software and provider of software consulting services.

BEA Systems S.A., Tour Manhattan 6, Place de l'Iris, F-92095 Paris La Defense Cedex, France

Tel: 33-1-41-45-7000   Fax: 33-1-41-45-7099

THE BEAR STEARNS & COMPANIES., INC.

245 Park Ave., New York, NY, 10167

Tel: (212) 272-2000   Fax: (212) 272-3092   www.bearstearns.com

Investment banking, securities broker/dealer and investment advisory services.

Bear Stearns Finance, S.A., 21-25 rue de Balzac, 8th Fl., F-75406 Paris Cedex 08, France

Tel: 33-1-42-99-6060   Fax: 33-1-42-99-6050

BEARIUM METALS CORPORATION

4180 S. Creek Road, Chattanooga, TN, 37406

Tel: (423) 622-9991   Fax: (423) 622-9991   www.bearium.com

Barium metal alloys.

Fonderies de Nogent, 91 rue Carnot Nogent sur Oise, BP 57, F-60105 Creil Cedex, France

BECHTEL GROUP INC.

50 Beale Street, PO Box 3965, San Francisco, CA, 94105-1895

Tel: (415) 768-1234   Fax: (415) 768-9038   www.bechtel.com

General contractors in engineering, construction and project management.

Bechtel International Corp., Centre Bassano, 38 rue de Bassano, F-75008 Paris, France

Tel: 33-1-47-20-5304   Fax: 33-1-47-20-5506

BECKMAN COULTER, INC.

4300 N. Harbor Boulevard, Fullerton, CA, 92834

Tel: (714) 871-4848   Fax: (714) 773-8898   www.beckmancoulter.com

Develop/mfr./marketing automated systems and supplies for biological analysis.

Beckman Coulter France S.A., Paris Nord II, 33 rue des Vanesses, BP 50359 Villepinte, F-95942 Roissy Cedex, France

Tel: 33-1-49-90-9000

BECTON DICKINSON AND COMPANY

One Becton Drive, Franklin Lakes, NJ, 07417-1880

Tel: (201) 847-6800   Fax: (201) 847-6475   www.bd.com

Mfr./sale medical supplies, devices and diagnostic systems.

Becton Dickinson European Divisions, 5 Chemin des Sources, BP 37, F-38241 Meylan, France

Becton Dickinson Pharmaceutical Systems, 11 rue Aristide Berges, BP 4, F-38800 Pont de Claix, France

BELDEN, INC.
7701 Forsyth Blvd., Ste. 800, St. Louis, MO, 63015

Tel: (314) 854-8000   Fax: (314) 854-8001   www.belden.com

Mfr. electronic wire and cable products.

Belden Electronics S.a.r.l., Immeuble le Cesar, 20 Place Louis Pradel, F-69001 Lyon, France

BELL SPORTS CORP.
6225 N. State Hwy. 161, Ste. 300, Irving, TX, 75038

Tel: (972) 417-6600   Fax: (972) 871-8676   www.bellsports.com

Mfr. bicycle and automotive racing helmets and accessories.

Euro-Bell SA, Z.I. du Gatling, rue Mathieu Vallat, F-42230 St. Etienne, France

BELLSOUTH CORPORATION LATIN AMERICA
1155 Peachtree Street NE, Ste. 400, Atlanta, GA, 30367

Tel: (404) 249-4800   Fax: (404) 249-4880   www.bellsouth.com

Mobile communications, telecommunications network systems.

Datech SA, 1 rue Marconi, Technopole Metz 2000, F-57070 Metz, France

BEN & JERRY'S HOMEMADE INC.
30 Community Drive, South Burlington, VT, 05403-6828

Tel: (802) 651-9600   Fax: (802) 651-9647   www.benjerry.com

Mfr. premium ice cream.

Ben & Jerry's International, Paris, France

BENTLY NEVADA CORPORATION
1631 Bently Parkway South, Minden, NV, 89423

Tel: (775) 782-3611   Fax: (775) 782-9259   www.bently.com

Provides hardware, software, and services for machinery information and management systems.

Bently Nevada France SARL, 30 ave. de l'Amiral Lemonnier, F-78160 Marly-le-Roi, France

LOUIS BERGER INTERNATIONAL INC.
100 Halsted Street, East Orange, NJ, 07019

Tel: (201) 678-1960   Fax: (201) 672-4284   www.louisberger.com

Consulting engineers, engaged in architecture, environmental and advisory services.

Louis Berger SARL, 71 rue Fondary, F-75015 Paris, France

Tel: 33-1-45-78-3939   Fax: 33-1-45-77-7469

BERLITZ CROSS-CULTURAL TRAINING INC.
400 Alexander Park, Princeton, NJ, 08540

Tel: (609) 514-9650   Fax: (609) 514-9689   www.berlitz.com

Consulting and management training services to bridge cultural gaps for international travelers as well as for business transferees and families.

Berlitz France S.A.S., 15 Place de la Nation, F-75011 Paris, France

Berlitz France S.A.S., 22 avenue des Nations, BP 500 79 Villepinte, F-95948 Roissy Cedex, France

BERNARD HODES GROUP
555 Madison Ave., New York, NY, 10022

Tel: (212) 935-4000   Fax: (212) 755-7324   www.hodes.com

Provides recruitment communications and staffing solutions.

Bernard Hodes Group, 40 Boulevard Henri Sellier, F-92150 Suresnes, France

BEST WESTERN INTERNATIONAL
6201 North 24th Place, Phoenix, AZ, 85106

Tel: (602) 957-4200   Fax: (602) 957-5740   www.bestwestern.com

International hotel chain.

Beau Manoir Hotel, 6 rue de l'arcade, F-75008 Paris, France

Grand Hotel Francais, 12 rue du Temple, F-33000 Bordeaux, France

Tel: 33-5-56-481035

BIJUR LUBRICATING CORPORATION

50 Kocher Dr., Bennington, VT, 05201-1994

Tel: (802) 447-2174   Fax: (802) 447-1365   www.bijur.com

Design and manufacture of grease and oil pumps.

Bijur Products Inc., BP 50, Z.I. de Courtaboeuf, F-91942 Orsay Les Ulis Cedex, France

Tel: 33-1-69-29-85-85 Fax: 33-1-69-07-76-27 Contact: John Pearce, Mng. Dir. Emp: 47

BINNEY & SMITH INC.

1100 Church Lane, PO Box 431, Easton, PA, 18044-0431

Tel: (610) 253-6271   Fax: (610) 250-5768   www.crayola.com

Mfr. crayons, art supplies and craft kits.

Binney & Smith Ltd., Succursale Francaise, 1 rue de la Mairie, F-60130 Saint-Remy-en-l'Eau, France

BIOGEN, INC.

14 Cambridge Center, Cambridge, MA, 02142

Tel: (617) 679-2000   Fax: (617) 679-2617   www.biogen.com

Engaged in medical research and development of autoimmune diseases.

Biogen Europe, 55 Avenue des Champs Pierreux, F-92012 Nanterre Cedex, France

Tel: 33-1-41-37-95-95 Fax: 33-1-40-97-00-53

Biogen France, Le Capitole, 55 Avenue des Champs Pierreux, F-92012 Nanterre Cedex, France

Tel: 33-1-41-37-95-95

BIO-RAD LABORATORIES INC.

1000 Alfred Nobel Drive, Hercules, CA, 94547

Tel: (510) 724-7000   Fax: (510) 724-3167   www.bio-rad.com

Mfr. life science research products, clinical diagnostics, analytical instruments.

Bio-Rad Laboratories, S.A., 3 boulevard Raymond Poincare, F-92430 Marnes La Coquette, France

Tel: 33-1-47-95-62-85   Fax: 33-1-47-95-61-81

BISSELL INC.

2345 Walker Road, NW, Grand Rapids, MI, 49504

Tel: (616) 453-4451   Fax: (616) 453-1383   www.bissell.com

Mfr. home care products.

Bissell SA, 27, Av. Ampere, Z.I. de Villemilan Wissous, France

BLACK & DECKER CORPORATION

701 E. Joppa Road, Towson, MD, 21286

Tel: (410) 716-3900   Fax: (410) 716-2933   www.blackanddecker.com

Mfr. power tools and accessories, security hardware, small appliances, fasteners, information systems and services.

Black & Decker Servitech, , 140 Ave. de la Republique, Bordeaux, France

Tel: 33-5-56-24-3838   Fax: 33-5-56-51-4471

BLACK BOX CORPORATION

1000 Park Dr., Lawrence, PA, 15055

Tel: (724) 746-5500   Fax: (724) 746-0746   www.blackbox.com

Direct marketer and technical service provider of communications, networking and related computer connectivity products.

Black Box France, 18 rue de L'Esterel, Silic 571, F-94653 Rungis Cedex, France

Tel: 33-1-45-60-6700   Fax: 33-1-45-60-6747   Contact: Norbest Prommdt, Gen. Mgr.

BLOOM ENGINEERING CO., INC.

5460 Horning Rd., Pittsburgh, PA, 15236

Tel: (412) 653-3500   Fax: (412) 653-2253   www.bloomeng.com

Mfr. custom engineered burners and combustion systems.

Bloom Engineering (Europa) GmbH, 8 rue du Marechal Juin, F-95210 Saint Gratien, France

Tel: 33-1-3405-1000 Fax: 33-1-34-05-10-01

BLUE OCEAN SOFTWARE, INC.

15310 Amberly Drive, Ste. 370, Tampa, FL, 33647

Tel: (813) 977-4553   Fax: (813) 979-4447   www.blueocean.com

Mfr. software.

Blue Ocean Software, c/o Kheisys, 24 Blvd. des Martyrs de Chateaubriant, Zone d'Activite du Val d'Argent, F-95100 Argenteuil, France

BMC SOFTWARE, INC.

2101 City West Blvd., Houston, TX, 77042-2827

Tel: (713) 918-8800   Fax: (713) 918-8000   www.bmc.com

Engaged in mainframe-related utilities software and services.

BMC Software, 24 rue Salomon de Rothschild, F-92150 Suresnes, France

BMC Software, Immeuble Danica, 21 avenue Georges Pompidou, F-69486 Lyon Cedex 03, France

BOART LONGYEAR COMPANY

2640 West 1700 South, PO Box 27314, Salt Lake City, UT, 84104

Tel: (801) 972-6430   Fax: (801) 977-3372   www.boartlongyear.com

Mfr. diamond drills, concrete cutting equipment and drill services.

Longyear France, BP 1, F-78191 Trappes Cedex, France

THE BOEING COMPANY

100 N. Riverside Plaza, Chicago, IL, 60606

Tel: (312) 544-2000   Fax: (312) 544-2082   www.boeing.com.

World's largest aerospace company; mfr. military and commercial aircraft, missiles and satellite launch vehicles.

The Boeing Company, Paris, France

BOISE CASCADE CORPORATION

1111 West Jefferson Street, PO Box 50, Boise, ID, 83728-0001

Tel: (208) 384-6161   Fax: (208) 384-7189   www.bc.com

Mfr./distributor paper and paper products, building products, office products.

Boise Cascade Office Products, Ltd., Paris, France

BOOZ-ALLEN & HAMILTON INC.

8283 Greensboro Drive, McLean, VA, 22102

Tel: (703) 902-5000   Fax: (703) 902-3333   www.bah.com

International management and technology consultants.

Booz Allen Hamilton France, 112 Ave. Kleber, F-75116 Paris Cedex 16, France

Tel: 33-1-44-34-3131   Fax: 33-1-44-34-3000

BORDEN CHEMICAL, INC.

180 East Broad Street, Columbus, OH, 43215

Tel: (614) 225-4000   Fax: www.bordenchem.com

Engaged in manufacture and sales of chemical products, including forest product and industrial resins, adhesives and UV coatings.

Borden Chemical France, 3 Rue Barbet, F-76250 Deville-Les Rouen, France

BORLAND SOFTWARE CORPORATION

100 Enterprise Way, Scotts Valley, CA, 95066

Tel: (831) 431-1000   Fax: (831) 431-4141   www.borland.com

Mfr. development software.

Borland France, 100 Terrasse Boeldieu, Tour Franklin, F-92042 La Défense 8 Cedex, France

Tel: 33-1-55-23-5500   Fax: 33-1-55-23-5570

BOSE CORPORATION

The Mountain, Framingham, MA, 01701-9168

Tel: (508) 879-7330   Fax: (508) 766-7543   www.bose.com

Mfr. quality audio equipment and speakers.

BOSE SA, 6 rue St. Vincent, F-78100 Saint Germain en Laye, France

Tel: 33-1-30616363

THE BOSTON CONSULTING GROUP

Exchange Place, 31st Fl., Boston, MA, 02109

Tel: (617) 973-1200   Fax: (617) 973-1339   www.bcg.com

Management consulting company.

The Boston Consulting Group, 4 rue d'Aguesseau, F-75008 Paris, France

Tel: 33-1-40-17-1010

BOSTON SCIENTIFIC CORPORATION (BSC)

One Scientific Place, Natick, MA, 01760-1537

Tel: (508) 650-8000   Fax: (508) 650-8923   www.bostonscientific.com

Developer, manufacturer and marketer of medical devices.

Antheor SNC, Site d'Activities Economiques de Chalembert, 4 rue Monge, F-86130 Juanay Clan, France

Tel: 33-5-49-62-3838   Fax: 33-5-49-62-8484

Boston Scientific International (European Hdqtrs.), Immeuble Vision Defense, 91 blvd National, F-92250 LaGarenne Colombes Cedex Paris, France

Tel: 33-1-46-49-6600   Fax: 33-1-46-49-6699

Boston Scientific, S.A., Par de l'Observatoire, Batiment B, 4 Ave. des Trois Peoples, F-78180 Montigny-Le-Bratonneux, France

Tel: 33-1-30-12-1649   Fax: 33-1-30-96-6010

BOURNS INC.

1200 Columbia Avenue, Riverside, CA, 92507

Tel: (909) 781-5500   Fax: (909) 781-5006   www.bourns.com

Mfr. resistive components and networks, precision potentiometers, panel controls, switches, transducers and surge protectors..

Bourns Ohmic SA, 21/23 rue des Ardennes, F-75019 Paris, France

BOWNE & COMPANY, INC.

345 Hudson Street, New York, NY, 10014

Tel: (212) 924-5500   Fax: (212) 229-3420   www.bowne.com

Financial printing and foreign language translation, localization (software), internet design and maintenance and facilities management.

Bowne Global Solutions, 5 rue Royale, 3rd Fl., F-75008 Paris, France

Tel: 33-1-44-94-3280   Fax: 33-1-44-94-3295   Contact: Antoine Antaki, Dir.

Bowne Global Solutions, 92-98, boulevard Victor Hugo, F-92115 Clichy, France

Tel: 33-1-58-74-92-00   Fax: 33-1-58-74-92-01

BOYDEN CONSULTING CORPORATION

364 Elwood Ave., Hawthorne, NY, 10502

Tel: (914) 747-0093   Fax: (914) 980-6147   www.boyden.com

International executive search firm.

Boyden Associates Ltd. - Search, 1 Rond-Point des Champs-Elysees, F-75008 Paris, France

Tel: 33-1-44-13-6700

Boyden International SARL Consulting, 38 rue Vauthier, F-92774 Boulogne Cedex, France

Tel: 33-1-46-99-1818

BOZELL GROUP

40 West 23rd Street, New York, NY, 10010

Tel: (212) 727-5000   Fax: (212) 645-9173   www.bozell.com

Advertising, marketing, public relations and media consulting.

Bozell France/Bozell Marketing/TN Media, 20 rue de L'Eglise 36, F-92522 Neuilly sur Seine, France

Tel: 33-1-41-92-1515   Fax: 33-1-41-92-1500   Contact: Brian Tucker, CEO

Bozell Terre Lune, 20 rue de L'Eglise 36, F-92522 Neuilly sur Seine, France

Tel: 33-1-41-92-1520   Fax: 33-1-41-92-1500   Contact: Serge Hugon, Mng. Dir.

BRADY CORPORATION

6555 W. Good Hope Road, Milwaukee, WI, 53223

Tel: (414) 358-6600   Fax: (414) 358-6600   www.whbrady.com

Mfr. industrial ID for wire marking, circuit boards; facility ID, signage, printing systems and software.

Signals S.A., Rond Point de la Republique, Z.I. de la Rochelle, F-17187 Perigny Cedex, France

W.H. Brady SARL, 2 Place Marcel Rebuffat, BP 362, Parc de Villejust, F-91959 Les Ulis Cedex, France

Tel: 33-1-69-31-9100   Fax: 33-1-69-31-1068   Contact: Max Squires, Country Sales/Mktg Dir.

BRANSON ULTRASONICS CORPORATION

41 Eagle Road, Danbury, CT, 06813-1961

Tel: (203) 796-0400   Fax: (203) 796-2285   www.branson-plasticsjoin.com

Engaged in design, development, manufacture and marketing of plastics joining, precision cleaning and processing equipment.

Branson Ultrasons (KBSA), 1 rue des Pyrenees, Silic 404, F-94573 Rungis Cedex, France

Tel: 33-4-50-43-96-50   Fax: 33-4-50-43-96-60

BRIGGS & STRATTON CORPORATION

PO Box 702, Milwaukee, WI, 53201

Tel: (414) 259-5333   Fax: (414) 259-9594   www.briggesandstratton.com

Mfr. air-cooled gasoline engines for outdoor power equipment.

Briggs & Stratton France, Attn: French Office, PO Box 72, Milwaukee, WI, 53201

BRIGHTPOINT, INC.

600 East 96th Street, Ste. 575, Indianapolis, IN, 46240

Tel: (317) 805-4100   Fax: (317) 805-4101   www.brightpoint.com

Provider of outsourced services in the global wireless telecommunications and data industry; distribution of wireless voice and data products.

Brightpoint France, 93 - Seine-Saint-Denis, 14 rue Davoust, F-93698 Pantin Cedex, France

Tel: 33-1-4810-1600   Fax: 33-1-4810-1699

BRINK'S INC.

Thorndal Circle, Darien, CT, 06820

Tel: (203) 662-7800   Fax: (203) 662-7968   www.brinks.com

Security transportation.

Brink's France, 61 rue Hautpoul, F-75019 Paris, France

BRIO SOFTWARE, INC.

4980 Great America Pkwy., Santa Clara, CA, 95054

Tel: (408) 496-7400   Fax: (408) 496-7420   www.brio.com

Mfr. software.

Brio Software, Le Capitole, 55 avenue des Champs Pierreux, F-92000 Nanterre Cedex, France

BRISTOL-MYERS SQUIBB COMPANY

345 Park Ave., New York, NY, 10154-0037

Tel: (212) 546-4000   Fax: (212) 546-4020   www.bms.com

Pharmaceutical and food preparations, medical and surgical instruments.

Bristol-Myers S.A., rue de la Maison Rouge, Le Mandinet, F-77185 Lognes, France

Bristol-Myers Squibb - Reg. Hdqtrs. - Africa/Paris, Quartier La Grande Arche, F-92057 Cedex 24, France

ConvaTec France, Tour Generale, F-92088 Paris Cedex 22, France

Laboratires Guieu Franceia Ltd., Z.I. de la Barogne, rue des 22 Arpents, F-77230 Lognes, France

Laboratoires ConvaTec, La Grande Arche Nord, F-92044 La Defense Paris Cedex, France

Mead Johnson S.A., 33, Ave. du Marechal, de Lattre de Tassign, France

SOFCA, rue des Longes, F-28232 Epernon, France

UPSA - France, Av. du Dr. Bru, F-47400 Tonneins, France

UPSA France Bon-Encontre, Z.I. Laville, F-47240 Bon-Encontre, France

Zimmer S.A. (Rungis), 62 rue des Gemeaux, Silic 582, F-94663 Rungis Cedex, France

BROADCOM CORPORATION INTERNATIONAL

16215 Alton Pkwy., Irvine, CA, 92619-7013

Tel: (949) 450-8700   Fax: (949) 450-8710   www.broadcom.com

Designs, develops and supplies integrated circuits and high density communication processors.

Broadcom Corporation, 54 rue de Fourqueux, F-78100 St Germain en Laye, France

Tel: 33-1-3904-1395

BROADVISION, INC.

585 Broadway, Redwood City, CA, 94063

Tel: (650) 261-5100   Fax: (650) 261-5900   www.broadvision.com

Develops and delivers an integrated suite of packaged applications for personalized enterprise portals.

BroadVision France, 155 rue Anatole, F-92300 Levallois-Perret, France

Tel: 33-1-4748-8000

BROWN BROTHERS HARRIMAN & COMPANY

140 Broadway, New York, NY, 10005

Tel: (212) 483-1818   Fax: (212) 493-8526   www.bbh.com

Leading provider of mergers and acquisition advisory services and private equity capital to private and closely held public companies.

Brown Brothers Harriman Corp., 12-14 Rond Point des Champs Elysees, F-75008 Paris, France

BROWN SHOE COMPANY, INC.

8300 Maryland Avenue, St. Louis, MO, 63105

Tel: (314) 854-4000   Fax: (314) 854-4274   www.brownshoe.com

Markets branded and private label footwear, including Dr. Scholl's, Air Step and Buster Brown.

Pagoda Intl. SARL, 6 rue St. Vincent, F-78100 St-Germain-en-Laye, France

BROWNING

1 Browning Place, Morgan, UT, 84050

Tel: (801) 876-2711   Fax: (801) 876-3331   www.browning.com

Sales and distribution of port firearms, fishing rods, etc.

Browning Sports France, S.A., 18 rue Salvatore Allende, Z.I. Molina-la-Chazotte, F-42350 La Taludiere, France

BUCK CONSULTANTS INC.

One Penn Plaza, New York, NY, 10119

Tel: (212) 330-1000   Fax: (212) 695-4184   www.buckconsultants.com

Employee benefit, actuarial and compensation consulting services.

Buck Paris, 35 Avenue de Friedland, F-75008 Paris, France

Tel: 33-1-5688-0235   Fax: 33-1-5688-0236   Contact: Claude Vala

LEO BURNETT, DIV. B-COM 3 GROUP

35 West Wacker Drive, Chicago, IL, 60601

Tel: (312) 220-5959   Fax: (312) 220-6533   www.leoburnett.com

Engaged in advertising, marketing, media buying and planning, and public relations.

Black Pencil SARL, 14 rue Alexandre Parodi, F-75010 Paris, France

Bordelais, Lemeunier & Leo Burnett, 185 ave. Charles de Gaulle, F-92521 Neuilly-sur-Seine, France

BURSON-MARSTELLER

230 Park Avenue South, New York, NY, 10003-1566

Tel: (212) 614-4000   Fax: (212) 614-4262   www.bm.com

Public relations/public affairs consultants.

Burson-Marsteller Paris, 6 rue Escudier, F-92772 Boulogre Billancourt Cedex, France

Tel: 33-1-41-86-76-76   Fax: 31-1-86-76-00   Emp: 42

BUTLER AUTOMATIC, INC.

41 Leona Drive, Middleborough, MA, 02346

Tel: (508) 923-0544　　　Fax: (508) 923-0885　　　www.butlerautomatic.com

Mfr. web splicing equipment.

Butler Automatic Inc., P.A.E. de Jourdies, 221 du Rhone, F-74800 St. Pierre-en-Faucigny, France

Tel: 33-4-5003-8520

BUTTERICK COMPANY, INC.

161 Avenue of the Americas, New York, NY, 10013

Tel: (212) 620-2500　　　Fax: (212) 620-2746　　　www.butterick.com

Prints sewing patterns and related magazines.

Vogue Pattern Service, 44 rue la Boetie, F-75008 Paris, France

CABOT CORPORATION

2 Seaport Lane, Ste. 1300, Boston, MA, 02210-2019

Tel: (617) 345-0100　　　Fax: (617) 342-6103　　　www.cabot-corp.com

Mfr. carbon blacks, plastics; oil and gas, information systems.

Berylco-Cabot Metaux Speciaux (Cabot Berylco Div.), BP 17, F-44220 Coueron, France

Berylco-Cabot Metaux Speciaux (Cabot Berylco Div.), 76-78 Champs Elyses, F-75008 Paris, France

Berylco-Cabot Metaux Speciaux, Div. Plastiques, 6 ave. Charles de Gaulle, F-78150 Le Chesnay Paris, France

CACI INTERNATIONAL INC.

1100 North Glebe Road, Arlington, VA, 22201

Tel: (703) 841-7800　　　Fax: (703) 841-7882　　　www.caci.com

Provides simulation technology/software and designs factories, computer networks, and communications systems for military, electronic commerce digital document management, logistics and Y2K remediation.

CACI International, Inc., Paris, France

CADENCE DESIGN SYSTEMS, INC.

2655 Seely Ave., Bldg. 5, San Jose, CA, 95134

Tel: (408) 943-1234　　　Fax: (408) 943-0513　　　www.cadence.com

Mfr. electronic design automation software.

Cadence Design Systems, 1080 Route des Dollines, F-06560 Valbonne, France

Tel: 33-4-8987-3000　Fax: 33-04-8987-3001

Cadence Design Systems, Batiment Avenir, 18 Grange Dame Rose, BP 128, Velizy-Cedex,, F-78140 Paris, France

CAHILL GORDON & REINDEL

80 Pine Street, New York, NY, 10005

Tel: (212) 701-3000　　　Fax: (212) 269-5420　　　www.cahill.com

Engaged in international law.

Cahill, Gordon & Reindel, Paris, France

CALGON CARBON CORPORATION

400 Calgon Carbon Drive, Pittsburgh, PA, 15230-0717

Tel: (412) 787-6700　　　Fax: (412) 787-4541　　　www.calgoncarbon.com

Mfr. activated carbon, related systems and services.

Chemviron Carbon, Immeuble "Expansion", 9-11 rue Georges Enesco, F-94008 Creteil Cedex, France

CALVIN KLEIN, INC.

205 West 39th Street, 4th Fl., New York, NY, 10018

Tel: (212) 719-2600　　　Fax: (212) 768-8922　　　www.calvinklein.com

Mfr. of high quality clothing and accessories

Calvin Klein Ltd., Paris, France

CAMBREX CORPORATION

1 Meadowlands Plaza, East Rutherford, NJ, 07063

Tel: (201) 804-3000　　　Fax: (201) 804-9852　　　www.cambrex.com

human health, animal health/agriculture and Mfr. biotechnology products and produce specialty chemicals.

Francochim, 129 Chemin des Cr»tes, F-31120 Foyrans, France

CAMPBELL SOUP COMPANY

Campbell Place, Camden, NJ, 08103-1799

Tel: (856) 342-4800   Fax: (856) 342-3878   www.campbellsoup.com

Mfr. food products.

Societe Francaise des Biscuits Delacre SA, Paris, France

CANBERRA INDUSTRIES, INC.

800 Research Parkway, Meriden, CT, 06450

Tel: (203) 238-2351   Fax: (203) 235-1347   www.canberra.com

Mfr. instruments for nuclear research.

Canberra Electronique SA, Z.I. de Savigny-le-Temple, 11 Rue de l'Etain, BP 15, F-77541 Savigny-le-Temple Cedex, France

Tel: 33-1-64411010

Canberra Eurisys, ZA de l'Observatoire 4 avenue des Frênes, BP 15, F-78067 St. Quentin Yvelines Cedex, France

CANDLE CORPORATION

201 N. Douglas Street, El Segundo, CA, 90245

Tel: (310) 535-3600   Fax: (310) 727-4287   www.candle.com

Mfr. management software.

Candle France, 13, Ave. de la Porte d'Italie, F-75013 Paris, France

CAPTURA, INC.

6710 108th Avenue NE, Kirkland, WA, 98033

Tel: (425) 803-6000   Fax: (425) 803-6100   www.captura.com

Mfr. automated payment software.

Captura International Ltd., Centre Etoile Balzac, 23, rue Balzac, F-75008 Paris, France

CARBOLINE COMPANY

350 Hanley Industrial Court, St. Louis, MO, 63144

Tel: (314) 644-1000   Fax: (314) 644-4617   www.carboline.com

Mfr. coatings and sealants.

StonCor Europe South, 14 allee Emile Reynaud, Bat. H, F-77200 Torcy, France

Tel: 33-1-600-64419   Fax: 33-1-600-51460

CARGILL, INC.

15407 McGinty Road West, Minnetonka, MN, 55440-5625

Tel: (612) 742-7575   Fax: (612) 742-7393   www.cargill.com

Food products, feeds, animal products.

Compagnie Cargill SA, BP 215, F-78108 St.Germain-en-laye Cedex Paris, France

CARLISLE SYNTEC SYSTEMS

PO Box 7000, Carlisle, PA, 17013

Tel: (717) 245-7000   Fax: (717) 245-9107   www.carlisle-syntec.com

Mfr. electrometric roofing and waterproofing systems.

Carlisle SynTec Systems SARL, Parc Club du Moulin a Vent, 33 ave. du Docteur G. Levy, F-69693 Vennissieux Cedex, France

CARLSON COMPANIES, INC.

PO Box 59159, Minneapolis, MN, 55459

Tel: (612) 550-4520   Fax: (612) 550-4580   www.cmg.carlson.com

Marketing services agency.

Issy-Les-Moullineaux IPC Groupe, 2 rue Maurice Hartmann, F-92137 Issy-les-Moulineaux, France

Tel: 33-1-40-95-2600

THE CARLYLE GROUP L.P.

1001 Pennsylvania Avenue, NW, Washington, DC, 20004-2505

Tel: (202) 347-2626   Fax: (202) 347-1818   www.thecarlylegroup.com

Global investor in defense contracts.

Carlyle Europe, 112 ave. Kelber, F-75116 Paris, France

Tel: 33-1-53-703520

CARPENTER TECHNOLOGY CORPORATION

PO Box 14662, Reading, PA, 19612-4662

Tel: (610) 208-2000   Fax: (610) 208-3214   www.cartech.com

Mfr. specialty steels and structural ceramics for casting industrial.

Carpenter Technology (France) SARL, 77 ave. Fernand Auberger, F-03700 Bellerive-sur-Allier, France

CARRIER CORPORATION

One Carrier Place, Farmington, CT, 06034-4015

Tel: (860) 674-3000   Fax: (860) 679-3010   www.carrier.com

Mfr./distributor/services A/C, heating and refrigeration equipment.

Carrier ETO Ltd., Tour Franklin, Defense 8, F-92042 Paris La Defense Cedex, France

Carrier SA, Montluel, France

Tel: 33-72-25-2121   Fax: 33-72-25-2248

CASCADE CORPORATION

2201 NE 201st Ave., Fairview, OR, 97024-9718

Tel: (503) 669-6300   Fax: (503) 669-6321   www.cascor.com

Mfr. hydraulic forklift truck attachments.

Cascade (France) SARL, 11 rue Jean Charcot, Zone Industrielle Sud, F-91421 Morangis Cedex, France

Mecalev S.A., Les Fontaines Douces, F-58260 La Machine, France

CATALINA MARKETING CORPORATION

200 Carillon Pkwy., St. Petersburg, FL, 33716

Tel: (727) 579-5000   Fax: (727) 570-8507   www.catmktg.com

Engaged in supermarket couponing on-line.

Catalina Marketing France, 60/62 rue Danjou, F-92517 Boulogne Cedex, France

Tel: 33-1-4694-5050

CATAPULT COMMUNICATIONS CORPORATION

160 South Whisman Road, Mountain View, CA, 94041

Tel: (650) 960-1025   Fax: (650) 960-1029   www.catapult.com

Mfr. test systems for telecommunications service providers.

Catapult Communications Corp., Centre d'Entreprises CGIA, 5-7, rue Marcelin Berthelot, F-92762 Antony Cedex, France

Tel: 33-1-55-59-5591

CATERPILLAR INC.

100 NE Adams Street, Peoria, IL, 61629-6105

Tel: (309) 675-1000   Fax: (309) 675-1182   www.cat.com

Mfr. earth/material-handling and construction machinery and equipment and engines.

Caterpillar Holding (France) S.A.R.L., 40-48 ave. Leon Blum, F-38100 Grenoble, France

F.G. Wilson S.A., Paris, France

CB RICHARD ELLIS SERVICES

200 N. Sepulveda Blvd., Ste. 300, El Segundo, CA, 90245-4380

Tel: (310) 563-8600   Fax: (310) 563-8670   www.cbrichardellis.com

Commercial real estate services.

CB Richard Ellis SA, 28/32 Avenue Victor Hugo, F-75116 Paris, France

CCITRIAD

804 Las Cimas Pkwy., Ste. 200, Austin, TX, 78746

Tel: (512) 328-2300 Fax: (512) 328-8209 www.cci-triad.com

Technology solutions for the automotive aftermarket and hardlines and lumber industries.

Triad Systems France, 2 Rue des Commeres, F-78310 Coignieres, France

Tel: 33-1-30-490607 Fax: 33-1-30-490209

CENTRA SOFTWARE, INC.

430 Bedford Street, Lexington, MA, 02421

Tel: (781) 861-7000 Fax: (781) 863-7288 www.centra.com

Mfr. on-line learning software.

Centra Software, 24 rue Jacques Ibert, F-92300 Levallois-Perret, France

Centra Software, 51 Boulevard de Courc, F-75008 Paris, France

CENTRAL NATIONAL-GOTTESMAN INC.

3 Manhattanville Road, Purchase, NY, 10577-2110

Tel: (914) 696-9000 Fax: (914) 696-1066 www.cng-inc.com

Distribution of pulp and paper products.

Central National France, S.A.R.L., 21 rue Auber, F-75009 Paris Cedex, France

Tel: 33-1-47-42-2415 Fax: 33-1-47-42-2429 Contact: Bogdan Pohl

CENTURY 21 REAL ESTATE CORPORATION

One Campus Drive, Parsippany, NJ, 07054-3826

Tel: (973) 496-5722 Fax: (973) 496-5527 www.century21.com

Engaged in real estate sales.

Century 21 France, S.A., rue des Cevennes Batiment 4, Petite Montagne Sud, F-91017 Evry Cedex Lisses, France

Tel: 33-1-69-11-1221 Contact: Frank Cluck, Gen. Mgr.

CEPHALON, INC.

145 Brandywine Pkwy., West Chester, PA, 19380

Tel: (610) 344-0200 Fax: (610) 344-0065 www.cephalon.com

Engaged in health science, research and development.

Cephalon France, 14 rue Albert Einstein, F-77420 Champs Sur Marne, France

Tel: 33-1-64-61-0505 Fax: 33-1-64-61-0500 Contact: Christian Lebreton

CERTEGY INC.

11720 Amber park Drive, Ste. 600, Alpharetta, GA, 30004

Tel: (678) 867-8000 Fax: (678) 867-8100 www.certegy.com

Provides credit, debit and merchant card processing, e-banking, check risk management and check cashing services to financial institutions and merchants worldwide.

Certegy France, Tour Franklin, La Defense 8, F-92042 Paris, France

CH2M HILL INC.

6060 South Willow Drive, Greenwood Village, CO, 80111

Tel: (303) 771-0900 Fax: (303) 770-2616 www.ch2m.com

Consulting engineers, planners, economists and scientists.

CH2M Hill, 37 Boulevard Aristide Briand, F-13100 Aix-en-Provence, France

CHARLES RIVER LABORATORIES INTERNATIONAL, INC.

251 Ballardvale Street, Wilmington, MA, 01887-1000

Tel: (978) 658-6000 Fax: (978) 658-7132 www.criver.com

Engaged in sales of pathogen-free, fertilized chicken eggs for drug testing.

Charles River France, Domaine de Oncins, BP 87, F-86953 L'Arbresle Cedex, France

CHECKPOINT SYSTEMS, INC.

101 Wolf Drive, Thorofare, NJ, 08086

Tel: (856) 848-1800   Fax: (856) 848-0937   www.checkpointsystems.com

Mfr. test, measurement and closed-circuit television systems.

Checkpoint Systems France SARL, 3 bd. Des Bouvets, F-92022 Nanterre Cedex, France

Tel: 33-1-55-69-6111   Fax: 33-1-55-69-6118   Contact: Gerald Valle, Mng. Dir.

CHEMFAB CORPORATION

701 Daniel Webster Hwy., PO Box 1137, Merrimack, NH, 03054

Tel: (603) 424-9000   Fax: (603) 424-9028   www.chemfab.com

Mfr. advanced polymer materials.

H.C.C. SA, 66, Pyrenees-Orientales, F-Languedoc-Roussillon Bompas, France

THE CHERRY CORPORATION

3600 Sunset Ave., PO Box 718, Waukegan, IL, 60087

Tel: (847) 662-9200   Fax: (847) 662-2990   www.cherrycorp.com

Mfr. electrical switches, electronic keyboards, controls and displays.

Cherry SARL, 1 ave. des Violettes, F-94384 Bonneuil Cedex, France

Tel: 33-1-437-72951   Fax: 33-1-437-72084

CHEVRON PHILLIPS CHEMICAL COMPANY LP

1301 McKinney Street, Houston, TX, 77010

Tel: (713) 754-2000   Fax: (713) 754-2016   www.chevron.com

Mfr. petro chemicals.

Chevron Chemical SA, 47 rue de Villiers, F-92527 Neuilly-sur-Seine, France

CHEVRON TEXACO CORPORATION

575 Market Street, San Francisco, CA, 94105-2856

Tel: (415) 894-7700   Fax: (415) 894-2248   www.chevrontexaco.com

Oil exploration, production and petroleum products.

ChevronTexaco France, 39 rue Cambon, F-75001 Paris, France

CHIEF INDUSTRIES INC.

3942 West Old Highway 30, Grand Island, NE, 68802-2078

Tel: (308) 382-8820   Fax: (308) 381-7221   www.chiefind.com

Mfr. grain bins, steel buildings, grain handling and drying equipment, elevator legs and components.

Phenix-Rousies Industries, S.A., F-59131 Rousies, France

Tel: 33-3-2769-4242   Fax: 33-3-27-64-9585

CHIRON CORPORATION

4560 Horton Street, Emeryville, CA, 94608-2916

Tel: (510) 655-8730   Fax: (510) 655-9910   www.chiron.com

Engaged in biotechnology; biopharmaceuticals, blood testing and vaccines.

Chiron France, 10 rue Chevreul, F-92150 Suresnes, France

CHOICE HOTELS INTERNATIONAL, INC.

10750 Columbia Pike, Silver Springs, MD, 20902

Tel: (301) 592-5000   Fax: (301) 592-6227   www.choicehotels.com

Hotel franchises, including Comfort Inn, Econo Lodge, Roadway Inn and Quality.

Choice Hotels France, Lieu-dit Les Champcueils BP 66, F-91223 Bretigny Sur orge Cedex, France

CHORDIANT SOFTWARE, INC.

20400 Stevens Creek Blvd., Ste. 400, Cupertino, CA, 95014-2217

Tel: (408) 517-6100   Fax: (408) 517-0270   www.chordiant.com

Mfr. customer relationship management software.

Chordiant Software, 54, Avenue Victor Hugo, F-92500 Paris, France

THE CHRISTIAN SCIENCE PUBLISHING SOCIETY

1 Norway Street, Boston, MA, 02115

Tel: (617) 450-2000   Fax: (617) 450-7575   www.christianscience.com

Publishing company.

The Christian Science Monitor, 4 rue de Casablanca, F-75015 Paris, France

Tel: 33-1-43-31-2290   Contact: Peter Ford   Emp: 1

THE CHUBB CORPORATION

15 Mountain View Road, Warren, NJ, 07061-1615

Tel: (908) 580-2000   Fax: (908) 580-3606   www.chubb.com

Holding company for property and casualty insurance and liability insurance for corporate executives.

Chubb Insurance Co. of Europe, SA, 9 rue Conde, F-33000 Bordeaux, France

Tel: 33-5-5600-1257   Fax: 33-5-56-44-2351

Chubb Insurance Company of Europe, S.A., 14, Parc Club de Gold, F-13856 Aix en Provence Cedex 03, France

Tel: 33-4-42-163525   Fax: 33-4-42-163526

Chubb Insurance Company of Europe, S.A., 5 bd Vincent Gache, BP 36204, F-44262 Nantes Cedex 02, France

Tel: 33-2-40-41-7378   Fax: 33-2-40-41-7388

Chubb Insurance Company of Europe, S.A., 298 Bd Clemenceau, F-59700 Marcq en Baroeul, France

Tel: 33-3-20-818506   Fax: 33-3-20-89-2373

Chubb Insurance Company of Europe, S.A., 16 Avenue de Matignon, F-75008 Paris, France

Tel: 33-1-45-61-7300   Fax: 33-1-45-61-9851

Chubb Insurance Company of Europe, SA, Le Forum Part Dieu 29, rue Maurice Flandin, F-69444 Lyon Cedex 03, France

Tel: 33-72-34-5204   Fax: 33-72-33-6098

CIENA CORPORATION

1201 Winterson Road, Linthicum, MD, 21090-2205

Tel: (410) 865-8500   Fax: (410) 694-5750   www.ciena.com

Mfr. optical network switching hardware.

CIENA Ltd., 7 Place d'Iena, F-75116 Paris, France

Tel: 33-1-5357-5778

CIGNA COMPANIES

One Liberty Place, Philadelphia, PA, 19192

Tel: (215) 761-1000   Fax: (215) 761-5511   www.cigna.com

Insurance, invest, health care and other financial services.

CIGNA France Compagnie d'Assurances, 5 rue de Turin, F-75008 Paris, France

CIGNA I, 5 rue de Turin, F-75008 Paris, France

CIGNA Insurance Co. of Europe SA/NV, 17 rue Ballu, F-75008 Paris, France

CIGNA Life Insurance Copany of Europe S.A.-N.V., Le Colisee-8 Ave. de l'Arche, F-92419 Courbevoi Paris Cedex, France

Tel: 33-1-559`-4545

Esis Intl. Inc., 5 rue Kleber, F-93100 Montreuil-sous-Bois, France

La Nouvelle SA, 14 rue Ballu, F-75009 Paris, France

CINCINNATI INCORPORATED

PO Box 11111, Cincinnati, OH, 45211

Tel: (513) 367-7100   Fax: (513) 367-7552   www.e-ci.com

Mfr. metal fabricating equipment.

O.G.R., 20 rue De La Liberte, F-95500 Gonesse, France

Tel: 33-1-39-87-0816   Fax: 33-1-39-85-2616

CINCINNATI MACHINE INC.

4701 Marburg Ave., Cincinnati, OH, 45209

Tel: (513) 841-8100   Fax: (513) 841-8919   www.cinmach.com

Mfr. of CNC machine tools, such as turning centers, vertical machining centers and horizontal machining centers.

Cincinnati Machine, Div. UNOVA Inc., 31, Avenue Pierre Brossolette, Immeuble Point Cardinal, F-91385 Chilly Mazarin, France

Tel: 33-1-60-49-13-30   Fax: 33-1-64-48-13-28

CINCOM SYSTEMS INC.

55 Merchant Street, Cincinnati, OH, 45446

Tel: (513) 612-2300   Fax: (513) 481-8332   www.cincom.com

Develop/distributor computer software.

Cincom Systems France, 13 Avenue de la porte d'Italie, F-75640 Paris, France

CISCO SYSTEMS, INC.

170 West Tasman Drive, San Jose, CA, 95134-1706

Tel: (408) 526-4000   Fax: (408) 526-4100   www.cisco.com

Develop/mfr./market computer hardware and software networking systems.

Cisco Systems Europe, s.a.r.l., Parc Evolic, Batiment L1/L, 16 Ave. du Quebec, BP 706 Villebon, F-91961 Courtaboeuf Cedex, France

Tel: 33-1-6918-6100   Fax: 33-1-6928-8326

CITIGROUP, INC.

399 Park Avenue, New York, NY, 10022

Tel: (212) 559-1000   Fax: (212) 559-3646   www.citigroup.com

Provides insurance and financial services worldwide.

Citigroup, Paris, France

Contact: Claude Jouven

CITRIX SYSTEMS, INC.

6400 NW 6th Way, Fort Lauderdale, FL, 33309

Tel: (954) 267-3000   Fax: (954) 267-9319   www.citrix.com

Developer of computer software.

Citrix Systems SARL, 84 Ave. du General Leclerc, F-92100 Boulogne-Billancourt, France

Tel: 33-1-55-60-1070   Fax: 33-1-55-60-1071

CLARCOR INC.

2323 Sixth Street, PO Box 7007, Rockford, IL, 61125

Tel: (815) 962-8867   Fax: (815) 962-0417   www.clarcor.com

Mfr. filtration products and consumer packaging products.

Facet France SARL, Div. CLARCOR, 22, Avenue des Nations, Z.I. Paris Nord II, B. P. 60055,, F-95972 Roissy CDG Cedex,, France

CLAYTON INDUSTRIES

4213 N. Temple City Blvd., El Monte, CA, 91731

Tel: (626) 443-9381   Fax: (626) 442-1701   www.claytonindustries.com

Mfr. steam generators, dynamometers and water treatment chemicals.

Clayton de France, S.A.R.L., CE No. 1433, 2 rue Du Ventoux Z.I. Petite Montagne, F-91019 Evry Cedex, France

Tel: 33-1-60-77-02-50   Fax: 33-1-60-77-01-11

CLEAR CHANNEL COMMUNICATIONS

200 East Basse Road, San Antonio, TX, 78209

Tel: (210) 822-2828   Fax: (210) 822-2299   www.clearchannel.com

Owns, manages, promotes and produces concerts and shows; programs and sells airtime for radio stations, owns and places outdoor advertising displays and provides agent services to athletes and broadcasters.

Dauphin Advertising, 21 Boulevard de la Madeleine, F-75001 Paris, France

Tel: 33-1-40-82-8282   Contact: Claude Duval

CLEARY GOTTLIEB STEEN & HAMILTON

One Liberty Plaza, New York, NY, 10006

Tel: (212) 225-2000   Fax: (212) 225-3999   www.cgsh.com

Engaged in international law.

Cleary, Gottlieb, Steen, & Hamilton, 41 ave. de Friedland, F-75008 Paris, France

CLUBCORP, INC.

3030 LBJ Freeway, Ste. 700, Dallas, TX, 75234

Tel: (972) 243-6191   Fax: (972) 888-7700   www.clubcorp.com

Operates high-end golf courses and resorts.

Paris International Golf Club, 18 Route du Golf, F-95560 Baillet-en-France, France

Tel: 33-5-34699000

CNA FINANCIAL CORPORATION

CNA Plaza, Chicago, IL, 60685

Tel: (312) 822-5000   Fax: (312) 822-6419   www.cna.com

Commercial property/casualty insurance policies.

CNA Insurance Company (Europe) Limited (CIE), Paris, France

CNH (CASE NEW HOLLAND) GLOBAL

100 South Saunders Road, Lake Forest, IL, 60045

Tel: (847) 955-3821   Fax: (847) 955-3961   www.casecorp.com

Mfr. and sale of agricultural and construction equipment.

CNH Europe, 18 Place des Nympheas, Z1 Paris Nord II, F-95915 Roissy CDG Cedex, France

Tel: 33-1-49-90-2300   Fax: 33-1-49-90-2587   Contact: Leopold Plattner, Pres. Eur/Africa/ME

CNH France S.A., 17 rue des Tournelles, F-60803 Crepy-en-Valois Cedex, France

Tel: 33-4494-3200   Fax: 33-4487-6869

CNH France S.A., 71 av. Georges Hannart, BP 109, F-59964 Croix Cedex, France

Tel: 33-2066-3900   Fax: 33-2066-3902

CNH France S.A., av. Georges Bataille, F-60670 Le Plessis-Belleville Cedex, France

CNH France S.A., Clos Saint Jean, BP 37, F-52102 St. Dizier, France

Tel: 33-2556-7900   Fax: 33-2505-2896

CNH France S.A., 28 route de Bailly, Tracy-le-Mont, F-60170 Ribecourt, France

Tel: 33-4475-5151   Fax: 33-4475-5100

COACH LEATHERWEAR COMPANY

516 West 34th Street, New York, NY, 10001

Tel: (212) 594-1850   Fax: (212) 594-1682   www.coach.com

Mfr. and sales of high-quality leather products, including handbags, wallets and shoes.

Coach at Boutique ALMA, 1 rue Henri Rivière, F-78200 Mantes-La-Jolie, France

THE COCA-COLA COMPANY

1 Coca Cola Plaza, Atlanta, GA, 30313

Tel: (404) 676-2121   Fax: (404) 676-6792   www.coca-cola.com

Mfr./marketing/distributor soft drinks, syrups and concentrates, juice and juice-drink products.

Coca-Cola France, Paris, France

COGNEX CORPORATION

1 Vision Drive, Natick, MA, 01760

Tel: (508) 650-3000   Fax: (508) 650-3333   www.cognex.com

Mfr. machine vision systems.

Cognex Corporation France, Immeuble le Patio, 104 Avenue Albert 1er, F-92563 Rueil Malmaison Cedex, France

Tel: 33-1-4777-1550   Fax: 33-1-4777-1555

COHERENT INC.

5100 Patrick Henry Drive, PO Box 54980, Santa Clara, CA, 95056

Tel: (408) 764-4000   Fax: (408) 764-4800   www.cohr.com

Mfr. lasers for science, industrial and medical.

Coherent SA, Domaine Technologique de Saclay, Batiment Azur 4 rue Rene Razel, F-91892 Orsay Cedex, France

COIN ACCEPTORS INC. (COINCO)

300 Hunter Ave., St. Louis, MO, 63124

Tel: (314) 725-0100   Fax: (314) 725-1243   www.coinco.com

Coin mechanisms for vending machinery.

Coin Acceptors Sarl, 1-3 Avenue Georges Clemenceau, F-93421 Villepinte Cedex, France

Tel: 33-1-5648-0505   Fax: 33-1-5648-0506

THE COLEMAN COMPANY, INC.

3600 N. Hydraulic, Wichita, KS, 67219

Tel: (316) 832-2700   Fax: (316) 832-2794   www.colemanoutdoors.com

Mfr. distributor and sales of camping and outdoor recreation products.

Coleman/ Campingaz Europe Head Office, BP 55, Route de Brignais, F-69563 Saint-Genis Laval Cedex, France

COLFAX PUMP GROUP, DIV. COLFAX INC.

1710 Airport Road, PO Box 5020, Monroe, NC, 28111-5020

Tel: (704) 289-6511   Fax: (704) 289-4839   www.colfaxpump.com

Mfr. rotary and centrifugal pumps.

Colfax Pumps rance, Za La Coudriere Rn 10, F-37210 Parcay Meslay, France

IMO Industries SARL, Techniparc, 3 ave. Boole, F-91240 St. Michel sur Orge, France

Morse Controls SARL, 3 ave. Rene Villemer, Z.A. du Thillay, F-95500 Le Thillay, France

Morse Controls SARL, 3 ave. Rene Villemer, Z.A. du Thillay, F-95500 Le Thillay, France

COLGATE-PALMOLIVE COMPANY

300 Park Ave., New York, NY, 10022

Tel: (212) 310-2000   Fax: (212) 310-2919   www.colgate.com

Mfr. pharmaceuticals, cosmetics, toiletries and detergents.

Colgate-Palmolive, 55 Blvd. de la Mission Marchand, F-92401 Courbevoie, France

COMDISCO HOLDING COMPANY

6111 N. River Road, Rosemont, IL, 60018

Tel: (847) 698-3000   Fax: (847) 518-5440   www.comdisco.com

Hi-tech asset and facility management and equipment leasing.

Comdisco France, 42 rue Pre Gaudry, Batiment 6, F-69007 Lyon, France

Tel: 33-4-72-763360

Comdisco France SA, Centre d'Affaires Le Louvre, 2 Place du Palais Royal, F-75044 Paris Cedex 1, France

COMMERCE ONE, INC.

4440 Rosewood Dr., Pleasanton, CA, 94588-3050

Tel: (925) 520-6000   Fax: (925) 520-6060   www.commerceone.com

Provides software and services.

Commerce One SARL, World Trade Center 2, Routes des Cretes Sophia Antipolis, F-06560 Valbonne, France

COMMWORKS CORPORATION

3800 Golf Road, Rolling Meadows, IL, 60008

Tel: (847) 262-5000   Fax: (847) 262-0327   www.commworks.com

Provides Internet protocol-based network access software and equipment.

Commworks Corporation, 1 Avenue de l'Atlantique, BP965 les Ulis, F-91976 Courtaboeuf Cedex, France

COMPUTER ASSOCIATES INTERNATIONAL INC.

One Computer Associates Plaza, Islandia, NY, 11788

Tel: (516) 342-5224   Fax: (516) 342-5329   www.cai.com

Integrated business software for enterprise computing and information management, application development, manufacturing, financial applications and professional services.

Computer Associates SA, 14 Ave. Francois Arago, F-92003 Nanterre Cedex, France

Tel: 33-1-40-97-5050

COMPUTER NETWORK TECHNOLOGY CORPORATION

6000 Nathan Lane, Plymouth, MN, 55442

Tel: (763) 268-6000   Fax: (763) 268-6800   www.cnt.com

Engaged in the sale of storage networking products for creating and connecting storage area networks.

CNT France, 77,81 Boulevard de la Republique, F-92250 La Garenne Colombes, France

COMPUTER SCIENCES CORPORATION

2100 East Grand Ave., El Segundo, CA, 90245

Tel: (310) 615-0311   Fax: (310) 322-9768   www.csc.com

Information technology services, management consulting, systems integration, outsourcing.

CSC Computer Sciences SA - French Division, Boulogne-Billancourt Cedex, France

Contact: Claude Czechowski, Pres.

COMPUTER TASK GROUP, INC.

800 Delaware Avenue, Buffalo, NY, 14209-2094

Tel: (716) 882-8000   Fax: (716) 887-7456   www.ctg.com

Provides data processing information through information technology.

CTG France, Tour Sesbastopol, 3 Quai Kelber, F-67080 Strasbough Cedex 3, France

COMPUWARE CORPORATION

31440 Northwestern Hwy., Farmington Hills, MI, 48334-2564

Tel: (248) 737-7300   Fax: (248) 737-7108   www.compuware.com

Develop and market software for enterprise and e-commerce solutions.

Compuware Sarl, 1 Avenue de la Cristallerie, F-92310 Sevres, France

Tel: 33-1-4114-2000   Fax: 33-1-4623-8889

COMSHARE INC.

555 Briarwood Circle, Ste. 200, Ann Arbor, MI, 48108-3302

Tel: (734) 994-4800   Fax: (734) 994-5895   www.comshare.com

Managerial application software.

Comshare SA, 73 blvd Haussmann, F-75008 Paris, France

COMVERSE, INC.

100 Quannapowitt Parkway, Wakefield, MA, 01880

Tel: (781) 246-9000   Fax: (781) 224-8143   www.comverse.com

Provides communications solutions.

Comverse Infosys France, 54-56 Ave du General Leclerc, F-92100 Boulogne Billancourt, France

Tel: 33-155-384-750   Fax: 33-155-384-755

CONAGRA FOODS, INC.

One ConAgra Drive, Omaha, NE, 68102-5001

Tel: (402) 595-4000   Fax: (402) 595-4707   www.conagra.com

Prepared/frozen foods, grains, flour, animal feeds, agro chemicals, poultry, meat, dairy products, including Healthy Choice, Butterball and Hunt's.

Gelazur SA (JV), Les Portes De L'Arenas Gate: C 455, Promenade Des Anglais, B.P. 291, F-06205 Nice Cedex 3, France

CONCURRENT COMPUTER CORPORATION

4375 River Green Pkwy., Duluth, GA, 30096

Tel: (678) 258-4000   Fax: (678) 258-4300   www.ccur.com

Mfr. computer systems and software.

Concurrent Computer France, S.A., Square Franklin, Montigny Le Bretonneux, BP 308, F-78054 St. Quentin En Yvelines Cedex, France

Tel: 33-13-085-3700   Fax: 33-13-460-3753

CONDE NAST PUBLICATIONS INC.

1440 Broadway, 11th Fl., New York, NY, 10018

Tel: (212) 286-3700   Fax: (212) 286-5960   www.condenast.com

Publishing company.

Les Editions Conde Nast SA, 4 Place de Palais Bourbon, F-75007 Paris, France

CONEXANT SYSTEMS, INC.

4311 Jamboree Road, PO Box C, Newport Beach, CA, 92658-8902

Tel: (949) 483-4600   Fax: (949) 483-4078   www.conexant.com

Provides semiconductor products for communications electronics.

Conexant Systems France S.A.S., Les Taissounieres, B1, 1680 Route des Dolines, BP 283, F-06905 Sophia Antipolis Cedex, France

Tel: 33-4-9300-3335   Fax: 33-4-9300-3303

Conexant Systems France S.A.S., Immeuble Le Franklin, 34 Ave Franklin Roosevelt, BP92, F-92159 Suresnes Cedex, France

Tel: 33-1-4144-3650   Fax: 33-1-4144-3690

CONOCO INC.

600 N. Dairy Ashford, Houston, TX, 77252

Tel: (281) 293-1000   Fax: (281) 293-1440   www.conoco.com

Oil, gas, coal, chemicals and minerals.

Continental Oil Co. of Niger, 17 ave. Matignon, F-75008 Paris, France

CONSTRUCTION SPECIALTIES INC.

3 Werner Way, Lebanon, NJ, 08833

Tel: (908) 236-0800   Fax: (908) 236-0801   www.c-sgroup.com

Mfr. architectural building products.

Construction Specialties Steel, 1 rue de la Cressonniere, F-27950 St. Marcel, France

Tel: 33-2-32648400   Contact: Philippe Luguet, Mng. Dir.

CONTINENTAL AIRLINES INC.

1600 Smith St., Houston, TX, 77002

Tel: (713) 324-5000   Fax: (713) 324-2637   www.continental.com

International airline carrier.

Continental Airlines Inc., Paris, France

CONVERGYS CORPORATION

201 E. 4th St., Cincinnati, OH, 45202

Tel: (513) 723-7000   Fax: (513) 421-8624   www.convergys.com

Engaged in data bill processing, telemarketing and customer services representation for major corporations.

Convergys Corporation, 153 Avenue d'Italie, F-75013 Paris, France

COOPER CAMERON CORPORATION

515 Post Oak Blvd., Ste.1200, Houston, TX, 77027

Tel: (713) 513-3300   Fax: (713) 513-3355   www.coopercameron.com

Mfr. oil and gas industry equipment.

Cooper Cameron France, Plaine Saint-Pierre, CS 620, F-34535 Beziers Cedex, France

Cooper Cameron France, 19 bis, Blvd. d'Argenson, F-92200 Neuilly-Sur-Seine Paris, France

COOPER INDUSTRIES INC.

6600 Travis Street, Ste. 5800, Houston, TX, 77002

Tel: (713) 209-8400   Fax: (713) 209-8995   www.cooperindustries.com

Mfr./distributor electrical products, tools, hardware and automotive products, fuses and accessories for electronic applications and circuit boards.

Cooper Hand Tools, Bonneuil, France

COOPERATIVE COMPUTING, INC.

804 Las Cimas Parkway, Ste. 200, Austin, TX, 78746

Tel: (512) 328-2300   Fax: (512) 326-6461   www.cci-triad.com

Mfr. information management software.

France Triad Systems, 2 Rue des Commeres, F-78310 Coignieres, France

COOPER-STANDARD AUTOMOTIVE GROUP

2401 South Gulley Road, Dearborn, MI, 48124

Tel: (313) 561-1100   Fax: (313) 561-6526   www.cooperstandard.com

Mfr. molded and extruded rubber and plastic products for automotive and appliance industry, retread tire industry.

Cooper Standard Automotive, 5 rue Auguste Desgenetais, F-76210 Bolbec, France
Tel: 33-2-3539-5999   Fax: 33-2-274-3538-4011

Cooper Standard Automotive, 9 rue Lois Rameau PBS, F-95871 Bezins, France
Tel: 33-1-34-23-3737   Fax: 33-1-39-47-1235

Cooper Standard Automotive, 1 rue Fond Valee, F-76170 Lillebonne, France
Tel: 33-2-3284-1600   Fax: 33-2-3538-1147

Cooper Standard Automotive, Route des Eaux, BP63, F-35503 Vitre Cedex, France
Tel: 33-2-9975-8740   Fax: 33-2-9975-8749

CORBIS CORPORATION

15395 SE 30th Place, Ste. 300, Bellevue, WA, 98007

Tel: (425) 641-4505   Fax: (425) 643-9740   www.corbis.com

Provides digital photograph imagery to creative professionals in magazine, book and newspaper publishing, advertising and graphic design and Internet and new media publishing.

Corbis France, Immeuble Zeus, 40, ave. des Terroirs de France, F-75611 Paris Cedex 12, France
Tel: 33-1-5333-3800

CORDIS CORPORATION

PO Box 25700, Miami, FL, 33102-5700

Tel: (305) 824-2000   Fax: (305) 824-2747   www.cordis.com

Mfr. medical devices and systems.

Cordis S.A., rue Camille Desmoulins 1, TSA 71001, F-92787 Issy-les-Moulineaux, France

CORNING INC.

One Riverfront Plaza, Corning, NY, 14831-0001

Tel: (607) 974-9000   Fax: (607) 974-8091   www.corning.com

Mfr. glass and specialty materials, consumer products; communications, laboratory services.

Corning S.A., B.P. 61, 44 Avenue de Valvins, F-77211 Avon Cedex, France
Tel: 33-1-6469-7521   Fax: 33-1-6422-8437

Corning S.A., B.P. No. 3, F-77167 Bagneaux-Sur-Loing, France
Tel: 33-1-6445-4000   Fax: 33-1-6445-4379

CORPORATE SOFTWARE (CORPSOFT INC.)

2 Edgewater Drive, Norwood, MA, 02062

Tel: (781) 440-1000   Fax: (781) 440-7070   www.corpsoft.com

Mfr. asset management software.

Corporate Software, 23 Ave. Louis Breguet, F-78142 Velizy Cedex, France
Tel: 33-1-3067-2500

CORRPRO COMPANIES, INC.

1090 Enterprise Drive, Medina, OH, 44256

Tel: (330) 725-6681   Fax: (330) 723-0244   www.corrpro.com

Engaged in full-services corrosion engineering and cathodic protection.

Corrpro Lyon, 16 Chemin des Pivolles, F-69150 Decines, France

Tel: 33-4-72-149494   Fax: 33-4-78-265174

COTY INC.

1325 Avenue of the Americas, New York, NY, 10019

Tel: (212) 479-4300   Fax: (212) 479-4399   www.coty.com

Fragrance, cosmetics and beauty treatments.

Coty Div. de Pfizer France, 86 rue de Paris, F-91101 Orsay Cedex 7, France

COUDERT BROTHERS LLP

1114 Ave. of the Americas, New York, NY, 10036-7794

Tel: (212) 626-4400   Fax: (212) 626-4120   www.coudert.com

Engaged in international law.

Coudert Freres, 52 Ave. des Champs-Elysees, F-75008 Paris, France

Tel: 33-1-53-83-6000   Fax: 33-1-53-83-6060   Contact: Jacques Buhart, Ptnr.

SG COWEN SECURITIES

1221 Avenue of the America, New York, NY, 10020

Tel: (212) 495-6000   Fax: (212) 380-8212   www.cowen.com

Securities research, trading, broker/dealer services; investment banking and asset management.

Cowen Securities, Tour Societe Generale, 17 Cours Valmy, F-92987 Paris, France

Tel: 33-1-4213-5500   Fax: 33-1-4244-1745   Contact: Patrick Halbers

CRAWFORD & COMPANY

5620 Glenridge Drive NE, Atlanta, GA, 30342

Tel: (404) 256-0830   Fax: (404) 847-4025   www.crawfordandcompany.com

Provides international insurance services engaged in risk management and claims adjustment.

Crawford & Company, 110/112 Rue Victor Hugo, F-92686 Levallois Perret Cedex, France

CROMPTON CORPORATION

One American Lane, Greenwich, CT, 06831

Tel: (203) 552-2000   Fax: (203) 552-2870   www.cromptoncorp.com

Mfr. dyes, colors, flavors, fragrances, specialty chemicals and industrial products.

Crompton Chemical SA, 10 rue Cambacere, F-75008 Paris, France

Crompton SA, Les Algorithmas-Thales, Saint Aubin, F-91197 Gif sur Yvette Cedex, France

A.T. CROSS COMPANY

One Albion Road, Lincoln, RI, 02865

Tel: (401) 333-1200   Fax: (401) 334-2861   www.cross.com

Mfr. writing instruments, leads, erasers and ink refills.

A.T. Cross France, 12 bis rue Keppler, F-75016 Paris, France

Tel: 33-1-5367-3130

CROWN CORK & SEAL COMPANY, INC.

One Crown Way, Philadelphia, PA, 19154-4599

Tel: (215) 698-5100   Fax: (215) 698-5201   www.crowncork.com

Mfr. metal and plastic packaging, including steel and aluminum cans for food, beverage and household products.

Crown Cork, Le Colisee 1, rue Fructidor, F-75830 Paris Cedex 17, France

Tel: 33-1-49-18-4000

Emballages Couronne SA, Crown Cork Co. France, BP 1, F-91170 Viry Chatillon, France

CROWN EQUIPMENT CORPORATION

40 South Washington Street, New Bremen, OH, 45869

Tel: (419) 629-2311   Fax: (419) 629-2900   www.crownlift.com

Mfr. and sales of forklift trucks and stackers.

Crown Manutention SNC, 9 rue Ampere, BP 107, F-95500 Gonesse, France

CULLIGAN INTERNATIONAL COMPANY

One Culligan Parkway, Northbrook, IL, 60062

Tel: (847) 205-6000   Fax: (847) 205-6030   www.culligan-man.com

Water treatment products and services.

Culligan France SA, 4 ave. du President Kennedy, F-78340 Les Clayes sous Bois Yvelines, France

Tel: 33-1-30-55-8055   Fax: 33-1-30-55-5623

CUMMINS, INC.

500 Jackson Street, PO Box 3005, Columbus, IN, 47202-3005

Tel: (812) 377-5000   Fax: (812) 377-4937   www.cummins.com

Mfr. diesel engines.

Cummins Diesel SA, 91 quai Emile Cormerais, ZI de la Loire, F-44800 Saint Herblain, France

Cummins Diesel Sales & Service /S, Hovedvejen 233B, F-08300 Rethel, France

Cummins Diesel Sales Corp., 39 rue Ampere, Z.I., F-69680 Chassieu, France

CUNO INCORPORATED

400 Research Pkwy., Meriden, CT, 06450

Tel: (203) 237-5541   Fax: (203) 238-8977   www.cuno.com

Mfr. water filtration products.

CUNO Europe S.A., Chemin du Contre-Halage, F-62730 Les Attaques, France

Tel: 33-3-2146-0200

Cuno Nantes, 11 rue de Chêne Lassé, PB 245, F-44818 Saint-Herblain Cedex, France

Tel: 33-2-4092-3355

CURTIS, MALLET-PREVOST, COLT & MOSLE LLP

101 Park Ave., Ste 3500, New York, NY, 10178

Tel: (212) 696-6000   Fax: (212) 697-1559   www.cm-p.com

International law firm.

Curtis, Mallet-Prevost, Colt & Mosle LLP, 15 rue d'Astorg, F-75008 Paris, France

Tel: 33-1-42-66-39-10

CURTISS-WRIGHT CORPORATION

1200 Wall Street West, Lyndhurst, NJ, 07071-0635

Tel: (201) 896-8400   Fax: (201) 438-5680   www.curtisswright.com

Mfr. precision components and systems, engineered services to aerospace, flow control and marine industry.

Metal Improvement Co. Inc., Zone Industrielle de St. Etienne, Rue de Cazenave, F-64100 Bayonne, France

Tel: 33-5-5955-4252

Metal Improvement Co. Inc., Zone Industrielle d'Amilly, F-45200 Montargis, France

CUSHMAN & WAKEFIELD INC.

51 West 52nd Street, New York, NY, 10019

Tel: (212) 841-7500   Fax: (212) 841-7867   www.cushwake.com

Engaged in commercial real estate services.

Cushman & Wakefield, 11/13 Avenue de Friedland, F-75008 Paris, France

CYPRESS SEMICONDUCTOR CORPORATION

3901 N. First Street, San Jose, CA, 95134-1599

Tel: (408) 943-2600   Fax: (408) 943-2796   www.cypress.com

Mfr. integrated circuits.

Cypress Semiconductor, Za De Courtaboeuf, 6 Avenue Des Andes, Miniparc, Bat No 8, F-91952 Les Ulis Cedex, France

Tel: 33-1-692-988-90   Fax: 33-1-690-755-71

CYTEC INDUSTRIES, INC.

5 Garret Mountain Plaza, West Paterson, NJ, 07424

Tel: (973) 357-3100   Fax: (973) 357-3054   www.cytec.com

Mfr. specialty chemicals and materials.

Cytec Industries S.A.R.L., 1 Place des Etats-Unis, Immeuble Liege, Silic 256, F-94568 Rungis Cedex, France

Tel: 33-1-41-80-17-00

D&B (DUN & BRADSTREET CORPORATION))

1 Diamond Hill Road, Murray Hill, NJ, 07974

Tel: (908) 665-5000   Fax: (908) 665-5524   www.dnb.com

Provides corporate credit, marketing and accounts-receivable management services and publishes financial information.

D&B France S.A., 345 Ave. Georges Clémenceau, Immeuble Défense Bergères, F-92882 Nanterre CTC Cedex 9, France

Tel: 33-1-40-77-0707

S&W, Boie Postale 15 05 Lyon, 4 Quai Jean-Moulin, F-6924 Lyon Cedex 01, France

Tel: 33-1-41-35-1700

DALLAS SEMICONDUCTOR CORPORATION

4401 South Beltway Parkway, Dallas, TX, 75244-3292

Tel: (972) 371-4000   Fax: (972) 371-4956   www.dalsemi.com

Design/mfr. computer chips and chip-based subsystems.

Dallas Semiconductor, 192 ave de General de Gaulle, F-92140 Clamart, France

Tel: 33-1-46-30-3026   Fax: 33-1-46-30-3061   Contact: Frederic Martin, District Sales Mgr.

Dallas Semiconductor, 3 La Garene Dulet, F-33610 Canejan, France

Tel: 33-5-56-89-6820   Fax: 33-5-56-89-6588   Contact: Yves Le Bras, Reg. Sales Mgr.

DANA CORPORATION

4500 Dorr Street, Toledo, OH, 43615

Tel: (419) 535-4500   Fax: (419) 535-4643   www.dana.com

Mfr./sales of automotive, heavy truck, off-highway, fluid and mechanical power components and engine parts, filters and gaskets.

Dana Corporation France, 33/35 Ave. Charles Edouard Jeannerel, Le Technoparc, F-78306 Poissy, France

Dana Corporation France, 2 Chemin Notre Dame de la Ronde, F-28100 Dreux, France

Floquet Monopole, 53 blvd Robespierre, BP31, F-78301 Poissy Cedex, France

Perfect Circle, Div. Dana, Le Technoparc, 1 rue Gustave Eiffel, F-78306 Poissy Cedex, France

Spicer France, 11 rue George Mangin, F-69400 Villefrance sur Saone, France

Warner & Turco, Route de Spay, BP 313, F-72007 Le Mans Cedex, France

DANIEL INDUSTRIES INC.

9753 Pine Lake Drive, PO Box 55435, Houston, TX, 77224

Tel: (713) 467-6000   Fax: (713) 827-3889   www.danielind.com

Fluid measurement, flow control, actuation and analytical products, services and integrated solutions primarily for natural gas and oil producers, transporters and refiners worldwide.

Daniel Industries/Emerson Process Management, 14, Rue Edison, BP 21, F-69671 Bron Cedex, France

DANZAS AEI, INC.

120 Tokeneke Road, PO Box 1231, Darien, CT, 06820

Tel: (203) 655-7900   Fax: (203) 655-5779   www.aeilogistics.com

International air freight forwarder.

Danzas AEI, 4, rue du Pâquier, F-21600 Longvic, France

Danzas AEI, Fret 5 Sogaris Porte 7, 1 rue de Pre, Bat 3317, F-95707 Roissy Cedex, France

Tel: 33-1-49-19-6826   Fax: 33-1-48-62-8982

Danzas AEI, F-59810 Aeroport de Lille Lesquin, France

D'ARCY MASIUS BENTON & BOWLES INC. (DMB&B)

1675 Broadway, New York, NY, 10019

Tel: (212) 468-3622   Fax: (212) 468-2987   www.darcyww.com

Full service international advertising and communications group.

DMB&B Europe, 10 blvd du Parc, F-92521 Neuilly Cedex, France

DATASCOPE CORPORATION

14 Phillips Pkwy., Montvale, NJ, 07645

Tel: (201) 391-8100   Fax: (201) 307-5400   www.datascope.com

Mfr. medical devices.

Cardiac SARL, Europarc Créteil, 123, Chemin des Bassins, F-94035 Créteil Cedex, France

Datascope SARL, Z.I Athelia 1, F-13705 La Ciotat Cedex, France

DATASTREAM SYSTEMS, INC.

50 Datastream Plaza, Greenville, SC, 29605

Tel: (864) 422-5001   Fax: (864) 422-5000   www.datastream.net

Mfr. asset management software.

Datastream SA, Zac des Deux Gares, 34 Avenue Franklin Roosevelt, F-92150 Suresnes, France

DAVIS POLK & WARDWELL

450 Lexington Ave., New York, NY, 10017

Tel: (212) 450-4000   Fax: (212) 450-4800   www.dpw.com

Engaged in international law.

Davis Polk & Wardwell, 15 Matignon, F-75088 Paris, France

Tel: 33-1-56-59-3600   Fax: 33-1-56-59-3690

DAYTON PROGRESS CORPORATION

500 Progress Road, Dayton, OH, 45449

Tel: (937) 859-5111   Fax: (937) 859-5353   www.daytonprogress.com

Engaged in the production of catalog and special punches, punch blanks and metal stamping tools.

Dayton Progress S.A., 105 Avenue de l'Epinette, BP 128, BP 128 Zone Industrielle, F-77107 Meaux Cedex, France

DAZEL CORPORATION

301 Congress Ave., Ste. 1100, Austin, TX, 78701

Tel: (512) 494-7300   Fax: (512) 494-7394   www.dazel.com

Mfr. software for information delivery solutions on documents and reports.

Dazel France, Tour Montparnasse, 33 avenue du Maine, F-75755 Paris, France

Tel: 33-1-5654-1122   Fax: 33-1-5654-1133

DDB WORLDWIDE COMMUNICATIONS GROUP

437 Madison Ave., New York, NY, 10022

Tel: (212) 415-2000   Fax: (212) 415-3417   www.ddbn.com

Advertising agency.

DDB Worldwide SA, 12/14 rue Mederic, F-75849 Paris Cedex 17, France

DEBEVOISE & PLIMPTON

919 Third Avenue, New York, NY, 10022

Tel: (212) 909-6000   Fax: (212) 909-6836   www.debevoise.com

Engaged in international law.

Debevoise & Plimpton, 21 Ave. George V, F-75008 Paris, France

Tel: 33-1-40-73-1212   Fax: 33-1-47-20-5082   Contact: James A. Kiernan, III, Mng. Prtn.   Emp: 36

DECHERT LLP

4000 Bell Atlantic Tower, 1717 Arch Street, Philadelphia, PA, 19103-2793

Tel: (215) 994-4000   Fax: (215) 994-2222   www.dechert.com

Engaged in international law.

Titmuss Sainer Dechert, 55 Ave. Kleber, F-75116 Paris, France

Tel: 33-1-53-65-0500   Fax: 33-1-53-65-0505

DEERE & COMPANY

One John Deere Place, Moline, IL, 61265

Tel: (309) 765-8000   Fax: (309) 765-5772   www.deere.com

Mfr./sale agricultural, construction, utility, forestry and lawn, grounds care equipment.

John Deere France, rue du Paradis, Ormes, BP 219, F-45144 St. Jean de la Ruelle Cedex, France

Tel: 33-238-72-3000   Fax: 33-238-74-8665

DELL COMPUTER CORPORATION

One Dell Way, Round Rock, TX, 78682-2222

Tel: (512) 338-4400   Fax: (512) 728-3653   www.dell.com

Direct marketer and supplier of computer systems.

Dell Computer, 1068 rue de la Vielle Poste, BP 9646, F-34054 Montepellier Cedex 1, France

Tel: 33-4-67-06-6000   Fax: 33-4-67-06-6001   Contact: Marie Eve Schauber, Mng. Dir.

Dell France/Putenux La Defense, 12-12 Bis rue Jean Jaures, Immeuble Plein Jour, F-92800 Puteaux la Defense, France

Tel: 33-1-47-62-6900   Fax: 33-1-47-62-6871   Contact: Marie Eve Schauber, Mng. Dir.

DELOITTE TOUCHE TOHMATSU INTERNATIONAL

1633 Broadway, New York, NY, 10019

Tel: (212) 492-4000   Fax: (212) 392-4154   www.deloitte.com

Accounting, audit, tax and management consulting services.

Deloitte & Touche, Paek Ave., 81 Blvd. se Stalingrad, F-69100 Villeurbanne, France

Deloitte Touche Tohmatsu, 185 ave Charles de Gaulle, F-92200 Neuilly sur Seine Cedex, France

DELPHAX TECHNOLOGIES

12500 Whitewater Drive, Minnetonka, MN, 55343-9420

Tel: (612) 939-9000   Fax: (612) 939-1151   www.delphax.com

Mfr. computer-controlled check coupon print systems.

Delphax Technologies, 8-10 rue du bois Sauvage, F-91055 Evry Cedex, France

DELTA AIR LINES INC.

Hartsfield International Airport, 1030 Delta Blvd., Atlanta, GA, 30320-6001

Tel: (404) 715-2600   Fax: (404) 715-5494   www.delta-air.com

Major worldwide airline; international air transport services.

Delta Air Lines Inc., Nice, France

Delta Air Lines Inc., Paris-De Gaulle, France

DENTSPLY INTERNATIONAL

570 West College Ave., PO Box 872, York, PA, 17405-0872

Tel: (717) 845-7511   Fax: (717) 843-6357   www.dentsply.com

Mfr. and distribution of dental supplies and equipment.

De Trey Dentsply SA, 72 rue de General-Leclerc, F-92270 Bois-Colombes, France

Dentsply France, 17 rue Michael Farady, F-78180 Montigny-le-Bretonneux, France

Tel: 33-1-30-14-7777

Dentsply Laboratoire SPAD, 14D rue Pierre de Coubertin, Paro de Mirande BP 242, F-21007 Dijon Cedex, France

Tel: 33-3-80-68-4848

Dentsply SIMFRA, 21 rue de Maurbeuge, F-75009 Paris, France

Tel: 33-1-48-78-0898

DHL WORLDWIDE EXPRESS

50 California Avenue, San Francisco, CA, 94111

Tel: (415) 677-6100   Fax: (415) 824-9700   www.dhl.com

Worldwide air express carrier.

DHL Worldwide Express, ZI. Paris Nord II, 241 rue de la Belle Etoile, BP 50252, F-95957 Roissy, France

Tel: 33-1-48-17-6600

DIAGNOSTIC PRODUCTS CORPORATION

5700 West 96th Street, Los Angeles, CA, 90045

Tel: (310) 645-8200   Fax: (310) 645-9999   www.dpcweb.com

Mfr. diagnostic products.

Dade Behring S.A., 19-29 rue du Capitaine Guynemer, F-92081 Paris La Defense, France

Tel: 33-1-4291-2166   Fax: 33-1-4291-2367

DPC, SAS, 90 Boulevard National, F-92257 La Garenne-Colombes Cedex, France

Tel: 33-1-55-66-86-00   Fax: 33-1-55-66-86-66

DIAMONDCLUSTER INTERNATIONAL, INC.

875 N. Michigan Avenue, Ste. 3000, Chicago, IL, 60611

Tel: (312) 255-5000   Fax: (312) 255-6000   www.diamondcluster.com

Engaged in electronic business development and support.

DiamondCluster International, Inc., 83, avenue Marceau, F-75016 Paris, France

Tel: 33-1-7098-9700   Fax: 33-1-7098-9710

DIEBOLD INC.

5995 Mayfair Road, North Canton, OH, 44720-8077

Tel: (330) 490-4000   Fax: (330) 490-3794   www.diebold.com

Mfr. automated banking systems; security services for banking industrial and related fields.

Diebold, 7, Rue de Dampierre, BLR-78282 Guyancourt Cedex, France

DIONEX CORPORATION

1228 Titan Way, PO Box 3603, Sunnyvale, CA, 94086-3603

Tel: (408) 737-0700   Fax: (408) 730-9403   www.dionex.com

Develop/mfr./market chromatography systems and related products.

Dionex - Bureau France Sud, 1210, rue Ampere, Z.I. Les Milles, F-13851 Aix en Provence Cedex 03, France

Dionex SA, 98 rue Albert Calmette, BPN 47, F-78354 Jouy en Josas Cedex, France

WALT DISNEY COMPANY

500 South Buena Vista Street, Burbank, CA, 91521

Tel: (818) 560-1000   Fax: (818) 560-1930   www.disney.com

Film/TV production, theme parks, resorts, publishing, recording and retail stores.

Walt Disney Productions SA, 52 ave. des Champs-Elysees, F-75008 Paris, France

DIVINE

1301 N. Elston Ave., Chicago, IL, 60622

Tel: (773) 394-6600   Fax: (773) 394-6601   www.divine.com

Software and services provider.

Divine, Inc., Immeuble le Viking, 67 Rue Anatole, F-92309 Levallois-Perret, France

DMC STRATEX NETWORKS, INC.

170 Rose Orchard Way, San Jose, CA, 95134

Tel: (408) 943-0777   Fax: (408) 944-1648   www.dmcstratexnetworks.com

Designs, manufactures, and markets advanced wireless solutions for wireless broadband access.

Stratex Networks, Le Calypso, 25 rue de la Petite Duranne, F-13857 Aix En Provence, France

Tel: 33-4-4290-4990   Fax: 33-4-4290-4999   Contact: Claude Echahamian

D-M-E COMPANY

29111 Stephenson Highway, Madison Heights, MI, 48071

Tel: (248) 398-6000   Fax: (248) 544-5705   www.dmeco.com

Manufacture and distribution of mold tooling, mold components, hot runner systems, and electronic controls for the plastics industry.

D-M-E France, Division DE MILACRON SAS, 1, Rue des Remparts, F-93 191 Noisy-le-Grand, France

Tel: 33-148-151-480

DOCUMENTUM, INC.

6801 Koll Center Pkwy., Pleasanton, CA, 94566

Tel: (925) 600-6800   Fax: (925) 600-6850   www.documentum.com

Mfr. content management software.

Documentum International Inc., 696 rue Yves Kermen, F-92658 Boulogne Billancourt Cedex, France

DONALDSON COMPANY, INC.

PO Box 1299, Minneapolis, MN, 55431

Tel: (952) 887-3131   Fax: (952) 887-3155   www.donaldson.com

Mfr. filtration systems and replacement parts.

Donaldson France, S.A., 4 Bis rue Maryse Bastie, F-69500 Bron, France

Tecnov Donaldson, S.A., Z-1 La Campagne, F-50420 Domjean, France

R.R. DONNELLEY & SONS COMPANY

77 West Wacker Drive, Chicago, IL, 60601-1696

Tel: (312) 326-8000   Fax: (312) 326-8543   www.rrdonnelley.com

Engaged in commercial printing and allied communication services.

R. R. Donnelley Financial, 23 rue Cambon, 4th Fl., F-75001 Paris, France

Tel: 33-1-5345-1900

R. R. Donnelley France S.A., 86 rue Regnault, F-75013 Paris, France

Tel: 33-1-42-16-6380

DONNELLY CORPORATION

49 West Third Street, Holland, MI, 49423-2813

Tel: (616) 786-7000   Fax: (616) 786-6034   www.donnelly.com

Mfr. fabricated, molded and coated glass products for the automotive and electronics industries.

Donnelly Euroglas Systems, 26 Avenue des Champs Pierreux, F-BP 11S-52201 Langres Cedex, France

Tel: 33-3-2584-3434   Fax: 33-32-584-3843   Contact: Mark Guiheneuf, Mgr.

Donnelly Hohe Paris Sarl, 26, Avenue des Champs Pierreux, F-92022 Nanterre Cedex, France

Tel: 33-1-46-69-9442   Fax: 33-1-46-69-9430

DOUBLE TWIST, INC.

2001 Broadway, Oakland, CA, 94612

Tel: (510) 628-0100   Fax: (510) 628-0108   www.doubletwist.com

Engaged in the development of software for medical research.

Double Twist Europe, 112 Avenue Kleber, F-75784 Paris Cedex 16, France

Tel: 33-1-4755-3038

DOUBLECLICK, INC.

450 West 33rd Street, New York, NY, 10001

Tel: (212) 683-0001   Fax: (212) 889-0062   www.doubleclick.net

Engaged in online advertising and e-mail marketing.

Doubleclick, Ltd., 16-18 rue Rivay, 2/F, F-92300 Levallois-Perret, France

Tel: 33-1-49-6683-83

DOVER CORPORATION

280 Park Ave., New York, NY, 10017-1292

Tel: (212) 922-1640   Fax: (212) 922-1656   www.dovercorporation.com

Holding company for varied industries; assembly and testing equipment, oil-well gear and other industrial products.

Imaje S.A., Div. Dover Corp., 9, rue Gaspard Monge, BP 110, F-26501 Bourg-les-Valence, France

THE DOW CHEMICAL COMPANY

2030 Dow Center, Midland, MI, 48674

Tel: (989) 636-1000   Fax: (989) 636-3228   www.dow.com

Mfr. chemicals, plastics, pharmaceuticals, agricultural products, consumer products.

Dow France S.A., 8 Route de Herrlisheim, F-67410 Drusenheim, France

DRAFT WORLDWIDE

633 North St. Clair Street, Chicago, IL, 60611-3211

Tel: (312) 944-3500   Fax: (312) 944-3566   www.draftworldwide.com

Full service international advertising agency, engaged in brand building, direct and promotional marketing.

DDW Santé, 3 blvd Paul Emile Victor, Ill de la Jalle, F-92528 Neuilly-sur-Seine Cedex, France

Tel: 33-1-47-47-7915 Fax: 33-1-47-47-7865 Contact: Loke Robert, Mng. Dir.

DraftWorldwide SA, 76 rue Thiers, F-92100 Boulogne, France

Tel: 33-1-47-61-8410 Fax: 33-1-47-61-8411 Contact: Jean-Paul Dupey, Pres. Europe

DRAKE BEAM MORIN INC.

100 Park Avenue, 11th Fl., New York, NY, 10017

Tel: (212) 692-7700   Fax: (212) 297-0426   www.dbm.com

Human resource management consulting and training.

DBM France, 44 rue Jeanne d'Arc, F-76000 Rouen, France

Tel: 33-23-571-8005 Fax: 33-23-571-7927

DBM France, 17 a 21 rue de Faubourg St. Honore, F-75008 Paris, France

Tel: 33-1-44-515280 Fax: 33-1-44-515282

DRESSER INSTRUMENT DIVISION

250 East Main Street, Stratford, CT, 06614-5145

Tel: (203) 378-8281   Fax: (203) 385-0357   www.dresserinstruments.com

Mfr. pressure gauges and temperature instruments.

Dresser Europe GmbH, 206, Rue des Campanules Le Mandinet, F-77185 Lognes, France

Tel: 33-1-6037-2530 Fax: 33-1-6037-2539

DRESSER-RAND COMPANY

PO Box 560, Paul Clark Drive, Olean, NY, 14760

Tel: (716) 375-3000   Fax: (716) 375-3178   www.dresser-rand.com

Mfr. generators, centrifugal compressors, turbines and control systems.

Dresser-Rand France, France

DRUGABUSE SCIENCES, INC.

330 Distel Circle, Ste. 150, Los Altos, CA, 94022

Tel: (650) 417-2300   Fax: (650) 417-2400   www.drugabusesciences.com

Mfr. treatments for drug and alcohol addiction.

DrugAbuse Sciences, 48 50 rue Boissonade, F-75014 Paris, France

DSP GROUP, INC.

3120 Scott Blvd., Santa Clara, CA, 95054

Tel: (408) 986-4300   Fax: (408) 986-4323   www.dspg.com

Mfr. speech compressor software.

DSP Group Europe SARL, Les Algorithmes, Bat. Aristote A, 2000 Route des Lucioles - BP29, F-06901 Sophia Antipolis, France

DUO-FAST CORPORATION

2400 Galvin Dr., Elgin, IL, 60123

Tel: (847) 783-5500   Fax: (847) 669-7301   www.duofast.com

Mfr. staplers, tackers and nailers.

Duo-Fast France, Zone Indus De La Petit Ile, BP 105, F-89300 Joigny Cedex, France

E.I. DUPONT DE NEMOURS & COMPANY

1007 Market Street, Wilmington, DE, 19898

Tel: (302) 774-1000   Fax: (302) 774-7321   www.dupont.com

Mfr. and sales of diversified chemicals, plastics, specialty products and fibers.

Du Pont de Nemours (France) S.A, Les Jardins d'Entreprise de Lyon Gerland, 213 Rue De Gerland-Bat B3, F-69007 Lyon, France

DuPont de Nemours S.A. Color Proofing, 3 Avenue du Canada, Parc Technopolis, B.P. 85, F-91943 Courtaboeuf Cedex, France

Contact: Catherine Moreau

Permatex France SA, Div. Dupont, Z.A. Les Bruottées, Voie Nouvelle, F- 21200 Vignolles, France

DUPONT PHOTOMASKS, INC. (DPI)

131 Old Settlers Blvd., Round Rock, TX, 78664

Tel: (512) 310-6500   Fax: (512) 255-9627   www.photomask.com

Mfr. photo masks for semiconductors.

DuPont Photomasks (France) SA, Avenue Victoire - Zone Industrielle, F-13106 Rousset Cedex, France

DuPont Photomasks (France) SA, European Technology Center, 224 Boulevard JF Kennedy, F-91105 Corbeil Essonnes Cedex, France

Tel: 33-1-6088-5151

DURACELL INTERNATIONAL INC.

8 Research Drive, Bethel, CT, 06801

Tel: (203) 796-4000   Fax: (203) 796-4745   www.duracell.com

Mfr. batteries.

Duracell France, Paris, France

EASTMAN & BEAUDINE INC.

5700 West Plano Parkway, Ste. 2800, Plano, TX, 75093

Tel: (972) 267-8891   Fax: (972) 267-8891   www.beaudine.com

Engaged in retained executive search and selection.

Eastman & Beaudine Inc., 3 rue de Penthievre, F-75008 Paris, France

EASTMAN CHEMICAL COMPANY

100 North Eastman Road, Kingsport, TN, 37662-5075

Tel: (423) 229-2000   Fax: (423) 229-1351   www.eastman.com

Mfr. plastics, chemicals, fibers.

Eastman Chemical B.V., 65 rue de Bercy, F-75012 Paris, France

Tel: 33-1-44-67-8899   Fax: 33-1-44-67-8888   Contact: Yves Hamon

EASTMAN KODAK COMPANY

343 State Street, Rochester, NY, 14650

Tel: (716) 724-4000   Fax: (716) 724-1089   www.kodak.com

Develop/mfr. photo and chemicals products, information management/video/copier systems, fibers/plastics for various industry.

Eastman Kodak Chemical Intl. SA, 1 Allee du 1er Mai, F-77423 Mame-laVallee Cedex, France

Kodak Industrie, Usine de fabrication, Route de Demigny, F-71102 Chalon-sur-Saone, France

Kodak Pathe, 8-26 rue Villiot, F-75594 Paris Cedex 12, France

Laboratoires et Services Kodak, Europarc, 1 rue Le Corbusier, F-94400 Creteil, France

EATON CORPORATION

Eaton Center, 1111 Superior Ave., Cleveland, OH, 44114-2584

Tel: (216) 523-5000   Fax: (216) 479-7068   www.eaton.com

Advanced technical products for transportation and industrial markets.

Eaton SA, Zone Industrial de Brais, Saint Nazaire, Loire Atlantique, France

ECOLAB INC.

370 N. Wabasha Street, St. Paul, MN, 55102

Tel: (651) 293-2233   Fax: (651) 293-2379   www.ecolab.com

Develop/mfr. premium cleaning, sanitizing and maintenance products and services for the hospitality, institutional, and residential markets.

Ecolab Ltd., Paris, France

Tel: 33-1-40-93-93-94

EDELMAN PUBLIC RELATIONS WORLDWIDE

200 East Randolph Drive, 62nd Fl., Chicago, IL, 60601

Tel: (312) 240-3000   Fax: (312) 240-0596   www.edelman.com

International independent public relations firm.

Edelman PR Worldwide, 54 rue Monceau, F-75008 Paris, France

Tel: 33-1-56-69-7500   Fax: 33-1-56-69-7575   Contact: Remy Ossard, Pres. Europe

J.D. EDWARDS & COMPANY

One Technology Way, Denver, CO, 80237

Tel: (303) 334-4000   Fax: (303) 334-4970   www.jdedwards.com

Computer software products.

J. D. Edwards, Sydec, 6 rue Thomas Mann, F-67200 Strasbourg, France

Tel: 33-88-27-94-94   Fax: 33-88-27-94-85

J. D. Edwards, Unilog, 9 Blvd. Gouvion St. Cyr, F-45849 Paris Cedex 17, France

Tel: 33-1-40-68-4000   Fax: 33-1-40-68-4020

J. D. Edwards, Progicentre, 8 Place Jean Monnet, BP 4543, F-45045 Orleans, France

Tel: 33-2-38-72-63-64   Fax: 33-2-38-72-00-88

J. D. Edwards, Focal, le 6 eme Ave., 75 cours Albert Thomas, F-69447 Lyon Cedex, France

Tel: 33-4-72-13-16-16   Fax: 33-4-72-34-55-38

J. D. Edwards, 104 bis rue de Reuilly, F-75012 Paris, France

Tel: 33-1-44-74-2000   Fax: 33-1-4474-2020

J. D. Edwards Eurexpert Conseil, Tour Manhattan, La Defense 2, 5-6 place de l'iris, F-92095 Paris, France

Tel: 33-1-46-93-75-00   Fax: 33-1-47-76-20-33

EG&G INC.

900 Clopper Road, Ste. 200, Gaithersburg, MD, 20878

Tel: (301) 840-3000   Fax: (301) 590-0502   www.egginc.com

Diversified R/D, mfr. and services.

EG&G Berthold, 62 ave. Foch, F-92250 la Garenne Colombes, France

EG&G Instruments Div., 1 rue du Gevaudan, CE 1734, ZI Petite Montagne Sud, F-91047 Evry Cedex, France

EG&G Sealol Callisto, 18 Ter rue des Osiers, BP 54 Coignieres, F-78311 Maurepas Cedex, France

EGL INC. (EAGLE GLOBAL LOGISTICS)

15350 Vickery Drive, Houston, TX, 77032

Tel: (281) 618-3100   Fax: (281) 618-3223   www.eagleusa.com

Ocean/air freight forwarding, customs brokerage, packing and wholesale, logistics management and insurance.

EGL Eagle Global Logistics, Zone De Fret, F-31703 Blagnac Cedex, France

Tel: 33-61-719-696   Fax: 33-61-304-511

EGL Eagle Global Logistics, Zone De Fret 4, Roissytech, 4 rue Du Cercle, B.P. 10169, F-95702 Roissy CDG Cedex, France

Tel: 33-1-48-62-4322   Fax: 33-1-48-62-0704

EGL Eagle Global Logistics, Gateway Department Zone De Fret, Bat 288, 1 Etag., Bur 1210, Orly Fret 690, F-94394 Orly, France

Tel: 33-1-49-75-3266   Fax: 33-1-49-75-3286

EGL Eagle Global Logistics, Aulnat Airport, Clermont Ferrand, F-63510 Aulnat, France

Tel: 33-736-27160   Fax: 33-736-27159

EGL Eagle Global Logistics, Zone De Fret, Satolas Aeroport, F-69125 Lyon, France

Tel: 33-72-227-990   Fax: 33-71-227-982

ELANCO ANIMAL HEALTH

500 East 96th Street, Ste. 125, Indianapolis, IN, 46240

Tel: (317) 276-3000   Fax: (317) 276-6116   www.elanco.com

Antibiotics and fine chemicals.

Elanco Animal Health, 203 Bureaux de la Colline, F-92213 Saint-Cloud, France

ELECTRO SCIENTIFIC INDUSTRIES, INC.

13900 NW Science Park Drive, Portland, OR, 97229

Tel: (503) 641-4141   Fax: (503) 643-4873   www.esi.com

Mfg. production and testing equipment used in manufacture of electronic components in pagers and cellular communication devices.

Electro Scientific Industries SARL, Cite Descartes, 1 allee Lorentz, F-77420 Champs-sur-Marne, France

Tel: 33-1-64-61-0011   Fax: 33-1-64-61-0016   Contact: Christian Saulnier

ELECTROGLAS INC.

6042 Silver Creek Valley Road, San Jose, CA, 95138

Tel: (408) 528-3000   Fax: (408) 528-3542   www.electroglas.com

Mfr. semi-conductor test equipment, automatic wafer probes.

Electroglas Intl. Inc., 13 Chemin du Levant, F-01210 Ferney Voltaire, France

ELECTRONIC DATA SYSTEMS, INC. (EDS)

5400 Legacy Dr., Plano, TX, 75024

Tel: (972) 604-6000   Fax: (972) 605-2643   www.eds.com

Engaged in systems integration, network and systems operations and management consulting.

EDS France, 4, avenue Pablo Picasso, F-92024 Nanterre Cedex, France

ELECTRONICS FOR IMAGING, INC. (EFI)

303 Velocity Way, Foster City, CA, 94404

Tel: (650) 357-3500   Fax: (650) 357-3907   www.efi.com

Design/mfr. computer software and hardware for color desktop publishing.

EFI France, Immeuble Atria, 5 Place des Marseilles, F-94227 Charenton-le-Pont Cedex, France

Tel: 33-1-4179 0000

ELECTRO-SCIENCE LABORATORIES, INC.

416 East Church Road, King of Prussia, PA, 19406

Tel: (610) 272-8000   Fax: (610) 272-6759   www.electroscience.com

Mfr. advanced thick film materials for hybrid microcircuits and other electronic packaging and component applications.

ESL (SNC), 7 rue de l'Avenir, F-92360 Meudon-la-Foret, France

EMC CORPORATION

35 Parkwood Drive, Hopkinton, MA, 01748-9103

Tel: (508) 435-1000   Fax: (508) 435-8884   www.emc.com

Designs/supplies intelligent enterprise storage and retrieval technology for open systems, mainframes and midrange environments.

EMC Aquitaine Midi + Pyrenes S.A., Aeropole 1, 5 Ave. Albert Durand, F-31700 Blaqnac Toulouse, France

Tel: 33-5-61-16-4-01

EMC Computer Systems France S.A., 3 rue du Parc, Immeuble Tourmaline, Oberhausbergen, F-67205 Strasbourge, France

Tel: 33-3-88-56-0083

EMC Computer Systems France S.A., Immeuble Le Discover 84, blvd Vivier Merle, F-69485 Lyon Cedex 09, France

Tel: 33-4-78-14-1320

EMC Computer Systems France S.A., 3 Ave. Pierre et Marie Curie, F-59260 Lezennes Lille, France

Tel: 33-3-20-71-4012

EMC Computer Systems France S.A., 6 Mail de l'Europe, La Celle, F-78170 St. Cloud, France

Tel: 33-1-30-82-5100

EMERSON & CUMING COMPOSITE MATERIALS, INC.

59 Walpole Street, Canton, MA, 02021

Tel: (781) 821-4250   Fax: (781) 821-0737   www.emersoncuming.com

Mfr. high performance encapsulants, adhesives and coatings for the automotive, telecommunications and electronic industries.

Emerson & Cuming France, Zone Industrielle Nord, B.P. 438, F-69655 Villefranche Cedex, France

Tel: 33-4-74-02-3960

EMERSON PROCESS MANAGEMENT

8301Cameron Road, Austin, TX, 78754

Tel: (512) 834-7689   Fax: (512) 832-3232   www.frco.com

Mfr. industrial process control equipment.

Emerson Process Management, 14, Rue Edison, BP 21, F-69671 Bron Cedex, France

EMERY FORWARDING

One Lagoon Drive, Ste. 400, Redwood City, CA, 94065

Tel: (650) 596-9600   Fax: (650) 596-7901   www.emeryworld.com

Freight transport, global logistics and air cargo.

Emery Forwarding, Fret 2, 3, rue du Trait-D'Union, BP 10408, F-95707 Roissy Airport Cedex, France

ENCAD, INC.

6059 Cornerstone Court West, San Diego, CA, 92121

Tel: (858) 452-0882   Fax: (858) 452-5618   www.encad.com

Mfr. large color printers for specialized graphics.

ENCAD Europe SA, 84/88 Blvd. de la Mission Marchand, F-92400 Courbevoie, France

Tel: 33-1-4199-9230

ENCYCLOPAEDIA BRITANNICA INC.

310 S. Michigan Ave., Chicago, IL, 60604

Tel: (312) 427-9700   Fax: (312) 294-2176   www.eb.com

Publishing; books.

Encyclopaedia Britannica, Immeuble Le Montcalm, 2 rue du Pont-Colbert, F-78023 Versailles Cedex, France
Encyclopedia Universalis, 10 rue Vercingetorix, F-75680 Paris Cedex 14, France

ENERGIZER HOLDINGS, INC.

533 Maryville University Dr., St. Louis, MO, 63141

Tel: (314) 985-2000   Fax: (214) 985-2205   www.energizer.com

Mfr. Eveready and Energizer brand batteries and lighting products.

Ralston Energy Systems, rue 5 Emile Pathe, F-78403 Chatou, France

Tel: 33-1-3480-1703   Fax: 33-1-3480-1800

ENERPAC

6101 N. Baker Road, PO Box 3241, Milwaukee, WI, 53201-3241

Tel: (414) 781-6600   Fax: (414) 781-1049   www.enerpac.com

Mfr. hydraulic cylinders, pumps, valves, presses, tools, accessories and system components.

ENERPAC S. A., BP 200, Parc d'Activities du Moulin de Massy, 1 rue du Saule Trapu, F-91882 Massy Cedex, France

ENGELHARD CORPORATION

101 Wood Avenue South, Iselin, NJ, 08830

Tel: (732) 205-5000   Fax: (732) 632-9253   www.engelhard.com

Mfr. pigments, additives, catalysts, chemicals, engineered materials.

Engelhard Corporation, 96 rue Saint-Charles, F-75015 Paris, France
Engelhard SA, 4 rue de Beaubourg, F-75004 Paris, France

EQUIFAX INC.

1550 Peachtree St. NW, Atlanta, GA, 30309

Tel: (404) 885-8000   Fax: (404) 888-5452   www.equifax.com

Provides information and knowledge-based solutions on consumers and businesses around the world.

TechniCob SA, 42 rue Poussin, F-75016 Paris, France

ERICO PRODUCTS INC.

34600 Solon Road, Cleveland, OH, 44139

Tel: (440) 248-0100   Fax: (440) 248-0723   www.erico.com

Mfr. electric welding apparatus and hardware, metal stampings, specialty fasteners.

Erico France SARL, BP 31, rue Benoit Fourneyron, One Industrielle Sud, F-42160 Andrezieux-Boutheon, France

Tel: 33-4-7736-5656

ERNST & YOUNG INTERNATIONAL

5 Times Square, New York, NY, 10036

Tel: (212) 773-3000   Fax: (212) 773-6350   www.eyi.com

Engaged in assurance and advisory business services, tax, law and corporate finance.

HSD Ernst & Young - Societe d'Avocates, Tour Manhattan, F-92095 Paris La Defense 2 Cedex 21, France

Tel: 33-1-46-93-6795   Fax: 33-1-47-67-0106   Contact: Jack Anderson

ESCO CORPORATION

2141 NW 25th Ave., Portland, OR, 97210

Tel: (503) 228-2141   Fax: (503) 778-6330   www.escocorp.com

Mfr. equipment for mining, construction and forestry industries.

ESCO Corp., Lyon, France

ESCO SA, BP 229, F-69803 Saint-Priest Cedex, France

ESCO TECHNOLOGIES INC.

8888 Ladue Road, Ste. 200, St. Louis, MO, 63124-2090

Tel: (314) 213-7200   Fax: (314) 213-7250   www.escostl.com

Electronic subassemblies and components.

Filtertek S.A., Div. ESCO, ZA du Prè de la Dame Jeanne, BP 11, F-60128 Plailly, France

Tel: 33-3-44-54-1990   Fax: 33-3-44-54-3892

ESTERLINE TECHNOLOGIES

10800 NE 8th Street, Ste. 600, Bellevue, WA, 98004

Tel: (425) 453-9400   Fax: (425) 453-2916   www.esterline.com

Mfr. equipment and instruments for industrial automation, precision measure, data acquisition.

Auxitrol Technologies S.A., Bureaux de la Colline, F-92213 Saint-Cloud Cedex, France

Tel: 33-149-116-565

International Precision Products BV, 6, rue de Général Pershing, Domaine de Picardie, Bat. F12, 3e étage, F-78000 Versailles, France

Tel: 33-1-39-54-31-11   Fax: 33-1-39-54-97-48

ETHYL CORPORATION

330 South 4th Street, PO Box 2189, Richmond, VA, 23219

Tel: (804) 788-5000   Fax: (804) 788-5688   www.ethyl.com

Provide additive chemistry solutions to enhance the performance of petroleum products.

Succursale d'Ethyl Europe SA, Tour Anjou, 33 Quai de Dion-Bouton, F- 92800 Puteaux-Cedex, France

Tel: 33-1-46939180   Fax: 33-1-47788717

EURO RSCG WORLDWIDE

350 Hudson Street, New York, NY, 10014

Tel: (212) 886-2000   Fax: (212) 886-2016   www.eurorscg.com

International advertising agency group.

Ailleurs Exactement, 38 bis rue du Fer a Moulin, Paris, France

EVOLUTIONARY TECHNOLOGIES INTERNATIONAL, INC.

816 Congress Avenue, Ste. 1300, Austin, TX, 78701

Tel: (512) 383-3000   Fax: (512) 383-3300   www.eti.com

Mfr. data integration management software.

EIT, Inc., 159 Rue de Silly, F-92641 Boulogne Cedex, France

Tel: 33-1-4100-1100

EXCELLON AUTOMATION

24751 Crenshaw Boulevard, Torrance, CA, 90505

Tel: (310) 534-6300   Fax: (310) 534-6777   www.excellon.com

PCB drilling and routing machines; optical inspection equipment.

Excellon France S.A.R.L., CE 1728, F-91047 Evry Cedex, France

Tel: 33-1-60862737   Fax: 33-1-60862535

EXIDE TECHNOLOGIES

210 Carnegie Center, Ste. 500, Princeton, NJ, 08540

Tel: (609) 627-7200 Fax: (609) 627-7217 www.exideworld.com

Mfr. lead-acid automotive and industrial batteries.

Exide France, Nanterre Cedex, France

EXXON MOBIL CORPORATION

5959 Las Colinas Blvd., Irving, TX, 75039-2298

Tel: (972) 444-1000 Fax: (972) 444-1882 www.exxonmobil.com

Petroleum exploration, production, refining; mfr. petroleum and chemicals products; coal and minerals.

Exxon Mobil Raffinage SAF, Raffinerie de Fos, Route de Guigonnet, F-13270 Fos-sur-mer, France

Exxon Mobil, Inc., 2 rue des Martinets, F-92500 Reveil Malmaison, France

Tel: 33-1-4710-6000 Fax: 33-1-470-5511

Exxon Mobil, Inc., 31 Place des Corolles, Courbevoie, France

Exxon Mobil, Inc., B.P. 138, F-76330 Notre-Dame de Gravenchon, France

Exxon Mobil, Inc., Chemin de Vermelles, BP 19, F-62440 Harnes, France

FAIR, ISAAC AND COMPANY, INC.

200 Smith Ranch Road, San Rafael, CA, 94903

Tel: (415) 472-2211 Fax: (415) 492-5691 www.fairisaac.com

Mfr. automated systems for credit and loan approvals.

Fair, Isaac and Co., Atria 21 Avenue Edouard Beling, F-92566 Rueil-Malmaison Cedex, France

Tel: 33-1-4196-8080 Fax: 33-1-4708-2808

FAIRCHILD PUBLICATIONS INC.

7 West 34th Street, New York, NY, 10001

Tel: (212) 630-4000 Fax: (212) 630-3563 www.fairchildpub.com

Magazine publishers: Women's Wear Daily, Supermarket News, Brand Marketing, Executive Technology, Footwear News, Salon News.

Fairchild Publications, 9 rue Royale, F-75008 Paris, France

Tel: 33-1-44-51-1300

FAXON COMPANY, INC.

15 Southwest Park, Westwood, MA, 02090

Tel: (781) 329-3350 Fax: (781) 329-9875 www.faxon.com

Library services; engaged in serials management and subscription services in the library marketplace.

RoweCom France, rue de la Prairie, Villebon sur Yvette, F-91121 Palaiseau Cedex, France

FEDERAL-MOGUL CORPORATION

26555 Northwestern Highway, PO Box 1966, Southfield, MI, 48034

Tel: (248) 354-7700 Fax: (248) 354-8983 www.federal-mogul.com

Mfr./distributor precision parts for automobiles, trucks, farm and construction vehicles.

Federal-Mogul Aftermarket France, 58, rue Juliette Adam - BP20, F-91192 Gif Sur Yvette, France

FEDEX CORPORATION

942 South Shady Grove Rd., Memphis, TN, 38120

Tel: (901) 369-3600 Fax: (901) 395-2000 www.fdxcorp.com

Package express delivery service.

Federal Express (France) SARL, 44/46 ave. du 8 Mai 1945, F-92390 Villeneuve la Garenne, France

Tel: 800-123 800

FELLOWES, INC.

1789 Norwood Avenue, Itasca, IL, 60143-109

Tel: (630) 893-1600 Fax: (630) 893-1648 www.fellowes.com

Mfr. of office products and accessories.

Fellowes, Inc., 1 Rue de Bray, Z.I. Sud Est, BP 251, F-35514 Cesson Sevigne Cedex, France

Tel: 33-299-227122

FERRO CORPORATION

1000 Lakeside Ave., Cleveland, OH, 44114-7000

Tel: (216) 641-8580   Fax: (216) 696-5784   www.ferro.com

Mfr. Specialty chemicals, coatings, plastics, colors, refractories.

Eurostar SA, Zone Industrielle, rue de la Ferme St. Ladre, BP 2, F-95470 Fosses, France

Tel: 33-1-34-47-4700   Fax: 33-1-34-68-5840

Ferro Chemicals SA, Etang de la Gafette, BP 28, F-13521 Port-de-Bouc Cedex, France

Tel: 33-42-40-7300   Fax: 33-42-40-7333   Contact: John McIlwraith, Mng. Dir.

Ferro France S.A.R.L., 43 rue Jeanne d'Arc, F-52115 Saint Dizier, France

Tel: 33-25-073333   Fax: 33-25-563606   Contact: J. Bonnal, Gen. Mgr.

FileNET CORPORATION

3565 Harbor Boulevard, Costa Mesa, CA, 92626

Tel: (714) 966-3400   Fax: (714) 966-3490   www.filenet.com

Provides integrated document management (IDM) software and services for internet and client server-based imaging, workflow, cold and electronic document management solutions.

FileNET France, Velizy Plus, Batiment C, 1 bis rue du Petit-Clamart, F-78140 Velizy, France

Tel: 33-1-40-83-0606   Fax: 33-1-40-94-9170

FINANCIAL GUARANTY INSURANCE COMPANY

115 Broadway, New York, NY, 10006

Tel: (212) 312-3000   Fax: (212) 312-3093   www.fgic.com

Engaged in insuring debt securities and investment, operation, and information services to state and local governments

Financial Guaranty Insurance Co. (Paris), 107 rue St.-Lazare, F-75009 Paris, France

FIREPOND, INC.

890 Winter Stret, Waltham, MA, 02451

Tel: (781) 487-8400   Fax: (781) 487-8450   www.firepond.com

Mfr. enterprise software.

Firepond France SAS, Immeuble Le Colisee, 12, Avenue de l'Arche, Faubourg de l'Arche, F-92400 Courbevoie, France

FISHER SCIENTIFIC INTERNATIONAL INC.

1 Liberty Lane, Hampton, NH, 03842

Tel: (603) 929-5911   Fax: (603) 929-0222   www.fisherscientific.com

Mfr. and distribution of science equipment, instruments, and supplies.

Fisher Scientific - S.A., 12 rue Gay Lussac, ZAC Clé de Saint Pierre, BP2, F-78996 Elancourt Cedex, France

Tel: 33-1-30-13-2400   Fax: 33-1-30-13-2424

FLEETBOSTON FINANCIAL CORPORATION

100 Federal Street, Boston, MA, 02110

Tel: (617) 434-2400   Fax: (617) 434-6943   www.fleet.com

Banking and insurance services.

FleetBoston S.A. - Paris, 104 Ave. des Champs-Elyseés, F-75008 Paris, France

Tel: 33-1-40-76-7500   Fax: 33-1-40-76-7595

FLOW INTERNATIONAL CORPORATION

23500 64th Avenue S., PO Box 97040, Kent, WA, 98064-9740

Tel: (253) 872-4900   Fax: (253) 813-3285   www.flowcorp.com

Mfr. high-pressure water jet cutting/cleaning equipment, powered scaffolding; concrete cleaning/removal.

Flow France, 38, Place des Pavillons, F-69007 Lyon, France

FLOWSERVE CORPORATION

222 W. Los Colinas Blvd., Irving, TX, 75039

Tel: (972) 443-6500   Fax: (972) 443-6858   www.flowserve.com

Mfr. chemicals equipment, pumps, valves, filters, fans and heat exchangers.

Flowserve SARL, Zone Industrielle Carre d'As 7, Rue de Louis Lepine, F-13500 Martigues, France

Contact: Gerard Riehs

Flowserve SARL, 12 Avenue du Quebec Silic 651, F-91965 Courtaboeuf, France
Contact: Charles Tulmets

FM GLOBAL INC.

1301 Atwood Avenue, Johnston, RI, 02919

Tel: (401) 275-3000   Fax: (401) 275-3029   www.fmglobal.com

Engaged in commercial and industrial property insurance and risk management, specializing in engineering-driven property protection.

FM Insurance Company, Ltd., Tour Europlaza, Défense 4, F-92927 Paris La Défensen Cedex, France
Tel: 33-1-46-93-9700

FMC CORPORATION

1735 Market St., Philadelphia, PA, 19103

Tel: (215) 299-6000   Fax: (215) 299-6618   www.fmc.com

Mfr. specialty chemicals, including alginate, carrageenan and microcrystalline cellulose.

FMC France, 614 rue Benoit Mulsant, F-69400 Villefranche-Sur-Seone, France
Tel: 33-4-7468-3546

FMC France, 222 rue Michael Carre, Bezons, France

FMC TECHNOLOGIES, INC.

200 E. Randolph Dr., Chicago, IL, 60601

Tel: (312) 861-6000   Fax: (312) 861-6176   www.fmctechnologies.com

Mfr. bulk material handling and automation equipment and cargo loaders.

FMC Energy Systems S.A., Route des Clerimois, BP 705, F-89107 Sens, France

FMR (FIDELITY INVESTMENTS)

82 Devonshire Street, Boston, MA, 02109

Tel: (617) 563-7000   Fax: (617) 476-6105   www.fidelity.com

Diversified financial services company offering investment management, retirement, brokerage, and shareholder services directly to individuals and institutions and through financial intermediaries.

Fidelity Investments SAS, 17 Ave. George V, F-75008 Paris, France
Tel: 33-1-53-67-5566

FOOT LOCKER INC.

112 West 34th Street, New York, NY, 10020

Tel: (212) 720-3700   Fax: (212) 553-2042   www.venatorgroup.com

Mfr./sales shoes and sneakers.

Foot Locker International, C.C. Lille Grand Place, F-59000 Lille, France
Tel: 33-3-20-13-9595

Foot Locker International, Centre Commercial Euralille, F-59777 Euralille, France
Tel: 33-3-20-13-1542

Foot Locker International, 20 Blvd Alexandre Lii, F-59140 Dunkerque, France
Tel: 33-3-2865-1223

Foot Locker International, C.C. Villeneuve 2, Case Nr 47, F-59658 Villeneuve D'Ascq, France
Tel: 33-3-20-47-0136

Foot Locker International, 22 Ave. du Giniral Leclerc, F-75014 Paris, France
Tel: 33-1-40-44-9901

Foot Locker International, C.C. Cite De L'Europe, F-62231 Calais, France
Tel: 33-3-21-36-3726

FORD MOTOR COMPANY

One American Road, Dearborn, MI, 48126

Tel: (313) 322-3000   Fax: (313) 322-9600   www.ford.com

Mfr./sales motor vehicles.

Ford France SA, 344 ave. Napoleon Bonaparte, BP 307, F-92506 Rueil Malmaison Cedex, France

FORMICA CORPORATION

10155 Reading Road, Cincinnati, OH, 45241-4805

Tel: (513) 786-3400   Fax: (513) 786-3082   www.formica.com

Mfr. decorative laminate, adhesives and solvents.

Formica SA, BP 19, F-77313 Marne La Vallee Cedex 2, France

FORTEL INC.

46832 Lakeview Blvd., Fremont, CA, 94538-6543

Tel: (510) 440-9600   Fax: (510) 440-9696   www.fortel.com

Mfr. e-business corporate software.

FORTEL SARL, 6, Rue Lionel Terray, F-92506 Rueil Malmaison Cedex, France

Tel: 33-155-94-0641

FOSTER WHEELER LTD.

Perryville Corporate Park, Clinton, NJ, 08809-4000

Tel: (908) 730-4000   Fax: (908) 730-4100   www.fwc.com

Manufacturing, engineering and construction.

Foster Wheeler France SA, BP 114, Z.I. de la Grande Campagne Nord, rue Branly, F-76330 N.D. de Gravenchon, France

Tel: 33-2-3539-5900   Fax: 33-2-3538-3128   Contact: R. Herpin, Mgr.

Foster Wheeler France SA, 31 rue des Bourdonnais, F-75021 Paris Cedex 1, France

Foster Wheeler France SA, 92 quai de Bercy, F-75597 Paris Cedex 12, France

Tel: 33-1-4346-4000   Fax: 33-1-4346-4700   Contact: G. Bonadies, Pres. & CEO

Foster Wheeler France SA, Clairiere de l'Anjoly, Bât. D, Ave. de l'Europe, F-13127 Vitrolles, France

Tel: 33-4-4275-1100   Fax: 33-4-4289-9154   Contact: A. Combier, Mgr

Foster Wheeler France SA, Bâtiment Pythagore-Les Algorithmes, Parc d'Innovation-rue Jean Sapidus, F-67400 Illkirch-Graffenstaden, France

Tel: 33-3-8840-8300   Fax: 33-3-8867-8202   Contact: P. Muller, Mgr.

FRANK RUSSELL COMPANY

909 A Street, Tacoma, WA, 98402

Tel: (253) 572-9500   Fax: (253) 591-3495   www.russell.com

Investment management and asset strategy consulting.

Frank Russell Company S.A., 6 rue Christophe Colomb, F-75008 Paris, France

Tel: 33-1-53-57-4020   Fax: 33-1-53-57-4021   Contact: Frédéric Jolly, Mng. Dir.   Emp: 7

THE FRANKLIN MINT

US Route 1, Media, PA, 19091-0001

Tel: (610) 459-6000   Fax: (610) 459-6880   www.franklinmint.com

Design/marketing collectibles and luxury items.

Le Medaillier Franklin SA, 4 ave. de l'Escouvrier, F-95207 Sarcelles, France

FRANKLIN RESOURCES, INC.

1 Franklin Pkwy., Bldg. 970, 1st Fl., San Mateo, CA, 94404

Tel: (415) 312-2000   Fax: (415) 312-5606   www.frk.com

Global and domestic investment advisory and portfolio management.

Templeton Global Strategic Services, S.A., 16 Ave. George V, F-75008 Paris, France

Tel: 33-1-40-73-8600   Fax: 33-1-40-73-8610

FRIED, FRANK, HARRIS, SHRIVER & JACOBSON

One New York Plaza, New York, NY, 10004-1980

Tel: (212) 859-8000   Fax: (212) 859-4000   www.ffhsj.com

International law firm.

Fried, Frank, Harris, Shriver & Jacobson, 7 rue Royale, F-75008 Paris, France

Tel: 33-1-40-17-0404   Fax: 33-1-40-17-0830   Contact: Eric Cafritz, Ptnr.

FRITZ COMPANIES, INC., DIV. UPS

706 Mission Street, Ste. 900, San Francisco, CA, 94103

Tel: (415) 904-8360   Fax: (415) 904-8661   www.fritz.com

Integrated transportation, sourcing, distribution and customs brokerage services.

Fritz Companies Inc., Le Harve, France

FRONTRANGE SOLUTIONS INC.

1125 Kelly Johnson Blvd., Colorado Springs, CO, 80820

Tel: (719) 531-5007   Fax: (719) 536-0620   www.frontrange.com

Mfr. customer support software.

FrontRange Solutions, 16/18, Avenue Morane Saulnier, Batiment A, F-78941 Vélizy Villacoublay Cedex, France

FRONTSTEP, INC.

2800 Corporate Exchange Drive, Ste. 400, Columbus, OH, 43231

Tel: (614) 523-7000   Fax: (614) 895-2504   www.frontstep.com

Mfr. management software.

Frontstep France, 173 Rue de la Croix Nivert, F-75015 Paris, France

FROST & SULLIVAN, INC.

7550 West Interstate 10, Ste. 910, San Antonio, TX, 78229

Tel: (210) 348-1000   Fax: (210) 348-1003   www.frost.com

Engaged in international marketing consulting and training.

Frost & Sullivan, 24 Rue de Londres, F-75009 Paris, France

FSI INTERNATIONAL INC.

3455 Lyman Boulevard, Chaska, MN, 55318-3052

Tel: (952) 448-5440   Fax: (952) 448-2825   www.fsi-intl.com

Manufacturing equipment for computer silicon wafers.

Metron Technology France, Z.I. de la Mariniere, Bondoufle, 6 rue Bernard Palissy, F-91912 Evry Cedex 9, France

Metron Technology France, Immeuble le Grenat, 3 Avenue Doyen Louis Weil, F-38024 Grenoble Cedex 1, France

H.B. FULLER COMPANY

1200 Willow Lake Blvd., Vadnais Heights, MN, 55110

Tel: (651) 236-5900   Fax: (651) 236-5898   www.hbfuller.com

Mfr./distributor adhesives, sealants, coatings, paints, waxes, sanitation chemicals.

EFTEC S.A., 131 blvd. Carnot, F-78110 Le Vesinet, France

Tel: 33-1-34-80-0667   Fax: 33-1-39-76-4826

H.B. Fuller France, Zone Industrielle, BP 12, F-76580 Le Trait, France

Tel: 33-235-059221   Fax: 33-235-373678

THE GAB ROBINS GROUP

Linden Plaza, 9 Campus Drive, Parsippany, NJ, 07054-4476

Tel: (973) 993-3400   Fax: (973) 993-9579   www.gabrobins.com

Engaged in insurance adjustments and claims.

GAB Robins, 17, rue Saulnier, F-75009 Paris, France

GALVESTON-HOUSTON COMPANY.

4900 Woodway, PO Box 2207, Houston, TX, 77056

Tel: (713) 966-2500   Fax: (713) 966-2575   www.hensleyind.com

Mfr. industrial equipment.

Compagnie Auxiliarie Industrielle, 57-59 rue Etienne-Marcel, F-93100 Montreuil, France

THE GAP

2 Folsom St., San Francisco, CA, 94105

Tel: (650) 952-4400   Fax: (650) 952-5884   www.gap.com

Clothing store chain.

The Gap, Paris, France

GARDNER-DENVER INC.

1800 Gardner Expressway, Quincy, IL, 62301

Tel: (217) 222-5400   Fax: (217) 228-8247   www.gardnerdenver.com

Mfr. portable air compressors and related drilling accessories.

Gardner-Denver S.A., 3 rue Charles, F-95870 Francois Daubigny Bezons, France

Tel: 33-1-34344120

GARLOCK SEALING TECHNOLOGIES

1666 Division Street, Palmyra, NY, 14522

Tel: (315) 597-4811   Fax: (315) 597-3216   www.garlock-inc.com

Mfr. of gaskets, packing, seals and expansion joints.

Cefilac, 90 rue de la Roche du Geai, F-42029 St. Etienne Cedex, France

Contact: Bruno Lagree

Garlock Sealing Technologies, BP 69, 5 Allee des Plantanes, F-59570 Bavay, France

THE GATES RUBBER COMPANY

990 S. Broadway, PO Box 5887, Denver, CO, 80217-5887

Tel: (303) 744-1911   Fax: (303) 744-4000   www.gatesrubber.com

Mfr. automotive and industrial belts and hoses.

Gates SA, rue des Grands Pres, BP 19, F-58026 Nevers Cedex, France

GATEWAY INC.

4545 Towne Centre Ct., San Diego, CA, 92121

Tel: (858) 799-3401   Fax: (858) 779-3459   www.gateway.com

Computers manufacture, sales and services.

Gateway France, Centre Commercial, Avenue du Général de Gaulle Entrée n° 7, Unit 134, F-93110 Rosny, France

Gateway France, 63 Boulevard Haussman, F-75008 Paris, France

GATX CORPORATION

500 West Monroe Street, Chicago, IL, 60661

Tel: (312) 621-6200   Fax: (312) 621-6648   www.gatxcapital.com

Lease and loan financing, residual guarantees.

GATX International Ltd., Centreda 1, Avenue Didier Daurat, F-31700 Blagnac, France

Tel: 33-561-77-39-40   Fax: 33-561-16-72-44   Contact: Mike D. Sanders

GE BETZ, DIV. GE SPECIALTY MATERIALS

4636 Somerton Road, PO Box 3002, Trevose, PA, 19053-6783

Tel: (215) 355-3300   Fax: (215) 953-5524   www.gebetz.com

Engaged in engineered chemical treatment of water and process systems in industrial, commercial and institutional facilities

GE Betz, Div. GE Specialty Materials, BP 43, 77312 Marne-la-Vallée, 77312 Marne-la-Vallée, France

Tel: 33-4-7540-2389   Contact: Jacques Romain

GE CAPITAL FLEET SERVICES

3 Capital Drive, Eden Prairie, MN, 55344

Tel: (612) 828-1000   Fax: (612) 828-2010   www.gefleet.com

Corporate vehicle leasing and services.

GE Capital Fleet Services, 41 rue le Corbusier, F-94046 Cedex Creteil, France

Tel: 33-1-4956-5000

GEN RE INTERMEDIARIES CORPORATION

PO Box 10216, Stamford, CT, 06904-2216

Tel: (203) 357-8883   Fax: (203) 328-6408   www.genre.com

Provides reinsurance services worldwide.

General Re Europe Ltd. - Paris, 119-121 Ave. des Champs Elysees, F-75008 Paris, France

Tel: 33-1-53-67-76-76   Fax: 33-1-40-70-91-60   Contact: Emmanuel Brouquier, VP

HartRe Company, Square Edouard VII, 26 boulevard des Capucines 6me Etage, F-75009 Paris, France

Tel: 33-15-818-3030   Fax: 33-14-456-0939   Contact: François Lanoote

La Kölnische Rück S.A., 121 Ave. des Champs-Elysées, F-75008 Paris, France

Tel: 33-1-5367-7676   Fax: 33-1-4070-9160   Contact: Bertrand Gautheron, Mng. Dir.

GENERAL BINDING CORPORATION

One GBC Plaza, Northbrook, IL, 60062

Tel: (847) 272-3700   Fax: (847) 272-1369   www.gbc.com

Engaged in the design, manufacture and distribution of branded office equipment, related supplies and thermal laminating films.

GBC France S.A., 1, allee des Bas Tilliers, Parc Les Barbanniers, F-92230 Gennevilliers Cedex, France

GENERAL DATACOMM INC.

6 Rubber Avenue, Naugatuck, CT, 06770

Tel: (203) 729-0271   Fax: (203) 729-2883   www.gdc.com

Mfr., sales and service of transportation equipment for communications networks.

General DataComm SARL, 14 rue Jules Saulnier, Parc du Colombier, BP 221, F-93200 St. Denis, France

GENERAL ELECTRIC CAPITAL CORPORATION

260 Long Ridge Road, Stamford, CT, 06927

Tel: (203) 357-4000   Fax: (203) 357-6489   www.gecapital.com

Financial, property, casualty insurance, computer sales and trailer leasing services.

GE Capital Equipement Finance, 2 Ave des Champs-Pierreux, F-92736 Nanterre Cedex, France

Tel: 33-1-55-07-1400   Fax: 33-1-5507-1402

GE Capital Equipement Finance, 8, Avenue Montaigne, F-93192 Noisy-le-Grand Cédex, France

GENERAL ELECTRIC COMPANY

3135 Easton Turnpike, Fairfield, CT, 06431

Tel: (203) 373-2211   Fax: (203) 373-3131   www.ge.com

Diversified manufacturing, technology and services.

GE Aircraft Engines, F-77750 Moissy Cramayel Villaroche, France

Tel: 33-6-212-2100

GE Capital Services GENSTAR Container, 30 rue D'Orleans, Paris, France

Tel: 33-1-47-45-0951

GE FANUC Automation, 45 rue du Bois Chaland, F-91029 Evry Cedex, France

Tel: 33-1-69-89-7020   Fax: 33-1-69-89-7049

General Electric France, 18 rue Horace Vernet, F-92136 Issy Les Moulineaux, France

Tel: 33-1-40-93-3336

GEPC Export Department, Route de Guise, BP 642, F-02322 St. Quentin Cedex, France

Tel: 33-3-23-50-7035   Fax: 33-3-23-50-7088

Nuovo Pignone, 19 Ave. de l'Opera, F-75001 Paris, France

Tel: 33-1-43-16-1496   Fax: 33-1-43-16-1499

GENERAL MOTORS ACCEPTANCE CORPORATION

3044 W. Grand Blvd., Detroit, MI, 48202

Tel: (313) 556-5000   Fax: (313) 556-5108   www.gmac.com

Automobile financing.

Banque de Credit General Motors, Tour Manhattan, F-92095 Paris Cedex 21, France

Banque de Credit GM, BP 354, F-33694 Merignac Cedex, France

Banque de Credit GM, Tour Credit Lyonnais, 129 rue Servient, F-69431 Lyon 03, France

GENERAL MOTORS CORPORATION

300 Renaissance Center, Detroit, MI, 48285

Tel: (313) 556-5000   Fax: (313) 556-5108   www.gm.com

Mfr. full line vehicles, automotive electronics, commercial technologies, telecommunications, space, finance.

Delco Remy Div. GM, BP 819, F-57208 Sarreguemines, France

Harrison Radiator Div. GM, BP 14, Zone Industrielle, F-08350 Donchery, France

Hydra-matic Div. GM, BP 33, F-67026 Strasbourg Cedex, France

GENICOM CORPORATION

4500 Daly Drive, Ste. 100, Chantilly, VA, 20151

Tel: (703) 633-8700   Fax: (703) 222-7629   www.genicom.com

Supplier of network systems, service and printer solutions.

CPG International S.A., 150, Avenue Joseph Kessel, Parc de la Grande Ile, F-78960 Voisins-le-Bretonneux, France

Tel: 33-1-69-542317   Contact: Michel Fargier

GENUITY, INC.

225 Presidential Way, Woburn, MA, 01801

Tel: (781) 865-2000   Fax: (781) 865-3936   www.genuity.com

R/D computer, communications, acoustics technologies and internetworking services.

Genuity France, 54 Avenue Hoche, F-75008 Paris, France

Tel: 33-1-5660 5273   Contact: Michel Azoulay

GENZYME CORPORATION

1 Kendall Square, Cambridge, MA, 02139-1562

Tel: (617) 252-7500   Fax: (617) 252-7600   www.genzyme.com

Mfr. healthcare products for enzyme deficient diseases.

Genzyme Europe BV, 9 Chaussee Jules Cesar, Batiment 2, BP 225, F-95523 Osny Cergy-Pontoise Cedex, France

Genzyme SA, 9 Chaussee Jules Cesar, Batiment 2, BP 225, F- 95523 Osny Cergy-Pointoise Cedex, France

Tel: 33-1-34-22-9570   Fax: 33-1-30-3-9919

GEORGIA-PACIFIC GROUP

133 Peachtree Street NE, 41st Floor, Atlanta, GA, 30303

Tel: (404) 652-4000   Fax: (404) 230-7008   www.gp.com

Mfr. and distribution of tissue, pulp, paper and building products and related chemicals.

Georgie-Pacific France, Usine d'Hondouville, F-27400 Louviers, France

GERBER SCIENTIFIC, INC.

83 Gerber Road West, South Windsor, CT, 06074

Tel: (860) 644-1551   Fax: (860) 644-5547   www.gerberscientific.com

Mfr. computer-based automated manufacturing and design systems for signs and graphics.

Gerber Technology, Batiment 7, Hall 7 bis, F-91571 Bievres Cedex, France

G-I HOLDINGS, INC.

1361 Alps Road, Wayne, NJ, 07470

Tel: (973) 628-3000   Fax: (973) 628-3326   www.gaf.com

Mfr. roofing and building materials.

G-I Holdings, Inc., BP 50007, F-95945 Roissy Charles de Gaulle Cedex, France

GIBSON, DUNN & CRUTCHER LLP

333 S. Grand Ave., Los Angeles, CA, 90071

Tel: (213) 229-7000   Fax: (213) 229-7520   www.gibsondunn.com

Engaged in international law.

Gibson, Dunn & Crutcher LLP, 166 rue du Faubourg Saint Honore, F-75008 Paris, France

Tel: 33-1-56-43-1300   Fax: 33-1-56-43-1333

GILEAD SCIENCES, INC.

333 Lakeside Dr, Foster City, CA, 94404

Tel: (650) 574-3000   Fax: (650) 578-9264   www.gilead.com

Engaged in healthcare research and development; biotech treatments for viruses.

NeXstar Pharaceutique, 39 rue Godot de Mauroy, F-75009 Paris, France

Tel: 33-1-4268-3450   Fax: 33-1-4266-2605

THE GILLETTE COMPANY

Prudential Tower Building, Boston, MA, 02199

Tel: (617) 421-7000   Fax: (617) 421-7123   www.gillette.com

Develop/mfr. personal care/use products: blades and razors, toiletries, cosmetics, stationery.

Braun France SA, Clichy Paris, France

Contact: Alain Calviera, Gen. Mgr.

Gillette Co./Waterman SA, 44 Saint-Herblain, F-75008 Paris, France

Tel: 33-1-4312-2370   Contact: Alain Calviera, Gen. Mgr.

Gillette France SA, Annecy, France

Contact: Alain Calviera, Gen. Mgr.

Oral-B Laboratories SA, Saint Herblain, France

Contact: Alain Calviera, Gen. Mgr.

Silk-Epil SA, La Farlede Toulon, France

Contact: Alain Calviera, Gen. Mgr.

Societe de Participations Financieres Gillette, Annecy Cedex, France

Contact: Alain Calviera, Gen. Mgr.

Societe Francaise d'Appareillages et d'Instrument de Mesure, Caluire Cedex, France

Contact: Alain Calviera, Gen. Mgr.

GILSON INC.

3000 W. Beltline Hwy, PO Box 620027, Middleton, WI, 53562-0027

Tel: (608) 836-1551   Fax: (608) 831-4451   www.gilson.com

Mfr. analytical/biomedical instruments.

Gilson International France S.A.S., 19, avenue des Entrepreneurs, B.P. 145, F-95400 Villiers-le-Bel, France

P.H. GLATFELTER COMPANY

96 South George St., Ste. 500, York, PA, 17401

Tel: (717) 225-4711   Fax: (717) 225-6834   www.glatfelter.com

Mfr. engineered and specialty printing papers.

Glatfelter Ltd., Paris, France

GLEASON CORPORATION

1000 University Ave., Rochester, NY, 14692

Tel: (716) 473-1000   Fax: (716) 461-4348   www.gleasoncorp.com

Mfr. gear making machine tools; tooling and services.

Gleason France, Paris Nord II, BP 60070 22 Avenue des Nation, F-95972 Roissy CDG Cedex, France

Tel: 33-1-49389000 Fax: 33-1-49389009

THE GOLDMAN SACHS GROUP

85 Broad Street, New York, NY, 10004

Tel: (212) 902-1000   Fax: (212) 902-3000   www.gs.com

Investment bankers; securities broker dealers.

Goldman Sachs Group, 2 rue de Thann, F-75017 Paris, France

Tel: 33-1-42-12-1000

GOODRICH CORPORATION

2730 West Tyvola Road, Charlotte, NC, 28217-4578

Tel: (704) 423-7000   Fax: (704) 423-7100   www.bfgoodrich.com

Engaged in aerospace and aeronautical systems and services, performance materials and engineered industrial products.

Cefilac, S.A., Div. Goodrich, 90 rue de la Roche du Geai, F-42029 Saint Etienne Cedex 1, France

Tel: 33-4-7743-5100

THE GOODYEAR TIRE & RUBBER COMPANY

1144 East Market Street, Akron, OH, 44316

Tel: (330) 796-2121   Fax: (330) 796-1817   www.goodyear.com

Mfr. tires, automotive belts and hose, conveyor belts, chemicals; oil pipeline transmission.

Cie. Francaise Goodyear SA, BP 310, F-92506 Rueil-Malmaison Cedex, France

GOSS INTERNATIONAL CORPORATION

700 Oakmont Lane, Westmont, IL, 60559-5546

Tel: (630) 850-5600 Fax: (630) 850-6310 www.gossgraphic.com

Engaged in the design and manufacture of advanced technology web offset press systems for the newspaper and commercial printing industries.

Goss Systemes Graphique SA, 20 Rue de Koufra, BP 61626, F-44316 Nantes Cedex 03, France

Tel: 33-240-18-6969 Fax: 33-240-93-2888 Contact: Eric Normand, SVP & Gen. Mgr.

W. R. GRACE & COMPANY

7500 Grace Drive, Columbia, MD, 21044

Tel: (410) 531-4000 Fax: (410) 531-4367 www.grace.com

Mfr. specialty chemicals and materials: packaging, health care, catalysts, construction, water treatment/process.

W. R. Grace Ltd., 33 Route de Gallardon, F-28234 Epernon Cedex, France

W.R. Grace S.A.S., 33 Route de Gallardon, F-28234 Epernon Cedex, France

Tel: 33-2-37-18-8600 Fax: 33-2-37-18-8686

GRACO INC.

88 - 11th Avenue NE, PO Box 1441, Minneapolis, MN, 55440-1441

Tel: (612) 623-6000 Fax: (612) 623-6777 www.graco.com

Mfr. systems and equipment to service fluid handling systems and automotive equipment.

Graco Puericulture, 155 Av. Jean Jaures, F-93531 Aubervilliers Cedex, France

Tel: 33-1-48-1179-24 Fax: 33-1-48-1179-24

GRAFTECH INTERNATIONAL LTD.

1521 Concord Pike, Ste. 301, Wilmington, DE, 19803

Tel: (302) 778-8277 Fax: (302) 778-8237 www.graftechinternational.com

Mfr. graphite electrodes for electrical products.

Carbone Savoie, 30 rue Louis Jouvet BP 16, F-69631 Vénissieux Cedex, France

Tel: 33-4-78-77-08-70 Fax: 33-4-78-09-05-22

GRANITE SYSTEMS, INC.

1228 Elm Street, Manchester, NH, 03101

Tel: (603) 625-0100 Fax: (603) 625-4812 www.granitesystems.com

Mfr. service resource management software.

Granite Systems, Inc., 455 Promenade des Anglais, Immeuble Air France, F-06200 Nice, France

Tel: 33-492-292805

GRANT THORNTON INTERNATIONAL

800 One Prudential Plaza, 130 E. Randolph Drive, Chicago, IL, 60601-6050

Tel: (312) 856-0001 Fax: (312) 616-7052 www.grantthornton.com

Accounting, audit, tax and management consulting services.

Grant Thornton France Exco France, 7 rue de Madrid, F-75008 Paris, France

Tel: 33-1-44-70-3000 Fax: 33-1-42-93-3216 Contact: André Zagouri

Grant Thornton France Exco France, 37 Ave. de la Foret Noire, BP 21/R1, F-67001 Strasbourg Cedex, France

Tel: 33-88-61-0802 Fax: 33-88-60-6710 Contact: Philippe Ley

Grant Thornton France Exco France, 46 bis rue des Hauts-Paves, B.P. 289, F-44010 Nantes Cedex 01, France

Tel: 33-40-20-2122 Fax: 33-40-08-0430 Contact: Michel Piau

Grant Thornton France Exco France, 156 blvd Delbecque, BP 99, F-59502 Douai Cedex Douai, France

Tel: 33-27-94-3000 Fax: 33-27-94-3001 Contact: Erik Voituriez

Grant Thornton France Exco France, 64 rue Francois Marceau, B.P. 208, F-33021 Bordeaux Cedex, France

Tel: 33-56-42-4344 Fax: 33-56-42-4380 Contact: Bernard Junières

GREAT LAKES CHEMICAL CORPORATION

500 East 96th Street, Ste. 500, Indianapolis, IN, 46240

Tel: (317) 715-3000   Fax: (317) 715-3050   www.greatlakeschem.com

Mfr. innovative specialty chemical solutions, including flame retardants and other polymer additives, water treatment chemicals, performance and fine chemicals, fire extinguishers.

Great Lakes Chemical France SA, 5 rue Francis de Pressensé, F-93210 Saint Denis La Plaine, France

Tel: 33-1-3441-6000

GREY GLOBAL GROUP

777 Third Ave., New York, NY, 10017

Tel: (212) 546-2000   Fax: (212) 546-1495   www.grey.com

International advertising agency.

Grey Communications Group, 63 bis rue de Sevres, F-92514 Boulogne-Billancourt Cedex, France

GRIFFITH LABORATORIES INC.

One Griffith Center, Alsip, IL, 60658

Tel: (708) 371-0900   Fax: (708) 597-3294   www.griffithlabs.com

Mfr. industrial food ingredients and equipment.

Griffith Labs Inc., Paris, France

Tel: 33-1-46-43-9393   Fax: 33-1-46-43-9394

GROVE WORLDWIDE LLC

1565 Buchanon Trail East, Shady Grove, PA, 17256

Tel: (717) 597-8121   Fax: (717) 593-4062   www.groveworldwide.com

Mfr. cranes.

Grove Worldwide, 16 Chaussee Jules Cesar, F-95523 Cergy Pontoise Cedex, France

GUIDANT CORPORATION

111 Monument Circle, 29th Fl., Indianapolis, IN, 46204

Tel: (317) 971-2000   Fax: (317) 971-2040   www.guidant.com

Mfr. cardiovascular therapeutic devices.

Guidant France S.A., 9 rue d'Estienne d'Orves, F-92504 Rueil Malmaison, France

Tel: 33-1-4714-4014

GUPTA TECHNOLOGIES

975 Island Drive, Redwood Shores, CA, 94065

Tel: (650) 596-3400   Fax: (650) 596-4900   www.centurasoft.com

Mfr. software and database management tools

Gupta Technologies, 10, Avenue du Québec - BP116, F-91944 Courtaboeuf Cedex, France

Tel: 33-1-60-92-41-09   Fax: 33-1-69-29-09-19

GUY CARPENTER & COMPANY, INC.

114 West 47th Street, New York, NY, 10036

Tel: (212) 323-1000   Fax: (212) 345-2494   www.guycarp.com

Engaged in global reinsurance and risk management.

Guy Carpenter & Company, S.A., 47-53 rue Raspail, F-92594 Levallois-Perret Cedex, France

Tel: 33-1-56-76-400   Fax: 33-1-41-27-9303   Contact: Bernard Paul

HAEMONETICS CORPORATION

400 Wood Road, Braintree, MA, 02184-9114

Tel: (781) 848-7100   Fax: (781) 848-5106   www.haemonetics.com

Mfr. automated blood processing systems and blood products.

Haemonetics France SARL, 46 bis rue Pierre Curie, Z.l. Les Gatines, F-78370 Plaisir, France

Tel: 33-1-308-141-41   Fax: 33-1-308-141-30

HAHT COMMERCE, INC.

400 Newton Road, Raleigh, NC, 27615

Tel: (919) 786-5100   Fax: (919) 786-5250   www.haht.com

Mfr. e-commerce software.

HAHT Commerce, 7 Place d'Iena, F-75116 Paris, France

HALLIBURTON COMPANY

500 North Akard Street, Ste. 3600, Dallas, TX, 75201-3391

Tel: (214) 978-2600   Fax: (214) 978-2685   www.halliburton.com

Engaged in diversified energy services, engineering and construction.

Halliburton Ltd., BP 209, F-64142 Billere Cedex, France

Tel: 33-59-32-1446   Fax: 33-59-62-1862

Halliburton Ltd., Le Florestan, 2 blvd Vauban, St. Quentin-En-Yvelines, F-78180 Montigney-Le-Bretonneux, France

Tel: 33-1-30-43-9898   Fax: 33-1-30-43-5662

Halliburton Ltd., rue de la foret, Zone Industriel Espinay Sous, F-91860 Epinay Sous Senart, France

Tel: 33-1-69-438135   Fax: 33-1-60-464038

HALLMARK CARDS INC.

2501 McGee Street, Kansas City, MO, 64108

Tel: (816) 274-5100   Fax: (816) 274-5061   www.hallmark.com

Mfr. greeting cards and related products.

Hallmark Group France, S.A., rue Eiffel, ZAC de Mercieres, F-60200 Compiegne, France

Tel: 33-3-44-51-5151

HA-LO INDUSTRIES, INC.

5800 West Touhy Avenue, Niles, IL, 60714

Tel: (847) 600-3000   Fax: (847) 600-4000   www.halo.com

Engaged in distribution of brand-awareness, promotional products.

Parsons International, 63 Avenue de l'Europe, F-77184 Emerainville, France

HAMILTON SUNSTRAND

One Hamilton Rd., Windsor Locks, CT, 06096-1010

Tel: (860) 654-6000   Fax: (860) 654-3469   www.hamiltonsunstrandcorp.com

Design/mfr. aerospace systems for commercial, regional, corporate and military aircraft.

Hamilton Sunstrand Corp., Zone Industrial Dijon Sud, B.P. 30, F-21604 Longvic Cedex, France

Tel: 33-3-80-38-33-01   Fax: 33-3-80-38-33-91

HARBORLITE CORPORATION

PO Box 100, Vicksburg, MI, 49097

Tel: (616) 649-1352   Fax: (616) 649-3707   www.worldminerals.com

Mining and process perlite filter media.

Harborlite France, 9 rue de Colonel de Rochebrune, BP 240, F-92504 Rueil-Malmaison Cedex, France

HARMAN INTERNATIONAL INDUSTRIES, INC.

1101 Pennsylvania Ave. NW, Ste. 1010, Washington, DC, 20004

Tel: (202) 393-1101   Fax: (202) 393-3064   www.harman.com

Mfr. audio and video equipment, loudspeakers and sound reinforcement equipment.

Harman France, 2, route de Tours, F-72500 Château du Loir, France

Harman France SA, 33 ave. du Marechal de Lattre de Tassigny, F-94127 Fontenay sous Bois Cedex, France

Harman France SA, 25 avenue de l'Europe, F-78400 Chatou, France

HARRIS CALORIFIC COMPANY

2345 Murphy Boulevard, Gainesville, GA, 30501

Tel: (770) 536-8801   Fax: (770) 536-0544   www.harriscal.com

Mfr./sales of gas welding and cutting equipment.

Harris France SARL, Div. Lincoln Electric, Avenue Franklin Roosevelt, BP 214, F-76121 Grand-Quevilly Cedex, France

HARRIS CORPORATION
1025 West NASA Blvd., Melbourne, FL, 32919

Tel: (407) 727-9100 Fax: (407) 727-9344 www.harris.com

Mfr. communications and information-handling equipment, including copying and fax systems.

Harris Semiconducteurs, Centrale Parc - Bat. Pasteur No. 4, Avenue Sully Prud'homme, F-92290 Chatenay-Malabry, France

Tel: 33-1-55-52-80-03 Fax: 33-1-55-52-80-13

HARVARD BIOSCIENCE, INC.
84 October Hill Road, Holliston, MA, 01746-1371

Tel: (508) 893-8999 Fax: (508) 429-5732 www.harvardbioscience.com

Mfr. tools for drug development.

Harvard Apparatus SARL, 6 avenue des Andes, Miniparc Bat. 8, F-91952 Les Ulis Cedex, France

Tel: 33-1-6446-0085 Fax: 33-1-6446-9438

HASBRO INDUSTRIES INC.
1027 Newport Ave., Pawtucket, RI, 02861

Tel: (401) 725-8697 Fax: (401) 727-5099 www.hasbro.com

Mfr. toy products, including games and puzzles, dolls and plush products.

Wizards, Div. Hasbro Industries, 2 rue du Nouveau Bercy, F-94220 Charenton Le Pont Paris, France

Tel: 33-1-4396-3565

HAUPPAUGE DIGITAL, INC.
91 Cabot Court, Hauppauge, NY, 11788

Tel: (631) 434-1600 Fax: (631) 434-3198 www.hauppauge.com

Mfr. circuit boards.

Hauppauge Computer Works, Sarl, 91 Avenue Kleber, Paris, France

Tel: 33-156-265-121

HAWORTH INC.
1 Haworth Center, Holland, MI, 49423-9576

Tel: (616) 393-3000 Fax: (616) 393-1570 www.haworth.com

Mfr. office furniture.

Haworth France, Mobilier & Ordo, 7, Terrasse des Retlets, La Defense 2 Cedex, France

Tel: 33-1-4197-4100

HAYNES INTERNATIONAL INC.
1020 W. Park Ave., PO Box 9013, Kokomo, IN, 46904-9013

Tel: (765) 456-6000 Fax: (765) 456-6905 www.haynesintl.com

Development and manufacture of high-performance nickel and cobalt based alloys for service in severe corrosion and high-temperature applications.

Haynes International, S.A.R.L., Boite Postale 9535, F-95061 Cergy Pontoise Cedex, France

Tel: 33-1-34-48-3100 Fax: 33-1-30-37-8022

HEIDRICK & STRUGGLES INTERNATIONAL, INC.
233 South Wacker Drive, Chicago, IL, 60606

Tel: (312) 496-1200 Fax: (312) 496-1290 www.heidrick.com

Executive search firm.

Heidrick & Struggles Intl. Inc., 112 Ave. Kleber, F-75784 Paris Cedex 18, France

Tel: 33-1-44-34-1700 Fax: 33-1-44-34-1717

HEIN-WERNER CORPORATION
2110 A Pewaukee Rd., PO Box 1606, Waukesha, WI, 53188

Tel: (262) 542-6611 Fax: (262) 542-7890 www.blackhawk-kj.com

Mfr. auto body repair equipment, engine rebuilding and brake repair equipment, hydraulic cylinders.

Blackhawk SA, Centre Eurofret, Rue du Rheinfeld, F-67026 Strasbourg, France

H.J. HEINZ COMPANY

600 Grant Street, Pittsburgh, PA, 15219

Tel: (412) 456-5700   Fax: (412) 456-6128   www.heinz.com

Processed food products and nutritional services.

Ets. Paul Paulet, Douarnenez, France

H.J. Heinz SARL, Paris, France

HELLER FINANCIAL INC.

500 West Monroe Street, Chicago, IL, 60661

Tel: (312) 441-7000   Fax: (312) 441-7367   www.hellerfin.com

Financial services.

Factofrance Heller, Tour Facto, F-92988 Paris La Défense Cedex 88, France

HENRY SCHEIN, INC.

135 Duryea Rd., Melville, NY, 11747

Tel: (516) 843-5500   Fax: (516) 843-5658   www.henryschein.com

Mfr. and supply dental equipment.

Henry Schein France SA, Immeuble Activille, 4, rue de Charenton, F-94140 Alfortville Cedex, France

Tel: 33-1-41-79-6565

HERCULES INC.

Hercules Plaza, 1313 N. Market Street, Wilmington, DE, 19894-0001

Tel: (302) 594-5000   Fax: (302) 594-5400   www.herc.com

Mfr. specialty chemicals, plastics, film and fibers, coatings, resins and food ingredients.

Hercules Chemical Ltd., Aklizay, France

Hercules France SA, 3 rue Eugene et Armaud Peugeot, F-92508 Rueil-Malmaison Cedex, France

Tel: 33-1-47-10-2400   Fax: 33-1-47-08-5075   Contact: Christian Tavaux

HERMAN MILLER INC.

855 East Main, Zeeland, MI, 49464

Tel: (616) 654-3000   Fax: (616) 654-5385   www.hermanmiller.com

Mfr. office furnishings.

Herman Miller et Cie, Immeuble Tivoli, 257 av Georges Clémenceau, F-92000 Nanterre Cedex, France

Tel: 33-1-5517-6262   Fax: 33-1-5517-6260

THE HERTZ CORPORATION

225 Brae Boulevard, Park Ridge, NJ, 07656-0713

Tel: (201) 307-2000   Fax: (201) 307-2644   www.hertz.com

Worldwide headquarters office for car rental, car leasing and equipment rental.

Hertz Rental Car, Paris, France

HEWITT ASSOCIATES LLC

100 Half Day Road, Lincolnshire, IL, 60069

Tel: (847) 295-5000   Fax: (847) 295-7634   www.hewitt.com

Employee benefits consulting firm.

Hewitt Associates, 20 Ave. André Malraux, F-92309 Levallois-Perret Cedex Paris, France

Tel: 33-1-47-59-3939

HEWLETT-PACKARD COMPANY

3000 Hanover Street, Palo Alto, CA, 94304-1185

Tel: (650) 857-1501   Fax: (650) 857-5518   www.hp.com

Mfr. computing, communications and measurement products and services.

Hewlett-Packard France, 5 Avenue Raymond Chanas, F-38053 Grenoble Cedex 09, France

HEXCEL CORPORATION

281 Tresser Blvd., Stamford, CT, 06901

Tel: (203) 969-0666   Fax: (203) 358-3977   www.hexcel.com

Honeycomb core materials, specialty chemicals, resins and epoxies.

Hexcel France, 3 avenue Condorcet, F-69608 Villeurbanne, France

Contact: Lionel Garnier

HILLENBRAND INDUSTRIES, INC.

700 State Route 46 East, Batesville, IN, 47006

Tel: (812) 934-7000   Fax: (812) 934-1963   www.hillenbrand.com

Holding company: mfr. hospital beds, incubators and caskets.

Hill-Rom Ltd., PB 14, ZI du Talhouet, F-56330 Pluvigner, France

Tel: 33-297-509275   Fax: 33-297-509202   Contact: Pascal Pouligny

HILTON HOTELS CORPORATION

9336 Civic Center Drive, Beverly Hills, CA, 90210

Tel: (310) 278-4321   Fax: (310) 205-7880   www.hiltonhotels.com

International hotel chain: Hilton International, Vista Hotels and Hilton National Hotels.

Hilton International Hotels, 18 Ave. de Suffren, F-75740 Paris Cedex 15, France

Noga Hilton Cannes, 50 blvd de la Croisette, F-06414 Cannes Cedex, France

Paris Hilton, 18 Ave. de Suffren, F-75740 Paris Cedex 15, France

HOGAN & HARTSON LLP

555 13th Street NW, Washington, DC, 20004-1109

Tel: (202) 637-5600   Fax: (202) 637-5910   www.hhlaw.com

Engaged in international law.

Hogan & Hartson, 12 Rue de la Paix, F-75002 Paris, France

Tel: 33-1-4261-5771   Contact: Alan Cariddi

HOLIDAY INN (BASS RESORTS) WORLDWIDE, INC.

3 Ravinia Drive, Ste. 2900, Atlanta, GA, 30346-2149

Tel: (770) 604-2000   Fax: (770) 604-5403   www.holidayinn.com

Hotels, restaurants and casinos.

Holiday Inn France, 69 Blvd. Victor, F-75015 Port de Versailles Paris, France

Holiday Inn France, 110 rue Jean Joures, F-59810 Lesquin Paris, France

Holiday Inn France, 4 ave. Charles Lindberg, Orly Airport, F-94656 Rungis Paris, France

HOLOGIC, INC.

35 Crosby Drive, Bedford, MA, 01730

Tel: (781) 999-7300   Fax: (781) 280-0669   www.hologic.com

Mfr. x-ray systems to measure bone density.

Hologic France, 35 rue du Saule Trapu, F-91882 Massy, France

Tel: 33-1-6013-3938   Fax: 33-1-6913-3441

HONEYWELL INTERNATIONAL INC.

Honeywell Plaza, Minneapolis, MN, 55408

Tel: (612) 951-1000   Fax: (612) 951-8537   www.honeywell.com

Develop/mfr. controls for home and building, industry, space and aviation, burglar and fire alarm systems.

Honeywell SA, Parc Technologique de St. Aubin, Route de l'Orme (CD 128), F-91190 Saint Aubin, France

Tel: 33-1-6919-8000   Fax: 33-1-6019-8181

HORWATH INTERNATIONAL ASSOCIATION

420 Lexington Avenue, Suite 526, New York, NY, 10170-0526

Tel: (212) 808-2000   Fax: (212) 808-2020   www.horwath.com

Public accountants and auditors.

Horwath France, 12 rue de Madrid, F-75008 Paris, France

HOUGHTON INTERNATIONAL INC.

PO Box 930, Madison & Van Buren Avenues, Valley Forge, PA, 19482-0930

Tel: (610) 666-4000   Fax: (610) 666-1376   www.houghtonintl.com

Mfr. specialty chemicals, hydraulic fluids and lubricants.

Produtec Houghton SA, 259 rue Benoit-Mulsant, ZAC Nord Est, BP 41, F-69652 Villefranche Cedex, France

Tel: 33-4-74-65-6500

HOWMEDICA OSTEONICS, INC.

59 Route 17 South, Allendale, NJ, 07401

Tel: (201) 507-7300   Fax: (201) 935-4873   www.howmedica.com

Mfr. of maxillofacial products (orthopedic implants).

Howmedica France, Lyon, France

Tel: 33-4-78-78-6060

HOWMET CASTINGS

9 Old Kings Hwy. South, Darien, CT, 06820

Tel: (203) 857-3120   Fax: (203) 857-3158   www.howmet.com

Mfr. precision investment castings, alloys, engineering and refurbishment for jet aircraft and industrial gas turbine (IGT) engine components.

Burgundy Casting, 26 rue de Pologne, F-71201 Le Creusot Cedex, France

Tel: 33-3-85-77-6600   Fax: 33-2-43-01-3413   Contact: Mike Hanrahan   Emp: 250

Evron Casting, Immeuble le Pereire, 6-8 Avenue Salvador Allerde, F- 93804 Epinay Sur Seine Cedex, France

Fax: 33-1-49-40-1594   Contact: Bernard Poissonnier

Gennevilliers Casting, 68 A 78 rue du Moulin de Cage, F-92300 Gennevilliers, France

Tel: 33-1-40-85-3600   Contact: Terry Zuk

Normandy Casting, Z.A.C. des Grandes Pres., F-14160 Dives sur Mer, France

Tel: 33-2-31-28-2930   Fax: 33-2-31-24-5866   Contact: Jean Castillon

HQ GLOBAL WORKPLACES INC.

15305 Dallas Parkway, Ste. 1400, Addison, TX, 75001

Tel: (972) 361-8221   Fax: (972) 361-8221   www.hq.com

Provides office outsourcing, officing solutions, including internet access, telecommunications, meeting rooms, furnished offices and team rooms, state-of-the-art videoconferencing, and trained on-site administrative support teams -

HQ Global Workplaces, 10 Place Vendôme, F-75001 Paris, France

Tel: 33-1-53-45-5454

HUBBARD ISA

PO Box 415, Walpole, NH, 03431

Tel: (603) 756-3311   Fax: (603) 756-9034   www.hubbard-isa.com

Poultry breeding R&D, poultry foundation breeding stock.

Hubbard ISA S.A.S, 119, avenue Maréchal de Saxe, F-69427 Lyon Cedex 3, France

J.M. HUBER CORPORATION

333 Thornall Street, Edison, NJ, 08818

Tel: (732) 549-8600   Fax: (732) 549-2239   www.huber.com

Diversified, multinational supplier of engineered materials, natural resources and technology-based services to customers spanning many industries, from paper and energy to plastics and construction.

Huber Engineered Materials, Clairefontaine, France

HUCK INTERNATIONAL INC.

3724 East Columbia Street, Tucson, AZ, 85714-3415

Tel: (520) 747-9898   Fax: (520) 750-7420   www.huck.com

Designer and manufacturer of high-performance, proprietary fasteners and fastener installation systems.

Huck SA, Clos d'Asseville, BP 4, F-95450 Us Par Vigny, France

HUGHES HUBBARD & REED LLP

One Battery Park Plaza, New York, NY, 10004-1482

Tel: (212) 837-6000 Fax: (212) 422-4726 www.hugheshubbard.com

Engaged in international law.

Hughes, Hubbard & Reed LLP, 47 ave. Georges Mandel, F-75116 Paris, France

Tel: 33-1-44-05-8000 Fax: 33-1-45-53-1504

HUNTSMAN CORPORATION

500 Huntsman Way, Salt Lake City, UT, 84108

Tel: (801) 532-5200 Fax: (801) 536-1581 www.huntsman.com

Mfr. and sales of specialty chemicals, industrial chemicals and petrochemicals.

Huntsman Tioxide, Boite Postale 89, 1 rue des Garennes, F-62102 Calais Cedex, France

HYATT CORPORATION

200 West Madison Street, Chicago, IL, 60606

Tel: (312) 750-1234 Fax: (312) 750-8578 www.hyatt.com

International hotel management.

Hyatt Regency Paris Madeleine Hotel, 24 blvd Malesherbes, F-75008 Paris, France

Tel: 33-1-55-27-1234 Fax: 33-1-55-27-1235

Hyatt Regency/Charles de Gaulle Hotel, 351 Ave. du Bois de la Pie, BP 40048, Paris Nord II, F-95912 Roissy CDG Cédex, France

Tel: 33-1-48-17-1234 Fax: 33-1-48-17-1717

HYPERION SOLUTIONS CORPORATION

1344 Crossman Avenue, Sunnyvale, CA, 94089

Tel: (408) 744-9500 Fax: (408) 744-0400 www.hyperion.com

Mfr. data analysis software tools.

Hyperion France, L'Albert 1er, 65 Avenue de Colmar, F-92507 Rueil Malmaison, France

Tel: 33-1-55-940120

i2 TECHNOLOGIES, INC.

11701 Luna Road, Dallas, TX, 75234

Tel: (214) 860-6106 Fax: (214) 860-6060 www.i2.com

Engaged in supply chain management; solutions to help companies collaborate on decision-making processes.

i2 Technologies France, 90 Boulevard National, 2/F, F-92250 LaGarenne-Colombes, France

IBM CORPORATION

1133 Westchester Avenue, White Plains, NY, 10604

Tel: (914) 765-1900 Fax: (914) 765-7382 www.ibm.com

Information products, technology and services.

IBM France, Centre de Relations Clientsa, BP 51, F-45802 Saint Jean de Braye, France

Tel: 33-8-01-835426 Fax: 33-8-01-329426

ICC INDUSTRIES INC.

460 Park Ave., New York, NY, 10022

Tel: (212) 521-1700 Fax: (212) 521-1794 www.iccchem.com

Manufacturing and trading of chemicals, plastics and pharmaceuticals.

Frutarom (UK) Ltd., Acticlub Bat A. rue Des Champs, Z.I. De La Pilaerie, F-59650 Villeneuve D'Ascq, France

Tel: 33-3-20-89-7020 Fax: 33-3-20-89-7400 Contact: Olivier Reiss

ICN PHARMACEUTICALS, INC.

3300 Hyland Ave., Costa Mesa, CA, 92626

Tel: (714) 545-0100 Fax: (714) 641-7268 www.icnpharm.com

Mfr. and distribution of pharmaceuticals.

ICN Pharmaceuticals, Inc., Parc Club D'Orsay, 4 rue Jean Rostand, F-91893 Orsay Cedex, France

Tel: 33-1-60-19-37-37 Fax: 33-1-60-19-34-60

ICO, INC.

5333 Westheimer, Ste. 600, Houston, TX, 77056

Tel: (281) 351-4100   Fax: (281) 335-2201   www.icoinc.com

Engaged in processing petrochemicals and reconditioning oil well drilling equipment.

WEDCO France SA, 3 Route de la Grande-Paroisse, Montereau, France

Tel: 33-1-64-32-4467   Fax: 33-1-64-32-4467   Contact: Olivier Vilcot, Mng. Dir.

ICORE INTERNATIONAL INC.

3780 Flightline Drive, Santa Rosa, CA, 95403-8227

Tel: (707) 535-2700   Fax: (707) 521-2524   www.icoreintl.com

Harness and conduit systems, battery connectors, etc.

Icore International France, 29 rue François de Tessan, F-77330 Ozoir la Ferriere, France

Tel: 33-1-6440-0110

IDEXX LABORATORIES, INC.

1 IDEXX Dr., Westbrook, ME, 04092-2041

Tel: (207) 856-0300   Fax: (207) 856-0346   www.idexx.com

Mfr. and sales of veterinary products.

IDEXX S.A.R.L., PB 232, F-95614 Cergy Pontoise, France

Tel: 33-1-3432-6200

IDT CORPORATION

520 Broad Street, Newark, NJ, 07102

Tel: (973) 438-1000   Fax: (973) 438-4002   www.idt.net

Engaged in domestic and international long distance telecommunications.

IDT France, 163-165 Avenue Charles de Gaulle, F-92200 Neuilly sur Seine, France

Tel: 33-1-4715-6966   Fax: 33-1-4715-6977

IFR SYSTEMS, INC.

10200 West York Street, Wichita, KS, 67215-8999

Tel: (316) 522-4981   Fax: (316) 524-2623   www.ifrsys.com

Mfr. electronic test and measurement equipment.

IFR Systems, 18 Rue du Plessis-Briard, Le Canal Courcouronnes, F-91023 Evry Cedex, France

IKON OFFICE SOLUTIONS

70 Valley Stream Parkway, Malvern, PA, 19355

Tel: (610) 296-8000   Fax: (610) 408-7022   www.ikon.com

Sales of office equipment, including fax machines, copiers and printers.

IKON Office Solutions, 58/60 Av de la Grande Armee, F-75017 Paris, France

Tel: 33-1-5381-1212   Fax: 33-1-5381-1234   Contact: Patrick Djunbushian

IKOS SYSTEMS, INC.

79 Great Oaks Blvd., San Jose, CA, 95119

Tel: (408) 284-0400   Fax: (408) 284-0401   www.ikos.com

Mfr. hardware and software.

IKOS Systems, Inc., Parc Victoria, 12, avenue de Scandinavie, F- 91969 Courtaboeuf Cedex, France

Tel: 33-1-60-92-36-90

ILLINOIS TOOL WORKS (ITW)

3600 West Lake Ave., Glenview, IL, 60025-5811

Tel: (847) 724-7500   Fax: (847) 657-4268   www.itw.com

Mfr. gears, tools, fasteners, sealants, plastic and metal components for industrial, medical, etc.

ITW de France, 305 Chaussee Jules Cesar, F-95250 Beauchamp, France

ITW de France, 20 rue Fizeau, F-75015 Paris, France

IMANAGE, INC.
950 Tower Lane, Ste. 500, Foster City, CA, 94404
Tel: (650) 356-1166   Fax: (650) 627-8751   www.imanage.com
Mfr. Web-based management software.
iManage France, 114 Bis Rue Michel Ane, F-75016 Paris, France

IMI NORGREN GROUP
5400 South Delaware Street, Littleton, CO, 80120-1663
Tel: (303) 794-2611   Fax: (303) 795-9487   www.usa.norgren.com
Mfr. pneumatic filters, regulators, lubricators, valves, automation systems, dryers, push-in fittings.
IMI Norgren SA, Zone Industrielle de Noisiel 1, BP 22, F-77422 Marne la Vall, France
Tel: 33-1-60-05-9212   Fax: 33-1-90-06-0852

IMPCO TECHNOLOGIES, INC.
16804 Gridley Place, Cerritos, CA, 90703
Tel: (562) 860-6666   Fax: (562) 809-1240   www.impco.ws
Mfr. fuel control processors.
IMPCO-BERU Technologies Sarl, 8 rue Jean Rostand, BP 364, F-69746 Genas, France
Tel: 33-472-795-990   Fax: 33-472-795-991

INDEL-DAVIS INC.
4401 S. Jackson Ave., Tulsa, OK, 74107
Tel: (918) 587-2151   Fax: (918) 446-1583   www.indel-davis.com
Engaged in web and graphic design and manufacture of toners and inks and oil field and seismic supplies.
Indel-Davis France, Actipol, Lot No 20, Boulevard De Beauborge, F-77183 Croissy Beauborg, France
Tel: 33-1-64807070   Fax: 33-1-64807700

INDUCTOTHERM INDUSTRIES
10 Indel Ave., PO Box 157, Rancocas, NJ, 08073-0157
Tel: (609) 267-9000   Fax: (609) 267-5705   www.inductotherm.com
Mfr. induction melting furnaces, induction power supplies, charging and preheating systems, automatic pouring systems and computer control systems.
Inductothermie France, 2 Quai De Seine, F-93200 Saint Denis, France
Inductothermie SA, 6-10 Quai de Seine, F-93200 St. Denis, France
Tel: 33-1-48-13-1080   Contact: Jean Lovens

INDUS INTERNATIONAL, INC.
3301 Windy Ridge Pkwy., Atlanta, GA, 30339
Tel: (770) 952-8444   Fax: (770) 955-2977   www.indus.com
Mfr. asset management software.
Indus International France, Immeuble Central Gare, 1 Place Charles de Gaule, F-78180 Montigny-le-Bretonneux, France

INFOGRAMES, INC.
417 Fifth Avenue, New York, NY, 10016
Tel: (212) 726-6500   Fax: (212) 679-3224   www.infogrames.com
Mfr. video games.
Infogrames France, Les Coteaux de Saône 13-15, rue des Draperies, F-69450 Saint Cyr au Mont d'Or, France

INFONET SERVICES CORPORATION
2160 East Grand Ave., El Segundo, CA, 90245-1022
Tel: (310) 335-2600   Fax: (310) 335-4507   www.infonet.com
Provider of Internet services and electronic messaging services.
Infonet France SA, 6 rue Jean Haures, F-92807 Puteaux Cedex, France
Tel: 33-1-46-92-2660   Fax: 33-1-46-92-0276

INFORMATICA CORPORATION

2100 Seaport Blvd., Redwood City, CA, 94063

Tel: (650) 385-5000   Fax: (650) 385-5500   www.informatica.com

Mfr. computer software.

Informatica France, 25 Quai Gallieni, F-92150 Suresnes, France

Tel: 33-1-4138-9200

INFORMATION BUILDERS INC.

Two Penn Plaza, New York, NY, 10121-2898

Tel: (212) 736-4433   Fax: (212) 967-6406   www.ibi.com

Design and manufacture enterprise reporting software.

Information Builders France SA, 78 Blvd. de la Republique, F-92100 Boulogne-Billancourt, France

INFORMATION RESOURCES, INC. (IRI)

150 N. Clinton St., Chicago, IL, 60661

Tel: (312) 726-1221   Fax: (312) 726-0360   www.infores.com

Provides bar code scanner services for retail sales organizations; processes, analyzes and sells data from the huge database created from these services.

IRI Secodip, 4 rue Andre-Derain, BP-49, F-78240 Chambourcy, France

Tel: 33-1-30-74-8282   Fax: 33-1-30-65-0945

INGERSOLL INTERNATIONAL INC.

707 Fulton Ave., Rockford, IL, 61103

Tel: (815) 987-6000   Fax: (815) 987-6725   www.ingersoll.com

Multinational supplier of special machine tools and services for the metalworking industries.

Ingersoll France, 41, Rue des Trois Fontanot, F-92024 Nanterre Cedex, France

Tel: 33-1-5517-2244   Fax: 33-1-5517-2249

INGERSOLL-RAND COMPANY

200 Chestnut Ridge Road, Woodcliff Lake, NJ, 07675

Tel: (201) 573-0123   Fax: (201) 573-3172   www.irco.com

Leading innovation and solutions provider for the major global markets of Security and Safety, Climate Control, Industrial Solutions and Infrastructure.

Compagnie Ingersoll-Rand, 5-7 Ave. Albert Einstein, F-78192 Trappes Cedex, France

Tel: 33-1-30-50-6110   Fax: 33-1-30-69-0327

Ingersoll-Dresser Pompes, 7230 Arnage rue d'Angers, Arnage, France

Ingersoll-Rand Equipements de Production, 111 ave. Roger Salengro, F-59450 Sin le Noble, France

I-R Montabert, 203 route de Grenoble, BP 671, F-69805 Saint-Priest Cedex, France

Torrington CEMC, 34 ave. Albert 1er, BP 35, F-92502 Rueil Malmaison Cedex, France

INGRAM MICRO INC.

1600 E. St. Andrew Place, Santa Ana, CA, 92799

Tel: (714) 566-1000   Fax: (714) 566-7940   www.ingrammicro.com

Engaged in wholesale distribution of microcomputer products.

Ingram Micro Inc., Carrefour de l'Europe, BP 221, F-59812 Lesquin Cedex, France

INKTOMI CORPORATION

4100 East Third Avenue, Foster City, CA, 94404

Tel: (650) 653-2800   Fax: (650) 653-2801   www.iktomi.com

Mfr. software to boost speeds of computer networks.

Inktomi Corporation, 54-56 Avenue Hoche, F-75008 Paris, France

Tel: 33-1-56-60-5060   Fax: 33-1-56-60-5061

INSIGHTFUL CORPORATION

1700 Westlake Avenue North, Ste. 500, Seattle, WA, 98109-3044

Tel: (206) 283-8802   Fax: (206) 283-8691   www.insightful.com

Mfr. statistical analysis software.

Insightful France, 7, rue Auber, F-31000 Toulouse, France

INSTINET

875 Third Ave., New York, NY, 10022

Tel: (212) 310-9500   Fax: (212) 832-5183   www.instinet.com

Online investment brokerage.

Instinet, Paris, France

INSTRON CORPORATION

100 Royal Street, Canton, MA, 02021-1089

Tel: (781) 575-5000   Fax: (781) 575-5751   www.instron.com

Mfr., markets and services materials testing instruments, systems and accessories.

Instron SA, 11 Parc Club Ariane, F-78284 Guyancourt Cedex, France

Tel: 33-1-3057-2353

INSUL-8 CORPORATION

10102 F Street, Omaha, NE, 68127

Tel: (402) 339-9300   Fax: (402) 339-9627   www.insul-8.com

Mfr. mobile electrification products; conductor bar and festoon equipment.

Delachaux S.A., Paris, France

Railtech, Div. Delachaux S.A., ZI du Bas Pré, F-59590 Raismes, France

INTEGRATED DEVICE TECHNOLOGY, INC. (IDT)

2975 Stender Way, Santa Clara, CA, 95054

Tel: (408) 727-6116   Fax: (408) 492-8674   www.idt.com

Mfr. high-performance semiconductors and modules.

Integrated Device Technology (IDT), 18 rue Saarinen, Bat Dublin, Silic 215, F-94518 Rungis Cedex, France

Tel: 33-1-41-80-85-00   Fax: 33-1-41-80-85-10

INTEL CORPORATION

2200 Mission College Blvd., Santa Clara, CA, 95052-8119

Tel: (408) 765-8080   Fax: (408) 765-1739   www.intel.com

Mfr. semiconductor, microprocessor and micro-communications components and systems.

Intel Semiconductor SARL, Tour Chenonceaux, 204, rond-point du Pont de Sevres, F-92516 Boulogne Billancourt, France

Tel: 33-1-4694-7171

INTER PARFUMS, INC.

551 Fifth Avenue, New York, NY, 10176

Tel: (212) 983-2640   Fax: (212) 983-4197   www.jeanphilippe.com

Engaged in the marketing and sales of brand name perfumes.

Inter Parfums, S.A., 4 Rond Point, Des Champs-Elysees, F-75008 Paris, France

INTERACTIVE DATA CORPORATION

22 Crosby Drive, Bedford, MA, 01730

Tel: (781) 687-8500   Fax: (781) 687-8289   www.interactivedatacorp.com

Engaged in subscription services.

Les Echos, Div. FT, 46 rue la Boetie, F-75008 Paris, France

INTER-CONTINENTAL HOTELS

3 Ravinia Drive, Suite 2900, Atlanta, GA, 30346-2149

Tel: (770) 604-2000   Fax: (770) 604-5403   www.interconti.com

Worldwide hotel and resort accommodations.

Carlton Inter-Continental Cannes, 58 La Croisette, BP 155, F-06406 Cannes Cedex, France

Tel: 33-493-064006

Inter-Continental Hotels, 5 Place de l'Opera, F-75009 Paris, France

Tel: 33-1-42-68-1380   Fax: 33-1-42-68-1531

INTERDEAN INTERCONEX, INC

55 Hunter Lane, Elmsford, NY, 10523-1317

Tel: (914) 347-6600   Fax: (914) 347-0129   www.interdean.com

Freight forwarding.

Interdean.Interconex, 515 Rue Helene-Boucher, PO Box 124, F - 78531 BUC Cedex Paris, France

Contact: Celine Delrue

INTERGRAPH CORPORATION

One Madison Industrial Park, Huntsville, AL, 35894-0001

Tel: (256) 730-2000   Fax: (256) 730-7898   www.intergraph.com

Develop/mfr. interactive computer graphic systems.

Intergraph (France) S.A., 95-101 rue Des Solets, Silic 578, F-94653 Rungis Cedex, France

Tel: 33-1-45-6-03000   Fax: 33-1-45-60-4885

Intergraph Nantes, Centre D'Affaires Nantais, 5 blvd Vincent Gauche, F-36204 Nantes Cedex 2, France

Tel: 33-240-417335   Fax: 33-240-353091

Intergraph Public Safety (France) S.A., 14 Parc Club Du Golf, F-13856 Aix-En-Provence Cedex 3, France

Tel: 33-44-2163587   Fax: 33-44-2163509

Intergraph S.A., Immeuble Cherbourg Helios, 120 rue Roger Glinel, B.P. 19, F-50460 Querqueville, France

Tel: 33-233-080120   Fax: 33-233-080082

INTERMAGNETICS GENERAL CORPORATION

450 Old Niskayuna Road, PO Box 461, Latham, NY, 12110-0461

Tel: (518) 782-1122   Fax: (518) 783-2601   www.igc.com

Design and manufacture of super conductive magnets, magnetic systems and conductors, cryogenic products, refrigerants.

Alsthom-Intermagnetics SA, 3 ave. de Trois Chenes, F-90018 Belfort Cedex, France

INTERMEC TECHNOLOGIES CORPORATION

6001 36th Avenue West, PO Box 4280, Everett, WA, 98203-9280

Tel: (425) 348-2600   Fax: (425) 355-9551   www.intermec.com

Mfr. and distributor automated data collection systems.

Intermec Scanner Technology Center, Intermec STC SA, Buro Parc 2, Voie no. 2, Rue de la Decoverte, BP 187, F-31676 Labege, France

Tel: 33-5-6139-9858   Fax: 33-5-6139-2000

INTERNATIONAL FLAVORS & FRAGRANCES INC.

521 West 57th Street, New York, NY, 10019-2960

Tel: (212) 765-5500   Fax: (212) 708-7132   www.iff.com

Design/mfr. flavors, fragrances and aroma chemicals.

International Flavors & Fragrances, 47 rue Victor Hugo, F-92270 Bois-Colombes, France

Tel: 33-1-4649-6060   Fax: 33-1-4781-8573

International Flavors & Fragrances, Boulevard de Beauregard, B.P.5, F-21601 Longvic-Dijon, France

Tel: 33-3-8073-7878   Fax: 33-3-8073-7899

INTERNATIONAL MANAGEMENT GROUP (IMG)

1360 East Ninth Street, Ste. 100, Cleveland, OH, 44114

Tel: (216) 522-1200   Fax: (216) 522-1145   www.imgworld.com

Manages athletes, sports academies and real estate facilities worldwide.

Golf Club France, Gold de Montpellier-Massane BP83, F-34670 Baillargues, France

Tel: 33-4-6791-2537   Fax: 33-4-6791-2530

IMG, 54 Avenue Marceau, F-75008 Paris, France

Tel: 33-1-4431-4431   Fax: 33-1-4431-4432

IMG Models, 16 Avenue de L'Opera, F-75001 Paris, France

Tel: 33-1-5535-1200   Fax: 33-1-5535-1201

Racing Club de Strasbourg-Football, Stade de la Meinau, 12 rue de 'Extenwoerth, F-67100 Strasbourg, France

Tel: 33-3-8844-5500   Fax: 33-3-8844-55011

INTERNATIONAL PAPER COMPANY

400 Atlantic Street, Stamford, CT, 06921

Tel: (203) 541-8000   Fax: (203) 358-6444   www.ipaper.com

Mfr./distributor container board, paper and wood products.

Aussedat Rey SA, Parc Ariane, 5/7 boulevard des Chenes, F-78284 Guyancourt Cedex, France
Tel: 33-1-40-83-4478

Comptoir des Bois de Brive, Chemin du Bois-de-Tulle, F-19100 La Pigeonnie Brive, France

Copadip, 115 ave. du President Wilson, F-93212 La Plaine St. Denis Cedex, France

Corimex SA, 1 rue du Petit Clamart, BP 5, F-78141 Velizy Villacoublay, France

Europapier SA, Route de Piscop, BP 35, F-95350 St. Brice sous Foret, France

Horsell Industries Graphiques, Peripole 208, F-94127 Fontenay sous Bois, France

Ilford-Anitec SA, BP 336, Chemin de la Fouillouse, F-69802 Saint-Priest, France

International Container/Bergvik SARL, 25 rue Michel Salles, F-92210 St. Cloud, France
Tel: 33-1-4771-1218

International Paper Cellulose, 36 ave. Hoche, F-75008 Paris, France

Iridium, 1 rue du Petit Clamart, F-78141 Velizy Villacoublay, France

Papeteries de France, 8a, 24 rue du Cheval Blanc, BP 198, F-93501 Pantin Cedex, France

Papeteries de Lancey, 1 rue du Petit Clamart, F-78141 Velizy Villacoublay, France

Papeteries J. Rezard, 21-23 blvd de la Muette, F-95140 Garges-les-Gonesse, France

Polyrey, 1 rue du Petit Clamart, BP 79, F-78143 Velizy Villacoublay, France

Promafor, Chemin du Bois-de-Tulle, F-19100 La Pigeonnie Brive, France

Societe de Reboisement, Chemin du Bois-de-Tulle, F-19100 La Pigeonnie Brive, France

Societe Immo des Papeteries de France, 1 rue du Petit Clamart, BP 5, F-78141 Velizy Villacoublay, France

Societe Moderne d'Emballage, 25 rue Michel Salles, F-92210 St. Cloud, France

Societe Normande de Carton Ondule, BP 3, F-61400 St. Langis les Montagne, France

Sofar, 25 rue Colonel Dumont, BP 481, F-38016 Grenoble Cedex, France

INTERNATIONAL RECTIFIER CORPORATION

233 Kansas Street, El Segundo, CA, 90245

Tel: (310) 322-3331   Fax: (310) 322-3332   www.irf.com

Mfr. power semiconductor components.

International Rectifier Corp., 32 rue des Processions, BP 61, F-91241 St. Michel sur Orge Cedex, France
Tel: 33-16-449-5959   Fax: 33-16-449-5969

INTERNATIONAL SPECIALTY PRODUCTS, INC.

1361 Alps Rd., Wayne, NJ, 07470

Tel: (973) 389-3083   Fax: (973) 628-4117   www.ispcorp.com

Mfr. specialty chemical products.

ISP (France) SA, ZAC Paris Nord II, BP 50007, F-95945 Roissy CDG Cédex, France
Tel: 33-1-49-9058   Fax: 33-1-49-9058

INTERVOICE-BRITE INC.

17811 Waterview Pkwy., Dallas, TX, 75206

Tel: (972) 454-8000   Fax: (972) 454-8707   www.intervoice.com

Mfr. telecom network hardware and software systems.

InterVoice-Brite Limited, Tour CIT, 3 rue de l'Arrivée, F-75749 Paris Cedex 15, France

INTERWOVEN, INC.

803 11th Avenue, Sunnyvale, CA, 94089

Tel: (408) 774-2000   Fax: (408) 774-2002   www.interwoven.com

Mfr. web content management software.

Interwoven SAS, 2 rue Troyon, F-92316 Sèvres Cedex, France
Tel: 33-1-4966-7676

INTRUSION, INC.

1101 East Arapaho Road, Richardson, TX, 75081

Tel: (972) 234-6400   Fax: (972) 234-1467   www.intrusion.com

Mfr. security software.

Intrusion.Com, SARL, 115 Avenue De Paris, F-94160 Saint-Mande, France

INVACARE CORPORATION

One Invacare Way, Elyria, OH, 44036

Tel: (440) 329-6000   Fax: (440) 366-6568   www.invacare.com

Mfr. home medical equipment, wheelchairs, respiratory care products, home care aids.

Invacare Poirier SA, Les Roches, F-37230 Fondettes, France

Tel: 33-2-47-62-6491   Fax: 33-2-47-62-6488

INVITROGEN CORPORATION

1600 Faraday Avenue, Carlsbad, CA, 92008

Tel: (760) 603-7200   Fax: (760) 602-6500   www.invitrogen.com

Mfr. products and kits for gene analysis.

Invitrogen SARL, BP 96, F-956130 Pontoise, France

IOMEGA CORPORATION

4435 Eastgate Mall, 3rd Fl., San Diego, CA, 92121

Tel: (858) 795-7000   Fax: (858) 795-7001   www.iomega.com

Mfr. data storage products.

Iomega, 70 ave. du General de Gaulle, F-94022 Creteil Cedex, France

IONICS INC.

65 Grove Street, Watertown, MA, 02172

Tel: (617) 926-2500   Fax: (617) 926-4304   www.ionics.com

Mfr. desalination equipment.

Eau et Industrie, 121 ave. du 8 Mai 1945, F-94170 Le Perreux, France

Ionics Europe, Paris, France

IR FLUID PRODUCTS

PO Box 151, Bryan, OH, 43506

Tel: (419) 636-4242   Fax: (419) 633-1674   www.irco.com

Mfr. fluid control products, including pumps, valves, cylinders, logic controls and air line components.

Ingersoll-Rand Material Handling, 111, avenue Roger Salengro, F-59450 Sin Le Noble, France

IRRIDELCO INTERNATIONAL CORPORATION

440 Sylvan Ave., Englewood Cliffs, NJ, 07632

Tel: (201) 569-3030   Fax: (201) 569-9237   www.irridelco.com

Mfr. and distributor of the most comprehensive lines of mechanical and micro irrigation; pumps and irrigation systems.

IDC France, Chemin d'Antonelle, F-13090 Aix En Provence, France

Tel: 33-4-42-92-1247   Fax: 33-442-92-1678   Contact: Jerome Lamy

ITT INDUSTRIES, INC.

4 West Red Oak Lane, White Plains, NY, 10604

Tel: (914) 641-2000   Fax: (914) 696-2950   www.ittind.com

Mfr. pumps, systems and services to move and control water/fluids and produces connectors, switches, keypads and cabling used in computing, telecommunications, aerospace and industrial applications, as well as network services.

Cannon/Switch Products, 2 Avenue Des Sablons Bouillants, F-77109 Meaux Cedex, France

Tel: 33-1-6024-515

KONI France, B.P. no. 9, F-06271 Villeneuve-Loubet Cedex, France

Tel: 33-4-9320-9070

ITT-GOULDS PUMPS INC.

2881 East Bayard Street, Seneca Falls, NY, 13148

Tel: (315) 568-2811   Fax: (315) 568-7651   www.gouldspumps.com

Mfr. industrial and water systems pumps.

ITT Richter France SA, 22/24 rue Lavoisier, F-92000 Nanterre Cedex, France

Tel: 33-1-41-3-6400   Fax: 33-1-41-3-6401

ITW DEVCON PLEXUS

30 Endicott Street, Danvers, MA, 01923

Tel: (978) 777-1100   Fax: (978) 774-0516   www.devcon-equip.com

Engaged in technology and products for OEM assembly, and maintenance/repair applications.

Devcon France SARL, 22 rue Paul Langevin, F-75002 Herblay, France

ITW RANSBURG FINISHING SYSTEMS

320 Phillips Ave., Toledo, OH, 43612

Tel: (419) 470-2000   Fax: (419) 470-2112   www.itwransburg.com

Engaged in the design, manufacture and marketing of liquid electrostatic paint application equipment.

ITW Surfaces & Finitions, 163 a 171 ave. des Aureats, BP 1453, F-26014 Valence, France

J. WALTER THOMPSON COMPANY

466 Lexington Ave., New York, NY, 10017

Tel: (212) 210-7000   Fax: (212) 210-6944   www.jwt.com

International advertising and marketing services.

J. Walter Thompson Co., Paris, France

JABIL CIRCUIT, INC.

10560 Ninth St. North, St. Petersburg, FL, 33716

Tel: (727) 557-9749   Fax: (727) 579-8529   www.jabil.com

Mfr. printed circuit boards, electronic components and systems.

Jabil Circuit France, 8, Rue de Kervézennec, BP 82 811, F-29228 Brest Cédex 2, France

JACOBS ENGINEERING GROUP INC.

1111 S. Arroyo Parkway, Pasadena, CA, 91105

Tel: (626) 578-3500   Fax: (626) 578-6916   www.jacobs.com

Engineering, design and consulting; construction and construction management; process plant maintenance.

3S/Serete, Z.A. Les Andenges, F-25420 Bart Sochoux, France

Tel: 33-3-81-90-41-72   Fax: 33-3-81-90-41-01   Contact: Bruno Leprince, Mgr.   Emp: 5

3S/Serete, La Triade, 167 Ave. de la Somme, BP 368, F-33694 Merignac Cedex Bordeaux, France

Tel: 33-5-56-47-7923   Fax: 33-5-56-47-7927   Contact: Jacques Coutou, Mgr.

3S/Serete, Le Stratége, BP 2746, F-31312 Labége Cedex, France

Tel: 33-5-61-29-9238   Fax: 33-4-61-39-9240

3S/Serete, Le Charlemayne, 132 Cours Charlemayne, F-69002 Lyon Cedex, France

Tel: 33-4-72-77-1050   Fax: 33-4-72-77-1051   Contact: Cyrille Bernal, Mgr.

3S/Serete, 26 rue du Chateau Des Rentiers, F-75013 Paris, France

Tel: 33-1-45-70-50-87   Fax: 33-1-45-86-09-02   Contact: Jean Levy, Chmn. & CEO

Prosys, 20 rue de Chateau Des Rentiers, F-75013 Paris, France

Tel: 33-1-45-70-57-12   Fax: 33-1-45-83-65-13   Contact: Jean Levy, Chmn. & CEO

Serete Constructions, 86 rue Regnault, F-75640 Paris Cedex 13, France

Tel: 33-1-45-70-5000   Fax: 33-1-45-70-5299   Contact: Pierre Larapldic, Chmn. & CEO

Serete Est, 23 Ollée Glück, BP 2331, F-68069 Hulhouse Cedex, France

Tel: 33-3-89-32-01-21   Fax: 33-3-89-42-30-48   Contact: Jacques Clerc, Mgr.

Serete Gestion & Industries, 18 rue Regnault, F-75640 Paris Cedex 13, France

Tel: 33-1-45-70-5000   Fax: 33-1-45-70-5024   Contact: Sylvie Biscorra, Mgr.

Serete Midi-Pryénees, Le Stratége, BP 2746, F-31312 Labége Cedex, France

Tel: 33-5-61-39-0506   Fax: 33-4-61-39-2575

Serete Sud-Est, Le Charlemayne, 140 Cours Charlemayne, F-69286 Lyon Cedex, France

Tel: 33-4-72-77-1050   Fax: 33-4-72-77-1051   Contact: Bernard Nicol, Mgr.

Serete Sud-Ouest, La Triade, 167 Ave. de la Somme, BP 368, F-33694 Merignac Cedex Bordeaux, France

Tel: 33-5-56-13-1616   Fax: 33-5-56-34-1064   Contact: Jean-Claude Berthelst, Mgr.   Emp: 20

JDA SOFTWARE GROUP, INC.

14400 N. 87th St., Scottsdale, AZ, 85260-3649

Tel: (480) 308-3000   Fax: (480) 308-3001   www.jda.com

Developer of information management software for retail, merchandising, distribution and store management.

JDA Software SA, 70 Boulevard de Courcelles, F-75017 Paris, France

Tel: 33-1-5679-2700   Fax: 33-1-4764-5050

JDS UNIPHASE CORPORATION

210 Baypoint Pkwy., San Jose, CA, 95134

Tel: (408) 434-1800   Fax: (408) 954-0760   www.jdsunph.com

Mfr. advanced fiber optic products for the cable television and telecommunications industries.

JDS Uniphase France, Mini-Parc des Andes - Bât 3 6, Avenue des Andes, F-91 940 Les Ulis, France

JOHNSON & JOHNSON

One Johnson & Johnson Plaza, New Brunswick, NJ, 08933

Tel: (732) 524-0400   Fax: (732) 214-0334   www.jnj.com

Mfr./distributor/R&D pharmaceutical, health care and cosmetic products.

Ethicon SA/Ethicon Endo-Surgery SA, 1, rue Camille Desmoulins, F-92787 Issy-Les-Moulineaux, France

Janssen-Cilag SA, 1, rue Camille Desmoulins 92787, F-92787 Issy-Les-Moulineaux, France

Johnson & Johnson Genset SA, 24, rue Royale, Paris, France

LifeScan France, 1 rue Camille Desmoulins, F-TSA 40007 Issy Les Moulineaux, France

Ortho-Clinical Diagnostics SA, Issy-Les-Moulineaux, France

RoC SA, F-92130 Issy-Les-Moulineaux, France

SC JOHNSON

1525 Howe St., Racine, WI, 53403

Tel: (262) 260-2000   Fax: (262) 260-2133   www.scjohnsonwax.com

Home, auto, commercial and personal care products and specialty chemicals.

SC Johnson SA, B.P. 606, F-95004 Cergy Paris, France

JOHNSON CONTROLS INC.

5757 N. Green Bay Ave., PO Box 591, Milwaukee, WI, 53201-0591

Tel: (414) 228-1200   Fax: (414) 228-2077   www.johnsoncontrols.com

Mfr. facility management and control systems and auto seating.

Johnson Control France SARL, 357 rue d'Estiennes d'Orves, F-92700 Colombes, France

Tel: 33-1-46-13-1600   Fax: 33-1-42-42- 4261   Contact: Bruno Nicholas

THE JOHNSON CORPORATION

805 Wood Street, Three Rivers, MI, 49093

Tel: (269) 278-1715   Fax: (269) 273-2230   www.joco.com

Mfr. rotary joints and siphon systems.

Johnson France, 13 rue Calmette et Guerin, F-78500 Sartrouville, France

Tel: 33-1-61043010

JOHNSON OUTDOORS, INC.

555 Main Street, Racine, WI, 53177

Tel: (262) 631-6600   Fax: (262) 631-6601   www.johnsonoutdoors.com

Mfr. diving, fishing, boating and camping sports equipment.

Scubapro France S.A., Nova Antipolis, Les Terriers Nord, 175 Allee Belle Vue, F-06600 Antibes, France

Tel: 33-4-92-913-030   Fax: 33-4-92-913-031

JONES LANG LASALLE

153 East 53rd Street, New York, NY, 10022

Tel: (212) 812-5700   Fax: (212) 421-3544   www.am.joneslanglasalle.com

International marketing consultants, leasing agents and property management advisors.

Jones Lang Wootton, France

JONES, DAY, REAVIS & POGUE

North Point, 901 Lakeside Ave., Cleveland, OH, 44114

Tel: (216) 586-3939   Fax: (216) 579-0212   www.jonesday.com

International law firm.

Jones, Day, Reavis & Pogue, 120 rue du Faubourg Saint-Honore, F-75008 Cedex Paris, France

Tel: 33-1-44-71-3939   Fax: 33-1-49-24-0471   Contact: Wesley R. Johnson, Jr., Ptnr.   Emp: 59

JPMORGAN PRIVATE BANK

345 Park Avenue, New York, NY, 10154-1002

Tel: (212) 483-2323   Fax: (212) 464-1120   www.jpmorgan.com

Engaged in private banking services.

JPMorgan Private Bank, 14, Place Vendome, F-75001 Paris, France

Tel: 33-1-4015-4500

JUKI UNION SPECIAL CORPORATION

8500 N.W. 17th St., Miami, FL, 33126

Tel: (305) 594-0059   Fax: (305) 594-0720   www.unionspecial.com

Mfr. sewing machines.

Union Special France SA, 33 rue Jean Jaures, BP 455, F-59814 Lesquin Cedex, France

Tel: 33-3-20-86-2003   Fax: 33-3-20-86-2118   Contact: E. Salu, Mng.

JUNIPER NETWORKS, INC.

1194 North Mathilda Ave., Sunnyvale, CA, 94089

Tel: (408) 745-2000   Fax: (408) 745-2100   www.juniper.net

Engaged in the design and sales of Internet Protocol routers for access networks.

Juniper Networks France, 70 Boulevard de Courcelles, F-75017 Paris, France

KADANT INC.

One Acton Place, Ste. 202, Acton, MA, 01720-3951

Tel: (978) 776-2000   Fax: (978) 635-1593   www.kandant.com

Mfr. paper recycling equipment.

Kadant, PO Box 46, 39 Rue de la Fontaine Ludot, F-51302 Vitry-le-Francois, France

Tel: 33-3-2674-8080   Fax: 33-3-26-72-0833

KAPPLER PROTECTIVE APPAREL & FABRICS

PO Box 218, 70 Grimes Drive, Guntersville, AL, 35976

Tel: (205) 505-4000   Fax: (205) 505-4004   www.kappler.com

Mfr. of protective apparel and fabrics.

Kappler France, rue de la Chanterie, BP 03, F-49180 St.Barthelemy-d'Anjou Cedex, France

Tel: 33-2-41-93-44-8   Fax: 33-2-41-37-1605   Contact: Serge Denis, Mng. Dir.   Emp: 10

KATY INDUSTRIES INC.

6300 South Syracuse Way, Ste. 300, Englewood, CO, 80111

Tel: (303) 290-9300   Fax: (303) 290-9344   www.katyindustries.com

Mfr. electronic and maintenance equipment for industrial and consumer markets.

Sofema, 206 rue de Fontenay, F-94300 Vincennes, France

Sofema SARL, 4 rue du Marechal Joffre, F-67240 Bischwiller, France

KAWNEER COMPANY, INC.

555 Guthridge Court, Norcross, GA, 30092

Tel: (770) 449-5555   Fax: (770) 734-1570   www.kawneer.com

Mfr. arch aluminum products for commercial construction.

Kawneer France SA, Rue de la Garenne, Zone Industrielle BP 24, F-34740 Vendargues, France

KB HOME

10990 Wilshire Blvd., Los Angeles, CA, 90024

Tel: (310) 231-4000   Fax: (310) 231-4222   www.kaufmanandbroad.com

Engaged in housing construction and financing.

Kaufman & Broad France, 44 rue de Washington, F-75408 Paris, France

Tel: 33-1-45-61-7000   Contact: Guy Nafilyan

A.T. KEARNEY INC.

5400 Legacy Dr., Plano, TX, 75201

Tel: (972) 604-4600   Fax: (972) 543-7680   www.atkearney.com

Management consultants and executive search.

A. T. Kearney Executive Search, 48 rue Jacques Dulud, F-92200 Neuilly-sur-Seine, France

Tel: 33-141-92-1092

A. T. Kearney Management Consultants S.A.S., 8-10 rue Victor Noir, F-92521 Neuilly-sur-Seine Cedex, France

Tel: 33-1-41-92-1111

KEITHLEY INSTRUMENTS INC.

28775 Aurora Road, Cleveland, OH, 44139

Tel: (440) 248-0400   Fax: (440) 248-6168   www.keithley.com

Mfr. electronic test/measure instruments, PC-based data acquisition hardware/software.

Keithley Instruments SARL, 3 allee de Garays, BP 60, F-91122 Palaiseau Cedex, France

KELLOGG BROWN & ROOT INC.

PO Box 4557, Houston, TX, 77210-4557

Tel: (713) 676-3011   Fax: (713) 676-8695   www.halliburton.com

Engaged in technology-based engineering and construction.

Kellogg Brown & Root, La Defense 6, F-92973 Paris Cedex, France

KELLOGG COMPANY

One Kellogg Square, PO Box 3599, Battle Creek, MI, 49016-3599

Tel: (616) 961-2000   Fax: (616) 961-2871   www.kelloggs.com

Mfr. ready-to-eat cereals and convenience foods.

Kellogg Products, Attn: French Office, One Kellogg Square, PO Box 3599, Battle Creek, MI, 49016-3599

KELLY SERVICES, INC.

999 W. Big Beaver Road, Troy, MI, 48084

Tel: (248) 362-4444   Fax: (248) 244-4154   www.kellyservices.com

Temporary help placement.

Societe Services Kelly (HQ), 73 blvd. Haussmann, F-75008 Paris, France

Tel: 33-1-44-94-6-64   Fax: 33-1-44-94-6465

THE KENDALL COMPANY TYCO HEALTHCARE

15 Hampshire Street, Mansfield, MA, 02048

Tel: (508) 261-8000   Fax: (508) 261-8542   www.kendallhq.com

Mfr. and markets a broad range of wound care, needles and syringes, electrodes, specialized paper, vascular therapy, urological care, incontinence care, and nursing care products.

Kendall France SA, 15, rue Marcelin Berthelot, F-92167 Antony Cedex, France

Tel: 33-1-46-74-7980   Fax: 33-1-423-70920

KENDLE INTERNATIONAL INC.

1200 Carew Tower, 441 Vine Street, Cincinnati, OH, 45202

Tel: (513) 381-5550   Fax: (513) 381-5870   www.kendle.com

Provides contract research and development services.

Kendle International, 13 Rue Jean-Pierre Timbaud, F-92130 Issy-Les Moulineaux, France

Tel: 33-1-4190-2600   Fax: 33-1-4642-9628

KENNAMETAL INC.

1600 Technology Way, PO Box 231, Latrobe, PA, 15650

Tel: (724) 539-5000   Fax: (724) 539-4710   www.kennametal.com

Tools, hard carbide and tungsten alloys for metalworking industry.

Kennametal Hertel France SA, POBox 201, F-91007 Evry Cedex, France

Tel: 33-1-69-77-8383   Fax: 33-1-69-77-8390

KEPNER-TREGOE INC.

PO Box 704, Princeton, NJ, 08542-0740

Tel: (609) 921-2806   Fax: (609) 497-0130   www.kepner-tregoe.com

Management consulting; specializing in strategy formulation, problem solving, decision making, project management, and cost reduction.

Kepner-Tregoe France SARL, 91 rue du Faubourg St. Honore, F-75370 Paris Cedex 8, France

Tel: 33-1-4471-3605   Fax: 33-1-4471-3572

KIMBERLY-CLARK CORPORATION

351 Phelps Drive, Irving, TX, 75038

Tel: (972) 281-1200   Fax: (972) 281-1435   www.kimberly-clark.com

Mfr./sales/distribution of consumer tissue, household and personal care products.

Kimberly-Clark France, 26, rue Armengaud, F-92210 Saint-Cloud, France

Tel: 33-1-41-12-15-25

Kimberly-Clark Industries SA, Orleans, France

LTR Industries SA, Villey-Saint-Etienne, France

Paperterie de Mauduit SA, Kerisole Quimperle, France

Papeterie de Malaucene SA, F-84340 Malaucene, France

KINETIC CONCEPTS, INC.

8023 Vantage Drive, San Antonio, TX, 78230-4728

Tel: (210) 524-9000   Fax: (210) 255-4524   www.KCI1.com

Mfr. specialized medical beds.

KCI Medical Equipment, Parc Gutenberg, 5, F-91126 Palaiseau, France

KINGSTON TECHNOLOGY COMPANY, INC.

17600 Newhope Street, Fountain Valley, CA, 92708

Tel: (714) 435-2600   Fax: (714) 435-2699   www.kingston.com

Mfr. memory modules.

Kingston Technology France, 171A, Avenue Charles De-Gaulle, F-92200 Neuilly-Sur-Seine, France

KIRKWOOD INDUSTRIES INC.

4855 W. 130th Street, Cleveland, OH, 44135-5182

Tel: (216) 267-6200   Fax: (216) 362-3804   www.kirkwood-ind.com

Mfr. manufacture of commutators, slip rings, carbon brushes and Cortem springs for the automotive, power tool and floor care industries.

Kirkwood Industries S.A., Division Nelco France, 1 Rue de L'artisanat, Zone Industrielle, F-68500 Guebwiller, France

KLA-TENCOR CORPORATION

160 Rio Robles, San Jose, CA, 95134

Tel: (408) 875-6000   Fax: (408) 875-3030   www.kia-tencor.ocm

Mfr. software and equipment.

KLA-Tencor, Le Clos Du Bois Guillaume, 14 Rue du Bois Sauvage, F-91007 Evry, France

Tel: 33-1-69-36-69-69   Fax: 33-1-60-78-74-06

KNIGHT INFRASTRUCTURE

549 West Randolph Street, Chicago, IL, 60661

Tel: (312) 577-3300   Fax: (312) 577-3526   www.knightinfrastructure.com

Engaged in architectural and engineering projects.

Knight Wendling SARL, 15 ave. Victor-Hugo, F-75116 Paris, France

KNOLL, INC.

1235 Water Street, East Greenville, PA, 18041

Tel: (215) 679-7991   Fax: (215) 679-3904   www.knoll.com

Mfr. and sale of office furnishings.

Knoll International, 268 Blvd. Saint Germain, F-75007 Paris, France

KOCH INDUSTRIES INC.

4111 East 37th Street North, Wichita, KS, 67220-3203

Tel: (316) 828-5500   Fax: (316) 828-5950   www.kochind.com

Oil, financial services, agriculture and Purina Mills animal feed.

Koch International S.A.R.L., 3 rue de La Haye, F-95731 Roissy Charles de Gaulle, France

Tel: 33-1-4816-4871   Fax: 33-1-4816-4857

KOCH-GLITSCH, INC.

4111 E. 37th Street North, Wichita, KS, 67220

Tel: (316) 828-5110   Fax: (316) 828-5263   www.koch-glitsch.com

Engaged in mass transfer, mist elimination, and motionless mixer technology.

Koch-Glitsch France, Chemin des Moines, BP 76, F-13632 Arles Cedex, France

Tel: 33-4-90-18-4800   Fax: 33-4-90-18-4807   Contact: Ian Shepherd

THE KOHLER COMPANY

444 Highland Drive, Kohler, WI, 53044

Tel: (920) 457-4441   Fax: (920) 459-1274   www.kohlerco.com

Plumbing products, ceramic tile and stone, cabinetry, furniture, engines, generators, switch gear and hospitality.

Dupont Sanitaire Chauffage, S.A., France

Holdiam S.A., Paris, France

Jacob Delafon/Neomediam, Paris, France

KORN/FERRY INTERNATIONAL

1800 Century Park East, Los Angeles, CA, 90067

Tel: (310) 843-4100   Fax: (310) 553-6452   www.kornferry.com

Engaged in executive search and management consulting.

Korn/Ferry International SA, 166 rue du Faubourg Saint-Honore, F-75008 Paris, France

Tel: 33-1-45-61-6660   Fax: 33-1-45-63-5667

KPMG CONSULTING INC.

1676 International Dr., McLean, VA, 22102

Tel: (703) 747-3000   Fax: (703) 747-8500   www.kpmg.com

Accounting and audit, tax and management consulting services.

Fidal Paris et International, 47 rue de Villiers, F-92200 Neuilly sur Seine, France

Tel: 33-1-46-39-40   Fax: 33-1-47-59-0078   Contact: Jean-Francis Blouet, Ptnr.

Fiduciaire Juridique et Fiscale de France, Le Montesquicu, Av. du Pr., F-33704 Bordeaux, France

KPMG Audit, 47 rue de Villiers, F-92200 Neuilly sur Seine, France

Tel: 33-1-46-39-4444   Fax: 33-1-47-58-7138   Contact: Jean Delsol, Ptnr.

KPMG International, 574 rue de Chantabord, F-73000 Lyon, France

KPMG International, Tour Framatome, 1 Place de la Coupole, F-92084 Paris La Défense, France

Tel: 33-1-47-93-2000   Fax: 33-1-47-96-2058   Contact: Patrick Laredo, Ptnr.

KPMG International, Tour Framatome, 1 Place de la Coupole, F-92084 Paris La Défense, France

Tel: 33-1-47-96-6760   Fax: 33-1-47-96-6750   Contact: Dominique Lecendreux, Ptnr.

KPMG International, 53 Ave. Montaigne, F-75008 Paris, France

Tel: 33-1-45-63-1540   Fax: 33-1-45-61-0925   Contact: Curtis H. Behrent, Ptnr.

KPMG International, Les Hauts de Villiers, 2 bis, rue de Villiers, F-92309 Paris, France

KRAMER LEVIN NAFTALIS & FRANKEL LLP

919 Third Avenue, New York, NY, 10022-3852

Tel: (212) 715-9100   Fax: (212) 715-8000   www.kramerlevin.com

Engaged in international law.

Kramer Levin Naftalis & Frankel, 47, avenue Hoche, F-7008 Paris, France

KROLL INC.

9023 Columbine Road, Eden Prairie, MN, 55347

Tel: (952) 937-1107   Fax: (952) 937-5815   www.knollworldwide.com

Mfr. of software and engaged in data recovery services.

Kroll Inc., 153, rue de Courcelles, F-75017 Paris, France

Tel: 33-1-42-67-3500 Fax: 33-1-42-67-7100

KROLL ONTRACK, INC.

9023 Columbine Rd., Eden Prairie, MN, 55347

Tel: (612) 937-1107   Fax: (612) 937-5815   www.krollontrack.com

Computer data evidence services company, rescuing lost or corrupted data, and software sales.

Kroll Ontrack, Inc., 2 impasse de la Noisette, F-91371 Verriéres-le-Buisson Cedex 413, France

Tel: 33-1-4919-2263 Fax: 33-1-4919-2237

KULICKE & SOFFA INDUSTRIES INC.

2101 Blair Mill Road, Willow Grove, PA, 19090

Tel: (215) 784-6000   Fax: (215) 659-7588   www.kns.com

Semiconductor assembly systems and services.

Caleo, 421 rue Helene Boucher, F-78532 Buc Cedex, France

K&S Test Products, Parc Ste. Victoire, Bat. 7, Quartier du Canet, F-13590 Meyreuil, France

KURT SALMON ASSOCIATES (KSA)

1355 Peachtree Street NE, Atlanta, GA, 30309

Tel: (404) 892-0321   Fax: (404) 898-9590   www.kurtsalmon.com

Management consulting: consumer products, retailing.

Cleversys, S.A., Div. Kurt Salmon, 22, rue de l' Arcade, F-75008 Paris, France

Tel: 33-140-07-1919

LA ROCHE INDUSTRIES INC.

1100 Johnson Ferry Road, NE, Atlanta, GA, 30342

Tel: (404) 851-0300   Fax: (404) 851-0421   www.larocheind.com

Mfr. and distribution of industrial ammonia and chlor-alkali chemicals.

ChlorAlp SAS, Pont-de-Claix, France

Emp: 225

LAM RESEARCH CORPORATION

4650 Cushing Pkwy., Fremont, CA, 94538

Tel: (510) 659-0200   Fax: (510) 572-6454   www.lamrc.com

Mfr. semiconductor processing equipment.

Lam Research Sarl, 5 Chemin des Sources, F-38240 Meylan, France

Tel: 33-476-61-4900 Fax: 33-476-61-4901

LANDOR ASSOCIATES

Klamath House, 1001 Front Street, San Francisco, CA, 94111-1424

Tel: (415) 955-1400   Fax: (415) 365-3190   www.landor.com

International marketing consulting firm, engaged in brand strategy, design, naming, digital branding, print literature design and research services.

Landor Associates, 44 rue des Petites Ecuries, F-75010 Paris, France

Tel: 33-1-53-34-3100 Fax: 33-1-53-34-3101 Contact: Jean-Louis Dumeu, Mng. Dir.

LANIER WORLDWIDE, INC.

2300 Parklake Drive, N.E., Atlanta, GA, 30345

Tel: (770) 496-9500   Fax: (770) 938-1020   www.lanier.com

Specialize in digital copiers and multi-functional systems.

Lanier France S.A., Bâtiment le Cérame, 47 ave des Genottes, F-95802 Cergy Pontoise, France

Tel: 33-1-47-67-7676   Fax: 33-1-47-67-7600

LEACH HOLDING CORPORATION

315 Post Road West, Westport, CT, 06880-4739

Tel: (203) 226-6577   Fax: (203) 226-6577   www.leachintl.com

Mfr. and design electrical switching and control devices for the aerospace and rail industries.

Leach International S.A., 2, Rue Goethe, F-57430 Sarralbe, France

Tel: 33-3-87-97-9897

LEARNING TREE INTERNATIONAL, INC.

6053 West Century Blvd., Los Angeles, CA, 90045-0028

Tel: (310) 417-9700   Fax: (310) 417-8684   www.learningtree.com

Information technology training services.

Learning Tree International SA (France), Espace Clichy, 68 rue Villenueve, F-92110 Clichy Cedex, France

Tel: 33-1-49-68-5308   Fax: 33-1-49-68-5374   Contact: Yann Houdent, Gen. Mgr.   Emp: 35

G. LEBLANC CORPORATION

7001 Leblanc Blvd., PO Box 1415, Kenosha, WI, 53141-1415

Tel: (414) 658-1644   Fax: (414) 658-2824   www.gleblanc.com

Mfr./sale/services musical wind instruments.

Leblanc France SA, 13 rue Georges-LeBlanc, BP 42, F-27750 La Couture Boussey, France

LeBOEUF, LAMB, GREENE & MacRAE LLP

125 West 55th Street, 12th Fl., New York, NY, 10019

Tel: (212) 424-8000   Fax: (212) 424-8500   www.llgm.com

International law firm.

LeBoeuf, Lamb, Greene & MacRae LLP, 130 rue du Faubourg, F-75008 Saint-Honore Paris, France

Tel: 33-1-5393-7700   Fax: 33-1-4256-0806   Contact: Rene de Monseignat

LECROY CORPORATION

700 Chestnut Ridge Road, Chestnut Ridge, NY, 10977

Tel: (845) 425-2000   Fax: (845) 425-8967   www.lecroy.com

Mfr. signal analyzers and electronic measurement systems.

LeCroy S.A., 1 Avenue de l'Atlantique, LP 903, Les Ulis, F-91976 Couraboeuf, France

Tel: 33-1-69-188320

LEGATO SYSTEMS, INC.

2350 West El Camino Real, Mountain View, CA, 94040

Tel: (650) 210-7000   Fax: (650) 210-7032   www.legato.com

Mfr. storage management software.

Legato Systems France, Batiment D, 2/4 Avenue de L'Europe, F-78140 Velizy, France

LEHMAN BROTHERS HOLDINGS INC.

*101 Hudson Street, Jersey City, NJ, 07302

Tel: (201) 524-2000   Fax: (201) 524-2000   www.lehman.com

Financial services, securities and merchant banking services.

Lehman Brothers, 21 rue Balzac, F-75008 Paris, France

Tel: 33-1-5389-3000

LEVI STRAUSS & COMPANY

1155 Battery St., San Francisco, CA, 94111-1230

Tel: (415) 544-6000   Fax: (415) 501-3939   www.levistrauss.com

Mfr. and distributor of casual wearing apparel, including jeans and sportswear.

Levi Strauss Continental, 6 ave. du Pacifique, BP115 Z.A., F-91944 Courtaboeuf Les Ulis, France

Tel: 33-1-69-86-8998   Fax: 33-1-64-46-5478

EDW. C. LEVY COMPANY

8800 Dix Avenue, Detroit, MI, 48209

Tel: (313) 843-7200   Fax: (313) 849-9444   www.edwclevy.com

Engaged in the process and production of aggregates.

Edw. C. Levy, Immeuble Poinfore, Zac Ban la Dame, F-54390 Frouard, France

LEXMARK INTERNATIONAL

740 W. New Circle Rd., Lexington, KY, 40550

Tel: (859) 232-2000   Fax: (859) 232-1886   www.lexmark.com

Develop, manufacture, supply of printing solutions and products, including laser, inkjet, and dot matrix printers.

Lexmark International S.N.C., Immeuble Newton, La Défense 5, 9 place des Vosges, F-92924 Paris Cedex, France

Tel: 33-1-46-67-4000

ELI LILLY & COMPANY

Lilly Corporate Center, Indianapolis, IN, 46285

Tel: (317) 276-2000   Fax: (317) 277-6579   www.lilly.com

Mfr. pharmaceuticals and animal health products.

Lilly France, rue du Colonel Lilly, F-6760 Fegersheim, France

Tel: 33-3-38-64-4000   Fax: 33-3-38-64-4022

Lilly France SA, 203 Bureaux de la Colline, F-92213 Saint-Cloud, France

Tel: 33-1-49-11-3434   Fax: 33-1-46-02-2767

LIMITORQUE

PO Box 11318, 5114 Woodall Road, Lynchburg, VA, 24506

Tel: (804) 528-4400   Fax: (804) 845-9736   www.limitorque.com

Mfr./marketing/services electric valve actuators.

Limitorque France, Alpha Forum Etoile, 2 rue Troyon, F-75017 Paris, France

Tel: 33-1-4055-4640   Fax: 33-1-4068-7962

LINCOLN ELECTRIC HOLDINGS

22801 St. Clair Ave., Cleveland, OH, 44117-1199

Tel: (216) 481-8100   Fax: (216) 486-8385   www.lincolnelectric.com

Mfr. arc welding and welding related products, oxy-fuel and thermal cutting equipment and integral AC motors.

Lincoln Electric Company France SA, Ave. Franklin Roosevelt, BP 214, F-76120 LeGrand Quevilly, France

Tel: 33-2-32-11-4040   Fax: 33-2-32-1104011

Lincoln Electric International, 2 blvd Albert 1 ER, F-94130 Nogent Sur Marne Paris, France

Tel: 33-1-43-24-6015   Fax: 33-1-43-24-6017   Contact: Jean Mazingue

LINEAR TECHNOLOGY CORPORATION

1630 McCarthy Blvd., Milpitas, CA, 95035

Tel: (408) 432-1900   Fax: (408) 434-6441   www.linear-tech.com

Mfr. linear integrated circuit chips.

Linear Technology S.A.R.L., Immeuble "Le Quartz", 58 Chemin De La Justice, F-92290 Chatenay Malabry, France

Tel: 33-1-41079555   Fax: 33-1-46314613

LIONBRIDGE TECHNOLOGIES, INC.

950 Winter St., Waltham, MA, 02451

Tel: (781) 434-6000   Fax: (781) 434-6034   www.lionbridge.com

Provides solutions for worldwide deployment of technology and content.

Lionbridge France, 6, avenue de Verdun, F-92250 La Garenne Colombes, France

LNP ENGINEERING PLASTICS

475 Creamery Way, Exton, PA, 19341

Tel: (610) 363-4500   Fax: (610) 363-4749   www.geplastics.com

Mfr. thermoplastic composites.

General Electric Plastics, ZI St. Guénault BP 67, F-91002 Evry-Cedex, France

LOCKHEED MARTIN CORPORATION

6801 Rockledge Drive, Bethesda, MD, 20817

Tel: (301) 897-6000   Fax: (301) 897-6652   www.imco.com

Design/mfr./management systems in fields of space, defense, energy, electronics and technical services.

CalComp S.A., Le Clemenceau, 205 Ave. Georges, F-92000 Nanterre Hermes, France

Tel: 33-1-47-29-5500   Fax: 33-1-47-29-1372

Lockheed Martin International, 4 rue de Penthievre, F-75008 Paris, France

Tel: 33-1-42-65-3981   Contact: G. Cass, VP

LORAL SPACE & COMMUNICATIONS LTD.

600 Third Ave., New York, NY, 10016

Tel: (212) 697-1105   Fax: (212) 338-5662   www.loral.com

Marketing coordination: defense electronics, communications systems.

Loral CyberStar, 90 avenue des Champs-Elysees, F-75008 Paris, France

Tel: 33-156-43-5072

LORD CORPORATION

2000 West Grandview Blvd, Erie, PA, 16514

Tel: (814) 868-0924   Fax: (814) 486-4345   www.lordcorp.com

Mfg. adhesives, coatings, chemicals, film products.

Lord Corporation, European Technology Center, 15 Boulevard d'Anvers, F-67000 Strasbourg, France

Lord Corporation, 10, Rue des Gaudines, F78100 Saint-Germain-En-Laye, France

Tel: 33-1-30-87-0578   Fax: 33-1-30-87-0827

LOST ARROW CORPORATION

259 West Santa Clara Street, Ventura, CA, 93001

Tel: (805) 643-8616   Fax: (805) 653-6355   www.patagonia.com

Mfr. high-end outdoor sportswear, via catalogues and specialty retailers, including Patagonia stores.

Patagonia Chamonix, 249 rue Paccard, F-74400 Chamonix, France

LOTUS DEVELOPMENT CORPORATION

1 Rogers Street, Cambridge, MA, 02142

Tel: (617) 577-8500   Fax: (617) 577-8500   www.lotus.com

Mfr. business software.

Immeuble Lotus France, La Defense 6, 35-41 rue du Capitaine Guynemer, F-92925 Paris La Defense Cedex, France

LSI LOGIC CORPORATION

1551 McCarthy Blvd., Milpitas, CA, 95035

Tel: (408) 433-8000   Fax: (408) 954-3220   www.lsilogic.com

Develop and manufacture semiconductors.

LSI Logic SA, 53 bis Ave. de l'europe, B.P. 139, Velizzy-Villacoublay, F-78148 Cedex Paris, France

Tel: 33-1-34-63-1313   Fax: 33-1-34-63-1319

LTX CORPORATION

LTX Park, University Ave., Westwood, MA, 02090

Tel: (617) 461-1000   Fax: (617) 326-4883   www.ltx.com

Design/mfr. computer-controlled semiconductor test systems.

LTX France SA, 50 Boulevard Rabelais, F-94100 Saint-Maur, France

Tel: 33-14-889-5240   Fax: 33-14-889-5375

THE LUBRIZOL CORPORATION

29400 Lakeland Blvd., Wickliffe, OH, 44092-2298

Tel: (440) 943-4200   Fax: (440) 943-5337   www.lubrizol.com

Mfr. chemicals additives for lubricants and fuels.

Lubrizol France SA, Tour Europe, F-92400 Courbevoie Paris Cedex 7, France

Tel: 33-1-41-25-1300

LUCENT TECHNOLOGIES, INC.

600 Mountain Ave., Murray Hill, NJ, 07974-0636

Tel: (908) 582-3000   Fax: (908) 582-2576   www.lucent.com

Design/mfr. wide range of public and private networks, communication systems and software, data networking systems, business telephone systems and microelectronics components.

TRT Lucent Technologies, 16 Ave. Descartes, F-92352 Le Plessis Robinson Cedex, France

Tel: 33-1-41-28-7000 Fax: 33-1-46-30-6224   Contact: Christelle Pollet, PR Mgr.

TRT Lucent Technologies, 49 rue de la Rebublique BP 26, F-76250 Deville-les -Rouen, France

Tel: 33-2-32-10-7000 Fax: 33-2-32-10-7010   Contact: Henri-Alain Rault, Location Head

LYDALL INC.

1 Colonial Road, PO Box 151, Manchester, CT, 06040

Tel: (860) 646-1233   Fax: (860) 646-4917   www.lydall.com

Mfr. converted paper products, paperboard, non-woven specialty media.

Axohm Axohm SA, Saint-Rivalain, F-56310 Melrand, France

Tel: 33-2-97285300 Fax: 33-2-9739-5890

LYONDELL CHEMICAL COMPANY

1221 McKinney St., Houston, TX, 77010

Tel: (713) 652-7200   Fax: (713) 309-2074   www.lyondell.com

Mfr. polymers and petrochemicals.

Lyondell Chemical Company, BP 201, F-13775 Fos-Sur-Mer Cedex, France

Tel: 33-4-4247-5100

Lyondell Chemical Products Europe, Inc., Z.I. du Pre Sarrazin, Boite Postale No. 34, F-60870 Villers Saint Paul, France

Tel: 33-4-4247-5100

Lyondell Chimie France, SNC, 12-14 Rond-Point des Champs Elysées, F-75008 Paris, France

M/A-COM INC.

1011 Pawtucket Boulevard, Lowell, MA, 01853-3295

Tel: (978) 442-5000   Fax: (978) 442-5354   www.macom.com

Mfr. radio frequency (RF) and microwave integrated circuits and IP Networks to the wireless telecommunications and defense-related industries.

M/A-COM Ltd., Div. Tyco, 29 Chaussee Jules Cesar, F-95300 Pontoise, France

Tel: 33-1-34-208888 Fax: 33-1-34208232

MacDERMID INC.

245 Freight Street, Waterbury, CT, 06702-0671

Tel: (203) 575-5700   Fax: (203) 575-7900   www.macdermid.com

Chemicals processing for metal industrial, plastics, electronics cleaners, strippers.

MacDermid France SA, rue de la Closerie, Z.I. du Clos aux Pois, C.E. 4831, F-91048 Evry Cedex, France

Tel: 33-1-60-86-1427 Fax: 33-1-60-86-1876

MACROMEDIA, INC.

600 Townsend Street, San Francisco, CA, 94103-4945

Tel: (415) 252-2000   Fax: (415) 626-9603   www.macromedia.com

Engaged in web publishing.

Macromedia France, 1, avenue Morane Saulnier, Immeuble St Exupéry, F-78140 Vélizy Villacoublay, France

MACTAC

4560 Darrow Road, Stow, OH, 44224

Tel: (330) 688-1111   Fax: (330) 688-2540   www.mactac.com

Mfr. pressure sensitive tapes, films and label materials.

MACtac France, 16, Avenue Arago, F-91420 Morangis, France

MAGNETROL INTERNATIONAL

5300 Belmont Road, Downers Grove, IL, 60515-4499

Tel: (630) 969-4000   Fax: (630) 969-9489   www.magnetrol.com

Mfr. level and flow instrumentation.

Magnetrol International, 11 rue Albert Einstein, Espace Descartes, F-77420 Champs-sur-Marne, France

Tel: 33-1-64-68-5828   Fax: 33-1-64-68-5827   Contact: Alain Demaitre, Sales Mgr.

MALLINCKRODT BAKER, INC.

222 Red School Lane, Phillipsburg, NJ, 08865

Tel: (908) 859-2151   Fax: (908) 859-9318   www.mallbaker.com

Mfr. of high purity chemicals and related products and services.

Mallinckrodt Baker, 33 Avenue Philippe Auguste, F-75011 Paris, France

Tel: 33-1-4464-8971   Fax: 33-1-4464-8973

MALLINCKRODT PHARMACUTICALS, INC.

675 McDonnell Blvd., Hazelwood, MO, 63042

Tel: (314) 654-2000   Fax: (314) 654-5380   www.mallinckrodt.com

Mfr. products for respiratory care.

Mallinckrodt France SARL, Parc d'Affaires Technopolis, 3 avenue du Canada, Les Ulis, F-91975 Courtaboeuf Cedex, France

Tel: 33-16-9821400   Fax: 33-16-9821500

MANPOWER INTERNATIONAL INC.

5301 N. Ironwood Rd., PO Box 2053, Milwaukee, WI, 53201-2053

Tel: (414) 961-1000   Fax: (414) 961-7081   www.manpower.com

Temporary help, contract service, training and testing.

Manpower France SARL, 9 rue Jacques Bingen, F-75017 Paris, France

Tel: 33-1-44-15-4040   Fax: 33-1-47-63-1077

MANUFACTURER'S SERVICES LTD. (MSL)

300 Baker Ave., Concord, MA, 01742-2125

Tel: (978) 287-5630   Fax: (978) 287-5635   www.manserve.com

Provides electronic manufacturing services to the medical, computer and peripherals industries.

MSL France, Site de Kerquessaud, BP 5429, F-44354 Guerande Cedex, France

MAPICS, INC.

1000 Windward Concourse Pkwy., Alpharetta, GA, 30005

Tel: (678) 319-8000   Fax: (678) 319-8000   www.mapics.com

Mfr. software.

MAPICS FRANCE, Le Danica, 21 avenue Georges Pompidou, F-69486 Lyon Cedex, France

MARCONI DATA SYSTEMS INC.

1500 Mittel Blvd., Wood Dale, IL, 60191

Tel: (630) 860-7300   Fax: (630) 616-3657   www.videojet.com

Mfr. computer peripherals and hardware, state-of-the-art industrial ink jet marking and coding products.

Videojet, Div. Marconi Data Systems, Parc Gutenberg, 7 vole la Cardon, BP n 81, F-91126 Palaiseau Cedex, France

Tel: 33-1-69-19-7000   Fax: 33-1-69-32-0145   Contact: Alain Legatelois

MARITZ INC.

1375 North Highway Drive, Fenton, MO, 63099

Tel: (636) 827-4000   Fax: (636) 827-3312   www.maritz.com

Engaged in travel and marketing services.

Maritz France, 2, Boulevard Georges Clemenceau, F-92400 Courbevoie, France

Tel: 33-1-41-16-2021

MARK IV INDUSTRIES INC.

501 John James Audubon Pkwy., PO Box 810, Amherst, NY, 14226-0810

Tel: (716) 689-4972   Fax: (716) 689-1529   www.mark-iv.com

Mfr. of engineered systems and components utilizing mechanical and fluid power transmission, fluid transfer, and power systems and components.

Dayco Europe SARL, Roissypole le Dome, 1 rue de la Haye, BP 10909, F-95731 Roissy CDG Cedex, France

Tel: 33-1-48-62-9351 Fax: 33-1-48-62-9352

Mark IV Systemes Moteurs S.A., 11 blvd d'Anvaux, F-36000 Chageauroux, France

Tel: 33-25-408-5959 Fax: 33-25-434-6130

Mark IV Systemes Moteurs S.A., 1 rue Charles Edouard Jeanneret, F-78306 Poissy Cedex, France

Tel: 33-1-3922-3423 Fax: 33-13911-3040

Mark IV Systemes Moteurs S.A., Z.Z. des Grands Pres., F-68370 Orbey, France

Tel: 33-329590-8806   Fax: 33-32950-8817

MARKEM CORPORATION

150 Congress Street, Keene, NH, 03431

Tel: (603) 352-1130   Fax: (603) 357-1835   www.markem.com.

Mfr. and sales of industrial marking, print machinery and hot stamping foils.

Markem France SA, 23 rue Auguste Perret, Z.A.C. de Petites, F-94808 Bruyeres Villejuif Cedex, France

Tel: 33-1-43-90-1100 Fax: 33-1-46-78-4763

MARLEY COOLING TOWER COMPANY

7401 West 129th Street, Overland Park, KS, 66213

Tel: (913) 664-7400   Fax: (913) 664-7641   www.marleyct.com

Cooling and heating towers and waste treatment systems.

Marley Cooling Tower (France), Polyparc 540 allee des Hetres, F-69760 Limonest, France

Tel: 33-4-7252-1700   Contact: Pierre-Yves Gerard

MARRIOTT INTERNATIONAL INC.

10400 Fernwood Rd., Bethesda, MD, 20817

Tel: (301) 380-3000   Fax: (301) 380-5181   www.marriott.com

Hotel services.

Marriott Courtyard Neuilly, 58 blvd Victor Hugo, F-92200 Neuilly, France

Tel: 33-155-636-465   Fax: 33-155-636-465

Paris Marriott Hotel, Champs Elysees, Paris, France

MARS INC.

6885 Elm Street, McLean, VA, 22101-3810

Tel: (703) 821-4900   Fax: (703) 448-9678   www.mars.com

Mfr. candy, snack foods, rice products and cat food.

Royal Canin, Div. Mars, RN 113 - BP 4, F-30470 Aimargues, France

Tel: 33-4-6673-6400   Contact: Henri Lagarde

MARSH & McLENNAN COS INC.

1166 Ave. of the Americas, New York, NY, 10036-2774

Tel: (212) 345-5000   Fax: (212) 345-4808   www.marshmac.com

Insurance agents/brokers, pension and investment management consulting services.

J&H Marsh & McLennan Global Broking Paris, 32 rue Lafitte, F-75009 Paris, France

Tel: 33-4-783-2071 Fax: 33-4-783-2070   Contact: Mohanned Dahbi

MASTERCARD INTERNATIONAL INC.

200 Purchase Street, Purchase, NY, 10577

Tel: (914) 249-2000   Fax: (914) 249-5475   www.mastercard.com

Provides financial payment systems globally.

MasterCard International Inc., Middle East/Africa Region, Tour Maine Montpaarnasse, 33 Ave. de Maine, F-75755 Paris Cedex 15, France

MATTEL INC.

333 Continental Blvd., El Segundo, CA, 90245-5012

Tel: (310) 252-2000   Fax: (310) 252-2179   www.mattel.com

Mfr. toys, dolls, games, crafts and hobbies.

Fisher-Price SA, rue de Gradoux, F-45800 St. Jean de Braye, France

Mattel France SA, 64-68 ave. de la Victoire, F-94310 Orly, France

MAURICE PINCOFFS COMPANY, INC.

Box 920919, Houston, TX, 77292

Tel: (713) 292-0503   Fax: (713) 681-8521   www.pincoffs.com

International marketing and distribution.

Maurice Pincoffs, 27-29 ave. de Saint Mande, F-75012 Paris, France

MAXON CORPORATION

201 East 18th Street, Muncie, IN, 47302

Tel: (765) 284-3304   Fax: (765) 286-8394   www.maxoncorp.com

Industry combustion equipment and valves.

Maxon S.A.R.L., 2 Avenue du Parc Le Campus, F-95033 Cergy Pontoise Cedex Paris, France

Tel: 33-1-34-20-1080   Fax: 33-1-34-20-1088

MAXTOR CORPORATION

500 McCarthy Blvd., Milpitas, CA, 95035

Tel: (408) 894-5000   Fax: (408) 432-4510   www.maxtor.com

Mfr. develops and markets hard disk drives for desktop computer systems.

Maxtor Europe S.A.R.L., 18 rue Saarinen, Silic 242, F-94568 Rungis Cedex, France

Tel: 33-1-41-80-0860   Fax: 33-1-46-86-4048

MAYER, BROWN, ROWE & MAW

190 S. LaSalle Street, Chicago, IL, 60603

Tel: (312) 782-0600   Fax: (312) 701-7711   www.mayerbrown.com

Engaged in international law.

Lambert & Lee, 13 Avenue Hoche, F-75008 Paris, France

Tel: 33-1-5353-4343

MAYFRAN INTERNATIONAL, INC.

PO Box 43038, Cleveland, OH, 44143

Tel: (440) 461-4100   Fax: (440) 461-5565   www.mayfran.com

Mfr. conveying systems, filtration equipment and separators that facilitate material handling and coolant recovery for automobile manufacturers and machine tool builders.

Mayfran France, Centre D'Affairs, PO Box 45, Paris-Nord, F-93153 LeBlanc Mesnil, France

Tel: 33-1-48-65-7800   Fax: 33-1-48-67-7629

MBIA INC.

113 King Street, Armonk, NY, 10504

Tel: (914) 273-4545   Fax: (914) 765-3299   www.mbia.com

Provides investment and treasury management services and insurance for municipal bonds.

MBIA Assurance, S.A., 112 Avenue Kléber, F-75116 Paris, France

Tel: 33-1-53-70-4343

McCANN-ERICKSON WORLDGROUP

750 Third Ave., New York, NY, 10017

Tel: (212) 697-6000   Fax: (212) 984-3575   www.mccann.com

International advertising and marketing services.

Joannis Schneider Conseil SA, 2 rue Voltaire, F-92309 Levallois Perret Cedex, France

McCann Erickson SA, rue de Villiere, F-92309 Levallois Perret Cedex, France

McDONALD'S CORPORATION

McDonald's Plaza, Oak Brook, IL, 60523

Tel: (630) 623-3000   Fax: (630) 623-7409   www.mcdonalds.com

Fast food chain stores.

McDonald's Corp., Paris, France

McKINSEY & COMPANY

55 East 52nd Street, New York, NY, 10022

Tel: (212) 446-7000   Fax: (212) 446-8575   www.mckinsey.com

Management and business consulting services.

McKinsey & Company, 79 avenue des Champs-Elysées, F-75008 Paris, France

Tel: 33-1-40-69-1400   Fax: 33-1-40-69-9393

MECHANICAL DYNAMICS, INC.

2300 Traverwood Drive, Ann Arbor, MI, 48105

Tel: (734) 994-3800   Fax: (734) 994-6418   www.adams.com

Mfr. Adams prototyping software for functional virtual prototyping solutions.

Mechanical Dynamics Sarl, 58 rue Pottier, F-7815 LeChesnay, France

Tel: 33-1-3966-040

MEDIA 100 INC.

450 Donald Lynch Blvd., Marlborough, MA, 01752

Tel: (508) 460-1600   Fax: (508) 481-8627   www.media100.com

Mfr. digital editing software and hardware.

Media 100 SA, BP 422, Bureau 300, World Trade Ctr., 2 CNIT, 2 Place de la Defense, F-92053 Paris, France

MEDICUS GROUP INTERNATIONAL

1675 Broadway, New York, NY, 10019

Tel: (212) 468-3100   Fax: (212) 468-3222   www.medicusgroup.com

Healthcare communications company engaged in professional advertising, sales promotion, global branding and launch planning.

Medicus 1 Team SA, 8 rue Bellini, F-75016 Paris Cedex 16, France

Tel: 33-1-53-65-6333   Contact: Dr. Jean-Marc Menat

MEMC ELECTRONIC MATERIALS, INC.

501 Pearl Drive, St. Peters, MO, 63376

Tel: (636) 474-5500   Fax: (636) 474-5161   www.memc.com

Mfg. and distribution of silicon wafers.

MEMC Huls France S.A., Tour Horizon, 52 quai de Dion Bouton, F-92806 Puteaux Cedex, France

Tel: 33-1-46-93-2305   Fax: 33-1-40-90-9281

MEMOREX CORPORATION

10100 Pioneer Blvd., Ste. 110, Santa Fe Springs, CA, 90670

Tel: (562) 906-2800   Fax: (562) 906-2848   www.memorex.com

Magnetic recording tapes, etc.

Memorex SA, 25 Blvd. de I'Amiral Bruix, F-75016 Paris, France

MENASHA CORPORATION

1645 Bergstrom Road, Neenah, WI, 54957-0367

Tel: (920) 751-1000   Fax: (920) 751-1236   www.menasha.com

Mfr. packaging and paperboard products.

Poly Hi Solidur France, Sub. Menasha, B.P. 95, F-57380 Faulquemont, France

MENTOR CORPORATION

201 Mentor Drive, Santa Barbara, CA, 93111

Tel: (805) 879-6000   Fax: (805) 967-7108   www.mentorcorp.com

Mfr. medical devices including breast implants.

Mentor Medical Systems France, S.A., 171 Avenue George Clemenceau, Bldg. D, F-92024 Nanterre Cedex, France

Tel: 33-1-1472-13366

MENTOR GRAPHICS

8005 SW Boeckman Road, Wilsonville, OR, 97070-7777

Tel: (503) 685-7000   Fax: (503) 685-1202   www.mentorg.com

Develop/mfr. software tools for embedded systems market.

Mentor Graphics, Immeuble Le Pasteur, 13/15 Rue Jeanne Braconnier, F-92360 Meudon La Foret, France

MERCER MANAGEMENT CONSULTING INC.

1166 Ave. of the Americas, New York, NY, 10036

Tel: (212) 345-3400   Fax: (212) 345-7414   www.mercermc.com

Provides clients with counsel in such areas as corporate and business strategy and growth planning, organizational development, and market and operations enhancement.

Mercer Management, 69 rue de Monceau, F-75008 Paris, France

Mercer Management Consulting, 28 avenue Victor Hugo, F-75116 Paris, France

MERCK & COMPANY, INC.

One Merck Drive, PO Box 100, Whitehouse Station, NJ, 08889-0100

Tel: (908) 423-1000   Fax: (908) 423-2592   www.merck.com

Pharmaceuticals, chemicals and biologicals.

Merck, Sharp & Dohme / Chibret, 3 ave. Hoche, F-75008 Paris, France

MERCURY COMPUTER SYSTEMS, INC.

199 Riverneck Rd., Chelmsford, MA, 01824

Tel: (978) 256-1300   Fax: (978) 256-3599   www.mc.com

Mfr. digital signal processing systems for the defense and medical imaging markets.

Mercury Computer Systems SARL, Les Ulis, France

MERCURY INTERACTIVE CORPORATION

1325 Borregas Ave., Sunnyvale, CA, 94089

Tel: (408) 822-5200   Fax: (408) 822-5300   www.merc-int.com

Mfr. computer software to decipher and eliminate "bugs" from systems.

Mercury Interactive France SARL, Ibis rue du Petit Clamart, Bâtiment E, F-78147 Vélizy, France

Tel: 33-1-40-83-6868   Fax: 33-1-40-83-6850

MERRILL CORPORATION

1 Merrill Circle, St. Paul, MN, 55108

Tel: (651) 646-4501   Fax: (651) 646-5332   www.merrillcorp.com

Engaged in document management and data services.

Merrill France, 4, Square Edouard VII, F-75009 Paris, France

MERRILL LYNCH & COMPANY, INC.

World Financial Center, 250 Vesey Street, New York, NY, 10281-1332

Tel: (212) 236-1000   Fax: (212) 449-2892   www.ml.com

Security brokers and dealers, investment and business services.

Merrill Lynch Capital Markets France, S.A., 96 Ave. Kleber, F-75761 Paris Cedex 16, France

Tel: 33-1-53-65-5555   Fax: 33-1-53-65-5600

MESTEK, INC.

260 North Elm St., Westfield, MA, 01085

Tel: (413) 568-9571   Fax: (413) 568-2969   www.mestek.com

Mfr. air diffusers, grilles and related equipment for air conditioning, heating and ventilation.

Anemotherm SA, 4749 rue Jean Bleuzen, F-92170 Vanves, France

META GROUP, INC.

208 Harbor Drive, PO Box 120061, Stamford, CT, 06912-0061

Tel: (203) 973-6700   Fax: (203) 359-8066   www.metagroup.com

Engaged in research and consulting, focusing on information technology and business transformation strategies.

META Group, 27 quai Anatole France, F-75007 Paris, France

Tel: 33-1-4550-1440

METAL IMPROVEMENT COMPANY

10 Forest Ave., Paramus, NJ, 07652

Tel: (201) 843-7800   Fax: (201) 843-3460   www.metalimprovement.com

Mfr. shot peening.

Shot Peening, Div. Metal Improvement, Zone Industrielle de St. Etienne, Rue De Cazenave, F-64100 Bayonne, France

Shot Peening, Div. Metal Improvement, Zone Industrielle d'Amilly, F-45200 Montargis, France

METASOLV, INC.

5560 Tennyson Pkwy., Plano, TX, 75024

Tel: (972) 403-8300   Fax: (972) 403-8333   www.metasolv.com

Mfr. software.

MetaSolv Software SAS, Sophia Antipolis, Zac du Font de l'Orme-Bat. C, 45, Allee Des Ormes, F-06250 Mougin, France

METROLOGIC INSTRUMENTS, INC.

90 Coles Road, Blackwood, NJ, 08012

Tel: (856) 225-8100   Fax: (856) 228-6673   www.metrologic.com

Mfr. and sales of hologram based, bar code scanner systems.

Metrologic Eria France S.A, 69 Rue de la Belle Etoile, ZI Paris Nord II BP 50057, F-95947 Roissy Cedex, France

METROMEDIA FIBER NETWORK, INC.

360 Hamilton Avenue, White Plains, NY, 10601

Tel: (914) 421-6700   Fax: (914) 421-6777   www.mfn.com

Mfr. urban fiber-optic networks for telecommunications providers.

Metromedia Fiber Network, 9 Energy Park, 130-136 Boulevard de Verdun, F-92400 Courbevoie, France

METRON TECHNOLOGY

1350 Old Bayshore Highway, Ste. 210, Burlingame, CA, 94010

Tel: (650) 401-4600   Fax: (650) 373-1135   www.metrontech.com

Global provider of marketing, sales, service and support solutions to semiconductor materials and equipment suppliers and semiconductor manufacturers.

Metron Technology (France) EURL, Immeuble le Grenat, 3, Avenue Doyen Louis Weil, F-38024 Grenoble Cedex l, France

M-I

PO Box 48242, Houston, TX, 77242-2842

Tel: (713) 739-0222   Fax: (713) 308-9503   www.midf.com

Developer, manufacturer and marketer of drilling and completion fluids and services.

M-I Drilling Fluids Intl B.V., Zone Induspal Avenue Joliot Curie, BP 205, Lons, F-64142 Billere Cedex, France

Tel: 33-559923551   Fax: 33-559923556

MICRO WAREHOUSE, INC.

535 Connecticut Ave., Norwalk, CT, 06854

Tel: (203) 899-4000   Fax: (203) 899-4203   www.warehouse.com

Catalog computer sales.

Inmac, 125 Avenue du Bois de la Pie, Roissy-en-France, F-95921 Roissy Cedex, France

MICROCHIP TECHNOLOGY INCORPORATED

2355 West Chandler Boulevard, Chandler, AZ, 85224

Tel: (602) 786-7200   Fax: (602) 899-9210   www.microchip.com

Mfr. electronic subassemblies and components.

AZ Microchip Technology SARL, Zone Industrielle de la Bonde, 2 rue Du Buisson aux Fraises, F-91300 Massy, France

Tel: 33-1-69-53-6320   Fax: 33-1-69-30-9079

LeadREP, 99 route de Versailles, F-91160 Champlain, France

Tel: 33-1-69-79-9350   Fax: 33-1-69-79-9359

MICROMERITICS INSTRUMENT CORPORATION

One Micromeritics Drive, Norcross, GA, 30093-1877

Tel: (770) 662-3620   Fax: (770) 662-3696   www.micromeritics.com

Mfr. analytical instruments.

Micromeritics France SA, 181 rue Henri Bessemer, F-60100 Creil, France

Tel: 33-3-4464-6080

MICROMUSE INC.

139 Townsend Street, San Francisco, CA, 94107

Tel: (415) 538-9090   Fax: (415) 538-9091   www.micromuse.com

Mfr. software for information technology.

Micromuse Ltd., 2, avenue de la Cristallerie, F-92310 Sevres, France

MICROSOFT CORPORATION

One Microsoft Way, Redmond, WA, 98052-6399

Tel: (425) 882-8080   Fax: (425) 936-7329   www.microsoft.com

Computer software, peripherals and services.

Microsoft Europe (European HQ), Tour Pacific, F-92977 Paris La Defense Cedex 77, France

Tel: 33-1-46-35-1010   Fax: 33-1-46-35-1030

Microsoft France SARL, 18 ave. du Quebec, Zone de Courteboeuf, F-91957 Les Ulis Cedex, France

Tel: 33-1-69-29-1111   Fax: 33-1-64-46-0660

MILACRON INC.

2090 Florence Ave., Cincinnati, OH, 45206

Tel: (513) 487-5000   Fax: (513) 487-5057   www.milacron.com

Metalworking and plastics technologies.

Ferromatik Milacron S.A., BP 173, rue Marie Curie, F-78313 Maurepas Cédex, France

Tel: 33-1-34821800   Fax: 33-1-30660469

MILLENNIUM CHEMICALS INC.

PO Box 7015, 230 Half Mile Road, Red Bank, NJ, 07701-7015

Tel: (732) 933-5000   Fax: (732) 933-5200   www.millenniumchem.com

Mfr. specialty chemicals for paints, perfumes, and flavorings.

Millennium Chemicals, 85 Avenue Victor Hugo, F-92563 Rueil Malmaison Cedex, France

Tel: 33-1-55-47-2250   Fax: 33-1-55-47-2251

MILLER ELECTRIC MFG. COMPANY

1635 W. Spencer Street, Appleton, WI, 54912-1079

Tel: (920) 734-9821   Fax: (920) 735-4125   www.millerwelds.com

Mfr. arc welding machines.

ITW Welding, 2, Voie Gallo Romaine, Z.A.C. de la Bonne Rencontre, F-77860 Quincy Voisins, France

MILTON ROY COMPANY

201 Ivyland Road, Ivylan, PA, 18974

Tel: (215) 441-0800   Fax: (215) 293-0468   www.miltonroy.com

Mfr. medical and industry equipment and process control instruments.

DOSAPRO-Milton Roy SA, 10 Grande rue, F-27360 Pont St. Pierre, France

Tel: 33-232-68-3000   Fax: 33-232-68-3093   Contact: Olivier Perrin

Robin Industries, 10 rue du bois Gasseau, BP 94, F-77212 Avon Cedex, France
Tel: 33-1-60-74-95-20

MINE SAFETY APPLIANCES COMPANY

121 Gamma Drive, PO Box 426, Pittsburgh, PA, 15230

Tel: (412) 967-3000   Fax: (412) 967-3452   www.msa.net

Safety equipment, industry filters.

MSA de France, 13 rue de la Guivernone, BP 617, F-95004 Cergy Pontoise, France

MINOLTA-QMS INC.

One Magnum Pass, PO Box 81250, Mobile, AL, 36618

Tel: (205) 633-4300   Fax: (205) 633-4866   www.qms.com

Mfr. of high-performance color and monochrome document printing solutions for office automation, electronic publishing, graphic design, and advanced imaging applications.

Minolta-QMS France, 1 bis rue du petit Clamart, BP 17, F-78142 Vélizy Cedex, France

MKS INSTRUMENTS INC.

6 Shattuck Road, Andover, MA, 01810-2449

Tel: (978) 975-2350   Fax: (978) 933-0750   www.astex.com

Provider of process infrastructure products and technologies that increase productivity in gas- and vacuum-based manufacturing.

AsTex France, Bat 5, Parc Club du Golf B, F-13856 Aix en Provence Cedex 3, France
Tel: 33-4-4297-5170   Fax: 33-4-4297-5179

MODEM MEDIA, INC.

230 East Avenue, Norwalk, CT, 06855

Tel: (203) 299-7000   Fax: (230) 299-7060   www.modemmedia.com

Provides on-line marketing and consulting services.

Modem Media Paris, 11 rue Mogador, F-75009 Paris, France
Tel: 33-1-42-818282   Contact: Carol Gué, Mng. Dir.

MODINE MANUFACTURING COMPANY

1500 DeKoven Ave., Racine, WI, 53403

Tel: (262) 636-1200   Fax: (262) 636-1424   www.modine.com

Mfr. heat-transfer products.

Modine Intl., 131-135 Blvd. Carnot, Bureau 441, F-78110 Le Vesinet, France

MODUS MEDIA, INC.

690 Canton Street, Westwood, MA, 02090

Tel: (781) 407-2000   Fax: (781) 407-3800   www.modusmedia.com

Engaged in outsourced manufacturing, fulfillment and distribution services.

Modus Media, Angers Solution Centre, Rue de la Nouette, Z.I. Angers Beaucouzé, F-49070 Beaucouzé, France
Tel: 33-2-41-22-04-00   Fax: 33-2-41-72-65-66

MOLEX INC.

2222 Wellington Court, Lisle, IL, 60532

Tel: (630) 969-4550   Fax: (630) 969-1352   www.molex.com

Mfr. electronic, electrical and fiber optic interconnection products and systems, switches, application tooling.

Molex France, 18 Parc Burospace, F-91571 Bièvres Cédex, France

MOLTECH POWER SYSTEMS

9062 South Rita Road, Tucson, AZ, 85747

Tel: (520) 799-7500   Fax: (520) 799-7501   www.moltechpower.com

Provides rechargeable battery solutions for industry applications.

Moltech Power Systems Nordic AB, Immeuble Apollo, 48 Cours Blaise Pascal, F-91004 Evry Cedex, France
Tel: 33-1-60871680   Fax: 33-1-60871681

MONSANTO

800 N. Lindbergh Boulevard, St. Louis, MO, 63167

Tel: (314) 694-1000   Fax: (314) 694-7625   www.monsanto.com

Life sciences company focusing on agriculture, nutrition, pharmaceuticals, health and wellness and sustainable development.

Asgrow France SA, Domaine de Mercie, F-82170 Monbequi, France

Monsanto Co. Chemical Group, Division Agriculture, Europarc du Chene, 11 rue Pascal, F-69673 Bron Cedex, France

Tel: 33-4-7214-4040   Fax: 33-4-7214-4141

Monsanto France SA, Immeuble Elysees La Defense, 7 Place de Dome, F-92056 Paris La Defense Cedex, France

Tel: 33-1-55-23-1201   Fax: 33-1-55-23-1212

Monsanto SAS, Station de Recherche, Boissay, F-28310 Toury, France

Monsanto SAS/Cargill, Croix de Pardies 21, F-40305 Peyrehorade Cedex, France

MOODY'S INVESTOR SERVICES, INC.

99 Church St., New York, NY, 10007

Tel: (212) 553-1658   Fax: (212) 553-0462   www.moodys.com

Publishes credit ratings.

Moody's France S.A., Services aux Investisseurs, 4 rue Auber, F-75009 Paris, France

Tel: 33-1-53-30-10-20

MOOG INC.

300 Jamison Road, East Aurora, NY, 14052-0018

Tel: (716) 652-2000   Fax: (716) 687-4471   www.moog.com

Mfr. precision control components and systems.

Moog SARL, 38 rue du Morvan, Silic 417, F-94573 Rungis, France

MORGAN ADVANCED MATERIALS AND TECHNOLOGY, INC.

441 Hall Ave., Saint Mary's, PA, 15857

Tel: (814) 781-1573   Fax: (814) 781-9262   www.mamat.com

Mfr. carbon graphite and silicon carbide components.

Marshall Morganite S.A., Z.I. 35, Rue Gay Lussac, B.P. 100, F-95505 Gonesse Cedex, France

J. P. MORGAN CHASE & CO. INC.

270 Park Ave., New York, NY, 10017

Tel: (212) 270-6000   Fax: (212) 622-9030   www.jpmorganchase.com

Provides integrated financial solutions for institutions and individuals worldwide, including asset management, investment banking and commercial banking.

J. P. Morgan Chase & Co., Washington Plaza, 42 rue Washington, F-75008 Paris, France

Tel: 33-1-53-77-1000   Fax: 33-1-53-77-1049

MORGAN STANLEY DEAN WITTER & CO.

1585 Broadway, New York, NY, 10036

Tel: (212) 761-4000   Fax: (212) 761-0086   www.msdw.com

Securities and commodities brokerage, investment banking, money management, personal trusts.

Morgan Stanley SA, 25 rue Balzac, F-75008 Paris, France

MOTOROLA, INC.

1303 East Algonquin Road, Schaumburg, IL, 60196

Tel: (847) 576-5000   Fax: (847) 538-5191   www.motorola.com

Mfr. communications equipment, semiconductors and cellular phones.

Motorola AIEG SA, 1 blvd Victor, F-75015 Paris, France

Tel: 33-1-53-78-1800   Fax: 33-1-53-78-1815

Motorola Electronique Automobile SA, 8, Blvd. Charles Detriche, F-49015 Angers, France

MPS GROUP, INC. (MODIS PROFESSIONAL SERVICES)

1 Independent Dr., Jacksonville, FL, 32202-5060

Tel: (904) 360-2000   Fax: (904) 360-2814   www.modispro.com

Engaged in staffing for professional services and information technology.

Modis, 6 av des Andes, BP 22, F-91941 Courtaboeuf, France

MQSOFTWARE, INC.

7575 Golden Valley Road, Ste. 140, Minneapolis, MN, 55427

Tel: (763) 546-9080   Fax: (763) 546-9083   www.mqsoftware.com

Mfr. enterprise application software.

MQSoftware France, 54 Rue Botzaris, F-75019 Paris, France

MRO SOFTWARE, INC.

100 Crosby Drive, Bedford, MA, 01730

Tel: (781) 280-2000   Fax: (781) 280-0207   www.mrosoftware.com

Design/sales of enterprise asset maintenance software.

MRO Software SARL, Immeuble Atria, 2 rue de Centre, Noisy-le-Grand, France

Tel: 33-1-48-15-5580   Fax: 33-1-48-15-5599   Contact: Pascal Robez, Gen. Mgr.   Emp: 12

MSC.SOFTWARE CORPORATION

2 MacArthur Place, Santa Ana, CA, 92707

Tel: (714) 540-8900   Fax: (714) 784-4056   www.mscsoftware.com

Develop finite element analysis software used in the field of computer-aided engineering.

MSC.Software SarL, Immeuble Burolines, 2ter, Avenue Marcel Doret, F-31700 Blagnac, France

MSC.Software SarL, Immeuble l'Europeen - 98, Allee des Champs Elysees, F-91042 Evry Cedex, France

MSC.Software SarL, Europarc du Chene Bat B3, 7 Rue Pascal, F-69500 Bron, France

MTI TECHNOLOGY CORPORATION

4905 East LaPalma Avenue, Anaheim, CA, 92807

Tel: (714) 970-0300   Fax: (714) 693-2202   www.mti.com

Mfr. data storage systems software.

MTI France S.A., 7 Avenue des Pommerots, BP 25, F-78400 Chatou, France

Tel: 33-1-3009-5200   Fax: 33-1-3009-5222

MTS SYSTEMS CORPORATION

14000 Technology Drive, Eden Prairie, MN, 55344-2290

Tel: (612) 937-4000   Fax: (612) 937-4515   www.mts.com

Develop/mfr. mechanical testing and simulation products and services, industry measure and automation instrumentation.

MTS France, 58 rue Auguste Perret, F-94043 Creteil Cedex, France

MUELLER INDUSTRIES, INC.

8285 Tournament Drive, Ste. 150, Memphis, TN, 38125

Tel: (901) 753-3200   Fax: (901) 753-3255   www.muellerindustries.com

Mfr. plumbing and heating products, refrigeration and A/C components, copper and copper alloy and metal forgings and extrusions.

Mueller Europe S.A., Roissypole Le Dome, 5 Rue De La Haye, F-95733 Roissy CDG Cedex, France

MULTIGRAPHICS INC.

431 Lakeview Court, Mt. Prospect, IL, 60056

Tel: (847) 375-1700   Fax: (847) 375-1810   www.multigraphics.com

Mfr./sale/service printing and print prod equipment, mailroom/bindery systems, services and supplies for graphics industry.

Multi Graphics Intl. SA, BP 307, 60 rue Berthelot, F-92402 Courbevoie Cedex, France

MYKROLIS CORPORATION

1 Patriots Park, Bedford, MA, 01730

Tel: (781) 695-7654   Fax: (781) 695-7639   www.mykrolis.com

Mfr. filtering equipment for gases and liquids.

Mykrolis Corporation, Parc d'Activités de Centr'Alp, 196, rue du Rocher de Lorzier, F-38430 Moirans, France

NATIONAL INSTRUMENTS CORPORATION

11550 N. Mopac Expwy., Austin, TX, 78759-3504

Tel: (512) 338-9119   Fax: (512) 794-5794   www.ni.com

Mfr. hardware and graphical software.

National Instruments, Centre D'Affaires Paris-Nord, BP 217, F-93153 Le Blanc-Mesnil Cedex, France

NATIONAL MACHINERY COMPANY

161 Greenfield St., Tiffin, OH, 44883-2471

Tel: (419) 447-5211   Fax: (419) 447-5299   www.nationalmachinery.com

Mfr. high-speed metal parts forming machines.

National Machinery Company, Paris, France

Tel: 33-1-4378-4084

NATIONAL SERVICE INDUSTRIES INC.

1420 Peachtree Street NE, Atlanta, GA, 30309

Tel: (404) 853-1000   Fax: (404) 853-1211   www.nationalservice.com

Mfr. envelopes and engaged in linen rentals.

Zep Europe, Paris, France

NATIONAL STARCH AND CHEMICAL COMPANY

10 Finderne Ave., Bridgewater, NJ, 08807-3300

Tel: (908) 685-5000   Fax: (908) 685-5005   www.nationalstarch.com

Mfr. adhesives and sealants, resins and specialty chemicals, electronic materials and adhesives, food products, industry starch.

National Starch & Chemical SA, PB 438, 299 rue Grange Morin, F-69400 Villefranche-sur-Saône, France

Tel: 33-4-74-02-3800   Fax: 33-4-74-02-3900

NATIONAL-OILWELL, INC.

PO Box 4638, Houston, TX, 77210-4638

Tel: (713) 960-5100   Fax: (713) 960-5428   www.natoil.com

Design, manufacture and sale of comprehensive systems and components used in oil and gas drilling and production.

National-Oilwell, 66 rue Cantgrel, F-75013 Paris, France

Tel: 33-1-44-24-2080   Fax: 33-1-44-24-0013

NAVIGATION TECHNOLOGIES CORPORATION

The Merchandise Mart, Ste. 900, Chicago, IL, 60654

Tel: (312) 894-7000   Fax: (312) 894-7050   www.navtech.com

Mfr. navigation systems for automobiles.

Navigation Technologies, Immeuble le Clemencia, 196, rue Houdan, F-92330 Sceaux, Paris, France

NCH CORPORATION

2727 Chemsearch Blvd., Irving, TX, 75062

Tel: (972) 438-0211   Fax: (972) 438-0707   www.nch.com

Engaged in manufacturing and specialty chemicals.

National Chemsearch France, Zone Industrielle, F-77160 Provins, France

NCR (NATIONAL CASH REGISTER)

1700 South Patterson Blvd., Dayton, OH, 45479

Tel: (937) 445-5000   Fax: (937) 445-7042   www.ncr.com

Mfr. automated teller machines and high-performance stationary bar code scanners.

NCR Ltd., 1 Square John H. Patterson, F-91749 Massy Cedex, France

Tel: 33-1-69-533573   Fax: 33-1-69-533545   Contact: Patrick Goasguen

THE NDP GROUP, INC.

900 West Shore Road, Port Washington, NY, 11050

Tel: (516) 625-0700   Fax: (516) 625-2347   www.npd.com

Engaged in consumer buying research.

NDP Group, 10, avenue Ledru Rollin, F-75012 Paris, France

NETEGRITY, INC.

52 Second Avenue, Waltham, MA, 02154

Tel: (781) 890-1700　　　Fax: (781) 487-7791　　　www.netegrity.com

Mfr. security software.

Netegrity France, CNIT Service Affaires, 2 Place de la Defense, BP 240, F-92053 Paris La Defense, France

Tel: 33-1-4692-23-55

NETIQ CORPORATION

3553 North First Street, San Jose, CA, 95134

Tel: (408) 856-3000　　　Fax: (408) 273-0578　　　www.netiq.com

Mfr. performance management software.

NetIQ, 126, rue du Général Galliéni, F-92643 Boulogne-Billancourt, France

NETMANAGE, INC.

10725 N. De Anza Blvd., Cupertino, CA, 95014

Tel: (408) 973-7171　　　Fax: (408) 257-6405　　　www.netmanage.com

Develop and manufacture computer software applications and tools.

NetManage SARL, Le Raspail, 53 Rue Raspail, F-92300 Levallois Perret, France

Tel: 33-1-4140-7777　Fax: 33-1-4140-7788

NETWORK ASSOCIATES, INC.

3965 Freedom Circle, Santa Clara, CA, 95054

Tel: (408) 988-3832　　　Fax: (408) 970-9727　　　www.networkassociates.com

Designs and produces network security and network management software and hardware.

Network Associates, 50 rue de Londres, F-75008 Paris, France

Tel: 33-1-44-90-8737　Fax: 33-1-45-22-7601

NETWORK COMPUTING DEVICES, INC. (NCDI)

301 Ravendale Drive, Mountain View, CA, 94043

Tel: (650) 694-0650　　　Fax: (650) 961-7711　　　www.ncd.com

Provider of server- and web-based computing solutions

NCD France, 5 bis, rue de Petit-Robinson, F-78353 Jouy-en-Josas Cedex, France

NETWORK EQUIPMENT TECHNOLOGIES INC.

6500 Paseo Padre Pkwy., Freemont, CA, 94555

Tel: (510) 713-7300　　　Fax: (510) 574-4000　　　www.net.com

Mfr./service networking products to info-intensive organizations.

NET SA, Z.I. Paris Nord II Parc des Reflets, 165 ave. de Bois de la Pie, BP 40041, F-95912 Poissy, France

NEUTROGENA CORPORATION

5760 West 96th Street, Los Angeles, CA, 90045

Tel: (310) 642-1150　　　Fax: (310) 337-5564　　　www.neutrogena.com

Mfr. facial cleansing, moisturizing products; body care, sun and hair care specialty products.

Neutrogena France, 5 rue de Logelbach, F-75017 Paris, France

NEVILLE CHEMICAL COMPANY

2800 Neville Road, Pittsburgh, PA, 15225-1496

Tel: (412) 331-4200　　　Fax: (412) 777-4234　　　www.nevchem.com

Mfr. hydrocarbon resins.

Les Derives Resiniques & Terpeniques (DRT) (JV), Dax Landes, France

NEW BALANCE ATHLETIC SHOE, INC.

Brighton Landing, 20 Guest Street, Boston, MA, 02135-2088

Tel: (617) 783-4000　　　Fax: (617) 787-9355　　　www.newbalance.com

Mfr. men's and women's athletic shoes.

New Balance France, 3, allee Maryse Bastie, Orlytech, F-91781 Wissous, France

NEW BRUNSWICK SCIENTIFIC COMPANY, INC.

44 Talmadge Road, Box 4005, Edison, NJ, 08818-4005

Tel: (732) 287-1200   Fax: (732) 287-4222   www.nbsc.com

Mfr. research and production equipment for life sciences.

New Brunswick Scientific S.A.R.L., 15 Allées de Bellefontaine, F-31100 Toulouse, France

Tel: 33-1-61-40-264706   Fax: 33-1-61-40-265423   Contact: Gerry Burgers, Gen. Mgr.

NEW HAMPSHIRE BALL BEARINGS INC. (NHBB)

9700 Independence Ave., Chatsworth, CA, 91311-4323

Tel: (818) 407-9300   Fax: (818) 407-9300   www.nhbb.com

Mfr. bearings and bearing assemblies.

NHBB, Bureau de Liaison, France, Immeuble GEPIC, 12 Rue de la Guivernone, F-95310 St. Ouen L-Aumône, France

THE NEW YORK TIMES COMPANY

229 West 43rd Street, New York, NY, 10036-3959

Tel: (212) 556-1234   Fax: (212) 556-7389   www.nytimes.com

Diversified media company including newspapers, magazines, television and radio stations, and electronic information and publishing.

International Herald Tribune SA, 6 Bis Rue des Graviers, F-92521 Neuilly Cedex, France

Tel: 33-1-4143-9300   Contact: Peter C. Goldmark, Chmn. & CEO

NEWELL RUBBERMAID

29 East Stephenson Street, Freeport, IL, 61032-0943

Tel: (815) 235-4171   Fax: (815) 489-8212   www.newellco.com

Mfr. hardware, housewares, and office products.

Ateliers 28/Newell Rubbermaid, Tremblay Les Villages, France

Reynolds S. A (JV), Valence, France

NEWPORT CORPORATION

1791 Deere Ave., PO Box 19607, Irvine, CA, 92606

Tel: (949) 863-3144   Fax: (949) 253-1800   www.newport.com

Engaged in the design, manufacture and marketing of high-precision components, instruments and integrated systems to the fiber optic communications, semiconductor equipment and aerospace and research markets.

Newport Micro Controle, 11 rue du Bois Sauvage, F-91055 Evry Cedex, France

Tel: 33-1-60-91-6868   Fax: 33-1-60-91-6869   Contact: Alain Danielo, VP European Operations.

NEXTIRA ONE

2800 Post Oak Boulevard, Ste. 200, Houston, TX, 77056

Tel: (713) 307-4000   Fax: (713) 307-4000   www.nextiraone.com

Provider of voice, data and converged technology.

NextiraOne Paris, Paris, France

AC NIELSEN COMPANY

177 Broad Street, Stamford, CT, 06901

Tel: (203) 961-3000   Fax: (203) 961-3190   www.acnielsen.com

Engaged in market and consumer research.

ACNielsen, 44 Blvd. de Grenelle, F-75732 Paris Cedex 15, France

NIKU CORPORATION

305 Main Street, Redwood City, CA, 94063

Tel: (650) 298-4600   Fax: (650) 298-4601   www.niku.com

Mfr. software.

Niku Corporation S.A., 84-88, Boulevard de la Mission, Marchard, F-92411 Courbevoie Cedex, France

Tel: 33-1-49047000

NORDSON CORPORATION

28601 Clemens Road, Westlake, OH, 44145-4551

Tel: (440) 892-1580   Fax: (440) 892-9507   www.nordson.com

Mfr. industry application equipment, sealants and packaging machinery.

Nordson France SA, 2 rue Niels Borh-l'Esplanade, Saint Thibault des Vignes, F-77462 Lagny sur Marre Cedex, France

Tel: 33-1-64-12-1400 Fax: 33-1-64-121452

NORRISEAL CONTROLS

PO Box 40525, Houston, TX, 77240-0525

Tel: (713) 466-3552   Fax: (713) 896-7386   www.norriseal.com

Mfr. butterfly valves, fittings and plugs primarily for the oil and gas industries.

TDS International, SA, Immeuble "Le Nautile", 32 Avenue de I'll St. Martin, F-92737 Nanterre Cedex, France

Tel: 33-1-47826464 Fax: 33-1-47699503

NORTON ABRASIVES COMPANY

1 New Bond Street, Worcester, MA, 01606

Tel: (508) 795-5000   Fax: (508) 795-5741   www.nortonabrasives.com

Mfr. abrasives for industrial manufacturing.

Carbo Abrasifs, Zone Industrielle, 8 rue De La Taxe, BP 45, F-28111 Luce Cedex, France

Tel: 33-237-916413 Fax: 33-237-342855

Christensen Diamond Products Co., Place de la Gare, F-78320 St. Denis la Verriere, France

Norton Houard SA, 33 Route de Blois, F-37400 Amboise, France

Norton SA, 178 ave. Paul-Vaillant-Couturier, La Courneuve, France

Norton SA, rue de l'Ambassadeur, F-78702 Couflane Ste. Honorine, France

NOVELL WORLDWIDE

1800 S. Novell Place, Provo, UT, 84606

Tel: (801) 861-7000   Fax: (801) 861-5555   www.novell.com

Develop/mfr. networking software and related equipment.

Novell France, Tour Framatome, 1 Place de la Coupole, F-Cedex 16 Paris, France

NOVELLUS SYSTEMS INC.

4000 North First Street, San Jose, CA, 95134

Tel: (408) 943-9700   Fax: (408) 943-3422   www.novellus.com

Mfr. chemical vapor deposition (CVD), physical vapor deposition (PVD) and copper electrofill systems.

Novellus Systems SARL, Parc de la Julienne, Bat D, 1 er etage, F-91830 LeCoudray-Montceaux, France

Tel: 33-1-64-93-7070 Fax: 33-1-64-93-8787

Novellus Systems SARL, 1488 Corniche de St. Ferreol, F-83510 Lorgues, France

Tel: 33-4-946-76952 Fax: 33-4-946-76990

NTL INCORPORATED

110 East 59th Street, New York, NY, 10022

Tel: (212) 906-8440   Fax: (212) 752-1157   www.ntl.com

Provides cable TV and Internet services.

NTL, 7-9, rue de la Croix Martre, F-91127 Palaiseau, France

Tel: 33-1-6919-5100 Fax: 33-1-6919-5199   Contact: Bernard Touraine

NU SKIN ENTERPRISES, INC.

75 West Center St., Provo, UT, 84601

Tel: (801) 345-6100   Fax: (801) 345-5999   www.nuskin.com

Develops and distributes premium-quality personal care and nutritional products.

NuSkin France, 90 Ave. des Champs Elysees, F-75008 Paris, France

NVF (NATIONAL VULCANIZED FIBRE) COMPANY

1166 Yorklyn Road, PO Box 68, Yorklyn, DE, 19736

Tel: (302) 239-5281   Fax: (302) 239-4406   www.nvf.com

Mfr. metal containers, steel products, laminated plastics and papers.

NVF Europe, F-69540 Irigny, France

NVIDIA CORPORATION

2701 San Tomas Expressway, Santa Clara, CA, 95050

Tel: (408) 486-2000   Fax: (408) 486-2200   www.nvidia.com

Mfr. graphics chips for video gamers and graphics designers.

NVIDIA France, 24 Rue Jacques Ibert, F-92300 Levallois Perret, France

NYPRO INC.

101 Union Street, Clinton, MA, 01510

Tel: (978) 365-9721   Fax: (978) 368-0236   www.nypro.com

Mfr. plastic parts for telecommunications industry.

Nypro France, ZA Jean Monnet, F-28630 Fontenay sur Sure, France

OCLI, INC. (OPTICAL COATING LABORATORY, INC.)

2789 Northpoint Pkwy., Santa Rosa, CA, 95407-7397

Tel: (707) 545-6440   Fax: (707) 525-7410   www.ocli.com

Mfr. thin film precision coated optical devices.

OCLI Optical Coating Lab EURL, Centre Vie, Batiment Le Tropic, Villejust, F-91969 Courtaboeuf Cedex, France

Tel: 33-1-69-07-0761

OFFICE DEPOT, INC.

2200 Old Germantown Road, Delray Beach, FL, 33445

Tel: (561) 278-4800   Fax: (561) 265-4406   www.officedepot.com

Discount office product retailer with warehouse-style superstores.

Office Depot France, Z.I. Senia Nord, 7 rue Des Alouettes, F-94320 Thiais, France

Tel: 33-1-17-32-525   Fax: 33-1-17-32-2526

Office Depot France, 3 Chemin De La Croix Brisse, F-92160 Antony Z.A. Paris, France

Tel: 33-1-46-11-7000   Fax: 33-1-46-11-7011

THE O'GARA COMPANY

1250 24th Street, NW, Suite 300, Washington, DC, 20037

Tel: (202) 835-1680   Fax: (202) 835-1685   www.ogara.com

Security and consulting services and vehicles.

Kroll Associates, 153 rue de Courcelles, F-75017 Paris, France

Tel: 33-1-42-67-3500   Fax: 33-1-42-67-7100

Labbe, S.A., Z.I. rue d'Armor, BP 414, F-22404 Lamballe Cedex, France

Tel: 33-2-96-501280   Fax: 33-2-96-34-7265   Contact: Jean-Philippe Tible

OGILVY & MATHER WORLDWIDE

309 West 49th Street, New York, NY, 10017-7399

Tel: (212) 237-4000   Fax: (212) 237-5123   www.ogilvypr.com

Engaged in public relations and communications.

Ogilvy Public Relations Worldwide, 40 Avenue George V, F-75008 Paris, France

Tel: 33-1-5357 9200   Fax: 33-1-5357 9202   Contact: Nick May

OHAUS CORPORATION

PO Bpx 2033,19a Chapin Road, Pine Brook, NJ, 07058

Tel: (973) 377-9000   Fax: (973) 593-0359   www.ohaus.com

Mfr. balances and scales for laboratories, industry and education.

Ohaus SARL, 85 rue Joseph-Bertrand, BP 30, F-78220 Viroflay, France

Tel: 33-1-3924-0193

OIL STATES INDUSTRIES

7701 South Cooper Street, Arlington, TX, 76017

Tel: (817) 468-1400   Fax: (817) 468-6250   www.oilstates.com

Mfr. drilling and production machinery and supplies for oil and gas production.

Oil States Industries, Inc., Rep Office, 36 Bd des Oceans, F-13275 Marseille Cedex 9, France

Tel: 33-491-291-833

THE OILGEAR COMPANY

2300 S. 51st Street, Milwaukee, WI, 53219

Tel: (414) 327-1700   Fax: (414) 327-0532   www.oilgear.com

Mfr. hydraulic power transmission machinery.

Oilgear Towler SA, Marne-la-Valee,, ZI de Pariest, Alle des Freres Montgolfier, F-77183 Croissy-Beaubourg, France

OLIN CORPORATION

501 Merritt Seven, Norwalk, CT, 06856-4500

Tel: (203) 750-3000   Fax: (203) 750-3292   www.olin.com

Mfr. chemicals, metals, sporting ammunition and copper and copper alloy sheets.

Olin SA-Hunt/Winchester, ZAC Paris Nord 11, 209 ave. des Nations, BP 60019, F-95970 Charles de Galle Cedex, France

OM GROUP, INC. (OMG)

3500 Terminal Tower, Cleveland, OH, 44113-2203

Tel: (216) 781-0083   Fax: (216) 781-0902   www.omgi.com

Producer and marketer of metal-based specialty chemicals.

Vasset S.A., 59. chemin de Moisselles, F95460 Ezanville, France

OMNICOM GROUP INC.

437 Madison Ave., New York, NY, 10022

Tel: (212) 415-3600   Fax: (212) 415-3530   www.omnicomgroup.com

International network of advertising, marketing, direct mail, public relations and consulting services.

BDDP Worldwide, 162-164 rue de Billancourt, F-92100 Boulogne Paris, France

Tel: 33-1-49-09-7010   Fax: 33-1-49-09-7633   Contact: Jean-marie Dru   Emp: 2,139

Rapp Collins, 5, rue Bucarest, F-75391 Paris Cedex 08, France

OMNOVA SOLUTIONS INC.

175 Ghent Road, Fairlawn, OH, 44333

Tel: (330) 869-4200   Fax: (330) 869-4288   www.omnova.com

Mfr. wall coverings and decorative building products and specialty chemicals.

OMNOVA Decorative & Building Products, 146 Boulevard Voltaire, F-92600 Asnières, France

OMNOVA Solutions SA, 33 Quai de Dion Bouton, F-92814 Paris, France

ONDEO NALCO COMPANY

Ondeo Nalco Center, 1601 W. Diehl Road, Naperville, IL, 60563-1198

Tel: (630) 305-1000   Fax: (630) 305-2900   www.ondeo-nalco.com

Mfr. specialty chemicals for water and waste water treatment, oil products and refining, industry processes; water and energy management service.

ONDEO Nalco France SARL, BP 179, rue Lavoisier, Z.I. de Coignieres-Maurepas, F-78313 Maurepas Cedex, France

Tel: 33-1-34-82-1200   Fax: 33-1-30-62-6806

ONYX SOFTWARE CORPORATION

3180 139th Avenue SE, Ste. 500, Bellevue, WA, 98005

Tel: (425) 451-8060   Fax: (425) 451-8277   www.onyx.com

Mfr. customer relationship management software.

Onyx Software France, 2 rue Victor Griffuelhes, F-92772 Boulogne Cedex, France

Tel: 33-1-4694-7575

OPEN MARKET, INC.

1 Wayside Road, Burlington, MA, 01803

Tel: (781) 359-3000   Fax: (781) 359-8111   www.openmarket.com

Mfr. catalog management software.

Open Market France SARL, 120 avenue Charles de Gaulle, F-92200 Neuilly sur Seine, France

Tel: 33-14640-3895

OPENWAVE SYSTEMS INC.

1400 Seaport Blvd., Redwood City, CA, 94063

Tel: (650) 480-8000   Fax: (650) 480-8100   www.openwave.com

Mfr. software for wireless telephones.

Openwave Systems, 235 Avenue Le Jour Se Leve, F-92100 Boulogne, France

OPTIO SOFTWARE, INC.

3015 Windward Plaza, Alpharetta, GA, 30005

Tel: (770) 576-3500   Fax: (770) 576-3699   www.optiosoftware.com

Mfr. information delivery software.

Optio Software Europe, 20 Quarter, Rue Schnapper, F-78175 Saint Germain-en-Laye, France

Tel: 33-1-3921-5959

ORACLE CORPORATION

500 Oracle Parkway, Redwood Shores, CA, 94065

Tel: (650) 506-7000   Fax: (650) 506-7200   www.oracle.com

Develop/manufacture software.

Oracle France, 65 rue des Trois Fontanot, F-92732 Nanterre Cedex, France

ORIEL INSTRUMENTS CORPORATION

150 Long Beach Boulevard, Stratford, CT, 06615

Tel: (203) 377-8282   Fax: (203) 378-2457   www.oriel.com

Mfr. optical goods.

L.O.T.-Oriel SARL, 4, Allee des Garays, F-91120 Palaiseau, France

Tel: 33-1-6919-4949   Fax: 33-1-6919-4930

OSMONICS INC.

5951 Clearwater Drive, Minnetonka, MN, 55343-8995

Tel: (952) 933-2277   Fax: (952) 933-0141   www.osmonics.com

Mfr. equipment, controls and components for the filtration and water-treatment industries.

Osmonics, Le Mee Sur Seine Paris, France

OTIS ELEVATOR COMPANY

One Farm Springs Road, Farmington, CT, 06032

Tel: (860) 676-6000   Fax: (860) 676-5111   www.otis.com

Mfr. elevators and escalators.

Otis Elevator Intl. Inc., 4 Place de La Defense, F-92974 Paris la Defense, France

OWENS-CORNING CORPORATION

One Owens Corning Pkwy., Toledo, OH, 43659

Tel: (419) 248-8000   Fax: (419) 248-8445   www.owenscorning.com

Mfr. building materials systems and composites systems.

Owens Corning France, 68 Clos du Prieure Rozereuilles, F-57160 Moulins les Metz, France

Owens-Corning France SA, 21 rue des Pervenches, F-31830 Plaisance du Touch, France

Tel: 33-5-6186-9839

Owens-Corning Isolation, 14 rue Ravelin, F-10001 Troyes Cedex, France

Tel: 33-3-2574-0303

PACCAR INC.

777 106th Ave. NE, Bellevue, WA, 98004

Tel: (425) 468-7400   Fax: (425) 468-8216   www.pacar.com

Heavy duty dump trucks, military vehicles.

PACCAR International, Les jardins de Farues, BP 140, F-84130 LePontet, France

Tel: 33-4-90-32-0621

PACIFIC SCIENTIFIC COMPANY

4301 Kishwaukee Street, PO Box 106, Rockford, IL, 61105-0106

Tel: (815) 226-3100   Fax: (815) 226-3148   www.pacsci.com

Mfr. high performance motors and drives.

Pacific Scientific SARL, 2 Allee des Garays, F-91124 Palaiseau, France

PALL CORPORATION

2200 Northern Boulevard, East Hills, NY, 11548-1289

Tel: (516) 484-5400   Fax: (516) 484-5228   www.pall.com

Specialty materials and engineering; filters and related fluid clarification equipment.

Pall Filtration Industrielle, Div. De Pall France, 3 rue des Gaudines, BP 5252, F-78175 St. Germain en Laye Cedex, France

Tel: 33-1-30-61-3953   Fax: 33-1-30-61-3898

Pall Gelman Sciences, Cite Descartes, 10 allee Lorentz, F-77420 Champs sur Marne, France

Tel: 33-1-6461-5252   Fax: 33-1-6461-5262

PALM, INC.

5470 Great American Pkwy., Santa Clara, CA, 95054

Tel: (408) 878-9000   Fax: (408) 878-2750   www.palm.com

Mfr. handheld computers, Palm Pilot.

Palm France SAS, 7 avenue Georges Pompidou, F-92593 Levallois-Perret Cedex, France

PANAMETRICS

221 Crescent Street, Waltham, MA, 02154

Tel: (781) 899-2719   Fax: (781) 899-1552   www.panametrics.com

Engaged in manufacture and distribution of ultrasonic testing equipment and process control instrumentation.

Panametrics, S.A., 11 rue du Renard, F-92250 La Garenne Colombes, France

Tel: 33-1-47-82-4281   Fax: 33-1-47-86-7490   Contact: Alan Chapas

Sofranel, 59 rue Parmentier, F-78500 Sartrouville, France

Tel: 33-1-39-13-8236   Fax: 33-1-39-13-1942

PANDUIT CORPORATION

17301 Ridgeland Ave., Tinley Park, IL, 60477-0981

Tel: (708) 532-1800   Fax: (708) 532-1811   www.panduit.com

Mfr. of network connectivity and electrical products.

Panduit SNC, 165 Avenue Jean Jaures, F-BP6 94701 Maisons-Alfort Cedex, France

PARADYNE NETWORKS, INC.

8545 126 Ave. North, Largo, FL, 33773

Tel: (727) 530-2000   Fax: (727) 530-2875   www.paradyne.com

Engaged in data communications and high-speed network access solutions.

Paradyne France, Paris, France

Tel: 33-4-9238-4801   Contact: Fouad Guendouz

PARAMETRIC TECHNOLOGY CORPORATION

140 Kendrick St., Needham, MA, 02494

Tel: (781) 370-5000   Fax: (781) 370-6000   www.ptc.com

Supplier of mechanical design automation and product data management software and services.

Parametric Technology S.A., Parc d'Activities de Limonest, 283 rue de l'Etang, F-69760 Linoest, France

Tel: 33-4-78-66-41-80   Fax: 33-4-78-35-94-11

Parametric Technology S.A., Technorparc Du Griffon, 511 Route de la Seds, F-13746 Vitolles Cedex, France
Tel: 33-4-42-40-5380   Fax: 33-4-42-10-5399

Parametric Technology S.A., Centre Atria, Ave. De L'Esperance, F-90000 Belfort, France
Tel: 33-3-88-56-93-50   Fax: 33-3-88-56-93-43

Parametric Technology S.A., Parc Curospace, Baitement 19, F-91573 Bievrex Cedex, France
Tel: 33-1-69-33-65-00   Fax: 33-1-69-33-65-65

Parametric Technology S.A., 1 rue Charles Lindbergh, F-44340 Nantes Bouguenais, France
Tel: 33-2-40-32-25-07   Fax: 32-2-40-04-10-80

Parametric Technology S.A., Novapole 18, rue de la Tullerie, F-38170 Seyssinet, France
Tel: 33-4-76-70-30-70   Fax: 33-4-76-70-30-96

Parametric Technology S.A., Place Francois Mitterrand 01, Tour Credit Lyonnais, F-59777 Eura Lille, France
Tel: 33-3-20-12-52-88   Fax: 33-3-20-12-52-87

Parametric Technology S.A., Technopole Metz 2000 Cescom, 4 rue Marconi, F-57070 Metz Cedex, France
Tel: 33-3-87-20-41-47   Fax: 33-3-87-20-41-48

Parametric Technology S.A., 1 Rond-Point Des Bruyeres N1, F-76300 Sottesville-Les-Rouen, France
Tel: 33-2-32-81-97-00   Fax: 32-2-32-81-97-01

Parametric Technology S.A., 13 rue des Granges Galand, BP 414, F-37554 Saint Avertin Cedex, France
Tel: 33-2-47-80-31-35   Fax: 33-2-47-27-89-64

Parametric Technology S.A., Parc Innolin, 3 rue du Golfe, F-33700 Merignac, France
Tel: 33-5-56-34-75-00   Fax: 33-5-56-34-74-12

Parametric Technology S.A., Aeropole 1, 5 Ave. Albert Durand, F-37160 Blagnac, France
Tel: 33-5-61-31-62-61   Fax: 33-5-61-71-35-00

Parametric Technology S.A., Parc Tertiaire Valparc, F-67205 Oberhausbergen, France
Tel: 33-3-90-20-50-50   Fax: 33-3-88-56-32-44

PAREXEL INTERNATIONAL CORPORATION

195 West Street, Waltham, MA, 02154
Tel: (781) 487-9900   Fax: (781) 487-0525   www.parexel.com
Provides contract medical, biotechnology, and pharmaceutical research and consulting services.

PAREXEL International, 124/126 rue de Provence, F-75008 Paris, France
Tel: 33-1-44-90-3200   Fax: 33-1-44-90-3232

PARK ELECTROCHEMICAL CORPORATION

5 Dakota Drive, Lake Success, NY, 11042
Tel: (516) 354-4100   Fax: (516) 354-4128   www.parkelectrochemical.com
Multi-layer laminate printed circuit materials, industry comps, plumbing hardware products.

Nelco SA, 72 Grande Rue, F-21310 Mirebeau-Sur-Beze, France

Neltec SA, Route des Usines, BP 25, Lannemezan, France
Tel: 33-562-985290

PARKER HANNIFIN CORPORATION

6035 Parkland Blvd., Cleveland, OH, 44124-4141
Tel: (216) 896-3000   Fax: (216) 896-4000   www.parker.com
Mfr. motion-control products.

Parker Hannifin Corp., Motion & Control/Parker Hannifin RAK, SA Centre Paris Pleyel, Tour Wuest, 153 Blvd. Anatole France, F-93521 St. Denis Cedex, France

Parker Hannifin Corp./Parker Hannifin RAK SA, Z.A.E. La Foret, F-74138 Contamine-sur-Arve, France

Parker Hannifin Corp./Parker Hannifin RAK SA, 8 rue Pierre Dechanet, BP 229, F-25303 Pontarlier Cedex, France

Parker Hannifin RAK SA, 17, rue des Buchillons, ZI du Mont-Blanc, BP 524, Ville-La-Grand, F-74112 Annemasse, France

Parker Hennifin Corp., Telemecanique, rue Henri Becquerel, BP 3124, F-27031 Evreux Cedex, France

PARTECH INTERNATIONAL

50 California Street, Ste. 3200, San Francisco, CA, 94111-4624

Tel: (415) 788-2929   Fax: (415) 788-6763   www.partechintl.com

Invests in startup and growth companies in information technology, communications and healthcare.

Partech International, 42 Avenue Raymond Poincaré, F-75116 Paris, France

Tel: 33-1-5365-6553   Contact: Philippe Herbert

PAUL, WEISS, RIFKIND, WHARTON & GARRISON

1285 Ave. of the Americas, New York, NY, 10019-6064

Tel: (212) 373-3000   Fax: (212) 373-2268   www.paulweiss.com

Law firm engaged in American and international law practice.

Paul, Weiss, Rifkind, Wharton & Garrison, 62 rue du Faubourg Saint-Honore, F-75008 Paris, France

Tel: 33-1-53-43-1414   Fax: 33-1-53-43-0023

THE PEELLE COMPANY

34 Central Ave., Hauppauge, NY, 11788-4734

Tel: (631) 231-6000   Fax: (631) 231-6059   www.peelledoor.com

Mfr., sales, service vertical sliding Freight Elevator Doors and related equipment.

Ascenseurs Fermetures, Rep. Peelle Company, 7 rue de la Croix Blanche, F-78618 Saint Leger en Yvelines, France

PEGASYSTEMS INC.

101 Main Street, Cambridge, MA, 02142-1590

Tel: (617) 374-9600   Fax: (617) 374-9620   www.pegasystems.com

Mfr. customer service software.

Pegasystems France, 72, rue du Faubourg Saint-Honoré, F-75008 Paris, France

PENTAIR, INC.

1500 County Road, B2 West, St. Paul, MN, 55113-3105

Tel: (612) 636-7920   Fax: (612) 636-5508   www.pentair.com

Diversified manufacturer operating in electrical and electronic enclosures, professional tools/equipment and water products.

Pentair Water Treatment Plant, B.P. 213 140 av. Roland Garros D Z.I., F-78532 Buc CEX, France

Tel: 33-1-39-24-1500   Fax: 33-1-39-56-0390

PEOPLESOFT INC.

4460 Hacienda Drive, Pleasanton, CA, 94588-8618

Tel: (925) 225-3000   Fax: (925) 694-4444   www.peoplesoft.com

Mfr. applications to manage business operations across computer networks.

PeopleSoft France, S.A., 153 rue de Courcelles, F-75017 Paris Cedex, France

Tel: 33-1-4429-5000   Fax: 33-1-4429-5001

PEPSiCO INC.

700 Anderson Hill Road, Purchase, NY, 10577-1444

Tel: (914) 253-2000   Fax: (914) 253-2070   www.pepsico.com

Beverages and snack foods.

PepsiCo de France SARL, Paris, France

PEREGRINE SYSTEMS, INC.

3611 Valley Centre Drive, San Diego, CA, 92130

Tel: (858) 481-5000   Fax: (858) 481-1751   www.peregrine.com

Mfr. resource planning software.

Peregrine Systems S.A., Tour Franklin, La Défense 8, F-92042 Paris, France

PEROT SYSTEMS CORPORATION

12404 Park Central Drive, Dallas, TX, 75251

Tel: (972) 340-5000   Fax: (972) 455-4100   www.perotsystems.com

Provides technology and business solutions.

Perot Systems HPS, 13 boulevard Haussmann, F-75009 Paris, France

PFIZER INC.

235 East 42nd Street, New York, NY, 10017-5755

Tel: (212) 573-2323   Fax: (212) 573-7851   www.pfizer.com

Research-based, global health care company.

CAL Pfizer, Paris, France

Climo SA, Paris, France

Laboratoire Beral SA, Paris, France

Orsim SA, Paris, France

Pfizer Diagnostic Products SARL, Paris, France

Pfizer SA, Paris, France

SA Benoist Girard & Cie., Paris, France

PRODUCTION GROUP INTERNATIONAL, INC.

2200 Wilson Blvd., Ste 200, Arlington, VA, 22201-3324

Tel: (703) 528-8484   Fax: (703) 528-1724   www.pgi.com

Provides major corporations with promotional events, planning and travel services, trade shows and exhibitions.

PGI/Spearhead, 18 rue Germain Pilon, F-75018 Paris Cedex, France

Tel: 33-1-4258-04 01

PHARMACIA CORPORATION

100 Route 206 North, Peapack, NJ, 07977

Tel: (908) 901-8000   Fax: (908) 901-8379   www.pharmacia.com

Mfr. pharmaceuticals, agricultural products, industry chemicals.

Pharmacia & Upjohn, BP 210, F-78051 St. Quentin Yvelines Cedex, France

Tel: 33-1-3064-3400   Fax: 33-1-3043-4445

PHH ARVAL VEHICLE MANAGEMENT

307 International Circle, Hunt Valley, MD, 21030

Tel: (410) 771-3600   Fax: (410) 771-2841   www.phh.com

Provides fleet leasing and fleet management services to corporate and government clients with sales, service, delivery, executive or specialized trucks fleets.

Arval Service Lease, 119-121 Grande rue, F-92318 Serves Paris Cedex, France

Tel: 33-1-41-14-1818

PHILIPP BROTHERS CHEMICALS INC.

1 Parker Plaza, 400 Kelby Street, Fort Lee, NJ, 07029

Tel: (201) 944-6020   Fax: (201) 944-7916   www.philipp-brothers.com

Mfr. industry and agricultural chemicals.

Phibrotec SA, 33 rue de la Baume, F-75008 Paris, France

PHILLIPS PETROLEUM COMPANY

Phillips Building, 411 S. Keeler Ave., Bartlesville, OK, 74004

Tel: (918) 661-6600   Fax: (918) 661-7636   www.phillips66.com

Crude oil, natural gas, liquefied petroleum gas, gasoline and petro-chemicals.

Phillips Petroleum International France, 37 ave. d'Lena, F-75116 Paris, France

PHILLIPS, DE PURY & LUXEMBOURG

3 West 57th Street, New York, NY, 10019

Tel: (212) 940-1200   Fax: (212) 688-1647   www.phillips-auctions.com

Auction house.

Phillips De Pury & Luxembourg, 72 Rue du Faubourg Saint-Honoré, Accès 9-11 Rue Montalivet, F-75008 Paris, France

PIC GROUP

2929 Seventh Avenue, Ste. 130, Berkeley, CA, 94710

Tel: (510) 848-8266   Fax: (510) 848-0324   www.pic.com

Engaged in biotechnology.

PIC France, Zoopole BP 48, F-22440 Ploufragan, France

Tel: 33-2-96-765050

PINNACLE SYSTEMS

280 North Bernardo Ave., Mountain View, CA, 94043

Tel: (650) 526-1600   Fax: (650) 526-1601   www.pinnaclesys.com

Designs, manufactures, markets and supports a wide range of high-quality digital solutions that enable businesses and consumers to create, store, distribute and view video programs.

Pinnacle Systems SARL, 99 Rue Pierre Sémard, F-92324 Chatillon, France

PINNACLE WORLDWIDE, INC.

1201 Marquette Ave., Ste. 300, Minneapolis, MN, 55403

Tel: (612) 338-2215   Fax: (612) 338-2572   www.pinnacleww.com

International network of independent public relations firms.

Self Images Relationes Publiques, 88 Avenue Kléber, F-75116 Paris, France

PIONEER HI-BRED INTERNATIONAL INC.

400 Locust Street, Ste. 800, Des Moines, IA, 50309

Tel: (515) 248-4800   Fax: (515) 248-4999   www.pioneer.com

Agricultural chemicals, farm supplies, biological products, research.

Pioneer France Mais SA, Aussonne Chemin de L'Enseigure, F-31840 Aussonne, France

PIONEER-STANDARD ELECTRONICS, INC.

6065 Parkland Blvd., Cleveland, OH, 44124

Tel: (440) 720-8500   Fax: (440) 720-8501   www.pios.com

Mfr. and distribution of electronic parts for computers and networking equipment.

Eurodis Electronics France, 30 Ave de L'Epi D'Or, F-94807 Villejuif Cedex, France

PITNEY BOWES INC.

1 Elmcroft Road, Stamford, CT, 06926-0700

Tel: (203) 356-5000   Fax: (203) 351-6835   www.pitneybowes.com

Mfr. postage meters, mailroom equipment, copiers, bus supplies, bus services, facsimile systems and financial services.

Pitney Bowes Finance S.A., Espace Clichy Batiment Andromede, 82 rue de Villeneuve, F-92587 Clichy Cedex Paris, France

Tel: 33-143-94-9925

PLANAR SYSTEMS, INC.

1400 NW Compton Drive, Beaverton, OR, 97006

Tel: (503) 690-1100   Fax: (503) 690-1541   www.planar.com

Mfr. of flat panel displays and liquid crystal displays.

Planar Systems SARL, 68, rue du Faubourg St-Honore, F-75008 Paris, France

Tel: 33-1-53-43-62-53   Contact: Thierry Farobbia

PLANET HOLLYWOOD INTERNATIONAL, INC.

8669 Commodity Circle, Orlando, FL, 32819

Tel: (407) 363-7827   Fax: (407) 363-4862   www.planethollywood.com

Theme-dining restaurant chain and merchandise retail stores.

Planet Hollywood International, Inc., Paris, France

PLANTRONICS

345 Encinal Street, Santa Cruz, CA, 95060

Tel: (831) 426-5858   Fax: (831) 425-5198   www.plantronics.com

Mfr. lightweight headsets and communications equipment and electrical and electronic appliances.

Plantronics France, 424 La Closerie Mont d'Est, F-93193 Noisy-le-Grand, France

Tel: 33-1-46-49-8300   Fax: 33-1-46-49-8309   Contact: William Amoyal, Sales Mgr.

PLATINUM EQUITY HOLDINGS

2049 Century Park East, Ste. 2700, Los Angeles, CA, 90067

Tel: (310) 712-1850   Fax: (310) 712-1848   www.peh.com

Engaged in the acquisition and strategic management of technology companies.

Alcatel Distribution Services Division, 54 rue La Boétie, F-75008 Paris Cedex 8, France

PLAYTEX APPAREL INC.

3330 Healy Drive, Winston Salem, NC, 27106

Tel: (336) 519-8688   Fax: (336) 519-6053   www.playtexbras.com

Mfr. intimate apparel.

Playtex France, BP 255, F-38356 La Tour du Pin, France

Contact: Lionel Maille

PLUMTREE SOFTWARE, INC.

500 Sansome Street, San Francisco, CA, 94111

Tel: (415) 263-8900   Fax: (415) 263-8991   www.plumtree.com

Mfr. organizational software.

Plumtree Software EURL, 12, Avenue de l'Arche, F-92419 Courbevoie, France

PNY TECHNOLOGIES, INC.

299 Webro Road, Parsippany, NJ, 07054

Tel: (973) 515-9700   Fax: (973) 560-5281   www.pny.com

Mfr. computer memory chips.

PNY Technologies, Inc., Zac du Phare, Rue Joseph Cugnot, BP-181, F-33708 Merignac Cedex, France

POLARIS INDUSTRIES INC.

2100 Highway 55, Medina, MN, 55440

Tel: (612) 542-0500   Fax: (612) 542-0599   www.polarisindustries.com

Mfr. snowmobiles and all-terrain recreational and utility vehicles.

Wintersnow, 2770 Avenue De Saint-Martin, F-74190 Passy, France

Tel: 33-4-5093-9614

POLAROID CORPORATION

784 Memorial Drive, Cambridge, MA, 02139

Tel: (781) 386-2000   Fax: (781) 386-3924   www.polaroid.com

Photographic equipment and supplies, optical products.

Polaroid (France) S.A., 41 Av des trois Peuples, Business Park Bat C, F-78180 Montigny le Bretonneux, France

POLYCOM, INC.

1565 Barber Lane, Milpitas, CA, 95035

Tel: (408) 526-9000   Fax: (408) 526-9100   www.polycom.com

Mfr. video conferencing systems, network bridging and multiplexing products, system peripherals.

Polycom, Inc., 38 rue de Villiers, F-92532 Levallois Perret Cedex, France

Tel: 33-1-41-49-5969   Fax: 33-1-41-49-5968

POLYONE CORPORATION

200 Public Square, Cleveland, OH, 44114-2304

Tel: (216) 589-4000   Fax: (216) 589-4077   www.polyone.com

Mfr. custom made compounded plastics, including polymer, elastomer, colorant and additive products.

PolyOne France SAS, R.N. 75, Tossiat, France

Tel: 33-4-74426970

PORTAL SOFTWARE, INC.

10200 S. De Anza Bolevard, Cupertino, CA, 95014

Tel: (408) 572-2000   Fax: (408) 572-2001   www.portal.com

Mfr. customer management and billing software.

Portal Software France, 54-56 Avenue Hoche, France

Tel: 33-1-5660-5110   Fax: 33-1-5660-5640

POTTERS INDUSTRIES INC.

PO Box 840, Valley Forge, PA, 19482-0840

Tel: (610) 651-4700   Fax: (610) 408-9724   www.pottersbeads.com

Mfr. glass spheres for road marking and industry applications.

Potters-Ballotini SA, Z.I. DuPont-Panay, 4 rue des Champs Elysees, F-03500 Saint-Pourcain-sur-Sioule, France

POWERQUEST CORPORATION

1359 North Research Way, Bldg. K, Box 1911, Orem, UT, 84059

Tel: (801) 437-8900   Fax: (801) 226-8941   www.powerquest.com

Provides storage lifecycle automation solutions.

PowerQuest France, Paris, France

Contact: Eric Heddeland

POWERWARE CORPORATION

8609 Six Forks Road, Raleigh, NC, 27615

Tel: (919) 870-3020   Fax: (919) 870-3100   www.powerware.com

Mfr./services uninterruptible power supplies and related equipment.

Powerware Electronics SA, Zac des Delâches, BP 77 - Gometz le Châtel, F-91940 Les Ulis, France

PPG INDUSTRIES

One PPG Place, Pittsburgh, PA, 15272

Tel: (412) 434-3131   Fax: (412) 434-2190   www.ppg.com

Mfr. coatings, flat glass, fiber glass, chemicals.

PPG Industries (France) SA, Immeuble SCOR, 1 ave. du President Wilson, F-92074 Paris La Defense Cedex, France

Sipsy Chimie Fine S.C.A., Route de Beaucouze, F-49240 Avrille, France

PR NEWSWIRE ASSOCIATION INC.

810 Seventh Avenue, 35th Fl., New York, NY, 10019

Tel: (212) 596-1500   Fax: (212) 541-6114   www.prnewswire.com

Distribution of news releases and photos to media organizations.

PR Newswire France, 39, rue Etienne Marcel, F-75001 Paris, France

PRAXAIR, INC.

39 Old Ridgebury Road, Danbury, CT, 06810-5113

Tel: (203) 837-2000   Fax: (203) 837-2450   www.praxair.com

Produces and distributes industrial and specialty gases.

Praxair S.A., 1-7 rue Traversiere, Silic 402, F-94573 Rungis Cedex, France

Tel: 33-1-49-78-4500   Fax: 33-1-46-75-9461

PRECISION CASTPARTS CORPORATION

4650 SW Macadam Ave., Ste. 440, Portland, OR, 97206

Tel: (503) 417-4800   Fax: (503) 417-4817   www.precast.com

Mfr. metal castings.

Precision Castparts Corp. France SA, F-64680 Ogeu Bains, France

PRECISION VALVE & TRIM, INC.

11923 Cloverland Ave, Baton Rouge, LA, 70809

Tel: (225) 752-5600   Fax: (225) 752-5400   www.precisionvalve.com

Mfr. aerosol valves.

Valve Precision SARL, 3 rue de la Croix Martre, BP 38, F-91120 Palaiseau, France

PRICEWATERHOUSECOOPERS LLP

1301 Ave. of the Americas, New York, NY, 10019

Tel: (212) 596-7000   Fax: (212) 259-1301   www.pwcglobal.com

Accounting and auditing, tax and management, and human resource consulting services.

PriceWaterhouseCoopers, 1 rue Daumier, F-13008 Marseille, France

Tel: 33-91-37-2736   Fax: 33-91-81-2-55

PriceWaterhouseCoopers, 1 Place Alfonse Jourdain, F-31000 Toulouse, France

Tel: 33-61-21-1871   Fax: 33-61-21-03-60

PriceWaterhouseCoopers, Le Sebastopol, 3 Quai Kleber, F-67055 Strausbourg Cedex, France

Tel: 33-88-22-2200   Fax: 33-88-75-6401

PriceWaterhouseCoopers, Parc de la Vatine, 20 rue Aron, F-76130 Mont Saint Aignan, France

Tel: 33-35-59-00-85   Fax: 33-35-59-9596

PriceWaterhouseCoopers, Parvis Sud de la Gare, 19 rue de Chatillon, F-35000 Rennes, France
Tel: 33-99-32-2100   Fax: 33-99-32-2032

PriceWaterhouseCoopers, 99 rue Nationale, F-59800 Lille, France
Tel: 33-20-12-5645   Fax: 33-20-12-5642

PriceWaterhouseCoopers, 1 rue de la Republique, F-69001 Lyon, France
Tel: 33-78-27-5060   Fax: 33-7-78-27-5029

PriceWaterhouseCoopers, Tour AIG, 34 place des Corolles, F-92908 Paris La Defense 2 Cedex 105, France
Tel: 33-1-41-26-1000   Fax: 33-1-41-26-4222

PriceWaterhouseCoopers, 1 allee Baco, BP 471, F-44015 Nantes Cedex, France
Tel: 33-40-89-7373   Fax: 33-40-48-4544

PRIDE INTERNATIONAL, INC.

5847 San Felipe, Ste. 3300, Houston, TX, 77057
Tel: (713) 789-1400   Fax: (713) 789-1430   www.prde.com
Provides drilling services.

Pride Forasol-Foramer, 16 bis, rue Grange Dame Rose, BP 100, F-78143 Velizy-Villacoublay Cedex, France

PRIMUS KNOWLEDGE SOLUTIONS, INC.

1601 Fifth Avenue, Ste. 1900, Seattle, WA, 98101
Tel: (206) 834-8100   Fax: (206) 834-8125   www.primus.com
Mfr. management software.

Primus Knowledge Solutions France, 17, Square Edouard VII, F-75009 Paris, France

PRINTRONIX INC.

14600 Myford Road, Irvine, CA, 92606
Tel: (714) 368-2300   Fax: (714) 368-2600   www.printronix.com
Mfr. computer printers.

Printronix France, 8 rue Parmentier, F-92800 Puteaux, France
Tel: 33-1-46-25-1900   Fax: 33-1-46-25-1919

PROCTER & GAMBLE COMPANY

One Procter & Gamble Plaza, Cincinnati, OH, 45202
Tel: (513) 983-1100   Fax: (513) 562-4500   www.pg.com
Personal care, food, laundry, cleaning and industry products.

Procter & Gamble France, 96 ave. Charles de Gaulle, F-92201 Neuilly sur Seine, France
Tel: 33-1-40-88-5923

PROCTER & GAMBLE PHARMACEUTICALS (P&GP)

17 Eaton Ave., Norwich, NY, 13815-1799
Tel: (607) 335-2111   Fax: (607) 335-2798   www.pg.com
Engaged in research dedicated to creating and delivering solutions that improve the health and well-being of people around the world.

Procter & Gamble Pharmaceuticals France, 96, avenue Charles de Gaulle, F-92201 Neuilly Sur Seine Cedex, France

PROSKAUER ROSE LLP

1585 Broadway, New York, NY, 10036
Tel: (212) 969-3000   Fax: (212) 969-2900   www.proskauer.com
Engaged in international law.

Dubarry Le Douarin & Veil, 9 rue Le Tasse, Trocadero Paris, France
Proskauer Rose LLP, 9 rue Le Tasse, Trocadero Paris, France
Contact: William Krisel

PRUDENTIAL FINANCIAL

751 Broad Street, Newark, NJ, 07102-3777
Tel: (973) 802-6000   Fax: (973) 802-2804   www.prudential.com
Sale of life insurance, financial services, asset management and brokerage.

Prudential-Bache International Limited, 9 Avenue Matignon, 2nd Floor, F-75008 Paris, France
Tel: 33-1-53-89-2929   Fax: 33-1-53-89-2900   Contact: Eric Bertier

PSC INC.

111 SW Fifth Avenue, Ste. 4100, Portland, OR, 97204-3644

Tel: (503) 553-3920   Fax: (503) 553-3940   www.pscnet.com

Mfr. and sales of bar code scanners.

PSC France, 12 avenue des Tropiques, Immeuble Avenue, Z.A. de Courtaboeuf - B.P. 1, F-91941 Les Ulis Cedex, France

PSI NET (PERFORMANCE SYSTEMS INTERNATIONAL INC.)

44983 Knoll Square, Ashburn, VA, 20147

Tel: (703) 726-4100   Fax: (703) 726-4200   www.psinet.com

Internet service provider.

PSINet France S.A.R.L., 8/10 rue Nieuport, F-78140 Vélizy, France

Tel: 33-1-346-319-19   Fax: 33-1-346-319-48   Contact: Moos Bulder, Reg. VP

PULSE ENGINEERING INC.

12220 World Trade Drive, PO 12235, San Diego, CA, 92112

Tel: (858) 674-8100   Fax: (858) 674-8262   www.pulseeng.com

Mfr. passive magnetic components and modules for use in Internet/broadband access, power, telecommunications and datacom applications.

Pulse France, Zone Industrielle, F-39270 Orgelet, France

QAD INC.

6450 Via Real, Carpinteria, CA, 93013

Tel: (805) 684-6614   Fax: (805) 566-4479   www.qad.com

Mfr. software.

QAD France, Immeuble Activille, 4 rue de Charenton, F-94140 Alfortville, France

QRS CORPORATION

1400 Marina Way South, Richmond, CA, 94804

Tel: (510) 215-5000   Fax: (510) 215-3980   www.qrs.com

Provides business-to-business electronic data systems and services.

QRS Paris, 10, Place Vendome, F-75001 Paris, France

QUAKER CHEMICAL CORPORATION

1 Quaker Park, 901 Hector St., Conshohocken, PA, 19428-0809

Tel: (610) 832-4000   Fax: (610) 832-8682   www.quakerchem.com

Mfr. developer, producer, and marketer of custom-formulated chemical specialty products.

Quaker Chemical S.A, 21 ave. Nobel, F-92396 Villeneuve la Garenne Cedex, France

Tel: 33-1-40.85.71.71   Contact: P. Peignoux

THE QUAKER OATS COMPANY

Quaker Tower, 321 North Clark Street, Chicago, IL, 60610-4714

Tel: (312) 222-7111   Fax: (312) 222-8323   www.quakeroats.com

Mfr. foods and beverages.

Quaker Oats France, 40 Blvd. de Dunkerque, F-13002 Marseille, France

QUALCOMM INC.

5775 Morehouse Dr., San Diego, CA, 92121-1714

Tel: (858) 587-1121   Fax: (858) 658-2100   www.qualcomm.com

Digital wireless telecommunications systems.

QUALCOMM, 2000 Route des Lucioles, 3/F, Sophia Antipolis, F-06560 Valbonne, France

QUARK, INC.

1800 Grant Street, Denver, CO, 80203

Tel: (303) 894-8888   Fax: (303) 894-3398   www.quark.com

Mfr. and sales of desktop publishing software.

Quark France, 32, rue Guy Moquet, F-92240 Malakoff, France

QUICK EAGLE NETWORKS INC.

217 Humboldt Court, Sunnyvale, CA, 94089

Tel: (408) 745-6200   Fax: (408) 745-6250   www.quickeagle.com

Mfr. digital multiplexers and network management software.

Quick Eagle Networks, 5, Place de la Pyramide, La Defence 9, Tour Ariane 33e etage, F-92088 Paris La Defense Cedex, France

Contact: Frederic Desnoes

QUIKSILVER, INC.

15202 Graham Sreet, Huntington Beach, CA, 92649

Tel: (714) 889-2200   Fax: (714) 889-2315   www.quiksilver.com

Mfr. sportswear and activewear.

Quiksilver Europe, Z. I. De Jalday, F-64500 St. Jean De Luz, France

QUINTILES TRANSNATIONAL CORPORATION

4709 Creekstone Dr., Durham, NC, 27703

Tel: (919) 998-2000   Fax: (919) 998-9113   www.quintiles.com

Mfr. pharmaceuticals.

Benefit International SNC, 3-5 rue Maurice Ravel Levallois-Perret, F-92594 Cedex, France

Innovex SARL, 1416 rue de la Vanne, F-92120 Montrouge, France

Quintiles S.A., 3-5 rue Maurice Ravel Levallois-Perret, F-92594 Cedex, France

QWEST COMMUNICATIONS INTERNATIONAL INC.

1801 California Street, Ste. 5200, Denver, CO, 80202

Tel: (303) 896-2020   Fax: (303) 793-6654   www.uswest.com

Tele-communications provider; integrated communications services.

KPNQwest (JV), Paris, France

RADIO SHACK CORPORATION

100 Throckmorton Street, Fort Worth, TX, 76102

Tel: (817) 390-3700   Fax: (817) 415-2647   www.tandy.com

Mfr. electronic and acoustic equipment; Radio Shack retail stores.

InterTAN, Inc., BP 147, Cergy Pointoise Cedex, France

RADISSON HOTELS INTERNATIONAL

Carlson Pkwy., PO Box 59159, Minneapolis, MN, 55459-8204

Tel: (612) 540-5526   Fax: (612) 449-3400   www.radisson.com

Operates, manages and franchises full-service hotels and resorts worldwide.

Radisson SAS Hotel, 223 Promenade des Anglais, F-06200 Nice, France

Tel: 33-4-93-37-17-17   Fax: 33-4-93-71-21-71

RAIN BIRD SPRINKLER MFG. CORPORATION

145 North Grand Ave., Glendora, CA, 91741-2469

Tel: (626) 963-9311   Fax: (626) 963-4287   www.rainbird.com

World's largest manufacturer of lawn sprinklers and irrigation systems equipment.

Rain Bird Europe, 535, rue Georges Claude, BP 72000, F-13792 Aix-en Provence Cedex 3, France

Tel: 33-4-42-24-4461   Fax: 33-4-42-24-2472

Rain Bird France, 415, rue Louis Armand, BP 72000, F-13792 Aix-en Provence Cedex 3, France

Tel: 33-4-42-24-4461   Fax: 33-4-42-24-2472   Contact: Eric Tortelier

RAINBOW TECHNOLOGY INC.

50 Technology Dr., Irvine, CA, 92618

Tel: (949) 450-7300   Fax: (949) 450-7450   www.rainbow.com

Mfr. computer related security products.

Microphar France, 122 ave. Charles de Gaulle, F-29522 Neuilly-sur-Seine Cedex, France

RATIONAL SOFTWARE CORPORATION

18880 Homestead Road, Cupertino, CA, 95014-0721

Tel: (408) 863-9900   Fax: (408) 863-4120   www.rationale.com

Mfr. application development software.

Rational Software, Immeuble de la Gare, 1, Place Charles de Gaulle, F-78180 Montigny le Bretonneux, France

RAY & BERNDTSON, INC.

301 Commerce, Ste. 2300, Fort Worth, TX, 76102

Tel: (817) 334-0500   Fax: (817) 334-0779   www.prb.com

Executive search, management audit and management consulting firm.

Ray & Berndtson, 73 Champs Elysées, F-75008 Paris, France

Tel: 33-1-53-77-2200   Fax: 33-1-53-77-2209   Contact: Xavier Alix, Mng. Ptnr.

RAYMOND JAMES FINANCIAL, INC.

880 Carillon Parkway, St. Petersburg, FL, 33716

Tel: (813) 573-3800   Fax: (813) 573-8244   www.rjf.com

Financial services; securities brokerage, asset management, and investment banking services.

Raymond James International, 14 rue de Berri, F-75008 Paris, France

Tel: 33-1-45-63-6345   Fax: 33-1-45-63-3047   Contact: E. Laussinotte

RAYOVAC CORPORATION

601 Rayovac Drive, Madison, WI, 53711-2497

Tel: (608) 275-3340   Fax: (608) 275-4577   www.rayovac.com

Mfr. batteries and lighting devices.

Rayovac Paris, Paris, France

RAYTHEON COMPANY

141 Spring Street, Lexington, MA, 02173

Tel: (781) 862-6600   Fax: (781) 860-2172   www.raytheon.com

Mfr. diversified electronics, appliances, energy and environmental products; publishing, industry and construction services.

Raytheon, 326 Bureaux de la Colline, F-92213 Saint Cloud Cedex, France

READER'S DIGEST ASSOCIATION, INC.

Reader's Digest Rd., Pleasantville, NY, 10570

Tel: (914) 238-1000   Fax: (914) 238-4559   www.readersdigest.com

Publisher of magazines and books and direct mail marketer.

Selection du Readers Digest SA, 1 a 7 ave. Louis Pasteur, F-92220 Bagneux, France

REALNETWORKS, INC.

PO Box 91123, Seattle, WA, 98111-9223

Tel: (206) 674-2700   Fax: (206) 674-2699   www.realnetworks.com

Mfr. software, including RealPlayer.

RealNetworks, Inc., 2 Place De La Defense BP, F-92053 Puteaux, France

Tel: 33-1-5517-4078

REDBACK NETWORKS, INC.

250 Holger Way, San Jose, CA, 95134

Tel: (408) 571-5000   Fax: (408) 541-0570   www.redbacknetworks.com

Mfr. equipment for high-speed internet connections.

Redback Networks France, 9, route du Colonel Moraine, F-92365 Meudon-La-Foret cedex, France

REEBOK INTERNATIONAL LTD.

1895 J. W. Foster Blvd., Canton, MA, 02021

Tel: (781) 401-5000   Fax: (781) 401-7402   www.reebok.com

Mfr. athletic shoes including casual, dress golf and walking shoes.

Reebok France SA, 184 rue Tabuteau, F-78532 Buc Cedex, France

REFCO GROUP LTD.

200 Liberty Street Tower A, New York, NY, 10281

Tel: (212) 693-7700   Fax: (212) 693-7856   www.refco.com

Commodity and security brokers engaged in the execution and clearing of futures and options and institutional asset management services.

Refco Futures Ltd., Paris, France

REFLEXITE TECHNOLOGY

120 Darling Drive, Avon, CT, 06001

Tel: (860) 676-7100   Fax: (860) 676-7199   www.reflexite.com

Mfr. plastic film, sheet, materials and shapes, optical lenses.

Reflexite France, Espace Florentin, 71 Chemin Du Moulin Carron, F-69570 Dardilly, France

Tel: 33-472-191910   Fax: 33-478-645833

RELIANCE STEEL & ALUMINUM COMPANY

350 S. Grand Ave., Ste. 5100, Los Angeles, CA, 90058

Tel: (213) 687-7700   Fax: (213) 687-8792   www.rsac.com

Provides customized metal processing services.

Valex Corporation, Div. Reliance Steel & Aluminum, 77 Sac St. Charles, F-13710 Fuv Eau, France

Tel: 33-4-4253-4641   Fax: 33-4-4253-4644   Contact: Daniel A. Mangan

REMINGTON PRODUCTS COMPANY, L.L.C.

60 Main Street, Bridgeport, CT, 06604

Tel: (203) 367-4400   Fax: (203) 332-4848   www.remington-products.com

Mfr. home appliances, electric shavers.

Remington Products Co., 65-75 Au Jean Mermoz, Batiment K, F-93120 La Courneuve, France

Tel: 33-1-48-35-3450   Fax: 33-1-48-35-0562   Contact: Pierre Pichard, Gen. Mgr.

RENAISSANCE HOTELS AND RESORTS

10400 Fernwood Road, Bethesda, MD, 20817

Tel: (301) 380-3000   Fax: (301) 380-5181   www.renaissancehotels.com

upscale, full-service hotel and resort chain under Marriott International, Inc.

Renaissance Paris Hotel, Le Defense Paris, France

Tel: 33-1-41-97-5050

RESMED INC.

1440 Danielson Street, Poway, CA, 92064

Tel: (858) 746-2400   Fax: (858) 880-1618   www.resmed.com

Mfr. sleep apnea aids, including nasal masks and accessories.

ResMed SA, Parc de la Bandonnière, 2 rue Maurice Audibert, F-69800 Saint-Priest, France

Tel: 33-4-37-251-251   Fax: 33-4-37-251-260

RESPIRONICS INC.

1501 Ardmore Blvd., Pittsburgh, PA, 15221-4401

Tel: (412) 731-2100   Fax: (412) 473-5011   www.respironics.com

Design/mfr. patient ventilation medical products.

Respironics International Inc., 77 rue de Paris, F-92100 Boulogne Billancourt, France

RETEK INC.

950 Nicollet Mall, Minneapolis, MN, 55403

Tel: (612) 587-5000   Fax: (612) 587-5100   www.retek.com

Mfr. retail management software.

Retek, 34 Boulevard Haussman, F-75009 Paris, France

Tel: 33-1-4801-4744   Fax: 33-1-4801-4746

REVLON INC.

625 Madison Ave., New York, NY, 10022

Tel: (212) 527-4000   Fax: (212) 527-4995   www.revlon.com

Mfr. cosmetics, fragrances, toiletries and beauty care products.

Revlon SA, 42 ave. Montaine, F-75008 Paris, France

Contact: Philippe Perrin, Gen. Mgr.

REXNORD CORPORATION

4701 West Greenfield Ave., Milwaukee, WI, 53214

Tel: (414) 643-3000   Fax: (414) 643-3078   www.rexnord.com

Mfr. power transmission and conveying components.

Rexnord PT France, La Belle Orge, F-88110 Raon, France

RHEOMETRIC SCIENTIFIC INC.

1 Possumtown Road, Piscataway, NJ, 08854

Tel: (732) 560-8550   Fax: (732) 560-7451   www.rheosci.com

Design/mfr. rheological instruments and systems.

Rheometric Scientific SARL, 7 rue Albert Einstein, F-77436 Marne la Vallee Cedex, France

RICHARDSON ELECTRONICS, LTD.

40 W 267 Keslinger Road, LaFox, IL, 60147-0393

Tel: (630) 208-2200   Fax: (630) 208-2550   www.rell.com

Mfr. and distribution of electron tubes and related equipment.

Richardson Electronics, BP 64, Zl de la Butte, F-91620 Nozay, France

RICHCO, INC.

5825 N. Tripp Ave., PO Box 804238, Chicago, IL, 60680

Tel: (773) 539-4060   Fax: (773) 539-6770   www.richco.com

Mfr. quality plastic fasteners, wire management devices, circuit board hardware, and custom components.

Richco France, Z.A. La Croix des Hormes, F-69250 Montanay, France

Tel: 33-4-72-08-7140

RIDGE TOOL COMPANY

400 Clark Street, Elyria, OH, 44035

Tel: (440) 323-5581   Fax: (440) 329-4853   www.ridgid.com

Mfr. hand and power tools for working pipe, drain cleaning equipment, etc.

Emerson Electric France SA, Div. Ridge Tool, Morangis, France

RIGHT MANAGEMENT CONSULTANTS, INC.

1818 Market Street, 33rd Fl., Philadelphia, PA, 19103-3614

Tel: (215) 988-1588   Fax: (215) 988-9112   www.right.com

Out placement and human resources consulting services.

Right Management Consultants, L. M. & P., 18-20 rue Foureroy, F-75017 Paris, France

Tel: 33-1-42-27-6300

Right Management Consultants, 152 Ave. de Malakoff, F-75116 Paris, France

Tel: 33-1-44-17-1888

ROBERT HALF INTERNATIONAL INC.

2884 Sand Hill Road, Ste. 200, Menlo Park, CA, 94025

Tel: (650) 234-6000   Fax: (650) 234-6999   www.rhii.com

World leader in personnel and specialized staffing services.

Robert Half Intl. Inc., 15/17 rue Marsollier, F-75002 Paris, France

Tel: 331-5504-1818

C. H. ROBINSON WORLDWIDE, INC. (CHR)

8100 Mitchell Road, Eden Prairie, MN, 55344

Tel: (612) 937-8500   Fax: (612) 937-6714   www.chrobinson.com

Global door-to-door freight forwarding services, including flexible transportation solutions and global logistics.

C. H. Robinson (CHR), 83 rue Saint Pierre, BP367, F-14016 Caen Cedex, France

Tel: 33-2-3115-1020

C. H. Robinson France, 15 avenue Jean Mermoz, 15 avenue Jean Mermoz, F-64000 Pau, France

C. H. Robinson France, 6 rue du Colonel Remy, F-14000 Caen, France

C. H. Robinson France, Zone de fret de Bordeaux, Bat 1, Port E, Rue de Barcelone, F-33521 Bruges Cedex, France

C.H. Robinson France, Technopole, 16 Rue Graham Bell, F-57070 Metz, France

C.H. Robinson France, 119 Route d'Heyrieux, F-69800 Saint Priest, France

ROCKWELL AUTOMATION, INC.

777 East Wisconsin Ave., Ste. 1400, Milwaukee, WI, 53202

Tel: (414) 212-5200   Fax: (414) 212-5201   www.rockwellautomation.com

Products and service for aerospace and defense, automotive, electronics, graphics and automation industry.

Rockwell Automation, 36 Avenue de L'Europe, F-78940 Velizy-Villacoublay, France

Tel: 33-1-3067-7200

Rockwell Semiconductor Systems S.A.S., Les Taissounières, B1, 1681 Route des Dolines, BP 283, F-06905 Sophia Antipolis Cedex, France

Tel: 33-1-49-06-3980   Fax: 33-1-49-06-3990

ROCKWELL COLLINS, INC.

400 Collins Road NE, Cedar Rapids, IA, 52498

Tel: (319) 295-1000   Fax: (319) 295-5429   www.rockwellcollins.com

Aviation electronics and communications equipment manufacturer.

Rockwell Collins SA, 6, avenue Didier Daurat, BP 8, F-31701 Blagnac Cedex, France

Tel: 33-5-6171-7700   Fax: 33-5-6171-5169

R.A. RODRIGUEZ, INC.

20 Seaview Boulevard, Port Washington, NY, 11050

Tel: (516) 625-8080   Fax: (516) 621-2424   www.rodriguez-usa.com

Distribution of ball and roller bearings, precision gears, mechanical systems and related products.

R. A. Rodriguez France, 12 rue George Clemenceau, F-78220 Viroflay, France

Tel: 33-1-30-24-1333

ROFIN-SINAR TECHNOLOGIES, INC.

45701 Mast St., Plymouth, MI, 48170

Tel: (734) 455-5400   Fax: (734) 455-2741   www.rofin-sinar.com

Mfr. industrial lasers.

ROFIN-SINAR France SA, 10, Allee du Cantal, Z.I. la Petite Montagne Sud, F-91018 Evry Cedex, France

Tel: 33-1-6911-3636

ROHM AND HAAS COMPANY

100 Independence Mall West, Philadelphia, PA, 19106

Tel: (215) 592-3000   Fax: (215) 592-3377   www.rohmhaas.com

Mfr. specialty chemicals.

Rohm and Haas France S.A.S, BP 48, F-02301 Chauny Cedex, France

Tel: 33-3-2338-3456

Rohm and Haas France S.A.S., Le Pressoir Vert, F-45400 Semoy, France

Tel: 33-2-3861-8100

Rohm and Haas France S.A.S., Site Atochem, Bat 201, BP 20, F-60870 Villers Saint Paul, France

Rohm and Haas France S.A.S., BP 27, F-67630 Lauterbourg, France

Tel: 33-38873-6000

Rohm and Haas France SA, 185 rue de Bercy, F-75579 Paris Cedex 12, France

Tel: 33-1-40-02-5000

Rohm and Haas France SA, 185 rue de Bercy, F-75579 Paris, France

Tel: 33-1-4002-5000

Rohm and Haas France SA European Laboratories, 371 rue L.V. Beethoven, Sophia Antipolis, F-06565 Valbonne Cedex, France

Tel: 33-193-95-5353

Shipley S.A.S, 3 rue Sigmund Freud, B.P. 55, F-69511 Vaulx-en-Velin Lyon, France

ROSENBLUTH INTERNATIONAL

2401 Walnut Street, Philadelphia, PA, 19103-4390

Tel: (215) 977-4000   Fax: (215) 977-4028   www.rosenbluth.com

Provides corporate business travel services.

Rosenbluth International, 19 avenue de la Bourdonnais, F-75007 Paris, France

ROWECOM, INC.

15 Southwest Park, Westwood, MA, 02090

Tel: (781) 410-3300   Fax: (781) 329-9875   www.rowe.com

On-line magazine and newspaper subscription services.

RoweCom France, Rue de la Prairie, Villebon sur Yvette, F-91121 Palaiseau Cedex, France

Tel: 33-1-6910-4700   Fax: 33-1-6910-4791

RPM INC.

PO Box 777, 2628 Pearl Road, Medina, OH, 44258

Tel: (330) 273-5090   Fax: (330) 225-8743   www.rpminc.com

Mfr. protective coatings and paints.

Rust-Oleum France S.A., B.P. 39, F-95322 St. Leu la Foret Cedex, France

Tel: 33-130-400044   Fax: 33-130-409980

RUDER FINN INC.

301 East 57th Street, New York, NY, 10022

Tel: (212) 593-6400   Fax: (212) 593-6397   www.ruderfinn.com

Engaged in public relations service and broadcast communications.

Ruder Finn France, 3 rue du Faubourg Saint Honore, F-75008 Paris, France

RUSSELL REYNOLDS ASSOCIATES INC.

200 Park Avenue, New York, NY, 10166-0002

Tel: (212) 351-2000   Fax: (212) 370-0896   www.russreyn.com

Executive recruiting services.

Russell Reynolds Associates Ltd., 7 Place Vendome, F-75001 Paris, France

Tel: 33-1-49-26-1300   Fax: 33-1-42-60-0385   Contact: Brigette Lemercier-Saltiel

RUST-OLEUM CORPORATION

11 Hawthorn Parkway, Vernon Hills, IL, 60061

Tel: (847) 367-7700   Fax: (847) 816-2300   www.rust-oleum.com

Rust preventive coatings.

Rust-Oleum/France S. A., 11 rue Jules Verne, St. Leu, France

Contact: Daniel Cormenier

RVSI (ROBOTIC VISION SYSTEMS, INC.)

5 Shawmut Road, Canton, MA, 02021

Tel: (781) 821-0830   Fax: (781) 828-8942   www.rvsi.com

Mfr. machine visions systems; bar code scanners and data collection equipment.

RVSI Europe S.A., Parc d'Activites des Bellevues, Immeuble Le Floride Allee Rosa, Luxembourg BP 258, F-95615 Cergy Pontoise Cedex, France

RVSI Robotic Vision Systems, 30 Chemin du Travers des Champs Guillaume, F-95240 Cormeilles en Paris, France

S1 CORPORATION

3500 Lenox Road, Ste. 200, Atlanta, GA, 30326-1108

Tel: (404) 923-3500   Fax: (404) 923-6727   www.s1.com

Mfr. on-line banking software.

S1 Paris, 33, avenue du Maine BP 31, F-75755 Paris Cedex 15, France

SAATCHI & SAATCHI

375 Hudson St., New York, NY, 10014

Tel: (212) 463-2000   Fax: (212) 463-9855   www.saatchi-saatchi.com

Provides advertising and marketing services.

Saatchi & Saatchi Business Communications, Paris, France

SABRE INC.

3150 Sabre Drive, Southlake, TX, 76092

Tel: (682) 605-1000   Fax: (682) 605-8267   www.sabre.com

Computerized travel reservation system.

Sabre France Sarl, 77, Street of Boetie, F-75008 Paris, France

Tel: 33-1-4420-6620   Fax: 33-1-4420-6644

SAFETY-KLEEN CORPORATION

1301 Gervais Street, Columbia, SC, 29201

Tel: (803) 933-4200   Fax: (803) 933-4345   www.safety-kleen.com

Solvent based parts cleaning service; sludge/solvent recycling service.

Sopia/Safety-Kleen France, 12 rue de Tilsitt, F-75008 Paris, France

SALANS HERTZFELD HEILBRONN CHRISTY & VIENER

620 Fifth Avenue, New York, NY, 10020-2457

Tel: (212) 632-5500   Fax: (212) 632-5555   www.salans.com

International law firm.

Salans Hertzfeld & Heilbronn, 9 rue Boissy d'Anglais, F-75008 Paris, France

SANFORD CORPORATION

2711 Washington Boulevard, Bellwood, IL, 60104

Tel: (708) 547-6650   Fax: (708) 547-6719   www.sanfordcorp.com

Mfr. inks, writing, drawing and drafting instruments.

Sanford Europe, 9-11 Rue Christophe Colomb, F-75008 Paris, France

SANMINA-SCI CORPORATION

2700 North First Street, San Jose, CA, 95134

Tel: (408) 964-3500   Fax: (408) 964-3799   www.sanmina-sci.com

Engaged in electronics contract manufacturing.

Sanmina Corporation France, rue des Fouleries, BP 69, F-28202 Chateaudun Cedex, France

Tel: 33-2-3497-3500

Sanmina-SCI France, Rue Des Fouleries, F-BP 69 Chateaudun, France

Tel: 33-134-630-888   Fax: 33-134-630-889

SARA LEE CORPORATION

3 First National Plaza, Chicago, IL, 60602-4260

Tel: (312) 726-2600   Fax: (312) 558-4995   www.saralee.com

Mfr./distributor food and consumer packaged goods, intimate apparel and knitwear.

Brossard/Sara Lee, Paris, France

Dim SA, 6 rue Marius Aufan, F-92300 Levallois-Perret Cedex, France

Sara Lee Personal Products, 28 rue Jacques Ibert, F-92300 Levallois-Perret Cedex, France

SAS INSTITUTE INC.

SAS Campus Drive, Cary, NC, 27513

Tel: (919) 677-8000   Fax: (919) 677-4444   www.sas.com

Mfr. and distribution of decision support software.

SAS Institute (France) Ltd., Gregy-sur-Yerres, France

Tel: 33-1-60-62-1111   Fax: 33-1-60-62-1199

SBC COMMUNICATIONS INC.

175 East Houston, San Antonio, TX, 78205

Tel: (210) 821-4105   Fax: (210) 351-5034   www.sbc.com

Engaged in telecommunications.

Group Cegetel (JV), 1 place Carpeaux, F-92915 Paris La Defense, France

Tel: 33-1-7107-0707   Contact: Jean-Marie Messier, Chmn.

Societe Francaise de Radiotelephone (SRF), Paris, France

SCANSOFT, INC.

9 Centennial Dr., Peabody, MA, 01960

Tel: (978) 977-2000   Fax: (978) 977-2436   www.scansoft.com

Mfr. digital imaging software for speech and language solutions.

ScanSoft, Inc., Paris, France

Tel: 33-1-5597-1720

SCHENECTADY INTERNATIONAL INC.

PO Box 1046, Schenectady, NY, 12301

Tel: (518) 370-4200   Fax: (518) 382-8129   www.siigroup.com

Mfr. electrical insulating varnishes, enamels, phenolic resins, alkylphenols.

Schenectady Europe SA, 916 ave. George Washington, F-62404 Bethune, France

Tel: 33-3-2157-3005   Fax: 33-3-2157-4301

SCHENKER USA INC.

150 Albany Ave., Freeport, NY, 11520

Tel: (516) 403-5416   Fax: (516) 377-3092   www.schenkerusa.com

Freight forwarders.

Jules Roy SA, 32 rue P. Brossolette Frankling Bldg., PO Box 263, F-76055 Le Havre Cedex, France

Tel: 33-2-35-195470   Fax: 33-2-35-214409

Jules Roy SA, 12 blvd Frederick Sauvage, PO Box 215, F-13014 Marseille Cedex 14, France

Tel: 33-4-91-02-0400   Fax: 33-4-91-02-8952

R. P. SCHERER CORPORATION

645 Martinsville Rd., Ste. 200, Basking Ridge, NJ, 07920

Tel: (908) 580-1500   Fax: (908) 580-9220   www.rpscherer.com

Mfr. pharmaceuticals; soft gelatin and two-piece hard shell capsules.

R.P. Scherer SA, 74, rue Principale, F-67930 Beinheim, France

Tel: 33-3-88-633131   Fax: 33-3-88-862248   Contact: Denis Vannson, Gen. Mgr.   Emp: 150

SCHERING-PLOUGH CORPORATION

One Giralda Farms, Madison, NJ, 07940-1000

Tel: (973) 822-7000   Fax: (973) 822-7048   www.sch-plough.com

Proprietary drug and cosmetic products.

Schering Plough, 92 rue Baudin, F-92307 Levallois-Perret Cedex, France

Tel: 33-1-41-96-3789   Contact: Daniel Pons

SCHLUMBERGER LIMITED

153 East 53rd St., 57th Fl., New York, NY, 10022-4624

Tel: (212) 350-9400   Fax: (212) 350-9457   www.slb.com

Engaged in oil and gas services, metering and payment systems, and produces semiconductor testing equipment and smart cards.

Schlumberger Limited, 42 rue Saint-Dominique, F-75007 Paris, France

A. SCHULMAN INC.

3550 West Market Street, Akron, OH, 44333

Tel: (330) 666-3751   Fax: (330) 668-7204   www.aschulman.com

Mfr./sale plastic resins and compounds.

A. Schulman Plastics SA, rue Alex Schuylman, F-08600 Givet, France

A. Schulman SA, Immeuble Dynasteur, 10/12 rue Andras Beck, F-92360 Meudon-la-Foret Paris, France

SCIENCE APPLICATIONS INTL. CORPORATION (SAIC)

10260 Campus Point Dr., San Diego, CA, 92121

Tel: (858) 826-6000   Fax: (858) 535-7589   www.saic.com

Engaged in research and engineering.

SAIC France, 2 Place De La Defense, Center 3, Suite 209, Cit., BP 464, F-92053 Paris La Defense, France

Tel: 33-1410-20333

SCIENTIFIC GAMES INTERNATIONAL

750 Lexington Avenue, 25th Fl., New York, NY, 10022

Tel: (212) 754-2233   Fax: (212) 754-2372   www.scientificgames.com

Mfr. video gaming machines and computerized pari-mutuel wagering systems used at racetracks.

Scientific Games International, 5-7 rue Salomon de Rothschild, F-92150 Suresnes, France

Tel: 33-141-44-3980   Fax: 33-141-44-3949

SCM MICROSYSTEMS, INC.

47211 Bayside Pkwy., Fremont, CA, 94538

Tel: (510) 360-2300   Fax: (510) 360-0211   www.scmmicro.com

Mfr. computer hardware for digital cameras.

SCM Microsystems,, ZE Athélia II, n° 216, avenue du Serpolet, F-13704 La Ciotat, Cedex, France

SEACOR SMIT INC.

11200 Richmond Avenue, Ste. 400, Houston, TX, 77042

Tel: (713) 782-5990   Fax: (713) 782-5991   www.seacorsmit.com

Engaged in offshore marine services.

SEACOR Marine SAS, 23 rue Notre-Dame des Victoires, F-75002 Paris, France

Tel: 33-1-53-40-2100

SEAGATE TECHNOLOGY, INC.

920 Disc Dr., Scotts Valley, CA, 95066

Tel: (408) 438-6550   Fax: (408) 438-7205   www.seagate.com

Develop computer technology, software and hardware.

Seagate Technology, Inc., 62 bis Ave. Andre Morizet, F-92643 Boulogne-Billancourt Cedex, France

Tel: 33-1-41-86-1000   Fax: 33-1-48-25-2861   Contact: Jean-Louis Cazenave, Dir.   Emp: 40

SEALED AIR CORPORATION

Park 80 East, Saddle Brook, NJ, 07663

Tel: (201) 791-7600   Fax: (201) 703-4205   www.sealedaircorp.com

Mfr. protective and specialty packaging solutions for industrial, food and consumer products.

Sealed Air S.A., 3 Ave. de la Mare, Z.A. des Béthunes, F-95310 Saint-Ouen-l´Aumone, France

Tel: 33-1-34-32-5950   Fax: 33-1-34-64-6385

G.D. SEARLE & COMPANY

5200 Old Orchard Road, Skokie, IL, 60077

Tel: (847) 982-7000   Fax: (847) 470-1480   www.searlehealthnet.com

Mfr. pharmaceuticals, health care, optical products and specialty chemicals.

Searle, Division of Monsanto France S.A., 2 Ave. de Guesclin, B.P. 285, F-27002 Evreux, France

Tel: 33-32-29-5800   Fax: 33-32-33-1248

SECURE COMPUTING CORPORATION

4810 Harwood Rd., San Jose, CA, 95124

Tel: (408) 979-6000   Fax: (408) 979-6101   www.sctc.com

Mfr. software.

Secure Computing International Sarl, La Grande Arche, Paroi Nord, 14eme Etage, Bureau 1410, F-92044 Paris la Defense, France

Tel: 33-1-4090-3105

SEDGWICK, DETERT, MORAN & ARNOLD

One Embarcadero Center, 16th Fl., San Francisco, CA, 94111

Tel: (415) 781-7900   Fax: (415) 781-2635   www.sdma.com

International law firm.

Sedgwick, Detert, Moran & Arnold, 104 Avenue Kléber, F-75116 Paris, France

Tel: 33-1-4704-5502   Fax: 33-1-4704-5502

SEEBEYOND TECHNOLOGY CORPORATION

404 East Huntington Drive, Monrovia, CA, 91016

Tel: (626) 471-6000   Fax: (626) 471-6104   www.seebeyond.com

Mfr. business software.

SeeBeyond France, 7, Place d'Iéna, 75116, F-75406 Paris, France

SELAS CORPORATION OF AMERICA

2034 S. Limekiln Pike, Dresher, PA, 19025

Tel: (215) 646-6600   Fax: (215) 646-3536   www.selas.com

Mfr. heat treating equipment for metal, glass, ceramic and chemical industry.

Selas SA, 3/5 Place du Village, F-92632 Gennevilliers Cedex, France

Contact: Christian Bailliart

SEMITOOL, INC.

655 West Reserve Drive, Kalispell, MT, 59901

Tel: (406) 752-2107   Fax: (406) 752-5522   www.semitool.com

Mfr. semiconductor manufacturing equipment.

Semitool France Sarl, 173 rue du Rocher de Lorzier, Parc du Pommarin, Centr'alp, F-38430 Moirans, France

SEMTECH CORPORATION

200 Flynn Road, Camarillo, CA, 93012-8790

Tel: (805) 498-2111   Fax: (805) 498-3804   www.semtech.com

Mfr. silicon rectifiers, rectifier assemblies, capacitors, switching regulators, AC/DC converters.

Semtech Ltd. France, 21 Ave. au Quebec, F-91951 Courtaboeuf Cedex, France

Tel: 33-1-69-28-2200   Fax: 33-1-69-28-1298

SENSIENT TECHNOLOGIES CORPORATION

777 E. Wisconsin Ave., Milwaukee, WI, 53202

Tel: (414) 271-6755   Fax: (414) 347-4783   www.sensient.com

Mfr. flavor applications for the beverage, bakery, confection, dairy, snack and savory markets.

Les Colorants Wackherr, Paris, France

SENSORMATIC ELECTRONICS CORPORATION

951 Yamato Road, Boca Raton, FL, 33431-0700

Tel: (561) 989-7000   Fax: (561) 989-7774   www.sensormatic.com

Electronic article surveillance equipment.

Sensormatic S.A., Parc de Haute Technologie 7, Rue Alexis de Tocqueville, F-92183 Antony Cedex, France

Tel: 33-1-40-96-2400   Fax: 33-1-40-96-0003

SEPRACOR INC.

111 Locke Drive, Marlborough, MA, 01752

Tel: (508) 481-6700   Fax: (508) 357-7499   www.sepracor.com

Engaged in drug patents.

BioSphere Medical (J/V), Bat. A - Parc des Nations Paris Nord 2, 383, Rue de la Belle Etoile, F-BP 50289 Roissy en France, France

SEQUA CORPORATION

200 Park Avenue, New York, NY, 10166

Tel: (212) 986-5500   Fax: (212) 370-1969   www.sequa.com

Mfr. aerospace products and systems, machinery and metal coatings, spec chemicals, automotive products.

Materiels Equipements Graphiques, 32-34 rue des Malines, Z.I. Les Malines, Lisses-Evry, France

SERVICE CORPORATION INTERNATIONAL

1929 Allen Parkway, Houston, TX, 77019

Tel: (713) 522-5141   Fax: (713) 525-5586   www.sci-corp.com

Operates funeral homes, cemeteries and crematoriums and sells caskets, burial vaults and cremation receptacles.

Pompes Funereraves Geneacuterales (PFG), Paris, France

SHEARMAN & STERLING

599 Lexington Ave., New York, NY, 10022-6069

Tel: (212) 848-4000   Fax: (212) 848-7179   www.shearman.com

Law firm engaged in general American and international financial and commercial practice.

Shearman & Sterling, 114 Ave. des Champs-Elysées, F-75008 Paris, France

Tel: 33-1-53-89-7000   Fax: 33-1-53-89-7070   Contact: Emmanuel Gaillard, Mng. Ptnr.

SHELDAHL, INC.

1150 Sheldahl Rd., Northfield, MN, 55057-9444

Tel: (507) 663-8000   Fax: (507) 663-8545   www.sheldahl.com

Mfr. electrical and electronic components and laminated plastic products/adhesive-based tapes and materials and adhesiveless Novaclad®.

CCI Eurolan/Sheldahl Europe, 71/78 rue Grand, F-92310 Sevres, France

SHIPLEY COMPANY, LLC

455 Forest Street, Marlborough, MA, 01752

Tel: (508) 481-7950   Fax: (508) 485-9113   www.shipley.com

Supplier of materials and processes technology to the microelectronics and printed wiring board industries.

Shipley S.A.S, 3 rue Sigmund Freud, B.P. 55, F-69511 Vaulx-en-Velin Lyon, France

Tel: 33-4-7880-0832   Fax: 33-4-7204-3778

Shipley SAS, La Tour de Lyon, 185 rue de Bercy, F-75579 Paris Cedex 12, France

Tel: 33-1-4002-5000   Fax: 33-1-4002-5008

SIEBEL SYSTEMS, INC.

2207 Bridgepointe Pkwy., San Mateo, CA, 94404

Tel: (650) 295-5000   Fax: (650) 295-5111   www.siebel.com

Provider of e-Business applications software.

Siebel Systems France SAS, 8, rue de Presbourg, F-75116 Paris, France

SIG DOBOY INC.

869 South Knowles Ave., New Richmond, WI, 54017-1797

Tel: (715) 246-6511   Fax: (715) 246-6539   www.doboy.com

Mfr. packaging machinery.

SIG Simonazzi, Tour Montparnasse, 3, avenue du Maine, F-75755 Paris Cédex 15, France

SIGNODE PACKAGING SYSTEMS

3610 West Lake Ave., Glenview, IL, 60025

Tel: (847) 724-6100   Fax: (847) 657-4392   www.signode.com

Mfr. industrial tools and machinery for packaging and strapping.

Signode France SA, 35 rue de la Motte, F-93308 Aubervilliers Cedex, France

SILICON GRAPHICS INC.

1600 Amphitheatre Pkwy., Mountain View, CA, 94043-1351

Tel: (650) 960-1980   Fax: (650) 932-0661   www.sgi.com

Design/mfr. special-effects computer graphic systems and software.

Espace Performance, Batiment J Bronze, F-35769 Saint Grégoire Cedex, France

Tel: 33-2-99-23-1280   Fax: 33-2-99-23-1895

Siege Social, 21 rue Albert Calmette, F-78350 Jouy-en-Josas Paris, France

Tel: 33-1-34-88-8000   Fax: 33-1-34-65-9619

SITEL CORPORATION

111 South Calver Street, Ste. 1900, Baltimore, MD, 21202

Tel: (410) 246-1505   Fax: (410) 246-0200   www.sitel.com

Provides outsourced customer management services.

SITEL France, 58, rue du Dessours, des Berges Batiment B, F-75013 Paris, France

SIX FLAGS, INC.

11501 Northeast Expwy., Oklahoma City, OK, 73131

Tel: (405) 475-2500   Fax: (405) 475-2555   www.sixflags.com

Owns and manages amusement parks.

Walibi Aquitaine Six Flags, F-47310 Roquefort, France

SKADDEN, ARPS, SLATE, MEAGHER & FLOM LLP

4 Times Square, New York, NY, 10036

Tel: (212) 735-3000   Fax: (212) 735-2000   www.sasmf.com

American/International law practice.

Skadden, Arps, Slate, Meagher & Flom LLP, 68 rue du Faubourg Saint-Honoré, F-75008 Paris, France

Tel: 33-1-40-75-4444   Fax: 33-1-49-53-0999

SKYWORKS SOLUTIONS, INC.

20 Sylvan Road, Woburn, MA, 01801

Tel: (781) 935-5150   Fax: (781) 824-4579   www.skyworksinc.com

Mfr. electronic and microwave components.

Skyworks Solutions, 34 Avenue Franklin Roosevelt, BP 92, F-92153 Suresnes Cedex, France

Contact: Philippe Roux

SLI, INC.

500 Chapman Street, Canton, MA, 02021

Tel: (781) 828-2948   Fax: (781) 828-2012   www.sli-lighting.com

Engaged in design, manufacture and sales of lighting systems, including lamps, fixtures and ballasts.

Sylvania Lighting SA, Züger Harry N., F-D-1217 Meyrin, France

SMITH INTERNATIONAL, INC.

PO Box 60068, Houston, TX, 77205-0068

Tel: (713) 443-3370   Fax: (713) 233-5996   www.smith.com

Mfr. drilling tools and equipment and provides related services for the drilling, completion and production sectors of the petroleum and mining industries.

Smith International France SARL, B.P. 217, Lons, F-64142 Billere Pau, France

Tel: 33-59-92-3550   Contact: Georges Italiano, District Mgr.

SMITHFIELD FOODS, INC.

200 Commerce Street, Smithfield, VA, 23430

Tel: (757) 365-3000   Fax: (757) 365-3017   www.smithfieldhams.com

Mfr. processed meats.

Societe Bretonne De Salaisons, BP 80359 Lampaul-Guimiliau, F-29403 Landivisiau Cedex, France

Tel: 33-2-9868-6868   Fax: 33-3-9868-6899   Contact: Adrien Czaja, Mgr.

SMURFIT-STONE CONTAINER CORPORATION

150 N. Michigan Ave., Chicago, IL, 60601-7568

Tel: (312) 346-6600   Fax: (312) 580-3486   www.smurfit-stone.net

Mfr. paper and paper packaging.

Societe Emballages des Cevennes SA, F-30410 Molieres-sur-Ceze, France

SNAP-ON INCORPORATED

10801 Corporate Dr., Pleasant Prairie, WI, 53158-1603

Tel: (262) 656-5200   Fax: (262) 656-5577   www.snapon.com

Mfr. auto maintenance, diagnostic and emission testing equipment, hand tools, hydraulic lifts and tire changers.

Snap-On Tools BV, ZI de la Petite, Montagne Sud, 13 allee du Dauphine, F-91008 Evry, France

SOFTWARE HOUSE INTERNATIONAL, INC.

2 Riverview Drive, Somerset, NJ, 08873

Tel: (732) 746-8888   Fax: (732) 764-8889   www.shi.com

Engaged in the distribution of software products.

SHI France, 23, rue Balzac, F-75008 Paris, France

SOLA INTERNATIONAL INC.

10690 W. Ocean Air Drive, Ste. 300, San Diego, CA, 92130

Tel: (858) 509-9899   Fax: (858) 509-9898   www.sola.com

Mfr. and sales of plastic and glass eyeglasses.

SOLA Optical S.A., 5 rue de Bitche, 57620 Goetzenbruck, Goetzenbruck, France

Tel: 33-87-96-96-08   Fax: 33-87-96-94-10

SOLECTRON CORPORATION

777 Gibraltar Drive, Milpitas, CA, 95035

Tel: (408) 957-8500   Fax: (408) 956-6075   www.solectron.com

Provides contract manufacturing services to equipment manufacturers.

Solectron Corporation, Chemin Departmental 109E, Canajan, BP 6, F-33611 Cestas Cedex, France

Tel: 33-5-57-12-7575   Fax: 33-5-57-12-7813

SONOCO PRODUCTS COMPANY

North Second Street, PO Box 160, Hartsville, SC, 29550

Tel: (843) 383-7000   Fax: (843) 383-7008   www.sonoco.com

Mfr. packaging for consumer and industrial market and recycled paperboard.

European Development Center, BP 1, 16 Chemin des Amoureux, F-89140 Pont-sur-Yonne, France

Tel: 33-3-86-672830

Papeteries du Rhin - Lhomme S.A., BP 148, F-68313 Illzach Cedex, France

Tel: 33-3-89-61-8584

Sonoco Consumer Products, Ltd., Zone Industrielle de Lievin, rue Francois Jacob, F-62800 Lievin, France

Tel: 33-2-1720033

Sonoco Gunther SA, F-70800 Fontaine les Luxeuil, France

Sonoco Lhomme S.A., 60 rue Gabriel Péri, F-59320 Haubourdin, France

Tel: 33-3-20-076040

Sonoco Lhomme S.A., BP 27, 88 rue de Lille, F-59520 Marquette-Lez-Lille, France

Tel: 33-3-20-14-9714   Fax: 33-3-20-13-1701

Sonoco Lhomme S.A., BP 1, Route de Paris, F-89140 Pont-sur-Yonne, France

Tel: 33-3-86-675000

Sonoco Pages S.A., Lieu-dit 'Mandete', F-09200 St-Girons, France

Tel: 33-5-61-66-2626

SOTHEBY'S HOLDINGS, INC.

1334 York Avenue, New York, NY, 10021

Tel: (212) 606-7000   Fax: (212) 606-7027   www.sothebys.com

Auction house specializing in fine art and jewelry.

Sotheby's Holdings, Inc., Galerie Charpentier, 76 rue du Faubourg Saint Honore, F-75008 Paris, France

Tel: 33-1-5305-5380

SPARTECH CORPORATION

120 S. Central, Ste. 1700, Clayton, MO, 63105-1705

Tel: (314) 721-4242   Fax: (314) 721-1447   www.spartech.com

Mfr. and sales of engineered thermoplastic materials and polymeric compounds.

Spartech Polycom, Z.I. Donchery, F-08350 Donchery, France

Tel: 33-3-2427-7580   Fax: 33-3-2427-7581

SPECTRIAN CORPORATION

350 West Java Drive, Sunnyvale, CA, 94089

Tel: (408) 745-5400   Fax: (408) 541-0263   www.spectrian.com

Mfr. linear power amplifiers.

Spectrian France, 22 rue Violet, F-75015 Paris Cedex, France

Tel: 33-1-45-79-10-77   Fax: 33-1-45-79-10-77

SPECTRUM CONTROL, INC.

8031 Avonia Road, Fairview, PA, 16415

Tel: (814) 835-1650   Fax: (814) 835-1651   www.spectrumcontrol.com

Mfr. control systems for telecommunications equipment.

Spectrum Control, 41/41 bis, Aenue de 'Europe, PB 264, F-78147 Velizy Cedex, France

SPENCER STUART MANAGEMENT CONSULTANTS

401 North Michigan Ave., Ste. 3400, Chicago, IL, 60611

Tel: (312) 822-0080   Fax: (312) 822-0116   www.spencerstuart.com

Executive recruitment firm.

Spencer Stuart & Associates Inc., 83 Ave. Marceau, F-75116 Paris, France

Tel: 33-1-53-57-8123   Fax: 33-1-53-57-8100   Contact: Henri dePitray

SPHERION CORPORATION

2050 Spectrum Boulevard, Fort Lauderdale, FL, 33309

Tel: (954) 938-7600   Fax: (954) 938-7666   www.spherion.com

Provides temporary personnel placement and staffing.

Michael Page Finance, 159 Ave. Achille Peretti, F-92200 Neuilly-sur-Seine Paris, France

Tel: 33-1-5948-3480

SPIROL INTERNATIONAL HOLDING CORPORATION

30 Rock Ave., Danielson, CT, 06239

Tel: (860) 774-8571   Fax: (860) 774-0487   www.spirol.com

Mfr. engineered fasteners, shims, automation equipment.

Spirol France, 21 rue de Baconnes, F-51430 Bezannes, France

Emp: 10

SPRAYING SYSTEMS COMPANY

PO Box 7900, Wheaton, IL, 60189-7900

Tel: (630) 665-5000   Fax: (630) 260-0842   www.spray.com

Designs and manufactures industrial spray products.

Spraying Systems France, 77 Avenue Aristide Briand, F-94118 Arcueil Cedex, France

SPS TECHNOLOGIES INC.

165 Township Line Rd., Two Pitcairn Place, Jenkintown, PA, 19046

Tel: (215) 517-2000   Fax: (215) 517-2032   www.spstech.com

Mfr. aerospace and industry fasteners, tightening systems, magnetic materials, super alloys.

SPS Technologies France, 46 Avenue Kleber, F-92700 Colombes, France

Tel: 33-5-6246-3004   Fax: 33-5-6246-3005   Contact: Frederic Fourcade

SPSS INC.

233 S. Wacker Dr., 11th Fl., Chicago, IL, 60606

Tel: (312) 651-6000   Fax: (312) 329-3668   www.spss.com

Mfr. statistical software.

SPSS France, 15, rue Marsollier, F-75002 Paris, France

SPX CORPORATION

700 Terrace Point Drive, PO Box 3301, Muskegon, MI, 49443-3301

Tel: (231) 724-5000   Fax: (231) 724-5720   www.spx.com

Mfr. auto parts, special service tools, engine and drive-train parts.

Automotive Diagnostics Intl., Technoparc, 15 rue Charles Edouard Jeanneret, F-78306 Poissy Cedex, France

Bear Export Division, BP 42, F-67450 Mundolsheim, France

Bear France SA, rue du Chemin de Fer, Wisconsin Building, ZAC de Lampertheim, F-67450 Lampertheim, France

Robinair Europe, Technoparc, 15 rue Charles Edouard Jeanneret, F-78306 Poissy Cedex, France

Sealed Power Europe, c/o Sealed Power Technologies Pringy SA, F-74370 Pringy, France

SSA GLOBAL TECHNOLOGIES, INC.

500 W. Madison St., Ste. 3200, Chicago, IL, 60661

Tel: (312) 258-6000   Fax: (312) 474-7500   www.ssax.com

Mfr. computer software.

SSA Global, Paris, France

THE ST. PAUL COMPANIES, INC.

385 Washington Street, St. Paul, MN, 55102

Tel: (651) 310-7911   Fax: (651) 310-8294   www.stpaul.com

Provides investment, insurance and reinsurance services.

Les Mutuelles duMans Assurances, 16 rue de Londres, F-75009 Paris, France

St. Paul International Insurance Company Ltd., 103 blvd. Haussmann, F-75008 Paris, France

Tel: 33-1-43-12-3282   Fax: 33-1-42-66-705

STANDARD COMMERCIAL CORPORATION

2201 Miller Rd., PO Box 450, Wilson, NC, 27894

Tel: (252) 291-5507   Fax: (252) 237-1109   www.sccgroup.com

Leaf tobacco dealers and processors and wool processors.

Standard Wool France SA, 157 rue de Roubaix, F-59336 Tourcoing, France

STANDARD MICROSYSTEMS CORPORATION

80 Arkay Drive, Hauppauge, NY, 11788

Tel: (631) 435-6000   Fax: (631) 273-5550   www.smsc.com

Telecommunications systems.

Insight France, Rungis, France

Tel: 33-1-4180-2900   Fax: 33-1-4686-6763

STANDEX INTERNATIONAL CORPORATION

6 Manor Parkway, Salem, NH, 03079

Tel: (603) 893-9701   Fax: (603) 893-7324   www.standex.com

Mfr. diversified graphics, institutional, industry, electronic and consumer products.

James Burn International SA, BP 134, 67 rue du Docteur Blaizot, F-61304 L'Aigle Cedex Orne, France

Tel: 33-233-842-150   Fax: 33-233-842-151   Contact: Guy Vatome, Mgr.

Mold-Tech S.A.R.L., Route Nationale 7, ZA Les Longues Raies, F-77310 Pringy, France

Tel: 33-1-60-65-7015   Fax: 33-1-60-65-6916   Contact: Patrick Cambier, Mgr.

STANLEY BOSTITCH FASTENING SYSTEMS

815 Briggs Street, East Greenwich, RI, 02818

Tel: (401) 884-2500   Fax: (401) 885-6511   www.stanleybostich.com

Mfr. stapling machines, stapling supplies, fastening systems and wire.

Stanley Bostitch, Maxonchamp, F-88360 Rupt sur Moselle, France

Stanley Bostitch France, BP 74, 112 ave. Charles de Gaulle, F-91423 Morangis Cedex, France

THE STANLEY WORKS

1000 Stanley Drive, PO Box 7000, New Britain, CT, 06053

Tel: (860) 225-5111   Fax: (860) 827-3987   www.stanleyworks.com

Mfr. hand tools and hardware.

Stanley Air Tools, Zone Immoparc, Route de Chartres, Bâtiment Loire 4, F-78197 Trappes, France

Stanley France, 112 Avenue Charles de Gaulle, F-91423 Morangis Cedex, France

Stanley Nirva, 17 Avenue industrielle, F-59520 Marquette Lez Lille, France

Stanley Tools, Rue Jouchoux, Zone Industrial Trepillot, F-25009 Besançon Cedex, France

STA-RITE INDUSTRIES INC.

293 Wright Street, Delavan, WI, 53115

Tel: (262) 728-5551   Fax: (262) 728-7323   www.sta-rite.com

Mfr. water pumps, filters and systems.

Nocchi Pompe, 6, Avenue de la Gloriette, Z.I. Flontcouverte, F-84000 Avignon, France

STARKEY LABORATORIES, INC.

6700 Washington Avenue South, Eden Prairie, MN, 55344

Tel: (952) 941-6401   Fax: (952) 947-4787   www.starkey.com

Mfr. custom in-the-ear hearing aids.

Starkey France, 23, rue Claude Nicolas Le Doux, Europarc Batiment 14, F-94000 Creteil, France

Tel: 33-1-4980-7474

STARTEC GLOBAL COMMUNICATIONS CORPORATION

1151 Seven Locks Road, Potomac, MD, 20854

Tel: (301) 610-4300   Fax: (301) 610-4301   www.startec.com

Provides international phone service.

Startec France, 30 rue Mozart, F-925787 Clichy Cedex, France

STARWOOD HOTELS & RESORTS WORLDWIDE

777 Westchester Avenue, White Plains, NY, 10604

Tel: (914) 640-8100   Fax: (914) 640-8316   www.starwoodhotels.com

Hotel operations including Sheraton, Westin, St. Regis, Four Points and Caesars.

Sheraton Sales Center, 89 Blvd. Haussmann, F-75008 Paris, France

STATE STREET CORPORATION

225 Franklin Street, Boston, MA, 02101

Tel: (617) 786-3000   Fax: (617) 654-3386   www.statestreet.com

Engaged in investment management and institutional investor services.

State Street Bank & Trust, 56 Avenue Samuel Champlain, F-34000 Montpellier, France

State Street Banque SA, 21/25 rue Balzac, F-75008 Paris, France

STEELCASE INC.

901 44th Street SE, Grand Rapids, MI, 49508

Tel: (616) 247-2710   Fax: (616) 248-7010   www.steelcase.com

Mfr. office, computer-support and systems furniture.

Steelcase Strafor SA, BP 6K, 56 rue Jean Giraudoux, F-67035 Strasbourg Cedex, France

STEINER CORPORATION

505 E. South Temple, Salt Lake City, UT, 84102

Tel: (801) 328-8831   Fax: (801) 363-5680   www.alsco.com

Mfr. soap and towel dispensers and uniforms.

Steiner Company International SA, 18, avenue Ferdinand-de-Lesseps, F-91422 Morangis, France

STELLENT, INC.

7777 Golden Triangle Drive, Eden Prairie, MN, 55344

Tel: (952) 903-2000   Fax: (952) 829-5424   www.stellent.com

Mfr. Web-based software products.

Stellent SARL, La Defense Colisee, 10, avenue de L'Arche, Faubourg de L'Arche, F-92419 Courbevoie, France

STEPAN COMPANY

22 West Frontage Rd., Northfield, IL, 60093

Tel: (847) 446-7500   Fax: (847) 501-2443   www.stepan.com

Mfr. basic intermediate chemicals.

Stepan Europe, BP 127, F-38340 Voreppe, France

STIEFEL LABORATORIES INC.

255 Alhambra Circle, Ste. 1000, Coral Gables, FL, 33134

Tel: (305) 443-3807   Fax: (305) 443-3467   www.stiefel.com

Mfr. pharmaceuticals, dermatological specialties.

Laboratoires Stiefel SARL, Z.I. du Petit Nanterre, 15 rue des Grands Pres, F-92000 Nanterre Cedex, France

STORAGE TECHNOLOGY CORPORATION

One Storagetech Dr., Louisville, CO, 80028-4377

Tel: (303) 673-5151   Fax: (303) 673-5019   www.stortek.com

Mfr., market, service information, storage and retrieval systems.

StorageTex European Ops S.A., 1 Rond-Point du General, Eisenhower, F-31106 Toulouse Cedex, France

Tel: 33-5-6214-3001   Fax: 33-5-6214-3030   Contact: Catherine Gaudeaux

STOWE WOODWARD MOUNT HOPE

One Technology Drive, Westborough, MA, 01581

Tel: (508) 616-9458   Fax: (508) 616-9479   www.stowewoodward.com

Mfr. roll covering and bowed roll technologies for the web handling industries.

Stowe Woodward France, 12 rue Jean Jaurés, F-69330 Meyzieu, France

Tel: 33-4-72 5770

STREAM INTERNATIONAL

85 Dan Road, Canton, MA, 02021

Tel: (781) 575-6800   Fax: (781) 575-6999   www.stream.com

Provider of outsourced technical support for major computer industry companies.

Steam International Services Corp., 23 ave. Louis Brequet, BP 257, F-78147 Velizy, France

Tel: 33-1-3067-1000   Fax: 3-1-3067-1005   Contact: Joop Heijenrath

THE STRUCTURE TONE ORGANIZATION

15 East 26th Street, New York, NY, 10010-1589

Tel: (212) 481-6100   Fax: (212) 685-9267   www.structuretone.com

Provides general contracting and construction management.

Structure Tone Organization, 390, rue St. Honore, F-75001 Paris, France

STRYKER CORPORATION

2725 Fairfield Rd., Kalamazoo, MI, 49002

Tel: (616) 385-2600   Fax: (616) 385-1062   www.strykercorp.com

Develops, manufactures and markets specialty surgical and medical products worldwide.

Stryker France, 13, rue de la Perdix, ZAC Paris Nord II, F-93290 Tremblay En, France

Contact: Bruno Corian

SUDLER & HENNESSEY

230 Park Avenue South, New York, NY, 10003-1566

Tel: (212) 614-4100   Fax: (212) 598-6933   www.sudler.com

Engaged in healthcare products advertising.

S&H/Paragraphe, 79 bis rue Dassault, F-92100 Boulogne Billancourt Paris, France

Tel: 33-1-46-10-5959   Fax: 33-1-46-10-5960   Contact: Catherine Verdieve

SULLAIR CORPORATION

3700 E. Michigan Blvd., Bldg. 1-2, Michigan City, IN, 46360

Tel: (219) 879-5451   Fax: (219) 874-1273   www.sullair.com

Mfr. high efficiency tandem compressors, vacuum systems, encapsulated compressors and air tools.

Sullair Europe SARL, Zone des Granges, BP 82, F-42602 Montbrison Cedex, France

Tel: 33-4-77-96-8470

SULLIVAN & CROMWELL

125 Broad Street, New York, NY, 10004-2498

Tel: (212) 558-4000   Fax: (212) 558-3588   www.sullcrom.com

Engaged in international law.

Sullivan & Cromwell, 8 Place Vendome, F-75001 Paris, France

SUN MICROSYSTEMS, INC.

901 San Antonio Road, Palo Alto, CA, 94303

Tel: (650) 960-1300   Fax: (650) 961-9131   www.sun.com

Computer peripherals and programming services.

Sun Microsystems France S.A., 13 Ave. Morane Saulnier, B.P. 53, F-78142 Velizy Cedex, France

Tel: 33-5-90-6157

SUNGARD DATA SYSTEMS

1285 Drummers Lane, Wayne, PA, 19087

Tel: (610) 341-8700   Fax: (610) 341-8851   www.sungard.com

Provides ASP solutions to the buyside investment management market.

SunGard Data Systems, 173 Bureaux de la Colline, Batiment E, F-92213 Saint-Cloud Paris, France

Tel: 33-1-49-11-3000   Contact: Bernard Hure

SUNRISE MEDICAL INC.

7477 East Dry Creek Parkway, Longmont, CO, 80503

Tel: (303) 218-4500   Fax: (303) 218-4590   www.sunrisemedical.com

Designs, manufactures and markets rehabilitation products and assistive technology devices for people with disabilities, and patient care products used in nursing homes, hospitals and homecare settings.

Sunrise Medical SA, Rochecorbon, Z.l La Planche, F-37210 Rochecorbon, France

Tel: 33-247-88-5858

SUPERIOR GRAPHITE COMPANY

10 South Riverside Plaza, Chicago, IL, 60606

Tel: (312) 559-2999   Fax: (312) 559-9064   www.graphitesgc.com

Mfr. natural and synthetic graphites, electrodes, lubricants, suspensions, carbide and carbon.

Foseco-SMC, 12 Ave. Marie Ampere, F-77420 Champs sur Marne, France

SYBASE, INC.

5000 Hacienda Dr., Dublin, CA, 94568

Tel: (925) 236-5000   Fax: (925) 236-4321   www.sybase.com

Design/mfg/distribution of database management systems, software development tools, connectivity products, consulting and technical support services..

Sybase France, 27 rue du Colonel Avia, F-75508 Paris Cedex 15, France

Tel: 33-1-41-90-4190   Fax: 33-1-41-90-4200

SYBRON DENTAL SPECIALTIES, INC.

1717 West Collins, Orange, CA, 92867

Tel: (714) 516-7400   Fax: (714) 516-7904   www.sybrondental.com

Mfr. consumable dental products, light curing instruments and plastics for dental use.

Kerr Succursale Francaise, 89 Boulevard Auguste Blanqui, F-75013 Paris, France

Tel: 33-1-4416-8860   Fax: 33-1-4416-8850

SYKES ENTERPRISES, INC.

100 N. Tampa Street, Ste. 3900, Tampa, FL, 33602

Tel: (813) 274-1000   Fax: (813) 273-0148   www.sykes.com

Provides information technology outsourcing services.

Sykes France, 1, Avenue de L`Atlantique, BP 970 Les Ulis, F-91976 Courtaboeuf Cedex, France

SYMANTEC CORPORATION

20330 Stevens Creek Blvd., Cupertino, CA, 95014-2132

Tel: (408) 253-9600   Fax: (408) 253-3968   www.symantec.com

Designs and produces PC network security and network management software and hardware.

Symantec SARL, 31-35 rue Gambetta, F-92150 Suresnes, France

Tel: 33-1-41-38-5700   Fax: 33-1-41-38-5729

SYMBOL TECHNOLOGIES, INC.

One Symbol Plaza, Holtsville, NY, 11742-1300

Tel: (631) 738-2400   Fax: (631) 738-5990   www.symbol.com

Mfr. Bar code-driven data management systems, wireless LAN's, and Portable Shopping System™.

Symbol Technologies France SA, Centre d'affaires d'Antony, 3, rue de la Renaissance, F-92184 Antony Cedex, France

Tel: 33-1-40-96-5200   Fax: 33-1-40-96-5252

SYNAVANT INC.

3445 Peachtree Road NE, Ste. 1400, Atlanta, GA, 30326

Tel: (404) 841-4000   Fax: (404) 841-4115   www.synavant.com

Mfr. support software for pharmaceutical industry.

Synavant, 185/187 Avenue du Général Leclerc, F-78220 Viroflay, France

SYNBIOTICS CORPORATION

11011 Via Frontera, San Diego, CA, 92127

Tel: (858) 451-3771   Fax: (858) 451-5719   www.synbiotics.

Mfr. diagnostic health care products for animal health care.

Synbiotics Europe, 2, rue Alexander Fleming, F-69367 Lyon Cedex 07, France

Tel: 33-472-761111

SYNOPSYS, INC.

700 East Middlefield Road, Mountain View, CA, 94043

Tel: (650) 962-5000   Fax: (650) 965-8637   www.synopsys.com

Mfr. electronic design automation software.

Synopsys SARL, 24 rue Saarinen Silic 217, F-94518 Rungis Cedex, France

Tel: 33-1-4512-0606   Fax: 33-1-4512-0707

Synopsys SARL, 1 allee de Certeze, F-18610 Gieres Grenoble, France

Tel: 33-4-763-7010

SYNPLICITY, INC.

935 Stewart Drive, Sunnyvale, CA, 94085

Tel: (408) 215-6000   Fax: (408) 990-0290   www.synplicity.com

Mfr. software.

Synplicity France, Europarc de Pichaury Bat B5, F-13856 Aix-en-Provence, France

SYNTEGRA

4201 Lexington Avenue North, Arden Hills, MN, 55126-6198

Tel: (651) 415-2999   Fax: (651) 415-4891   www.cdc.com

Engaged in consulting and systems integration.

Syntegra France, Le Capitole, 55 Ave. des Champs Pierreux, F-92012 Nanterre Cedex Paris, France

Tel: 33-1-41-37-8000   Fax: 33-1-41-37-8001

SYSTEMAX INC.

22 Harbor Park Dr., Port Washington, NY, 11050

Tel: (516) 608-7000   Fax: (516) 608-7111   www.systemax.com

Direct marketer of computers and related products to businesses.

HCS Misco France, BP 69, Verrieres le Buisson, F-91371 Cedex Paris, France

Tel: 33-1-6993-2121

TACONIC LTD.

PO Box 69, 136 Coon Brook Road, Petersburg, NY, 12138

Tel: (518) 658-3202   Fax: (518) 658-3204   www.4taconic.com

Mfr. Teflon/silicone-coated fiberglass fabrics, tapes and belts; specialty tapes and circuit board substrates.

Taconic France, Za Des Vernays, Leiu-Dit "Lecouarnet", F-74210 Doussard, France

Tel: 33-450-443147   Fax: 33-450-448845

TARANTELLA, INC.

425 Encinal Street, Santa Cruz, CA, 95060

Tel: (831) 425-7222　　　Fax: (831) 427-5400　　　www.tarantella.com

Mfr. server software.

Tarantella France, 6, rue de Clignancourt, F-75018 Paris, France

TBWA WORLDWIDE

488 Madison Avenue, 6th Floor, New York, NY, 10022

Tel: (212) 804-1000　　　Fax: (212) 804-1200　　　www.tbwachiat.com

International full service advertising agency.

TBWA, Paris, France

TEAM, INC.

Box 123, 200 Hermann Dr., Alvin, TX, 77511

Tel: (281) 331-6154　　　Fax: (281) 331-4107　　　www.teamindustrialservices.com

Consulting, engineering and rental services.

Team Inc. Europe B.V., Paris, France

Tel: 33-442-39-7438　Fax: 33-442-39-7422

TECA CORPORATION (THERMO ELECTRIC COOLING AMERICA

4048 West Schubert, Chicago, IL, 60639

Tel: (773) 342-4900　　　Fax: (773) 342-0191　　　www.thermoelectric.com

Mfr. solid state cooling products, including air-conditioners, cold plates and liquid chillers.

Thermo Electric SA, 25 rue Pasteur, F-94456 Limeil Brevannes Cedex, France

TECH DATA CORPORATION

5350 Tech Data Drive, Clearwater, FL, 33760

Tel: (727) 539-7429　　　Fax: (727) 538-7876　　　www.techdata.com

Distributor of computer systems, software and related equipment.

Tech Data (TD), 29 Av. Henri Barbusse, 390 Bobiny, Cedex, France

TECH/OPS SEVCON INC.

40 North Avenue, Burlington, MA, 01803

Tel: (781) 229-7896　　　Fax: (781) 229-8603　　　www.sevcon.com

Design, manufacture, and marketing of microprocessor based control systems for battery powered vehicles.

Sevcon SA, 12, rue Jean Poulmarch, F-95100 Argenteuil, France

TECHNITROL INC.

1210 Northbrook Drive, #385, Trevose, PA, 19053

Tel: (215) 355-2900　　　Fax: (215) 355-7397　　　www.technitrol.com

Mfr. of electronic components, electrical contacts, and other parts/materials.

Technitrol Inc., Attn: French Office, 1210 Northbrook Drive Suite 285, Trevose, PA, 19053

TECHNOLOGY SOLUTIONS COMPANY (TSC)

205 N. Michigan Ave., Ste. 1500, Chicago, IL, 60601

Tel: (312) 228-4500　　　Fax: (312) 228-4501　　　www.techsol.com

Designs computer information systems and strategic business and management consulting for major corporations.

TSC Europe, 19 Boulevard Malesherbes, F-75008 Paris, France

Tel: 33-1-55-27-3663　Fax: 33-1-55-27-3847　Contact: Philippe Villaeys

TECUMSEH PRODUCTS COMPANY

100 E. Patterson Street, Tecumseh, MI, 49286-1899

Tel: (517) 423-8411　　　Fax: (517) 423-8526　　　www.tecumseh.com

Mfr. of hermetic compressors for air conditioning and refrigeration products, gasoline engines and power train components for lawn and garden applications, and pumps.

L'Unite Hermetique, F-38290 La Verpilliere, France

TIGER Moteurs Industriels, 1A 3 rue d'Anjou, Z.A. des Bethunes-St. Oune l'Aumone, BP 9094, F-95073 Cergy Pontoise Cedex, France

TEKELEC

26580 West Agoura Road, Calabasas, CA, 91302

Tel: (818) 880-5656   Fax: (818) 880-6993   www.tekelec.com

Mfr. telecommunications testing equipment.

Tekelec Europe, 5 rue Carle Vernet, F-92315 Sevres Cedex, France

Tel: 33-1-46-23-25-63

TEKTRONIX INC.

14200 SW Karl Braun Dr., PO Box 500, Beaverton, OR, 97077

Tel: (503) 627-7111   Fax: (503) 627-2406   www.tek.com

Mfr. test and measure, visual systems/color printing and communications/video and networking products.

Tektronix S.A. France, Batiment Omega Tech 3, Ave. de Canada, BP13, F-91941 Courtaboeuf Les Ulis Cedex, France

Tel: 33-1-69-86-8181   Fax: 33-1-69-07-0937

TELCORDIA TECHNOLOGIES, INC.

445 South Street, Morristown, NJ, 07960-6438

Tel: (973) 829-2000   Fax: (973) 829-3172   www.telecordia.com

Mfr. telecom software.

Telcordia Technologies Inc./SAIC, 2229 route des Cretes, F-06560 Sophia Antipolis, France

Telcordia Technologies Inc./SAIC, 10/12 av. de l'arche, F-92 419 Courbevoie Cedex, France

Tel: 33-1-4691-8849

TELEFLEX INC.

630 W. Germantown Pike, Ste. 450, Plymouth Meeting, PA, 19462

Tel: (610) 834-6301   Fax: (610) 834-8307   www.teleflex.com

Design, manufacture and marketing of mechanical and electro-mechanical systems, control systems and surgical devices.

Asept Inmed S.A., Le Faget, France

Pilling Weck Europe, Le Faget, France

Rüsch France S.A.R.L., Betschdorf, France

Sermatech Manufacturing Group, LaPacaudiere, France

TFX Marine European Sales Office, LaRochelle, France

United Parts France S.A., Cluses Cedex, France

TELEX COMMUNICATIONS INC.

12000 Portland Ave. South, Burnsville, MN, 55337

Tel: (952) 884-4051   Fax: (952) 884-0043   www.telexcommunications.com

Mfr. communications, audio-visual and professional audio products.

EVI Audio France, S.A., Parc de Courcerin, Allee Lech Walesa, F-77185 Lognes Marne La Vallee, France

TELLABS INC.

1415 W. Diehl Rd., Naperville, IL, 60563

Tel: (630) 378-8800   Fax: (630) 852-7346   www.tellabs.com

Design/mfr./service voice/data transport and network access systems.

Tellabs France, 6 Parc Club Ariane, Bâtiment Mercure, Boulevard des Chênes, F-78284 Guyancourt Cedex, France

TENNECO AUTOMOTIVE INC.

500 North Field Drive, Lake Forest, IL, 60045

Tel: (847) 482-5241   Fax: (847) 482-5295   www.tenneco-automotive.com

Mfr. automotive parts, exhaust systems and service equipment.

Gillet Tubes Technologies S.A.R.L., Re des Fontangues, Zone Industrielle, B.P. 31, F-55400 Etain, France

Tel: 33-29-83-2250   Fax: 33-29-87-8900   Contact: Juergen Blum, Mgr.   Emp: 125

Monroe France, 7 Ave de Fief, F-95310 Saint Ouen L' Aumone, France

Walker France SA, BP 4149, La Croix des Landes, F-53500 Ernee, France

Tel: 33-2-43-59-1160   Fax: 33-2-43-59-1166   Contact: Daniel Bellanger, Mgr.   Emp: 627

TERADATA

1700 South Patterson Blvd., Dayton, OH, 45479

Tel: (937) 445-5000   Fax: (937) 445-1682   www.teradata.com

Mfr. software to store information.

Teradata Div., NCR, 1, Square John H. Patterson, F-91749 Massy, France

TERADYNE INC.

321 Harrison Ave., Boston, MA, 02118

Tel: (617) 482-2700   Fax: (617) 422-2910   www.teradyne.com

Mfr. electronic test equipment and blackplane connection systems.

Teradyne SA, ZAC Kleber Batiment F, 165 blvd. de Valmy, F-92700 Colombes, France

TEXAS INSTRUMENTS INC.

12500 TI Blvd., Dallas, TX, 75266

Tel: (972) 995-3773   Fax: (972) 995-4360   www.ti.com

Mfr. semiconductor devices, electronic electro-mechanical systems, instruments and controls.

Texas Instruments France, Velizy, France

TEXTRON INC.

40 Westminster Street, Providence, RI, 02903

Tel: (401) 421-2800   Fax: (401) 421-2878   www.textron.com

Mfr. Aerospace (Bell Helicopter and Cessna Aircraft), industry and consumer products, fasteners and financial services.

Avdel SA, 33 Bis, Rue des Ardennes, F-75017 Paris Cedex 19, France

Tel: 33-1-40-40-8000   Fax: 33-1-40-40-8040   Contact: Marie-Claude Vaquie

THERMO ELECTRON CORPORATION

81 Wyman Street, Waltham, MA, 02454-9046

Tel: (781) 622-1000   Fax: (781) 622-1207   www.thermo.com

Develop, mfr., sale of process equipment &instruments for energy intensive and healthcare industries.

Nicolet Biomedical SARL, 1 rue Blaise Pascal, Batiment C, B.P. 144, F-7816 Trappes Cedex, France

THERMO FINNIGAN CORPORATION

355 River Oaks Parkway, San Jose, CA, 95134-1991

Tel: (408) 433-4800   Fax: (408) 433-4823   www.thermo.com

Mfr. mass spectrometers.

Thermo Finnigan, 12 Avenue des Tropiques, Z. A de courtaboeuf-BP 141, F-91944 Les Ulis, France

Contact: Rene Petit

THERMO NICOLET CORPORATION

5225 Verona Road, Madison, WI, 53711-4495

Tel: (608) 276-6100   Fax: (608) 276-6222   www.nicolet.com

Mfr. infrared spectrometers and oscilloscopes and medical electro-diagnostic equipment.

Thermo Optek S.A.R.L., Zone d'Activites du Pas du Lac, 1 Square Franklin, F-78180 Montigny le Bretonneux, France

Tel: 33-1-3930-5300

THERMO RAMSEY INC.

501 90th Avenue NW, Minneapolis, MN, 55433

Tel: (763) 783-2500   Fax: (763) 780-2525   www.thermoramsey.com

Mfr. of industrial control products.

Thermo Ramsey, 63 Place du Commerce, F-78370 Plaisir, France

THERMON MANUFACTURING COMPANY

100 Thermon Drive, PO Box 609, San Marcos, TX, 78667-0609

Tel: (512) 396-5801   Fax: (512) 396-3627   www.thermon.com

Mfr. steam and electric heat tracing systems, components and accessories.

Thermon France, 1 a 15 rue de Valmy, Lot #10, F-93100 Montreuil, France

THETFORD CORPORATION

7101 Jackson Road, PO Box 1285, Ann Arbor, MI, 48106

Tel: (734) 769-6000   Fax: (734) 769-2023   www.thetford.com

Mfr. sanitation products and chemicals.

Thetford S.A.R.L., BP 204, F-95614 Cergy Pontoise Cedex, France

THOMAS & BETTS CORPORATION

8155 T&B Blvd., Memphis, TN, 38125

Tel: (901) 252-5000   Fax: (901) 685-1988   www.tnb.com

Mfr. elect/electronic connectors and accessories.

Thomas & Betts France, 57 Place de la Seine, Silic 120, F-94513 Rungis Cedex, France

THOMAS PUBLISHING COMPANY

5 Penn Plaza, New York, NY, 10007

Tel: (212) 695-0500   Fax: (212) 290-7362   www.thomaspublishing.com

Publishing magazines and directories.

Editions Thomas/Elsevier SA, 128 rue Daguesseau, F-92100 Boulogne-Billancourt, France

THQ, INC.

27001 Agoura Road, Ste. 325, Calabasas Hills, CA, 91301

Tel: (818) 871-5000   Fax: (818) 591-1615   www.thw.com

Engaged in publishing of video game titles.

THQ Entertainment, 32, rue de Paradis, F-75010 Paris, France

TIBCO SOFTWARE INC.

3165 Porter Drive, Palo Alto, CA, 94304

Tel: (650) 846-5000   Fax: (650) 846-1005   www.tibco.com

Mfr. software and provides e-commerce, consulting, and support services. (JV of Reuters UK)

TIBCO Software Inc., 70 Avenue du General de Gaulle, F-92058 Puteaux La Defense Cedex, France
Tel: 33-1-5813-5560

TIDEWATER INC.

601 Poydras Street, Ste.1900, New Orleans, LA, 70130

Tel: (504) 568-1010   Fax: (504) 566-4582   www.tdw.com

Marine service and equipment to companies engaged in exploration, development and production of oil, gas and minerals.

S.A.M.I. (Socite D'Affretement), SA, 35 rue Bergere, F-75009 Paris, France
Tel: 33-1-44-83-68-68   Fax: 33-1-44-83-68-69

THE TIMBERLAND COMPANY

200 Domain Drive, Stratham, NH, 03885

Tel: (603) 772-9500   Fax: (603) 773-1640   www.timberland.com

Design/mfr. footwear, apparel and accessories for men and women.

Timberland SARL, Space Antipolis Immeuble 9, 2323 Chemin de St. Bernard, F-06220 Vallauris, France

TIMEX CORPORATION

555 Christian Rd., Middlebury, CT, 06762

Tel: (203) 573-5000   Fax: (203) 573-7019   www.timex.com

Mfr. watches, clocks, timing instruments.

Usine Kelton, 1 rue Denis Papin, F-25011 Besancon, France

THE TIMKEN COMPANY

1835 Dueber Ave. SW, PO Box 6932, Canton, OH, 44706-0932

Tel: (330) 438-3000   Fax: (330) 471-4118   www.timken.com

Mfr. tapered roller bearings and quality alloy steels.

Timken France, 2 rue Timken, BP 89, F-68002 Colmar Cedex, France

TIMKEN SUPER PRECISION

PO Box 547 Precision Park, Keene, NH, 03431-0547

Tel: (603) 352-0310   Fax: (603) 355-4553   www.timken.com

Mfr., sales and distribution of bearings, tape guides and systems for missiles, etc.

Timken Super Precision, Succersale France, 14 Bureau A101 Bis, rue de Mal Foch, F-77780 Bourron-Marlotte, France

Tel: 33-1-644-59880

TITANIUM METALS CORPORATION (TIMET)

1999 Broadway, Suite 4300, Denver, CO, 80202

Tel: (303) 296-5600   Fax: (303) 296-5650   www.timet.com

Produce light weight titanium sponge (metal) for aerospace and auto industries.

TIMET France SARL, Avenue Paul Girod, F-73400 Ugine, France

TIW CORPORATION

12300 S. Main Street, PO Box 35729, Houston, TX, 77035

Tel: (713) 729-2110   Fax: (713) 728-4767   www.tiwtools.com

Mfr. liner hanger equipment, production packers, safety and kelly valves.

TIW France, Paris, France

Tel: 33-1-30-50-12-16   Fax: 33-4-92-74-64-52

TMP WORLDWIDE, INC.

622 Third Ave., New York, NY, 10017

Tel: (212) 351-7000   Fax: (212) 658-0540   www.tmpw.com

#1 Yellow Pages agency and a leader in the recruitment and interactive advertising fields.

TMP Worldwide Advertising & Communications, 3 Boulevard Bineau, F-92594 Levallois Perret, France

TMP Worldwide Advertising & Communications, 8 rue Duquesne, F-69006 Lyon, France

TOGETHERSOFT CORPORATION

900 Main Campus Drive, Ste. 500, Raleigh, NC, 27606

Tel: (919) 833-5550   Fax: (919) 833-5533   www.togethersoft.com

Mfr. software.

TogetherSoft France, 104 Avenue Albert Premier, F-92563 Rueil Malmaison Cedex, France

TOKHEIM CORPORATION

PO Box 360, 10501 Corporate Drive, Fort Wayne, IN, 46845

Tel: (219) 470-4600   Fax: (219) 482-2677   www.tokheim.com

Engaged in design, manufacture and service of electronic and mechanical petroleum marketing systems.

Tokheim Europe, AC Paris Nord 2, B.P. 40027, F-95912 Roissy Cedex, France

Tokheim Services France, 9, ave. Galilee, F-92350 Les Plessis Robinson, France

Tokheim Sofitam, Foute de Soliers, F-14540 Grentheville, France

Tokheim Sofitam Applications, 5, rue des Chardonnerets ZAC, F-93290 Paris-Nord 2, France

TOPFLIGHT CORPORATION

277 Commerce Dr., Glen Rock, PA, 17327

Tel: (717) 227-5400   Fax: (717) 227-1415   www.topflight.com

Commercial printing and service paper.

Topflight France, Chatou Cedex, France

TOTES ISOTONER CORPORATION

9655 International Blvd., PO Box 465658, Cincinnati, OH, 45246

Tel: (513) 682-8200   Fax: (513) 682-8602   www.totes.com

Mfr. rubber and plastic footwear, slippers, umbrellas.

Totes France, Paris, France

TOWERS PERRIN

335 Madison Ave., New York, NY, 10017-4605

Tel: (212) 309-3400   Fax: (212) 309-0975   www.towers.com

Management consulting services.

Towers Perrin, Tor Neptune La Defense 1, 20 Place de Seine, F-92086 Paris la Defense Cedex, France

Tel: 33-1-4102-0202 Fax: 33-1-4102-5454

TOYS R US INC.

461 From Road, Paramus, NJ, 07652

Tel: (201) 262-7800   Fax: (201) 845-0973   www.toysrus.com

Retail stores: toys and games, sporting goods, computer software, books, records.

Toys R Us SARL, 2 rue Thomas Edison, Evry, F-91044 Essonne, France

THE TRANE COMPANY

3600 Pammel Creek Road, La Crosse, WI, 54601

Tel: (608) 787-2000   Fax: (608) 787-4990   www.trane.com

Mfr. distribution and service of A/C systems and equipment.

Societe Trane, 5, blvd. de la Grande Thumine, ZAC du Jas de Bouffan, F-13090 Aix-en-Provence, France

Societe Trane, 1 rue des Ameriques, BP 6, F-88191 Golbey Cedex, France

Societe Trane, Direction Regionale Nord, 62 rue des Meuniers, F-92220 Bagneux, France

Societe Trane, Direction Regionale Sud, Allee de la Combe, F-69380 Lissieu, France

TRANSATLANTIC HOLDINGS, INC.

80 Pine Street, New York, NY, 10005

Tel: (212) 770-2000   Fax: (212) 289-6801   www.transre.com

Engaged in reinsurance.

TRC Paris, 4 Rue Auber, F-75009 Paris, France

TRANSOCEAN INC.

4 Greenway Plaza, Houston, TX, 77046

Tel: (713) 232-7500   Fax: (713) 232-7027   www.deepwater.com

Engaged in oil and gas offshore drilling.

Transocean Inc., 50, Avenue Jean-Jaures Building Z, F-92542 Montrouge Cedex, France

TRANSWITCH CORPORATION

3 Enterprise Drive, Shelton, CT, 06484

Tel: (203) 929-8810   Fax: (203) 926-9453   www.transwitch.com

Design and manufacture of mixed signal semiconductors.

TranSwitch France, 5-7 Rue Marcelin Berthelot, F-92762 Antony Cedex, France

TRANTER PHE, INC.

PO Box 2289, Wichita Falls, TX, 76306

Tel: (940) 723-7125   Fax: (940) 723-1131   www.tranter.com

Mfr. heat exchangers.

SWEP France SA, 77 Rue Auguste Renoir, ZI Croix Sant Marc, BP 135, F-93623 Aulnay-sous-Bois Cedex, France

Tel: 33-1-48-19-8709 Fax: 33-1-48-69-3415

TREIBACHER SCHLEIFMITTEL CORPORATION

2000 College Ave., Niagara Falls, NY, 14305

Tel: (716) 286-1234   Fax: (716) 286-1224   www.treibacher-schleifm.com

Mfr. abrasives.

Treibacher Schleifmittel, Parc Club du Golf, Batiment 22, F-13856 Aix en Provence Cedex 3, France

TRENWICK GROUP LTD.

1 Canterbury Green, Stamford, CT, 06901

Tel: (203) 353-5500   Fax: (203) 353-5550   www.trenwick.com

Insurance holding group.

Trenwick International, 264 Rue du Faubourg Saint Honore, F-75008 Paris, France

TRIMBLE NAVIGATION LIMITED

645 N. Mary Ave., Sunnyvale, CA, 94086

Tel: (408) 481-8000   Fax: (408) 481-2000   www.trimble.com

Design/mfr. electronic geographic instrumentation.

Trimble Navigation France S.A., Centre d'Affairs Les Econdeaux, F-93800 Epinay sur Seine, France

Tel: 33-2-99-26-3181   Fax: 33-2-99-26-3900

TRIPOS, INC.

1699 S. Hanley Road, St. Louis, MO, 63144

Tel: (314) 647-1099   Fax: (314) 647-9241   www.tripos.com

Mfr. pharmaceutical software for research.

Tripos SARL, Buromaster, 2, rue Luigi Galvani, F-92160 Antony, France

Tel: 33-1-46-11-4444

TRIUMPH GROUP, INC.

1255 Drummer Lane, Ste. 200, Wayne, PA, 19087

Tel: (610) 975-0420   Fax: (610) 975-0563   www.triumphgrp.com

Mfr. aircraft engines and parts.

CBS, 189-191 rue Paul Vailant Couturier, F-94140 Alfortville, France

TROPICANA PRODUCTS, INC.

1001 13th Avenue East, Bradenton, FL, 34208

Tel: (941) 747-4461   Fax: (941) 665-5330   www.tropicana.com

Marketer and producer of branded juices, including Tropicana, Dole, Looza and Copella.

Loóza Distribution France S.A., 67 rue de Margueri, F-60370 Hermes, France

Tropicana France, Continental Square Batiment Uranus, Place de Londeres, F-95727 Roissy, France

TRUSERV CORPORATION

8600 West Bryn Mawr, Chicago, IL, 60631-3505

Tel: (773) 695-5000   Fax: (773) 695-6541   www.truserv.com

Dealer-owned, independent, hardware store cooperative.

TruServ Corporation, Paris, France

TRW INC.

1900 Richmond Road, Cleveland, OH, 44124-2760

Tel: (216) 291-7000   Fax: (216) 291-7932   www.trw.com

Electric and energy-related products, automotive and aerospace products, tools and fasteners.

Gemmer France, 97 rue de Verdun, F-92151 Suresnes Seine, France

Le Thillot, Vosges, France

Societe de Mecanique de Pringy, 74 Pringy, Haute Savoie, France

Societe Hydro-Mecanique Pleuger, 21 rue de la Mouchetierre, ZI d'Ingres, Saint Jean de la Ruelle, F-45140 Orleans, France

Societe Metallurgique G. Jeudy, 31 rue des Forges, F-67130 Schirmeck, France

TRW Composants Electroniques, ave. de la Jalle Re, F-33300 Bordeaux-Lac, France

TRW Mission Hydrosys. SA, Monceau Commerce Bldg., 38 rue de Lisbonne, F-75008 Paris, France

TTI, INC.

2441 Northeast Pkwy., Fort Worth, TX, 76106-1896

Tel: (817) 740-9000   Fax: (817) 740-9898   www.ttiinc.com

Distribution of resistors and capacitors, including cables and sockets.

TTI, Inc., Buro Frankreich Claredent, F-19360 Malemort, France

TUPPERWARE CORPORATION

14901 S. Orange Blossom Trail, Orlando, FL, 32837

Tel: (407) 826-5050   Fax: (407) 826-8268   www.tupperware.com

Engaged in direct selling of plastic household products.

Tupperware France, Paris, France

TUTHILL CORPORATION

8500 S. Madison Street, Burr Ridge, Il, 60521

Tel: (630) 382-4900   Fax: (630) 362-4999   www.tuthill.com

Mfr. diversified industrial products, including auto controls, pedals, axels, pneumatic systems and pumps.

Tuthill Corporation, 7, rue de Biches, Ville-la-Grand, F-74112 Annemasse Cedex, France

TW METALS INC.

760 Constitution Drive, Ste. 204, Exton, PA, 19341

Tel: (610) 458-1300   Fax: (610) 458-1399   www.twmetals.com

Engaged in metals distribution and processing.

Philip Cornes Ltd., Rue Jean Monet, Za Des Varigionas, F-451 30 Saint Aye, France

Contact: Christian Belleux

TYCO CAPITAL

1211 Avenue of the Americas, New York, NY, 10036

Tel: (212) 536-1390   Fax: (212) 536-1912   www.citgroup.com

Engaged in commercial finance.

Newcourt SNC, Le Patio de Rueil, 104 Avenue Albert 1er, F-92500 Rueil Malmaison Paris, France

Tel: 33-147-529500

UAL CORPORATION

1200 E. Algonquin Rd., Chicago, IL, 60007

Tel: (847) 700-4000   Fax: (847) 700-4081   www.ual.com

Air transportation, passenger and freight services.

United Airlines, 40 rue Jean Jaures, F-93176 Bagnolet Cedex, France

UNION CARBIDE CORPORATION

39 Old Ridgebury Road, Danbury, CT, 06817

Tel: (203) 794-2000   Fax: (203) 794-6269   www.unioncarbide.com

Mfr. industrial chemicals, plastics and resins.

Union Carbide Chemicals France SA, 4 Place des Etats-Unis, F-94518 Rungis, France

UNISYS CORPORATION.

PO Box 500, Union Meeting Road, Blue Bell, PA, 19424

Tel: (215) 986-4011   Fax: (215) 986-6850   www.unisys.com

Mfr./marketing/servicing electronic information systems.

Unisys France Sa, La Palette Orange, Cergy, F-95015 Val d'Oise, France

UNITED PARCEL SERVICE, INC.

55 Glenlake Parkway, NE, Atlanta, GA, 30328

Tel: (404) 828-6000   Fax: (404) 828-6593   www.ups.com

International package-delivery service.

Espaces Express UPS, 34 blvd. Malesherbes, F-75008 Paris, France

Tel: 800-877-877

UNITED STATES SURGICAL CORPORATION

150 Glover Ave., Norwalk, CT, 06856

Tel: (203) 845-1000   Fax: (203) 847-0635   www.ussurg.com

Mfr./development/market surgical staplers, laparoscopic instruments and sutures.

U.S. Surgical, Div. Tyco Healthcare, 50 rue Pierre Curie, Z.I. les Gatines, F-78370 Plaisir, France

UNITED TECHNOLOGIES CORPORATION

One Financial Plaza, Hartford, CT, 06103

Tel: (860) 728-7000   Fax: (860) 728-7979   www.utc.com

Mfr. aircraft engines, elevators, A/C, auto equipment, space and military electronic and rocket propulsion systems. Products include Pratt and Whitney, Otis elevators, Carrier heating and air conditioning and Sikorsky helicopters.

United Technologies Intl. Operations Inc., 141 rue de Saussure, F-75017 Paris, France

UNIVERSAL SECURITY INSTRUMENTS, INC.

PO Box 825, Binghamton, NY, 13902-0825

Tel: (607) 779-7689   Fax: (607) 779-7301   www.uic.com

Provider of innovative electronic circuit assembly technology and equipment, integrated system solutions, and process expertise.

Universal Instruments SARL, Gennevilliers, France

Tel: 33-1-41-11-4123   Fax: 33-1-40-86-9954

UNIVERSAL WEATHER & AVIATION INC.

8787 Tallyho Road, Houston, TX, 77061

Tel: (713) 944-1622   Fax: (713) 943-4650   www.univ-wea.com

Provides service management, and worldwide weather and communications to the corporate aviation community.

Universal Aviation France SA, Aeroport de Paris Bourget, Hangar 5, Bat 44, Le Bourget, F-93350 Seine St. Denis, France

Tel: 33-1-4835-9638   Fax: 33-1-4835-8546   Contact: Sandrine Laroche-Jackson

UNUM PROVIDENT

2211 Congress Street, Portland, ME, 04122

Tel: (207) 770-2211   Fax: (207) 770-4510   www.unum.com

Disability and special risk insurance.

Unum France, 21/23 rue Renan, F- 69007 Lyon, France

Tel: 33-4-78-619797

UOP LLC

25 East Algonquin Road, Des Plaines, IL, 60017

Tel: (847) 391-2000   Fax: (847) 391-2253   www.uop.com

Engaged in developing and commercializing technology for license to the oil refining, petrochemical and gas processing industries.

UOP France SARL, 24 rue Saarinen, SILIC 252, F-94568 Rungis Cedex, France

Tel: 33-1-41-80-1660   Fax: 33-1-41-80-1666

URS CORPORATION

100 California Street, Ste. 500, San Francisco, CA, 94111

Tel: (415) 774-2700   Fax: (415) 398-1905   www.urscorp.com

Engineering, environmental and construction management services.

Dames & Moore, 2 rue de Marly-le-Roi, F-78150 Le Chesnay, France

Dames & Moore France, 87, avenue François Arago, F-92017 Nanterre Cedex, France

URSCHEL LABORATORIES INC.

2503 Calumet Ave., PO Box 2200, Valparaiso, IN, 46384-2200

Tel: (219) 464-4811   Fax: (219) 462-3879   www.urschel.com

Design/mfr. precision food processing equipment.

Urschel Intl. Ltd., Orly Fret 747, F-94398 Orly Aerogare Cedex, France

US AIRWAYS GROUP, INC.

2345 Crystal Drive, Arlington, VA, 22227

Tel: (703) 872-7000   Fax: (703) 294-5096   www.usairways.com

Commercial airline.

USAir Inc., Charles de Gaulle Airport, BP 20247, F-95712 Paris Roisy, France

UUNET

22001 Loudoun County Pkwy., Ashburn, VA, 20147

Tel: (703) 206-5600   Fax: (703) 206-5601   www.uu.net

World's largest Internet service provider; World Wide Web hosting services, security products and consulting services to businesses, professionals, and on-line service providers.

UUNET France, 215 Avenue Georges, Le Clemenceau 2, F-92000 Nanterre Cedex, France

Tel: 33-1-56-38-22-00   Fax: 33-156-38-2201   Contact: Jerome Lecat

VALHI INC.

5430 LBJ Freeway, Ste. 1700, Dallas, TX, 75240

Tel: (972) 233-1700   Fax: (972) 450-4278

Holding company engaged in the chemicals, component products, titanium metals and waste management industries.

Bentone-Sud SA, 11 ave. Morane Saulnier, F-78140 Yvelines, France

Societe Industrielle du Titane SA, 45 rue de Courcelles, F-75008 Paris, France

VALMONT INDUSTRIES INC.

1 Valmont Plaza, Omaha, NE, 68154

Tel: (402) 963-1000   Fax: (402) 963-1199   www.valmont.com

Mfr. irrigation systems, steel lighting, utility and communication poles.

Sermeto - Industrial Equipment Division, Les Rebrillons, F-03330 Creuzier-Le-Neuf, France

Tel: 33-470-58-4740   Fax: 33-470-58-0022

Valmont Sermeto-Charmeil, Les Martoulets-B.P.1, F-03110 Charmeil, France

Tel: 33-470-58-8686   Fax: 33-470-58-8687   Contact: Philippe Guidez

Valmont Tubalco, Vallee de Couzon, F-42800 Rive-de-Gier, France

Tel: 33-477-83-0010   Fax: 33-477-83-7425   Contact: Paul von Iseghem

VALSPAR CORPORATION

1101 South Third Street, Minneapolis, MN, 55415-1259

Tel: (612) 332-7371   Fax: (612) 375-7723   www.valspar.com

Mfr. paints and coatings.

The Valspar (France) Corporation, S.A., Boîte Postale 51, 14 Rue Chanay, F-71700 Tournus, France

VARIAN MEDICAL SYSTEMS, INC.

3050 Hansen Way, Palo Alto, CA, 94304-100

Tel: (650) 493-4000   Fax: (650) 424-5358   www.varian.com

Mfr. microwave tubes and devices, analytical instruments, semiconductor process and medical equipment, vacuum systems.

Varian Medical France, C.A.A. Tolbiac-Massena, C.E. 16, 5 rue Watt, F-75644 Paris Cedex 13, France

VARIAN SEMICONDUCTOR EQUIPMENT ASSOCIATES, INC. (VSEA)

35 Dory Road, Gloucester, MA, 01930

Tel: (978) 281-2000   Fax: (978) 283-5391   www.vsea.com

Mfr. semiconductors and ion implantation systems.

Varian Semiconductor Equipment Assocates, Les Conquerants, 1 Avenue de l'Atlantique, BP 906, F-91976 Courtaboeuf Cedex, France

Tel: 33-1-6986-3838

VASCO DATA SECURITY INTERNATIONAL, INC.

1901 South Meyers Road, Ste. 210, Oakbrook Terrace, IL, 60181

Tel: (630) 932-8844   Fax: (630) 932-8852   www.vasco.com

Mfr. and sales of security computer software.

Vasco France, Immeuble Titanium, rue Cantelaudette, F-22210 Lormont, France

Vasco France, 4, Place de la Defense, F-02074 Paris, France

VEECO INSTRUMENTS INC.

100 Sunnyside Blvd., Woodbury, NY, 11797

Tel: (516) 677-0200   Fax: (516) 677-9125   www.veeco.com

Mfr. surface profiler, atomic force microscopes, leak and plating thickness detectors and semiconductor products.

Veeco S.A., 11 rue Maire Poussepin, Zi de la Gare, F-91412 Dourdan, France

Tel: 33-1-64-59-3520   Fax: 33-1-64-59-7222

VEEDER-ROOT COMPANY

125 Powder Forest Drive, PO Box 2003, Simsbury, CT, 06070-2003

Tel: (860) 651-2700   Fax: (860) 651-2704   www.veeder.com

Mfr. of automatic tank gauging systems.

Veeder-Root SARL, ZI des Mardelles, 94-106 rue Blaise Pascal, F-93600 Aulnay Sous Bois, France

VELCRO USA INC.

406 Brown Avenue, Manchester, NH, 03108

Tel: (603) 669-4892   Fax: (603) 669-9271   www.velcro.com

Mfr./sales of Velcro brand hook and loop fasteners, plastic buckles and metal hardware and cable control straps.

Systems de Fermeture S.A., Zone d'Activite Valnor, BP62, 21-23 rue Des Jeunes Chiens, F-95508 Le Thillay, France

Tel: 33-1-39-88100   Fax: 33-1-39-889161

VENTIV HEALTH, INC.

1114 Avenue of the Americas, 8th Fl., New York, NY, 10036

Tel: (212) 768-8000   Fax: (212) 768-7387   www.ventiv.com

Provides sales and marketing services for pharmaceutical companies.

Ventiv Health, 2, rue du Docteur Lombard, F-92441 Issy Les Moulineaux Cedex, France

Tel: 33-1-5697-5000   Fax: 33-1-5697-5040

VENTURE INDUSTRIES

33662 James J. Pompo Drive, Fraser, MI, 48026-0278

Tel: (586) 294-1500   Fax: (586) 296-8863   www.ventureindustries.com

Mfr. and sales of plastic automotive components.

Venture Industries, Burnhaupt, France

VERIFONE, INC.

4988 Great America Pkwy., Santa Clara, CA, 94054-1200

Tel: (408) 496-0444   Fax: (408) 919-5105   www.verifone.com

Mfr. electronic payment software and hardware.

VeriFone SA, 22 Rue Leon Jouhaux, F-75010 Paris, France

VERINT SYSTEMS INC.

234 Crossways Park Drive, Woodbury, NY, 11797

Tel: (516) 677-7300   Fax: (516) 677-7197   www.verintsystems.com

Mfr. and sales of analytic software.

Verint Systems, 54-56 Avenue du General Leclerc, F-92100 Boulogne-Billancourt, France

VERISIGN, INC.

1350 Charleston Rd., Mountain View, CA, 94043

Tel: (650) 961-7500   Fax: (650) 961-7300   www.verisign.com

Mfr. software.

Certplus, 1, place de la Méditerranée, F-95200 Sarcelles, France

Tel: 33-1-3438-4900

Certplus, 36, rue Guynemer, 92447 Issy les Moulineaux Cedex, France

Tel: 33-1-4648-2080

VERITAS SOFTWARE INC.

350 Ellis Street, Mountain View, CA, 94043

Tel: (650) 527-8000   Fax: (650) 527-8050   www.veritas.com

Mfr. of storage management software for data protection, application availability, and disaster recovery.

VERITAS France, 17, avenue de l'Arche, Courbevoie Cedex, F-92671 Paris, France

Tel: 33-1-4145-0202

VERITY, INC.

894 Ross Drive, Sunnyvale, CA, 94089

Tel: (408) 541-1500   Fax: (408) 541-1600   www.verity.com

Mfr. software to simplify management of information.

Verity France, 14 Place Marie Jeanne Bassot, F-92593 Levallois Perret Cedex, France

Tel: 33-1-4149-0450

VERIZON COMMUNICATIONS INC.

1095 Ave. of the Americas, New York, NY, 10036

Tel: (212) 395-2121   Fax: (212) 395-1285   www.verizon.com

Telecommunications.

Cable & Wireless France, 3 Rue Dareau, Paris, France

Tel: 33-1-4313-6800   Fax: 33-1-4313-6868

VERIZON WIRELESS, INC.

180 Washington Valley Rd., Bedminster, NJ, 07921

Tel: (908) 306-7000   Fax: (908) 306-6927   www.verizonwireless.com

Engaged in mobile phone operations.

Societe Francais du Radiotelephone, 1 Place Carpeaux, F-92915 Paris, France

VERSATA, INC.

300 Lakeside Drive, Ste. 1500, Oakland, CA, 94612

Tel: (510) 238-4100   Fax: (510) 238-4101   www.versata.com

Mfr. software.

Versata France, 13, rue Camille Desmoulins, F-92441 Issy Les Moulineaux Cedex, France

VERTEX INTERACTIVE, INC.

22 Audrey Place, Fairfield, NJ, 07004

Tel: (973) 777-3500   Fax: (973) 472-0814   www.vertexinteractive.com

Mfr. software.

Vertex Interactive France, 63, Rue d'Emerainville, Buroplus pariest, F-77437 Marne-laVallee Cedex 2, France

Vertex/VSM France, ZAC des Gatines, 17 Avenue du Garigliano, F-91601 91601, France

Tel: 33-1-6954-2328

VERTICALNET, INC.

300 Chester Field Pkwy., Malvern, PA, 19355

Tel: (610) 240-0600   Fax: (610) 240-9470   www.verticalnet.com

Engaged in e-commerce software.

Verticalnet European Hdqrts., Les Espaces de Sophia, BP 37, F-06901 Sophia Antipolis, France

Tel: 33-4-9295-2518   Fax: 33-4-9202-8631

VESTAR CAPITAL PARTNERS

245 Park Avenue, 41st Fl., New York, NY, 10167

Tel: (212) 949-6500   Fax: (212) 808-4922   www.vestarcapital.com

Engaged in management buyouts, recapitalizations and growth capital investments.

Vestar Capital Partners Europe, 1, Rond Point Des Champs Elysees, F-75008 Paris, France

Tel: 33-1-5856-6010   Contact: Robert L. Rosner

VF CORPORATION

628 Green Valley Road, Suite 500, Greensboro, NC, 27408

Tel: (336) 547-6000   Fax: (336) 547-7630   www.vfc.com

Mfr./marketing apparel including Lee and Wrangler jeans, Jansport backpacks and Healthtex.

VF Intimate Apparel, 65 ave. Kleber, F-75116 Paris, France

VIACOM INC.

1515 Broadway, 28th Fl., New York, NY, 10036-5794

Tel: (212) 258-6000   Fax: (212) 258-6358   www.viacom.com

Communications, publishing and entertainment.

Films Paramount SA, 1 rue Meyerbeer, F-75009 Paris, France

VIASYS HEALTHCARE INC.

227 Washington Street, Ste. 200, Conshohocken, PA, 19428

Tel: (610) 862-0800   Fax: (610) 862-0836   www.viasyshealthcare.com

Mfr. medical instruments and devices.

Medical Service Recherches, 29 Rue de Monthlery, SILIC 140, F-94523 Rungis, France

Tel: 33-1-45-60-58-37   Fax: 33-1-45-60-58-37   Contact: John Chamaaah

VIASYS Healthcare SARL, 1, Rue du Fort, BP 127, F-67118 Geispolsheim-Gare, France

VIASYSTEMS GROUP, INC.

101 South Hanley Road, Ste. 40, St. Louis, MO, 63105

Tel: (314) 727-2087   Fax: (314) 719-2255   www.viasystems.com

Engaged in contract manufacturing of printed circuit boards.

Viasystems EMS France, 49, rue de la République B.P. 26, F-76250 Deville-les-Rouen, France

VICOR CORPORATION

25 Frontage Rd., Andover, MA, 01810-5413

Tel: (978) 470-2900   Fax: (978) 749-3536   www.vicr.com

Designs, manufactures, and markets modular power components and complete configurable and custom power systems.

Vicor France, 6 Parc Ariane, Immeuble "Le Mercure", F-78284 Guyancourt Cedex, France

VIEWLOCITY, INC.

3475 Piedmont Road, Ste. 1700, Atlanta, GA, 30305

Tel: (404) 267-6400   Fax: (404) 267-6500   www.viewlocity.com

Mfr. supply chain management software.

Viewlocity France, 37 rue Adam Ledoux, F-92400 Courbevoie Paris, France

VIEWSONIC CORPORATION

381 Brea Canyon Road, Walnut, CA, 91789

Tel: (909) 444-8888   Fax: (909) 869-7958   www.viewsonic.com

Mfr. displays.

ViewSonic SARL, Le Parc Barbanniers, 1 Allee Des Bas Tilliers, F-92230 Gennevilliers, France

Tel: 33-1-41-47-4900   Fax: 33-1-41-47-4910

VIGNETTE CORPORATION

1601 South Mopac Expwy., Bldg. 3, Austin, TX, 78746-5776

Tel: (512) 741-4300   Fax: (512) 741-4500   www.vignette.com

Mfr. software.

Vignette France, La Grande Arche, Paroi Nord, F-92044 Paris, France

THE VIKING CORPORATION

210 N. Industrial Park Rd., Hastings, MI, 49058

Tel: (616) 945-9501   Fax: (616) 945-9599   www.vikingcorp.com

Mfr. fire extinguishing equipment.

Sprinkler Viking SARL, 43 Blvd. Chilperic, F-77500 Chelles, France

VISHAY INTERTECHNOLOGY INC.

63 Lincoln Hwy., Malvern, PA, 19355

Tel: (610) 644-1300   Fax: (610) 296-0657   www.vishay.com

Mfr. resistors, strain gages, capacitors, inductors, printed circuit boards.

Aztronic Societe Nouvelle, Z.I. de Bellitourne, AZE, F-53200 Chateau-Gontier, France

Nicolitch, 1 ave. du Bois de L'Epine, BP 143, F-91005 Evry Cedex, France

Sfernice SA, 199 Blvd. de la Madeleine, BP 159, F-06003 Nice Cede, France

Sprague, 8 ave. du Danemark, F-37100 Tours, France

Vishay Geka/Sovcor, 11 Chemin de Ronde, BP 8, F-78110 Le Vesinet, France

VISHAY SILICONIX INC.

2201 Laurelwood Drive, Santa Clara, CA, 95054

Tel: (408) 988-8000   Fax: (408) 970-3950   www.siliconix.com

Mfr. power IC's and analog signal processing devices for computers, cell phones, fixed communications networks, automobiles, and other electronic systems.

Vishay Siliconix SARL, Centre Commercial de l'Echat, Place de l'Europe, F-94019 Creteil Cedex, France

VISKASE COMPANIES, INC.

6855 West 65th Street, Chicago, IL, 60638

Tel: (630) 789-4900   Fax: (708) 496-4412   www.viskase.com

Production of nonedible cellulose casing for sausages.

Viskase S.A., Usine de Beauvais, 10 Chaussee Feldtrappe B.P. 20923, France

Viskase S.A., 9, rue Pierre de Coubertin, F-88155 Thaon-les-Vosges Cedex, France

VIVITAR CORPORATION

1280 Rancho Conejo Blvd, Newbury Park, CA, 91320

Tel: (805) 498-7008   Fax: (805) 498-5086   www.vivitar.com

Mfr. photographic equipment, electronic supplies.

Vivitar France SA, 48, rue Léonard de Vinci, BP 177, F-95691 Goussainville Cedex, France

Tel: 33-1-34-38-7800

VOLT INFORMATION SCIENCES, INC.

560 Lexington Avenue, 16th Fl., New York, NY, 10022-6828

Tel: (212) 704-2400   Fax: (212) 704-2417   www.volt.com

Staffing services and telecommunication services.

Autologic Intl. Ltd., 26 rue Robert Witxhitz, F-94200 Ivy-Sur-Seine Paris, France

Tel: 33-1-45-21-6960   Fax: 33-1-46-71-5049

VTEL PRODUCTS CORPORATION

108 Wild Basin Road, Austin, TX, 78746

Tel: (512) 314-2700   Fax: (512) 314-2792   www.vtel.com

Design, development, manufacture and sale of PC-based videoconferencing systems through reseller channels.

VTEL France SA, 15 rue J.B. Berlier, F-75013 Paris, France

Tel: 33-1-53-94-6161   Fax: 33-1-53-94-6171   Contact: Jean-Christophe Lenglart

WABTEC CORPORATION

1001 Air Brake Ave., Wilmerding, PA, 15148

Tel: (412) 825-1000   Fax: (412) 825-1501   www.wabtec.com

Mfr. equipment for locomotives, railway freight cars, and passenger transit vehicles

Railroad Friction Products Corporation, Wissenbourg, France

WACHOVIA CORPORATION

301 South College Street, Ste. 4000, Charlotte, NC, 28288-0013

Tel: (704) 374-6161   Fax: (704) 383-1240   www.wachovia.com

Engaged in commercial and retail banking services.

Wachovia Corporation, 9 Rue Royale, F-75008 Paris, France

THE WACKENHUT CORPORATION

4200 Wackenhut Dr., Ste. 100, Palm Beach Gardens, FL, 33410

Tel: (561) 622-5656   Fax: (561) 691-6736   www.wackenhut.com

Security systems and services.

Wackenhut France, 9-11 ave. Michelet, F-93400 Saint Ouen Paris, France

Tel: 33-1-49-48-7956   Fax: 33-1-40-10-1771

WALBRO ENGINE MANAGEMENT

7400 N. Oracle Road, Ste. 310, Tucson, AZ, 85704

Tel: (520) 877-3000   Fax: (520) 877-3006   www.walbro.com

Mfr. motor vehicle accessories and parts, automotive fluid carrying systems.

TI Group Automotive Systems, Boulevard de l'Industrie Z.I., F-37530 Nazelles-Negron, France

Tel: 33-2-27-23-4000

TI Group Automotive Systems, ZI Technoland, F-25600 Brognard, France

WALL COLMONOY CORPORATION

30261 Stephenson Hwy., Madison Heights, MI, 48071

Tel: (248) 585-6400   Fax: (248) 585-7960   www.wallcolmonoy.com

Mfr. hard-surfacing and brazing alloys, equipment and services, aircraft exhaust systems.

Wall Colmonoy France, 9, rue des Aulnettes, F-95104 Argenteuil, France

Tel: 33-1-30-25-9860   Fax: 33-1-30-25-9865   Contact: Gerard Caville   Emp: 12

THE WARNACO GROUP INC.

90 Park Ave., New York, NY, 10016

Tel: (212) 661-1300   Fax: (212) 687-0480   www.warnaco.com

Mfr./sales intimate apparel and men's and women's sportswear.

Lejaby, Div. Warnaco, Avenue du Loup Pendu, F-69140 Rillieux la Pape, France

WARNER BROS.

4000 Warner Boulevard, Bldg.170, 3rd Fl., Burbank, CA, 91522

Tel: (818) 954-6000   Fax: (818) 977-4040   www.wbitv.com

Distributor TV programming and theatrical features.

Warner Bros., 33 Ave. de Wagram, F-75057 Paris, France

Tel: 33-1-55-37-5966   Fax: 33-1-55-37-5968   Contact: Michel Lecourt, VP

WARNER ELECTRIC COMPANY

449 Gardner St., South Beloit, IL, 61080

Tel: (815) 389-3771   Fax: (815) 389-2582   www.warnernet.com

Global supplier of Power Transmission and Motion Control Solution Systems; automotive, industry brakes, and clutches.

Warner & Tourco, Rte de Spay, BP 313, F-72700 Allonnes, France

Tel: 33-243-43-6363   Fax: 33-243-6340

THE WASHINGTON POST COMPANY

1150 15th St. NW, Washington, DC, 20071

Tel: (202) 334-6000   Fax: (202) 334-4536   www.washpostco.com

Engaged in magazine publishing, cable and television broadcasting, educational services and the Internet.

International Herald Tribune, 181 Avenue Charles-de-Gaulle, F-91521 Neuilly Cedex, France

Tel: 33-1-41-43-9300

Newsweek Inc., 162 rue du Faubourg Saint Honore, F-75008 Paris, France

WATERS CORPORATION

34 Maple Street, Milford, MA, 01757

Tel: (508) 478-2000   Fax: (508) 872-1990   www.waters.com

Mfr./distribute liquid chromatographic instruments and test and measurement equipment.

Waters SA, 6 rue Jean Pierre Timbaud, F-78180 Montigny le Bretonneux, France

WATLOW ELECTRIC MFG. COMPANY

12001 Lackland Rd., St. Louis, MO, 63146-4039

Tel: (314) 878-4600   Fax: (314) 434-1020   www.watlow.com

Mfr. electrical heating units, electronic controls, thermocouple wire, metal-sheathed cable, infrared sensors.

Watlow France SARL, Immeuble Somag, 16 rue Ampere, F-95307 Cergy Pontoise Cedex, France

Tel: 33-1-30-73-2425   Fax: 33-1-34-73-2875

WATSON WYATT & COMPANY HOLDINGS

1717 H Street NW, Washington, DC, 20006-3807

Tel: (202) 715-7000   Fax: (202) 715-7700   www.watsonwyatt.com

Creates compensation and benefits programs for major corporations.

Watson Wyatt SARL, 3/5 rue Scheffer, F-75016 Paris, France

Contact: Eric Van Effenterre

WATTS INDUSTRIES, INC.

815 Chestnut Street, North Andover, MA, 01845-6098

Tel: (978) 688-1811   Fax: (978) 688-5841   www.wattsind.com

Designs/mfr./sales of industry valves and safety control products.

Etablissements Trubert SA, 6 ave. Gustave Eiffel, Gellainville, BP 339, F-28630 Chartres Cedex, France

Watts-SFR, 13 rue Jean Jacques Rousseau, F-80390 Fressenneville, France

WD-40 COMPANY

1061 Cudahy Place, San Diego, CA, 92110-3998

Tel: (619) 275-1400   Fax: (619) 275-5823   www.wd40.com

Mfr. branded multiple-purpose lubrication, protection and general maintenance products.

WD-40 Company, Europac De Chene, Batiment C3, 11 Rue Edison, F-695000 Bron, France

Tel: 33-4-72-146-747   Fax: 33-4-72-146-749

WEATHERFORD INTERNATIONAL, INC.

515 Post Oak Blvd. Ste. 600, Houston, TX, 77027-3415

Tel: (713) 287-8400   Fax: (713) 963-9785   www.weatherford.com

Oilfield services, products and equipment; mfr. marine cranes for oil and gas industry.

Weatherford SA, rue Marie Joliot Curie, Z.I., BP 130, F-64143 Lons Cedex, France

Tel: 33-5-59-622664   Fax: 33-5-59-323197

WEBER-STEPHEN PRODUCTS COMPANY

200 East Daniels Road, Palatine, IL, 60067-6266

Tel: (847) 934-5700   Fax: (847) 934-0291   www.weberbq.com

Mfr./sales Weber cooking systems and barbeque and gas grills.

Le Creuset/Weber-Stephen, rue Olivier Deguise, F-02230 Frenoy LeGrand, France

Tel: 33-3-23-06-2222   Fax: 33-3-23-09-0662

WEBMETHODS, INC.

3930 Pender Drive, Fairfax, VA, 22030

Tel: (703) 460-2500   Fax: (703) 460-2599   www.webmethods.com

Mfr. automated business software.

WebMethods France, 58 Avenue Hoche, F-75008 Paris, France

WEBSENSE, INC.

10240 Sorrento Valley Road, San Diego, CA, 92121

Tel: (858) 320-8000   Fax: (858) 458-2950   www.websense.com

Mfr. software.

Websense, 54/56 Avenue Hoche, F-75008 Paris, France

Tel: 33-1-5660-5814

WEIGHT WATCHERS INTERNATIONAL, INC.

175 Crossways Park Dr., Woodbury, NY, 11797

Tel: (516) 390-1400   Fax: (516) 390-1763   www.weightwatchers.com

Weight loss programs.

Weight Watchers France, Le Florilege, 4 Allee de la Frasnerie, B.P. 64.F, F-748330 Fontenay-le-Fleury, France

WELCH ALLYN INC.

4341 State Street Road, Skaneateles Falls, NY, 13153

Tel: (315) 685-4100   Fax: (315) 685-4091   www.welchallyn.com

Mfr. fiber optic products and medical diagnostic equipment.

Welch Allyn France, 814 Rue Chales de Gaulle, F-77100 Mareu, France

Tel: 33-1-6009-3366

WELLS LAMONT CORPORATION

6640 W. Touhy Avenue, Niles, IL, 60714

Tel: (847) 647-8200   Fax: (847) 647-6943   www.wellslamontindustry.com

Mfr. industrial protective work gloves and industrial rainwear.

Wells Lamont Europe, 11 Bis Avenue Du General Mazillier, F-21140 Semur-En-Auxois, France

Tel: 33-3-80-89-93-40   Fax: 33-3-80-96-60-11

WEST PHARMACEUTICAL SERVICES, INC.

101 Gordon Drive, Lionville, PA, 19341-0645

Tel: (610) 594-2900   Fax: (610) 594-3000   www.westpharma.com

Mfr. packaging and plastic components for health care and consumer products.

West Pharmaceutical Services, 38 rue Robert Degon BP 26, F-2170 Le Nouvion-En-Thierache, France

WESTERN DIGITAL CORPORATION

20511 Lake Forest Dr., Lake Forest, CA, 92630-7741

Tel: (949) 672-7000   Fax: (949) 672-5408   www.westerndigital.com

Mfr. hard disk drives, video graphics boards, VLSI.

Western Digital Corp., Parc Club Orsay Universite, Batiment N, 3 rue Jean Rostand, Orsay Cedex, France

WESTERN RESOURCES, INC.

818 Kansas Ave., Topeka, KS, 66612

Tel: (785) 575-6300   Fax: (785) 575-1796   www.wstnres.com

Engaged in security monitoring, natural gas and electricity.

Protection One Europe Holding, Div. Western Resources, 140 Bd Malesherbes, F-75017 Paris, France

WHIRLPOOL CORPORATION

2000 N. M-63, Benton Harbor, MI, 49022-2692

Tel: (616) 923-5000   Fax: (616) 923-5443   www.whirlpoolcorp.com

Mfr., market home appliances: Whirlpool, Roper, KitchenAid, Estate, and Inglis.

Whirlpool Europe BV, Amiens, France

WHITE & CASE LLP

1155 Ave. of the Americas, New York, NY, 10036-2767

Tel: (212) 819-8200   Fax: (212) 354-8113   www.whitecase.com

Engaged in international law.

White & Case LLP, Avocates au Barreau de Paris, Toque Générale: J002, 11 blvd de la Madeleine, F-75001 Paris, France

Tel: 33-1-55-04-1515   Fax: 33-1-55-04-1516   Contact: Michael Hancock

WHITTMAN-HART & USWEB/CKS

311 S. Wacker Drive, Ste. 3500, Chicago, IL, 60606-6621

Tel: (312) 922-9200   Fax: (312) 913-3020   www.uswebcks.com

Internet professional services firm; design and implementation services for multimedia marketing programs.

USWeb/CKS France, 95 rue Marcel Dassault, F-92100 Boulogne Billancourt, France

Tel: 33-1-46-94-9842   Contact: Robert T. Clarkson

WIDIA VALENITE INC

31700 Research Park Dr., Madison Heights, MI, 48071-4627

Tel: (248) 589-1000   Fax: (248) 597-4820   www.valenite.com

Cemented carbide, high speed steel, ceramic and diamond cutting tool products, etc.

Widia Valenite France S.A., BP 65, Boutheon Cedex, F-42162 Andrezieux, France

WILLAMETTE INDUSTRIES, INC.

1300 SW Fifth Ave., Ste. 3800, Portland, OR, 97201

Tel: (503) 227-5581   Fax: (503) 273-5603   www.wii.com

Mfr./sales and distribution of paper and wood products.

Willamette Europe, One Industrielle, B.P. 50, F-40110 Morcenx Orcenx, France

Tel: 33-5-58-82-5900   Fax: 33-5-58-07-9136

Willamette Europe Darso SAS, F-40260 Linxe, France

T.D. WILLIAMSON INC.

6801 S. 65th West Avenue, Tulsa, OK, 74131-2444

Tel: (918) 447-5100   Fax: (918) 446-6327   www.tdwilliamson.com

Mfr. equipment and provide service for pipeline maintenance.

TDW, Ltd., ba 11 rue de L'Atome, BP 81, Zone Industriele, F-67802 Bischheim Cedex, France

WILLKIE FARR & GALLAGHER

787 Seventh Avenue, New York, NY, 10019-6099

Tel: (212) 821-8000   Fax: (212) 821-8111   www.willkie.com

International law firm.

Willkie Farr & Gallagher, 21-23 rue de la Ville l'Evêque, F-75008 Paris, France

Tel: 33-1-5- 43-4500

WILSON, ELSER, MOSKOWITZ, EDELMAN & DICKER LLP

150 East 42nd St., New York, NY, 10017

Tel: (212) 490-3000   Fax: (212) 490-3038   www.wemed.com

International law firm.

Honig Buffat Mettetal, WEMED Société D' Avocats, 21, Rue Magellan, F-75008 Paris, France

Tel: 33-1-44-43-88-88   Fax: 33-1-44-43-88-77   Contact: Gérard Honig

WIND RIVER SYSTEMS, INC.

500 Wind River Way, Alameda, CA, 94501

Tel: (510) 748-4100   Fax: (510) 749-2010   www.isi.com

Develops and markets computer software products and services.

Wind River Systems S.A.R.L., 19 Avenue de Norvège, Immeuble OSLO Bâtiment 3, Z.A. de Courtaboeuf 1, F-91953 Les Ulis Cédex, France

Tel: 33-1-60-92-63-00   Fax: 33-1-60-92-63-15

WINSTON & STRAWN

35 West Wacker Drive, Ste. 4200, Chicago, IL, 60601-9703

Tel: (312) 558-5600   Fax: (312) 558-5700   www.winston.com

International law firm.

Winston & Strawn, 6 rue de Cirque, F-75008 Paris, France

Tel: 33-1-42-25-1055   Contact: Paul Bishop, Ptnr.

HARRY WINSTON INC.

718 Fifth Ave., New York, NY, 10019

Tel: (212) 245-2000   Fax: (212) 245-2000   www.harry-winston.com

Diamonds and lapidary work.

Harry Winston de New York SARL, 29 ave. Montaigne, F-75008 Paris, France

Tel: 33-1-4720-0309

WOODHEAD INDUSTRIES INC.

Three Parkway North, Ste. 550, Deerfield, IL, 60015

Tel: (847) 236-9300   Fax: (847) 236-0503   www.woodhead.com

Develop/mfr./sale/distributor elect/electronic, fiber optic and ergonomic special-function, non-commodity products.

Woodhead Connectivity S.A., 57, Rue Jacquard Z.I., F-77400 Lagny Sur Marne, France

WORLD COURIER INC.

45 Southfield Avenue, Ste. 3450, Stamford, CT, 06902-7210

Tel: (203) 975-9333   Fax: (203) 316-9455   www.worldcourier.com

International courier service.

World Courier France, F-10484 Roissy Paris, France

WORLD MINERALS INC.

130 Castilian Drive, Santa Barbara, CA, 93117

Tel: (805) 562-0200   Fax: (805) 562-0298   www.worldminerals.com

Mfr. premium quality diatomite and perlite products.

World Minerals France SA, 257 avenue Georges Clemenceau, F-92745 Nanterre Cedex, France

Tel: 33-1-41-91-5711

WORLDCOM, INC.

500 Clinton Center Drive, Clinton, MS, 39060

Tel: (601) 360-8600   Fax: (601) 360-8616   www.wcom.com

Telecommunications; serving local, long distance and Internet customers domestically and internationally. **Corporation under worldwide reorganization under Chapter 11 Bankruptcy; new data unavailable for this edition.*

WorldCom International, 125 ave. des Champs-Elysees, F-75008 Paris, France

WORLDXCHANGE COMMUNICATIONS

9999 Willow Creek Road, San Diego, CA, 92131

Tel: (858) 547-4933   Fax: (800) 995-4502   www.worldxchange.com

Provides international, long distance telecommunications services worldwide.

WorldxChange Communications S.A., Paris, France

WRIGHT MEDICAL GROUP, INC.

5677 Airline Road, Arlington, TN, 38002

Tel: (901) 867-9971   Fax: (901) 867-9534   www.wmt.com

Mfr. orthopedic reconstructive implants.

Wright Cremascoli Ortho SA, Zone Industrielle la Farlede, Rue Pasteur BP 222, F-83089 Toulon Cedex 09, France

Wright Cremascoli Ortho Technique, Europarc - Le Hameau C, 127, chemin des Bassins, F-94035 Creteil Cedex, France

WM WRIGLEY JR. COMPANY

410 N. Michigan Ave., Chicago, IL, 60611-4287

Tel: (312) 644-2121   Fax: (312) 644-0353   www.wrigley.com

Mfr. chewing gum.

Wrigley France S.N.C., Zone Industrielle, BP 29, F-68600 Neufbrisach Biesheim, France

WRQ, INC.

1500 Dexter Avenue North, Seattle, WA, 98109

Tel: (206) 217-7100   Fax: (206) 217-7515   www.wrq.com

Mfr. software.

WRQ Software SA, Le Dôme BP 10913, 2, rue de la Haye, F-95731 Roissy Cedex, France

WYETH

5 Giralda Farms, Madison, NJ, 07940-0874

Tel: (973) 660-5000   Fax: (973) 660-7026   www.wyeth.com

Mfr. consumer healthcare products.

Whitehall Wyeth Consumer Healthcare, 80 Avenue du Général de Gaulle, F-92800 Puteaux, France

Tel: 33-1-41-02-7777

WYETH PHARMACEUTICALS

555 E. Lancaster Ave., Wayne, PA, 19087-5109

Tel: (610) 971-5400   Fax: (610) 995-4668   www.wyeth.com

Mfr. antibiotics and pharmaceutical products.

Wyeth-Lederle, Le Wilson 2, 80 Avenue du President Wilson Puteaux, F-92031 Paris Cedex, France

Tel: 33-1-4102-7000   Fax: 33-1-4102-7010

WYNN OIL COMPANY

1050 West Fifth Street, PO Box 9510, Azusa, CA, 91702-9510

Tel: (626) 334-0231   Fax: (626) 334-6463   www.wynnusa.com

Mfr. of specialty chemicals, equipment and related service programs for automotive and industrial markets.

Wynn's Automotive France, Z.A. Europark, 2, Avenue Léonard de Vinci, F-33608 Pessac, France

Emp: 87

Wynn's France SA (Industrial), 11 ave. Dubonnet, F-92407 Courbevoie Cedex, France

Tel: 33-1-49-04-0420   Fax: 33-1-47-89-9670   Contact: Bernard-Lionel Poulard, Mng. Dir.   Emp: 95

WYSE TECHNOLOGY INC.

3471 North First Street, San Jose, CA, 95134

Tel: (408) 473-1200   Fax: (408) 473-2080   www.wyse.com

Mfr. computer network terminals.

Wyse Technology, Immeuble Mercure, 6 Parc Club Arlane, F-78284 Guyancourt Cedex, France

Tel: 33-1-3944-0044   Fax: 33-1-3452-0930

XANSER CORPORATION

2435 N. Central Expwy, 7th Fl., Richardson, TX, 75080

Tel: (972) 699-4000   Fax: (972) 699-4025   www.xanser.com

Engaged in information technology services.

Furmanite France, BP 308, F-59351 Douai, France

XELUS, INC.

290 Woodcliff Drive, Fairport, NY, 14450

Tel: (716) 248-9660   Fax: (716) 248-9199   www.xelus.com

Mfr. equipment and repair service software.

Xelus, Inc., 42 Ave. Montaigne, F-75008 Paris, France

XEROX CORPORATION

800 Long Ridge Road, PO Box 1600, Stamford, CT, 06904

Tel: (203) 968-3000   Fax: (203) 968-4312   www.xerox.com

Mfr. document processing equipment, systems and supplies.

Xerox Research Centre Europe, 6 chemin de Maupertuis, 38240 Meylan, France

Xerox SA, 90 chemin du Roy d'Espagne, BP 171, F-13279 Marseille Cedex 09, France

Tel: 33-4-91-76-70-00   Fax: 33-4-91-76-60-10

Xerox SA, 20 rue Garibaldi, F-69451 Lyon Cedex 06, France

Tel: 33-4-72-69-22-69   Fax: 33-4-72-69-23-91

Xerox SA, ZI La Pilaterie, F-59700 Marcq En Baroeul, France

Tel: 33-3-20-66-7100   Fax: 33-3-20-66-7171

Xerox SA, 7 rue Touzet, F-93586 St.-Ouen Cedex, France

Xerox SA, 20 place des Halles, Tour Europe, F-67000 Strasbourg, France

Tel: 33-3-88-25-48-00   Fax: 33-3-88-25-48-12

Xerox SA, 1 rue Celestin Freinet, BP 2069, F-44201 Nantes Cedex 02, France

Tel: 33-2-51-88-80-80   Fax: 33-2-51-88-80-00

XILINX INC.

2100 Logic Drive, San Jose, CA, 95124-3400

Tel: (408) 559-7778   Fax: (408) 559-7114   www.xilinx.com

Programmable logic and related development systems software.

Xilinx SARL, Espace Jouy Technology, 21 rue Albert Calmette Bt. C, F-78353 Jouy En Josas Cedex, France

XIRCOM, INC.

2300 Corporate Center Drive, Thousand Oaks, CA, 91320

Tel: (805) 376-9300   Fax: (805) 376-9311   www.xircom.com

Mfr. PC card network adapters and modems.

Xircom France SARL, 41 Bis Avenue de l'Europe, BP 264, F-78147 Velizy Cedex, France

X-RITE, INC.

3100 44th Street SW, Grandville, MI, 49418

Tel: (616) 534-7663   Fax: (616) 534-9215   www.xrite.com

Mfr. precision measurement devices, systems and processes that enhance the measurement of color, light and shape.

X-Rite Méditerranée, Parc du moulin de Massy, 35, rue du Saule Trapu, F-92168 Massy, France

Tel: 33-1-6953-6620

XTRA CORPORATION

200 Nyala Farms Rd., Westport, CT, 06880

Tel: (203) 221-1005   Fax: (203) 221-9024   www.xtracorp.com

Holding company: leasing.

XTRA International, Paris, France

YAHOO! INC.

701 First Avenue, Sunnyvale, CA, 94089

Tel: (408) 439-3300   Fax: (408) 439-3301   www.yahoo-inc.com

Internet media company providing specialized content, free electronic mail and community offerings and commerce.

Yahoo! Inc., 14 Place Marie-Jeanne Bassot, F-92593 Levallois-Perret Paris Cedex, France

Tel: 33-1-46-39-5582   Fax: 33-1-46-39-0070

YELLOW CORPORATION

10990 Roe Ave., PO Box 7270, Overland Park, KS, 66207

Tel: (913) 696-6100   Fax: (913) 696-6116   www.yellowcorp.com

Commodity transportation.

Frans Maas Sud Transports Internationaux Snc, C.E.N. 116 Route du Bassin N.1, F-92631 Gennevilliers Cedex, France

Frans Maas Sud Transports Internationaux Snc, Z.I. De Revoisson, rue Calmette, F- 69740 Genas, France

YORK INTERNATIONAL CORPORATION

631 South Richland Ave., York, PA, 17403

Tel: (717) 771-7890   Fax: (717) 771-6212   www.york.com

Mfr. heating, ventilating, air conditioning and refrigeration equipment.

Le Froid Industriel-York SA, BP 10, F-44471 Carquefou Nantes, France

York Neige-Nantes, 18 rue Gustave Eiffel, B.P. 66, F-44980 Ste. Luce sur Loire, France

Tel: 33-2-4018-4600   Fax: 33-2-5185-0193

YOUNG & RUBICAM INC.

285 Madison Ave., New York, NY, 10017

Tel: (212) 210-3000   Fax: (212) 370-3796   www.yr.com

Advertising, public relations, direct marketing and sales promotion, corporate and product ID management.

Young & Rubicam France SA, 23 allee Maillasson, BP 73, F-92105 Boulogne Cedex, France

ZEBRA TECHNOLOGIES CORPORATION

333 Corporate Woods Pkwy., Vernon Hills, IL, 60061-3109

Tel: (847) 634-6700   Fax: (847) 913-8766   www.zebracorporation.com

Mfr. bar code systems.

Zebra Technologies France, 50, Rue Marcel Dassault, F-92100 Boulogne Billancourt, France

ZIMMER HOLDINGS, INC.

345 East Main St., Warsaw, IN, 46580

Tel: (574) 267-6131   Fax: (574) 372-4988   www.zimmer.com

Engaged in design and manufacture of orthopedic products.

Zimmer SAS, B.P. 337, F-13799 Aix-en-Provence Cedex 3, France

Tel: 33-442-97-72-60   Fax: 33-442-97-72-55

JOHN ZINK COMPANY

11920 East Apache, Tulsa, OK, 74121-1220

Tel: (918) 234-1800   Fax: (918) 234-2700   www.johnzink.com

Engaged in the development and manufacture of next-generation combustion products, technologies and clean-air solutions that power global industry.

Koch International, John Zink Division, 71A Rue des Hautes Patures, F-92737 Nanterre Cedex, France

ZOLL MEDICAL CORPORATION

32 Second Avenue, Burlington, MA, 01803

Tel: (781) 229-0020   Fax: (781) 272-5578   www.zoll.com

Mfr. electrical resuscitation devices and equipment.

ZOLL Medical France, 11 Bis Rud Du Colisee, F75 608 Paris, France

French Antilles

AON CORPORATION

200 East Randolph, Chicago, IL, 60601

Tel: (312) 381-1000   Fax: (312) 381-6032   www.aon.com

Insurance brokers worldwide; underwrites accident and health insurance, specialty and professional insurance; and provides risk management consultation.

AON Worldwide / Wachter Assurances, rue Ferdinand Forest, Z.I. Jarry, 97122 Baie Mahault, Guadeloupe

Tel: 590-326-701   Fax: 590-326-686   Contact: M. Wachter

DHL WORLDWIDE EXPRESS

50 California Avenue, San Francisco, CA, 94111

Tel: (415) 677-6100   Fax: (415) 824-9700   www.dhl.com

Worldwide air express carrier.

DHL Worldwide Express, z.I. Acajou, Californie, 97232 Le Lamentin, Martinique

Tel: 596-504-141

EGL INC. (EAGLE GLOBAL LOGISTICS)

15350 Vickery Drive, Houston, TX, 77032

Tel: (281) 618-3100   Fax: (281) 618-3223   www.eagleusa.com

Ocean/air freight forwarding, customs brokerage, packing and wholesale, logistics management and insurance.

EGL Eagle Global Logistics, Sotrama BP 802, Canal Alaric Ouest, Route Portuaire de L'Hydrobase, 97207 Fort-de-France, Martinique

Tel: 596-512-035   Fax: 596-516-017

EGL Eagle Global Logistics, Bat. Fret, Aeroport du Raizet, Pointe-a-Pitre, Guadeloupe

Tel: 590-830-708   Fax: 590-835-426

EGL Eagle Global Logistics, rue H. Becquerel, Z.I. De Jarry, 97122 Baie-Bahault Point-a-Pitre, Guadeloupe

Tel: 590-268-062   Fax: 590-268-519

EXXON MOBIL CORPORATION

5959 Las Colinas Blvd., Irving, TX, 75039-2298

Tel: (972) 444-1000   Fax: (972) 444-1882   www.exxonmobil.com

Petroleum exploration, production, refining; mfr. petroleum and chemicals products; coal and minerals.

Exxon Mobil, Inc., Martinique

IBM CORPORATION

1133 Westchester Avenue, White Plains, NY, 10604

Tel: (914) 765-1900   Fax: (914) 765-7382   www.ibm.com

Information products, technology and services.

IBM Martinique, Martinique

Tel: 596-753-000   Fax: 596-753-261

KPMG CONSULTING INC.

1676 International Dr., McLean, VA, 22102

Tel: (703) 747-3000   Fax: (703) 747-8500   www.kpmg.com

Accounting and audit, tax and management consulting services.

Fiduciaire de France, Lotissement Acajou, Californie, 97232 Le Lamentin, Martinique

Fiduciaire de France, Immeuble SCI-BTB, Voie Principale Z.I. Jarry, 97122 Baie Mahault, Guadeloupe

French Guiana

EGL INC. (EAGLE GLOBAL LOGISTICS)

15350 Vickery Drive, Houston, TX, 77032

Tel: (281) 618-3100   Fax: (281) 618-3223   www.eagleusa.com

Ocean/air freight forwarding, customs brokerage, packing and wholesale, logistics management and insurance.

EGL Eagle Global Logistics, Immeuble de Fret R4, Aeroport de Rochambeau, Matoury 97341, Ceyenne CAY, French Guiana

Tel: 594-357-836   Fax: 594-358-961

IBM CORPORATION

1133 Westchester Avenue, White Plains, NY, 10604

Tel: (914) 765-1900   Fax: (914) 765-7382   www.ibm.com

Information products, technology and services.

IBM French Guiana, French Guiana

Tel: 594-311-241   Fax: 594-305-609

French Polynesia

BANK OF HAWAII CORPORATION

130 Merchant Street, Honolulu, HI, 96813

Tel: (808) 643-3888   Fax: (808) 537-8440   www.boh.com

Engaged in commercial and consumer banking services.

Bank of Hawaii Corporation, PO Box 1602, Papeete, Tahiti French Polynesia

DHL WORLDWIDE EXPRESS

50 California Avenue, San Francisco, CA, 94111

Tel: (415) 677-6100   Fax: (415) 824-9700   www.dhl.com

Worldwide air express carrier.

DHL Worldwide Express, Boite Poste 6480 FAAA, Papeete, Tahiti French Polynesia

Tel: 689-830024

KPMG CONSULTING INC.

1676 International Dr., McLean, VA, 22102

Tel: (703) 747-3000   Fax: (703) 747-8500   www.kpmg.com

Accounting and audit, tax and management consulting services.

Fidupac S.A., Fare-Ute, Papeete, Tahiti French Polynesia

Tel: 689-427542   Fax: 689-413297   Contact: Gilles Redon, Sr. Ptnr.

Gabon

AMERADA HESS CORPORATION

1185 Avenue of the Americas, New York, NY, 10036

Tel: (212) 997-8500   Fax: (212) 536-8390   www.hess.com

Crude oil and natural gas.

Amerada Hess Production Gabon, PO Box 20316, Libreville, Gabon

ANADARKO PETROLEUM CORPORATION

17001 Northchase Drive, Houston, TX, 77060

Tel: (281) 875-1101   Fax: (281) 874-3316   www.anadarko.com

Exploration, development, production and marketing of oil and gas.

Andarko Gabon Company, Boulevard Bord de Mer, Ste. 720, B.P. 2081, Libreville, Gabon

Tel: 241-44-37-46   Fax: 241-44-37-48

BAKER HUGHES INCORPORATED

3900 Essex Lane, Ste. 1200, Houston, TX, 77027

Tel: (713) 439-8600   Fax: (713) 439-8699   www.bakerhughes.com

Develop and apply technology to drill, complete and produce oil and natural gas wells; provide separation systems to petroleum, municipal, continuous process and mining industries.

Baker Oil Tools, PO Box 587, Port Gentil, Gabon

Tel: 241-553612   Fax: 241-550928

CITIGROUP, INC.

399 Park Avenue, New York, NY, 10022

Tel: (212) 559-1000   Fax: (212) 559-3646   www.citigroup.com

Provides insurance and financial services worldwide.

Citigroup, Blvd. Quaben & rue Kringer, BP 3940, Libreville, Gabon

Contact: Nuhad K. Saliba

COOPER CAMERON CORPORATION

515 Post Oak Blvd., Ste.1200, Houston, TX, 77027

Tel: (713) 513-3300   Fax: (713) 513-3355   www.coopercameron.com

Mfr. oil and gas industry equipment.

Cooper Cameron Gabon, B.P. No. 869, Port Gentil, Gabon

DHL WORLDWIDE EXPRESS

50 California Avenue, San Francisco, CA, 94111

Tel: (415) 677-6100   Fax: (415) 824-9700   www.dhl.com

Worldwide air express carrier.

DHL Worldwide Express, rue Victor Schoelcher, BP 6113, Libreville, Gabon

Tel: 241-721170

ERNST & YOUNG INTERNATIONAL

5 Times Square, New York, NY, 10036

Tel: (212) 773-3000   Fax: (212) 773-6350   www.eyi.com

Engaged in assurance and advisory business services, tax, law and corporate finance.

Ernst & Young International, Immeuble Sonagar, Ave. du Colonel Parant, BP 1013, Libreville, Gabon

Tel: 241-74-3217   Fax: 241-72-64-94   Contact: Bernard Esteve

FRITZ COMPANIES, INC., DIV. UPS

706 Mission Street, Ste. 900, San Francisco, CA, 94103

Tel: (415) 904-8360   Fax: (415) 904-8661   www.fritz.com

Integrated transportation, sourcing, distribution and customs brokerage services.

Fritz Companies Inc., Gabon

GENERAL ELECTRIC COMPANY

3135 Easton Turnpike, Fairfield, CT, 06431

Tel: (203) 373-2211   Fax: (203) 373-3131   www.ge.com

Diversified manufacturing, technology and services.

GE Medical Systems Europe, BP 20320, Libreville, Gabon

GLOBAL SANTA FE CORPORATION

777 North Eldridge Pkwy., Houston, TX, 77079

Tel: (281) 496-8000   Fax: (281) 531-1260   www.gsfdrill.com

Offshore contract drilling, turnkey drilling, oil and gas exploration and production.

Global SantaFe, Port Gentil, Gabon

HALLIBURTON COMPANY

500 North Akard Street, Ste. 3600, Dallas, TX, 75201-3391

Tel: (214) 978-2600   Fax: (214) 978-2685   www.halliburton.com

Engaged in diversified energy services, engineering and construction.

Halliburton S.A.S., Zone Industrielle Oprag, B.P. 917, Port Gentil, Gabon

HELMERICH & PAYNE INC.

Utica at Twenty-First, Tulsa, OK, 74114-1398

Tel: (918) 742-5531   Fax: (918) 743-2671   www.hpinc.com

Engaged in contract drilling and oil and gas exploration and production.

Helmerich & Payne (Gabon), Boite Postal 20381, Libreville, Gabon

INTER-CONTINENTAL HOTELS

3 Ravinia Drive, Suite 2900, Atlanta, GA, 30346-2149

Tel: (770) 604-2000   Fax: (770) 604-5403   www.interconti.com

Worldwide hotel and resort accommodations.

Leconi Palace Inter-Continental Franceville, PO Box 735, Franceville, Gabon

Tel: 241-67-74-16   Fax: 241-67-74-19

LEXMARK INTERNATIONAL

740 W. New Circle Rd., Lexington, KY, 40550

Tel: (859) 232-2000   Fax: (859) 232-1886   www.lexmark.com

Develop, manufacture, supply of printing solutions and products, including laser, inkjet, and dot matrix printers.

Revendeur Lexmark, BP 1079, Libreville, Gabon

Tel: 241-73-3988

MARATHON OIL COMPANY

5555 San Felipe Road, Houston, TX, 77056

Tel: (713) 629-6600   Fax: (713) 296-2952   www.marathon.com

Oil and gas exploration.

Marathon Oil Company, Port Gentil, Gabon

M-I

PO Box 48242, Houston, TX, 77242-2842

Tel: (713) 739-0222   Fax: (713) 308-9503   www.midf.com

Developer, manufacturer and marketer of drilling and completion fluids and services.

IMCO SARL, Barge 106, Boite Postale 507, Port Gentil, Gabon

OCCIDENTAL PETROLEUM CORPORATION

10889 Wilshire Blvd., Los Angeles, CA, 90024

Tel: (310) 208-8800   Fax: (310) 443-6690   www.oxy.com

Petroleum and petroleum products, chemicals, plastics.

Occidental of Gabon Inc., Gabon

PRICEWATERHOUSECOOPERS LLP

1301 Ave. of the Americas, New York, NY, 10019

Tel: (212) 596-7000   Fax: (212) 259-1301   www.pwcglobal.com

Accounting and auditing, tax and management, and human resource consulting services.

PriceWaterhouseCoopers, BP 584, Port-Gentil, Gabon

Tel: 241-55-33-24   Fax: 241-55-16-28

PriceWaterhouseCoopers, rue Alfred-Marche, BP 2164, Libreville, Gabon

Tel: 241-761-2371   Fax: 241-74-43-25

STARWOOD HOTELS & RESORTS WORLDWIDE

777 Westchester Avenue, White Plains, NY, 10604

Tel: (914) 640-8100   Fax: (914) 640-8316   www.starwoodhotels.com

Hotel operations including Sheraton, Westin, St. Regis, Four Points and Caesars.

Sheraton Re-Ndama Hotel, Boite Postale 4064, Libreville, Gabon

WEATHERFORD INTERNATIONAL, INC.

515 Post Oak Blvd. Ste. 600, Houston, TX, 77027-3415

Tel: (713) 287-8400   Fax: (713) 963-9785   www.weatherford.com

Oilfield services, products and equipment; mfr. marine cranes for oil and gas industry.

Weatherford Intl., Boite Postale 654, Port Gentil, Gabon

Tel: 241-56-0826   Fax: 241-56-0828

XEROX CORPORATION

800 Long Ridge Road, PO Box 1600, Stamford, CT, 06904

Tel: (203) 968-3000   Fax: (203) 968-4312   www.xerox.com

Mfr. document processing equipment, systems and supplies.

Electra Xerox, BP 613, Libreville, Gabon

Tel: 241-761-502   Fax: 241-741-776

Gambia

DHL WORLDWIDE EXPRESS

50 California Avenue, San Francisco, CA, 94111

Tel: (415) 677-6100   Fax: (415) 824-9700   www.dhl.com

Worldwide air express carrier.

DHL Worldwide Express, 71 Hagan St., Banjul, Gambia

Tel: 220-228414

KPMG CONSULTING INC.

1676 International Dr., McLean, VA, 22102

Tel: (703) 747-3000   Fax: (703) 747-8500   www.kpmg.com

Accounting and audit, tax and management consulting services.

KPMG International, Meridien Bank Bldg., 3/4 Buckle St., Banjul, Gambia

THE WACKENHUT CORPORATION

4200 Wackenhut Dr., Ste. 100, Palm Beach Gardens, FL, 33410

Tel: (561) 622-5656   Fax: (561) 691-6736   www.wackenhut.com

Security systems and services.

Wackenhut International Inc.-Gambia, PO Box 2506 SK, Serekunda, Gambia

Tel: 220-46-3772   Fax: 220-46-0009

XEROX CORPORATION

800 Long Ridge Road, PO Box 1600, Stamford, CT, 06904

Tel: (203) 968-3000   Fax: (203) 968-4312   www.xerox.com

Mfr. document processing equipment, systems and supplies.

Shyben Hadi & Sons, 3A Russell St., PO Box 184, Banjul, Gambia

Tel: 220-21-226-659   Fax: 220-21-228-827

Georgia

DHL WORLDWIDE EXPRESS

50 California Avenue, San Francisco, CA, 94111

Tel: (415) 677-6100   Fax: (415) 824-9700   www.dhl.com

Worldwide air express carrier.

DHL Worldwide Express, Tsereteli Ave. 105, Tbilisi 380019, Georgia

Tel: 995-8832-999568

INTERDEAN INTERCONEX, INC

55 Hunter Lane, Elmsford, NY, 10523-1317

Tel: (914) 347-6600   Fax: (914) 347-0129   www.interdean.com

Freight forwarding.

Interdean.Interconex, 13-1A-5 Digomi Massive, Tbilisi 380059, Georgia

Contact: Giorgi Koberidze

McCANN-ERICKSON WORLDGROUP

750 Third Ave., New York, NY, 10017

Tel: (212) 697-6000   Fax: (212) 984-3575   www.mccann.com

International advertising and marketing services.

KEDI McCann-Erickson, Tbilisi, Georgia

Kedi McCann-Erickson, 12A Asatiani St., Tbilisi 380077, Georgia

ORION MARINE CORPORATION

79 West Monroe Street, Ste. 1105, Chicago, IL, 60603

Tel: (312) 263-5153   Fax: (312) 263-4233   www.orion-marine.com

Ocean transportation.

LTT Tbilisi, Barmonov St. 1, Tbilisi 380008, Georgia

Tel: 995-32-986545   Fax: 995-39-320215   Contact: Klaus Droege

PALMS & COMPANY, INC. (U.S. FUR EXCHANGE)

515 Lake Street South, Bldg., Ste. 103, Kirkland, WA, 98033

Tel: (425) 828-6774   Fax: (425) 827-5528   www.peterpalms.com

Engaged in general import and export and web-design, web-promotion and e-commerce.

Palms & Co. (Georgia) Inc., PO Box 25, Lutsk-23, City Volyn Region 262023, Ukraine

Contact: Dr. Oleg Jourin

WESTERN WIRELESS CORPORATION

3650 131st Avenue SE, Ste. 400, Bellevue, WA, 98006

Tel: (425) 586-8700   Fax: (425) 586-8666   www.wwireless.com

Provides wireless communication services.

MagtiCom Gsm, Ltd., Div. Western Wireless International, T'bilisi, Georgia

Germany

24 HOUR FITNESS WORLDWIDE INC.

5020 Franklin Drive, Pleasanton, CA, 94588

Tel: (925) 416-3100   Fax: (925) 416-3146   www.24hourfitness.com

Owns and manages fitness centers.

24 Hour Fitness, Hermannplatz 10, D-10967 Berlin, Germany

24/7 REAL MEDIA, INC.

1250 Broadway, New York, NY, 10001-3701

Tel: (212) 231-7100   Fax: (212) 760-1774   www.247media.com

Provides global online advertising, sponsorships, e-commerce and direct marketing solutions to advertisers and Web publishers.

24/7 Media Germany, AM Weingarten 25, D-60487 Frankfurt, Germany

Tel: 49-69-90-59612

24/7 Media Germany, Gladbacher Strasse 6, D-40219 Dusseldorf, Germany

Tel: 49-211-600-0111

3COM CORPORATION

5400 Bayfront Plaza, Santa Clara, CA, 95052-8145

Tel: (408) 326-5000   Fax: (408) 326-5001   www.3com.com

Engaged in the development and manufacture of computer networking products and systems.

3Com GmbH, Schiersteiner Strasse 84, D-65187 Wiesbaden, Germany

Tel: 49-611-973-660   Fax: 49-611-97366-99

3Com GmbH, Office Unterfoehring, Muenchner Str. 12, D-85774 Unterföhring, Germany

Tel: 49-89-992200   Fax: 49-89-9577-220

3Com GmbH, Borsigstr. 13, D-40880 Ratingen, Germany

Tel: 49-2102-4030

3Com GmbH, Kaiserin-Augusta-Allee 111, D-10553 Berlin, Germany

Tel: 49-30-3498790   Fax: 49-30-34987999

3Com GmbH, Gustav-Heinemann-Ring 123, D-81739 Münich, Germany

Tel: 49-89-627-320   Fax: 49-89-627-32-233

3D SYSTEMS CORPORATION

26081 Avenue Hall, Valencia, CA, 91355

Tel: (805) 295-5600   Fax: (805) 294-8406   www.3dsystems.com

Mfr. computer lasers.

3D Systems, Roentgenstrasse 41, D-64291 Darmstadt, Germany

THE 3DO COMPANY

100 Cardinal Way, Ste. 425, Redwood City, CA, 94063

Tel: (650) 385-3000   Fax: (650) 385-3184   www.3do.com

Mfr. entertainment software.

UBI Soft GmbH, Zimmerstraße 19, D-40215 Dusseldorf, Germany

3M (MINNESOTA MINING & MFG.)

3M Center, St. Paul, MN, 55144-1000

Tel: (651) 733-1110   Fax: (651) 733-9973   www.mmm.com

Mfr. diversified products for industry, consumer, health care, imaging, communications, transport, safety, etc.

3M Deutschland GmbH, Carl-Schurz-Strasse 1, D-41453 Neuss, Germany

Tel: 49-2131-14-3000   Fax: 49-2131-14-3470   Contact: Reinhold Hiersemann

3M TOUCH SYSTEMS, INC.

300 Griffin Brook Park Drive, Methuen, MA, 01844

Tel: (978) 659-9000   Fax: (978) 659-9100   www.microtouch.com

Mfr. Touchscreen Sensors, Touch Monitors, and Industrial Computer Products.

3M Touch Systems GmbH, Schiess-Str. 55, D-40549 Düsseldorf, Germany

Tel: 49-211-59907-0

AAF INTERNATIONAL (AMERICAN AIR FILTER)

10300 Ormsby Park Place, Ste. 600, Louisville, KY, 40232-5690

Tel: (502) 637-0011   Fax: (502) 637-0321   www.aafintl.com

Mfr. air filtration and pollution control and noise control equipment.

AAF GmbH, Postfach 130618, D-44316 Dortmund, Germany

Tel: 49-231-921-0330   Fax: 49-231-921-03323

AAVID THERMAL TECHNOLOGIES, INC.

1 Eagle Square, Ste. 509, Concord, NH, 03301

Tel: (603) 224-1117   Fax: (603) 224-6673   www.aatt.com

Mfr. fluid dynamics software.

Aavid Thermalloy, Hirtenstrasse 3, D-73271 Holzmaden, Germany

Tel: 49-7023-909990

ABBOTT LABORATORIES

100 Abbott Park Rd., Abbott Park, IL, 60064

Tel: (847) 937-6100   Fax: (847) 937-1511   www.abbott.com

Development, manufacture and sale of diversified health care products and services.

Abbott GmbH, Postfach 2103, D-65011 Wiesbaden, Germany

Tel: 49-6122-580

ABS (AMERICAN BUREAU OF SHIPPING)

ABS Plaza, 16855 Northchase Drive, Houston, TX, 77060

Tel: (281) 877-6000   Fax: (281) 877-6344   www.eagle.org

Classification and certification of ships and offshore structures, development and technical assistance.

ABS Europe Ltd., Limbecker Platz 1, D-45127 Essen, Germany

ACADIA PHARMACEUTICALS INC.

3911 Sorrento Valley Blvd., San Diego, CA, 92121

Tel: (858) 558-2871   Fax: (858) 558-2872   www.acadia-pharm.com

Engaged in gene development and related drug products.

ACADIA Pharmaceuticals A/S, Febriksparken 58, D-2600 Glostrup, Germany

Tel: 45-4329-3000   Fax: 45-4329-3030

ACCELRYS INC.

9685 Scranton Road, San Diego, CA, 92121-3752

Tel: (858) 799-5000   Fax: (858) 799-5100   www.accelrys.com

Mfr. software for drug research.

Accelrys GmbH, Inselkammerstrasse 1, D-82008 Unterhaching-Muenchen, Germany

Tel: 49-89-614593

ACCENTURE LTD.

1345 Avenue of the Americas, New York, NY, 10105

Tel: (917) 452-4400   Fax: (917) 527-9915   www.accenture.com

Provides management and technology consulting services.

Accenture, Otto-Volger-StraBe 15, D-65843 Sulzbach/Frankfurt, Germany

Tel: 49-6196-5760   Fax: 49-6196-57-6710

ACCLAIM ENTERTAINMENT, INC.

One Acclaim Plaza, Glen Cove, NY, 11542

Tel: (516) 656-5000   Fax: (516) 656-2040   www.acclaim.com

Mfr. video games.

Acclaim Entertainment GmbH, Leuchtenbergring 20, D-81677 Münich, Germany

Tel: 49-89-4-12190

ACCO WORLD CORPORATION

300 Tower Parkway, Lincolnshire, IL, 60069

Tel: (847) 541-9500   Fax: (847) 541-5750   www.accobrands.com

Provides services in the office and computer markets and manufactures paper fasteners, clips, metal fasteners, binders and staplers.

ACCO International GmbH, Schorndorfer Str. 69, A-73635 Rudersberg-Steinenberg, Germany

Tel: 49-7183-3003-158   Fax: 49-7183-3003-95   Contact: Ines Klockenbusch

ACCURIDE INTERNATIONAL, INC.

12311 Shoemaker Ave., Santa Fe Springs, CA, 90670-4721

Tel: (562) 903-0200   Fax: (562) 903-0208   www.accuride.com

Mfr. drawer slides.

Accuride International, Postfach 1464, D-65573 Diez Lahn, Germany

ACE CONTROLS INC.

23435 Industrial Park Drive, Farmington Hills, MI, 48024

Tel: (248) 476-0213   Fax: (248) 276-2470   www.acecontrols.com

Industry hydraulic shock absorbers, cylinders, valves and automation controls.

ACE Stossdampfer GmbH, Herzogstrasse 28, Postfach 3161, D-40764 Langenfeld, Germany

Tel: 49-2173-922610   Fax: 49-2173-922619

ACETO CORPORATION

One Hallow Lane, Ste. 201, Lake Success, NY, 11042-1215

Tel: (516) 627-6000   Fax: (516) 627-6093   www.aceto.com

Engaged in the distribution of chemicals.

Aceto Holding GmbH, Klettgaustrasse 21, D-79761 Waldshut-Tiengen, Germany

Tel: 49-7741-807-210

Aceto Pharma GmbH, Winterhuder Weg 27, D22085 Hamburg, Germany

ACHESON COLLOIDS INDUSTRIES, INC.

1600 Washington Avenue, Port Huron, MI, 48060

Tel: (810) 984-5581   Fax: (810) 984-1446   www.nationalstarch.com

Chemicals, chemical preparations, paints and lubricating oils.

Acheson Industries Deutschland, Postfach 7, D-89156 Dornstadt, Germany

Tel: 49-7348-20010   Fax: 49-7348-200127

ACME UNITED CORPORATION

1931 Black Rock Turnpike, Fairfield, CT, 06432

Tel: (203) 332-7330   Fax: (203) 576-0007   www.acmeunited.com

Mfr. mathematics tools, including rulers, protractors, compasses and scissors.

Emil Schlemper GmbH, PO Box 13 02 39, D-42680 Solingen, Germany

Tel: 49-212-23245-0   Fax: 49-212-332181

ACTEL CORPORATION

955 East Arquest Avenue, Sunnyvale, CA, 94086-4533

Tel: (408) 739-1010   Fax: (408) 739-1540   www.actel.com

Mfr. integrated circuits.

Actel GmbH, Lohweg 27, D-85375 Neufahrn, Germany

ACTION PERFORMANCE COMPANIES, INC.

4707 East Baseline Road, Phoenix, AZ, 85042

Tel: (602) 337-3700   Fax: (602) 337-3750   www.action-performance.com

Mfr. licensed motorsports collectibles.

Minichamps, Div. Action Performance, Napoleonsberg 99, D-52076 Aachen, Germany

ACTIONPOINT, INC.

1299 Parkmoor Avenue, San Jose, CA, 95126

Tel: (408) 325-3800   Fax: (408) 325-3985   www.actionpoint.com

Develops software for e-commerce.

ActionPoint GmbH, Nymphenburger Str. 136, D-80636 Münich, Germany

Tel: 49-89-189516

ACTIVISION

3100 Ocean Park Boulevard, Santa Monica, CA, 90405

Tel: (310) 255-2000   Fax: (310) 255-2100   www.activision.com

Development and manufacture of entertainment software and video games.

Activision Germany, Auf der Haar 47, Postfach 1553, D-332245 Guterloh, Germany

Tel: 49-5-241-480811   Fax: 49-5-241-480848   Emp: 11

ACTUATE CORPORATION

701 Gateway Boulevard, South San Francisco, CA, 94080

Tel: (650) 837-2000   Fax: (650) 827-1560   www.actuate.com

Develops software.

Actuate Germany GmbH, Lyoner Strasse 34, D-60576 Frankfurt Main, Germany

ADAC LABORATORIES, INC.

540 Alder Drive, Milpitas, CA, 95035

Tel: (408) 321-9100   Fax: (408) 321-9536   www.adaclabs.com

Mfr. cameras and equipment for nuclear medicine.

ADAC Laboratories GmbH, Grossenbaumer Weg 6, D-40472 Dusseldorf, Germany

ADAPTEC INC.

691 South Milpitas Boulevard, Milpitas, CA, 95035

Tel: (408) 945-8600   Fax: (408) 262-2533   www.adaptec.com

Design/mfr./marketing hardware and software solutions.

Adaptec GmbH, Munchner Strasse 17, D-85540 Haar, Germany

ADE CORPORATION

80 Wilson Way, Westwood, MA, 02090

Tel: (781) 467-3500   Fax: (781) 467-0500   www.ade.com

Mfr. semiconductor wafers and computer disks.

ADE International GmbH, Klausnerring 17, D-85551 Kirschheim Heimstetten, Germany

Tel: 49-89-909-9610   Fax: 49-89-909-96120

ADEMCO INTERNATIONAL

1769 N.W. 79th Avenue, Miami, FL, 33126

Tel: (305) 477-5204   Fax: (305) 477-5404   www.ademcoint.com

Mfr. security, fire and burglary systems and products.

ADEMCO Sicherheitseinrichtungen GmbH, Postfach 4125, D-7302 Ostfildern 1, Germany

ADEPT TECHNOLOGY, INC.

150 Rose Orchard Way, San Jose, CA, 95134

Tel: (408) 432-0888   Fax: (408) 434-6267   www.adept.com

Mfr. robots for industries.

Adept Technology GmbH, Otto-Hahn-Str. 23, D-44227 Dortmund, Germany

Tel: 49-231-758940

ADEXA, INC.

5933 West Century Blvd., 12th Fl., Los Angeles, CA, 90045

Tel: (310) 338-8444 Fax: (310) 338-9878 www.adexa.com

Mfr. supply chain management software.

Adexa GmbH, Lillenthalstrasse 29, D-85339 Hallbergmoos Munich, Germany

ADOBE SYSTEMS INCORPORATED

345 Park Avenue, San Jose, CA, 95110

Tel: (408) 536-6000 Fax: (408) 537-6000 www.adobe.com

Engaged in print technology and distributor of Acrobat Reader.

Adobe Systems GmbH, Ohmstraße 1, D-85716 Unterschleißheim, Germany

ADVANCED BRAIN TECHNOLOGIES (ABT)

PO Box 1088, Ogden, UT, 84402

Tel: (801) 622-5676 Fax: (801) 622-5676 www.advancedbrain.com

Engaged in research to create products, programs, and services that enhance health, learning and productivity.

Soundlife Media GMBH, Lutticherstr. 15, D-50674 Cologne, Germany

ADVANCED DIGITAL INFORMATION CORPORATION

11431 Willows Rd. NE, PO Box 97057, Redmond, WA, 98073

Tel: (425) 881-8004 Fax: (425) 881-2296 www.adic.com

Mfr. computer storage systems.

ADIC GmbH, Lilienthalstr.25 / 2.OG, D-85399 Münich, Germany

Tel: 49-811-99871-0

ADVANCED ENERGY INDUSTRIES, INC.

1625 Sharp Point Drive, Fort Collins, CO, 80525

Tel: (970) 221-4670 Fax: (970) 221-5583 www.advanced-energy.com

Mfr. semiconductors.

Advanced Energy GmbH, Raiffeisenstrasse 32, D-70794 Filderstadt, Germany

ADVANCED MICRO DEVICES INC.

1 AMD Place, Sunnyvale, CA, 94086

Tel: (408) 732-2400 Fax: (408) 982-6164 www.amd.com

Mfr. integrated circuits for communications and computation industry.

Advanced Micro Devices GmbH, Rosenheimerstrasse 143B, D-81671 Münich, Germany

Advanced Micro Devices GmbH, Siemensstrasse 6, D-61352 Bad Homburg, Germany

Tel: 49-6172-92670

ADVANCED MP TECHNOLOGY, INC.

1010 Calle Sombra, San Clemente, CA, 92673-6480

Tel: (949) 492-3113 Fax: (949) 492-5068 www.advancedmp.com

Engaged in distribution of electronic components.

Advanced MP Technology, Carl-Theodor-Reiffenstein-Platz, D-60313 Frankfurt, Germany

ADVANCED PRODUCTS COMPANY

33 Defco Park Road, North Haven, CT, 06473

Tel: (203) 239-3341 Fax: (203) 234-7233 www.advpro.com

Mfr. metallic and PTFE seals and gaskets.

Advanced Products, Karl Arnold Strasse 63, D-5130 Geilenkirchen Gilrath, Germany

ADVANSTAR COMMUNICATIONS INC.

545 Boylston Steet, Boston, MA, 02116

Tel: (617) 267-6500 Fax: (617) 267-6900 www.advanstar.com

Provides business to business marketing services.

Advanstar Communications GmbH, Landsberger Str. 101, D-45219 Essen, Germany

Tel: 49-2054-1048-90 Fax: 49-2054-10489-29

AERONAUTICAL INSTRUMENTS & RADIO COMPANY

234 Garibaldi Ave., Lodi, NJ, 07644

Tel: (973) 473-0034   Fax: (973) 473-8748   www.femareps.com

Provides the development, sales, manufacture and maintenance of complete military navigational systems and industrial equipment with spare parts.

Elan GmbH, Freudenber Str. 27, D-6200 Weisbaden Schienstien, Germany

AGCO CORPORATION

4205 River Green Parkway, Duluth, GA, 30096-2568

Tel: (770) 813-9200   Fax: (770) 813-6038   www.agcocorp.com

Mfr. farm equipment and machinery.

AGCO GmbH & Co., Am Sande 20, D-37213 Witzenhausen, Germany

AGCO GmbH & Co., Johann-Georg-Fendtstraße 4, D-87616 Marktoberdorf, Germany
Tel: 49-8342-770   Fax: 49-8342-77-220

AGILE SOFTWARE CORPORATION

1 Almaden Blvd., San Jose, CA, 95113-2253

Tel: (408) 975-3900   Fax: (408) 271-4862   www.agilesoft.com

Mfr. software for supply chain management.

Agile Software GmbH, Keltenring 13, D-82041 Oberhaching, Germany

AGILENT TECHNOLOGIES, INC.

395 Page Mill Road, PO Box 10395, Palo Alto, CA, 94303

Tel: (650) 752-5000   Fax: (650) 752-5633   www.agilent.com

Mfr. communications components.

Agilent Technologies GmbH, Bereich Halbleiter, Eschenstr. 5, D-82024 Taufkirchen, Germany
Tel: 49-89-6141-2300

AIG AMERICAN INTERNATIONAL GROUP INC.

70 Pine Street, New York, NY, 10270

Tel: (212) 770-7000   Fax: (212) 509-9705   www.aig.com

Worldwide insurance and financial services.

AIG Europe S.A., Oberlendau 76-78, D-60323 Frankfurt, Germany

AIR PRODUCTS AND CHEMICALS, INC.

7201 Hamilton Boulevard, Allentown, PA, 18195-1501

Tel: (610) 481-4911   Fax: (610) 481-5900   www.airproducts.com

Mfr. industry gases and related equipment, specialty chemicals, environmental/energy systems.

Air Products GmbH, Hauptverwaltung Hattingen, Huettenstrasse 50, D-4320 Hattingen Ruhr, Germany

AIRBORNE INC.

3101 Western Ave., PO Box 662, Seattle, WA, 98121

Tel: (206) 285-4600   Fax: (206) 281-1444   www.airborne.com

Air transport services.

RGW Express Airfreight GmbH, Postfach 750433, D-60534 Frankfurt, Germany
Tel: 49-6969-80080   Fax: 49-6969-800840

AKAMAI TECHNOLOGIES, INC.

500 Technology Square, Cambridge, MA, 02139

Tel: (617) 250-3000   Fax: (617) 250-3001   www.akamai.com

Develops routing technologies for websites.

Akamai Technologies EMEA, Heisenbergbogen 2, D-85609 Dornach, Germany
Tel: 49-89-9400-6101   Fax: 49-89-9400-6006

ALBANY INTERNATIONAL CORPORATION

1373 Broadway, Albany, NY, 12204

Tel: (518) 445-2200   Fax: (518) 445-2265   www.albint.com

Mfr. broadwoven and engineered fabrics, plastic products, filtration media.

Filtra GmbH, Postfach 5, Filtrastr. 5, D-4730 Ahlen 5, Germany

Filtra GmbH, Postfach 1640, Steinackerstr 20, D-7858 Weil Rhein, Germany

ALCOA INC.

Alcoa Center, 201 Isabella Street at 7th Street Bridge, Pittsburgh, PA, 15212-5858

Tel: (412) 553-4545   Fax: (412) 553-4498   www.alcoa.com

World's leading producer of aluminum and alumina; mining, refining, smelting, fabricating and recycling.

Alcoa Automotive Structures GmbH, Soest, Germany

Alcoa Chemie GmbH, Ludwigshafen, Germany

Alcoa Deutschland GmbH, Oldendorfer Strasse 9, D-49324 Melle, Germany

Tel: 49-5422-94470   Contact: Reinhard Deipenwisch

Alcoa Extrusions Hannover GmbH & Co. KG, Hannover, Germany

Michels GmbH & Co., KG, Herzebrock, Germany

Stribel GmbH, Frickenhausen, Germany

ALCOA FUJIKURA LTD.

800 Crescent Centre Drive, Ste. 600, Franklin, TN, 37067

Tel: (615) 778-6000   Fax: (615) 778-5927   www.alcoa-fujikura.com

Mfr. optical ground wire, tube cable, fiber optic connectors and automotive wiring harnesses. (JV of Alcoa USA).

Alcoa Fujikura Ltd., Dieselstrabe 64-72, D-33442 Herzebrock-Clarholz, Germany

Tel: 49-5245-449-207   Fax: 49-5245-449-390   Contact: James Edwards, VP Europe

ALLEGHENY LUDLUM CORPORATION

1000 Six PPG Place, Pittsburgh, PA, 15222

Tel: (412) 394-2805   Fax: (412) 394-2800   www.alleghenyludlum.com

Mfr. steel and alloys.

Allegheny Rodney, Duesseldorf, Germany

Tel: 49-211-513-560-0   Fax: 49-211-513-560-50

ALLEGHENY TECHNOLOGIES INC.

1000 Six PPG Place, Pittsburgh, PA, 15222

Tel: (412) 394-2800   Fax: (412) 394-2805   www.alleghenytechnologies.com

Diversified mfr. aviation and electronics, specialty metals, industrial and consumer products.

Allegheny Rodney, Postfach 1326, Kleinbeckstasse 7, D-45549 Sprockhovel, Germany

Tel: 49-2324-97360

Allegheny Technologies, Hagenauer Str. 42, D-65203 Wiesbaden, Germany

Allvac Ltd., Div. Teledyne GmbH, Sternstrasse 5, D-40479 Dusseldorf, Germany

Titanium International GmbH, Tiefenbroicher Weg 35, D-40472 Dusseldorf, Germany

ALLEGIANCE HEALTHCARE CORPORATION

1430 Waukegan Road, McGaw Park, IL, 60085

Tel: (847) 689-8410   Fax: (847) 578-4437   www.allegiance.net

Manufactures and distributes medical, surgical, respiratory therapy and laboratory products.

Allegiance Deutschland GmbH, Edisonstrasse 3-4, Unterschleissheim, D-85716 München, Germany

Tel: 49-89-31788   Fax: 49-89-31788-788   Contact: Josef Bernlochner, Mgr.

ALLEGIS GROUP INC.

6992 Columbia Gateway Dr., Bldg. D, Columbia, MD, 21046

Tel: (410) 540-7000   Fax: (410) 540-7099   www.aerotek.com

Recruitment and placement services.

Allegis Group, GW2, Ludwie-Erhaldt-Rin 94, D-15827 Dahlewitz, Germany

ALLENBERG COTTON COMPANY, INC.

PO Box 3254, Cordova, TN, 38018-3254

Tel: (901) 383-5000   Fax: (901) 383-5010   www.hohenbergbros.com

Engaged in cotton merchandising.

Allenberg Baumwoll GmbH, Ostertorsteinweg 57a, D-2800 Bremen, Germany

ALLEN-BRADLEY COMPANY, INC.

1201 South Second Street, Milwaukee, WI, 53204

Tel: (414) 382-2000   Fax: (414) 382-4444   www.ab.com

Mfr. electrical controls and information devices.

Allen-Bradley GmbH, Robert-Bosch Strasse 5, D-6072 Dreieich-Sprendlingen, Germany

Allen-Bradley GmbH, Duesselbergerstr. 15, D-5657 Haan 2 Gruiten, Germany

ALLERGAN INC.

2525 Dupont Drive, Irvine, CA, 92612

Tel: (714) 246-4500   Fax: (714) 246-6987   www.allergan.com

Mfr. therapeutic eye care products and skin care pharmaceuticals.

Pharm-Allergan GmbH, Postfach 10 06 61, D-76260 Ettlingen, Germany

Tel: 49-7243-5010   Fax: 49-7243-501-100

ALLIANCE GAMING CORPORATION

6601 S. Bermuda Road, Las Vegas, NV, 89119

Tel: (702) 270-7600   Fax: (702) 263-5636   www.ally.com

Mfr. gaming machines.

Bally Gaming GmbH, Sokelantstrasse 35, D-30185 Hannover, Germany

Bally Wulff Automaten GmbH, Maybachufer 48-51, D-12045 Berlin, Germany

Tel: 49-30-620-020

THE ALLSTATE CORPORATION

Allstate Plaza, 2775 Sanders Road, Northbrook, IL, 60062-6127

Tel: (847) 402-5000   Fax: (847) 836-3998   www.allstate.com

Personal property, auto and life insurance.

Allstate Direct AG, Postfach 140 165, D-14301 Berlin, Germany

ALOHA TECHNOLOGIES, LTD.

1320 Tennis Drive, Bedford, TX, 76022

Tel: (817) 252-9400   Fax: (817) 252-9490   www.alohapos.com

Provider of point-of-sale (POS) software and information solutions for the foodservice and hospitality industries.

Aloha Systems Europe GmbH, Bettinastrasse 30, D-60325 Frankfurt am Main 1, Germany

Tel: 49-69-9746-1124   Fax: 49-69-9746-1155

ALSTON & BIRD LLP

90 Park Avenue, New York, NY, 10016-1387

Tel: (212) 210-9400   Fax: (212) 210-9444   www.alston.com

International law firm.

Alston & Bird LLP, Brienner Strasse 11, D-80333 München, Germany

ALTERA CORPORATION

101 Innovation Drive, San Jose, CA, 95134

Tel: (408) 544-7000   Fax: (408) 544-8303   www.altera.com

Mfr. high-density programmable chips for semi-conductor industry.

Altera GmbH, Max-Planck-Str. 5, D-85716 Unterschleissheim, Germany

Tel: 49-89-32-18250

ALTIRIS, INC.

588 West 400 South, Lindon, UT, 84042

Tel: (801) 226-8500   Fax: (801) 226-8506   www.altiris.com

Mfr. IT systems management software.

Altiris International GmbH, Am Gierath 20, D-40885 Ratingen, Germany

Contact: Stanislav Bologov

AMAZON.COM, INC.

1200 12th Ave. South, Ste. 1200, Seattle, WA, 98144-2734

Tel: (206) 266-1000   Fax: (206) 266-4206   www.amazon.com

Computer site that offers books, CDs, DVDS, videos, toys, tools, and electronics.

Amazon.Com GmbH, Lilienthalstr. 2, D-8399 Hallbergmoos b. Münich, Germany

AMERICAN APPRAISAL ASSOCIATES INC.

411 E. Wisconsin Ave., Ste. 1900, Milwaukee, WI, 53202

Tel: (414) 271-7240   Fax: (414) 271-1041   www.american-appraisal.com

Valuation consulting services.

American Appraisal Associates, Reinhardtstrasse 27b, D-10117 Berlin, Germany

Tel: 49-3028-4849-50

AMERICAN AXLE & MANUFACTURING HOLDINGS, INC.

1840 Holbrook Ave., Detroit, MI, 48212

Tel: (313) 974-2000   Fax: (313) 974-3090   www.aam.com

Mfr. axles, propeller shafts and chassis components.

American Axle & Manufacturing, GmbH, Pfarrer-Weiss-Weg 10, Ulm, Germany

Contact: Ulrich Stockert, Dir.

ABC, INC.

77 West 66th Street, 13th Fl., New York, NY, 10023

Tel: (212) 456-7777   Fax: (212) 456-6384   www.abc.com

Radio/TV production and broadcasting.

Overseas Media GmbH, Schiller Str. 19-25, Frankfurt Main, Germany

AMERICAN EXPRESS COMPANY

90 Hudson Street, Jersey City, NJ, 07302

Tel: (212) 640-2000   Fax: (212) 619-9802   www.americanexpress.com

Engaged in travel, travelers cheques, charge card and financial services.

American Express Foreign Exchange, Promenadeplatz 6, Bayerischer Hof, Münich, Germany

AMERICAN MANAGEMENT SYSTEMS, INC. (AMS)

4050 Legato Road, 10th Fl., Fairfax, VA, 22033

Tel: (703) 267-8000   Fax: (703) 267-5073   www.amsinc.com

Provides integrated IT solutions, outsourcing, and transformation services.

AMS Management Systems Deutschland GmbH, Querstrasse 8-10, D-60322 Frankfurt, Germany

Tel: 49-69-95-51-11-0   Fax: 49-69-95-51-11-99   Contact: James W. Sheaffer, Mng. Dir.   Emp: 300

AMERICAN MEDICAL SYSTEMS HOLDING, INC.

10700 Bren Road West, Minnetonka, MN, 55343

Tel: (952) 933-4666   Fax: (952) 930-6157   www.visitams.com

Mfr. urological devices.

American Medical Systems GmbH, Kronenstrasse 3, D-10117 Berlin, Germany

Tel: 49-3020-64390   Contact: Marco Kalms

AMERICAN STANDARD COMPANIES, INC.

One Centennial Avenue, Piscataway, NJ, 08855-6820

Tel: (732) 980-3000   Fax: (732) 980-6118   www.americanstandard.com

Mfr. automotive, plumbing, heating, air conditioning products and medical diagnostics systems.

DiaSorin GmbH, Heltofer Strasse 12, D-40472 Dusseldorf, Germany

Tel: 49-211-47220   Fax: 49-211-472-2333

Ideal Standard GmbH, Euskirchenerstr. 80, Postfach 549, D-5300 Bonn, Germany

AMERICAN TECHNICAL CERAMICS CORPORATION

17 Stepar Place, Huntington Station, NY, 11746

Tel: (631) 622-4700   Fax: (631) 622-4748   www.alceramics.com

Mfr. ceramic porcelain capacitors and ceramic-based electronic products.

American Tehcnical Ceramics, Marienstrasse 5, D-85567 Grafing, Germany

Tel: 49-80-92-851086   Fax: 49-80-92-851087

AMERON INTERNATIONAL CORPORATION

245 South Los Robles Ave., Pasadena, CA, 91109-7007

Tel: (626) 683-4000   Fax: (626) 683-4060   www.ameron.com

Mfr. steel pipe systems, concrete products, traffic and lighting poles, protective coatings.

Ameron BV, Rheinstr. 21, D-6000 Frankfurt, Germany

AMETEK INC.

37 N. Valley Road, PO Box 1764, Paoli, PA, 19301-0801

Tel: (610) 647-2121   Fax: (610) 296-3412   www.ametek.com

Mfr. instruments, electric motors and engineered materials.

AMETEK GmbH, Rudolf-Diesel-Strasse 16, D-040670 Meerbusch, Germany

Tel: 49-2159-9136 Fax: 49-2159-9136039

AMETEK GmbH, Schleusingen, Jagerhausstrasse 5, D-98553 Schleusingen, Germany

Tel: 49-36841240   Fax: 49-3684124220

AMF BOWLING WORLDWIDE, INC.

8100 AMF Drive, Richmond, VA, 23111

Tel: (804) 730-4000   Fax: (804) 559-6276   www.amf.com

Operates bowling alleys.

AMF Bowling Products, Niederlassung Deutschland, Anna-Birle Strasse 3A, D-55252 Mainz-Kastel, Germany

Tel: 49-6134-25947   Contact: Peter Knopp

AMGEN INC.

One Amgen Center Drive, Thousand Oaks, CA, 91320-1799

Tel: (805) 447-1000   Fax: (805) 499-2694   www.amgen.com

Biotechnology research and pharmaceuticals.

Amgen GmbH, Reisstrasse 25, D-80992 Münich, Germany

Tel: 49-89-1490-960

AMPEX CORPORATION

1228 Douglas Avenue, Redwood City, CA, 94063-3199

Tel: (650) 367-2011   Fax: (650) 367-4669   www.ampex.com

Mfr. extremely high-performance digital data storage, data retrieval and image processing systems for a broad range of corporate scientific and government applications.

Ampex Europa GmbH., Otto-Volger-Strasse 7C, D-65842 Sulzbach Taunus Frankfurt, Germany

Tel: 49-6196-76520   Fax: 49-6196-76529   Contact: Willy Bjorklund   Emp: 13

AMPHENOL CORPORATION

358 Hall Ave., Wallingford, CT, 06492-7530

Tel: (203) 265-8900   Fax: (203) 265-8793   www.amphenol.com

Mfr. electronic interconnect penetrate systems and assemblies.

Amphenol-Tuchel Electronics, August-Haeusser-Strasse 10, D-74080 Heilbronn, Germany

Tel: 49-7131-9290

AMR CORPORATION (AMERICAN AIRLINES)

4333 Amon Carter Boulevard, Ft. Worth, TX, 76155

Tel: (817) 963-1234   Fax: (817) 967-9641   www.amrcorp.com

Air transport services.

American Airlines Inc., Monckebergstr. 31, D-2000 Hamburg 1, Germany

American Airlines Inc., Terminal C/Rm. 2234, Flughafen, D-4000 Düsseldorf 30, Germany

American Airlines Inc., Airport Münich, Rm. 430, D-8000 Münich 87, Germany

AMSTED INDUSTRIES INC.

205 North Michigan Ave., Chicago, IL, 60601

Tel: (312) 645-1700 Fax: (312) 819-8523 www.amsted.com

Privately-held, diversified manufacturer of products for the construction and building markets, general industry and the railroads.

Keystone Industries, Karl George Bahntechnik, Rheinstrassee 15, D-57638 Neitersen, Germany

Tel: 49-2681-8080

AMWAY CORPORATION

7575 Fulton Street East, Ada, MI, 49355-0001

Tel: (616) 787-6000 Fax: (616) 787-6177 www.amway.com

Mfr./sale home care, personal care, nutrition and houseware products.

Amway GmbH, Benzstrasse 11A, D-8039 Puchheim, Germany

ANACOMP INC.

12365 Crosthwaite Circle, Poway, CA, 92064

Tel: (858) 679-9797 Fax: (858) 748-9482 www.anacomp.com

Engaged in electronic information management services and products.

Anacomp GmbH, Abraham Lincoln Str. 28, D-6200 Wiesbaden, Germany

ANALOG DEVICES INC.

1 Technology Way, Norwood, MA, 02062

Tel: (781) 329-4700 Fax: (781) 326-8703 www.analog.com

Mfr. integrated circuits and related devices.

Analog Devices GmbH, Edelsbergstrasse 8-10, D-8000 Münich, Germany

ANC RENTAL CORPORATION

200 S. Andrews Ave., Ft. Lauderdale, FL, 33301

Tel: (954) 320-4000 Fax: (954) 320-4077 www.ancrental.com

Engaged in car rental services, including National Car Rental and Alamo Rent A Car.

National Car Rental, Franfurter Ring 243, D-8000 Münich 46, Germany

ANDERSEN

33 West Monroe Street, Chicago, IL, 60603

Tel: (312) 580-0033 Fax: (312) 507-6748 www.andersen.com

Accounting and audit, tax and management consulting services. **Firm under worldwide reorganization; new data unavailable for this edition.

Arthur Andersen & Co., GmbH, Mergenthalerallee 10-12, Postfach 5323, D-65760 Eschborn Frankfurt, Germany

Tel: 49-6196-9960

ANDREW CORPORATION

10500 West 153rd Street, Orland Park, IL, 60462

Tel: (708) 349-3300 Fax: (708) 349-5410 www.andrew.com

Designer, manufacturer, and supplier of communications equipment, services, and systems.

Andrew GmbH, Julius-Moserstrasse, 13, D-75179 Pforzheim, Germany

Tel: 49-7231-140150 Fax: 49-7231-140151

Andrew GmbH, Freischützstrasse 96, D-81927 Münich, Germany

Tel: 49-89-99271-100 Fax: 49-89-99271-120

Andrew GmbH Kommunikationssysteme, Daniel-Eckhardt-Strasse 3a, D-43356 Essen, Germany

Tel: 49-201-836070 Fax: 49-201-8360720

ANIXTER INTERNATIONAL INC..

4711 Golf Road, Skokie, IL, 60076

Tel: (847) 677-2600 Fax: (847) 677-8557 www.anixter.com

Distributor wiring systems/products for voice, video, data and power applications.

Anixter Germany, Wittestrasse 30, Haus JVOG, D-13509 Berlin, Germany

Tel: 49-30-435-6830

Anixter Germany, Gottlieb-Daimler-Strasse 55, D-71711 Murr bei Stuttgart, Germany

Tel: 49-7144-26940 Fax: 49-7144-2694-111

ANSELL HEALTHCARE INCORPORATED

200 Schulz Drive, Red Bank, NJ, 07701

Tel: (732) 345-5400   Fax: (732) 219-5114   www.ansellhealthcare.com

Mfr. industrial gloves, rubber and plastic products, protective clothing.

Ansell Healthcare Germany, Stahlgruberring 3, D-81829 Münich, Germany

Tel: 49-89-451180

ANSWERTHINK, INC.

1001 Brickell Bay Drive, Ste. 3000, Miami, FL, 33131

Tel: (305) 375-8005   Fax: (305) 379-8810   www.answerthink.com

Engaged in e-commerce strategies.

Answerthink GmbH, Rathausplatz 12-14, D-65760 Eschborn, Germany

Tel: 49-6196-77726-0

ANSYS TECHNOLOGIES, INC.

25200 Commercentre Drive, Lake Forest, CA, 92630-8810

Tel: (949) 770-9381   Fax: (949) 770-0863   www.ansysinc.com

Develops, manufactures, and markets leading edge technology disposable medical diagnostic products.

ANSYS Technologies, GmbH, Steinmetzstr, 20, D-41061 Mönchengladbach, Germany

Tel: 49-2161-189756   Fax: 49-2161-189602   Contact: ,

AOL TIME WARNER

75 Rockefeller Plaza, New York, NY, 10019

Tel: (212) 484-8000   Fax: (212) 275-3046   www.aoltimewarner.com

Engaged in media and communications; provides internet services, communications, publishing and entertainment.

AOL Time Warner Bertelsmann AG (JV), Gütersloh, Germany

AOL Time Warner Germany, Münich, Germany

Time-Life International GmbH, Akadamiestrasse 7, D-8000 Münich 40, Germany

AON CORPORATION

200 East Randolph, Chicago, IL, 60601

Tel: (312) 381-1000   Fax: (312) 381-6032   www.aon.com

Insurance brokers worldwide; underwrites accident and health insurance, specialty and professional insurance; and provides risk management consultation.

AON Deutschland GmbH, 180 Darmstädter Landstrasse, D-60598 Frankfurt, Germany

Tel: 49-69-686-0730   Fax: 49-69-686-07349   Contact: Klaus P. Obereigner

API MOTION INC.

45 Hazelwood Dr., Amherst, NY, 14228

Tel: (716) 691-9100   Fax: (716) 691-9181   www.apimotion.com

Engaged in motion control solutions using motors and drives, motor gear heads, resolver and encoder feedback devices.

API Motion Deutschland GmbH, Gulichstrasse 12, D-75179 Pforzheim, Germany

APOGENT TECHNOLOGIES INC.

48 Congress Street, Portsmouth, NH, 03801

Tel: (603) 433-6131   Fax: (603) 431-0860   www.apogent.com

Design, mfr. & sell products for laboratories, clinical research, industrial markets & analytical products.

Gerhard Menzel GmbH & Co. KG, Postfach 3157, D-38021 Braunschweig, Germany

Kerr GmbH, Listrasse 28, D-76185 Karlsruhe, Germany

Nunc GmbH, Postfach 12 05 43, D-65083 Wiesbaden, Germany

Ormco Dental GmbH & Co. KG, Hauptstrasse 102-A, D-88161 Lindenberg Allgau, Germany

APPLE COMPUTER, INC.

One Infinite Loop, Cupertino, CA, 95014

Tel: (408) 996-1010   Fax: (408) 974-2113   www.apple.com

Personal computers, peripherals and software.

Apple Computers GmbH, Ingolstadterstr. 20, D-8000 Münich 45, Germany

APPLERA CORPORATION

301 Merritt 7, Norwalk, CT, 06851

Tel: (203) 840-2000   Fax: (203) 840-2312   www.applera.com

Leading supplier of systems for life science research and related applications.

Applied Biosystems, Paul Ehrlich Strasse 17, D-63225 Langen, Germany

Applied Biosystems GmbH, Brunnenweg 13, D-64331 Weiterstadt, Germany

Tel: 49-6150-1010

APPLIED MATERIALS, INC.

3050 Bowers Ave., Santa Clara, CA, 95054-3299

Tel: (408) 727-5555   Fax: (408) 727-9943   www.appliedmaterials.com

Supplies manufacturing systems and services to the semiconductor industry.

Applied Materials G.m.b.H, Buchenstrasse 16b, D-01097 Dresden, Germany

Tel: 49-351-8002-30 Fax: 49-351-8002-310

Applied Materials G.m.b.H - Training Center, Gutenbergstrasse 25, D-85748 Garching-Hochbrck, Germany

Tel: 49-89-329-4830 Fax: 49-89-329-48310

APPLIX, INC.

289 Turnpike Rd., Westboro, MA, 01581

Tel: (508) 870-0300   Fax: (508) 366-4873   www.applix.com

Engaged in business productivity application software.

APPLIX, Inc., Boschetsrieder Straße 67, D-81379 Muenchen, Germany

Tel: 49-89-7485-890 Fax: 49-89-7485-8920

APPLIX, Inc., Hildesheimer Straße 53, D-30169 Hannover, Germany

Tel: 49-0511-807-1161

APPLIX, Inc., Westendstraße 19, D-60325 Frankfurt, Germany

Tel: 49-69-97546-447

APRISMA MANAGEMENT TECHNOLOGIES, INC.

273 Corporate Drive, Portsmouth, NH, 03801

Tel: (603) 334-2100   Fax: (603) 334-2784   www.aprisma.com

Mfr. software.

Aprisma EMEA, Im Gefierth 13d, D-63303 Dreieich, Germany

APW, INC.

N22 W23685 Ridgeview Parkway West, Waukesha, WI, 53188-1013

Tel: (262) 523-7600   Fax: (262) 523-7624   www.apw1.com

Mfr. hi-pressure tools, vibration control products, consumables, technical furniture and enclosures.

APW GmbH, Mundelheimer Weg 51, Postfach 30 01 13, D-40472 Düsseldorf, Germany

AQUENT

711 Boylston Street, Boston, MA, 02116

Tel: (617) 535-5000   Fax: (617) 535-6001   www.aquent.com

Engaged in temporary, specialized employment.

AQUENT, Mullerstrasse 27, D-80469 Münich, Germany

AQUENT, Hedderichstraße 104, D-60596 Frankfurt, Germany

Tel: 49-69-603262

ARAMARK CORPORATION

1101 Market Street, Philadelphia, PA, 19107-2988

Tel: (215) 238-3000   Fax: (215) 238-3333   www.aramark.com

Provides managed services for food, work and safety clothing, education, recreation and facilities.

ARAMARK GmbH, Martin-Behaim-Str. 6, D-63263 Neu Isenburg, Germany

Tel: 49-6-102-745-220 Fax: 49-6-102-745-234 Contact: Udo Luerssen, Pres.

ARBOR ACRES FARM INC.

439 Marlborough Road, Glastonbury, CT, 06033

Tel: (860) 633-4681   Fax: (860) 633-2433   www.aaf.com

Producers of male and female broiler breeders, commercial egg layers.

Arbor Acres Europe, Hasselbusch 4, D-26197 Grossenkneten, Germany

Contact: Tyark Osterndorff

ARBORTEXT, INC.

1000 Victors Way, Ann Arbor, MI, 48108

Tel: (734) 997-0200   Fax: (734) 997-0201   www.arbortext.com

Mfr. publishing software.

Arbortext, Humboldstraße 12, D-85609 Münich, Germany

ARIBA, INC.

1565 Charleston Rd., Mountain View, CA, 94043

Tel: (650) 930-6200   Fax: (650) 930-6300   www.ariba.com

Mfr. software.

Ariba Germany, Feringastrasse 6, D-85774 Unterfoehring Münich, Germany

ARMOR HOLDINGS, INC.

1400 Marsh Landing Parkway, Ste. 112, Jacksonville, FL, 32250

Tel: (904) 741-5400   Fax: (904) 741-5403   www.armorholdings.com

Holding company engaged in security products and services.

COP Zentrale, Klenauer Str. 1A, D-86561 Oberweilenbach, Germany

ARMSTRONG HOLDINGS, INC.

2500 Columbia Avenue, Lancaster, PA, 17604-3001

Tel: (717) 397-0611   Fax: (717) 396-2787   www.armstrong.com

Mfr. and marketing interior furnishings and specialty products for building, auto and textile industry.

Armstrong Floor Products Europe GmbH, Robert Bosch Strasse 10, D-48153 Münster, Germany

Tel: 49-251-760-30

ARROW ELECTRONICS INC.

25 Hub Drive, Melville, NY, 11747

Tel: (516) 391-1300   Fax: (516) 391-1640   www.arrow.com

Distributor of electronic components and computer products.

Spoerle Electronic, Im Gefierth 11 a, D-63303 Dreiech, Germany

Tel: 49-6103-30-40   Fax: 49-6103-30-45-25   Contact: Carlo Giersch, Chmn.

Spoerle GmbH, Postfach 33 52, D-37023 Gottingen, Germany

ARROW INTERNATIONAL, INC.

2400 Bernville Rd., Reading, PA, 19605

Tel: (610) 378-0131   Fax: (610) 374-5360   www.arrowintl.com

Develop, manufacture, and marketing of medical devices.

Arrow Deutschland GmbH, Justus-von-Liebig-Strasse 2, D-85435 Erding, Germany

Tel: 49-8122-98200   Fax: 49-8122-40384   Contact: Klaus Holzer

ART TECHNOLOGY GROUP, INC.

25 First Street, Cambridge, MA, 02141

Tel: (617) 386-1000   Fax: (617) 386-1111   www.atg.com

Mfr. application service software.

Art Technology Group GmbH, Frankfurter Welle, An der Welle 4, D-60422 Frankfurt, Germany

ARVIN MERITOR INC

2135 W. Maple Rd., Troy, MI, 48084-7186

Tel: (248) 435-1000   Fax: (248) 435-1393   www.arvinmeritor.com

Mfr. of automotive exhaust systems and ride control products, axles and power-steering pumps.

ArvinMeritor Exhaust Germany (Zeuna Stärker), Ufestrasse 6, D-57413 Finnentrop, Germany

Tel: 49-2721-517-0   Fax: 49-2721-517-48   Contact: Andreas Schmitz, Engineer

ASCENTIAL SOFTWARE CORPORATION

50 Washington Street, Westboro, MA, 01581

Tel: (508) 366-3888   Fax: (508) 366-3669   www.ascentialsoftware.com

Mfr. software.

Ascential Software GmbH, Landsberger Strasse 302, D-80687 Münich, Germany

ASERA INC.

600 Clipper Drive, Ste. 100, Belmont, CA, 94002

Tel: (650) 769-1200   Fax: (650) 769-1234   www.asera.com

Engaged in eBusiness solutions.

Asera GmbH, Hans-Pinsel-Straße 4, D-85540 Haar, Germany

ASG (ALLEN SYSTEMS GROUP)

1333 Third Avenue South, Naples, FL, 34102

Tel: (941) 435-2200   Fax: (941) 263-3692   www.asg.com

Mainframe computer software, specializing in OnMark 2000 software.

ASG Central Europe, Max-Planck-Straße 15a, D-40699 Erkrath Düsseldorf, Germany

Tel: 49-211-75658-0

ASG Central Europe, Münchnerstr 14, D-85774 Unterföhring, Germany

Tel: 49-89-45-716-300

ASHLAND OIL INC.

50 E. RiverCenter Blvd., Box 391, Covington, KY, 41012-0391

Tel: (859) 815-3333   Fax: (859) 815-5053   www.ashland.com

Petroleum exploration, refining and transportation; mfr. chemicals, oils and lubricants.

Ashland-Suedchemie Gremolith AG, 16-18 Ricewood Road, D-40721 Hilden, Germany

Ashland-Suedchemie-Kernfest GmbH, Postfach 440, Reisholzstrasse 16, D-4010 Hilden, Germany

ASPECT COMMUNICATIONS CORPORATION

1310 Ridder Park Dr., San Jose, CA, 95131-2312

Tel: (408) 325-2200   Fax: (408) 325-2260   www.aspect.com

Mfr. software and related equipment.

Aspect GmbH, Frankfurter Straße 233, D-63263 Neu-Isenburg, Germany

Tel: 49-6102-5670

ASPEN TECHNOLOGY, INC.

10 Canal Park, Cambridge, MA, 02141

Tel: (617) 949-1000   Fax: (617) 949-1030   www.aspentec.com

Mfr. software for chemists and refineries.

AspenTech Europe SA, Am Seestern 24, D-40547 Düsseldorf, Germany

Tel: 49-211-596-787

ASSOCIATED MERCHANDISING CORPORATION

500 Seventh Ave., 2nd Fl., New York, NY, 10018

Tel: (212) 819-6600   Fax: (212) 819-6701   www.theamc.com

Retail service organization; apparel, shoes and accessories.

Associated Merchandising Corp., Bleichstrasse 2-4, D-6000 Frankfurt/Main 1, Germany

ASSOCIATED PRESS INC.

50 Rockefeller Plaza, New York, NY, 10020-1605

Tel: (212) 621-1500   Fax: (212) 621-5447   www.ap.com

News gathering agency.

The Associated Press, Berlin, Germany

Tel: 49-30-399-9250

The Associated Press GmbH, Moselstr. 27, Frankfurt am Main 1, Germany

Tel: 49-69-272300

ATMEL CORPORATION

2325 Orchard Pkwy., San Jose, CA, 95131

Tel: (408) 441-0311   Fax: (408) 436-4200   www.atmel.com

Design, manufacture and marketing of advanced semiconductors.

Atmel Gmbh, Pulverstrasse 55, D-22880 Wedel, Germany

Tel: 49-4103-93160

ATTACHMATE CORPORATION

3617 131st Avenue SE, Bellevue, WA, 98006-1332

Tel: (425) 644-4010   Fax: (425) 747-9924   www.attachmate.com

Mfr. connectivity software.

Attachmate Germany GmbH, Stefan-George-Ring 6, D-81929 München, Germany

Tel: 49-89-99-3510   Fax: 49-89-99-351-111

Attachmate International Sales, Schimmelbuschstrasse 9, D-40699 Erkrath-Hochdahl, Germany

Tel: 49-21-04-93980   Fax: 49-21-04-939850

Attachmate International Sales, Schnackenburgallee 15, D-22525 Hamburg, Germany

Tel: 49-40-85-32660   Fax: 49-40-85-326632

Attachmate International Sales, Untere Waldplatze 2, D-70569 Stuttgart, Germany

Tel: 49-711-67-9680   Fax: 49-711-67-96833

Attachmate International Sales, Lurgiallee 6-8, D-60439 Frankfurt/Main, Germany

Tel: 49-69-958210-0   Fax: 49-69-958210-20

AUTODESK INC.

111 McInnis Parkway, San Rafael, CA, 94903

Tel: (415) 507-5000   Fax: (415) 507-6112   www.autodesk.com

Develop/marketing/support computer-aided design, engineering, scientific and multimedia software products.

Autodesk GmbH, Hansastrasse 28, D-8000 München 21, Germany

Tel: 49-89-547690   Fax: 49-89-5769433

AUTOMATIC DATA PROCESSING INC.

One ADP Blvd., Roseland, NJ, 07068

Tel: (973) 994-5000   Fax: (973) 994-5387   www.adp.com

Data processing services.

ADP Autonom Computer GmbH, Heddernheimer Landstrasse 144, D-60439 Frankfurt, Germany

Tel: 49-69-58-040   Fax: 49-69-5804-241   Contact: Gabriele Bauer

AUTOMATIC SWITCH CO. (ASCO)

50-60 Hanover Rd., Florham Park, NJ, 07932

Tel: (973) 966-2000   Fax: (973) 966-2628   www.asco.com

Mfr. solenoid valves, emergency power controls, pressure and temperature switches.

ASCO GmbH & Co., PO Box 101138, D-40831 Ratingen 1, Germany

Tel: 49-2102-8501-0   Fax: 49-2102-850136   Contact: H. Hummel

AUTOSPLICE INC.

10121 Barnes Canyon Road, San Diego, CA, 92121

Tel: (858) 535-0077   Fax: (858) 535-0130   www.autosplice.com

Mfr. electronic components.

Autosplice Europe GmbH, Waldstrasse 12, D-90579 Langenzenn Laubendorf, Germany

Tel: 49-9102-9957-12   Fax: 49-9102-9957-19   Contact: Wolfgang Blust

AUTO-TROL TECHNOLOGY CORPORATION

12500 North Washington Street, Denver, CO, 80241-2400

Tel: (303) 452-4919   Fax: (303) 252-2249   www.auto-trol.com

Develops, markets and integrates computer-based solutions for industrial companies and government agencies worldwide.

Auto-Trol Technology GmbH, Heltorfer Strasse 6, D-40472 Düsseldorf, Germany

Tel: 49-211-907-950   Emp: 3

AVERY DENNISON CORPORATION

150 N. Orange Grove Blvd., Pasadena, CA, 91103

Tel: (626) 304-2000   Fax: (626) 792-7312   www.averydennison.com

Mfr. pressure-sensitive adhesives and materials, office products, labels, tags, retail systems, Carter's Ink and specialty chemicals.

Avery Maschinen GmbH, Kollaustrasse 105, D-2000 Hamburg, Germany

Fasson Handelsgesellschaft GmbH, Alte Strasse 39, Dortmund, Germany

AVID TECHNOLOGY, INC.

1 Park West, Tewksbury, MA, 01876

Tel: (978) 640-6789   Fax: (978) 640-1366   www.avid.com

Mfr. animation design software and digital and audio systems.

Avid Technology GmbH, Isar Office Park, Am Soeldermoos, D-85399 Hallbergmoos, Germany

Fax: 49-811-55-20999

AVNET INC.

2211 South 47th Street, Phoenix, AZ, 85034

Tel: (480) 643-2000   Fax: (480) 643-4670   www.avnet.com

Distributor electronic components, computers and peripherals.

Avnet EMG Gmbh, Wolfenbutteler Str. 33, D-81829 Münich, Germany

Tel: 49-531-220-7330   Fax: 49-531-220-7335

BFI Ibexsa Elektronik GmbH, Assar Gabrielssonstrasse 1B, D-61328 Steinberg, Germany

Tel: 49-6074-40980   Fax: 49-6074-409810

AVOCENT CORPORATION

4991 Corporate Drive, Huntsville, AL, 35805

Tel: (256) 430-4000   Fax: (250) 430-4030   www.avocent.com

Mfr. computer hardware.

Avocent Munich, Dachauer Straße 2-4, D-33803 Steinhagen, Germany

AVON PRODUCTS, INC.

1345 Avenue of the Americas, New York, NY, 10105-0196

Tel: (212) 282-5000   Fax: (212) 282-6049   www.avon.com

Mfr. direct seller of cosmetics and beauty-related items.

Avon Cosmetics GmbH, Postfach 400140, D-8000 Münich 40, Germany

Tel: 49-8165-720   Fax: 49-8165-721226   Contact: Walter Biel

AXCELIS TECHNOLOGIES, INC.

55 Cherry Hill Drive, Beverly, MA, 01915

Tel: (978) 787-4000   Fax: (978) 787-4200   www.axcelis.com

Mfr. implantation devices.

Axcelis Technologies, Henschelring 11, D-95551 Kirchheim, Germany

B&P PROCESS EQUIPMENT AND SYSTEMS LLC

1000 Hess Ave., Saginaw, MI, 48601

Tel: (989) 757-1300   Fax: (989) 757-1301   www.bpprocess.com

Mfr. stand-alone machines and complete turnkey systems for food and chemicals processing.

Baker Perkins Holding Ltd., Compounding Technology, Schlusselbergstraße 7, D-84453 Muhldorf, UK

Tel: 49-8631-379425   Contact: Harald Possler

BADGER METER INC.

PO Box 245036, Milwaukee, WI, 53224-9536

Tel: (414) 355-0400   Fax: (414) 371-5956   www.badgermeter.com

Mfr. liquid meters and controls.

Badger Meter Europe GmbH, Karlstrasse 11, D-72660 Beuren, Germany

Tel: 49-7025-9208-0   Fax: 49-7025-9208-25   Contact: Hors Gras   Emp: 25

BAIN & COMPANY, INC.

Two Copley Place, Boston, MA, 02116

Tel: (617) 572-2000   Fax: (617) 572-2427   www.bain.com

Strategic management consulting services.

Bain & Co. Germany Inc., Thomas-Wimmer-Ring 3, D-8000 Münich 22, Germany

Tel: 49-89-290-110   Fax: 48-89-290-11-113

ROBERT W. BAIRD & CO. INCORPORATED

PO Box 672, Milwaukee, WI, 53201

Tel: (414) 765-3500   Fax: (414) 765-3600   www.rwbaird.com

Engaged in investment banking, serving individuals, corporations, municipalities and institutional investors.

Granville Baird, Haus am Hafen, Steinhoeft 5-7, D-20459 Hamburg, Germany

Tel: 49-40-3748-0210   Contact: Wolfgang Alvano

BAKER & McKENZIE

130 East Randolph Drive, Ste. 2500, Chicago, IL, 60601

Tel: (312) 861-8000   Fax: (312) 861-2899   www.bakerinfo.com

International legal services.

Döser Amereller Noack / Baker & McKenzie, Friedrichstrasse 79-80, D-10117 Berlin, Germany

Tel: 49-30-20387-600   Fax: 49-30-20387-699   Contact: Carl H. Andres, Ptnr.

Döser Amereller Noack / Baker & McKenzie, Palais am Lembachplatz, Ottostrasse 8, D-80333 Münich, Germany

Tel: 49-89-552380   Fax: 49-89-55238-199   Contact: Walter R. Henle, Ptnr.

Döser Amereller Noack / Baker & McKenzie, Bethmannstrasse 50-54, D-60311 Frankfurt/Main, Germany

Tel: 49-69-299080   Fax: 49-69-29908108   Contact: Horst Amereller, Ptnr.

BAKER HUGHES INCORPORATED

3900 Essex Lane, Ste. 1200, Houston, TX, 77027

Tel: (713) 439-8600   Fax: (713) 439-8699   www.bakerhughes.com

Develop and apply technology to drill, complete and produce oil and natural gas wells; provide separation systems to petroleum, municipal, continuous process and mining industries.

Baker Hughes Process, Dillenburger Str. 100, D-51105 Cologne, Germany

Tel: 49-221-9856-0 Fax: 49-221-9856-202

Baker Oil Tools GmbH, Christensenstrasse 1, D-29221 Celle, Germany

Tel: 49-5141-2030 Fax: 49-5141-203626

BAKER PETROLITE CORPORATION

3900 Essex Lane, Houston, TX, 77027

Tel: (713) 599-7400   Fax: (713) 599-7592   www.bakerhughes.com

Mfr. specialty chemical treating programs, performance-enhancing additives and related equipment and services.

Petrolite GmbH, Kaiser Friedrich Promenade 59, Postfach 2031, D-6380 Bad Homburg 1, Germany

BALDOR ELECTRIC COMPANY

5711 R.S. Boreham Jr. Street, Fort Smith, AR, 72908

Tel: (501) 646-4711   Fax: (501) 648-5792   www.baldor.com

Mfr. electric motors.

Baldor ASR GmbH, Dieselstrasse 22, Kirchheim, D-85551 Münich, Germany

Tel: 49-89-90508-0

BALDWIN TECHNOLOGY COMPANY, INC.

12 Commerce Drive, Shelton, CT, 06484

Tel: (203) 402-1000   Fax: (203) 402-5500   www.baldwintech.com

Mfr./services material handling, accessories, control and prepress equipment for print industry.

Baldwin Grafotec GmbH, Derchinger Strasse 137, D-86165 Augsburg, Germany

Tel: 49-821-79420 Fax: 49-821-794222   Contact: Dr. Rolf Enders, Geschäftsführer

BANK OF AMERICA CORPORATION

Bank of America Corporate Center, Charlotte, NC, 28255

Tel: (415) 622-3530   Fax: (704) 386-6699   www.bankofamerica.com

Financial services.

Bank of America NT & SA, Ulmenstrasse 30, Postfach 110243, D-60325 Frankfurt, Germany

Tel: 49-69-7100-1461   Fax: 49-69-7100-1261   Contact: Rudi Perkowsky, VP

THE BANK OF NEW YORK

One Wall Street, New York, NY, 10286

Tel: (212) 495-1784   Fax: (212) 495-2546   www.bankofny.com

Banking services.

The Bank of New York, Niedenau 61-63, Postfach 60077, D-60235 Frankfurt/Main 17, Germany

Tel: 49-69-971510   Fax: 49-69-721798

BANK ONE CORPORATION

One Bank One Plaza, Chicago, IL, 60670

Tel: (312) 732-4000   Fax: (312) 732-3366   www.fcnbd.com

Provides financial products and services.

Bank One, NA, Hochstrasse 35-37, D-60313 Frankfurt/Main, Germany

Tel: 49-69-299876-0   Fax: 49-69-299876-80   Contact: Volker Loeser, Branch Mgr.

C. R. BARD, INC.

730 Central Ave., Murray Hill, NJ, 07974

Tel: (908) 277-8000   Fax: (908) 277-8078   www.crbard.com

Mfr. health care products.

C.R. Bard GmbH, Siemenstrasse 1, D-8044 Unterschleissheim München, Germany

BARRA, INC.

2100 Milvia Street, Berkeley, CA, 94704

Tel: (510) 548-5442   Fax: (510) 548-4374   www.barra.com

Mfr. analytical software for private investors and portfolio managers.

BARRA International, Ltd., Goethestraße 5, D-60313 Frankfurt, Germany

Tel: 49-69-28-1700

BARRY CONTROLS INC.

40 Guest Street, PO Box 9105, Brighton, MA, 02135-9105

Tel: (617) 787-1555   Fax: (617) 254-7381   www.barrymounts.com

Mfr./sale vibration isolation mounting devices.

Barry Controls Intl. GmbH, Karl Liebknecht Str. 30, Postfach 1137, D-65479 Raunheim, Germany

BASE TEN SYSTEMS, INC.

528 Primrose Ct., Belle Mead, NJ, 08502

Tel: (908) 359-1867   Fax: (908) 359-1867   www.base10.com

Mfr. software for pharmaceutical companies.

Base Ten Electronics GmbH, Am Söldnermoos 10, D-85399 Hallbergmoos, Germany

Tel: 49-811-5598-0

BATES WORLDWIDE INC.

498 Seventh Avenue, New York, NY, 10018

Tel: (212) 297-7000   Fax: (212) 986-0270   www.batesww.com

Advertising, marketing, public relations and media consulting.

Bates Dialog Direkt Marketing, Hanauer Landstrasse 287-289, D-60314 Frankfurt, Germany

Tel: 49-69-405-7203   Fax: 49-69-405-72359   Contact: Relner Blau, Dir.

Bates Germany GmbH, Hanauer Landstrasse 287-289, D-60314 Frankfurt am Main 1, Germany

Tel: 49-69-405-7200   Fax: 49-69-405-72-359   Contact: Ulrich Voigel, CEO

BATTELLE MEMORIAL INSTITUTE

505 King Ave., Columbus, OH, 43201-2693

Tel: (614) 424-6424   Fax: (614) 424-3260   www.battelle.org

Develops new technologies, commercializes products, and provides solutions for industry and government.

Battelle Europe, Am Romerhof 35, D-6000 Frankfurt Main 90, Germany

BAUSCH & LOMB INC.

One Bausch & Lomb Place, Rochester, NY, 14604-2701

Tel: (716) 338-6000   Fax: (716) 338-6007   www.bausch.com

Mfr. vision care products and accessories.

Bausch & Lomb GmbH (Vision Care), Max-Planck-Str. 6, D-85609 Dornach, Germany

Dr. Mann Pharma Fabrik, GmbH, Brunsbuetteler Damm 165 - 173, D-13581 Berlin, Germany

Dr. Winzer Pharma GmbH, Lizweg 7, D-82140 Olching, Germany

BAX GLOBAL INC.

16808 Armstrong Ave., PO Box 19571, Irvine, CA, 92623

Tel: (949) 752-4000   Fax: (949) 260-3182   www.baxworld.com

Air freight forwarder.

BAX Global, c/o Wendschlag & Pohl, Frachthalle Tegel Airport, D-100051 Berlin, Germany

BAXTER INTERNATIONAL INC.

One Baxter Parkway, Deerfield, IL, 60015

Tel: (847) 948-2000   Fax: (847) 948-3948   www.baxter.com

Mfr. products and provide services in the field of the administration of medication and bioscience.

Baxter Deutschland GmbH, Edisonstrasse 3-4, D-85716 Unterschleissheim Münich, Germany

BBDO WORLDWIDE

1285 Ave. of the Americas, New York, NY, 10019

Tel: (212) 459-5000   Fax: (212) 459-6645   www.bbdo.com

Multinational group of advertising agencies.

BBDO Group Germany, Düsseldorf, Germany

BDO SEIDMAN, LLP   BELGIUM

130 East Randolph Street, Chicago, IL, 60601

Tel: (312) 856-9100   Fax: (312) 856-1379   www.bdo.com

International accounting and financial consulting firm.

BDO Deutsche Warentreuhand Aktiengesellschaft, Grüneburgweg 12, D-60322 Frankfurt, Germany

Tel: 49-69-95-9410   Fax: 49-69-55-4335   Contact: Dr. Hans-Joachim Jacob

BEA SYSTEMS, INC.

2315 North First Street, St. Jose, CA, 95131

Tel: (408) 570-8000   Fax: (408) 570-8091   www.beasys.com

Develops communications management software and provider of software consulting services.

BEA Systems GmbH, Martin-Behaim-Straße 8, D-63263 Neu-Isenburg, Germany

BECKER & POLIAKOFF, P.A.

Emerald Lake Corporate Park, 3111 Stirling Road, Fort Lauderdale, FL, 33312

Tel: (954) 987-7550   Fax: (954) 985-4176   www.becker-poliakoff.com

Law firm; advice and assistance with foreign investments.

Becker & Poliakoff, P.A., Wicke Rechtsanwälte, Friedrich-Ebert-Anlage 56, D-60325 Frankfurt, Germany

BECKMAN COULTER, INC.

4300 N. Harbor Boulevard, Fullerton, CA, 92834

Tel: (714) 871-4848   Fax: (714) 773-8898   www.beckmancoulter.com

Develop/mfr./marketing automated systems and supplies for biological analysis.

Beckman Coulter GmbH, Europark Fichtenhain B 13, D-47807 Krefeld, Germany

Tel: 49-21-51-3335

BELDEN, INC.

7701 Forsyth Blvd., Ste. 800, St. Louis, MO, 63015

Tel: (314) 854-8000   Fax: (314) 854-8001   www.belden.com

Mfr. electronic wire and cable products.

Belden-EIW GmbH & Co. KG, Am Krebsgraben 1-3, Postfach 13 40, D-78048 Villingen-Schwenningen, Germany

BELLSOUTH CORPORATION LATIN AMERICA

1155 Peachtree Street NE, Ste. 400, Atlanta, GA, 30367

Tel: (404) 249-4800   Fax: (404) 249-4880   www.bellsouth.com

Mobile communications, telecommunications network systems.

E-Plus Mobilfunk GmbH, E-Plus Platz 1, D-40468 Düsseldorf, Germany

Tel: 49-211-4480

BEMIS COMPANY, INC.

222 South 9th Street, Ste. 2300, Minneapolis, MN, 55402-4099

Tel: (612) 376-3000   Fax: (612) 376-3180   www.bemis.com

Mfr. flexible packaging materials and specialty coated and graphics products.

Hayssen Europa GmbH, Postfach 3280, D-7500 Karlsruhe l, Germany

BENTLY NEVADA CORPORATION

1631 Bently Parkway South, Minden, NV, 89423

Tel: (775) 782-3611   Fax: (775) 782-9259   www.bently.com

Provides hardware, software, and services for machinery information and management systems.

Bently Nevada GmbH, Postfach 60, Hermannstr. 25, D-6078 Neu-Isenburg, Germany

BERLITZ CROSS-CULTURAL TRAINING INC.

400 Alexander Park, Princeton, NJ, 08540

Tel: (609) 514-9650   Fax: (609) 514-9689   www.berlitz.com

Consulting and management training services to bridge cultural gaps for international travelers as well as for business transferees and families.

Berlitz Deutschland GmbH, Marienplatz 18/19, D-80331 Münich, Germany

BEST WESTERN INTERNATIONAL

6201 North 24th Place, Phoenix, AZ, 85106

Tel: (602) 957-4200   Fax: (602) 957-5740   www.bestwestern.com

International hotel chain.

Hotel Domicil, Thomas-Mann-Strasse 24-26, D-53111 Bonn, Germany

BHA GROUP HOLDINGS, INC.

8800 East 63rd Street, Kansas City, MO, 64133

Tel: (816) 356-8400   Fax: (816) 353-1873   www.bha.com

Mfr. air pollution control replacement parts.

BHA Group GmbH, Filtrastrasse 507, D-59222 Ahlen, Germany

Tel: 49-2528-300

BICC GENERAL

4 Tesseneer Drive, Highland Heights, KY, 41076

Tel: (859) 572-8000   Fax: (859) 572-8444   www.generalcable.com

Mfr., marketing and distribution of copper, aluminum and fiber optic wire and cable products for the communications, energy and electrical markets.

BICC General, Riedelstrasse 1, D-12347 Berlin, Germany

BIJUR LUBRICATING CORPORATION

50 Kocher Dr., Bennington, VT, 05201-1994

Tel: (802) 447-2174   Fax: (802) 447-1365   www.bijur.com

Design and manufacture of grease and oil pumps.

Delimon GmbH, Armistraße 15, Postfach 402052, D-40227 Düsseldorf, Germany

Tel: 49-211-7774-0 Fax: 49-211-7774-210

BIOGEN, INC.

14 Cambridge Center, Cambridge, MA, 02142

Tel: (617) 679-2000   Fax: (617) 679-2617   www.biogen.com

Engaged in medical research and development of autoimmune diseases.

Biogen GmbH, Carl-Zeiss Ring 6, D-85737 Ismaning, Germany

Tel: 49-89-99-6170

BIOMET, INC.

56 East Bell Drive, Warsaw, IN, 46682

Tel: (574) 267-6639   Fax: (574) 267-8137   www.biomet.com

Mfr. orthopedic medical devices.

Walter Lorenz Surgical, Inc., Jechtinger Strasse 8, D-79111 Freiburg, Germany

BIO-RAD LABORATORIES INC.

1000 Alfred Nobel Drive, Hercules, CA, 94547

Tel: (510) 724-7000   Fax: (510) 724-3167   www.bio-rad.com

Mfr. life science research products, clinical diagnostics, analytical instruments.

Bio-Rad Laboratories Inc., Heidemannstraße 164, Postfach 45 01 33, D-80901 Münich, Germany

BIOSOURCE INTERNATIONAL, INC.

542 Flynn Road, Camarillo, CA, 93012

Tel: (805) 987-0086   Fax: (805) 383-5386   www.biosource.com

Engaged in biotech research.

BioSource GmbH, Neuenhoferstr. 84, D-42657 Solingen, Germany

Contact: Jozef Van Genechten

BIRD MACHINE COMPANY

100 Neponset Street, South Walpole, MA, 02071

Tel: (508) 668-0400   Fax: (508) 668-6855   www.bakerhughes.com

Specializes in solid-liquid separation utilizing a broad range of centrifugation and filtration equipment.

Bird Machine, Dillenburger Str. 100, D-51105 Cologne, Germany

Tel: 49-221-9856-535   Fax: 49-221-9856-102

BLACK & DECKER CORPORATION

701 E. Joppa Road, Towson, MD, 21286

Tel: (410) 716-3900   Fax: (410) 716-2933   www.blackanddecker.com

Mfr. power tools and accessories, security hardware, small appliances, fasteners, information systems and services.

Black & Decker Kundendienst, , Black & Decker-Strasse 40, D-65510 Idstein, Germany

Tel: 49-6-126-212483   Fax: 49-6-126-212770

DeWalt Kundendienst, , Richard-Klinger-Strasse, D-65510 Idstein, Germany

Tel: 49-6-126-212483   Fax: 49-6-126-212770

Zentral-Kundendienst ELU International, , Richard-Klinger-Strasse, D-65510 Idstein, Germany

Tel: 49-6-126-212483   Fax: 49-6-126-212770

BLACK & VEATCH LLP

8400 Ward Pkwy., PO Box 8405, Kansas City, MO, 64114

Tel: (816) 339-2000   Fax: (816) 339-2934   www.bv.com

Engaged in engineering, construction and consulting, specializing in infrastructure development in the fields of energy, water and information.

PROWA - Black & Veatch GmbH, Magdeburger Strasse 38, D-06112 Halle, Germany

Tel: 49-345-2125-0   Fax: 49-345-2125-201   Contact: Klaus Klingel

BLACK BOX CORPORATION

1000 Park Dr., Lawrence, PA, 15055

Tel: (724) 746-5500   Fax: (724) 746-0746   www.blackbox.com

Direct marketer and technical service provider of communications, networking and related computer connectivity products.

Black Box Deutschland, Ludwigsforum, Ludwigstrasse 456, D-85399 Hallbergmoos, Germany

Tel: 49-811-5541-0   Fax: 49-811-5541-499   Contact: Michael Balmforth, Gen. Mgr.

BLOOM ENGINEERING CO., INC.

5460 Horning Rd., Pittsburgh, PA, 15236

Tel: (412) 653-3500   Fax: (412) 653-2253   www.bloomeng.com

Mfr. custom engineered burners and combustion systems.

Bloom Engineering Company, Büro Ost, AM Bahnhof 1, D-09599 Freiberg/Sachsen, Germany

Bloom Engineering Company (Europa) GmbH, Büttgenbachstrasse 14, D-40549 Dusseldorf, Germany

Tel: 49-211-500910   Fax: 49-211-501397

BLOUNT INTERNATIONAL, INC

4520 Executive Park Dr., Montgomery, AL, 36116-1602

Tel: (334) 244-4000   Fax: (334) 271-8130   www.blount.com

Mfr. cutting chain and equipment, timber harvest and handling equipment and riding mowers.

Blount GmbH, Postfach 1146, Reinhardstrasse 23, D-71112 Gartringen, Germany

Tel: 49-7034-92850   Fax: 49-7034-26754   Contact: Roland Stolz, Mgr.

BLUE OCEAN SOFTWARE, INC.

15310 Amberly Drive, Ste. 370, Tampa, FL, 33647

Tel: (813) 977-4553   Fax: (813) 979-4447   www.blueocean.com

Mfr. software.

Blue Ocean Software, In der Fuhr 4, D-51789 Lindlar, Germany

Tel: 49-2207-700539   Contact: Margarete Roesch

BMC INDUSTRIES INC.

One Meridian Crossings, Ste. 850, Minneapolis, MN, 55423

Tel: (612) 851-6000   Fax: (612) 851-6065   www.bmcind.com

Design/mfr./marketing precision etched products, electroformed components, special printed circuits, ophthalmic devices.

BMC Europe GmbH, Renkenrunsstrasse 24-26, D-79379 Mullheim, Germany

Tel: 49-7631-802-115   Fax: 49-7631-802-311   Contact: John Springer, Mng. Dir.   Emp: 300

BMC SOFTWARE, INC.

2101 City West Blvd., Houston, TX, 77042-2827

Tel: (713) 918-8800   Fax: (713) 918-8000   www.bmc.com

Engaged in mainframe-related utilities software and services.

BMC Software, Postfach 71 01 49, D-60491 Frankfurt, Germany

BMC Software, Amsinckstraße 57, D-20097 Hamburg, Germany

BOART LONGYEAR COMPANY

2640 West 1700 South, PO Box 27314, Salt Lake City, UT, 84104

Tel: (801) 972-6430   Fax: (801) 977-3372   www.boartlongyear.com

Mfr. diamond drills, concrete cutting equipment and drill services.

Longyear GmbH, Postfach 460, Grafftring 1, D-3100 Celle, Germany

BOBCAT COMPANY

250 E. Beaton Drive, PO Box 6000, West Fargo, ND, 58078-8700

Tel: (701) 241-8700   Fax: (701) 241-8704   www.melroe.com

Mfr. heavy equipment.

Bobcat Parts Trading Company GmbH, Solinger Strasse 2, D-45481 Mulheim, Germany

THE BOEING COMPANY

100 N. Riverside Plaza, Chicago, IL, 60606

Tel: (312) 544-2000   Fax: (312) 544-2082   www.boeing.com.

World's largest aerospace company; mfr. military and commercial aircraft, missiles and satellite launch vehicles.

The Boeing Company, Geschaftsfuhrung, Postfach 51 01 43, D-13361 Berlin, Germany

BOISE CASCADE CORPORATION

1111 West Jefferson Street, PO Box 50, Boise, ID, 83728-0001

Tel: (208) 384-6161   Fax: (208) 384-7189   www.bc.com

Mfr./distributor paper and paper products, building products, office products.

Boise Cascade Office Products, Ltd., Hamburg, Germany

BOOZ-ALLEN & HAMILTON INC.

8283 Greensboro Drive, McLean, VA, 22102

Tel: (703) 902-5000   Fax: (703) 902-3333   www.bah.com

International management and technology consultants.

Booz Allen & Hamilton GmbH, Lenbachplatz 3, D-80333 München, Germany

Tel: 49-89-545250   Fax: 49-89-545-25500

Booz Allen & Hamilton GmbH, Mainzer Landstrasse/16, D-60325 Frankfurt, Germany

Tel: 49-69-971670   Fax: 49-69-97167-400

Booz, Allen & Hamilton Inc., Koenigsallee 106, D-40215 Düsseldorf, Germany

Tel: 49-211-38900   Fax: 49-211-371002

BORG-WARNER AUTOMOTIVE INC.

200 S. Michigan Ave., Chicago, IL, 60604

Tel: (312) 322-8500   Fax: (312) 461-0507   www.bwauto.com

Mfr. automotive components; provider of security services.

Borg-Warner Automotive GmbH, Postfach 40, D-68767 Ketsch, Germany

Borg-Warner Automotive GmbH, Postfach 101360, D-69003 Heidelberg, Germany

BOSE CORPORATION

The Mountain, Framingham, MA, 01701-9168

Tel: (508) 879-7330   Fax: (508) 766-7543   www.bose.com

Mfr. quality audio equipment and speakers.

BOSE GmbH, Max-Planck-Strasse 36, Postfach 1125, D-61381 Friedrichsdorf, Germany

THE BOSTON CONSULTING GROUP

Exchange Place, 31st Fl., Boston, MA, 02109

Tel: (617) 973-1200   Fax: (617) 973-1339   www.bcg.com

Management consulting company.

The Boston Consulting Group, GmbH, Westend-Carree, Gruneburgweg 18, D-60322 Frankfurt am Main, Germany

Tel: 49-711-16-23-3

The Boston Consulting Group, GmbH, Heinrich-Heine-Allee 1, D-40213 Düsseldorf, Germany

Tel: 49-211-13830

The Boston Consulting Group, GmbH, Chilehaus A, Fischertwiete 2, D-20095 Hamburg, Germany

Tel: 49-40-301-82

The Boston Consulting Group, GmbH, Sendlinger Str. 7, D-80331 München, Germany

Tel: 49-89-23-17-40

The Boston Consulting Group, GmbH, Kronprinzstr. 28, D-70173 Stuttgart, Germany

Tel: 49-69-9-15-02

BOSTON SCIENTIFIC CORPORATION (BSC)

One Scientific Place, Natick, MA, 01760-1537

Tel: (508) 650-8000   Fax: (508) 650-8923   www.bostonscientific.com

Developer, manufacturer and marketer of medical devices.

Boston Scientific Medizintechnik GmbH, Christinenstrasse 2, D-40880 Ratinger, Germany

Tel: 49-2102-489-3   Fax: 49-2102-489-439

BOURNS INC.

1200 Columbia Avenue, Riverside, CA, 92507

Tel: (909) 781-5500   Fax: (909) 781-5006   www.bourns.com

Mfr. resistive components and networks, precision potentiometers, panel controls, switches, transducers and surge protectors..

Bourns GmbH, Postfach 100644, Brietestrasse 2, D-7000 Stuttgart 10, Germany

BOWNE & COMPANY, INC.

345 Hudson Street, New York, NY, 10014

Tel: (212) 924-5500   Fax: (212) 229-3420   www.bowne.com

Financial printing and foreign language translation, localization (software), internet design and maintenance and facilities management.

Bowne Global Solutions, Bettinastrasse 30, D-60325 Frankfurt am Main, Germany

Tel: 49-69-9714-760 Fax: 49-69-72-43-41   Contact: Matthew Gould, Mgr.

Bowne Global Solutions, Inselkammerstraße 11, D-82008 Unterhaching Münich, Germany

Tel: 49-89-666-790   Fax: 49-89-666-79166

BOYDEN CONSULTING CORPORATION

364 Elwood Ave., Hawthorne, NY, 10502

Tel: (914) 747-0093   Fax: (914) 980-6147   www.boyden.com

International executive search firm.

Boyden Intl. GmbH, Kathaarina-Heinroth-Ufer 1, D-10787 Berlin, Germany

Tel: 49-30-23-09090

Boyden Intl. GmbH, Postfach 1724, Ferinandstr., D-61348 Bad Homburg-v.d.H, Germany

Tel: 49-6172-180200

BOZELL GROUP

40 West 23rd Street, New York, NY, 10010

Tel: (212) 727-5000   Fax: (212) 645-9173   www.bozell.com

Advertising, marketing, public relations and media consulting.

Bozell Direct Friends, Werbesgentur fur Direct Marketing GmbH, Borsteler Chaussee 55, D-22453 Hamburg, Germany

Tel: 49-40-514-320   Fax: 49-40-514-32200   Contact: Uwe H. Drescher, Chmn.

Bozell Werbeaentur GmbH, Hansaallee 16, D-60322 Frankfurt am Main 1, Germany

Tel: 49-69-1530-920   Fax: 49-69-1530-9215   Contact: Dietmar Steuer, Mng. Dir.

BRADY CORPORATION

6555 W. Good Hope Road, Milwaukee, WI, 53223

Tel: (414) 358-6600   Fax: (414) 358-6600   www.whbrady.com

Mfr. industrial ID for wire marking, circuit boards; facility ID, signage, printing systems and software.

W.H. Brady GmbH, Lagerstrasse 13, D-64807 Dieburg, Germany

Tel: 49-6071-960-3   Fax: 49-6071-960-400   Contact: Christian Thomczek, Country Mgr.

BRANSON ULTRASONICS CORPORATION

41 Eagle Road, Danbury, CT, 06813-1961

Tel: (203) 796-0400   Fax: (203) 796-2285   www.branson-plasticsjoin.com

Engaged in design, development, manufacture and marketing of plastics joining, precision cleaning and processing equipment.

Branson GmbH, Waldstraße 53-55, D-63128 Dietzenbach-Steinberg, Germany

Tel: 49-6074-4970   Fax: 49-6074-497499

BRIGGS & STRATTON CORPORATION

PO Box 702, Milwaukee, WI, 53201

Tel: (414) 259-5333   Fax: (414) 259-9594   www.briggesandstratton.com

Mfr. air-cooled gasoline engines for outdoor power equipment.

Briggs & Stratton Deutschland GmbH, Attn: German Office, PO Box 72, Milwaukee, WI, 53201

BRIGHTPOINT, INC.

600 East 96th Street, Ste. 575, Indianapolis, IN, 46240

Tel: (317) 805-4100   Fax: (317) 805-4101   www.brightpoint.com

Provider of outsourced services in the global wireless telecommunications and data industry; distribution of wireless voice and data products.

Brightpoint GmbH, An der Stadtweide 17, D-46446 Willich, Germany

Tel: 49-2154-9390

BRINK'S INC.

Thorndal Circle, Darien, CT, 06820

Tel: (203) 662-7800   Fax: (203) 662-7968   www.brinks.com

Security transportation.

Brink's Deutschland GmbH, Insterburger Straße 7a, D-60487 Frankfurt/Main, Germany

BRIO SOFTWARE, INC.

4980 Great America Pkwy., Santa Clara, CA, 95054

Tel: (408) 496-7400   Fax: (408) 496-7420   www.brio.com

Mfr. software.

Brio Software GmbH, Moosacher Straße 56A, D-80809 München, Germany

BRISTOL-MYERS SQUIBB COMPANY

345 Park Ave., New York, NY, 10154-0037

Tel: (212) 546-4000   Fax: (212) 546-4020   www.bms.com

Pharmaceutical and food preparations, medical and surgical instruments.

Bristol-Myers - Regensburg Plant, Postfach 177, Donaustaufer Strasse 378, D-8400 Regensburg, Germany

ConvaTec Germany, Volkartstrasse 83, D-8000 München 19, Germany

ConvaTech Vertriebs GmbH, Ein Unter. der, Volkartstrasse 3, D-80636 München, Germany

S+G Implants GmbH, Grapengieberstrasse 34, D-2400 Lubeck, Germany

Zimmer Chirurgie GmbH, Waldstrasse 23, D-6057 Dietzenbach, Germany

BROADCOM CORPORATION INTERNATIONAL

16215 Alton Pkwy., Irvine, CA, 92619-7013

Tel: (949) 450-8700   Fax: (949) 450-8710   www.broadcom.com

Designs, develops and supplies integrated circuits and high density communication processors.

Broadcom Germany, Eggersgrub 2, D-84149 Velden, Germany

Tel: 49-8742-918710   Fax: 49-8742-918711

BROBECK PHLEGER & HARRISON LLP

Spear Street Tower, One Market St., San Francisco, CA, 94105

Tel: (415) 442-0900   Fax: (415) 442-1010   www.brobeck.com

Engaged in international law.

Brobeck Hale and Dorr, Maximilianstraße 31, D-80539 München, Germany

BROOKS-PRI AUTOMATION, INC.

15 Elizabeth Drive, Chelmsford, MA, 01824

Tel: (978) 262-2400   Fax: (978) 262-2500   www.brooks.com

Mfr. tool automation products.

Brooks Automation GmbH, Göschwitzer Strasse 25, D-07745 Jena, Germany

Tel: 49-3641-65-4000   Fax: 49-3641-65-4444

Brooks Automation GmbH, Freisinger Strasse 32, D-85737 Ismaning, Germany

Tel: 49-89-9621-026-0   Fax: 49-89-9621-026-99

BROWNING

1 Browning Place, Morgan, UT, 84050

Tel: (801) 876-2711   Fax: (801) 876-3331   www.browning.com

Sales and distribution of port firearms, fishing rods, etc.

Browning Sports GmbH, Allscheidt 7, D-40883 Ratingen, Germany

BRUSH WELLMAN ENGINEERED MATERIALS INC.

17876 St. Clair Ave., Cleveland, OH, 44110

Tel: (216) 486-4200   Fax: (216) 383-4091   www.beminc.com

Mfr. beryllium, beryllium alloys and ceramics, specialty metal systems and precious metal products.

Brush Wellman GmbH, Motorstrasse 34, D-70499 Stuttgart, Germany

Tel: 49-711-830-930   Fax: 49-711-833-822

BUCKEYE TECHNOLOGIES, INC.

1001 Tillman St., Memphis, TN, 38108-0407

Tel: (901) 320-8100　　Fax: (901) 320-8131　　www.bkitech.com

Mfr. specialty cellulose and absorbency products.

Buckeye Technologies GmbH, Glückstadt, Germany

BUCKMAN LABORATORIES INTERNATIONAL, INC.

1258 N. McLean Blvd., Memphis, TN, 38108-0308

Tel: (901) 278-0330　　Fax: (901) 276-5343　　www.buckman.com

Mfr. specialty chemicals.

Buckman Laboratories GmbH, Marienbader Platz 22, D-61348 Bad Homburg, Germany

LEO BURNETT, DIV. B-COM 3 GROUP

35 West Wacker Drive, Chicago, IL, 60601

Tel: (312) 220-5959　　Fax: (312) 220-6533　　www.leoburnett.com

Engaged in advertising, marketing, media buying and planning, and public relations.

Kastner & Partner GmbH, Werbeagentur, Kennedyallee 94, D-6000 Frankfurt/Main 1, Germany

Michale Conrad & Leo Burnett GmbH, Feuerbachstrasse 26, D-6000 Frankfurt/Main 1, Germany

BURSON-MARSTELLER

230 Park Avenue South, New York, NY, 10003-1566

Tel: (212) 614-4000　　Fax: (212) 614-4262　　www.bm.com

Public relations/public affairs consultants.

Burson-Marsteller GmbH, Untermainkai 20, D-60329 Frankfurt/Main, Germany

Tel: 49-69-23-8090　Fax: 49-69-23-80944　Emp: 50

Burson-Marsteller Hamburg, Hopensack 19, D-20457 Hamburg, Germany .

Tel: 49-40-32110　Fax: 49-40-3233-1199

BUSINESS WIRE

44 Montgomery Street, 39th Fl., San Francisco, CA, 94104

Tel: (415) 986-4422　　Fax: (415) 788-5335　　www.businesswire.com

Engaged in distribution of electronic news to worldwide news databases.

Business Wire Frankfurt, Nibelungenplatz 3, D-60318 Frankfurt am Main 1, Germany

Tel: 49-6991-50660

CABLE DESIGN TECHNOLOGIES CORPORATION

661 Andersen Drive, Plaza 7, Pittsburgh, PA, 15220

Tel: (412) 937-2300　　Fax: (412) 937-9690　　www.cdtc.com

Mfr. computer connector copper, fiber optic and composite cables.

HEW CDT, Gewerbegebiet Klingsiepen 12, D-51688 Wipperfurth, Germany

Tel: 49-2267-6830

CABOT CORPORATION

2 Seaport Lane, Ste. 1300, Boston, MA, 02210-2019

Tel: (617) 345-0100　　Fax: (617) 342-6103　　www.cabot-corp.com

Mfr. carbon blacks, plastics; oil and gas, information systems.

Cabot GmbH, Postfach 901120, Hanau 9, Germany

Deloro Stellite GmbH (Weartec Div.), Postfach 520, Carl-Spaeterstr. 11, D-5400 Koblenz, Germany

Deutssche Beryllium GmbH (Cabot Berylco Div.), Postfach 1620, D-6370 Oberursel, Germany

Nickel Contor Deutschland GmbH (Hitec Div.), Taunusanlage 21, D-6000 Frankfurt/Main 1, Germany

CACI INTERNATIONAL INC.

1100 North Glebe Road, Arlington, VA, 22201

Tel: (703) 841-7800　　Fax: (703) 841-7882　　www.caci.com

Provides simulation technology/software and designs factories, computer networks, and communications systems for military, electronic commerce digital document management, logistics and Y2K remediation.

CACI International, Inc., Frankfurt am Main, Germany

CADENCE DESIGN SYSTEMS, INC.

2655 Seely Ave., Bldg. 5, San Jose, CA, 95134

Tel: (408) 943-1234   Fax: (408) 943-0513   www.cadence.com

Mfr. electronic design automation software.

Cadence Design Systems GmbH, Mozartstrasse 2, D-85622 Feldkirchen, Germany

Tel: 49-89-4563-0

CALBIOCHEM-NOVABIOCHEM CORPORATION

10394 Pacific Center Court, San Diego, CA, 92121

Tel: (858) 450-9600   Fax: (858) 453-3552   www.calbiochem.com

Mfr. biochemicals, immunochemicals and reagents.

CN Biosciences GmbH, Postfach 1167, Lisztweg 1, D-6232 Bad Soden, Germany

CALDERA INTERNATIONAL

355 South 520 West, Ste. 100, Linden, UT, 84057

Tel: (801) 765-4999   Fax: (801) 765-1313   www.caldera.com

Provides integrated solutions for small-to-medium businesses, retail operations, telecommunications and other vertical markets.

Caldera GmbH, Norsk-Data-Strasse 3, D-61352 Bad Homburg, Germany

Contact: Hans Bayer

CALGON CARBON CORPORATION

400 Calgon Carbon Drive, Pittsburgh, PA, 15230-0717

Tel: (412) 787-6700   Fax: (412) 787-4541   www.calgoncarbon.com

Mfr. activated carbon, related systems and services.

Calgon Carbon GmbH, Robert-Hoch-Strasse 5-7, D-6078 Neu-Isenburg, Germany

CAMBREX CORPORATION

1 Meadowlands Plaza, East Rutherford, NJ, 07063

Tel: (201) 804-3000   Fax: (201) 804-9852   www.cambrex.com

human health, animal health/agriculture and Mfr. biotechnology products and produce specialty chemicals.

Cambrex GmbH, Wettsteinstrasse 4, D-82024 Taufkirchen, Germany

Tel: 49-89-612-00821   Fax: 49-86-612-00825

Midas Pharmachemie GmbH, Weingasse, D-366535 Gau-Algesheim, Germany

Tel: 49-61-329900

CAMPBELL SOUP COMPANY

Campbell Place, Camden, NJ, 08103-1799

Tel: (856) 342-4800   Fax: (856) 342-3878   www.campbellsoup.com

Mfr. food products.

Campbell Grocery Products, GmbH, Frankfurt/Main, Germany

Eugen Lacroix, GmbH, Frankfurt/Main, Germany

CANBERRA INDUSTRIES, INC.

800 Research Parkway, Meriden, CT, 06450

Tel: (203) 238-2351   Fax: (203) 235-1347   www.canberra.com

Mfr. instruments for nuclear research.

Canberra Eurisys GmbH, Walter-Flex-Str. 66, D-65428 Rüsselsheim, Germany

Tel: 49 -6142-7382-0

Canberra Packard GmbH, Robert Bosch Str. 32, D-633303 Dreieich, Germany

CARBOLINE COMPANY

350 Hanley Industrial Court, St. Louis, MO, 63144

Tel: (314) 644-1000   Fax: (314) 644-4617   www.carboline.com

Mfr. coatings and sealants.

StonCor Germany, Schumanstrabe 18, D-52146 Wurlselen, Germany

Tel: 49-2405-44-1148   Fax: 49-2405-44-1169

CARGILL, INC.

15407 McGinty Road West, Minnetonka, MN, 55440-5625

Tel: (612) 742-7575   Fax: (612) 742-7393   www.cargill.com

Food products, feeds, animal products.

Deutsche Cargill GmbH, Ruedekenstrasse 51, Am Hafen, D-38239 Salzgitter-Beddingen, Germany

CARLSON COMPANIES, INC.

PO Box 59159, Minneapolis, MN, 55459

Tel: (612) 550-4520   Fax: (612) 550-4580   www.cmg.carlson.com

Marketing services agency.

LPP Carlson, Kreuzberger Ring 64, D-65205 Weisbaden, Germany

Tel: 49- 611-778-470   Fax: 49-611-778-4766

THE CARLYLE GROUP L.P.

1001 Pennsylvania Avenue, NW, Washington, DC, 20004-2505

Tel: (202) 347-2626   Fax: (202) 347-1818   www.thecarlylegroup.com

Global investor in defense contracts.

Carlyle Europe, ResidenzstraBe 18, D-80333 Münich, Germany

Tel: 49-89-29-19-580

CARPENTER COMPANY

5016 Monument Avenue, Richmond, VA, 23220

Tel: (904) 359-0800   Fax: (804) 353-0694   www.carpenter.com

Mfr. polyurethane foam and chemicals.

Carpenter GmbH, Industrial Road, D-99334 Ichtershausen Thoerey, Germany

CARPENTER TECHNOLOGY CORPORATION

PO Box 14662, Reading, PA, 19612-4662

Tel: (610) 208-2000   Fax: (610) 208-3214   www.cartech.com

Mfr. specialty steels and structural ceramics for casting industrial.

Carpenter Technology (Deutschland) GmbH, Waldenbucher Strasse 22, D-7032 Sindelfingen 1, Germany

CARRIER CORPORATION

One Carrier Place, Farmington, CT, 06034-4015

Tel: (860) 674-3000   Fax: (860) 679-3010   www.carrier.com

Mfr./distributor/services A/C, heating and refrigeration equipment.

Carrier GmbH, Münich, Germany

Tel: 49-89-321-540   Fax: 49-89-321-5410

CASCADE CORPORATION

2201 NE 201st Ave., Fairview, OR, 97024-9718

Tel: (503) 669-6300   Fax: (503) 669-6321   www.cascor.com

Mfr. hydraulic forklift truck attachments.

Cascade GmbH, Klosterhofweg 52, D-4050 Münich, Germany

CAT PUMPS

1681 94th Lane NE, Minneapolis, MN, 55449-4324

Tel: (763) 780-5440   Fax: (763) 780-2958   www.catpumps.com

Mfr./distributor pumps.

Cat Pumps Deutschland GmbH, Buchwiese 2, D-65510 Idstein, Germany

Tel: 49-6126-9303-0   Contact: Juergen Uhlig

CATAPULT COMMUNICATIONS CORPORATION

160 South Whisman Road, Mountain View, CA, 94041

Tel: (650) 960-1025   Fax: (650) 960-1029   www.catapult.com

Mfr. test systems for telecommunications service providers.

Catapult Communications Corp., Lechwiesenstrasse 56, D-86899 Landsberg/Lech, Germany

CATERPILLAR INC.

100 NE Adams Street, Peoria, IL, 61629-6105

Tel: (309) 675-1000   Fax: (309) 675-1182   www.cat.com

Mfr. earth/material-handling and construction machinery and equipment and engines.

Caterpillar Holding Germany GmbH, Münich, Germany

Claas Caterpillar Europe GmbH & Co. KG, Unterschleissheim, Germany

CB RICHARD ELLIS SERVICES

200 N. Sepulveda Blvd., Ste. 300, El Segundo, CA, 90245-4380

Tel: (310) 563-8600   Fax: (310) 563-8670   www.cbrichardellis.com

Commercial real estate services.

CB Richard Ellis GmbH, Maximilianstrasse 27, D-80539 Münich, Germany

CB Richard Ellis GmbH, Feuerbachstrasse 26/32, D-60325 Frankfurt am Main, Germany

CBS TELEVISION NETWORK

51 West 52nd Street, New York, NY, 10019

Tel: (212) 975-4321   Fax: (212) 975-9387   www.cbs.com

TV/radio broadcasting, mfr. electronic systems for industry/defense, financial and environmental services.

H. Maihak AG, Samperstr. 38, D-2000 Hamburg 60, Germany

Westinghouse Controlmatic GmbH, Postfach 560200, D-6000 Frankfurt 56, Germany

CCH INCORPORATED

2700 Lake Cook Road, Riverwoods, IL, 60015

Tel: (847) 267-7000   Fax: (800) 224-8299   www.cch.com

Provides tax and business law information and software for accounting, legal, human resources, securities and health care professionals.

CCH Europe GmbH, Parkstrasse 71-73, D-65191 Wiesbaden, Germany

CEILCOTE AIR POLLUTION CONTROL

14955 Sprague Road, Strongsville, OH, 44136

Tel: (440) 243-0700   Fax: (440) 234-3486   www.ceilcoteapc.com

Mfr. corrosion-resistant material, air pollution control equipment, construction services.

Air-Cure GmbH, Ostendstrasse 1, D-64319 Pfungstadt, Germany

Tel: 49-6157-91-55-0

CENTRA SOFTWARE, INC.

430 Bedford Street, Lexington, MA, 02421

Tel: (781) 861-7000   Fax: (781) 863-7288   www.centra.com

Mfr. on-line learning software.

Centra Software GmbH, Merowinger Straße 3, D-41238 Mönchengladbach, Germany

CENTRAL NATIONAL-GOTTESMAN INC.

3 Manhattanville Road, Purchase, NY, 10577-2110

Tel: (914) 696-9000   Fax: (914) 696-1066   www.cng-inc.com

Distribution of pulp and paper products.

Europcell GmbH, Bruchköbeler Landstr. 71, D-63452 Hanau, Germany

Tel: 49-6181-98660   Fax: 49-6181-986620

CEPHALON, INC.

145 Brandywine Pkwy., West Chester, PA, 19380

Tel: (610) 344-0200   Fax: (610) 344-0065   www.cephalon.com

Engaged in health science, research and development.

Cephalon Germany, Hippmannstrasse 13, D-80639 Münich, Germany

Tel: 49-89-1709-4499   Fax: 49-89-1709-4495   Contact: Uwe Mascheck

CH2M HILL INC.

6060 South Willow Drive, Greenwood Village, CO, 80111

Tel: (303) 771-0900   Fax: (303) 770-2616   www.ch2m.com

Consulting engineers, planners, economists and scientists.

CH2M Hill, Stephan-Lochner-Straße 2, D-53175 Bonn, Germany

CHARLES RIVER LABORATORIES INTERNATIONAL, INC.

251 Ballardvale Street, Wilmington, MA, 01887-1000

Tel: (978) 658-6000   Fax: (978) 658-7132   www.criver.com

Engaged in sales of pathogen-free, fertilized chicken eggs for drug testing.

Charles River Wiga, Sandhofer WEG 7, D-97633 Sutzfeld, Germany

CHART INDUSTRIES, INC.

5885 Landerbrook Drive, Cleveland, OH, 44124

Tel: (440) 753-1490   Fax: (440) 753-1491   www.chart-ind.com

Mfr. cryogenic storage and shipping containers and related industrial products.

Chart Europe GmbH, Brosshauser Strasse 20, D-42697 Solingen, Germany

Tel: 49-212-700-570   Fax: 49-212-700-577

CHECKPOINT SYSTEMS, INC.

101 Wolf Drive, Thorofare, NJ, 08086

Tel: (856) 848-1800   Fax: (856) 848-0937   www.checkpointsystems.com

Mfr. test, measurement and closed-circuit television systems.

Checkpoint Systems Deutschland GmbH, Forumstrasse 2, D-41468 Neuss, Germany

Tel: 49-2131-93190 Fax: 49-2131-33303   Contact: Volker Kalkowski, Mng. Dir.

CHEMETALL OAKITE

50 Valley Road, Berkeley Heights, NJ, 07922-2798

Tel: (908) 464-6900   Fax: (908) 464-7914   www.oakite.com

Mfr. chemical products for industry cleaning and metal treating.

Chemetall GmbH Group, Frankfurt/Main, Germany

THE CHERRY CORPORATION

3600 Sunset Ave., PO Box 718, Waukegan, IL, 60087

Tel: (847) 662-9200   Fax: (847) 662-2990   www.cherrycorp.com

Mfr. electrical switches, electronic keyboards, controls and displays.

Cherry GmbH, Cherrystraße, D-91275 Auerbach/Opf, Germany

Tel: 49-96-43180   Fax: 49-96-4318262

Cherry GmbH, Industriestrasse 19, D-91275 Auerbach/Opf., Germany

Tel: 49-96-43180   Fax: 49-96-4318406

CHESTERTON BLUMENAUER BINSWANGER

Two Logan Square, 4th Floor, Philadelphia, PA, 19103-2759

Tel: (215) 448-6000   Fax: (215) 448-6238   www.cbbi.com

Real estate and related services.

Chesterton Blumenauer Binswanger, Stadthausbrucke 5, D-20355 Hamburg, Germany

Contact: David Kenney

Engel & Völkers, Baringstr. 8, D-30159 Hannover, Germany

Contact: Thomas Buhre

Engel & Völkers, Thomasiusstrasse 21, D-04109 Leipzig, Germany

Engel & Völkers, Thomasiusstrasse 21, D-04109 Leipzig, Germany

Contact: Michael Weise

Engel & Völkers, Werdener Strasse 6, Georg-Glock-Strasse 2, D-40227 Dusseldorf, Germany

Contact: Ulrich Dahl

Engel & Völkers, Kochstr. 22 / Charlottenstr., D-10969 Berlin, Germany

Engel & Völkers, Charlottenplatz 6, D-70173 Stuttgart, Germany

A.W. CHESTERTON COMPANY

225 Fallon Road, Stoneham, MA, 02180

Tel: (781) 438-7000   Fax: (781) 438-8971   www.chesterton.com

Mfr. of industrial fluid sealing, hydraulic, pneumatic and maintenance products.

Chesterton International (Deutschland) GmbH, Carl-Zeiss-Ring 9, D-85737 Ismaning, Germany

Chesterton International (Deutschland) GmbH, Trierer Str. 12, D-68309 Mannheim, Germany

CHEVRON PHILLIPS CHEMICAL COMPANY LP

1301 McKinney Street, Houston, TX, 77010

Tel: (713) 754-2000   Fax: (713) 754-2016   www.chevron.com

Mfr. petro chemicals.

Orogil KG, Mainzer Str. 172, Postfach 190369, D-6000 Frankfurt/Main, Germany

CHICAGO BRIDGE & IRON COMPANY (CBI)

10200 Grogan's Mill Road, Suite 300, The Woodlands, TX, 77380

Tel: (281) 774-2200   Fax: (281) 774-2202   www.chicago-bridge.com

Holding company: engaged in metal plate fabricating, construction and oil and gas drilling.

CBI Industriestahlbau GmbH, D-4650 Gelsenkirchen, Germany

CHICAGO RAWHIDE INDUSTRIES (CRI)

735 Tollgate Road, Elgin, IL, 60123

Tel: (847) 742-7840   Fax: (847) 742-7845   www.chicago-rawhide.com

Mfr. shaft and face seals.

CR Elastomere GmbH, Dusseldorf Str. 121, D-51379 Leverkusen-Opladen, Germany

CHILD CUSTODY CONSULTANTS

400 West Tenth Street, Suite 204, Santa Ana, CA, 92701

Tel: (714) 285-1104   Fax: (714) 285-1136   www.laislaw.com

Facilitators in child custody and visitation issues.

Child Custody Consultants, Ronald E. Lais, Inc., Nockherstrasse 2, D-81541 Münich, Germany
Tel: 49-89-62-4080   Fax: 49-89-62-408-444

CHIQUITA BRANDS INTERNATIONAL INC.

250 East Fifth Street, Cincinnati, OH, 45202

Tel: (513) 784-8000   Fax: (513) 784-8030   www.chiquita.com

Sale and distribution of bananas, fresh fruits and processed foods.

Chiquita Brands International, Münich, Germany

CHIRON CORPORATION

4560 Horton Street, Emeryville, CA, 94608-2916

Tel: (510) 655-8730   Fax: (510) 655-9910   www.chiron.com

Engaged in biotechnology; biopharmaceuticals, blood testing and vaccines.

Chiron Behring GmbH, Emil Von Behring Strasse 76, D-35041 Marburg, Germany
Tel: 49-6421-393-264

CHOICE HOTELS INTERNATIONAL, INC.

10750 Columbia Pike, Silver Springs, MD, 20902

Tel: (301) 592-5000   Fax: (301) 592-6227   www.choicehotels.com

Hotel franchises, including Comfort Inn, Econo Lodge, Roadway Inn and Quality.

Choice Hotels International, Stahlgruberring 1, D-81829 Münich, Germany

CHORDIANT SOFTWARE, INC.

20400 Stevens Creek Blvd., Ste. 400, Cupertino, CA, 95014-2217

Tel: (408) 517-6100   Fax: (408) 517-0270   www.chordiant.com

Mfr. customer relationship management software.

Chordiant Software GmbH, An der Welle 4, D-60322 Frankfurt, Germany

THE CHUBB CORPORATION

15 Mountain View Road, Warren, NJ, 07061-1615

Tel: (908) 580-2000   Fax: (908) 580-3606   www.chubb.com

Holding company for property and casualty insurance and liability insurance for corporate executives.

Chubb Insurance Co. of Europe, SA, Martin-Luther-Platz 28, D-40212 Düsseldorf, Germany

Tel: 49-211-8773-0 Fax: 49-211-8773-333

Chubb Insurance Company of Europe, SA, Niederlassung Munchen, Josephspitalstrabe 15, D-80332 Münich, Germany

Tel: 49-89-54551-0 Fax: 49-89-54551-12

Chubb Insurance Company of Europe, SA, Freiherr Von Stein Strasse II, D-60323 Frankfurt/Main Strasse II, Germany

Tel: 49-69-97-12160 Fax: 49-69-97-122633

Chubb Insurance Company of Europe, SA, Fleethof Stadthausbrueke 1-3, D-20355 Hamburg, Germany

Tel: 49-36-98050 Fax: 49-36-980590

CIENA CORPORATION

1201 Winterson Road, Linthicum, MD, 21090-2205

Tel: (410) 865-8500   Fax: (410) 694-5750   www.ciena.com

Mfr. optical network switching hardware.

CIENA Ltd., Box A5, 15 Lyoner Strasse, D-80528 Frankfurt, Germany

Tel: 49-6966-57-7125

CIGNA COMPANIES

One Liberty Place, Philadelphia, PA, 19192

Tel: (215) 761-1000   Fax: (215) 761-5511   www.cigna.com

Insurance, invest, health care and other financial services.

CIGNA Insurance Co. of Europe SA/NV, Erlenstrasse 2-6, D-6000 Frankfurt/Main, Germany

Esis Intl. Inc., Erlenstrasse 2-6, D-6000 Frankfurt/Main, Germany

Insurance Co. of North America, Direktion Fuer Deutschland, Erlenstrasse 2-6, D-6000 Frankfurt/Main, Germany

CINCOM SYSTEMS INC.

55 Merchant Street, Cincinnati, OH, 45446

Tel: (513) 612-2300   Fax: (513) 481-8332   www.cincom.com

Develop/distributor computer software.

Cincom Systems Deutschland, Am Kronberger Hang, D-65824 Schwalbach, Germany

Cincom Systems GmbH, Industriestrasse 3, D-70565 Stuttgart, Germany

Cincom Systems GmbH, 19 Im Hargarten, D-54316 Pluwig, Germany

Cincom Systems Inc., Holsteiner Chaussee 303b, D-22457 Hamburg, Germany

CINEMARK USA INC.

3900 Dallas Pkwy., Ste. 500, Plano, TX, 75093

Tel: (972) 665-1000   Fax: (972) 665-1004   www.cinemark.com

Operates multiplex cinemas.

Cinemark, Herne 13, Dusseldorf, Germany

CISCO SYSTEMS, INC.

170 West Tasman Drive, San Jose, CA, 95134-1706

Tel: (408) 526-4000   Fax: (408) 526-4100   www.cisco.com

Develop/mfr./market computer hardware and software networking systems.

Cisco Systems GmbH, Isar Buero Park, Lilienthalstrasse 9, D-85399 Hallbergmoos, Germany

Tel: 49-811-55430 Fax: 49-811-554310

CITIGROUP, INC.

399 Park Avenue, New York, NY, 10022

Tel: (212) 559-1000   Fax: (212) 559-3646   www.citigroup.com

Provides insurance and financial services worldwide.

Citigroup, Neue Mainzer Strasse 75, D-60311 Frankfurt, Germany

Contact: Willy P. Socquet

CITRIX SYSTEMS, INC.

6400 NW 6th Way, Fort Lauderdale, FL, 33309

Tel: (954) 267-3000   Fax: (954) 267-9319   www.citrix.com

Developer of computer software.

Citrix GmbH (Europe HQ), Am Soeldnermoos 17, D-85399 Hallbergmoos, Germany

Tel: 49-89-607687-10   Fax: 49-89-607687-11

CLAYTON INDUSTRIES

4213 N. Temple City Blvd., El Monte, CA, 91731

Tel: (626) 443-9381   Fax: (626) 442-1701   www.claytonindustries.com

Mfr. steam generators, dynamometers and water treatment chemicals.

Clayton Deutschland GmbH, Mevissenstrasse 64a, D-47803 Krefeld, Germany

Tel: 49-2151-8775-0   Fax: 49-2151-8775-22

CLEARY GOTTLIEB STEEN & HAMILTON

One Liberty Plaza, New York, NY, 10006

Tel: (212) 225-2000   Fax: (212) 225-3999   www.cgsh.com

Engaged in international law.

Cleary, Gottlieb, Steen & Hamilton, Main Tower, Neue Mainzer Strasse 52, Ulmenstrasse 37-39, D-60311 Frankfurt/Main, Germany

CNA FINANCIAL CORPORATION

CNA Plaza, Chicago, IL, 60685

Tel: (312) 822-5000   Fax: (312) 822-6419   www.cna.com

Commercial property/casualty insurance policies.

CNA Insurance Company (Europe) Limited (CIE), München, Germany

CNH (CASE NEW HOLLAND) GLOBAL

100 South Saunders Road, Lake Forest, IL, 60045

Tel: (847) 955-3821   Fax: (847) 955-3961   www.casecorp.com

Mfr. and sale of agricultural and construction equipment.

CNH GmbH, Heinrich-Fuchs-Strasse 124, D-69126 Heidelberg, Germany

Tel: 49-6221-318-600   Fax: 49-6221-318-680   Contact: Gunther Apfalter

CNH Harvesting Systems, Berghausstrasse 1, Postfach 110, D-01841 Neustadt, Germany

Tel: 49-3596-53-2405   Fax: 49-3506-53-2202   Contact: Herbert Wolf, Gen. Mgr.

COACH LEATHERWEAR COMPANY

516 West 34th Street, New York, NY, 10001

Tel: (212) 594-1850   Fax: (212) 594-1682   www.coach.com

Mfr. and sales of high-quality leather products, including handbags, wallets and shoes.

Coach at E.C. Trading, Burgmauer 12, D-50667 Cologne, Germany

THE COCA-COLA COMPANY

1 Coca Cola Plaza, Atlanta, GA, 30313

Tel: (404) 676-2121   Fax: (404) 676-6792   www.coca-cola.com

Mfr./marketing/distributor soft drinks, syrups and concentrates, juice and juice-drink products.

Coca-Cola Eastern Europe GmbH, Frankenstrasse 348, D-4300 Essen, Germany

Contact: John P. Sechi

Coca-Cola GmbH, Max-Keith-Strasse 66, D-45136 Essen, Germany

Contact: John P. Sechi

COGNEX CORPORATION

1 Vision Drive, Natick, MA, 01760

Tel: (508) 650-3000   Fax: (508) 650-3333   www.cognex.com

Mfr. machine vision systems.

Cognex Corporation Germany, Greschbachstrasse 12, D-76229 Karlsruhe, Germany

Tel: 49-721-96187-0   Fax: 49-721-61566-1

COGNIZANT TECHNOLOGY SOLUTIONS CORPORATION

500 Glenpointe Centre West, Teaneck, NJ, 07666

Tel: (201) 801-0233   Fax: (201) 801-0243   www.cognizant.com

Provides software development , application management, computer date corrections, and currency conversion.

Cognizant Technology Solutions, Hahnstrasse 30-32, D-60528 Frankfurt, Germany

COHERENT INC.

5100 Patrick Henry Drive, PO Box 54980, Santa Clara, CA, 95056

Tel: (408) 764-4000   Fax: (408) 764-4800   www.cohr.com

Mfr. lasers for science, industrial and medical.

Coherent GmbH, Diesenstrasse 5-b, D-64807 Dieburg, Germany

Lambda Physik GmbH, Hans-Bockler-Strasse 12, D-37079 Gottingen, Germany

COHU, INC.

12367 Crosthwaite Circle, Poway, CA, 92064

Tel: (858) 848-8100   Fax: (858) 848-8185   www.cohu.com

Mfr. semiconductor test handling systems.

Macrotron Systems, Ammerthalstrasse 7, D-95551 Kirchheim Münich, Germany

Tel: 49-89-45111-0   Fax: 49-89-45111-102

COIN ACCEPTORS INC. (COINCO)

300 Hunter Ave., St. Louis, MO, 63124

Tel: (314) 725-0100   Fax: (314) 725-1243   www.coinco.com

Coin mechanisms for vending machinery.

Coin Acceptors GmbH, Siemensring 44D, D-47877 Willich, Germany

Tel: 49-2154-205000   Fax: 49-12154-205002

THE COLEMAN COMPANY, INC.

3600 N. Hydraulic, Wichita, KS, 67219

Tel: (316) 832-2700   Fax: (316) 832-2794   www.colemanoutdoors.com

Mfr. distributor and sales of camping and outdoor recreation products.

Coleman Deutschland GmbH, Ezetilstr., D-6303 Hungen 3, Germany

COLFAX CORPORATION

9211 Forest Hill Avenue, Ste. 109, Richmond, VA, 23235

Tel: (804) 560-4070   Fax: (804) 560-4076   www.colfaxcorp.com

Mfr. industrial clutches and brakes and motion control products and components.

Stieber GmbH, Div. Colfax, Dieselstraße 14, D-85748 Garching, Germany

Stieber GmbH, Div. Colfax, Hatschekstraße 36, D-69126 Heidelberg, Germany

COLFAX PUMP GROUP, DIV. COLFAX INC.

1710 Airport Road, PO Box 5020, Monroe, NC, 28111-5020

Tel: (704) 289-6511   Fax: (704) 289-4839   www.colfaxpump.com

Mfr. rotary and centrifugal pumps.

Allweiler GmbH, Postfach 202123, D-46223 Bottrop, Germany

Tel: 49-2045-96660

Allweiler GmbH, Postfach 1140, D-78301 Radolfzell, Germany

IMO Industries GmbH, Dorn-Assenheimer Strasse 27, D-61201 Reichelsheim, Germany

IMO Industries GmbH, Morse Teleflex, Hoeseler Strasse 40, D-42579 Heiligenhaus, Germany

IMO-Pumpen, Hamelner Strasse 52, Postfach 1228, D-32678 Barntrup, Germany

COLGATE-PALMOLIVE COMPANY

300 Park Ave., New York, NY, 10022

Tel: (212) 310-2000   Fax: (212) 310-2919   www.colgate.com

Mfr. pharmaceuticals, cosmetics, toiletries and detergents.

Colgate-Palmolive GmbH, Liebigstr. 2-20, D-22113 Hamburg, Germany

COMCAST CORPORATION

1500 Market St., Philadelphia, PA, 19102

Tel: (215) 665-1700   Fax: (215) 981-7790   www.comcast.com

Provides cable and broadband services and QVC electronic retailing.

QVC Deutschland GmbH, Kaistrasse 7-9, D-40221 Dusseldorf, Germany

Tel: 49-211-300-0   Fax: 49--211-3007-100

COMDISCO HOLDING COMPANY

6111 N. River Road, Rosemont, IL, 60018

Tel: (847) 698-3000   Fax: (847) 518-5440   www.comdisco.com

Hi-tech asset and facility management and equipment leasing.

Comdisco Deutschland GmbH, Dusseldorf, Germany

COMMERCE ONE, INC.

4440 Rosewood Dr., Pleasanton, CA, 94588-3050

Tel: (925) 520-6000   Fax: (925) 520-6060   www.commerceone.com

Provides software and services.

Commerce One GmbH, Wamslerstrasse 2, D-81829 Münich, Germany

COMMWORKS CORPORATION

3800 Golf Road, Rolling Meadows, IL, 60008

Tel: (847) 262-5000   Fax: (847) 262-0327   www.commworks.com

Provides Internet protocol-based network access software and equipment.

Commworks Corporation, Max Planck Strasse 3, D-85609 Aschheim bei Münich, Germany

COMPUTER ASSOCIATES INTERNATIONAL INC.

One Computer Associates Plaza, Islandia, NY, 11788

Tel: (516) 342-5224   Fax: (516) 342-5329   www.cai.com

Integrated business software for enterprise computing and information management, application development, manufacturing, financial applications and professional services.

Computer Associates GmbH, Hauptverwaltung, Marienburgstrasse 35, D-64297 Darmstadt, Germany

Tel: 49-6151-4-9490

COMPUTER NETWORK TECHNOLOGY CORPORATION

6000 Nathan Lane, Plymouth, MN, 55442

Tel: (763) 268-6000   Fax: (763) 268-6800   www.cnt.com

Engaged in the sale of storage networking products for creating and connecting storage area networks.

CNT Germany, Voltastrasse 6, D-63128 Dietzenbach, Germany

Contact: Thomas Riedl

CNT GmbH, Voltastrasse 6, D-63128 Dietzenbach, Germany

COMPUTER SCIENCES CORPORATION

2100 East Grand Ave., El Segundo, CA, 90245

Tel: (310) 615-0311   Fax: (310) 322-9768   www.csc.com

Information technology services, management consulting, systems integration, outsourcing.

CSC Computer Sciences GmbH -Plöenzke, Kiedrich/Rheingau, Germany

Contact: Klaus C. Plöenzke, CEO

COMPUWARE CORPORATION

31440 Northwestern Hwy., Farmington Hills, MI, 48334-2564

Tel: (248) 737-7300   Fax: (248) 737-7108   www.compuware.com

Develop and market software for enterprise and e-commerce solutions.

Compuware GmbH, Hauert 1, D-44227 Dortmund, Germany

COMSHARE INC.

555 Briarwood Circle, Ste. 200, Ann Arbor, MI, 48108-3302

Tel: (734) 994-4800   Fax: (734) 994-5895   www.comshare.com

Managerial application software.

Comshare GmbH, Comshare Haus, Waltherstrasse 78, D-5000 Cologne 80, Germany

COMVERSE, INC.

100 Quannapowitt Parkway, Wakefield, MA, 01880

Tel: (781) 246-9000   Fax: (781) 224-8143   www.comverse.com

Provides communications solutions.

Comverse Infosys GmbH, Am Storrenacker 2, D-76139 Karlsruhe, Germany

Tel: 49-721-625-310   Fax: 49-721-625-3119

CONAGRA FOODS, INC.

One ConAgra Drive, Omaha, NE, 68102-5001

Tel: (402) 595-4000   Fax: (402) 595-4707   www.conagra.com

Prepared/frozen foods, grains, flour, animal feeds, agro chemicals, poultry, meat, dairy products, including Healthy Choice, Butterball and Hunt's.

ConAgra Inc., Münich, Germany

CONCERTO SOFTWARE

6 Technology Park Drive, Westford, MA, 01886

Tel: (978) 952-0200   Fax: (978) 952-0201   www.concerto.com

Mfr. call-center software for telephone operations.

Concerto GmbH, Hayn Parc 11, An der Trift 65, D-63303 Dreieich BRD, Germany

Tel: 49-6103-90230

THE CONCOURS GROUP, INC.

800 Rockmead Drive, Ste. 151, Kingwood, TX, 77339

Tel: (281) 359-3464   Fax: (281) 359-3443   www.concoursgroup.com

Provides e-business information technology.

Concours Group GmbH, Frauenstrasse 32, D-80469 Münich, Germany

Tel: 49-89-2109-516

CONCURRENT COMPUTER CORPORATION

4375 River Green Pkwy., Duluth, GA, 30096

Tel: (678) 258-4000   Fax: (678) 258-4300   www.ccur.com

Mfr. computer systems and software.

Concurrent Computer Corporation GmbH, Lena-Christ Strasse 46, Martinsried, D-82152 Planegg Münich, Germany

Tel: 49-89-856-030   Fax: 49-89-856-03150

Concurrent Computer Corporation GmbH, Schunannstrasse 7, D-64287 Darmstadt, Germany

Tel: 49-6151-712069   Fax: 49-6151-7111267

Concurrent Computer Corporation GmbH, Scheibenhardter Strasse 10, D-76275 Ettlingen/Ettlingenweir, Germany

Tel: 49-7243-90922

Concurrent Computer Corporation GmbH, Kampstrasse 53, D-52525 Heinsberg, Germany

Tel: 49-161-323-1097

CONEXANT SYSTEMS, INC.

4311 Jamboree Road, PO Box C, Newport Beach, CA, 92658-8902

Tel: (949) 483-4600   Fax: (949) 483-4078   www.conexant.com

Provides semiconductor products for communications electronics.

Conexant Systems Germany GmbH, Paul-Gerhardt-Allee 50A, D-81245 Münich, Germany

Tel: 49-89-829-13220   Fax: 49-89-834-2734

CONOCO INC.

600 N. Dairy Ashford, Houston, TX, 77252

Tel: (281) 293-1000   Fax: (281) 293-1440   www.conoco.com

Oil, gas, coal, chemicals and minerals.

CONDEA Petrochemie GmbH, Fritz-Staiger-Str., Postfach 2212, Brunsbuettel, Germany

Conoco Mineraloel GmbH, Hudtwalckerstr. 2-8, D-2000 Hamburg 39, Germany

CONTINENTAL AIRLINES INC.

1600 Smith St., Houston, TX, 77002

Tel: (713) 324-5000   Fax: (713) 324-2637   www.continental.com

International airline carrier.

Continental Airlines Inc., Münich, Germany

THE COOPER COMPANIES, INC.

6140 Stoneridge Mall Rd., Ste. 590, Pleasanton, CA, 94588

Tel: (925) 460-3600   Fax: (925) 460-3649   www.coopercos.com

Mfr. contact lenses and gynecological instruments.

Cooper Surgical Leisegang Medical GmbH, Berlin, Germany

COOPER INDUSTRIES INC.

6600 Travis Street, Ste. 5800, Houston, TX, 77002

Tel: (713) 209-8400   Fax: (713) 209-8995   www.cooperindustries.com

Mfr./distributor electrical products, tools, hardware and automotive products, fuses and accessories for electronic applications and circuit boards.

Apparatebau Hundsbach GmbH, Baden-Baden, Germany

CEAG Sicherheilslechnik GmbH, Senator-Schwartz-Reng 26, D-59494 Soest, Germany

Tel: 49-2921-690

CEAG Sicherheitstechnik GmbH, Münich, Germany

Tel: 49-29-21690   Fax: 49-29-2169-630

Cooper Hand Tools Div., Besigheim, Germany

Cooper Power Tools Div., Westhausen, Germany

Metronix Elektronik GmbH, Braunschweig, Germany

COOPER TURBOCOMPRESSOR

3101 Broadway, PO Box 209, Buffalo, NY, 14225-0209

Tel: (716) 896-6600   Fax: (716) 896-1233   www.turbocompressor.com

Provides products and services for centrifugal air compression equipment for manufacturing and process air applications.

Cooper Turbocompressor GmbH, Heinrichstrasse 169, D-40239 Dusseldorf, Germany

Tel: 49-211-613051   Fax: 49-211-614718

CORBIS CORPORATION

15395 SE 30th Place, Ste. 300, Bellevue, WA, 98007

Tel: (425) 641-4505   Fax: (425) 643-9740   www.corbis.com

Provides digital photograph imagery to creative professionals in magazine, book and newspaper publishing, advertising and graphic design and Internet and new media publishing.

Corbis Germany, Kaistrabe 6, D-40221 Dusseldorf, Germany

Tel: 49-211-912-820

CORDIS CORPORATION

PO Box 25700, Miami, FL, 33102-5700

Tel: (305) 824-2000   Fax: (305) 824-2747   www.cordis.com

Mfr. medical devices and systems.

Cordis Germany, Rheinische Strasse 2, D-42781 Haan, Germany

CORNING INC.

One Riverfront Plaza, Corning, NY, 14831-0001

Tel: (607) 974-9000   Fax: (607) 974-8091   www.corning.com

Mfr. glass and specialty materials, consumer products; communications, laboratory services.

Corning International GmbH, Abraham-Lincoln-Strasse 30, D-65189 Wiesbaden, Germany

Tel: 49-611-7366-100   Fax: 49-611-7366-143

CORPORATE SOFTWARE (CORPSOFT INC.)

2 Edgewater Drive, Norwood, MA, 02062

Tel: (781) 440-1000   Fax: (781) 440-7070   www.corpsoft.com

Mfr. asset management software.

Corporate Software, Gutenbergstrasse 1, D-85737 Ismaning, Germany

Tel: 49-89-94580-0

COUDERT BROTHERS LLP

1114 Ave. of the Americas, New York, NY, 10036-7794

Tel: (212) 626-4400   Fax: (212) 626-4120   www.coudert.com

Engaged in international law.

Coudert Brothers, Markgrafenstrasse 36, Am Gendarmenmarkt, D-10117 Berlin, Germany

Tel: 49-30-202-2990   Fax: 49-30-202-29929   Contact: Dr. Karl H. Pilny

COVANTA ENERGY CORPORATION

40 Lane Road, Fairfield, NJ, 07004

Tel: (973) 882-9000   Fax: (973) 882-9121   www.covantenergy.com

Engaged in power generation.

Covanta Energy GmbH, Niederlassung Wurzburg, Am Sonnenhof 16, D-97076 Wurzburg, Germany

CRAIN COMMUNICATIONS INC.

1155 Gratiot Avenue, Detroit, MI, 48207-2997

Tel: (313) 446-6000   Fax: (313) 446-6100   www.crain.com

Publishes business and trade journals.

Crain Communications, Technopark Oberpfaffenhofen, Argelsrieder Feld13, D-82234 Oberpfaffenhofen, Germany

Tel: 49-815-390-7400

CRANE COMPANY

100 First Stamford Place, Stamford, CT, 06907

Tel: (203) 363-7300   Fax: (203) 363-7359   www.craneco.com

Diversified mfr. and distribution of engineered industrial products and the largest American distributor of doors, windows and millwork.

National Rejectors Inc. GmbH, Zum Fruchthof 6, D-2150 Buxtehude, Germany

CREDENCE SYSTEMS CORPORATION

215 Fourier Avenue, Fremont, CA, 94539

Tel: (510) 657-7400   Fax: (510) 623-2560   www.credence.com

Mfr. software for semiconductor production.

Credence Systems Europe GmbH, Inselkammerstrasse 10, D-82008 Münich, Germany

Tel: 49-89-630-20825

CRITICARE SYSTEMS INC.

20925 Crossroads Circle, Waukesha, WI, 53186

Tel: (262) 798-8282   Fax: (262) 798-8491   www.csiusa.com

Develop/mfr. diagnostic and therapeutic products and patient monitoring systems..

Criticare Systems Inc. Europe, Gotzenmuhlweg 66, D-6380 Bad Homburg, Germany

Medlog GmbH, Gotzenmuhlweg 66, D-6380 Bad Homburg, Germany

CROMPTON CORPORATION

One American Lane, Greenwich, CT, 06831

Tel: (203) 552-2000   Fax: (203) 552-2870   www.cromptoncorp.com

Mfr. dyes, colors, flavors, fragrances, specialty chemicals and industrial products.

Crompton GmbH, Grueneburgweg 16-18, D-6000 Frankfurt/Main 1, Germany

Crompton Polymers & Resins BV, Postfach 1160, Max-Wolf-Strasse 7, Industriegebiet West, D-6497 Steinau an der Strasse, Germany

Crompton Vinyl Additives GmbH, Chemiestrasse 22, D-68623 Lampertheim, Germany

Davis-Standard GmbH, Mettmanner Strasse 51, Postfach 15 65, D-40675 Erkrath, Germany

A.T. CROSS COMPANY

One Albion Road, Lincoln, RI, 02865

Tel: (401) 333-1200   Fax: (401) 334-2861   www.cross.com

Mfr. writing instruments, leads, erasers and ink refills.

A.T. Cross GmbH, Rheinallee 189, Postfach 1220, D-55120 Mainz, Germany

Tel: 49-6131-626010

CROWN CORK & SEAL COMPANY, INC.

One Crown Way, Philadelphia, PA, 19154-4599

Tel: (215) 698-5100   Fax: (215) 698-5201   www.crowncork.com

Mfr. metal and plastic packaging, including steel and aluminum cans for food, beverage and household products.

Bender-Werke GmbH, Postfach 245, D-6710 Frankenthal Pfalz, Germany

CROWN EQUIPMENT CORPORATION

40 South Washington Street, New Bremen, OH, 45869

Tel: (419) 629-2311   Fax: (419) 629-2900   www.crownlift.com

Mfr. and sales of forklift trucks and stackers.

Crown Gabelstapler GmbH, Kronstadterstr. 11, D-8000 Münich 80, Germany

DELTEK SYSTEMS, INC.

7887 East Belleview Avenue, Ste. 1000, Englewood, CO, 80111

Tel: (303) 796-2850   Fax: (303) 804-4088   www.csgsys.com

Mfr. customer service software.

CSG International GmbH, Lyonerstrasse 26, D-60528 Frankfurt, Germany

Tel: 49-69-677-33-415

CSX CORPORATION

901 East Cary Street, Richmond, VA, 23860

Tel: (804) 782-1400   Fax: (804) 782-6747   www.csx.com

Provides freight delivery and contract logistics services.

CSX Terminal Germersheim (CTG), Wörthstrasse 13, D-76726 Germersheim, Germany

Tel: 49-7274-70825   Fax: 49-7274-70840

CULLIGAN INTERNATIONAL COMPANY

One Culligan Parkway, Northbrook, IL, 60062

Tel: (847) 205-6000   Fax: (847) 205-6030   www.culligan-man.com

Water treatment products and services.

Culligan Deutschland GmbH, Jagerhofstrasse 3, D-40880 Ratingen, Germany

Tel: 49-2102-40740   Fax: 49-2102-443960

CUMMINS, INC.

500 Jackson Street, PO Box 3005, Columbus, IN, 47202-3005

Tel: (812) 377-5000   Fax: (812) 377-4937   www.cummins.com

Mfr. diesel engines.

Cummins Diesel Deutschland GmbH, Postfach 1134, D-6080 Grob-Gerau, Germany

Cummins Diesel Deutschland GmbH, Odenwaldstraße 23, D-64521 Groß-Gerau, Germany

Tel: 49-6152-1740

CUNO INCORPORATED

400 Research Pkwy., Meriden, CT, 06450

Tel: (203) 237-5541   Fax: (203) 238-8977   www.cuno.com

Mfr. water filtration products.

CUNO GmbH, Wilh.-Theodor-Romheld, D-Str. 32, D-55130 Mainz, Germany

CURTIS, MALLET-PREVOST, COLT & MOSLE LLP

101 Park Ave., Ste 3500, New York, NY, 10178

Tel: (212) 696-6000   Fax: (212) 697-1559   www.cm-p.com

International law firm.

Curtis, Mallet-Prevost, Colt & Mosle LLP, Staufenstrasse 42, D-60323 Frankfurt am Main, Germany

Tel: 49-69-971-442-0

CURTISS-WRIGHT CORPORATION

1200 Wall Street West, Lyndhurst, NJ, 07071-0635

Tel: (201) 896-8400   Fax: (201) 438-5680   www.curtisswright.com

Mfr. precision components and systems, engineered services to aerospace, flow control and marine industry.

Metal Improvement Co. (MIC), Sommerauer Strasse 6, D-91555 Feuchtwangen, Germany

Tel: 49-9852-67030

Metal Improvement Co. (MIC), Otto-Hahn-Strasse 3, D-459423 Unna, Germany

CUSHMAN & WAKEFIELD INC.

51 West 52nd Street, New York, NY, 10019

Tel: (212) 841-7500   Fax: (212) 841-7867   www.cushwake.com

Engaged in commercial real estate services.

Cushman & Wakefield, Georg-Glock-Straße 8, D-40474 Dusseldorf, Germany

CUTLER-HAMMER, DIV. EATON CORP.

173 Heatherdown Drive, Westerville, OH, 43082

Tel: (614) 882-3282   Fax: (614) 895-7111   www.cutlerhammer.com

Mfr. electrical control products and power distribution equipment.

Eaton GmbH (Cutler-Hammer), Oranienpassage 1, D-57258 Freudenberg, Germany

Tel: 49-2734-46-63-0   Fax: 49-2734-4-76-05

CYLINK CORPORATION

3131 Jay Street, Santa Clara, CA, 95054

Tel: (408) 855-6000   Fax: (408) 855-6100   www.cyllink.com

Develop and manufactures encryption software.

Algorithmic Research GmbH, Siemensstrasse 100, D-63755 Alzenau, Germany

Tel: 49-6023-948560   Fax: 49-6023-948589

CYPRESS SEMICONDUCTOR CORPORATION

3901 N. First Street, San Jose, CA, 95134-1599

Tel: (408) 943-2600   Fax: (408) 943-2796   www.cypress.com

Mfr. integrated circuits.

Cypress Semiconductor, Muenchener Str. 15A, D-85604 Zorneding, Germany

Tel: 49-8106-2448-0   Fax: 49-8106-2008-7

CYTEC INDUSTRIES, INC.

5 Garret Mountain Plaza, West Paterson, NJ, 07424

Tel: (973) 357-3100   Fax: (973) 357-3054   www.cytec.com

Mfr. specialty chemicals and materials.

Cytec Industries B.V., Hermann-Klammt Str. 3, D-41460 Neuss, Germany

Tel: 49-2131-9524-0

D&B (DUN & BRADSTREET CORPORATION))

1 Diamond Hill Road, Murray Hill, NJ, 07974

Tel: (908) 665-5000   Fax: (908) 665-5524   www.dnb.com

Provides corporate credit, marketing and accounts-receivable management services and publishes financial information.

D&B Schimmelpfeng GmbH, Hahnstrasse 31-35, D-60528 Frankfurt/Main, Germany

Tel: 49-69-663030

DALLAS SEMICONDUCTOR CORPORATION

4401 South Beltway Parkway, Dallas, TX, 75244-3292

Tel: (972) 371-4000   Fax: (972) 371-4956   www.dalsemi.com

Design/mfr. computer chips and chip-based subsystems.

Dallas Semiconductor, Am Soldnermoos 17, D-85399 Hallbergmoos, Germany

Tel: 49-811-600960   Fax: 49-811-6009620   Contact: David Thomas, Area Sales Mgr.

DANA CORPORATION

4500 Dorr Street, Toledo, OH, 43615

Tel: (419) 535-4500   Fax: (419) 535-4643   www.dana.com

Mfr./sales of automotive, heavy truck, off-highway, fluid and mechanical power components and engine parts, filters and gaskets.

ATV Antriebstechnik Vertriers Gmbh, Benzstrasse 1, D-7448 Wolfschlugen, Germany

Erwin Hengstler Hydraulik GmbH, Postfach 1220, Schaetzlestrasse 2-8, D-7613 Hausach, Germany

Perfect Circle, Div. Dana, Hannoversche Strasse, D-30890 Barginhausen, Germany

Stieber Fiormstrag GmbH, Dieselstrasse 14, D-8046 Garching, Germany

Thermoplast + Apparatebau GmbH, Postfach 1220, Black u. Decker-Str. 25, D-65510 Idstein/Taunus, Germany

Victor Rinz Dichtungs GmbH, Reinzstrasse 3-7, Postfach 1909, D-89229 Neu-Ulm, Germany

Tel: 49-731-70460   Fax: 49-731-719089

Warner Electric GmbH, Postfach 2008, D-7440 Nurtingen, Germany

Weatherhead GmbH, Dieselstrasse 14, D-8046 Garching, Germany

DANAHER CORPORATION

1250 24th St. NW, Ste. 800, Washington, DC, 20037

Tel: (202) 828-0850   Fax: (202) 828-0860   www.danaher.com

Mfr. hand tools and motion controls.

Danaher Corporation, c/o Dr. Bruno Lange, Willstätterstr. 11, D-40549 Düsseldorf, Germany

Tel: 49-211-52-880   Fax: 49-211-52-88231

Danaher GmbH, Willstaetterstr. 11, D-40649 Dusseldorf, Germany

Danaher GmbH, Uhlandstrasse 49, D-78554 Aldingen, Germany

Danaher GmbH, Koningsweg 10, D-14163 Berlin, Germany

Tel: 49-30809-860   Contact: Dr. Bruno Lang

Eduard Bautz GmbH + Co.KG, Robert-Bosch-Strasse 10, D-64331 Weiterstadt, Germany

Tel: 49-6151-8796-10   Fax: 49-6151-8796-123

DANIEL INDUSTRIES INC.

9753 Pine Lake Drive, PO Box 55435, Houston, TX, 77224

Tel: (713) 467-6000   Fax: (713) 827-3889   www.danielind.com

Fluid measurement, flow control, actuation and analytical products, services and integrated solutions primarily for natural gas and oil producers, transporters and refiners worldwide.

Daniel Messtechnik, Gartenstraße 2/12, D-1591 Potsdam, Germany

Tel: 49-331-76-10   Fax: 49-331-76-14-01

DANZAS AEI, INC.

120 Tokeneke Road, PO Box 1231, Darien, CT, 06820

Tel: (203) 655-7900   Fax: (203) 655-5779   www.aeilogistics.com

International air freight forwarder.

Danzas AEI, Frankfurter Str. 93, D-65479 Raunheim, Germany

Tel: 49-6142-20060   Fax: 49-6142-200660

Danzas AEI, Fasanenweg 4, D-65451 Kelsterbach Frankfurt, Germany

Tel: 49-69-6107-7020   Fax: 49-69--6107-702390

D'ARCY MASIUS BENTON & BOWLES INC. (DMB&B)

1675 Broadway, New York, NY, 10019

Tel: (212) 468-3622   Fax: (212) 468-2987   www.darcyww.com

Full service international advertising and communications group.

DMB&B Europe, Karlplatz 21, D-4000 Düsseldorf 1, Germany

Dorger Dialog, Kaufmannshaus, Bleichenbruecke 10, D-2000 Hamburg 36, Germany

DATA I/O CORPORATION

10525 Willows Road NE, Redmond, WA, 98073-9746

Tel: (425) 881-6444   Fax: (425) 882-1043   www.dataio.com

Mfr. computer testing devices.

Data I/O Germany, Münich, Germany

Tel: 49-8-985-8580

DATA TRANSLATION INC.

100 Locke Drive, Marlborough, MA, 01752-1192

Tel: (508) 481-3700   Fax: (508) 481-8620   www.datx.com

Mfr. peripheral boards for image and array processing micro-computers.

Data Translation GmbH, Im Weilerlen 10, D-74321 Bietigheim-Bissingen, Germany

Tel: 49-7142-95310

DATASCOPE CORPORATION

14 Phillips Pkwy., Montvale, NJ, 07645

Tel: (201) 391-8100   Fax: (201) 307-5400   www.datascope.com

Mfr. medical devices.

Datascope GmbH, Zeppelinstrasse 2-4, D-64625 Bensheim, Germany

Tel: 49-6251-17050

Datascope GmbH, Fabrikstrasse 35, D-64625 Bensheim, Germany

DATUM INC.

9975 Toledo Way, Irvine, CA, 92618-1819

Tel: (949) 598-7500   Fax: (949) 598-7555   www.datum.com

Mfr. high-precision measuring equipment.

Datum GmbH, Fichtenstraße 25, D-85649 Hofolding, Germany

DAVIS POLK & WARDWELL

450 Lexington Ave., New York, NY, 10017

Tel: (212) 450-4000   Fax: (212) 450-4800   www.dpw.com

Engaged in international law.

Davis Polk & Wardwell, MesseTurm, D-60308 Frankfurt am Main, Germany

Tel: 49-69-9757030   Fax: 49-69-747744

DAYTON PROGRESS CORPORATION

500 Progress Road, Dayton, OH, 45449

Tel: (937) 859-5111   Fax: (937) 859-5353   www.daytonprogress.com

Engaged in the production of catalog and special punches, punch blanks and metal stamping tools.

Schneider Stanznormalien GmbH, Im Heidegraben 8 Postfach 1165, D-61401 Oberursel, Germany

DAZEL CORPORATION

301 Congress Ave., Ste. 1100, Austin, TX, 78701

Tel: (512) 494-7300   Fax: (512) 494-7394   www.dazel.com

Mfr. software for information delivery solutions on documents and reports.

Dazel Germany, Regus Business Centre GmbH, Frankfurt Atricom Box A5, Lyoner Strasse 15, D-60528 Frankfurt Niederrad, Germany

DDB WORLDWIDE COMMUNICATIONS GROUP

437 Madison Ave., New York, NY, 10022

Tel: (212) 415-2000   Fax: (212) 415-3417   www.ddbn.com

Advertising agency.

DDB GmbH, Postfach 1065, Osterholzallee 76, D-7140 Ludwigsburg, Germany

DDB GmbH, Schadowstrasse 48/50, D-4000 Düsseldorf 1, Germany

DDB GmbH, Streitfeldstrasse 19, D-8000 Münich 80, Germany

Heye & Partner GmbH, Ottobrunner Strasse 28, Unteraching, D-8025 Münich, Germany

Heye & Partner GmbH, Mittelweg 17, D-2000 Hamburg 13, Germany

DEERE & COMPANY
One John Deere Place, Moline, IL, 61265
Tel: (309) 765-8000   Fax: (309) 765-5772   www.deere.com
Mfr./sale agricultural, construction, utility, forestry and lawn, grounds care equipment.
John Deere Internatinal GmbH, Steubenstrasse 36-42, D-68163 Mannheim, Germany
Tel: 49-621-829-01   Fax: 49-621-829-8427

DELL COMPUTER CORPORATION
One Dell Way, Round Rock, TX, 78682-2222
Tel: (512) 338-4400   Fax: (512) 728-3653   www.dell.com
Direct marketer and supplier of computer systems.
Dell Computer GmbH, Monzastrasse 4, D-63225 Langen, Germany
Tel: 49-6103-971-0 Fax: 49-6103-971-701   Contact: Hans-Jurgen Mammitesch, Mng. Dir.

DELOITTE TOUCHE TOHMATSU INTERNATIONAL
1633 Broadway, New York, NY, 10019
Tel: (212) 492-4000   Fax: (212) 392-4154   www.deloitte.com
Accounting, audit, tax and management consulting services.
Deloitte & Touche GmbH, Schumannstrase 27, D-60325 Frankfurt/Main, Germany

DELTA AIR LINES INC.
Hartsfield International Airport, 1030 Delta Blvd., Atlanta, GA, 30320-6001
Tel: (404) 715-2600   Fax: (404) 715-5494   www.delta-air.com
Major worldwide airline; international air transport services.
Delta Air Lines Inc., Frankfurt, Germany

DENTSPLY INTERNATIONAL
570 West College Ave., PO Box 872, York, PA, 17405-0872
Tel: (717) 845-7511   Fax: (717) 843-6357   www.dentsply.com
Mfr. and distribution of dental supplies and equipment.
Denstsply GmbH, Postfach 101074, Eisenbahntrasse 180, D-63303 Dreieich, Germany
Tel: 49-6103-6070
Dentsply Gendex, Albert-Einstein, Ring 13, D-22761 Hamburg, Germany
Tel: 49-4089-96880
Dentsply GmbH, Postfach 5346, DeTrey Strasse 1, D-78467 Konstanz 12, Germany
Tel: 49-7531-5830

DETROIT DIESEL CORPORATION
13400 Outer Drive West, Detroit, MI, 48239
Tel: (313) 592-5000   Fax: (313) 592-5058   www.detroitdiesel.com
Mfr. diesel and aircraft engines and heavy-duty transmissions.
Diesel Und Getriebe Service, Wernher Von Braun Strasse 11, D-6500 Mainz-Hechtsheim, Germany
Tel: 49-61-315-8070   Fax: 49-61-315-80714

DHL WORLDWIDE EXPRESS
50 California Avenue, San Francisco, CA, 94111
Tel: (415) 677-6100   Fax: (415) 824-9700   www.dhl.com
Worldwide air express carrier.
DHL Worldwide Express, Lyoner Strasse 20, D-60528 Frankfurt, Germany
Tel: 49-69-66-904494

DIAGNOSTIC PRODUCTS CORPORATION
5700 West 96th Street, Los Angeles, CA, 90045
Tel: (310) 645-8200   Fax: (310) 645-9999   www.dpcweb.com
Mfr. diagnostic products.
DPC Biermann GmbH, Hohe Strasse 4-8, D-61231 Bad Nauheim, Germany
Tel: 49-6032-994-00   Fax: 49-6032-994-200

THE DIAL CORPORATION

15501 North Dial Blvd., Scottsdale, AZ, 85260-1619

Tel: (480) 754-3425   Fax: (480) 754-1098   www.dialcorp.com

Mfr. soaps, detergents, air fresheners, specialty personal care products and Armour Star canned meats.

Dial/Henkel LLC (JV), Henkelstrasse 67, D-40589 Düsseldorf, Germany

Tel: 49-211-797-3533   Fax: 49-211-798-4040

DIAMONDCLUSTER INTERNATIONAL, INC.

875 N. Michigan Avenue, Ste. 3000, Chicago, IL, 60611

Tel: (312) 255-5000   Fax: (312) 255-6000   www.diamondcluster.com

Engaged in electronic business development and support.

DiamondCluster International, Inc., Managementberatung, Platz 1a, D-80331 Münich, Germany

Tel: 49-8924-2420

DICTAPHONE CORPORATION

3191 Broadbridge Ave., Stratford, CT, 06497-2559

Tel: (203) 381-7000   Fax: (203) 381-7100   www.dictaphone.com

Mfr./sale dictation, telephone answering and multi-channel voice communications recording systems.

Dictaphone Deutschland GmbH, Siemenstrasse 8a, D-61352 Bad-Homburg, Germany

Tel: 49-6172-682682

DIEBOLD INC.

5995 Mayfair Road, North Canton, OH, 44720-8077

Tel: (330) 490-4000   Fax: (330) 490-3794   www.diebold.com

Mfr. automated banking systems; security services for banking industrial and related fields.

Diebold Germany GmbH, Zur Falkenburg 84, D-48432 Rheine, Germany

Tel: 49-2572-2881   Fax: 49-2572-151208

DIGI INTERNATIONAL INC.

11001 Bren Road East, Minnetonka, MN, 55343

Tel: (952) 912-3444   Fax: (952) 912-4952   www.digi.com

Mfr. computer hardware.

Digi International GmbH, Joseph-von-Fraunhofer-Str. 23, D-44227 Dortmund, Germany

Tel: 49-231-97-47-0   Fax: 49-231-97-47-111

DIMON INCORPORATED

512 Bridge Street, PO Box 681, Danville, VA, 24543-0681

Tel: (804) 792-7511   Fax: (804) 791-0377   www.dimon.com

One of world's largest importer and exporters of leaf tobacco.

DIMON Rotag A.G., PO Box 10 01 02, D-76231 Karlsruhe, Germany

Tel: 49-721-509-010   Fax: 49-721-509-0111

DIONEX CORPORATION

1228 Titan Way, PO Box 3603, Sunnyvale, CA, 94086-3603

Tel: (408) 737-0700   Fax: (408) 730-9403   www.dionex.com

Develop/mfr./market chromatography systems and related products.

Dionex GmbH, Am Woertzgarten 10, D-65510 Idstein, Germany

DISCOVERY COMMUNICATIONS, INC.

7700 Wisconsin Avenue, Bethesda, MD, 20814

Tel: (301) 986-0444   Fax: (301) 771-4064   www.discovery.com

Owns and operates cable networks.

Discovery Channel Betriebs GmbH, Robert-Buerkle-Str. 2, D-85737 Ismaning, Germany

Tel: 49-89-9956

WALT DISNEY COMPANY

500 South Buena Vista Street, Burbank, CA, 91521

Tel: (818) 560-1000   Fax: (818) 560-1930   www.disney.com

Film/TV production, theme parks, resorts, publishing, recording and retail stores.

Walt Disney Productions GmbH, Savignystr 76, D-6000 Frankfurt/Main, Germany

DMC STRATEX NETWORKS, INC.

170 Rose Orchard Way, San Jose, CA, 95134

Tel: (408) 943-0777   Fax: (408) 944-1648   www.dmcstratexnetworks.com

Designs, manufactures, and markets advanced wireless solutions for wireless broadband access.

DMC Stratex Networks, Gute Anger 3, D-85356 Freising, Germany

Tel: 49-8161-9927-0   Contact: Torsten Langhammer, Mgr.

D-M-E COMPANY

29111 Stephenson Highway, Madison Heights, MI, 48071

Tel: (248) 398-6000   Fax: (248) 544-5705   www.dmeco.com

Manufacture and distribution of mold tooling, mold components, hot runner systems, and electronic controls for the plastics industry.

D-M-E Normalien GmbH, Neckarsulmer Strasse 47, D-74194 Neuenstadt, Germany

Tel: 49-7139-920

DO ALL COMPANY

254 North Laurel Ave., Des Plaines, IL, 60016

Tel: (847) 803-7380   Fax: (847) 699-7524   www.doall.com

Distributors of machinery tools, metal cutting tools, instruments and industrial supplies for metalworking industry.

DoALL GmbH, Kleberstrasse 5, D-4020 Mettmann, Germany

DOCUMENTUM, INC.

6801 Koll Center Pkwy., Pleasanton, CA, 94566

Tel: (925) 600-6800   Fax: (925) 600-6850   www.documentum.com

Mfr. content management software.

Documentum International Inc., Erlenhof Park, Unterhaching, Inselkammerstrasse 2, D-82008 Unterhaching, Germany

DOLE FOOD COMPANY, INC.

One Dole Drive, Westlake Village, CA, 91362

Tel: (818) 874-4000   Fax: (818) 879-6615   www.dole.com

Produces/distributes fresh fruits and vegetables and canned juices and fruits.

Dole Food Company, Münich, Germany

DONALDSON COMPANY, INC.

PO Box 1299, Minneapolis, MN, 55431

Tel: (952) 887-3131   Fax: (952) 887-3155   www.donaldson.com

Mfr. filtration systems and replacement parts.

Donaldson Gesellschaft m.b.H., Postfach 1251, D-48233 Dülmen, Germany

Ultrafilter International AG, Haan, Germany

Contact: Dirk G. Kronsbein

DONNA KARAN INTERNATIONAL INC.

550 Seventh Avenue, New York, NY, 10018

Tel: (212) 789-1500   Fax: (212) 921-3526   www.donnakaran.com

Design/manufacture/sale men's, women's, and children's clothes.

Donna Karan International, Quartier 206, Friedrichstrasse 71, Germany

R.R. DONNELLEY & SONS COMPANY

77 West Wacker Drive, Chicago, IL, 60601-1696

Tel: (312) 326-8000   Fax: (312) 326-8543   www.rrdonnelley.com

Engaged in commercial printing and allied communication services.

R. R. Donnelley Deutschland GmbH, Bockenheimer Landstrasse 39, 5th Fl., D-60325 Frankfurt am Main, Germany

Tel: 49-69-1708-8300   Fax: 49-69-1708-8143

DONNELLY CORPORATION

49 West Third Street, Holland, MI, 49423-2813

Tel: (616) 786-7000   Fax: (616) 786-6034   www.donnelly.com

Mfr. fabricated, molded and coated glass products for the automotive and electronics industries.

Donnelly Hohe GmbH & Co. KG, Industriestrasse 10-16, D97904 Dorfprozelten, Germany

Tel: 49-9376-8-2001   Fax: 49-9376-8-2450

Hohe GmbH & Co. KG, Hauptstrasse 36, D-97903 Collenberg, Germany

Tel: 49-93-768-0   Fax: 49-93-768-1133   Contact: Hans Huber, CEO

DOREMUS & COMPANY, INC.

200 Varick Street, New York, NY, 10271

Tel: (212) 366-3000   Fax: (212) 366-3629   www.doremus.com

Advertising and public relations.

Advantage Doremus, Westend-Terrassen, Oberlindau, D-54-56 60323 Frankfurt, Germany

Tel: 49-69-71005-0   Fax: 49-69-71005-333

DOUBLECLICK, INC.

450 West 33rd Street, New York, NY, 10001

Tel: (212) 683-0001   Fax: (212) 889-0062   www.doubleclick.net

Engaged in online advertising and e-mail marketing.

Doubleclick GmbH, Phoenixhof, Ruhstrasse 11a, D-22761 Hamburg, Germany

Tel: 49-408-53570

Doubleclick GmbH, Koelner Strasse 10, D-65760 Eshborn, Germany

Tel: 49-6196-400-870

Doubleclick GmbH, Scheinerstrasse 7, D-81679 Münich, Germany

Doubleclick GmbH, Kolner Strasse 17, D-40211 Dusseldorf, Germany

DOVER CORPORATION

280 Park Ave., New York, NY, 10017-1292

Tel: (212) 922-1640   Fax: (212) 922-1656   www.dovercorporation.com

Holding company for varied industries; assembly and testing equipment, oil-well gear and other industrial products.

European Lift Engineering, Schleswigstrabe 3, GMB, D-30853 Langenhagen, Germany

Tel: 49-511-972420   Fax: 49-511-9723730

THE DOW CHEMICAL COMPANY

2030 Dow Center, Midland, MI, 48674

Tel: (989) 636-1000   Fax: (989) 636-3228   www.dow.com

Mfr. chemicals, plastics, pharmaceuticals, agricultural products, consumer products.

Dow Chemical GmbH, Wiesenhuttenstr. 18, D-6000 Frankfurt/Main, Germany

Dow Chemical GmbH, Werk Stade Butzenflether Sand, D-2160 Stade-Butzfletz, Germany

Dow Chemical GmbH, Briennerstrasse 44, D-8000 Münich 2, Germany

Dow Chemical GmbH, Kommandantendeich 8, D-2160 Stade, Germany

Dow Chemical GmbH, Winterhunder Weg 29/31, D-2000 Hamburg 76, Germany

Dow Chemical GmbH, Grunerstr. 46, D-4000 Düsseldorf 1, Germany

Dow Chemical GmbH, Gansheidestr. 55, D-7000 Stuttgart 1, Germany

Dow Deutschland Inc., Werk Rheinmünster, Industriestr. 1, D-77836 Rheinmünster, Germany

DRAFT WORLDWIDE

633 North St. Clair Street, Chicago, IL, 60611-3211

Tel: (312) 944-3500   Fax: (312) 944-3566   www.draftworldwide.com

Full service international advertising agency, engaged in brand building, direct and promotional marketing.

DraftWorldwide GmbH, Wandsbeker Zollstrasse 15, D-22041 Hamburg, Germany

Tel: 49-40-6891-35-85   Fax: 49-40-6891-35-87

Mailpool, Birkenwaldstrasse 200, D-70191 Stuttgart, Germany

Tel: 49-7-11-257-3050   Fax: 49-7-11-257-9240   Contact: E. Wolff, Co-Mng. Dir.

Mailpool, TheresienstraBe 10, D-04129 Leipzig, Germany

Tel: 49-34-9120-833   Fax: 49-341-9120-847   Contact: Christina Dorn, Supervisor

Peter Reincke/DraftWorldwide, Mühlstrasse 98a, D-63741 Aschaffenburg, Germany

Tel: 49-6021-4024-0   Fax: 49-6021-4024-13   Contact: Peter Richard Reincke

DRAKE BEAM MORIN INC.

100 Park Avenue, 11th Fl., New York, NY, 10017

Tel: (212) 692-7700   Fax: (212) 297-0426   www.dbm.com

Human resource management consulting and training.

DBM Deutschland Hdqtrs., v. Rundstedt & Partner GmbH, Konigsalle 70, D-40212 Düsseldorf, Germany

Tel: 49-211-83-9612   Fax: 49-211-13-4322

DRESSER INSTRUMENT DIVISION

250 East Main Street, Stratford, CT, 06614-5145

Tel: (203) 378-8281   Fax: (203) 385-0357   www.dresserinstruments.com

Mfr. pressure gauges and temperature instruments.

Dresser Europe, Postfach 11 20, Max-Planck-Strasse 1, D-52499 Baesweiler, Germany

Tel: 49-2401-8080   Fax: 49-2401-7027

DRESSER-RAND COMPANY

PO Box 560, Paul Clark Drive, Olean, NY, 14760

Tel: (716) 375-3000   Fax: (716) 375-3178   www.dresser-rand.com

Mfr. generators, centrifugal compressors, turbines and control systems.

Dresser-Rand GmbH, Postfach 101629, D-46016 Oberhausen, Germany

DRS TECHNOLOGIES, INC.

5 Dylvan Way, Parsippany, NJ, 07054

Tel: (973) 898-1500   Fax: (973) 898-4730   www.drs.com

Mfr. software and equipment for diagnostic and retrieval systems.

DRS Hadland GMBH, Gaissacher Str., D-81371 Münich, Germany

DT INDUSTRIES, INC.

907 West 5th Street, Dayton, OH, 45407

Tel: (937) 586-5600   Fax: (937) 586-5601   www.dtindustries.com

Mfr automated production equipment and packaging systems for the pharmaceutical and food industries.

DT Industries, Carl-Borgward Str. 11, D-56566 Neuwied, Germany

DUNHAM-BUSH INC.

101 Burgess Road, Harrisonburg, VA, 22801

Tel: (540) 574-6600   Fax: (540) 574-6618   www.dunham-bush.com

Provides innovative solutions for the heating, air conditioning and refrigeration segments.

Dunham-Bush GmbH, Wiesenstr. 5, D-6140 Bensheim 1, Germany

E.I. DUPONT DE NEMOURS & COMPANY

1007 Market Street, Wilmington, DE, 19898

Tel: (302) 774-1000   Fax: (302) 774-7321   www.dupont.com

Mfr. and sales of diversified chemicals, plastics, specialty products and fibers.

Du Pont de Nemours (Deutschland) GmbH, Hans-Bocklerstr. 33, D-4000 Düsseldorf Nord, Germany

DuPont Deutschland Holding, Industriestrasse 1, D-76684 Oestringen, Germany

Tel: 49-7253-91-2182   Fax: 49-7253-91-2195

Permatex GmbH, Div. Dupont, Rieter Tal, D-71665 Vaihingen/Enz, Germany

DVI, INC.

2500 york Road, Jamison, PA, 18929

Tel: (215) 488-5000   Fax: (215) 488-5010   www.dvifs.com

Engaged in financing of medical equipment.

DVI Germany, Furstenbergerstr. 143, D-60322 Frankfurt, Germany

DYN CORPORATION

11710 Plaza America Drive, Reston, VA, 20190

Tel: (703) 261-5000   Fax: (703) 261-5090   www.dyncorp.com

Engaged in diversified technical services.

ITS Intl. Service, Schiersteiner Str. 52, Lindsey Air Station, D-6200 Wiesbaden, Germany

E.PIPHANY, INC.

1900 South Norfolk Street, Ste. 310, San Mateo, CA, 94403

Tel: (650) 356-3800   Fax: (650) 356-3801   www.epiphany.com

Mfr. analytical software.

E.piphany Deutschland GmbH, Elisabethstr. 91, D-80797 Münich, Germany

Tel: 49-89-5908-2350

EASTMAN CHEMICAL COMPANY

100 North Eastman Road, Kingsport, TN, 37662-5075

Tel: (423) 229-2000   Fax: (423) 229-1351   www.eastman.com

Mfr. plastics, chemicals, fibers.

Eastman Chemical B.V, Zweigniederlassung Koeln, Charlottenstrasse 61, D-51149 Köln, Germany

Eastman Chemical Jaegar GmbH, Ottensener Str. 20-22, D-40599 Dusseldorf, Germany

Tel: 49-211-979-5521

EASTMAN KODAK COMPANY

343 State Street, Rochester, NY, 14650

Tel: (716) 724-4000   Fax: (716) 724-1089   www.kodak.com

Develop/mfr. photo and chemicals products, information management/video/copier systems, fibers/plastics for various industry.

Eastman Chemical Intl. AG, Xantenerstr. 105, D-5000 Cologne 60, Germany

Kodak AG, Postfach 60 03 45, Hedelfinger Strasse, D-7000 Stuttgart 60, Germany

EASTMAN RESINS, INC.

1 Terra Way, 8601 95th St., Pleasant Prairie, WI, 53158

Tel: (262) 947-7300   Fax: (262) 947-7328   www.lawter.com

Resins, pigments and coatings.

Eastman Resins Lawter International GmbH, Kolnerstrasse 114, D-502226 Frechen, Germany

Tel: 49-2234-120-52   Fax: 49-2234-583-44

EATON CORPORATION

Eaton Center, 1111 Superior Ave., Cleveland, OH, 44114-2584

Tel: (216) 523-5000   Fax: (216) 479-7068   www.eaton.com

Advanced technical products for transportation and industrial markets.

Aeroquip Division, Eaton Corp., Chemical Containment Systems, Carl-Benz-Strasse 9, D-82205 Gilching, Germany

Eaton GmbH, Am Lindenkamp 31, D-5620 Velbert Rheinland, Germany

EBSCO INDUSTRIES

PO Box 1943, Birmingham, AL, 35201

Tel: (205) 991-6600   Fax: (205) 995-1586   www.ebscoind.com

Engaged in information management services, journal and periodical subscription services, fishing lure manufacturing, custom printing, loose-leaf binder manufacturing and specialty office and computer furniture sales and distribution.

EBSCO Subscription Services, Bodenstedtstrasse 6, D-6200 Wiesbaden, Germany

ECOLAB INC.

370 N. Wabasha Street, St. Paul, MN, 55102

Tel: (651) 293-2233   Fax: (651) 293-2379   www.ecolab.com

Develop/mfr. premium cleaning, sanitizing and maintenance products and services for the hospitality, institutional, and residential markets.

Henkel-Ecolab (JV), IDR Gebaude, Reisholzer Werftrasse 42, D-4000 Düsseldorf, Germany

Tel: 49-211-9893-101

ECOLOGY AND ENVIRONMENT INC.

368 Pleasant View Drive, Lancaster, NY, 14086-1397

Tel: (716) 684-8060   Fax: (716) 684-0844   www.ecolen.com

Environmental, scientific and engineering consulting.

E&E Umwelt Baratung GmbH, Chemnitzer Strassse 13, Postfach 7, D-09222 Gruna, Germany

EDDIE BAUER INC.

15010 NE 36th Street, Redmond, WA, 98073

Tel: (425) 882-6100   Fax: (425) 882-6383   www.eddiebauer.com

Clothing retailer and mail order catalog company.

Eddie Bauer Inc., Münich, Germany

EDELMAN PUBLIC RELATIONS WORLDWIDE

200 East Randolph Drive, 62nd Fl., Chicago, IL, 60601

Tel: (312) 240-3000   Fax: (312) 240-0596   www.edelman.com

International independent public relations firm.

Edelman PR Worldwide, Bettinastrasse 64, D-60325 Frankfurt am Main 1, Germany

Tel: 49-69-75-61-990   Fax: 49-69-75-61-9910   Contact: Eduard Weber-Bemnet, Mng. Dir.

J.D. EDWARDS & COMPANY

One Technology Way, Denver, CO, 80237

Tel: (303) 334-4000   Fax: (303) 334-4970   www.jdedwards.com

Computer software products.

J. D. Edwards, Monzastrasse 2B, D-63885 Langen, Germany

Tel: 49-6103-7620   Fax: 49-6103-762299

J. D. Edwards, Osterbekstrasse 90b, D-22083 Hamburg, Germany

Tel: 49-40-27814-5   Fax: 49-40-27814-799

EFCO

1800 NE Broadway Ave., Des Moines, IA, 50316-0386

Tel: (515) 266-1141   Fax: (515) 266-7970   www.efco-usa.com

Mfr. systems for concrete construction.

EFCO Schalungsbau GmbH, Bahnhofstrasse 1, D-82402 Seeshaupt, Germany

EG&G INC.

900 Clopper Road, Ste. 200, Gaithersburg, MD, 20878

Tel: (301) 840-3000   Fax: (301) 590-0502   www.egginc.com

Diversified R/D, mfr. and services.

EG&G Berthold, Calmbacher Strasse 22, Postfach 100163, D-75323 Bad Wildbad, Germany

EG&G GmbH Reticon, Hohenlindener Str. 12, D-81677 Münich, Germany

EG&G GmbH/Instrument Div., Hohenlindener Str. 12, D-81677 Münich, Germany

EG&G GmbH/Sealol Euroseals, Weher Koeppel 6, D-65013 Wiesbaden, Germany

EG&G Heimann Optoelectronics GmbH, Weher Koeppel 6, D-65199 Wiesbaden, Germany

EGL INC. (EAGLE GLOBAL LOGISTICS)

15350 Vickery Drive, Houston, TX, 77032

Tel: (281) 618-3100   Fax: (281) 618-3223   www.eagleusa.com

Ocean/air freight forwarding, customs brokerage, packing and wholesale, logistics management and insurance.

EGL Eagle Global Logistics, C. T. Nordhafen, Gate House 3, D-27568 Bremerhaven, Germany

Tel: 49-471-400-97   Fax: 49-471-412-055

EGL Eagle Global Logistics, Langer Kornweg 19-23, Alfa Haus, 3rd Fl., D-65451 Kelsterbach, Germany
Tel: 49-6107-750-924   Fax: 49-6107-907-318

EGL Eagle Global Logistics, Aeropark Ratingen-West, Broichhofstrasse 5, D-40880 Ratingen, Germany
Tel: 49-2102-474-077   Fax: 49-2101-471-204

EGL Eagle Global Logistics, Martinistrasse 33, D-28195 Bremen, Germany
Tel: 49-421-366-90   Fax: 49-421-366-9666

EGL Eagle Global Logistics, Am Suedpark 10, D-65241 Kelsterbach, Germany
Tel: 49-6107-750-980   Fax: 49-6107-790-945

EGL Eagle Global Logistics, Flughafenstrasse, Frachtgebaude, D-01109 Dresden, Germany
Tel: 49-351-881-4830   Fax: 49-351-881-4831

EGL Eagle Global Logistics, Frachthalle 2, Room 185-186, D-51147 Cologne, Germany
Tel: 49-2203-402-174   Fax: 49-2203-402-238

EGL Eagle Global Logistics, Flughafen, Frachtgebaude, D-70629 Stuttgart, Germany
Tel: 49-711-798-013   Fax: 49-711-795-644

EGL Eagle Global Logistics, Flughafen, Franchtgebaude, 1st Fl., D-13405 Berlin, Germany
Tel: 49-30-410-13397   Fax: 49-30-413-5659

EGL Eagle Global Logistics, Cadolto Geb., Flughfenstrasse 100, D-90411 Nuernberg, Germany
Tel: 49-911-356-9300   Fax: 49-911-365-9301

EGL Eagle Global Logistics, Billhorner Deich 96, D-20539 Hamburg, Germany
Tel: 49-40-788-700   Fax: 49-40-788-70111

EGL Eagle Global Logistics, Flughafen Fuhlsbuettel, Frachtgebaeude 150, Room 2010-2113, D-22335 Hamburg, Germany
Tel: 49-40-507-5200-1   Fax: 49-40-506-564

EGL Eagle Global Logistics, Flughafen Muenchen, Air Cargo Ctr., Modul F, 3rd Fl., Rm. 327-331, D-85356 München, Germany
Tel: 49-89-975-9437-0   Fax: 49-89-975-9437-6

ELANCO ANIMAL HEALTH

500 East 96th Street, Ste. 125, Indianapolis, IN, 46240

Tel: (317) 276-3000   Fax: (317) 276-6116   www.elanco.com

Antibiotics and fine chemicals.

Elanco Animal Health, Teichweg 3, D-35396 Giessen, Germany

ELECTRIC FURNACE COMPANY

435 Wilson Street, Salem, OH, 44460

Tel: (330) 332-4661   Fax: (330) 332-1853   www.electricfurnace.com

Mfr./design heat treating furnaces for metals industrial.

Electric Furnace GmbH, Lohstätte 4, Postfach 1327, D-47513 Kleve, Germany
Tel: 49-2821-77590 Fax: 49-2821-18235

ELECTRO SCIENTIFIC INDUSTRIES, INC.

13900 NW Science Park Drive, Portland, OR, 97229

Tel: (503) 641-4141   Fax: (503) 643-4873   www.esi.com

Mfg. production and testing equipment used in manufacture of electronic components in pagers and cellular communication devices.

Electro Scientific Industries GmbH, Riesstrasse 17, D-80992 München, Germany
Tel: 49-89-149-0070 Fax: 49-89-149-00720   Contact: Robert Meisenbacher

ELECTROGLAS INC.

6042 Silver Creek Valley Road, San Jose, CA, 95138

Tel: (408) 528-3000   Fax: (408) 528-3542   www.electroglas.com

Mfr. semi-conductor test equipment, automatic wafer probes.

Electroglas GmbH, Carl-Zeiss Strasse 5, D-85748 Garching, Germany

ELECTRONIC DATA SYSTEMS, INC. (EDS)

5400 Legacy Dr., Plano, TX, 75024

Tel: (972) 604-6000   Fax: (972) 605-2643   www.eds.com

Engaged in systems integration, network and systems operations and management consulting.

EDS Germany, Eisenstrasse 56, D-65428 Ruesselsheim, Germany

ELECTRONICS FOR IMAGING, INC. (EFI)

303 Velocity Way, Foster City, CA, 94404

Tel: (650) 357-3500   Fax: (650) 357-3907   www.efi.com

Design/mfr. computer software and hardware for color desktop publishing.

EFI GmbH, Luegallee 18, D-40545 Düesseldorf, Germany

Tel: 49-211-576841

EFI GmbH, Kaiserwerther Strasse 115, D-40880 Ratingen Düesseldorf, Germany

Tel: 49 2102-74540

ELECTRO-SCIENCE LABORATORIES, INC.

416 East Church Road, King of Prussia, PA, 19406

Tel: (610) 272-8000   Fax: (610) 272-6759   www.electroscience.com

Mfr. advanced thick film materials for hybrid microcircuits and other electronic packaging and component applications.

ESL Deutschland, Sendinger Tor Platz 8, D-8000 Münich 2, Germany

EMC CORPORATION

35 Parkwood Drive, Hopkinton, MA, 01748-9103

Tel: (508) 435-1000   Fax: (508) 435-8884   www.emc.com

Designs/supplies intelligent enterprise storage and retrieval technology for open systems, mainframes and midrange environments.

EMC Computer Systems Deutschland GmbH, Boeblinger Strabe 29, D-71229 Leonberg Stuttgartt, Germany

Tel: 49-7152-979340

EMC Computer Systems Deutschland GmbH, Hammfelddamm 6, D-41460 Neuss Düsseldorf, Germany

Tel: 49-2131-9191-0

EMC Computer Systems Deutschland GmbH, Schwalbach/TS, D-65824 Frankfurt, Germany

Tel: 49-6196-4728-0

EMC Computer Systems Deutschland GmbH, Osterbekstrabe 906, D-22083 Hamburg, Germany

Tel: 49-40-271315-00

EMC Computer Systems Deutschland GmbH, Messerschmittstrasse 4, D-80992 Münich, Germany

Tel: 49-89-143132-0

EMC Computer Systems Deutschland GmbH, Stefan-George-Ring 6, D-81929 Münich, Germany

Tel: 49-89-930960-0

EMC Computer Systems Deutschland GmbH, Suedwestpark 92, D-90449 Neurnberg, Germany

Tel: 49-911-688698-0

EMC Computer Systems Deutschland GmbH, Auguste-Victoria-Allee 4, D-13403 Berlin, Germany

Tel: 49-30-417071-0

EMERSON & CUMING COMPOSITE MATERIALS, INC.

59 Walpole Street, Canton, MA, 02021

Tel: (781) 821-4250   Fax: (781) 821-0737   www.emersoncuming.com

Mfr. high performance encapsulants, adhesives and coatings for the automotive, telecommunications and electronic industries.

Emerson & Cuming GmbH, Emil-von-Behring-Strasse 2, D-60439 Frankfurt am Main 1, Germany

EMERSON PROCESS MANAGEMENT

8301Cameron Road, Austin, TX, 78754

Tel: (512) 834-7689   Fax: (512) 832-3232   www.frco.com

Mfr. industrial process control equipment.

Emerson Process Management, Robert-Bosch-Str. 21, D-64625 Bensheim, Germany

Emerson Process Management, Argelsrieder Feld 3, D-82234 Wessling, Germany

Emerson Process Management, Reiherstieg 6, D-21217 Seevetal, Germany

EMERY FORWARDING

One Lagoon Drive, Ste. 400, Redwood City, CA, 94065

Tel: (650) 596-9600   Fax: (650) 596-7901   www.emeryworld.com

Freight transport, global logistics and air cargo.

Emery Forwarding, Langer Komweg 8, D-65451 Kelsterbach Frankfurt Main, Germany

ENCAD, INC.

6059 Cornerstone Court West, San Diego, CA, 92121

Tel: (858) 452-0882   Fax: (858) 452-5618   www.encad.com

Mfr. large color printers for specialized graphics.

ENCAD Europe SA, Alte Landstrasse 21, D-85521 Ottobrunn, Germany

Tel: 49-89-6603-903

ENCYCLOPAEDIA BRITANNICA INC.

310 S. Michigan Ave., Chicago, IL, 60604

Tel: (312) 427-9700   Fax: (312) 294-2176   www.eb.com

Publishing; books.

Encyclopaedia Britannica (Germany) Ltd., Hildebrandtstrasse 4, D-40215 Dusseldorf, Germany

ENERGIZER HOLDINGS, INC.

533 Maryville University Dr., St. Louis, MO, 63141

Tel: (314) 985-2000   Fax: (214) 985-2205   www.energizer.com

Mfr. Eveready and Energizer brand batteries and lighting products.

Ralston Energy Systems, Max Planck Strasse 30, PO Box 3243, D-40699 Erkrath Dusseldorf, Germany

Tel: 49-11-2002109   Fax: 49-211-20020

ENERPAC

6101 N. Baker Road, PO Box 3241, Milwaukee, WI, 53201-3241

Tel: (414) 781-6600   Fax: (414) 781-1049   www.enerpac.com

Mfr. hydraulic cylinders, pumps, valves, presses, tools, accessories and system components.

ENERPAC Applied Power GmbH, PO Box 300113, D-40401 Düsseldorf, Germany

ENGELHARD CORPORATION

101 Wood Avenue South, Iselin, NJ, 08830

Tel: (732) 205-5000   Fax: (732) 632-9253   www.engelhard.com

Mfr. pigments, additives, catalysts, chemicals, engineered materials.

Engelhard-Clal Germany, Lise-Meitner Strasse 7, D-63303 Dreieich, Germany

Tel: 49-61-03-93450

ENRON CORPORATION

1400 Smith Street, Houston, TX, 77002-7369

Tel: (713) 853-6161   Fax: (713) 853-3129   www.enron.com

Exploration, production, transportation and distribution of integrated natural gas and electricity. **Corporation under worldwide reorganization; new data unavailable for this edition.

Enron Energie GmbH, Brosenstrasse 2-4, D-60313 Frankfurt, Germany

Tel: 49-69-1330-80

Tacke Windenergie GmbH, Holsterfeld 5A, D-48499 Salzbergen, Germany

Tel: 49-597-197-0871

EPICOR SOFTWARE CORPORATION

195 Technology Drive, Irvine, CA, 92618

Tel: (949) 585-4000   Fax: (949) 450-4419   www.epicor.com

Mfr. software for e-business.

Epicor Deutschland GmbH, Gutenbergstrasse 3, D-85716 Unterschleißheim München, Germany

Tel: 49-89-317060

EPRESENCE, INC.

120 Flanders Road, Westboro, MA, 01581

Tel:　(508) 898-1000　　　Fax:　(508) 898-1755　　　www.epresence.com

Provides electronic business services.

e-Presence Germany, Kapellenstr. 10, D-85622 Feldkirchen, Germany

Tel: 49-89-990-2240

ERICO PRODUCTS INC.

34600 Solon Road, Cleveland, OH, 44139

Tel:　(440) 248-0100　　　Fax:　(440) 248-0723　　　www.erico.com

Mfr. electric welding apparatus and hardware, metal stampings, specialty fasteners.

Erico GmbH, Postfach Steinalben, D-66851 Schwanenmuehle, Germany

Tel: 49-63-079-1810

ERNST & YOUNG INTERNATIONAL

5 Times Square, New York, NY, 10036

Tel:　(212) 773-3000　　　Fax:　(212) 773-6350　　　www.eyi.com

Engaged in assurance and advisory business services, tax, law and corporate finance.

Ernst & Young GmbH, Eschersheimer Landstrasse 14, D-60322 Frankfurt am Main, Germany

Tel: 49-69-152-08-01　Fax: 49-69-152-08-550　Contact: Karin Skiba

ESCO CORPORATION

2141 NW 25th Ave., Portland, OR, 97210

Tel:　(503) 228-2141　　　Fax:　(503) 778-6330　　　www.escocorp.com

Mfr. equipment for mining, construction and forestry industries.

ESCO Corp., Moenchengladbach, Germany

ESCO TECHNOLOGIES INC.

8888 Ladue Road, Ste. 200, St. Louis, MO, 63124-2090

Tel:　(314) 213-7200　　　Fax:　(314) 213-7250　　　www.escostl.com

Electronic subassemblies and components.

Filtertek, GmbH, Div. ESCO, Rudolf-Diesel - Street 2, D-406 Meerbush, Germany

Tel: 49-2159-92300

ESTERLINE TECHNOLOGIES

10800 NE 8th Street, Ste. 600, Bellevue, WA, 98004

Tel:　(425) 453-9400　　　Fax:　(425) 453-2916　　　www.esterline.com

Mfr. equipment and instruments for industrial automation, precision measure, data acquisition.

Excellon Europe GmbH, Juston-von-Liebig-Str. 19, D-6057 Dietzenbach, Germany

Tel: 49-6074-3000

International Precision Products Gmbh, Arabellastrasse 5 / 203, D-81925 Münich, Germany

Tel: 49-89-920905-0　Fax: 49-89-920905-19

ETHYL CORPORATION

330 South 4th Street, PO Box 2189, Richmond, VA, 23219

Tel:　(804) 788-5000　　　Fax:　(804) 788-5688　　　www.ethyl.com

Provide additive chemistry solutions to enhance the performance of petroleum products.

Ethyl Mineraloel-Additives GmbH, Oberstrasse 14b, D-20144 Hamburg, Germany

Tel: 49-40-42-92-90-0

EURO RSCG WORLDWIDE

350 Hudson Street, New York, NY, 10014

Tel:　(212) 886-2000　　　Fax:　(212) 886-2016　　　www.eurorscg.com

International advertising agency group.

ABC Berlin, Kurfuerstendamm 66, Berlin, Germany

EXCELLON AUTOMATION

24751 Crenshaw Boulevard, Torrance, CA, 90505

Tel: (310) 534-6300　　　Fax: (310) 534-6777　　　www.excellon.com

PCB drilling and routing machines; optical inspection equipment.

Excellon Europa GmbH, PO Box 1328, D-36113 Dietzenbach, Germany

Tel: 49-6074-3000　Fax: 49-6074-300-160

EXCELON INC.

25 Mall Road, Burlington, MA, 01803

Tel: (781) 674-5000　　　Fax: (781) 674-5010　　　www.exceloncorp.com

Developer of object-oriented database management systems software.

eXcelon Deutschland GmbH, Kreuzberger Ring 64, D-65205 Wiesbaden, Germany

Tel: 49-611-977190　Fax: 49-611-977-1919

EXE TECHNOLOGIES, INC.

8787 N. Stemmons Fwy., Dallas, TX, 75247-3702

Tel: (214) 775-6000　　　Fax: (214) 775-0911　　　www.exe.com

Provides a complete line of supply chain management execution software for WMS.

EXE Technologies GmbH, Lilenthalstrasse 25, D-85399 Hallbergmoos Munich, Germany

EXELIXIS, INC.

170 Harbor Way, South San Francisco, CA, 94080

Tel: (650) 837-7000　　　Fax: (650) 837-7226　　　www.exelixis.com

Engaged in drug testing.

Artemis Pharmaceuticals GmbH, Neurather Ring 1, D-51063 Köln, Germany

Tel: 49-221-964-53-10　Contact: Monika Hahn

Exelixis Deutschland GmbH, Spemannstr.35, D-72076 Tübingen, Germany

EXIDE TECHNOLOGIES

210 Carnegie Center, Ste. 500, Princeton, NJ, 08540

Tel: (609) 627-7200　　　Fax: (609) 627-7217　　　www.exideworld.com

Mfr. lead-acid automotive and industrial batteries.

Exide Germany, Budingen, Germany

EXPEDITORS INTERNATIONAL OF WASHINGTON INC.

1015 Third Avenue, 12th Fl., Seattle, WA, 98104-1182

Tel: (206) 674-3400　　　Fax: (206) 682-9777　　　www.expd.com

Air/ocean freight forwarding, customs brokerage, international logistics solutions.

Expeditors International GmbH - Frankfurt, Langer Kornweg 27-29, D-65451 Kelsterbach, Germany

Tel: 49-6107-7990　Fax: 49-6107-63179

EXXON MOBIL CORPORATION

5959 Las Colinas Blvd., Irving, TX, 75039-2298

Tel: (972) 444-1000　　　Fax: (972) 444-1882　　　www.exxonmobil.com

Petroleum exploration, production, refining; mfr. petroleum and chemicals products; coal and minerals.

Brigitta Erdgas GmbH, Katstadtring 2, D-2000 Hamburg 60, Germany

Exxon Mobil, Inc., Postfach 10 03 55, D-85003 Ingolstadt, Germany

Exxon Mobil, Inc., Kapstadtring 2, D-2000 Hamburg 60, Germany

Exxon Mobil, Inc., Neusser Landstrasse 16, D-50735 Köln, Germany

Tel: 49-221-770-31

Exxon Mobil, Inc., Neusser Landestrasse 16, D-50735 Köln, Germany

Tel: 49-221-77031　Fax: 49-221-770-3320

FABREEKA INTERNATIONAL INC.

1023 Turnpike, PO Box 210, Stoughton, MA, 02072

Tel: (781) 341-3655   Fax: (781) 341-3983   www.fabreeka.com

Mfr. vibration isolation materials; consulting and engineering services.

Fabreeka Deutschland GmbH, Postfach 103, D-64570 Buttelborn, Germany

Tel: 49-6152-9597-0   Fax: 49-6152-9597-40

FACTSET RESEARCH SYSTEMS, INC.

1 Greenwich Plaza, Greenwich, CT, 06830

Tel: (203) 863-1599   Fax: (203) 863-1501   www.factset.com

Provides on-line investment research services to financial institutions.

FactSet Limited, An der Welle 3, D-60322 Frankfurt, Germany

Tel: 49-69-7706-1600

FAEGRE & BENSON LLP

2200 Norwest Center, 90 South Seventh Street, Minneapolis, MN, 55402-3901

Tel: (612) 336-3000   Fax: (612) 336-3026   www.faegre.com

International law firm.

Faegre & Benson LLP, Theodor-Heuss-Allee 108, D-60486 Frankfurt am Main, Germany

Tel: 49-69-971-227-0   Fax: 49-69-971-227-70   Contact: Philip B. Haleen, Ptnr.

FAIR, ISAAC AND COMPANY, INC.

200 Smith Ranch Road, San Rafael, CA, 94903

Tel: (415) 472-2211   Fax: (415) 492-5691   www.fairisaac.com

Mfr. automated systems for credit and loan approvals.

Fair, Isaac and Co., Berliner Strasse 207-211, D-65205 Wiesbaden, Germany

Tel: 49-611-97850

FAIRCHILD AEROSPACE CORPORATION

10823 NE Entrance Rd., San Antonio, TX, 78216

Tel: (210) 824-9421   Fax: (210) 824-9476   www.faidor.com

Mfr. turboprop aircraft.

Fairchild Dornier, PO Box 1103, Airfield Oberpfassenhofen, D-8230 Wessling, Germany

Tel: 49-8153-300

THE FALK CORPORATION

3001 West Canal Street, PO Box 492,, Milwaukee, WI, 53208-4200

Tel: (414) 342-3131   Fax: (414) 937-4359   www.falkcorp.com

Designers and manufacturers of power transmission equipment including gears, geared reducers and drives, couplings.

Falk Germany, 5 Burgbergstrasse, D-87527 Sonthofen, Germany

FARREL CORPORATION

25 Main Street, Ansonia, CT, 06401

Tel: (203) 736-5500   Fax: (203) 735-6267   www.farrel.com

Mfr. polymer processing equipment.

Farrel-Rockstedt GmbH, Haupstrasse 1, D-5481 Schalkenbach, Germany

FEDERAL-MOGUL CORPORATION

26555 Northwestern Highway, PO Box 1966, Southfield, MI, 48034

Tel: (248) 354-7700   Fax: (248) 354-8983   www.federal-mogul.com

Mfr./distributor precision parts for automobiles, trucks, farm and construction vehicles.

Federal-Mogul Friction Products GmbH, Klosterstrasse 16, D-51709 Marienheide, Germany

Federal-Mogul GmbH, Otto-Hahn-Strausse 26-28, D-65520 Bad Camberg, Germany

Glyco AG, Münich, Germany

Glyco Antriebstechnik GmbH, Münich, Germany

Glyco KG, Münich, Germany

FEDEX CORPORATION

942 South Shady Grove Rd., Memphis, TN, 38120

Tel: (901) 369-3600   Fax: (901) 395-2000   www.fdxcorp.com

Package express delivery service.

Federal Express (Deutschland) GmbH, Flughafen, Gebaude 192, D-2000 Hamburg 63, Germany
Tel: 800-1230800

Federal Express (Deutschland) GmbH, Wanheimer Str. 61, D-4000 Düsseldorf 30, Germany
Tel: 800-1230800

Federal Express (Deutschland) GmbH, Kleiner Kornweg 6-24, D-6092 Kezsterbach, Germany
Tel: 800-1230800

Federal Express (Deutschland) GmbH, Stahlgruberring 32, D-8000 Münich 82, Germany
Tel: 800-1230800

FEI CORPORATION

7451 NW Evergreen Pkwy., Hillsboro, OR, 97124-5830

Tel: (503) 640-7500   Fax: (503) 640-7509   www.feicompany.com

Design and mfr. of charged particle beam systems serving the research, development and production needs of customers in semiconductor, data storage, and industry/institute markets.

FEI Deutschland GmbH, Kirchenstrasse 2, D-85622 Feldkirchen, Germany
Tel: 45-561-9983611

FELLOWES, INC.

1789 Norwood Avenue, Itasca, IL, 60143-109

Tel: (630) 893-1600   Fax: (630) 893-1648   www.fellowes.com

Mfr. of office products and accessories.

Fellowes GmbH, Dieselstrabe 27, D-30827 Garbsen, Germany
Tel: 49-51-3149-770

FENDER MUSICAL INSTRUMENTS CORPORATION

7975 N. Hayden Road, Ste. C-100, Scottsdale, AZ, 85258

Tel: (480) 596-9690   Fax: (480) 596-1384   www.fender.com

Mfr. electric guitars and stringed instruments.

Fender Musica Instruments GmbH, Dusseldorf, Germany

FERRO CORPORATION

1000 Lakeside Ave., Cleveland, OH, 44114-7000

Tel: (216) 641-8580   Fax: (216) 696-5784   www.ferro.com

Mfr. Specialty chemicals, coatings, plastics, colors, refractories.

Ferro GmbH, Postfach 1032, Langenbergstrasse 10, D-67657 Kaiserslautern, Germany
Tel: 49-631-41640   Fax: 49-631-4164-147   Contact: C.L. Kolff

Ferro GmbH, Electro Materials Division, Obere Vorstadt 16, D-71063 Sindelfingen, Germany
Tel: 49-7031-809003   Fax: 49-7031-809694

Ferro GmbH Enamel Lab, Amt Schwarzenberg, Robert-Koch Strasse 16a, D-9430 Schwarzenberg, Germany
Tel: 49-3774-22066   Fax: 49-3774-25567

Ferro Plastics GmbH, Osningstrasse 12, D-33605 Bielefeld, Germany
Tel: 49-521-25084   Fax: 49-521-25086

Ruhr Pulverlack GmbH, Zur Alten Ruhr 4, D-59755 Arnsberg, Germany
Tel: 49-2932-62990   Fax: 49-2932-629936   Contact: Gunter Jung, Dir.

FIBERMARK, INC.

161 Wellington Rd., Brattleboro, VT, 05302

Tel: (802) 257-0365   Fax: (802) 257-5900   www.fibermark.com

Mfr. specialty fiber-based materials, including insulating printed circuit boards, air filters, vacuum cleaner bags and tape substrates.

FiberMark Gessner and Filter Media, GmbH, Otto Von Steinbeis-Strasse 14b, D-83052 Bruckmühl, Germany
Tel: 49-8062-703-0

FiberMark Lahnstein GmbH, Auf Brühl 15-27, D-56112 Lahnstein, Germany

Tel: 49-2621-177-0

FileNET CORPORATION

3565 Harbor Boulevard, Costa Mesa, CA, 92626

Tel: (714) 966-3400   Fax: (714) 966-3490   www.filenet.com

Provides integrated document management (IDM) software and services for internet and client server-based imaging, workflow, cold and electronic document management solutions.

FileNET GmbH, Dietrich-Bonhoeffer-Strasse 4, D-61380 Bad Homburg v.d.H, Germany

Tel: 49-6172-963-0   Fax: 49-6172-963-478

FIREPOND, INC.

890 Winter Stret, Waltham, MA, 02451

Tel: (781) 487-8400   Fax: (781) 487-8450   www.firepond.com

Mfr. enterprise software.

Firepond Deutschland GmbH, Niederkasseler Lohweg 185, D-40547 Dusseldorf, Germany

FIRESTONE POLYMERS

381 W. Wilbeth Road, Akron, OH, 44301

Tel: (330) 379-7864   Fax: (330) 379-7875   www.firesyn.com

Mfr. polymers; rubber, plastics and adhesives

HSH Chemie GmbH, PO Box 10 24 25, D-20017 Hamburg, Germany

Tel: 49-40-32-1011   Fax: 49-40-33-6623   Contact: Stephan Löhden

FISCHER IMAGING CORPORATION

12300 North Grant Street, Denver, CO, 80241

Tel: (303) 452-6800   Fax: (303) 452-4335   www.fischerimaging.com

Engaged in the design, manufacture and marketing of specialty mammography and X-ray systems that aid in the early diagnosis and treatment of disease.

Fischer Imaging Europe A/S, Hummelsbuetteler Steindamm 78 A, D-22851 Norderstedt, Germany

FISHER SCIENTIFIC INTERNATIONAL INC.

1 Liberty Lane, Hampton, NH, 03842

Tel: (603) 929-5911   Fax: (603) 929-0222   www.fisherscientific.com

Mfr. and distribution of science equipment, instruments, and supplies.

Fisher Scientific GmbH, Liebigstrasse 16, D-61130 Nidderau, Germany

Tel: 49-6187-20190   Fax: 49-6187-201949

Fisher Scientific GmbH, Binnerheide 33, D-58239 Schwerte, Germany

Tel: 49-2304-9325   Fax: 49-2304-932-950

FLEETBOSTON FINANCIAL CORPORATION

100 Federal Street, Boston, MA, 02110

Tel: (617) 434-2400   Fax: (617) 434-6943   www.fleet.com

Banking and insurance services.

FleetBoston Frankfurt, Postfach 17 05 38, D-60069 Frankfurt, Germany

Tel: 49-69-97265-0   Fax: 49-69-721162

FLOW INTERNATIONAL CORPORATION

23500 64th Avenue S., PO Box 97040, Kent, WA, 98064-9740

Tel: (253) 872-4900   Fax: (253) 813-3285   www.flowcorp.com

Mfr. high-pressure water jet cutting/cleaning equipment, powered scaffolding; concrete cleaning/removal.

Flow Europe GmbH, Gewerbestr. 95, D-75015 Bretten, Germany

FLOWSERVE CORPORATION

222 W. Los Colinas Blvd., Irving, TX, 75039

Tel: (972) 443-6500   Fax: (972) 443-6858   www.flowserve.com

Mfr. chemicals equipment, pumps, valves, filters, fans and heat exchangers.

Drametallic Europe GmbH, Blumenstrasse 10, Post 201108, D-6072 Drieich 2, Germany

Flowserve GmbH, Rotenburgerstrasse 21, D-27389 Fintel, Germany

FLUOR CORPORATION

One Enterprise Drive, Aliso Viejo, CA, 92656-2606

Tel: (949) 349-2000 Fax: (949) 349-5271 www.flour.com

Engineering and construction services.

Fluor Daniel GmbH, Buero Leipzig, Ellenburger Strasse 15a, D-7050 Leipzig, Germany

FM GLOBAL INC.

1301 Atwood Avenue, Johnston, RI, 02919

Tel: (401) 275-3000 Fax: (401) 275-3029 www.fmglobal.com

Engaged in commercial and industrial property insurance and risk management, specializing in engineering-driven property protection.

FM Germany, Eschersheimer Landstrasse 55, D-60322 Frankfurt am Main, Germany

FMC CORPORATION

1735 Market St., Philadelphia, PA, 19103

Tel: (215) 299-6000 Fax: (215) 299-6618 www.fmc.com

Mfr. specialty chemicals, including alginate, carrageenan and microcrystalline cellulose.

FMC GmbH, Hoheluftchausee 153, Nordestedt Hamburg, Germany

Tel: 49-40-534-33415

FMR (FIDELITY INVESTMENTS)

82 Devonshire Street, Boston, MA, 02109

Tel: (617) 563-7000 Fax: (617) 476-6105 www.fidelity.com

Diversified financial services company offering investment management, retirement, brokerage, and shareholder services directly to individuals and institutions and through financial intermediaries.

Fidelity International Ltd., Frankfort, Germany

FOOT LOCKER INC.

112 West 34th Street, New York, NY, 10020

Tel: (212) 720-3700 Fax: (212) 553-2042 www.venatorgroup.com

Mfr./sales shoes and sneakers.

Foot Locker International, Wilhelm Leuscnerstrasse 1, D-67547 Worms, Germany

Tel: 49-6241-23391

Foot Locker International, Hauptstrasse 63, D-69117 Heidelberg, Germany

Tel: 49-6221-21344

Foot Locker International, Q 1-3, D-68161 Mannheim, Germany

Tel: 49-621-14334

Foot Locker International, Kaiserstrasse 1-3, D-97070 Wurzburg, Germany

Tel: 49-931-17077

Foot Locker International, Spitalstrasse, 18-20, D-97421 Schweinfurt, Germany

Tel: 49-9721-24681

Foot Locker International, Ludwigstrasse 20, D-64283 Darmstadt, Germany

Tel: 49-6151-28862

FORD MOTOR COMPANY

One American Road, Dearborn, MI, 48126

Tel: (313) 322-3000 Fax: (313) 322-9600 www.ford.com

Mfr./sales motor vehicles.

Ford-Werke AG, Werke Koeln-Niehl, Henry Ford Str., Postfach 604002, D-5000 Cologne 60, Germany

FORMICA CORPORATION

10155 Reading Road, Cincinnati, OH, 45241-4805

Tel: (513) 786-3400 Fax: (513) 786-3082 www.formica.com

Mfr. decorative laminate, adhesives and solvents.

Formica Vertriebs GmbH, Belgische Allee 9, D-53842 Troisdorf, Germany

FORRESTER RESEARCH, INC.

400 Technology Square, Cambridge, MA, 02139

Tel: (617) 497-7090   Fax: (617) 868-0577   www.forrester.com

Provides clients an analysis of the effect of changing technologies on their operations.

Forrester Research GmbH, Hanauer Landstraße 135-137, D-60314 Frankfurt am Main, Germany

Tel: 49-69-4308910   Fax: 49-69-43089110

FORTEL INC.

46832 Lakeview Blvd., Fremont, CA, 94538-6543

Tel: (510) 440-9600   Fax: (510) 440-9696   www.fortel.com

Mfr. e-business corporate software.

FORTEL GmbH, Norsk-Data-Str. 1, D-61352 Bad Homburg, Germany

Tel: 49-6172-483250   Fax: 49-6172-483252

FOSSIL, INC.

2280 N. Greenville Avenue, Richardson, TX, 75082

Tel: (972) 234-2525   Fax: (972) 234-4669   www.fossil.com

Mfr. fashion watches

Fossil GmbH, Innerlohener Str. 10-12, D-83355 Erlstatt, Germany

FOSTER WHEELER LTD.

Perryville Corporate Park, Clinton, NJ, 08809-4000

Tel: (908) 730-4000   Fax: (908) 730-4100   www.fwc.com

Manufacturing, engineering and construction.

Foster Wheeler Energi GmbH, Hohenstaufenstrasse 4, D-40547 Düsseldorf, Germany

Tel: 49-211-559-0551   Fax: 49-211-559-0553

FRANKLIN ELECTRIC COMPANY, INC.

400 East Spring Street, Bluffton, IN, 46714-3798

Tel: (219) 824-2900   Fax: (219) 824-2909   www.fele.com

Mfr./distribute electric motors, submersible motors and controls.

Franklin Electric Europa GmbH, Rudolf-Diesel-Straße 20, D-54516 Wittlich, Germany

Tel: 49-6571-105-0   Fax: 49-6571-105-520

THE FRANKLIN MINT

US Route 1, Media, PA, 19091-0001

Tel: (610) 459-6000   Fax: (610) 459-6880   www.franklinmint.com

Design/marketing collectibles and luxury items.

Franklin Mint GmbH, Im Taubental 5, D-41468 Neuss bei Düsseldorf, Germany

FRANKLIN RESOURCES, INC.

1 Franklin Pkwy., Bldg. 970, 1st Fl., San Mateo, CA, 94404

Tel: (415) 312-2000   Fax: (415) 312-5606   www.frk.com

Global and domestic investment advisory and portfolio management.

Templeton Global Strategic Services (Deutschland) GmbH, Taunusanlage 11, D-60329 Frankfurt, Germany

Tel: 49-1-80-232-4632   Fax: 49-69-272-23120

FRITZ COMPANIES, INC., DIV. UPS

706 Mission Street, Ste. 900, San Francisco, CA, 94103

Tel: (415) 904-8360   Fax: (415) 904-8661   www.fritz.com

Integrated transportation, sourcing, distribution and customs brokerage services.

Fritz Companies Inc., Berlin, Germany

FRONTRANGE SOLUTIONS INC.

1125 Kelly Johnson Blvd., Colorado Springs, CO, 80820

Tel: (719) 531-5007   Fax: (719) 536-0620   www.frontrange.com

Mfr. customer support software.

FrontRange Solutions Deutschland GmbH, Einsteinstrasse 14, D-85716 Unterschleissheim, Germany

FROST & SULLIVAN, INC.

7550 West Interstate 10, Ste. 910, San Antonio, TX, 78229

Tel: (210) 348-1000   Fax: (210) 348-1003   www.frost.com

Engaged in international marketing consulting and training.

Frost & Sullivan, Klemmensstrausse 9, D-60487 Frankfurt, Germany

FSI INTERNATIONAL INC.

3455 Lyman Boulevard, Chaska, MN, 55318-3052

Tel: (952) 448-5440   Fax: (952) 448-2825   www.fsi-intl.com

Manufacturing equipment for computer silicon wafers.

Metron Technology GmbH, PO Box 1156, D-85622 München, Germany

Tel: 49-89-90-4740

FULBRIGHT & JAWORSKI LLP

1301 McKinney Street, Ste. 5100, Houston, TX, 77010

Tel: (713) 651-5151   Fax: (713) 651-5246   www.fulbright.com

Engaged in international law.

Fulbright & Jaworski, Prinzregentenstr. 50, D-80538 München, Germany

H.B. FULLER COMPANY

1200 Willow Lake Blvd., Vadnais Heights, MN, 55110

Tel: (651) 236-5900   Fax: (651) 236-5898   www.hbfuller.com

Mfr./distributor adhesives, sealants, coatings, paints, waxes, sanitation chemicals.

H.B. Fuller Europe - Group Office, Salzbrücker Strasse 1-4, D-21335 Lüeneburg, Germany

Tel: 49-4131-705296   Fax: 49-4131-705299

H.B. Fuller GmbH, An der Roten Bleiche 2-3, D-21335 Lüeneburg, Germany

Tel: 49-4131-705360   Fax: 49-4131-705227

H.B. Fuller, GmbH, Postfach 83 04 52, D-81704 München, Germany

THE GAP

2 Folsom St., San Francisco, CA, 94105

Tel: (650) 952-4400   Fax: (650) 952-5884   www.gap.com

Clothing store chain.

The Gap, München, Germany

GARDNER-DENVER INC.

1800 Gardner Expressway, Quincy, IL, 62301

Tel: (217) 222-5400   Fax: (217) 228-8247   www.gardnerdenver.com

Mfr. portable air compressors and related drilling accessories.

Gardner Denver Wittig GmbH, Johann-Sutter-Straße 6+8, D-79650 Schopfheim, Germany

Tel: 49-7622-394-0

GARLOCK SEALING TECHNOLOGIES

1666 Division Street, Palmyra, NY, 14522

Tel: (315) 597-4811   Fax: (315) 597-3216   www.garlock-inc.com

Mfr. of gaskets, packing, seals and expansion joints.

Garlock GmbH, Falkenweg 1, D-41468 Neuss, Germany

Tel: 49-2131-3490 Fax: 49-2131-349-222   Contact: Harold Poppke, Mng. Dir.

Garlock Sealing Technologies, Hans-Boeckler-Straße 32, D-64521 Gross-Gerau, Germany

THE GATES RUBBER COMPANY

990 S. Broadway, PO Box 5887, Denver, CO, 80217-5887

Tel: (303) 744-1911   Fax: (303) 744-4000   www.gatesrubber.com

Mfr. automotive and industrial belts and hoses.

Gates GmbH, Postfach 1428, D-52015 Aachen 1, Germany

GATEWAY INC.

4545 Towne Centre Ct., San Diego, CA, 92121

Tel: (858) 799-3401   Fax: (858) 779-3459   www.gateway.com

Computers manufacture, sales and services.

Gateway Deutschland GmbH, Hoechstrasse 94, D-65835 Leiderbach, Germany

GATX CORPORATION

500 West Monroe Street, Chicago, IL, 60661

Tel: (312) 621-6200   Fax: (312) 621-6648   www.gatxcapital.com

Lease and loan financing, residual guarantees.

GATX Financial Services GmbH, Mainzer Landstrasse 49, D-60329 Frankfurt, Germany

Tel: 49-69-238-5210   Contact: Michael Stahl, VP

GE BETZ, DIV. GE SPECIALTY MATERIALS

4636 Somerton Road, PO Box 3002, Trevose, PA, 19053-6783

Tel: (215) 355-3300   Fax: (215) 953-5524   www.gebetz.com

Engaged in engineered chemical treatment of water and process systems in industrial, commercial and institutional facilities

GE Betz, Div. GE Specialty Materials, Siemensring 44, D-47877 Willich 1, Germany

GEN RE INTERMEDIARIES CORPORATION

PO Box 10216, Stamford, CT, 06904-2216

Tel: (203) 357-8883   Fax: (203) 328-6408   www.genre.com

Provides reinsurance services worldwide.

Die Kölnische Rück., Postfach 10 22 44, D-50462 Köln, Germany

Tel: 49-221-97380   Fax: 49-221-9738494   Contact: Dr. Peter Lütke-Bornefeld, Mng. Dir.

General Re Europe Ltd. - Cologne, Niederlassung Deutschland, 5th Fl. Sedanstrasse 8, D-50668 Cologne, Germany

Tel: 49-221-9738-160   Fax: 49-221-9738-1619   Contact: Andreas Kessler, VP

HartRe Company, Mauerkircherstrasse 8, D-81679 München, Germany

Tel: 49-89-998-4030   Fax: 49-89-998-4033   Contact: Chris Genillard, Gen. Mgr.

GENCORP INC.

Hwy. 50 and Aerojet Rd., Ranchero Cordova, CA, 95853

Tel: (916) 355-4000   Fax: (916) 355-2459   www.gencorp.com

Mfr. aerospace, defense and automotive products.

GenCorp Henniges, Am Buchholz 4, D-31547 Rehburg Loccum, Germany

GENERAL BINDING CORPORATION

One GBC Plaza, Northbrook, IL, 60062

Tel: (847) 272-3700   Fax: (847) 272-1369   www.gbc.com

Engaged in the design, manufacture and distribution of branded office equipment, related supplies and thermal laminating films.

GBC Deutschland GmbH, Rather Str. 28, D-4000 Düsseldorf 30, Germany

GBC Deutschland GmbH, Uferweg 40-44, D-63571 Gelnhausen, Germany

GENERAL DYNAMICS CORPORATION

3190 Fairview Park Drive, Falls Church, VA, 22042-4523

Tel: (703) 876-3000   Fax: (703) 876-3125   www.gendyn.com

Mfr. aerospace equipment, submarines, strategic systems, armored vehicles, defense support systems.

General Dynamics Intl. Corp., Buerohaus Am Stadtpark, Koblenzer Str. 99, Bad Godesbert, D-53001 Bonn, Germany

GENERAL ELECTRIC CAPITAL CORPORATION

260 Long Ridge Road, Stamford, CT, 06927

Tel: (203) 357-4000   Fax: (203) 357-6489   www.gecapital.com

Financial, property, casualty insurance, computer sales and trailer leasing services.

ERC Group, Div. GE Capital, Maria-Theresia-StraBe 35, D-81675 München, Germany

Tel: 49-89-92280   Fax: 49-89-9228-395

ERC Group, Div. GE Capital, Sachsenring 83, D-50677 Köln, Germany

Tel: 49-241-93690   Fax: 49--241-9369-205

GENERAL ELECTRIC COMPANY

3135 Easton Turnpike, Fairfield, CT, 06431

Tel: (203) 373-2211   Fax: (203) 373-3131   www.ge.com

Diversified manufacturing, technology and services.

GE Capital Services GENSTAR container, Grosser Burstah 2000 11, Hamburg, Germany

Tel: 49-40-378-9030

GE FANUC Automation, Bernhauser Strasse 22, D-73765 Neuhausen A.D.F., Germany

Tel: 49-71-5818-7400   Fax: 49-71-5818-7400

General Electric Deutschland, Praunhimer Landdstrasse 50, D-60488 Frankfurt am Main, Germany

Tel: 49-69-9760-7348   Fax: 49-69-7682-091   Contact: Arno Bohn, Pres.

GEPC Germany, Buechekstrasse 63, D-53227 Bonn, Germany

Tel: 49-22-844-543   Fax: 49-22-844-5468

Nuovo Pignone, Rennbahnstrasse 72-74, D-60528 Frankfurt am Main, Germany

Tel: 49-6-9678-7021   Fax: 49-6-967-1988

GENERAL MOTORS ACCEPTANCE CORPORATION

3044 W. Grand Blvd., Detroit, MI, 48202

Tel: (313) 556-5000   Fax: (313) 556-5108   www.gmac.com

Automobile financing.

Opel Bank GmbH, Am Fernmeldeamt 15, Postfach 102817, D-4300 Essen, Germany

Opel Bank GmbH, Stahlstrasse 34, D-6090 Russelsheim, Germany

Opel Bank GmbH, Grosse Bleichen 21, Postfach 304050, D-2000 Hamburg, Germany

Opel Bank GmbH, Prielmayerstrasse 1, Postfach 201826, D-8000 Münich, Germany

Opel Bank GmbH, IHZ Friedrichstr., D-1086 Berlin, Germany

Opel Bank GmbH, Postfach 4666, Herschelstrasse 32, Hanover 1, Germany

Opel Bank GmbH, Postfach 103643, D-7000 Stuttgart 10, Germany

GENERAL MOTORS CORPORATION

300 Renaissance Center, Detroit, MI, 48285

Tel: (313) 556-5000   Fax: (313) 556-5108   www.gm.com

Mfr. full line vehicles, automotive electronics, commercial technologies, telecommunications, space, finance.

Adam Opel AG, D-6090 Russelsheim, Germany

Contact: Robert W. Hendry, Chmn.

Unicables SA, c/o Kabelwerke Reinshagen GmbH, Reinshagenstr. 1, D-5600 Wuppertal 21, Germany

GENICOM CORPORATION

4500 Daly Drive, Ste. 100, Chantilly, VA, 20151

Tel: (703) 633-8700   Fax: (703) 222-7629   www.genicom.com

Supplier of network systems, service and printer solutions.

CPG International GmbH, Robert-Bosch-Straße 26-28, D-63225 Langen, Germany

Contact: Dirk De Waegeneire

GENTNER COMMUNICATIONS, INC.

1825 Research Way, Salt Lake City, UT, 84119

Tel: (801) 975-7200   Fax: (801) 977-0087   www.gentner.com

Provides audio and video conferencing products and services.

Gentner, Div. Clearone Communications, Leonhardstr. 16-18, D-90443 Nuremberg, Germany

Tel: 49-911-955159-0   Fax: 49-911-955159-10

GENUITY, INC.

225 Presidential Way, Woburn, MA, 01801

Tel: (781) 865-2000   Fax: (781) 865-3936   www.genuity.com

R/D computer, communications, acoustics technologies and internetworking services.

Genuity GmbH, Gartenstrasse 27, D-61352 Bad Homburg, Germany

Tel: 49-6172-6726-00

GENZYME CORPORATION

1 Kendall Square, Cambridge, MA, 02139-1562

Tel: (617) 252-7500   Fax: (617) 252-7600   www.genzyme.com

Mfr. healthcare products for enzyme deficient diseases.

Genzyme GmbH, Lowenplatz 5, D-65428 Russelsheim, Germany

Tel: 49-6142-6909-0

GEO LOGISTICS CORPORATION

1521 E. Dyer Rd., Santa Ana, CA, 92705

Tel: (714) 513-3000   Fax: (714) 513-3120   www.geo-logistics.com

Engaged in freight forwarding, warehousing and distribution services, specializing in heavy cargo.

GeoLogisics GmbH, PO Box 12 07, D-88322 Aulendorf, Germany

Tel: 49-7525-9219-0   Fax: 49-7525-490

GeoLogisics GmbH, PO Box 13 05 50, D-40555 Dusseldorf, Germany

Tel: 49-211-9-9520   Fax: 49-211-995-2199

GEORGIA-PACIFIC GROUP

133 Peachtree Street NE, 41st Floor, Atlanta, GA, 30303

Tel: (404) 652-4000   Fax: (404) 230-7008   www.gp.com

Mfr. and distribution of tissue, pulp, paper and building products and related chemicals.

Ashland-Südchemie-Kernfest GmbH, Div. Georgia-Pacific Group, Dieselstrasse 35-41, D5603 Wülfrath, Germany

Tel: 49-2058-7850

GERBER SCIENTIFIC, INC.

83 Gerber Road West, South Windsor, CT, 06074

Tel: (860) 644-1551   Fax: (860) 644-5547   www.gerberscientific.com

Mfr. computer-based automated manufacturing and design systems for signs and graphics.

Gerber Technology, Stahlgruberring 23, D-81829 München, Germany

G-I HOLDINGS, INC.

1361 Alps Road, Wayne, NJ, 07470

Tel: (973) 628-3000   Fax: (973) 628-3326   www.gaf.com

Mfr. roofing and building materials.

G-I Holdings, Inc., Postfach 1380, D-5020 Frechen, Germany

GIBSON, DUNN & CRUTCHER LLP

333 S. Grand Ave., Los Angeles, CA, 90071

Tel: (213) 229-7000   Fax: (213) 229-7520   www.gibsondunn.com

Engaged in international law.

Gibson, Dunn & Crutcher GmbH, Widenmayerstrasse 10, D-80538 München, Germany

Tel: 49-89-189-33-0   Fax: 49-89-189-33-333   Contact: Christoph Hoebbel, Prtn.

GILEAD SCIENCES, INC.

333 Lakeside Dr, Foster City, CA, 94404

Tel: (650) 574-3000   Fax: (650) 578-9264   www.gilead.com

Engaged in healthcare research and development; biotech treatments for viruses.

NeXstar Pharmaceutals GmbH, Fraunhoferstrasse 22, D-82152 Martinsried/München, Germany

Tel: 49-89-899-8900   Fax: 49-89-899-89090

THE GILLETTE COMPANY

Prudential Tower Building, Boston, MA, 02199

Tel: (617) 421-7000   Fax: (617) 421-7123   www.gillette.com

Develop/mfr. personal care/use products: blades and razors, toiletries, cosmetics, stationery.

Braun AB, Kronberg/Ts., Germany

Braun de Mexico GmbH, Kronberg/Ts., Germany

Braun do Brasil GmbH, Kronberg/Ts., Germany

Consul GmbH, Kronberg/Ts., Germany

Contact: Norbert Koll, Gen. Mgr.

Gillette, Business Unit Oral B, Frankfurter Strasse 145, D-61476 Kronberg, Germany
Contact: Norbert Koll, Gen. Mgr.
Gillette Beteiligungs GmbH, Berlin, Germany
Contact: Norbert Koll, Gen. Mgr.
Gillette Continental Trading GmbH, Florsheim, Germany
Contact: Norbert Koll, Gen. Mgr.
Gillette Deutschland GmbH & Co., Berlin, Germany
Contact: Norbert Koll, Gen. Mgr.
Gillette Verwaltungs GmbH, Berlin, Germany
Contact: Norbert Koll, Gen. Mgr.
Helit Innovative Buroproduckte GmbH, Kierspe, Germany
Contact: Norbert Koll, Gen. Mgr.
Oral-B Laboratories GmbH, Frankfurt/Main, Germany
Contact: Norbert Koll, Gen. Mgr.
WEBA Betriebsrenten-Verwaltungs GmbH, Kronberg/Taunus, Germany
Contact: Norbert Koll, Gen. Mgr.

GILSON INC.
3000 W. Beltline Hwy, PO Box 620027, Middleton, WI, 53562-0027
Tel: (608) 836-1551   Fax: (608) 831-4451   www.gilson.com
Mfr. analytical/biomedical instruments.

Abimed Analysen-Technik Gmbh, Otto-Hahn-Strasse 17, D-65520 Bad Camberg, Germany

GIW INDUSTRIES, INC.
5000 Wrightsboro Rd., Grovetown, GA, 30813
Tel: (706) 863-1011   Fax: (706) 860-5897   www.giwindustries.com
Mfr. slurry pumps.

KSB Service GmbH, Leunawerk II Bau 3024, D-06236 Leuna, Germany

P.H. GLATFELTER COMPANY
96 South George St., Ste. 500, York, PA, 17401
Tel: (717) 225-4711   Fax: (717) 225-6834   www.glatfelter.com
Mfr. engineered and specialty printing papers.

Papierfabrik Schoeller & Hoesch GmbH, Münich, Germany

GLEASON CORPORATION
1000 University Ave., Rochester, NY, 14692
Tel: (716) 473-1000   Fax: (716) 461-4348   www.gleasoncorp.com
Mfr. gear making machine tools; tooling and services.

Gleason-Hurth, Maschinen und Werkzeuge GmbH, Moosacher Str. 36, D-80809 Münich, Germany
Tel: 49-89-354010   Fax: 49-89-35401-643
Gleason-Pfauter
Maschinenfabrik GmbH, Daimlerstr 14, D-71634 Ludwigsburg, Germany
Gleason-Pfauter/Maschinenfabrik GmbH, Daimlerstrasse 14, D-71636 Luwigsburg, Germany
Tel: 49-7141-4040 Fax: 49-7141-404500

GLOBAL SILVERHAWK INTERNATIONAL MOVING
1000 Burnett Avenue, Concord, CA, 94520
Tel: (510) 609-7080   Fax: (510) 609-7081   www.globalsilverhawk.com
International moving and forwarding.

Global Silverhawk, Opelstrasse 30, D-6082 Moerfelden, Germany
Tel: 49-6105-92520   Contact: William Gibbon, Gen. Mgr.
Global Silverhawk, Auf Dem Dransdorferberg 64, D-53121 Bonn, Germany
Tel: 49-228-66-40-11   Contact: Jurgen Thielen, Gen. Mgr.

THE GOLDMAN SACHS GROUP

85 Broad Street, New York, NY, 10004

Tel: (212) 902-1000   Fax: (212) 902-3000   www.gs.com

Investment bankers; securities broker dealers.

Goldman Sachs Group, MesseTurm, Friedrich-Ebert-Anlage 49, D-60308 Frankfurt am Main, Germany

Tel: 49-69-7532-1000

GOODRICH CORPORATION

2730 West Tyvola Road, Charlotte, NC, 28217-4578

Tel: (704) 423-7000   Fax: (704) 423-7100   www.bfgoodrich.com

Engaged in aerospace and aeronautical systems and services, performance materials and engineered industrial products.

Goodrich Hella Aerospace Lighting Systems, Bertramstraße 8, D 59557 Lippstadt, Germany

Tel: 49-2941-7676 0

THE GOODYEAR TIRE & RUBBER COMPANY

1144 East Market Street, Akron, OH, 44316

Tel: (330) 796-2121   Fax: (330) 796-1817   www.goodyear.com

Mfr. tires, automotive belts and hose, conveyor belts, chemicals; oil pipeline transmission.

Deutsche Goodyear GmbH, Xantener Str. 105, Postfach 100508, D-5000 Cologne 60, Germany

Gummiwerke Fulda GmbH, Kuenzellerstr. 59/61, D-6400 Fulda, Germany

W. L. GORE & ASSOCIATES, INC.

555 Paper Mill Road, Newark, DE, 19711

Tel: (302) 738-4880   Fax: (302) 738-7710   www.gorefabrics.com

Mfr. electronic, industrial filtration, medical and fabric products.

W. L. Gore & Associates GmbH, Hermann-Oberth-Strasse 22, D-85640 Putzbrunn, Germany

Tel: 49-89-4612-0

GOSS INTERNATIONAL CORPORATION

700 Oakmont Lane, Westmont, IL, 60559-5546

Tel: (630) 850-5600   Fax: (630) 850-6310   www.gossgraphic.com

Engaged in the design and manufacture of advanced technology web offset press systems for the newspaper and commercial printing industries.

Goss Graphic Systems, Ottostrasse 25, Postfach 1207, D-63150 Heusenstamm, Germany

Tel: 49-6104-6994-0

W. R. GRACE & COMPANY

7500 Grace Drive, Columbia, MD, 21044

Tel: (410) 531-4000   Fax: (410) 531-4367   www.grace.com

Mfr. specialty chemicals and materials: packaging, health care, catalysts, construction, water treatment/process.

Grace GmbH, Erlengang 31, D-22844 Norderstedt, Germany

Tel: 49-40-526010   Fax: 49-40-52601-511

Grace GmbH, In der Hollerhecke 1, D-67547 Worms, Germany

Tel: 49-6241-4030   Fax: 49-6241-403211

GRACO INC.

88 - 11th Avenue NE, PO Box 1441, Minneapolis, MN, 55440-1441

Tel: (612) 623-6000   Fax: (612) 623-6777   www.graco.com

Mfr. systems and equipment to service fluid handling systems and automotive equipment.

Graco GmbH, Moselstrasse 19, D-41464 Neuss, Germany

GRANT THORNTON INTERNATIONAL

800 One Prudential Plaza, 130 E. Randolph Drive, Chicago, IL, 60601-6050

Tel: (312) 856-0001   Fax: (312) 616-7052   www.grantthornton.com

Accounting, audit, tax and management consulting services.

Grant Thornton GmbH, RitterstraBe 2a, Bechsteinhaus, D-10969 Berlin, Germany

Tel: 49-30-61-69-0412   Fax: 49-30-61-69-0499   Contact: Norbert Jost

Grant Thornton GmbH, Warburgstrasse 50, D-20354 Hamburg, Germany

Tel: 49-40-415-22280   Fax: 49-40-415-22111   Contact: Dr Wolfgang Wawrzinek

GREAT LAKES CHEMICAL CORPORATION

500 East 96th Street, Ste. 500, Indianapolis, IN, 46240

Tel: (317) 715-3000   Fax: (317) 715-3050   www.greatlakeschem.com

Mfr. innovative specialty chemical solutions, including flame retardants and other polymer additives, water treatment chemicals, performance and fine chemicals, fire extinguishers.

Great Lakes Chemical GmbH, Sattlerweg 8, D-51429 Bergisch Gladbach, Germany

Tel: 49-2204-9543-150

GREAT PLAINS SOFTWARE, INC.

1 Long Tree Road, Fargo, ND, 58104

Tel: (701) 281-6500   Fax: (701) 281-6868   www.greatplains.com

Mfr. supply chain management software.

Great Plains Software, Industriestraße 10, D-82256 Furstenfeldbruck, Germany

Tel: 49-8141-8887-0

GREENFIELD INDUSTRIES INC.

470 Old Evans Road, Evans, GA, 30809

Tel: (706) 863-7708   Fax: (706) 860-8559   www.gfi.com

Mfr. high-speed rotary cutting tools.

Kemmer Europe, Hartmetall Feinwerkzeuge, Hangendeinbacherstrasse 4, D-73527 Schwabisch Gmund, Germany

GREG MANNING AUCTIONS, INC.

775 Passaic Avenue, West Caldwell, NJ, 07006

Tel: (973) 882-0004   Fax: (973) 882-3499   www.gregmanning.com

Specialty auction house; dealing primarily in stamps.

GMAI Europe, Feldbergstrasse 57, D-61440 Oberursel, Germany

GREY GLOBAL GROUP

777 Third Ave., New York, NY, 10017

Tel: (212) 546-2000   Fax: (212) 546-1495   www.grey.com

International advertising agency.

Grey Europe, Schanzenstrasse 82, D-40549 Düsseldorf, Germany

Grey Gruppe Deutschland, Corneliusstrasse 168-24, D-40215 Düsseldorf, Germany

GRIFFITH LABORATORIES INC.

One Griffith Center, Alsip, IL, 60658

Tel: (708) 371-0900   Fax: (708) 597-3294   www.griffithlabs.com

Mfr. industrial food ingredients and equipment.

Griffith Labs Inc., Heidelberg, Germany

Tel: 49-6221-301-027   Fax: 49-6221-302-484

GRIFFON CORPORATION

100 Jericho Quadrangle, Jericho, NY, 11753

Tel: (516) 938-5544   Fax: (516) 938-5564   www.griffoncorp.com

Mfr. residential and industrial garage doors and related products and services for the home building and replacement markets.

Böhme Verpackungsfolien GmbH & Co, Dombühl, Germany

Contact: Ulrich W. Böhme

GROVE WORLDWIDE LLC

1565 Buchanon Trail East, Shady Grove, PA, 17256

Tel: (717) 597-8121   Fax: (717) 593-4062   www.groveworldwide.com

Mfr. cranes.

Grove GmbH, Helmholtzstrasse 12 Postfach 5026, D-40750 Langenfeld, Germany

GTSI CORP.

3901 Stonecroft Blvd., Chantilly, VA, 20151-1010

Tel: (703) 502-2000   Fax: (703) 222-5204   www.gtsi.com

Engaged in the sale and resale of computers and software to local governments.

GTSI Corp., Mallau Strasse 59, D-68219 Mannheim, Germany

Tel: 49-621-871-0681

GUIDANT CORPORATION

111 Monument Circle, 29th Fl., Indianapolis, IN, 46204

Tel: (317) 971-2000   Fax: (317) 971-2040   www.guidant.com

Mfr. cardiovascular therapeutic devices.

Guidant B.V. & Co. Medizintechnik KG, Wingertschecke 6, D-35392 Giessen, Germany

Tel: 49-641-922-210

GULTON GRAPHIC INSTRUMENTS, INC.

212 Durham Ave., Metuchen, NJ, 08840

Tel: (732) 548-6500   Fax: (732) 548-6781   www.gulton.com

Mfr. electronic instruments, controls and communications equipment.

Electro Voice Div., Unternehmenbereich der Gulton GmbH, Laerchenstr. 99, Postfach 831164, D-6230 Frankfurt/Main 80, Germany

GUPTA TECHNOLOGIES

975 Island Drive, Redwood Shores, CA, 94065

Tel: (650) 596-3400   Fax: (650) 596-4900   www.centurasoft.com

Mfr. software and database management tools

Gupta Technologies GmbH, Riesstrasse 15-17, D-80992 München, Germany

Tel: 49-89-7481210   Fax: 49-89-7851771

GUY CARPENTER & COMPANY, INC.

114 West 47th Street, New York, NY, 10036

Tel: (212) 323-1000   Fax: (212) 345-2494   www.guycarp.com

Engaged in global reinsurance and risk management.

Guy Carpenter & Company, GmbH, Brienner Strasse 14, D-80333 München, Germany

Tel: 49-89-26-6030   Fax: 49-89-286-6033   Contact: Klaus Riechmann

HAEMONETICS CORPORATION

400 Wood Road, Braintree, MA, 02184-9114

Tel: (781) 848-7100   Fax: (781) 848-5106   www.haemonetics.com

Mfr. automated blood processing systems and blood products.

Haemonetics Germany GmbH, Rohrauerstrasse 72, D-81477 München, Germany

Tel: 49-89-785-8070   Fax: 49-89-780-9779

HALLIBURTON COMPANY

500 North Akard Street, Ste. 3600, Dallas, TX, 75201-3391

Tel: (214) 978-2600   Fax: (214) 978-2685   www.halliburton.com

Engaged in diversified energy services, engineering and construction.

Halliburton GmbH, Postfach 1248, D-49361 Vechta, Germany

Tel: 49-4441-93930   Fax: 49-4441-939333

Halliburton GmbH, Postfach 3250, D-29227 Celle, Germany

Tel: 49-5141-9990   Fax: 49-5141-999390

HA-LO INDUSTRIES, INC.

5800 West Touhy Avenue, Niles, IL, 60714

Tel: (847) 600-3000   Fax: (847) 600-4000   www.halo.com

Engaged in distribution of brand-awareness, promotional products.

HA-LO GmbH, Spaldingstraße 74, D-20097 Hamburg, Germany

HAMILTON SUNSTRAND

One Hamilton Rd., Windsor Locks, CT, 06096-1010

Tel: (860) 654-6000   Fax: (860) 654-3469   www.hamiltonsunstrandcorp.com

Design/mfr. aerospace systems for commercial, regional, corporate and military aircraft.

Hamilton Sunstrand Corp., Frankfurt, Germany

HARLEY-DAVIDSON INTERNATIONAL

3700 West Juneau Ave., Milwaukee, WI, 53201

Tel: (414) 342-4680   Fax: (414) 343-4621   www.harleydavidson.com

Mfr. motorcycles, recreational and commercial vehicles, parts and accessories.

Harley-Davidson GmbH, 7 Industriestrasse, D-6096 Raunheim, Germany

HARMAN INTERNATIONAL INDUSTRIES, INC.

1101 Pennsylvania Ave. NW, Ste. 1010, Washington, DC, 20004

Tel: (202) 393-1101   Fax: (202) 393-3064   www.harman.com

Mfr. audio and video equipment, loudspeakers and sound reinforcement equipment.

Harman Deutschland GmbH, Hunderstrasse 1, D-7100 Heilbronn, Germany

HARRIS CALORIFIC COMPANY

2345 Murphy Boulevard, Gainesville, GA, 30501

Tel: (770) 536-8801   Fax: (770) 536-0544   www.harriscal.com

Mfr./sales of gas welding and cutting equipment.

Harris Calorific Deutschland GmbH, 586 Iserlohn, Masteweg 7, Germany

HARRIS CORPORATION

1025 West NASA Blvd., Melbourne, FL, 32919

Tel: (407) 727-9100   Fax: (407) 727-9344   www.harris.com

Mfr. communications and information-handling equipment, including copying and fax systems.

Harris Semiconductors, Richard-Reitzner-Allee 4, D-85540 Haar, Germany

Tel: 49-89-462-63-0   Fax: 49-89-462-63-133

Harris Semiconductors, Kolumbusstrasse 35/1, D-71063 Sindelfingen, Germany

Tel: 49-7031-8-69-40   Fax: 49-7031-87-38-49

HARSCO CORPORATION

PO Box 8888, 350 Poplar Church Rd., Camp Hill, PA, 17001-8888

Tel: (717) 763-7064   Fax: (717) 763-6424   www.harsco.com

Metal reclamation and mill services, infrastructure and construction and process industry products.

Taylor Wharton Harsco GmbH, Postfach 30 03005, D-4600 Dortmund 30, Germany

Taylor Wharton Harsco GmbH, Postfach 1470, D-25804 Husum, Germany

HARTFORD STEAM BOILER INSPECTION & INSURANCE CO.)

One State Street, PO Box 5024, Hartford, CT, 06102-5024

Tel: (860) 722-1866   Fax: (860) 722-5770   www.hsb.com

Provides specialty insurance products and inspection services.

Hartford Stream Boiler GmbH, Box 15 20, Frerener Str. 13, D-49785 Lingen Ems, Germany

Contact: Doris M. Gillert, Mng. Dir.

HARVARD BIOSCIENCE, INC.

84 October Hill Road, Holliston, MA, 01746-1371

Tel: (508) 893-8999   Fax: (508) 429-5732   www.harvardbioscience.com

Mfr. tools for drug development.

Hugo Sachs Elektronik, Harvard Apparatus GmbH, Gruenstrasse 1, D-79232 March - Hugstetten, Germany

HASBRO INDUSTRIES INC.

1027 Newport Ave., Pawtucket, RI, 02861

Tel: (401) 725-8697   Fax: (401) 727-5099   www.hasbro.com

Mfr. toy products, including games and puzzles, dolls and plush products.

Hasbro Deutschland GmbH, Max-Planck-Straße 10, D-63128 Dietzenbach, Germany

HAUPPAUGE DIGITAL, INC.

91 Cabot Court, Hauppauge, NY, 11788

Tel: (631) 434-1600   Fax: (631) 434-3198   www.hauppauge.com

Mfr. circuit boards.

Hauppauge Computer Works GmbH, Krefelder Str. 669, D-41066 Mönchengladbach, Germany

Tel: 49-02161-69488-0   Fax: 49-02161-69488-15

HAYES LEMMERZ INTERNATIONAL

15300 Centennial Dr., Northville, MI, 48167

Tel: (734) 737-5000   Fax: (734) 737-2003   www.hayes-lemmerz.com

Mfr. steel and aluminum car wheels.

Hayes Lemmerz System Service, Margot-Kalinke-Strasse 9, D-80939 Münich, Germany

Hayes Lemmerz System Service, Friedrich-List-Strasse 6, Ind. Area Hansalinie, D-28309 Bremen, Germany

Tel: 49-421-458-760

Hayes Lemmerz Werke GmbH, Postfach 11 20, D-53621 Konigswinter, Germany

HEIDRICK & STRUGGLES INTERNATIONAL, INC.

233 South Wacker Drive, Chicago, IL, 60606

Tel: (312) 496-1200   Fax: (312) 496-1290   www.heidrick.com

Executive search firm.

Heidrick & Struggles • Mülder & Partner, Airport Ctr. 1, Hugo-Eckerner-Ring, D-60549 Frankfurt, Germany

Tel: 49-69-69-70020   Fax: 49-69-69-700299

Heidrick & Struggles Mülder & Partner, Theresienstraße 29, D-01097 Dresden, Germany

HEIN-WERNER CORPORATION

2110 A Pewaukee Rd., PO Box 1606, Waukesha, WI, 53188

Tel: (262) 542-6611   Fax: (262) 542-7890   www.blackhawk-kj.com

Mfr. auto body repair equipment, engine rebuilding and brake repair equipment, hydraulic cylinders.

Blackhawk GmbH, Postfach 2064, Karlstrasse 1, D-7640 Kehl, Germany

H.J. HEINZ COMPANY

600 Grant Street, Pittsburgh, PA, 15219

Tel: (412) 456-5700   Fax: (412) 456-6128   www.heinz.com

Processed food products and nutritional services.

H.J. Heinz GmbH, Cologne, Germany

HELLER FINANCIAL INC.

500 West Monroe Street, Chicago, IL, 60661

Tel: (312) 441-7000   Fax: (312) 441-7367   www.hellerfin.com

Financial services.

Heller Bank A.G., Weberstraße 21, D-55130 Mainz, Germany

HENRY SCHEIN, INC.

135 Duryea Rd., Melville, NY, 11747

Tel: (516) 843-5500   Fax: (516) 843-5658   www.henryschein.com

Mfr. and supply dental equipment.

Henry Schein Dentina, Max-Stromeyer-Strasse 170, C-D, D-78467 Konstanz, Germany

Tel: 49-7531-992100

HERCULES INC.

Hercules Plaza, 1313 N. Market Street, Wilmington, DE, 19894-0001

Tel: (302) 594-5000   Fax: (302) 594-5400   www.herc.com

Mfr. specialty chemicals, plastics, film and fibers, coatings, resins and food ingredients.

Hercules Chemicals Ltd., Germany

Hercules GmbH, Curslacker Neur Diech 66, D-2050 Hamburg 80, Germany

Pomosin AG, Von-Herwath-Strasse, D-2443 Grossenbrode, Germany

HERMAN MILLER INC.

855 East Main, Zeeland, MI, 49464

Tel: (616) 654-3000   Fax: (616) 654-5385   www.hermanmiller.com

Mfr. office furnishings.

Herman Miller Deutschland, Kaiserswerther Str. 85, D-40878 Ratingen, Germany

HERSHEY FOODS CORPORATION

100 Crystal A Drive, Hershey, PA, 17033

Tel: (717) 534-6799   Fax: (717) 534-6760   www.hersheys.com

Mfr. chocolate, mints, gum, food and confectionery products.

Gubor Schokoladenfabrik GbmH, Neuenburger Strasse, D-79373 Mullheim Schwarzwald, Germany

HEWITT ASSOCIATES LLC

100 Half Day Road, Lincolnshire, IL, 60069

Tel: (847) 295-5000   Fax: (847) 295-7634   www.hewitt.com

Employee benefits consulting firm.

Hewitt Associates GmbH, Hagenauer Strasse 42, D-65203 Wiesbaden, Germany

Tel: 49-611-928830

HEWLETT-PACKARD COMPANY

3000 Hanover Street, Palo Alto, CA, 94304-1185

Tel: (650) 857-1501   Fax: (650) 857-5518   www.hp.com

Mfr. computing, communications and measurement products and services.

Hewlett-Packard GmbH, Herrenberger Strasse 140, D-71034 Boebligen, Germany

HILLENBRAND INDUSTRIES, INC.

700 State Route 46 East, Batesville, IN, 47006

Tel: (812) 934-7000   Fax: (812) 934-1963   www.hillenbrand.com

Holding company: mfr. hospital beds, incubators and caskets.

Hill-Rom GmbH, Kurhessen Strasse 11, D-64546 Morfelden, Germany

Tel: 49-6105-932-100   Fax: 49-6105-932-102

HILTON HOTELS CORPORATION

9336 Civic Center Drive, Beverly Hills, CA, 90210

Tel: (310) 278-4321   Fax: (310) 205-7880   www.hiltonhotels.com

International hotel chain: Hilton International, Vista Hotels and Hilton National Hotels.

Hilton International Hotels, Kaiserstrasse 47, D-60329 Frankfurt/Main, Germany

Hilton International Hotels, Georg Glock Strasse 20, D-40474 Düsseldorf, Germany

Munich City Hilton, Rosenheimer Strasse 15, D-81667 Münich, Germany

HOGAN & HARTSON LLP

555 13th Street NW, Washington, DC, 20004-1109

Tel: (202) 637-5600   Fax: (202) 637-5910   www.hhlaw.com

Engaged in international law.

Hogan & Hartson Raue LLP, Potsdamer Platz 1, D-10785 Berlin, Germany

HOLIDAY INN (BASS RESORTS) WORLDWIDE, INC.

3 Ravinia Drive, Ste. 2900, Atlanta, GA, 30346-2149

Tel: (770) 604-2000   Fax: (770) 604-5403   www.holidayinn.com

Hotels, restaurants and casinos.

Holiday Inn Munich, Schleissheimerstr. 188, D-8000 Münich 40, Germany

Holiday Inn Munich, Leapoldstr. 200, D-8000 Münich 40, Germany

Holiday Inn Stuttgart-Munchingen, Siemensstr 50, D-7015 Stuttgart/Munchingen, Germany

Holiday Inn Stuttgart-Sindelfingen, Schwertstr. 65, D-7032 Sindelfingen 3, Germany

Holiday Inn Trier, Zurmaienerstr. 164, D-5500 Trier, Germany

Holiday Inn Viernheim-Mannheim, Bgm Neffstr. 12, D-6806 Viemheim, Germany

Holiday Inn Wolfsburg, Rathausstr. 1, D-3180 Wolfsburg, Germany

HOLLINGSWORTH & VOSE COMPANY

112 Washington Street, East Walpole, MA, 02032

Tel: (508) 668-0295   Fax: (508) 668-3557   www.hollingsworth-vose.com

Mfr. technical and industrial papers and non-woven fabrics.

Hollingsworth & Vose (J.C. Binzer), D-35116 Hatzfeld, Germany

Tel: 49-646-7801-4205

Hollingsworth & Vose Europe NV, Norsk-Data Strasse 1, D-61352 Bad Homburg, Germany

HOLOPHANE CORPORATION

214 Oakwood Ave., Newark, OH, 43055

Tel: (740) 349-4130   Fax: (740) 349-4426   www.holophane.com

Mfr. and marketer of premium quality, highly engineered, lighting systems targeted to the industrial, commercial and outdoor markets.

Holophane, Hauptstrasse 66,, D-56858 Peterswald-Löffelscheid, Germany

Contact: Bernd Gutgesell

HONEYWELL INTERNATIONAL INC.

Honeywell Plaza, Minneapolis, MN, 55408

Tel: (612) 951-1000   Fax: (612) 951-8537   www.honeywell.com

Develop/mfr. controls for home and building, industry, space and aviation, burglar and fire alarm systems.

Honeywell AG, Kaiserleistrasse 39, D-63067 Offenbach, Germany

Tel: 49-69-806-40   Fax: 49-69-818620

HORWATH INTERNATIONAL ASSOCIATION

420 Lexington Avenue, Suite 526, New York, NY, 10170-0526

Tel: (212) 808-2000   Fax: (212) 808-2020   www.horwath.com

Public accountants and auditors.

AWT-Allgemeine, Wirtschattreuhand GmbH, Leonhard-Mall-Bogen, D-8000 Münich 70, Germany

Dr. Lipfert GmbH, Postfach 103023, Alexanderstr. 12, D-7000 Stuttgart 1, Germany

Dr. Lipfert GmbH, Berner Strasse 49, D-6000 Frankfurt/Main 56, Germany

Horwath & Gelbert GmbH, Berner Strasse 49, D-6000 Frankfurt/Main 56, Germany

RWT Reutlinger Wirtschaftsreuhand GmbH, Charlottenstrasse 45-51, D-72764 Reutlingen, Germany

Tel: 49-7121-489-226

HOUGHTON INTERNATIONAL INC.

PO Box 930, Madison & Van Buren Avenues, Valley Forge, PA, 19482-0930

Tel: (610) 666-4000   Fax: (610) 666-1376   www.houghtonintl.com

Mfr. specialty chemicals, hydraulic fluids and lubricants.

Houghton Deutschland GmbH, Robert-Koch-Str., 6 D-65479 Raunheim/Main, Germany

Tel: 49-61-42-9430

Houghton Durferrit GmbH Thermotechnik, PO Box 1853, D-63406 Hanau, Germany

Tel: 49-6181-59-426

Houghton Lubricor GmbH, Werkstrasse 26, D-52076 Aachen, Germany

Tel: 49-2408-1406-0

HOWMEDICA OSTEONICS, INC.

59 Route 17 South, Allendale, NJ, 07401

Tel: (201) 507-7300   Fax: (201) 935-4873   www.howmedica.com

Mfr. of maxillofacial products (orthopedic implants).

Howmedica Germany GmbH, Kiel, Germany

Tel: 49-4348-7020

Howmedica International Inc., Richard-Wagner-Str. 27, D-5000 Cologne 1, Germany

HQ GLOBAL WORKPLACES INC.

15305 Dallas Parkway, Ste. 1400, Addison, TX, 75001

Tel: (972) 361-8221   Fax: (972) 361-8221   www.hq.com

Provides office outsourcing, officing solutions, including internet access, telecommunications, meeting rooms, furnished offices and team rooms, state-of-the-art videoconferencing, and trained on-site administrative support teams -

HQ Global Workplaces, Arabellapark Center, Weltenburger Strasse 70, D-81677 Münich, Germany

Tel: 49-89-92-40-4290

HUNT CORPORATION

2005 Market Street, Philadelphia, PA, 19103

Tel: (215) 656-0300   Fax: (215) 656-3700   www.hunt-corp.com

Mfr. office, art and craft, and presentation products.

ADEMCO-Seal GmbH, Ulrichstrasse 15B, D-7014 Kornwestheim, Germany

HUNTSMAN CORPORATION

500 Huntsman Way, Salt Lake City, UT, 84108

Tel: (801) 532-5200   Fax: (801) 536-1581   www.huntsman.com

Mfr. and sales of specialty chemicals, industrial chemicals and petrochemicals.

Huntsman Polyurethanes GmbH, Land-Au 30, D-94454 Deggendorf, Germany

Tel: 49-991-27040   Contact: R. Oertel

Huntsman Tioxide Europe GmbH, Am Brüll 17, D-40878 Ratingen, Germany

HYATT CORPORATION

200 West Madison Street, Chicago, IL, 60606

Tel: (312) 750-1234   Fax: (312) 750-8578   www.hyatt.com

International hotel management.

Grand Hyatt Berlin Hotel, Marlene-Dietrich Platz 2, D-10785 Berlin, Germany

Tel: 49-30-2553-1234   Fax: 49-30-2553-1235

Hyatt Regency Cologne Hotel, Kennedy-Ufer 2A, D-50679 Cologne Deutz, Germany

Tel: 49-221-828-1234   Fax: 49-221-828-1370

Hyatt Regency Mainz Hotel, Malakoff-Terrasse 1, D-55116 Mainz, Germany

Tel: 49-6131-73-1234   Fax: 49-6131-73-1235

HYPERCOM CORPORATION

2851 West Kathleen Road, Phoenix, AZ, 85053

Tel: (602) 504-5000   Fax: (602) 504-4578   www.hypercom.com

Mfr. point-of-sale systems.

Hypercom GmbH, Am Holzweg, D-65830 Kriftel, Germany

Tel: 49-6192-4020   Contact: Martin Croot

HYPERION SOLUTIONS CORPORATION

1344 Crossman Avenue, Sunnyvale, CA, 94089

Tel: (408) 744-9500   Fax: (408) 744-0400   www.hyperion.com

Mfr. data analysis software tools.

Hauptniederlassung Frankfurt, Platz der Einheit 1, D-60327 Frankfurt/Main, Germany

Tel: 49-69-505050

Niederlassung Duesseldorf, Heinrich-Heine-Allee 53, D-40213 Düsseldorf, Germany

Niederlassung Germany, Muenchner Strasse 16, D-85774 Unterfoehring, Germany

Niederlassung Germany, Fritz-Elsas-Strasse 38, D-70174 Stuttgart, Germany

Niederlassung Germany, Zuerich Haus, Domstrasse 17, D-20095 Hamburg, Germany

i2 TECHNOLOGIES, INC.

11701 Luna Road, Dallas, TX, 75234

Tel: (214) 860-6106   Fax: (214) 860-6060   www.i2.com

Engaged in supply chain management; solutions to help companies collaborate on decision-making processes.

i2 Technologies Germany, Richard-Reitzner-Allee 8, D-85540 Haar by Münich, Germany

IBM CORPORATION

1133 Westchester Avenue, White Plains, NY, 10604

Tel: (914) 765-1900   Fax: (914) 765-7382   www.ibm.com

Information products, technology and services.

IBM Deutschland Direct GmbH, Am Fichtenberg 1, D-71083 Herrenberg, Germany

Tel: 49-7032-152720   Fax: 49-7032-153777

ICN PHARMACEUTICALS, INC.

3300 Hyland Ave., Costa Mesa, CA, 92626

Tel: (714) 545-0100   Fax: (714) 641-7268   www.icnpharm.com

Mfr. and distribution of pharmaceuticals.

ICN Biomedicals, Thüringer Straße 15, D-37269 Eschwege, Germany

Tel: 49-5651-921-0

ICORE INTERNATIONAL INC.

3780 Flightline Drive, Santa Rosa, CA, 95403-8227

Tel: (707) 535-2700   Fax: (707) 521-2524   www.icoreintl.com

Harness and conduit systems, battery connectors, etc.

Icore International GmbH, Höhestrasse 31-33, D-61348 Bad Homburg, Germany

Tel: 49-6172-67730

IDEXX LABORATORIES, INC.

1 IDEXX Dr., Westbrook, ME, 04092-2041

Tel: (207) 856-0300   Fax: (207) 856-0346   www.idexx.com

Mfr. and sales of veterinary products.

IDEXX GmbH, Ober-Saulheimer Strasse 23, D-55286 Worrstadt, Germany

Tel: 49-6732-94420

IDT CORPORATION

520 Broad Street, Newark, NJ, 07102

Tel: (973) 438-1000   Fax: (973) 438-4002   www.idt.net

Engaged in domestic and international long distance telecommunications.

IDT Germany GmbH, Gruneburgweg 12, D-60322 Frankfurt, Germany

Tel: 49-69-548-100

IGATE CORPORATION

680 Andersen Drive, Foster Plaza 10, Pittsburgh, PA, 15220

Tel: (412) 503-4450   Fax: (412) 503-4490   www.igatecorp.com

Provides IT services.

iGate, Mascot Systems Divison, Curiestrasse 2, D-70563 Stuttgart, Germany

Tel: 49-711-67400-312   Fax: 49-711-67400-200

iGate, Mascot Systems Divison, Fritz-Vomfelde-Str. 34, D-40547 Dusseldorf, Germany

Tel: 49-211-53883-200   Fax: 49-211-53883-238

IKON OFFICE SOLUTIONS

70 Valley Stream Parkway, Malvern, PA, 19355

Tel: (610) 296-8000   Fax: (610) 408-7022   www.ikon.com

Sales of office equipment, including fax machines, copiers and printers.

IKON Office Solutions, Berner Str. 34, D-60437 Frankfurt, Germany

Tel: 49-69-952010-0

IKON Office Solutions, Buttnerstr 13, D-30165 Hannover, Germany

Tel: 49-511-358840

IKON Office Solutions Holding GmbH, Julius-Vosseler-Str. 100-102, D-22527 Hamburg, Germany

Tel: 49-40-561-9900   Fax: 49-40-560-4998   Contact: John Murphy

IKOS SYSTEMS, INC.

79 Great Oaks Blvd., San Jose, CA, 95119

Tel: (408) 284-0400   Fax: (408) 284-0401   www.ikos.com

Mfr. hardware and software.

IKOS Systems GmbH, Ottobrunner Straße 37, D-82008 Unterhaching, Germany

ILLINOIS TOOL WORKS (ITW)

3600 West Lake Ave., Glenview, IL, 60025-5811

Tel: (847) 724-7500   Fax: (847) 657-4268   www.itw.com

Mfr. gears, tools, fasteners, sealants, plastic and metal components for industrial, medical, etc.

ITW-Ateco GmbH, Stormannstr. 43, Norderstedt, Germany

IMATION CORPORATION

One Imation Place, Oakdale, MN, 55128

Tel: (612) 704-4000   Fax: (612) 704-3444   www.imation.com

Dry laser-imaging film systems.

Imation GmbH, Hilden, Germany

Tel: 49-2103-9830

IMI NORGREN GROUP

5400 South Delaware Street, Littleton, CO, 80120-1663

Tel: (303) 794-2611   Fax: (303) 795-9487   www.usa.norgren.com

Mfr. pneumatic filters, regulators, lubricators, valves, automation systems, dryers, push-in fittings.

IMI Norgren GmbH, Postfach 11 20, Bruckstrasse 93, D-46519 Alpern/Niederrhein, Germany

Tel: 49-28-02-490   Fax: 49-28-02-49356

IMMUNOMEDICS, INC.

300 American Road, Morris Plains, NJ, 07950

Tel: (973) 605-8200   Fax: (973) 605-8282   www.immunomedics.com

Engaged in the development of cancer drug therapies.

Immunomedics Europe, Otto-Roehm-Str. 69, D-64293 Darmstadt, Germany

Tel: 49-6151-66-71566

IMPCO TECHNOLOGIES, INC.

16804 Gridley Place, Cerritos, CA, 90703

Tel: (562) 860-6666   Fax: (562) 809-1240   www.impco.ws

Mfr. fuel control processors.

IMPCO-BERU Technologies GmbH, Perchstätten 16, D-35428 Langgöns, Germany

Tel: 49-6403-911-330   Fax: 49-6403-911-335

IMS HEALTH INCORPORATED

1499 Post Rd., Fairfield, CT, 06430

Tel: (203) 222-4200   Fax: (203) 222-4276   www.imshealth.com

Provides sales management reports and prescription tracking reports for pharmaceutical and health-care companies.

IMS Health GmbH & Co., Hahnstrasse 30-32, D-60528 Frankfurt Main, Germany

Tel: 69-66-0401   Fax: 69-66-04299

INDEL-DAVIS INC.

4401 S. Jackson Ave., Tulsa, OK, 74107

Tel: (918) 587-2151   Fax: (918) 446-1583   www.indel-davis.com

Engaged in web and graphic design and manufacture of toners and inks and oil field and seismic supplies.

Indel-Davis GmbH, Karl Heinz Beckurts-Strasze, D-5170 Julich, Germany

Tel: 49-2461-690-751   Fax: 49-2461-690-759

INDUCTOTHERM INDUSTRIES

10 Indel Ave., PO Box 157, Rancocas, NJ, 08073-0157

Tel: (609) 267-9000   Fax: (609) 267-5705   www.inductotherm.com

Mfr. induction melting furnaces, induction power supplies, charging and preheating systems, automatic pouring systems and computer control systems.

AB Plan GmbH, Gewerbestrasse 4A, D-83404 Ainring, Germany

Tel: 49-8654-48880   Contact: Helmuth Ronig

Guardscan GmbH, Damm-Strasse 8, D-30982 Pattensen, Germany

INDUSTRIAL ACOUSTICS COMPANY

1160 Commerce Ave., Bronx, NY, 10462

Tel: (718) 931-8000   Fax: (718) 863-1138   www.industrialacoustics.com

Design/mfr. acoustic structures for sound conditioning and noise control.

Industrial Acoustics GmbH, Sohlweg 24, D-4055 Niederkruchten, Germany

INFICON HOLDING

Two Technology Place, Syracuse, NY, 13057

Tel: (315) 434-1100   Fax: (315) 437-3803   www.inficon.com

Provides instrumentation for monitoring, analysis, control, leak detection and plasma cleaning in the semiconductor, vacuum coatings, air conditioning and refrigeration markets.

Inficon GmbH, Bonner Strasse 498, D-50968 Cologne, Germany

Tel: 49-221-3474-2222

INFOGRAMES, INC.

417 Fifth Avenue, New York, NY, 10016

Tel: (212) 726-6500   Fax: (212) 679-3224   www.infogrames.com

Mfr. video games.

Infogrames Germany, Robert Bosch Strasse 18, D-63303 Dreieich Sprendlingen, Germany

INFONET SERVICES CORPORATION

2160 East Grand Ave., El Segundo, CA, 90245-1022

Tel: (310) 335-2600   Fax: (310) 335-4507   www.infonet.com

Provider of Internet services and electronic messaging services.

Infonet Network Services Deutschland GmbH, Lyonerstrase 14, D-60494 Frankfurt am Main, Germany

Tel: 49-69-665-220   Fax: 49-69-666-4566

INFORMATION BUILDERS INC.

Two Penn Plaza, New York, NY, 10121-2898

Tel: (212) 736-4433   Fax: (212) 967-6406   www.ibi.com

Design and manufacture enterprise reporting software.

Information Builders Deutschland GmbH, Leopoldstrasse 236-238, D-80807 Münich, Germany

INFORMATION RESOURCES, INC. (IRI)

150 N. Clinton St., Chicago, IL, 60661

Tel: (312) 726-1221   Fax: (312) 726-0360   www.infores.com

Provides bar code scanner services for retail sales organizations; processes, analyzes and sells data from the huge database created from these services.

GfK Panel Services, Nordwestring 101, Postfach 2854, D-90319 Nurenberg 90, Germany

Tel: 49-911-395-3202   Fax: 49-911-395-4013

INGERSOLL INTERNATIONAL INC.

707 Fulton Ave., Rockford, IL, 61103

Tel: (815) 987-6000   Fax: (815) 987-6725   www.ingersoll.com

Multinational supplier of special machine tools and services for the metalworking industries.

Ingersoll GmbH, Daimlerstraße 22, D-57299 Burbach, Germany

Tel: 49-2736-493-01   Fax: 49-2736-493-244

INGERSOLL-RAND COMPANY

200 Chestnut Ridge Road, Woodcliff Lake, NJ, 07675

Tel: (201) 573-0123   Fax: (201) 573-3172   www.irco.com

Leading innovation and solutions provider for the major global markets of Security and Safety, Climate Control, Industrial Solutions and Infrastructure.

G. Klemm Bohrtechnik GmbH, Wintersohler Str. 5, D-57489 Drolshagen-Wenkhausen, Germany

Ingersoll-Rand GmbH, Gwerbeallee 17, D-45478 Mulheim/Ruhr, Germany

Tel: 49-208-99940 Fax: 49-208-9994-486

Ingersoll-Rank Waterjet Cutting Systems, European HQ, Auf der Laukert II, D-61231 Bad Nauheim, Germany

Ingersol-Rand ABG, Kuhbruckenstrasse 18, Postfach 10133, D-31785 Hameln, Germany

Pleuger Worthington GmbH, Friedrich-Ebert Damm 105, D-2000 Hamburg 70, Germany

Torrington Nadellagher GmbH, Werkstrasse 5, Postfach 1263/1264, D-33788 Halle Westfalen, Germany

INGRAM MICRO INC.

1600 E. St. Andrew Place, Santa Ana, CA, 92799

Tel: (714) 566-1000   Fax: (714) 566-7940   www.ingrammicro.com

Engaged in wholesale distribution of microcomputer products.

Ingram Micro Inc., Münich, Germany

INKTOMI CORPORATION

4100 East Third Avenue, Foster City, CA, 94404

Tel: (650) 653-2800   Fax: (650) 653-2801   www.iktomi.com

Mfr. software to boost speeds of computer networks.

Inktomi Corporation, Platz der Einheit 1, D-60327 Frankfurt, Germany

Tel: 49-69-97503-119

Inktomi Corporation, Maximilianstr. 35a, D-80539 Münich, Germany

Tel: 49-89-24218-109

INSIGHTFUL CORPORATION

1700 Westlake Avenue North, Ste. 500, Seattle, WA, 98109-3044

Tel: (206) 283-8802   Fax: (206) 283-8691   www.insightful.com

Mfr. statistical analysis software.

Insightful Germany, Schillstrasse 10, D-10785 Berlin, Germany

INSTINET

875 Third Ave., New York, NY, 10022

Tel: (212) 310-9500   Fax: (212) 832-5183   www.instinet.com

Online investment brokerage.

Instinet, Germany

INSTRON CORPORATION

100 Royal Street, Canton, MA, 02021-1089

Tel: (781) 575-5000   Fax: (781) 575-5751   www.instron.com

Mfr., markets and services materials testing instruments, systems and accessories.

Instron Schenck Testing Systems GmbH, Landwehrstrasse 65, D-64293 Darmstadt, Germany

Tel: 49-6151-32-47-00

INTEGRATED DEVICE TECHNOLOGY, INC. (IDT)

2975 Stender Way, Santa Clara, CA, 95054

Tel: (408) 727-6116   Fax: (408) 492-8674   www.idt.com

Mfr. high-performance semiconductors and modules.

Integrated Device Technology (IDT), Kornblumenstrasse 6, D-74232 Abstadt-Happenbach, Germany

Tel: 49-7062-90620   Fax: 49-7062-96195

Integrated Device Technology (IDT), Max-Planck-Strasse 17, D-85716 Unterschleissheim, Germany

Tel: 49-89-374-48-100   Fax: 49-89-374-48-210

INTEGRATED SILICON SOLUTION, INC.

2231 Lawson Lane, Santa Clara, CA, 95054-3311

Tel: (408) 588-0800   Fax: (408) 588-0805   www.issiusa.com

Mfr. high-speed memory chips and SRAMs.

Integrated Silicon Solution, Inc., Planegg, Germany
Tel: 49-89-899-30193   Fax: 49-89-899-0399

INTEL CORPORATION

2200 Mission College Blvd., Santa Clara, CA, 95052-8119

Tel: (408) 765-8080   Fax: (408) 765-1739   www.intel.com

Mfr. semiconductor, microprocessor and micro-communications components and systems.

Intel Semiconductor GmbH, Seidl 27, D-82008 Münich, Germany
Tel: 49-89-99143-0

INTERACTIVE DATA CORPORATION

22 Crosby Drive, Bedford, MA, 01730

Tel: (781) 687-8500   Fax: (781) 687-8289   www.interactivedatacorp.com

Engaged in subscription services.

Financial Times, Stubbenhuk 3, Eingang Haus Nr. 5, 5. Stock, D-20459 Hamburg, Germany

INTER-CONTINENTAL HOTELS

3 Ravinia Drive, Suite 2900, Atlanta, GA, 30346-2149

Tel: (770) 604-2000   Fax: (770) 604-5403   www.interconti.com

Worldwide hotel and resort accommodations.

Forum Hotel Berlin, Alexanderplatz, D-10178 Berlin, Germany
Tel: 49-30-2389   Fax: 49-30-2389-4305

Hotel Inter-Continental Leipzig, Gerberstrasse 15, D-04105 Leipzig, Germany
Tel: 49-341-988-0   Fax: 49-341-988-1229

Inter-Continental Hotels, Moselstrasse 4, D-60329 Frankfurt am Main, Germany
Tel: 49-69-27-40140   Fax: 49-69-23-0255

INTERGRAPH CORPORATION

One Madison Industrial Park, Huntsville, AL, 35894-0001

Tel: (256) 730-2000   Fax: (256) 730-7898   www.intergraph.com

Develop/mfr. interactive computer graphic systems.

Intergraph (Deutschland) GmbH, Reuterstrasse 161, D-53113 Bonn, Germany
Tel: 49-228-9140956   Fax: 49-228-9140957

Intergraph (Deutschland) GmbH, Robert-Bosch-Strasse 5, Dreieich-Sprendlingen, D-63303 Frankfurt, Germany
Tel: 49-610-33770   Fax: 49-610-337-7100

Intergraph (Deutschland) GmbH, Münich, Germany
Tel: 49-40-278500   Fax: 49-40-273360

Intergraph (Deutschland) GmbH, Zettachring 4, Stuttgart, Germany
Tel: 49-7-117253500   Fax: 49-7-117288913

Intergraph (Deutschland) GmbH, Alt-Moabit 96b, D-10559 Berlin, Germany
Tel: 49-3-03999120   Fax: 49-3-03919427

Intergraph (Deutschland) GmbH, Paul-Thomas-Strasse 58, D-40599 Düsseldorf, Germany
Tel: 49-211-97460   Fax: 49-211-9746150

INTERMEC TECHNOLOGIES CORPORATION

6001 36th Avenue West, PO Box 4280, Everett, WA, 98203-9280

Tel: (425) 348-2600   Fax: (425) 355-9551   www.intermec.com

Mfr. and distributor automated data collection systems.

Intermec Technologies GmbH, Schiess-Strasse 44a, D-40549 Düsseldorf, Germany
Tel: 49-211-536010   Fax: 49-211-5360150

INTERNATIONAL COMPONENTS CORPORATION

420 N. May Street, Chicago, IL, 60622

Tel: (312) 829-2525   Fax: (312) 829-0213   www.icc-charge.com

Mfr. portable, rechargeable power, control and accessory products.

International Components GmbH (ICG), Kleinreuther Weg 120, D-90425 Nuremberg, Germany

INTERNATIONAL FLAVORS & FRAGRANCES INC.

521 West 57th Street, New York, NY, 10019-2960

Tel: (212) 765-5500   Fax: (212) 708-7132   www.iff.com

Design/mfr. flavors, fragrances and aroma chemicals.

International Flavors & Fragrances GmbH, Postfach 302789, D-2000 Hamburg 36, Germany
Tel: 49-40-355358-0   Fax: 49-40-355358-23

International Flavors & Fragrances GmbH, Emmerich/Rheim, Germany

INTERNATIONAL MANAGEMENT GROUP (IMG)

1360 East Ninth Street, Ste. 100, Cleveland, OH, 44114

Tel: (216) 522-1200   Fax: (216) 522-1145   www.imgworld.com

Manages athletes, sports academies and real estate facilities worldwide.

IMG GmbH, Magdalenenstrasse 7, D-20148 Hamburg, Germany
Tel: 49-4041-40040   Fax: 49-4041-400420

Nick Bollettieri Tennis Academy, Pachter Roland Mank, Am Golfplaz 1, Bad Saarow, Germany
Tel: 49-33631-63-700   Fax: 49-33631-63-710

Sporting Club Berlin, International Tennis Center, Am Golfplatz 1, Bad Saarow, D-155526 Berlin, Germany
Tel: 49-33-631-37000   Fax: 49-33-631-63710

Sportpark Buhl IMG, Hagenichstraße 10, D-77815 Buhl, Germany
Tel: 49-7223-940-8630   Fax: 49-7223-940-8613

INTERNATIONAL PAPER COMPANY

400 Atlantic Street, Stamford, CT, 06921

Tel: (203) 541-8000   Fax: (203) 358-6444   www.ipaper.com

Mfr./distributor container board, paper and wood products.

Anitec Image (Deutschland) GmbH, Bachemer Landstrasse 29, Postfach 40 01 51, D-5000 Cologne 40, Germany

Aussedat Rey Deutschland GmbH, Volmerswerther Strasse 20, D-4000 Düsseldorf 1, Germany

Bergvik Chemie GmbH, Bahrenfelder Str. 244, D-2000 Hamburg 50, Germany

Freundorfer GmbH, Steinerstrasse 11, Postfach 70 06 60, D-8000 Münich 70, Germany

Hammerhill Paper GmbH, Duisburger Landstrasse 25, D-4000 Düsseldorf 31, Germany

Ilford Photo GmbH, An der Gohrsmuhle, D-5060 Bergisch Gladbach 2, Germany

Joost & Preuss GbmH, Rodingsmarkt 14, D-2000 Hamburg 11, Germany

Zanders Feinpapiere AG, An der Gohrsmuhle, D-5060 Bergisch Gladbach 2, Germany

INTERNATIONAL RECTIFIER CORPORATION

233 Kansas Street, El Segundo, CA, 90245

Tel: (310) 322-3331   Fax: (310) 322-3332   www.irf.com

Mfr. power semiconductor components.

International Rectifier Corp., Saalburgstrasse 157, D-61350 Bad Homburg, Germany
Tel: 49-6172-96590   Fax: 49-6172-965933

INTERNATIONAL SPECIALTY PRODUCTS, INC.

1361 Alps Rd., Wayne, NJ, 07470

Tel: (973) 389-3083   Fax: (973) 628-4117   www.ispcorp.com

Mfr. specialty chemical products.

ISP Global Technologies Deutschland GmbH, Emil Hofman-Strasse 1 a, D-50996 Cologne-Rodenkirchen, Germany
Tel: 49-2236-96490   Fax: 49-2236-9649

INTERVOICE-BRITE INC.

17811 Waterview Pkwy., Dallas, TX, 75206

Tel: (972) 454-8000   Fax: (972) 454-8707   www.intervoice.com

Mfr. telecom network hardware and software systems.

InterVoice-Brite GmbH, Bleichstrasse 1-3, D-65183 Wiesbaden, Germany

Tel: 49-611-18444-0   Fax: 49-611-18444-44

INTERWOVEN, INC.

803 11th Avenue, Sunnyvale, CA, 94089

Tel: (408) 774-2000   Fax: (408) 774-2002   www.interwoven.com

Mfr. web content management software.

Interwoven Gmbh, Carl-Zeiss-Ring 19-19a, D-85737 Ismaning, Germany

INTRUSION, INC.

1101 East Arapaho Road, Richardson, TX, 75081

Tel: (972) 234-6400   Fax: (972) 234-1467   www.intrusion.com

Mfr. security software.

Intrusion.Com, GmbH, Erfurter Strasse 29, D-85386 Eching, Germany

INVACARE CORPORATION

One Invacare Way, Elyria, OH, 44036

Tel: (440) 329-6000   Fax: (440) 366-6568   www.invacare.com

Mfr. home medical equipment, wheelchairs, respiratory care products, home care aids.

Invacare Deutschland GmbH, Dehmer Strasse 66, D-32549 Bad Oeynhausen, Germany

Tel: 49-5731-7540   Fax: 49-5731-754-111

INVITROGEN CORPORATION

1600 Faraday Avenue, Carlsbad, CA, 92008

Tel: (760) 603-7200   Fax: (760) 602-6500   www.invitrogen.com

Mfr. products and kits for gene analysis.

Invitrogen GmbH, Technologiepark Karlsruhe, Emmy-Noether Strasse 10, D-76131 Karlsruhe, Germany

IOMEGA CORPORATION

4435 Eastgate Mall, 3rd Fl., San Diego, CA, 92121

Tel: (858) 795-7000   Fax: (858) 795-7001   www.iomega.com

Mfr. data storage products.

Iomega, Konigsallee 60/F, D-4000 Düsseldorf 1, Germany

IPSEN INDUSTRIES INC.

894 Ipsen Rd., Cherry Valley, IL, 61016

Tel: (815) 332-4941   Fax: (815) 332-7625   www.ipsen-intl.com

Heat treating equipment.

Ipsen International GmbH, Postfach 1447, D-47514 Kleve, Germany

Tel: 49-2821-804-0   Fax: 49-2821-804-324

IR FLUID PRODUCTS

PO Box 151, Bryan, OH, 43506

Tel: (419) 636-4242   Fax: (419) 633-1674   www.irco.com

Mfr. fluid control products, including pumps, valves, cylinders, logic controls and air line components.

IR Fluid Products, Kaiserswerther Str. 49-51, Postfach 1152, D-4030 Ratingen 1, Germany

IRIDIUM LLC

1600 Wilson Boulevard, Suite 1000, Washington, DC, 20009

Tel: (202) 408-3800   Fax: (202) 408-3801   www.iridium.com

Consortium of companies sharing the construction and implementation of a global satellite communications system.

Iridium Communications Germany GmbH (ICG), Iridium North Europe Reg. HQ, Jagerhofstrasse 19-20, D-40479 Düsseldorf, Germany

Tel: 49-211-4973-200   Fax: 49-211-4973-112   Contact: Thomas Loewenthal, Dir.

IRRIDELCO INTERNATIONAL CORPORATION

440 Sylvan Ave., Englewood Cliffs, NJ, 07632

Tel: (201) 569-3030   Fax: (201) 569-9237   www.irridelco.com

Mfr. and distributor of the most comprehensive lines of mechanical and micro irrigation; pumps and irrigation systems.

Irrigation & Industrial Development Corp. GmbH, Niddastr 42-44, D-6000 Frankfurt, Germany

ITT INDUSTRIES, INC.

4 West Red Oak Lane, White Plains, NY, 10604

Tel: (914) 641-2000   Fax: (914) 696-2950   www.ittind.com

Mfr. pumps, systems and services to move and control water/fluids and produces connectors, switches, keypads and cabling used in computing, telecommunications, aerospace and industrial applications, as well as network services.

ITT Industries- Fluid Handling Systems, Talhausstrasse 14, D-68766 Hockenheim, Germany

Tel: 49-6205-2008-512   Fax: 49-6205-2008-550

ITT Systems Intl. Corp., Bldg. 3113 Daenner Kaserne, Mannheimer Strasse, D-6750 Kaiserslautern, Germany

KONI Germany, Industriegebiet, D-56424 Ebernhahn, Germany

Tel: 49-2623-602-30   Fax: 49-2623-602-30

Richter Chemie-Technik, Otto-Schott Strasse 2, D-47906 Kempen, Germany

Tel: 49-2151-1460   Fax: 49-2152-146190

ITT-GOULDS PUMPS INC.

2881 East Bayard Street, Seneca Falls, NY, 13148

Tel: (315) 568-2811   Fax: (315) 568-7651   www.gouldspumps.com

Mfr. industrial and water systems pumps.

Vogel Ochsner Pumpen GmbH, Yorckstraße 24, D-40476 Düsseldorf, Germany

Tel: 49-211-480206   Fax: 49-211-480208

ITW DEVCON PLEXUS

30 Endicott Street, Danvers, MA, 01923

Tel: (978) 777-1100   Fax: (978) 774-0516   www.devcon-equip.com

Engaged in technology and products for OEM assembly, and maintenance/repair applications.

ITW Devcon GmbH, Siemansstr. 15, D-4030 Ratingen 4 Lantare, Germany

Tel: 49-431-718830

ITW RANSBURG FINISHING SYSTEMS

320 Phillips Ave., Toledo, OH, 43612

Tel: (419) 470-2000   Fax: (419) 470-2112   www.itwransburg.com

Engaged in the design, manufacture and marketing of liquid electrostatic paint application equipment.

ITW Oberflaechentechnik GmbH, Justus-Von-Liebigstr 31, D-6057 Dietzenbach 1, Germany

IXYS CORPORATION

3540 Bassett Street, Santa Clara, CA, 95054

Tel: (408) 982-0700   Fax: (408) 748-9788   www.ixys.com

Mfr. semiconductors and modules.

IXYS Semiconductor GmbH, Edisonstrasse 15, D-68623 Lampertheim, Germany

J. WALTER THOMPSON COMPANY

466 Lexington Ave., New York, NY, 10017

Tel: (212) 210-7000   Fax: (212) 210-6944   www.jwt.com

International advertising and marketing services.

DSB&K Frakfurt, Frankfurt, Germany

J. Walter Thompson Co., Frankfurt, Germany

JASON INCORPORATED

411 E. Wisconsin Ave., Ste 2100, Milwaukee, WI, 53202

Tel: (414) 277-9300   Fax: (414) 277-9445   www.jasoninc.com

Mfr. and sales auto trim and finishing products.

Suroflex GmbH, Eiserhammerstrass 9, D-92237 Sulzbach-Rosenburg, Germany

Tel: 49-9661-9040   Fax: 49-9661-9222

JDA SOFTWARE GROUP, INC.

14400 N. 87th St., Scottsdale, AZ, 85260-3649

Tel: (480) 308-3000   Fax: (480) 308-3001   www.jda.com

Developer of information management software for retail, merchandising, distribution and store management.

JDA Software GmbH, Garather Schlossallee 19, D-40595 Duesseldorf, Germany

Tel: 49-6966-554-266   Fax: 49-6966-554-100

JDS UNIPHASE CORPORATION

210 Baypoint Pkwy., San Jose, CA, 95134

Tel: (408) 434-1800   Fax: (408) 954-0760   www.jdsunph.com

Mfr. advanced fiber optic products for the cable television and telecommunications industries.

JDS Uniphase GmbH, Leipziger Strasse 4, D-85386 Eching, Germany

JDS Uniphase Photonics GmbH & Co. KG, Bruchsaler Strasse 22, Waghaeusel-Kirrlach, Germany

JEUNIQUE BEAUTY FOR ALL SEASONS, INC.

19501 E. Walnut Dr., City of Industry, CA, 91748

Tel: (909) 598-8598   Fax: (909) 594-8258   www.jeunique.com

Mfr. and direct sales of vitamins, food supplements, cosmetics and diet products.

Jeunique Beauty For All Seasons., Ginnheimer Strasse 24, D-65760 Eschborn, Germany

JLG INDUSTRIES INC.

One JLG Drive, McConnellsburg, PA, 17233-9533

Tel: (717) 485-5161   Fax: (717) 485-6417   www.jlg.com

Mfr. aerial work platforms and vertical personnel lifts.

JLG Deutschland GmbH, Max Planck Strasse 21, D-27721 Ritterhude/Ihlpohl Bei Bremen, Germany

Tel: 49-42-1693-5000   Fax: 49-42-1693-5035

JOHNS MANVILLE CORPORATION

717 17th Street, Denver, CO, 80202

Tel: (303) 978-2000   Fax: (303) 978-2318   www.jm.com

Mfr. fiberglass insulation, roofing products and systems, fiberglass material and reinforcements, filtration mats.

Johns Manville International, Postfach 1555, D-97865 Wertheim, Germany

JOHNSON & JOHNSON

One Johnson & Johnson Plaza, New Brunswick, NJ, 08933

Tel: (732) 524-0400   Fax: (732) 214-0334   www.jnj.com

Mfr./distributor/R&D pharmaceutical, health care and cosmetic products.

DePuy Orthopädie GmbH, Sulzbach, Germany

Ethicon GmbH/Ethicon Endo-Surgery (Europe) GmbH, Robert-Kochstr. 15, D-2000 Norderstedt, Germany

Janssen-Cilag GmbH, Rosellen, Germany

Johnson & Johnson GmbH, Postfach 103161, D-40022 Düsseldorf, Germany

Johnson & Johnson Medical GmbH, Postfach 1364, D-22803 Norderstedt, Germany

LifeScan GmbH, D-69141 Neckargemund, Germany

Ortho-Clinical Diagnostics GmbH, Postfach 1340, D-69141 Neckargemund, Germany

Penaten GmbH, Postfach 1680, D-53588 Bad Honnef, Germany

SC JOHNSON

1525 Howe St., Racine, WI, 53403

Tel: (262) 260-2000   Fax: (262) 260-2133   www.scjohnsonwax.com

Home, auto, commercial and personal care products and specialty chemicals.

SC Johnson, Postfach 1100, Solingen, D-5657 Haan Rhld, Germany

JOHNSON CONTROLS INC.

5757 N. Green Bay Ave., PO Box 591, Milwaukee, WI, 53201-0591

Tel: (414) 228-1200   Fax: (414) 228-2077   www.johnsoncontrols.com

Mfr. facility management and control systems and auto seating.

JCI Regelungstechnik GmbH, Industriesstrasse 20-30, Burcheid, Germany

Tel: 49-2174-65-110

JCI Regelungstechnik GmbH, Alderstrasse 1, D-45307 Essen, Germany

Tel: 49-201-55880   Fax: 49-201-5588280   Contact: Peter Pienker, Branch Mgr.

THE JOHNSON CORPORATION

805 Wood Street, Three Rivers, MI, 49093

Tel: (269) 278-1715   Fax: (269) 273-2230   www.joco.com

Mfr. rotary joints and siphon systems.

Johnson Deutschland GmbH, Carl-Leverkus-Strasse 10a, D-40764 Langenfeld, Germany

JOHNSON OUTDOORS, INC.

555 Main Street, Racine, WI, 53177

Tel: (262) 631-6600   Fax: (262) 631-6601   www.johnsonoutdoors.com

Mfr. diving, fishing, boating and camping sports equipment.

Jack Wolfskin, Ausrustung fur Draussen GmbH, Limburger Strasse 38-40, D-65510 Idstein/Ts., Germany

Tel: 49-6126-9540   Fax: 49-6126-954159

Scubapro Germany, Rheinvogtstrasse 17, D-79713 Bad Sackingen-Wallbach, Germany

Tel: 49-7761-92100   Fax: 49-7761-921030

JONES LANG LASALLE

153 East 53rd Street, New York, NY, 10022

Tel: (212) 812-5700   Fax: (212) 421-3544   www.am.joneslanglasalle.com

International marketing consultants, leasing agents and property management advisors.

Jones Lang Wootton, Germany

JONES, DAY, REAVIS & POGUE

North Point, 901 Lakeside Ave., Cleveland, OH, 44114

Tel: (216) 586-3939   Fax: (216) 579-0212   www.jonesday.com

International law firm.

Jones, Day, Reavis & Pogue, 20/F, Hochhaus am Park, Grüneburgweg 102, D-60323 Frankfurt am Main, Germany

Tel: 49-69-9726-3939   Fax: 49-69-9726-3993   Contact: Ansgar Rempp, Prtn.   Emp: 62

JPMORGAN PRIVATE BANK

345 Park Avenue, New York, NY, 10154-1002

Tel: (212) 483-2323   Fax: (212) 464-1120   www.jpmorgan.com

Engaged in private banking services.

JPMorgan Private Bank, Börsenstrasse 2-4, D-60313 Frankfurt am Main, Germany

JUKI UNION SPECIAL CORPORATION

8500 N.W. 17th St., Miami, FL, 33126

Tel: (305) 594-0059   Fax: (305) 594-0720   www.unionspecial.com

Mfr. sewing machines.

Union Special GmbH, Raiffeisenstrasse3, Po Box 1148, D-71696 Moglingen, Germany

Tel: 49-7141-2470   Fax: 49-7141-247-100   Contact: A. Briegel, Mng.

JUNIPER NETWORKS, INC.

1194 North Mathilda Ave., Sunnyvale, CA, 94089

Tel: (408) 745-2000   Fax: (408) 745-2100   www.juniper.net

Engaged in the design and sales of Internet Protocol routers for access networks.

Juniper Networks GmbH, Im Atricon, Lyoner Strasse 15, D-60528 Frankfurt, Germany

JUPITER MEDIA METRIX INC.

21 Astor Place, New York, NY, 10003

Tel: (212) 780-6060   Fax: (212) 780-6075   www.jmm.com

Engaged in research services to determine audience measurement.

Jupiter Media Metrix Inc., Pilotystrasse 4, D-80538 München, Germany

Tel: 49-89-23035-315

K-2, INC.

4900 South Eastern Ave., Los Angeles, CA, 90040

Tel: (323) 724-2800   Fax: (323) 724-8174   www.k2sports.com

Mfr. sporting goods, recreational and industrial products.

K2 Sport and Mode GmbH, Seeshaupter Strasse 60, D-8237 Penzberg, Germany

Tel: 49-8856-9010

KADANT INC.

One Acton Place, Ste. 202, Acton, MA, 01720-3951

Tel: (978) 776-2000   Fax: (978) 635-1593   www.kandant.com

Mfr. paper recycling equipment.

Kadant, Rheinstrasse 57, D-77694 Kehl, Germany

KATY INDUSTRIES INC.

6300 South Syracuse Way, Ste. 300, Englewood, CO, 80111

Tel: (303) 290-9300   Fax: (303) 290-9344   www.katyindustries.com

Mfr. electronic and maintenance equipment for industrial and consumer markets.

Schon & Cie AG, Im Gehornerwald 2, D-6780 Pirmasems 17, Germany

KAWNEER COMPANY, INC.

555 Guthridge Court, Norcross, GA, 30092

Tel: (770) 449-5555   Fax: (770) 734-1570   www.kawneer.com

Mfr. arch aluminum products for commercial construction.

Kawneer GmbH, Stenglingser Weg 65-78, D-41207 Mönchengladbach, Germany

A.T. KEARNEY INC.

5400 Legacy Dr., Plano, TX, 75201

Tel: (972) 604-4600   Fax: (972) 543-7680   www.atkearney.com

Management consultants and executive search.

A. T. Kearney GmbH, Maximilianstrasse 40, D-80539 Münich, Germany

Tel: 49-89-290-620

A. T. Kearney GmbH, Am Festungsgraben 1, D-10117 Berlin, Germany

Tel: 49-30-2202-260

A. T. Kearney GmbH, Am Hauptbahnhof 9, D-70173 Stuttgart, Germany

Tel: 49-711-132550

A. T. Kearney GmbH, Jan-Wellem-Platz 3, D-40212 Düsseldorf, Germany

Tel: 49-211-1377-0

A. T. Kearney GmbH, Charlottenstrasse 57, D-10117 Berlin, Germany

Tel: 49-30-202-260

KEITHLEY INSTRUMENTS INC.

28775 Aurora Road, Cleveland, OH, 44139

Tel: (440) 248-0400   Fax: (440) 248-6168   www.keithley.com

Mfr. electronic test/measure instruments, PC-based data acquisition hardware/software.

Keithley Instruments GmbH, Landsberger Str. 65, D-82110 Germering, Germany

KELLOGG BROWN & ROOT INC.

PO Box 4557, Houston, TX, 77210-4557

Tel: (713) 676-3011   Fax: (713) 676-8695   www.halliburton.com

Engaged in technology-based engineering and construction.

Kellogg Brown & Root/Philip Morris (JV), Haberstrasse 10, D-12057 Berlin, Germany

KELLOGG COMPANY

One Kellogg Square, PO Box 3599, Battle Creek, MI, 49016-3599

Tel: (616) 961-2000   Fax: (616) 961-2871   www.kelloggs.com

Mfr. ready-to-eat cereals and convenience foods.

Kellogg (Deutschland) GmbH, Auf der Muggenburg 30, Bremen, Germany, D-Bremen

KELLY SERVICES, INC.

999 W. Big Beaver Road, Troy, MI, 48084

Tel: (248) 362-4444   Fax: (248) 244-4154   www.kellyservices.com

Temporary help placement.

Kelly Services (Deutschland) GmbH, Ludwig-Erhard-Str. 37, D-20459 Hamburg, Germany

Tel: 49-40-31-77310   Fax: 49-40-317-3112

KENDA SYSTEMS INC.

One Stiles Road, Salem, NH, 03079

Tel: (603) 898-7884   Fax: (603) 898-3016   www.kenda.com

Computer programming services.

Kenda Systems GmbH, Am Seerten 24, D-40547 Düsseldorf, Germany

Tel: 49-211-596-789

THE KENDALL COMPANY TYCO HEALTHCARE

15 Hampshire Street, Mansfield, MA, 02048

Tel: (508) 261-8000   Fax: (508) 261-8542   www.kendallhq.com

Mfr. and markets a broad range of wound care, needles and syringes, electrodes, specialized paper, vascular therapy, urological care, incontinence care, and nursing care products.

CDK Holding Deutschland GmbH, Postfach 1217, D-93328 Neustadt/Donau, Germany

Tel: 49-951-60470   Fax: 49-951-68392

CDK Holding Deutschland GmbH, Postfach 1217, D-9333 Neustadt/Donau, Germany

Tel: 49-94-45-959-0   Fax: 49-94-45-959-155

OFA Bamberg, Postfach 1480, D-96005 Bamberg, Germany

Tel: 49-951-60470   Fax: 49-951-68392

KENNAMETAL INC.

1600 Technology Way, PO Box 231, Latrobe, PA, 15650

Tel: (724) 539-5000   Fax: (724) 539-4710   www.kennametal.com

Tools, hard carbide and tungsten alloys for metalworking industry.

Kennametal Hertel AG, Werkzeuge + Hartstoffe, Postfach 1751, D-90707 Fürth, Germany

Tel: 49-911-97350   Fax: 49-911-9735-388

Kennametal Hertel GmbH, Max Planck Str. 13, Postfach 1347, D-61364 Friedrichsdorf, Germany

Tel: 49-61-72-7370   Fax: 49-61-72-78490

KEPNER-TREGOE INC.

PO Box 704, Princeton, NJ, 08542-0740

Tel: (609) 921-2806   Fax: (609) 497-0130   www.kepner-tregoe.com

Management consulting; specializing in strategy formulation, problem solving, decision making, project management, and cost reduction.

Kepner-Tregoe GmbH, An der Alster 17, D-20099 Hamburg, Germany

Tel: 49-40-284075-0   Fax: 49-40-284075-28

KERR-McGEE CORPORATION

123 Robert S. Kerr Ave., Oklahoma City, OK, 73102

Tel: (405) 270-1313   Fax: (405) 270-3123   www.kerr-mcgee.com

Engaged in oil and gas exploration and manufacture of inorganic chemicals.

Kerr-McGee Pigments GmbH & Co. KG, Gebäude R 54, Rheinuferstrasse 7-9, D-47829 Krefeld, Germany

KI

1330 Bellevue Street, Green Bay, WI, 54302

Tel: (920) 468-8100   Fax: (920) 468-0280   www.ki.com

Mfr. ergonomic furniture for schools, businesses and health care organizations.

Krueger International GmbH, Wacker Fabrik, Ober-Ramstaedter-Strasse 96 H1, D-64367 Mühltal Darmstad, Germany

Contact: Matthias Jaenecke, Mng. Dir.

KIMBERLY-CLARK CORPORATION

351 Phelps Drive, Irving, TX, 75038

Tel: (972) 281-1200   Fax: (972) 281-1435   www.kimberly-clark.com

Mfr./sales/distribution of consumer tissue, household and personal care products.

Hakle-Kimberly, Carl-Spaeter-Strasse 17, D-56070 Koblenz-Rheinhafen, Germany

Tel: 49-261-9227-477

KINETIC CONCEPTS, INC.

8023 Vantage Drive, San Antonio, TX, 78230-4728

Tel: (210) 524-9000   Fax: (210) 255-4524   www.KCI1.com

Mfr. specialized medical beds.

KCI Medical GmbH, Am Klingenweg 10, D-65396 Wiesbaden, Germany

KINETICSYSTEMS CORPORATION

900 N. State Street, Lockport, IL, 60441

Tel: (815) 838-0005   Fax: (815) 838-4424   www.kscorp.com

Mfr. electronic data acquisition and process control systems.

KineticSystems Technical Support Center, Heinitzstrasse 49, D-58097 Hagen, Germany

Tel: 49-2331-870595

KINGSTON TECHNOLOGY COMPANY, INC.

17600 Newhope Street, Fountain Valley, CA, 92708

Tel: (714) 435-2600   Fax: (714) 435-2699   www.kingston.com

Mfr. memory modules.

Kingston Technology GmbH, Hoferstrasse 1, D-81737 Münich, Germany

KIRKWOOD INDUSTRIES INC.

4855 W. 130th Street, Cleveland, OH, 44135-5182

Tel: (216) 267-6200   Fax: (216) 362-3804   www.kirkwood-ind.com

Mfr. manufacture of commutators, slip rings, carbon brushes and Cortem springs for the automotive, power tool and floor care industries.

Kirkwood Industries GmbH, Kautt & Bux Werk Herrenberg, Schiessmauer 9, D-71083 Herrenberg, Germany

Kirkwood Industries GmbH, Hochgerichtstr. 37, D-72280 Dornstetten, Germany

KLA-TENCOR CORPORATION

160 Rio Robles, San Jose, CA, 95134

Tel: (408) 875-6000   Fax: (408) 875-3030   www.kia-tencor.ocm

Mfr. software and equipment.

KLA-Tencor, Junkersstrasse 3, D-82178 Puchheim, Germany

Tel: 49-89-8902-170   Fax: 49-89-8902-1799

KNIGHT INFRASTRUCTURE

549 West Randolph Street, Chicago, IL, 60661

Tel: (312) 577-3300   Fax: (312) 577-3526   www.knightinfrastructure.com

Engaged in architectural and engineering projects.

Knight Wendling Consulting Gmbh, Heinz-Schmöle-Strasse 12, D-40227 Dusseldorf, Germany

KNOLL, INC.

1235 Water Street, East Greenville, PA, 18041

Tel: (215) 679-7991   Fax: (215) 679-3904   www.knoll.com

Mfr. and sale of office furnishings.

Knoll International GmbH, Gottlieb-Dailer Strasse 35, D-71711 Murr, Germany

Tel: 49-71-442-01243

KOCH-GLITSCH, INC.

4111 E. 37th Street North, Wichita, KS, 67220

Tel: (316) 828-5110   Fax: (316) 828-5263   www.koch-glitsch.com

Engaged in mass transfer, mist elimination, and motionless mixer technology.

Koch-Glitsch GmbH, Dipl. - Ing. Hans Stratmann, Marienstrasse 3.D-59302 Oelde i, Westfalen, Germany

Koch-Glitsch GmbH, Grosser Stellweg 23, D-68519 Viernheim, Germany

KODAK POLYCHROME GRAPHICS

401 Merritt 7, Norwalk, CT, 06851

Tel: (203) 845-7000   Fax: (203) 845-7113   www.kodak.com

Metal offset plates, coating specialties, graphic arts films.

Kodak Polychrome GmbH, Seesenerstr. 11, D-3360 Osterrode, Germany

KOHN PEDERSEN FOX ASSOCIATES PC

111 West 57th Street, New York, NY, 10019

Tel: (212) 977-6500   Fax: (212) 956-2526   www.kpf.com

Engaged in architectural design and planning.

Kohn Pedersen Fox GmbH, Bulowstrasse 66, D-10783 Berlin, Germany

KORN/FERRY INTERNATIONAL

1800 Century Park East, Los Angeles, CA, 90067

Tel: (310) 843-4100   Fax: (310) 553-6452   www.kornferry.com

Engaged in executive search and management consulting.

Korn/Ferry International, Koenigsallee 64, D-40212 Düsseldorf, Germany

Tel: 49-211-55-8650   Fax: 49-211-55-86555

Korn/Ferry International GmbH, Lyoner Strasse 15, Atricom, D-60528 Frankfurt/Main, Germany

Tel: 49-69-669-0170   Fax: 49-69-669-01766

KPMG CONSULTING INC.

1676 International Dr., McLean, VA, 22102

Tel: (703) 747-3000   Fax: (703) 747-8500   www.kpmg.com

Accounting and audit, tax and management consulting services.

KPMG Deutsche Treuhand-Gesellschaft AG, HessbrDhlstrasse 21, D-70565 Stuttgart, Germany

KPMG Deutsche Treuhand-Gesellschaft AG, Bahnofstrasse 30-32, D-65185 Wiesbaden, Germany

KPMG Deutsche Treuhand-Gesellschaft AG, Spitalerhof, Kurze Mahren 1, D-20095 Hamburg, Germany

KPMG Deutsche Treuhand-Gesellschaft AG, Marie-Curie-Strasse 30, D-60439 Frankfurt Main, Germany

KPMG International, Barbarossplatz 1a, D-50674 Cologne, Germany

Tel: 49-221-207300   Fax: 49-221-207-3209   Contact: Axel Berger, Ptnr.

KPMG International, Olof-Palme-Strasse 31, National Office, D-60439 Frankfurt/Main, Germany

KPMG International, KurfDrstendamm 207-208, D-10719 Berlin, Germany

KPMG International, Elektrastrasse 6, D-81925 Münich, Germany

KPMG International, Am Bommeshof 35, D-40474 Düsseldorf, Germany

KROLL INC.

9023 Columbine Road, Eden Prairie, MN, 55347

Tel: (952) 937-1107   Fax: (952) 937-5815   www.knollworldwide.com

Mfr. of software and engaged in data recovery services.

Kroll Inc., Arndtstraße 11, D-60325 Frankfurt Main, Germany

KROLL ONTRACK, INC.

9023 Columbine Rd., Eden Prairie, MN, 55347

Tel: (612) 937-1107   Fax: (612) 937-5815   www.krollontrack.com

Computer data evidence services company, rescuing lost or corrupted data, and software sales.

Kroll Ontrack, Inc., Hanns-Klemm-Straße 5, D-71034 Böblingen, Germany

Tel: 49-7031-644-150   Fax: 49-7031-644-100

KULICKE & SOFFA INDUSTRIES INC.

2101 Blair Mill Road, Willow Grove, PA, 19090

Tel: (215) 784-6000   Fax: (215) 659-7588   www.kns.com

Semiconductor assembly systems and services.

K&S Test Products, Laerchenstrasse 4, D-92361 Berngau, Germany

Minitron Elektronik GmbH, Ettinger Strasse 20, D-85057 Ingolstadt, Germany

Simac Masic Europe, Dientzenhofer Strasse 7, D-83098 Brannenburg, Germany

KURT SALMON ASSOCIATES (KSA)

1355 Peachtree Street NE, Atlanta, GA, 30309

Tel: (404) 892-0321   Fax: (404) 898-9590   www.kurtsalmon.com

Management consulting: consumer products, retailing.

Kurt Salmon Associates GmbH, Rheindorfer Weg 13, D-40591 Düsseldorf, Germany

THE L. S. STARRETT COMPANY

121 Crescent Street, Athol, MA, 01331

Tel: (978) 249-3551   Fax: (978) 249-8495   www.starrett.com

Mfr. measuring tools and precision instruments.

Starrett GmbH, Feldwies 12, D-61389 Schmitten Taunus, Germany

L-3 COMMUNICATIONS HOLDINGS, INC.

600 Third Avenue, New York, NY, 10016

Tel: (212) 697-1111   Fax: (212) 490-0731   www.L-3com.com

Design and manufacture of high-tech communications systems, including specialized flight recorders.

L-3 Communications ELAC Nautik GmbH, Virtrieb, Neufeld Straße, D-24118 Kiel, Germany

Tel: 49-431-883-0   Emp: 40

LA ROCHE INDUSTRIES INC.

1100 Johnson Ferry Road, NE, Atlanta, GA, 30342

Tel: (404) 851-0300   Fax: (404) 851-0421   www.larocheind.com

Mfr. and distribution of industrial ammonia and chlor-alkali chemicals.

LII Europe GmbH, Industriepark Höchst, Gebäude C 526, D-65926 Frankfurt am Main, Germany

Tel: 49-69-305-0   Contact: Dr. Marcell Peuckert   Emp: 360

LADAS & PARRY

26 West 61st Street, New York, NY, 10023

Tel: (212) 708-1800   Fax: (212) 246-8959   www.ladasparry.com

International law firm.

Ladas & Parry, Altheimer ECK 2, D-80331 Münich, Germany

Tel: 49-89-269077   Fax: 49-89-269040

LAM RESEARCH CORPORATION

4650 Cushing Pkwy., Fremont, CA, 94538

Tel: (510) 659-0200   Fax: (510) 572-6454   www.lamrc.com

Mfr. semiconductor processing equipment.

Lam Research GmbH, Oskar-Messter-Strasse 24, D-85737 Ismaning, Germany

Tel: 49-89-96099-0   Fax: 49-89-96099-227

LAMSON & SESSIONS COMPANY

25701 Science Park Drive, Cleveland, OH, 44122

Tel: (216) 464-3400   Fax: (216) 464-1455   www.lamson-sessions.com

Mfr. thermoplastic enclosures, fittings, conduit and pipe, and wiring devices for the electrical, telecommunications, consumer, power and waste water markets.

Lamson & Sessions GmbH, Postfach 5144, D-5970 Plettenberg 5, Germany

LANDIS GARDNER

20 East Sixth Street, Waynesboro, PA, 17268-2050

Tel: (717) 762-2161   Fax: (717) 765-5143   www.landisgardner.com

Engaged in the design and manufacture of precision cylindrical and centerless grinders, and single and double-disc grinding machines.

Honsberg Lamb GmbH, Walter-Freitag-Straße 35, D-42899 Remscheid-Lüttringhausen, Germany

Honsberg Lamb GmbH, Hastener Str. 22-26, D-42855 Remscheid, Germany

LANDOR ASSOCIATES

Klamath House, 1001 Front Street, San Francisco, CA, 94111-1424

Tel: (415) 955-1400   Fax: (415) 365-3190   www.landor.com

International marketing consulting firm, engaged in brand strategy, design, naming, digital branding, print literature design and research services.

Landor Associates, Pickhuben 6, Sandtorkaihof, D-20457 Hamburg, Germany

Tel: 49-40-378-5670   Fax: 49-40-378-56718   Contact: Ulf-Bruen Drechsel, Mng. Dir.

LANDS' END INC.

1 Lands' End Lane, Dodgeville, WI, 53595

Tel: (608) 935-9341   Fax: (608) 935-4260   www.landsend.com

Clothing, home furnishings and mail order catalog company.

Lands' End GmbH, In Der Langwiese, D-66693 Mettlach, Germany

Tel: 49-6864-971-0 Fax: 49-6864-921-111   Contact: Stephen Bechwar, Mng. Dir.   Emp: 100

LANIER WORLDWIDE, INC.

2300 Parklake Drive, N.E., Atlanta, GA, 30345

Tel: (770) 496-9500   Fax: (770) 938-1020   www.lanier.com

Specialize in digital copiers and multi-functional systems.

Lanier Deutschland GmbH, IM Taubental 6, D-41468 Neuss, Germany

Tel: 49-2131-387-0   Fax: 49-2131-387-203

Lanier Deutschland GmbH, Wendenstr. 309, D-20537 Hamburg, Germany

Tel: 49-40-251-527-20   Fax: 49-40-251-527-15

Lanier Deutschland GmbH, Pestalozzi Str. 5-8, D-1318 Berlin, Germany

Tel: 49-30-486-37-625   Fax: 49-30-486-37-627

Lanier Deutschland GmbH, Motorstrasse 4, D-70499 Stuttgart, Germany

Tel: 49-711-83098-31   Fax: 49-711-83098-20

LEACH HOLDING CORPORATION

315 Post Road West, Westport, CT, 06880-4739

Tel: (203) 226-6577   Fax: (203) 226-6577   www.leachintl.com

Mfr. and design electrical switching and control devices for the aerospace and rail industries.

J&M, Robert-Bosch-Straße 83, D-73431 Aalen, Germany

Leach International GmbH, Hoferstrasse 5, D-86720 Nordlingen, Germany

LRE Technologie Partner GmbH, Frankfurter Ring 15, D-80807 Münich, Germany

LRE Technologie Partner GmbH, Hofer Straße 5, D-86720 Nördlingen, Germany

LEAR CORPORATION

21557 Telegraph Road, Southfield, MI, 48086-5008

Tel: (248) 746-1500   Fax: (248) 746-1722   www.lear.com

Mfr. and distribute automotive materials and car seats.

Lear Corporation, Ebersburg, Germany

Lear Corporation (Keiper Car Seating Division), Bremen, Germany

Lear Corporation (Keiper Car Seating Division), Besigheim, Germany

Lear Corporation (Opel Division), Gustavsburg, Germany

Lear Corporation (Opel Division), Eisenbach, Germany

LECROY CORPORATION

700 Chestnut Ridge Road, Chestnut Ridge, NY, 10977

Tel: (845) 425-2000   Fax: (845) 425-8967   www.lecroy.com

Mfr. signal analyzers and electronic measurement systems.

LeCroy GmbH, Postfach 103767, D-69027 Heidelberg, Germany

Tel: 49-6221-82700

LEGATO SYSTEMS, INC.

2350 West El Camino Real, Mountain View, CA, 94040

Tel: (650) 210-7000   Fax: (650) 210-7032   www.legato.com

Mfr. storage management software.

Legato Systems Germany GmbH, Einsteinstrasse 12, D-85716 Unterschleissheim, Germany

Tel: 49-89-899-692-0

LEGGETT & PLATT, INC.

1 Leggett Road, Carthage, MO, 64836

Tel: (417) 358-8131   Fax: (417) 358-5840   www.leggett.com

Mfr. components for bedding and furniture.

Spühl AG, Div. Leggett & Platt, St.Gallen, Grüntalstrasse 23, D-9303 Wittenbach, Germany

LEHMAN BROTHERS HOLDINGS INC.

*101 Hudson Street, Jersey City, NJ, 07302

Tel: (201) 524-2000   Fax: (201) 524-2000   www.lehman.com

Financial services, securities and merchant banking services.

Lehman Brothers, Grueneburgweg #18, D-60322 Frankfurt, Germany

Tel: 49-69-153070

LEVI STRAUSS & COMPANY

1155 Battery St., San Francisco, CA, 94111-1230

Tel: (415) 544-6000   Fax: (415) 501-3939   www.levistrauss.com

Mfr. and distributor of casual wearing apparel, including jeans and sportswear.

Levi Strauss Germany GmbH, Levi Strauss Alee 18-20, D-63 150 Heusenstamm, Germany

Tel: 49-6104-6010   Fax: 49-6104-601350

LEVOLOR KIRSCH, DIV. LEVOLOR HARDWARE

4110 Premier Drive, High Point, NC, 27265

Tel: (336) 812-8181   Fax: (336) 659-5614   www.kirsch.com

Mfr. drapery hardware and accessories, wood shelving, woven wood shades, etc.

Sani-Kirsch Inc. & Co. KG, Bornbarch 8, D-22848 Norderstedt, Germany

LEXMARK INTERNATIONAL

740 W. New Circle Rd., Lexington, KY, 40550

Tel: (859) 232-2000   Fax: (859) 232-1886   www.lexmark.com

Develop, manufacture, supply of printing solutions and products, including laser, inkjet, and dot matrix printers.

Lexmark Deutschland, GmbH, Postfach 1560, D-63115 Dietzenbach, Germany

ELI LILLY & COMPANY

Lilly Corporate Center, Indianapolis, IN, 46285

Tel: (317) 276-2000   Fax: (317) 277-6579   www.lilly.com

Mfr. pharmaceuticals and animal health products.

Beiersdorf-Lilly GmbH, Wiesingerweg 25, D-20253 Hamburg, Germany

Lilly Deutschland GmbH, Saalburgstrasse 153, D-61350 Bad Homburg, Germany

Tel: 49-6172-2730   Fax: 49-6172-273-283

Lilly Deutschland GmbH, Teichweg 3, D-35396 Giessen, Germany

LINCOLN ELECTRIC HOLDINGS

22801 St. Clair Ave., Cleveland, OH, 44117-1199

Tel: (216) 481-8100   Fax: (216) 486-8385   www.lincolnelectric.com

Mfr. arc welding and welding related products, oxy-fuel and thermal cutting equipment and integral AC motors.

Lincoln Smitweld GmbH, Heinrich Hertz-Strasse 16, D-40699 Erkrath-Unterfeldhaus, Germany

Tel: 49-211-92-550   Fax: 49-211-92-55179   Contact: Knut Pink, Mng. Ptnr.

Uhrhan & Schwill GmbH, Max-Keith Strasse 39, D-45136 Essen, Germany

Tel: 49-201-259-61   Fax: 49-201-256-538   Contact: Heinrich Schwill, Mng. Dir.

LINCOLN INDUSTRIAL

1 Lincoln Way, St. Louis, MO, 63120

Tel: (314) 679-4200   Fax: (314) 424-5359   www.lincolnindustrial.com

Mfr. lubrication equipment and materials dispensing equipment.

Lincoln GmbH, Heinrich-Hertz Strasse 2-8, D-69190 Walldorf, Germany

Tel: 49-6227-33-0   Fax: 49-6227-33-259

LINEAR TECHNOLOGY CORPORATION

1630 McCarthy Blvd., Milpitas, CA, 95035

Tel: (408) 432-1900   Fax: (408) 434-6441   www.linear-tech.com

Mfr. linear integrated circuit chips.

Linear Technology GmbH, Oskar-Messter-Str. 24, D-85737 Ismaning, Germany

Tel: 49-89-9624550   Fax: 49-89-963147

LIONBRIDGE TECHNOLOGIES, INC.

950 Winter St., Waltham, MA, 02451

Tel: (781) 434-6000   Fax: (781) 434-6034   www.lionbridge.com

Provides solutions for worldwide deployment of technology and content.

Lionbridge Hamburg, Mexikoring 19, D-22297 Hamburg, Germany

LNP ENGINEERING PLASTICS

475 Creamery Way, Exton, PA, 19341

Tel: (610) 363-4500   Fax: (610) 363-4749   www.geplastics.com

Mfr. thermoplastic composites.

General Electric Plastics, Iron route 5, D-65428 Ruesselsheim, Germany

LOCKHEED MARTIN CORPORATION

6801 Rockledge Drive, Bethesda, MD, 20817

Tel: (301) 897-6000   Fax: (301) 897-6652   www.imco.com

Design/mfr./management systems in fields of space, defense, energy, electronics and technical services.

CalComp GmbH, Hermann-Klammt-Strase, Postfach 10 03 02, D-41403 Neuss, Germany

Contact: R. Winfried, VP

CalComp GmbH, Nilolaus-Otto-Strasse 29, D-7022 Leinfelden-Echterdingen, Germany

CalComp GmbH, Hansaallee, D-4000 Düsseldorf 1, Germany

CalComp GmbH, Elmshorner Strasse 7-11, D-2080 Pinneberg, Germany

CalComp GmbH, Max Planckstrasse 25, D-6072 Dreieich, Germany

Lockheed Martin GmbH, Arn Michaelshof 4/B, D-53177 Bonn, Germany

Tel: 49-228-1620   Fax: 49-228-957-1611   Contact: Manfred Wiese, Dir

Lockheed Martin Intl. GmbH, Turmstasse 10, D-53175 Bonn, Germany

Mountain Gate Data Systems GmbH, D-86633 Neuburg, Germany

LORAL SPACE & COMMUNICATIONS LTD.

600 Third Ave., New York, NY, 10016

Tel: (212) 697-1105   Fax: (212) 338-5662   www.loral.com

Marketing coordination: defense electronics, communications systems.

Loral CyberStar, Bruesseler Str. 7, D-30539 Hannover, Germany

Tel: 49-511-87430

LORD CORPORATION

2000 West Grandview Blvd, Erie, PA, 16514

Tel: (814) 868-0924   Fax: (814) 486-4345   www.lordcorp.com

Mfg. adhesives, coatings, chemicals, film products.

Agomet Klebstoffe, Postfach 602, D-6450 Hanau 1, Germany

Lord GmbH, Osterladekop 89b, D-21635 Jork, Germany

Tel: 49-4162-9128-77   Fax: 49-4162-9128-78

Lord GmbH, Zettachring 10, 3 OG, D-70567 Stuttgart, Germany

PAR Oberflächenchemie GmbH, Ottostrasse 28, D-41836 Hückelhoven, Germany

Tel: 49-2433-4084   Fax: 49-2433-4816

LOST ARROW CORPORATION

259 West Santa Clara Street, Ventura, CA, 93001

Tel: (805) 643-8616   Fax: (805) 653-6355   www.patagonia.com

Mfr. high-end outdoor sportswear, via catalogues and specialty retailers, including Patagonia stores.

Patagonia Munich, Leopoldstrasse 47, D-80802 Münich, Germany

LSI LOGIC CORPORATION

1551 McCarthy Blvd., Milpitas, CA, 95035

Tel: (408) 433-8000   Fax: (408) 954-3220   www.lsilogic.com

Develop and manufacture semiconductors.

LSI Logic GmbH, Orleansstrasse 4, D-81669 Münich, Germany

Tel: 49-89-458-330   Fax: 49-89-458-33108

LSI Logic GmbH, Mittlerer Pfad 4, D-70499 Stuttgart, Germany

Tel: 49-711-13-9690

LTX CORPORATION

LTX Park, University Ave., Westwood, MA, 02090

Tel: (617) 461-1000   Fax: (617) 326-4883   www.ltx.com

Design/mfr. computer-controlled semiconductor test systems.

LTX (Deutschland) GmbH, AM Hochacker 5, D-85630 Grasbrunn Neukeferloh, Germany

Tel: 49-89-4623550   Fax: 49-89-46235510

THE LUBRIZOL CORPORATION

29400 Lakeland Blvd., Wickliffe, OH, 44092-2298

Tel: (440) 943-4200   Fax: (440) 943-5337   www.lubrizol.com

Mfr. chemicals additives for lubricants and fuels.

Langer & Co. GmbH, Ritterhude, Germany

Tel: 49-421-69-333

Lubrizol Coatings Additives Company GmbH, Kurze Muehren 3, D-2000 Hamburg 1, Germany

Tel: 49-40-32-32-820

LUCENT TECHNOLOGIES, INC.

600 Mountain Ave., Murray Hill, NJ, 07974-0636

Tel: (908) 582-3000   Fax: (908) 582-2576   www.lucent.com

Design/mfr. wide range of public and private networks, communication systems and software, data networking systems, business telephone systems and microelectronics components.

Lucent Technologies Network Systems, GmbH, Thiern-und-Taxis-Str. 10, D-90411 Nuernberg, Germany

Tel: 49-228-917-77-62   Fax: 49-911-526-3890   Contact: Harald Kettenbach, PR Mgr.

Optimay Lucent Technologies Int'l GmbH, Orleansstrasse 4, D-81669 Münich, Germany

Tel: 49-89-45-91-83   Fax: 49-89-45-91-84-74   Contact: Sam Goodner, Pres. & CEO

LYDALL INC.

1 Colonial Road, PO Box 151, Manchester, CT, 06040

Tel: (860) 646-1233   Fax: (860) 646-4917   www.lydall.com

Mfr. converted paper products, paperboard, non-woven specialty media.

Lydall Gerhardi & Cie GmbH & Co., Ludenscheid, Germany

LYNX THERAPEUTICS, INC.

25861 Industrial Boulevard, Hayward, CA, 94545

Tel: (510) 670-9300   Fax: (510) 670-9302   www.lynxgen.com

Engaged in gene research.

Axaron Bioscience AG, Im Neuenheimer Feld 515, D-69120 Heidelberg, Germany

Tel: 49-6221-454-6

LYONDELL CHEMICAL COMPANY

1221 McKinney St., Houston, TX, 77010

Tel: (713) 652-7200   Fax: (713) 309-2074   www.lyondell.com

Mfr. polymers and petrochemicals.

Lyondell Chemical GmbH, Kaiserwerther Straße 115, D-40880 Ratingen, Germany

M/A-COM INC.

1011 Pawtucket Boulevard, Lowell, MA, 01853-3295

Tel: (978) 442-5000   Fax: (978) 442-5354   www.macom.com

Mfr. radio frequency (RF) and microwave integrated circuits and IP Networks to the wireless telecommunications and defense-related industries.

M/A-COM Ltd., Div. Tyco, Building 6408, Room 686, Rupert-Mayer-Str. 44, D-81359 Münich, Germany

Tel: 49-89-722-33990   Fax: 49-89-722-63567

MacDERMID INC.

245 Freight Street, Waterbury, CT, 06702-0671

Tel: (203) 575-5700   Fax: (203) 575-7900   www.macdermid.com

Chemicals processing for metal industrial, plastics, electronics cleaners, strippers.

MacDermid GmbH, Industrial 37, D-76707 Hambrucken, Germany

Tel: 49-7455-7171   Fax: 49-7455-9539

MACKIE DESIGNS INC.

16220 Wood-Red Road, NE, Woodinville, WA, 98072

Tel: (425) 487-4333   Fax: (425) 487-4337   www.mackie.com

Mfr. speakers, amplifiers, monitors and digital consoles.

Mackie Designs Deutschland GmbH, Kuhlmannstraße 7, D-48282 Emsdetten, Germany

Tel: 49-2572-960-4218   Fax: 49-2572-960-4210

MACROMEDIA, INC.

600 Townsend Street, San Francisco, CA, 94103-4945

Tel: (415) 252-2000   Fax: (415) 626-9603   www.macromedia.com

Engaged in web publishing.

Macromedia Northern Europe, Gewerbepark 6, D-93333 Neustadt, Germany

Tel: 49-9445-95490   Fax: 49-9445-21908

MACTAC

4560 Darrow Road, Stow, OH, 44224

Tel: (330) 688-1111   Fax: (330) 688-2540   www.mactac.com

Mfr. pressure sensitive tapes, films and label materials.

MACtac, Mathias-Brüggen-Straße, 140, D-50829 Köln, Germany

MAGNETROL INTERNATIONAL

5300 Belmont Road, Downers Grove, IL, 60515-4499

Tel: (630) 969-4000   Fax: (630) 969-9489   www.magnetrol.com

Mfr. level and flow instrumentation.

Magnetrol International, Schlossstrasse 76, D-51429 Bergisch Gladbach 1, Germany

Tel: 49-2204-9536-0   Fax: 49-2204-9536-53   Contact: Dieter Greiner

MALLINCKRODT BAKER, INC.

222 Red School Lane, Phillipsburg, NJ, 08865

Tel: (908) 859-2151   Fax: (908) 859-9318   www.mallbaker.com

Mfr. of high purity chemicals and related products and services.

Mallinckrodt Baker, Im Leuschnerpark 4, D-64347 Griesheim, Germany

Tel: 49-6155-667939   Fax: 49-6155-667940

MALLINCKRODT PHARMACUTICALS, INC.

675 McDonnell Blvd., Hazelwood, MO, 63042

Tel: (314) 654-2000   Fax: (314) 654-5380   www.mallinckrodt.com

Mfr. products for respiratory care.

Mallinckrodt Medical GmbH, Josef-Dietzgen-Straße 1-3, D-53773 Hennef, Germany

Tel: 49-22428870   Fax: 49-22426070

MANHATTAN ASSOCIATES, INC.

2300 Windy Ridge Pkwy., Ste. 700, Atlanta, GA, 30339

Tel: (770) 955-7070   Fax: (770) 955-0302   www.manh.com

Mfr. supply chain management software.

Manhattan Associates, Lohrstrasse 78/80, D-56068 Koblenz, Germany

MANPOWER INTERNATIONAL INC.

5301 N. Ironwood Rd., PO Box 2053, Milwaukee, WI, 53201-2053

Tel: (414) 961-1000   Fax: (414) 961-7081   www.manpower.com

Temporary help, contract service, training and testing.

Manpower-Planen-Leisten GmbH, Stiftstrasse 30, D-60313 Frankfurt/Main 1, Germany

Tel: 49-69-299-8050   Fax: 49-69-296-582

MARCONI DATA SYSTEMS INC.

1500 Mittel Blvd., Wood Dale, IL, 60191

Tel: (630) 860-7300   Fax: (630) 616-3657   www.videojet.com

Mfr. computer peripherals and hardware, state-of-the-art industrial ink jet marking and coding products.

Videojet, Div. Marconi Data Systems, An der Meil 1, D-65555 Limburg, Germany

Tel: 49-6431-9940 Fax: 49-6431-994-112   Contact: Nicole Heinzkill

MARITZ INC.

1375 North Highway Drive, Fenton, MO, 63099

Tel: (636) 827-4000   Fax: (636) 827-3312   www.maritz.com

Engaged in travel and marketing services.

Maritz GmbH, Goltsteinstr. 28, D-40211 Dusseldorf, Germany

Tel: 49-211-99100-0

Maritz GmbH, Rosenstraße 17, D-20095 Hamburg, Germany

MARK IV INDUSTRIES INC.

501 John James Audubon Pkwy., PO Box 810, Amherst, NY, 14226-0810

Tel: (716) 689-4972   Fax: (716) 689-1529   www.mark-iv.com

Mfr. of engineered systems and components utilizing mechanical and fluid power transmission, fluid transfer, and power systems and components.

Dayco Europe GmbH, Max-Born-Strasse 2-4, D-68519 Viernheim, Germany

Tel: 49-6204-6060-0   Fax: 49-6204-6895

MARKEM CORPORATION

150 Congress Street, Keene, NH, 03431

Tel: (603) 352-1130   Fax: (603) 357-1835   www.markem.com.

Mfr. and sales of industrial marking, print machinery and hot stamping foils.

Markem GmbH, Westpreussenstrasse 33, D-47809 Krefeld Linn Düsseldorf, Germany

Tel: 49-2151-94-88-0   Fax: 49-2151-94-88-20

MARLEY COOLING TOWER COMPANY

7401 West 129th Street, Overland Park, KS, 66213

Tel: (913) 664-7400   Fax: (913) 664-7641   www.marleyct.com

Cooling and heating towers and waste treatment systems.

Marley Kuhllturm GmbH, PO Box 34 02 61, D-40441 Düsseldorf, Germany

Tel: 49-203-997790   Fax: 49-203-741642

MARRIOTT INTERNATIONAL INC.

10400 Fernwood Rd., Bethesda, MD, 20817

Tel: (301) 380-3000   Fax: (301) 380-5181   www.marriott.com

Hotel services.

Bremen Marriott Hotel, Bremen, Germany

Frankfurt Marriott Hotel, Frankfurt, Germany

Hamburg Marriott Hotel and Golf Club, Hamburg, Germany

Marriott Courtyard Berlin-Koepenick, Grunanerstrassee 3-15, D-12557 Berlin, Germany

Tel: 49-30-65479-0 Fax: 49-30-65479-555

Marriott Courtyard Frankfurt Messe, Oeserstrasse 180, Frankfurt, D-65933 Hessen, Germany

Tel: 49-69-3905-0 Fax: 49-69-3808218

MARS INC.

6885 Elm Street, McLean, VA, 22101-3810

Tel: (703) 821-4900   Fax: (703) 448-9678   www.mars.com

Mfr. candy, snack foods, rice products and cat food.

Mars Schokladenvertrieb GmbH, Worringerstr. 7-9, D-4000 Düsseldorf, Germany

MARSH & McLENNAN COS INC.

1166 Ave. of the Americas, New York, NY, 10036-2774

Tel: (212) 345-5000   Fax: (212) 345-4808   www.marshmac.com

Insurance agents/brokers, pension and investment management consulting services.

Gradmann & Holler Group, Kerknerstrasse 50, D-70182 Stuttgart, Germany

Tel: 49-7-112-3800   Fax: 49-7-112-380622   Contact: Dr. George Brauchle

Gradmann & Holler Group, Kasernenstrasse 69, D-40213 Düsseldorf, Germany

Tel: 49-2-118-9870   Fax: 49-211-898-7369   Contact: Dr. Christian Doenecke

Gradmann & Holler Holding, Pacellistrasse 14, D-80333 Münich, Germany

Tel: 49-892-905-6620   Fax: 49-892-905-6619   Contact: Peter Hesse

Gradmann & Holler Kiefhaber GmbH, Cremon 3, D-20457 Hamburg, Germany

Tel: 49-40-37-6920   Fax: 49-40-3769-2622   Contact: Harald Sack

Gradmann & Holler Kiefhaber GmbH, Versicherungsmalder, Alt-Moabit 101 B, D-10559 Berlin, Germany

Tel: 49-30-399-9450   Fax: 49-303-999-4519   Contact: Bernd Kaiser

Gradmann & Holler Kiefhaber GmbH, Herriotstrasse 3, D-60528 Frankfurt/Main, Germany

Tel: 49-69-66760   Fax: 49-69-667-6522   Contact: Hans Theo Niklas

MARY KAY COSMETICS INC.

16251 No. Dallas Pkwy, Dallas, TX, 75248

Tel: (972) 687-6300   Fax: (972) 687-1609   www.marykay-cosmetic.com

Mfr. and direct sales of cosmetics and toiletries.

Mary Kay Cosmetics GmbH, Lilienthalstrasse 5, D-82178 Puchheim, Germany

Tel: 49-89-8009000 Fax: 49-89-80090090

MASCO CORPORATION

21001 Van Born Road, Taylor, MI, 48180

Tel: (313) 274-7400   Fax: (313) 374-6666   www.masco.com

Mfr. faucets, cabinets, locks and numerous home improvement, building and home furnishings products.

Alfred Reinecke GmbH & Co., Koebbingser Muehle 2, D-58640 Iserlohn, Germany

Tel: 49-2371-94900

Alma Kuchen Aloys Meyer GmbH & Co., Von-Rontgen-StraBe 8-14, D-48683 Ahaus, Germany

Tel: 49-2561-69465

E. Missel GmbH, Hortensienweg 2/27, D-70374 Stuttgart, Germany

Tel: 49-711-5308-106

Gebhardt Ventilatoren GmbH & Co., 74638 Waldenburg, Gebhardstrasse 19-25, PO Box 40, D-74636 Waldenburg, Germany

Tel: 49-7942-1010

Horst Breuer GmbH, Meerpfac 27-31, D-56566 Neuwied, Germany

Tel: 49-2631-86-07-45

Jung Pumpen GmbH & Co., Industriestr. 4-6 - Postfach 1341, D-4803 Steinhagen, Germany

Tel: 49-5204-170

SKS Gmbh & Co., KG, EisenbahnstraBe 2, D-47198 Duisburg Homburg, Germany

Tel: 49-2066-20-040

MATRIXONE, INC.

210 Littleton Road, Westford, MA, 01886

Tel: (978) 589-4000   Fax: (978) 589-5700   www.matrixone.com

Mfr. software.

MatrixOne GmbH, Zettachring 8A, D-70567 Stuttgart, Germany

MATTEL INC.

333 Continental Blvd., El Segundo, CA, 90245-5012

Tel: (310) 252-2000   Fax: (310) 252-2179   www.mattel.com

Mfr. toys, dolls, games, crafts and hobbies.

Fisher-Price Spielwaren GmbH, Bruehler Str. 101, D-50389 Wesseling, Germany

Mattel GmbH, An der Trift 75, D-63303 Dreieich, Germany

MAXITROL COMPANY

23555 Telegraph Road, PO Box 2230, Southfield, MI, 48037-2230

Tel: (248) 356-1400   Fax: (248) 356-0829   www.maxitrol.com

Mfr. gas pressure regulators, emergency shut-off valves, electronic temp controls.

Mertik Maxitrol GmbH, Industrie Strasse, D-4403 Senden, Germany

Tel: 49-3947-400-0   Fax: 49-3947-400-200

MAXON CORPORATION

201 East 18th Street, Muncie, IN, 47302

Tel: (765) 284-3304   Fax: (765) 286-8394   www.maxoncorp.com

Industry combustion equipment and valves.

Maxon GmbH, Niederlassung Stuttgart, Gottlieb-Daimler-Strasse 1, D-71394 Kernen Stuttgart, Germany

Tel: 49-7151-949040   Fax: 49-7151-949044

Maxon GmbH, Steeler-Strasse 491, D-45276 Essen, Germany

Tel: 49-201-85-1160   Fax: 49-201-851-1661

MAXTOR CORPORATION

500 McCarthy Blvd., Milpitas, CA, 95035

Tel: (408) 894-5000   Fax: (408) 432-4510   www.maxtor.com

Mfr. develops and markets hard disk drives for desktop computer systems.

Maxtor Europe GmbH, Max-von-Eyth-Str. 3, D-85737 Ismaning, Germany

Tel: 49-89-962-4190   Fax: 49-89-968572

MAYER, BROWN, ROWE & MAW

190 S. LaSalle Street, Chicago, IL, 60603

Tel: (312) 782-0600   Fax: (312) 701-7711   www.mayerbrown.com

Engaged in international law.

Mayer, Brown, Rowe & Maw, An Lyskirchen 14, D-50676 Cologne, Germany

Tel: 49-221-921-5210   Fax: 49-221-921-5214   Contact: Kim D. Larsen, Mng. Ptnr.

MAYFRAN INTERNATIONAL, INC.

PO Box 43038, Cleveland, OH, 44143

Tel: (440) 461-4100   Fax: (440) 461-5565   www.mayfran.com

Mfr. conveying systems, filtration equipment and separators that facilitate material handling and coolant recovery for automobile manufacturers and machine tool builders.

Mayfran GmbH, Postfach 230124, Alfredstr. 295, D-4300 Essen, Germany

May-Fran GmbH, Fruehlingstr. 52, D-4300 Essen, Germany

McCANN-ERICKSON WORLDGROUP

750 Third Ave., New York, NY, 10017

Tel: (212) 697-6000   Fax: (212) 984-3575   www.mccann.com

International advertising and marketing services.

Art McCann GmbH, Großer Hasenpfad 44, D-60598 Frankfurt/Main, Germany

McCann-Erickson Hamburg GmbH, Neuerwall 41, Postfach 303640, D-2000 Hamburg 36, Germany

McDERMOTT WILL & EMERY

227 W. Monroe Street, Chicago, IL, 60606-5096

Tel: (312) 372-2000   Fax: (312) 984-7700   www.mwe.com

Engaged in international law.

McDermott Will & Emery, Elisabethstraße 91, D-80797 Munich, Germany

McDermott Will & Emery, Stadtor 1, 15/F, D-40219 Dusseldorf, Germany

McDONALD'S CORPORATION

McDonald's Plaza, Oak Brook, IL, 60523

Tel: (630) 623-3000   Fax: (630) 623-7409   www.mcdonalds.com

Fast food chain stores.

McDonald's Corp., Münich, Germany

THE McGRAW-HILL COMPANIES

1221 Avenue of the Americas, New York, NY, 10020

Tel: (212) 512-2000   Fax: (212) 512-2703   www.mccgraw-hill.com

Books, magazines, information systems, financial service, publishing and broadcast operations.

McGraw-Hill Book Co. GmbH, Lademannbogen 136, Postfach 630520, D-2000 Hamburg 63, Germany

McKINSEY & COMPANY

55 East 52nd Street, New York, NY, 10022

Tel: (212) 446-7000   Fax: (212) 446-8575   www.mckinsey.com

Management and business consulting services.

McKinsey & Company, St.-Apern-Strasse 1, D-50667 Cologne, Germany

Tel: 49-221-20870   Fax: 49-221-2087-700

McKinsey & Company, Am Sandtorkai 77, D-20457 Hamburg, Germany

Tel: 49-40-3612-10   Fax: 49-40-3612-1700

McKinsey & Company, Birkenwaldstrasse 149, D-70191 Stuttgart, Germany

Tel: 49-711-25535   Fax: 49-711-2553-700

McKinsey & Company, Prinzregenstrasse 22, D-80538 Münich, Germany

Tel: 49-89-55940   Fax: 49-89-5594-700

McKinsey & Company, Taunustor 2, D-60311 Frankfurt am Main, Germany

Tel: 49-69-71620   Fax: 49-69-7162-700

McKinsey & Company, Königsallee 60C, D-40027 Düsseldorf, Germany

Tel: 49-211-13640   Fax: 49-211-1364-700

McKinsey & Company, Kurfürstendamm 185, D-10707 Berlin, Germany

Tel: 49-30-88-452-0   Fax: 49-30-88-452-700

McKinsey & Company -, Frankfurt, BTO, Taunustor 2, D-60311 Frankfurt am Main, Germany

Tel: 49-69-71620   Fax: 49-69-7162-700

JOHN J. McMULLEN ASSOCIATES INC. (JJMA)

4300 King Street, Alexandria, VA, 22302

Tel: (703) 418-0100   Fax: (703) 933-6774   www.jjma.com

Engaged in marine engineering and naval architecture.

John J. McMullen GmbH, Glockengiestr-Wall 20, D-2000 Hamburg 1, Germany

MEADE INSTRUMENTS CORPORATION

6001 Oak Canyon, Irvine, CA, 92618-5200

Tel: (949) 451-1450   Fax: (949) 451-1460   www.meade.com

Engaged in the design and manufacture of telescopes and accessories for amateur astronomers.

Meade Instruments Europe, Siemensstrasse 6, D-46325 Borken, Germany

Tel: 49-2861-9317   Fax: 49-2861-2294

Meade Instruments Europe, Lochhamer Schlag 5, D-82166 Graefelfing, Germany

Tel: 49-89-898-896-00   Fax: 49-89-898-996-01

MECHANICAL DYNAMICS, INC.

2300 Traverwood Drive, Ann Arbor, MI, 48105

Tel: (734) 994-3800   Fax: (734) 994-6418   www.adams.com

Mfr. Adams prototyping software for functional virtual prototyping solutions.

Ing. Buro Kik- Are Care, Rheingaustrasse 22, D-12161 Berlin, Germany

Tel: 49-30-8270-2776

Mechanical Dynamics GmbH, Universitatsstraße 51, D-35037 Marburg/Lahn, Germany

Tel: 49-6421-17070   Contact: Jurgen Fett, VP

Mechanical Dynamics GmbH, Joseph-Dollinger-Bogen 12, D-80807 München, Germany

Tel: 49-89-546-44622

Mechanical Dynamics GmbH, Mollenbachstrasse 23, D-71229 Loenberg, Germany

Tel: 49-7152-399800

MEDIA 100 INC.

450 Donald Lynch Blvd., Marlborough, MA, 01752

Tel: (508) 460-1600   Fax: (508) 481-8627   www.media100.com

Mfr. digital editing software and hardware.

Media 100 GmbH, Hallbergmoos, Germany

MEDTRONIC, INC.

7000 Central Ave. N.E., Minneapolis, MN, 55432-5604

Tel: (763) 514-4000   Fax: (763) 514-4879   www.medtronic.com

Mfr., sales and service of electrotherapeutic medical devices, specializing in implantable and invasive therapies.

Medtronic GmbH, Am Seestern 3, D-40547 Düsseldorf, Germany

Tel: 49-21152930

MEMC ELECTRONIC MATERIALS, INC.

501 Pearl Drive, St. Peters, MO, 63376

Tel: (636) 474-5500   Fax: (636) 474-5161   www.memc.com

Mfg. and distribution of silicon wafers.

MEMC Electronic Materials, Inc., Limeetrasse 111, D-81243 München, Germany

Tel: 49-89-89-87666-30   Fax: 49-89-89-7666-40

MEMOREX CORPORATION

10100 Pioneer Blvd., Ste. 110, Santa Fe Springs, CA, 90670

Tel: (562) 906-2800   Fax: (562) 906-2848   www.memorex.com

Magnetic recording tapes, etc.

Memorex GmbH, Hauptverwaltung, Hahnstr. 41, D-6000 Frankfurt/Main 71, Germany

MENASHA CORPORATION

1645 Bergstrom Road, Neenah, WI, 54957-0367

Tel: (920) 751-1000   Fax: (920) 751-1236   www.menasha.com

Mfr. packaging and paperboard products.

Poly Hi Solidur, Sub. Menasha, PO Box 1264, D-48685 Vreden, Germany

MENTOR CORPORATION

201 Mentor Drive, Santa Barbara, CA, 93111

Tel: (805) 879-6000   Fax: (805) 967-7108   www.mentorcorp.com

Mfr. medical devices including breast implants.

Mentor Deutschland GmbH, Ludwigsforum, Ludwigstrasse 45/Haus C, D-85399 Hallbergmoos, Germany

Tel: 49-8116-00500

MENTOR GRAPHICS

8005 SW Boeckman Road, Wilsonville, OR, 97070-7777

Tel: (503) 685-7000   Fax: (503) 685-1202   www.mentorg.com

Develop/mfr. software tools for embedded systems market.

Mentor Graphics GmbH, Wanheimerstr. 43, D-40472 Dusseldorf, Germany

MERCER MANAGEMENT CONSULTING INC.

1166 Ave. of the Americas, New York, NY, 10036

Tel: (212) 345-3400   Fax: (212) 345-7414   www.mercermc.com

Provides clients with counsel in such areas as corporate and business strategy and growth planning, organizational development, and market and operations enhancement.

Mercer Management Consulting GmbH`, Stefan-George-Ring 2, D-81929 München, Germany

MERCK & COMPANY, INC.

One Merck Drive, PO Box 100, Whitehouse Station, NJ, 08889-0100

Tel: (908) 423-1000   Fax: (908) 423-2592   www.merck.com

Pharmaceuticals, chemicals and biologicals.

Merck, Sharp & Dohme GmbH, Lindenplatz 1, D-85540 Haar, Germany

MERCURY INTERACTIVE CORPORATION

1325 Borregas Ave., Sunnyvale, CA, 94089

Tel: (408) 822-5200   Fax: (408) 822-5300   www.merc-int.com

Mfr. computer software to decipher and eliminate "bugs" from systems.

Mercury Interactive GmbH, Inselkammerstrasse 1, D-82008 Unterhaching bei München, Germany

Tel: 49-89-613767-0   Fax: 49-89-613767-60

MERRILL CORPORATION

1 Merrill Circle, St. Paul, MN, 55108

Tel: (651) 646-4501   Fax: (651) 646-5332   www.merrillcorp.com

Engaged in document management and data services.

Merrill Germany GmbH, Grueneburgweg 1418, D-60322 Frankfurt, Germany

MERRILL LYNCH & COMPANY, INC.

World Financial Center, 250 Vesey Street, New York, NY, 10281-1332

Tel: (212) 236-1000   Fax: (212) 449-2892   www.ml.com

Security brokers and dealers, investment and business services.

Merrill Lynch Bank AG, Neue Mainzer Straße 52, D-60311 Frankfurt, Germany

Tel: 49-69-2994

Merrill Lynch International Bank, Moehlstrasse 2, D-81675 München, Germany

Tel: 49-89-41305

Merrill Lynch International Bank Limited, Ottostraße 8, D-80333 München, Germany

Tel: 49-89-41305 0

MESTEK, INC.

260 North Elm St., Westfield, MA, 01085

Tel: (413) 568-9571   Fax: (413) 568-2969   www.mestek.com

Mfr. air diffusers, grilles and related equipment for air conditioning, heating and ventilation.

Anemostat Raumlufttechnik, Grafenmuhlenweg 19, D-5000 Cologne 80, Germany

META GROUP, INC.

208 Harbor Drive, PO Box 120061, Stamford, CT, 06912-0061

Tel: (203) 973-6700   Fax: (203) 359-8066   www.metagroup.com

Engaged in research and consulting, focusing on information technology and business transformation strategies.

META Group, Friedrich-Ebert-Damm 143, D-22047 Hamburg, Germany

METAL IMPROVEMENT COMPANY

10 Forest Ave., Paramus, NJ, 07652

Tel: (201) 843-7800   Fax: (201) 843-3460   www.metalimprovement.com

Mfr. shot peening.

Shot Peening, Div. Metal Improvement, Hans-Bockler-Str. 5, D-64521 Gross-Gerau, Germany

METROLOGIC INSTRUMENTS, INC.

90 Coles Road, Blackwood, NJ, 08012

Tel: (856) 225-8100   Fax: (856) 228-6673   www.metrologic.com

Mfr. and sales of hologram based, bar code scanner systems.

Metrologic Instruments GmbH, Dornierstrasse 2, Puchheim b., D-82178 Münich, Germany

Tel: 49-89-89019-0   Fax: 49-89-89019-200

METROMEDIA FIBER NETWORK, INC.

360 Hamilton Avenue, White Plains, NY, 10601

Tel: (914) 421-6700   Fax: (914) 421-6777   www.mfn.com

Mfr. urban fiber-optic networks for telecommunications providers.

Metromedia Fiber Network Inc., Eschborner Landstrasse 112, D-60489 Frankfurt, Germany

Tel: 49-69-905 54-0

METRON TECHNOLOGY

1350 Old Bayshore Highway, Ste. 210, Burlingame, CA, 94010

Tel: (650) 401-4600   Fax: (650) 373-1135   www.metrontech.com

Global provider of marketing, sales, service and support solutions to semiconductor materials and equipment suppliers and semiconductor manufacturers.

Metron GmbH, Königsbrücker Str. 61A, D-01099 Dresden, Germany

Tel: 49-351-82 95 90   Fax: 49-35-82 95 950

M-I

PO Box 48242, Houston, TX, 77242-2842

Tel: (713) 739-0222   Fax: (713) 308-9503   www.midf.com

Developer, manufacturer and marketer of drilling and completion fluids and services.

M-I Drilling Fluids Intl. B.V., Grafftring 5-7, D-29227 Celle, Germany

Tel: 49-5141-98410   Fax: 49-5141-84064

MICRO WAREHOUSE, INC.

535 Connecticut Ave., Norwalk, CT, 06854

Tel: (203) 899-4000   Fax: (203) 899-4203   www.warehouse.com

Catalog computer sales.

Micro Warehouse GmbH, Postfach 108, D-55247 Mainz-Kastel, Germany

MICROCHIP TECHNOLOGY INCORPORATED

2355 West Chandler Boulevard, Chandler, AZ, 85224

Tel: (602) 786-7200   Fax: (602) 899-9210   www.microchip.com

Mfr. electronic subassemblies and components.

AZ Microchip Technology GmbH, Gustav-Heinemann-Ring 125, D-81739 Münich, Germany

Tel: 49-89-627-1440   Fax: 49-89-627-1444

MICROMERITICS INSTRUMENT CORPORATION

One Micromeritics Drive, Norcross, GA, 30093-1877

Tel: (770) 662-3620   Fax: (770) 662-3696   www.micromeritics.com

Mfr. analytical instruments.

Micromeritics GmbH, Erftstrasse 54, D-41238 Mönchengladbach, Germany

Tel: 49-2166-98708-0

MICROMUSE INC.

139 Townsend Street, San Francisco, CA, 94107

Tel: (415) 538-9090   Fax: (415) 538-9091   www.micromuse.com

Mfr. software for information technology.

Micromuse Ltd., Hamborner Straße 53, D- 40472 Dusseldorf, Germany

MICRON TECHNOLOGY, INC.

8000 S. Federal Way, Boise, ID, 83707-0006

Tel: (208) 368-4000   Fax: (208) 368-4435   www.micron.com

Mfr. random-access memory chips and semi-conductor memory components.

Micron Semiconductor GmbH, Sternstrasse 20, D-85609 Aschheim, Germany

Tel: 49-89-904-8720   Fax: 49-89-904-87250

MICROSOFT CORPORATION

One Microsoft Way, Redmond, WA, 98052-6399

Tel: (425) 882-8080   Fax: (425) 936-7329   www.microsoft.com

Computer software, peripherals and services.

Microsoft Eastern Europe, Edisonstrasse 1, D-8044 Unterschleissheim Münich, Germany

Microsoft Germany GmbH, Edisonstrasse 1, D-85716 Unterschleissheim Münich, Germany

Tel: 49-89-31760   Fax: 49-89-3176-1000

MILACRON INC.

2090 Florence Ave., Cincinnati, OH, 45206

Tel: (513) 487-5000   Fax: (513) 487-5057   www.milacron.com

Metalworking and plastics technologies.

Ferromatik Milacron Maschinenbau GmbH, Riegelerstr. 4, D-79364 Malterdingen, Germany

Tel: 49-7644-78-0

MILLENNIUM CHEMICALS INC.

PO Box 7015, 230 Half Mile Road, Red Bank, NJ, 07701-7015

Tel: (732) 933-5000   Fax: (732) 933-5200   www.millenniumchem.com

Mfr. specialty chemicals for paints, perfumes, and flavorings.

Millennium Chemicals, Neuer Markt 1, D-42781 Haan, Germany

Tel: 49-2119-93010

MINDSPEED TECHNOLOGIES

4000 MacArthur, Newport Beach, CA, 92660-3095

Tel: (949) 579-3000   Fax: (945) 579-3020   www.mindspeed.com

Mfr. integrated circuits.

Mindspeed Technologies, Paul-Gehardt-Allee 50 A, D-81245 Münich, Germany

MINE SAFETY APPLIANCES COMPANY

121 Gamma Drive, PO Box 426, Pittsburgh, PA, 15230

Tel: (412) 967-3000   Fax: (412) 967-3452   www.msa.net

Safety equipment, industry filters.

Auergesellschaft GmbH, Thiemannstr. 1-11, Postfach 440208, D-100044 Berlin, Germany

MSA Europe, Thiemannstr. 1-11, Postfach 440208, D-100044 Berlin, Germany

MINOLTA-QMS INC.

One Magnum Pass, PO Box 81250, Mobile, AL, 36618

Tel: (205) 633-4300   Fax: (205) 633-4866   www.qms.com

Mfr. of high-performance color and monochrome document printing solutions for office automation, electronic publishing, graphic design, and advanced imaging applications.

Minolta-QMS GmbH, Gustav-Heinemann-Ring 212, D-81739 Münich, Germany

MINTEQ INTERNATIONAL INC.

395 Grove City Road, Slippery Rock, PA, 16057

Tel: (724) 794-3000   Fax: (724) 794-4455   www.mineralstech.com

Mfr./market specialty refractory and metallurgical products and application systems.

MINTEQ International GmbH, Kuhstrabe 23-25, D-47051 Duisburg, Germany

Tel: 49-203-2-86480   Fax: 49-203-2-864848   Contact: David Rosenberg/Christian Wasmuht, Mgrs.   Emp: 23

MKS INSTRUMENTS INC.

6 Shattuck Road, Andover, MA, 01810-2449

Tel: (978) 975-2350   Fax: (978) 933-0750   www.astex.com

Provider of process infrastructure products and technologies that increase productivity in gas- and vacuum-based manufacturing.

ENI Germany GmbH, Sielminger Str. 63, D-70771 Leinfelden-Echterdingen, Germany

Tel: 49-0711-947-700   Fax: 49-0711-947-7025

MODEM MEDIA, INC.

230 East Avenue, Norwalk, CT, 06855

Tel: (203) 299-7000   Fax: (230) 299-7060   www.modemmedia.com

Provides on-line marketing and consulting services.

Modem Media Mex, Isartalstrasse 49, D-80469 Münich, Germany

Tel: 49-89-7461660   Contact: Juergen Funk, Mng. Dir.

MODINE MANUFACTURING COMPANY

1500 DeKoven Ave., Racine, WI, 53403

Tel: (262) 636-1200   Fax: (262) 636-1424   www.modine.com

Mfr. heat-transfer products.

Modine GmbH, Burgsteinfurter Damm, D-4445 Neuenkirchen, Germany

Modine GmbH, Efeustrasse 10, D-8000 Münich 21, Germany

Modine Manufacturing Co., Bernhause, Germany

MOLECULAR DEVICES CORPORATION

1311 Orleans Drive, Sunnyvale, CA, 94089

Tel: (408) 747-1700   Fax: (408) 747-3601   www.moleculardevices.com

Engaged in the development and manufacture of pharmaceuticals.

Molecular Devices GmbH, Gutenbergstr. 10, D-85737 Ismaning/Munchen, Germany

MOLEX INC.

2222 Wellington Court, Lisle, IL, 60532

Tel: (630) 969-4550   Fax: (630) 969-1352   www.molex.com

Mfr. electronic, electrical and fiber optic interconnection products and systems, switches, application tooling.

Molex Services GmbH, Felix-Wankel-Strasse 11, D-74078 Heilbronn-Biberach, Germany

Tel: 49-7066-95550   Fax: 49-7066-9555-29

MONSANTO

800 N. Lindbergh Boulevard, St. Louis, MO, 63167

Tel: (314) 694-1000   Fax: (314) 694-7625   www.monsanto.com

Life sciences company focusing on agriculture, nutrition, pharmaceuticals, health and wellness and sustainable development.

Monsanto Deutschland GmbH, Vogelsanger Weg 91, D-40470 Dusseldorf, Germany

Tel: 49-211-367-50   Fax: 49-211-367-5341

MOODY'S INVESTOR SERVICES, INC.

99 Church St., New York, NY, 10007

Tel: (212) 553-1658   Fax: (212) 553-0462   www.moodys.com

Publishes credit ratings.

Moody's Deutschland GmbH, Taunusanlage 11, D-60329 Frankfurt, Germany

Tel: 49-69-2-42-84-0

MOOG INC.

300 Jamison Road, East Aurora, NY, 14052-0018

Tel: (716) 652-2000   Fax: (716) 687-4471   www.moog.com

Mfr. precision control components and systems.

Moog GmbH, Hanns Klemmstr. 28, D-71030 Boblingen, Germany

MORGAN ADVANCED MATERIALS AND TECHNOLOGY, INC.

441 Hall Ave., Saint Mary's, PA, 15857

Tel: (814) 781-1573   Fax: (814) 781-9262   www.mamat.com

Mfr. carbon graphite and silicon carbide components.

Morganite GmbH, Walporzheimer Strasse 100, D-53474 Bad Neuenahr-Ahrweiler, Germany

J. P. MORGAN CHASE & CO. INC.

270 Park Ave., New York, NY, 10017

Tel: (212) 270-6000   Fax: (212) 622-9030   www.jpmorganchase.com

Provides integrated financial solutions for institutions and individuals worldwide, including asset management, investment banking and commercial banking.

J. P. Morgan Chase & Co., Grueneburgweg 2, D-60322 Frankfurt am Main, Germany

Tel: 49-69-7158-2500   Fax: 49-69-7158-2209

J. P. Morgan Chase & Co., Ulmenstrasse 30, D-60325 Frankfurt am Main, Germany

J. P. Morgan Chase & Co., Munzgasse 2, D-01067 Dresden, Germany

J. P. Morgan Chase & Co., GlockengieBerwall 26, D-20095 Hamburg, Germany

J. P. Morgan Chase & Co., Unter den Linden 12, D-10117 Berlin, Germany

Tel: 49-30-2039-450   Fax: 49-30-2039-4510

MORGAN STANLEY DEAN WITTER & CO.

1585 Broadway, New York, NY, 10036

Tel: (212) 761-4000   Fax: (212) 761-0086   www.msdw.com

Securities and commodities brokerage, investment banking, money management, personal trusts.

Morgan Stanley Bank AG, Rahmhofstrasse 2-4, D-60313 Frankfurt, Germany

MORGAN, LEWIS & BOCKIUS LLP

1701 Market St., Philadelphia, PA, 19103-6993

Tel: (215) 963-5000   Fax: (215) 963-5299   www.morganlewis.com

International law firm.

Morgan, Lewis & Bockius LLP, Guiollettstraße 54, D-60325 Frankfurt am Main, Germany

Tel: 49-69-714-0070   Fax: 49-69-714-007-10   Contact: Robert V. Daly, Mng. Ptnr.   Emp: 29

MOTIVE COMMUNICATIONS, INC.

12515 Research Blvd., Bldg., Austin, TX, 78759-2220

Tel: (512) 339-8335   Fax: (512) 339-9040   www.motive.com

Mfr. customer service software.

Motive Communications, Leopoldstrasse 236, D-80807 Münich, Germany

MOTOROLA, INC.

1303 East Algonquin Road, Schaumburg, IL, 60196

Tel: (847) 576-5000   Fax: (847) 538-5191   www.motorola.com

Mfr. communications equipment, semiconductors and cellular phones.

Motorola GmbH, Heinrich-Hertz-Strasse 1, D-65232 Taunusstein, Germany

Tel: 49-6128-700   Fax: 49-6128-72920

MPS GROUP, INC. (MODIS PROFESSIONAL SERVICES)

1 Independent Dr., Jacksonville, FL, 32202-5060

Tel: (904) 360-2000   Fax: (904) 360-2814   www.modispro.com

Engaged in staffing for professional services and information technology.

Modis, Euro Haus, Lyoner Str 26, Frankfurt, Germany

MQSOFTWARE, INC.

7575 Golden Valley Road, Ste. 140, Minneapolis, MN, 55427

Tel: (763) 546-9080   Fax: (763) 546-9083   www.mqsoftware.com

Mfr. enterprise application software.

MQSoftware GmbH, Sarrazinstrasse 17, D-12159 Berlin, Germany

Tel: 49-30-85-98970

MRO SOFTWARE, INC.

100 Crosby Drive, Bedford, MA, 01730

Tel: (781) 280-2000   Fax: (781) 280-0207   www.mrosoftware.com

Design/sales of enterprise asset maintenance software.

MRO Software, Stadionstrasse 6, D-70771 Leinfelden-Echterdingen, Germany

MSC.SOFTWARE CORPORATION

2 MacArthur Place, Santa Ana, CA, 92707

Tel: (714) 540-8900   Fax: (714) 784-4056   www.mscsoftware.com

Develop finite element analysis software used in the field of computer-aided engineering.

MSC.Software GmbH, Im Rudert 2, D-35043 Marburg, Germany

MSC.Software GmbH, Carl-Zeiss-Strasse 2, D-63755 Alzenau, Germany

MSC.Software GmbH, Am Moosfeld 13, D-81829 Münich, Germany

MTI TECHNOLOGY CORPORATION

4905 East LaPalma Avenue, Anaheim, CA, 92807

Tel: (714) 970-0300   Fax: (714) 693-2202   www.mti.com

Mfr. data storage systems software.

MTI Technology GmbH, Otto-Von-Guericke-Ring 15, D-652 Wiesbaden, Germany

Tel: 49-61-229950   Fax: 49-61-2299-5100

MTI Technology GmbH, Orleansstrasse 4, D-81669 Münich, Germany

Tel: 49-89-4587-570   Fax: 49-89-4587-5750

MTS SYSTEMS CORPORATION

14000 Technology Drive, Eden Prairie, MN, 55344-2290

Tel: (612) 937-4000   Fax: (612) 937-4515   www.mts.com

Develop/mfr. mechanical testing and simulation products and services, industry measure and automation instrumentation.

MTS Systems GmbH, Mochentaler Weg 18, D-89584 Ehingen, Germany

Tel: 49-7393-917730   Fax: 49-7393-917731   Contact: Thomas Weiß

MTS Systems GmbH, Erchanbertstrasse 8, D-81929 Münich, Germany

Tel: 49-89-9393-1026   Fax: 49-89-9393-1027   Contact: Eckehard Werner

MULTIGRAPHICS INC.

431 Lakeview Court, Mt. Prospect, IL, 60056

Tel: (847) 375-1700   Fax: (847) 375-1810   www.multigraphics.com

Mfr./sale/service printing and print prod equipment, mailroom/bindery systems, services and supplies for graphics industry.

Multi Graphics GmbH, Robert-Bosch-Str. 18, Postfach 10-20-08, D-6072 Dreieich B. Frankfurt Main, Germany

MULTILINK TECHOLOGY CORPORATION

300 Atrium Drive, 2nd Fl., Somerset, NJ, 08873-4105

Tel: (732) 537-3700   Fax: (732) 805-9177   www.mltc.com

Mfr. high-band, mixed-signal integrated circuits.

Multilink Technology GmbH, Hallerstr. 6, D-10557 Berlin, Germany

Multilink Technology GmbH, Truderinger Strasse 17, D-81677 Münich, Germany

Multilink Technology GmbH, Bessemerstr. 80, D-44793 Bochum, Germany

Tel: 49-234-91173-12

MYKROLIS CORPORATION

1 Patriots Park, Bedford, MA, 01730

Tel: (781) 695-7654   Fax: (781) 695-7639   www.mykrolis.com

Mfr. filtering equipment for gases and liquids.

Mykrolis GmbH, Grenzstrasse 28, D-01109 Dresden, Germany

NAMCO CONTROLS CORPORATION

2013 West Meeting Street, Lancaster, SC, 29720

Tel: (803) 286-8491   Fax: (803) 289-1389   www.namcocontrols.com

Mfr. sensors, switches and encoders.

Namco Controls GmbH, Mittelfeld 10, D-25379 Hezhorn, Germany

THE NASH ENGINEERING COMPANY

9 Trefoil Drive, Trumbull, CT, 06611

Tel: (203) 459-3900   Fax: (203) 459-3511   www.nasheng.com

Mfr. air and gas compressors, vacuum pumps.

Elmo Vacuum Technology GmbH, Humboldtstraße 59, D-90459 Nürnberg, Germany

Contact: Erich Michael Wenzel

NATIONAL MACHINERY COMPANY

161 Greenfield St., Tiffin, OH, 44883-2471

Tel: (419) 447-5211   Fax: (419) 447-5299   www.nationalmachinery.com

Mfr. high-speed metal parts forming machines.

National Machinery Europe GmbH, Klingenhofstrabe 5, D-90411 Nürnberg, Germany

Tel: 49-911-519.0

NATIONAL SEMICONDUCTOR CORPORATION

2900 Semiconductor Dr., PO Box 58090, Santa Clara, CA, 95052-8090

Tel: (408) 721-5000   Fax: (408) 739-9803   www.national.com

Engaged in producing computer-on-a-chip solutions for the information highway.

National Semiconductor, Livry-Gargon Str. 10, D-82256 Fuerstenfeldbruck, Germany

Tel: 49-8141-35-0   Fax: 49-8141-351-506   Contact: Roland Anderson, VP & Gen. Mgr.   Emp: 300

NATIONAL STARCH AND CHEMICAL COMPANY

10 Finderne Ave., Bridgewater, NJ, 08807-3300

Tel: (908) 685-5000   Fax: (908) 685-5005   www.nationalstarch.com

Mfr. adhesives and sealants, resins and specialty chemicals, electronic materials and adhesives, food products, industry starch.

National Starch & Chemical GmbH, Postfach 17 01 63, D-67418 Neustadt Weinstrasse, Germany

Tel: 49-6327-3820   Fax: 49-6327-382-259

NATIONWIDE

One Nationwide Plaza, Columbus, OH, 43215-2220

Tel: (614) 249-7111   Fax: (614) 249-7705   www.nationwide.com

Insurance services.

Neckura Versicherungs AG, Oberstedter Str. 14, Postfach 1480, D-6370 Oberursel/Ts. 1, Germany

NAVIGATION TECHNOLOGIES CORPORATION

The Merchandise Mart, Ste. 900, Chicago, IL, 60654

Tel: (312) 894-7000   Fax: (312) 894-7050   www.navtech.com

Mfr. navigation systems for automobiles.

Navigation Technologies NavTech GmbH, Otto-Volger-Str. 17, D-65843 Sulzbach, Germany

NCR (NATIONAL CASH REGISTER)

1700 South Patterson Blvd., Dayton, OH, 45479

Tel: (937) 445-5000   Fax: (937) 445-7042   www.ncr.com

Mfr. automated teller machines and high-performance stationary bar code scanners.

NCR GmbH, Ulmer Strasse 160, D-86135 Augsburg, Germany

Tel: 49-821-405-8030   Fax: 49-821-405-8013   Contact: Walter Muecke, Dir.

NCUBE CORPORATION

1825 NW 167th Place, Beaverton, OR, 97006

Tel: (503) 629-5088   Fax: (503) 645-1737   www.ncube.com

Mfr. computer servers.

nCUBE Deutschland GmbH, Hanauerstrasse 56, D-80992 Münich, Germany

NDCHEALTH CORPORATION

National Data Plaza, Atlanta, GA, 30329-2010

Tel: (404) 728-2000   Fax: (404) 728-2551   www.ndchealth.com

Mfr. billing management software.

NDCHealth GmbH & Co. KG, Auf der Lind 10, D-65529 Waldems-Esch, Germany

THE NDP GROUP, INC.

900 West Shore Road, Port Washington, NY, 11050

Tel: (516) 625-0700   Fax: (516) 625-2347   www.npd.com

Engaged in consumer buying research.

NPD Group, Intelect Markforschung GmbH, Nordwestring 101, D-90319 Nuremberg, Germany

NELSON, MULLINS, RILEY & SCARBOROUGH LLP

PO Box 11070, Colombia, SC, 29211-1070

Tel: (803) 799-2000   Fax: (803) 799-2000   www.nmrs.com

Engaged in international law.

Nelson Mullins GmbH, Brienner Sraße 12A, D-80333 Munich, Germany

Contact: Oliver Bolthausen

NEON SYSTEMS, INC.

14100 Southwest Fwy., Ste. 500, Sugar Land, TX, 77478

Tel: (281) 491-4200   Fax: (281) 242-3880   www.neonsys.com

Mfr. security management software.

NEON Systems Germany, martin-Behaim-Strausse 12, D-63263 Neu-Isenburg, Germany

Tel: 49-61-23-0060

NETEGRITY, INC.

52 Second Avenue, Waltham, MA, 02154

Tel: (781) 890-1700   Fax: (781) 487-7791   www.netegrity.com

Mfr. security software.

Netegrity GmbH, Eurohaus, Lyoner Straße 26,, D-60529 Frankfurt, Germany

Tel: 49-69-6-65-770

NETMANAGE, INC.

10725 N. De Anza Blvd., Cupertino, CA, 95014

Tel: (408) 973-7171   Fax: (408) 257-6405   www.netmanage.com

Develop and manufacture computer software applications and tools.

NetManage Software GmbH, Mühlweg 2, D-82054 Sauerlach, Germany

NetManage Software GmbH, Donaustrasse 7, D-63452 Hanau, Germany

NetManage Software GmbH, Ruhrallee 5, D-45525 Hattingen, Germany

NETWORK APPLIANCE, INC.

495 E. Java Drive, Sunnyvale, CA, 94089

Tel: (408) 822-6000   Fax: (408) 822-4501   www.netapp.com

Engaged in data storage market equipment.

NetApp GmbH, Eschbaum 2, D-84424 Isen/Eschbaum, Germany

NETWORK ASSOCIATES, INC.

3965 Freedom Circle, Santa Clara, CA, 95054

Tel: (408) 988-3832   Fax: (408) 970-9727   www.networkassociates.com

Designs and produces network security and network management software and hardware.

Network Associates GmbH, Ohmstrasse 1, D-85716 Unterschleissheim, Germany

Tel: 49-89-3707-0   Fax: 49-89-3707-1199

Network Associates GmbH, Luisenweg 40, D-20537 Hamburg, Germany

Tel: 49-40-2531-0   Fax: 49-40-2531-2829

NETWORK COMPUTING DEVICES, INC. (NCDI)

301 Ravendale Drive, Mountain View, CA, 94043

Tel: (650) 694-0650   Fax: (650) 961-7711   www.ncd.com

Provider of server- and web-based computing solutions

NCD GmbH, Freischutzstrasse 92 /II, D-81927 München, Germany

NEUTROGENA CORPORATION

5760 West 96th Street, Los Angeles, CA, 90045

Tel: (310) 642-1150   Fax: (310) 337-5564   www.neutrogena.com

Mfr. facial cleansing, moisturizing products; body care, sun and hair care specialty products.

Neutrogena GmbH, Postfach 1216, Rheydter Str. 1-3, D-4052 Korschenbroich, Germany

NEW BALANCE ATHLETIC SHOE, INC.

Brighton Landing, 20 Guest Street, Boston, MA, 02135-2088

Tel: (617) 783-4000   Fax: (617) 787-9355   www.newbalance.com

Mfr. men's and women's athletic shoes.

New Balance Germany, Ganghoferstraße 45, D-82216 Gernlinden, Germany

NEW BRUNSWICK SCIENTIFIC COMPANY, INC.

44 Talmadge Road, Box 4005, Edison, NJ, 08818-4005

Tel: (732) 287-1200   Fax: (732) 287-4222   www.nbsc.com

Mfr. research and production equipment for life sciences.

New Brunswick Scientific GmbH, In der Au 14, D-72622 Nürtingen, Germany

Tel: 49-7022-932490   Fax: 49-7022-932486   Contact: Gerry Burgers, Gen. Mgr.

NEW HAMPSHIRE BALL BEARINGS INC. (NHBB)

9700 Independence Ave., Chatsworth, CA, 91311-4323

Tel: (818) 407-9300   Fax: (818) 407-9300   www.nhbb.com

Mfr. bearings and bearing assemblies.

NHBB, c/o NMB Minebca GmbH, Siemensstr. 30, D-63225 Langen, Germany

NEW HORIZONS WORLDWIDE, INC.

1900 S. State College Blvd., Anaheim, CA, 92806-6135

Tel: (714) 940-8000   Fax: www.newhorizons.com

Provides customer-focused computer training choices, through computer training centers.

New Horizons Worldwide, Hansaallee 247, D-40549 Düsseldorf, Germany

Tel: 49-211-280-48-0   Fax: 49-211-280-48-48

THE NEW YORK TIMES COMPANY

229 West 43rd Street, New York, NY, 10036-3959

Tel: (212) 556-1234   Fax: (212) 556-7389   www.nytimes.com

Diversified media company including newspapers, magazines, television and radio stations, and electronic information and publishing.

International Herald Tribune (IHT), Friedrichstrasse 15, D-60323 Frankfurt/Main, Germany

Tel: 49-69-97-12-5000

NEWELL RUBBERMAID

29 East Stephenson Street, Freeport, IL, 61032-0943

Tel: (815) 235-4171   Fax: (815) 489-8212   www.newellco.com

Mfr. hardware, housewares, and office products.

Gardinia Groujp, Isny, Germany

Rotring Group, Hamburg, Germany

NEWPORT CORPORATION

1791 Deere Ave., PO Box 19607, Irvine, CA, 92606

Tel: (949) 863-3144   Fax: (949) 253-1800   www.newport.com

Engaged in the design, manufacture and marketing of high-precision components, instruments and integrated systems to the fiber optic communications, semiconductor equipment and aerospace and research markets.

Newport GmbH, Holzhofalle 19, D-64295 Darmstadt, Germany

Tel: 49-6151-36210   Fax: 49-6151-362150

AC NIELSEN COMPANY

177 Broad Street, Stamford, CT, 06901

Tel: (203) 961-3000   Fax: (203) 961-3190   www.acnielsen.com

Engaged in market and consumer research.

ACNielsen, Ludwig-Landmann-Strasse 405, D-6000 Frankfurt Main 90, Germany

NIKU CORPORATION

305 Main Street, Redwood City, CA, 94063

Tel: (650) 298-4600   Fax: (650) 298-4601   www.niku.com

Mfr. software.

Niku Corporation GmbH, Oskar-Messter-Str. 33, D-85737 Ismaning, Germany

NL INDUSTRIES, INC.

16825 Northchase Drive, Ste. 1200, Houston, TX, 77060-2544

Tel: (281) 423-3300   Fax: (281) 423-3236   www.nl-ind.com

Producer of titanium dioxide pigments.

Kronos Marketing, Div. NL Industries, Peschstrasse 5, D-51373 Leverkusen, Germany

NORDSON CORPORATION

28601 Clemens Road, Westlake, OH, 44145-4551

Tel: (440) 892-1580   Fax: (440) 892-9507   www.nordson.com

Mfr. industry application equipment, sealants and packaging machinery.

Nordson Deutschland GbmH, Postfach 3234, Heinrich-Hertz-Strasse 42, D-40699 Erkrath 1, Germany

Tel: 49-211-92050 Fax: 49-211-254652

Nordson Engineering GmbH, Postfach 2165, Lilienthalstrasse 6, D-21337 Luneburg, Germany

Tel: 49-4131-8940   Fax: 49-4131-894-149

NORTON ABRASIVES COMPANY

1 New Bond Street, Worcester, MA, 01606

Tel: (508) 795-5000   Fax: (508) 795-5741   www.nortonabrasives.com

Mfr. abrasives for industrial manufacturing.

Christensen Diamond Products GmbH, Postfach 309, Heerstr. 61, D-3100 Braunschweiger, Germany

Norton GmbH, Vorgebirgsstr. 10, D-5047 Wesseling, Germany

NOVELL WORLDWIDE

1800 S. Novell Place, Provo, UT, 84606

Tel: (801) 861-7000   Fax: (801) 861-5555   www.novell.com

Develop/mfr. networking software and related equipment.

Novell GmbH, Niederlassung Munich, Joseph-Dollinger-Bogen 9, D-80807 München, Germany

NOVELLUS SYSTEMS INC.

4000 North First Street, San Jose, CA, 95134

Tel: (408) 943-9700   Fax: (408) 943-3422   www.novellus.com

Mfr. chemical vapor deposition (CVD), physical vapor deposition (PVD) and copper electrofill systems.

Novellus Systems GmbH, Ingolstaedter Strasse 22, D-80807 Münich, Germany

Tel: 49-893-50152-0   Fax: 49-89-350-152-99

Novellus Systems GmbH, Manfred Von Ardenne, Ring 20, D-01099 Dresden, Germany

Tel: 49-351-89252-10   Fax: 49-351-89252-20

NOVEON INTERNATIONAL

9911 Brecksville Road, Cleveland, OH, 44141-3427

Tel: (216) 447-5000   Fax: (216) 447-5669   www.noveoninc.com

Mfr. specialty chemicals.

Noveon Pharma GmbH & Co. KG, Georg-Reismuller-Str. 36, D-80999 Münich, Germany

Tel: 49-89-8106-335

NRG ENERGY, INC.

901 Marquette Avenue, Ste. 2300, Minneapolis, MN, 55402

Tel: (612) 373-5300   Fax: (612) 373-5466   www.nrgenergy.com

Electric power generation.

NRG Energy Development GmbH, Friedrichstrasse 50, D-10117 Berlin, Germany

Tel: 49-30-20-65-9219   Fax: 49-30-20-65-9330

NTL INCORPORATED

110 East 59th Street, New York, NY, 10022

Tel: (212) 906-8440   Fax: (212) 752-1157   www.ntl.com

Provides cable TV and Internet services.

NTL, Otto-Hahn-Ring 6, D-81739 Münich, Germany

Tel: 49-89-636-41325 Fax: 49-89-636-53484   Contact: Andrea Rohmeder, PR

NU SKIN ENTERPRISES, INC.

75 West Center St., Provo, UT, 84601

Tel: (801) 345-6100   Fax: (801) 345-5999   www.nuskin.com

Develops and distributes premium-quality personal care and nutritional products.

NuSkin Germany GmbH, Ginnheimer Strasse 4, D-65760 Eschborn, Germany

NUMATICS INC.

1450 North Milford Road, Highland, MI, 48357

Tel: (248) 887-4111   Fax: (248) 887-9190   www.numatics.com

Mfr. control valves and manifolds.

Numatics GmbH, Otto von Guericke Str. 13, D-5205 St. Augustin 3, Germany

Tel: 49-2241-3160-0   Fax: 49-2241-316040

NVIDIA CORPORATION

2701 San Tomas Expressway, Santa Clara, CA, 95050

Tel: (408) 486-2000   Fax: (408) 486-2200   www.nvidia.com

Mfr. graphics chips for video gamers and graphics designers.

NVIDIA GmbH, Adenauer-Strasse 20-B1, D-52146 Wurselen, Germany

OAK TECHNOLOGY, INC.

139 Kifer Court, Sunnyvale, CA, 94086

Tel: (408) 737-0888   Fax: (408) 737-3838   www.oaktech.com

Engaged in the design and manufacture of semiconductors.

Oak Technology, Hohe Strasse 28, D-44139 Dortmund, Germany

Tel: 231-914442-0 Fax: 231-914442-2

OCCIDENTAL PETROLEUM CORPORATION

10889 Wilshire Blvd., Los Angeles, CA, 90024

Tel: (310) 208-8800   Fax: (310) 443-6690   www.oxy.com

Petroleum and petroleum products, chemicals, plastics.

Kleinholz Mineraloel GmbH, Huysenallee 66-68, Postfach 856, D-4300 Essen, Germany

Mineraloel KG, Jungfernstieg 51, D-2000 Hamburg 36, Germany

Occidental Oil GmbH, Graf-Adolf-Str. 73, D-4000 Düsseldorf, Germany

OCLI, INC. (OPTICAL COATING LABORATORY, INC.)

2789 Northpoint Pkwy., Santa Rosa, CA, 95407-7397

Tel: (707) 545-6440   Fax: (707) 525-7410   www.ocli.com

Mfr. thin film precision coated optical devices.

OCLI Germany, Alte Heerstrasse 14, D-38644 Goslar, Germany

Tel: 49-5321-3590

OCLI Optical Coating Laboratory GmbH, Tilsiter Strasse 12, D-64354 Reinheim, Germany

Tel: 49-6162-93210

THE O'GARA COMPANY

1250 24th Street, NW, Suite 300, Washington, DC, 20037

Tel: (202) 835-1680   Fax: (202) 835-1685   www.ogara.com

Security and consulting services and vehicles.

Kroll Associates Frankfurt, Germany, Bleidensstrasse 6, D-60311 Frankfurt Am Main, Germany

Tel: 49-69-299840   Fax: 49-69-29984-170

OGILVY & MATHER WORLDWIDE

309 West 49th Street, New York, NY, 10017-7399

Tel: (212) 237-4000   Fax: (212) 237-5123   www.ogilvypr.com

Engaged in public relations and communications.

Ogilvy Healthcare, Burgplatz 21-22, D-40213 Düsseldorf, Germany

Tel: 49-211-1367-0   Contact: Maria Unland

Ogilvy Healthcare, Geleitsstrasse 25, D-60599 Frankfurt, Germany

Tel: 49-69 609101-0   Contact: Sabine Kreusch

OHAUS CORPORATION

PO Bpx 2033,19a Chapin Road, Pine Brook, NJ, 07058

Tel: (973) 377-9000   Fax: (973) 593-0359   www.ohaus.com

Mfr. balances and scales for laboratories, industry and education.

Ohaus Germany GmbH, An der Johanneskirche 6, D-35390 Giessen, Germany

Tel: 49-641-71023

THE OILGEAR COMPANY

2300 S. 51st Street, Milwaukee, WI, 53219

Tel: (414) 327-1700   Fax: (414) 327-0532   www.oilgear.com

Mfr. hydraulic power transmission machinery.

Oilgear Towler GmbH, Im Gotthelf 8, D-65795 Hattersheim, Germany

OLIN CORPORATION

501 Merritt Seven, Norwalk, CT, 06856-4500

Tel: (203) 750-3000   Fax: (203) 750-3292   www.olin.com

Mfr. chemicals, metals, sporting ammunition and copper and copper alloy sheets.

Olin Chemicals GmbH, Ander Hoffnung 125, D-40885 Ratingen, Germany

Tel: 49-2102-77-110

OM GROUP, INC. (OMG)

3500 Terminal Tower, Cleveland, OH, 44113-2203

Tel: (216) 781-0083   Fax: (216) 781-0902   www.omgi.com

Producer and marketer of metal-based specialty chemicals.

OMG Europe GmbH, Muensterstrasse 248, D-40470 Düsseldorf, Germany

Tel: 49-211-961-880   Fax: 49-211-614-629

OMNICARE, INC.

100 E. River Center Blvd., Covington, KY, 41011

Tel: (859) 392-3300   Fax: (859) 392-3333   www.omnicare.com

Provides pharmaceutical and nursing home services.

IFNS (Institut Fur Numerische Statistik), Cologne, Germany

Contact: Dr. Wolfgang Haase

ON TECHNOLOGY CORPORATION

880 Winter Street, B.dg. 4, Waltham, MA, 02451-1449

Tel: (781) 487-3300   Fax: (781) 487-3301   www.on.com

Mfr. asset management software.

ON Technology Europe GmbH, Enzianstrasse 4, D-82319 Starnberg, Germany

Tel: 49-8151-3690 Fax: 49-8151-369-100

ONDEO NALCO COMPANY

Ondeo Nalco Center, 1601 W. Diehl Road, Naperville, IL, 60563-1198

Tel: (630) 305-1000   Fax: (630) 305-2900   www.ondeo-nalco.com

Mfr. specialty chemicals for water and waste water treatment, oil products and refining, industry processes; water and energy management service.

Deutsche ONDEO Nalco Chemie GmbH, Postfach 970110, D-6000 Frankfurt Main 90, Germany

Tel: 49-69-793-40 Fax: 49-69-793-4295

ONYX SOFTWARE CORPORATION

3180 139th Avenue SE, Ste. 500, Bellevue, WA, 98005

Tel: (425) 451-8060   Fax: (425) 451-8277   www.onyx.com

Mfr. customer relationship management software.

Onyx Software Germany, Franziskaner Strasse 38, D-81669 München, Germany

OPEN MARKET, INC.

1 Wayside Road, Burlington, MA, 01803

Tel: (781) 359-3000   Fax: (781) 359-8111   www.openmarket.com

Mfr. catalog management software.

Open Market GmbH, Hessenring 119, D-61348 Bad Homburg, Germany

OPENWAVE SYSTEMS INC.

1400 Seaport Blvd., Redwood City, CA, 94063

Tel: (650) 480-8000   Fax: (650) 480-8100   www.openwave.com

Mfr. software for wireless telephones.

Openwave Systems, Leopold Str. 244, D-80807 München, Germany

OPNEXT, INC.

1 Christopher Way, Eatontown, NJ, 07724

Tel: (732) 544-3400   Fax: (732) 544-3540   www.opnext.com

Mfr. optoelectronic components for fiber optic data and voice communications networks.

OpNext Europe, Dornacher Str 3, D-85622 Feldkirchen Bei, Germany

Tel: 49-89-99180-215 Fax: 49-89-99180-352

ORACLE CORPORATION

500 Oracle Parkway, Redwood Shores, CA, 94065

Tel: (650) 506-7000   Fax: (650) 506-7200   www.oracle.com

Develop/manufacture software.

Oracle Deutschland GmbH, Hauptverwaltung, Hanover Strasse 87, D-8000 München 50, Germany

ORC MACRO INTERNATIONAL INC.

11785 Beltsville Dr., Calverton, MD, 20705-3119

Tel: (301) 572-0200   Fax: (301) 572-0999   www.macroint.com

Engaged in research and evaluation, training, consulting and information technology.

Macro Internatinoal Inc., Im Brohl 16, D- 614 Kronberg/Ts., Germany

Tel: 49-61-7395-0862   Fax: 49-61-7395-0863   Contact: Douglas Ziurys, Mng. Dir.

ORIEL INSTRUMENTS CORPORATION

150 Long Beach Boulevard, Stratford, CT, 06615

Tel: (203) 377-8282   Fax: (203) 378-2457   www.oriel.com

Mfr. optical goods.

L.O.T.-Oriel GmbH & CO KG, Im Tiefen See 58, D-64293 Darmstadt, Germany

Tel: 49-6151-88-060

OSMONICS INC.

5951 Clearwater Drive, Minnetonka, MN, 55343-8995

Tel: (952) 933-2277   Fax: (952) 933-0141   www.osmonics.com

Mfr. equipment, controls and components for the filtration and water-treatment industries.

Osmonics GmbH, Düsseldorf, Germany

OTIS ELEVATOR COMPANY

One Farm Springs Road, Farmington, CT, 06032

Tel: (860) 676-6000   Fax: (860) 676-5111   www.otis.com

Mfr. elevators and escalators.

Otis Escalator GmbH, Industriestrasse 2, D-31655 Stadthagen, Germany

Otis GmbH, Otisstrasse 33, D-13507 Berlin, Germany

OWENS-CORNING CORPORATION

One Owens Corning Pkwy., Toledo, OH, 43659

Tel: (419) 248-8000   Fax: (419) 248-8445   www.owenscorning.com

Mfr. building materials systems and composites systems.

Deutsche Owens-Corning Glasswool GmbH, Idsteiner Strasse 82, D-65232 Taunusstein-Neuhof, Germany

Owens-Corning Fiberglas Deutschland GmbH, Königsberger Ring 82, D-30559 Hannover, Germany

PACIFIC ARCHITECTS & ENGINEERS INC. (PAE)

888 South Figueroa Street, 17th Fl., Los Angeles, CA, 90017

Tel: (213) 481-2311   Fax: (213) 481-7189   www.paechl.com

Technical engineering services.

PAE GmbH Planning & Construction, Kurhessen Strasse 1, D-64546 Moerfelden-Walldorf, Germany

Tel: 49-6105-91110   Fax: 49-6105-33069   Contact: John D. Pawulak, Mgr.   Emp: 10

PALL CORPORATION

2200 Northern Boulevard, East Hills, NY, 11548-1289

Tel: (516) 484-5400   Fax: (516) 484-5228   www.pall.com

Specialty materials and engineering; filters and related fluid clarification equipment.

Pall Filtrationstechnik GmbH, Philipp-Reis Strasse 6, D-63303 Frankfurt, Germany

Tel: 49-6-103-3070   Fax: 49-6-103-34037

Pall Gelman Sciences, Arheilger Weg 6, D-64380 Robdorf, Germany

Tel: 49-6-154-60220   Fax: 49-6-154-602260

Pall Rochem, Stenzelring 14A, D-2102 Hamburg 93, Germany

Tel: 49-4-75-27940   Fax: 49-4-75-279434

PANAMETRICS

221 Crescent Street, Waltham, MA, 02154

Tel: (781) 899-2719   Fax: (781) 899-1552   www.panametrics.com

Engaged in manufacture and distribution of ultrasonic testing equipment and process control instrumentation.

Panametrics Gmbh, Analysen-und Prüftechnik, Rudolf-Diesel-Strabe 1, D-65719 Hofheim, Germany

Tel: 49-6122-8090   Fax: 49-6122-8147   Contact: Hans-Juergen Boeger

PANDUIT CORPORATION

17301 Ridgeland Ave., Tinley Park, IL, 60477-0981

Tel: (708) 532-1800   Fax: (708) 532-1811   www.panduit.com

Mfr. of network connectivity and electrical products.

Panduit GmbH, In der Au 25, D-61440 Oberursel, Germany

PAPER CONVERTING MACHINE COMPANY

PO Box 19005, 2300 S. Ashland Ave., Green Bay, WI, 54307

Tel: (920) 494-5601   Fax: (920) 494-8865   www.pcmc.com

Mfr. converting machinery for the sanitary tissue, flexible packaging and disposables nonwovens industries.

Paper Converting Machine Europe GmbH, PO Box 10 04 39, D-76258 Ettlingen, Germany

Tel: 49-7243-72580

PARAMETRIC TECHNOLOGY CORPORATION

140 Kendrick St., Needham, MA, 02494

Tel: (781) 370-5000   Fax: (781) 370-6000   www.ptc.com

Supplier of mechanical design automation and product data management software and services.

Parametric Technology GmbH, In deu Spoeck 6, D-77656 Offenburg, Germany

Tel: 49-781-6102   Fax: 49-781-61229

Parametric Technology GmbH, Rudower Stasse 90/94, D-12351 Berlin, Germany

Tel: 49-30-60008-319   Fax: 49-30-60008-619

Parametric Technology GmbH, Otto-Brenner Strasse 207-209, D-33604 Bielefeld, Germany

Tel: 49-52-19276-131   Fax: 49-52-19276-132

Parametric Technology GmbH, In den Dauen 6, D-53117 Bonn, Germany

Tel: 49-22-8555-1240   Fax: 49-22-8555-110

Parametric Technology GmbH, Parkallee 117, D-28209 Bremen, Germany

Tel: 49-421-3475-619   Fax: 49-421-3499-827

Parametric Technology GmbH, Paulinenstasse 94, D-88046 Griedrichshafen, Germany

Tel: 49-7541-3811-0   Fax: 49-7541-3811-15

Parametric Technology GmbH, Sachsenfeld 4, 4th Fl., D-20097 Hamburg, Germany

Tel: 49-40-23505-666   Fax: 49-40-235085-665

Parametric Technology GmbH, Wilhemshoher Allee 239, D-34121 Kassel, Germany

Tel: 49-561-935-3134   Fax: 49-561-935-3100

Parametric Technology GmbH, Salomonstasse 17, D-04129 Leipzig, Germany

Tel: 49-341-994-0360   Fax: 49-341-994-0361

Parametric Technology GmbH, Edisonstasse 8, D-85716 Unteerschlessheim, Germany

Tel: 49-89-32106-0   Fax: 49-89-32106-150

Parametric Technology GmbH, Geschaegtsstelle Nuremberg, Kleinreuther Weg 120, D-90425 Nuremburg, Germany

Tel: 49-911-3651-126   Fax: 49-911-3651-131

Parametric Technology GmbH, Geschastsstelle Hannover, Hildesheimer Stasse 53, D-30169 Kassel, Germany

Tel: 49-511-8071-130   Fax: 49-511-8071-132

Parametric Technology GmbH, Kaiserswerter Strasse 115, D-40882 Ratingen, Germany

Tel: 49-2102-742-60   Fax: 49-2102-742-6666

Parametric Technology GmbH, Zettachring 2, D-70567 Stuttgart, Germany

Tel: 49-711-7287-265   Fax: 49-711-7280-396

Parametric Technology GmbH, Simemensstasse 9, D-63263 Neu-Isenburg, Germany

Tel: 49-6102-782-5   Fax: 49-6102-782-666

PAREXEL INTERNATIONAL CORPORATION

195 West Street, Waltham, MA, 02154

Tel: (781) 487-9900   Fax: (781) 487-0525   www.parexel.com

Provides contract medical, biotechnology, and pharmaceutical research and consulting services.

PAREXEL International, Klinikum Westend Haus 18, Spandauer Damm 130, D-14050 Berlin, Germany

Tel: 49-30-306850   Fax: 49-30-30685-299

PAREXEL International, Schleussnerstr. 90, D-63263 Neu-Isenburg, Germany
Tel: 49-6102-71620 Fax: 49-6102-716222

PAREXEL LOGOS, Kartauserstrasse 47, D-79102 Freiburg, Germany
Tel: 49-761-282800 Fax: 49-761-34086

PARKER HANNIFIN CORPORATION
6035 Parkland Blvd., Cleveland, OH, 44124-4141
Tel: (216) 896-3000   Fax: (216) 896-4000   www.parker.com
Mfr. motion-control products.

Hauser Elektronik GmbH, Postfach 1720, D-77607 Offenburg, Germany

Parker GmbH Fluid Verbindungsteile, Postfach 1120, Freiherr-vom-Stein-Strasse, D-35325 Mucke, Germany

Parker Hannefin GmbH, Automotive & Refrigeration Group, Postfach 1120, D-35322 Mucke, Germany

Parker Hannifin Corp., Polyflex Div. Europe, An der Tuckbleiche 4, D-68623 Lampertheim Huttenfeld, Germany

Parker Hannifin Corp., Seal Products/Parker Praedifa GmbH, Praezisions-Dichtungen,, Postfach 40, Stuifenstrasse 55, D-74385 Pleidelsheim, Germany

Parker Hannifin GmbH, Romerweg 13, D-78727 Oberndorf am Neckar, Germany

Parker Hannifin GmbH, Heimchenweg 8, D-65929 Frankfurt/Main, Germany

Parker Hannifin GmbH, Johann-Strauss-Strasse 51, D-70794 Filderstadt, Germany

Parker Hannifin GmbH, Ermeto Div., Am Metallwerk 9, D-33659 Bielefeld, Germany

Parker Hannifin NMF GmbH, Delmenhorster Str. 10, D-50735 Cologne, Germany

Parker Hannifin NMF GmbH, Hydraulic Control Div., Gutenbergstrasse 36, D-41564 Kaarst, Germany

Parker Hannifin Schrader Bellows GmbH, Heidestr. 71, D-42549 Velbert, Germany

Parker Praedifa GmbH, Postfach 1641, D-74306 Beitigheim-Bissingen, Germany

PEDDINGHAUS CORPORATION
300 North Washington Avenue, Bradley, IL, 60915
Tel: (815) 937-3800   Fax: (815) 937-4003   www.peddinghaus.com
Mfr./distribute structure steel and plate-fabricating equipment.

Peddinghaus Anlagen Und Maschinen GmbH (PAM), Hasslinghauser Strasse 150, D-58285 Geelsberg, Germany
Tel: 49-2332-9126-25 Fax: 49-2332-9126-28

PENTAIR, INC.
1500 County Road, B2 West, St. Paul, MN, 55113-3105
Tel: (612) 636-7920   Fax: (612) 636-5508   www.pentair.com
Diversified manufacturer operating in electrical and electronic enclosures, professional tools/equipment and water products.

FLEX-Elektrowerkzeuge GmbH, Bahnhofstrasse 15, D-71711 Steinheim Murr, Germany

Pentair Enclosures, Langenalber Strasse 96-100, D-75332 Straubenhardt, Germany

PENWEST PHARMACEUTICAL CO.
2981 Route 22, Patterson, NY, 12563-9970
Tel: (845) 878-3414   Fax: (845) 878-3484   www.penw.com
Engaged in the research, development and commercialization of novel drug delivery technologies.

Penwest Pharmaceuticals GmbH, Am Kummerling 21-25, D-55294 Bodenheim, Germany

PEOPLESOFT INC.
4460 Hacienda Drive, Pleasanton, CA, 94588-8618
Tel: (925) 225-3000   Fax: (925) 694-4444   www.peoplesoft.com
Mfr. applications to manage business operations across computer networks.

PeopleSoft GmbH, Haus 13i-3-OG, Postfach 39, Friedrich-Ebert-Straße, D-51429 Bergisch Gladbach, Germany
Tel: 49-2204-84-2980

PEPSiCO INC.
700 Anderson Hill Road, Purchase, NY, 10577-1444
Tel: (914) 253-2000   Fax: (914) 253-2070   www.pepsico.com
Beverages and snack foods.

Florida Intl. Fruchsaftgetraenke GmbH, Münich, Germany

PepsiCo GmbH, Münich, Germany

PEREGRINE SYSTEMS, INC.

3611 Valley Centre Drive, San Diego, CA, 92130

Tel: (858) 481-5000   Fax: (858) 481-1751   www.peregrine.com

Mfr. resource planning software.

Peregrine Systems GmbH, Bürohaus ATRICOM, Lyoner Strasse 15, D-60528 Frankfurt, Germany

PERKIN ELMER, INC.

45 William Street, Wellesley, MA, 02481

Tel: (781) 237-5100   Fax: (781) 431-4255   www.perkinelmer.com

Mfr. equipment and devices to detect explosives and bombs on airline carriers.

PerkinElmer Life Sciences, Wenzel-Jaksch-Str. 31, D-65199 Wiesbaden, Germany

PEROT SYSTEMS CORPORATION

12404 Park Central Drive, Dallas, TX, 75251

Tel: (972) 340-5000   Fax: (972) 455-4100   www.perotsystems.com

Provides technology and business solutions.

HPS GmbH, Hahnstrasse 43, D-60528 Frankfort, Germany

Tel: 49-0-69-664-46400

PERVASIVE SOFTWARE INC.

12365 Riata Trace Pkwy., Austin, TX, 78727

Tel: (512) 231-6000   Fax: (512) 231-6010   www.pervasive.com

Mfr. software.

Pervasive EMEAA, Frankfurter Strasse 151d, Frankfurt, Germany

PFAUDLER, INC.

1000 West Ave., PO Box 23600, Rochester, NY, 14692-3600

Tel: (716) 235-1000   Fax: (716) 436-9644   www.pfaudler.com

Mfr. glass lined reactors, storage vessels and reglassing services.

Pfaudler-Werke GmbH, Postfach 1780, Pfaudler Strasse, D-6830 Schwetzingen, Germany

Tel: 49-620-2850   Fax: 49-620-222-412

PFIZER INC.

235 East 42nd Street, New York, NY, 10017-5755

Tel: (212) 573-2323   Fax: (212) 573-7851   www.pfizer.com

Research-based, global health care company.

C.H. Buer GmbH, Münich, Germany

Forster & Hug KG, Münich, Germany

Heinrich Mack Nachf. Gmbh & Co. KG, Buro Karlsruhe, Pfizerstraße 1, D-76139 Karlsruhe, Germany

Hilekes GmbH, Münich, Germany

Leibinger GmbH, Freiburg, Germany

Pfizer GmbH, Heinrich-Mack-Straße 35, D-89257 Illertissen, Germany

Tel: 49-28-02-2000

Pfizer Holding und Verwaltungs GmbH, Pfizerstraße 1, D-76139 Karlstruhe, Germany

Taylor Kosmetic GmbH, Pfizerstraße 1, D-76139 Karlstruhe, Germany

PHARMACIA CORPORATION

100 Route 206 North, Peapack, NJ, 07977

Tel: (908) 901-8000   Fax: (908) 901-8379   www.pharmacia.com

Mfr. pharmaceuticals, agricultural products, industry chemicals.

Pharmacia GmbH, Am Wolfsmantel 46, D-91058 Erlangen, Germany

Tel: 49-9131-620   Fax: 49-9131-621202

PHELPS DODGE CORPORATION

2600 North Central Ave., Phoenix, AZ, 85004-3089

Tel: (602) 234-8100   Fax: (602) 234-8337   www.phelpsdodge.com

Copper, minerals, metals and special engineered products for transportation and electrical markets.

Columbian Carbon Deutschland GmbH, Antwerpenstrasse 1, D-2103 Hamburg 95, Germany

Columbian Chemicals GmbH, Hannover, Germany

PHH ARVAL VEHICLE MANAGEMENT

307 International Circle, Hunt Valley, MD, 21030

Tel: (410) 771-3600   Fax: (410) 771-2841   www.phh.com

Provides fleet leasing and fleet management services to corporate and government clients with sales, service, delivery, executive or specialized trucks fleets.

PHH Vehicle Management Services, Stäblistrasse 8, D-81477 Münich, Germany

Tel: 49-89-780440

PHILIP SERVICES CORP. INDUSTRIAL GROUP

9700 Higgins Road, Ste. 750, Rosemont, IL, 60018

Tel: (847) 685-9752   Fax: (847) 685-9775   www.philipinc.com

Trucking, refuse systems, staffing and numerous industrial-oriented services.

Industrial Services Philip Services (Europe), Landshuterstrasse 56, D-84130 Dingolfing, Germany

Tel: 49-87-31-72-5100 Fax: 49-87-31-72-5864   Contact: Gernot Waltenstorfer

PHILIPP BROTHERS CHEMICALS INC.

1 Parker Plaza, 400 Kelby Street, Fort Lee, NJ, 07029

Tel: (201) 944-6020   Fax: (201) 944-7916   www.philipp-brothers.com

Mfr. industry and agricultural chemicals.

Ferro Metal & Chemical Corp., Münich, Germany

Tel: 44-118-959-1961

PHILLIPS PETROLEUM COMPANY

Phillips Building, 411 S. Keeler Ave., Bartlesville, OK, 74004

Tel: (918) 661-6600   Fax: (918) 661-7636   www.phillips66.com

Crude oil, natural gas, liquefied petroleum gas, gasoline and petro-chemicals.

Phillips Petroleum International GmbH, Ulmenstr. 37, D-6000 Frankfurt/Main, Germany

PHILLIPS, DE PURY & LUXEMBOURG

3 West 57th Street, New York, NY, 10019

Tel: (212) 940-1200   Fax: (212) 688-1647   www.phillips-auctions.com

Auction house.

Phillips De Pury & Luxembourg, Maximiliansplatz 12a, D-80333 Münich, Germany

PHOENIX TECHNOLOGIES LTD.

411 East Plumeria Drive, San Jose, CA, 95134

Tel: (408) 570-1000   Fax: (408) 570-1001   www.phoenix.com

Mfr. BIOS software.

Phoenix Technologies GmbH, Landsbergerstrasse 318, D-80687 Münich, Germany

Tel: 49-89 -58- 999-0   Fax: 49-89-58-999-499

PHOTRONICS, INC.

1061 E. Indiantown Rd., Ste. 310, Jupiter, FL, 33477

Tel: (561) 745-1222   Fax: (561) 747-1432   www.photronics.com

Mfr. high-precision quartz photomasks for semiconductors.

Photronics Germany, Grenzstrasse 28, D-01109 Dresden, Germany

Tel: 33-450-426-4   Fax: 33-450-426-494   Contact: Dominique Varloud

PIERCE & STEVENS CORPORATION

710 Ohio Street, Buffalo, NY, 14203

Tel: (716) 856-4910   Fax: (716) 856-0942   www.dualite-spheres.com

Mfr. coatings, adhesives and specialty chemical for packaging and graphic arts..

Lehmann & Voss & Co., Alsteruler 19, D-20354 Hamburg, Germany

PINNACLE SYSTEMS

280 North Bernardo Ave., Mountain View, CA, 94043

Tel: (650) 526-1600   Fax: (650) 526-1601   www.pinnaclesys.com

Designs, manufactures, markets and supports a wide range of high-quality digital solutions that enable businesses and consumers to create, store, distribute and view video programs.

Pinnacle Systems GmbH, Rüdesheimer Strasse 11-13, D-80686 Münich, Germany

Pinnacle Systems GmbH, Frankfurter Str. 3, D-80331 Braunschweig, Germany

Tel: 49-531-2183-0

PIONEER HI-BRED INTERNATIONAL INC.

400 Locust Street, Ste. 800, Des Moines, IA, 50309

Tel: (515) 248-4800   Fax: (515) 248-4999   www.pioneer.com

Agricultural chemicals, farm supplies, biological products, research.

Pioneer Hi-Bred Northern Europe GmbH, Apensener Str. 198, PO Box 1464, D-2150 Buxtehude, Germany

PIONEER-STANDARD ELECTRONICS, INC.

6065 Parkland Blvd., Cleveland, OH, 44124

Tel: (440) 720-8500   Fax: (440) 720-8501   www.pios.com

Mfr. and distribution of electronic parts for computers and networking equipment.

Eurodis Enatechnik, Pascalkehre 1, D-24551 Quickborn, Germany

PITNEY BOWES INC.

1 Elmcroft Road, Stamford, CT, 06926-0700

Tel: (203) 356-5000   Fax: (203) 351-6835   www.pitneybowes.com

Mfr. postage meters, mailroom equipment, copiers, bus supplies, bus services, facsimile systems and financial services.

Pitney Bowes Deutschland GmbH, Tiergartenstrasse 7, D-64636 Happenheim, Germany

Tel: 49-6252-7080   Fax: 49-6252-708-206   Contact: Klaus Karl, Mng. Dir.   Emp: 600

PLANAR SYSTEMS, INC.

1400 NW Compton Drive, Beaverton, OR, 97006

Tel: (503) 690-1100   Fax: (503) 690-1541   www.planar.com

Mfr. of flat panel displays and liquid crystal displays.

Planar Systems GmbH, Fürstenrieder Strasse 279a, D-81377 Münich, Germany

Tel: 49-89-741-201-64   Fax: 49-89-741-201-02   Contact: Raine Bornwasser

PLANET HOLLYWOOD INTERNATIONAL, INC.

8669 Commodity Circle, Orlando, FL, 32819

Tel: (407) 363-7827   Fax: (407) 363-4862   www.planethollywood.com

Theme-dining restaurant chain and merchandise retail stores.

Planet Hollywood International, Inc., Berlin, Germany

Planet Hollywood International, Inc., Promenade 1, Centro, Oberhausen Nord Rhein, D-46047 Westjalen, Germany

PLANTRONICS

345 Encinal Street, Santa Cruz, CA, 95060

Tel: (831) 426-5858   Fax: (831) 425-5198   www.plantronics.com

Mfr. lightweight headsets and communications equipment and electrical and electronic appliances.

Plantronics GmbH, Gildenweg 7, D-50354 Hurth, Germany

Tel: 49-2233-3990   Fax: 49-2233-399399

PLUMTREE SOFTWARE, INC.

500 Sansome Street, San Francisco, CA, 94111

Tel: (415) 263-8900   Fax: (415) 263-8991   www.plumtree.com

Mfr. organizational software.

Plumtree Software GmbH, Humboldtstr. 12, 85609, D-85609 Münich, Germany

POET HOLDINGS, INC.

999 Baker Way, Ste. 200, San Mateo, CA, 94404

Tel: (650) 577-2500   Fax: (650) 286-4630   www.poet.com

Mfr. software.

Poet Holdings GmbH, Kattjahren 4-8, D-22359 Hamburg, Germany

Poet Software GmbH, Suskindstrasse 4, D-81929 Münich, Germany

Poet Software GmbH, SAP Partner Port, Altrottstrasse 31, D-69190 Walldorf, Germany

POLARIS INDUSTRIES INC.

2100 Highway 55, Medina, MN, 55440

Tel: (612) 542-0500   Fax: (612) 542-0599   www.polarisindustries.com

Mfr. snowmobiles and all-terrain recreational and utility vehicles.

Taubenreuther GmbH, Postfach 2008, D-95326 Kulmbach, Germany

Tel: 49-922-195-6222

POLAROID CORPORATION

784 Memorial Drive, Cambridge, MA, 02139

Tel: (781) 386-2000   Fax: (781) 386-3924   www.polaroid.com

Photographic equipment and supplies, optical products.

Polaroid GmbH, Postfach 101563, D63015 Offenbach, Germany

R.L. POLK & COMPANY

26955 Northwestern Hwy., Southfield, MI, 48034

Tel: (248) 728-7111   Fax: (248) 393-2860   www.polk.com

Directories and direct mail advertising.

Portica GmbH, Von-Galen Str. 35, D-4152 Kempen 1, Germany

POLYCOM, INC.

1565 Barber Lane, Milpitas, CA, 95035

Tel: (408) 526-9000   Fax: (408) 526-9100   www.polycom.com

Mfr. video conferencing systems, network bridging and multiplexing products, system peripherals.

Polycom GmbH, Messeturm, Box 23, D-60208 Frankfurt am Main, Germany

Tel: 49-69-975-44503   Fax: 49-69-975-44928

Polycom GmbH, Demo Center Düsseldorf, Wilhelm-Marx-Haus, Heinrich-Heine-Allee 53, D-40213 Düsseldorf, Germany

Tel: 49-211-8307205   Fax: 49-211-8308370

Polycom GmbH, Büropark Oktavian, Feringstrasse 6, D-85774 Münich-Unterfohring, Germany

Tel: 49-89-992-110   Fax: 49-89-992-11200

PORTAL SOFTWARE, INC.

10200 S. De Anza Bolevard, Cupertino, CA, 95014

Tel: (408) 572-2000   Fax: (408) 572-2001   www.portal.com

Mfr. customer management and billing software.

Portal Software GmbH, Ernst-Abbe-Strasse 10, D-25451 Quickborn, Germany

Tel: 49-4106-760-0   Fax: 49-4106-760-199

Portal Software GmbH, Gartenstrasse 25, D-61352 Bad Homburg, Germany

Tel: 49-6172-9446-0   Fax: 49-6172-9446-29

Portal Software GmbH, Oskar-Messter-Strasse 33, D-85737 Ismaning, Germany

Tel: 49-89-665507-0

PORTER PRECISION PRODUCTS COMPANY

2734 Banning Road, PO Box 538706, Cincinnati, OH, 45239

Tel: (513) 923-3777   Fax: (513) 923-1111   www.porterpunch.com

Mfr. piercing punches and die supplies for metal stamping and tool/die industry.

Porter Intl. GmbH, Am Gewerbepark 23, D-6108 Gros-Umstadt, Germany

POTTERS INDUSTRIES INC.

PO Box 840, Valley Forge, PA, 19482-0840

Tel: (610) 651-4700   Fax: (610) 408-9724   www.pottersbeads.com

Mfr. glass spheres for road marking and industry applications.

Potters-Ballotini, Benderstrasse 8, D-40625 Düsseldorf, Germany

Potters-Ballotini GmbH, Morschheimerstr. 9, Postfach 1226, D-67292 Kirchheimbolanden, Germany

POWERQUEST CORPORATION

1359 North Research Way, Bldg. K, Box 1911, Orem, UT, 84059

Tel: (801) 437-8900   Fax: (801) 226-8941   www.powerquest.com

Provides storage lifecycle automation solutions.

PowerQuest GmbH, Max-Planck-Straße 13, D-85716 Unterschleißheim, Germany

POWERWARE CORPORATION

8609 Six Forks Road, Raleigh, NC, 27615

Tel: (919) 870-3020   Fax: (919) 870-3100   www.powerware.com

Mfr./services uninterruptible power supplies and related equipment.

Powerware Electronics GmbH, Bem Alten Bahnhof 1, D-76530 Baden Baden, Germany

Tel: 49-7221-9388-0   Fax: 49-7221-9388-33

PPG INDUSTRIES

One PPG Place, Pittsburgh, PA, 15272

Tel: (412) 434-3131   Fax: (412) 434-2190   www.ppg.com

Mfr. coatings, flat glass, fiber glass, chemicals.

PPG Industries Lacke GmbH, Stackenbergstrasse 34, D-42329 Wuppertal, Germany

PPG Industries Lackfabrik GmbH, Werner-Siemensstrasse 1, D-76356 Weingarten, Germany

PR NEWSWIRE ASSOCIATION INC.

810 Seventh Avenue, 35th Fl., New York, NY, 10019

Tel: (212) 596-1500   Fax: (212) 541-6114   www.prnewswire.com

Distribution of news releases and photos to media organizations.

PR Newswire Europe GmbH, Bockenheimer Landstrasse 43, D-60325 Frankfurt, Germany

PRAXAIR, INC.

39 Old Ridgebury Road, Danbury, CT, 06810-5113

Tel: (203) 837-2000   Fax: (203) 837-2450   www.praxair.com

Produces and distributes industrial and specialty gases.

Praxair GmbH, Justus-von-Liebig Strasse 2, D-64580 Biebesheim/Rhein, Germany

Tel: 49-6258-8980   Fax: 49-6258-89850

PRECISION VALVE & TRIM, INC.

11923 Cloverland Ave, Baton Rouge, LA, 70809

Tel: (225) 752-5600   Fax: (225) 752-5400   www.precisionvalve.com

Mfr. aerosol valves.

Deutsche Prazisions Ventil GmbH, Schulstr. 33, D-6234 Battersheim Main, Germany

PRG-SCHULTZ INTERNATIONAL INC.

2300 Windy Ridge Pkwy., Ste. 100 N, Atlanta, GA, 30339-8426

Tel: (770) 779-3900   Fax: (770) 898-2996   www.prgx.com

Engaged in comprehensive recovery auditing and process improvement services.

PRG-Schultz Germany, Inc., Robert-Bosch-Strasse 25A, D-63225 Langen, Germany

Tel: 49-6103-20-111-30   Fax: 49-6103-20-111-33

PRICEWATERHOUSECOOPERS LLP

1301 Ave. of the Americas, New York, NY, 10019

Tel: (212) 596-7000   Fax: (212) 259-1301   www.pwcglobal.com

Accounting and auditing, tax and management, and human resource consulting services.

PriceWaterhouseCoopers, Arnulfstrasse 25, Postfach 20 16 42, D-80016 Münich, Germany

Tel: 49-89-55-14-80   Fax: 49-89-55-14-8-222

PriceWaterhouseCoopers, Heilbronner Strasse 190, Postfach 10 38 53, D-70033 Stuttgart, Germany

Tel: 49-711-1652-0   Fax: 49-711-1652-222

PriceWaterhouseCoopers, Mozartstrasse 1, Postfach 405, D-04004 Leipzig, Germany

Tel: 49-341-2135-6   Fax: 49-341-2135-777

PriceWaterhouseCoopers, ABC-Strasse 45, Postfach 30 40 69, D-20313 Hamburg, Germany

Tel: 49-40-3-55-56-0   Fax: 49-40-3-55-56-123

PriceWaterhouseCoopers, Gervinusstrasse 15, D-60322 Frankfurt am Main, Germany

Tel: 49-69-15204-600   Fax: 49-69-15204-666

PriceWaterhouseCoopers, Graf-Recke-Strasse 82, Postfach 17 02 64, D-40083 Düsseldorf, Germany

Tel: 49-211-9615-01   Fax: 49-211-9615-700

PriceWaterhouseCoopers, Ostra-Allee 25, Postfach 12 03 11, D-01004 Dresden, Germany

Tel: 49-351-4860260   Fax: 49-351-4860245

PriceWaterhouseCoopers, An der Muhle 3, D-13507 Berlin, Germany

Tel: 49-30-43902-0   Fax: 49-30-43902-999

PRINTRONIX INC.

14600 Myford Road, Irvine, CA, 92606

Tel: (714) 368-2300   Fax: (714) 368-2600   www.printronix.com

Mfr. computer printers.

Printronix GmbH, Goethering 56, D-63067 Offenbach, Germany

Tel: 49-69-829-7060   Fax: 49-69-829-70622

PROCTER & GAMBLE COMPANY

One Procter & Gamble Plaza, Cincinnati, OH, 45202

Tel: (513) 983-1100   Fax: (513) 562-4500   www.pg.com

Personal care, food, laundry, cleaning and industry products.

Procter & Gamble GmbH, Sulzbacherstr. 40, D-65824 Schwalbach/Ts., Germany

PROCTER & GAMBLE PHARMACEUTICALS (P&GP)

17 Eaton Ave., Norwich, NY, 13815-1799

Tel: (607) 335-2111   Fax: (607) 335-2798   www.pg.com

Engaged in research dedicated to creating and delivering solutions that improve the health and well-being of people around the world.

Procter & Gamble Pharmaceuticals GmbH, Postfach 100161, D-64201 Darmstadt, Germany

PROQUEST COMPANY

300 N. Zeeb Road, Ann Arbor, MI, 48103

Tel: (734) 761-4700   Fax: (734) 997-4040   www.bellhowell.com

Engaged in information management services; publishers of electronic content for the academic, library, automotive and power sports industries.

ProQuest Information and Learning Company, Grüner Weg 8, D-61169 Friedberg, Germany

PROXIM CORPORATION

510 DeGuigne Drive, Sunnyvale, CA, 94089

Tel: (408) 731-2700   Fax: (408) 731-3675   www.proxim.com

Mfr. wireless modems.

Proxim GmbH, Rosenstrasse 2, D-10178 Berlin, Germany

PRUDENTIAL FINANCIAL

751 Broad Street, Newark, NJ, 07102-3777

Tel: (973) 802-6000   Fax: (973) 802-2804   www.prudential.com

Sale of life insurance, financial services, asset management and brokerage.

Prudential-Bache International Limited, Mainzer Landstrasse 46, 13th Floor, D-60325 Frankfurt, Germany

Tel: 49-69-971350   Fax: 49-69-97135241   Contact: David G. Traughber

PSC INC.

111 SW Fifth Avenue, Ste. 4100, Portland, OR, 97204-3644

Tel: (503) 553-3920   Fax: (503) 553-3940   www.pscnet.com

Mfr. and sales of bar code scanners.

PSC GmbH, Guerickeweg 7 + 9, D-64291 Darmstadt, Germany

PSI NET (PERFORMANCE SYSTEMS INTERNATIONAL INC.)

44983 Knoll Square, Ashburn, VA, 20147

Tel: (703) 726-4100   Fax: (703) 726-4200   www.psinet.com

Internet service provider.

Interactive Network GmbH (INX), Hardenbergplatz 2, D-10623 Berlin, Germany

Tel: 49-30-254-310   Fax: 49-30-254-31299   Contact: Moos Bulder, Reg. VP

PSINet Germany GmbH, Carl-Zeiss-Ring 21, D-85737 Ismaning, Germany

Tel: 49-89-96-28-70   Fax: 49-89-9620-94-25   Contact: Moos Bulder, Reg. VP

PULSE ENGINEERING INC.

12220 World Trade Drive, PO 12235, San Diego, CA, 92112

Tel: (858) 674-8100   Fax: (858) 674-8262   www.pulseeng.com

Mfr. passive magnetic components and modules for use in Internet/broadband access, power, telecommunications and datacom applications.

Pulse GmbH, Raiffensenstrasse 2, D-63110 Rodgau, Germany

QUALCOMM INC.

5775 Morehouse Dr., San Diego, CA, 92121-1714

Tel: (858) 587-1121   Fax: (858) 658-2100   www.qualcomm.com

Digital wireless telecommunications systems.

QUALCOMM Germany, München Airport Business Center, Soeldnermoos 17, Entrance B, 4/F, D-85399 Hallbergmoos, Germany

QUALITROL CORPORATION

1385 Fairport Road, Fairport, NY, 14450

Tel: (716) 586-1515   Fax: (716) 377-0220   www.qualitrolcorp.com

Mfr. gauges and thermometers.

Qualitrol GmbH, Industriestr., Postfach 1170, D-6222 Geisenheim, Germany

QUANTUM

500 McCarthy Blvd., Milpitas, CA, 95035

Tel: (408) 894-4000   Fax: (408) 894-3218   www.quantum.com

Mfr. computer peripherals.

Quantum GmbH, Berner Strasse 28, D-60437 Frankfurt, Germany

Tel: 49-69-950767-91

QUARK, INC.

1800 Grant Street, Denver, CO, 80203

Tel: (303) 894-8888   Fax: (303) 894-3398   www.quark.com

Mfr. and sales of desktop publishing software.

Quark GmbH, Eglosheimer Strabe, 41, D-71636 Ludwigsburg, Germany

QUICK EAGLE NETWORKS INC.

217 Humboldt Court, Sunnyvale, CA, 94089

Tel: (408) 745-6200   Fax: (408) 745-6250   www.quickeagle.com

Mfr. digital multiplexers and network management software.

Quick Eagle Networks, Neumarkt-Galerie, D-50667 Koeln Cologne, Germany

QUINTILES TRANSNATIONAL CORPORATION

4709 Creekstone Dr., Durham, NC, 27703

Tel: (919) 998-2000   Fax: (919) 998-9113   www.quintiles.com

Mfr. pharmaceuticals.

Innovex (Biodesign) GmbH, Quintiles Phase I, Services Obere Hardtstr. 8-16, D-79114 Freiburg, Germany

Quintiles GmbH, Schleussnerstrasse 42, D-63236 Neu-Isenburg, Germany

QWEST COMMUNICATIONS INTERNATIONAL INC.

1801 California Street, Ste. 5200, Denver, CO, 80202

Tel: (303) 896-2020   Fax: (303) 793-6654   www.uswest.com

Tele-communications provider; integrated communications services.

KPNQwest (JV), Frankfurt, Germany

RADIO SHACK CORPORATION

100 Throckmorton Street, Fort Worth, TX, 76102

Tel: (817) 390-3700   Fax: (817) 415-2647   www.tandy.com

Mfr. electronic and acoustic equipment; Radio Shack retail stores.

Memtek Co., Hahnstr. 41, D-6000 Frankfurt, Germany

Tandy Intl. Electronics, Christenenstr. 11, D-4030 Ratingen 2, Germany

RADISSON HOTELS INTERNATIONAL

Carlson Pkwy., PO Box 59159, Minneapolis, MN, 55459-8204

Tel: (612) 540-5526   Fax: (612) 449-3400   www.radisson.com

Operates, manages and franchises full-service hotels and resorts worldwide.

Radisson Hotels Intl., Attn: German Office, Carlson Parkway, PO Box 59159, Minneapolis, MN, 55459-8204

Radisson SAS Hotel, Karl-Liebknecht-Strasse 5, D-10178 Berlin, Germany

Tel: 49-30-23-82-8   Fax: 49-30-23-82-7590

RADISYS CORPORATION

5445 NE Dawson Creek Drive, Hillsboro, OR, 97124

Tel: (503) 615-1100   Fax: (503) 615-1121   www.radisys.com

Mfr. embedded computer systems.

RadiSys GmbH, Haringstrasse 19, D-85635 Hoehenkirchen, Germany

RAIN BIRD SPRINKLER MFG. CORPORATION

145 North Grand Ave., Glendora, CA, 91741-2469

Tel: (626) 963-9311   Fax: (626) 963-4287   www.rainbird.com

World's largest manufacturer of lawn sprinklers and irrigation systems equipment.

Rain Bird Deutschland, Siedlerstrasse 46, D-71126 Gäufelden-Nebringen, Germany

Tel: 49-7032-99010   Fax: 49-7032-99010   Contact: Rolf Kruger

RAINBOW TECHNOLOGY INC.

50 Technology Dr., Irvine, CA, 92618

Tel: (949) 450-7300   Fax: (949) 450-7450   www.rainbow.com

Mfr. computer related security products.

IBV Informatik AG, Lerzenstr. 27, CH-8953 Dietikon, Switzerland

IBV Informatik GmbH, Fabrikstr. 5, D-79539 Lörrach, Germany

Rainbow Technologies GmbH, Oskar-Messter-Strasse 16, D-8045 Ismaning, Germany

RATIONAL SOFTWARE CORPORATION

18880 Homestead Road, Cupertino, CA, 95014-0721

Tel: (408) 863-9900   Fax: (408) 863-4120   www.rationale.com

Mfr. application development software.

Rational Software GmbH, Keltenring 15, D-82041 Oberhaching, Germany

RAY & BERNDTSON, INC.

301 Commerce, Ste. 2300, Fort Worth, TX, 76102

Tel: (817) 334-0500   Fax: (817) 334-0779   www.prb.com

Executive search, management audit and management consulting firm.

Ray & Berndtson, Olof-Palme-StraBe 35, D-60393 Frankfurt, Germany

Tel: 49-69-95777-01   Fax: 49-69-95777-901   Contact: Theo Gehlen, Mng. Ptnr.

RAYMOND JAMES FINANCIAL, INC.

880 Carillon Parkway, St. Petersburg, FL, 33716

Tel: (813) 573-3800   Fax: (813) 573-8244   www.rjf.com

Financial services; securities brokerage, asset management, and investment banking services.

Raymond James Deutschland, Lange Str. 8, D-70173 Stuttgart, Germany

Tel: 49-711-222-9740   Fax: 49-711-227-0999   Contact: F. Reissland

Raymond James Deutschland GmbH & Co. KG, Moerser Strasse 100, D-40667 Meerbusch, Germany

Tel: 49-213-293-070   Fax: 49-213-293-0714

RAYOVAC CORPORATION

601 Rayovac Drive, Madison, WI, 53711-2497

Tel: (608) 275-3340   Fax: (608) 275-4577   www.rayovac.com

Mfr. batteries and lighting devices.

Rayovac Europe BV, Hellbreite 11, D-32791 Lage, Germany

RAYTECH CORPORATION

4 Corporate Drive, Ste. 295, Shelton, CT, 06484

Tel: (203) 925-8000   Fax: (203) 925-8088   www.raytech.com

Mfr. friction components and products for automotive and construction industry.

Raybestos Industrie Produkte GmbH, Industriestraße 7, D-54497 Morbach, Germany

RAYTHEON COMPANY

141 Spring Street, Lexington, MA, 02173

Tel: (781) 862-6600   Fax: (781) 860-2172   www.raytheon.com

Mfr. diversified electronics, appliances, energy and environmental products; publishing, industry and construction services.

Raytheon Marine GmbH, Zeystraße 16 - 24, D-24106 Kiel, Germany

Contact: Bernhardt Schell

RAZORFISH, INC.

32 Mercer Street, New York, NY, 10013

Tel: (212) 966-5960   Fax: (212) 966-6915   www.razorfish.com

Engaged in consulting and web services.

Razorfish GmbH, Solmsstrasse 8, D-60486 Frankfurt, Germany

Tel: 49-69-9726580

Razorfish GmbH, Gutshof Menterschwaige, Menterschweigstrasse 4, D-81545 München, Germany

Tel: 49-89-64-2000

READER'S DIGEST ASSOCIATION, INC.

Reader's Digest Rd., Pleasantville, NY, 10570

Tel: (914) 238-1000   Fax: (914) 238-4559   www.readersdigest.com

Publisher of magazines and books and direct mail marketer.

Reader's Digest Verlag Das Beste GmbH, Augustenstr. 1, D-7000 Stuttgart 1, Germany

RECOTON CORPORATION

2950 Lake Emma Road, Lake Mary, FL, 32746

Tel: (407) 333-8900   Fax: (407) 333-8903   www.recoton.com

Mfr. electronic accessories and aftermarket products for computers and office equipment.

Recoton GmbH, Lise Meitner Strasse 9, D-50259 Pulheim, Germany

Tel: 49-2234-807-0333   Fax: 49-2234-807-0332

REEBOK INTERNATIONAL LTD.

1895 J. W. Foster Blvd., Canton, MA, 02021

Tel: (781) 401-5000   Fax: (781) 401-7402   www.reebok.com

Mfr. athletic shoes including casual, dress golf and walking shoes.

Reebok Deutschland GmbH, Keltenring 14, D-82039 Oberhaching, Germany

REFCO GROUP LTD.

200 Liberty Street Tower A, New York, NY, 10281

Tel: (212) 693-7700   Fax: (212) 693-7856   www.refco.com

Commodity and security brokers engaged in the execution and clearing of futures and options and institutional asset management services.

Refco Futures Ltd., Hamburg, Germany

REFLEXITE TECHNOLOGY

120 Darling Drive, Avon, CT, 06001

Tel: (860) 676-7100   Fax: (860) 676-7199   www.reflexite.com

Mfr. plastic film, sheet, materials and shapes, optical lenses.

Fresnel Optics, GmbH, Flurstedter Marktweg 13, D-99510 Apolda, Germany

Tel: 49-3644-50110 Fax: 49-3644-501150   Contact: Olivier Bulcourt, Mgr.

REGAL-BELOIT CORPORATION

200 State Street, Beloit, WI, 53512-0298

Tel: (608) 364-8800   Fax: (608) 364-8818   www.regal-beloit.com

Mfr. power transmission equipment, perishable cutting tools.

Mastergear GmbH, Postfach 1216, D-61260 Neu-Anspach, Germany

Tel: 49-6081-94300 Fax: 49-6081-943030

REGENT SPORTS CORPORATION

PO Box 11357, Hauppauge, NY, 11788

Tel: (516) 234-2800   Fax: (516) 234-2948   www.regent-halex.com

Mfr. sporting goods equipment, including Spalding, MacGregor, Regent and Halex.

Regent Sports GmbH Germany, Pfarrweg 1, D-8035 Gauting, Germany

RELIANCE GROUP HOLDINGS, INC.

55 East 52nd Street, New York, NY, 10055

Tel: (212) 909-1100   Fax: (212) 909-1864   www.rgh.com

Financial and insurance management services.

Reliance National Insurance Co. (Europe) Ltd., Niederlassung München, Ottostrasse 5, D-80333 Münich, Germany

Tel: 49-89-550-8956 Fax: 49-89-550-8956

Reliance National Insurance Co. (Europe) Ltd., Direktion für Deutschland, Kaiser-Wilhelm-Ring 50, D-50672 Köln, Germany

Tel: 49-221-912-7670 Fax: 49-221-912-7676

RELIANT ENERGY, INC.

1111 Louisiana Street, Houston, TX, 77002

Tel: (713) 207-3000   Fax: (713) 207-0206   www.houind.com

Provides gas and electric services.

Reliant Energy Trading & Marketing, Frankfurt, Germany

REMINGTON ARMS COMPANY, INC.

870 Remington Drive, PO Box 700, Madison, NC, 27025

Tel: (336) 548-8700   Fax: (336) 548-7801   www.remington.com

Mfr. sporting firearms and ammunition.

Remington Arms GmbH, Postfach 3266, Wurzburg, Germany

REMINGTON PRODUCTS COMPANY, L.L.C.

60 Main Street, Bridgeport, CT, 06604

Tel: (203) 367-4400   Fax: (203) 332-4848   www.remington-products.com

Mfr. home appliances, electric shavers.

Remington Products GmbH, Niederlassung Deutschland, Siemensstrasse 7, D-8849 Riedlingen, Germany

Tel: 49-7371-9325-0

RENAISSANCE HOTELS AND RESORTS

10400 Fernwood Road, Bethesda, MD, 20817

Tel: (301) 380-3000   Fax: (301) 380-5181   www.renaissancehotels.com

upscale, full-service hotel and resort chain under Marriott International, Inc.

Renaissance Hamburg Hotel, Hamburg, Germany

Tel: 49-40-349-180

Renaissance Hotel, Chemnitz, Germany

Tel: 49-221-203-40

REQUISITE TECHNOLOGY, INC.

10955 Westmoor Drive, Ste. 100, Westminster, CO, 80021

Tel: (303) 474-2200   Fax: (303) 474-2211   www.requisite.com

Mfr. software.

Requisite Technology GmbH, Otto-Hesse Strasse 19, D-64293 Darmstadt, Germany

Tel: 49-615-1667-7100

RESMED INC.

1440 Danielson Street, Poway, CA, 92064

Tel: (858) 746-2400   Fax: (858) 880-1618   www.resmed.com

Mfr. sleep apnea aids, including nasal masks and accessories.

ResMed GmbH & Co. KG, Rudolfstraße 10, D-41068 Mönchengladbach, Germany

Tel: 49-2161-3521

RESPIRONICS INC.

1501 Ardmore Blvd., Pittsburgh, PA, 15221-4401

Tel: (412) 731-2100   Fax: (412) 473-5011   www.respironics.com

Design/mfr. patient ventilation medical products.

Respironics Deutschland GmbH, Gewerbestrasse 17, D-82211 Herrsching, Germany

RETEK INC.

950 Nicollet Mall, Minneapolis, MN, 55403

Tel: (612) 587-5000   Fax: (612) 587-5100   www.retek.com

Mfr. retail management software.

Retek GmbH, Hans-Henny-Jahnn-Weg 9, D-22085 Hamburg, Germany

Tel: 49-40-284-193-79

REVELL-MONOGRAM LLC

8601 Waukegan Rd., Morton Grove, IL, 60053

Tel: (847) 966-3500   Fax: (847) 767-5857   www.revell-monogram.com

Mfr. plastic hobby kits.

Revell Metal AG, Henschelstr. 20-30, D-4980 Buende 1, Germany

REVLON INC.

625 Madison Ave., New York, NY, 10022

Tel: (212) 527-4000   Fax: (212) 527-4995   www.revlon.com

Mfr. cosmetics, fragrances, toiletries and beauty care products.

Deutsche Revlon GmbH, Tiefenbroicher Weg 15, D-4000 Düsseldorf, Germany

REXNORD CORPORATION

4701 West Greenfield Ave., Milwaukee, WI, 53214

Tel: (414) 643-3000   Fax: (414) 643-3078   www.rexnord.com

Mfr. power transmission and conveying components.

Rexnord Antriebstechnik GmbH, Obsener Strasse 79-83, D-31789 Hameln, Germany

Rexnord Kette GmbH & Co. KG, Postfach 120, D-57501 Betzdorf, Germany

RHEOMETRIC SCIENTIFIC INC.

1 Possumtown Road, Piscataway, NJ, 08854

Tel: (732) 560-8550   Fax: (732) 560-7451   www.rheosci.com

Design/mfr. rheological instruments and systems.

Rheometric Scientific GmbH, Schwanheimer Strasse 144a, D-64625 Bensheim, Germany

RICHARDSON ELECTRONICS, LTD.

40 W 267 Keslinger Road, LaFox, IL, 60147-0393

Tel: (630) 208-2200   Fax: (630) 208-2550   www.rell.com

Mfr. and distribution of electron tubes and related equipment.

Richardson Elecronics, Sperberhorst 11, D-22459 Hamburg, Germany

RICHCO, INC.

5825 N. Tripp Ave., PO Box 804238, Chicago, IL, 60680

Tel: (773) 539-4060   Fax: (773) 539-6770   www.richco.com

Mfr. quality plastic fasteners, wire management devices, circuit board hardware, and custom components.

Richco Plastic Deutschland GmbH, Breslauer Weg 31, D-82358 Geretsfried, Germany

Tel: 49-8171-43280

RIDGE TOOL COMPANY

400 Clark Street, Elyria, OH, 44035

Tel: (440) 323-5581   Fax: (440) 329-4853   www.ridgid.com

Mfr. hand and power tools for working pipe, drain cleaning equipment, etc.

Ridge Tool GmbH, Limburg Lahn, Germany

RIGHT MANAGEMENT CONSULTANTS, INC.

1818 Market Street, 33rd Fl., Philadelphia, PA, 19103-3614

Tel: (215) 988-1588   Fax: (215) 988-9112   www.right.com

Out placement and human resources consulting services.

Right Management Consultants, Senefelderstr. 166, D-6050 Offenbach Frankfurt, Germany

THE RITZ-CARLTON HOTEL COMPANY, L.L.C.

3414 Peachtree Road NE, Ste. 300, Atlanta, GA, 30326

Tel: (404) 237-5500   Fax: (404) 365-9643   www.ritzcarlton.com

5-star hotel and restaurant chain.

The Ritz-Carlton Hotel Company, Westendstrasse 19, D-60325 Frankfurt/Main, Germany

Tel: 49-69-975-46224

C. H. ROBINSON WORLDWIDE, INC. (CHR)

8100 Mitchell Road, Eden Prairie, MN, 55344

Tel: (612) 937-8500   Fax: (612) 937-6714   www.chrobinson.com

Global door-to-door freight forwarding services, including flexible transportation solutions and global logistics.

C. H. Robinson (CHR), Konrad-Adenauer Allee 61, D-86150 Augsburg, Germany

ROCKWELL AUTOMATION, INC.

777 East Wisconsin Ave., Ste. 1400, Milwaukee, WI, 53202

Tel: (414) 212-5200   Fax: (414) 212-5201   www.rockwellautomation.com

Products and service for aerospace and defense, automotive, electronics, graphics and automation industry.

Rockwell Automation, Dusselberger Str. 15, D-42781 Haan-Gruiten, Germany

Tel: 49-2104-9600

R.A. RODRIGUEZ, INC.

20 Seaview Boulevard, Port Washington, NY, 11050

Tel: (516) 625-8080   Fax: (516) 621-2424   www.rodriguez-usa.com

Distribution of ball and roller bearings, precision gears, mechanical systems and related products.

R. A. Rodriguez GmbH, rue De Wattrelos 17, D-52249 Eschweiler, Germany

Tel: 49-2403-7800 Fax: 49-2403-78050 Contact: Gunther Schulz, Mng. Dir.

ROFIN-SINAR TECHNOLOGIES, INC.

45701 Mast St., Plymouth, MI, 48170

Tel: (734) 455-5400   Fax: (734) 455-2741   www.rofin-sinar.com

Mfr. industrial lasers.

ROFIN-SINAR Laser GmbH, Berzeliusstraße 83, D-22113 Hamburg, Germany

Tel: 49-40-733-630

ROHM AND HAAS COMPANY

100 Independence Mall West, Philadelphia, PA, 19106

Tel: (215) 592-3000   Fax: (215) 592-3377   www.rohmhaas.com

Mfr. specialty chemicals.

Morton International GmbH, Reinhard-Reichnow-Strasse 4, D-8618 Strullendorf, Germany

Morton International GmbH, Hefenrignstrasse 1, D-49090 Osnabruck, Germany

Morton International GmbH, Beim Struckenberge 11, D-2823 Bremen, Germany

Tel: 49-541-91410

Rohm and Haas GmbH, In der Kron 4, D-60489 Frankfurt/Main, Germany

Tel: 49-69-789960

Shipley GmbH, Wolf-Hirt-Str. 12, PO Box 507, D-73706 Esslingen, Germany

Tel: 49-711-931-320

ROPER INDUSTRIES, INC.

160 Ben Burton Road, Bogart, GA, 30622

Tel: (706) 369-7170   Fax: (706) 353-6496   www.roperind.com

Mfr. analytical instruments.

Roper Scientific, Rosenheimer Landstr. 87, D-85521 Ottobrunn, Germany

ROXIO, INC.

455 El Camino Real, Santa Clara, CA, 95050

Tel: (408) 367-3100   Fax: (408) 367-3101   www.roxio.com

Mfr. CD recording software.

Roxio GmbH, Jens-Otto-Krag-Str. 11, D-52146 Wurselen, Germany

Tel: 49-2405-45080

ROYAL APPLIANCE MFG. COMPANY

7005 Cochran Rd., Glenwillow, OH, 44139

Tel: (440) 996-2000   Fax: (440) 996-2030   www.royalappliance.com

Mfr. vacuum cleaners.

Royal Appliances Mfg. GmbH, Weisshausstrasse 21, D-5000 Cologne 41, Germany

RUSSELL REYNOLDS ASSOCIATES INC.

200 Park Avenue, New York, NY, 10166-0002

Tel: (212) 351-2000   Fax: (212) 370-0896   www.russreyn.com

Executive recruiting services.

Russell Reynolds Associates Inc., Messe Turm, Ludwig-Erhard-Anlage, D-60308 Frankfurt/Main, Germany

Tel: 49-69-7560900   Fax: 49-69-756090-11   Contact: Harald Grosser

Russell Reynolds Associates Inc., Heilwigstraße 33, D-20249 Hamburg, Germany

Tel: 49-40-4806610   Fax: 49-40-480661-40   Contact: Harald Grosser

RVSI (ROBOTIC VISION SYSTEMS, INC.)

5 Shawmut Road, Canton, MA, 02021

Tel: (781) 821-0830   Fax: (781) 828-8942   www.rvsi.com

Mfr. machine visions systems; bar code scanners and data collection equipment.

RVSI Europe (central) GmbH, Industriestrasse 20, D-61381 Friedrichsdorf, Germany

RVSI Robotic Vision Systems, Otto-Hahn-Str. 40, D-61381 Friedrichsdorf-Koeppern, Germany

RWD TECHNOLOGIES, INC.

10480 Little Paluxent Pkwy., Ste. 1200, Columbia, MD, 21044-3530

Tel: (410) 730-4377   Fax: (410) 964-0039   www.rwd.com

Mfr. software and services.

RWD Technologies, SAP Partners Port, Altrottstrasse 31, D-69190 Walldorf, Germany

RYDER SYSTEM, INC.

3600 NW 82nd Ave., Miami, FL, 33166

Tel: (305) 500-3726   Fax: (305) 500-4129   www.ryder.com

Integrated logistics, full-service truck leasing, truck rental and public transportation services.

Ryder Deutschland, Parsevalstrasse 9A, D-40468 Düsseldorf, Germany

Tel: 49-211-472-100   Fax: 49-211-472-1099

S1 CORPORATION

3500 Lenox Road, Ste. 200, Atlanta, GA, 30326-1108

Tel: (404) 923-3500   Fax: (404) 923-6727   www.s1.com

Mfr. on-line banking software.

S1 Munich, Karlsplatz 11, D-80335 München, Germany

SAATCHI & SAATCHI

375 Hudson St., New York, NY, 10014

Tel: (212) 463-2000   Fax: (212) 463-9855   www.saatchi-saatchi.com

Provides advertising and marketing services.

Saatchi & Saatchi Advertising, Frankfurt, Germany

SAFETY COMPONENTS INTERNATIONAL, INC.

41 Stevens Street, Greenville, SC, 29605

Tel: (864) 240-2600   Fax: (864) 240-2728   www.safetycomponents.com

Mfr. automobile airbag cushions and components..

Automotive Safety Components, Maybachstrasse 7, D-31135 Hildesheim, Germany

SAFETY-KLEEN CORPORATION

1301 Gervais Street, Columbia, SC, 29201

Tel: (803) 933-4200   Fax: (803) 933-4345   www.safety-kleen.com

Solvent based parts cleaning service; sludge/solvent recycling service.

Safety-Kleen GmbH Reinigungstechnik, Auf dem Huls 16, D-4020 Mettmann, Germany

SANDISK CORPORATION

140 Caspian Court, Sunnyvale, CA, 94089

Tel: (408) 542-0500   Fax: (408) 542-0503   www.sandisk.com

Mfr. storage based, flash memory products.

SanDisk GmbH, Karlsruher Str. 2C, D-30519 Hannover, Germany

SunDisk Southern Europe, Rudolf-Diesel-Str.3, D-40822 Mettmann, Germany

Contact: Karl Kleemann

SANFORD CORPORATION

2711 Washington Boulevard, Bellwood, IL, 60104

Tel: (708) 547-6650   Fax: (708) 547-6719   www.sanfordcorp.com

Mfr. inks, writing, drawing and drafting instruments.

Sanford GmbH, Schnackenburgallee 45, D-22525 Hamburg, Germany

Tel: 49-40-85-56-22-67

SAPIENT CORPORATION

1 Memorial Drive, Cambridge, MA, 02142

Tel: (617) 621-0200   Fax: (617) 621-1300   www.sapient.com

Engaged in information technology and consulting services.

Sapient Dusseldorf, Furstenwall 65, D-40219 Dusseldorf, Germany

Tel: 49-211-60-116

Sapient GmbH, Schaefflerhof, Maffeistrasse 3, D-80333 Münich, Germany
Tel: 49-89-255-58853

SAS INSTITUTE INC.

SAS Campus Drive, Cary, NC, 27513
Tel: (919) 677-8000   Fax: (919) 677-4444   www.sas.com
Mfr. and distribution of decision support software.

SAS Institute GmbH (European Hdqtrs.), Neuenheimer Landstrasse 28-30, Postfach 10 53 40, D-69043 Heidelberg, Germany
Tel: 49-6221-4160   Fax: 49-6221-474850

SBS TECHNOLOGIES, INC.

2400 Louisiana Blvd. NE, Ste. 600, Albuquerque, NM, 87110
Tel: (505) 875-0600   Fax: (505) 875-0400   www.sbs.com
Mfr. high-tech computer components.

SBS Technologies Germany, Memminger Str. 14, D-86159 Augsburg, Germany
Tel: 49-821-5034175   Contact: Kurt Herbert

SCHENECTADY INTERNATIONAL INC.

PO Box 1046, Schenectady, NY, 12301
Tel: (518) 370-4200   Fax: (518) 382-8129   www.siigroup.com
Mfr. electrical insulating varnishes, enamels, phenolic resins, alkylphenols.

Schenectady Europe GmbH, Grossmannstrasse 105, D-20539 Hamburg, Germany
Tel: 49-40-78-946   Fax: 49-40-78-946-276

SCHENKER USA INC.

150 Albany Ave., Freeport, NY, 11520
Tel: (516) 403-5416   Fax: (516) 377-3092   www.schenkerusa.com
Freight forwarders.

Schenker International Deutschland GmbH, PO Box 42 01 65, D-30855 Hannover, Germany
Tel: 49-511-7408560   Fax: 49-511-740-85639   Contact: Håkan Larsson

Schenker International Deutschland GmbH, Cargo Term. A+B, 4 Etage, PO Box 23 19 44, D-85356 Münich, Germany
Tel: 49-89-97-5900   Fax: 49-89-97-590090

Schenker International Deutschland GmbH, PO Box 11 03 13, D-20457 Hamburg, Germany
Tel: 49-40-36135   Fax: 49-40-36135-216

Schenker International Deutschland GmbH, Ruhrorter Strasse 9-21, PO Box 10 26 64, D-68219 Mannheim, Germany
Tel: 49-621-8046-785   Fax: 49-621-8046-666

R. P. SCHERER CORPORATION

645 Martinsville Rd., Ste. 200, Basking Ridge, NJ, 07920
Tel: (908) 580-1500   Fax: (908) 580-9220   www.rpscherer.com
Mfr. pharmaceuticals; soft gelatin and two-piece hard shell capsules.

R.P. Scherer GmbH, Postfach 1243, D-69402 Eberbach/Baden, Germany
Tel: 49-6271-8402 Fax: 49-6271-842700   Contact: Dr. Gunter Blankenhorn, Gen. Mgr.   Emp: 1,000

SCHERING-PLOUGH CORPORATION

One Giralda Farms, Madison, NJ, 07940-1000
Tel: (973) 822-7000   Fax: (973) 822-7048   www.sch-plough.com
Proprietary drug and cosmetic products.

Essex Tierarznei Ndl der Essex Pharma GmbH, Dr. Christian Wirth Thomas, Dehler Str. 27, D-81737 Münich, Germany
Tel: 49-89-62731-430

SCHLEGEL SYSTEMS

1555 Jefferson Road, PO Box 23197, Rochester, NY, 14692-3197

Tel: (716) 427-7200   Fax: (716) 427-9993   www.schlegel.com

Mfr. engineered perimeter sealing systems for residential and commercial construction; fibers; rubber product.

Schlegel GmbH, Bredowstrasse 33, D-22113 Hamburg, Germany

SCHLUMBERGER LIMITED

153 East 53rd St., 57th Fl., New York, NY, 10022-4624

Tel: (212) 350-9400   Fax: (212) 350-9457   www.slb.com

Engaged in oil and gas services, metering and payment systems, and produces semiconductor testing equipment and smart cards.

Messerchmidt Apparate GmbH, Haenseatenstrasse 1, Postfach 1348, D-30834 Langenhagen, Germany

Schlumberger Sema Telecom GmbH, Otto-Hahn Strasse 36, D-63303 Dreieich, Germany

Schlumberger Systems GmbH, Hanhnstr. 70, D-60528 Frankfurt, Germany

Tel: 49-69-668042-0   Fax: 49-69-668042-42

A. SCHULMAN INC.

3550 West Market Street, Akron, OH, 44333

Tel: (330) 666-3751   Fax: (330) 668-7204   www.aschulman.com

Mfr./sale plastic resins and compounds.

A. Schulman GmbH, Huttenstr. 211, D-50170 Kerpen Sindorf, Germany

SCIENCE APPLICATIONS INTL. CORPORATION (SAIC)

10260 Campus Point Dr., San Diego, CA, 92121

Tel: (858) 826-6000   Fax: (858) 535-7589   www.saic.com

Engaged in research and engineering.

SAIC C/O Detesystem GmbH, Hahnstrasse 43D, D-605 Frankfurt, Germany

Tel: 49-69-665313490

SCIENTIFIC GAMES INTERNATIONAL

750 Lexington Avenue, 25th Fl., New York, NY, 10022

Tel: (212) 754-2233   Fax: (212) 754-2372   www.scientificgames.com

Mfr. video gaming machines and computerized pari-mutuel wagering systems used at racetracks.

Scientific Games International, Fischerried 33, D-82362 Weilheim, Germany

Tel: 49-881-93940   Fax: 49-881-939415

SCIENTIFIC-ATLANTA, INC.

5030 Sugarloaf Pkwy., Lawrenceville, GA, 30044

Tel: (770) 903-5000   Fax: (770) 236-6777   www.sciatl.com

Mfr. cable set-top boxes, modems, transmission and distribution equipment.

Scientific-Atlanta Central Europe GmbH, Westerbachstraße 28, D-61476 Kronberg, Germany

Tel: 49-6173-928-0

SCM MICROSYSTEMS, INC.

47211 Bayside Pkwy., Fremont, CA, 94538

Tel: (510) 360-2300   Fax: (510) 360-0211   www.scmmicro.com

Mfr. computer hardware for digital cameras.

SCM Microsystems GmbH, European Hdqrts., Oskar-Messter-Str. 13, D-85737 Ismaning, Germany

Tel: 49-89-9595-5000   Fax: 49-89-9595-5555

SEAGATE TECHNOLOGY, INC.

920 Disc Dr., Scotts Valley, CA, 95066

Tel: (408) 438-6550   Fax: (408) 438-7205   www.seagate.com

Develop computer technology, software and hardware.

Seagate Technology GmbH, Messerschmittstrasse 4, D-80992 München, Germany

Tel: 49-89-14305000   Fax: 49-89-14305100   Contact: Hans-Dieter Blaser, VP   Emp: 25

SEALED AIR CORPORATION

Park 80 East, Saddle Brook, NJ, 07663

Tel: (201) 791-7600   Fax: (201) 703-4205   www.sealedaircorp.com

Mfr. protective and specialty packaging solutions for industrial, food and consumer products.

Sealed Air GmbH, Max-Planck Strasse 15, D-61381 Friedrichsdorf, Germany

Tel: 49-6172-760635   Fax: 49-6172-760637

G.D. SEARLE & COMPANY

5200 Old Orchard Road, Skokie, IL, 60077

Tel: (847) 982-7000   Fax: (847) 470-1480   www.searlehealthnet.com

Mfr. pharmaceuticals, health care, optical products and specialty chemicals.

Heumann Pharma GmbH & Co., Nürnberger Str. 12, D-90537 Feucht, Germany

Tel: 49-9128-404-0   Fax: 49-9128-404-581

Searle East Europe & Candarel, Frankfurter Strasse 181, D-6078 Neu-Isenberg, Germany

SECURE COMPUTING CORPORATION

4810 Harwood Rd., San Jose, CA, 95124

Tel: (408) 979-6000   Fax: (408) 979-6101   www.sctc.com

Mfr. software.

Secure Computing GmbH, Luise-Kiesselbach-Platz 35, D-81377 Münich, Germany

Tel: 49-89-71-04-6100

SEEBEYOND TECHNOLOGY CORPORATION

404 East Huntington Drive, Monrovia, CA, 91016

Tel: (626) 471-6000   Fax: (626) 471-6104   www.seebeyond.com

Mfr. business software.

SeeBeyond Deutschland GmbH, Martin-Behaim-Strabe 8, D-63263 Neu-Isenburg, Germany

SeeBeyond GmbH, Falkenbergpark Berlin-Sud, Paradiesstrasse 206a, D-12526 Berlin, Germany

SELAS CORPORATION OF AMERICA

2034 S. Limekiln Pike, Dresher, PA, 19025

Tel: (215) 646-6600   Fax: (215) 646-3536   www.selas.com

Mfr. heat treating equipment for metal, glass, ceramic and chemical industry.

Selas Waermetechnik GmbH, Christenenstrasse 2, D-40880 Ratingen, Germany

SEMITOOL, INC.

655 West Reserve Drive, Kalispell, MT, 59901

Tel: (406) 752-2107   Fax: (406) 752-5522   www.semitool.com

Mfr. semiconductor manufacturing equipment.

Semitool Halbleitertechnik Vertriebs GmbH, Ahornstrasse 30, D-83451 Piding, Germany

SEMTECH CORPORATION

200 Flynn Road, Camarillo, CA, 93012-8790

Tel: (805) 498-2111   Fax: (805) 498-3804   www.semtech.com

Mfr. silicon rectifiers, rectifier assemblies, capacitors, switching regulators, AC/DC converters.

Semtech Germany GmbH, General-von-Nagel-Strasse 5, D-85354 Freising, Germany

Tel: 49-8161-140-123

SENCO PRODUCTS INC.

8485 Broadwell Road, Cincinnati, OH, 45244

Tel: (513) 388-2000   Fax: (513) 388-2026   www.senco.com

Mfr. industry nailers, staplers, fasteners and accessories.

Deutsche Senco Industrie-Erzeugnisse GmbH & Co. KG, Gelsenkirchenerstr. 27, Postfach 10 68 67, D-28001 Bremen, Germany

SENSIENT TECHNOLOGIES CORPORATION

777 E. Wisconsin Ave., Milwaukee, WI, 53202

Tel: (414) 271-6755   Fax: (414) 347-4783   www.sensient.com

Mfr. flavor applications for the beverage, bakery, confection, dairy, snack and savory markets.

C. Melchers GmbH & Company, Bremen, Germany

SENSORMATIC ELECTRONICS CORPORATION

951 Yamato Road, Boca Raton, FL, 33431-0700

Tel: (561) 989-7000   Fax: (561) 989-7774   www.sensormatic.com

Electronic article surveillance equipment.

Sensormatic GmbH, Am Schimmersfeld 7, D-40880 Ratingen, Germany

Tel: 49-2102-431-303   Fax: 49-2102-431-341   Contact: Karl-Heinz Hollung

SEQUENOM, INC.

3595 John Hopkins Court, San Diego, CA, 92121-1331

Tel: (858) 202-9000   Fax: (858) 202-9001   www.sequenon.com

Engaged in biotechnology.

Sequenom GmbH, Mendelssohnstrasse 15D, D-22761 Hamburg, Germany

Tel: 49-40-899676-0   Contact: Karsten Shmidt, Mng. Dir.

THE SERVICEMASTER COMPANY

2300 Warrenville Road, Downers Grove, IL, 60515-1700

Tel: (630) 271-1300   Fax: (630) 271-2710   www.svm.com

Provides residential consumer services, including lawn care and landscape maintenance, termite and pest control, plumbing, heating and air conditioning maintenance and repair.

ServiceMaster Operations-Germany GmbH, Lange Strasse 33, D-7293 Pfalzgrafenweiler, Germany

Terminix, Münich, Germany

SHAKESPEARE FISHING TACKLE GROUP

3801 Westmore Drive, Columbia, SC, 29223

Tel: (803) 754-7000   Fax: (803) 754-7342   www.shakespeare-fishing.com

Mfr. fishing tackle.

Shakespeare Intl. GmbH, Postfach 420 424, D-5000 Cologne 41, Germany

THE SHAW GROUP INC.

4171 Essen Lane, Baton Rouge, LA, 70809

Tel: (225) 932-2500   Fax: (225) 932-2661   www.shawgrp.com

Vertically-integrated provider of complete piping systems, and comprehensive engineering, procurement and construction services.

IT Infrastructure & Environmental GmbH, Merkurstrasse 60, D-67663 Kaiserslautern, Germany

SHEARMAN & STERLING

599 Lexington Ave., New York, NY, 10022-6069

Tel: (212) 848-4000   Fax: (212) 848-7179   www.shearman.com

Law firm engaged in general American and international financial and commercial practice.

Shearman & Sterling, Couvenstrasse 8, D-40211 Düsseldorf, Germany

Tel: 49-211-178-880   Fax: 49-211-178-8888   Contact: Georg F. Thoma, Mng. Ptnr.

Shearman & Sterling, Bockenheimer Landstrasse 55, D-60325 Frankfurt/Main, Germany

Tel: 49-69-971070   Fax: 49-69-97107-100   Contact: Georg F. Thoma, Mng. Ptnr.

SHIPLEY COMPANY, LLC

455 Forest Street, Marlborough, MA, 01752

Tel: (508) 481-7950   Fax: (508) 485-9113   www.shipley.com

Supplier of materials and processes technology to the microelectronics and printed wiring board industries.

Shipley GmbH, Gewerbestrasse 19, D-75217 Birkenfeld, Germany

Tel: 49-70-82-79140

SHURE INCORPORATED

222 Hartrey Ave., Evanston, IL, 60202-3696

Tel: (847) 866-2200   Fax: (847) 866-2279   www.shure.com

Mfr. microphones, teleconferencing systems, circuitry products.

Shure Distribution GmbH, Wannenäcker Straße 28, D-74078 Heilbronn, Germany

Contact: Markus Winkler, Mng. Dir.

SIEBEL SYSTEMS, INC.

2207 Bridgepointe Pkwy., San Mateo, CA, 94404

Tel: (650) 295-5000   Fax: (650) 295-5111   www.siebel.com

Provider of e-Business applications software.

Siebel Systems Deutschland GmbH, Düsseldorf Airport, Hamborner Strasse 53, D-40472 Düsseldorf, Germany

SIG DOBOY INC.

869 South Knowles Ave., New Richmond, WI, 54017-1797

Tel: (715) 246-6511   Fax: (715) 246-6539   www.doboy.com

Mfr. packaging machinery.

SIG Beverages International, Brüsseler Straße 13, D-53842 Troisdorf, Germany

SIGNODE PACKAGING SYSTEMS

3610 West Lake Ave., Glenview, IL, 60025

Tel: (847) 724-6100   Fax: (847) 657-4392   www.signode.com

Mfr. industrial tools and machinery for packaging and strapping.

Signode Bernpak GmbH, Greul 1a, D-42897 Remscheid, Germany

Signode Pan-European Consumable Systems, Magusstrasse 18, D-46535 Dinslaken, Germany

Signode Pan-European Metals Systems, Magnustrasse 18, D-46535 Dinslaken, Germany

Signode System GmbH, Magnustrasse 18, D-46535 Dinslaken, Germany

SILICON GRAPHICS INC.

1600 Amphitheatre Pkwy., Mountain View, CA, 94043-1351

Tel: (650) 960-1980   Fax: (650) 932-0661   www.sgi.com

Design/mfr. special-effects computer graphic systems and software.

Silicon GmbH, Münich, Germany

SIMPLICITY PATTERN COMPANY, INC.

2 Park Avenue, 12th Fl., New York, NY, 10016

Tel: (212) 372-0500   Fax: (212) 372-0628   www.simplicity.com

Dress patterns.

Simplicity Modeschnitt GmbH, Postfach 101664, D-5000 Cologne 1, Germany

J.R. SIMPLOT COMPANY, INC.

999 Main Street, Ste. 1300, Boise, ID, 83702

Tel: (208) 336-2110   Fax: (208) 389-7515   www.simplot.com

Fresh/frozen fruits and vegetables, animal feeds, fertilizers.

Simplot Europe GmbH & Co. KG, Kielsgrassen 6, Monheim, Germany

SITEL CORPORATION

111 South Calver Street, Ste. 1900, Baltimore, MD, 21202

Tel: (410) 246-1505   Fax: (410) 246-0200   www.sitel.com

Provides outsourced customer management services.

SITEL, Europark Fichtenhain A17, D-48807 Krefeld, Germany

Contact: Jorg Diepenseifen

SIX FLAGS, INC.

11501 Northeast Expwy., Oklahoma City, OK, 73131

Tel: (405) 475-2500   Fax: (405) 475-2555   www.sixflags.com

Owns and manages amusement parks.

Warner Bros Movie World, GmbH & Co Kg, Warner Allee 1, D-46244 Bottrop, Germany

SKADDEN, ARPS, SLATE, MEAGHER & FLOM LLP

4 Times Square, New York, NY, 10036

Tel: (212) 735-3000   Fax: (212) 735-2000   www.sasmf.com

American/International law practice.

Skadden, Arps, Slate, Meagher & Flom LLP, MesseTurm, 27th Fl., D-60308 Frankfurt am Main, Germany

Tel: 49-69-9757-3000   Fax: 49-69-9757-3050   Contact: Hilary S. Foulkes, Partner

SKYWORKS SOLUTIONS, INC.

20 Sylvan Road, Woburn, MA, 01801

Tel: (781) 935-5150   Fax: (781) 824-4579   www.skyworksinc.com

Mfr. electronic and microwave components.

Skyworks Solutions, Paul-Gehardt-Allee 50 A, D-81245 Münich, Germany

SL INDUSTRIES, INC.

520 Fellowship Road, Ste. A-114,, Mount Laurel, NJ, 08054

Tel: (609) 727-1500   Fax: (609) 727-1683   www.slindustries.com

Mfr./design electronic protection and power fluctuation devices.

Elektro-Metall Export GmbH, Manchinger Str. 116, D-85053 Ingolstadt, Germany

SMITH INTERNATIONAL, INC.

PO Box 60068, Houston, TX, 77205-0068

Tel: (713) 443-3370   Fax: (713) 233-5996   www.smith.com

Mfr. drilling tools and equipment and provides related services for the drilling, completion and production sectors of the petroleum and mining industries.

Smith International Deutschland GmbH, Grafftring 5-7, D-29227 Celle, Germany

Tel: 49-514-801-243   Contact: Dietmar Muckstein, Area Mgr.

SMURFIT-STONE CONTAINER CORPORATION

150 N. Michigan Ave., Chicago, IL, 60601-7568

Tel: (312) 346-6600   Fax: (312) 580-3486   www.smurfit-stone.net

Mfr. paper and paper packaging.

Europa Carton AG, Spitalerstrasse 11, D-2000 Hamburg 1, Germany

SNAP-ON INCORPORATED

10801 Corporate Dr., Pleasant Prairie, WI, 53158-1603

Tel: (262) 656-5200   Fax: (262) 656-5577   www.snapon.com

Mfr. auto maintenance, diagnostic and emission testing equipment, hand tools, hydraulic lifts and tire changers.

Sun Electric Deutschland GmbH, Postfach 100609, D-4020 Mettmann, Germany

Tel: 49-2104-7990   Fax: 49-2104-799212   Contact: H. Laube, Mng. Dir.

SOLECTRON CORPORATION

777 Gibraltar Drive, Milpitas, CA, 95035

Tel: (408) 957-8500   Fax: (408) 956-6075   www.solectron.com

Provides contract manufacturing services to equipment manufacturers.

Force Computers, Inc., Prof. Messerschmitt Strasse 1, D-85579 Neubiberg Münich, Germany

Tel: 49-89-608-140   Fax: 49-89-609-7793

Solectron Corporation, Solectronstrasse 1, D-71083 Herrenberg, Germany

Tel: 49-70-329-980   Fax: 49-70-329-98222

SONOCO PRODUCTS COMPANY

North Second Street, PO Box 160, Hartsville, SC, 29550

Tel: (843) 383-7000   Fax: (843) 383-7008   www.sonoco.com

Mfr. packaging for consumer and industrial market and recycled paperboard.

Sonoco Consumer Products GmbH, Nikolaus-Otostrasse, D-56727 Mayer-Oft, Germany

Tel: 49-2651-4876

Sonoco Deutschland GmbH, Fennastrasse 94, D-48529 Nordhorn, Germany

Tel: 49-5921-8831-0

Sonoco Deutschland GmbH, Lauda Plant, Tauberstrasse 36, D-97922 Lauda - Königshofen, Germany
Tel: 49-9343-7017

Sonoco Engraph Machine Division, Am Webrhabn, D-40211 Düsseldorf, Germany
Tel: 49-211-35 68 68

Sonoco IPD GmbH, Düren Plant, Math v.d. Drieschstrasse 2, D-52399 Merzenich Girbelsrath, Germany
Tel: 49-2421-704-0

Sonoco OPV Hülsen GmbH, Industriestrasse 6-9, Postfach 1154, D-77741 Neuried Altenheim, Germany
Tel: 49-7807-990

Sonoco Plastics GmbH, Lindestrasse 20, D-53842 Troisdorf, Germany
Tel: 49-2241-48000

SOTHEBY'S HOLDINGS, INC.
1334 York Avenue, New York, NY, 10021
Tel: (212) 606-7000   Fax: (212) 606-7027   www.sothebys.com
Auction house specializing in fine art and jewelry.

Sotheby's Holdings, Inc., Mendelssohnstrasse 66, D-60325 Frankfurt am Main 1, Germany
Tel: 49-69-7407-87   Contact: Nina Buhne

Sotheby's Holdings, Inc., Odeansplatz 16, D-80539 Münich, Germany
Tel: 49-89-291-3151   Contact: Heinrich Graf von Spreti, Pres.

THE SOUTHERN COMPANY
270 Peachtree Street, N.W., Atlanta, GA, 30303
Tel: (404) 506-5000   Fax: (404) 506-0642   www.southernco.com
Electric utility.

Southern Energy, Inc., 3 Markgrafenstrasse, D-10117 Berlin, Germany
Tel: 49-30-2092-4000   Fax: 49-30-2092-4200   Contact: Jason Harlan, Dir.

SPARKLER FILTERS INC.
PO Box 19, Conroe, TX, 77305-0019
Tel: (936) 756-4471   Fax: (936) 539-1165   www.sparklerfilters.com
Mfr. chemical process filtration industry.

Sparkler Filters Europe GmbH, Belvedered Allee 23C, D-99425 Weimar, Germany

SPECTRA-PHYSICS, INC.
1335 Terra Bella Avenue, Bldg. 7, Mountain View, CA, 94043
Tel: (650) 961-2550   Fax: (650) 968-5215   www.spectra-physics.com
Mfr. lasers.

Spectra-Physics GmbH, Guerickeweg 7, D-64291 Darmstadt, Germany

Spectra-Physics LAS GmbH, Ruhlsdorfer Str. 95,, D-14532 Stahnsdorf, Germany

SPECTRUM CONTROL, INC.
8031 Avonia Road, Fairview, PA, 16415
Tel: (814) 835-1650   Fax: (814) 835-1651   www.spectrumcontrol.com
Mfr. control systems for telecommunications equipment.

Spectrum Control, Hansastrasse 6, D-91126 Schwabach, Germany
Tel: 49-91227950

SPEEDFAM-IPEC INC.
305 N. 54th Street, Chandler, AZ, 85226-2416
Tel: (480) 961-1600   Fax: (480) 705-2793   www.sfamipec.com
Mfr. semiconductors.

SpeedFam-IPEC GmbH, Hendrichstrasse 42a, D-01099 Dresden, Germany
Tel: 49-351-888-5960   Fax: 49-351-888-5966

SPENCER STUART MANAGEMENT CONSULTANTS

401 North Michigan Ave., Ste. 3400, Chicago, IL, 60611

Tel: (312) 822-0080   Fax: (312) 822-0116   www.spencerstuart.com

Executive recruitment firm.

Spencer Stuart & Associates Inc., Albstrasse 14, D-70597 Stuttgart, Germany

Tel: 49-711-97682-0   Fax: 49-711-97682-82   Contact: Hermann Sendele

Spencer Stuart & Associates Inc., Konigsallee 82, D-40212 Düsseldorf, Germany

Tel: 49-211-864070   Fax: 49-211-132975   Contact: Hermann Sendele

Spencer Stuart & Associates Inc., Prinzregentenstrasse 61, D-81675 Münich, Germany

Tel: 49-89-455553-0   Fax: 49-89-455553-33   Contact: Hermann Sendele

SPERRY-SUN DRILLING SERVICES

PO Box 60070, Houston, TX, 77205

Tel: (281) 871-5100   Fax: (281) 871-5742   www.sperry-sun.com

Provides drilling services to the oil and gas drilling industry.

Sperry-Sun c/o DB Stratabit GmbH, Hunaustrasse 7a, D-9227 Celle Westercelle, Germany

SPHERION CORPORATION

2050 Spectrum Boulevard, Fort Lauderdale, FL, 33309

Tel: (954) 938-7600   Fax: (954) 938-7666   www.spherion.com

Provides temporary personnel placement and staffing.

Michael Page Finance, Mainzer Landstrasse 39, D-60329 Frankfort, Germany

Tel: 49-9-242-6180

Michael Page Finance, Graf-Adolf-Strasse 70, D-40210 Düsseldorf, Germany

Tel: 49-211-177-220

SPRAYING SYSTEMS COMPANY

PO Box 7900, Wheaton, IL, 60189-7900

Tel: (630) 665-5000   Fax: (630) 260-0842   www.spray.com

Designs and manufactures industrial spray products.

Feinbau Maschinen GmbH, Postfach 1340, D-7065 Winterbach, Germany

Spraying Systems Deutschland, Grossmoorring 9, D-2100 Hamburg 90, Germany

SPS TECHNOLOGIES INC.

165 Township Line Rd., Two Pitcairn Place, Jenkintown, PA, 19046

Tel: (215) 517-2000   Fax: (215) 517-2032   www.spstech.com

Mfr. aerospace and industry fasteners, tightening systems, magnetic materials, super alloys.

Unbrako Schrauben SPS GmbH, Postfach 2180, Ernst-Sach-Str. 11, D-5400 Koblenz, Germany

Fax: 49-421-3795-663   Contact: Peter Danisch

SPSS INC.

233 S. Wacker Dr., 11th Fl., Chicago, IL, 60606

Tel: (312) 651-6000   Fax: (312) 329-3668   www.spss.com

Mfr. statistical software.

SPSS GmbH Software, Rosenheimer Str. 30, D-81669 Münich 22, Germany

SPX CORPORATION

700 Terrace Point Drive, PO Box 3301, Muskegon, MI, 49443-3301

Tel: (231) 724-5000   Fax: (231) 724-5720   www.spx.com

Mfr. auto parts, special service tools, engine and drive-train parts.

Allen Motordiagnose Systeme/SPX Deutschland GmbH, Dieselstrasse 10, D-63512 Hainburg, Germany

Bear Automobil Servicegerate, Postfach 1108, D-77671 Kehl, Germany

Kent-Moore & Euroline, Alfred Nobel Str. 12, Postfach 1528, D-68519 Viernheim, Germany

Lowener OTC Tool GbmH, Industriestrasse 67, D-40764 Langenfeld, Germany

Sealed Power Europe, Postfach 1355, D-3013 Barsinghausen, Germany

SPX Deutschland, Alfred-Nobel-Strasse 12, Postfach 1528, D-68519 Viernheim, Germany

THE ST. PAUL COMPANIES, INC.

385 Washington Street, St. Paul, MN, 55102

Tel: (651) 310-7911   Fax: (651) 310-8294   www.stpaul.com

Provides investment, insurance and reinsurance services.

St. Paul Deutschland, Neue Weyerstrasse 6, D-50676 Cologne, Germany

Tel: 49-221-92-44-70   Fax: 49-221-92-44-710   Contact: Bodo Sartorius, Mgr.

Victoria Verischerung AG, Victoriaplatz 1, D-40198 Düsseldorf, Germany

STANDARD COMMERCIAL CORPORATION

2201 Miller Rd., PO Box 450, Wilson, NC, 27894

Tel: (252) 291-5507   Fax: (252) 237-1109   www.sccgroup.com

Leaf tobacco dealers and processors and wool processors.

Leafco Trading GmbH, D-2000 Hamburg, Germany

Standard Wool GmbH, Schwachhauser Heerstrasse 57, D-2800 Bremen, Germany

Werkhof GmbH, Brook 6, D-20457 Hamburg, Germany

Werkhof GmbH, An der Alster 18, D-2000 Hamburg 1, Germany

STANDARD MICROSYSTEMS CORPORATION

80 Arkay Drive, Hauppauge, NY, 11788

Tel: (631) 435-6000   Fax: (631) 273-5550   www.smsc.com

Telecommunications systems.

Standard Microsystems GmbH, Johanneskirchner Str. 100, D-81927 Münich, Germany

Tel: 49-89-9592-990   Fax: 49-89-9592-9990

STANDEX INTERNATIONAL CORPORATION

6 Manor Parkway, Salem, NH, 03079

Tel: (603) 893-9701   Fax: (603) 893-7324   www.standex.com

Mfr. diversified graphics, institutional, industry, electronic and consumer products.

James Burn International GbmH, Postfach 540752, D-22507 Hamburg, Germany

Tel: 49-40-540-7013   Fax: 49-40-540-7090   Contact: Peter Timm, Mgr.

Roehlen Industries/Europe, Postfach 130665, D-47758 Krefeld 1, Germany

Tel: 49-2151-37120   Fax: 49-2151-3712-58   Contact: Giorgio Mazza, Mgr.

Standex International GmbH, PO Box 130665, D-47758 Krefeld 1, Germany

Tel: 49-2151-37120   Fax: 49-2151-371258   Contact: Eckhard Roeder, Mgr.

Standex International GmbH, Mold-Tech Div. South, Postfach 1444, D-74604 Oehringen, Germany

Tel: 49-7941-91700   Fax: 49-7941-9170-33

STANLEY BOSTITCH FASTENING SYSTEMS

815 Briggs Street, East Greenwich, RI, 02818

Tel: (401) 884-2500   Fax: (401) 885-6511   www.stanleybostich.com

Mfr. stapling machines, stapling supplies, fastening systems and wire.

Stanley Bostitch GmbH, Postfach 1349, Oststr. 26, D-2000 Norderstedt l Bez-Hamburg, Germany

THE STANLEY WORKS

1000 Stanley Drive, PO Box 7000, New Britain, CT, 06053

Tel: (860) 225-5111   Fax: (860) 827-3987   www.stanleyworks.com

Mfr. hand tools and hardware.

Stanley Air Tools, Frankfurterstrasse 74, D-64521 Gross-Gerau, Germany

Stanley Fastening Systems, Oststrasse 26, D-22844 Norderstedt, Germany

Stanley Home Décor GmbH, Industriestrasse 3-5, D-91632 Wieseth, Germany

STAPLES, INC.

500 Staples Dr., Framingham, MA, 01702

Tel: (508) 253-3000   Fax: (508) 253-8989   www.staples.com

Superstore for office supplies and equipment.

MAXI Papier, Am Werder 1, D-21073 Hamburg, Germany

Tel: 49-40-76741-0   Fax: 49-40-76741-299

MAXI Papier Direct, Warehouse Bldg., HalskestraBe 1, D-21465 Reinbek, Germany
Tel: 49-40-76741-278   Fax: 49-40-727-309-11

STAR TELECOMMUNICATIONS, INC.
223 East De La Guerra Street, Santa Barbara, CA, 93101
Tel: (805) 899-1962   Fax: (805) 899-2972   www.startel.com
Provides long-distance telecommunications services.

Star Germany, Voltastrasse 1a, D-60486 Frankfurt am Main, Germany
Tel: 49-699-8240-0 Fax: 49-699-8240-100

STA-RITE INDUSTRIES INC.
293 Wright Street, Delavan, WI, 53115
Tel: (262) 728-5551   Fax: (262) 728-7323   www.sta-rite.com
Mfr. water pumps, filters and systems.

Sta-Rite Industries GmbH, Wiesenstr 6, D-64347 Griesheim, Germany
Tel: 49-6155-8417-0   Fax: 49-6155-8417-99   Contact: Gert Van de Sand   Emp: 17

STARKEY LABORATORIES, INC.
6700 Washington Avenue South, Eden Prairie, MN, 55344
Tel: (952) 941-6401   Fax: (952) 947-4787   www.starkey.com
Mfr. custom in-the-ear hearing aids.

Starkey GmbH, Rugenbarg 69, D-22848 Norderstedt, Germany

STARTEC GLOBAL COMMUNICATIONS CORPORATION
1151 Seven Locks Road, Potomac, MD, 20854
Tel: (301) 610-4300   Fax: (301) 610-4301   www.startec.com
Provides international phone service.

Startec Global GmbH, Weismullerstrasse 25, D-60314 Frankfurt, Germany

STARWOOD HOTELS & RESORTS WORLDWIDE
777 Westchester Avenue, White Plains, NY, 10604
Tel: (914) 640-8100   Fax: (914) 640-8316   www.starwoodhotels.com
Hotel operations including Sheraton, Westin, St. Regis, Four Points and Caesars.

Sheraton Sales Center, Ander Hauptwache 11, D-6000 Frankfurt/Main 1, Germany

STATE STREET CORPORATION
225 Franklin Street, Boston, MA, 02101
Tel: (617) 786-3000   Fax: (617) 654-3386   www.statestreet.com
Engaged in investment management and institutional investor services.

State Street Global GmbH, Brienner Strasse 59, D-80333 München, Germany

STEINER CORPORATION
505 E. South Temple, Salt Lake City, UT, 84102
Tel: (801) 328-8831   Fax: (801) 363-5680   www.alsco.com
Mfr. soap and towel dispensers and uniforms.

Steiner Company International SA, Im GewerbegebiePesch 13A, D-50767 Köln, Germany

STEINWAY MUSICAL INSTRUMENTS, INC.
800 South St., Ste.305, Waltham, MA, 02453
Tel: (781) 894-9770   Fax: (781) 894-9803   www.steinway.com
Manufacture and marketing of pianos.

Steinway & Sons Hamburg, Rindenburg 10, Postfach 54 07 48, D-22525 Hamburg, Germany
Tel: 49-40-853-910 Fax: 49-40-853-91199   Contact: Thomas Kurrer, Mng. Dir.   Emp: 400

STELLENT, INC.
7777 Golden Triangle Drive, Eden Prairie, MN, 55344
Tel: (952) 903-2000   Fax: (952) 829-5424   www.stellent.com
Mfr. Web-based software products.

Stelleng GmbH, Claudia Str. 2B, D-51149 Köln, Germany

STEPAN COMPANY
22 West Frontage Rd., Northfield, IL, 60093

Tel: (847) 446-7500   Fax: (847) 501-2443   www.stepan.com

Mfr. basic intermediate chemicals.

Stepan Germany, Wesseling, Germany

STIEFEL LABORATORIES INC.
255 Alhambra Circle, Ste. 1000, Coral Gables, FL, 33134

Tel: (305) 443-3807   Fax: (305) 443-3467   www.stiefel.com

Mfr. pharmaceuticals, dermatological specialties.

Stiefel Laboratorium GmbH, Muhlheimer Strasse 231, D-63075 Offenbach/Main, Germany

STONERIDGE, INC.
9400 E. Market Stret, Warren, OH, 4484

Tel: (330) 856-2443   Fax: (220) 856-2611   www.stroneridge.com

Mfr. electrical and electronic components for automobiles and trucks.

Stoneridge GmbH, Wilhelm-Theodor-Roemheld-Strasse 14, D-55130 Mainz, Germany

STORAGE TECHNOLOGY CORPORATION
One Storagetech Dr., Louisville, CO, 80028-4377

Tel: (303) 673-5151   Fax: (303) 673-5019   www.stortek.com

Mfr., market, service information, storage and retrieval systems.

StorageTek GmbH, Industriestrasse 30-34, D-65760 Eschborn, Germany

StorageTekv GmbH, Groninger Str. 25, D-13347 Berlin, Germany

STOWE WOODWARD MOUNT HOPE
One Technology Drive, Westborough, MA, 01581

Tel: (508) 616-9458   Fax: (508) 616-9479   www.stowewoodward.com

Mfr. roll covering and bowed roll technologies for the web handling industries.

Gummiwerke Becker AG, Robert-Koch Str. 3, Postfach 1126, D-7920 Heidenhein, Germany

Stowe Woodward AG, Hellweg 184-194, D-33758 Schloß Holte, Germany

Stowe Woodward AG, Am Langen Graben 22, D-52353 Düren, Germany

STREAM INTERNATIONAL
85 Dan Road, Canton, MA, 02021

Tel: (781) 575-6800   Fax: (781) 575-6999   www.stream.com

Provider of outsourced technical support for major computer industry companies.

Stream International GmbH, Komturstrasse 18, D-12099 Berlin, Germany

THE STRUCTURE TONE ORGANIZATION
15 East 26th Street, New York, NY, 10010-1589

Tel: (212) 481-6100   Fax: (212) 685-9267   www.structuretone.com

Provides general contracting and construction management.

Structure Tone Organization, Geleitsstrasse 8, D-60599 Frankfurt, Germany

SUDLER & HENNESSEY
230 Park Avenue South, New York, NY, 10003-1566

Tel: (212) 614-4100   Fax: (212) 598-6933   www.sudler.com

Engaged in healthcare products advertising.

Sudler & Hennessey GmbH, Kleyerstrasse 25, D-60326 Frankfurt am Main, Germany
Tel: 49-69-75-06-03   Fax: 49-69-75-06-15-42   Contact: Thomas Schmidt-Breber, Mng. Dir.

SULLIVAN & CROMWELL
125 Broad Street, New York, NY, 10004-2498

Tel: (212) 558-4000   Fax: (212) 558-3588   www.sullcrom.com

Engaged in international law.

Sullivan & Cromwell, Neue Mainzer Strasse 52, D-60311 Frankfurt am Main, Germany

SUN MICROSYSTEMS, INC.

901 San Antonio Road, Palo Alto, CA, 94303

Tel: (650) 960-1300　　　Fax: (650) 961-9131　　　www.sun.com

Computer peripherals and programming services.

Sun Microsystems, Personalabteilung, Bretonischer Ring 3, D-85630 Grasbrunn, Germany

SUNBEAM CORPORATION

2381 Executive Center Dr., Boca Raton, FL, 33431

Tel: (561) 912-4100　　　Fax: (561) 912-4567　　　www.sunbeam.com

Mfr. household and personal grooming appliances; Sunbeam, Mr. Coffee, First Alert, Mixmaster and Oster.

Oster Intl. GmbH, Schreberstrasse 18, D-6050 Offenbach/Main, Germany

SUNGARD DATA SYSTEMS

1285 Drummers Lane, Wayne, PA, 19087

Tel: (610) 341-8700　　　Fax: (610) 341-8851　　　www.sungard.com

Provides ASP solutions to the buyside investment management market.

SunGard Data Systems, Wilhelm-Leuschner-Strasse 14, D-60329 Frankfurt am Main, Germany

Tel: 49-69-2561440　　Contact: George Zafirakis, Pres.

SUNRISE MEDICAL INC.

7477 East Dry Creek Parkway, Longmont, CO, 80503

Tel: (303) 218-4500　　　Fax: (303) 218-4590　　　www.sunrisemedical.com

Designs, manufactures and markets rehabilitation products and assistive technology devices for people with disabilities, and patient care products used in nursing homes, hospitals and homecare settings.

Sunrise Medical GmbH, Industriegebiet, D-69254 Malsch, Germany

SUPRA PRODUCTS INC.

4001 Fairview Industrial Drive S.E., Salem, OR, 97302-1067

Tel: (503) 581-9101　　　Fax: (503) 364-1285　　　www.supra-products.com

Mfr. lockboxes and provides key and access management products.

KEMAS GmbH, Würstenbrander Str. 9, D-09353 Oberlungwitz, Germany

SYBASE, INC.

5000 Hacienda Dr., Dublin, CA, 94568

Tel: (925) 236-5000　　　Fax: (925) 236-4321　　　www.sybase.com

Design/mfg/distribution of database management systems, software development tools, connectivity products, consulting and technical support services..

Sybase Germany GmbH, An der Trift 65, D-63303 Dreieich, Germany

Tel: 49-6103-890500　　Fax: 49-6103-890566

Sybase Germany GmbH, Mainzer Landstrasse 45/34 OG, D-62305 Frankfurt am Main, Germany

Tel: 49-69-170820　　Fax: 49-69-170-82111

Sybase Germany GmbH, Heidenkampsweg 41, D-20097 Hamburg, Germany

Tel: 49-4023-7809-0　　Fax: 49-4023-7809-55

Sybase Germany GmbH, Zettachring 2A, D-70567 Stuttgart, Germany

Tel: 49-711-900-5220　　Fax: 49-711-5222

Sybase Germany GmbH, Am Steestern 8, D-40547 Düsseldorf, Germany

Tel: 49-2115-9760　　Fax: 49-2115-9761-11

SYBRON DENTAL SPECIALTIES, INC.

1717 West Collins, Orange, CA, 92867

Tel: (714) 516-7400　　　Fax: (714) 516-7904　　　www.sybrondental.com

Mfr. consumable dental products, light curing instruments and plastics for dental use.

Kerr International, Div. Sybron Dental, Liststrasse 28, D-76185 Karlsruhe, Germany

Tel: 49-721-95567-0

SYKES ENTERPRISES, INC.

100 N. Tampa Street, Ste. 3900, Tampa, FL, 33602

Tel: (813) 274-1000   Fax: (813) 273-0148   www.sykes.com

Provides information technology outsourcing services.

Sykes GmbH, Adenauerstrasse 20, C2, D-52146 Wurselen, Germany

SYMANTEC CORPORATION

20330 Stevens Creek Blvd., Cupertino, CA, 95014-2132

Tel: (408) 253-9600   Fax: (408) 253-3968   www.symantec.com

Designs and produces PC network security and network management software and hardware.

Symantec (Deutschland) GmbH, Kaiserwerther Str. 115, D-40880 Ratingen, Germany

Tel: 49-2102-74530   Fax: 49-2102-7452-922

SYMBOL TECHNOLOGIES, INC.

One Symbol Plaza, Holtsville, NY, 11742-1300

Tel: (631) 738-2400   Fax: (631) 738-5990   www.symbol.com

Mfr. Bar code-driven data management systems, wireless LAN's, and Portable Shopping System™.

Symbol Technologies Germany GmbH, Grabenstraße 5, D-40213 Düsseldorf, Germany

Tel: 49-211-32-04-52 Fax: 49-211-32-04-70

Symbol Technologies Germany GmbH, Waldstrasse 68, D-63128 Dietzenbach, Germany

Tel: 49-60-74-490-20   Fax: 49-60-74-427-95

Symbol Technologies Germany GmbH, Gotensraße 12, D-20097 Hamburg, Germany

Tel: 49-40-235-3990   Fax: 49-40-235-39999

SYNAVANT INC.

3445 Peachtree Road NE, Ste. 1400, Atlanta, GA, 30326

Tel: (404) 841-4000   Fax: (404) 841-4115   www.synavant.com

Mfr. support software for pharmaceutical industry.

Synavant GmbH, Carl-Zeiss-Ring 3, D-85737 Ismaning, Germany

Contact: Joerg Medelnik

SYNCHRONICITY SOFTWARE, INC.

201 Forest Street, Marlboro, MA, 01752

Tel: (508) 485-4122   Fax: (508) 485-7514   www.synchronicity.com

Mfr. communications software.

Synchronicity Software, Herterich Str. 174, 1/F, D-81476 München, Germany

SYNOPSYS, INC.

700 East Middlefield Road, Mountain View, CA, 94043

Tel: (650) 962-5000   Fax: (650) 965-8637   www.synopsys.com

Mfr. electronic design automation software.

Synopsys GmbH, Europa-Forum-II Bldg., Karl-hammerschmidt-Strasse 34, D-85609 Aschheim/Dornach, Germany

SYNPLICITY, INC.

935 Stewart Drive, Sunnyvale, CA, 94085

Tel: (408) 215-6000   Fax: (408) 990-0290   www.synplicity.com

Mfr. software.

Synplicity GmbH, Humboldstrasse 12, D-85609 Dornach, Germany

Contact: Willi Ahnen

SYNTEGRA

4201 Lexington Avenue North, Arden Hills, MN, 55126-6198

Tel: (651) 415-2999   Fax: (651) 415-4891   www.cdc.com

Engaged in consulting and systems integration.

Syntegra GmbH, Stressmannallee 30, D-60596 Frankfurt, Germany

Tel: 49-69-630-5271   Fax: 49-69-630-5695

SYNTEL, INC.

525 East Big Beaver Road, Ste. 300, Troy, MI, 48083

Tel: (248) 619-2800   Fax: (248) 619-2888   www.syntelinc.com

Provides applications outsourcing and IT consulting services.

Syntel Deutschland GmbH, Lenbachplatz 3, D- 80333 Münich, Germany

Tel: 49-89-544-15511   Fax: 49-89-544-15599

SYSTEMAX INC.

22 Harbor Park Dr., Port Washington, NY, 11050

Tel: (516) 608-7000   Fax: (516) 608-7111   www.systemax.com

Direct marketer of computers and related products to businesses.

Misco Germany Inc., Im Gefierth 14-16, D-63303 Dreieich, Germany

Tel: 49-6103-305305

TARANTELLA, INC.

425 Encinal Street, Santa Cruz, CA, 95060

Tel: (831) 425-7222   Fax: (831) 427-5400   www.tarantella.com

Mfr. server software.

Tarantella GmbH, Zimmersmühlenweg 68, D-61440 Oberursel, Germany

TBWA WORLDWIDE

488 Madison Avenue, 6th Floor, New York, NY, 10022

Tel: (212) 804-1000   Fax: (212) 804-1200   www.tbwachiat.com

International full service advertising agency.

Planet Communications, Frankfurt, Germany

TBWA GmbH, Frankfurt, Germany

TECA CORPORATION (THERMO ELECTRIC COOLING AMERICA

4048 West Schubert, Chicago, IL, 60639

Tel: (773) 342-4900   Fax: (773) 342-0191   www.thermoelectric.com

Mfr. solid state cooling products, including air-conditioners, cold plates and liquid chillers.

Thermo Electric GmbH, Postfach 900 406, Fuggerstrasse 34a, D-51114 Cologne, Germany

TECH DATA CORPORATION

5350 Tech Data Drive, Clearwater, FL, 33760

Tel: (727) 539-7429   Fax: (727) 538-7876   www.techdata.com

Distributor of computer systems, software and related equipment.

Macrotron, Münich, Germany

TECHNE CORPORATION

614 McKinley Place NE, Minneapolis, MN, 55413

Tel: (612) 379-8854   Fax: (612) 379-6580   www.techne-corp.com

Mfr. controls and instruments for blood analysis.

R&D Systems GmbH, Borsigstrasse 7, D-65205 Wiesbaden, Germany

TECHNITROL INC.

1210 Northbrook Drive, #385, Trevose, PA, 19053

Tel: (215) 355-2900   Fax: (215) 355-7397   www.technitrol.com

Mfr. of electronic components, electrical contacts, and other parts/materials.

Pulse Engineering Electronic Components, Huchenfeld, Germany

TECHNOLOGY SOLUTIONS COMPANY (TSC)

205 N. Michigan Ave., Ste. 1500, Chicago, IL, 60601

Tel: (312) 228-4500   Fax: (312) 228-4501   www.techsol.com

Designs computer information systems and strategic business and management consulting for major corporations.

TSC Europe, Vor den Siebenburgen 2, D-50676 Köln, Germany

Tel: 49-221-93-1224 Fax: 49-221-93-122499   Contact: Robert Philipp

TECUMSEH PRODUCTS COMPANY

100 E. Patterson Street, Tecumseh, MI, 49286-1899

Tel: (517) 423-8411   Fax: (517) 423-8526   www.tecumseh.com

Mfr. of hermetic compressors for air conditioning and refrigeration products, gasoline engines and power train components for lawn and garden applications, and pumps.

Tecnamotor Deutschland Vertrieb GmbH, Necklenbroicher Str. 52-54, D-4005 Meerbusch 1, Germany

TEKELEC

26580 West Agoura Road, Calabasas, CA, 91302

Tel: (818) 880-5656   Fax: (818) 880-6993   www.tekelec.com

Mfr. telecommunications testing equipment.

Tekelec Europe GmbH, Kapuzinerstrasse 9, D-80337 München, Germany

Tel: 49-89-516-4100

TEKTRONIX INC.

14200 SW Karl Braun Dr., PO Box 500, Beaverton, OR, 97077

Tel: (503) 627-7111   Fax: (503) 627-2406   www.tek.com

Mfr. test and measure, visual systems/color printing and communications/video and networking products.

Tektronix GmbH, Stolberger Str. 200, D-50933 Cologne, Germany

Tel: 49-221-94770   Fax: 49-221-9477-200

TELEFLEX INC.

630 W. Germantown Pike, Ste. 450, Plymouth Meeting, PA, 19462

Tel: (610) 834-6301   Fax: (610) 834-8307   www.teleflex.com

Design, manufacture and marketing of mechanical and electro-mechanical systems, control systems and surgical devices.

Medical Device Safety Service GmbH, Burckhardtstr. 1, D-30163 Hannover, Germany

Pilling Weck GmbH, D-63791 Karlstein am Main, Germany

Rüsch Care Vertriebs GmbH, Kernen, Germany

SermeTel Technical Services GmbH, Heiligenhaus, Germany

Telair International GmbH, Bayernwerkstrasse 39 g, D-857 57 Karlsfeld, Germany

United Parts Driver Control Systems GmbH, Wiesbaden, Germany

Willy Rüsch AG, Willy-Rüsch-StraBe 4-10, D-71394 Kernen, Germany

Tel: 49-7151-406-0   Fax: 49-7151-406-130

TELEX COMMUNICATIONS INC.

12000 Portland Ave. South, Burnsville, MN, 55337

Tel: (952) 884-4051   Fax: (952) 884-0043   www.telexcommunications.com

Mfr. communications, audio-visual and professional audio products.

Telex EVI Audio GmbH, Hirschberger Ring 45, D-94315 Straubing, Germany

TELLABS INC.

1415 W. Diehl Rd., Naperville, IL, 60563

Tel: (630) 378-8800   Fax: (630) 852-7346   www.tellabs.com

Design/mfr./service voice/data transport and network access systems.

Tellabs Germany, Marsstr. 22, D-80335 München, Germany

TENNANT COMPANY

701 North Lilac Drive, Minneapolis, MN, 55440

Tel: (763) 540-1208   Fax: (763) 540-1437   www.tennantco.com

Mfr. industry floor maintenance sweepers and scrubbers and floor coatings.

Tennant GmbH & Co. KG, Weststrasse 22, Postfach 10 09 52, D-42809 Remscheid, Germany

Tel: 49-2191-92810   Fax: 49-2191-928129

TENNECO AUTOMOTIVE INC.

500 North Field Drive, Lake Forest, IL, 60045

Tel: (847) 482-5241   Fax: (847) 482-5295   www.tenneco-automotive.com

Mfr. automotive parts, exhaust systems and service equipment.

Gillet Aggassysteme Zwickau GmbH, Postfach 862, Hilferdingste 8, D-08056 Zwickau, Germany

Tel: 49-375-8250

Monroe Auto Equipment GmbH, Herzog-Adolph-Strasse 4, D-6420 Konigstein/TS, Germany

Walker Deutschland GmbH, Waldgartenstrasse 4, D-68642 Buerstadt, Germany

Tel: 49-6206-70255   Fax: 49-6206-70226   Contact: Horst Hermann, Mgr.

Walker Gillet Europe GmbH, Luitpoldstrasse 83, Postfach 95, D-67477 Edenkoben, Germany

Tel: 49-6323-470   Fax: 49-6323-47-2299   Contact: Lutz Kesselring, Mng. Dir.   Emp: 65

TERADATA

1700 South Patterson Blvd., Dayton, OH, 45479

Tel: (937) 445-5000   Fax: (937) 445-1682   www.teradata.com

Mfr. software to store information.

Teradata Div., NCR, Ulmer Straßw 160, D-86156 Augsburg, Germany

TERADYNE INC.

321 Harrison Ave., Boston, MA, 02118

Tel: (617) 482-2700   Fax: (617) 422-2910   www.teradyne.com

Mfr. electronic test equipment and blackplane connection systems.

Teradyne GmbH, Dingolfinger Strasse 2, D-81673 Münich, Germany

Zehntel GmbH, Paul-Gerhardt-Allee 50, D-81245 Münich, Germany

TEREX CORPORATION

500 Post Road East, Ste. 320, Westport, CT, 06880

Tel: (203) 222-7170   Fax: (203) 222-7976   www.terex.com

Mfr. lifting and earthmoving equipment.

O&K Mining GmbH, Karl-Funke-Str. 36, D-44149 Dortmund, Germany

Tel: 49-0231-9223   Fax: 49-0231-922-5005

TEXAS INSTRUMENTS INC.

12500 TI Blvd., Dallas, TX, 75266

Tel: (972) 995-3773   Fax: (972) 995-4360   www.ti.com

Mfr. semiconductor devices, electronic electro-mechanical systems, instruments and controls.

Texas Instruments GmbH, Freising, Germany

Texas Instruments GmbH, Haggertystrasse 1, D-8050 Freising, Germany

TEXTRON INC.

40 Westminster Street, Providence, RI, 02903

Tel: (401) 421-2800   Fax: (401) 421-2878   www.textron.com

Mfr. Aerospace (Bell Helicopter and Cessna Aircraft), industry and consumer products, fasteners and financial services.

Avdel GmbH, Postfach 30 07 63, D-30835 Langenhagen, Germany

Tel: 49-511-72880   Fax: 49-511-7288133

Klauke Textron, Auf Dem Knappe 46, Postfach 10 05 52, D-42805 Remscheid, Germany

Tel: 49-2-191-9070   Fax: 49-2-191-907201   Contact: Karl-Gustav Diederichs, Mng. Dir.

Sükosim Verbindungselemente, Zeller Weg 25, D-7187 Schrozberg, Germany

Tel: 49-7935-71-0   Fax: 49-7935-71-488

THE MARMON GROUP, INC.

200 West Adams, Ste. 2211, Chicago, IL, 60606

Tel: (312) 372-9500   Fax: (312) 845-5305   www.marmon.com

Holding company for diversified manufacturing and service firms.

DWL Elektronische Systeme GmbH, Langerach 4, D-78354 Sipplingen, Germany

Tel: 49-7551-9206-0

THERMO ELECTRON CORPORATION

81 Wyman Street, Waltham, MA, 02454-9046

Tel: (781) 622-1000   Fax: (781) 622-1207   www.thermo.com

Develop, mfr., sale of process equipment &instruments for energy intensive and healthcare industries.

Jaeger Toennies, Div. Thermo Electron Corp., Leibnizstrasse 7, D-9204 Hoechberg, Germany
Tel: 49-931-4972-0

Nicolet Biomedical Germany, Saalackerstrasse 8, D-63801 Kleinostheim, Germany
Tel: 49-6027-4698

Van Hengel Instrumente GmbH, Baiertalerstr. 24-26, D-6908 Wiesloch, Germany

THERMO FINNIGAN CORPORATION

355 River Oaks Parkway, San Jose, CA, 95134-1991

Tel: (408) 433-4800   Fax: (408) 433-4823   www.thermo.com

Mfr. mass spectrometers.

Thermo Finnigan, Boschring 12, D- 63329 Egelsbach, Germany

Thermo Finnigan MAT GmbH, Barkhausenstrasse 2, D-28197 Bremen, Germany

THERMO NICOLET CORPORATION

5225 Verona Road, Madison, WI, 53711-4495

Tel: (608) 276-6100   Fax: (608) 276-6222   www.nicolet.com

Mfr. infrared spectrometers and oscilloscopes and medical electro-diagnostic equipment.

Nicolet Instrument GmbH, Senefelderstr. 162, D-63069 Offenbach Main, Germany
Tel: 49-69-98408-0   Fax: 49-69-98408-122

THERMO RAMSEY INC.

501 90th Avenue NW, Minneapolis, MN, 55433

Tel: (763) 783-2500   Fax: (763) 780-2525   www.thermoramsey.com

Mfr. of industrial control products.

Thermo Ramsey, Max-Eyth-Str. 45, D-4200 Oberhausen 11, Germany

THERMON MANUFACTURING COMPANY

100 Thermon Drive, PO Box 609, San Marcos, TX, 78667-0609

Tel: (512) 396-5801   Fax: (512) 396-3627   www.thermon.com

Mfr. steam and electric heat tracing systems, components and accessories.

Thermon Deutschland, Dillenburger Strasse 26, D-57299 Burbach, Germany

THETFORD CORPORATION

7101 Jackson Road, PO Box 1285, Ann Arbor, MI, 48106

Tel: (734) 769-6000   Fax: (734) 769-2023   www.thetford.com

Mfr. sanitation products and chemicals.

Thetford GmbH, Schallbruch 14, D-42781 Haan, Germany

THOMAS & BETTS CORPORATION

8155 T&B Blvd., Memphis, TN, 38125

Tel: (901) 252-5000   Fax: (901) 685-1988   www.tnb.com

Mfr. elect/electronic connectors and accessories.

Thomas & Betts GmbH, Postfach 1274, Theodor-Heuss-Str. 7-9, D-6073 Egelsbach, Germany

THOMAS GROUP, INC.

5221 N. O'Connor Blvd., Ste. 500, Irving, TX, 75039-3714

Tel: (972) 869-3400   Fax: (972) 443-1701   www.thomasgroup.com

Engaged in management consulting services.

Thomas Group GmbH, Aculeum, Hahnstra 43, D-60528 Frankfurt, Germany
Contact: Phillip J. Lovell, Pres.

THOMAS INDUSTRIES INC.

4360 Brownsboro Road, Ste. 300, Louisville, KY, 40232

Tel: (502) 893-4600   Fax: (502) 893-4685   www.thomasind.com

Mfr. lighting fixtures and specialty pumps and compressors for global OEM applications.

ASF Thomas Industries GmbH, Hahnerbergerstrasse 173-185, Postfach 15 02 20, D-42349 Kronenberg, Germany

ASF Thomas Industries GmbH, Postfach 1214, Luitpoldstrasse 28, D-8940 Memmingen, Germany

ASF Thomas Industries GmbH, Siemensstraße 4, Industriegebiet Nord, D-82178 Puchheim, Germany

Contact: Peter Bissinger, VP

THOMAS PUBLISHING COMPANY

5 Penn Plaza, New York, NY, 10007

Tel: (212) 695-0500   Fax: (212) 290-7362   www.thomaspublishing.com

Publishing magazines and directories.

Elsevier-Thomas Fachverlag, Postfach 1869, D-6500 Mainz, Germany

THQ, INC.

27001 Agoura Road, Ste. 325, Calabasas Hills, CA, 91301

Tel: (818) 871-5000   Fax: (818) 591-1615   www.thw.com

Engaged in publishing of video game titles.

THQ Entertainment GmbH, Kimplerstrasse 278, D-47807 Krefeld, Germany

Contact: Riidiger Moersch

TIBCO SOFTWARE INC.

3165 Porter Drive, Palo Alto, CA, 94304

Tel: (650) 846-5000   Fax: (650) 846-1005   www.tibco.com

Mfr. software and provides e-commerce, consulting, and support services. (JV of Reuters UK)

TIBCO Software GmbH, Balanstrasse 49, D-81541 München, Germany

Tel: 49-89-48956-000

TIFFANY & COMPANY

727 Fifth Ave., New York, NY, 10022

Tel: (212) 755-8000   Fax: (212) 605-4465   www.tiffany.com

Mfr./retail fine jewelry, silverware, china, crystal, leather goods, etc.

Tiffany & Co. Munich, Residenzstrasse 11, D-80333 München, Germany

Tel: 49-89-29-00430

THE TIMBERLAND COMPANY

200 Domain Drive, Stratham, NH, 03885

Tel: (603) 772-9500   Fax: (603) 773-1640   www.timberland.com

Design/mfr. footwear, apparel and accessories for men and women.

Timberland World Trading GmbH, Rodelweg 7, D-82067 Ebenhausen, Germany

TIMEX CORPORATION

555 Christian Rd., Middlebury, CT, 06762

Tel: (203) 573-5000   Fax: (203) 573-7019   www.timex.com

Mfr. watches, clocks, timing instruments.

Timex Corp., Wurmbergerstr. 125, D-7530 Pforzhelm, Germany

TIMKEN SUPER PRECISION

PO Box 547 Precision Park, Keene, NH, 03431-0547

Tel: (603) 352-0310   Fax: (603) 355-4553   www.timken.com

Mfr., sales and distribution of bearings, tape guides and systems for missiles, etc.

Timken Super Precision, Obertorstrasse 3, D-97737 Gemunden, Germany

Tel: 49-9351-3013

TITANIUM METALS CORPORATION (TIMET)

1999 Broadway, Suite 4300, Denver, CO, 80202

Tel: (303) 296-5600   Fax: (303) 296-5650   www.timet.com

Produce light weight titanium sponge (metal) for aerospace and auto industries.

TIMET GmbH, Dinnendahlstrasse 31, D-40235 Düsseldorf, Germany

TIW CORPORATION

12300 S. Main Street, PO Box 35729, Houston, TX, 77035

Tel: (713) 729-2110   Fax: (713) 728-4767   www.tiwtools.com

Mfr. liner hanger equipment, production packers, safety and kelly valves.

TIW GmbH, Vogelberg 33a, D-3100 Celle, Germany

Tel: 49-5141-81041

TMP WORLDWIDE, INC.

622 Third Ave., New York, NY, 10017

Tel: (212) 351-7000   Fax: (212) 658-0540   www.tmpw.com

#1 Yellow Pages agency and a leader in the recruitment and interactive advertising fields.

TMP Worldwide Advertising & Communications, Hohenstaufenstrasse 7, D-65189 Wiesbaden, Germany

TOGETHERSOFT CORPORATION

900 Main Campus Drive, Ste. 500, Raleigh, NC, 27606

Tel: (919) 833-5550   Fax: (919) 833-5533   www.togethersoft.com

Mfr. software.

TogetherSoft Germany, Curiestraße 4, D-70563 Stuttgart, Germany

TogetherSoft GmbH, Bessemerstrasse 82, D-12103 Berlin, Germany

TogetherSoft GmbH, Herr Achim Ruder, Curiestrasse 4, D-70563 Stuttgart, Germany

TOKHEIM CORPORATION

PO Box 360, 10501 Corporate Drive, Fort Wayne, IN, 46845

Tel: (219) 470-4600   Fax: (219) 482-2677   www.tokheim.com

Engaged in design, manufacture and service of electronic and mechanical petroleum marketing systems.

Tokheim GmbH, Lothstrasse 1a, D-80335 München, Germany

Tel: 49-89-18953-0   Fax: 49-89-18953-399

THE TORRINGTON COMPANY

59 Field St., PO Box 1008, Torrington, CT, 06790

Tel: (860) 626-2000   Fax: (860) 496-3625   www.torrington.com

Mfr. precision bearings, motion control components and automotive steering assemblies.

Torrington Nadellager GmbH, Kuensebeck, Germany

TOWERS PERRIN

335 Madison Ave., New York, NY, 10017-4605

Tel: (212) 309-3400   Fax: (212) 309-0975   www.towers.com

Management consulting services.

Tillinghast Towers Perrin, Im Trutz 55, D-60322 Frankfurt Main 1, Germany

Tel: 49-69-1505-50

Tillinghast Towers Perrin, Neue Wyerstrasse 6, D-50675 Cologne, Germany

Tel: 49-221-921-2340

TOYS R US INC.

461 From Road, Paramus, NJ, 07652

Tel: (201) 262-7800   Fax: (201) 845-0973   www.toysrus.com

Retail stores: toys and games, sporting goods, computer software, books, records.

Toys R Us GmbH, Koehlstrasse 8, D-50827 Ossendorf, Germany

THE TRANE COMPANY

3600 Pammel Creek Road, La Crosse, WI, 54601

Tel: (608) 787-2000 Fax: (608) 787-4990 www.trane.com

Mfr. distribution and service of A/C systems and equipment.

H.W. Schmidt Klimakalte GmbH, Forstrasse 196A, D-70193 Stuttgart 1, Germany

Trane Klima Technisches Buero GmbH, Wilhelm-Spathstrasse 45D, D-90461 Nürnberg, Germany

Trane Klima und Kaeltetechnisches Buero GmbH, Lilienthal Strasse 6, D-82205 Münich Gilching, Germany

Trane Technisches Buero Dusseldorf GmbH, Am Kiekenbusch 15, D-47269 Duisburg 29, Germany

Trane Technisches Buero Frankfurt GmbH, Ohmstrasse 7, D-63477 Maintal 1, Germany

Trane Technisches Buero Hamburg GmbH, Fabriciusstrasse 15, D-22177 Hamburg, Germany

TRANSWITCH CORPORATION

3 Enterprise Drive, Shelton, CT, 06484

Tel: (203) 929-8810 Fax: (203) 926-9453 www.transwitch.com

Design and manufacture of mixed signal semiconductors.

TranSwitch Germany, Leonhardsweg 4, Unterhaching, D-82008 Münich, Germany

Tel: 49-8179-925757

TRANTER PHE, INC.

PO Box 2289, Wichita Falls, TX, 76306

Tel: (940) 723-7125 Fax: (940) 723-1131 www.tranter.com

Mfr. heat exchangers.

SWEP Warmetauscher Deutschland AG, Kathe-Paulus-Strasse 9, Postfach 10 12 14, Daimlerring 29, D-31112 Hildesheim, Germany

Tel: 49-5121-75200 Fax: 49-5121-54011

TREIBACHER SCHLEIFMITTEL CORPORATION

2000 College Ave., Niagara Falls, NY, 14305

Tel: (716) 286-1234 Fax: (716) 286-1224 www.treibacher-schleifm.com

Mfr. abrasives.

Treibacher Schleifmittel GmbH, Postfach 1116, D-79719 Laufenburg, Germany

TRIBUNE COMPANY

435 North Michigan Ave., Chicago, IL, 60611

Tel: (312) 222-9100 Fax: (312) 222-9100 www.tribune.com

Media company engaged in television and radio broadcasting, publishing and interactive.

Learning Intl. GmbH, Werfstrasse 20-22, D-40549 Düsseldorf, Germany

TRICON GLOBAL RESTAURANTS INC.

1441 Gardner Lane, Louisville, KY, 40213

Tel: (502) 874-1000 Fax: (502) 874-8315 www.triconglobal.com

Owns and operates KFC, Taco Bell and Pizza Hut restaurant food chains.

Pizza Hut Restauration GmbH & Co., Münich, Germany

TRIMBLE NAVIGATION LIMITED

645 N. Mary Ave., Sunnyvale, CA, 94086

Tel: (408) 481-8000 Fax: (408) 481-2000 www.trimble.com

Design/mfr. electronic geographic instrumentation.

Trimble Navigation Deutschland GmbH, HaringstraBe 19, D-85635 Hohenkirchen, Germany

Tel: 49-8102-7433-0 Fax: 49-8102-7433-133

TRIPOINT GLOBAL COMMUNICATIONS

PO Box 368, Conover, NC, 28613

Tel: (828) 464-4141 Fax: (828) 464-4147 www.vertencomm.com

High-tech holding company; microwave components, amplifiers, converters, terminal network workstations, voice, video and data applications.

Vertex Antennentechnik GmbH, Baumstrasse 50, D-41798 Duisburg, Germany

Tel: 49-206-620960 Fax: 49-206-6209611 Contact: Dr. Karl-Heinz Stenvers, Pres.

TRIPOS, INC.

1699 S. Hanley Road, St. Louis, MO, 63144

Tel: (314) 647-1099   Fax: (314) 647-9241   www.tripos.com

Mfr. pharmaceutical software for research.

Tripos GmbH, Martin-Kollar-Strasse 13, D-81829 Münich, Germany

Tel: 49-89-4510-30

TROPICANA PRODUCTS, INC.

1001 13th Avenue East, Bradenton, FL, 34208

Tel: (941) 747-4461   Fax: (941) 665-5330   www.tropicana.com

Marketer and producer of branded juices, including Tropicana, Dole, Looza and Copella.

Tropicana Deutschland GmbH, Kackerstrasse 11, D-52072 Aachen-Laurensberg, Germany

TRW AUTOMOTIVE, INC.

12025 Tech Center Drive, Livonia, MI, 48150

Tel: (734) 266-2600   Fax: (734) 266-5702   www.trw.com

Mfr. steering gears, power steering pumps, columns, linkage.

TRW Automotive Europe, Industriestrasse 2-8, D-78315 Radolfzell, Germany

Tel: 49-7732-809-342   Fax: 49-7732-809-421

TRW INC.

1900 Richmond Road, Cleveland, OH, 44124-2760

Tel: (216) 291-7000   Fax: (216) 291-7932   www.trw.com

Electric and energy-related products, automotive and aerospace products, tools and fasteners.

Repa Feinstanzwerk GmbH, D-7071 Lindach Uber Schwaebisch Guend, Germany

Teves-Thompson GmbH, D-3013 Barsinghausen Hannover, Germany

TRW Carr Europe, Rennbahnstr. 72, D-6000 Frankfurt 71, Germany

Werner Messmer GmbH, Industriestrasse 2-8, D-7760 Radolfzell am Bodensee, Germany

TTI, INC.

2441 Northeast Pkwy., Fort Worth, TX, 76106-1896

Tel: (817) 740-9000   Fax: (817) 740-9898   www.ttiinc.com

Distribution of resistors and capacitors, including cables and sockets.

TTI, Inc., Frankenring 16, D-30853 Langenhagen Hannover, Germany

TTI, Inc., Streiflacher Strasse 7, D-82110 Germering, Germany

TUTOGEN MEDICAL, INC.

925 Allwood Road, Clifton, NJ, 07012

Tel: (973) 365-2799   Fax: (973) 365-1690   www.tutogen.com

Engaged in sterilization of transplanted tissue for use in surgical procedures.

Tutogen Medical GmbH, Industriestrasse 6, D-91077 Neunkirchen, Germany

Tel: 49-9134-9998   Fax: 49-9134-9988419

TYCO CAPITAL

1211 Avenue of the Americas, New York, NY, 10036

Tel: (212) 536-1390   Fax: (212) 536-1912   www.citgroup.com

Engaged in commercial finance.

Newcourt, Div. Tyco Capital, Alexanderstrasse 59, D-60489 Frankfurt, Germany

Tel: 49-69-247-840

W. S. TYLER INC.

8570 Tyler Road, Mentor, OH, 44060

Tel: (440) 974-1047   Fax: (440) 974-0921   www.wstyler.com

Mfr. vibrating screens, lab equipment and related screening media, crushing equipment.

Haver and Boecker GmbH, Ennigerloher StraBe 64, D-59302 Oelde, Germany

Tel: 49-2522-30-0   Fax: 49-2522-30404

Haver and Boecker GmbH, Ennigerloher StraBe 64, D-59302 Oelde, Germany

Tel: 49-2522-30-0   Fax: 49-2522-30404

UAL CORPORATION

1200 E. Algonquin Rd., Chicago, IL, 60007

Tel: (847) 700-4000   Fax: (847) 700-4081   www.ual.com

Air transportation, passenger and freight services.

United Airlines, Munchenerstr. 7, D-6000 Frankfurt Main, Germany

UNION CARBIDE CORPORATION

39 Old Ridgebury Road, Danbury, CT, 06817

Tel: (203) 794-2000   Fax: (203) 794-6269   www.unioncarbide.com

Mfr. industrial chemicals, plastics and resins.

Union Carbide Deutschland GmbH, Morsenbroicher Weg 200, D-4000 Düsseldorf 30, Germany

UNISYS CORPORATION.

PO Box 500, Union Meeting Road, Blue Bell, PA, 19424

Tel: (215) 986-4011   Fax: (215) 986-6850   www.unisys.com

Mfr./marketing/servicing electronic information systems.

Unisys Deutschland GmbH, Am Unisys Park 1, D-6231 Sulzbach, Germany

UNITED PARCEL SERVICE, INC.

55 Glenlake Parkway, NE, Atlanta, GA, 30328

Tel: (404) 828-6000   Fax: (404) 828-6593   www.ups.com

International package-delivery service.

UPS Deutschland OHG, Droopweg 31, D-20537 Hamburg, Germany

Fax: 49-2131-947-2233

UNITED STATES SURGICAL CORPORATION

150 Glover Ave., Norwalk, CT, 06856

Tel: (203) 845-1000   Fax: (203) 847-0635   www.ussurg.com

Mfr./development/market surgical staplers, laparoscopic instruments and sutures.

U.S. Surgical, Div. Tyco Healthcare, Gewerbepark 1, D-93333 Neustadt/Donau, Germany

UNITED TECHNOLOGIES CORPORATION

One Financial Plaza, Hartford, CT, 06103

Tel: (860) 728-7000   Fax: (860) 728-7979   www.utc.com

Mfr. aircraft engines, elevators, A/C, auto equipment, space and military electronic and rocket propulsion systems. Products include Pratt and Whitney, Otis elevators, Carrier heating and air conditioning and Sikorsky helicopters.

Carrier GmbH, Vogelsbergstr. 3, D-6082 Moerfelden Walldorf, Germany

Carrier GmbH, Aarstr. 247, D-6204 Taunusstein 4, Germany

Carrier GmbH, Beckmesserstr. 4, D-8000 Münich 81, Germany

Flohr Otis GmbH, Wichmannstr. 5, D-100030 Berlin, Germany

Flohr Otis GmbH, Industriestr. 2, D-3060 Stadthagen, Germany

Flohr Otis GmbH, Fichrstr. 1-10, D-1000 Borsigwalde Berlin 27, Germany

UNIVERSAL SECURITY INSTRUMENTS, INC.

PO Box 825, Binghamton, NY, 13902-0825

Tel: (607) 779-7689   Fax: (607) 779-7301   www.uic.com

Provider of innovative electronic circuit assembly technology and equipment, integrated system solutions, and process expertise.

Universal Instruments GmbH, Bad Vilbel, Germany

Tel: 49-6101-8080   Fax: 49-6101-808-222

UNOVA INC.

21900 Burbank Blvd., Woodland Hills, CA, 91367-7418

Tel: (818) 992-3000   Fax: (818) 992-2848   www.unova.com

Automated data collection, mobile computing and manufacturing systems.

Honsberg Lamb, Hastener Strasse 22-26, Postfach 14 02 80, D42855 Remscheid, Germany

UOP LLC

25 East Algonquin Road, Des Plaines, IL, 60017

Tel: (847) 391-2000   Fax: (847) 391-2253   www.uop.com

Engaged in developing and commercializing technology for license to the oil refining, petrochemical and gas processing industries.

Universal Matthey Products (Deutschland) GmbH, Steinhof 39, D-40699 Erkrath, Germany

Tel: 49-211-24903-25   Fax: 49-211-249109

URS CORPORATION

100 California Street, Ste. 500, San Francisco, CA, 94111

Tel: (415) 774-2700   Fax: (415) 398-1905   www.urscorp.com

Engineering, environmental and construction management services.

Dames & Moore, Leberstrasse 37, D-10829 Berlin, Germany

Dames & Moore, Frintroper Strasse 53, D-45355 Essen, Germany

Dames & Moore, Goernestrasse 32, D-20249 Hamburg, Germany

Dames & Moore, Hoechster Strasse 92, D-65835 Liederbach/Ts., Germany

URSCHEL LABORATORIES INC.

2503 Calumet Ave., PO Box 2200, Valparaiso, IN, 46384-2200

Tel: (219) 464-4811   Fax: (219) 462-3879   www.urschel.com

Design/mfr. precision food processing equipment.

Urschel Intl. Ltd., Dieselstr. 7, D-61239 Ober-Morlen, Germany

US AIRWAYS GROUP, INC.

2345 Crystal Drive, Arlington, VA, 22227

Tel: (703) 872-7000   Fax: (703) 294-5096   www.usairways.com

Commercial airline.

USAir Inc., Rhein/Main Flughafen, Postfach 22, D-0549 Frankfurt, Germany

USAA

9800 Fredericksburg Road, San Antonio, TX, 78288-3533

Tel: (210) 498-2211   Fax: (210) 498-9940   www.usaa.com

Provides financial services, life, property and casualty insurance and consumer sales services primarily to military and U.S. government personnel and their families.

USAA, Frankfurt, Germany

USFILTER WALLACE & TIERNAN

1901 West Garden Road, Vineland, NJ, 08360

Tel: (609) 507-9000   Fax: (609) 507-4125   www.usfwt.com

Mfr. disinfections and chemical feed equipment.

USFilter Wallace & Tiernan GmbH, Postfach 1563, D-89305 Gunzburg, Germany

Tel: 49-8221-9040   Fax: 49-8221-904203   Contact: Gunther Fuhrer

USFilter Wallace & Tiernan GmbH, Auf der Weide 10, D-89312 Gunzburg-Wasserburg, Germany

Tel: 49-8221-9040

USG CORPORATION

125 South Franklin Street, Chicago, IL, 60606-4678

Tel: (312) 606-4000   Fax: (312) 606-4093   www.usg.com

Holding company for the building products industry.

Donn Products GmbH, Münich, Germany

UTILICORP UNITED INC.

20 W. Ninth St., Kansas City, MO, 64105

Tel: (816) 421-6600   Fax: (816) 472-6281   www.utilicorp.com

Electric and gas utility.

Utilicorp United, Münich, Germany

UTILX CORPORATION

PO Box 97009, Kent, WA, 98064-9709

Tel: (253) 395-0200   Fax: (253) 395-1040   www.utilx.com

Mfr. utility construction machinery and guided boring systems and provides cable restoration services.

CableCURE, Hermannstrasse 20, D-31737 Rinteln, Germany

Tel: 49-5751-918715   Contact: Hermann Schmidt

UUNET

22001 Loudoun County Pkwy., Ashburn, VA, 20147

Tel: (703) 206-5600   Fax: (703) 206-5601   www.uu.net

World's largest Internet service provider; World Wide Web hosting services, security products and consulting services to businesses, professionals, and on-line service providers.

UUNET Deutschland GmbH, Sebrathweg 20, D-44149 Dortmund, Germany

Tel: 49-231-972-00   Fax: 49-231-972-1111   Contact: Karsten Lerenth

VALHI INC.

5430 LBJ Freeway, Ste. 1700, Dallas, TX, 75240

Tel: (972) 233-1700   Fax: (972) 450-4278

Holding company engaged in the chemicals, component products, titanium metals and waste management industries.

Bentone-Chemie GmbH, Titanstrasse, D-2890 Niedrsachs, Germany

Kronos Titan GmbH, Postfach 100720, Leverkusen, Germany

VALMONT INDUSTRIES INC.

1 Valmont Plaza, Omaha, NE, 68154

Tel: (402) 963-1000   Fax: (402) 963-1199   www.valmont.com

Mfr. irrigation systems, steel lighting, utility and communication poles.

Valmont Mastbau GmbH & Co KG, D-33106 Paderborn, Germany

Tel: 49-5251-500400   Fax: 49-5251-5004045   Contact: Udo Ruesing

VALSPAR CORPORATION

1101 South Third Street, Minneapolis, MN, 55415-1259

Tel: (612) 332-7371   Fax: (612) 375-7723   www.valspar.com

Mfr. paints and coatings.

Valspar GmbH, Pfalzstraße 2, D-42781 Haan, Germany

VARIAN MEDICAL SYSTEMS, INC.

3050 Hansen Way, Palo Alto, CA, 94304-100

Tel: (650) 493-4000   Fax: (650) 424-5358   www.varian.com

Mfr. microwave tubes and devices, analytical instruments, semiconductor process and medical equipment, vacuum systems.

Varian GmbH, Postfach 11 14 45, D-64229 Darmstadt, Germany

Tel: 49-6151-7030

VARIAN SEMICONDUCTOR EQUIPMENT ASSOCIATES, INC. (VSEA)

35 Dory Road, Gloucester, MA, 01930

Tel: (978) 281-2000   Fax: (978) 283-5391   www.vsea.com

Mfr. semiconductors and ion implantation systems.

Varian Semiconductor Equipment Assocates, Carl-Zeiss-Ring 23, D-85737 Ismaning Münich, Germany

Varian Semiconductor Equipment Assocates, Zettachring 2A, Postfach 81 06 49, D-70567 Stuttgart, Germany

VASCULAR SOLUTIONS, INC.

2495 Xenium Lane North, Minneapolis, MN, 55441

Tel: (763) 656-4300   Fax: (763) 656-4250   www.vascularsolutions.com

Mfr. and sales of medical devices related to vascular procedures.

Vascular Solutions GmbH, Universitatsstrasse 140, D-44799 Bochum, Germany

VASTERA, INC.

45025 Aviation Drive, Ste. 300, Dulles, VA, 20166

Tel: (703) 661-9006   Fax: (703) 742-4580   www.vastera.com

Helps companies to define and deploy best business processes for trade and manages their global trade operations.

Vastera GmbH, Wesostrasse 21, D-76327 Pfinztal, Germany

VEECO INSTRUMENTS INC.

100 Sunnyside Blvd., Woodbury, NY, 11797

Tel: (516) 677-0200   Fax: (516) 677-9125   www.veeco.com

Mfr. surface profiler, atomic force microscopes, leak and plating thickness detectors and semiconductor products.

Veeco GmbH, Wissenschaftliche Geraete, D-85716 Unterschleissheim Münich, Germany

Tel: 49-89-317-8250   Fax: 49-89-317-3440

VEEDER-ROOT COMPANY

125 Powder Forest Drive, PO Box 2003, Simsbury, CT, 06070-2003

Tel: (860) 651-2700   Fax: (860) 651-2704   www.veeder.com

Mfr. of automatic tank gauging systems.

Veeder-Root GmbH, Uhlandstrasse 49, D-78554 Aldingen, Germany

VELCON FILTERS INC.

4525 Centennial Blvd., Colorado Springs, CO, 80919-3350

Tel: (719) 531-5855   Fax: (719) 531-5690   www.velcon.com

Mfr. filtration and coalescing products for airports, terminals, refineries, bulk storage plants, and utility companies.

Warner Lewis Jr. Industrie-Filter GmbH, Fasanenweg 5, D-6092 Kelsterbach/Frankfurt/Main, Germany

VELCRO USA INC.

406 Brown Avenue, Manchester, NH, 03108

Tel: (603) 669-4892   Fax: (603) 669-9271   www.velcro.com

Mfr./sales of Velcro brand hook and loop fasteners, plastic buckles and metal hardware and cable control straps.

Velcro GmbH, 2 Siemens-Strasse, D-74343 Sachsenheim, Germany

Tel: 49-7147-9900   Fax: 49-7147-99011

VENTIV HEALTH, INC.

1114 Avenue of the Americas, 8th Fl., New York, NY, 10036

Tel: (212) 768-8000   Fax: (212) 768-7387   www.ventiv.com

Provides sales and marketing services for pharmaceutical companies.

Ventiv Health, Fleck 34-36, D-83661 Lenggries, Germany

VERISIGN, INC.

1350 Charleston Rd., Mountain View, CA, 94043

Tel: (650) 961-7500   Fax: (650) 961-7300   www.verisign.com

Mfr. software.

D-Trust, Kommandantenstraße 15, D-10969 Berlin, Germany

VERITAS SOFTWARE INC.

350 Ellis Street, Mountain View, CA, 94043

Tel: (650) 527-8000   Fax: (650) 527-8050   www.veritas.com

Mfr. of storage management software for data protection, application availability, and disaster recovery.

VERITAS Germany, Humboldtstraße 6, Gewerbegebiet Dornach, D- 85609 Aschheim, Germany

VERITY, INC.

894 Ross Drive, Sunnyvale, CA, 94089

Tel: (408) 541-1500   Fax: (408) 541-1600   www.verity.com

Mfr. software to simplify management of information.

Verity Deutschland GmbH, Babenhäuser Straße 50, D-63762 Großostheim, Germany

Tel: 49-6026-9710-0   Fax: 49-6026-971020

VERIZON WIRELESS, INC.

180 Washington Valley Rd., Bedminster, NJ, 07921

Tel: (908) 306-7000   Fax: (908) 306-6927   www.verizonwireless.com

Engaged in mobile phone operations.

Vodafone D2, AM Seestem, D-40547 Dusseldorf, Germany

VERSATA, INC.

300 Lakeside Drive, Ste. 1500, Oakland, CA, 94612

Tel: (510) 238-4100   Fax: (510) 238-4101   www.versata.com

Mfr. software.

Versata GmbH, Flughafenstr. 52, D-22335 Hamburg, Germany

Versata GmbH, Forumstr. 24, D-41468 Neuss, Germany

Versata GmbH, Steinheimer Str. 117, D-63500 Seligenstadt, Germany

VF CORPORATION

628 Green Valley Road, Suite 500, Greensboro, NC, 27408

Tel: (336) 547-6000   Fax: (336) 547-7630   www.vfc.com

Mfr./marketing apparel including Lee and Wrangler jeans, Jansport backpacks and Healthtex.

H.I.S. Sportswear AG, München, Germany

VIACOM INC.

1515 Broadway, 28th Fl., New York, NY, 10036-5794

Tel: (212) 258-6000   Fax: (212) 258-6358   www.viacom.com

Communications, publishing and entertainment.

KirchGroup, München, Germany

VIAD CORPORATION

1850 North Central Ave., Phoenix, AZ, 85077

Tel: (602) 207-4000   Fax: (602) 207-5900   www.viad.com

Provides convention, exhibit design and production services.

Voblo Innenausbau GmbH, Siemenstrasse 19, D-42551 Velbert, Germany

Tel: 49-2051-28110   Fax: 49-2051-281128

VIASYS HEALTHCARE INC.

227 Washington Street, Ste. 200, Conshohocken, PA, 19428

Tel: (610) 862-0800   Fax: (610) 862-0836   www.viasyshealthcare.com

Mfr. medical instruments and devices.

Erich Jaeger GmbH, Leibnizstraße 7, D-97204 Hochberg, Germany

Jaeger Toennies, Leibnizstrasse 7, D-97204 Hoechberg, Germany

VICOR CORPORATION

25 Frontage Rd., Andover, MA, 01810-5413

Tel: (978) 470-2900   Fax: (978) 749-3536   www.vicr.com

Designs, manufactures, and markets modular power components and complete configurable and custom power systems.

Vicor Germany GmbH, Adalperostraße 29, D-85737 Ismaning, Germany

VIEWLOCITY, INC.

3475 Piedmont Road, Ste. 1700, Atlanta, GA, 30305

Tel: (404) 267-6400   Fax: (404) 267-6500   www.viewlocity.com

Mfr. supply chain management software.

Viewlocity GmbH, Mary-Sommerville-Strasse 3, D-28359 Bremen, Germany

VIEWSONIC CORPORATION

381 Brea Canyon Road, Walnut, CA, 91789

Tel: (909) 444-8888   Fax: (909) 869-7958   www.viewsonic.com

Mfr. displays.

ViewSonic Germany, Hanns-Martin-Schleyer-Strasse 18A, D-47877 Willich, Germany

VIRAGE LOGIC CORPORATION

46501 Landing Pkwy., Fremont, CA, 94538

Tel: (510) 360-8000　　　Fax: (510) 360-8099　　　www.viragelogic.com

Mfr. software.

Virage Logic Corporation, Julius-Echter-Str.11, D-96106 Ebern, Germany

VISHAY INTERTECHNOLOGY INC.

63 Lincoln Hwy., Malvern, PA, 19355

Tel: (610) 644-1300　　　Fax: (610) 296-0657　　　www.vishay.com

Mfr. resistors, strain gages, capacitors, inductors, printed circuit boards.

Draloric Electronic GmbH, Porschestrasse 18, D-8950 Kaufbeuren, Germany

Measurements Group GmbH, Am Lochhamer Schlag 6, D-8032 Lochham München, Germany

Roederstein GmbH, Schillerstrasse 2, D-8300 Landshut, Germany

Vishay Electronic GmbH, Geheimrat-Rosenthal-Str. 100, 95100 Postfach 1180, D-95092 Selb, Germany

Tel: 49-9287-710

VISHAY SILICONIX INC.

2201 Laurelwood Drive, Santa Clara, CA, 95054

Tel: (408) 988-8000　　　Fax: (408) 970-3950　　　www.siliconix.com

Mfr. power IC's and analog signal processing devices for computers, cell phones, fixed communications networks, automobiles, and other electronic systems.

Vishay Siliconix GmbH, Postfach 1340, Johannesstr. 27, D-7024 Filderstadt, Germany

VISHAY VITRAMON INC.

PO Box 544, Bridgeport, CT, 06601

Tel: (203) 268-6261　　　Fax: (203) 261-4446　　　www.vitramon.com

Ceramic capacitors.

Vitramon GmbH, Muhlbachstr. 7, Postfach 1420, D-7150 Backnang Waldrems, Germany

VISTEON CORPORATION

5500 Auto Club Drive, Dearborn, MI, 48126

Tel: (313) 755-2800　　　Fax: (313) 755-7983　　　www.visteon.com

Mfr. and sales of auto parts.

Visteon GmbH, Wuelfrath, Germany

VITAL SIGNS, INC.

20 Campus Road, Totowa, NJ, 07512

Tel: (973) 790-1330　　　Fax: (973) 790-3307　　　www.vital-signs.com

Mfr. disposable medical products for critical care procedures.

BREAS Medical GmbH, Div. Vital Signs, Bahnhofstrasse 26, DE-822 11 Herrsching, Germany

Tel: 49-8152-37210

VITESSE SEMICONDUCTOR CORPORATION

741 Calle Plano, Camarillo, CA, 93012

Tel: (805) 388-3700　　　Fax: (805) 389-7188　　　www.vitesse.com

Mfr. integrated circuits.

Vitesse Semiconductor, Altstadt 296, D-84036 Landshut, Germany

Tel: 49-871-9663344　Fax: 49-871-9663343　Contact: Hermann Helmbold

Vitesse Semiconductor GmbH, Zwoelferweg 2, D-86836 Lagerlechfeld, Germany

Tel: 49-8232-78-626　Fax: 49-8232-78-627　Contact: Harald King

VIVITAR CORPORATION

1280 Rancho Conejo Blvd, Newbury Park, CA, 91320

Tel: (805) 498-7008　　　Fax: (805) 498-5086　　　www.vivitar.com

Mfr. photographic equipment, electronic supplies.

Vivitar Photo-Electronik GmbH, Vivitarstr. 7-9, Postfach 1564, D-6238 Hofheim/TS, Germany

VOLT INFORMATION SCIENCES, INC.

560 Lexington Avenue, 16th Fl., New York, NY, 10022-6828

Tel: (212) 704-2400   Fax: (212) 704-2417   www.volt.com

Staffing services and telecommunication services.

Autologic Intl. Ltd., Frankfurter Strasse 63-69, D-65760 Eschborn, Germany

Tel: 49-6196-481796   Fax: 49-6196-42389

VTEL PRODUCTS CORPORATION

108 Wild Basin Road, Austin, TX, 78746

Tel: (512) 314-2700   Fax: (512) 314-2792   www.vtel.com

Design, development, manufacture and sale of PC-based videoconferencing systems through reseller channels.

VTEL Deutschland GmbH, Industriestr. 18, D-89423 Gundelfingen, Germany

WACHOVIA CORPORATION

301 South College Street, Ste. 4000, Charlotte, NC, 28288-0013

Tel: (704) 374-6161   Fax: (704) 383-1240   www.wachovia.com

Engaged in commercial and retail banking services.

Wachovia GmbH, Gansemarkt 44, D-20354 Hamburg, Germany

THE WACKENHUT CORPORATION

4200 Wackenhut Dr., Ste. 100, Palm Beach Gardens, FL, 33410

Tel: (561) 622-5656   Fax: (561) 691-6736   www.wackenhut.com

Security systems and services.

Wackenhut Central Europe GmbH, Tulpenhofstrasse 18, D-68067 Offenbach/Main, Germany

Tel: 49-69-817025

WAHL CLIPPER CORPORATION

2902 N. Locust Street, Sterling, IL, 61081

Tel: (815) 625-6525   Fax: (815) 625-1193   www.wahlclipper.com

Mfr. hair clippers, beard and mustache trimmers, shavers, pet clippers and soldering irons.

Moser Elektrogeräte GmbH, Roggenbachweg 9, D-78089 Unterkirnach, Germany

WALBRO ENGINE MANAGEMENT

7400 N. Oracle Road, Ste. 310, Tucson, AZ, 85704

Tel: (520) 877-3000   Fax: (520) 877-3006   www.walbro.com

Mfr. motor vehicle accessories and parts, automotive fluid carrying systems.

TI Group Automotive Systems, Heidelberg Engineering Centre, Dischingerstr 11, D-69123 Heidelberg, Germany

Tel: 49-6221-74910

TI Group Automotive Systems, Lochfeldstr. 33, D-76437 Rastatt, Germany

WAL-MART STORES INC.

702 SW 8th Street, Bentonville, AR, 72716-8611

Tel: (501) 273-4000   Fax: (501) 273-1917   www.wal-mart.com

Retailer.

Wal-Mart Stores Inc. (Wertkauf), München, Germany

THE WARNACO GROUP INC.

90 Park Ave., New York, NY, 10016

Tel: (212) 661-1300   Fax: (212) 687-0480   www.warnaco.com

Mfr./sales intimate apparel and men's and women's sportswear.

Warnaco, München, Germany

WARNER ELECTRIC COMPANY

449 Gardner St., South Beloit, IL, 61080

Tel: (815) 389-3771   Fax: (815) 389-2582   www.warnernet.com

Global supplier of Power Transmission and Motion Control Solution Systems; automotive, industry brakes, and clutches.

Stieber GmbH, Hatschekstrasse 36, D-69126 Heidelberg, Germany

Tel: 49-6221-30470   Fax: 49-6221-304717

Warner Electric GmbH, Postfach 2008, D-72610 Nürtinger, Germany

Tel: 49-7022-5040   Fax: 49-7022-55091

WASHINGTON GROUP INTERNATIONAL, INC.

720 Park Blvd., PO Box 73, Boise, ID, 83729

Tel: (208) 386-5000   Fax: (208) 386-7186   www.wgint.com

Engaged in engineering and construction.

Washington Group International, Inc., Wiesenstrasse 20, D-06727 Theissen, Germany

Tel: 49-3441-684-611   Fax: 49-3441-684-415

Washington Group International, Inc., Hagenauer Strasse 42, D-65203 Wiesbaden, Germany

Tel: 49-611-18-2500   Fax: 49-611-18-85959

THE WASHINGTON POST COMPANY

1150 15th St. NW, Washington, DC, 20071

Tel: (202) 334-6000   Fax: (202) 334-4536   www.washpostco.com

Engaged in magazine publishing, cable and television broadcasting, educational services and the Internet.

International Herald Tribune, Friedrichstrasse 15, D-60323 Frankfurt/Main, Germany

Tel: 49-69-97-12-5020

WASTE MANAGEMENT, INC.

1001 Fannin Street, Ste. 4000, Houston, TX, 77002

Tel: (713) 512-6200   Fax: (713) 512-6299   www.wastemanagement.com

Environmental services and disposal company; collection, processing, transfer and disposal facilities.

WMD Waste Management (Deutschland) GmbH, Im Teelbruch 134b, D-45219 Essen, Germany

Contact: Wolfgang Otte, Mgr.

WATERS CORPORATION

34 Maple Street, Milford, MA, 01757

Tel: (508) 478-2000   Fax: (508) 872-1990   www.waters.com

Mfr./distribute liquid chromatographic instruments and test and measurement equipment.

Waters GmbH, Siemensstr. 20, D-6078 Neu-Isenburg, Germany

Waters GmbH, Hauptstraße 87, D-65760 Eschborn Eschborn, Germany

WATLOW ELECTRIC MFG. COMPANY

12001 Lackland Rd., St. Louis, MO, 63146-4039

Tel: (314) 878-4600   Fax: (314) 434-1020   www.watlow.com

Mfr. electrical heating units, electronic controls, thermocouple wire, metal-sheathed cable, infrared sensors.

Watlow Electric Mfg. Co. GmbH, Lauchwasenstr. 1, Postfach 1165, D-76709 Kronau, Germany

Tel: 49-7253-9400-50   Fax: 49-7253-9400-99

WATSON WYATT & COMPANY HOLDINGS

1717 H Street NW, Washington, DC, 20006-3807

Tel: (202) 715-7000   Fax: (202) 715-7700   www.watsonwyatt.com

Creates compensation and benefits programs for major corporations.

Watson Wyatt GmbH, Konigsallee 86, D-40212 Dusseldorf, Germany

Tel: 49-211-8228-0   Fax: 49-211-8228-100   Contact: Thierry Hamon

WATTS INDUSTRIES, INC.

815 Chestnut Street, North Andover, MA, 01845-6098

Tel: (978) 688-1811   Fax: (978) 688-5841   www.wattsind.com

Designs/mfr./sales of industry valves and safety control products.

Watts MTR GmbH, Rudolf-Diesel-Strabe 5, Gewerbegebiet Ottmarsheim, D-74354 Besigheim, Germany

WD-40 COMPANY

1061 Cudahy Place, San Diego, CA, 92110-3998

Tel: (619) 275-1400   Fax: (619) 275-5823   www.wd40.com

Mfr. branded multiple-purpose lubrication, protection and general maintenance products.

WD-40 Company, Verkaufsburo Deutschland, Hessenring 113, D-61348 Bad Homburg, Germany

Tel: 49-61-726-77450   Fax: 49-61-726-77499

WEATHERFORD INTERNATIONAL, INC.

515 Post Oak Blvd. Ste. 600, Houston, TX, 77027-3415

Tel: (713) 287-8400   Fax: (713) 963-9785   www.weatherford.com

Oilfield services, products and equipment; mfr. marine cranes for oil and gas industry.

Weatherford Oil Tool GmbH, Hainhauser Weg 150, D-3012 Langenhagen 6, Germany

Tel: 49-511-7702-300   Fax: 49-511-7705-333

WEAVEXX

11120 Capital Blvd., Wake Forest, NC, 27587

Tel: (919) 556-7235   Fax: (919) 556-2432   www.weavexx.com

Mfr. forming fabrics, press felts, dryer fabrics, and wet-end drainage equipment for all grades of paper and machine types.

Wangner Finckh Group, Münich, Germany

JERVIS B. WEBB COMPANY

34375 W.Twelve Mile Rd., Farmington Hills, MI, 48331

Tel: (248) 553-1220   Fax: (248) 553-1237   www.jervisbwebb.com

Mfr. integrators of material handling systems solutions.

Hechert & Schmid GmbH, Vaihingen, Germany

WEBER MARKING SYSTEMS INC.

711 West Algonquin Road, Arlington Heights, IL, 60005-4457

Tel: (847) 364-8500   Fax: (847) 364-8575   www.webermarking.com

Mfr. label printing systems and custom labels.

Weber Marking Systems GmbH, Postfach/Box 0154, Honnefer Str. 41, D-53572 Unkel/Rhein, Germany

WEBER-STEPHEN PRODUCTS COMPANY

200 East Daniels Road, Palatine, IL, 60067-6266

Tel: (847) 934-5700   Fax: (847) 934-0291   www.weberbq.com

Mfr./sales Weber cooking systems and barbeque and gas grills.

Le Creuset/Weber-Stephen, Zeppelinstrasse 9, D-73274 Notzingen, Germany

Tel: 49-7021-97-490   Fax: 49-7021-480-214

WEBMETHODS, INC.

3930 Pender Drive, Fairfax, VA, 22030

Tel: (703) 460-2500   Fax: (703) 460-2599   www.webmethods.com

Mfr. automated business software.

WebMethods, Stefan-George-Ring 29, D-81929 Münich, Germany

WebMethods, Lyoner Straße 15, Atricom Box A5, D-60528 Frankfurt, Germany

WEBSENSE, INC.

10240 Sorrento Valley Road, San Diego, CA, 92121

Tel: (858) 320-8000   Fax: (858) 458-2950   www.websense.com

Mfr. software.

Websense GmbH, Arnulfstrasse 27, D-80335 Münich, Germany

WEIL, GOTSHAL & MANGES LLP

767 Fifth Ave., New York, NY, 10153

Tel: (212) 310-8000   Fax: (212) 310-8007   www.weil.com

Engaged in international law.

Weil, Gotshal & Manges GmbH, Maintower, Box 19, 31st floor, Neue Mainzer Strasse 52-58, D-60311 Frankfurt, Germany

Tel: 49-69-216-59-600   Fax: 49-69-216-59-699   Contact: Esther Habich

WELCH ALLYN INC.

4341 State Street Road, Skaneateles Falls, NY, 13153

Tel: (315) 685-4100   Fax: (315) 685-4091   www.welchallyn.com

Mfr. fiber optic products and medical diagnostic equipment.

Welch Allyn GmbH, Zollerstrasse 2-4, D-72417 Jungingen, Germany

Tel: 49-7477-927173   Fax: 49-7477-9271-90

WELLMAN INC.

595 Shrewsbury Avenue, Shrewsbury, NJ, 07702

Tel: (732) 212-3300   Fax: (732) 212-3344   www.wellmaninc.com

Mfr. and sale of polyester products, including Fortrel brand polyester textile fibers, polyester fibers made from recycled raw materials and PermaClear PET (polyethylene terephthalate) resins.

Wellman International GmbH, Alterhellweg 1111, D-4800 Dortmund 70, Germany

Tel: 49-2-316-1181

WEST PHARMACEUTICAL SERVICES, INC.

101 Gordon Drive, Lionville, PA, 19341-0645

Tel: (610) 594-2900   Fax: (610) 594-3000   www.westpharma.com

Mfr. packaging and plastic components for health care and consumer products.

West Pharmaceutical Services, Leimberg 33, D-52222 Stolberg, Germany

West Pharmaceutical Services, Stolberger Strasse 21-41, D-52249 Eschweiler, Germany

WESTERN DIGITAL CORPORATION

20511 Lake Forest Dr., Lake Forest, CA, 92630-7741

Tel: (949) 672-7000   Fax: (949) 672-5408   www.westerndigital.com

Mfr. hard disk drives, video graphics boards, VLSI.

Western Digital Deutschland, Samdorfer Str. 26, D-3000 Münich, Germany

WHIRLPOOL CORPORATION

2000 N. M-63, Benton Harbor, MI, 49022-2692

Tel: (616) 923-5000   Fax: (616) 923-5443   www.whirlpoolcorp.com

Mfr., market home appliances: Whirlpool, Roper, KitchenAid, Estate, and Inglis.

Whirlpool Europe BV, Schorndorf, Germany

WHITE ELECTRONIC DESIGNS CORPORATION (WEDC)

3601 East University Drive, Phoenix, AZ, 85034

Tel: (602) 437-1520   Fax: (602) 437-1731   www.whiteedc.com

Mfr. of high density memory modules and micro processor MCMs; state of the art micro-electronics devices.

White Electronic Designs, Lettenfeldstr. 15, D-90592 Schwarzenbruck, Germany

Tel: 49-9183-9029-24-0   Contact: Juergen Eichner

WHITTMAN-HART & USWEB/CKS

311 S. Wacker Drive, Ste. 3500, Chicago, IL, 60606-6621

Tel: (312) 922-9200   Fax: (312) 913-3020   www.uswebcks.com

Internet professional services firm; design and implementation services for multimedia marketing programs.

USWeb/CKS Germany, Neumann Reichardt Str. 27-33, D-22041 Hamburg, Germany

Tel: 49-40-657-33800   Contact: Robert T. Clarkson

WIDIA VALENITE INC

31700 Research Park Dr., Madison Heights, MI, 48071-4627

Tel: (248) 589-1000   Fax: (248) 597-4820   www.valenite.com

Cemented carbide, high speed steel, ceramic and diamond cutting tool products, etc.

Widia GmbH, Carl-Benz Strasse 4, D-74876 Sinsheim, Germany

JOHN WILEY & SONS INC.

605 Third Ave., New York, NY, 10158-0012

Tel: (212) 850-6000   Fax: (212) 850-6088   www.wiley.com

Develops, publishes, and sells products in print and electronic media for the educational, professional, scientific, technical, medical, and consumer markets

Wiley VCH Verlag GmbH, Pappelallee 3, D-69469 Weinheim, Germany

Tel: 49-6201-6060   Fax: 49-6201-606328

WILLKIE FARR & GALLAGHER

787 Seventh Avenue, New York, NY, 10019-6099

Tel: (212) 821-8000   Fax: (212) 821-8111   www.willkie.com

International law firm.

Willkie Farr & Gallagher, Frankfurter Welle, An der Welle 4, D-60322 Frankfurt, Germany

WILMER, CUTLER & PICKERING (WCP)

2445 M Street, NW, Washington, DC, 20037-1420

Tel: (202) 663-6000   Fax: (202) 663-6363   www.wilmer.com

International law firm.

Wilmer, Cutler & Pickering (WCP), Friedrichstrasse 95, D-10117 Berlin, Germany

WILSON, ELSER, MOSKOWITZ, EDELMAN & DICKER LLP

150 East 42nd St., New York, NY, 10017

Tel: (212) 490-3000   Fax: (212) 490-3038   www.wemed.com

International law firm.

Bach, Langheid & Dallmayr (Wilson Elser affiliate), Uhlandstrasse 19 IV, D-10623 Berlin, Germany

Tel: 49-221-944-0270

Bach, Langheid & Dallmayr (Wilson Elser affiliate), Oeder Weg 52-54, D-60318 Frankfurt/Main, Germany

Tel: 49-8954-58-77-0   Contact: Reinhard Dallmayr

Bach, Langheid & Dallmayr (Wilson Elser affiliate), Beethovenstrasse 5-13, D-50674 Köln, Germany

Tel: 49-221-944-027-0   Fax: 49-221-944-027-7   Contact: Dr. Peter Bach

WIND RIVER SYSTEMS, INC.

500 Wind River Way, Alameda, CA, 94501

Tel: (510) 748-4100   Fax: (510) 749-2010   www.isi.com

Develops and markets computer software products and services.

Wind River Systems GmbH, Chilehaus A, Fischertwiete 2, D-20095 Hamburg, Germany

Tel: 49-40-32005-202

Wind River Systems GmbH, Freisinger Straße 34, D-85737 Ismaning, Germany

Tel: 49-89-962445-0

Wind River Systems GmbH, Zettachring 4, D-70567 Stuttgart, Germany

Tel: 49-71-17-27-23-53-0

WINTEC INDUSTRIES, INC.

4280 Technology Drive, Fremont, CA, 94538

Tel: (510) 770-9239   Fax: (510) 770-9338   www.wintecindustries.com

Mfr. integrated circuits.

Tecwin Technology GmbH, Stettiner Str. 20A, D-30916 Isernhagen, Germany

WOODHEAD INDUSTRIES INC.

Three Parkway North, Ste. 550, Deerfield, IL, 60015

Tel: (847) 236-9300   Fax: (847) 236-0503   www.woodhead.com

Develop/mfr./sale/distributor elect/electronic, fiber optic and ergonomic special-function, non-commodity products.

Woodhead Connectivity GmbH, GewerbestraBe 60, D-75015 Bretten-"G"Ishausen, Germany

WOODWARD GOVERNOR COMPANY

5001 N. Second Street, PO Box 7001, Rockford, IL, 61125-7001

Tel: (815) 877-7441   Fax: (815) 639-6033   www.woodward.com

Mfr./service speed control devices and systems for aircraft turbines, industrial engines and turbines.

Woodward Governor Germany, GmbH, Frankenhaeuser Strasse 21a, D-06537 Kelbra, Germany

Tel: 49-34651-3590   Fax: 49-34651-35999   Contact: Jacques van Oppen   Emp: 50

Woodward Governor Germany, GmbH, Koethener Chaussee 46, D-06385 Aken Elbe, Germany

Tel: 49-34909-8800   Fax: 49-34909-82049   Contact: Pieter Jan van Rijnbach   Emp: 50

WORLD AIRWAYS, INC.

HLH Building, 101 World Drive, Peachtree City, GA, 30269

Tel: (770) 632-8000   Fax: (770) 632-8075   www.worldair.com

Engaged in air transport leasing.

World Airways GmbH, Frankfort, Germany

Tel: 49-6107-903025

WORLDCOM, INC.

500 Clinton Center Drive, Clinton, MS, 39060

Tel: (601) 360-8600   Fax: (601) 360-8616   www.wcom.com

*Telecommunications; serving local, long distance and Internet customers domestically and internationally. **Corporation under worldwide reorganization under Chapter 11 Bankruptcy; new data unavailable for this edition.*

WorldCom International, Langstrasse 50, D-6450 Hanau, Germany

WORLDXCHANGE COMMUNICATIONS

9999 Willow Creek Road, San Diego, CA, 92131

Tel: (858) 547-4933   Fax: (800) 995-4502   www.worldxchange.com

Provides international, long distance telecommunications services worldwide.

WorldxChange Communications GmbH, Wilhelm-Marx-Haus, Heinrich-Heine-Allee 53, D-40213 Düsseldorf, Germany

Tel: 49-211-8307-204   Fax: 49-211-8307-378   Emp: 40

WRIGHT MEDICAL GROUP, INC.

5677 Airline Road, Arlington, TN, 38002

Tel: (901) 867-9971   Fax: (901) 867-9534   www.wmt.com

Mfr. orthopedic reconstructive implants.

Wright Cremascoli Ortho, Alter Postweg 41, D-21614 Buxtehude, Germany

WM WRIGLEY JR. COMPANY

410 N. Michigan Ave., Chicago, IL, 60611-4287

Tel: (312) 644-2121   Fax: (312) 644-0353   www.wrigley.com

Mfr. chewing gum.

Wrigley GmbH, Albrecht Duerer Str. 2, Postfach 1414, D-8025 Unterhaching, Germany

WRQ, INC.

1500 Dexter Avenue North, Seattle, WA, 98109

Tel: (206) 217-7100   Fax: (206) 217-7515   www.wrq.com

Mfr. software.

WRQ Software GmbH, Halskestraße 1, D-40880 Ratingen, Germany

WUNDERMAN

675 Avenue of the Americas, New York, NY, 10010

Tel: (212) 941-3000   Fax: (212) 941-2000   www.wunderman.com

Engaged in direct marketing.

Wunderman, GmbH, Kleyerstrasse 19, D-60326 Frankfurt, Germany

Contact: Jörg Puphal

WYETH

5 Giralda Farms, Madison, NJ, 07940-0874

Tel: (973) 660-5000   Fax: (973) 660-7026   www.wyeth.com

Mfr. consumer healthcare products.

Wyeth Consumer Healthcare, Regina-Protmann-Straße 16, D-48159 Münster, Germany

Tel: 49-251-9271-8

WYETH PHARMACEUTICALS

555 E. Lancaster Ave., Wayne, PA, 19087-5109

Tel: (610) 971-5400   Fax: (610) 995-4668   www.wyeth.com

Mfr. antibiotics and pharmaceutical products.

Wyeth-Pharma GmbH, Wienburgstrasse 207, D-48159 Münster, Germany

Tel: 49-251-2040

WYNN OIL COMPANY

1050 West Fifth Street, PO Box 9510, Azusa, CA, 91702-9510

Tel: (626) 334-0231   Fax: (626) 334-6463   www.wynnusa.com

Mfr. of specialty chemicals, equipment and related service programs for automotive and industrial markets.

Wynn's Deutschland GmbH, Gothaer Str. 4, D-40880 Ratinger, Germany

Tel: 49-2102-48-0300   Fax: 49-2102-48-0310

WYSE TECHNOLOGY INC.

3471 North First Street, San Jose, CA, 95134

Tel: (408) 473-1200   Fax: (408) 473-2080   www.wyse.com

Mfr. computer network terminals.

Wyse Technology, Humboldt Park Haus 7, Humboldtstrasse 10, D-85609 Aschheim/Dornach, Germany

Tel: 49-89-460099

XEROX CORPORATION

800 Long Ridge Road, PO Box 1600, Stamford, CT, 06904

Tel: (203) 968-3000   Fax: (203) 968-4312   www.xerox.com

Mfr. document processing equipment, systems and supplies.

Rank Xerox GmbH, Emanuel-Leutze Strasse 20, D-40547 Düsseldorf, Germany

Tel: 49-211-9900   Fax: 49-211-990-7832

Rank Xerox GmbH, Heesenetrasse 70, D-40549 Düsseldorf 11, Germany

Tel: 49-211-9900   Fax: 49-211-9907832

XILINX INC.

2100 Logic Drive, San Jose, CA, 95124-3400

Tel: (408) 559-7778   Fax: (408) 559-7114   www.xilinx.com

Programmable logic and related development systems software.

Xilinx GmbH, Dorfstrasse 1, D-85609 Ascheim Münich, Germany

XIRCOM, INC.

2300 Corporate Center Drive, Thousand Oaks, CA, 91320

Tel: (805) 376-9300   Fax: (805) 376-9311   www.xircom.com

Mfr. PC card network adapters and modems.

Xircom Europe GmbH, Am Soldnermoos 17, D-85399 Hallbergmoos, Germany

X-RITE, INC.

3100 44th Street SW, Grandville, MI, 49418

Tel: (616) 534-7663   Fax: (616) 534-9215   www.xrite.com

Mfr. precision measurement devices, systems and processes that enhance the measurement of color, light and shape.

X-Rite GmbH, Stollwerckstr. 32, D-51149 Köln, Germany

Tel: 49-2203-91450

XTRA CORPORATION

200 Nyala Farms Rd., Westport, CT, 06880

Tel: (203) 221-1005   Fax: (203) 221-9024   www.xtracorp.com

Holding company: leasing.

XTRA International, Bremen, Germany

YAHOO! INC.

701 First Avenue, Sunnyvale, CA, 94089

Tel: (408) 439-3300   Fax: (408) 439-3301   www.yahoo-inc.com

Internet media company providing specialized content, free electronic mail and community offerings and commerce.

Yahoo! Deutschland, Riesstraße 25, Haus C, D-80992 Münich, Germany

Tel: 49-89-143-12576   Fax: 49-89-143-12575

YANTRA CORPORATION

1 Park West, Tewksbury, MA, 01876

Tel: (978) 513-6000   Fax: (978) 513-6006   www.yantra.com

Mfr. software providing supply chain solutions for the extended enterprise.

Yantra GmbH, Maximillanstrasse 35A, D-80539 Münich, Germany

Tel: 49-89-24218417   Fax: 49-89-24218303

YELLOW CORPORATION

10990 Roe Ave., PO Box 7270, Overland Park, KS, 66207

Tel: (913) 696-6100   Fax: (913) 696-6116   www.yellowcorp.com

Commodity transportation.

FM Deutschland GmbH, Poststrase 58, D-4143 Nettetal-Kaldenkirchen, Germany

FM Deutschland GmbH, Schollersheiderstrasse 2-4, D-40822 Mettmann, Germany

FM Deutschland GmbH, Carl-Benz Strasse 9, D-71634 Ludwigsburg, Germany

YORK INTERNATIONAL CORPORATION

631 South Richland Ave., York, PA, 17403

Tel: (717) 771-7890   Fax: (717) 771-6212   www.york.com

Mfr. heating, ventilating, air conditioning and refrigeration equipment.

York International GmbH, Gottlieb Daimler Str. 6, Postfach 100465, D-68165 Mannheim, Germany

Tel: 49-621-468222

York, Kalte und Klimatechnik GmbH, Postfach 100465, D-6800 Mannheim 1, Germany

YOUNG & RUBICAM INC.

285 Madison Ave., New York, NY, 10017

Tel: (212) 210-3000   Fax: (212) 370-3796   www.yr.com

Advertising, public relations, direct marketing and sales promotion, corporate and product ID management.

Young & Rubicam GmbH Werbung, Postfach 4665, Bleichstr. 64, D-6000 Frankfurt/Main, Germany

ZEBRA TECHNOLOGIES CORPORATION

333 Corporate Woods Pkwy., Vernon Hills, IL, 60061-3109

Tel: (847) 634-6700   Fax: (847) 913-8766   www.zebracorporation.com

Mfr. bar code systems.

Zebra Technologies Germany, Birkenwaldstr. 38, D-63179 Obertshausen, Germany

Tel: 49-6104-70990

ZILOG, INC.

532 Race Street, San Jose, CA, 95126

Tel: (408) 558-8500   Fax: (408) 558-8300   www.zilog.com

Mfr. integrated circuits.

ZILOG Gmbh, Thomas-Dehler-Str. 18, D-81737 Münich, Germany

ZIMMER HOLDINGS, INC.

345 East Main St., Warsaw, IN, 46580

Tel: (574) 267-6131   Fax: (574) 372-4988   www.zimmer.com

Engaged in design and manufacture of orthopedic products.

Zimmer GmbH, Maria-Merian-Str. 7, D-24145 Kiel-Wellsee, Germany

Tel: 49-4317-1940

ZIPPERTUBING COMPANY

13000 S. Broadway, PO Box 61129, Los Angeles, CA, 90061

Tel: (310) 527-0488   Fax: (310) 767-1714   www.zippertubing.com

Mfr. zip-on plastic tubing, wire markers, pipe insulation, EMI shielding.

Zipper-Technik GmbH, Wernher von Braun Strasse 3, D-63238 Neu Isenburg, Germany

ZOLL MEDICAL CORPORATION

32 Second Avenue, Burlington, MA, 01803

Tel: (781) 229-0020   Fax: (781) 272-5578   www.zoll.com

Mfr. electrical resuscitation devices and equipment.

ZOLL Medical Deutschland, Schillingsrotter Str. 23, D-50996 Cologne, Germany

Tel: 49-22-139-89340

ZOLTEK COMPANIES, INC.

3101 McKelvey Road, St. Louis, MO, 63044

Tel: (314) 291-5110   Fax: (314) 291-8536   www.zoltek.com

Engaged in production and manufacture of carbon fibers.

Zoltek Europe GmbH, Hallbergmooser Str. 5, D-85445 Schwaig, Germany

ZONE LABS, INC.

1060 Howard Street, San Francisco, CA, 94103

Tel: (415) 341-8200   Fax: (415) 341-8299   www.zonelabs.com

Mfr. computer anti-virus software.

Zone Labs GmbH, Dusseldorfer Str. 40A, D-65760 Eschborn, Germany

Tel: 49-6196-773-670   Fax: 49-6196-773-6777

ZYGO CORPORATION

Laurel Brook Road, Middlefield, CT, 06455

Tel: (860) 347-8506   Fax: (860) 347-8372   www.zygo.com

Mfr. high-precision, electro-optical measuring equipment.

Syncotec Neue Tech GmbH, Loherstrasse 4, D-35614 Asslar, Germany

Tel: 49-644-188-889   Fax: 49-644-181-588

ZygoLOT GmbH, Im Tiefen See 58, D-64293 Darmstadt, Germany

Tel: 49-6151-8806-27   Fax: 49-6151-8806-88   Contact: Thorsten Glaschke

Ghana

LOUIS BERGER INTERNATIONAL INC.

100 Halsted Street, East Orange, NJ, 07019

Tel: (201) 678-1960   Fax: (201) 672-4284   www.louisberger.com

Consulting engineers, engaged in architecture, environmental and advisory services.

Louis Berger International Inc., Water Sector, Restructuring Secretariat, PO Box M43, Accra, Ghana

Tel: 233-21-764111   Fax: 233-21764111

CIGNA COMPANIES

One Liberty Place, Philadelphia, PA, 19192

Tel: (215) 761-1000   Fax: (215) 761-5511   www.cigna.com

Insurance, invest, health care and other financial services.

Crusader Co. (Ghana) Ltd., Samlotte House, Kwame Nkrumah Ave., Accra, Ghana

CMS ENERGY CORPORATION

330 Town Center Dr., Ste. 1100, Dearborn, MI, 48126

Tel: (313) 436-9200   Fax: (313) 436-9225   www.cmsenergy.com

Independent power plant operator.

CMS Energy/Takoradi Power Co, Akoradi, Ghana

DELOITTE TOUCHE TOHMATSU INTERNATIONAL

1633 Broadway, New York, NY, 10019

Tel: (212) 492-4000   Fax: (212) 392-4154   www.deloitte.com

Accounting, audit, tax and management consulting services.

Deloitte & Touche, 4 Liberation Rd., PO Box 453, Accra, Ghana

Deloitte & Touche Consulting, 350 Nima Ave., North Ridge, Accra, Ghana

DHL WORLDWIDE EXPRESS

50 California Avenue, San Francisco, CA, 94111

Tel: (415) 677-6100   Fax: (415) 824-9700   www.dhl.com

Worldwide air express carrier.

DHL Worldwide Express, North Ridge Cresent, House C913/3, PO Box 207, Accra, Ghana

Tel: 233-21-221647

EGL INC. (EAGLE GLOBAL LOGISTICS)

15350 Vickery Drive, Houston, TX, 77032

Tel: (281) 618-3100   Fax: (281) 618-3223   www.eagleusa.com

Ocean/air freight forwarding, customs brokerage, packing and wholesale, logistics management and insurance.

EGL Eagle Global Logistics, No. 2 Cargo Village, Kotoka International Airport, PO Box 16774, Accra North, Ghana

Tel: 233-21-772-667   Fax: 233-21-775-419

ERNST & YOUNG INTERNATIONAL

5 Times Square, New York, NY, 10036

Tel: (212) 773-3000   Fax: (212) 773-6350   www.eyi.com

Engaged in assurance and advisory business services, tax, law and corporate finance.

Associates of Ernst & Young/ Owusu & Fiadjoe, PO Box 2239 Asylum Down, Accra, Ghana

Tel: 233-21-227054   Fax: 233-21-234335   Contact: Kwame Nini Owusu

GREY GLOBAL GROUP

777 Third Ave., New York, NY, 10017

Tel: (212) 546-2000   Fax: (212) 546-1495   www.grey.com

International advertising agency.

Insight Advertising, Accra, Ghana

H.J. HEINZ COMPANY

600 Grant Street, Pittsburgh, PA, 15219

Tel: (412) 456-5700   Fax: (412) 456-6128   www.heinz.com

Processed food products and nutritional services.

Star-Kist Europe Inc., Tema, Ghana

J. WALTER THOMPSON COMPANY

466 Lexington Ave., New York, NY, 10017

Tel: (212) 210-7000   Fax: (212) 210-6944   www.jwt.com

International advertising and marketing services.

Ghana Advertising & Marketing, Accra, Ghana

SC JOHNSON

1525 Howe St., Racine, WI, 53403

Tel: (262) 260-2000   Fax: (262) 260-2133   www.scjohnsonwax.com

Home, auto, commercial and personal care products and specialty chemicals.

SC Johnson, PO Box C537, Cantonments, Accra, Ghana

KAISER ALUMINUM CORPORATION

5847 San Felipe, Ste. 2600, Houston, TX, 77057-3010

Tel: (713) 267-3777   Fax: (713) 267-3701   www.kaiseral.com

Aluminum refining and manufacturing.

Volta Aluminum Company Ltd., Tema, Ghana

KPMG CONSULTING INC.

1676 International Dr., McLean, VA, 22102

Tel: (703) 747-3000   Fax: (703) 747-8500   www.kpmg.com

Accounting and audit, tax and management consulting services.

KPMG International, 2nd Fl., Mobil House, Liberia Rd., Accra, Ghana

Tel: 233-21-664881   Fax: 233-21-667909   Contact: Albert N. Kotey, Sr. Ptnr.

KPMG International, Ivory Coast (Cote d'Ivoire), Ghana

MARS INC.

6885 Elm Street, McLean, VA, 22101-3810

Tel: (703) 821-4900   Fax: (703) 448-9678   www.mars.com

Mfr. candy, snack foods, rice products and cat food.

Mars Ltd., Airport, PO Box M 109, Accra, Ghana

MAXXAM INC.

5847 San Felipe, Ste. 2600, Houston, TX, 77057

Tel: (713) 975-7600   Fax: (713) 267-3701

Holding company for aluminum and timber products and real estate industries.

MAXXAM Inc., Ghana

McCANN-ERICKSON WORLDGROUP

750 Third Ave., New York, NY, 10017

Tel: (212) 697-6000   Fax: (212) 984-3575   www.mccann.com

International advertising and marketing services.

STB&A, Accra, Ghana

PFIZER INC.

235 East 42nd Street, New York, NY, 10017-5755

Tel: (212) 573-2323   Fax: (212) 573-7851   www.pfizer.com

Research-based, global health care company.

Pfizer Ltd., Ghana

PHILLIPS PETROLEUM COMPANY

Phillips Building, 411 S. Keeler Ave., Bartlesville, OK, 74004

Tel: (918) 661-6600   Fax: (918) 661-7636   www.phillips66.com

Crude oil, natural gas, liquefied petroleum gas, gasoline and petro-chemicals.

Phillips Petroleum Co. (Ghana), Private Post Box, Central Post Office, Accra, Ghana

PRICEWATERHOUSECOOPERS LLP

1301 Ave. of the Americas, New York, NY, 10019

Tel: (212) 596-7000   Fax: (212) 259-1301   www.pwcglobal.com

Accounting and auditing, tax and management, and human resource consulting services.

PriceWaterhouseCoopers, PO Box 16009, Airport, Accra, Ghana

Tel: 233-21-772088   Fax: 233-21-772934

THE ST. PAUL COMPANIES, INC.

385 Washington Street, St. Paul, MN, 55102

Tel: (651) 310-7911   Fax: (651) 310-8294   www.stpaul.com

Provides investment, insurance and reinsurance services.

New India Assurance Co. (Ghana) Ltd., Queensway Building, D-619/4 Kimberley Ave., PO Box 138, Accra, Ghana

UNITED PARCEL SERVICE, INC.

55 Glenlake Parkway, NE, Atlanta, GA, 30328

Tel: (404) 828-6000   Fax: (404) 828-6593   www.ups.com

International package-delivery service.

UPS Ghana, Danquah Circle, PO Box C693, Cantonments Accra, Ghana

Tel: 223-21-762509   Fax: 233-21-772487

THE WACKENHUT CORPORATION

4200 Wackenhut Dr., Ste. 100, Palm Beach Gardens, FL, 33410

Tel: (561) 622-5656   Fax: (561) 691-6736   www.wackenhut.com

Security systems and services.

Wackenhut Ghana Ltd., Belmont Place, E153/3 Gamel Abdul Nasser Ave., PO Box C2616, Cantonments Accra, Ghana

Tel: 233-21-224276   Fax: 233-21-220302

XEROX CORPORATION

800 Long Ridge Road, PO Box 1600, Stamford, CT, 06904

Tel: (203) 968-3000   Fax: (203) 968-4312   www.xerox.com

Mfr. document processing equipment, systems and supplies.

Interlink Communications, Ring Rd. Central, PO Box 15930, Accra, Ghana

Tel: 233-21-226-659

Gibraltar

BDO SEIDMAN, LLP   BELGIUM

130 East Randolph Street, Chicago, IL, 60601

Tel: (312) 856-9100   Fax: (312) 856-1379   www.bdo.com

International accounting and financial consulting firm.

BDO Fidees, PO Box 575, Ste. 2C, Eurolife Building, 1 Corral Rd., Gibraltar

Tel: 350-42686   Fax: 350-42701   Contact: Timothy J. Revill

DELOITTE TOUCHE TOHMATSU INTERNATIONAL

1633 Broadway, New York, NY, 10019

Tel: (212) 492-4000   Fax: (212) 392-4154   www.deloitte.com

Accounting, audit, tax and management consulting services.

Deloitte & Touche, Imossi House, PO Box 758, 1/5 Irish Town, Gibraltar

DHL WORLDWIDE EXPRESS

50 California Avenue, San Francisco, CA, 94111

Tel: (415) 677-6100   Fax: (415) 824-9700   www.dhl.com

Worldwide air express carrier.

DHL AI Couriers Ltd., 11 Engineer Lane, PO Box 532, Gibraltar

Tel: 350-73775   Fax: 350-74389

ERNST & YOUNG INTERNATIONAL

5 Times Square, New York, NY, 10036

Tel: (212) 773-3000   Fax: (212) 773-6350   www.eyi.com

Engaged in assurance and advisory business services, tax, law and corporate finance.

Ernst & Young International, Ste. 5, International House, Bell Lane, Gibraltar

Tel: 350-79799   Fax: 350-75141   Contact: Kenneth A. Robinson

GRANT THORNTON INTERNATIONAL

800 One Prudential Plaza, 130 E. Randolph Drive, Chicago, IL, 60601-6050

Tel: (312) 856-0001   Fax: (312) 616-7052   www.grantthornton.com

Accounting, audit, tax and management consulting services.

Grant Thornton International, Suite 944, Europort Gibraltar, Gibraltar

HORWATH INTERNATIONAL ASSOCIATION

420 Lexington Avenue, Suite 526, New York, NY, 10170-0526

Tel: (212) 808-2000   Fax: (212) 808-2020   www.horwath.com

Public accountants and auditors.

Horwath Mutual Trust, 50 Town Range, Suites 7B & 8B, Gibraltar

KPMG CONSULTING INC.

1676 International Dr., McLean, VA, 22102

Tel: (703) 747-3000   Fax: (703) 747-8500   www.kpmg.com

Accounting and audit, tax and management consulting services.

KPMG International, Regal House, Queensway, Gibraltar

Tel: 350-74015   Fax: 350-74016   Contact: Francis A. Isola, Sr. Ptnr.

PRICEWATERHOUSECOOPERS LLP

1301 Ave. of the Americas, New York, NY, 10019

Tel: (212) 596-7000   Fax: (212) 259-1301   www.pwcglobal.com

Accounting and auditing, tax and management, and human resource consulting services.

PriceWaterhouseCoopers, PO Box 615, Europort, Gibraltar

Tel: 350-41992   Fax: 350-41996

XEROX CORPORATION

800 Long Ridge Road, PO Box 1600, Stamford, CT, 06904

Tel: (203) 968-3000   Fax: (203) 968-4312   www.xerox.com

Mfr. document processing equipment, systems and supplies.

Image Graphics Ltd., c/o Holiday Inn, 21/23 Governor's Parade, Gibraltar

Tel: 350-76834   Fax: 350-71892

Greece

3COM CORPORATION

5400 Bayfront Plaza, Santa Clara, CA, 95052-8145

Tel: (408) 326-5000   Fax: (408) 326-5001   www.3com.com

Engaged in the development and manufacture of computer networking products and systems.

3Com Greece, 90 Kifissias Avenue, GR-15125 Marousi Athens, Greece

Tel: 30-1-809-9675

3M (MINNESOTA MINING & MFG.)

3M Center, St. Paul, MN, 55144-1000

Tel: (651) 733-1110   Fax: (651) 733-9973   www.mmm.com

Mfr. diversified products for industry, consumer, health care, imaging, communications, transport, safety, etc.

3M Hellas Ltd., Kifissias 20, GR-151-25 Maroussi Athens, Greece

Tel: 30-1-68-85-300   Fax: 30-1-68-43-281

AAF INTERNATIONAL (AMERICAN AIR FILTER)

10300 Ormsby Park Place, Ste. 600, Louisville, KY, 40232-5690

Tel: (502) 637-0011   Fax: (502) 637-0321   www.aafintl.com

Mfr. air filtration and pollution control and noise control equipment.

AAF Environmental Control Epe, 2 Papada Street, GR-115-25 Athens, Greece

ABBOTT LABORATORIES

100 Abbott Park Rd., Abbott Park, IL, 60064

Tel: (847) 937-6100   Fax: (847) 937-1511   www.abbott.com

Development, manufacture and sale of diversified health care products and services.

Abbott Laboratories Hellas S.A., 512 Vouliagmenis AV, GR-174-56 Alimos Athens, Greece

ABS (AMERICAN BUREAU OF SHIPPING)

ABS Plaza, 16855 Northchase Drive, Houston, TX, 77060

Tel: (281) 877-6000   Fax: (281) 877-6344   www.eagle.org

Classification and certification of ships and offshore structures, development and technical assistance.

ABS Europe, Akti Miaouli & Filellinon St. 1-3, PO Box 80139, GR-185-10 Pireaus, Greece

ACCENTURE LTD.

1345 Avenue of the Americas, New York, NY, 10105

Tel: (917) 452-4400   Fax: (917) 527-9915   www.accenture.com

Provides management and technology consulting services.

Accenture, 24 Kifissias Ave., GR-152-31 Chalandri Athens, Greece

Tel: 30-1-6776-4004   Fax: 30-1-6776-405

AIG AMERICAN INTERNATIONAL GROUP INC.

70 Pine Street, New York, NY, 10270

Tel: (212) 770-7000   Fax: (212) 509-9705   www.aig.com

Worldwide insurance and financial services.

AILCO, 119 Kifissias Avenue, GR-151-24 Marcusi Athens, Greece

AMERICAN APPRAISAL ASSOCIATES INC.

411 E. Wisconsin Ave., Ste. 1900, Milwaukee, WI, 53202

Tel: (414) 271-7240   Fax: (414) 271-1041   www.american-appraisal.com

Valuation consulting services.

American Appraisal Associates, 54, Vassilissis Sophias Avenue, GR-115 28 Athens, Greece

Contact: Pavlos M. Zeccos

AMERICAN EXPRESS COMPANY

90 Hudson Street, Jersey City, NJ, 07302

Tel: (212) 640-2000   Fax: (212) 619-9802   www.americanexpress.com

Engaged in travel, travelers cheques, charge card and financial services.

American Express Foreign Exchange, 7 Hermou Street, GR-10563 Athens, Greece

AMERICAN LOCKER GROUP INC.

608 Allen Street, Jamestown, NY, 14701-3966

Tel: (716) 664-9600   Fax: (716) 483-2822   www.americanlocker.com

Mfr. coin-operated locks and office furniture.

MTI, 2 Ergaton Tipou Street, Ilioupolis 163 46, Athens, Greece

Tel: 30-1-9959063   Contact: Panos Thomadakis

ANC RENTAL CORPORATION

200 S. Andrews Ave., Ft. Lauderdale, FL, 33301

Tel: (954) 320-4000   Fax: (954) 320-4077   www.ancrental.com

Engaged in car rental services, including National Car Rental and Alamo Rent A Car.

National Car Rental, 7 Stadium St., Athens, Greece

ANDERSEN

33 West Monroe Street, Chicago, IL, 60603

Tel: (312) 580-0033   Fax: (312) 507-6748   www.andersen.com

*Accounting and audit, tax and management consulting services. **Firm under worldwide reorganization; new data unavailable for this edition.*

Arthur Andersen/ S. Pantzopoulos & Co., Syngrou Ave. 377, GR-175-64 Athens, Greece

Tel: 30-1-9302-063

ANIXTER INTERNATIONAL INC..

4711 Golf Road, Skokie, IL, 60076

Tel: (847) 677-2600   Fax: (847) 677-8557   www.anixter.com

Distributor wiring systems/products for voice, video, data and power applications.

Anixter Greece Network Systems Ltd., 282 Messogion Ave, GR-155-62 Holargos Athens, Greece

Tel: 30-1-653-5073   Fax: 30-1-653-1509

AON CORPORATION

200 East Randolph, Chicago, IL, 60601

Tel: (312) 381-1000   Fax: (312) 381-6032   www.aon.com

Insurance brokers worldwide; underwrites accident and health insurance, specialty and professional insurance; and provides risk management consultation.

AON Hellenic Bain Hogg SA, 320, Sygrou Avenue, GR-176-73 Athens, Greece

Tel: 30-10-955-2500   Fax: 30-10-957 6116   Contact: Stavros C. Papagiannopoulos

AON Turner Reinsurance Services SA, 7, Granikou Street, GR-151 25 Athens, Greece

Tel: 30-10-610-7025   Contact: Gerald Turner

APPLERA CORPORATION

301 Merritt 7, Norwalk, CT, 06851

Tel: (203) 840-2000   Fax: (203) 840-2312   www.applera.com

Leading supplier of systems for life science research and related applications.

Analytical Instruments S.A., 9 Tzavella Strasse, GR-152 31 Chalandri Athens, Greece

ARROW INTERNATIONAL, INC.

2400 Bernville Rd., Reading, PA, 19605

Tel: (610) 378-0131   Fax: (610) 374-5360   www.arrowintl.com

Develop, manufacture, and marketing of medical devices.

Arrow Hellas A.E.E., Leoforos Kifissias 294 & Narvarinou, Halandri, GR-152-32 Athens, Greece

Tel: 30-1-68-13024   Fax: 30-1-68-18145   Contact: Paula Kondopoulos

ASSOCIATED MERCHANDISING CORPORATION

500 Seventh Ave., 2nd Fl., New York, NY, 10018

Tel: (212) 819-6600   Fax: (212) 819-6701   www.theamc.com

Retail service organization; apparel, shoes and accessories.

Associated Merchandising Corp., 220 Messagion St., Holargos, GR-155-61 Athens, Greece

AT&T CORPORATION

295 N. Maple Ave., Basking Ridge, NJ, 07920-1002

Tel: (908) 221-2000   Fax: (908) 221-2528   www.att.com

Engaged in long distance telecommunications.

AT&T (Greece) Ltd., 64 Kifissias Ave., GR-151-25 Maroussi Athens, Greece

BANK OF AMERICA CORPORATION

Bank of America Corporate Center, Charlotte, NC, 28255

Tel: (415) 622-3530   Fax: (704) 386-6699   www.bankofamerica.com

Financial services.

Bank of America NT & SA, 39 Panepistimiou St., PO Box 3630, GR-105-64 Athens, Greece

Tel: 30-1-325-1901   Fax: 30-1-323-1376   Contact: Leonidas Metaxas, VP

BATES WORLDWIDE INC.

498 Seventh Avenue, New York, NY, 10018

Tel: (212) 297-7000   Fax: (212) 986-0270   www.batesww.com

Advertising, marketing, public relations and media consulting.

Bates Hellas, 11b Konitsis St., GR-151-25 Maroussi Athens, Greece

Tel: 30-1-612-5520   Fax: 30-1-805-0138   Contact: Yannis Papagiannacopoulos, CEO

BAUSCH & LOMB INC.

One Bausch & Lomb Place, Rochester, NY, 14604-2701

Tel: (716) 338-6000   Fax: (716) 338-6007   www.bausch.com

Mfr. vision care products and accessories.

Bausch & Lomb Greece, 73 Apostolopou Street, GR-152-31 Chalandri Athens, Greece

BAXTER INTERNATIONAL INC.

One Baxter Parkway, Deerfield, IL, 60015

Tel: (847) 948-2000   Fax: (847) 948-3948   www.baxter.com

Mfr. products and provide services in the field of the administration of medication and bioscience.

Baxter (Hellas) EPE, 67 Daskaroli St. & Gr. Lambraki St., GR-166-75 Flytada, Greece

BBDO WORLDWIDE

1285 Ave. of the Americas, New York, NY, 10019

Tel: (212) 459-5000   Fax: (212) 459-6645   www.bbdo.com

Multinational group of advertising agencies.

BBDO Group, Athens, Greece

BDO SEIDMAN, LLP   BELGIUM

130 East Randolph Street, Chicago, IL, 60601

Tel: (312) 856-9100   Fax: (312) 856-1379   www.bdo.com

International accounting and financial consulting firm.

BDO Kolokotronis & Co., 16 Metsovou St., GR-175-63 Paleo Firo Athens, Greece

Tel: 30-1-9317-117   Fax: 30-1-93-12-319   Contact: Loizos E. Kolokotronis

BEBE STORES, INC.

380 Valley Drive, Brisbane, CA, 94005

Tel: (415) 715-3900   Fax: (415) 715-3939   www.bebe.com

Mfr. contemporary clothes for young women.

Bebe Stores, Inc., Milioni 12, Kolonaki, GR-106-74 Athens, Greece

BENTLY NEVADA CORPORATION

1631 Bently Parkway South, Minden, NV, 89423

Tel: (775) 782-3611   Fax: (775) 782-9259   www.bently.com

Provides hardware, software, and services for machinery information and management systems.

Tesims SA, PO Box 80285, GR-185-10 Piraeus, Greece

LOUIS BERGER INTERNATIONAL INC.

100 Halsted Street, East Orange, NJ, 07019

Tel: (201) 678-1960   Fax: (201) 672-4284   www.louisberger.com

Consulting engineers, engaged in architecture, environmental and advisory services.

Mott Berger Joint Venture, 205 Alexander Ave., 3rd Fl., GR-115-23 Athens, Greece
Tel: 30-1-641-7543   Fax: 30-1-641-7543

BEST WESTERN INTERNATIONAL

6201 North 24th Place, Phoenix, AZ, 85106

Tel: (602) 957-4200   Fax: (602) 957-5740   www.bestwestern.com

International hotel chain.

Hotel Europa, Ancient Olympia, Piloponnese, Greece

BOYDEN CONSULTING CORPORATION

364 Elwood Ave., Hawthorne, NY, 10502

Tel: (914) 747-0093   Fax: (914) 980-6147   www.boyden.com

International executive search firm.

Boyden Associates Ltd., 12 Kinitsis St., GR-151-25 Maroussi, Greece
Tel: 30-1-6127-777

BOZELL GROUP

40 West 23rd Street, New York, NY, 10010

Tel: (212) 727-5000   Fax: (212) 645-9173   www.bozell.com

Advertising, marketing, public relations and media consulting.

Solid Advertising, Artemidos 3, Paradissos, Amarusius Athens, Greece
Tel: 30-1-685-5000   Fax: 30-1-685-5009   Contact: Stavros Leoussis, Mng. Dir.

BRANSON ULTRASONICS CORPORATION

41 Eagle Road, Danbury, CT, 06813-1961

Tel: (203) 796-0400   Fax: (203) 796-2285   www.branson-plasticsjoin.com

Engaged in design, development, manufacture and marketing of plastics joining, precision cleaning and processing equipment.

Control Technik SA, 22 Vas Georglou Str., GR-11635 Athens, Greece

BRISTOL-MYERS SQUIBB COMPANY

345 Park Ave., New York, NY, 10154-0037

Tel: (212) 546-4000   Fax: (212) 546-4020   www.bms.com

Pharmaceutical and food preparations, medical and surgical instruments.

Bristol Hellas A.E.B.E., 11th KLM., Athens-Lamia National Rd., Athens, Greece
ConvaTec Greece, 22nd KLM National Rd., GR-114-51 Metamorfosi, Greece
ConvaTec, Div. Bristol-Myers Squibb, 357-359 Messoghion Ae., GR-152-31 Chalandri, Greece
Tel: 30-1-6501-582

LEO BURNETT, DIV. B-COM 3 GROUP

35 West Wacker Drive, Chicago, IL, 60601

Tel: (312) 220-5959   Fax: (312) 220-6533   www.leoburnett.com

Engaged in advertising, marketing, media buying and planning, and public relations.

Leo Burnett Company, 371 Sygrou Ave., GR-175-64 Athens, Greece

CAMBREX CORPORATION

1 Meadowlands Plaza, East Rutherford, NJ, 07063

Tel: (201) 804-3000   Fax: (201) 804-9852   www.cambrex.com

human health, animal health/agriculture and Mfr. biotechnology products and produce specialty chemicals.

Chemico-Technica Renos J. Sashpelis SA, 8 SP Donda Street, Athens, Greece

Tel: 30-1-922-6391

CARGILL, INC.

15407 McGinty Road West, Minnetonka, MN, 55440-5625

Tel: (612) 742-7575   Fax: (612) 742-7393   www.cargill.com

Food products, feeds, animal products.

Diamandouros Brothers S.A., 5 Mimnermou and Rigillis Street, Athens, Greece

CARRIER CORPORATION

One Carrier Place, Farmington, CT, 06034-4015

Tel: (860) 674-3000   Fax: (860) 679-3010   www.carrier.com

Mfr./distributor/services A/C, heating and refrigeration equipment.

Carrier Hellas SA, 4c, Andersen & Moraiti 93, GR-115 25 Athens, Greece

THE CHERRY CORPORATION

3600 Sunset Ave., PO Box 718, Waukegan, IL, 60087

Tel: (847) 662-9200   Fax: (847) 662-2990   www.cherrycorp.com

Mfr. electrical switches, electronic keyboards, controls and displays.

G. Parpanelas & Co., Salaminos 10, GR-546-25 Thessaloniki, Greece

Tel: 30-31-51-8485   Fax: 30-31-51-7156

CHEVRON TEXACO CORPORATION

575 Market Street, San Francisco, CA, 94105-2856

Tel: (415) 894-7700   Fax: (415) 894-2248   www.chevrontexaco.com

Oil exploration, production and petroleum products.

ChevronTexaco Greece, Katchaki, Athens, Greece

CIGNA COMPANIES

One Liberty Place, Philadelphia, PA, 19192

Tel: (215) 761-1000   Fax: (215) 761-5511   www.cigna.com

Insurance, invest, health care and other financial services.

CIGNA Insurance Co. (Hellas) SA, Phidippidou 2, Ampelokipi, GR-115-26 Athens, Greece

CIGNA Insurance Co. of Europe SA/NV, Apollo Tower, 17/F, GR-115-23 Athens, Greece

CISCO SYSTEMS, INC.

170 West Tasman Drive, San Jose, CA, 95134-1706

Tel: (408) 526-4000   Fax: (408) 526-4100   www.cisco.com

Develop/mfr./market computer hardware and software networking systems.

Cisco Systems Greece, Caravel Hotel, Ste. 427, Vas. Alexandrou 2, Athens, Greece

Tel: 30-1-7253-725   Fax: 30-1-7253-770

CITIGROUP, INC.

399 Park Avenue, New York, NY, 10022

Tel: (212) 559-1000   Fax: (212) 559-3646   www.citigroup.com

Provides insurance and financial services worldwide.

Citigroup, 8 Othonos St., GR 105-57 Athens, Greece

Contact: Efstratios-George A. Arapoglou

THE COCA-COLA COMPANY

1 Coca Cola Plaza, Atlanta, GA, 30313

Tel: (404) 676-2121   Fax: (404) 676-6792   www.coca-cola.com

Mfr./marketing/distributor soft drinks, syrups and concentrates, juice and juice-drink products.

Coca-Cola Hellas SA, 26 Kifissias Ave. & 2 Paradissou Str., GR-15125 Maroussi, Greece

Tel: 30-10-688-8191

COLGATE-PALMOLIVE COMPANY

300 Park Ave., New York, NY, 10022

Tel: (212) 310-2000   Fax: (212) 310-2919   www.colgate.com

Mfr. pharmaceuticals, cosmetics, toiletries and detergents.

Colgate-Palmolive (Hellas) SA, 89 Athinon St., Piraeus, Greece

COMPUWARE CORPORATION

31440 Northwestern Hwy., Farmington Hills, MI, 48334-2564

Tel: (248) 737-7300   Fax: (248) 737-7108   www.compuware.com

Develop and market software for enterprise and e-commerce solutions.

Compuware Corporation, 59 Valtetsio Street, GR-132-31 Athens, Greece

CONCURRENT COMPUTER CORPORATION

4375 River Green Pkwy., Duluth, GA, 30096

Tel: (678) 258-4000   Fax: (678) 258-4300   www.ccur.com

Mfr. computer systems and software.

Concurrent Hellas, 2 Vas Georgiou St., GR-151-22 Maroussi Athens, Greece

Tel: 30-1-612-8935   Fax: 30-1-612-8934

CRAWFORD & COMPANY

5620 Glenridge Drive NE, Atlanta, GA, 30342

Tel: (404) 256-0830   Fax: (404) 847-4025   www.crawfordandcompany.com

Provides international insurance services engaged in risk management and claims adjustment.

Crawford & Company, 10 Athinas Street, GR-176 73 Kalithea, Greece

DANZAS AEI, INC.

120 Tokeneke Road, PO Box 1231, Darien, CT, 06820

Tel: (203) 655-7900   Fax: (203) 655-5779   www.aeilogistics.com

International air freight forwarder.

Danzas AEI, 20 Satovriandou Str, PO Box 8518, GR-100-10 Athens, Greece

Tel: 30-1-524-6512   Fax: 30-1-524-6134

D'ARCY MASIUS BENTON & BOWLES INC. (DMB&B)

1675 Broadway, New York, NY, 10019

Tel: (212) 468-3622   Fax: (212) 468-2987   www.darcyww.com

Full service international advertising and communications group.

International Marketing & Promotions, 8 Koumbari St., GR-106-74 Athens, Greece

DDB WORLDWIDE COMMUNICATIONS GROUP

437 Madison Ave., New York, NY, 10022

Tel: (212) 415-2000   Fax: (212) 415-3417   www.ddbn.com

Advertising agency.

Olympic DDB SA, 124 Kifissias Ave., GR-115-26 Athens, Greece

DELOITTE TOUCHE TOHMATSU INTERNATIONAL

1633 Broadway, New York, NY, 10019

Tel: (212) 492-4000   Fax: (212) 392-4154   www.deloitte.com

Accounting, audit, tax and management consulting services.

Deloitte & Touche Hadjipavlou Sofianos & Cambanis SA, 250-254 Kifissias Ave., GR-152-31 Halandri Athens, Greece

DELTA AIR LINES INC.

Hartsfield International Airport, 1030 Delta Blvd., Atlanta, GA, 30320-6001

Tel: (404) 715-2600   Fax: (404) 715-5494   www.delta-air.com

Major worldwide airline; international air transport services.

Delta Air Lines Inc., Athens, Greece

DHL WORLDWIDE EXPRESS

50 California Avenue, San Francisco, CA, 94111

Tel: (415) 677-6100   Fax: (415) 824-9700   www.dhl.com

Worldwide air express carrier.

DHL Worldwide Express, Alimou 44 & Rome 17, GR-174-55 Alimos Athens, Greece

Tel: 30-1-989-0000

DIAGNOSTIC PRODUCTS CORPORATION

5700 West 96th Street, Los Angeles, CA, 90045

Tel: (310) 645-8200   Fax: (310) 645-9999   www.dpcweb.com

Mfr. diagnostic products.

DPC N.Tsakiris S.A., Ionias Oreokastro, PO Box 238, GR-570-08 Thessaloniki, Greece

Tel: 30-31-783-891   Fax: 30-31-784-712

DIMON INCORPORATED

512 Bridge Street, PO Box 681, Danville, VA, 24543-0681

Tel: (804) 792-7511   Fax: (804) 791-0377   www.dimon.com

One of world's largest importer and exporters of leaf tobacco.

DIMON Hellas Tobacco S.A., 19 Thermaikou Street, GR- 564-30 Stavroupoli Thessaloniki, Greece

DIONEX CORPORATION

1228 Titan Way, PO Box 3603, Sunnyvale, CA, 94086-3603

Tel: (408) 737-0700   Fax: (408) 730-9403   www.dionex.com

Develop/mfr./market chromatography systems and related products.

Hellamco, PO Box 65074, GR154-10 Psyhiko-Athens, Greece

DMC STRATEX NETWORKS, INC.

170 Rose Orchard Way, San Jose, CA, 95134

Tel: (408) 943-0777   Fax: (408) 944-1648   www.dmcstratexnetworks.com

Designs, manufactures, and markets advanced wireless solutions for wireless broadband access.

DMC Stratex Networks, 2 Eratoshenous Str., GR-116-35 Athens, Greece

Tel: 30-1-752-2066

DRAFT WORLDWIDE

633 North St. Clair Street, Chicago, IL, 60611-3211

Tel: (312) 944-3500   Fax: (312) 944-3566   www.draftworldwide.com

Full service international advertising agency, engaged in brand building, direct and promotional marketing.

DraftWorldwide Hellas, 172 N. Plastera St., Agious Anargerous, Athens, Greece

Tel: 30-1-269-0373   Fax: 30-1-269-1827   Contact: Chris Gaitanaria, CEO

DRAKE BEAM MORIN INC.

100 Park Avenue, 11th Fl., New York, NY, 10017

Tel: (212) 692-7700   Fax: (212) 297-0426   www.dbm.com

Human resource management consulting and training.

DBM Greece, c/o S & S Consulting, Apollo Tower, Ste. 12B4, 64 Louise Reincourt St., GR-115-23 Athens, Greece

Tel: 30-1-648-4235   Fax: 30-1-692-3452

E.I. DUPONT DE NEMOURS & COMPANY

1007 Market Street, Wilmington, DE, 19898

Tel: (302) 774-1000   Fax: (302) 774-7321   www.dupont.com

Mfr. and sales of diversified chemicals, plastics, specialty products and fibers.

DuPont Agros Hellas S.A., 12 Solomou & Vas.Georgiou Str., GR-152 32 Halandri, Greece

Tel: 30-1-688-9784   Fax: 30-1-688-9789   Contact: Virginia Gioka

EASTMAN KODAK COMPANY

343 State Street, Rochester, NY, 14650

Tel: (716) 724-4000   Fax: (716) 724-1089   www.kodak.com

Develop/mfr. photo and chemicals products, information management/video/copier systems, fibers/plastics for various industry.

Kodak (Near East) Inc., PO Box 8253, GR-100-10 Athens, Greece

EATON CORPORATION

Eaton Center, 1111 Superior Ave., Cleveland, OH, 44114-2584

Tel: (216) 523-5000   Fax: (216) 479-7068   www.eaton.com

Advanced technical products for transportation and industrial markets.

Eaton Intl. Inc., 6 Queen Frederikis St., Glyfada, Athens, Greece

ECOLAB INC.

370 N. Wabasha Street, St. Paul, MN, 55102

Tel: (651) 293-2233   Fax: (651) 293-2379   www.ecolab.com

Develop/mfr. premium cleaning, sanitizing and maintenance products and services for the hospitality, institutional, and residential markets.

Ecolab Ltd., Athens, Greece

Tel: 30-1-68-11010

J.D. EDWARDS & COMPANY

One Technology Way, Denver, CO, 80237

Tel: (303) 334-4000   Fax: (303) 334-4970   www.jdedwards.com

Computer software products.

Softecon, 25 Mavromateon Str. & Kotsika, GR-104-34 Athens, Greece

Tel: 30-1-825-3803   Fax: 30-1-821-8249

EGL INC. (EAGLE GLOBAL LOGISTICS)

15350 Vickery Drive, Houston, TX, 77032

Tel: (281) 618-3100   Fax: (281) 618-3223   www.eagleusa.com

Ocean/air freight forwarding, customs brokerage, packing and wholesale, logistics management and insurance.

EGL Eagle Global Logistics, 226 Syngrou Ave., GR-176-72 Athens, Greece

Tel: 30-1-958-1349   Fax: 30-1-952-1988

EGL Eagle Global Logistics, 7 Tantalou St., Thessaloniki, Greece

Tel: 30-31-517-184   Fax: 30-31-532-174

EMERSON PROCESS MANAGEMENT

8301Cameron Road, Austin, TX, 78754

Tel: (512) 834-7689   Fax: (512) 832-3232   www.frco.com

Mfr. industrial process control equipment.

TEVEX, A. Sarafides & Co. E.E., 4, Argyrokastrou Street, GR-15235 Vrilissia-Athens, Greece

ERNST & YOUNG INTERNATIONAL

5 Times Square, New York, NY, 10036

Tel: (212) 773-3000   Fax: (212) 773-6350   www.eyi.com

Engaged in assurance and advisory business services, tax, law and corporate finance.

Ernst & Young International, 3-5 Ilisson St., GR-115 Athens, Greece

Tel: 30-1-748-8610-20   Fax: 30-1-788-2044   Contact: Themis Lianopoulos

EURO RSCG WORLDWIDE

350 Hudson Street, New York, NY, 10014

Tel: (212) 886-2000   Fax: (212) 886-2016   www.eurorscg.com

International advertising agency group.

EURO RSCG, 4 Priynis Street, Nea Smyrni, Athens, Greece

EXPEDITORS INTERNATIONAL OF WASHINGTON INC.

1015 Third Avenue, 12th Fl., Seattle, WA, 98104-1182

Tel: (206) 674-3400   Fax: (206) 682-9777   www.expd.com

Air/ocean freight forwarding, customs brokerage, international logistics solutions.

Expeditors/Planair Ltd., Androutsou 4 St, GR-117-41 Athens, Greece

FEDERAL-MOGUL CORPORATION

26555 Northwestern Highway, PO Box 1966, Southfield, MI, 48034

Tel: (248) 354-7700   Fax: (248) 354-8983   www.federal-mogul.com

Mfr./distributor precision parts for automobiles, trucks, farm and construction vehicles.

Federal-Mogul de Venezuela CA, Athens, Greece

FERRO CORPORATION

1000 Lakeside Ave., Cleveland, OH, 44114-7000

Tel: (216) 641-8580   Fax: (216) 696-5784   www.ferro.com

Mfr. Specialty chemicals, coatings, plastics, colors, refractories.

Ferro B.V., 14. Makedonias Str., GR-151-24 Maroussi Athens, Greece

Tel: 30-1-8062486

FMC CORPORATION

1735 Market St., Philadelphia, PA, 19103

Tel: (215) 299-6000   Fax: (215) 299-6618   www.fmc.com

Mfr. specialty chemicals, including alginate, carrageenan and microcrystalline cellulose.

FMC Greece, Arkadiou 38 and Dzavela Streets, Kato Chalandri, Athens, Greece

FRITZ COMPANIES, INC., DIV. UPS

706 Mission Street, Ste. 900, San Francisco, CA, 94103

Tel: (415) 904-8360   Fax: (415) 904-8661   www.fritz.com

Integrated transportation, sourcing, distribution and customs brokerage services.

Fritz Companies Inc., Athens, Greece

GENERAL DYNAMICS CORPORATION

3190 Fairview Park Drive, Falls Church, VA, 22042-4523

Tel: (703) 876-3000   Fax: (703) 876-3125   www.gendyn.com

Mfr. aerospace equipment, submarines, strategic systems, armored vehicles, defense support systems.

Hellenic Business Development & Investment Co. SA, 32 Kifissias Ave., Marousi Athens, Greece

GENERAL MOTORS CORPORATION

300 Renaissance Center, Detroit, MI, 48285

Tel: (313) 556-5000   Fax: (313) 556-5108   www.gm.com

Mfr. full line vehicles, automotive electronics, commercial technologies, telecommunications, space, finance.

General Motors Hellas ABEE, PO Box 61020, Amaroussion, GR-151-10 Athens, Greece

GENZYME CORPORATION

1 Kendall Square, Cambridge, MA, 02139-1562

Tel: (617) 252-7500   Fax: (617) 252-7600   www.genzyme.com

Mfr. healthcare products for enzyme deficient diseases.

Jasonpharm & Co., Div. Genzyme Ltd., Ymittou 97, GR-116-33 Athens, Greece

Tel: 30-1-751-7608

GILEAD SCIENCES, INC.

333 Lakeside Dr, Foster City, CA, 94404

Tel: (650) 574-3000   Fax: (650) 578-9264   www.gilead.com

Engaged in healthcare research and development; biotech treatments for viruses.

NeXstar Pharmaceuticals, Inc., 602A Vouliagmenis Avenue, GR-16452 Argiroupolis Athens, Greece

Tel: 30-1-996-8758   Fax: 30-1-996-8777

THE GILLETTE COMPANY

Prudential Tower Building, Boston, MA, 02199

Tel: (617) 421-7000 Fax: (617) 421-7123 www.gillette.com

Develop/mfr. personal care/use products: blades and razors, toiletries, cosmetics, stationery.

Gillette Greece, c/o Marvo ABEE, 21 Spirou Merkouri Str, GR-14452 Metamorfossi Attikis, Greece

Contact: Domenico Ottavis, Gen. Mgr.

GILSON INC.

3000 W. Beltline Hwy, PO Box 620027, Middleton, WI, 53562-0027

Tel: (608) 836-1551 Fax: (608) 831-4451 www.gilson.com

Mfr. analytical/biomedical instruments.

Meditec S.A., 29 Paradisou & Zagoras str., GR-151-25 Athens, Greece

THE GOODYEAR TIRE & RUBBER COMPANY

1144 East Market Street, Akron, OH, 44316

Tel: (330) 796-2121 Fax: (330) 796-1817 www.goodyear.com

Mfr. tires, automotive belts and hose, conveyor belts, chemicals; oil pipeline transmission.

Goodyear Hellas SAIC, 94 Kifissou Ave., PO Box 41092, GR-122-10 Aibaleo Athens, Greece

W. R. GRACE & COMPANY

7500 Grace Drive, Columbia, MD, 21044

Tel: (410) 531-4000 Fax: (410) 531-4367 www.grace.com

Mfr. specialty chemicals and materials: packaging, health care, catalysts, construction, water treatment/process.

Grace Hellas E.P.E., 20 Lagoumitzi St., GR-176-71 Kallitha Athens, Greece

Tel: 30-1-9231-404 Fax: 30-1-9235-993

GRANT THORNTON INTERNATIONAL

800 One Prudential Plaza, 130 E. Randolph Drive, Chicago, IL, 60601-6050

Tel: (312) 856-0001 Fax: (312) 616-7052 www.grantthornton.com

Accounting, audit, tax and management consulting services.

Grant Thornton SA, 99 Pratinou & Nereidon Str., GR-116-34 Athens, Greece

Tel: 30-172- 53315 Contact: Vassilis Kazas

GREY GLOBAL GROUP

777 Third Ave., New York, NY, 10017

Tel: (212) 546-2000 Fax: (212) 546-1495 www.grey.com

International advertising agency.

Grey Athens, 294 Syngrou Ave., GR-176-73 Kalithea Athens, Greece

HALLIBURTON COMPANY

500 North Akard Street, Ste. 3600, Dallas, TX, 75201-3391

Tel: (214) 978-2600 Fax: (214) 978-2685 www.halliburton.com

Engaged in diversified energy services, engineering and construction.

Halliburton Ltd., PO Box 1525, GR-651-10 Kavala, Greece

Tel: 30-51-831-842 Fax: 30-51-831-842

HARRIS CORPORATION

1025 West NASA Blvd., Melbourne, FL, 32919

Tel: (407) 727-9100 Fax: (407) 727-9344 www.harris.com

Mfr. communications and information-handling equipment, including copying and fax systems.

EBV Elektronik, Anaxagora St. 1, GR-177-78 Travros Athens, Greece

Tel: 30-1-325-3626 Fax: 30-1-32-16-063

HASBRO INDUSTRIES INC.

1027 Newport Ave., Pawtucket, RI, 02861

Tel: (401) 725-8697 Fax: (401) 727-5099 www.hasbro.com

Mfr. toy products, including games and puzzles, dolls and plush products.

Hasbro Industries, Athens, Greece

H.J. HEINZ COMPANY

600 Grant Street, Pittsburgh, PA, 15219

Tel: (412) 456-5700　　　Fax: (412) 456-6128　　　www.heinz.com

Processed food products and nutritional services.

COPAIS SA, Athens, Greece

HEWLETT-PACKARD COMPANY

3000 Hanover Street, Palo Alto, CA, 94304-1185

Tel: (650) 857-1501　　　Fax: (650) 857-5518　　　www.hp.com

Mfr. computing, communications and measurement products and services.

Hewlett-Packard Hellas, 62 Kifissias Ave., GR-151-25 Marousi Athens, Greece

HILTON HOTELS CORPORATION

9336 Civic Center Drive, Beverly Hills, CA, 90210

Tel: (310) 278-4321　　　Fax: (310) 205-7880　　　www.hiltonhotels.com

International hotel chain: Hilton International, Vista Hotels and Hilton National Hotels.

Hilton International Hotels, 46 Vassilissis Sofias Ave., GR-115-28 Athens, Greece

HOLIDAY INN (BASS RESORTS) WORLDWIDE, INC.

3 Ravinia Drive, Ste. 2900, Atlanta, GA, 30346-2149

Tel: (770) 604-2000　　　Fax: (770) 604-5403　　　www.holidayinn.com

Hotels, restaurants and casinos.

Holiday Inn Inc., Michalacopoulou 50, Ilissia, Athens, Greece

HONEYWELL INTERNATIONAL INC.

Honeywell Plaza, Minneapolis, MN, 55408

Tel: (612) 951-1000　　　Fax: (612) 951-8537　　　www.honeywell.com

Develop/mfr. controls for home and building, industry, space and aviation, burglar and fire alarm systems.

Honeywell E.P.E., 313 Irakliou Ave., 1-3 Viotias Str., Neon Iraklion, Athens, Greece

Tel: 30-1-284-8049　Fax: 30-1-284-8055

HORWATH INTERNATIONAL ASSOCIATION

420 Lexington Avenue, Suite 526, New York, NY, 10170-0526

Tel: (212) 808-2000　　　Fax: (212) 808-2020　　　www.horwath.com

Public accountants and auditors.

Alexander, Young & Co., 5-7 Filellinon St., GR-185-36 Piraeus, Greece

Euroauditing S.A., 25 Stournari Street, GR-106-82 Athens, Greece

Tel: 30-1-380-0082

HOWMEDICA OSTEONICS, INC.

59 Route 17 South, Allendale, NJ, 07401

Tel: (201) 507-7300　　　Fax: (201) 935-4873　　　www.howmedica.com

Mfr. of maxillofacial products (orthopedic implants).

Howmedica Greece, Athens, Greece

Tel: 30-1-330-4318

IBM CORPORATION

1133 Westchester Avenue, White Plains, NY, 10604

Tel: (914) 765-1900　　　Fax: (914) 765-7382　　　www.ibm.com

Information products, technology and services.

IBM Hellas S.A., 284 Kifissias Ave., GR-152-32 Halandri, Greece

Tel: 30-1-688-1220　Fax: 30-1-680-1300

INFONET SERVICES CORPORATION

2160 East Grand Ave., El Segundo, CA, 90245-1022

Tel: (310) 335-2600　　　Fax: (310) 335-4507　　　www.infonet.com

Provider of Internet services and electronic messaging services.

Infonet Greece, 99 Kifissias Ave., GR-151-81 Marousi, Greece

Tel: 30-1-611-53756　Fax: 30-1-806-4299

INFORMATION RESOURCES, INC. (IRI)

150 N. Clinton St., Chicago, IL, 60661

Tel: (312) 726-1221   Fax: (312) 726-0360   www.infores.com

Provides bar code scanner services for retail sales organizations; processes, analyzes and sells data from the huge database created from these services.

Information Resources Hellas, 133 Michalakopoulou St., GR-115-27 Athens, Greece

Tel: 30-1-7488-241   Fax: 30-1-7488-240

INTER-CONTINENTAL HOTELS

3 Ravinia Drive, Suite 2900, Atlanta, GA, 30346-2149

Tel: (770) 604-2000   Fax: (770) 604-5403   www.interconti.com

Worldwide hotel and resort accommodations.

Athenaeum Inter-Continental Athens, 89-93 Syngrou Ave., GR-117-45 Athens, Greece

Tel: 30-1-920-6000   Fax: 30-1-924-3000

INTERGRAPH CORPORATION

One Madison Industrial Park, Huntsville, AL, 35894-0001

Tel: (256) 730-2000   Fax: (256) 730-7898   www.intergraph.com

Develop/mfr. interactive computer graphic systems.

Intergraph Hellas S.A, 237 Messogion Ave., GR-154-51 Neo Psychiko Athens, Greece

Tel: 30-1-6729091   Fax: 30-1-6729094

INTERMEC TECHNOLOGIES CORPORATION

6001 36th Avenue West, PO Box 4280, Everett, WA, 98203-9280

Tel: (425) 348-2600   Fax: (425) 355-9551   www.intermec.com

Mfr. and distributor automated data collection systems.

Intermec Hellas, 125 Michalakopoulou Ave., GR-115-27 Athens, Greece

ITT-GOULDS PUMPS INC.

2881 East Bayard Street, Seneca Falls, NY, 13148

Tel: (315) 568-2811   Fax: (315) 568-7651   www.gouldspumps.com

Mfr. industrial and water systems pumps.

Goulds Pumps - Athens, Achileos Kyrou 4 Neo Psychiko, GR-115-25 Athens, Greece

J. WALTER THOMPSON COMPANY

466 Lexington Ave., New York, NY, 10017

Tel: (212) 210-7000   Fax: (212) 210-6944   www.jwt.com

International advertising and marketing services.

Spot Thompson Athens, Athens, Greece

JOHNSON & JOHNSON

One Johnson & Johnson Plaza, New Brunswick, NJ, 08933

Tel: (732) 524-0400   Fax: (732) 214-0334   www.jnj.com

Mfr./distributor/R&D pharmaceutical, health care and cosmetic products.

Janssen-Cilag Pharmaceutical S.A.C.I., 246 Kifissias Ave., Halandri, Athens, Greece
Johnson & Johnson Hellas SA, PO Box 65069, GR-154-10 Psychico Athens, Greece
Johnson & Johnson Medical Products SA, Athens, Greece

SC JOHNSON

1525 Howe St., Racine, WI, 53403

Tel: (262) 260-2000   Fax: (262) 260-2133   www.scjohnsonwax.com

Home, auto, commercial and personal care products and specialty chemicals.

SC Johnson, 479 Messogion Ave., GR-153 Aghia Paraskevi Athens, Greece

KENNAMETAL INC.

1600 Technology Way, PO Box 231, Latrobe, PA, 15650

Tel: (724) 539-5000   Fax: (724) 539-4710   www.kennametal.com

Tools, hard carbide and tungsten alloys for metalworking industry.

Kennametal / D.Panayoditis - J. Tsatsis S.A., GR-183-46 Moschaton Athens, Greece

Tel: 30-1-4810-81789   Fax: 30-1-3014-829673

KORN/FERRY INTERNATIONAL

1800 Century Park East, Los Angeles, CA, 90067

Tel: (310) 843-4100   Fax: (310) 553-6452   www.kornferry.com

Engaged in executive search and management consulting.

Korn/Ferry International, Athens, Greece

Tel: 30-1-777-7718   Fax: 30-1-748-9511

KPMG CONSULTING INC.

1676 International Dr., McLean, VA, 22102

Tel: (703) 747-3000   Fax: (703) 747-8500   www.kpmg.com

Accounting and audit, tax and management consulting services.

KPMG International, 3 Stratigou Tombra St., GR-153-42 Aghia Paraskevi, Greece

Tel: 30-1-606-2100   Fax: 30-1-606-2111   Contact: Marios T. Kyriacou, Sr. Ptnr.

LANIER WORLDWIDE, INC.

2300 Parklake Drive, N.E., Atlanta, GA, 30345

Tel: (770) 496-9500   Fax: (770) 938-1020   www.lanier.com

Specialize in digital copiers and multi-functional systems.

Lanier Hellas AEBE, Eleon 29, GR-145-64 Kifissias Athens, Greece

Tel: 30-1-807-8212   Fax: 30-1-807-8014

LEVI STRAUSS & COMPANY

1155 Battery St., San Francisco, CA, 94111-1230

Tel: (415) 544-6000   Fax: (415) 501-3939   www.levistrauss.com

Mfr. and distributor of casual wearing apparel, including jeans and sportswear.

Levi Strauss Hellas, AEBE, 11 Argonafton Street, GR-152-32 Halandri Athens, Greece

Tel: 30-1-685-6350   Fax: 30-1-685-6271

ELI LILLY & COMPANY

Lilly Corporate Center, Indianapolis, IN, 46285

Tel: (317) 276-2000   Fax: (317) 277-6579   www.lilly.com

Mfr. pharmaceuticals and animal health products.

Pharmaserve-Lilly Saci, 15th KLM National Rd., Athens-Lamia, GR-145-64 Kifissias Athens, Greece

Tel: 30-1-629-4600   Fax: 30-1-629-4610

LOCKHEED MARTIN CORPORATION

6801 Rockledge Drive, Bethesda, MD, 20817

Tel: (301) 897-6000   Fax: (301) 897-6652   www.imco.com

Design/mfr./management systems in fields of space, defense, energy, electronics and technical services.

Lockheed Martin International S.A., 9 Giannitson Street, Holargos, GR-155-62 Athens, Greece

Tel: 30-1-654-7082   Fax: 30-1-653-6632   Contact: Alex K. Papadimitrious, Dir.

Lockheed-Hellas S.A., 64 Kifissias Ave., 32 Maroussi, GR-151-25 Athens, Greece

THE LUBRIZOL CORPORATION

29400 Lakeland Blvd., Wickliffe, OH, 44092-2298

Tel: (440) 943-4200   Fax: (440) 943-5337   www.lubrizol.com

Mfr. chemicals additives for lubricants and fuels.

Lubrizol Greece, Athens, Greece

Tel: 30-1-933-5367

MARRIOTT INTERNATIONAL INC.

10400 Fernwood Rd., Bethesda, MD, 20817

Tel: (301) 380-3000   Fax: (301) 380-5181   www.marriott.com

Hotel services.

Athlens Ledra Marriott Hotel, Athens, Greece

MARSH & McLENNAN COS INC.

1166 Ave. of the Americas, New York, NY, 10036-2774

Tel: (212) 345-5000   Fax: (212) 345-4808   www.marshmac.com

Insurance agents/brokers, pension and investment management consulting services.

Marsh & McLennan-Hellas LLC, 124 Kifissias Ave., Ambelokipi, GR-115-26 Athens, Greece

Tel: 30-1-685-7575   Fax: 30-1-685-7573   Contact: Panayiotis Lisseos

McCANN-ERICKSON WORLDGROUP

750 Third Ave., New York, NY, 10017

Tel: (212) 697-6000   Fax: (212) 984-3575   www.mccann.com

International advertising and marketing services.

McCann-Erickson (Hellas) LLC, 7 Ventiri St., GR-115-28 Athens, Greece

McDONALD'S CORPORATION

McDonald's Plaza, Oak Brook, IL, 60523

Tel: (630) 623-3000   Fax: (630) 623-7409   www.mcdonalds.com

Fast food chain stores.

McDonald's Corp., Athens, Greece

THE McGRAW-HILL COMPANIES

1221 Avenue of the Americas, New York, NY, 10020

Tel: (212) 512-2000   Fax: (212) 512-2703   www.mccgraw-hill.com

Books, magazines, information systems, financial service, publishing and broadcast operations.

McGraw-Hll Hellas, 21A Patriarchou Gregoriou E. Str., 153 41 Ag., Paraskevi Athens, Greece

MECHANICAL DYNAMICS, INC.

2300 Traverwood Drive, Ann Arbor, MI, 48105

Tel: (734) 994-3800   Fax: (734) 994-6418   www.adams.com

Mfr. Adams prototyping software for functional virtual prototyping solutions.

Omega Vision 2000 s.a., Ravine 22, #1 Kolonaki, GR-115-21 Athens, Greece

Tel: 30-1-725-2044

MERCK & COMPANY, INC.

One Merck Drive, PO Box 100, Whitehouse Station, NJ, 08889-0100

Tel: (908) 423-1000   Fax: (908) 423-2592   www.merck.com

Pharmaceuticals, chemicals and biologicals.

Merck, Sharp & Dohme Inc., Athens Tower, Messogion 2-4, Athens, Greece

MERRILL LYNCH & COMPANY, INC.

World Financial Center, 250 Vesey Street, New York, NY, 10281-1332

Tel: (212) 236-1000   Fax: (212) 449-2892   www.ml.com

Security brokers and dealers, investment and business services.

Merrill Lynch, Pierce, Fenner & Smith Hellas LLC, 17 Valaorithous Street, GR-106-71 Athens, Greece

Tel: 30-1-361-8916   Fax: 30-1-364-8046

META GROUP, INC.

208 Harbor Drive, PO Box 120061, Stamford, CT, 06912-0061

Tel: (203) 973-6700   Fax: (203) 359-8066   www.metagroup.com

Engaged in research and consulting, focusing on information technology and business transformation strategies.

Pliroforiki S.A., Div. META Group, 438 Acharnon Str., GR-111 43 Athens, Greece

M-I

PO Box 48242, Houston, TX, 77242-2842

Tel: (713) 739-0222   Fax: (713) 308-9503   www.midf.com

Developer, manufacturer and marketer of drilling and completion fluids and services.

MIOL Greece, PO Box 1291, GR-651-10 Kavala, Greece

Tel: 30-51-223530   Fax: 30-51-837017

MICROSOFT CORPORATION

One Microsoft Way, Redmond, WA, 98052-6399

Tel: (425) 882-8080   Fax: (425) 936-7329   www.microsoft.com

Computer software, peripherals and services.

Microsoft Greece, 64 Kifissias Ave., Polis Centre, GR-151-25 Maroussi Athens, Greece

Tel: 30-1-680-6775   Fax: 30-1-680-6780

MONSANTO

800 N. Lindbergh Boulevard, St. Louis, MO, 63167

Tel: (314) 694-1000   Fax: (314) 694-7625   www.monsanto.com

Life sciences company focusing on agriculture, nutrition, pharmaceuticals, health and wellness and sustainable development.

Monsanto Hellas EPE, 29 Michaiakoulou Street, GR-11528 Athens, Greece

J. P. MORGAN CHASE & CO. INC.

270 Park Ave., New York, NY, 10017

Tel: (212) 270-6000   Fax: (212) 622-9030   www.jpmorganchase.com

Provides integrated financial solutions for institutions and individuals worldwide, including asset management, investment banking and commercial banking.

J. P. Morgan Chase & Co., 3 Korai St., PO Box3005, GR-102-10 Athens, Greece

J. P. Morgan Chase & Co., PO Box 89, 95 Akti Miaouli, GR-185-10 Piraeus, Greece

Tel: 30-1-42-90-678   Fax: 30-1-42-90-693

MOTOROLA, INC.

1303 East Algonquin Road, Schaumburg, IL, 60196

Tel: (847) 576-5000   Fax: (847) 538-5191   www.motorola.com

Mfr. communications equipment, semiconductors and cellular phones.

Motorola Greece, 22 Kifissias Ave., GR-151-25 Maroussi Athens, Greece

Tel: 30-1-689-0898   Fax: 30-1-684-3079

NATIONAL INSTRUMENTS CORPORATION

11550 N. Mopac Expwy., Austin, TX, 78759-3504

Tel: (512) 338-9119   Fax: (512) 794-5794   www.ni.com

Mfr. hardware and graphical software.

National instruments Hellas, B' Merarchias 17, GR-185 35 Piraeus, Greece

NEW HORIZONS WORLDWIDE, INC.

1900 S. State College Blvd., Anaheim, CA, 92806-6135

Tel: (714) 940-8000   Fax: www.newhorizons.com

Provides customer-focused computer training choices, through computer training centers.

New Horizons Worldwide, 70, Panormou, GR-11523 Athens, Greece

AC NIELSEN COMPANY

177 Broad Street, Stamford, CT, 06901

Tel: (203) 961-3000   Fax: (203) 961-3190   www.acnielsen.com

Engaged in market and consumer research.

ACNielsen, 196 Sygrou Ave., GR-176-71 Kallithea Athens, Greece

NL INDUSTRIES, INC.

16825 Northchase Drive, Ste. 1200, Houston, TX, 77060-2544

Tel: (281) 423-3300   Fax: (281) 423-3236   www.nl-ind.com

Producer of titanium dioxide pigments.

Kronos Marketing, Div. NL Industries, 16 Xanthippou Str., GR-15561 Holargos, Greece

NORDSON CORPORATION

28601 Clemens Road, Westlake, OH, 44145-4551

Tel: (440) 892-1580   Fax: (440) 892-9507   www.nordson.com

Mfr. industry application equipment, sealants and packaging machinery.

Meltko S.A., 54 Korai Str., GR-183-45 Moschato Athens, Greece

Tel: 30-1-940-7907

OGILVY & MATHER WORLDWIDE

309 West 49th Street, New York, NY, 10017-7399

Tel: (212) 237-4000   Fax: (212) 237-5123   www.ogilvypr.com

Engaged in public relations and communications.

Stigma Communication Ltd./Ogilvy, 7 Granikou Street, GR-151-25 Maroussi Athens, Greece

Contact: Marina Leonidhopoulos

OPTEK TECHNOLOGY, INC.

1215 West Crosby Road, Carrollton, TX, 75006

Tel: (972) 323-2200   Fax: (972) 323-2208   www.optekinc.com

Mfr. standard and custom sensors utilizing infrared and magnetic devices.

Optrionics Yet, El. Venizelou 222, Pal. Faliro, GR-175-63 Athens, Greece

OTIS ELEVATOR COMPANY

One Farm Springs Road, Farmington, CT, 06032

Tel: (860) 676-6000   Fax: (860) 676-5111   www.otis.com

Mfr. elevators and escalators.

C. Veremis Otis SA, 38 Bouboulinco St., GR-106-82 Athens, Greece

PANAMETRICS

221 Crescent Street, Waltham, MA, 02154

Tel: (781) 899-2719   Fax: (781) 899-1552   www.panametrics.com

Engaged in manufacture and distribution of ultrasonic testing equipment and process control instrumentation.

Meta Engineering, 54 Agias Marinis St., GR-151-27 Melissia Athens Hellas, Greece

Tel: 30-1-613-0929   Fax: 30-1-613-1329

PANDUIT CORPORATION

17301 Ridgeland Ave., Tinley Park, IL, 60477-0981

Tel: (708) 532-1800   Fax: (708) 532-1811   www.panduit.com

Mfr. of network connectivity and electrical products.

Panduit Greece, 56 AG. Paraskevis St., GR-167-77 Elliniko, Greece

Tel: 30-1-9931816

PEPSiCO INC.

700 Anderson Hill Road, Purchase, NY, 10577-1444

Tel: (914) 253-2000   Fax: (914) 253-2070   www.pepsico.com

Beverages and snack foods.

PepsiCo IVI SA, Athens, Greece

PFIZER INC.

235 East 42nd Street, New York, NY, 10017-5755

Tel: (212) 573-2323   Fax: (212) 573-7851   www.pfizer.com

Research-based, global health care company.

Pfizer Hellas AE, Athens, Greece

PHARMACIA CORPORATION

100 Route 206 North, Peapack, NJ, 07977

Tel: (908) 901-8000   Fax: (908) 901-8379   www.pharmacia.com

Mfr. pharmaceuticals, agricultural products, industry chemicals.

Pharmacia & Upjohn Hellas S.A., 62-66 Marinou Antypa Str., GR-141 21 Neo Iraklio Athens, Greece

Tel: 30-1-2710-600   Fax: 30-1-2720-075

PHELPS DODGE CORPORATION

2600 North Central Ave., Phoenix, AZ, 85004-3089

Tel:　(602) 234-8100　　　Fax:　(602) 234-8337　　　www.phelpsdodge.com

Copper, minerals, metals and special engineered products for transportation and electrical markets.

Viem Metal Works SA, 115 Kifissias Ave., GR-115-24 Athens, Greece

PIC GROUP

2929 Seventh Avenue, Ste. 130, Berkeley, CA, 94710

Tel:　(510) 848-8266　　　Fax:　(510) 848-0324　　　www.pic.com

Engaged in biotechnology.

PIC Greece, Zoforos SA, 23 Krionerious Avenue, Athens, Greece

PINNACLE WORLDWIDE, INC.

1201 Marquette Ave., Ste. 300, Minneapolis, MN, 55403

Tel:　(612) 338-2215　　　Fax:　(612) 338-2572　　　www.pinnacleww.com

International network of independent public relations firms.

Connective Communication Ltd., V. Sofias Ave., 5 Xenias Str., GR-115-27 Athens, Greece

PIONEER HI-BRED INTERNATIONAL INC.

400 Locust Street, Ste. 800, Des Moines, IA, 50309

Tel:　(515) 248-4800　　　Fax:　(515) 248-4999　　　www.pioneer.com

Agricultural chemicals, farm supplies, biological products, research.

Athens HellaSeed, 15 Fleming Street, Marousi Athens, Greece

PRICEWATERHOUSECOOPERS LLP

1301 Ave. of the Americas, New York, NY, 10019

Tel:　(212) 596-7000　　　Fax:　(212) 259-1301　　　www.pwcglobal.com

Accounting and auditing, tax and management, and human resource consulting services.

PriceWaterhouseCoopers, Europa Plaza, 5th Fl., 330 El Venizelou (Thisseos) Ave., GR-176-75 Kallithea Athens, Greece

Tel: 30-1-9308180　Fax: 30-1-9308182

PROCTER & GAMBLE COMPANY

One Procter & Gamble Plaza, Cincinnati, OH, 45202

Tel:　(513) 983-1100　　　Fax:　(513) 562-4500　　　www.pg.com

Personal care, food, laundry, cleaning and industry products.

Procter & Gamble Hellas SA, 165 Syngrou Ave., GR-171-21 N. Smyrni Athens, Greece

Tel: 30-1-939-4300

QUINTILES TRANSNATIONAL CORPORATION

4709 Creekstone Dr., Durham, NC, 27703

Tel:　(919) 998-2000　　　Fax:　(919) 998-9113　　　www.quintiles.com

Mfr. pharmaceuticals.

Quintiles Athens, Themistocleous 25, GR-151-25 Maroussi Athens, Greece

ROHM AND HAAS COMPANY

100 Independence Mall West, Philadelphia, PA, 19106

Tel:　(215) 592-3000　　　Fax:　(215) 592-3377　　　www.rohmhaas.com

Mfr. specialty chemicals.

Rohm and Haas Greece Ltd., 9 Leontariou St., Alsoupolis, GR-142-35 Nea Ionia Athens, Greece

Tel: 30-1-6843-780

SAATCHI & SAATCHI

375 Hudson St., New York, NY, 10014

Tel:　(212) 463-2000　　　Fax:　(212) 463-9855　　　www.saatchi-saatchi.com

Provides advertising and marketing services.

Adel Saatchi & Saatchi Advertising, Athens, Greece

SANFORD CORPORATION
2711 Washington Boulevard, Bellwood, IL, 60104
Tel: (708) 547-6650   Fax: (708) 547-6719   www.sanfordcorp.com
Mfr. inks, writing, drawing and drafting instruments.
Sanford Hellas GmbH, Amikis Str. 1, GR-11522 Athens, Greece

SCHENKER USA INC.
150 Albany Ave., Freeport, NY, 11520
Tel: (516) 403-5416   Fax: (516) 377-3092   www.schenkerusa.com
Freight forwarders.
Schenker A.E., Zefyrou St., 12 Paleo Faliro, PO Box 77281, Athens, Greece
Tel: 30-1-950-2111   Fax: 30-1-930-1560

SCHERING-PLOUGH CORPORATION
One Giralda Farms, Madison, NJ, 07940-1000
Tel: (973) 822-7000   Fax: (973) 822-7048   www.sch-plough.com
Proprietary drug and cosmetic products.
Schering-Plough Veterinary S.A., 63 Ag. Dimitriou str., GR-174-55 Alimos Athens, Greece

G.D. SEARLE & COMPANY
5200 Old Orchard Road, Skokie, IL, 60077
Tel: (847) 982-7000   Fax: (847) 470-1480   www.searlehealthnet.com
Mfr. pharmaceuticals, health care, optical products and specialty chemicals.
Serale Vianex, 38 Kifissias St., GR-151-25 Athens, Greece
Tel: 30-1-958-8325   Fax: 30-1-958-5078

SNAP-ON INCORPORATED
10801 Corporate Dr., Pleasant Prairie, WI, 53158-1603
Tel: (262) 656-5200   Fax: (262) 656-5577   www.snapon.com
Mfr. auto maintenance, diagnostic and emission testing equipment, hand tools, hydraulic lifts and tire changers.
Snap-On Tools Intl. Ltd., PO Box 65033, GR-154-10 Psychico Athens, Greece

SOLUTIA INC.
575 Maryville Center Dr, St. Louis, MO, 63141
Tel: (314) 674-1000   Fax: (314) 694-8686   www.solutia.com
Mfr. specialty chemical based products.
Solutia Europe SA/NV, Tatoiou 122 and Parthenonos St., GR-146-71 Nea Erithrea Athens, Greece

SONOCO PRODUCTS COMPANY
North Second Street, PO Box 160, Hartsville, SC, 29550
Tel: (843) 383-7000   Fax: (843) 383-7008   www.sonoco.com
Mfr. packaging for consumer and industrial market and recycled paperboard.
Evien (Office), 2-Vas. Georgion St., GR-546-40 Thessaloniki, Greece
Tel: 30-31-84-1474
Evien (Plant), PO Box 96, GR-570-08 Ionia Thessaloniki, Greece
Tel: 30-31-78-0098

SPRAYING SYSTEMS COMPANY
PO Box 7900, Wheaton, IL, 60189-7900
Tel: (630) 665-5000   Fax: (630) 260-0842   www.spray.com
Designs and manufactures industrial spray products.
Spraying Systems Hellas SA, 4 Tziraion Street, GR-117-42 Athens, Greece

SPSS INC.
233 S. Wacker Dr., 11th Fl., Chicago, IL, 60606
Tel: (312) 651-6000   Fax: (312) 329-3668   www.spss.com
Mfr. statistical software.
SPSS BI Greece SA, 74 Panormou Str, GR-115 23 Athens, Greece

THE ST. PAUL COMPANIES, INC.

385 Washington Street, St. Paul, MN, 55102

Tel: (651) 310-7911   Fax: (651) 310-8294   www.stpaul.com

Provides investment, insurance and reinsurance services.

Olympic Victoria General Insurance Co., S.A., 21 Tsimiski, GR-546-24 Thessaloniki, Greece

STANDARD COMMERCIAL CORPORATION

2201 Miller Rd., PO Box 450, Wilson, NC, 27894

Tel: (252) 291-5507   Fax: (252) 237-1109   www.sccgroup.com

Leaf tobacco dealers and processors and wool processors.

Exelka SA, 6 Km Simmachiki Odos, GR-570-13 Paleokastro Thessoloniki, Greece

Transhellenic Tobacco SA, Salonika, Greece

THE STANLEY WORKS

1000 Stanley Drive, PO Box 7000, New Britain, CT, 06053

Tel: (860) 225-5111   Fax: (860) 827-3987   www.stanleyworks.com

Mfr. hand tools and hardware.

The Stanley Works, PO Box 75018, 32 Sfigosstrasse, GR-117 45 Athens, Greece

STIEFEL LABORATORIES INC.

255 Alhambra Circle, Ste. 1000, Coral Gables, FL, 33134

Tel: (305) 443-3807   Fax: (305) 443-3467   www.stiefel.com

Mfr. pharmaceuticals, dermatological specialties.

Stiefel Laboratories SA, PO Box 67247, GR-151-92 Melissia Athens, Greece

SYNAVANT INC.

3445 Peachtree Road NE, Ste. 1400, Atlanta, GA, 30326

Tel: (404) 841-4000   Fax: (404) 841-4115   www.synavant.com

Mfr. support software for pharmaceutical industry.

Synavant, 68 Alimou Avenue, GR-174 55 Alimos, Greece

TBWA WORLDWIDE

488 Madison Avenue, 6th Floor, New York, NY, 10022

Tel: (212) 804-1000   Fax: (212) 804-1200   www.tbwachiat.com

International full service advertising agency.

TBWA Producta, Athens, Greece

THE TRANE COMPANY

3600 Pammel Creek Road, La Crosse, WI, 54601

Tel: (608) 787-2000   Fax: (608) 787-4990   www.trane.com

Mfr. distribution and service of A/C systems and equipment.

Trane Hellas, 7 Zoodohou, Pigis 3, GR-152-31 Halandri Athens, Greece

UNION CARBIDE CORPORATION

39 Old Ridgebury Road, Danbury, CT, 06817

Tel: (203) 794-2000   Fax: (203) 794-6269   www.unioncarbide.com

Mfr. industrial chemicals, plastics and resins.

Union Carbide Middle East Ltd., PO Box Psyhico 65045, GR-154-10 Athens, Greece

UNITED PARCEL SERVICE, INC.

55 Glenlake Parkway, NE, Atlanta, GA, 30328

Tel: (404) 828-6000   Fax: (404) 828-6593   www.ups.com

International package-delivery service.

UPS Greece Inc. - Head Office, 98a Alimou Ave., GR-164-52 Argiroupoli Athens, Greece
Tel: 30-1-9966840

UNITED TECHNOLOGIES CORPORATION

One Financial Plaza, Hartford, CT, 06103

Tel: (860) 728-7000   Fax: (860) 728-7979   www.utc.com

Mfr. aircraft engines, elevators, A/C, auto equipment, space and military electronic and rocket propulsion systems. Products include Pratt and Whitney, Otis elevators, Carrier heating and air conditioning and Sikorsky helicopters.

Carrier Intl. Corp., 2-4 Mesogion St., Athens, Greece

UNIVERSAL CORPORATION

1501 N. Hamilton Street, Richmond, VA, 23230

Tel: (804) 359-9311   Fax: (804) 254-3582   www.universalcorp.com

Holding company for tobacco and commodities.

Gretoba SA, PO Box 169, Thessaloniki, Greece

UUNET

22001 Loudoun County Pkwy., Ashburn, VA, 20147

Tel: (703) 206-5600   Fax: (703) 206-5601   www.uu.net

World's largest Internet service provider; World Wide Web hosting services, security products and consulting services to businesses, professionals, and on-line service providers.

UUNET Hellas, 90 Kifissias Avenue, GR-151-25 Marousi Athens, Greece

VERIZON COMMUNICATIONS INC.

1095 Ave. of the Americas, New York, NY, 10036

Tel: (212) 395-2121   Fax: (212) 395-1285   www.verizon.com

Telecommunications.

STET Hellas Telecommunications S.A., 60 Kifissias Avenue, GR-151-25 Maroussi Athens, Greece

Tel: 30-1-618-6000   Fax: 30-1-610-6504   Contact: Roberto Rovera, CEO

THE VIKING CORPORATION

210 N. Industrial Park Rd., Hastings, MI, 49058

Tel: (616) 945-9501   Fax: (616) 945-9599   www.vikingcorp.com

Mfr. fire extinguishing equipment.

Viking Greece, Karali 19, GR-156-69 Papagou Athens, Greece

THE WACKENHUT CORPORATION

4200 Wackenhut Dr., Ste. 100, Palm Beach Gardens, FL, 33410

Tel: (561) 622-5656   Fax: (561) 691-6736   www.wackenhut.com

Security systems and services.

Wackenhut Security (Hellas) Ltd., 100 Kapodistriou St., GR-142-35 Alsoupolis Athens, Greece

Tel: 30-1-2714-870   Fax: 30-1-2714-500

WENDY'S INTERNATIONAL, INC.

4288 West Dublin Granville Roads, Dublin, OH, 43017-0256

Tel: (614) 764-3100   Fax: (614) 764-3459   www.wendysintl.com

Fast food restaurant chain.

Wendy's International, Athens, Greece

WHIRLPOOL CORPORATION

2000 N. M-63, Benton Harbor, MI, 49022-2692

Tel: (616) 923-5000   Fax: (616) 923-5443   www.whirlpoolcorp.com

Mfr., market home appliances: Whirlpool, Roper, KitchenAid, Estate, and Inglis.

Whirlpool Europe BV, Athens, Greece

WORLD COURIER INC.

45 Southfield Avenue, Ste. 3450, Stamford, CT, 06902-7210

Tel: (203) 975-9333   Fax: (203) 316-9455   www.worldcourier.com

International courier service.

World Courier Hellas, 27 Skoufa St., Athens, Greece

WUNDERMAN

675 Avenue of the Americas, New York, NY, 10010

Tel: (212) 941-3000   Fax: (212) 941-2000   www.wunderman.com

Engaged in direct marketing.

Wunderman Greece, 137 Chrysostomou Smirnis Street, GR-18346 Moshato Athens, Greece

WYETH

5 Giralda Farms, Madison, NJ, 07940-0874

Tel: (973) 660-5000   Fax: (973) 660-7026   www.wyeth.com

Mfr. consumer healthcare products.

Wyeth, Whitehall Div., 517 Vouliagmenis Avenue, 163 41 Ilioupolis, Athens, Greece

WYETH PHARMACEUTICALS

555 E. Lancaster Ave., Wayne, PA, 19087-5109

Tel: (610) 971-5400   Fax: (610) 995-4668   www.wyeth.com

Mfr. antibiotics and pharmaceutical products.

Wyeth Hellas SA, Chrysostomou Smyrnis, 126 Kyprou Ave., Argyroupolis Athens, Greece

Tel: 30-1-998-1600

XEROX CORPORATION

800 Long Ridge Road, PO Box 1600, Stamford, CT, 06904

Tel: (203) 968-3000   Fax: (203) 968-4312   www.xerox.com

Mfr. document processing equipment, systems and supplies.

Rank Xerox Greece SA, 127 Syngrou Ave., Kalithea, GR-117-45 Athens, Greece

Tel: 30-1-931-1000   Fax: 30-1-931-1075

YORK INTERNATIONAL CORPORATION

631 South Richland Ave., York, PA, 17403

Tel: (717) 771-7890   Fax: (717) 771-6212   www.york.com

Mfr. heating, ventilating, air conditioning and refrigeration equipment.

York Hellas S.A., 62 Kifissias Avenue, GR-115-26 Athens, Greece

YOUNG & RUBICAM INC.

285 Madison Ave., New York, NY, 10017

Tel: (212) 210-3000   Fax: (212) 370-3796   www.yr.com

Advertising, public relations, direct marketing and sales promotion, corporate and product ID management.

Geo Young & Rubicam Inc., Athens, Greece

Greenland

DELOITTE TOUCHE TOHMATSU INTERNATIONAL

1633 Broadway, New York, NY, 10019

Tel: (212) 492-4000   Fax: (212) 392-4154   www.deloitte.com

Accounting, audit, tax and management consulting services.

Deloitte & Touche, Postbox 20, Skibshavnsvej 22, 3900 Nuuk, Greenland

DHL WORLDWIDE EXPRESS

50 California Avenue, San Francisco, CA, 94111

Tel: (415) 677-6100   Fax: (415) 824-9700   www.dhl.com

Worldwide air express carrier.

DHL Worldwide Express, CPH CO, Greenland

Tel: 45-7013-1131

POLARIS INDUSTRIES INC.

2100 Highway 55, Medina, MN, 55440

Tel: (612) 542-0500   Fax: (612) 542-0599   www.polarisindustries.com

Mfr. snowmobiles and all-terrain recreational and utility vehicles.

Polaris Import Greenland, Po Box 142, Qivittoqarfik Nr. 17, 3911 Holsteinsborg, Greenland

Contact: Ole Andersen

Grenada

AON CORPORATION

200 East Randolph, Chicago, IL, 60601

Tel: (312) 381-1000   Fax: (312) 381-6032   www.aon.com

Insurance brokers worldwide; underwrites accident and health insurance, specialty and professional insurance; and provides risk management consultation.

AON Worldwide / L.H. Williams Marketing Agency Ltd., Gore St., PO Box 213, St. George's, Grenada

Tel: 471-440-2179   Fax: 471-440-4187   Contact: L.H. Williams

LOUIS BERGER INTERNATIONAL INC.

100 Halsted Street, East Orange, NJ, 07019

Tel: (201) 678-1960   Fax: (201) 672-4284   www.louisberger.com

Consulting engineers, engaged in architecture, environmental and advisory services.

Louis Berger International Inc., PO Box 445, St. George's, Grenada

Tel: 471-444-4687   Fax: 471-444-4822

DHL WORLDWIDE EXPRESS

50 California Avenue, San Francisco, CA, 94111

Tel: (415) 677-6100   Fax: (415) 824-9700   www.dhl.com

Worldwide air express carrier.

DHL Worldwide Express, Carenage, PO Box 188, St. George's, Grenada

Tel: 599-542-952

FRITZ COMPANIES, INC., DIV. UPS

706 Mission Street, Ste. 900, San Francisco, CA, 94103

Tel: (415) 904-8360   Fax: (415) 904-8661   www.fritz.com

Integrated transportation, sourcing, distribution and customs brokerage services.

Fritz Companies Inc., St. George's, Grenada

RENAISSANCE HOTELS AND RESORTS

10400 Fernwood Road, Bethesda, MD, 20817

Tel: (301) 380-3000   Fax: (301) 380-5181   www.renaissancehotels.com

upscale, full-service hotel and resort chain under Marriott International, Inc.

Renaissance Grenada Resort, St. George's, Grenada

Tel: 809-221-2222

Guam

AON CORPORATION

200 East Randolph, Chicago, IL, 60601

Tel: (312) 381-1000   Fax: (312) 381-6032   www.aon.com

Insurance brokers worldwide; underwrites accident and health insurance, specialty and professional insurance; and provides risk management consultation.

AON Insurance Micronesia (Guam) Inc., Aon Building, Hengi Plaza, Tamuning, Guam, 96911

Tel: 671-646-3681   Fax: 671-646-8084   Contact: Garry J. Curran

BRISTOL-MYERS SQUIBB COMPANY

345 Park Ave., New York, NY, 10154-0037

Tel: (212) 546-4000   Fax: (212) 546-4020   www.bms.com

Pharmaceutical and food preparations, medical and surgical instruments.

Bristol-Myers (Guam), PO Box 9007, Tamuning, Guam, 96911

CITIGROUP, INC.

399 Park Avenue, New York, NY, 10022

Tel: (212) 559-1000   Fax: (212) 559-3646   www.citigroup.com

Provides insurance and financial services worldwide.

Citigroup, 402 East Marine Drive, PO Box FF, Agana, Guam, 69632

Tel: 671-475-4121   Contact: Renzo C. Viegas

DELOITTE TOUCHE TOHMATSU INTERNATIONAL

1633 Broadway, New York, NY, 10019

Tel: (212) 492-4000   Fax: (212) 392-4154   www.deloitte.com

Accounting, audit, tax and management consulting services.

Deloitte & Touche, 361 South Marine Drive, Tamuning, Guam, 966911

DHL WORLDWIDE EXPRESS

50 California Avenue, San Francisco, CA, 94111

Tel: (415) 677-6100   Fax: (415) 824-9700   www.dhl.com

Worldwide air express carrier.

DHL Worldwide Express, c/o Republic Express, PO Box 497, Koror Palau, Guam, 96940

Tel: 671-646-1765

EA ENGINEERING, SCIENCE AND TECHNOLOGY

11019 McCormick Road, Hunt Valley, MD, 21031

Tel: (410) 584-7000   Fax: (410) 771-1625   www.eaest.com

Environmental engineering and consulting, pollution control and water resources management.

EA International, Inc., PO Box 4355, AFBB, Yigo, Guam, 96929-4355

EA International, Inc., PO Box 4355, Andersen AFB, Yigo, Guam, 96929

Tel: 671-366-5231   Fax: 671-366-3902   Contact: Joel L. Lazzeri, Installation Mgr.   Emp: 8

EGL INC. (EAGLE GLOBAL LOGISTICS)

15350 Vickery Drive, Houston, TX, 77032

Tel: (281) 618-3100   Fax: (281) 618-3223   www.eagleusa.com

Ocean/air freight forwarding, customs brokerage, packing and wholesale, logistics management and insurance.

EGL Eagle Global Logistics, Harmon Industrial Park, Guam

Tel: 671-649-6291   Fax: 671-649-6290

ERNST & YOUNG INTERNATIONAL

5 Times Square, New York, NY, 10036

Tel: (212) 773-3000   Fax: (212) 773-6350   www.eyi.com

Engaged in assurance and advisory business services, tax, law and corporate finance.

Ernst & Young International, Orlean Pacific Plaza, Ste. B 201, 865 South Marine Drive, Tamuning, Guam, 96911

Tel: 671-649-3700 Fax: 671-649-3920   Contact: Lance Kamigaki

FRITZ COMPANIES, INC., DIV. UPS

706 Mission Street, Ste. 900, San Francisco, CA, 94103

Tel: (415) 904-8360   Fax: (415) 904-8661   www.fritz.com

Integrated transportation, sourcing, distribution and customs brokerage services.

Fritz Companies Inc., Guam

HILTON HOTELS CORPORATION

9336 Civic Center Drive, Beverly Hills, CA, 90210

Tel: (310) 278-4321   Fax: (310) 205-7880   www.hiltonhotels.com

International hotel chain: Hilton International, Vista Hotels and Hilton National Hotels.

Guam Hilton, Tumon Bay, PO Box 11199, Tamuning, Guam, 96931

HYATT CORPORATION

200 West Madison Street, Chicago, IL, 60606

Tel: (312) 750-1234   Fax: (312) 750-8578   www.hyatt.com

International hotel management.

Hyatt Regency Guam Resort, 1155 Pale San Vitores Rd., Tumon, Guam, 96911

Tel: 671-647-1234   Fax: 671-647-1235

KRONOS INCORPORATED

297 Billerica Road, Chelmsford, MA, 01824

Tel: (978) 250-9800   Fax: (978) 367-5900   www.kronos.com

Mfr. timekeeping systems software.

APS, Inc, Suite 118A, Agana Shopping Center, PO Box GH, Agana,, Guam, 96910

LOCKHEED MARTIN CORPORATION

6801 Rockledge Drive, Bethesda, MD, 20817

Tel: (301) 897-6000   Fax: (301) 897-6652   www.imco.com

Design/mfr./management systems in fields of space, defense, energy, electronics and technical services.

Airport Group International, Inc., AB Wonpat Int'l Airport, PO Box 7418, Tamuning, Guam, 96931

MOTOROLA, INC.

1303 East Algonquin Road, Schaumburg, IL, 60196

Tel: (847) 576-5000   Fax: (847) 538-5191   www.motorola.com

Mfr. communications equipment, semiconductors and cellular phones.

Motorola Guam, 215 Rojas No. 123, Harmon, Guam, 96911

Tel: 671-647-6140   Fax: 671-647-6130

OUTBACK STEAKHOUSE, INC.

2202 N. Westshore Blvd. 5th Fl., Tampa, FL, 33607

Tel: (813) 282-1225   Fax: (813) 282-1209   www.outback.com

Chain of casual steak restaurants.

Outback Steakhouse, Inc., 1411 Pale San Vitores, Tamuning, Guam, 96911

Tel: 671-646-1543

PLANET HOLLYWOOD INTERNATIONAL, INC.

8669 Commodity Circle, Orlando, FL, 32819

Tel: (407) 363-7827   Fax: (407) 363-4862   www.planethollywood.com

Theme-dining restaurant chain and merchandise retail stores.

Planet Hollywood International, Inc., Guam

THE SHAW GROUP INC.

4171 Essen Lane, Baton Rouge, LA, 70809

Tel: (225) 932-2500   Fax: (225) 932-2661   www.shawgrp.com

Vertically-integrated provider of complete piping systems, and comprehensive engineering, procurement and construction services.

Shaw Environmental & Infrastructure, Ste. 602, GCIC Bldg., 414 West Soledad Avenue, Hagatna, Guam, 96910-5065

THE ST. PAUL COMPANIES, INC.

385 Washington Street, St. Paul, MN, 55102

Tel: (651) 310-7911   Fax: (651) 310-8294   www.stpaul.com

Provides investment, insurance and reinsurance services.

Moylans Insurance Underwriters, Inc., 101 Agana Shopping Center, Guam

Guatemala

3M (MINNESOTA MINING & MFG.)

3M Center, St. Paul, MN, 55144-1000

Tel: (651) 733-1110   Fax: (651) 733-9973   www.mmm.com

Mfr. diversified products for industry, consumer, health care, imaging, communications, transport, safety, etc.

3M Guatemala SA, Km. 13 Calzada Roosevelt 12-33, Z.3 Mixco, Guatemala City, Guatemala

Tel: 502-2-591-1236   Fax: 502-2-593-4177

ABBOTT LABORATORIES

100 Abbott Park Rd., Abbott Park, IL, 60064

Tel: (847) 937-6100   Fax: (847) 937-1511   www.abbott.com

Development, manufacture and sale of diversified health care products and services.

Abbott Laboratories, S.A., Apartado Postal 37, Guatemala City 01901, Guatemala

AIG AMERICAN INTERNATIONAL GROUP INC.

70 Pine Street, New York, NY, 10270

Tel: (212) 770-7000   Fax: (212) 509-9705   www.aig.com

Worldwide insurance and financial services.

La Compania de Seguros SA, 7 a Av.- 12-23, Zona 9, Edif. Elisa, Nivel 3, Guatemala City, Guatemala

ALBERTO-CULVER COMPANY

2525 Armitage Ave., Melrose Park, IL, 60160

Tel: (708) 450-3000   Fax: (708) 450-3354   www.alberto.com

Mfr./marketing personal care and household brand products.

Alberto-Culver de Guatemala SA, 10a Av. 18-67, Zona 11, Col. Mariscal, Guatemala City, Guatemala

AMERICAN BILTRITE INC.

57 River Street, Wellesley Hills, MA, 02181

Tel: (781) 237-6655   Fax: (781) 237-6880   www.americanbiltriteinc.com

Mfr. vinyl composition and rubber floor coverings and produces pressure sensitive tape and rubber matting.

American Biltrite Guatemala Ltd., Guatemala

AMERICAN STANDARD COMPANIES, INC.

One Centennial Avenue, Piscataway, NJ, 08855-6820

Tel: (732) 980-3000   Fax: (732) 980-6118   www.americanstandard.com

Mfr. automotive, plumbing, heating, air conditioning products and medical diagnostics systems.

Industria Centroamericana de Sanitarios SA, Aptdo. 2553, Guatemala City, Guatemala

AMWAY CORPORATION

7575 Fulton Street East, Ada, MI, 49355-0001

Tel: (616) 787-6000   Fax: (616) 787-6177   www.amway.com

Mfr./sale home care, personal care, nutrition and houseware products.

Amway de Guatemala SA, 7a Av. 6-69, Zona 9, Guatemala City, Guatemala

ANC RENTAL CORPORATION

200 S. Andrews Ave., Ft. Lauderdale, FL, 33301

Tel: (954) 320-4000   Fax: (954) 320-4077   www.ancrental.com

Engaged in car rental services, including National Car Rental and Alamo Rent A Car.

National Car Rental, 14 Calle 1-42, Zona 10, Guatemala City, Guatemala

ANDERSEN

33 West Monroe Street, Chicago, IL, 60603

Tel: (312) 580-0033   Fax: (312) 507-6748   www.andersen.com

*Accounting and audit, tax and management consulting services. **Firm under worldwide reorganization; new data unavailable for this edition.*

Andersen Worldwide, Diagonal 6 10-65, Zona 10, Centro Gerencial Las Margaritas, 50 Nivel, Guatemala City 01010, Guatemala

Tel: 502-2-332-7939

AON CORPORATION

200 East Randolph, Chicago, IL, 60601

Tel: (312) 381-1000   Fax: (312) 381-6032   www.aon.com

Insurance brokers worldwide; underwrites accident and health insurance, specialty and professional insurance; and provides risk management consultation.

AON Worldwide / AISFA (Agencia Independiente de Seg. y Fias), Av. Reforma 6-64, Zona 9, Guatemala City, Guatemala

Tel: 502-2-336-0921   Fax: 502-2-339-0929   Contact: Moises Cupersmith

AVIS GROUP HOLDINGS, INC.

6 Sylvan Way, Parsippany, NJ, 07054

Tel: (973) 222-3000   Fax: (973) 222-4381   www.avis.com

Car rental services.

Avis Group Holdings Ltd., 12 Calle 2-73, Zona 9, Guatemala City, Guatemala

AVON PRODUCTS, INC.

1345 Avenue of the Americas, New York, NY, 10105-0196

Tel: (212) 282-5000   Fax: (212) 282-6049   www.avon.com

Mfr. direct seller of cosmetics and beauty-related items.

Avon Productos de Guatemala, Apartado Postal 3004-A, Guatemala City, Guatemala

Tel: 502-5943-0600   Fax: 502-5943-0589   Contact: Estela Matamoros, Mgr.

BATES WORLDWIDE INC.

498 Seventh Avenue, New York, NY, 10018

Tel: (212) 297-7000   Fax: (212) 986-0270   www.batesww.com

Advertising, marketing, public relations and media consulting.

PM&S Bates CentroAmerica, 4a Av. 15-70, Zona 10, Edif. Paladlum, 10 nival, Of. 10, Guatemala City, Guatemala

Tel: 502-2-366-4384   Fax: 502-2-366-4391   Contact: Armando S. Esponda, Pres.

BDO SEIDMAN, LLP   BELGIUM

130 East Randolph Street, Chicago, IL, 60601

Tel: (312) 856-9100   Fax: (312) 856-1379   www.bdo.com

International accounting and financial consulting firm.

Platero Reyes y Asociados, 12 Calle 2-04, Zona 9, Edif. Plaza del Sol, 4º Nivel, Of. 413, Guatemala City, Guatemala

Tel: 502-2-331-9744   Fax: 502-2-331-4217   Contact: Mauricio Platero

BEST WESTERN INTERNATIONAL

6201 North 24th Place, Phoenix, AZ, 85106

Tel: (602) 957-4200   Fax: (602) 957-5740   www.bestwestern.com

International hotel chain.

BW Royal Palace, 6 Av. 12-66, Zona 1, Guatemala City 01010, Guatemala

Tel: 502-2325-125

BRISTOL-MYERS SQUIBB COMPANY

345 Park Ave., New York, NY, 10154-0037

Tel: (212) 546-4000   Fax: (212) 546-4020   www.bms.com

Pharmaceutical and food preparations, medical and surgical instruments.

Compania Bristol-Myers de Centro America, Blvd. Liberacion 5-55, Zona 9, Guatemala City, Guatemala

LEO BURNETT, DIV. B-COM 3 GROUP

35 West Wacker Drive, Chicago, IL, 60601

Tel: (312) 220-5959   Fax: (312) 220-6533   www.leoburnett.com

Engaged in advertising, marketing, media buying and planning, and public relations.

Leo Burnett - Comunica, 5ta Av. 6-39, Zona 14, Col. El Campo, Guatemala City, Guatemala

CARBOLINE COMPANY

350 Hanley Industrial Court, St. Louis, MO, 63144

Tel: (314) 644-1000   Fax: (314) 644-4617   www.carboline.com

Mfr. coatings and sealants.

Sigma Quimica, 12 Calle 5-34, Zona 1, Guatemala City, Guatemala

CARGILL, INC.

15407 McGinty Road West, Minnetonka, MN, 55440-5625

Tel: (612) 742-7575   Fax: (612) 742-7393   www.cargill.com

Food products, feeds, animal products.

Hohenberg Bros. Ltd., Aptdo. 2857, Guatemala City, Guatemala

CATERPILLAR INC.

100 NE Adams Street, Peoria, IL, 61629-6105

Tel: (309) 675-1000   Fax: (309) 675-1182   www.cat.com

Mfr. earth/material-handling and construction machinery and equipment and engines.

Caterpillar Energy Company, Guatemala

CHESTERTON BLUMENAUER BINSWANGER

Two Logan Square, 4th Floor, Philadelphia, PA, 19103-2759

Tel: (215) 448-6000   Fax: (215) 448-6238   www.cbbi.com

Real estate and related services.

Binswanger Guatemala, Ingenieros Valuadores, 7avenida 3-33, Zona 9, of. 605, Guatemala City, Guatemala

CHEVRON TEXACO CORPORATION

575 Market Street, San Francisco, CA, 94105-2856

Tel: (415) 894-7700   Fax: (415) 894-2248   www.chevrontexaco.com

Oil exploration, production and petroleum products.

ChevronTexaco, Av. Petapa 23-01, Zona 12, Guatemala City, Guatemala

CIGNA COMPANIES

One Liberty Place, Philadelphia, PA, 19192

Tel: (215) 761-1000   Fax: (215) 761-5511   www.cigna.com

Insurance, invest, health care and other financial services.

Empresa Guatemalteco CIGNA de Seguros, S.A., 6a. Ave 20-25, Zona 10, Edi Plaza Maritima, 100 Nivel, Guatemala City 01010, Guatemala

CITIGROUP, INC.

399 Park Avenue, New York, NY, 10022

Tel: (212) 559-1000   Fax: (212) 559-3646   www.citigroup.com

Provides insurance and financial services worldwide.

Citigroup, Ave. Reforma 15-45, Zona 10, Guatemala City, Guatemala

Tel: 502-2-333-6574   Fax: 502-2-333-6860   Contact: Juan Miró, VP & Gen. Mgr.

THE COCA-COLA COMPANY

1 Coca Cola Plaza, Atlanta, GA, 30313

Tel: (404) 676-2121   Fax: (404) 676-6792   www.coca-cola.com

Mfr./marketing/distributor soft drinks, syrups and concentrates, juice and juice-drink products.

Industria de Cafe, Guatemala

COLGATE-PALMOLIVE COMPANY

300 Park Ave., New York, NY, 10022

Tel: (212) 310-2000 Fax: (212) 310-2919 www.colgate.com

Mfr. pharmaceuticals, cosmetics, toiletries and detergents.

Colgate-Palmolive (Central America) Inc., Av. del Ferrocarril 49-65, Zona 12, Guatemala City, Guatemala

CONTINENTAL AIRLINES INC.

1600 Smith St., Houston, TX, 77002

Tel: (713) 324-5000 Fax: (713) 324-2637 www.continental.com

International airline carrier.

Continental Airlines Inc., Guatemala

DANZAS AEI, INC.

120 Tokeneke Road, PO Box 1231, Darien, CT, 06820

Tel: (203) 655-7900 Fax: (203) 655-5779 www.aeilogistics.com

International air freight forwarder.

Danzas AEI, c/o Comar Guatemala, 24 Ave. 41-81, Zona 12, Interior Almacendora Integrada, Guatemala City, Guatemala

Tel: 502-4743-3686 Fax: 502-4743-3697

D'ARCY MASIUS BENTON & BOWLES INC. (DMB&B)

1675 Broadway, New York, NY, 10019

Tel: (212) 468-3622 Fax: (212) 468-2987 www.darcyww.com

Full service international advertising and communications group.

DMBB Dos Puntos, 17 Av. 42-26, Zona 8, Guatemala City, Guatemala

Tel: 502-471-8262 Fax: 502-472-5103 Contact: Estuardo Aguilar, Pres.

DDB WORLDWIDE COMMUNICATIONS GROUP

437 Madison Ave., New York, NY, 10022

Tel: (212) 415-2000 Fax: (212) 415-3417 www.ddbn.com

Advertising agency.

Publinac DDB, Guatemala City, Guatemala

DELOITTE TOUCHE TOHMATSU INTERNATIONAL

1633 Broadway, New York, NY, 10019

Tel: (212) 492-4000 Fax: (212) 392-4154 www.deloitte.com

Accounting, audit, tax and management consulting services.

Lara & Coyoy, CPA, 7a. Av. 7-07, Zona 9, 4 Nivel, Apartado Postal 646-A, Guatemala City, Guatemala

DHL WORLDWIDE EXPRESS

50 California Avenue, San Francisco, CA, 94111

Tel: (415) 677-6100 Fax: (415) 824-9700 www.dhl.com

Worldwide air express carrier.

DHL Worldwide Express, 7a. Av. 2-42, Zona 9, Guatemala City 01009, Guatemala

Tel: 502-2-323023

THE DIAL CORPORATION

15501 North Dial Blvd., Scottsdale, AZ, 85260-1619

Tel: (480) 754-3425 Fax: (480) 754-1098 www.dialcorp.com

Mfr. soaps, detergents, air fresheners, specialty personal care products and Armour Star canned meats.

International Soap & Cosmetics (ISC), 10 Ave. 5-49, Zona 14, Guatemala City 01014, Guatemala

Tel: 502-366-6880 Fax: 502-337-2537

DIMON INCORPORATED

512 Bridge Street, PO Box 681, Danville, VA, 24543-0681

Tel: (804) 792-7511 Fax: (804) 791-0377 www.dimon.com

One of world's largest importer and exporters of leaf tobacco.

DIMON Guatemala S.A., Km. 12.5 Carretera A Villa Canales, Boca del Monte, Guatemala City, Guatemala

DOVER CORPORATION

280 Park Ave., New York, NY, 10017-1292

Tel: (212) 922-1640   Fax: (212) 922-1656   www.dovercorporation.com

Holding company for varied industries; assembly and testing equipment, oil-well gear and other industrial products.

De Elevadores, S.A. - Eveva Compañia Internacional, 14 Ave. 15-01, Zona 12, Guatemala City, Guatemala

Tel: 502-473-0362   Fax: 502-473-1092

Guatemale, C.A., 3a. Ave. 16-38, Zona 10, Guatemala City, Guatemala

Tel: 502-268-1315   Fax: 502-63-1745

THE DOW CHEMICAL COMPANY

2030 Dow Center, Midland, MI, 48674

Tel: (989) 636-1000   Fax: (989) 636-3228   www.dow.com

Mfr. chemicals, plastics, pharmaceuticals, agricultural products, consumer products.

Dow Quimica de Guatemala Ltda., Guatemala City, Guatemala

ECOLAB INC.

370 N. Wabasha Street, St. Paul, MN, 55102

Tel: (651) 293-2233   Fax: (651) 293-2379   www.ecolab.com

Develop/mfr. premium cleaning, sanitizing and maintenance products and services for the hospitality, institutional, and residential markets.

Ecolab Ltd., Guatemala City, Guatemala

Tel: 502-2-599-3697

EGL INC. (EAGLE GLOBAL LOGISTICS)

15350 Vickery Drive, Houston, TX, 77032

Tel: (281) 618-3100   Fax: (281) 618-3223   www.eagleusa.com

Ocean/air freight forwarding, customs brokerage, packing and wholesale, logistics management and insurance.

EGL Eagle Global Logistics, Edif. Galerias Reforma, Av. Reforma 8-60, Zona 9. Of. 319, Guatemala City, Guatemala

Tel: 502-2-394-037   Fax: 502-2-394-039

ENRON CORPORATION

1400 Smith Street, Houston, TX, 77002-7369

Tel: (713) 853-6161   Fax: (713) 853-3129   www.enron.com

*Exploration, production, transportation and distribution of integrated natural gas and electricity. **Corporation under worldwide reorganization; new data unavailable for this edition.*

Puerto Quetzal Power Corp., Km 112 Carretera A Iztapa, Puerto Quetzal Escuintla, Guatemala

ERNST & YOUNG INTERNATIONAL

5 Times Square, New York, NY, 10036

Tel: (212) 773-3000   Fax: (212) 773-6350   www.eyi.com

Engaged in assurance and advisory business services, tax, law and corporate finance.

Lizarralde, Ayestas, Asturias y Ramos Ernst & Young, 13 Calle 1-51, Zona 10, Guatemala City, Guatemala

Tel: 502-2-321-249   Fax: 502-2-315-687   Contact: Carlos Asturias

FEDERAL-MOGUL CORPORATION

26555 Northwestern Highway, PO Box 1966, Southfield, MI, 48034

Tel: (248) 354-7700   Fax: (248) 354-8983   www.federal-mogul.com

Mfr./distributor precision parts for automobiles, trucks, farm and construction vehicles.

Federal-Mogul de Guatemala SA, Guatemala

FERRO CORPORATION

1000 Lakeside Ave., Cleveland, OH, 44114-7000

Tel: (216) 641-8580   Fax: (216) 696-5784   www.ferro.com

Mfr. Specialty chemicals, coatings, plastics, colors, refractories.

J.C. Niemann (Rep), Calle Mariscal Cruz 10-69, Zone 5, Guatemala City, Guatemala

Tel: 502-2-315454   Contact: Juan Niemann

FRITZ COMPANIES, INC., DIV. UPS

706 Mission Street, Ste. 900, San Francisco, CA, 94103

Tel: (415) 904-8360 Fax: (415) 904-8661 www.fritz.com

Integrated transportation, sourcing, distribution and customs brokerage services.

Fritz Companies Inc., Guatemala City, Guatemala

H.B. FULLER COMPANY

1200 Willow Lake Blvd., Vadnais Heights, MN, 55110

Tel: (651) 236-5900 Fax: (651) 236-5898 www.hbfuller.com

Mfr./distributor adhesives, sealants, coatings, paints, waxes, sanitation chemicals.

Kativo de Guatemala SA, Guatemala City 2061, Guatemala

Tel: 502-2-477-4873 Fax: 502-2-477-5393

THE GILLETTE COMPANY

Prudential Tower Building, Boston, MA, 02199

Tel: (617) 421-7000 Fax: (617) 421-7123 www.gillette.com

Develop/mfr. personal care/use products: blades and razors, toiletries, cosmetics, stationery.

Gillette de Centro America SA, Guatemala City, Guatemala

Jafra Cosmeticos de Guatemala SA, Guatemala City, Guatemala

THE GOODYEAR TIRE & RUBBER COMPANY

1144 East Market Street, Akron, OH, 44316

Tel: (330) 796-2121 Fax: (330) 796-1817 www.goodyear.com

Mfr. tires, automotive belts and hose, conveyor belts, chemicals; oil pipeline transmission.

Gran Industrial de Neumaticos Centroamericana SA, Aptdo. 1946, 50 Calle 23-70, Zona 12, Guatemala City 01012, Guatemala

GRANT THORNTON INTERNATIONAL

800 One Prudential Plaza, 130 E. Randolph Drive, Chicago, IL, 60601-6050

Tel: (312) 856-0001 Fax: (312) 616-7052 www.grantthornton.com

Accounting, audit, tax and management consulting services.

Grant Thornton - Pineda Tezo Y Asociados, S.C., 15 Avda 15-81, Zona 13, Guatemala City, Guatemala

Contact: Sergio L. Pineda

GREY GLOBAL GROUP

777 Third Ave., New York, NY, 10017

Tel: (212) 546-2000 Fax: (212) 546-1495 www.grey.com

International advertising agency.

Tobar & Conde Publicidad, Guatemala City, Guatemala

GRIFFITH LABORATORIES INC.

One Griffith Center, Alsip, IL, 60658

Tel: (708) 371-0900 Fax: (708) 597-3294 www.griffithlabs.com

Mfr. industrial food ingredients and equipment.

Griffith Labs Inc., Guatemala City, Guatemala

Tel: 502-2-223-8643 Fax: 502-2-234-0555

GUILFORD MILLS INC.

4925 West Market Street, PO Box 26969, Greensboro, NC, 27407

Tel: (336) 316-4000 Fax: (336) 316-4059 www.guilfordmills.com

Mfr. textiles.

Guilford Mills, Inc., 2nd Avenida 10-37, Zona 10, Guatemala

Tel: 502-261-0437 Fax: 502-261-0447 Contact: Venicio Savedra

HALLIBURTON COMPANY

500 North Akard Street, Ste. 3600, Dallas, TX, 75201-3391

Tel: (214) 978-2600   Fax: (214) 978-2685   www.halliburton.com

Engaged in diversified energy services, engineering and construction.

Halliburton Ltd., 2 a. Calle 15-96, Zona 13, 01013 Ciudad de Guatemala, Guatemala

Tel: 502-2-318-185   Fax: 502-2-325-096

HORWATH INTERNATIONAL ASSOCIATION

420 Lexington Avenue, Suite 526, New York, NY, 10170-0526

Tel: (212) 808-2000   Fax: (212) 808-2020   www.horwath.com

Public accountants and auditors.

Bocanegra, Cruz y Associados, Ave Reforma 1-50, Zona 9, Edif. El Reformador, Nivel 4, Guatemala City, Guatemala

HYATT CORPORATION

200 West Madison Street, Chicago, IL, 60606

Tel: (312) 750-1234   Fax: (312) 750-8578   www.hyatt.com

International hotel management.

Hyatt Regency Guatemala Hotel, Calzada Roosevelt 22-43, Zona 11, Guatamala City, Guatemala

Tel: 502-440-1234   Fax: 502-440-4050

IBM CORPORATION

1133 Westchester Avenue, White Plains, NY, 10604

Tel: (914) 765-1900   Fax: (914) 765-7382   www.ibm.com

Information products, technology and services.

IBM de Guatemala SA, Guatemala City, Guatemala

IMATION CORPORATION

One Imation Place, Oakdale, MN, 55128

Tel: (612) 704-4000   Fax: (612) 704-3444   www.imation.com

Dry laser-imaging film systems.

Imation de Guatemala, S.A., Calzada Roosevelt 22-43, Zona 11, Edificio Tikal Futura, Torre Sol, Nivel, Piso 7, Oficina 70, Guatemala City, Guatemala

INFORMATION RESOURCES, INC. (IRI)

150 N. Clinton St., Chicago, IL, 60661

Tel: (312) 726-1221   Fax: (312) 726-0360   www.infores.com

Provides bar code scanner services for retail sales organizations; processes, analyzes and sells data from the huge database created from these services.

Grupo de Servicios de Informacion, SA GSI/IRI, Plaza GSI, 5 Av. 6-39, Zona 14, Condominio Las Plazas, Guatemala City, Guatemala

Tel: 502-337-3751   Fax: 502-337-3744

IRRIDELCO INTERNATIONAL CORPORATION

440 Sylvan Ave., Englewood Cliffs, NJ, 07632

Tel: (201) 569-3030   Fax: (201) 569-9237   www.irridelco.com

Mfr. and distributor of the most comprehensive lines of mechanical and micro irrigation; pumps and irrigation systems.

IDC Guatemala, 13 Calle B - 4-50, Zona 3, Guatemala City, Guatemala

Tel: 502-251-4354   Fax: 502-202-3274   Contact: Leonel Santa Cruz

J. WALTER THOMPSON COMPANY

466 Lexington Ave., New York, NY, 10017

Tel: (212) 210-7000   Fax: (212) 210-6944   www.jwt.com

International advertising and marketing services.

APCU-Thompson, Guatemala City, Guatemala

JOHNSON & JOHNSON

One Johnson & Johnson Plaza, New Brunswick, NJ, 08933

Tel: (732) 524-0400   Fax: (732) 214-0334   www.jnj.com

Mfr./distributor/R&D pharmaceutical, health care and cosmetic products.

Johnson & Johnson Guatemala SA, Aptdo. 2067, Guatemala City, Guatemala

KELLOGG COMPANY

One Kellogg Square, PO Box 3599, Battle Creek, MI, 49016-3599

Tel: (616) 961-2000   Fax: (616) 961-2871   www.kelloggs.com

Mfr. ready-to-eat cereals and convenience foods.

Kellogg's de Centro America SA, Attn: Guatemalan Office, One Kellogg Square, PO Box 3599, Battle Creek, MI, 49016-3599

KOPPERS INDUSTRIES INC.

436 Seventh Ave., Pittsburgh, PA, 15219-1800

Tel: (412) 227-2000   Fax: (412) 227-2333   www.koppers.com

Construction materials and services; chemicals and building products.

Impregnadora de Madera de Guatemala SA, 8a Calle 2-31, Zona l, Guatemala City, Guatemala

KPMG CONSULTING INC.

1676 International Dr., McLean, VA, 22102

Tel: (703) 747-3000   Fax: (703) 747-8500   www.kpmg.com

Accounting and audit, tax and management consulting services.

KPMG Aldana, Salazar, Garcia & Asociados, Centro Financiero, Torre I, Nivel 16, 7a. Av. 5-10, Zona 4, Guatemala City, Guatemala

Tel: 502-334-2628   Fax: 502-331-5477   Contact: Arturo Aldana, Sr. Ptnr.

LANIER WORLDWIDE, INC.

2300 Parklake Drive, N.E., Atlanta, GA, 30345

Tel: (770) 496-9500   Fax: (770) 938-1020   www.lanier.com

Specialize in digital copiers and multi-functional systems.

Lanier de Guatemala, S.A., 5a. Av. 11-24, Zona 9, PO Box 885 A, Guatemala City, Guatemala

Tel: 502-2-331-8083   Fax: 502-2-331-4770

MARRIOTT INTERNATIONAL INC.

10400 Fernwood Rd., Bethesda, MD, 20817

Tel: (301) 380-3000   Fax: (301) 380-5181   www.marriott.com

Hotel services.

Guatemala City Marriott, Guatemala City, Guatemala

Tel: 502-2-331-2070

MARSH & McLENNAN COS INC.

1166 Ave. of the Americas, New York, NY, 10036-2774

Tel: (212) 345-5000   Fax: (212) 345-4808   www.marshmac.com

Insurance agents/brokers, pension and investment management consulting services.

Consultores de Seguros S.A., 2 Avenuda 8-48, Zona 9, Edif. Profesional, 2 Nivel, Guatemala City 01009, Guatemala

Tel: 502-2-239-2595   Fax: 502-2-239-2596

Tecniseguros Cia. Ltda., Av. Reforma 9-00, zona 9, Edif. Plaza Panamericana, 6o. Nivel, Guatemala City, Guatemala

Tel: 502-2-332-1555   Fax: 502-2-331-1917   Contact: Enrique Fernandez B.

MARY KAY COSMETICS INC.

16251 No. Dallas Pkwy, Dallas, TX, 75248

Tel: (972) 687-6300   Fax: (972) 687-1609   www.marykay-cosmetic.com

Mfr. and direct sales of cosmetics and toiletries.

Masdel S.A. Mary Kay, 6a Calle 1-41, Zona 9, Guatemala City, Guatemala

McCANN-ERICKSON WORLDGROUP

750 Third Ave., New York, NY, 10017

Tel: (212) 697-6000   Fax: (212) 984-3575   www.mccann.com

International advertising and marketing services.

McCann-Erickson Centroamericana (Guatemala) SA, Aptdo. 390, 7a Av. 5-10, Zona 4, Centro Financiero, Torre 11, Guatemala City, Guatemala

MERLE NORMAN COSMETICS INC.

9130 Bellance Ave., Los Angeles, CA, 90045

Tel: (310) 641-3000   Fax: (310) 641-7144   www.merlenorman.com

Mfr., sales and distribution of cosmetics.

Merle Norman Cosmetics, 1600 Calle 200, Zone 145, Central, Guatemala

MONSANTO

800 N. Lindbergh Boulevard, St. Louis, MO, 63167

Tel: (314) 694-1000   Fax: (314) 694-7625   www.monsanto.com

Life sciences company focusing on agriculture, nutrition, pharmaceuticals, health and wellness and sustainable development.

Monsanto Guatemala Inc., Edificio Columbus Center, Nivel 13, Avenida Las Americas 18-891, Zona 14, Ciudad de Guatemala, Guatemala

J. P. MORGAN CHASE & CO. INC.

270 Park Ave., New York, NY, 10017

Tel: (212) 270-6000   Fax: (212) 622-9030   www.jpmorganchase.com

Provides integrated financial solutions for institutions and individuals worldwide, including asset management, investment banking and commercial banking.

J. P. Morgan Chase & Co., Aptdo. 40-F, Guatemala City, Guatemala

MYERS INTERNATIONAL INC.

1293 South Main Street, Akron, OH, 44301

Tel: (330) 253-5592   Fax: (330) 253-0035   www.myerstiresupply.com

Mfr. tire retreading and maintenance equipment and supplies.

Orientadores Comerciales S.A., Myers De Guatemala, 3 ra Calle 5-49, Zona 9, Guatemala

Tel: 502-360-0608   Fax: 502-360-0628

NORDSON CORPORATION

28601 Clemens Road, Westlake, OH, 44145-4551

Tel: (440) 892-1580   Fax: (440) 892-9507   www.nordson.com

Mfr. industry application equipment, sealants and packaging machinery.

Maquinsa, 10 Calle 0-78, Zona 14, Plaza San Judas, Of. 201, Guatemala, C.A. 01014, Guatemala

PAN-AMERICAN LIFE INSURANCE COMPANY

Pan American Life Center, 601 Poydras St., New Orleans, LA, 70130-0219

Tel: (504) 566-1300   Fax: (504) 566-3600   www.panamericanlife.com

Insurance services.

Compania de Seguros Panamericana SA, Edif. Plaza Panamericana, Av. Reforma 9-00, Zona 9, Guatemala City, Guatemala

Tel: 502-2-332-5922   Fax: 502-2-331-5026   Contact: Salvador Ortega, VP & Gen. Mgr.   Emp: 95

PAPA JOHN'S INTERNATIONAL, INC.

2002 Papa John's Blvd., Louisville, KY, 40299-2334

Tel: (502) 266-5200   Fax: (502) 266-2925   www.papajohns.com

Retailer and pizza franchiser.

Papa John's International Inc., Anillo Periférico, Zona 11, Centro Comercial Las Majadas, Local 27, Cd. de Guatemala, Guatemala

Tel: 502-474-2441

PENETONE CORPORATION

74 Hudson Avenue, Tenafly, NJ, 07670

Tel: (201) 567-3000   Fax: (201) 569-5340   www.west-penetone.com

Sanitary equipment and supplies.

West Chemical Products de Guatemala, 3a Calle 10-25, Zona 12, Guatemala City, Guatemala

PEPSiCO INC.

700 Anderson Hill Road, Purchase, NY, 10577-1444

Tel: (914) 253-2000   Fax: (914) 253-2070   www.pepsico.com

Beverages and snack foods.

PepsiCo Interamericana de Guatemala SA, Guatemala

PHARMACIA CORPORATION

100 Route 206 North, Peapack, NJ, 07977

Tel: (908) 901-8000   Fax: (908) 901-8379   www.pharmacia.com

Mfr. pharmaceuticals, agricultural products, industry chemicals.

Pharmacia & Upjohn, S.A., Tikal Futura, Torre sol, Nivel 19, Calzada Roosevelt 22-43, Zona 11, Guatemala City 01011, Guatemala

Tel: 502-440-4250

PHELPS DODGE CORPORATION

2600 North Central Ave., Phoenix, AZ, 85004-3089

Tel: (602) 234-8100   Fax: (602) 234-8337   www.phelpsdodge.com

Copper, minerals, metals and special engineered products for transportation and electrical markets.

Fabrica de Conductores Elecricos, Apartado Postal 2856, Guatemala City, Guatemala

PHILIP MORRIS COMPANIES, INC.

120 Park Ave., New York, NY, 10017

Tel: (917) 663-5000   Fax: (917) 663-2167   www.philipmorris.com

Mfr. cigarettes and tobacco and consumer food products (Kraft Foods).

Nabisco Royal Guatemala, KM 13.5 Carretera Roosevelt, 12 Av. 0-68, Zona 2, Guatemala City, Guatemala

PRICEWATERHOUSECOOPERS LLP

1301 Ave. of the Americas, New York, NY, 10019

Tel: (212) 596-7000   Fax: (212) 259-1301   www.pwcglobal.com

Accounting and auditing, tax and management, and human resource consulting services.

PriceWaterhouseCoopers, Edif. Tivoli Plaza 6a, Calle 6-38, AP 868 Guatemala City 9, Guatemala

Tel: 502-2-345080   Fax: 502-2-312819

PROCTER & GAMBLE COMPANY

One Procter & Gamble Plaza, Cincinnati, OH, 45202

Tel: (513) 983-1100   Fax: (513) 562-4500   www.pg.com

Personal care, food, laundry, cleaning and industry products.

Procter & Gamble, Diagonal 6 10-65, Nivel 16, Centro Gerencial Las Margaritas, Zona 10, Guatemala City 01010, Guatemala

RAYOVAC CORPORATION

601 Rayovac Drive, Madison, WI, 53711-2497

Tel: (608) 275-3340   Fax: (608) 275-4577   www.rayovac.com

Mfr. batteries and lighting devices.

Rayovac Guatemala S.A., Avenida Hincapié 14-71 Zona 13, Guatemala City, Guatemala

RIVIANA FOODS INC.

2777 Allen Parkway, 15th Fl., Houston, TX, 77019

Tel: (713) 529-3251   Fax: (713) 529-1661   www.rivianafoods.com

Process, market and distribute branded and private-label rice products.

Alimentos Kern de Guatemala SA, Km. 6.5 Carretera al Atlantico, Zona 18, Guatemala City 01018, Guatemala

RUDDICK CORPORATION

301 S. Tryon St., Ste. 1800, Charlotte, NC, 28202

Tel: (704) 372-5404   Fax: (704) 372-6409   www.amefird.com

Mfr. industrial sewing thread for worldwide industrial and consumer markets.

Hilos A&E de Guatemala, Lote 7-B, Parque Industrial Zeta, La Union SA, Zona Franca, Autopista A Amatitlan KM30, Guatemala

SCHENKER USA INC.

150 Albany Ave., Freeport, NY, 11520

Tel: (516) 403-5416   Fax: (516) 377-3092   www.schenkerusa.com

Freight forwarders.

Schenker Internacional, SA, 5 Ave. 3-30, Zone 13, PO Box 1159, Guatemala City 01901, Guatemala

Tel: 502-475-4260   Fax: 502-475-4259

SEARS ROEBUCK & COMPANY

3333 Beverly Road, Hoffman Estates, IL, 60179

Tel: (847) 286-2500   Fax: (847) 286-1517   www.sears.com

Diversified general merchandise.

Sears Roebuck SA, Aptdo. 513, Guatemala City, Guatemala

SENSIENT TECHNOLOGIES CORPORATION

777 E. Wisconsin Ave., Milwaukee, WI, 53202

Tel: (414) 271-6755   Fax: (414) 347-4783   www.sensient.com

Mfr. flavor applications for the beverage, bakery, confection, dairy, snack and savory markets.

Levaduras Universal, Km. 16 Carretera Roosevelt, Guatemala City, Guatemala

THE STANLEY WORKS

1000 Stanley Drive, PO Box 7000, New Britain, CT, 06053

Tel: (860) 225-5111   Fax: (860) 827-3987   www.stanleyworks.com

Mfr. hand tools and hardware.

Stanley Latin America, Edif. Epresariales Montemaria, Oficina 120, Zona 11, Calzada Aguilar Batres 45-54, Guatemala City, Guatemala

STARWOOD HOTELS & RESORTS WORLDWIDE

777 Westchester Avenue, White Plains, NY, 10604

Tel: (914) 640-8100   Fax: (914) 640-8316   www.starwoodhotels.com

Hotel operations including Sheraton, Westin, St. Regis, Four Points and Caesars.

Conquistador Sheraton Hotel, Via 5 4-68, Zona 4, Guatemala City, Guatemala

U.S. WHEAT ASSOCIATES

1620 "I" Street NW, Ste. 801, Washington, DC, 20006-4005

Tel: (202) 463-0999   Fax: (202) 785-1052   www.uswheat.org

Market development for wheat products.

U.S. Wheat Associates Inc., 15 Av. A 3-67, Zona 13, Guatemala City, Guatemala

UAL CORPORATION

1200 E. Algonquin Rd., Chicago, IL, 60007

Tel: (847) 700-4000   Fax: (847) 700-4081   www.ual.com

Air transportation, passenger and freight services.

United Airlines, Guatemala

UNION CARBIDE CORPORATION

39 Old Ridgebury Road, Danbury, CT, 06817

Tel: (203) 794-2000   Fax: (203) 794-6269   www.unioncarbide.com

Mfr. industrial chemicals, plastics and resins.

Union Carbide Guatemala, Guatemala City, Guatemala

UNITED PARCEL SERVICE, INC.

55 Glenlake Parkway, NE, Atlanta, GA, 30328

Tel: (404) 828-6000   Fax: (404) 828-6593   www.ups.com

International package-delivery service.

UPS / Courier Internacional S.A., 12 Calle 5-53, Zona 10, Guatemala City, Guatemala

Tel: 502-2-360-6470   Fax: 502-2-332-6607

THE WACKENHUT CORPORATION

4200 Wackenhut Dr., Ste. 100, Palm Beach Gardens, FL, 33410

Tel: (561) 622-5656   Fax: (561) 691-6736   www.wackenhut.com

Security systems and services.

Wackenhut de Guatemala SA (WAGSA), Calle 14 8-51, Zona 10, Barrio Santa Clara, Guatemala

Tel: 502-2-335803   Fax: 502-2-634560

Wackenhut Electronics S.A., 14 Calle 7-49, Zona 9, 2ndo Nivel, Interior, Portal Belmont, Guatemala

Tel: 502-344834   Fax: 502-317553

WENDY'S INTERNATIONAL, INC.

4288 West Dublin Granville Roads, Dublin, OH, 43017-0256

Tel: (614) 764-3100   Fax: (614) 764-3459   www.wendysintl.com

Fast food restaurant chain.

Wendy's International, Guatemala

WORLD COURIER INC.

45 Southfield Avenue, Ste. 3450, Stamford, CT, 06902-7210

Tel: (203) 975-9333   Fax: (203) 316-9455   www.worldcourier.com

International courier service.

World Courier Guatemala SA, Edif. el Triangulo, 7a Av. 6-53, Zona 4, Guatemala City, Guatemala

WORLDXCHANGE COMMUNICATIONS

9999 Willow Creek Road, San Diego, CA, 92131

Tel: (858) 547-4933   Fax: (800) 995-4502   www.worldxchange.com

Provides international, long distance telecommunications services worldwide.

WorldxChange Communications S.A., Guatemala

XEROX CORPORATION

800 Long Ridge Road, PO Box 1600, Stamford, CT, 06904

Tel: (203) 968-3000   Fax: (203) 968-4312   www.xerox.com

Mfr. document processing equipment, systems and supplies.

Xerox De Guatemala, S.A., Av. Hincapie 14-71, Zona 13, Ciudad De Guatemala 01013, Guatemala

Tel: 502-2-334-4811   Fax: 501-2-334-4876

YOUNG & RUBICAM INC.

285 Madison Ave., New York, NY, 10017

Tel: (212) 210-3000   Fax: (212) 370-3796   www.yr.com

Advertising, public relations, direct marketing and sales promotion, corporate and product ID management.

Eco Young & Rubicam, Guatemala City, Guatemala

Guinea

ALCOA INC.
Alcoa Center, 201 Isabella Street at 7th Street Bridge, Pittsburgh, PA, 15212-5858
Tel: (412) 553-4545   Fax: (412) 553-4498   www.alcoa.com
World's leading producer of aluminum and alumina; mining, refining, smelting, fabricating and recycling.
Halco (Mining), Inc., Sangaredi, Guinea

LOUIS BERGER INTERNATIONAL INC.
100 Halsted Street, East Orange, NJ, 07019
Tel: (201) 678-1960   Fax: (201) 672-4284   www.louisberger.com
Consulting engineers, engaged in architecture, environmental and advisory services.
Louis Berger International Inc., Immeuble de M. Fofana, Quartier Camayenne, Boite Postale 383, Conakry, Guinea
Tel: 224-462023   Fax: 224-462023

THE COCA-COLA COMPANY
1 Coca Cola Plaza, Atlanta, GA, 30313
Tel: (404) 676-2121   Fax: (404) 676-6792   www.coca-cola.com
Mfr./marketing/distributor soft drinks, syrups and concentrates, juice and juice-drink products.
Bonagui, Guinea

DHL WORLDWIDE EXPRESS
50 California Avenue, San Francisco, CA, 94111
Tel: (415) 677-6100   Fax: (415) 824-9700   www.dhl.com
Worldwide air express carrier.
DHL Worldwide Express, 4 blvd Ave. de la Republique, Conakry, Guinea
Tel: 224-411766

ERNST & YOUNG INTERNATIONAL
5 Times Square, New York, NY, 10036
Tel: (212) 773-3000   Fax: (212) 773-6350   www.eyi.com
Engaged in assurance and advisory business services, tax, law and corporate finance.
FFA Ernst & Young, Immeuble SAADI, Ave. de la Republique, B.P. 1762, Conakry, Guinea
Tel: 224-41-28-31   Fax: 224-41-28-31

OCEANEERING INTERNATIONAL INC.
11911 FM 529, Houston, TX, 77041
Tel: (713) 329-4500   Fax: (713) 329-4951   www.oceaneering.com
Transportation equipment, underwater service to offshore oil and gas industry.
Oceaneering Inc., Aeropuerto Carreterra KM 5, Malabo, Equatorial Guinea, APDO 925 Correos, Guinea

TRANSOCEAN INC.
4 Greenway Plaza, Houston, TX, 77046
Tel: (713) 232-7500   Fax: (713) 232-7027   www.deepwater.com
Engaged in oil and gas offshore drilling.
Transocean Inc., Banapa Street, Carretera de Luba, Malabo, Guinea
Transocean Inc., Banapa Street, Carretera de Luba, Malabo, Guinea

XEROX CORPORATION
800 Long Ridge Road, PO Box 1600, Stamford, CT, 06904
Tel: (203) 968-3000   Fax: (203) 968-4312   www.xerox.com
Mfr. document processing equipment, systems and supplies.
Xeroguinee, BP 114, Conakry, Guinea
Tel: 224-414-774   Fax: 224-414-803

Guyana

AON CORPORATION
200 East Randolph, Chicago, IL, 60601

Tel: (312) 381-1000   Fax: (312) 381-6032   www.aon.com

Insurance brokers worldwide; underwrites accident and health insurance, specialty and professional insurance; and provides risk management consultation.

AON Worldwide / Insurance Brokers-Guyana Ltd., 125 Carmichael St., South Cummingsburg, PO Box 10750, Georgetown, Guyana

Tel: 592-2-67261   Fax: 592-2-53187   Contact: E.W. Adams

CHEVRON TEXACO CORPORATION
575 Market Street, San Francisco, CA, 94105-2856

Tel: (415) 894-7700   Fax: (415) 894-2248   www.chevrontexaco.com

Oil exploration, production and petroleum products.

ChevtonTexaco West Indies Ltd., 45 Main Street, Georgetown, Guyana

COLGATE-PALMOLIVE COMPANY
300 Park Ave., New York, NY, 10022

Tel: (212) 310-2000   Fax: (212) 310-2919   www.colgate.com

Mfr. pharmaceuticals, cosmetics, toiletries and detergents.

Colgate-Palmolive (Guyana) Ltd., R.1 Ruimveldt, Georgetown, Guyana

DELOITTE TOUCHE TOHMATSU INTERNATIONAL
1633 Broadway, New York, NY, 10019

Tel: (212) 492-4000   Fax: (212) 392-4154   www.deloitte.com

Accounting, audit, tax and management consulting services.

Deloitte & Touche, 77 Brickdam, PO Box 10506, Stabroek Georgetown, Guyana

DHL WORLDWIDE EXPRESS
50 California Avenue, San Francisco, CA, 94111

Tel: (415) 677-6100   Fax: (415) 824-9700   www.dhl.com

Worldwide air express carrier.

DHL Worldwide Express, 50 East Fifth Sreet, Alberttown, Georgetown, Guyana

Tel: 592-4-2019

ERNST & YOUNG INTERNATIONAL
5 Times Square, New York, NY, 10036

Tel: (212) 773-3000   Fax: (212) 773-6350   www.eyi.com

Engaged in assurance and advisory business services, tax, law and corporate finance.

Christopher L. Ram & Co., 157 C. Waterloo St., Georgetown, Guyana

Tel: 592-2-74891   Fax: 592-2-54221   Contact: Christopher Ram

IBM CORPORATION
1133 Westchester Avenue, White Plains, NY, 10604

Tel: (914) 765-1900   Fax: (914) 765-7382   www.ibm.com

Information products, technology and services.

IBM Guyana, Guyana

Tel: 592-826900   Fax: 592-826969

KPMG CONSULTING INC.

1676 International Dr., McLean, VA, 22102

Tel: (703) 747-3000   Fax: (703) 747-8500   www.kpmg.com

Accounting and audit, tax and management consulting services.

KPMG International, 9 Church Path, Georgetown, Guyana

Tel: 592-2-78825   Fax: 592-2-78824   Contact: Nizam Ali, Sr. Ptnr.

PRICEWATERHOUSECOOPERS LLP

1301 Ave. of the Americas, New York, NY, 10019

Tel: (212) 596-7000   Fax: (212) 259-1301   www.pwcglobal.com

Accounting and auditing, tax and management, and human resource consulting services.

PriceWaterhouseCoopers, 145 Crown Street, PO Box 10351, Georgetown 6, Guyana

Tel: 592-2-62904   Fax: 592-2-53849

Haiti

AIG AMERICAN INTERNATIONAL GROUP INC.

70 Pine Street, New York, NY, 10270

Tel: (212) 770-7000   Fax: (212) 509-9705   www.aig.com

Worldwide insurance and financial services.

Compagnie d'Assurance d'Haiti SA, 158 rue de Centre, Port-au-Prince, Haiti

AMR CORPORATION (AMERICAN AIRLINES)

4333 Amon Carter Boulevard, Ft. Worth, TX, 76155

Tel: (817) 963-1234   Fax: (817) 967-9641   www.amrcorp.com

Air transport services.

American Airlines Inc., Cite de l'Exposition, Francois Duvalier Intl. Airport, Port-au-Prince, Haiti

AON CORPORATION

200 East Randolph, Chicago, IL, 60601

Tel: (312) 381-1000   Fax: (312) 381-6032   www.aon.com

Insurance brokers worldwide; underwrites accident and health insurance, specialty and professional insurance; and provides risk management consultation.

AON Worldwide / Bain Hogg Insurance Brokers, 184 rue Pavee, Port-au-Prince, Haiti

Tel: 809-567-7178   Fax: 809-541-9333   Contact: M.R. Redondo

AVIS GROUP HOLDINGS, INC.

6 Sylvan Way, Parsippany, NJ, 07054

Tel: (973) 222-3000   Fax: (973) 222-4381   www.avis.com

Car rental services.

Avis Group Holdings Ltd., rue Mais Gate, Port-au-Prince, Haiti

CITIGROUP, INC.

399 Park Avenue, New York, NY, 10022

Tel: (212) 559-1000   Fax: (212) 559-3646   www.citigroup.com

Provides insurance and financial services worldwide.

Citigroup, 242 Delmas Rd., PO Box 1688, Port-au-Prince, Haiti

Contact: Gladys M. Coupet

DANZAS AEI, INC.

120 Tokeneke Road, PO Box 1231, Darien, CT, 06820

Tel: (203) 655-7900   Fax: (203) 655-5779   www.aeilogistics.com

International air freight forwarder.

Danzas AEI, International Airport of Maia Gate (PAP), Cargo Section, Port-au-Prince, Haiti

Tel: 509-460102   Fax: 509-463522

DHL WORLDWIDE EXPRESS

50 California Avenue, San Francisco, CA, 94111

Tel: (415) 677-6100   Fax: (415) 824-9700   www.dhl.com

Worldwide air express carrier.

DHL Worldwide Express, 17 BIS. Route de L'Aeroport, Port au Prince, Haiti

Tel: 509-464800

EGL INC. (EAGLE GLOBAL LOGISTICS)

15350 Vickery Drive, Houston, TX, 77032

Tel: (281) 618-3100   Fax: (281) 618-3223   www.eagleusa.com

Ocean/air freight forwarding, customs brokerage, packing and wholesale, logistics management and insurance.

EGL Eagle Global Logistics, Hamaserco Bldg., Door No. 4, Airport Rd., PO Box 1795, Port-au-Prince, Haiti

Tel: 509-46-3253   Fax: 509-46-5540

FRITZ COMPANIES, INC., DIV. UPS

706 Mission Street, Ste. 900, San Francisco, CA, 94103

Tel: (415) 904-8360   Fax: (415) 904-8661   www.fritz.com

Integrated transportation, sourcing, distribution and customs brokerage services.

Fritz Companies Inc., Port-au-Prince, Haiti

HOLIDAY INN (BASS RESORTS) WORLDWIDE, INC.

3 Ravinia Drive, Ste. 2900, Atlanta, GA, 30346-2149

Tel: (770) 604-2000   Fax: (770) 604-5403   www.holidayinn.com

Hotels, restaurants and casinos.

Holiday Inn, rue Capois 10, B.P. 1429, Dwin, Port-au-Prince, Haiti

KPMG CONSULTING INC.

1676 International Dr., McLean, VA, 22102

Tel: (703) 747-3000   Fax: (703) 747-8500   www.kpmg.com

Accounting and audit, tax and management consulting services.

KPMG International, 47 Route de l'Aeroport, Port-au-Prince, Haiti

Tel: 509-464854   Fax: 509-460625   Contact: Mireille Mérové-Pierre, Sr. Ptnr.

NORTON ABRASIVES COMPANY

1 New Bond Street, Worcester, MA, 01606

Tel: (508) 795-5000   Fax: (508) 795-5741   www.nortonabrasives.com

Mfr. abrasives for industrial manufacturing.

Norton SA, Meu's Bldg., B.P. 652, Port-au-Prince, Haiti

RUDDICK CORPORATION

301 S. Tryon St., Ste. 1800, Charlotte, NC, 28202

Tel: (704) 372-5404   Fax: (704) 372-6409   www.amefird.com

Mfr. industrial sewing thread for worldwide industrial and consumer markets.

American & Efird Haiti, Batiments 1 Et 2, Complexe Industriel Des Nimes, Route De l' Aeroport, Port-au-Prince, Haiti

Honduras

AIG AMERICAN INTERNATIONAL GROUP INC.

70 Pine Street, New York, NY, 10270

Tel: (212) 770-7000   Fax: (212) 509-9705   www.aig.com

Worldwide insurance and financial services.

American Home Assurance Co., Edif Los Costanos, Blvd. Morazan, Tegucigalpa, Honduras

AMERICAN BILTRITE INC.

57 River Street, Wellesley Hills, MA, 02181

Tel: (781) 237-6655   Fax: (781) 237-6880   www.americanbiltriteinc.com

Mfr. vinyl composition and rubber floor coverings and produces pressure sensitive tape and rubber matting.

Compania Hulera SA, Aptdo. 164, San Pedro Sula, Honduras

AON CORPORATION

200 East Randolph, Chicago, IL, 60601

Tel: (312) 381-1000   Fax: (312) 381-6032   www.aon.com

Insurance brokers worldwide; underwrites accident and health insurance, specialty and professional insurance; and provides risk management consultation.

AON Worldwide / Consultores y Corredores de Seguros, 6 Av. 2 y 3 Calles, N.O. Plaza G.M.C., San Pedro Sula, Honduras

Tel: 504-552-2595   Fax: 504-550-9644   Contact: Rene Kattan

APPLERA CORPORATION

301 Merritt 7, Norwalk, CT, 06851

Tel: (203) 840-2000   Fax: (203) 840-2312   www.applera.com

Leading supplier of systems for life science research and related applications.

Analytical Instruments, Ave. Colon No. 523, Piso 2, Tegucigalpa, Honduras

AVON PRODUCTS, INC.

1345 Avenue of the Americas, New York, NY, 10105-0196

Tel: (212) 282-5000   Fax: (212) 282-6049   www.avon.com

Mfr. direct seller of cosmetics and beauty-related items.

Productos Avon S.A., Apartado Postal "1763", San Pedro Sula, Honduras

Tel: 504-52-6118   Fax: 504-57-3883   Contact: Napoleon Garcia, Div. Sales Mgr.

LOUIS BERGER INTERNATIONAL INC.

100 Halsted Street, East Orange, NJ, 07019

Tel: (201) 678-1960   Fax: (201) 672-4284   www.louisberger.com

Consulting engineers, engaged in architecture, environmental and advisory services.

Louis Berger International Inc., Unidad Coordinadoro-BID, Ed. Inatlantic, 2da Planta 2da Av., Entre Calle1y2, San Predo Sula, Honduras

BEST WESTERN INTERNATIONAL

6201 North 24th Place, Phoenix, AZ, 85106

Tel: (602) 957-4200   Fax: (602) 957-5740   www.bestwestern.com

International hotel chain.

Best Western International, San Pedro Sula, Honduras

BW Posada Real Copan, Km 164 Carr, San Pedro Sula, Copan Ruins 23400, Honduras

Tel: 504-614-483

BRISTOL-MYERS SQUIBB COMPANY

345 Park Ave., New York, NY, 10154-0037

Tel: (212) 546-4000   Fax: (212) 546-4020   www.bms.com

Pharmaceutical and food preparations, medical and surgical instruments.

Compania Bristol-Myers de Centro America, Col. John F. Kennedy, Tegucigalpa, Honduras

LEO BURNETT, DIV. B-COM 3 GROUP

35 West Wacker Drive, Chicago, IL, 60601

Tel: (312) 220-5959   Fax: (312) 220-6533   www.leoburnett.com

Engaged in advertising, marketing, media buying and planning, and public relations.

Calderon Publicidad, Tegucigalpa, Honduras

CALMAQUIP ENGINEERING CORPORATION

7240 N.W. 12th Street, Miami, FL, 33121

Tel: (305) 592-4510   Fax: (305) 593-9618   www.calmaquip.com

Engineering project management

Calmaquip Ingenieros de Honduras SA, Aptdo. 845, blvd Morazan 1518, Barrio de Guacerique, Comayaguela, Honduras

CARGILL, INC.

15407 McGinty Road West, Minnetonka, MN, 55440-5625

Tel: (612) 742-7575   Fax: (612) 742-7393   www.cargill.com

Food products, feeds, animal products.

Alcon (Alimentos Concentrados Nacionales SA), Aptdo. 283, San Pedro Sula, Bufalo, Cortes, Honduras

CHIQUITA BRANDS INTERNATIONAL INC.

250 East Fifth Street, Cincinnati, OH, 45202

Tel: (513) 784-8000   Fax: (513) 784-8030   www.chiquita.com

Sale and distribution of bananas, fresh fruits and processed foods.

Tela Railroad Co., Aptdo. Aereo 30, San Pedro Sula, Honduras

CITIGROUP, INC.

399 Park Avenue, New York, NY, 10022

Tel: (212) 559-1000   Fax: (212) 559-3646   www.citigroup.com

Provides insurance and financial services worldwide.

Citigroup, Blvd. Suyapa, Tegucigalpa Francisco, Morazan 3434, Honduras

Contact: Patricia Ferro

COLGATE-PALMOLIVE COMPANY

300 Park Ave., New York, NY, 10022

Tel: (212) 310-2000   Fax: (212) 310-2919   www.colgate.com

Mfr. pharmaceuticals, cosmetics, toiletries and detergents.

Colgate-Palmolive Inc., Dos Cuadros al Norte de Granitos, Terrazas Contiguo Honduprint, Tegucigalpa, Honduras

CONTINENTAL AIRLINES INC.

1600 Smith St., Houston, TX, 77002

Tel: (713) 324-5000   Fax: (713) 324-2637   www.continental.com

International airline carrier.

Continental Airlines Inc., Honduras

DANZAS AEI, INC.

120 Tokeneke Road, PO Box 1231, Darien, CT, 06820

Tel: (203) 655-7900   Fax: (203) 655-5779   www.aeilogistics.com

International air freight forwarder.

Danzas AEI, c/o Cormar Honduras - Ave. Independencia, 8a Calle B - No. Q-6 Col. 15 de Setiembre, Comayaguela, Tegucigalpa, Honduras

Tel: 504-2-342-612

DDB WORLDWIDE COMMUNICATIONS GROUP

437 Madison Ave., New York, NY, 10022

Tel: (212) 415-2000   Fax: (212) 415-3417   www.ddbn.com

Advertising agency.

Adcom/DDB Needham Worldwide, San Pedro Sula, Honduras

DHL WORLDWIDE EXPRESS

50 California Avenue, San Francisco, CA, 94111

Tel: (415) 677-6100   Fax: (415) 824-9700   www.dhl.com

Worldwide air express carrier.

DHL Worldwide Express, Col. Palmira, Ave. Republica of Chile, Frente Of. Principal Banexpo, Tegucigalpa, Honduras

Tel: 504-39-4882

DOLE FOOD COMPANY, INC.

One Dole Drive, Westlake Village, CA, 91362

Tel: (818) 874-4000   Fax: (818) 879-6615   www.dole.com

Produces/distributes fresh fruits and vegetables and canned juices and fruits.

Agropecuaria el Porvenir S.A. (Agropor, Honduras

ECOLAB INC.

370 N. Wabasha Street, St. Paul, MN, 55102

Tel: (651) 293-2233   Fax: (651) 293-2379   www.ecolab.com

Develop/mfr. premium cleaning, sanitizing and maintenance products and services for the hospitality, institutional, and residential markets.

Ecolab Ltd., Tegucigalpa, Honduras

Tel: 504-553-4679

EGL INC. (EAGLE GLOBAL LOGISTICS)

15350 Vickery Drive, Houston, TX, 77032

Tel: (281) 618-3100   Fax: (281) 618-3223   www.eagleusa.com

Ocean/air freight forwarding, customs brokerage, packing and wholesale, logistics management and insurance.

EGL Eagle Global Logistics, 2a Calle - 4a Ave., A #238 Col. Palmira, PO Box 988, Tegucigalpa, Honduras

Tel: 504-532-600   Fax: 504-577-000

EGL Eagle Global Logistics, 4a Calle - 4a Ave., N.O. #29, Edif. Bonilla Gastel #2 Barrio Guamilito, PO Box 298, San Pedro Sula, Honduras

Tel: 504-532-600   Fax: 504-577-000

ERNST & YOUNG INTERNATIONAL

5 Times Square, New York, NY, 10036

Tel: (212) 773-3000   Fax: (212) 773-6350   www.eyi.com

Engaged in assurance and advisory business services, tax, law and corporate finance.

Morales Palao William y Asociados, Apdo. Postal 2232, San Pedro Sula, Honduras

Tel: 504-31-3712   Fax: 504-313709   Contact: David O. Palo

FRITZ COMPANIES, INC., DIV. UPS

706 Mission Street, Ste. 900, San Francisco, CA, 94103

Tel: (415) 904-8360   Fax: (415) 904-8661   www.fritz.com

Integrated transportation, sourcing, distribution and customs brokerage services.

Fritz Companies Inc., San Pedro de Sula, Honduras

H.B. FULLER COMPANY

1200 Willow Lake Blvd., Vadnais Heights, MN, 55110

Tel: (651) 236-5900   Fax: (651) 236-5898   www.hbfuller.com

Mfr./distributor adhesives, sealants, coatings, paints, waxes, sanitation chemicals.

H.B. Fuller Co., Kativo de Honduras, 454 Tegucigalpa, Honduras

Tel: 504-32-2039   Fax: 504-32-0436

H.B. Fuller Co., Kativo de Honduras, San Pedro Sula, Honduras

H.B. Fuller Honduras, S.A., San Pedro Sula 1103, Honduras

Tel: 504-51-7914   Fax: 504-51-7510

GARAN, INC.

350 Fifth Avenue, New York, NY, 10118

Tel: (212) 563-2000   Fax: (212) 971-2250

Designs, manufactures and markets apparel for men, women and children.

Garan de Honduras, Honduras

GREY GLOBAL GROUP

777 Third Ave., New York, NY, 10017

Tel: (212) 546-2000   Fax: (212) 546-1495   www.grey.com

International advertising agency.

Talento Publicidad, Tegucigalpa, Honduras

GRIFFITH LABORATORIES INC.

One Griffith Center, Alsip, IL, 60658

Tel: (708) 371-0900   Fax: (708) 597-3294   www.griffithlabs.com

Mfr. industrial food ingredients and equipment.

Griffith Labs Inc., San Pedro Sula, Honduras

Tel: 504-52-2938   Fax: 504-52-7071

HOLIDAY INN (BASS RESORTS) WORLDWIDE, INC.

3 Ravinia Drive, Ste. 2900, Atlanta, GA, 30346-2149

Tel: (770) 604-2000   Fax: (770) 604-5403   www.holidayinn.com

Hotels, restaurants and casinos.

Holiday Inn, Calle Peatonal, Aptdo. 175, Tegucigalpa, Honduras

HORWATH INTERNATIONAL ASSOCIATION

420 Lexington Avenue, Suite 526, New York, NY, 10170-0526

Tel: (212) 808-2000   Fax: (212) 808-2020   www.horwath.com

Public accountants and auditors.

Fajardo Fernandez y Asociados, Barrio El Benque, 9, Avenida S.O. No. 13, Apartado Postal 99, San Pedro Sula, Honduras

IBM CORPORATION

1133 Westchester Avenue, White Plains, NY, 10604

Tel: (914) 765-1900   Fax: (914) 765-7382   www.ibm.com

Information products, technology and services.

IBM de Honduras SA, Edificio Sonisa, Colonia San Ignacio, Tegucigalpa, Honduras

Tel: (504) 232-2319   Fax: (504) 239-1915

INTER-CONTINENTAL HOTELS

3 Ravinia Drive, Suite 2900, Atlanta, GA, 30346-2149

Tel: (770) 604-2000   Fax: (770) 604-5403   www.interconti.com

Worldwide hotel and resort accommodations.

Camino Real Inter-Continental San Pedro Sula, Col. Hernandez y Blvd. del Sur, Multiplaza Mall, San Pedro Sula, Honduras

Tel: 504-50-5555   Fax: 504-50-6255

J. WALTER THOMPSON COMPANY

466 Lexington Ave., New York, NY, 10017

Tel: (212) 210-7000   Fax: (212) 210-6944   www.jwt.com

International advertising and marketing services.

APCU-Thompson, Tegucigalpa, Honduras

KIMBERLY-CLARK CORPORATION

351 Phelps Drive, Irving, TX, 75038

Tel: (972) 281-1200　　Fax: (972) 281-1435　　www.kimberly-clark.com

Mfr./sales/distribution of consumer tissue, household and personal care products.

Kimberly-Clark Co. de Honduras SA de CV, San Pedro Sula, Honduras

KPMG CONSULTING INC.

1676 International Dr., McLean, VA, 22102

Tel: (703) 747-3000　　Fax: (703) 747-8500　　www.kpmg.com

Accounting and audit, tax and management consulting services.

KPMG International, Edif. Barnco Atlantida SA, 7 piso, No. 703, la. Calle N.O. 3 a. Av., San Pedro Sula, Honduras

KPMG International, Col. Palmire 2da Calle, 2da Av., Casa No. 417, Tegucigalpa, Honduras

Tel: 504-32-2806　Fax: 504-32-5925　Contact: Armando Barnica, Sr. Ptnr.

MARSH & McLENNAN COS INC.

1166 Ave. of the Americas, New York, NY, 10036-2774

Tel: (212) 345-5000　　Fax: (212) 345-4808　　www.marshmac.com

Insurance agents/brokers, pension and investment management consulting services.

Correduria Internacional de Seguros, Edif. Cruz-Heath, 3 Av. 6 Calle, Col. Alameda, Tegucigalpa 1876, Honduras

Tel: 504-32-2676　Fax: 504-39-3558

Teciseguros S. de R.L., Edif. Rivera & Cia., 3er piso, San Pedro Sula, Honduras

Tel: 504-5-553-3069　Fax: 504-5-552-7418　Contact: Claudo Guell

McCANN-ERICKSON WORLDGROUP

750 Third Ave., New York, NY, 10017

Tel: (212) 697-6000　　Fax: (212) 984-3575　　www.mccann.com

International advertising and marketing services.

McCann-Erickson Centroamericana S de RL (Honduras), Edif. Banco Atlantida, piso 8, Aptdo. 802, San Pedro Sula, Honduras

McDONALD'S CORPORATION

McDonald's Plaza, Oak Brook, IL, 60523

Tel: (630) 623-3000　　Fax: (630) 623-7409　　www.mcdonalds.com

Fast food chain stores.

McDonald's Corp., Honduras

THE McGRAW-HILL COMPANIES

1221 Avenue of the Americas, New York, NY, 10020

Tel: (212) 512-2000　　Fax: (212) 512-2703　　www.mccgraw-hill.com

Books, magazines, information systems, financial service, publishing and broadcast operations.

McGraw-Hill Honduras, Colonia Luis Landa, Cuarta Calle Case E-, Tegucigalpa, Honduras

Tel: 504-322-475

J. P. MORGAN CHASE & CO. INC.

270 Park Ave., New York, NY, 10017

Tel: (212) 270-6000　　Fax: (212) 622-9030　　www.jpmorganchase.com

Provides integrated financial solutions for institutions and individuals worldwide, including asset management, investment banking and commercial banking.

J. P. Morgan Chase & Co., Aptdo. 57-C, 5a Calle y 7a. Av., San Pedro Sula, Honduras

PAN-AMERICAN LIFE INSURANCE COMPANY

Pan American Life Center, 601 Poydras St., New Orleans, LA, 70130-0219

Tel: (504) 566-1300　　Fax: (504) 566-3600　　www.panamericanlife.com

Insurance services.

Pan-American Life Insurance Co., Av. Republica de Chile 804, Edif. PALIC, Tegucigalpa, Honduras

Tel: 504-232-8774　Fax: 504-232-3907　Contact: Alberto Agurcia　Emp: 105

PERKIN ELMER, INC.

45 William Street, Wellesley, MA, 02481

Tel: (781) 237-5100   Fax: (781) 431-4255   www.perkinelmer.com

Mfr. equipment and devices to detect explosives and bombs on airline carriers.

PerkinElmer Honduras, Avenida Colon Casa #523, 2do Piso, Joyeria Handal, Frente a Bancasa Apdo. 5, Tegucigalpa, Honduras

PHELPS DODGE CORPORATION

2600 North Central Ave., Phoenix, AZ, 85004-3089

Tel: (602) 234-8100   Fax: (602) 234-8337   www.phelpsdodge.com

Copper, minerals, metals and special engineered products for transportation and electrical markets.

Electro Conductores de Honduras SA de CV (ECOHSA), Aptdo. 3192, Tegucigalpa, Honduras

PRICEWATERHOUSECOOPERS LLP

1301 Ave. of the Americas, New York, NY, 10019

Tel: (212) 596-7000   Fax: (212) 259-1301   www.pwcglobal.com

Accounting and auditing, tax and management, and human resource consulting services.

PriceWaterhouseCoopers, Col. Loma Linda Norte, Bloque F-3 Calle, Diagonal Gema No 1, Tegucigalpa, Honduras
Tel: 504-32-01-51   Fax: 504-31-19-06

PriceWaterhouseCoopers, Edif. Banco Atlantida, No 903, Apartado 563, San Pedro Sula, Honduras
Tel: 504-53-3060   Fax: 504-52-6728

RAYOVAC CORPORATION

601 Rayovac Drive, Madison, WI, 53711-2497

Tel: (608) 275-3340   Fax: (608) 275-4577   www.rayovac.com

Mfr. batteries and lighting devices.

Rayovac Honduras, Comayaguella, Honduras

SEARS ROEBUCK & COMPANY

3333 Beverly Road, Hoffman Estates, IL, 60179

Tel: (847) 286-2500   Fax: (847) 286-1517   www.sears.com

Diversified general merchandise.

Sears Roebuck & Cia., Pasaje Valle, San Pedro Sula, Honduras

UNITED PARCEL SERVICE, INC.

55 Glenlake Parkway, NE, Atlanta, GA, 30328

Tel: (404) 828-6000   Fax: (404) 828-6593   www.ups.com

International package-delivery service.

UPS / Courier Internacional S.A., Edif. Maya, Frente Hotel Maya, Primer piso, Local 4, Tegucigalpa, Honduras
Tel: 504-31-4-755   Fax: 504-31-1244

THE WACKENHUT CORPORATION

4200 Wackenhut Dr., Ste. 100, Palm Beach Gardens, FL, 33410

Tel: (561) 622-5656   Fax: (561) 691-6736   www.wackenhut.com

Security systems and services.

Seguridad Tecnica S.A. de C.V., Col. Miramontes, Av. Altiplano, Casa 1411, Tegucigalpa, Honduras
Tel: 504-32-0778   Fax: 504-32-2926

Wackenhut Honduras SA, Col. Miramontes, Av. Altiplano, Casa 1411, Tegucigalpa, Honduras
Tel: 504-32-0778   Fax: 504-32-2926

THE WARNACO GROUP INC.

90 Park Ave., New York, NY, 10016

Tel: (212) 661-1300   Fax: (212) 687-0480   www.warnaco.com

Mfr./sales intimate apparel and men's and women's sportswear.

Warnaco, San Pedro Sula, Honduras

WENDY'S INTERNATIONAL, INC.

4288 West Dublin Granville Roads, Dublin, OH, 43017-0256

Tel: (614) 764-3100   Fax: (614) 764-3459   www.wendysintl.com

Fast food restaurant chain.

Wendy's International, Honduras

XEROX CORPORATION

800 Long Ridge Road, PO Box 1600, Stamford, CT, 06904

Tel: (203) 968-3000   Fax: (203) 968-4312   www.xerox.com

Mfr. document processing equipment, systems and supplies.

Xerox De Honduras, S.A., Apt. Postal 897, Col. La Paloma No. 2401, Blvd. Morazan, Tegucigalpa D.C., Honduras

Tel: 504-38-2211   Fax: 504-31-3689

YOUNG & RUBICAM INC.

285 Madison Ave., New York, NY, 10017

Tel: (212) 210-3000   Fax: (212) 370-3796   www.yr.com

Advertising, public relations, direct marketing and sales promotion, corporate and product ID management.

Delfos Publicidad, Teguicgalpa, Honduras

Hong Kong PRC

24 HOUR FITNESS WORLDWIDE INC.

5020 Franklin Drive, Pleasanton, CA, 94588

Tel: (925) 416-3100   Fax: (925) 416-3146   www.24hourfitness.com

Owns and manages fitness centers.

24 Hour Fitness, 1 Wellington Street, Central, Hong Kong PRC

Tel: 852-2522-5229

3COM CORPORATION

5400 Bayfront Plaza, Santa Clara, CA, 95052-8145

Tel: (408) 326-5000   Fax: (408) 326-5001   www.3com.com

Engaged in the development and manufacture of computer networking products and systems.

3Com Asia Ltd., 23/F, Li Po Chun Chambers, 189 Des Voeux Rd., Central, Hong Kong PRC

Tel: 852-2501-1111 Fax: 852-2537-1149

3D SYSTEMS CORPORATION

26081 Avenue Hall, Valencia, CA, 91355

Tel: (805) 295-5600   Fax: (805) 294-8406   www.3dsystems.com

Mfr. computer lasers.

3D Systems, Honest Motor Building, 21/F, 9-11 Leighton Road, Causeway Bay, Hong Kong PRC

3D/INTERNATIONAL INC.

1900 West Loop South, Ste. 400, Houston, TX, 77027

Tel: (713) 871-7000   Fax: (713) 871-7456   www.3di.com

Engaged in design, management and environmental services.

3D/I-Hong Kong, 17/F, Malaysia Bldg., 50 Gloucester Rd., Wanchai, Hong Kong PRC

3M (MINNESOTA MINING & MFG.)

3M Center, St. Paul, MN, 55144-1000

Tel: (651) 733-1110   Fax: (651) 733-9973   www.mmm.com

Mfr. diversified products for industry, consumer, health care, imaging, communications, transport, safety, etc.

3M Hong Kong Ltd., 5/F, Victoria Ctr., 15 Watson Rd., Northpoint, Causeway Bay, Hong Kong PRC

Tel: 852-2806-6111 Fax: 852-5807-1308

3M TOUCH SYSTEMS, INC.

300 Griffin Brook Park Drive, Methuen, MA, 01844

Tel: (978) 659-9000   Fax: (978) 659-9100   www.microtouch.com

Mfr. Touchscreen Sensors, Touch Monitors, and Industrial Computer Products.

3M Touch Systems, Limited, 15 Watson Road, 5/F, North Point, Hong Kong PRC

Tel: 852-2333-6138

ABBOTT LABORATORIES

100 Abbott Park Rd., Abbott Park, IL, 60064

Tel: (847) 937-6100   Fax: (847) 937-1511   www.abbott.com

Development, manufacture and sale of diversified health care products and services.

Abbott Laboratories, Ltd., Room 301, Block B, 3/F, Sea View Estate, Watson Road, North Point, Hong Kong PRC

Tel: 852-2-566-8711

ABS (AMERICAN BUREAU OF SHIPPING)

ABS Plaza, 16855 Northchase Drive, Houston, TX, 77060

Tel: (281) 877-6000   Fax: (281) 877-6344   www.eagle.org

Classification and certification of ships and offshore structures, development and technical assistance.

ABS Pacific, 58-64 Queen's Road East, 15/F, Hong Kong PRC

ACCENTURE LTD.

1345 Avenue of the Americas, New York, NY, 10105

Tel: (917) 452-4400   Fax: (917) 527-9915   www.accenture.com

Provides management and technology consulting services.

Accenture, Wing On Centre, 23/F, 111 Connaught Rd., Central, Hong Kong PRC

Tel: 852-2852-0388   Fax: 852-2850-8956

ACCO WORLD CORPORATION

300 Tower Parkway, Lincolnshire, IL, 60069

Tel: (847) 541-9500   Fax: (847) 541-5750   www.accobrands.com

Provides services in the office and computer markets and manufactures paper fasteners, clips, metal fasteners, binders and staplers.

ACCO Asia Limited, The Lee Gardens 40th Fl., 33 Hysan Avenue, Causeway Bay, Hong Kong PRC

ACCO Asia Limited, Room 5001-5006, 50/F Hopewell Centre, 183 Queen's Road East, Wanchai, Hong Kong PRC

Tel: 852-2576-8021   Fax: 852-2504-0993

ACTERNA CORPORATION

20400 Observation Drive, Germantown, MD, 20876

Tel: (301) 353-1550   Fax: (301) 353-1536   www.acterna.com

Develop, manufacture and market communications test instruments, systems, software and services.

Acterna Corporation, Room 902, 9th. Floor, First Pacific Bank Centre, 56 Gloucester Road, Wanchai, Hong Kong PRC

ACTION INSTRUMENTS INC.

8601 Aero Drive, San Diego, CA, 92123

Tel: (619) 279-5726   Fax: (619) 279-6290   www.actionio.com

Mfr. electronic instruments and industrial measurements computers.

Action Instruments (China) Ltd., 24/F, Unit D, Gee Change Hong Centre, 65 Wong Chuk Hang Road, Hong Kong PRC

Contact: Eliza Leung

ADAPTEC INC.

691 South Milpitas Boulevard, Milpitas, CA, 95035

Tel: (408) 945-8600   Fax: (408) 262-2533   www.adaptec.com

Design/mfr./marketing hardware and software solutions.

Adaptec Hong Kong, Unit 10, 18/F, Tower II, Lippo Centre, 89 Queensway, Hong Kong PRC

ADEMCO INTERNATIONAL

1769 N.W. 79th Avenue, Miami, FL, 33126

Tel: (305) 477-5204   Fax: (305) 477-5404   www.ademcoint.com

Mfr. security, fire and burglary systems and products.

ADEMCO (Hong Kong) Ltd., Flat A&B, 7/F, CDW Bldg., 388 Castle Peak Rd., Tseun Wan N.T., Hong Kong PRC

Tel: 852-2405-2323   Fax: 852-2415-3112

ADVANCED DIGITAL INFORMATION CORPORATION

11431 Willows Rd. NE, PO Box 97057, Redmond, WA, 98073

Tel: (425) 881-8004   Fax: (425) 881-2296   www.adic.com

Mfr. computer storage systems.

ADIC Hong Kong, 1 Harbour View Street, 18/F, Central, Hong Kong PRC

ADVANCED MICRO DEVICES INC.

1 AMD Place, Sunnyvale, CA, 94086

Tel: (408) 732-2400   Fax: (408) 982-6164   www.amd.com

Mfr. integrated circuits for communications and computation industry.

Advanced Micro Devices Far East Ltd., Ste. 4504-11 Natwest Tower, 1 Matheson Street, Causeway Bay, Hong Kong PRC

Tel: 852-2956-0388   Fax: 852-2956-0588

ADVANCED MP TECHNOLOGY, INC.

1010 Calle Sombra, San Clemente, CA, 92673-6480

Tel: (949) 492-3113   Fax: (949) 492-5068   www.advancedmp.com

Engaged in distribution of electronic components.

Advanced MP Technology, 26 Harbour Road, Wanchai, Hong Kong PRC

Tel: 852-2877-0383

ADVANSTAR COMMUNICATIONS INC.

545 Boylston Steet, Boston, MA, 02116

Tel: (617) 267-6500   Fax: (617) 267-6900   www.advanstar.com

Provides business to business marketing services.

Advanstar Asia Ltd., 26/F Pacific Plaza, 410 Des Voeux Road West, Hong Kong PRC

Tel: 852-2559-2772   Fax: 852-2559-7002

THE AES CORPORATION

1001 North 19th Street, Arlington, VA, 22209

Tel: (703) 522-1315   Fax: (703) 528-4510   www.aesc.com

Gas and electric utility.

AES Orient, 26/F Entertainment Building, 30 Queen's Road Central, Hong Kong PRC

Tel: 852-2842-5111   Fax: 852-2530-1673

AETNA INC.

151 Farmington Avenue, Hartford, CT, 06156

Tel: (860) 273-0123   Fax: (860) 275-2677   www.aetna.com

Managed health care, annuities, individual retirement and group pension services, and asset management products worldwide.

Aetna Hong Kong, Hong Kong PRC

AFFILIATED COMPUTER SERVICES, INC.

2828 North Haskell Ave., Dallas, TX, 75204

Tel: (214) 841-6111   Fax: (214) 821-8315   www.acs-inc.com

Provides data processing outsourcing services and ATM operations.

ACS Innovations International (HK) Ltd, Unit A & B, 17/Fl. V Ga Building, 532 Castle Peak Road, Kowloon, Hong Kong PRC

Tel: 852-2148-3230   Contact: Omiya Lee

AGERE SYSTEMS

555 Union Boulevard, Allentown, PA, 18109-3286

Tel: (610) 712-4323   Fax: (610) 712-4106   www.agere.com

Mfr. of communications chips.

Agere Systems Hong Kong Ltd., Suites 3201 & 3210-12, Tower 2, The Gateway, Harbor City, Tsim Sha Tsui, Hong Kong PRC

Tel: 852-3129-2000

AGRA BAYMONT, INC.

14100 58th St. North, Clearwater, FL, 33760-3796

Tel: (727) 578-0100   Fax: (727) 577-6946   www.baymont.com

Provides data conversion, maintenance, and implementation services for utility, public, and commercial industries and offers services in photogram metric mapping, remote sensing, imagery analysis, and resource mapping.

AGRA Baymont Representative, Smart Technology, Room 601 Opulent Building, 402-406 Hennessy Road, Wanchai, Hong Kong PRC

Tel: 852-2-504-5260   Fax: 852-2-504-4965   Contact: Alex Henshaw

AIG AMERICAN INTERNATIONAL GROUP INC.

70 Pine Street, New York, NY, 10270

Tel: (212) 770-7000   Fax: (212) 509-9705   www.aig.com

Worldwide insurance and financial services.

AIG International Inc., 2809-11, Ceitibank Tower, 3 Garden Road, Central, Hong Kong PRC

AIR PRODUCTS AND CHEMICALS, INC.

7201 Hamilton Boulevard, Allentown, PA, 18195-1501

Tel: (610) 481-4911   Fax: (610) 481-5900   www.airproducts.com

Mfr. industry gases and related equipment, specialty chemicals, environmental/energy systems.

Air Products Asia Inc., Room 1901, ETE Tower 838, 89 Queensway, Central, Hong Kong PRC

Contact: Wayne A. Hinman, Pres.

AJC INTERNATIONAL, INC.

5188 Roswell Road NW, Atlanta, GA, 30342

Tel: (404) 252-6750   Fax: (404) 252-9340   www.ajcfood.com

Engaged in food marketing.

AJC International, 1801 Jubilee Centre, 18 Fenwick Street, Wanchai, Hong Kong PRC

Tel: 852-2543-4264

ALBERTO-CULVER COMPANY

2525 Armitage Ave., Melrose Park, IL, 60160

Tel: (708) 450-3000   Fax: (708) 450-3354   www.alberto.com

Mfr./marketing personal care and household brand products.

Alberto-Culver (HK) Ltd., Rm. 110-111, Stanhope House, 738 King's Rd., Quarry Bay, Hong Kong PRC

ALCONE MARKETING GROUP

4 Studebaker, Irvine, CA, 92618

Tel: (949) 770-4400   Fax: (949) 770-2957   www.alconemarketing.com

Engaged in sales promotion and marketing services.

Alcone Marketing Group, Unit 2113, Miramar Tower 21/F, 1-23 Kimberley Road, Tsimshatsui Kowloon, Hong Kong PRC

Tel: 852-2311-4491 Fax: 852-2316-2937 Contact: May Leung

ALLEGHENY TECHNOLOGIES INC.

1000 Six PPG Place, Pittsburgh, PA, 15222

Tel: (412) 394-2800   Fax: (412) 394-2805   www.alleghenytechnologies.com

Diversified mfr. aviation and electronics, specialty metals, industrial and consumer products.

Allegheny Technologies, New World Centre, East Wing, #918, 24 Salisbury Rd., Tsim Sha Tsui, Hong Kong PRC

ALLEN TELECOM

25101 Chagrin Boulevard, Beachwood, OH, 44122-5619

Tel: (216) 765-5818   Fax: (216) 765-0410   www.allentele.com

Mfr. communications equipment, automotive bodies and parts, electronic components.

Allen Telecom Ltd., Room 1605-07, Remington Ctr., 23 Hung To Rd., Kwun Tong, Kowloon, Hong Kong PRC

Tel: 852-2839-1844 Fax: 852-2839-4864 Contact: James Fong

ALLEN-BRADLEY COMPANY, INC.

1201 South Second Street, Milwaukee, WI, 53204

Tel: (414) 382-2000   Fax: (414) 382-4444   www.ab.com

Mfr. electrical controls and information devices.

Rockwell Automation/Allen-Bradley (Hong Kong) Ltd., Room 1006, Block B, Seaview Estate, 2-8 Watson Rd., Hong Kong PRC

ALLERGAN INC.

2525 Dupont Drive, Irvine, CA, 92612

Tel: (714) 246-4500   Fax: (714) 246-6987   www.allergan.com

Mfr. therapeutic eye care products and skin care pharmaceuticals.

Allergan Asia Limited, Unit 3001, New Metroplaza, Tower 1, 223 Hing Fong Rd., Kwai Chung NT, Hong Kong PRC

Tel: 852-2480-3330 Fax: 852-2424-0213

ALLTEL CORPORATION

1 Allied Drive, Little Rock, AR, 72202

Tel: (501) 905-8000   Fax: (501) 905-6444   www.alltel.com

Full range outsourcing services.

ALLTEL Systems Ltd. Hong Kong, Suite 3610, Syun Tak Centre, 200 Connaught Rd., Hong Kong PRC

ALTERA CORPORATION

101 Innovation Drive, San Jose, CA, 95134

Tel: (408) 544-7000   Fax: (408) 544-8303   www.altera.com

Mfr. high-density programmable chips for semi-conductor industry.

Altera International, Ltd., Suites 908-920, 9/F Tower 1, Metroplaza, 223 Hing Fong Road, Kwai Fong New Territories, Hong Kong PRC

AMC ENTERTAINMENT INC.

106 West 14th Street, Kansas City, MO, 64121-9615

Tel: (816) 221-4000   Fax: (816) 480-4617   www.amctheatres.com

Operates movie theater chains.

AMC Festival Walk 11, 80 Tat Chee Avenue, Level U/G, Kowloon Tong, Hong Kong PRC

Tel: 852-2397-2310

AMERICAN APPRAISAL ASSOCIATES INC.

411 E. Wisconsin Ave., Ste. 1900, Milwaukee, WI, 53202

Tel: (414) 271-7240   Fax: (414) 271-1041   www.american-appraisal.com

Valuation consulting services.

American Appraisal Hong Kong Ltd., 2901, Central Plaza, 18 Harbour Rd., Wanchai, Hong Kong PRC

Tel: 852-2-511-5200   Fax: 852-2-511-9626   Contact: Patrick Wu

AMERICAN STANDARD COMPANIES, INC.

One Centennial Avenue, Piscataway, NJ, 08855-6820

Tel: (732) 980-3000   Fax: (732) 980-6118   www.americanstandard.com

Mfr. automotive, plumbing, heating, air conditioning products and medical diagnostics systems.

World Standard Ltd., 14-16F, St. John's Bldg., 33 Garden Road, Central, Hong Kong PRC

Tel: 852-2971-3610

AMF BOWLING WORLDWIDE, INC.

8100 AMF Drive, Richmond, VA, 23111

Tel: (804) 730-4000   Fax: (804) 559-6276   www.amf.com

Operates bowling alleys.

AMF Bowling Products, Chung Nam Bldg., 9/F, 1 Lockhart Road, Wanchai, Hong Kong PRC

Tel: 852-2866-6466   Contact: John Farinholt

AMGEN INC.

One Amgen Center Drive, Thousand Oaks, CA, 91320-1799

Tel: (805) 447-1000   Fax: (805) 499-2694   www.amgen.com

Biotechnology research and pharmaceuticals.

Amgen Greater China, Ltd., Dah Sing Financial Centre 15/F, 108 Gloucester Road, Wanchai, Hong Kong PRC

Tel: 852-2802-9033   Fax: 852-2827-7043

AMPEX CORPORATION

1228 Douglas Avenue, Redwood City, CA, 94063-3199

Tel: (650) 367-2011   Fax: (650) 367-4669   www.ampex.com

Mfr. extremely high-performance digital data storage, data retrieval and image processing systems for a broad range of corporate scientific and government applications.

Ampex Ferrotec Ltd., 603 Tai Nan West St., 6/F & 7/F, Kowloon, Hong Kong PRC

Ampex World Operations SA, 709-11, World Finance Ctr., Harbour City, Canton Rd., Tsim Sha Tsui, Hong Kong PRC

AMPHENOL CORPORATION

358 Hall Ave., Wallingford, CT, 06492-7530

Tel: (203) 265-8900   Fax: (203) 265-8793   www.amphenol.com

Mfr. electronic interconnect penetrate systems and assemblies.

Amphenol East Asia Limited, 22/F, Railway Plaza, 39 Chatham Road South, TST Kowloon, Hong Kong PRC

Tel: 852-2699-2663   Fax: 852-2688-0974

AMR CORPORATION (AMERICAN AIRLINES)

4333 Amon Carter Boulevard, Ft. Worth, TX, 76155

Tel: (817) 963-1234   Fax: (817) 967-9641   www.amrcorp.com

Air transport services.

American Airlines Inc., Caxton House, 1 Duddell St., Hong Kong PRC

AMWAY CORPORATION

7575 Fulton Street East, Ada, MI, 49355-0001

Tel: (616) 787-6000   Fax: (616) 787-6177   www.amway.com

Mfr./sale home care, personal care, nutrition and houseware products.

Amway Intl. Inc., 26/F, Citicorp Centre, 18 Whitfield Rd., Causeway Bay, Hong Kong PRC

ANDERSEN

33 West Monroe Street, Chicago, IL, 60603

Tel: (312) 580-0033   Fax: (312) 507-6748   www.andersen.com

Accounting and audit, tax and management consulting services. **Firm under worldwide reorganization; new data unavailable for this edition.

Andersen Worldwide, Wing On Centre, 25/F, 111 Connaught Rd. Central, GPO Box 3289, Hong Kong PRC

Tel: 852-2852-0222

ANDREA ELECTRONICS CORPORATION

45 Melville Park Road, Melville, NY, 11747

Tel: (631) 719-1800   Fax: (631) 719-1950   www.andreaelectronics.com

Mfr. noise reduction electronic headsets, handsets and microphones.

Andrea ANC Manufacturing, Room 817, 2/F, Blk. B, Seaview Estate, 2-8 Watson Road, Hong Kong PRC

ANDREW CORPORATION

10500 West 153rd Street, Orland Park, IL, 60462

Tel: (708) 349-3300   Fax: (708) 349-5410   www.andrew.com

Designer, manufacturer, and supplier of communications equipment, services, and systems.

Andrew Hong Kong Ltd., Suite 1901, East Asia Aetna Tower, 308-320 Des Voeux Rd., Central, Hong Kong PRC

Tel: 852-2515-7500   Fax: 852-2515-7599

AOL TIME WARNER

75 Rockefeller Plaza, New York, NY, 10019

Tel: (212) 484-8000   Fax: (212) 275-3046   www.aoltimewarner.com

Engaged in media and communications; provides internet services, communications, publishing and entertainment.

AOL Time Warner Hong Kong, Hong Kong PRC

AON CORPORATION

200 East Randolph, Chicago, IL, 60601

Tel: (312) 381-1000   Fax: (312) 381-6032   www.aon.com

Insurance brokers worldwide; underwrites accident and health insurance, specialty and professional insurance; and provides risk management consultation.

AON Holdings Asia Ltd., AON China Building, 29 Queen's Road Central, Hong Kong, Hong Kong PRC

Tel: 852-2861-6666   Fax: 852-2866-6691   Contact: Joseph Wu

AON Risk Services Hong Kong Ltd., 9/F, Asian House 1, Wanchai, Hong Kong PRC

Tel: 852-2862-4200   Fax: 852-2862-4200   Contact: Anthony Langridge

APAR INFOTECH CORPORATION

160 Technology Drive, Canonsburg, PA, 15317

Tel: (724) 745-7100   Fax: (724) 745-6494   www.apar.com

Provides software development.

Apar Infotech Services, 1006, World Wide House, 19 Des Voeux Road, Central, Hong Kong PRC

APL LOGISTICS

1111 Broadway, Oakland, CA, 94607

Tel: (510) 272-8000   Fax: (510) 272-7421   www.apllogistics.com

Provides ocean container shipping and logistics services.

APL Hong Kong, 16/F, New T&T Centre, 7 Canton Road, Tsimshatsui, Kowloon, Hong Kong PRC

Tel: 852-2302-7555   Fax: 852-2827-4181

APOGENT TECHNOLOGIES INC.

48 Congress Street, Portsmouth, NH, 03801

Tel: (603) 433-6131   Fax: (603) 431-0860   www.apogent.com

Design, mfr. & sell products for laboratories, clinical research, industrial markets & analytical products.

Erie-Watala Glass Co. Ltd., Unit 401-405, World Wide Industrial Centre, 43-47 Shan Mei St., Fo Tan Shatin, Hong Kong PRC

APPLE COMPUTER, INC.

One Infinite Loop, Cupertino, CA, 95014

Tel: (408) 996-1010   Fax: (408) 974-2113   www.apple.com

Personal computers, peripherals and software.

Apple Computer Intl. Ltd., 2401, NatWest Tower, Times Square, Causeway Bay, Hong Kong PRC

Tel: 852-2506-8888   Fax: 852-2506-2833   Contact: Vincent Tai, Gen. Mgr.

APPLERA CORPORATION

301 Merritt 7, Norwalk, CT, 06851

Tel: (203) 840-2000   Fax: (203) 840-2312   www.applera.com

Leading supplier of systems for life science research and related applications.

Analytical Instruments, Room 1112-13, New East Ocean Centre, 9 Science Museum Road, Tsim Sha Tsui East, Hong Kong PRC

APPLICA INCORPORATED

5980 Miami Lakes Drive, Hialeah, FL, 33014

Tel: (305) 362-2611   Fax: (305) 364-0635   www.applicainc.com

Mfr. and distributor of a broad range of household appliances for major retailers and appliance distributors.

Durable Electrical Metal Factory, Ltd., 1/F, Efficiency House, 35 Tai Yau St., San Po Kong, Kowloon, Hong Kong PRC

Contact: Lai Kin, Chmn.

APW, INC.

N22 W23685 Ridgeview Parkway West, Waukesha, WI, 53188-1013

Tel: (262) 523-7600   Fax: (262) 523-7624   www.apw1.com

Mfr. hi-pressure tools, vibration control products, consumables, technical furniture and enclosures.

APW Products Hong Kong, 2304 & 2309, Wharf Cable Tower, 9 Hoi Shing Road, Tsuen Wan, Hong Kong PRC

ARCHER DANIELS MIDLAND COMPANY (ADM)

4666 Faries Parkway, Decatur, IL, 62526

Tel: (217) 424-5200   Fax: (217) 424-6196   www.admworld.com

Grain processing: flours, grains, oils and flax fiber.

ADM Asia Pacific, Ltd., Hong Kong PRC

ARIBA, INC.

1565 Charleston Rd., Mountain View, CA, 94043

Tel: (650) 930-6200   Fax: (650) 930-6300   www.ariba.com

Mfr. software.

Ariba Hong Kong, One Pacific Place, 39/F, 88 Queensway, Hong Kong PRC

ARMOR HOLDINGS, INC.

1400 Marsh Landing Parkway, Ste. 112, Jacksonville, FL, 32250

Tel: (904) 741-5400   Fax: (904) 741-5403   www.armorholdings.com

Holding company engaged in security products and services.

Armor Group Asia Pacific, One Capital Place 22/F, 18 Luard Road, Wanchai, Hong Kong PRC

Tel: 852-2530-1111   Contact: P. Layton

ARMSTRONG HOLDINGS, INC.

2500 Columbia Avenue, Lancaster, PA, 17604-3001

Tel: (717) 397-0611   Fax: (717) 396-2787   www.armstrong.com

Mfr. and marketing interior furnishings and specialty products for building, auto and textile industry.

Armstrong World Industries (HK) Ltd., 19/F, Cindic Topwer, 128 Gloucester Road, Hong Kong PRC

Tel: 852-2585-7800   Fax: 852-2598-7181

ARROW ELECTRONICS INC.

25 Hub Drive, Melville, NY, 11747

Tel: (516) 391-1300   Fax: (516) 391-1640   www.arrow.com

Distributor of electronic components and computer products.

Arrow Asia Pacific Ltd., 20/F, Tower Two Ever Gain Plaza, 88 Container Port Road, Kwai Chung, Hong Kong PRC

Tel: 852-2484-2484   Fax: 852-2484-2468   Contact: John Tam, Pres.

ASCENTIAL SOFTWARE CORPORATION

50 Washington Street, Westboro, MA, 01581

Tel: (508) 366-3888   Fax: (508) 366-3669   www.ascentialsoftware.com

Mfr. software.

Ascential Software, 2801 Central Plaza, 18 Harbour Road, Wanchai, Hong Kong PRC

ASG (ALLEN SYSTEMS GROUP)

1333 Third Avenue South, Naples, FL, 34102

Tel: (941) 435-2200   Fax: (941) 263-3692   www.asg.com

Mainframe computer software, specializing in OnMark 2000 software.

ASG Hong Kong, Suite 1415-16, Sun Hung Kai Centre, 14/F, 30 Harbour Road, Wanchai, Hong Kong PRC

ASHLAND OIL INC.

50 E. RiverCenter Blvd., Box 391, Covington, KY, 41012-0391

Tel: (859) 815-3333   Fax: (859) 815-5053   www.ashland.com

Petroleum exploration, refining and transportation; mfr. chemicals, oils and lubricants.

Valvoline International Inc., 12/F, Jubilee Commercial Bldg., 42-46 Gloucester Rd., Wanchai, Hong Kong PRC

ASSOCIATED MERCHANDISING CORPORATION

500 Seventh Ave., 2nd Fl., New York, NY, 10018

Tel: (212) 819-6600   Fax: (212) 819-6701   www.theamc.com

Retail service organization; apparel, shoes and accessories.

Associated Merchandising Corp., 5/F, West Wing Tsim Sha Tsui Centre, 66 Mody Rd., Kowloon, Hong Kong PRC

ASSOCIATED PRESS INC.

50 Rockefeller Plaza, New York, NY, 10020-1605

Tel: (212) 621-1500   Fax: (212) 621-5447   www.ap.com

News gathering agency.

The Associated Press, Telecom House, 3 Gloucester Rd., Wan Chai, Hong Kong PRC

Tel: 852-2802-4324

AT&T CORPORATION

295 N. Maple Ave., Basking Ridge, NJ, 07920-1002

Tel: (908) 221-2000   Fax: (908) 221-2528   www.att.com

Engaged in long distance telecommunications.

AT&T Asia Pacific Inc., Shell Tower, 30/F, Times Square, 1 Matheson St., Causeway Bay, Hong Kong PRC

ATMEL CORPORATION

2325 Orchard Pkwy., San Jose, CA, 95131

Tel: (408) 441-0311　　　Fax: (408) 436-4200　　　www.atmel.com

Design, manufacture and marketing of advanced semiconductors.

Atmel Asia Ltd., Chinachem Golden Plaza, 77 Mody Road, Tsimhatsui East Kowloon, Hong Kong PRC

Tel: 852-2721-9778

ATTACHMATE CORPORATION

3617 131st Avenue SE, Bellevue, WA, 98006-1332

Tel: (425) 644-4010　　　Fax: (425) 747-9924　　　www.attachmate.com

Mfr. connectivity software.

Attachmate Hong Kong Ltd., Units 2701-3, 27/F, Vicwood Plaza, 199 Des Voeux Road, Central, Hong Kong PRC

Tel: 852-2572-8988　Fax: 852-2572-7497

AUDIO VISUAL SERVICES CORPORATION

111 West Ocean Blvd, Ste., Long Beach, CA, 90802

Tel: (562) 366-0620　　　Fax: (562) 366-0628　　　www.avservicecorp.com

Plans and produces meetings, events, and media campaigns: creates film/video presentations; supports in-house communications and training programs: and supplies audio-visual equipment.

Audio Visual Services, 15/F, Kinwick Centre, 32 Hollywood Rd., Central, Hong Kong PRC

Tel: 852-2805-1767　Fax: 852-2805-1768

AUTODESK INC.

111 McInnis Parkway, San Rafael, CA, 94903

Tel: (415) 507-5000　　　Fax: (415) 507-6112　　　www.autodesk.com

Develop/marketing/support computer-aided design, engineering, scientific and multimedia software products.

Autodesk Far East Ltd., Units 414-416, 4/F, Hong Kong Industrial Technology Centre, 72 Tat Chee Ave., Kowloon Tong, Hong Kong PRC

Tel: 852-2824-2338　Fax: 852-2824-3228

AUTOMATIC SWITCH CO. (ASCO)

50-60 Hanover Rd., Florham Park, NJ, 07932

Tel: (973) 966-2000　　　Fax: (973) 966-2628　　　www.asco.com

Mfr. solenoid valves, emergency power controls, pressure and temperature switches.

ASCO Asia, Hong Kong, Branson Ultrasonics Asia Pacific Co. Inc., 5A Pioneer Bldg., 213 Wai Yip St., Kwun Tong Kowloon, Hong Kong PRC

Tel: 852-2343-8580　Fax: 852-2790-1771　Contact: Tony Wong

AVERY DENNISON CORPORATION

150 N. Orange Grove Blvd., Pasadena, CA, 91103

Tel: (626) 304-2000　　　Fax: (626) 792-7312　　　www.averydennison.com

Mfr. pressure-sensitive adhesives and materials, office products, labels, tags, retail systems, Carter's Ink and specialty chemicals.

Dennison Trading Hong Kong Ltd., 1301-3, Lu Plaza, 2 Wing Yip Street, Kwun Tong Kowloon, Hong Kong PRC

Tel: 852-2802-9618　Fax: 852-2588-1344

Soabar Systems (HK) Ltd., 16 Westland Rd., Quarry Bay, Hong Kong PRC

AVICI SYSTEMS INC.

101 Billerica Avenue, Bldg. 2, North Billerica, MA, 01862

Tel: (978) 964-2000　　　Fax: (978) 955-2100　　　www.avici.com

Engaged in telecommunications.

Avici Systems International, 39/F, One Pacific Place, 88 Queensway, Admiralty, Hong Kong PRC

Tel: 852-2273-5128

AVIS GROUP HOLDINGS, INC.

6 Sylvan Way, Parsippany, NJ, 07054

Tel: (973) 222-3000　　　Fax: (973) 222-4381　　　www.avis.com

Car rental services.

Avis Group Holdings Ltd., Bonaventure House, 85-91 Leighton Rd., Causeway Bay, Hong Kong PRC

AVNET INC.

2211 South 47th Street, Phoenix, AZ, 85034

Tel: (480) 643-2000　　Fax: (480) 643-4670　　www.avnet.com

Distributor electronic components, computers and peripherals.

Avnet WKK Components Ltd., 16/F, Spectrum Tower, 53 Hung To Road, Kwun Tong, Kowloon, Hong Kong PRC

Tel: 852-217-65388　Fax: 852-279-02182

AVOCENT CORPORATION

4991 Corporate Drive, Huntsville, AL, 35805

Tel: (256) 430-4000　　Fax: (250) 430-4030　　www.avocent.com

Mfr. computer hardware.

Avocent Hong Kong, 1402 Kwai Hung Holdings Centre, 89 King's Road, North Point, Hong Kong PRC

AVON PRODUCTS, INC.

1345 Avenue of the Americas, New York, NY, 10105-0196

Tel: (212) 282-5000　　Fax: (212) 282-6049　　www.avon.com

Mfr. direct seller of cosmetics and beauty-related items.

Avon Cosmetics Hong Kong Ltd., 3601 Bond St., East Tower, Queensway, Hong Kong PRC

Contact: Jose Ferreira, Pres. Asia-Pacific

AVX CORPORATION

801 17th Ave. South, Myrtle Beach, SC, 29577

Tel: (843) 448-9411　　Fax: (843) 448-7139　　www.avxcorp.com

Mfr. multilayer ceramic capacitors.

AVX/Kyocera Asia Ltd., Hilder Centre, 3/F, 2 Sung Ping St., Hunghom Kowloon, Hong Kong PRC

BAIN & COMPANY, INC.

Two Copley Place, Boston, MA, 02116

Tel: (617) 572-2000　　Fax: (617) 572-2427　　www.bain.com

Strategic management consulting services.

Bain & Company (Hong Kong), 10/F, One Pacific Place, 88 Queensway, Hong Kong PRC

Tel: 852-2978-8800　Fax: 852-2978-8801

BAKER & McKENZIE

130 East Randolph Drive, Ste. 2500, Chicago, IL, 60601

Tel: (312) 861-8000　　Fax: (312) 861-2899　　www.bakerinfo.com

International legal services.

Baker & McKenzie, 14/F, Hutchison House, 10 Harcourt Rd., Hong Kong PRC

Tel: 852-2846-1888　Fax: 852-2845-2476

BAKER HUGHES INCORPORATED

3900 Essex Lane, Ste. 1200, Houston, TX, 77027

Tel: (713) 439-8600　　Fax: (713) 439-8699　　www.bakerhughes.com

Develop and apply technology to drill, complete and produce oil and natural gas wells; provide separation systems to petroleum, municipal, continuous process and mining industries.

Baker Hughes Inc., c/o Star Business Centre, Ste. 1229, Satr House, 3 Salisbury Rd., TST Kowloon, Hong Kong PRC

Tel: 852-2314-4416　Fax: 852-2736-9631

BALDWIN TECHNOLOGY COMPANY, INC.

12 Commerce Drive, Shelton, CT, 06484

Tel: (203) 402-1000　　Fax: (203) 402-5500　　www.baldwintech.com

Mfr./services material handling, accessories, control and prepress equipment for print industry.

Baldwin Asia Pacific Ltd., Unit A, 26/F, Seaview Plaza, 283 Shaukeiwan Rd., Hong Kong PRC

Tel: 852-2811-2987　Fax: 852-2811-0641　Contact: Akira Hara, Pres.

Baldwin Printing Controls Ltd., Unit A, 26/F, Seaview Plaza, 283 Shaukeiwan Rd., Hong Kong PRC

Tel: 852-2811-2987　Fax: 852-2811-0641　Contact: Simon Li, Mgr.

BALL CORPORATION
10 Longs Peak Drive, Broomfield, CO, 80021

Tel: (303) 469-3131   Fax: (303) 460-2127   www.ball.com

Mfr. metal beverage and food containers, glass containers, aerospace systems and services.

Ball Asia Pacific Ltd., Hong Kong PRC

BANK OF AMERICA CORPORATION
Bank of America Corporate Center, Charlotte, NC, 28255

Tel: (415) 622-3530   Fax: (704) 386-6699   www.bankofamerica.com

Financial services.

BA Asia Ltd., Bank of America Tower, 14/F, 12 Harcourt Rd., GPO Box 799, Hong Kong PRC
Tel: 852-2847-6467   Fax: 852-2847-6566   Contact: Frances Taylor

Bank of America - Asia Region, Devon House, 17/F, 979 King's Rd., Quarry Bay, Hong Kong PRC
Tel: 852-2597-3888   Fax: 852-2597-3886   Contact: Robert P. Morrow III

Bank of America NT & SA, Bank of America Tower, 2/F, 12 Harcourt Rd., GPO Box 472, Hong Kong PRC
Tel: 852-2847-5882   Fax: 852-2847-5200   Contact: D.H. Garschagen, EVP

BANK OF HAWAII CORPORATION
130 Merchant Street, Honolulu, HI, 96813

Tel: (808) 643-3888   Fax: (808) 537-8440   www.boh.com

Engaged in commercial and consumer banking services.

Bank of Hawaii Corporation, 6201, Central Plaza, 18 Harbour Road, Wan Chai, Hong Kong PRC
Tel: 852-2588-9488

THE BANK OF NEW YORK
One Wall Street, New York, NY, 10286

Tel: (212) 495-1784   Fax: (212) 495-2546   www.bankofny.com

Banking services.

The Bank of New York, New Henry House, 7/F, 10 Ice House St., GPO Box 67, Hong Kong PRC
Tel: 852-2840-9888   Fax: 852-2810-5279

Wing Hang Bank Limited, 161 Queen's Road, Central, Hong Kong PRC

BANK ONE CORPORATION
One Bank One Plaza, Chicago, IL, 60670

Tel: (312) 732-4000   Fax: (312) 732-3366   www.fcnbd.com

Provides financial products and services.

Bank One, NA, 13/F Jardine House, 1 Connaught Place, Hong Kong PRC
Tel: 852-2844-9222   Fax: 852-2844-9318   Contact: Richard L. Kolehmainen, Head of Office

C. R. BARD, INC.
730 Central Ave., Murray Hill, NJ, 07974

Tel: (908) 277-8000   Fax: (908) 277-8078   www.crbard.com

Mfr. health care products.

Bard International, Fleet House, 901, 38 Gloucester Rd., Wanchai, Hong Kong PRC

BARRA, INC.
2100 Milvia Street, Berkeley, CA, 94704

Tel: (510) 548-5442   Fax: (510) 548-4374   www.barra.com

Mfr. analytical software for private investors and portfolio managers.

BARRA International, Ltd., 1910 Jardine House, 1 Connaught Place, Central, Hong Kong PRC
Tel: 852-2521-3083

BATES WORLDWIDE INC.
498 Seventh Avenue, New York, NY, 10018

Tel: (212) 297-7000   Fax: (212) 986-0270   www.batesww.com

Advertising, marketing, public relations and media consulting.

Bates 141 Hong Kong, 17/F, The Lee Gardens, 33 Hysan Ave., Causeway Bay, Hong Kong PRC
Tel: 852-2103-6666   Fax: 852-2520-6660   Contact: Simon Holt, Dir.

Bates Graffix Ltd., 4/F, Golden Star Bldg., 11 Lockhart Rd., Wanchai, Hong Kong PRC
Tel: 852-2527-2766   Contact: S. Siu, Mgr.

Bates Hong Kong, 18/F, The Lee Gardens, 33 Hysan Ave., Causeway Bay, Hong Kong PRC
Tel: 852-2103-6666   Contact: Jeffrey Yu, CEO

BAUSCH & LOMB INC.

One Bausch & Lomb Place, Rochester, NY, 14604-2701
Tel: (716) 338-6000   Fax: (716) 338-6007   www.bausch.com
Mfr. vision care products and accessories.

Bausch & Lomb (Hong Kong) Ltd., Shaukeiwan, Hong Kong PRC

Bausch & Lomb Hong Kong, 26/F, Cityplaza 1, Taikooshing, Hong Kong PRC

BAX GLOBAL INC.

16808 Armstrong Ave., PO Box 19571, Irvine, CA, 92623
Tel: (949) 752-4000   Fax: (949) 260-3182   www.baxworld.com
Air freight forwarder.

BAX Global, 2/F, Sunhing Chekiang Godown, 8 Sze Shan St., Yau Tong, Kowloon, Hong Kong PRC
Tel: 852-2379-9280   Fax: 852-2379-9289

BAXTER INTERNATIONAL INC.

One Baxter Parkway, Deerfield, IL, 60015
Tel: (847) 948-2000   Fax: (847) 948-3948   www.baxter.com
Mfr. products and provide services in the field of the administration of medication and bioscience.

Baxter Healthcare Ltd., Rm 2003-6, CRC Protective Tower, 38 Gloucester Road, Wanchai, Hong Kong PRC
Tel: 852-2-802-4535

BBDO WORLDWIDE

1285 Ave. of the Americas, New York, NY, 10019
Tel: (212) 459-5000   Fax: (212) 459-6645   www.bbdo.com
Multinational group of advertising agencies.

BBDO Asia Pacific, Hong Kong PRC

BBDO Hong Kong, Hong Kong PRC

BDO SEIDMAN, LLP   BELGIUM

130 East Randolph Street, Chicago, IL, 60601
Tel: (312) 856-9100   Fax: (312) 856-1379   www.bdo.com
International accounting and financial consulting firm.

BDO Asia Pacific Reg. Office, 29/F, Wing On Centre, 111 Connaught Road, Central, Hong Kong PRC
Tel: 852-2541-5041   Fax: 852-2815-0002   Contact: Floyd T. Chan, Reg. Dir.

BDO China, 29/F, Wing On Centre, 111 Connaught Road, Central, Hong Kong PRC
Tel: 852-2541-5041   Fax: 852-2815-0002   Contact: Jennifer Y. Yip

BDO Mcabe Lo & Co., 29/F, Wing On Centre, 111 Connaught Road, Central, Hong Kong PRC
Tel: 852-2541-5041   Fax: 852-2815-0002   Contact: Albert Au

BEA SYSTEMS, INC.

2315 North First Street, St. Jose, CA, 95131
Tel: (408) 570-8000   Fax: (408) 570-8091   www.beasys.com
Develops communications management software and provider of software consulting services.

BEA Systems HK Ltd., Room 1701, 17/F, Cityplaza One, 1111 King's Road, Taikoo Shing, Island East, Hong Kong PRC
Tel: 852-2290-9222

THE BEAR STEARNS & COMPANIES., INC.

245 Park Ave., New York, NY, 10167
Tel: (212) 272-2000   Fax: (212) 272-3092   www.bearstearns.com
Investment banking, securities broker/dealer and investment advisory services.

Bear Stearns Asia Ltd., Citibank Tower, Citibank Plaza, 26/F, 3 Garden Rd., Hong Kong PRC
Tel: 852-2593-2700   Fax: 852-2593-2870

BECHTEL GROUP INC.

50 Beale Street, PO Box 3965, San Francisco, CA, 94105-1895

Tel: (415) 768-1234   Fax: (415) 768-9038   www.bechtel.com

General contractors in engineering, construction and project management.

Bechtel International Corp., 22/F, Li Po Chun Chambers, 189 Des Voeux Rd., Central, Hong Kong PRC

Tel: 852-2970-7000   Fax: 852-2840-1272

BECKMAN COULTER, INC.

4300 N. Harbor Boulevard, Fullerton, CA, 92834

Tel: (714) 871-4848   Fax: (714) 773-8898   www.beckmancoulter.com

Develop/mfr./marketing automated systems and supplies for biological analysis.

Beckman Coulter Hong Kong Ltd., Oxford House, 12/F, 979 King's Road, TaiKoo Place, Hong Kong PRC

Tel: 852-2814-7431

BEL FUSE INC.

198 Van Vorst Street, Jersey City, NJ, 07302

Tel: (201) 432-0463   Fax: (201) 432-9542   www.belfuse.com

Mfr. electronic components for networking, fuses, delay lines, hybrids and magnetic products.

Bel Fuse Ltd., 8/F, 8 Luk Hop St., San Po Kong, Kowloon, Hong Kong PRC

BELDEN, INC.

7701 Forsyth Blvd., Ste. 800, St. Louis, MO, 63015

Tel: (314) 854-8000   Fax: (314) 854-8001   www.belden.com

Mfr. electronic wire and cable products.

Belden International, Inc., 2/F, Shui On Centre, 6-8 Harbour Road, Wanchai, Hong Kong PRC

BELLSOUTH CORPORATION LATIN AMERICA

1155 Peachtree Street NE, Ste. 400, Atlanta, GA, 30367

Tel: (404) 249-4800   Fax: (404) 249-4880   www.bellsouth.com

Mobile communications, telecommunications network systems.

BellSouth Intl., Hong Kong PRC

LOUIS BERGER INTERNATIONAL INC.

100 Halsted Street, East Orange, NJ, 07019

Tel: (201) 678-1960   Fax: (201) 672-4284   www.louisberger.com

Consulting engineers, engaged in architecture, environmental and advisory services.

Louis Berger Finance & Dev. Co., Ltd., GPO Box 8764, Central District, Hong Kong PRC

Tel: 852-2523-6111   Fax: 852-2845-9584

BERNARD HODES GROUP

555 Madison Ave., New York, NY, 10022

Tel: (212) 935-4000   Fax: (212) 755-7324   www.hodes.com

Provides recruitment communications and staffing solutions.

Bernard Hodes Group (Hong Kong), 18/F, Centre Point, 181-183 Gloucester Road, Hong Kong PRC

BIO-RAD LABORATORIES INC.

1000 Alfred Nobel Drive, Hercules, CA, 94547

Tel: (510) 724-7000   Fax: (510) 724-3167   www.bio-rad.com

Mfr. life science research products, clinical diagnostics, analytical instruments.

Bio-Rad Pacific Limited, Unit 1111, New Kowloon Plaza, 38 Tai Kok Tsui Road, Kowloon, Hong Kong PRC

Tel: 852-2789-3300   Fax: 852-2789-1257

BLACK & VEATCH LLP

8400 Ward Pkwy., PO Box 8405, Kansas City, MO, 64114

Tel: (816) 339-2000   Fax: (816) 339-2934   www.bv.com

Engaged in engineering, construction and consulting, specializing in infrastructure development in the fields of energy, water and information.

Binnie Black & Veatch Hong Kong Ltd., New Town Tower 11/F, Pak Hok Ting St., Shatin NT, Hong Kong PRC

Tel: 852-2601-1000   Fax: 852-2601-3988   Contact: Martin D. McMillan

BLACKROCK, INC.

345 Park Avenue, New York, NY, 10154

Tel: (212) 754-5560   Fax: (212) 409-3123   www.blackrock.com

Engaged in investment management services.

BlackRock Inc., Jardine House, Ste. 3717-3718, 1 Connaught Place, Central, Hong Kong PRC

Tel: 852-2111-2738   Fax: 852-2111-0051

BLOOMBERG L.P.

499 Park Ave., New York, NY, 10022

Tel: (212) 318-2000   Fax: (212) 940-1954   www.bloomberg.com

Publishes magazines and provides TV, radio and newspaper wire services.

Bloomberg L.P., Hong Kong PRC

BMC SOFTWARE, INC.

2101 City West Blvd., Houston, TX, 77042-2827

Tel: (713) 918-8800   Fax: (713) 918-8000   www.bmc.com

Engaged in mainframe-related utilities software and services.

BMC Software, Suite 5501, 55/F, Central Plaza, 18 Harbour Road, Wanchai, Hong Kong PRC

BONTEX INC.

One Bondex Drive, Buena Vista, VA, 24416

Tel: (540) 261-2181   Fax: (540) 261-3784   www.bontex.com

Engaged in development and distribution of advanced materials, systems for a broad range of applications.

Bontex Hong Kong, Flat B3, Paterson Bldg., 7 Great George Street, Causeway Bay, Hong Kong PRC

BOOZ-ALLEN & HAMILTON INC.

8283 Greensboro Drive, McLean, VA, 22102

Tel: (703) 902-5000   Fax: (703) 902-3333   www.bah.com

International management and technology consultants.

Booz Allen & Hamilton (HK) Ltd., 1306-07 Grand Central Plaza, Shatin Rural Committee Road Shatin, Hong Kong PRC

Tel: 852-2634-1878   Fax: 852-2634-1879

THE BOSTON CONSULTING GROUP

Exchange Place, 31st Fl., Boston, MA, 02109

Tel: (617) 973-1200   Fax: (617) 973-1339   www.bcg.com

Management consulting company.

The Boston Consulting Group, 34/F, Shell Tower, Times Square, Causeway Bay, Hong Kong PRC

Tel: 852-2506-2111

BOSTON SCIENTIFIC CORPORATION (BSC)

One Scientific Place, Natick, MA, 01760-1537

Tel: (508) 650-8000   Fax: (508) 650-8923   www.bostonscientific.com

Developer, manufacturer and marketer of medical devices.

Boston Scientific Hong Kong Ltd., Unit 1403, Kodak House II, 39 Healthy St. East, North Point, Hong Kong PRC

Tel: 852-2563-1227   Fax: 852-2563-5276

BOURNS INC.

1200 Columbia Avenue, Riverside, CA, 92507

Tel: (909) 781-5500   Fax: (909) 781-5006   www.bourns.com

Mfr. resistive components and networks, precision potentiometers, panel controls, switches, transducers and surge protectors..

Bourns Asia Pacific Inc., Room 905, Tower 3, 33 Canton, Tsim Shat Sui Kowloon, Hong Kong PRC

BOWNE & COMPANY, INC.

345 Hudson Street, New York, NY, 10014

Tel: (212) 924-5500   Fax: (212) 229-3420   www.bowne.com

Financial printing and foreign language translation, localization (software), internet design and maintenance and facilities management.

Bowne Financial Print, 3402, Citibank Tower, Citibank Plaza, Central, Hong Kong PRC

Tel: 852-2526-0688   Fax: 852-2526-1200   Contact: Paul Dalton, Mng. Dir.

BOYDEN CONSULTING CORPORATION

364 Elwood Ave., Hawthorne, NY, 10502

Tel: (914) 747-0093   Fax: (914) 980-6147   www.boyden.com

International executive search firm.

Boyden Associates Ltd., 1 on Hing Terrace, 10/F, Wyndham St., Central, Hong Kong PRC

Tel: 852-2868-3882

BOZELL GROUP

40 West 23rd Street, New York, NY, 10010

Tel: (212) 727-5000   Fax: (212) 645-9173   www.bozell.com

Advertising, marketing, public relations and media consulting.

Bozell Hong Kong, 6/F, Sino Plaza, 256 Gloucester Rd., Causeway Bay, Hong Kong PRC

Tel: 852-2892-8698   Fax: 852-2892-8797   Contact: Gary Tse, Mgr.

Bozell Tong Barnes PR, Room 805B, Sino Plaza, 256 Gloucester Rd., Causeway Bay, Hong Kong PRC

Tel: 852-2575-0448   Fax: 852-2573-4823   Contact: Wendy Tong Barnes, Dir.

Bozell Worldwide, Inc. (Asia Pacific), 6/F, Sino Plaza, 256 Gloucester Rd., Causeway Bay, Hong Kong PRC

Tel: 852-2892-8678   Fax: 852-2892-8765   Contact: Roger Winter, CEO

Grant Advertising, Room 303, Sino Plaza, 256 Gloucester Rd., Causeway Bay, Hong Kong PRC

Tel: 852-2893-7171   Fax: 852-2893-3799   Contact: Dionne Kung, Gen. Mgr.

BRADY CORPORATION

6555 W. Good Hope Road, Milwaukee, WI, 53223

Tel: (414) 358-6600   Fax: (414) 358-6600   www.whbrady.com

Mfr. industrial ID for wire marking, circuit boards; facility ID, signage, printing systems and software.

Brady Corporation S.E.A. Pte. Ltd., Unit 1803-04, 18/F, CRE Centre, 889 Chenng Shawan Road, Kowloon, Hong Kong PRC

Tel: 852-2370-2082   Fax: 852-2359-3164

BRAND FARRAR BUXBAUM LLP

515 S. Flower Street, Ste. 3500, Los Angeles, CA, 90017-2201

Tel: (213) 228-0288   Fax: (213) 426-6222

International law firm specializing in cross-border disputes and business transactions; intellectual property.

Brand Farrar Buxbaum LLP, Ste. 1408-10, Shui On Centre, 6-8 Harbour Rd., Wanchai, Hong Kong PRC

Tel: 852-2523-7001   Fax: 852-2845-0947   Contact: Messrs. Farrar & Buxbaum, Sr. Ptnrs

BRANSON ULTRASONICS CORPORATION

41 Eagle Road, Danbury, CT, 06813-1961

Tel: (203) 796-0400   Fax: (203) 796-2285   www.branson-plasticsjoin.com

Engaged in design, development, manufacture and marketing of plastics joining, precision cleaning and processing equipment.

Branson Ultrasonics (Asia Pacific) Co. Ltd., 5/F, Trinity Industrial Bldg., 10 Shing Yip St., Kwun Tong, Kowloon, Hong Kong PRC

Tel: 852-2790-3393   Fax: 852-2341-2716

BRIGHTPOINT, INC.

600 East 96th Street, Ste. 575, Indianapolis, IN, 46240

Tel: (317) 805-4100   Fax: (317) 805-4101   www.brightpoint.com

Provider of outsourced services in the global wireless telecommunications and data industry; distribution of wireless voice and data products.

Brightpoint Asia Ltd., Unit C, 16/F, World Trust Tower, 50 Stanley Street, Central, Hong Kong PRC

Tel: 852-2537-4838   Fax: 852-2898-3520

BRISTOL-MYERS SQUIBB COMPANY

345 Park Ave., New York, NY, 10154-0037

Tel: (212) 546-4000   Fax: (212) 546-4020   www.bms.com

Pharmaceutical and food preparations, medical and surgical instruments.

BMS (Hong Kong), 29 Wong Chuk Hang Rd., Aberdeen, Hong Kong PRC

Bristol-Myers Squibb - Reg. HQ/ Hong Kong, Vita Tower, 8/F, Block B, 29 Wong Chuk Hang Rd., Hong Kong PRC

ConvaTec Pacific, Unit D, 16/F, Manulife Tower, 169 Electric Road, North Point, Hong Kong PRC

Tel: 852-2510-6500

BROADVISION, INC.

585 Broadway, Redwood City, CA, 94063

Tel: (650) 261-5100   Fax: (650) 261-5900   www.broadvision.com

Develops and delivers an integrated suite of packaged applications for personalized enterprise portals.

BroadVision Hong Kong, Room 6403, Central Plaza, 18 Harbour Road, Wanchai, Hong Kong PRC

Tel: 852-2824-4238

BROWN BROTHERS HARRIMAN & COMPANY

140 Broadway, New York, NY, 10005

Tel: (212) 483-1818   Fax: (212) 493-8526   www.bbh.com

Leading provider of mergers and acquisition advisory services and private equity capital to private and closely held public companies.

Brown Brothers Harriman, Gloucester Tower, 22/F, The Landmark, Central, Hong Kong PRC

Tel: 852-2877-3222

BROWN SHOE COMPANY, INC.

8300 Maryland Avenue, St. Louis, MO, 63105

Tel: (314) 854-4000   Fax: (314) 854-4274   www.brownshoe.com

Markets branded and private label footwear, including Dr. Scholl's, Air Step and Buster Brown.

Pagoda Intl. Footwear, 3/F, Two Harbour Front, 22 Tak Fung St., The Harbourfront, Hung Hom Kowloon, Hong Kong PRC

BRYAN CAVE LLP

211 North Broadway, St. Louis, MO, 63102

Tel: (314) 259-2000   Fax: (314) 259-2020   www.bryancave.com

International law firm.

Bryan Cave LLP, Lippo Centre, Tower One 37/F, 89 Queensway, Hong Kong PRC

Contact: John V. Lonsberg

BUCK CONSULTANTS INC.

One Penn Plaza, New York, NY, 10119

Tel: (212) 330-1000   Fax: (212) 695-4184   www.buckconsultants.com

Employee benefit, actuarial and compensation consulting services.

Buck Consultants, 32/F, One Exchange Sq., 8 Connaught Place, Central, Hong Kong PRC

BULOVA CORPORATION

One Bulova Ave., Woodside, NY, 11377-7874

Tel: (718) 204-3300   Fax: (718) 204-3546   www.bulova.com

Mfr. timepieces, watches and clocks, watch parts, batteries and precision defense products.

Bulova Watch Intl. Ltd., Unit 2-3, 3/F, Siu Wai Ind. Centre, 29-33 Wing Hong St., Cheung Sha Wan, Kowloon, Hong Kong PRC

LEO BURNETT, DIV. B-COM 3 GROUP

35 West Wacker Drive, Chicago, IL, 60601

Tel: (312) 220-5959	Fax: (312) 220-6533	www.leoburnett.com

Engaged in advertising, marketing, media buying and planning, and public relations.

Leo Burnett Ltd., 9/F, Mount Parker House, 1111 King's Road, Quarry Bay, Hong Kong PRC

Contact: Alan Treadgold

BURSON-MARSTELLER

230 Park Avenue South, New York, NY, 10003-1566

Tel: (212) 614-4000	Fax: (212) 614-4262	www.bm.com

Public relations/public affairs consultants.

Burson-Marsteller (HK) Ltd., 14/F, Stanhope House, 738 King's Rd., North Point, Hong Kong PRC

Tel: 852-2880-0229	Fax: 852-2856-1101

CADENCE DESIGN SYSTEMS, INC.

2655 Seely Ave., Bldg. 5, San Jose, CA, 95134

Tel: (408) 943-1234	Fax: (408) 943-0513	www.cadence.com

Mfr. electronic design automation software.

Cadence Design Systems, Tower 2, 03-07 The Gateway, 25 Canton Road Tsimshatsui, Kowloon, Hong Kong PRC

Tel: 852-2377-7111

CALLAWAY GOLF COMPANY

2180 Rutherford Rd., Carlsbad, CA, 92008-8815

Tel: (760) 931-1771	Fax: (760) 931-8013	www.callawaygolf.com

Mfr. and sales of golf clubs.

Callaway/Sportsmark Trading, Rm. 409-10, Haiphong Mansion, 4/F, 53-55 Haiphong Road, Tsim Sha Tsui Kowloon, Hong Kong PRC

Tel: 852-272-13366	Fax: 852-272-13268

CALTEX CORPORATION

PO Box 619500, Dallas, TX, 75261-9500

Tel: (972) 830-1000	Fax: (972) 830-1081	www.caltex.com

Petroleum products.

Caltex Oil Hong Kong Ltd., GPO Box 147, Hong Kong PRC

CALVIN KLEIN, INC.

205 West 39th Street, 4th Fl., New York, NY, 10018

Tel: (212) 719-2600	Fax: (212) 768-8922	www.calvinklein.com

Mfr. of high quality clothing and accessories

Calvin Klein Ltd., Hong Kong PRC

CAMBREX CORPORATION

1 Meadowlands Plaza, East Rutherford, NJ, 07063

Tel: (201) 804-3000	Fax: (201) 804-9852	www.cambrex.com

human health, animal health/agriculture and Mfr. biotechnology products and produce specialty chemicals.

Biesterfeld Asia Pacific Ltd., 1608, South Tower, World Finance Center, Harbour City, Canton Road, TST Kowloon, Hong Kong PRC

CAMPBELL SOUP COMPANY

Campbell Place, Camden, NJ, 08103-1799

Tel: (856) 342-4800	Fax: (856) 342-3878	www.campbellsoup.com

Mfr. food products.

Campbell Soup Asia Ltd., Hong Kong PRC

Contact: Andrew Hughson, VP

CANTOR FITZGERALD LP

299 Park Avenue, New York, NY, 10171

Tel: (212) 821-6710   Fax: (212) 821-6710   www.cantor.com

Engaged in fixed income securities and stocks.

Cantor Fitzgerald, 1 Harbour View Street, Ste. 2507, Central, Hong Kong PRC

CAPITAL CONTROLS COMPANY, INC.

3000 Advance Lane, PO Box 211, Colmar, PA, 18915-0211

Tel: (215) 997-4000   Fax: (215) 997-4062   www.capitalcontrols.com

Mfr./services water disinfecting products and systems.

Capital Controls Co. Ltd., Unit 1408 Riley House, 88 Lei Muk Road, Kwai Chung, Hong Kong PRC

Contact: Gary Tse

THE CAPITAL GROUP COS INC.

333 South Hope Street, Los Angeles, CA, 90071

Tel: (213) 486-9200   Fax: (213) 486-9557   www.capgroup.com

Investment management.

Capital Research Company, Suite2601, One International Finance Ctr., No. 1 Harbour View Street, Hong Kong PRC

Tel: 852-2842-1000   Fax: 852-2810-6788

CARGILL, INC.

15407 McGinty Road West, Minnetonka, MN, 55440-5625

Tel: (612) 742-7575   Fax: (612) 742-7393   www.cargill.com

Food products, feeds, animal products.

Cargill Hong Kong Ltd., 36/F, One Pacific Place, 88 Queensway, Central, Hong Kong PRC

CARLISLE COMPANIES INC.

13925 Ballantyne Corporate Place, Ste. 400, Charlotte, NC, 28277

Tel: (704) 501-1100   Fax: (704) 501-1190   www.carlisle.com

Engaged in rubber, plastics and friction technologies.

Carlisle Companies Hong Kong, 1204-5, Great Eagle Centre, 23 Harbour Road, Wanchai, Hong Kong PRC

Tel: 852-2511-5800   Contact: Kevin G. Forster

CARLISLE SYNTEC SYSTEMS

PO Box 7000, Carlisle, PA, 17013

Tel: (717) 245-7000   Fax: (717) 245-9107   www.carlisle-syntec.com

Mfr. electrometric roofing and waterproofing systems.

Carlisle Asia Pacific, 1204-5, Great Eagle Centre, 23 Harbour Road, Wanchai, Hong Kong PRC

Tel: 852-2511-5800   Fax: 852-2824-4747

THE CARLYLE GROUP L.P.

1001 Pennsylvania Avenue, NW, Washington, DC, 20004-2505

Tel: (202) 347-2626   Fax: (202) 347-1818   www.thecarlylegroup.com

Global investor in defense contracts.

Carlyle Asia, Asia Pacific Finance Tower, 32/F, 3 Garden Road, Hong Kong PRC

Tel: 852-2878-7000   Fax: 852-2878-7007   Contact: John J. Ying, Mng. Dir

CARRIER CORPORATION

One Carrier Place, Farmington, CT, 06034-4015

Tel: (860) 674-3000   Fax: (860) 679-3010   www.carrier.com

Mfr./distributor/services A/C, heating and refrigeration equipment.

Carrier China Ltd., Shatin NT, Hong Kong PRC

Tel: 852-2694-3111   Fax: 852-2691-2845

Carrier Hong Kong Ktd., PO Box 260, Shatin Post Office, NT, Hong Kong PRC

Carrier Transicold (HK) Ltd., King's Rd., Hong Kong PRC

CATERPILLAR INC.

100 NE Adams Street, Peoria, IL, 61629-6105

Tel: (309) 675-1000   Fax: (309) 675-1182   www.cat.com

Mfr. earth/material-handling and construction machinery and equipment and engines.

Caterpillar (HK) Ltd., c/o Caterpillar Far East Ltd., Sun Hung Kai Centre, 30 Harbour Rd., GPO 3069, Wanchai, Hong Kong PRC

Caterpillar Far East Ltd., Sun Hung Kai Centre, 30 Harbour Rd., GPO 3069, Wanchai, Hong Kong PRC

CB RICHARD ELLIS SERVICES

200 N. Sepulveda Blvd., Ste. 300, El Segundo, CA, 90245-4380

Tel: (310) 563-8600   Fax: (310) 563-8670   www.cbrichardellis.com

Commercial real estate services.

CB Richard Ellis Ltd., 1130, Ocean Center, Harbour City Tsimshatsui, Kowloon, Hong Kong PRC

CB Richard Ellis Ltd., 32/F, Bank of China Tower, 1 Garden Rd., Central, Hong Kong PRC

Tel: 852-2820-2800   Fax: 852-2810-0380   Contact: David Runciman, Chmn.

CB Richard Ellis Ltd., Suite 3401, Central Plaza, 18 Harbour Rd., Wanchai, Hong Kong PRC

CCH INCORPORATED

2700 Lake Cook Road, Riverwoods, IL, 60015

Tel: (847) 267-7000   Fax: (800) 224-8299   www.cch.com

Provides tax and business law information and software for accounting, legal, human resources, securities and health care professionals.

CCH Hong Kong Limited, Room 801-2, Luk Yu Building, 24-26 Stanley Street, Central, Hong Kong PRC

Tel: 852-2526-7614   Fax: 852-2521-7874

C-COR.NET CORP.

60 Decibel Road, State College, PA, 16801

Tel: (814) 238-2461   Fax: (814) 238-4065   www.c-cor.com

Design/mfr. amplifiers, fiber optics electronic equipment for data and cable TV systems.

C-COR.net Hong Kong, 4/F, Flat 4B, 48 Crestmont Villa, Discovery Bay, Hong Kong PRC

Tel: 852-2914-2705   Fax: 852-2914-2460   Contact: Howard Rupert, Mgr.

CDM INTERNATIONAL INC.

50 Hampshire Street, Cambridge, MA, 02139

Tel: (617) 452-6000   Fax: (617) 452-8000   www.cdm.com

Consulting engineers.

CDM Hong Kong, Room 4305-12, Metroplaza Tower 1, 223 Hing Fong Rd., Kwai Fong, Hong Kong PRC

Tel: 852-2428-2332

CELLSTAR CORPORATION

1730 Briercroft Ct., Carrollton, TX, 75006

Tel: (972) 466-5000   Fax: (972) 466-0288   www.cellstar.com

Provides wireless communications products.

CellStar Asia Pacific, 509-510, 5/FL, Block B, Sing Tao Bldg. 1, Wang Kwong Road, Kowloon, Hong Kong PRC

Tel: 852-2-757-0998   Fax: 852-2-759-5255

CENDANT CORPORATION

9 West 57th Street, New York, NY, 10019

Tel: (212) 413-1800   Fax: (212) 413-1918   www.cendant.com

Membership-based, direct marketer offering shopping/travel/insurance and dining discount programs

Europe Tax Free Shopping, Pacific Leisure Group, 10/F, Tung Ming Bldg., 40 Des Voeux Rd., Central, Hong Kong PRC

Tel: 852-2525-1365   Fax: 852-252-53290

CENTRAL NATIONAL-GOTTESMAN INC.

3 Manhattanville Road, Purchase, NY, 10577-2110

Tel: (914) 696-9000   Fax: (914) 696-1066   www.cng-inc.com

Distribution of pulp and paper products.

Central National Hong Kong Ltd., New Trend Centre, Rm. 1504, 704 Prince Edward Rd. East, Sanpo Kong Kowloon, Hong Kong PRC

Tel: 852-2398-7666   Fax: 852-2398-7570   Contact: Ian K. Y. Fung

CENTURY 21 REAL ESTATE CORPORATION

One Campus Drive, Parsippany, NJ, 07054-3826

Tel: (973) 496-5722   Fax: (973) 496-5527   www.century21.com

Engaged in real estate sales.

Century 21 Hong Kong, Ste. 1207, 12/F, Wing Shan Tower, 173 Des Voeux Rd., Central, Hong Kong PRC

Tel: 852-2869-7221   Fax: 852-2522-8596

CHADBOURNE & PARKE LLP

30 Rockefeller Plaza, New York, NY, 10112-0127

Tel: (212) 408-5100   Fax: (212) 541-5369   www.chadbourne.com

Engaged in international law.

Chadbourne & Parke, Suite 2203, Tower I Lippo Centre, 89 Queensway, Hong Kong PRC

Tel: 852-2842-5400   Fax: 852-2521-7527   Contact: N. Theodore Zink

CHEMETALL OAKITE

50 Valley Road, Berkeley Heights, NJ, 07922-2798

Tel: (908) 464-6900   Fax: (908) 464-7914   www.oakite.com

Mfr. chemical products for industry cleaning and metal treating.

Chemetall Hong Kong Ltd., Unit 8 10/F, Block 3, 18 Tin Hau Road Tuen Mun, Nan Fung Industrial City, Hong Kong PRC

THE CHERRY CORPORATION

3600 Sunset Ave., PO Box 718, Waukegan, IL, 60087

Tel: (847) 662-9200   Fax: (847) 662-2990   www.cherrycorp.com

Mfr. electrical switches, electronic keyboards, controls and displays.

Cherasia Ltd., 14/F, Block B,, North Point Industrial Bldg., 499 Kings Rd., North Point, Hong Kong PRC

Tel: 852-2565-6678   Fax: 852-2565-6827

CHESTERTON BLUMENAUER BINSWANGER

Two Logan Square, 4th Floor, Philadelphia, PA, 19103-2759

Tel: (215) 448-6000   Fax: (215) 448-6238   www.cbbi.com

Real estate and related services.

Chesterton Petty Ltd., 1113 New T&T Centre, Harbour City, 1 Connaught Place, Kowloon, Hong Kong PRC

THE CHUBB CORPORATION

15 Mountain View Road, Warren, NJ, 07061-1615

Tel: (908) 580-2000   Fax: (908) 580-3606   www.chubb.com

Holding company for property and casualty insurance and liability insurance for corporate executives.

Federal Insurance Co., Rm. 1801-3, Harcourt House, 39 Gloucester Rd., Wanchai, Hong Kong PRC

Tel: 852-2861-3668   Fax: 852-2861-2681

CIENA CORPORATION

1201 Winterson Road, Linthicum, MD, 21090-2205

Tel: (410) 865-8500   Fax: (410) 694-5750   www.ciena.com

Mfr. optical network switching hardware.

CIENA Ltd., 181 Queen's Road, 20/F, Central, Hong Kong PRC

CIGNA COMPANIES

One Liberty Place, Philadelphia, PA, 19192

Tel: (215) 761-1000　　　Fax: (215) 761-5511　　　www.cigna.com

Insurance, invest, health care and other financial services.

CIGNA Property & Casualty Insurance Co., 29/F, Office Tower, Convention Plaza, 1 Harbour Rd., Wanchai, Hong Kong PRC

CIGNA Worldwide Insurance Co., 16/F, East Point Centre, 555 Hennessy Rd., Causeway Bay, Hong Kong PRC

Esis Intl. Inc., 5/F, Edinburgh Tower, The Landmark, 15 Queen's Rd., Central, Hong Kong PRC

Insurance Co. of North America, 29/F, Office Tower, Convention Plaza, 1 Harbour Rd., PO Box 703, Wanchai, Hong Kong PRC

CINCOM SYSTEMS INC.

55 Merchant Street, Cincinnati, OH, 45446

Tel: (513) 612-2300　　　Fax: (513) 481-8332　　　www.cincom.com

Develop/distributor computer software.

Cincom Distribution, c/o Pro-Technic, G/F & Blks. A-C & J, 4/F, Kwai Shun Industrial Centre,, 51-63 Container Port Road, Kwai Chung, Hong Kong PRC

Tel: 852-24282727　Fax: 852-24804764

CIRRUS LOGIC, INC.

4210 South industrial Drive, Austin, TX, 78744

Tel: (512) 445-7222　　　Fax: (512) 445-7581　　　www.cirrus.com

Engaged in manufacture of semiconductors and integrated circuits for entertainment devices.

Cirrus Logic, 80 Shanghai Street, 20/F, Kowloon, Hong Kong PRC

Tel: 852-2376-0801

CISCO SYSTEMS, INC.

170 West Tasman Drive, San Jose, CA, 95134-1706

Tel: (408) 526-4000　　　Fax: (408) 526-4100　　　www.cisco.com

Develop/mfr./market computer hardware and software networking systems.

Cisco Systems Hong Kong, Ltd., Ste. 1009, Great Eagle Centre, 23 Harbour Rd., Wanchai, Hong Kong PRC

Tel: 852-583-9110　Fax: 852-824-9528

CITIGROUP, INC.

399 Park Avenue, New York, NY, 10022

Tel: (212) 559-1000　　　Fax: (212) 559-3646　　　www.citigroup.com

Provides insurance and financial services worldwide.

Citigroup, 8/F, Dorst House, Taikoo Place, 979 King's Rd., Quarry Bay, Hong Kong PRC

Tel: 852-2810-1961　Fax: 852-2860-0222　Contact: Stephen Long

CITRIX SYSTEMS, INC.

6400 NW 6th Way, Fort Lauderdale, FL, 33309

Tel: (954) 267-3000　　　Fax: (954) 267-9319　　　www.citrix.com

Developer of computer software.

Citrix Systems HK Ltd., Suite 5A, Floor 17, Sino Plaza, 255-257 Gloucester Road, Causeway Bay, Hong Kong PRC

Tel: 852-2838-8939

CLARCOR INC.

2323 Sixth Street, PO Box 7007, Rockford, IL, 61125

Tel: (815) 962-8867　　　Fax: (815) 962-0417　　　www.clarcor.com

Mfr. filtration products and consumer packaging products.

Clarcor, Flat 3, 9/F, Port Centre, 38 Chengtu Rd., Aberdeen, Hong Kong PRC

CLEARY GOTTLIEB STEEN & HAMILTON

One Liberty Plaza, New York, NY, 10006

Tel: (212) 225-2000　　　Fax: (212) 225-3999　　　www.cgsh.com

Engaged in international law.

Cleary, Gottlieb, Steen & Hamilton, 56/F, Bank of China Tower, One Garden Rd., Hong Kong PRC

THE CLOROX COMPANY

1221 Broadway, PO Box 24305, Oakland, CA, 94623-1305

Tel: (510) 271-7000   Fax: (510) 832-1463   www.clorox.com

Mfr. soap and detergents, and domestic consumer packaged products.

Clorox (Far East) Ltd., Hong Kong PRC

COACH LEATHERWEAR COMPANY

516 West 34th Street, New York, NY, 10001

Tel: (212) 594-1850   Fax: (212) 594-1682   www.coach.com

Mfr. and sales of high-quality leather products, including handbags, wallets and shoes.

Coach Leatherwear Co., Landmark Boutique Shop, G4, G/F, 5-17 Pedder Street, Central, Hong Kong PRC

THE COCA-COLA COMPANY

1 Coca Cola Plaza, Atlanta, GA, 30313

Tel: (404) 676-2121   Fax: (404) 676-6792   www.coca-cola.com

Mfr./marketing/distributor soft drinks, syrups and concentrates, juice and juice-drink products.

Coca-Cola Central Pacific Ltd., GPO Box 916, Hong Kong PRC

Swire Bottlers, GPO Box 916, Hong Kong PRC

COGNEX CORPORATION

1 Vision Drive, Natick, MA, 01760

Tel: (508) 650-3000   Fax: (508) 650-3333   www.cognex.com

Mfr. machine vision systems.

Cognex Hong Kong, Unit 3506, 35/F., Tower 2, Lippo Centre, 89 Queensway, Admiralty, Hong Kong PRC

Tel: 852-28019618   Fax: 852-28019617

COHERENT INC.

5100 Patrick Henry Drive, PO Box 54980, Santa Clara, CA, 95056

Tel: (408) 764-4000   Fax: (408) 764-4800   www.cohr.com

Mfr. lasers for science, industrial and medical.

Coherent Pacific, Unit No. 1515-18, Level 15, Tower II, Grand Century Plaza, 193 Prince Edward Rd. West, Mongkok Kowloon, Hong Kong PRC

Tel: 852-2174-2800

COLFAX CORPORATION

9211 Forest Hill Avenue, Ste. 109, Richmond, VA, 23235

Tel: (804) 560-4070   Fax: (804) 560-4076   www.colfaxcorp.com

Mfr. industrial clutches and brakes and motion control products and components.

Warner Electric, 71-75 Container Port Road, Unit 4A, Kwai Chung, Hong Kong PRC

Tel: 852-2-615-9313   Fax: 852-2-6159162

COLGATE-PALMOLIVE COMPANY

300 Park Ave., New York, NY, 10022

Tel: (212) 310-2000   Fax: (212) 310-2919   www.colgate.com

Mfr. pharmaceuticals, cosmetics, toiletries and detergents.

Colgate-Palmolive Hong Kong Ltd., 11/F, Caroline Centre, 28 Yun Ping Rd., Causeway Bay, Hong Kong PRC

COMMERCIAL METALS COMPANY (CMC)

7800 Stemmons Fwy., Dallas, TX, 75247

Tel: (214) 689-4300   Fax: (214) 689-4320   www.commercialmetals.com

Metal collecting/processing, steel mills and metal trading.

CMC Far East Ltd., Unit C, 128 Gloucester Rd., Hong Kong PRC

COMPUTER ASSOCIATES INTERNATIONAL INC.

One Computer Associates Plaza, Islandia, NY, 11788

Tel: (516) 342-5224   Fax: (516) 342-5329   www.cai.com

Integrated business software for enterprise computing and information management, application development, manufacturing, financial applications and professional services.

Computer Associates Intl. Ltd., Suite 3008, 30/F, 12 Convention Plaza, Office Tower, 1 Harbour Rd., Wanchai, Hong Kong PRC

Tel: 852-2587-1388

COMPUWARE CORPORATION

31440 Northwestern Hwy., Farmington Hills, MI, 48334-2564

Tel: (248) 737-7300   Fax: (248) 737-7108   www.compuware.com

Develop and market software for enterprise and e-commerce solutions.

Compuware Asia - Pacific Ltd., Lincoln House, Level 11, 28 Tong Chong Street, Quarry Bay, Hong Kong PRC

COMVERSE, INC.

100 Quannapowitt Parkway, Wakefield, MA, 01880

Tel: (781) 246-9000   Fax: (781) 224-8143   www.comverse.com

Provides communications solutions.

Comverse Infosys Hong Kong, Room 1105, Emperor Centre, 288 Hennessy Road, Wanchai, Hong Kong PRC

Tel: 852-2574-7192   Fax: 852-2904-7676

CONAIR CORPORATION

1 Cummings Point Road, Stamford, CT, 06904

Tel: (203) 351-9000   Fax: (203) 351-9180   www.conair.com

Mfr. personal care and household appliances.

Continental Conair Ltd., World Trade Tower II, Kwun Tong, Kowloon, Hong Kong PRC

CONCURRENT COMPUTER CORPORATION

4375 River Green Pkwy., Duluth, GA, 30096

Tel: (678) 258-4000   Fax: (678) 258-4300   www.ccur.com

Mfr. computer systems and software.

Concurrent Computer Hong Kong Ltd., Unit 1701, 17/F, Stanhope House, 738 King's Rd., Quarry Bay, Hong Kong PRC

Tel: 852-2-880-0802   Fax: 852-2-880-0664

CONE MILLS CORPORATION

3101 N. Elm Street, PO Box 26540, Greensboro, NC, 27415-6540

Tel: (336) 379-6220   Fax: (336) 379-6287   www.cone.com

Mfr. denims, flannels, chamois and other fabrics.

Burlton International Ltd., Rm. 1307, New Treasure Centre, 10 Ng Fong St., San Po Kong, Kowloon, Hong Kong PRC

Tel: 852-2721-2213   Fax: 852-2723-1117   Contact: Benjamin Cheung

CONEXANT SYSTEMS, INC.

4311 Jamboree Road, PO Box C, Newport Beach, CA, 92658-8902

Tel: (949) 483-4600   Fax: (949) 483-4078   www.conexant.com

Provides semiconductor products for communications electronics.

Conexant Systems Asia Pacific Limited, Ste. 8-10 Harbour Centre - 13/F, 25 Harbour Road, Wanchai, Hong Kong PRC

Tel: 852-2-827-0181   Fax: 852-2-827-6488

CONTIGROUP COMPANIES, INC.

277 Park Avenue, New York, NY, 10172

Tel: (212) 207-5100   Fax: (212) 207-2910   www.contigroup.com

Engaged in cattle feed and pork/poultry producers.

Asian Industries Merchandising, United Centre, 35/F, 95 Queensway, Hong Kong PRC

Tel: 852-2823-6111   Fax: 852-2528-0797   Contact: Michael A. Hoer, SVP

COPELAND CORPORATION

1675 West Campbell Road, Sidney, OH, 45365-0669

Tel: (937) 498-3011   Fax: (937) 498-3334   www.copeland-corp.com

Producer of compressors and condensing units for commercial and residential air conditioning and refrigeration equipment.

Copeland Hong Kong, 10/F, Pioneer Building, 213 Wai Yip Street, Kwun Tong Kowloon, Hong Kong PRC

CORBIS CORPORATION

15395 SE 30th Place, Ste. 300, Bellevue, WA, 98007

Tel: (425) 641-4505   Fax: (425) 643-9740   www.corbis.com

Provides digital photograph imagery to creative professionals in magazine, book and newspaper publishing, advertising and graphic design and Internet and new media publishing.

Corbis Hong Kong, 33 Lockhart Road, Ste. 1506, Wan Chai, Hong Kong PRC

Tel: 852-2215-8000

CORNING INC.

One Riverfront Plaza, Corning, NY, 14831-0001

Tel: (607) 974-9000   Fax: (607) 974-8091   www.corning.com

Mfr. glass and specialty materials, consumer products; communications, laboratory services.

Corning Hong Kong Ltd., Manulife Tower, 34/F, 169 Electric Road, North Point, Hong Kong PRC

Tel: 852-2807-2723   Fax: 852-2807-2152

CORPORATE SOFTWARE (CORPSOFT INC.)

2 Edgewater Drive, Norwood, MA, 02062

Tel: (781) 440-1000   Fax: (781) 440-7070   www.corpsoft.com

Mfr. asset management software.

Corporate Software, 12 Harcourt Road, 8/F, Bank of America Tower, Central, Hong Kong PRC

Tel: 852-2584-6206

CORRPRO COMPANIES, INC.

1090 Enterprise Drive, Medina, OH, 44256

Tel: (330) 725-6681   Fax: (330) 723-0244   www.corrpro.com

Engaged in full-services corrosion engineering and cathodic protection.

Corrpro Companies Far East Ltd., Room 1008, Block B, Sea View Estate, No. 2-8 Watson Rd., North Point, Hong Kong PRC

Tel: 852-2541-6875   Fax: 852-2541-7543   Contact: Colin Man

COUDERT BROTHERS LLP

1114 Ave. of the Americas, New York, NY, 10036-7794

Tel: (212) 626-4400   Fax: (212) 626-4120   www.coudert.com

Engaged in international law.

Coudert Brothers, 25/F, 9 Queen's Rd., Central, Hong Kong PRC

Tel: 852-2218-9100   Fax: 852-2868-1417   Contact: Henry J. Uscinski, Ptnr.

COVANTA ENERGY CORPORATION

40 Lane Road, Fairfield, NJ, 07004

Tel: (973) 882-9000   Fax: (973) 882-9121   www.covantenergy.com

Engaged in power generation.

Covanta Energy Corporation, Entertainment Bldg., Ste. 24B, 30 Queens Road, Central, Hong Kong PRC

Tel: 852-280-17474

CRAVATH, SWAINE & MOORE

Worldwide Plaza, 825 Eighth Ave., New York, NY, 10019-7475

Tel: (212) 474-1000   Fax: (212) 474-3700   www.cravath.com

International law firm.

Cravath, Swaine & Moore, Ste. 2609, Asia Pacific Finance Tower, Citibank Plaza, 3 Garden Rd., Central, Hong Kong PRC

Tel: 852-2509-7200

CRAWFORD & COMPANY

5620 Glenridge Drive NE, Atlanta, GA, 30342

Tel: (404) 256-0830   Fax: (404) 847-4025   www.crawfordandcompany.com

Provides international insurance services engaged in risk management and claims adjustment.

Crawford & Company, 1-9 On Hing Terrace, 21/F, Central, Hong Kong PRC

CSX CORPORATION

901 East Cary Street, Richmond, VA, 23860

Tel: (804) 782-1400   Fax: (804) 782-6747   www.csx.com

Provides freight delivery and contract logistics services.

CSX World Terminals Hong Kong Ltd., Kennese Tam Berth 3, Kwai Chung Container Port, Kowloon, Hong Kong PRC

Tel: 852-2489-5012

CTS CORPORATION

905 Northwest Boulevard, Elkhart, IN, 46514

Tel: (219) 293-7511   Fax: (219) 293-6146   www.ctscorp.com

Mfr. designs, produces and sells passive, electro-mechanical, hybrid and interconnect components for OEMs.

CTS Hong Kong, Room 501, No. 1 Hung To Road, Kwun Tong, Kowloon, Hong Kong PRC

CUBIC CORPORATION

9333 Balboa Ave., PO Box 85587, San Diego, CA, 92123

Tel: (858) 277-6780   Fax: (858) 277-1878   www.cubic.com

Automatic fare collection equipment, training systems.

Cubic Transportation Far East Ltd., Units 1102-3, 11/F, Tower Enterprise Square, 8 Sheny Yuet Rd., Kowloon Bay, Hong Kong PRC

Tel: 852-2331-7888   Fax: 852-2331-3182

CUMMINS, INC.

500 Jackson Street, PO Box 3005, Columbus, IN, 47202-3005

Tel: (812) 377-5000   Fax: (812) 377-4937   www.cummins.com

Mfr. diesel engines.

Cummins Engine H.K. Ltd., Unison Industrial Centre, 2/F, 27-31 Au Pui Wan Street, Fo Tan Shatin N.T., Hong Kong PRC

CURTIS, MALLET-PREVOST, COLT & MOSLE LLP

101 Park Ave., Ste 3500, New York, NY, 10178

Tel: (212) 696-6000   Fax: (212) 697-1559   www.cm-p.com

International law firm.

Curtis, Mallet-Prevost, Colt & Mosle LLP, 401, St. George's Bldg., 2 Ice House St., Central, Hong Kong PRC

CUSHMAN & WAKEFIELD INC.

51 West 52nd Street, New York, NY, 10019

Tel: (212) 841-7500   Fax: (212) 841-7867   www.cushwake.com

Engaged in commercial real estate services.

Cushman & Wakefield, 5 Queen's Road Central, 6/F, Hong Kong PRC

Contact: Richard Middleton

CYPRESS SEMICONDUCTOR CORPORATION

3901 N. First Street, San Jose, CA, 95134-1599

Tel: (408) 943-2600   Fax: (408) 943-2796   www.cypress.com

Mfr. integrated circuits.

Cypress Semiconductor, Unit 1307-08, Tower 1, Metroplaza, Hing Fong Road, N.T., Hong Kong PRC

Tel: 852-2420-2568   Fax: 852-2427-0335

LEO A. DALY

8600 Indian Hills Drive, Omaha, NE, 68114

Tel: (402) 393-1100   Fax: (402) 393-1200   www.leoadaly.com

Planning, architecture, engineering and interior design services.

Leo A. Daly Pacific Ltd., 10/F, CNAC Bldg., 10 Queen's Rd., Central, Hong Kong PRC

Tel: 852-2567-4321   Fax: 852-2885-3507   Contact: Michael R. Fowler   Emp: 11

DANA CORPORATION

4500 Dorr Street, Toledo, OH, 43615

Tel: (419) 535-4500   Fax: (419) 535-4643   www.dana.com

Mfr./sales of automotive, heavy truck, off-highway, fluid and mechanical power components and engine parts, filters and gaskets.

Shui Hing Manufacturing Co. Ltd., Block B., Marvel Ind. Bldg., 4/F, 17-23 Kwai Fung Crescent, Kwai Chung NT, Hong Kong PRC

DANZAS AEI, INC.

120 Tokeneke Road, PO Box 1231, Darien, CT, 06820

Tel: (203) 655-7900   Fax: (203) 655-5779   www.aeilogistics.com

International air freight forwarder.

Danzas AEI, AEI Warehouse & Distribution Centre, Units 3-6, G/F, Pacific Trade Centre, Kai Hing Rd., Kowloon Bay, Hong Kong PRC

Tel: 852-2750-2051   Fax: 852-2798-8246

Danzas AEI, Room 28, 1/F, Pacific Trade Centre, 2 Kai Hing Rd., Kowloon Bay, Hong Kong PRC

Tel: 852-2796-3668   Fax: 852-2796-6533

D'ARCY MASIUS BENTON & BOWLES INC. (DMB&B)

1675 Broadway, New York, NY, 10019

Tel: (212) 468-3622   Fax: (212) 468-2987   www.darcyww.com

Full service international advertising and communications group.

DMB&B Asia Pacific, 6/F, Devon House, 979 King's Rd., Quarry Bay, Hong Kong PRC

Tel: 852-2590-5888   Fax: 852-2856-9905   Contact: Alan Thompson, Mng. Dir.

DATASCOPE CORPORATION

14 Phillips Pkwy., Montvale, NJ, 07645

Tel: (201) 391-8100   Fax: (201) 307-5400   www.datascope.com

Mfr. medical devices.

Datascope Hong Kong, Billion Trade Centre, 1801, 31 Hung To Road, Kwun Tong, Kowloon, Hong Kong PRC

DAVIS POLK & WARDWELL

450 Lexington Ave., New York, NY, 10017

Tel: (212) 450-4000   Fax: (212) 450-4800   www.dpw.com

Engaged in international law.

Davis Polk & Wardwell, The Hong Kong Club Bldg., 3A Chater Rd., Hong Kong PRC

Tel: 852-2533-3300   Fax: 852-2533-3388

DAY RUNNER, INC.

2750 W. Moore Avenue, Fullerton, CA, 92833

Tel: (714) 680-3500   Fax: (714) 680-0538   www.dayrunner.com

Mfg./distribution of paper-based organizers.

Day Runner Hong Kong Ltd., Room 2509, Harbour Centre, 25 Harbour Rd., Wanchai, Hong Kong PRC

Tel: 852-2583-9218   Fax: 852-2827-4333   Contact: Daniel Kwan

DDB WORLDWIDE COMMUNICATIONS GROUP

437 Madison Ave., New York, NY, 10022

Tel: (212) 415-2000   Fax: (212) 415-3417   www.ddbn.com

Advertising agency.

DDB Asia Pacific Ltd., 17/F, Citicorp Centre, 18 Whitfield Rd., Causeway Bay, Hong Kong PRC

DEBEVOISE & PLIMPTON

919 Third Avenue, New York, NY, 10022

Tel: (212) 909-6000   Fax: (212) 909-6836   www.debevoise.com

Engaged in international law.

Debevoise & Plimpton, 13/F, Entertainment Bldg., 30 Queen's Rd., Central, Hong Kong PRC

Tel: 852-2810-7918   Fax: 852-2810-9828   Contact: Jeffrey S. Wood, Mng. Ptnr.   Emp: 12

DECISION STRATEGIES FAIRFAX INTERNATIONAL

33 East 33rd Street, New York, NY, 10016

Tel: (212) 935-4040   Fax: (212) 935-4046   www.dsfx.com

Provides discreet consulting, investigative, business intelligence and security services to corporations, financial and investment institutions, law firms and governments worldwide.

Decision Strategies, Room 704, 1 Lyndhurst Terrace, Central District, Hong Kong PRC

Tel: 852-2522-1352   Fax: 852-2536-0469

DELL COMPUTER CORPORATION

One Dell Way, Round Rock, TX, 78682-2222

Tel: (512) 338-4400   Fax: (512) 728-3653   www.dell.com

Direct marketer and supplier of computer systems.

Dell Computer Asia Ltd., 1001, Stanhope House, 734-738 King's Rd., Quarry Bay, Hong Kong PRC

Tel: 852-2508-0500   Fax: 852-2887-2040   Contact: Diane Chan, Gen. Mgr.

DELOITTE TOUCHE TOHMATSU INTERNATIONAL

1633 Broadway, New York, NY, 10019

Tel: (212) 492-4000   Fax: (212) 392-4154   www.deloitte.com

Accounting, audit, tax and management consulting services.

Deloitte Touche Tohmatsu, Wing on Centre, 22/F, 111 Connaught Rd., Central, Hong Kong PRC

DENTSPLY INTERNATIONAL

570 West College Ave., PO Box 872, York, PA, 17405-0872

Tel: (717) 845-7511   Fax: (717) 843-6357   www.dentsply.com

Mfr. and distribution of dental supplies and equipment.

Dentsply Asia Inc., 23/F, Gee Chang Hong Centre, 65 Wong Chuk Hang Rd., Aberdeen, Hong Kong PRC

Tel: 852-2870-0336

DETROIT DIESEL CORPORATION

13400 Outer Drive West, Detroit, MI, 48239

Tel: (313) 592-5000   Fax: (313) 592-5058   www.detroitdiesel.com

Mfr. diesel and aircraft engines and heavy-duty transmissions.

China Diesel Support Services, Unit B, 10/F, Alex Ind. Bldg., Cheung Sha Wan, Kowloon, Hong Kong PRC

DEWEY BALLANTINE LLP

1301 Avenue of the Americas, New York, NY, 10019

Tel: (212) 259-8000   Fax: (212) 259-6333   www.deweyballantine.com

International law firm.

Dewey Ballantine LLP, Ste. 3907, Asia Pacific Finance Tower, Citibank Plaza, 3 Garden Rd., Central, Hong Kong PRC

Tel: 852-2509-7000   Fax: 852-2509-70883

DHL WORLDWIDE EXPRESS

50 California Avenue, San Francisco, CA, 94111

Tel: (415) 677-6100   Fax: (415) 824-9700   www.dhl.com

Worldwide air express carrier.

DHL Worldwide Express, 13 Mok Cheong St., Tokwawan, Kowloon, Hong Kong PRC

Tel: 852-2765-8111

DICTAPHONE CORPORATION

3191 Broadbridge Ave., Stratford, CT, 06497-2559

Tel: (203) 381-7000   Fax: (203) 381-7100   www.dictaphone.com

Mfr./sale dictation, telephone answering and multi-channel voice communications recording systems.

Dictaphone International, Room 801, Stanhope House, 738 King's Road, Hong Kong PRC

Tel: 852-2709-1163

DIEBOLD INC.

5995 Mayfair Road, North Canton, OH, 44720-8077

Tel: (330) 490-4000   Fax: (330) 490-3794   www.diebold.com

Mfr. automated banking systems; security services for banking industrial and related fields.

Diebold Hong Kong, 148 Electric Road, 23/F, North Point, Hong Kong PRC

DIGI INTERNATIONAL INC.

11001 Bren Road East, Minnetonka, MN, 55343

Tel: (952) 912-3444   Fax: (952) 912-4952   www.digi.com

Mfr. computer hardware.

Digi International (HK), Suite 1101-02, 11/F, K Wah Centre, 191 Java Road, North Point, Hong Kong PRC

Tel: 852-2833-1008   Fax: 852-2572-9989

DILLINGHAM CONSTRUCTION CORPORATION

5960 Inglewood Dr., Pleasanton, CA, 94588-8535

Tel: (925) 463-3300   Fax: (925) 463-1571   www.dillinghamconstruction.com

Engaged in construction services for the commercial, industrial, and marine markets.

Dillingham Construction (HK) Ltd., 90,4 Tower Two, South Seas Centre, 75 Mody St., Tsim Sha Tsui East, Kowloon, Hong Kong PRC

DIMON INCORPORATED

512 Bridge Street, PO Box 681, Danville, VA, 24543-0681

Tel: (804) 792-7511   Fax: (804) 791-0377   www.dimon.com

One of world's largest importer and exporters of leaf tobacco.

Intabex International Limited, Unit 1004, Technology Plaza, 29-35 Sha Tsui Road, Tsuen Wan N.T., Hong Kong PRC

Tel: 852-2492-3868   Fax: 852-2417-2256

DIONEX CORPORATION

1228 Titan Way, PO Box 3603, Sunnyvale, CA, 94086-3603

Tel: (408) 737-0700   Fax: (408) 730-9403   www.dionex.com

Develop/mfr./market chromatography systems and related products.

Techcomp, Rm. 505, Shui Hing Ctr., 13 Sheung Yuet Road, Kowloon Bay Kowloon, Hong Kong PRC

DISCOVERY COMMUNICATIONS, INC.

7700 Wisconsin Avenue, Bethesda, MD, 20814

Tel: (301) 986-0444   Fax: (301) 771-4064   www.discovery.com

Owns and operates cable networks.

Discovery Communications, Inc, 2601 Tower 2, 89 Queensway, Admiralty, Hong Kong PRC

Tel: 852-2817-6639

D-M-E COMPANY

29111 Stephenson Highway, Madison Heights, MI, 48071

Tel: (248) 398-6000   Fax: (248) 544-5705   www.dmeco.com

Manufacture and distribution of mold tooling, mold components, hot runner systems, and electronic controls for the plastics industry.

DME Ltd., Bank of America Tower, Room 705-8, 7/F, 12 Harcourt Road, Admiralty, Hong Kong PRC

Tel: 852-2795-1035   Fax: 852-2110-9843

DONALDSON COMPANY, INC.

PO Box 1299, Minneapolis, MN, 55431

Tel: (952) 887-3131   Fax: (952) 887-3155   www.donaldson.com

Mfr. filtration systems and replacement parts.

Donaldson Far East Ltd., United A & B & C, 21/F, CDW Bldg., 388 Castle Peak Rd., Tsuen Wan N.T., Hong Kong PRC

Tel: 852-2402-2830   Fax: 852-2493-2928   Contact: Elick Shum

R.R. DONNELLEY & SONS COMPANY

77 West Wacker Drive, Chicago, IL, 60601-1696

Tel: (312) 326-8000   Fax: (312) 326-8543   www.rrdonnelley.com

Engaged in commercial printing and allied communication services.

R. R. Donnelley Financial Ltd., Asia Pacific Finance Tower, Suite 805, Citibank Plaza, 3 Garden Rd., Central, Hong Kong PRC

Tel: 852-2522-3803

DOREMUS & COMPANY, INC.

200 Varick Street, New York, NY, 10271

Tel: (212) 366-3000   Fax: (212) 366-3629   www.doremus.com

Advertising and public relations.

Doremus & Co., 16/F Asia Orient Tower, Town Place 33 Lockhart Road, Wanchai, Hong Kong PRC

Tel: 852-2861-2721   Fax: 852-2536-9416   Contact: Richard Beccle

DORSEY & WHITNEY LLP

50 South Sixth Street, Ste. 1500, Minneapolis, MN, 55402

Tel: (612) 340-2600   Fax: (612) 340-2868   www.dorseylaw.com

International law firm.

Dorsey & Whitney LLP, One Pacific Place, Ste. 3008, 88 Queensway, Hong Kong PRC

Tel: 852-2526-5000   Fax: 852-2524-3000   Contact: Zhao Zhang, Mng. Ptnr.   Emp: 6

DOUBLECLICK, INC.

450 West 33rd Street, New York, NY, 10001

Tel: (212) 683-0001   Fax: (212) 889-0062   www.doubleclick.net

Engaged in online advertising and e-mail marketing.

Doubleclick, Ltd., 11 Pedder Street, 6/F, Central, Hong Kong PRC

THE DOW CHEMICAL COMPANY

2030 Dow Center, Midland, MI, 48674

Tel: (989) 636-1000   Fax: (989) 636-3228   www.dow.com

Mfr. chemicals, plastics, pharmaceuticals, agricultural products, consumer products.

Dow Chemical Hong Kong Ltd., Gammon House, 12 Harbour Rd., PO Box 711, Hong Kong PRC

DOW JONES & COMPANY, INC.

200 Liberty Street, New York, NY, 10281

Tel: (212) 416-2000   Fax: (212) 416-4348   www.dj.com

Publishing and financial news services.

Asian Wall Street Journal, GPO Box 9825, Hong Kong PRC

DRAFT WORLDWIDE

633 North St. Clair Street, Chicago, IL, 60611-3211

Tel: (312) 944-3500   Fax: (312) 944-3566   www.draftworldwide.com

Full service international advertising agency, engaged in brand building, direct and promotional marketing.

DraftWorldwide, 7/F, Siu On Centre, 188 Lockhard Rd., Wanchai, Hong Kong PRC

Tel: 852-2531-8828   Fax: 852-2824-4386   Contact: Ana Lee, Pres.

DRAKE BEAM MORIN INC.

100 Park Avenue, 11th Fl., New York, NY, 10017

Tel: (212) 692-7700   Fax: (212) 297-0426   www.dbm.com

Human resource management consulting and training.

DBM Hong Kong, Printing House, 16/F, 6 Duddell St., Central, Hong Kong PRC

Tel: 852-2840-0838   Fax: 852-2877-3721

DRESSER INSTRUMENT DIVISION

250 East Main Street, Stratford, CT, 06614-5145

Tel: (203) 378-8281   Fax: (203) 385-0357   www.dresserinstruments.com

Mfr. pressure gauges and temperature instruments.

Dresser Trading Div., American Chamber of Commerce Building, 1030 Swire House, Hong Kong PRC

DSP GROUP, INC.

3120 Scott Blvd., Santa Clara, CA, 95054

Tel: (408) 986-4300   Fax: (408) 986-4323   www.dspg.com

Mfr. speech compressor software.

DSP Solutions Ltd., Rm. 24, 3/F, Block B, Proficient Ind. Center, 6 Wang Chui Rd., Kowloon Bay, Hong Kong PRC

Tel: 852-2795-7421   Fax: 852-2305-0640

DST SYSTEMS, INC.

333 West 11th Street, Kansas City, MO, 64105

Tel: (816) 435-1000   Fax: (816) 435-8618   www.dstsystems.com

Mfr. financial software.

DST International Hong Kong Ltd., 19/F Kinwick Centre, 32 Hollywood Road, Central, Hong Kong PRC

E.I. DUPONT DE NEMOURS & COMPANY

1007 Market Street, Wilmington, DE, 19898

Tel: (302) 774-1000   Fax: (302) 774-7321   www.dupont.com

Mfr. and sales of diversified chemicals, plastics, specialty products and fibers.

DuPont Teijin Films China Limited, 1122 New World Office Bldg., Salisbury Road, Kowloon, Hong Kong PRC

Tel: 852 2734 5345

DURACELL INTERNATIONAL INC.

8 Research Drive, Bethel, CT, 06801

Tel: (203) 796-4000   Fax: (203) 796-4745   www.duracell.com

Mfr. batteries.

Duracell Asia Ltd., 1602, World Finance Centre South Tower, Harbour City, Canton Rd., Kowloon, Hong Kong PRC

EASTMAN CHEMICAL COMPANY

100 North Eastman Road, Kingsport, TN, 37662-5075

Tel: (423) 229-2000   Fax: (423) 229-1351   www.eastman.com

Mfr. plastics, chemicals, fibers.

Eastman Chemical Hong Kong Ltd., 1-3 Wang Lok St., Yuen Long Industrial Estate, Yuen Long New Territories, Hong Kong PRC

Tel: 852-2473-7188   Fax: 852-2474-0913   Contact: J. Ron Hilderbrand, Mgr.

Eastman Chemical Ltd., 1/F, Kodak House 1, 321 Java Rd., North Point, Hong Kong PRC

Tel: 852-2565-6330   Fax: 852-2880-9729   Contact: Bruce Chiu

EASTMAN KODAK COMPANY

343 State Street, Rochester, NY, 14650

Tel: (716) 724-4000   Fax: (716) 724-1089   www.kodak.com

Develop/mfr. photo and chemicals products, information management/video/copier systems, fibers/plastics for various industry.

Eastman Chemical Intl. Ltd., 1/F, Kodak House, 321 Java Rd., North Point, Hong Kong PRC

Eastman Kodak Asia-Pacific Ltd., 2/F, Kodak House, 321 Java Rd., North Point, Hong Kong PRC

ECOLAB INC.

370 N. Wabasha Street, St. Paul, MN, 55102

Tel: (651) 293-2233   Fax: (651) 293-2379   www.ecolab.com

Develop/mfr. premium cleaning, sanitizing and maintenance products and services for the hospitality, institutional, and residential markets.

Ecolab Ltd., Hong Kong PRC

Tel: 852-2341-4202

EDELMAN PUBLIC RELATIONS WORLDWIDE

200 East Randolph Drive, 62nd Fl., Chicago, IL, 60601

Tel: (312) 240-3000   Fax: (312) 240-0596   www.edelman.com

International independent public relations firm.

Edelman PR Worldwide, Room 3701-2, 37/F, Windsor House, 311 Gloucester Rd., Causeway Bay, Hong Kong PRC

Tel: 852-2804-1338 Fax: 852-2804-1301   Contact: Clara Shek, Gen. Mgr.

J.D. EDWARDS & COMPANY

One Technology Way, Denver, CO, 80237

Tel: (303) 334-4000   Fax: (303) 334-4970   www.jdedwards.com

Computer software products.

J. D. Edwards, Unit A, 24/F, Entertainment Bldg., 30 Queens Rd., Central, Hong Kong PRC

Tel: 852-2844-7400 Fax: 852-2590-9618

System-Pro Solutions Ltd., 8/F, West Warwick House, Taiko Place, 979 King's Rd., Quarry Bay, Hong Kong PRC

Tel: 852-2844-7400 Fax: 852-2521-4782

EGL INC. (EAGLE GLOBAL LOGISTICS)

15350 Vickery Drive, Houston, TX, 77032

Tel: (281) 618-3100   Fax: (281) 618-3223   www.eagleusa.com

Ocean/air freight forwarding, customs brokerage, packing and wholesale, logistics management and insurance.

EGL Eagle Global Logistics, Room 2004-5, Devon House, 979 King's Rd., Quarry Bay, Hong Kong PRC

Tel: 852-2590-9822 Fax: 852-2590-9130

ELANCO ANIMAL HEALTH

500 East 96th Street, Ste. 125, Indianapolis, IN, 46240

Tel: (317) 276-3000   Fax: (317) 276-6116   www.elanco.com

Antibiotics and fine chemicals.

Elanco Agricultural & Industrial Products, 1026-1030 Prince's Bldg., 10 Chater Rd., Hong Kong PRC

ELECTRO SCIENTIFIC INDUSTRIES, INC.

13900 NW Science Park Drive, Portland, OR, 97229

Tel: (503) 641-4141   Fax: (503) 643-4873   www.esi.com

Mfg. production and testing equipment used in manufacture of electronic components in pagers and cellular communication devices.

Asia Industrial Technology Ltd. ECS - Test, Room 1318, Level 13, Tower 1, Grand Central Plaza, 138 Shatin Rural Committee Rd., Shatin NT, Hong Kong PRC

Tel: 852-2558-8110 Fax: 852-2558-8139   Contact: Jackie Wong

ELECTROGLAS INC.

6042 Silver Creek Valley Road, San Jose, CA, 95138

Tel: (408) 528-3000   Fax: (408) 528-3542   www.electroglas.com

Mfr. semi-conductor test equipment, automatic wafer probes.

Electroglas Intl. Inc., Room 1901, Park-In Comm. Ctr., 56 Dundas St., Kowloon, Hong Kong PRC

ELECTRONIC DATA SYSTEMS, INC. (EDS)

5400 Legacy Dr., Plano, TX, 75024

Tel: (972) 604-6000   Fax: (972) 605-2643   www.eds.com

Engaged in systems integration, network and systems operations and management consulting.

EDS Hong Kong, 3 Garden Road, 33/F, Central, Hong Kong PRC

Tel: 852-2867-9888

ELECTRONICS FOR IMAGING, INC. (EFI)

303 Velocity Way, Foster City, CA, 94404

Tel: (650) 357-3500 Fax: (650) 357-3907 www.efi.com

Design/mfr. computer software and hardware for color desktop publishing.

EFI Hong Kong, 28/F, Soundwill Plaza, 38 Russell Street, Causeway Bay, Hong Kong PRC

Tel: 852 2922 1668

EMC CORPORATION

35 Parkwood Drive, Hopkinton, MA, 01748-9103

Tel: (508) 435-1000 Fax: (508) 435-8884 www.emc.com

Designs/supplies intelligent enterprise storage and retrieval technology for open systems, mainframes and midrange environments.

EMC Computer Systems Hong Kong, Room 1101-3, Cityplaza 4, Tiakoosing, Hong Kong PRC

Tel: 852-2839-9600

EMERSON PROCESS MANAGEMENT

8301Cameron Road, Austin, TX, 78754

Tel: (512) 834-7689 Fax: (512) 832-3232 www.frco.com

Mfr. industrial process control equipment.

Emerson Process Management, Unit B, 7/F, Seabright Plaza, Shell St., North Point, Hong Kong PRC

Tel: 852-2571-1681 Fax: 852-2887-7750

Emerson Process Management, Unit 2302, 23/F, Malaysia Bldg., 50 Gloucester Rd., Wanchai, Hong Kong PRC

Tel: 852-2802-9368 Fax: 852-2827-8670 Contact: Andrew Ho, Mgr.

EMERSON RADIO CORPORATION

9 Entin Road, Parsippany, NJ, 07054

Tel: (973) 884-5800 Fax: (973) 428-2033 www.emersonradio.com

Consumer electronics, radios, TV and VCR, tape recorders and players, computer products.

Emerson Radio HK Ltd., Suite 1009-1015, World Shopping Ctr., Harbor City Phase 1, 7 Canton Rd., Kowloon, Hong Kong PRC

EMERY FORWARDING

One Lagoon Drive, Ste. 400, Redwood City, CA, 94065

Tel: (650) 596-9600 Fax: (650) 596-7901 www.emeryworld.com

Freight transport, global logistics and air cargo.

Emery Forwarding, Unit 9-15, 15/F, Kwong Sang Hong Centre, 151-153 Hoi Bun Rd., Swun Tong Kowloon, Hong Kong PRC

Tel: 852-2796-3883

ENCAD, INC.

6059 Cornerstone Court West, San Diego, CA, 92121

Tel: (858) 452-0882 Fax: (858) 452-5618 www.encad.com

Mfr. large color printers for specialized graphics.

ENCAD Hong Kong, Suite 1901-3, Chinachem Leighton Plaza, 29 Leighton Road, Causeway Bay, Hong Kong PRC

Tel: 852-2881-8969

ENERGIZER HOLDINGS, INC.

533 Maryville University Dr., St. Louis, MO, 63141

Tel: (314) 985-2000 Fax: (214) 985-2205 www.energizer.com

Mfr. Eveready and Energizer brand batteries and lighting products.

Eveready Batteries Hong Kong Ltd., Rm 1601-1605, China Resources Building, 26 Harbour Road, Wan Chai, Hong Kong PRC

Tel: 852-2956-2333 Fax: 852-2956-2686

ENERPAC

6101 N. Baker Road, PO Box 3241, Milwaukee, WI, 53201-3241

Tel: (414) 781-6600   Fax: (414) 781-1049   www.enerpac.com

Mfr. hydraulic cylinders, pumps, valves, presses, tools, accessories and system components.

ENERPAC, Workingberg Commercial Room 907, 41-47 Marble Road, North Point, Hong Kong PRC

Tel: 852-2561-6295   Fax: 852-2561-6772

ENGELHARD CORPORATION

101 Wood Avenue South, Iselin, NJ, 08830

Tel: (732) 205-5000   Fax: (732) 632-9253   www.engelhard.com

Mfr. pigments, additives, catalysts, chemicals, engineered materials.

Engelhard Corporation, Room 1001-2, Yuenfoong Centre, 150-160 Castle Peak Rd., Yuen Long NT, Hong Kong PRC

Engelhard-Clal Hong Kong, 21 Ma Tau Wei Road, 6/F, Blk. B2, Hunghom, Kowloon, Hong Kong PRC

Tel: 852-2365-0301

EPICOR SOFTWARE CORPORATION

195 Technology Drive, Irvine, CA, 92618

Tel: (949) 585-4000   Fax: (949) 450-4419   www.epicor.com

Mfr. software for e-business.

Epicor Hong Kong, 10 Cityplaza One, 1111 King's Road, Taikoo Shing, Hong Kong PRC

ERICO PRODUCTS INC.

34600 Solon Road, Cleveland, OH, 44139

Tel: (440) 248-0100   Fax: (440) 248-0723   www.erico.com

Mfr. electric welding apparatus and hardware, metal stampings, specialty fasteners.

Erico Products, 2/F, Block A ,Po Yip Building, 62-70 Texaco Road, Tsuen Wan NT, Hong Kong PRC

Tel: 852-2764-8808

ERIE CONTROLS LTD.

4000 South 13th Street, Milwaukee, WI, 53221

Tel: (414) 483-0524   Fax: (414) 483-6610   www.eriecontrols.com

Mfr. controls and valves.

Erie Controls Hong Kong, 22nd Fl. Silver Tech Tower, 26 Cheung Lee Street, Chai Wan, Hong Kong PRC

Tel: 852-2515-3713   Fax: 852-2898-2935

ERNST & YOUNG INTERNATIONAL

5 Times Square, New York, NY, 10036

Tel: (212) 773-3000   Fax: (212) 773-6350   www.eyi.com

Engaged in assurance and advisory business services, tax, law and corporate finance.

Ernst & Young International, 17/F, Hutchison, 10 Harcourt Rd., Central, Hong Kong PRC

Tel: 852-2585-2642   Fax: 852-2827-9523   Contact: Jason Felton

ESS TECHNOLOGY, INC.

48401 Fremont Blvd., Fremont, CA, 94538

Tel: (510) 492-1088   Fax: (510) 492-1098   www.esstech.com

Mfr. audio chips.

ESS Technology, Inc., Unit 1, 18/F, Westley Square, 48 Hoi Yuen Road, Kwun Tong Kowloon, Hong Kong PRC

Tel: 852-2418-0860   Fax: 852-2619-0053

EURO RSCG WORLDWIDE

350 Hudson Street, New York, NY, 10014

Tel: (212) 886-2000   Fax: (212) 886-2016   www.eurorscg.com

International advertising agency group.

EURO RSCG Partnership, 21/F, Devon House, Taikoo Place, 979 King's Road, Quarry Bay, Hong Kong PRC

EXABYTE CORPORATION

1635 38th Street, Boulder, CO, 80301

Tel: (303) 442-4333   Fax: (303) 417-7170   www.exabyte.com

Mfr. computer hardware, including tape drives and cartridges.

Exabyte Hong Kong Representative Office, Unit A 22/F Winsan Tower, 98 Thomson Road, Wanchai, Hong Kong PRC

Tel: 852-2295-6370

EXCELLON AUTOMATION

24751 Crenshaw Boulevard, Torrance, CA, 90505

Tel: (310) 534-6300   Fax: (310) 534-6777   www.excellon.com

PCB drilling and routing machines; optical inspection equipment.

Wong's Kong King Intl.Ltd., 11/F, WKK Building, 418A Kwun Tong Road, Kowloon, Hong Kong PRC

Tel: 852-2-357-8888 Fax: 852-2-341-9339

EXE TECHNOLOGIES, INC.

8787 N. Stemmons Fwy., Dallas, TX, 75247-3702

Tel: (214) 775-6000   Fax: (214) 775-0911   www.exe.com

Provides a complete line of supply chain management execution software for WMS.

EXE Technologies, Inc. Hong Kong, Rm. 805, 8/F, BOC Credit Card Centre, 68 Connaught Rd. West, Hong Kong PRC

Tel: 852-2804-1881 Fax: 852-2849-8916

EXPEDITORS INTERNATIONAL OF WASHINGTON INC.

1015 Third Avenue, 12th Fl., Seattle, WA, 98104-1182

Tel: (206) 674-3400   Fax: (206) 682-9777   www.expd.com

Air/ocean freight forwarding, customs brokerage, international logistics solutions.

EI Freight (HK) Ltd., 201, South Seas Centre, Tower 2, 75 Mody Rd., Tsim Sha Tsui East, Kowloon, Hong Kong PRC

Tel: 852-2739-2399 Fax: 852-2721-9734

EXXON MOBIL CORPORATION

5959 Las Colinas Blvd., Irving, TX, 75039-2298

Tel: (972) 444-1000   Fax: (972) 444-1882   www.exxonmobil.com

Petroleum exploration, production, refining; mfr. petroleum and chemicals products; coal and minerals.

Exxon Mobil, Inc., 18 Harbour Road, Central Plaza, 22/F, Wanchai, Hong Kong PRC

Exxon Mobil, Inc., St. George's Bldg., 2 Ice House St., Hong Kong PRC

FACTSET RESEARCH SYSTEMS, INC.

1 Greenwich Plaza, Greenwich, CT, 06830

Tel: (203) 863-1599   Fax: (203) 863-1501   www.factset.com

Provides on-line investment research services to financial institutions.

FactSet Limited, Bank of China Tower, Level 25, One Garden Road, Central, Hong Kong PRC

Tel: 852-2251-1833

FAIRCHILD SEMICONDUCTOR INTERNATIONAL, INC.

82 Running Hill Road, South Portland, ME, 04106

Tel: (207) 775-8100   Fax: (207) 761-0392   www.fairchildsemi.com

Mfr. semiconductor chips.

Fairchild Semiconductor Ltd., 19/F., CMG Tower, The Gateway II, 15 Canton Road, Tsimshatsui, Kowloon, Hong Kong PRC

Tel: 852-2722-8338 Fax: 852-2722-8383

FALLON WORLDWIDE

50 South Sixth Street, Minneapolis, MN, 55402

Tel: (612) 758-2345   Fax: (612) 758-2346   www.fallon.com

Advertising and marketing agency.

Fallon Hong Kong, 23/F The Workstation, 43 Lyndhurst Terrace, Hong Kong PRC

Tel: 852-2854-1366 Contact: Calvin Soh

FEDERAL-MOGUL CORPORATION

26555 Northwestern Highway, PO Box 1966, Southfield, MI, 48034

Tel: (248) 354-7700   Fax: (248) 354-8983   www.federal-mogul.com

Mfr./distributor precision parts for automobiles, trucks, farm and construction vehicles.

Federal-Mogul World Trade Hong Kong Ltd., Kwai Chung, Hong Kong PRC

FEDEX CORPORATION

942 South Shady Grove Rd., Memphis, TN, 38120

Tel: (901) 369-3600   Fax: (901) 395-2000   www.fdxcorp.com

Package express delivery service.

Federal Express (HK) Ltd., 100 Sung Wong Toi Rd., Tokwawan Kowloon, Hong Kong PRC

Tel: 852-273-03333

FEI CORPORATION

7451 NW Evergreen Pkwy., Hillsboro, OR, 97124-5830

Tel: (503) 640-7500   Fax: (503) 640-7509   www.feicompany.com

Design and mfr. of charged particle beam systems serving the research, development and production needs of customers in semiconductor, data storage, and industry/institute markets.

FEI Hong Kong Company Ltd., Room 2604, Greenfield Tower, Concordia Plaza, 1 Science Museum Road, TST East, Hong Kong PRC

FERRO CORPORATION

1000 Lakeside Ave., Cleveland, OH, 44114-7000

Tel: (216) 641-8580   Fax: (216) 696-5784   www.ferro.com

Mfr. Specialty chemicals, coatings, plastics, colors, refractories.

Ferro Far East Ltd., PO Box 98436, Tsim Sha Tsui, Kowloon, Hong Kong PRC

Tel: 852-2724-6193   Fax: 852-2724-6837   Contact: Ronald L. Klassen, Mng. Dir.

FIDUCIARY TRUST COMPANY INTERNATIONAL

175 Federal Street, Boston, MA, 02110

Tel: (617) 482-5270   Fax: (617) 482-5270   www.ftc.com

Banking services.

Fiduciary Trust (Intl.) SA, Hong Kong PRC

FileNET CORPORATION

3565 Harbor Boulevard, Costa Mesa, CA, 92626

Tel: (714) 966-3400   Fax: (714) 966-3490   www.filenet.com

Provides integrated document management (IDM) software and services for internet and client server-based imaging, workflow, cold and electronic document management solutions.

FileNET Hong Kong Ltd., Unit 3206-7, 32/F, Shui On Centre, 8 Harbour Rd., Wanchai, Hong Kong PRC

Tel: 852-2563-5822   Fax: 852-2811-5631

FLACK + KURTZ INC.

475 Fifth Ave., 8th Fl., New York, NY, 10017

Tel: (212) 532-9600   Fax: (212) 689-7489   www.flackandkurtz.com

Consulting engineers for building services, i.e.., HVAC, electrical, lighting, plumbing/hydraulics, life safety, fire protection and telecommunications.

Flack + Kurtz Asia, Ltd., Asian House, 19/F, 1 Hennesy Rd., Wanchai, Hong Kong PRC

Tel: 852-2893-3316   Fax: 852-2838-2708   Contact: Henry DiGregorio   Emp: 6

FLEETBOSTON FINANCIAL CORPORATION

100 Federal Street, Boston, MA, 02110

Tel: (617) 434-2400   Fax: (617) 434-6943   www.fleet.com

Banking and insurance services.

FleetBoston - Hong Kong, Jardine House, 1 Connaught Place, Sts. 801-809, Central, Hong Kong PRC

Tel: 852-2526-4361   Fax: 852-2845-9222

FM GLOBAL INC.

1301 Atwood Avenue, Johnston, RI, 02919

Tel: (401) 275-3000   Fax: (401) 275-3029   www.fmglobal.com

Engaged in commercial and industrial property insurance and risk management, specializing in engineering-driven property protection.

FM Global, Unit 1117, Level 11, Tower One, 193 Prince Edward Road West, Mongkok, Kowloon, Hong Kong PRC

FMC CORPORATION

1735 Market St., Philadelphia, PA, 19103

Tel: (215) 299-6000   Fax: (215) 299-6618   www.fmc.com

Mfr. specialty chemicals, including alginate, carrageenan and microcrystalline cellulose.

FMC Hong Kong, Central Plaza Ste. 2401-02, 18 Harbour Road, Hong Kong PRC

Tel: 852-2839-6600

FMR (FIDELITY INVESTMENTS)

82 Devonshire Street, Boston, MA, 02109

Tel: (617) 563-7000   Fax: (617) 476-6105   www.fidelity.com

Diversified financial services company offering investment management, retirement, brokerage, and shareholder services directly to individuals and institutions and through financial intermediaries.

Fidelity Investments Management (HK) Ltd., PO Box 92053, Tsim Sha Tsui Post Office, Kowloon, Hong Kong PRC

Tel: 852-2629-2626   Fax: 852-2956-2346

FORTUNE BRANDS

300 Tower Parkway, Lincolnshire, IL, 60069

Tel: (847) 484-4400   Fax: (800) 310-5960   www.fortunebrands.com

Mfr. diversified consumer products including Masterbrand, Acco office products, Jim Bean distillery products, Footjoy and Titleist golf products and Moen bath products.

Fortune Brands International Corporation, Ste. 4003, The Lee Gardens, 33 Hysan Avenue, Causeway Bay, Hong Kong PRC

Tel: 852-2506-0660   Fax: 852-2506-0671

Moen International Inc., 33 Hysan Avenue, Ste. 4003, Causeway Bay, Hong Kong PRC

Tel: 852-2506-0670   Fax: 852-2506-0672

FRANKLIN COVEY COMPANY

2200 W. Parkway Blvd., Salt Lake City, UT, 84119-2331

Tel: (801) 975-1776   Fax: (801) 977-1431   www.franklincovey.com

Provides productivity and time management products and seminars.

Franklin Covey Taiwan, 7/F-3, No. 9, 1/F, Admiralty Center Tower 1, 18 Harcourt Road, Hong Kong PRC

Tel: 886-2731-7115   Fax: 886-2711-5285

THE FRANKLIN MINT

US Route 1, Media, PA, 19091-0001

Tel: (610) 459-6000   Fax: (610) 459-6880   www.franklinmint.com

Design/marketing collectibles and luxury items.

Franklin Mint Ltd., Unit 5-7, 19/F, Tower III Enterprise Square, 9 Sheung Yuet Road, Kowloon Bay, Hong Kong PRC

FRANKLIN RESOURCES, INC.

1 Franklin Pkwy., Bldg. 970, 1st Fl., San Mateo, CA, 94404

Tel: (415) 312-2000   Fax: (415) 312-5606   www.frk.com

Global and domestic investment advisory and portfolio management.

Templeton Asset Management Ltd., Hong Kong Branch Office, Shui On Centre, 2701, 6-8 Harbour Rd., Wan Chai, Hong Kong PRC

Tel: 852-2877-7733   Fax: 852-2877-5401

Templeton Franklin Investment Services (Asia) Ltd., Shui On Centre, 2701, 6-8 Harbour Rd., Wan Chai, Hong Kong PRC

Tel: 852-2877-7733   Fax: 852-2877-5401

FRITZ COMPANIES, INC., DIV. UPS

706 Mission Street, Ste. 900, San Francisco, CA, 94103

Tel: (415) 904-8360   Fax: (415) 904-8661   www.fritz.com

Integrated transportation, sourcing, distribution and customs brokerage services.

Fritz Air Freight (HK) Ltd., 3/F, Goodwin "A", Sunshine Kowloon Bay Cargo Centre, 59 Tai Yip St., Kowloon, Hong Kong PRC

Fritz Companies Asian Hdqtrs., Suite 906-10, Tai Building, 49 Austin Road, Tsim Sha Tsui, Kowloon, Hong Kong PRC

Fritz Transportation Intl. (HK) Ltd., 9/F, Tai Building, 49 Austin Road, Tsim Sha Tsui, Kowloon, Hong Kong PRC

FRONTSTEP, INC.

2800 Corporate Exchange Drive, Ste. 400, Columbus, OH, 43231

Tel: (614) 523-7000   Fax: (614) 895-2504   www.frontstep.com

Mfr. management software.

Frontstep Hong Kong, 1606-08 MLC Tower, 248 Queen's Road East, Wanchai, Hong Kong PRC

FSI INTERNATIONAL INC.

3455 Lyman Boulevard, Chaska, MN, 55318-3052

Tel: (952) 448-5440   Fax: (952) 448-2825   www.fsi-intl.com

Manufacturing equipment for computer silicon wafers.

Metron Technology Ltd., Unit E, 5/F, China Overseas Building, 139 Hennessy Road, Wanchai, Hong Kong PRC

FULBRIGHT & JAWORSKI LLP

1301 McKinney Street, Ste. 5100, Houston, TX, 77010

Tel: (713) 651-5151   Fax: (713) 651-5246   www.fulbright.com

Engaged in international law.

Fulbright & Jaworski, The Hong Kong Club Bldg., 19/F, 3A Chater Rd., Central, Hong Kong PRC
Tel: 852-2523-3200   Fax: 852-2523-3255

H.B. FULLER COMPANY

1200 Willow Lake Blvd., Vadnais Heights, MN, 55110

Tel: (651) 236-5900   Fax: (651) 236-5898   www.hbfuller.com

Mfr./distributor adhesives, sealants, coatings, paints, waxes, sanitation chemicals.

H.B. Fuller International Inc., Asia/Pacific Area Office, Suite 2605, 26/F, Sino Plaza, 255-257 Glouchester Rd., Causeway Bay, Hong Kong PRC
Tel: 852-2832-9622   Fax: 852-2892-1680

GALILEO INTERNATIONAL, INC.

1 Campus Dr., Parsippany, NJ, 07054

Tel: (973) 518-4000   Fax: (973) 518-4085   www.galileo.com

Operates computerized reservation systems (CRS) for travel.

Galileo International Asia, Vicwood Plaza, 33/F, 199 Des Voeux Road, Central, Hong Kong PRC
Tel: 852-2821-2288   Fax: 852-2821-2299

THE GATES RUBBER COMPANY

990 S. Broadway, PO Box 5887, Denver, CO, 80217-5887

Tel: (303) 744-1911   Fax: (303) 744-4000   www.gatesrubber.com

Mfr. automotive and industrial belts and hoses.

GNAPCO Pte. Ltd., Duke Wellington House, 7/F, 14-24 Wellington Street, Central, Hong Kong PRC
Tel: 852-2525-1306   Fax: 852-2810-4289

GATX CORPORATION

500 West Monroe Street, Chicago, IL, 60661

Tel: (312) 621-6200   Fax: (312) 621-6648   www.gatxcapital.com

Lease and loan financing, residual guarantees.

GATX Leasing Hong Kong Ltd., Ste. 2705, Two Pacific Place, 88 Wueensway, Hong Kong PRC

GE BETZ, DIV. GE SPECIALTY MATERIALS

4636 Somerton Road, PO Box 3002, Trevose, PA, 19053-6783

Tel: (215) 355-3300   Fax: (215) 953-5524   www.gebetz.com

Engaged in engineered chemical treatment of water and process systems in industrial, commercial and institutional facilities

GE Betz, Div. GE Specialty Materials, Unit 1501, Greenfield Tower, Concordia Plaza, 1 Science Museum Rd., Tsimshatsui East Kowloon, Hong Kong PRC

GEMSTAR-TV GUIDE INTERNATIONAL, INC.

135 North Los Robles Avenue, Ste. 800, Pasadena, CA, 91101

Tel: (626) 792-5700   Fax: (626) 792-0257   www.gemstar.com

Mfr. technology for VCR programming.

Gemstar Asia, Man Lok Centre, 23 Man Lok Street, Hung Hom Kowloon, Hong Kong PRC

Tel: 852-2766-8445   Fax: 852-2363-3942

GEN RE INTERMEDIARIES CORPORATION

PO Box 10216, Stamford, CT, 06904-2216

Tel: (203) 357-8883   Fax: (203) 328-6408   www.genre.com

Provides reinsurance services worldwide.

Cologne Reinsurance Company plc., 68/F, Central Plaza, 18 Harbour Rd., Wanchai, Hong Kong PRC

Tel: 852-2598-2388   Fax: 852-2598-2398   Contact: Jackie Y.C. Chun, Gen. Mgr.

General Re Financial Products Ltd. - Hong Kong, 68/F, Central Plaza, 18 Harbour Rd., Wanchai, Hong Kong PRC

Tel: 852-2598-2488   Fax: 852-2598-2408   Contact: James Kao

Hartford Re Company, Unit 3304-06, World Trade Centre, 280 Gloucester Road, Causeway Bay, Hong Kong PRC

Tel: 852-2840-5100   Fax: 852-2840-1980   Contact: Daniel Stau, Gen. Mgr.

GENERAL DATACOMM INC.

6 Rubber Avenue, Naugatuck, CT, 06770

Tel: (203) 729-0271   Fax: (203) 729-2883   www.gdc.com

Mfr., sales and service of transportation equipment for communications networks.

General DataComm Intl., 803 Century Square, 1-13 D'Aguilar St., Central, Hong Kong PRC

GENERAL ELECTRIC CAPITAL CORPORATION

260 Long Ridge Road, Stamford, CT, 06927

Tel: (203) 357-4000   Fax: (203) 357-6489   www.gecapital.com

Financial, property, casualty insurance, computer sales and trailer leasing services.

ERC Group, Div. GE Capital, Ste. 2807-8, Citibank Tower, Citibank Plaza, 3 Garden Rd., Hong Kong PRC

Tel: 852-2509-6888

GENERAL ELECTRIC COMPANY

3135 Easton Turnpike, Fairfield, CT, 06431

Tel: (203) 373-2211   Fax: (203) 373-3131   www.ge.com

Diversified manufacturing, technology and services.

GE Capital Global Projects, 15-16/F, The Lee Gardens, Central, Hong Kong PRC

Tel: 852-2100-6717   Fax: 852-2100-8198

GE International, 15/FThe Lee Gardens, Central, Hong Kong PRC

Tel: 852-2100-8382   Fax: 852-2100-6688

GE Silicones Hong Kong, 25 Canton Road, Tsimshatsui, Kowloon, Hong Kong PRC

Tel: 852-2629-0888   Fax: 852-2629-0803

GT Engineering and Associates, 17/F, Pacific Trade Centre, 2 Kai Hing Road, Kowloon Bay, Hong Kong PRC

Tel: 852-2795-9988   Fax: 852-2705-9799

NBC GE, NBC Asia Ltd., 15/F, 8 Commercial Tower, Chaiwan, Hong Kong PRC

Tel: 852-2965-6800   Fax: 852-2965-6882

GENUITY, INC.

225 Presidential Way, Woburn, MA, 01801

Tel: (781) 865-2000　　　Fax: (781) 865-3936　　　www.genuity.com

R/D computer, communications, acoustics technologies and internetworking services.

Genuity Hong Kong, One Pacific Place, 39/F, 88 Queensway, Admiralty, Hong Kong PRC

GEO LOGISTICS CORPORATION

1521 E. Dyer Rd., Santa Ana, CA, 92705

Tel: (714) 513-3000　　　Fax: (714) 513-3120　　　www.geo-logistics.com

Engaged in freight forwarding, warehousing and distribution services, specializing in heavy cargo.

GeoLogistics Ltd., 93 Kwai Fuk Road, 20/F, Kwai Chung NT, Hong Kong PRC

Tel: 852-2211-8998　Fax: 852-23-2877

GeoLogistics Ltd., G57, Airfreight Forwarding Center, Chek Lap Kok, Hong Kong PRC

Tel: 852-2237-1469　Fax: 852-22-37-1483

GERBER SCIENTIFIC, INC.

83 Gerber Road West, South Windsor, CT, 06074

Tel: (860) 644-1551　　　Fax: (860) 644-5547　　　www.gerberscientific.com

Mfr. computer-based automated manufacturing and design systems for signs and graphics.

Gerber Technology, 123 Hoi Bun Road, Tower II, 10/F, Kowloon, Hong Kong PRC

THE GILLETTE COMPANY

Prudential Tower Building, Boston, MA, 02199

Tel: (617) 421-7000　　　Fax: (617) 421-7123　　　www.gillette.com

Develop/mfr. personal care/use products: blades and razors, toiletries, cosmetics, stationery.

Colton Trading Co. Ltd., Hong Kong PRC

Contact: William Yeoh, Gen. Mgr.

Gillette (Hong Kong) Ltd., North Point, Hong Kong PRC

Contact: Ying Meng Lai, Mgr.

Gillette Far East Trading Ltd., 16/F Island Place Tower, 510 King's Road, North Point, Hong Kong PRC

Contact: Ying Meng Lai, Mgr.

GILSON INC.

3000 W. Beltline Hwy, PO Box 620027, Middleton, WI, 53562-0027

Tel: (608) 836-1551　　　Fax: (608) 831-4451　　　www.gilson.com

Mfr. analytical/biomedical instruments.

World Ways, 172-176 Wing Lok Street, 2/F, Winfull Commercial Bldg., Hong Kong PRC

GIW INDUSTRIES, INC.

5000 Wrightsboro Rd., Grovetown, GA, 30813

Tel: (706) 863-1011　　　Fax: (706) 860-5897　　　www.giwindustries.com

Mfr. slurry pumps.

KSB Jebsen China Ltd., 24/F, Caroline Centre, 28 Yun Ping Rd., Hong Kong PRC

GLENAYRE ELECTRONICS LTD.

11360 Lakefield Drive, Duluth, GA, 30097

Tel: (770) 283-1000　　　Fax: (770) 497-3982　　　www.glenayre.com

Mfr. infrastructure components and pagers.

Glenayre Electronics (Hong Kong) Ltd., Units 2104-2105, Chow Tai Fook Centre, 580A Nathan Rd., Kowloon, Hong Kong PRC

Tel: 852-2838-3236　Fax: 852-2838-3231

GLOBAL SILVERHAWK INTERNATIONAL MOVING

1000 Burnett Avenue, Concord, CA, 94520

Tel: (510) 609-7080　　　Fax: (510) 609-7081　　　www.globalsilverhawk.com

International moving and forwarding.

Santa Fe Transport International Ltd, 302-308 Hennessy Road, 18/F, Wanchai, Hong Kong PRC

Tel: 852-2574-6204

THE GOLDMAN SACHS GROUP

85 Broad Street, New York, NY, 10004

Tel: (212) 902-1000   Fax: (212) 902-3000   www.gs.com

Investment bankers; securities broker dealers.

Goldman Sachs Group, Asia Pacific Finance Tower, Citibank Plaza, 37/F, 3 Garden Road, Central, Hong Kong PRC

Tel: 852-2978-1000

W. L. GORE & ASSOCIATES, INC.

555 Paper Mill Road, Newark, DE, 19711

Tel: (302) 738-4880   Fax: (302) 738-7710   www.gorefabrics.com

Mfr. electronic, industrial filtration, medical and fabric products.

W. L. Gore & Associates Ltd., Hong Kong PRC

W. R. GRACE & COMPANY

7500 Grace Drive, Columbia, MD, 21044

Tel: (410) 531-4000   Fax: (410) 531-4367   www.grace.com

Mfr. specialty chemicals and materials: packaging, health care, catalysts, construction, water treatment/process.

W.R. Grace (Hong Kong) Ltd., Devon House, 20/F, 979 King's Rd., Quarry Bay, Hong Kong PRC

Tel: 852-2590-2828   Fax: 852-2811-2661

GRACO INC.

88 - 11th Avenue NE, PO Box 1441, Minneapolis, MN, 55440-1441

Tel: (612) 623-6000   Fax: (612) 623-6777   www.graco.com

Mfr. systems and equipment to service fluid handling systems and automotive equipment.

Graco Hong Kong, 21-08 Well Fung Industrial Ctr., 57-76 Ta Chuen Ping St., Kwai Chung New Territory, Hong Kong PRC

Tel: 852-2395-3189   Fax: 852-2392-0837

GRAFTECH INTERNATIONAL LTD.

1521 Concord Pike, Ste. 301, Wilmington, DE, 19803

Tel: (302) 778-8277   Fax: (302) 778-8237   www.graftechinternational.com

Mfr. graphite electrodes for electrical products.

UCAR International Trading Inc., Room 302B, 3/F, AIA Plaza, 18 Hysan Avenue, Causeway Bay, Hong Kong PRC

Tel: 852-2739-2820   Fax: 852-2610-1469

GRANT THORNTON INTERNATIONAL

800 One Prudential Plaza, 130 E. Randolph Drive, Chicago, IL, 60601-6050

Tel: (312) 856-0001   Fax: (312) 616-7052   www.grantthornton.com

Accounting, audit, tax and management consulting services.

Grant Thornton Byrne, Lippo Centre, Lippo Tower, 40/F, 89 Queensway, Hong Kong PRC

Tel: 852-2840-1188   Fax: 852-2840-0789   Contact: Kevin O'Shaughnessy

Grant Thornton International, 37/F, Wu Chung House, 213 Queen's Rd. East, Wanchai, Hong Kong PRC

Tel: 852-2838-0099   Fax: 852-2838-0211   Contact: Gabriel R. Azedo

PCS International, 803, Regent Centre, 88 Queen's Rd., Central, Hong Kong PRC

GREAT LAKES CHEMICAL CORPORATION

500 East 96th Street, Ste. 500, Indianapolis, IN, 46240

Tel: (317) 715-3000   Fax: (317) 715-3050   www.greatlakeschem.com

Mfr. innovative specialty chemical solutions, including flame retardants and other polymer additives, water treatment chemicals, performance and fine chemicals, fire extinguishers.

Great Lakes Chemical (Far East) Ltd., Units 05-6, 30/F, Soundwill Plaza, 38 Russell Street, Causeway Bay, Hong Kong PRC

Tel: 852-2258-2233   Fax: 852-2258-2266

GREENFIELD INDUSTRIES INC.

470 Old Evans Road, Evans, GA, 30809

Tel: (706) 863-7708   Fax: (706) 860-8559   www.gfi.com

Mfr. high-speed rotary cutting tools.

Rogers Tool Works Inc., 1903, Shiu Lam Bldg., 23 Luard Rd., Wan Chai, Hong Kong PRC

GREY GLOBAL GROUP

777 Third Ave., New York, NY, 10017

Tel: (212) 546-2000   Fax: (212) 546-1495   www.grey.com

International advertising agency.

Grey Hong Kong, Manulife Tower, 34/F, 169 Electric Rd., North Point, Hong Kong PRC

GRIFFITH LABORATORIES INC.

One Griffith Center, Alsip, IL, 60658

Tel: (708) 371-0900   Fax: (708) 597-3294   www.griffithlabs.com

Mfr. industrial food ingredients and equipment.

Griffith Laboratories Ltd., 8/F, Supreme Industrial Bldg., 15 Shan Mei St., Fo-Tan Shatin New Territories, Hong Kong PRC

Tel: 852-2688-6119   Fax: 852-2688-6126

GUIDANT CORPORATION

111 Monument Circle, 29th Fl., Indianapolis, IN, 46204

Tel: (317) 971-2000   Fax: (317) 971-2040   www.guidant.com

Mfr. cardiovascular therapeutic devices.

Guidant Hong Kong, CRC Protective Tower, Ste. 2201, 38 Gloucester Road, Wanchai, Hong Kong PRC

Tel: 852-2827-2338   Fax: 852-2593-2222

GUILFORD MILLS INC.

4925 West Market Street, PO Box 26969, Greensboro, NC, 27407

Tel: (336) 316-4000   Fax: (336) 316-4059   www.guilfordmills.com

Mfr. textiles.

Guilford Mills, Inc., Unit 702, 7F, Lippo Sun Plaza, 28 Canton Road, Tsimshatsui Kowloon, Hong Kong PRC

Tel: 852-2730-9922   Fax: 852-2376-5922   Contact: Matthew Tsang

GUY CARPENTER & COMPANY, INC.

114 West 47th Street, New York, NY, 10036

Tel: (212) 323-1000   Fax: (212) 345-2494   www.guycarp.com

Engaged in global reinsurance and risk management.

Guy Carpenter & Company Limited, Miramar Tower, Ste. 2118, 1-23 Kimberly Road Tsimshatsui, Kowloon, Hong Kong PRC

Tel: 852-2582-3500   Fax: 852-2827-5551   Contact: Lawrence Liao

HAEMONETICS CORPORATION

400 Wood Road, Braintree, MA, 02184-9114

Tel: (781) 848-7100   Fax: (781) 848-5106   www.haemonetics.com

Mfr. automated blood processing systems and blood products.

Haemonetics Hong Kong Ltd., Ste. 1314, 13/F, Two Pacific Place, 88 Queensway, Hong Kong PRC

Tel: 852-2868-9218   Fax: 852-2801-4380

HALLMARK CARDS INC.

2501 McGee Street, Kansas City, MO, 64108

Tel: (816) 274-5100   Fax: (816) 274-5061   www.hallmark.com

Mfr. greeting cards and related products.

Hallmark Cards Asia Ltd., Rm. 1501, Stanhope House, 734-738 King's Rd., Quarry Bay, Hong Kong PRC

Tel: 852-2811-8551

HA-LO INDUSTRIES, INC.

5800 West Touhy Avenue, Niles, IL, 60714

Tel: (847) 600-3000   Fax: (847) 600-4000   www.halo.com

Engaged in distribution of brand-awareness, promotional products.

Parsons International, Ltd., 38 Tai Kok Tsui Road, Kowloon, Hong Kong PRC

HANDY & HARMAN

555 Theodore Fremd Ave., Rye, NY, 10580

Tel: (914) 921-5200   Fax: (914) 925-4496   www.handyha

Precious and specialty metals for industry, refining, scrap metal; diversified industrial mfr.

Handy & Harman (HK) Ltd., 6/F, King Fook Bldg., 30-32 Des Voeux Rd., Central, Hong Kong PRC

HARCOURT GENERAL, INC.

27 Boylston St., Chestnut Hill, MA, 02467

Tel: (617) 232-8200   Fax: (617) 739-1395   www.harcourt.com

Publisher of educational materials.

Harcourt General Asia Pte.Ltd., Rm. 803, 8/F, 331 Cheung Sha Wan Rd., Kowloon, Hong Kong PRC

Tel: 852-8108-6882   Fax: 852-2861-3956   Contact: Joe Lam, Mgr.

HARRIS CORPORATION

1025 West NASA Blvd., Melbourne, FL, 32919

Tel: (407) 727-9100   Fax: (407) 727-9344   www.harris.com

Mfr. communications and information-handling equipment, including copying and fax systems.

Harris Semiconductor China Ltd., Unit 1801-2, 18/F, 83 Austin Road, Tsimshatsui, Kowloon, Hong Kong PRC

Tel: 852-2723-6339   Fax: 852-2724-4369

HARTFORD STEAM BOILER INSPECTION & INSURANCE CO.)

One State Street, PO Box 5024, Hartford, CT, 06102-5024

Tel: (860) 722-1866   Fax: (860) 722-5770   www.hsb.com

Provides specialty insurance products and inspection services.

Hartford Steam Boiler, 2705, Universal Trade Centre, 3 Arbuthnot Rd., Central, Hong Kong PRC

HARTMARX CORPORATION

101 North Wacker Drive, Chicago, IL, 60606

Tel: (312) 372-6300   Fax: (312) 444-2710   www.hartmarx.com

Mfr. licensing men's and women's apparel.

Hartmarx Far East, Unit 809, 8/F, Tower 2, Cheung Sha Wan Rd., Kowloon, Hong Kong PRC

HAWORTH INC.

1 Haworth Center, Holland, MI, 49423-9576

Tel: (616) 393-3000   Fax: (616) 393-1570   www.haworth.com

Mfr. office furniture.

Haworth Furniture, 248 Queen's Road East, Wanchai, Hong Kong PRC

HEIDRICK & STRUGGLES INTERNATIONAL, INC.

233 South Wacker Drive, Chicago, IL, 60606

Tel: (312) 496-1200   Fax: (312) 496-1290   www.heidrick.com

Executive search firm.

Heidrick & Struggles Intl. Inc., The Bank of China Tower, One Garden Rd., 54/F, Central, Hong Kong PRC

Tel: 852-2802-8887   Fax: 852-2519-8411

HELLER FINANCIAL INC.

500 West Monroe Street, Chicago, IL, 60661

Tel: (312) 441-7000   Fax: (312) 441-7367   www.hellerfin.com

Financial services.

East Asia Heller Limited, Ste. 901-903, Central Plaza, 18 Harbour Road, Wanchai, Hong Kong PRC

Tel: 852-2586-0000

HELLER, EHRMAN, WHITE & McAULIFFE

333 Bush Street, Ste. 3000, San Francisco, CA, 94104-2878

Tel: (415) 772-6000   Fax: (415) 772-6268   www.hewm.com

Engaged in international law.

Heller, Ehrman, White & McAuliffe, 63-8-09 The Center, 99 Queen's Road, Central, Hong Kong PRC

Tel: 852-2526-6381   Fax: 852-2810-6242

HERCULES INC.

Hercules Plaza, 1313 N. Market Street, Wilmington, DE, 19894-0001

Tel: (302) 594-5000   Fax: (302) 594-5400   www.herc.com

Mfr. specialty chemicals, plastics, film and fibers, coatings, resins and food ingredients.

Hercochem (HK) Ltd., 11/F, Tower 3, China Hong Kong City, 33 Canton Rd., Tsim Sha Tsui Kowloon, Hong Kong PRC

Tel: 852-2527-2638

Hercules Asia Pacific/Hercules China Ltd., 1907-8, Harcourt House, 39 Gloucester Rd., Wanchai, Hong Kong PRC

Tel: 852-2527-2638   Fax: 852-2528-1598

HEWITT ASSOCIATES LLC

100 Half Day Road, Lincolnshire, IL, 60069

Tel: (847) 295-5000   Fax: (847) 295-7634   www.hewitt.com

Employee benefits consulting firm.

Hewitt Associates, Suite 2601-05, Shell Tower Times Square, 1 Matheson St., Causeway Bay, Hong Kong PRC

Tel: 852-2877-8600

HEWLETT-PACKARD COMPANY

3000 Hanover Street, Palo Alto, CA, 94304-1185

Tel: (650) 857-1501   Fax: (650) 857-5518   www.hp.com

Mfr. computing, communications and measurement products and services.

Hewlett-Packard Hong Kong Ltd. Hdqtrs.- Asia Pacific, 19/F, Cityplaza One, 1111 King's Road, Taikoo Shing, Hong Kong PRC

Tel: 852-2-599-7777

HILTON HOTELS CORPORATION

9336 Civic Center Drive, Beverly Hills, CA, 90210

Tel: (310) 278-4321   Fax: (310) 205-7880   www.hiltonhotels.com

International hotel chain: Hilton International, Vista Hotels and Hilton National Hotels.

Hilton International Company, Rm. 2102, Lippo Tower Lippo Centre, 89 Queensway, Admiralty, Hong Kong PRC

HOLIDAY INN (BASS RESORTS) WORLDWIDE, INC.

3 Ravinia Drive, Ste. 2900, Atlanta, GA, 30346-2149

Tel: (770) 604-2000   Fax: (770) 604-5403   www.holidayinn.com

Hotels, restaurants and casinos.

Holiday Inn Hong Kong, PO Box 95555, 50 Nathan Rd., Hong Kong PRC

HONEYWELL INTERNATIONAL INC.

Honeywell Plaza, Minneapolis, MN, 55408

Tel: (612) 951-1000   Fax: (612) 951-8537   www.honeywell.com

Develop/mfr. controls for home and building, industry, space and aviation, burglar and fire alarm systems.

Honeywell Ltd., New Bright Bldg., 5/F, 11 Sheung Yuet Rd., Kowloon Bay, Hong Kong PRC

Tel: 852-2331-9133   Fax: 852-2331-9998

HORWATH INTERNATIONAL ASSOCIATION

420 Lexington Avenue, Suite 526, New York, NY, 10170-0526

Tel: (212) 808-2000   Fax: (212) 808-2020   www.horwath.com

Public accountants and auditors.

Horwath Asia Pacific, Bank of America Tower, 6/F, 12 Harcourt Rd., Central, Hong Kong PRC

Contact: Alan Johnson

HOUGHTON INTERNATIONAL INC.

PO Box 930, Madison & Van Buren Avenues, Valley Forge, PA, 19482-0930

Tel: (610) 666-4000   Fax: (610) 666-1376   www.houghtonintl.com

Mfr. specialty chemicals, hydraulic fluids and lubricants.

Houghton Oils & Chemicals, Unit B, 16/F, Full Win Commercial Ctr., 573 Nathan Road, Kowloon, Hong Kong PRC

Tel: 852-2770-8211

HOWMEDICA OSTEONICS, INC.

59 Route 17 South, Allendale, NJ, 07401

Tel: (201) 507-7300   Fax: (201) 935-4873   www.howmedica.com

Mfr. of maxillofacial products (orthopedic implants).

Hong Kong Surgical Products Ltd., Hong Kong PRC

Tel: 852-2527-9974

HUBBELL INCORPORATED

584 Derby Milford Road, Orange, CT, 06477

Tel: (203) 799-4100   Fax: (203) 799-4208   www.hubbell.com

Electrical wiring components.

Hubbell S.E. Asia Pte. Ltd., Room 112, I/F, Sun House, 90 Connaught Road, Central, Hong Kong PRC

Tel: 852-2534-0812   Fax: 852-2851-8146

HUNTON & WILLIAMS

951 East Byrd Street, East Tower, Richmond, VA, 23219-4074

Tel: (804) 788-8200   Fax: (804) 788-8218   www.hunton.com

Engaged in international law.

Hunton & Williams, 23/F, CITIC Tower, 1 Tim Mei Ave., Central, Hong Kong PRC

Tel: 852-2841-9100   Fax: 852-2841-9191   Contact: Edward B. Koehler, Mng. Ptnr.   Emp: 16

HUSSMANN INTERNATIONAL

12999 St. Charles Rock Road, Bridgeton, MO, 63044

Tel: (314) 291-2000   Fax: (314) 291-5144   www.hussmann.com

Mfr. refrigeration and environmental control systems for food industrial.

Hussmann Tempcool (Hong Kong) Limited, Unit B, 25/F, 609-611, Tai Nan West Street, Cheung Sha Wan, Kowloon, Hong Kong PRC

Tel: 852-2765-8022   Fax: 852-2765-0283

HYATT CORPORATION

200 West Madison Street, Chicago, IL, 60606

Tel: (312) 750-1234   Fax: (312) 750-8578   www.hyatt.com

International hotel management.

Hyatt Regency Hong Kong, 67 Nathan Rd., Kowloon, Hong Kong PRC

Tel: 852-2311-1234   Fax: 852-2739-8701

HYPERCOM CORPORATION

2851 West Kathleen Road, Phoenix, AZ, 85053

Tel: (602) 504-5000   Fax: (602) 504-4578   www.hypercom.com

Mfr. point-of-sale systems.

Hypercom Asia, Ltd., 21/F, Metro Centre II, 21 Lam Hing Street, Kowloon Bay, Kowloon, Hong Kong PRC

Tel: 852-2561-6800   Fax: 852-2561-5890

HYPERION SOLUTIONS CORPORATION

1344 Crossman Avenue, Sunnyvale, CA, 94089

Tel: (408) 744-9500   Fax: (408) 744-0400   www.hyperion.com

Mfr. data analysis software tools.

Niederlassung Hong Kong, 18 Harbour Road, 32/F, Wanchai, Hong Kong PRC

Tel: 852-2598-7900   Fax: 852-2914-2972

i2 TECHNOLOGIES, INC.

11701 Luna Road, Dallas, TX, 75234

Tel: (214) 860-6106   Fax: (214) 860-6060   www.i2.com

Engaged in supply chain management; solutions to help companies collaborate on decision-making processes.

i2 Technologies Hong Kong, Suites 3001-3, NatWest Tower, Times Square, 1 Matheson Street, Causeway Bay, Hong Kong PRC

Tel: 852-2506-1338

IBM CORPORATION

1133 Westchester Avenue, White Plains, NY, 10604

Tel: (914) 765-1900　　　　Fax: (914) 765-7382　　　　www.ibm.com

Information products, technology and services.

IBM Hong Kong/Southeast Asia, 10/F, Hong Kong Telecom Tower, Taikoo Place, 979 King's Road, Quarry Bay, Hong Kong PRC

Tel: 852-2825-6222　Fax: 852-2810-0210

ICC INDUSTRIES INC.

460 Park Ave., New York, NY, 10022

Tel: (212) 521-1700　　　　Fax: (212) 521-1794　　　　www.iccchem.com

Manufacturing and trading of chemicals, plastics and pharmaceuticals.

ICC (Hong Kong) Ltd., Rm. 1110, West Wing, New World Office Bldg., 20 Salisbury Rd., Tsimshatsui East Kowloon, Hong Kong PRC

Tel: 852-2366-1678　Fax: 852-2367-1377　Contact: Helen Ho So-King

IFR SYSTEMS, INC.

10200 West York Street, Wichita, KS, 67215-8999

Tel: (316) 522-4981　　　　Fax: (316) 524-2623　　　　www.ifrsys.com

Mfr. electronic test and measurement equipment.

IFR Hong Kong, 302-308 Hennessy, Rm. 702, Wanchai, Hong Kong PRC

ILLINOIS TOOL WORKS (ITW)

3600 West Lake Ave., Glenview, IL, 60025-5811

Tel: (847) 724-7500　　　　Fax: (847) 657-4268　　　　www.itw.com

Mfr. gears, tools, fasteners, sealants, plastic and metal components for industrial, medical, etc.

ITW Dynatec Hong Kong, No. 6 25/F Sunrise Ind. Bldg., 16-26 Wang Wo Tsai Street, Tsuen Wan, Hong Kong PRC

IMATION CORPORATION

One Imation Place, Oakdale, MN, 55128

Tel: (612) 704-4000　　　　Fax: (612) 704-3444　　　　www.imation.com

Dry laser-imaging film systems.

Imation Hong Kong, Two Chinachem Exchange Square, 30/F, 338 King's Road, North Point, Hong Kong PRC

Tel: 852-2161-2888

IMI NORGREN GROUP

5400 South Delaware Street, Littleton, CO, 80120-1663

Tel: (303) 794-2611　　　　Fax: (303) 795-9487　　　　www.usa.norgren.com

Mfr. pneumatic filters, regulators, lubricators, valves, automation systems, dryers, push-in fittings.

IMI Norgren Ltd., 14/F, Hale Weal Industrial Bldg., 22-28 Tai Chung Rd., Tseun Wan, Hong Kong PRC

Tel: 852-2492-7608　Fax: 852-2498-5878

IMPERIAL TOY CORPORATION

2060 East Seventh Street, Los Angeles, CA, 90021

Tel: (213) 489-2100　　　　Fax: (213) 489-4467　　　　www.imperialtoy.com

Mfr. plastic toys and novelties.

Fred Kort Intl. Ltd., 501-2, Peninsula Centre 67, Mody Rd., Tsim Shu Tsui East, Kowloon, Hong Kong PRC

INDUSTRIAL ACOUSTICS COMPANY

1160 Commerce Ave., Bronx, NY, 10462

Tel: (718) 931-8000　　　　Fax: (718) 863-1138　　　　www.industrialacoustics.com

Design/mfr. acoustic structures for sound conditioning and noise control.

Industrial Acoustics Co. (HK) Ltd., 15/F, Honour Industrial Centre, Unit 12, 6 Sun Yip St., Chai Wan, Hong Kong PRC

INFONET SERVICES CORPORATION

2160 East Grand Ave., El Segundo, CA, 90245-1022

Tel: (310) 335-2600   Fax: (310) 335-4507   www.infonet.com

Provider of Internet services and electronic messaging services.

Infonet Hong Kong, Telcom Services - Infonet Section, 31/F, Hong Kong Telecom Tower, Taikoo Place, 979 King's Road, Quarry Bay, Hong Kong PRC

Tel: 852-2883-6383   Fax: 852-2962-5359

INGERSOLL-RAND COMPANY

200 Chestnut Ridge Road, Woodcliff Lake, NJ, 07675

Tel: (201) 573-0123   Fax: (201) 573-3172   www.irco.com

Leading innovation and solutions provider for the major global markets of Security and Safety, Climate Control, Industrial Solutions and Infrastructure.

Ingersoll-Rand Asia Pacific Inc., Ste. 1201-3, 12/F, Central Plaza, 18 Harbour Rd., Wanchai, Hong Kong PRC

Tel: 852-2527-0183   Fax: 852-2824-2589

INGRAM MICRO INC.

1600 E. St. Andrew Place, Santa Ana, CA, 92799

Tel: (714) 566-1000   Fax: (714) 566-7940   www.ingrammicro.com

Engaged in wholesale distribution of microcomputer products.

Ingram Micro Hong Kong, 17/F, Seaview Centre, 139 Hoi Bun Road, Kwun Tong Kowloon, Hong Kong PRC

INSTINET

875 Third Ave., New York, NY, 10022

Tel: (212) 310-9500   Fax: (212) 832-5183   www.instinet.com

Online investment brokerage.

Instinet, Hong Kong PRC

INTEGRATED SILICON SOLUTION, INC.

2231 Lawson Lane, Santa Clara, CA, 95054-3311

Tel: (408) 588-0800   Fax: (408) 588-0805   www.issiusa.com

Mfr. high-speed memory chips and SRAMs.

Integrated Silicon Solution, Inc., Hong Kong PRC

Tel: 852-2319-2212   Fax: 852-2768-8704

INTEL CORPORATION

2200 Mission College Blvd., Santa Clara, CA, 95052-8119

Tel: (408) 765-8080   Fax: (408) 765-1739   www.intel.com

Mfr. semiconductor, microprocessor and micro-communications components and systems.

Intel Semiconductor Ltd., 32/F, Two Pacific Place, 88 Queensway, Central, Hong Kong PRC

Tel: 852-2844-4555

INTELLIGROUP, INC.

499 Thornall Street, Edison, NJ, 08837

Tel: (732) 590-1600   Fax: (732) 362-2100   www.intelligroup.com

Provides systems integration, customer software and Internet application development.

Intelligroup Hong Kong Ltd., Wing On Centre, 25/F, 111 Connaught Road, Central, Hong Kong PRC

Contact: Madhukar Joshi

INTERACTIVE DATA CORPORATION

22 Crosby Drive, Bedford, MA, 01730

Tel: (781) 687-8500   Fax: (781) 687-8289   www.interactivedatacorp.com

Engaged in subscription services.

FT Interactive Data, Hong Kong PRC

INTER-CONTINENTAL HOTELS

3 Ravinia Drive, Suite 2900, Atlanta, GA, 30346-2149

Tel: (770) 604-2000   Fax: (770) 604-5403   www.interconti.com

Worldwide hotel and resort accommodations.

Inter-Continental Hotels, Unit 4701, Central Plaza, 18 Harbour Road, Wanchai, Hong Kong PRC

Tel: 852-2827-1010   Fax: 852-2827-0505

INTERDEAN INTERCONEX, INC

55 Hunter Lane, Elmsford, NY, 10523-1317

Tel: (914) 347-6600   Fax: (914) 347-0129   www.interdean.com

Freight forwarding.

Interconex Far East Ltd., Units 2612-2624, Level 26 Metroplaza Tower, 223 Hing Fong Rd., Kwai Chung NT, Hong Kong PRC

Tel: 852-2480-3122   Fax: 852-2428-2881   Contact: Phil Hamill, Mgr.

INTERGEN (INTERNATIONAL GENERATING CO., LTD.)

15 Wayside Road, Burlington, MA, 01803-4609

Tel: (781) 933-3000   Fax: (781) 933-3001   www.intergen.com

Global power and fuel asset development company; develops, owns and operates electric power plants and related distribution facilities.

InterGen (HK) Limited, Tower One Lippo Centre, 41/F, 89 Queensway, Hong Kong PRC

Tel: 852-2912-8200   Fax: 852-2537-6400

INTERGRAPH CORPORATION

One Madison Industrial Park, Huntsville, AL, 35894-0001

Tel: (256) 730-2000   Fax: (256) 730-7898   www.intergraph.com

Develop/mfr. interactive computer graphic systems.

Intergraph Asia Pacific Ltd., Tai Yau Building, Rooms 901-910, 181 Johnston Road, Wanchai, Hong Kong PRC

Tel: 852-2-8933621   Fax: 852-2572-9787

Intergraph Hong Kong Ltd., Units 401-4, 72 Tat Chee Ave., Hong Kong Industrial Technology Centre, Kowloon, Hong Kong PRC

Tel: 852-2593-1600   Fax: 852-2802-0781

INTERMEC TECHNOLOGIES CORPORATION

6001 36th Avenue West, PO Box 4280, Everett, WA, 98203-9280

Tel: (425) 348-2600   Fax: (425) 355-9551   www.intermec.com

Mfr. and distributor automated data collection systems.

Intermec Technologies Corporation, 1 Harbor Road, Unit 2602, Wan Chai, Hong Kong PRC

Tel: 852-2574-9777   Fax: 852-2574-9725

INTERNATIONAL COMPONENTS CORPORATION

420 N. May Street, Chicago, IL, 60622

Tel: (312) 829-2525   Fax: (312) 829-0213   www.icc-charge.com

Mfr. portable, rechargeable power, control and accessory products.

Fabricators Intl. Ltd., 11/F, Safety Godown Industrial Bldg., 56 Ka Yip St., Chai Wan, Hong Kong PRC

INTERNATIONAL FLAVORS & FRAGRANCES INC.

521 West 57th Street, New York, NY, 10019-2960

Tel: (212) 765-5500   Fax: (212) 708-7132   www.iff.com

Design/mfr. flavors, fragrances and aroma chemicals.

International Flavors & Fragrances Far East Ltd., 11/F, Watson Centre, 18-2 Kung Yip St., Kwai Chung, NT Kowloon, Hong Kong PRC

INTERNATIONAL MANAGEMENT GROUP (IMG)

1360 East Ninth Street, Ste. 100, Cleveland, OH, 44114

Tel: (216) 522-1200   Fax: (216) 522-1145   www.imgworld.com

Manages athletes, sports academies and real estate facilities worldwide.

IMG, Sunning Plaza, 12/F, 10 Hysan Avenue, Causeway Bay, Hong Kong PRC

Tel: 852-2-894-0288   Fax: 852-2-882-2557

INTERNATIONAL PAPER COMPANY

400 Atlantic Street, Stamford, CT, 06921

Tel: (203) 541-8000   Fax: (203) 358-6444   www.ipaper.com

Mfr./distributor container board, paper and wood products.

International Paper Co. (Far East) Ltd., 1008 Bank of America Tower, 12 Harcourt Rd., Hong Kong PRC

Veratec Nonwoven (Asia) Ltd., Suite 2112-2113, 21/F, Shui On Centre, 6-8 Harbour Rd., Hong Kong PRC

INTERNATIONAL RECTIFIER CORPORATION

233 Kansas Street, El Segundo, CA, 90245

Tel: (310) 322-3331   Fax: (310) 322-3332   www.irf.com

Mfr. power semiconductor components.

International Rectifier Corp., Unit 2210-2212, 22/F, Paul Y Centre, Hong Kong PRC

Tel: 852-2803-738   Fax: 852-2540-5835

INTERNATIONAL SPECIALTY PRODUCTS, INC.

1361 Alps Rd., Wayne, NJ, 07470

Tel: (973) 389-3083   Fax: (973) 628-4117   www.ispcorp.com

Mfr. specialty chemical products.

ISP (Hong Kong) Ltd., Ste. 1102, Ming An Plaza, No. 8 Sunning Road, Causeway Bay, Hong Kong PRC

Tel: 852-2881-6108   Fax: 852-2895-1250

INTERSIL CORPORATION

7585 Irvine Center Drive, Ste. 100, Irvine, CA, 92618

Tel: (949) 341-7000   Fax: (949) 341-7123   www.intersil.com

Designs innovative wireless networking and high performance analog solutions.

Intersil Corporation, Unit 1804 18/F Guangdong, 83 Austin Road, Kowloon, Hong Kong PRC

Tel: 852-2723-6339

INTERWOVEN, INC.

803 11th Avenue, Sunnyvale, CA, 94089

Tel: (408) 774-2000   Fax: (408) 774-2002   www.interwoven.com

Mfr. web content management software.

Interwoven, 1 Garden Road, Central, Hong Kong PRC

INVITROGEN CORPORATION

1600 Faraday Avenue, Carlsbad, CA, 92008

Tel: (760) 603-7200   Fax: (760) 602-6500   www.invitrogen.com

Mfr. products and kits for gene analysis.

Invitrogen Hong Kong Limited, 8/F Concord Tech Centre, 98 Texaco Road, Tsuen Wan, Hong Kong PRC

Tel: 852-2407-8450

IR FLUID PRODUCTS

PO Box 151, Bryan, OH, 43506

Tel: (419) 636-4242   Fax: (419) 633-1674   www.irco.com

Mfr. fluid control products, including pumps, valves, cylinders, logic controls and air line components.

Ingersoll-Rand, 625 Kings Road, 23/F, North Point, Hong Kong PRC

IVAX CORPORATION

4400 Biscayne Blvd., Miami, FL, 33137

Tel: (305) 575-6000   Fax: (305) 575-6055   www.ivax.com

Mfr. pharmaceuticals.

IVAX Asia, 3301 Hopewell Centre, 183 Queen's Road East, Wanchai, Hong Kong PRC

J. WALTER THOMPSON COMPANY

466 Lexington Ave., New York, NY, 10017

Tel: (212) 210-7000   Fax: (212) 210-6944   www.jwt.com

International advertising and marketing services.

J. Walter Thompson Co., Wanchai, Hong Kong PRC

JABIL CIRCUIT, INC.

10560 Ninth St. North, St. Petersburg, FL, 33716

Tel: (727) 557-9749   Fax: (727) 579-8529   www.jabil.com

Mfr. printed circuit boards, electronic components and systems.

Jabil Circuit, 11/F Tower 6, The Gateway Harbour City, Tsim Sha Tsui, Kowloon, Hong Kong PRC

Tel: 852-2668-7668 Fax: 852-2639-1794

JDA SOFTWARE GROUP, INC.

14400 N. 87th St., Scottsdale, AZ, 85260-3649

Tel: (480) 308-3000   Fax: (480) 308-3001   www.jda.com

Developer of information management software for retail, merchandising, distribution and store management.

JDA Software Group, 28/F, 38 Russell Street, Causeway Bay, Hong Kong PRC

Tel: 852-2106-1116 Fax: 852-2900-1195

JLG INDUSTRIES INC.

One JLG Drive, McConnellsburg, PA, 17233-9533

Tel: (717) 485-5161   Fax: (717) 485-6417   www.jlg.com

Mfr. aerial work platforms and vertical personnel lifts.

JLG Equipment Services Ltd., Landmark North 39, Level 11, Lung Sum Avenue, Sheung Shui N.T., Hong Kong PRC

Tel: 852-2639-5783 Fax: 852-2639-5797

JOHNSON & JOHNSON

One Johnson & Johnson Plaza, New Brunswick, NJ, 08933

Tel: (732) 524-0400   Fax: (732) 214-0334   www.jnj.com

Mfr./distributor/R&D pharmaceutical, health care and cosmetic products.

Janssen-Cilag Ltd., GPO 9733, Hong Kong PRC

Johnson & Johnson (Hong Kong) Ltd., GPO 9733, Hong Kong PRC

Johnson & Johnson Medical Hong Kong Ltd., GPO 9733, Hong Kong PRC

SC JOHNSON

1525 Howe St., Racine, WI, 53403

Tel: (262) 260-2000   Fax: (262) 260-2133   www.scjohnsonwax.com

Home, auto, commercial and personal care products and specialty chemicals.

SC Johnson, 20/F, OTB Bldg., 160 Gloucester Rd., Wanchai, Hong Kong PRC

JOHNSON CONTROLS INC.

5757 N. Green Bay Ave., PO Box 591, Milwaukee, WI, 53201-0591

Tel: (414) 228-1200   Fax: (414) 228-2077   www.johnsoncontrols.com

Mfr. facility management and control systems and auto seating.

Johnson Controls Hong Kong Ltd., Unit 1501, 5/F, Devon House, Taikoo Place, 979 King's Rd., Quarry Bay, Hong Kong PRC

Tel: 852-2590-0012 Fax: 852-2516-5648 Contact: Wing-On Yau, Branch Mgr.

JOHNSON OUTDOORS, INC.

555 Main Street, Racine, WI, 53177

Tel: (262) 631-6600   Fax: (262) 631-6601   www.johnsonoutdoors.com

Mfr. diving, fishing, boating and camping sports equipment.

Scubapro Asia/Pacific, 1208, Block A, M.P. Industrial Centre, 18 Ka Yip St., Chai Wan, Hong Kong PRC

Tel: 852-2556-7338 Fax: 852-2898-9872

JONES APPAREL GROUP INC.

250 Rittenhouse Circle, Bristol, PA, 19007

Tel: (215) 785-4000   Fax: (215) 785-1795   www.jny.com

Designs and markets a broad range of women's career sportswear, suits, and dresses, casual sportswear and jeans wear.

Jones Intl. Ltd., Cheung Sha Wan Plaza, Tower 1, 833 Cheung Sha Wan, Kowloon, Hong Kong PRC

JONES LANG LASALLE

153 East 53rd Street, New York, NY, 10022

Tel: (212) 812-5700   Fax: (212) 421-3544   www.am.joneslanglasalle.com

International marketing consultants, leasing agents and property management advisors.

Jones Lang Wootton, Hong Kong PRC

JONES, DAY, REAVIS & POGUE

North Point, 901 Lakeside Ave., Cleveland, OH, 44114

Tel: (216) 586-3939   Fax: (216) 579-0212   www.jonesday.com

International law firm.

Jones, Day, Reavis & Pogue, 29/F, Entertainment Bldg., 30 Queen's Rd., Central, Hong Kong PRC

Tel: 852-2526-6895   Fax: 852-2868-5871   Contact: W. Anthony Stewart, Ptnr.   Emp: 14

JUKI UNION SPECIAL CORPORATION

8500 N.W. 17th St., Miami, FL, 33126

Tel: (305) 594-0059   Fax: (305) 594-0720   www.unionspecial.com

Mfr. sewing machines.

Union Special Far East Ltd., 223 Hing Fong Rd., Kwai Fong NT, Hong Kong PRC

JUNIPER NETWORKS, INC.

1194 North Mathilda Ave., Sunnyvale, CA, 94089

Tel: (408) 745-2000   Fax: (408) 745-2100   www.juniper.net

Engaged in the design and sales of Internet Protocol routers for access networks.

Juniper Networks, Natwest Tower, Ste. 1601-06, Times Square, 1 Matheson Street, Causeway Bay, Hong Kong PRC

Tel: 852-2332-3636   Fax: 852-2574-7803

Juniper Networks Hong Kong, Ste. 1601-06, Natwest Tower, Times Square, 1 Matheson Street, Causeway Bay, Hong Kong PRC

KAYE, SCHOLER, FIERMAN, HAYS & HANDLER, LLP

425 Park Ave., New York, NY, 10022-3598

Tel: (212) 836-8000   Fax: (212) 836-8689   www.kayescholer.com

American and international law practice.

Kaye, Scholer, Fierman, Hays & Handler, LLP, Suite 2006-2010, No. 1 Harbour View Street, Central, Hong Kong PRC

Tel: 852-2845-8989   Fax: 852-2845-3682

A.T. KEARNEY INC.

5400 Legacy Dr., Plano, TX, 75201

Tel: (972) 604-4600   Fax: (972) 543-7680   www.atkearney.com

Management consultants and executive search.

A. T. Kearney (Hong Kong) Ltd., Level 31, One Pacofic Place, 88 Queensway, Hong Kong PRC

Tel: 852-2501-1400

KELLEY DRYE & WARREN LLP

101 Park Ave., New York, NY, 10178

Tel: (212) 808-7800   Fax: (212) 808-7898   www.kelleydrye.com

Engaged in international law.

Kelley Drye & Warren LLP, Suite 509-10, Tower Two Lippo Centre, 89 Queensway, Hong Kong PRC

Tel: 852-2869-0821   Fax: 852-2869-0049

KELLWOOD COMPANY

600 Kellwood Pkwy., Chesterfield, MO, 63017

Tel: (314) 576-3100   Fax: (314) 576-3434   www.kellwood.com

Mfr./marketing/sale primarily women's apparel and recreational camping products.

Smart Shirts Ltd., 55 King Yip St., Kwun Tong, Kowloon, Hong Kong PRC

Tel: 852-279-75111   Fax: 852-234-32715   Contact: Jesse C. P. Zee, Mng. Dir

KENNAMETAL INC.

1600 Technology Way, PO Box 231, Latrobe, PA, 15650

Tel: (724) 539-5000   Fax: (724) 539-4710   www.kennametal.com

Tools, hard carbide and tungsten alloys for metalworking industry.

Kennametal Hardpoint Hong Kong Ltd., Room C, 9/F, V Ga Bldg., 532-532A Castle Peak Rd., Kowloon, Hong Kong PRC

Tel: 852-2314-9209   Fax: 852-2314-9207

KEPNER-TREGOE INC.

PO Box 704, Princeton, NJ, 08542-0740

Tel: (609) 921-2806   Fax: (609) 497-0130   www.kepner-tregoe.com

Management consulting; specializing in strategy formulation, problem solving, decision making, project management, and cost reduction.

Kepner-Tregoe Southeast Asia Ltd, Level 25 Bank of China Tower, 1 Garden Road, Central, Hong Kong PRC

KIMBERLY-CLARK CORPORATION

351 Phelps Drive, Irving, TX, 75038

Tel: (972) 281-1200   Fax: (972) 281-1435   www.kimberly-clark.com

Mfr./sales/distribution of consumer tissue, household and personal care products.

Kimberly-Clark (Hong Kong) Ltd., Hong Kong PRC

KNIGHT-RIDDER INC.

50 W. San Fernando Street, San Jose, CA, 95113

Tel: (408) 938-7700   Fax: (408) 938-7700   www.kri.com

Engaged in newspaper and Internet publishing.

Knight-Ridder Financial/Asia, Citibank Tower, Suite 501-4, Citibank Plaza, 3 Garden Rd., Central, Hong Kong PRC

KNOLL, INC.

1235 Water Street, East Greenville, PA, 18041

Tel: (215) 679-7991   Fax: (215) 679-3904   www.knoll.com

Mfr. and sale of office furnishings.

Knoll International, Inc. c/o Comer Co., Ltd., 902 The Lee Gardens, 33 Hysan Avenue, Hong Kong

Tel: 85-22-881-8734

THE KOHLER COMPANY

444 Highland Drive, Kohler, WI, 53044

Tel: (920) 457-4441   Fax: (920) 459-1274   www.kohlerco.com

Plumbing products, ceramic tile and stone, cabinetry, furniture, engines, generators, switch gear and hospitality.

The Kohler Company, 1110B, Tower 2, China Hong Kong City, 33 Canton Rd., Kowloon, Hong Kong PRC

Tel: 852-2730-2383   Fax: 852-2730-2318   Contact: George Tam, Sr. Area Mgr.

KORN/FERRY INTERNATIONAL

1800 Century Park East, Los Angeles, CA, 90067

Tel: (310) 843-4100   Fax: (310) 553-6452   www.kornferry.com

Engaged in executive search and management consulting.

Korn/Ferry International Ltd., 808 Gloucester Tower, The Landmark, Central, Hong Kong PRC

Tel: 852-2521-5457   Fax: 852-2810-1632

KPMG CONSULTING INC.

1676 International Dr., McLean, VA, 22102

Tel: (703) 747-3000   Fax: (703) 747-8500   www.kpmg.com

Accounting and audit, tax and management consulting services.

KPMG International, 8/F, Prince's Bldg., 10 Chater Rd., Hong Kong PRC

Tel: 852-2522-60   Fax: 852-2845-2588   Contact: Marvin K.T. Cheung, Sr. Ptnr.

KRAFT FOODS INTERNATIONAL, INC., DIV. PHILIP MORRIS COS.

Three Lakes Drive, Northfield, IL, 60093

Tel: (847) 646-2000   Fax: (847) 646-6005   www.kraftfoods.com

Processor, distributor and manufacturer of food products.

Kraft Foods Asia/Pacific, One Pacific Place, 15/F, 88 Queensway, Hong Kong PRC

KRAS WORLDWIDE, INC.

2 Old Mill Lane, Media, PA, 19063

Tel: (215) 736-0981   Fax: (215) 736-8953   www.kras.com

Mfr. precision tools and machinery for electronic and plastics industrial.

Kras Asia Ltd., 78 Hung To Rd., Kwun Tong, Kowloon, Hong Kong PRC

KROLL INC.

9023 Columbine Road, Eden Prairie, MN, 55347

Tel: (952) 937-1107   Fax: (952) 937-5815   www.knollworldwide.com

Mfr. of software and engaged in data recovery services.

Kroll Asia Pacific Headquarters, Suite 1701-1702 Central Plaza, 18 Harbour Road, Wanchai, Hong Kong PRC

Tel: 852-2884-7788   Fax: 852-2568-8505

KULICKE & SOFFA INDUSTRIES INC.

2101 Blair Mill Road, Willow Grove, PA, 19090

Tel: (215) 784-6000   Fax: (215) 659-7588   www.kns.com

Semiconductor assembly systems and services.

Kulicke & Soffa (Asia) Ltd., 21/F, Yen Sheng Centre, 64 Hoi Yen Rd., Kwun Tong, Kowloon, Hong Kong PRC

Tel: 852-2955-3668   Fax: 852-2955-3666   Contact: Randy Wan, Sales Dir.

THE KULJIAN CORPORATION

3700 Science Center, Philadelphia, PA, 19104

Tel: (215) 243-1900   Fax: (215) 243-1909

Studies, design, engineering, construction management and site supervision.

Development Consultants Intl., 9/F, Hyde Ctr., 223 Gloucester Rd., Hong Kong PRC

KURT SALMON ASSOCIATES (KSA)

1355 Peachtree Street NE, Atlanta, GA, 30309

Tel: (404) 892-0321   Fax: (404) 898-9590   www.kurtsalmon.com

Management consulting: consumer products, retailing.

Kurt Salmon Associates Inc., Units 2101-2, 21/F, 83 Austin Rd., Kowloon, Hong Kong PRC

LANDOR ASSOCIATES

Klamath House, 1001 Front Street, San Francisco, CA, 94111-1424

Tel: (415) 955-1400   Fax: (415) 365-3190   www.landor.com

International marketing consulting firm, engaged in brand strategy, design, naming, digital branding, print literature design and research services.

Landor Hong Kong, Kinwick Centre, 17/F, 32 Hollywood Road, Central, Hong Kong PRC

Tel: 852-2851-8173   Fax: 852-2544-9199   Contact: Michael Ip

LATHAM & WATKINS

633 West 5th St., Ste. 4000, Los Angeles, CA, 90071-2007

Tel: (213) 485-1234   Fax: (213) 891-8763   www.lw.com

International law firm.

Latham & Watkins, Ste. 2205A, 22/F, No. 9 Queen's Rd., Central, Hong Kong PRC

Tel: 852-2522-7886   Fax: 852-2522-7006

LEARNING TREE INTERNATIONAL, INC.

6053 West Century Blvd., Los Angeles, CA, 90045-0028

Tel: (310) 417-9700   Fax: (310) 417-8684   www.learningtree.com

Information technology training services.

Learning Tree International Ltd. (Hong Kong), Ste. No. 5, 16/F, Queen's Place, 74 Queen's Rd., Central, Hong Kong PRC

Tel: 852-2111-7700 Fax: 852-2530-2902 Contact: James Webb Emp: 3

LECROY CORPORATION

700 Chestnut Ridge Road, Chestnut Ridge, NY, 10977

Tel: (845) 425-2000   Fax: (845) 425-8967   www.lecroy.com

Mfr. signal analyzers and electronic measurement systems.

LeCroy Corporation, Units 1503, Causeway Bay Plaza, Phase 2, 463-483 Lockhart Road, Causeway Bay, Hong Kong PRC

Tel: 852-2834-5630

LEGATO SYSTEMS, INC.

2350 West El Camino Real, Mountain View, CA, 94040

Tel: (650) 210-7000   Fax: (650) 210-7032   www.legato.com

Mfr. storage management software.

Legato Systems, 2/F Shui on Centre, 6-8 Harbour Road, Hong Kong PRC

LEHMAN BROTHERS HOLDINGS INC.

*101 Hudson Street, Jersey City, NJ, 07302

Tel: (201) 524-2000   Fax: (201) 524-2000   www.lehman.com

Financial services, securities and merchant banking services.

Lehman Brothers, One Pacific Place, Level 38-39, 88 Queensway, Hong Kong PRC

Tel: 852-2869-3000

LEVI STRAUSS & COMPANY

1155 Battery St., San Francisco, CA, 94111-1230

Tel: (415) 544-6000   Fax: (415) 501-3939   www.levistrauss.com

Mfr. and distributor of casual wearing apparel, including jeans and sportswear.

Levi Strauss (Far East) Ltd., Unit A & B, 10/F, CDW Building, 388 Castle Peak Road, Tseun Wan NT, Hong Kong PRC

Tel: 852-2412-8088 Fax: 852-2402-3067

LEXMARK INTERNATIONAL

740 W. New Circle Rd., Lexington, KY, 40550

Tel: (859) 232-2000   Fax: (859) 232-1886   www.lexmark.com

Develop, manufacture, supply of printing solutions and products, including laser, inkjet, and dot matrix printers.

Lexmark International (China) Limited, Rm. 3301, Hong Kong Telecom Tower, TaiKoo Place, 979 King's Road, Quarry Bay, Hong Kong PRC

Tel: 852-2866-8900 Fax: 852-2866-8911

LIBERTY MUTUAL GROUP

175 Berkeley Street, Boston, MA, 02117

Tel: (617) 357-9500   Fax: (617) 350-7648   www.libertymutual. com

Provides workers' compensation insurance and operates physical rehabilitation centers and provides risk prevention management.

Liberty International (H.K.) Ltd., 25 Westlands Road, Quarry Bay 504, 5 DCH Commercial Center, Hong Kong PRC

ELI LILLY & COMPANY

Lilly Corporate Center, Indianapolis, IN, 46285

Tel: (317) 276-2000   Fax: (317) 277-6579   www.lilly.com

Mfr. pharmaceuticals and animal health products.

Eli Lilly Asia, Inc., 3/F., Hua Fu Commercial Bldg., 111 Queen's Rd. West, Hong Kong PRC

Tel: 852-2572-0160 Fax: 852-2572-7893

LINEAR TECHNOLOGY CORPORATION

1630 McCarthy Blvd., Milpitas, CA, 95035

Tel: (408) 432-1900   Fax: (408) 434-6441   www.linear-tech.com

Mfr. linear integrated circuit chips.

Linear Technology Corporation Ltd., Unit 2109, Metroplaza, Tower 2, 223 Hing Fong Road, Kwai Fong N.T., Hong Kong PRC

Tel: 852-2428-0303   Fax: 852-2348-0885

LoBUE ASSOCIATES, INC.

1771 East Flamingo Road, Ste. 219A, Las Vegas, NV, 89119

Tel: (702) 989-6940   Fax: (702) 433-4021   www.lobue.com

Management consulting services for financial services industry.

LoBue Associates Inc., 1133, Central Bldg., 1 Pedder St., GPO Box 11308, Central, Hong Kong PRC

Tel: 852-841-7758   Fax: 852-810-1868

LOCKHEED MARTIN CORPORATION

6801 Rockledge Drive, Bethesda, MD, 20817

Tel: (301) 897-6000   Fax: (301) 897-6652   www.imco.com

Design/mfr./management systems in fields of space, defense, energy, electronics and technical services.

CalComp Asia Pacific Ltd., Sts. 701-704, 7/F Chinachem Exchange Square, 1 Hoi Wan Street, Quarry Bay, Hong Kong PRC

Lockheed Martin International, Ltd., Three Exchange Square, Rms.1004-1006, Central, Hong Kong PRC

Contact: B. Miller

Lockheed Martin International, Ltd., Rm. 1904, Wing On Centre, 111 Connaught Road, Central, Hong Kong PRC

Contact: L. Fung, Mgr.

Lockheed Martin International, Ltd., c/o Cathay Pacific Airways Ltd., Engineering Dept. Kai Tak Airport, Hong Kong PRC

Lockheed Martin Intl. Ltd., Two Pacific Place, Suite 1907, 88 Queensway, Hong Kong PRC

LORAL SPACE & COMMUNICATIONS LTD.

600 Third Ave., New York, NY, 10016

Tel: (212) 697-1105   Fax: (212) 338-5662   www.loral.com

Marketing coordination: defense electronics, communications systems.

Loral CyberStar Asia-Pacific, Central Plaza, 35/F, 18 Harbour Road, Wan Chai, Hong Kong PRC

LORD CORPORATION

2000 West Grandview Blvd, Erie, PA, 16514

Tel: (814) 868-0924   Fax: (814) 486-4345   www.lordcorp.com

Mfg. adhesives, coatings, chemicals, film products.

Lord Thermoset, 2001 Shun Tak Centre West Tower, 200 Connaught Road, Central, Hong Kong PRC

Tel: 852-2546-4777   Fax: 852-2546-8111

LSI LOGIC CORPORATION

1551 McCarthy Blvd., Milpitas, CA, 95035

Tel: (408) 433-8000   Fax: (408) 954-3220   www.lsilogic.com

Develop and manufacture semiconductors.

LSI Logic Hong Kong Limited, Kowloon Tong Office, Unit 301-302, 3/F, Tech Centre, 72 Tat Chee Avenue, Kowloon Tong, Hong Kong PRC

LSI Logic Hong Kong Ltd., 7/F, Southeast Industrial Building, 611-619 Castle Peak Road, Tsuen Wan N.T., Hong Kong PRC

LUCENT TECHNOLOGIES, INC.

600 Mountain Ave., Murray Hill, NJ, 07974-0636

Tel: (908) 582-3000   Fax: (908) 582-2576   www.lucent.com

Design/mfr. wide range of public and private networks, communication systems and software, data networking systems, business telephone systems and microelectronics components.

Lucent Technologies Asia/Pacific (HK) Ltd., 29/F, Shell Tower, Times Square, 1 Matheson Street, Causeway Bay, Hong Kong PRC

Tel: 852-2506-8000   Fax: 852-2506-9621   Contact: Jonnie Oden, PR Mgr.

LYONDELL CHEMICAL COMPANY

1221 McKinney St., Houston, TX, 77010

Tel: (713) 652-7200   Fax: (713) 309-2074   www.lyondell.com

Mfr. polymers and petrochemicals.

Lyondell Asia Pacific, Ltd., The Lee Gardens, 41/F, 33 Hysan Avenue, Causeway Bay, Hong Kong PRC

Tel: 852-2-822-2668

M/A-COM INC.

1011 Pawtucket Boulevard, Lowell, MA, 01853-3295

Tel: (978) 442-5000   Fax: (978) 442-5354   www.macom.com

Mfr. radio frequency (RF) and microwave integrated circuits and IP Networks to the wireless telecommunications and defense-related industries.

M/A-COM Ltd., Div. Tyco, 21/F, Unit A, CNT Tower, No. 338 Hennessey Road, Wanchai, Hong Kong PRC

Tel: 852-2521-4567   Fax: 852-2845-1847

M/A-COM Ltd., Div. Tyco, 601 N. Mur-Len, Suite 21B, Wanchai, Hong Kong PRC

Tel: 852-2521-4567

Welllink Communications, Ltd., Unit 602, Westlands Centre, 20 Westlands Road, Quarry Bay, Hong Kong PRC

Tel: 852-2884-4128   Fax: 852-2885-0113

MacDERMID INC.

245 Freight Street, Waterbury, CT, 06702-0671

Tel: (203) 575-5700   Fax: (203) 575-7900   www.macdermid.com

Chemicals processing for metal industrial, plastics, electronics cleaners, strippers.

MacDermid Asian Ltd./ MacDermid Hong Kong, Ltd., 9/F, Block A&B, Tai Ping Industrial Park, 51 Ting Kok Road, Tao Po New Territories, Hong Kong PRC

Tel: 852-2667-8283   Fax: 852-2667-5063

MacDermid Hong Kong Ltd., 10/F, Block C/D, 2-12 Au Pui Wan St., Fo Tan Sha Tin NT, Hong Kong PRC

MACROMEDIA, INC.

600 Townsend Street, San Francisco, CA, 94103-4945

Tel: (415) 252-2000   Fax: (415) 626-9603   www.macromedia.com

Engaged in web publishing.

Macromedia Hong Kong Ltd, Unit A, 27/F, EIB Centre, 40-44 Bonham Strand E, Sheung Wan, Hong Kong PRC

Tel: 852-2191-2562   Fax: 852-2191-2391

MACROVISION CORPORATION

1341 Orleans Dr., Sunnyvale, CA, 94089

Tel: (408) 743-8600   Fax: (408) 743-8610   www.macrovision.com

Provider of digital rights management technologies for the home video, enterprise software and consumer interactive software markets.

Macrovision Hong Kong, 30/F Entertainment Building, 30 Queen's Road Central, Hong Kong PRC

Tel: 852-2168-0625   Contact: Masao Kumei

MANPOWER INTERNATIONAL INC.

5301 N. Ironwood Rd., PO Box 2053, Milwaukee, WI, 53201-2053

Tel: (414) 961-1000   Fax: (414) 961-7081   www.manpower.com

Temporary help, contract service, training and testing.

Manpower Hong Kong Ltd., Prince's Building, Suite 1216, 12/F, Central, Hong Kong PRC

Tel: 852-28-68-2328   Fax: 852-281-06473

MAPICS, INC.

1000 Windward Concourse Pkwy., Alpharetta, GA, 30005

Tel: (678) 319-8000   Fax: (678) 319-8000   www.mapics.com

Mfr. software.

MAPICS China Ltd., Level 25, Bank of China Tower, 1 Garden Road, Central, Hong Kong PRC

MARKET FACTS INC.
3040 Salt Creek Lane, Arlington Heights, IL, 60005

Tel: (847) 590-7000   Fax: (847) 590-7010   www.marketfacts.com

Market research services.

AMI - Asia Market Intelligence, 9/F, Leighton Centre, 77 Leighton Road, Causeway Bay, Hong Kong PRC

Tel: 852-2281-5388   Fax: 852-2281-5918

MARRIOTT INTERNATIONAL INC.
10400 Fernwood Rd., Bethesda, MD, 20817

Tel: (301) 380-3000   Fax: (301) 380-5181   www.marriott.com

Hotel services.

JW Marriott Hotel, Hong Kong PRC

Tel: 852-2525-9966

MARSH & McLENNAN COS INC.
1166 Ave. of the Americas, New York, NY, 10036-2774

Tel: (212) 345-5000   Fax: (212) 345-4808   www.marshmac.com

Insurance agents/brokers, pension and investment management consulting services.

J&H Marsh & McLennan Consulting (Far East) Ltd., 805B-808, Empire Centre, 68 Mody Rd., Tsimshatsui, Kowloon, Hong Kong PRC

Tel: 852-2301-7000   Fax: 852-2576-6419   Contact: Sidney Ku

J&H Marsh & McLennan Ltd., Ste. 2118, 21/F, Miramar Tower 1-23, Kimberley Rd., Tsimshatsui, Kowloon, Hong Kong PRC

Tel: 852-2301-7000   Fax: 852-2576-3340   Contact: Sidney Ku

MARY KAY COSMETICS INC.
16251 No. Dallas Pkwy, Dallas, TX, 75248

Tel: (972) 687-6300   Fax: (972) 687-1609   www.marykay-cosmetic.com

Mfr. and direct sales of cosmetics and toiletries.

Mary Kay Limited, 133 Wanchai Road, 16/F, Wanchai, Hong Kong PRC

Tel: 852-2922-8133   Fax: 852-2845-7103

MASCO CORPORATION
21001 Van Born Road, Taylor, MI, 48180

Tel: (313) 274-7400   Fax: (313) 374-6666   www.masco.com

Mfr. faucets, cabinets, locks and numerous home improvement, building and home furnishings products.

Maitland-Smith Ltd., 4-5/F, Wyler Centre, 210 Tai Lin Pai Rd., Kwai Chung NT, Hong Kong PRC

Universal Furniture Ltd., 3/F, Yo To Sang Bldg., 37 Queens Rd., Central, Hong Kong PRC

MASS MUTUAL FINANCIAL GROUP
1295 State Street, Springfield, MA, 01111

Tel: (413) 788-8411   Fax: (413) 744-6005   www.massmutual.com

Individual insurance, personal accident insurance, credit and group life insurance.

MassMutual Asia, Mass Mutual Tower, 12/F, 38 Gloucester Road, Hong Kong PRC

Tel: 852-2919-9000   Fax: 852-2576-6756

MASTERCARD INTERNATIONAL INC.
200 Purchase Street, Purchase, NY, 10577

Tel: (914) 249-2000   Fax: (914) 249-5475   www.mastercard.com

Provides financial payment systems globally.

MasterCard International Inc., Suite 1401-04, 14/F, Dah Sing Financial Ctr, 108 Gloucester Road, Wanchai, Hong Kong PRC

MATTEL INC.
333 Continental Blvd., El Segundo, CA, 90245-5012

Tel: (310) 252-2000   Fax: (310) 252-2179   www.mattel.com

Mfr. toys, dolls, games, crafts and hobbies.

Arco Toys Ltd., World Finance Ctr., South Tower, 17-19 Canton Rd., Kowloon, Hong Kong PRC

Fisher-Price (Hong Kong) Ltd., 92 Grandville Rd., Tsim Sha Tsui, Kowloon, Hong Kong PRC

Mattel (HK) Ltd., Len Shing Ind. Bldg. 4, Ah Kung Ngam Village Rd., Shau Kei Wan, Hong Kong PRC

Pacific American Buying Service Ltd., Seaview Estate, 8 Watson's Rd., North Point, Hong Kong PRC

MAXTOR CORPORATION

500 McCarthy Blvd., Milpitas, CA, 95035

Tel: (408) 894-5000   Fax: (408) 432-4510   www.maxtor.com

Mfr. develops and markets hard disk drives for desktop computer systems.

Maxtor Asia Pacific Ltd., Sun Hung Kai Center, Room 802-807, 30 Harbour Road, Wanchai, Hong Kong PRC

Tel: 852-2585-4500

McCANN-ERICKSON WORLDGROUP

750 Third Ave., New York, NY, 10017

Tel: (212) 697-6000   Fax: (212) 984-3575   www.mccann.com

International advertising and marketing services.

McCann-Erickson (H.K.) Ltd., 1/F, Sunning Plaza, 10 Hysan Avenue, Hong Kong PRC

McDONALD'S CORPORATION

McDonald's Plaza, Oak Brook, IL, 60523

Tel: (630) 623-3000   Fax: (630) 623-7409   www.mcdonalds.com

Fast food chain stores.

McDonald's Corp., Hong Kong PRC

THE McGRAW-HILL COMPANIES

1221 Avenue of the Americas, New York, NY, 10020

Tel: (212) 512-2000   Fax: (212) 512-2703   www.mccgraw-hill.com

Books, magazines, information systems, financial service, publishing and broadcast operations.

McGraw-Hill Intl Enterprises, Inc., Ste. 2309-10, One Hung To Road, Kwun Tong, Kowloon, Hong Kong PRC

Tel: 852-2730-6640

McKINSEY & COMPANY

55 East 52nd Street, New York, NY, 10022

Tel: (212) 446-7000   Fax: (212) 446-8575   www.mckinsey.com

Management and business consulting services.

McKinsey & Company, 31/F, Asia Pacific Finance Tower, Citibank Plaza, 3 Garden Rd., Hong Kong PRC

Tel: 852-2868-1188   Fax: 852-2845-9985

MEADWESTVACO CORPORATION

One High Ridge Park, Stamford, CT, 06905

Tel: (203) 461-7400   Fax: (212) 318-5055   www.meadwestvaco.com

Mfr. paper, packaging, chemicals.

Meadwestvaco Hong Kong Ltd., Bank of America Tower, 3705, 12 Harcourt Rd., Central, Hong Kong PRC

MEASUREMENT SPECIALTIES, INC.

80 Little Falls Road, Fairfield, NJ, 07004

Tel: (973) 808-1819   Fax: (973) 808-1787   www.msiusa.com

Designer and manufacturer of sensors and sensor-based consumer products.

Measurement Limited, Chinachem Golden Plaza, 10/F, 77 Mody Road, Tsimshatsui East, Kowloon, Hong Kong PRC

Tel: 852-2420-9088   Fax: 852-2422-7682

MECHANICAL DYNAMICS, INC.

2300 Traverwood Drive, Ann Arbor, MI, 48105

Tel: (734) 994-3800   Fax: (734) 994-6418   www.adams.com

Mfr. Adams prototyping software for functional virtual prototyping solutions.

IMAG Industries, Inc., Rm. 406, Wing On Plaza, 62 Mody Rd., Tsimshatsui E. Kowloon, Hong Kong PRC

MEDTRONIC, INC.

7000 Central Ave. N.E., Minneapolis, MN, 55432-5604

Tel: (763) 514-4000   Fax: (763) 514-4879   www.medtronic.com

Mfr., sales and service of electrotherapeutic medical devices, specializing in implantable and invasive therapies.

Medtronic International, Ltd., 1602 Manulife Plaza, 33 Hysan Avenue, Causeway Bay, Hong Kong PRC

Tel: 852-2891-4456   Fax: 852-2891-6830

MELLON FINANCIAL CORPORATION

One Mellon Bank Center, Pittsburgh, PA, 15258-0001

Tel: (412) 234-5000   Fax: (412) 236-1662   www.mellon.com

Commercial and trade banking and foreign exchange.

Mellon Asia Ltd., Citibank Tower, Suite 3202, 3 Garden Rd., Central, Hong Kong PRC

THE MENTHOLATUM COMPANY, INC.

707 Sterling Drive, Orchard Park, NY, 14127-1587

Tel: (716) 677-2500   Fax: (716) 674-3696   www.mentholatum.com

Mfr. of non-prescription pharmaceuticals, healthcare and cosmeceutical products and medical devices.

Mentholatum Ltd., 1616-21, Tower 1, Grand Central Plaza, 138 Shatin Rural Committee Road, Shatin N.T., Hong Kong PRC

Tel: 852-2699-0078   Fax: 852-2694-7636

MENTOR GRAPHICS

8005 SW Boeckman Road, Wilsonville, OR, 97070-7777

Tel: (503) 685-7000   Fax: (503) 685-1202   www.mentorg.com

Develop/mfr. software tools for embedded systems market.

Mentor Hong Kong Ltd., Unit 1205, 12/F, Sino Plaza, 255 Gloucester Road, Causeway Bay, Hong Kong PRC

MERCER MANAGEMENT CONSULTING INC.

1166 Ave. of the Americas, New York, NY, 10036

Tel: (212) 345-3400   Fax: (212) 345-7414   www.mercermc.com

Provides clients with counsel in such areas as corporate and business strategy and growth planning, organizational development, and market and operations enhancement.

Mercer Management Consulting, 32/F, NatWest Tower, Times Square, One Matheson Street, Causeway Bay, Hong Kong PRC

MERCK & COMPANY, INC.

One Merck Drive, PO Box 100, Whitehouse Station, NJ, 08889-0100

Tel: (908) 423-1000   Fax: (908) 423-2592   www.merck.com

Pharmaceuticals, chemicals and biologicals.

Merck, Sharp & Dohme (Asia) Ltd., 1401 Guardian House, 3201 Kwan Road, Hong Kong PRC

MERRILL LYNCH & COMPANY, INC.

World Financial Center, 250 Vesey Street, New York, NY, 10281-1332

Tel: (212) 236-1000   Fax: (212) 449-2892   www.ml.com

Security brokers and dealers, investment and business services.

Merrill Lynch International, 17/F Asia Pacific Finance Tower, 3 Garden Road, Central, Hong Kong PRC

Tel: 852-536-3888   Fax: 852-2536-3789

METRON TECHNOLOGY

1350 Old Bayshore Highway, Ste. 210, Burlingame, CA, 94010

Tel: (650) 401-4600   Fax: (650) 373-1135   www.metrontech.com

Global provider of marketing, sales, service and support solutions to semiconductor materials and equipment suppliers and semiconductor manufacturers.

Metron Technology (Asia) Ltd., Unit E, 5th Floor, China Overseas Bldg, Wanchai, Hong Kong PRC

Tel: 852-2891-7128   Fax: 852-2574-580

METROPOLITAN LIFE INSURANCE COMPANY

1 Madison Ave., New York, NY, 10010-3603

Tel: (212) 578-3818   Fax: (212) 252-7294   www.metlife.com

Insurance and retirement savings products and services.

Metropolitan Life Insurance Co. of Hong Kong Ltd., Bank of East Asia Building, 11/F, 10 Des Voeux Road, Central, Hong Kong PRC

MICRO AGE, INC.

1330 West Southern Avenue, Tempe, AZ, 85282-1896

Tel: (480) 366-2000   Fax: (480) 966-7339   www.microage.com

Computer systems integrator, software products and telecommunications equipment.

Hercules Data Comm, Hong Kong PRC

MICROCHIP TECHNOLOGY INCORPORATED

2355 West Chandler Boulevard, Chandler, AZ, 85224

Tel: (602) 786-7200   Fax: (602) 899-9210   www.microchip.com

Mfr. electronic subassemblies and components.

Microchip Asia Pacific Hdqtrs., Rm 3801, B Tower, Two Metroplaza, Dwai Fong N.T., Hong Kong PRC

Tel: 852-2401-1200   Fax: 852-2401-3431

MICROMUSE INC.

139 Townsend Street, San Francisco, CA, 94107

Tel: (415) 538-9090   Fax: (415) 538-9091   www.micromuse.com

Mfr. software for information technology.

Micromuse, 39/F, One Pacific Place, 88 Queensway, Admiralty, Hong Kong PRC

MICROSEMI CORPORATION

2830 South Fairview St., Santa Ana, CA, 92704

Tel: (714) 979-8220   Fax: (714) 557-5989   www.microsemi.com

Design, manufacture and market analog, mixed-signal and discrete semiconductors.

Microsemi (H.K.) Ltd., 5-7/F, Meeco Industrial Bldg., 53-55 Au Pui Wan St., Fotan NT, Hong Kong PRC

Tel: 852-2692-1202

MICROSOFT CORPORATION

One Microsoft Way, Redmond, WA, 98052-6399

Tel: (425) 882-8080   Fax: (425) 936-7329   www.microsoft.com

Computer software, peripherals and services.

Microsoft Hong Kong, 20/F, City Plaza 3, 12 Taikoo Wan Rd., Quarry Bay, Hong Kong PRC

Tel: 852-2804-4200   Fax: 852-2560-2217

MILBANK, TWEED, HADLEY & McCLOY LLP

1 Chase Manhattan Plaza, New York, NY, 10005-1413

Tel: (212) 530-5000   Fax: (212) 530-5219   www.milbank.com

International law practice.

Milbank, Tweed, Hadley & McCloy, 3007, Alexandra House, 16 Chater Rd., Central, Hong Kong PRC

Tel: 852-2971-4888   Fax: 852-2840-0792

MILLENNIUM CHEMICALS INC.

PO Box 7015, 230 Half Mile Road, Red Bank, NJ, 07701-7015

Tel: (732) 933-5000   Fax: (732) 933-5200   www.millenniumchem.com

Mfr. specialty chemicals for paints, perfumes, and flavorings.

Millennium Chemicals, China Hong Kong Tower, 22/F, 8-12 Hennessy Road, Wanchai, Hong Kong PRC

Tel: 852-2528-4667

MILLIMAN USA, INC.

1301 Fifth Avenue, Ste. 3800, Seattle, WA, 98101

Tel: (206) 624-7940   Fax: (206) 340-1380   www.milliman.com

Engaged in actuarial consulting services.

Milliman Asia, 1803 Tower One, Lippo Centre, 89 Queensway, Hong Kong PRC

Tel: 852-2147-9678   Fax: 852-2147-9879

MILLIPORE CORPORATION

80 Ashby Road, PO Box 9125, Bedford, MA, 01730

Tel: (781) 533-6000   Fax: (781) 533-3110   www.millipore.com

Mfr. flow and pressure measurement and control components; precision filters, hi-performance liquid chromatography instruments.

Millipore Asia Ltd., Central Plaza, Ste. 3201, 18 Harbour Road, Wanchai, Hong Kong PRC

MINOLTA-QMS INC.

One Magnum Pass, PO Box 81250, Mobile, AL, 36618

Tel: (205) 633-4300   Fax: (205) 633-4866   www.qms.com

Mfr. of high-performance color and monochrome document printing solutions for office automation, electronic publishing, graphic design, and advanced imaging applications.

Minolta-QMS AsiaPacific, Flat J-11, Grenville House, 1-3 Magazine Gap Rd., Hong Kong PRC

MIRANT CORPORATION

1155 Perimeter Center West, Ste. 100, Atlanta, GA, 30338

Tel: (678) 579-5000   Fax: (678) 579-5754   www.mirant.com

Engaged in natural gas and electricity.

Mirant Asia-Pacific Ltd., 18/F, PCCW Tower, 979 King's Road, Taikoo Place, Quarry Bay, Hong Kong PRC

MODEM MEDIA, INC.

230 East Avenue, Norwalk, CT, 06855

Tel: (203) 299-7000   Fax: (230) 299-7060   www.modemmedia.com

Provides on-line marketing and consulting services.

Modem Media Hong Kong, Ste. 2601 2604-05, Sio Plaza, 256 Gloucester Road, Causeway Bay, Hong Kong PRC

Tel: 852-2923-5777   Fax: 852-2891-2210   Contact: Eve Chu, Mng. Dir.

MOEN INC.

25300 Al Moen Drive, North Olmstead, OH, 44070

Tel: (440) 962-2000   Fax: (440) 962-2089   www.moen.com

Mfr. faucets, plumbing and bath accessories.

Moen China, Rooms 5001-06, Hopewell Centre, 183 Queen's Rd. East, Wanchai, Hong Kong PRC

Moen Hong Kong, Rooms 5001-06, Hopewell Centre, 183 Queen's Rd. East, Wanchai, Hong Kong PRC

MOLEX INC.

2222 Wellington Court, Lisle, IL, 60532

Tel: (630) 969-4550   Fax: (630) 969-1352   www.molex.com

Mfr. electronic, electrical and fiber optic interconnection products and systems, switches, application tooling.

Molex Hong Kong/China Ltd., 2/F., Block A, Shatin Industrial Center, 5-7 Yuen Shun Circuit, Siu Lek Yuen, Shatin, Hong Kong PRC

Tel: 852-2637-3111   Fax: 852-2637-5990

MOLTECH POWER SYSTEMS

9062 South Rita Road, Tucson, AZ, 85747

Tel: (520) 799-7500   Fax: (520) 799-7501   www.moltechpower.com

Provides rechargeable battery solutions for industry applications.

Moltech Power Systems (Asia) Limited, Room 1518, Shatin Galleria, 18-24 Shan Mei Street, Fo Tan, Hong Kong PRC

Tel: 852-2601-2839   Fax: 852-2693-3793

MONSANTO

800 N. Lindbergh Boulevard, St. Louis, MO, 63167

Tel: (314) 694-1000   Fax: (314) 694-7625   www.monsanto.com

Life sciences company focusing on agriculture, nutrition, pharmaceuticals, health and wellness and sustainable development.

Monsanto Far East Ltd., 2/F, City Plaza 3, 14 Taikoo Wan Road, Taikoo Shing, Hong Kong PRC

Tel: 852-2831-9121

MOODY'S INVESTOR SERVICES, INC.

99 Church St., New York, NY, 10007

Tel: (212) 553-1658   Fax: (212) 553-0462   www.moodys.com

Publishes credit ratings.

Moody's Asia Pacific, Ltd., Central Tower, 15/F, 22-28 Queens Rd., Central, Hong Kong PRC

Tel: 852-2509-0200

Moody's Asia-Pacfic Ltd., Room 2510-2514, International Finance Centre Tower One, One Harbour Street View, Central, Hong Kong PRC

Tel: 852-2509-0200

MOOG INC.

300 Jamison Road, East Aurora, NY, 14052-0018

Tel: (716) 652-2000   Fax: (716) 687-4471   www.moog.com

Mfr. precision control components and systems.

Moog Controls Hong Kong Ltd., Unit 2915-6, 29/F, Tower 1, Metroplaza, 223 Hing Fong Rd., Kwaichung, Hong Kong PRC

MORGAN ADVANCED MATERIALS AND TECHNOLOGY, INC.

441 Hall Ave., Saint Mary's, PA, 15857

Tel: (814) 781-1573   Fax: (814) 781-9262   www.mamat.com

Mfr. carbon graphite and silicon carbide components.

Morganite Hong Kong Company Limited, Unit 4-6, 11/F, Siu Wai Industrial Centre, 29-33 Wing Hong Street, Cheung Sha Wan, Kowloon, Hong Kong PRC

J. P. MORGAN CHASE & CO. INC.

270 Park Ave., New York, NY, 10017

Tel: (212) 270-6000   Fax: (212) 622-9030   www.jpmorganchase.com

Provides integrated financial solutions for institutions and individuals worldwide, including asset management, investment banking and commercial banking.

J. P. Morgan Chase & Co., 720 Nathan Rd., Mongkok Kowloon, Hong Kong PRC

J. P. Morgan Chase & Co., G/F, China Life Insurance Bldg., 313-317B Hennessy Rd., Hong Kong PRC

J. P. Morgan Chase & Co., G/F, Shanghai Industrial Investment Bldg., 48-62 Hennessy Rd., Wanchai, Hong Kong PRC

J. P. Morgan Chase & Co., G/F, Shop 30-33, Silvercord Centre, 30 Canton Rd., Tsim Sha Tsui, Kowloon, Hong Kong PRC

J. P. Morgan Chase & Co., 40/F, One Exchange Square, Connaught Place, Hong Kong PRC

Tel: 852-2841-6008   Fax: 852-2841-4396

J. P. Morgan Chase & Co., Alexander House, 6 Ice House St., Central, Hong Kong PRC

J. P. Morgan Chase & Co., 39/F, One Exchange Square, Connaught Place, Hong Kong PRC

Tel: 852-2843-1234   Fax: 852-2841-4396

J. P. Morgan Chase & Co., 15-22/F, Chase Manhattan Tower, Shatin, Hong Kong PRC

Tel: 852-2685-5111   Fax: 852-2685-5099

MORGAN STANLEY DEAN WITTER & CO.

1585 Broadway, New York, NY, 10036

Tel: (212) 761-4000   Fax: (212) 761-0086   www.msdw.com

Securities and commodities brokerage, investment banking, money management, personal trusts.

Morgan Stanley Asia Ltd., 31/F, 3 Exchange Place, Hong Kong PRC

Morgan Stanley Dean Witter (Hong Kong), 3408, Edinburg Tower, 15 Queen's Rd., Central, Hong Kong PRC

MORRISON & FOERSTER

425 Market Street, San Francisco, CA, 94105

Tel: (415) 268-7000   Fax: (415) 268-7522   www.mofo.com

Engaged in international law.

Morrison & Foerster, Entertainment Bldg., 23/F, 30 Queen's Rd., Central, Hong Kong PRC

MOTOROLA, INC.

1303 East Algonquin Road, Schaumburg, IL, 60196

Tel: (847) 576-5000   Fax: (847) 538-5191   www.motorola.com

Mfr. communications equipment, semiconductors and cellular phones.

Motorola Asia Pacific Ltd., NatWest Tower, Times Square, 1 Matheson St., Causeway Bay, Hong Kong PRC

Tel: 852-2599-2800   Fax: 852-2506-2454

Motorola Semiconductors HK Ltd., 7/F, Profit Industrial Bldg., 1-15 Kwai Fund Crescent, Kwai Chung NT, Hong Kong PRC

Tel: 852-2480-8333   Fax: 852-2419-2896

MRO SOFTWARE, INC.

100 Crosby Drive, Bedford, MA, 01730

Tel: (781) 280-2000   Fax: (781) 280-0207   www.mrosoftware.com

Design/sales of enterprise asset maintenance software.

MRO Software, 19/F One International Finance Centre, 1 Harbour View Street, Central, Hong Kong PRC

Tel: 852-2565-3500   Fax: 852 2565 3500

MTS SYSTEMS CORPORATION

14000 Technology Drive, Eden Prairie, MN, 55344-2290

Tel: (612) 937-4000   Fax: (612) 937-4515   www.mts.com

Develop/mfr. mechanical testing and simulation products and services, industry measure and automation instrumentation.

MTS Systems (Hong Kong) Ltd., Beverley Commercial Center, Suite 831, 87-105 Chatham Rd. South, Tsim-Sha-Tsui, Hong Kong PRC

MULTEX.COM, INC.

100 Williams Street, 7th Fl., New York, NY, 10038

Tel: (212) 607-2500   Fax: (212) 607-2510   www.multex.com

Distributes financial information of corporations via the internet to professional investors.

Multex.com Asia, 1 Wellington Road, Silver Fortune Plaza, 21/F, Central, Hong Kong PRC

Tel: 852-2810-0039   Fax: 852-2810-0939

NATIONAL INSTRUMENTS CORPORATION

11550 N. Mopac Expwy., Austin, TX, 78759-3504

Tel: (512) 338-9119   Fax: (512) 794-5794   www.ni.com

Mfr. hardware and graphical software.

National Instruments Hong Kong, 19 On Sum Street, Ste. 210, Shatin, N.T., Hong Kong PRC

NATIONAL MACHINERY COMPANY

161 Greenfield St., Tiffin, OH, 44883-2471

Tel: (419) 447-5211   Fax: (419) 447-5299   www.nationalmachinery.com

Mfr. high-speed metal parts forming machines.

National Machinery Company, Hong Kong PRC

Tel: 852-2597-5044

NATIONAL SEMICONDUCTOR CORPORATION

2900 Semiconductor Dr., PO Box 58090, Santa Clara, CA, 95052-8090

Tel: (408) 721-5000   Fax: (408) 739-9803   www.national.com

Engaged in producing computer-on-a-chip solutions for the information highway.

National Semiconductor HK Ltd., Suite 2501, Mirai Tower, 1-23 Kimberly Rd., Tsim Shatsui Kowloon, Hong Kong PRC

Tel: 852-2737-1654   Fax: 852-2736-9960   Contact: Martin Kidgell, Reg. VP

NATIONAL STARCH AND CHEMICAL COMPANY

10 Finderne Ave., Bridgewater, NJ, 08807-3300

Tel: (908) 685-5000　　　　Fax: (908) 685-5005　　　　www.nationalstarch.com

Mfr. adhesives and sealants, resins and specialty chemicals, electronic materials and adhesives, food products, industry starch.

National Starch & Chemical Ltd., Suite 513-4, 5/F, Tower 1, Cheung Sha Wan Plaza, 833 Cheung Sha Wan Rd., Kowloon, Hong Kong PRC

Tel: 852-2745-7799　Fax: 852-2745-7063

NCH CORPORATION

2727 Chemsearch Blvd., Irving, TX, 75062

Tel: (972) 438-0211　　　　Fax: (972) 438-0707　　　　www.nch.com

Engaged in manufacturing and specialty chemicals.

National Chemsearch, 75/F, 31 Ng Fong St., San Po Kong, Kowloon, Hong Kong PRC

NCR (NATIONAL CASH REGISTER)

1700 South Patterson Blvd., Dayton, OH, 45479

Tel: (937) 445-5000　　　　Fax: (937) 445-7042　　　　www.ncr.com

Mfr. automated teller machines and high-performance stationary bar code scanners.

NCR Asia Ltd., 25/F, Office Tower, Convention Plaza, 1 Harbour Rd., Wanchai, Hong Kong PRC

Tel: 852-2859-6067　Fax: 852-2517-1381　Contact: Jolene Wong, Mgr.

NETIQ CORPORATION

3553 North First Street, San Jose, CA, 95134

Tel: (408) 856-3000　　　　Fax: (408) 273-0578　　　　www.netiq.com

Mfr. performance management software.

NetIQ Corporation, Room 40 C&D, Regus Shui On Centre, 2/F Shui On Centre, 6-8 Harbour Road, Wanchai, Hong Kong PRC

NETWORK ASSOCIATES, INC.

3965 Freedom Circle, Santa Clara, CA, 95054

Tel: (408) 988-3832　　　　Fax: (408) 970-9727　　　　www.networkassociates.com

Designs and produces network security and network management software and hardware.

Network Associates, Plaza 2000, 14/F, 2-4 Russell Street, Causeway Bay, Hong Kong PRC

Tel: 852-2892-9500　Fax: 852-2832-9530

NEW HORIZONS WORLDWIDE, INC.

1900 S. State College Blvd., Anaheim, CA, 92806-6135

Tel: (714) 940-8000　　　　Fax:　　　　www.newhorizons.com

Provides customer-focused computer training choices, through computer training centers.

New Horizons Worldwide, 201 Harbour Centre, 2/F, 25 Harbour Road, Wan Chai,, Hong Kong PRC

Tel: 852-2155-1800　Fax: 852-2155-1880

NEW YORK LIFE INSURANCE COMPANY

51 Madison Ave., New York, NY, 10010

Tel: (212) 576-7000　　　　Fax: (212) 576-4291　　　　www.newyorklife.com

Insurance services.

New York Life Insurance Co. of Hong Kong, Unit 3201, Shui On Centre, 6 Harbor Road, Wanchai, Hong Kong PRC

THE NEW YORK TIMES COMPANY

229 West 43rd Street, New York, NY, 10036-3959

Tel: (212) 556-1234　　　　Fax: (212) 556-7389　　　　www.nytimes.com

Diversified media company including newspapers, magazines, television and radio stations, and electronic information and publishing.

International Herald Tribune (IHT), 1201, K.Wah Centre, 191 Java Road, North Point, Hong Kong PRC

Tel: 852-2922-1188

NIBCO INC.

1516 Middlebury St., PO Box 1167, Elkhart, IN, 46515-1167

Tel: (219) 295-3000   Fax: (219) 295-3307   www.nibco.com

Mfr. fluid handling products for residential, commercial, industrial and fire protection markets.

NIBCO Pacific (Flow Controls) Ltd., Empireland Commercial Bldg., 6/F, 81-85 Lockhart Rd., Wanchai, Hong Kong PRC

Tel: 852-2512-8398   Fax: 852-2570-9428

AC NIELSEN COMPANY

177 Broad Street, Stamford, CT, 06901

Tel: (203) 961-3000   Fax: (203) 961-3190   www.acnielsen.com

Engaged in market and consumer research.

ACNielsen, 2/F, Warwick House East Wing, Taikoo Place 979 King's Road, Quarry Bay, Hong Kong PRC

Tel: 852-2563-9688

NIKE INC.

One Bowerman Drive, Beaverton, OR, 97005

Tel: (503) 671-6453   Fax: (503) 671-6300   www.nike.com

Mfr. athletic footwear, equipment and apparel.

Nike Hong Kong, The Gateway, 26/F, Tower 1, 25 Canton Road, Tsimshatsui, Kowloon, Hong Kong PRC

NORDSON CORPORATION

28601 Clemens Road, Westlake, OH, 44145-4551

Tel: (440) 892-1580   Fax: (440) 892-9507   www.nordson.com

Mfr. industry application equipment, sealants and packaging machinery.

Nordson Application Equipment Inc., Topsail Plaza, Room 708, No. 11 On Sum St., Siu Lek Yuen, Shatin N.T., Hong Kong PRC

Tel: 852-2687-2828   Fax: 852-2687-4748

NORTEK INC.

50 Kennedy Plaza, Providence, RI, 02903

Tel: (401) 751-1600   Fax: (401) 751-4610   www.nortek-inc.com

Mfr. residential and commercial building products.

Linear HK Mfg. Ltd., 19/F, Honour Industrial Centre, 6 Sun Yip St., Chai Wan, Hong Kong PRC

NORTHERN TRUST CORPORATION

50 South LaSalle Street, Chicago, IL, 60675

Tel: (312) 630-6000   Fax: (312) 630-1512   www.ntrs.com

Engaged in banking and financial services.

The Northern Trust Company of Hong Kong, Suite 703-4 One Pacific Place, 88 Queensway, Hong Kong PRC

NORTON ABRASIVES COMPANY

1 New Bond Street, Worcester, MA, 01606

Tel: (508) 795-5000   Fax: (508) 795-5741   www.nortonabrasives.com

Mfr. abrasives for industrial manufacturing.

Norton International, Inc, 1001, Trans Asia Centre, 18 Kin Hong Street, Kwai Chung N.T., Hong Kong PRC

Tel: 852-2589-3589   Fax: 852-2547-4848

NOVELL WORLDWIDE

1800 S. Novell Place, Provo, UT, 84606

Tel: (801) 861-7000   Fax: (801) 861-5555   www.novell.com

Develop/mfr. networking software and related equipment.

Novell Hong Kong, China Resources Building, Room 4601-5, 26 Harbour Road, Wanchai, Hong Kong PRC

NOVEON INTERNATIONAL

9911 Brecksville Road, Cleveland, OH, 44141-3427

Tel: (216) 447-5000   Fax: (216) 447-5669   www.noveoninc.com

Mfr. specialty chemicals.

Noveon Asia Pacific Limited, 2813-17 East Tower, Shun Tak Centre, 168-200 Connaught Road Central, Sheung Wan, Hong Kong PRC

Tel: 85-22-508-1021

NVIDIA CORPORATION

2701 San Tomas Expressway, Santa Clara, CA, 95050

Tel: (408) 486-2000   Fax: (408) 486-2200   www.nvidia.com

Mfr. graphics chips for video gamers and graphics designers.

Best Union Electronics, Unit 8, 12/F, Fook Ho Bldg., 19 Sheung Yuet Roar, Kowloon Bay, Kowloon, Hong Kong PRC

OCLI, INC. (OPTICAL COATING LABORATORY, INC.)

2789 Northpoint Pkwy., Santa Rosa, CA, 95407-7397

Tel: (707) 545-6440   Fax: (707) 525-7410   www.ocli.com

Mfr. thin film precision coated optical devices.

Opton Ltd., Suite 1106, Shatin Galleria, 18-24 Shan Mei Street, Fo Tan, Shatin NT, Hong Kong PRC

Tel: 852-2687-2350   Fax: 852-2687-6529

S&T Enterprises Ltd. (Rep Office), Room 404, Block F, Sea View Estate, 2-8 Watson Road, North Point, Hong Kong PRC

THE O'GARA COMPANY

1250 24th Street, NW, Suite 300, Washington, DC, 20037

Tel: (202) 835-1680   Fax: (202) 835-1685   www.ogara.com

Security and consulting services and vehicles.

Kroll Associates (Asia) Ltd., Room 906/911, 9/F, Mount Parker House, 1111 King's Rd., Taikoo Shing, Hong Kong PRC

Tel: 852-2884-7788   Fax: 852-2568-8505

OGILVY & MATHER WORLDWIDE

309 West 49th Street, New York, NY, 10017-7399

Tel: (212) 237-4000   Fax: (212) 237-5123   www.ogilvypr.com

Engaged in public relations and communications.

Ogilvy Public Relations Worldwide, Mount Parker House, 7/F, Taikoo Shing, Hong Kong PRC

Ogilvy Public Relations Worldwide, The Center, 99 Queen's Road, Central, Hong Kong PRC

Tel: 852-2567-4461   Fax: 852-2885-3227   Contact: Debby Cheung

OLIN CORPORATION

501 Merritt Seven, Norwalk, CT, 06856-4500

Tel: (203) 750-3000   Fax: (203) 750-3292   www.olin.com

Mfr. chemicals, metals, sporting ammunition and copper and copper alloy sheets.

Olin Industrial (HK) Ltd., 1111, Peninsula Centre, 67 Mody Road, Tsim Sha Tsui East, Kowloon, Hong Kong PRC

Tel: 852-2366-8303   Fax: 852-2367-1309

O'MELVENY & MYERS LLP

400 South Hope Street, Ste. 1500, Los Angeles, CA, 90017-2801

Tel: (213) 430-6000   Fax: (213) 430-6407   www.omelveny.com

Engaged in international law.

O'Melveny & Myers, 89 Queensway, Ste. 1905, Central, Hong Kong PRC

Tel: 852-2523-8266   Contact: Daniel Deshon

OMNICOM GROUP INC.

437 Madison Ave., New York, NY, 10022

Tel: (212) 415-3600   Fax: (212) 415-3530   www.omnicomgroup.com

International network of advertising, marketing, direct mail, public relations and consulting services.

BBDO Asia Pacific, 38/F, Dorset House, Taikoo Place, 979 King's Road, Quarry Bay, Hong Kong PRC

Rapp Collins, 1111 King's Road, Ste. 1712, Tai Koo Shing, Hong Kong PRC

ONDEO NALCO COMPANY

Ondeo Nalco Center, 1601 W. Diehl Road, Naperville, IL, 60563-1198

Tel: (630) 305-1000   Fax: (630) 305-2900   www.ondeo-nalco.com

Mfr. specialty chemicals for water and waste water treatment, oil products and refining, industry processes; water and energy management service.

ONDEO Nalco Chemical (HK) Ltd., 1806, Tower 6,, China Hong Kong City, 33 Canton Rd., Kowloon, Hong Kong PRC

Tel: 852-2736-3033   Fax: 852-2736-1317

ONYX SOFTWARE CORPORATION

3180 139th Avenue SE, Ste. 500, Bellevue, WA, 98005

Tel: (425) 451-8060   Fax: (425) 451-8277   www.onyx.com

Mfr. customer relationship management software.

Onyx Software Hong Kong, Harcourt House #1010, 39 Gloucester Road, Wanchai, Hong Kong PRC

Tel: 852-2868-2727

OPENWAVE SYSTEMS INC.

1400 Seaport Blvd., Redwood City, CA, 94063

Tel: (650) 480-8000   Fax: (650) 480-8100   www.openwave.com

Mfr. software for wireless telephones.

Openwave Systems, Dah Sing Financial Centre, 25/F, 108 Gloucester Road, Wanchai, Hong Kong PRC

Tel: 852-3416-9000   Fax: 852-3416-9222

OPINION RESEARCH CORPORATION

23 Orchard Road, Skillman, NJ, 08558

Tel: (908) 281-5100   Fax: (908) 281-5103   www.opinionresearch.com

Engaged in market research.

Opinion Research, 1602 Ming An Plaza I, 8 Sunning Road, Causeway Bay, Hong Kong PRC

Tel: 852-2882-3042

ORACLE CORPORATION

500 Oracle Parkway, Redwood Shores, CA, 94065

Tel: (650) 506-7000   Fax: (650) 506-7200   www.oracle.com

Develop/manufacture software.

Oracle Hong Kong, Hong Kong PRC

ORC MACRO INTERNATIONAL INC.

11785 Beltsville Dr., Calverton, MD, 20705-3119

Tel: (301) 572-0200   Fax: (301) 572-0999   www.macroint.com

Engaged in research and evaluation, training, consulting and information technology.

ORC Macro, 1602 Ming An Plaza I, 8 Sunning Road, Causeway Bay, Hong Kong PRC

Tel: 852-2882-3042   Fax: 852-2882-4515

OSMONICS INC.

5951 Clearwater Drive, Minnetonka, MN, 55343-8995

Tel: (952) 933-2277   Fax: (952) 933-0141   www.osmonics.com

Mfr. equipment, controls and components for the filtration and water-treatment industries.

Osmonics Asia/Pacific Ltd., Suite F, 15/F, Cameron Plaza, 23-25A Cameron Rd., Kowloon TST, Hong Kong PRC

OTIS ELEVATOR COMPANY

One Farm Springs Road, Farmington, CT, 06032

Tel: (860) 676-6000   Fax: (860) 676-5111   www.otis.com

Mfr. elevators and escalators.

Otis Elevator Co., 5/F, Luk Kwok Centre, 72 Gloucester Rd., Wanchai, Hong Kong PRC

Otis Elevator Co. Ltd., GPO Box 82, Hong Kong PRC

OUTBACK STEAKHOUSE, INC.

2202 N. Westshore Blvd. 5th Fl., Tampa, FL, 33607

Tel: (813) 282-1225   Fax: (813) 282-1209   www.outback.com

Chain of casual steak restaurants.

Outback Steakhouse, Inc., Level 2, 398 Castle Peak Road, Tsuen Wan NT, Hong Kong PRC

Tel: 852-2940-0682

PALL CORPORATION

2200 Northern Boulevard, East Hills, NY, 11548-1289

Tel: (516) 484-5400   Fax: (516) 484-5228   www.pall.com

Specialty materials and engineering; filters and related fluid clarification equipment.

Pall Asia International Ltd., Room 2806-7, Shu on Centre, 6-8 Harbour Road, Wanchai, Hong Kong PRC

Tel: 852-2583-9610   Fax: 852-2511-5773

PANDUIT CORPORATION

17301 Ridgeland Ave., Tinley Park, IL, 60477-0981

Tel: (708) 532-1800   Fax: (708) 532-1811   www.panduit.com

Mfr. of network connectivity and electrical products.

Panduit Hong Kong, Suite 3310, 33/F, The Gateway, Tower 1, 25 Canton Road, Tsimshatsui Kowloon, Hong Kong PRC

PARADYNE NETWORKS, INC.

8545 126 Ave. North, Largo, FL, 33773

Tel: (727) 530-2000   Fax: (727) 530-2875   www.paradyne.com

Engaged in data communications and high-speed network access solutions.

Paradyne Far East Corp., Room 901, Wing On Centre, 111 Connaught Rd., Central, Hong Kong PRC

PARAMETRIC TECHNOLOGY CORPORATION

140 Kendrick St., Needham, MA, 02494

Tel: (781) 370-5000   Fax: (781) 370-6000   www.ptc.com

Supplier of mechanical design automation and product data management software and services.

Parametric Tecnology (Hong Kong) Ltd., 37/F, Suite 3703-4, Central Plaza, 18 Harbour Road, Wanchai, Hong Kong PRC

Tel: 852-2802-8982   Fax: 852-2587-9095

PARKER HANNIFIN CORPORATION

6035 Parkland Blvd., Cleveland, OH, 44124-4141

Tel: (216) 896-3000   Fax: (216) 896-4000   www.parker.com

Mfr. motion-control products.

Parker Hannifin Hong Kong Ltd., Hong Kong Worsted Mills Ind. Bldg., #2104, 31-39 Wo Tong Tsui St., Kwai Chung NT, Hong Kong PRC

PARSONS BRINCKERHOFF INC.

One Penn Plaza, New York, NY, 10119-0061

Tel: (212) 465-5000   Fax: (212) 465-5096   www.pbworld.com

Provides planning, engineering, construction management and operations and maintenance services.

PB Kennedy & Donkin Transportation Limited, Suite 602-4, New Town Tower, 10-18 Pak Hok Ting Street, Sha Tin NT, Hong Kong PRC

Tel: 852-2698-8986   Fax: 852-2684-9119

PARSONS CORPORATION

100 West Walnut Street, Pasadena, CA, 91124

Tel: (626) 440-2000   Fax: (626) 440-4919   www.parsons.com

Engaged in engineering, procurement, and construction management services.

Parsons Asia Pacific, 39 E, One Robinson Place, 70 Robinson Road, Hong Kong PRC

Tel: 852-2915-2957

PAUL, WEISS, RIFKIND, WHARTON & GARRISON

1285 Ave. of the Americas, New York, NY, 10019-6064

Tel: (212) 373-3000   Fax: (212) 373-2268   www.paulweiss.com

Law firm engaged in American and international law practice.

Paul, Weiss, Rifkind, Wharton & Garrison, 13/F, Hong Kong Club Bldg., 3A Chater Rd., Central, Hong Kong PRC

Tel: 852-2536-9933   Fax: 852-2536-9622

J.C. PENNEY COMPANY, INC.

6501 Legacy Drive, Plano, TX, 75024-3698

Tel: (972) 431-1000   Fax: (972) 431-1977   www.jcpenney.com

Markets family apparel, shoes, home furnishings, jewelry, and offers credit cards.

J. C. Penney Purchasing Corp., 617 Peninsula Centre, 67 Mody Rd., Tsim Sha Tsui E., Kowloon, Hong Kong PRC

PENTON MEDIA

1300 E. 9th St., Cleveland, OH, 44114

Tel: (216) 696-7000   Fax: (216) 696-7648   www.penton.com

Publisher of industrial/trade magazines.

Penton Media Asia Ltd., 7/F, 9 Des Vouex Road West, Hong Kong PRC

Tel: 852-2975-9051   Fax: 852-2857-6144

Penton Media Asia, Ltd., 9 Des Vouex Road West, 7/F, Hong Kong PRC

PEOPLESOFT INC.

4460 Hacienda Drive, Pleasanton, CA, 94588-8618

Tel: (925) 225-3000   Fax: (925) 694-4444   www.peoplesoft.com

Mfr. applications to manage business operations across computer networks.

PeopleSoft Hong Kong Ltd., 8/F, 12 Harcourt Road, Central, Hong Kong PRC

Tel: 85-2-258-46180

PEREGRINE SYSTEMS, INC.

3611 Valley Centre Drive, San Diego, CA, 92130

Tel: (858) 481-5000   Fax: (858) 481-1751   www.peregrine.com

Mfr. resource planning software.

Peregrine Systems, Inc., Level 32 Entertainment Building, 30 Queen's Road Central, Hong Kong PRC

PERKIN ELMER, INC.

45 William Street, Wellesley, MA, 02481

Tel: (781) 237-5100   Fax: (781) 431-4255   www.perkinelmer.com

Mfr. equipment and devices to detect explosives and bombs on airline carriers.

PerkinElmer Hong Kong, Room 1409, Kodak House II, 39 Healthy Street East, North Point, Hong Kong PRC

Tel: 852-2590-0238

PERKINS COIE LLP

1201 Third Avenue, Ste. 4800, Seattle, WA, 98101-3099

Tel: (206) 583-8888   Fax: (206) 583-8500   www.perkinscoie.com

Engaged in international law.

Perkins Coie, 17/F Standard Chartered Bank Bldg., 4 Des Voeux Road, Central, Hong Kong PRC

PEROT SYSTEMS CORPORATION

12404 Park Central Drive, Dallas, TX, 75251

Tel: (972) 340-5000   Fax: (972) 455-4100   www.perotsystems.com

Provides technology and business solutions.

HPS Hong Kong, 18/F, One International Finance Centre, 1 Harbour View Street, Central, Hong Kong PRC

Tel: 852-21668772   Fax: 852-2166 8444

PHARMACIA CORPORATION

100 Route 206 North, Peapack, NJ, 07977

Tel: (908) 901-8000   Fax: (908) 901-8379   www.pharmacia.com

Mfr. pharmaceuticals, agricultural products, industry chemicals.

Pharmacia & Upjohn Ltd., 18/F, Allied Kajima Building, 138 Gloucester Road, Wanchai, Hong Kong PRC

Tel: 852-2598-4988   Fax: 852-2824-4265

PHELPS DODGE CORPORATION

2600 North Central Ave., Phoenix, AZ, 85004-3089

Tel: (602) 234-8100   Fax: (602) 234-8337   www.phelpsdodge.com

Copper, minerals, metals and special engineered products for transportation and electrical markets.

Phelps Dodge Intl. Corp., Hong Kong PRC

PHILIP MORRIS COMPANIES, INC.

120 Park Ave., New York, NY, 10017

Tel: (917) 663-5000   Fax: (917) 663-2167   www.philipmorris.com

Mfr. cigarettes and tobacco and consumer food products (Kraft Foods).

Philip Morris Asia Inc., Two Pacific Place, 23/F, 88 Queensway, Hong Kong PRC

PHILLIPS PETROLEUM COMPANY

Phillips Building, 411 S. Keeler Ave., Bartlesville, OK, 74004

Tel: (918) 661-6600   Fax: (918) 661-7636   www.phillips66.com

Crude oil, natural gas, liquefied petroleum gas, gasoline and petro-chemicals.

Phillips Petroleum Co. Asia, 9/F, Citibank Towe, 8 Queen's Rd., Central, Hong Kong PRC

Phillips Petroleum Intl. Inc., 501 Cosmopolitan Bldg., 10 Stanley St., Hong Kong PRC

PHOENIX TECHNOLOGIES LTD.

411 East Plumeria Drive, San Jose, CA, 95134

Tel: (408) 570-1000   Fax: (408) 570-1001   www.phoenix.com

Mfr. BIOS software.

Phoenix Technologies Ltd., Unit 04,9/F, Chevalier, Commercial Centre, No. 8, Wang Hoi Road, Kowloon Bay, Kowloon, Hong Kong PRC

Tel: 852-27997719   Fax: 852-23464846

PILLSBURY WINTHROP LLP

50 Fremont Street, San Francisco, CA, 94105

Tel: (415) 983-1000   Fax: (415) 983-1200   www.pillsburylaw.com

International law firm.

Pillsbury Winthrop LLP, 3102, Tower Two, Lippo Centre, Queensway, Hong Kong PRC

Tel: 852-2530-3400

PIONEER-STANDARD ELECTRONICS, INC.

6065 Parkland Blvd., Cleveland, OH, 44124

Tel: (440) 720-8500   Fax: (440) 720-8501   www.pios.com

Mfr. and distribution of electronic parts for computers and networking equipment.

WPI International, Commercial Center, Tower B, Rm. 809, 37-39 Ma Tau Wai Road, Humghom Kowloon, Hong Kong PRC

Tel: 852-2365-4860

PITNEY BOWES INC.

1 Elmcroft Road, Stamford, CT, 06926-0700

Tel: (203) 356-5000   Fax: (203) 351-6835   www.pitneybowes.com

Mfr. postage meters, mailroom equipment, copiers, bus supplies, bus services, facsimile systems and financial services.

Pitney Bowes Asian Operations, 10/F, Beverly House, 93-107 Lockhart Rd., Wanchai, Hong Kong PRC

Tel: 852-2528-9011   Fax: 852-2527-4077   Contact: Henri Ho, VP Asian Operations   Emp: 100

Pitney Bowes Hong Kong Inc., 21/F, Beverly House, 93-107 Lockhart Road, Wanchai, Hong Kong PRC

PLAINS COTTON COOPERATIVE ASSOCIATES

3301 East 50th Street, Lubbock, TX, 79404

Tel: (806) 763-8011   Fax: (806) 762-7333   www.pcca.com

Merchandisers of raw cotton to domestic and foreign textile mills.

Amerasia Intl. Ltd., 4/F, Solar House, 26 Des Voeux Rd., Central, Hong Kong PRC

PLANET HOLLYWOOD INTERNATIONAL, INC.

8669 Commodity Circle, Orlando, FL, 32819

Tel: (407) 363-7827   Fax: (407) 363-4862   www.planethollywood.com

Theme-dining restaurant chain and merchandise retail stores.

Planet Hollywood International, Inc., Kowloon, Hong Kong PRC

PLANTRONICS

345 Encinal Street, Santa Cruz, CA, 95060

Tel: (831) 426-5858   Fax: (831) 425-5198   www.plantronics.com

Mfr. lightweight headsets and communications equipment and electrical and electronic appliances.

Plantronics Hong Kong, 1801 Yue Xiu Building, 160 - 174 Lockhart Road, Wanchai, Hong Kong PRC

PLUMTREE SOFTWARE, INC.

500 Sansome Street, San Francisco, CA, 94111

Tel: (415) 263-8900   Fax: (415) 263-8991   www.plumtree.com

Mfr. organizational software.

Plumtree Software Hong Kong Ltd.,, Suite 3208-11, Shell Tower Times Square, Causeway Bay, Hong Kong PRC

THE PMI GROUP, INC.

601 Montgomery Street, San Francisco, CA, 94111

Tel: (415) 788-7878   Fax: (415) 291-6191   www.pmigroup.com

Mortgage insurer.

PMI Mortgage Insurance Ltd., One International Finance Centre, 18/F, 1 Harbour View Street, Central, Hong Kong PRC

POLAROID CORPORATION

784 Memorial Drive, Cambridge, MA, 02139

Tel: (781) 386-2000   Fax: (781) 386-3924   www.polaroid.com

Photographic equipment and supplies, optical products.

Polaroid Far East Ltd., 36/F Manulife Plaza, The Lee Gardens, 33 Hysan Avenue, Causeway Bay, Hong Kong PRC
Tel: 852-2894-0333   Fax: 852-2895-1382

POLYCOM, INC.

1565 Barber Lane, Milpitas, CA, 95035

Tel: (408) 526-9000   Fax: (408) 526-9100   www.polycom.com

Mfr. video conferencing systems, network bridging and multiplexing products, system peripherals.

Polycom, Inc., Room 3401, Citibank Plaza, Citibank Tower, 3 Garden Road, Central, Hong Kong PRC
Tel: 852-2821-4700   Fax: 852-2821-4800

PORTAL SOFTWARE, INC.

10200 S. De Anza Bolevard, Cupertino, CA, 95014

Tel: (408) 572-2000   Fax: (408) 572-2001   www.portal.com

Mfr. customer management and billing software.

Portal Software Hong Kong, Suite 6406-7, 64/F.,Central Plaza, 18 Harbour Road, Wanchai, Hong Kong PRC
Tel: 852-2585-2200

POWER-ONE, INC.

740 Calle Plano, Camarillo, CA, 93012

Tel: (805) 987-8741   Fax: (805) 388-0476   www.power-one.com

Mfr. converters and voltage power switchers for electronic equipment.

Power-One Ltd., 1216 Peninsula Square, 18 Sung On Street, Hunghom, Kowloon, Hong Kong PRC
Tel: 852-2578-4412

PPG INDUSTRIES

One PPG Place, Pittsburgh, PA, 15272

Tel: (412) 434-3131   Fax: (412) 434-2190   www.ppg.com

Mfr. coatings, flat glass, fiber glass, chemicals.

PPG Industries International Inc., Cityplaza One, Suite 1010-1015, 111 King's Rd., Taikoo Shing, Hong Kong PRC

PRESTON GATES & ELLIS LLP

701 Fifth Avenue, Ste. 5000, Seattle, WA, 98104

Tel: (206) 623-7580   Fax: (206) 623-7022   www.prestongates.com

Engaged in international law.

Preston Gates & Ellis LLP, 10 Harcourt Road, Central, Hong Kong PRC

Tel: 852-2511-5100

PRG-SCHULTZ INTERNATIONAL INC.

2300 Windy Ridge Pkwy., Ste. 100 N, Atlanta, GA, 30339-8426

Tel: (770) 779-3900   Fax: (770) 898-2996   www.prgx.com

Engaged in comprehensive recovery auditing and process improvement services.

PRG-Schultz Singapore Pte Ltd., Hong Kong Branch, Suite 2209, 39 Healthy Street, East North Point, Hong Kong PRC

PRICEWATERHOUSECOOPERS LLP

1301 Ave. of the Americas, New York, NY, 10019

Tel: (212) 596-7000   Fax: (212) 259-1301   www.pwcglobal.com

Accounting and auditing, tax and management, and human resource consulting services.

PriceWaterhouseCoopers, Prince's Building, 22/F, GPO Box 690, Hong Kong PRC

Tel: 852-2826-2111   Fax: 852-2810-9888   Contact: Augustine YY Lo

PRIMAVERA SYSTEMS, INC.

3 Bala Plaza West, Ste. 700, Bala Cynwyd, PA, 19004

Tel: (610) 667-8600   Fax: (610) 667-7894   www.primavera.com

Mfr. project management software.

Primavera Systems, Inc., The Gateway, Tower 2, Ste. 3009, 25 Canton Road Tsimshatsui, Kowloon, Hong Kong PRC

PRIMEDIA

745 Fifth Avenue, New York, NY, 10151

Tel: (212) 745-0100   Fax: (212) 745-0121   www.primedia.com

Engaged in integrated marketing solutions and publisher of special interest magazines.

Primedia International, Rm 902, AIA Plaza, 18 Hysan Avenue, Causeway Bay, Hong Kong PRC

THE PRINCIPAL FINANCIAL GROUP

711 High Street, Des Moines, IA, 50392-9950

Tel: (515) 248-8288   Fax: (515) 248-8049   www.principal.com

Insurance and investment services.

Principal Insurance Company (Hong Kong) Ltd., Unit 1001-3, Central Plaza, 18 Harbour Rd., Wanchai, Hong Kong PRC

Tel: 852-2827-1628   Fax: 852-2827-1618   Contact: Rex Auyeung, Mgr.

Principal International Asia, Ltd., Unit 1001-3, Central Plaza, 18 Harbour Rd., Wanchai, Hong Kong PRC

Tel: 852-2827-1628   Fax: 852-2827-1618   Contact: Christopher Reddy, Mktg. Dir.

PRUDENTIAL FINANCIAL

751 Broad Street, Newark, NJ, 07102-3777

Tel: (973) 802-6000   Fax: (973) 802-2804   www.prudential.com

Sale of life insurance, financial services, asset management and brokerage.

Prudential Reinsurance Co. (USA), 2906, Windsor Houser, 311 Gloucester Rd., Causeway Bay, Hong Kong PRC

PSC INC.

111 SW Fifth Avenue, Ste. 4100, Portland, OR, 97204-3644

Tel: (503) 553-3920   Fax: (503) 553-3940   www.pscnet.com

Mfr. and sales of bar code scanners.

PSC Hong Kong, Bank of America Tower 8/F, 12 Harcourt Road, Hong Kong PRC

Tel: 852-2-584-6210

PSI NET (PERFORMANCE SYSTEMS INTERNATIONAL INC.)

44983 Knoll Square, Ashburn, VA, 20147

Tel: (703) 726-4100   Fax: (703) 726-4200   www.psinet.com

Internet service provider.

Linkage Online Limited, 69-71 King Yip Street, Kwun Tong, Kowloon, Hong Kong PRC

Tel: 852-23-31-81-23   Fax: 852-27-95-12-62   Contact: Chi H. Kwan, SVP, Asia

PUBLIC SERVICE ENTERPRISE GROUP (PSEG)

80 Park Plaza, Newark, NJ, 07101

Tel: (973) 430-7000   Fax: (973) 623-5389   www.pseg.com

Electric and gas utility.

Meiya Power Company, Room 1701-6, Harbour Centre, 25 Harbour Road, Wanchai, Hong Kong PRC

Tel: 852-2593-3222   Fax: 852-2519-0313   Contact: Colin S. Tam

PULSE ENGINEERING INC.

12220 World Trade Drive, PO 12235, San Diego, CA, 92112

Tel: (858) 674-8100   Fax: (858) 674-8262   www.pulseeng.com

Mfr. passive magnetic components and modules for use in Internet/broadband access, power, telecommunications and datacom applications.

Pulse Engineering Inc., 19/F, China United Plaza, 1008 Tai Nan West Street, Cheung Sha Wan Kowloon, Hong Kong PRC

QUAKER CHEMICAL CORPORATION

1 Quaker Park, 901 Hector St., Conshohocken, PA, 19428-0809

Tel: (610) 832-4000   Fax: (610) 832-8682   www.quakerchem.com

Mfr. developer, producer, and marketer of custom-formulated chemical specialty products.

Quaker Chemical Ltd., East Asia Aetna Tower, 26/F, 308 Des Voeux Rd., Central, Hong Kong PRC

Tel: 852-2854-3311   Contact: Daniel S. Ma, Mng. Dir.

QUANTUM

500 McCarthy Blvd., Milpitas, CA, 95035

Tel: (408) 894-4000   Fax: (408) 894-3218   www.quantum.com

Mfr. computer peripherals.

Quantum Hong Kong Ltd., Great Eagle Centre 32/F, 23 Harbour Rd., Wanchai, Hong Kong PRC

Tel: 852-2519-8606

QUINTILES TRANSNATIONAL CORPORATION

4709 Creekstone Dr., Durham, NC, 27703

Tel: (919) 998-2000   Fax: (919) 998-9113   www.quintiles.com

Mfr. pharmaceuticals.

Quintiles Hong Kong Limited, Room No. 1602, Ming An Plaza Phase II, 8 Sunning Road, Causeway Bay, Hong Kong PRC

RADIO SHACK CORPORATION

100 Throckmorton Street, Fort Worth, TX, 76102

Tel: (817) 390-3700   Fax: (817) 415-2647   www.tandy.com

Mfr. electronic and acoustic equipment; Radio Shack retail stores.

A & A International (YICHI-HK) Ltd., 1406-1411, World Commerce Centre, Harbour City, Phase 1, Kowloon, Hong Kong PRC

RATIONAL SOFTWARE CORPORATION

18880 Homestead Road, Cupertino, CA, 95014-0721

Tel: (408) 863-9900   Fax: (408) 863-4120   www.rationale.com

Mfr. application development software.

Rational Software, Suite 1406, 14/F, Cityplaza Four, 12 Taikoo Wan Road, Taikoo Shing, Hong Kong PRC

RAY & BERNDTSON, INC.

301 Commerce, Ste. 2300, Fort Worth, TX, 76102

Tel: (817) 334-0500   Fax: (817) 334-0779   www.prb.com

Executive search, management audit and management consulting firm.

Ray & Berndtson, Allied Capital Resources Bldg., 8/F, 32-28 Ice House St., Central, Hong Kong PRC

Tel: 852-522-4118 Fax: 852-877-2418   Contact: David S. Seabrook, Mng. Ptnr.

RAYOVAC CORPORATION

601 Rayovac Drive, Madison, WI, 53711-2497

Tel: (608) 275-3340   Fax: (608) 275-4577   www.rayovac.com

Mfr. batteries and lighting devices.

Rayovac Far East Corp, Room 720-723, Hollywood Plaza, 610 Nathan Rd., Mongkok Kowloon, Hong Kong PRC

READER'S DIGEST ASSOCIATION, INC.

Reader's Digest Rd., Pleasantville, NY, 10570

Tel: (914) 238-1000   Fax: (914) 238-4559   www.readersdigest.com

Publisher of magazines and books and direct mail marketer.

Reader's Digest Assn. Far East Ltd., 3A Kung Ngam Village Rd., Shaukiwan, Hong Kong PRC

RECOTON CORPORATION

2950 Lake Emma Road, Lake Mary, FL, 32746

Tel: (407) 333-8900   Fax: (407) 333-8903   www.recoton.com

Mfr. electronic accessories and aftermarket products for computers and office equipment.

Recoton Hong Kong, Unit F-J 5/F Block 2, Kawi Tak Ind Centre, 15-33 Kwai Tak Street, Kwai Chung, Hong Kong PRC

Tel: 852-498-1223 Fax: 852-411-1993

REDBACK NETWORKS, INC.

250 Holger Way, San Jose, CA, 95134

Tel: (408) 571-5000   Fax: (408) 541-0570   www.redbacknetworks.com

Mfr. equipment for high-speed internet connections.

Redback Networks Hong Kong, Shun Tak Centre, 168-200 Connaught Road, Central, Hong Kong PRC

Tel: 852-9861-1873 Fax: 852-2291-4219

REEBOK INTERNATIONAL LTD.

1895 J. W. Foster Blvd., Canton, MA, 02021

Tel: (781) 401-5000   Fax: (781) 401-7402   www.reebok.com

Mfr. athletic shoes including casual, dress golf and walking shoes.

Reebok Intl. Asia-Pacific, Gitic Centre,17/F, 24-32 Queen's Rd. E., Wanchai, Hong Kong PRC

RELIANCE GROUP HOLDINGS, INC.

55 East 52nd Street, New York, NY, 10055

Tel: (212) 909-1100   Fax: (212) 909-1864   www.rgh.com

Financial and insurance management services.

Reliance National (Asia) Ltd., Suite 2106-7, Lippo House, Causeway Bay Plaza 2, 463 Lockhart Rd., Causeway Bay, Hong Kong PRC

Tel: 852-2892-2179 Fax: 852-3833-5694   Contact: Christopher J. Cron, Dir.

The Hong Kong Chinese Insurance Company, Ltd., 24/F, Lippo House Causeway Bay Plaza 2, 463 Lockhart Rd., Causeway Bay, Hong Kong PRC

Tel: 852-2572-5488 Fax: 852-2672-5007   Contact: Paul Ng, Mgr.

RENA WARE DISTRIBUTORS INC.

PO Box 97050, Redmond, WA, 98073-9750

Tel: (425) 881-6171   Fax: (425) 882-7500   www.renaware.com

Mfr. stainless steel cookware and water filtration products.

Rena Ware Limited, Room 1902, C.C. Wu Bldg., 302-308 Hennessy Road, Wanchai, Hong Kong PRC

RENAISSANCE HOTELS AND RESORTS

10400 Fernwood Road, Bethesda, MD, 20817

Tel: (301) 380-3000   Fax: (301) 380-5181   www.renaissancehotels.com

upscale, full-service hotel and resort chain under Marriott International, Inc.

Renaissance Harbour View Hong Kong, Hong Kong PRC

Tel: 852-2375-1133

RESOURCES CONNECTION, INC.

695 Town Center Drive, Ste. 600, Costa Mesa, CA, 92626

Tel: (714) 430-6400   Fax: (714) 426-6090   www.resourcesconnection.com

Provides accounting and financial professional services.

Resources Connection, Citibank Tower, Ste. 3201, 3 Garden Road, Central, Hong Kong PRC

RESPIRONICS INC.

1501 Ardmore Blvd., Pittsburgh, PA, 15221-4401

Tel: (412) 731-2100   Fax: (412) 473-5011   www.respironics.com

Design/mfr. patient ventilation medical products.

Respironics Asia Pacific, 3/F, Microtron Building, 38 Hung To Road Kwun Tong, Kowloon, Hong Kong PRC

Respironics HK Ltd., 38 Hung To Rd., Kwun Tong, Kowloon, Hong Kong PRC

Tel: 852-23-434218

REVLON INC.

625 Madison Ave., New York, NY, 10022

Tel: (212) 527-4000   Fax: (212) 527-4995   www.revlon.com

Mfr. cosmetics, fragrances, toiletries and beauty care products.

Revlon Hong Kong Ltd., 7/F, 64-66 To Kwa Wan Rd., Kowloon, Hong Kong PRC

Contact: Patrick Lee, Gen. Mgr.

RICH PRODUCTS CORPORATION

One Robert Rich Way, Buffalo, NY, 14213

Tel: (716) 878-8000   Fax: (716) 878-8765   www.richs.com

Mfr. non-dairy products and icings, fillings, dry cake mixes, baked goods and desserts, frozen seafood and specialty meat products.

Rich Products Corp., Room 702A, Euro Trade Centre, 13-14 Connaught Rd., Central, Hong Kong PRC

RIDGE TOOL COMPANY

400 Clark Street, Elyria, OH, 44035

Tel: (440) 323-5581   Fax: (440) 329-4853   www.ridgid.com

Mfr. hand and power tools for working pipe, drain cleaning equipment, etc.

Ridge Tool Hong Kong, c/o Emerson Electric Asia Ltd., 3904, Central Plaza, 18 Harbour Rd., Wanchai, Hong Kong PRC

Tel: 852-2802-9223   Fax: 852-2857-9433

RIGHT MANAGEMENT CONSULTANTS, INC.

1818 Market Street, 33rd Fl., Philadelphia, PA, 19103-3614

Tel: (215) 988-1588   Fax: (215) 988-9112   www.right.com

Out placement and human resources consulting services.

Right D&A, 1903 Tower II, Lippo Centre, 89 Queensway, Hong Kong PRC

Contact: Stephen Lazar

THE RITZ-CARLTON HOTEL COMPANY, L.L.C.

3414 Peachtree Road NE, Ste. 300, Atlanta, GA, 30326

Tel: (404) 237-5500   Fax: (404) 365-9643   www.ritzcarlton.com

5-star hotel and restaurant chain.

The Ritz-Carlton Hong Kong, 3 Connaught Rd., Central, Hong Kong PRC

Tel: 852-2877-6666

ROCKWELL AUTOMATION, INC.

777 East Wisconsin Ave., Ste. 1400, Milwaukee, WI, 53202

Tel: (414) 212-5200   Fax: (414) 212-5201   www.rockwellautomation.com

Products and service for aerospace and defense, automotive, electronics, graphics and automation industry.

Rockwell Automation Asia Pacific, 27/F, Citicorp Centre, 18 Whitfield Road, Causeway Bay, Hong Kong PRC

Tel: 852-2887-4788

Rockwell Intl. (Asia Pacific) Ltd., Suite 1306-10, Harbour Centre, 25 Harbour Rd., Wanchai, Hong Kong PRC

Tel: 852-2827-0181   Fax: 852-2827-6488

ROGERS CORPORATION

One Technology Drive, PO Box 188, Rogers, CT, 06263-0188

Tel: (860) 774-9605   Fax: (860) 779-5509   www.rogers-corp.com

Mfr. specialty materials including elastomers, circuit laminates and moldable composites.

Rogers Southeast Asia, Inc, 118 Connaught Road Wan, Sheung Wan, Hong Kong PRC

ROHM AND HAAS COMPANY

100 Independence Mall West, Philadelphia, PA, 19106

Tel: (215) 592-3000   Fax: (215) 592-3377   www.rohmhaas.com

Mfr. specialty chemicals.

Rohm and Haas Hong Kong Ltd., Unit A, 17/F, On Hin Bldg., No.1 On Hing Terrace, Central, Hong Kong PRC

Tel: 852-2868-1383

Shipley Chemicals (Hong Kong). Ltd., Unit 1301, New Town Tower, 10-18 Pak Hok Ting St., Shantin N.T., Hong Kong PRC

Tel: 852-2694-0661

ROSENBLUTH INTERNATIONAL

2401 Walnut Street, Philadelphia, PA, 19103-4390

Tel: (215) 977-4000   Fax: (215) 977-4028   www.rosenbluth.com

Provides corporate business travel services.

Rosenbluth International, Taikoo Place, 979 King's Road, Quarry Bay, Hong Kong PRC

Tel: 852 2815 3263

T. ROWE PRICE ASSOCIATES, INC.

100 East Pratt Street, Baltimore, MD, 21202

Tel: (410) 345-2000   Fax: (410) 345-2394   www.troweprice.com

Investment and portfolio asset management.

Rowe Price-Fleming International, Hong Kong PRC

Contact: Mark J.T. Edwards

RUDDICK CORPORATION

301 S. Tryon St., Ste. 1800, Charlotte, NC, 28202

Tel: (704) 372-5404   Fax: (704) 372-6409   www.amefird.com

Mfr. industrial sewing thread for worldwide industrial and consumer markets.

American & Efird (HK) Ltd., Unit 1501, Tsuen Wan Ind. Centre, 15/F, 220-248 Texaco Road, Tsuen Wan NT, Hong Kong PRC

RUSSELL REYNOLDS ASSOCIATES INC.

200 Park Avenue, New York, NY, 10166-0002

Tel: (212) 351-2000   Fax: (212) 370-0896   www.russreyn.com

Executive recruiting services.

Russell Reynolds Associates Inc., 3801-4, Edinburgh Tower, 15 Queen's Rd., The Landmark, Central, Hong Kong PRC

Tel: 852-2523-9123   Fax: 852-284-59044   Contact: Raymond C.P. Tang

S1 CORPORATION

3500 Lenox Road, Ste. 200, Atlanta, GA, 30326-1108

Tel: (404) 923-3500   Fax: (404) 923-6727   www.s1.com

Mfr. on-line banking software.

S1 Hong Kong, 2/F, Shui On Centre, 8 Harbour Road, Wanchai, Hong Kong PRC

SALOMON SMITH BARNEY HOLDINGS INC.

388 Greenwich Street, New York, NY, 10013

Tel: (212) 816-6000   Fax: (212) 816-8915   www.smithbarney.com

Securities dealers and underwriters.

Salomon Smith Barney Holdings, 2907 Alexandra House, 15-20 Chater Rd., Hong Kong PRC

SANFORD CORPORATION

2711 Washington Boulevard, Bellwood, IL, 60104

Tel: (708) 547-6650   Fax: (708) 547-6719   www.sanfordcorp.com

Mfr. inks, writing, drawing and drafting instruments.

Sanford International, 255-257 Gloucester Road, 21/F, Causway Bay, Hong Kong PRC

SANMINA-SCI CORPORATION

2700 North First Street, San Jose, CA, 95134

Tel: (408) 964-3500   Fax: (408) 964-3799   www.sanmina-sci.com

Engaged in electronics contract manufacturing.

Sanmina-SCI Asia, 22 Kai Cheung Road, Kowloon Bay, Hong Kong PRC

Tel: 85-8-2953-9988   Fax: 85-2-2799-2398

SAS INSTITUTE INC.

SAS Campus Drive, Cary, NC, 27513

Tel: (919) 677-8000   Fax: (919) 677-4444   www.sas.com

Mfr. and distribution of decision support software.

SAS Institute (China) Ltd., Talkoo Shing, Hong Kong PRC

Tel: 852-2568-4280   Fax: 852-2-568-7218

SCHENKER USA INC.

150 Albany Ave., Freeport, NY, 11520

Tel: (516) 403-5416   Fax: (516) 377-3092   www.schenkerusa.com

Freight forwarders.

Schenker (H.K.) Ltd., China Resources Bldg., Suite 3801-5, 26 Harbour Rd., PO Box 6611, Wanchai, Hong Kong PRC

Tel: 852-2585-9688   Fax: 852-2827-5363

SCHERING-PLOUGH CORPORATION

One Giralda Farms, Madison, NJ, 07940-1000

Tel: (973) 822-7000   Fax: (973) 822-7048   www.sch-plough.com

Proprietary drug and cosmetic products.

Plough Consumer Products (Asia) Ltd., 304 Watsons Estate B, 6 Watson Rd., Hong Kong PRC

SCHOLASTIC CORPORATION

555 Broadway, New York, NY, 10012

Tel: (212) 343-6100   Fax: (212) 343-6934   www.scholastic.com

Publishing/distribution educational and children's magazines, books, software.

Scholastic Hong Kong Ltd., Tung Sung Hing Commercial Ctr., 20-22 Granville Rd., Kowloon, Hong Kong PRC

Tel: 852-2722-6161   Contact: Linda H. Warfel, Reg. Dir.

THE CHARLES SCHWAB CORPORATION

101 Montgomery Street, San Francisco, CA, 94104

Tel: (415) 627-7000   Fax: (415) 627-8840   www.schawb.com

Financial services; discount brokerage, retirement accounts.

Schwab International, 3301, Two Exchange Square, Central, Hong Kong PRC

SCIENTECH, INC.

2650 McCormick Drive, Suite 300, Clearwater, FL, 33759

Tel: (727) 669-3003   Fax: (727) 669-3100   www.scientech.com

worldwide provider of expert services to the energy and telecommunication markets

Scientech Hong Kong, Yu Yuet Lai Bldg., 10/F, 43 Wyndham St., Central, Hong Kong PRC

SCIENTIFIC GAMES INTERNATIONAL

750 Lexington Avenue, 25th Fl., New York, NY, 10022

Tel: (212) 754-2233   Fax: (212) 754-2372   www.scientificgames.com

Mfr. video gaming machines and computerized pari-mutuel wagering systems used at racetracks.

Scientific Games International, Inter-Continental, 7/F, Plaza 94 Granville Road, Tsim Sha Tsui, Kowloon, Hong Kong PRC

Tel: 852-2723-7911   Fax: 852-2723-8711

SCIENTIFIC-ATLANTA, INC.

5030 Sugarloaf Pkwy., Lawrenceville, GA, 30044

Tel: (770) 903-5000   Fax: (770) 236-6777   www.sciatl.com

Mfr. cable set-top boxes, modems, transmission and distribution equipment.

Scientific-Atlanta (HK) Ltd., Tower 1, Lippo Centre, 89 Queensway Road, Admiralty, Central, Hong Kong PRC

Tel: 852-2522-5059   Fax: 852-2522-5624   Contact: William.Katherman

SDI TECHNOLOGIES

1299 Main St., Rahway, NJ, 07065

Tel: (732) 574-9000   Fax: (732) 574-3797   www.sdidirect.com

Mfr. clock radios and electronic products.

SDI Technologies, Kowloon Centre, 29-43 Ashley Rd., Kowloon, Hong Kong PRC

SDI Technologies, Hong Kong PRC

SEAGATE TECHNOLOGY, INC.

920 Disc Dr., Scotts Valley, CA, 95066

Tel: (408) 438-6550   Fax: (408) 438-7205   www.seagate.com

Develop computer technology, software and hardware.

Seagate Technology, Rm. 1001, Energy Plaza, 92 Granville Rd., Tsim Sha Tsui East, Kowloon, Hong Kong PRC

Tel: 852-2368-9918   Fax: 852-2368-7173   Contact: Chia Hyaw Seong, Dir.   Emp: 10

SEALED AIR CORPORATION

Park 80 East, Saddle Brook, NJ, 07663

Tel: (201) 791-7600   Fax: (201) 703-4205   www.sealedaircorp.com

Mfr. protective and specialty packaging solutions for industrial, food and consumer products.

Sealed Air (Far East) Ltd., 9/F, Wing Kwai Ind. Bldg., 2-8 Wang Wo Tsai St., Tsuen Wan NT, Hong Kong PRC

Tel: 852-2407-3367   Fax: 852-2407-3385

G.D. SEARLE & COMPANY

5200 Old Orchard Road, Skokie, IL, 60077

Tel: (847) 982-7000 Fax: (847) 470-1480 www.searlehealthnet.com

Mfr. pharmaceuticals, health care, optical products and specialty chemicals.

Searle Hong Kong, Unit 3106, Level 31, Metro Plaza Tower II, 223 Hing Fong Rd., Kai Chung N.T., Hong Kong PRC

Tel: 852-423-0923 Fax: 852-423-1169

SEI INVESTMENTS COMPANY

1 Freedom Valley Drive, Oaks, PA, 19456-1100

Tel: (610) 676-1000 Fax: (610) 676-2995 www.seic.com

Accounting, evaluation and financial automated systems and services.

SEI Investments, 1201, Chinachem Leighton Plaza, 29 Leighton Rd., Causeway Bay, Hong Kong PRC

Tel: 852-2575-4772 Fax: 852-2575-3772 Contact: Vincent W. Chu, Mng. Dir.

SEMTECH CORPORATION

200 Flynn Road, Camarillo, CA, 93012-8790

Tel: (805) 498-2111 Fax: (805) 498-3804 www.semtech.com

Mfr. silicon rectifiers, rectifier assemblies, capacitors, switching regulators, AC/DC converters.

Dragon Technology Distribution Co., Ltd., Rm. 903, Landmark North, Sheung Shui N.T., Hong Kong PRC

Tel: 852-2303-0711 Fax: 852-2317-7522

THE SERVICEMASTER COMPANY

2300 Warrenville Road, Downers Grove, IL, 60515-1700

Tel: (630) 271-1300 Fax: (630) 271-2710 www.svm.com

Provides residential consumer services, including lawn care and landscape maintenance, termite and pest control, plumbing, heating and air conditioning maintenance and repair.

ServiceMaster Hong Kong, Hong Kong PRC

SHAKESPEARE FISHING TACKLE GROUP

3801 Westmore Drive, Columbia, SC, 29223

Tel: (803) 754-7000 Fax: (803) 754-7342 www.shakespeare-fishing.com

Mfr. fishing tackle.

Shakespeare Hong Kong Ltd., 175 Hoi Bun Rd., Jwun Tong, Kowloon, Hong Kong PRC

THE SHAW GROUP INC.

4171 Essen Lane, Baton Rouge, LA, 70809

Tel: (225) 932-2500 Fax: (225) 932-2661 www.shawgrp.com

Vertically-integrated provider of complete piping systems, and comprehensive engineering, procurement and construction services.

Organic Waste Technologies HK Ltd., Pik Wan Road, Lin Tak Road Lam Tin, Kowloon, Hong Kong PRC

SHAW INDUSTRIES, INC.

616 E. Walnut Ave., Dalton, GA, 30720

Tel: (706) 278-3812 Fax: (706) 275-3735 www.shawinc.com

Mfr. carpet.

Shaw Industries, Inc., Hong Kong PRC

SHEARMAN & STERLING

599 Lexington Ave., New York, NY, 10022-6069

Tel: (212) 848-4000 Fax: (212) 848-7179 www.shearman.com

Law firm engaged in general American and international financial and commercial practice.

Shearman & Sterling, Standard Chartered Bank Bldg., 4 Des Voeux Rd., Central, Hong Kong PRC

Tel: 852-2978-8000 Fax: 852-2978-8099 Contact: Edward L. Turner III, Mng. Ptnr.

SHIPLEY COMPANY, LLC

455 Forest Street, Marlborough, MA, 01752

Tel: (508) 481-7950   Fax: (508) 485-9113   www.shipley.com

Supplier of materials and processes technology to the microelectronics and printed wiring board industries.

Shipley Asia, Ltd., 15 On Lok Mun Street, On Lok Tsuen, Fanling N.T., Hong Kong PRC

Tel: 852-2680-16888   Fax: 852-2680-06333

Shipley Chemicals Ltd., Unit 1303, New Town Tower, 10-18 Pok Hok Ting St., Shatin NT, Hong Kong PRC

Tel: 852-2694-0661   Fax: 852-2694-0939   Contact: R. Leung

SHURE INCORPORATED

222 Hartrey Ave., Evanston, IL, 60202-3696

Tel: (847) 866-2200   Fax: (847) 866-2279   www.shure.com

Mfr. microphones, teleconferencing systems, circuitry products.

Shure Asia Limited, Unit 701, 7/F, Top Glory Tower, 26 2 Gloucester Road, Causeway Bay, Hong Kong PRC

Tel: 852-2893-4290   Fax: 852-2893-4055   Contact: Tom Anderson

SIDLEY AUSTIN BROWN & WOOD, LLP

10 South Dearborn, Bank One Plaze, Chicago, IL, 60603

Tel: (312) 853-7000   Fax: (312) 853-7036   www.sidley.com

Engaged in international law.

Sidley Austin Brown & Wood LLP, Bank Of China Tower, One Garden Rd., Central, Hong Kong PRC

Tel: 852-2509-7888   Fax: 852-2509-3110

SIGMA-ALDRICH CORPORATION

3050 Spruce Street, St. Louis, MO, 63103

Tel: (314) 771-5765   Fax: (314) 771-5757   www.sigma-aldrich.com

Chemicals and biochemical's, aluminum and structural steel components.

Tin Hang Technology Limited, Unit 1204-06, 69 Jervois Street, Sheung Wan, Hong Kong PRC

Tel: 852-2817-2121

SIGNODE PACKAGING SYSTEMS

3610 West Lake Ave., Glenview, IL, 60025

Tel: (847) 724-6100   Fax: (847) 657-4392   www.signode.com

Mfr. industrial tools and machinery for packaging and strapping.

Signode Hong Kong Ltd., Unit B, 9/F, Kin Yip Factory Bldg., 9 Cheung Yee St., Kowloon, Hong Kong PRC

SILICON GRAPHICS INC.

1600 Amphitheatre Pkwy., Mountain View, CA, 94043-1351

Tel: (650) 960-1980   Fax: (650) 932-0661   www.sgi.com

Design/mfr. special-effects computer graphic systems and software.

Silicon Graphics Ltd., Rooms 513-522, 5/F, Hong Kong Industrial Tech Centre, 72 Tat Chee Ave., Kowloon, Hong Kong PRC

Tel: 852-2784-3111   Fax: 852-2778-9100

THE SIMCO COMPANY, INC.

1178 Bordeaux Dr., Sunnyvale, CA, 94089

Tel: (408) 734-9750   Fax: (408) 734-9754   www.simco.com

Provides electronics and commercial calibration services.

Simco Company c/o CO Packaging Corp(HK) Ltd., 4/F, Din Wai Industrial Bldg., 13 On Chuen St., On Lok Tsuen, Fanling NT, Hong Kong PRC

Tel: 852-2785-2230   Fax: 852-2947-5770

SIMPLEX GRINNELL

100 Simplex Dr., Westminster, MA, 01441

Tel: (978) 731-2500   Fax: (978) 731-7052   www.simplexgrinnell.com

Provides safety, fire detection, integrated security, communications, time and attendance and workforce management systems.

SimplexGrinnell International Pty. Ltd., Units 1101-2, Stelux House, 698 Prince Edward Road East, San Po Kong, Kowloon, Hong Kong PRC

SIMPSON THACHER & BARTLETT

425 Lexington Ave., New York, NY, 10017

Tel: (212) 455-2000   Fax: (212) 455-2502   www.simpsonthacher.com

Engaged in international law.

Simpson Thacher & Bartlett, Asia Pacific Tower, 32/F, 3 Garden Rd., Central, Hong Kong PRC

Tel: 852-2514-7600   Fax: 852-2869-7694   Contact: John E. Riley, Ptnr.

SKADDEN, ARPS, SLATE, MEAGHER & FLOM LLP

4 Times Square, New York, NY, 10036

Tel: (212) 735-3000   Fax: (212) 735-2000   www.sasmf.com

American/International law practice.

Skadden, Arps, Slate, Meagher & Flom LLP, 30/F, Tower Two Lippo Centre, 89 Queensway, Central, Hong Kong PRC

Tel: 852-2820-0700   Fax: 852-2820-0727   Contact: Robert C. Hinkley, Partner

SKIDMORE OWINGS & MERRILL LLP

224 S. Michigan Ave., Ste. 1000, Chicago, IL, 60604-2707

Tel: (312) 554-9090   Fax: (312) 360-4545   www.som.com

Engaged in architectural and engineering services.

SOM Inc., Trium Pacific Place, Suite 4606, 88 Queensway, Hong Kong PRC

Tel: 852-2877-4606   Fax: 852-2810-6056

SKYTEL COMMUNICATIONS, INC.

515 E. Amite St., Jackson, MS, 39201

Tel: (601) 944-1300   Fax: (601) 944-3900   www.skytel.com

Provides wireless messaging services, radio paging services and systems implementation.

SkyTel Services Ltd., Hong Kong PRC

SKYWORKS SOLUTIONS, INC.

20 Sylvan Road, Woburn, MA, 01801

Tel: (781) 935-5150   Fax: (781) 824-4579   www.skyworksinc.com

Mfr. electronic and microwave components.

Skyworks Solutions, Rm 2532, Sun Hung Kai Centre,, 30 Harbour Rd,, Wanchai, Hong Kong PRC

WILBUR SMITH ASSOCIATES (WSA)

PO Box 92, Columbia, SC, 29202

Tel: (803) 758-4500   Fax: (803) 251-2064   www.wilbursmith.com

Consulting engineers.

Wilbur Smith Associates Inc., Unit 803-6, 8/F, Two Harbourfront, 22 Tak Fung Street, Hung Hom Kowloon, Hong Kong PRC

Tel: 852-2359-5738   Fax: 852-2385-7215   Contact: Chang Tai Tseng

SOFTWARE HOUSE INTERNATIONAL, INC.

2 Riverview Drive, Somerset, NJ, 08873

Tel: (732) 746-8888   Fax: (732) 764-8889   www.shi.com

Engaged in the distribution of software products.

SHI Hong Kong, 19/F One International Finance Centre, 1 Harbour View Street, Central, Hong Kong PRC

Tel: 852-2166-8293

SOLA INTERNATIONAL INC.

10690 W. Ocean Air Drive, Ste. 300, San Diego, CA, 92130

Tel: (858) 509-9899   Fax: (858) 509-9898   www.sola.com

Mfr. and sales of plastic and glass eyeglasses.

SOLA Hong Kong, Shui Hing Centre, 13, Sheung Yuet Road, Kowloon Bay, Kowloon, Hong Kong PRC

SOLUTIA INC.

575 Maryville Center Dr, St. Louis, MO, 63141

Tel: (314) 674-1000   Fax: (314) 694-8686   www.solutia.com

Mfr. specialty chemical based products.

Solutia Hong Kong Limited, 18 Harbour Road, Unit 1706, Central Plaza, Wanchai, Hong Kong PRC

Tel: 852-28283232

SONOCO PRODUCTS COMPANY

North Second Street, PO Box 160, Hartsville, SC, 29550

Tel: (843) 383-7000   Fax: (843) 383-7008   www.sonoco.com

Mfr. packaging for consumer and industrial market and recycled paperboard.

Sonoco Asia Recycling Ltd., Two Pacific Place, Suite 1101, 88 Queensway, Hong Kong PRC

Tel: 852-2514-4300   Fax: 852-2869-6201

SOTHEBY'S HOLDINGS, INC.

1334 York Avenue, New York, NY, 10021

Tel: (212) 606-7000   Fax: (212) 606-7027   www.sothebys.com

Auction house specializing in fine art and jewelry.

Sotheby's Holdings, Inc., 4-4A Des Boeux Road Central, 5/F, Hong Kong PRC

Tel: 852-2524-8121   Fax: 852-1810-6238   Contact: Carlton C. Rochell Jr.

THE SOUTHERN COMPANY

270 Peachtree Street, N.W., Atlanta, GA, 30303

Tel: (404) 506-5000   Fax: (404) 506-0642   www.southernco.com

Electric utility.

Consolidated Electric Power Asia (Cepa), 18/F, Hong Kong Telecom Tower, 979 King's Rd., Quarry Bay, Hong Kong PRC

Tel: 852-2179-3333   Fax: 852-2179-3334   Contact: Raymond D. Hill, Mng. Dir.

SPENCER STUART MANAGEMENT CONSULTANTS

401 North Michigan Ave., Ste. 3400, Chicago, IL, 60611

Tel: (312) 822-0080   Fax: (312) 822-0116   www.spencerstuart.com

Executive recruitment firm.

Spencer Stuart & Associates Inc., 17/F, Bank of East Asia Bldg., 10 Des Voeux Rd., Central, Hong Kong PRC

Tel: 852-2521-8373   Fax: 852-2810-5246   Contact: Martin Tang

SPHERION CORPORATION

2050 Spectrum Boulevard, Fort Lauderdale, FL, 33309

Tel: (954) 938-7600   Fax: (954) 938-7666   www.spherion.com

Provides temporary personnel placement and staffing.

Michael Page Finance, One Pacific Place, Suite 601, Hong Kong PRC

Tel: 852-2530-2000

Michael Page Sales & Marketing, One Pacific Place, Suite 601, Hong Kong PRC

Tel: 852-2918-1333

SPRINGS INDUSTRIES INC.

205 N. White Street, PO Box 70, Fort Mill, SC, 29716

Tel: (803) 547-1500   Fax: (803) 547-1772   www.springs.com

Mfr. and sales of home furnishings, finished fabrics and industry textiles.

Springs Asia, 202, Wing on Plaza, 62 Mody Rd., TST East, Kowloon, Hong Kong PRC

Tel: 852-2722-7671   Fax: 852-2722-1259   Contact: T. Arimitsu

SPRINT CORPORATION

2330 Shawnee Mission Parkway, Westwood, KS, 66205

Tel: (913) 624-3000   Fax: (913) 624-3281   www.sprint.com

Telecommunications equipment and services.

Sprint Corporation, Two Pacific Place, Suite 1212, 88 Queensway, Hong Kong PRC

SPSS INC.

233 S. Wacker Dr., 11th Fl., Chicago, IL, 60606

Tel: (312) 651-6000   Fax: (312) 329-3668   www.spss.com

Mfr. statistical software.

SPSS Hong Kong, Westlands Centre 18/F, 20 Westlands Road, Quarry Bay, Hong Kong PRC

SQUIRE, SANDERS & DEMPSEY

4900 Key Tower, 127 Public Square, Cleveland, OH, 44114-1304

Tel: (216) 479-8500   Fax: (216) 479-8780   www.ssd.com

Engaged in international law.

Squire, Sanders & Dempsey, Room 4008, Gloucester Tower, The Landmark, 11 Pedder Street, Central, Hong Kong PRC

Tel: 852-2509-9977   Fax: 852-2509-9772   Contact: James S. Tsang

THE ST. PAUL COMPANIES, INC.

385 Washington Street, St. Paul, MN, 55102

Tel: (651) 310-7911   Fax: (651) 310-8294   www.stpaul.com

Provides investment, insurance and reinsurance services.

QBE Insurance Hong Kong Ltd., Allied Kajima Building, 16th Floor, 138 Gloucester Road, Wanchai, Hong Kong PRC

THE STANLEY WORKS

1000 Stanley Drive, PO Box 7000, New Britain, CT, 06053

Tel: (860) 225-5111   Fax: (860) 827-3987   www.stanleyworks.com

Mfr. hand tools and hardware.

The Stanley Works Hong Kong Ltd., 1433 Central Bldg., Pedder St., Hong Kong PRC

STARTEC GLOBAL COMMUNICATIONS CORPORATION

1151 Seven Locks Road, Potomac, MD, 20854

Tel: (301) 610-4300   Fax: (301) 610-4301   www.startec.com

Provides international phone service.

Startec Global, 22/F, Sino Favour Centre, 1 On Yip Street, Chai Wan, Hong Kong PRC

STARWOOD HOTELS & RESORTS WORLDWIDE

777 Westchester Avenue, White Plains, NY, 10604

Tel: (914) 640-8100   Fax: (914) 640-8316   www.starwoodhotels.com

Hotel operations including Sheraton, Westin, St. Regis, Four Points and Caesars.

Sheraton Hong Kong Hotel & Towers, 20 Nathan Rd., Kowloon, Hong Kong PRC

Tel: 852-2369-1111   Fax: 852-2739-8707

STATE STREET CORPORATION

225 Franklin Street, Boston, MA, 02101

Tel: (617) 786-3000   Fax: (617) 654-3386   www.statestreet.com

Engaged in investment management and institutional investor services.

State Street Trust (HK) Ltd., Two Exchange Square, 32/F, 8 Connaught Place, Central, Hong Kong PRC

Tel: 852-2103-0275   Contact: Raymond Hood

STEPAN COMPANY

22 West Frontage Rd., Northfield, IL, 60093

Tel: (847) 446-7500   Fax: (847) 501-2443   www.stepan.com

Mfr. basic intermediate chemicals.

Stepan, House 15, 63 Deep Water Bay Rd., Deep Water Bay, Hong Kong PRC

STERIS CORPORATION

5960 Heisley Road, Mentor, OH, 44060

Tel: (440) 354-2600   Fax: (440) 639-4459   www.steris.com

Mfr. sterilization and infection control equipment, surgical tables, lighting systems for health, pharmaceutical and scientific industries.

Steris Corporation, 34/F, Uint D, Manulife Tower, 169 Electric Rd., North Point, Hong Kong PRC

STIEFEL LABORATORIES INC.

255 Alhambra Circle, Ste. 1000, Coral Gables, FL, 33134

Tel: (305) 443-3807　　　　Fax: (305) 443-3467　　　　www.stiefel.com

Mfr. pharmaceuticals, dermatological specialties.

Stiefel Laboratories Limited, 601B, Tower 2, Cheung Sha Wan Plaza, 833 Cheung Sha Wan Road, Kowloon, Hong Kong PRC

STORAGE TECHNOLOGY CORPORATION

One Storagetech Dr., Louisville, CO, 80028-4377

Tel: (303) 673-5151　　　　Fax: (303) 673-5019　　　　www.stortek.com

Mfr., market, service information, storage and retrieval systems.

StorageTek North Asia Limited, Ste. 6201, Central Plaza, 18, Harbour Road, Wanchai, Hong Kong PRC

Tel: 852-8200-0791　Fax: 852-8200-0792　Contact: Brian Knott

THE STRUCTURE TONE ORGANIZATION

15 East 26th Street, New York, NY, 10010-1589

Tel: (212) 481-6100　　　　Fax: (212) 685-9267　　　　www.structuretone.com

Provides general contracting and construction management.

Structure Tone Organization, 23/F Chinachem Johnson Plaza, 178-186 Johnston Road, Wanchai, Hong Kong PRC

STRYKER CORPORATION

2725 Fairfield Rd., Kalamazoo, MI, 49002

Tel: (616) 385-2600　　　　Fax: (616) 385-1062　　　　www.strykercorp.com

Develops, manufactures and markets specialty surgical and medical products worldwide.

Stryker Hong Kong, Tower Citibank Plaza, 3, Ste. 2501, Hong Kong PRC

Tel: 852-2840-4400　Fax: 852-2804-6303　Contact: Jackarine Yu

SULLIVAN & CROMWELL

125 Broad Street, New York, NY, 10004-2498

Tel: (212) 558-4000　　　　Fax: (212) 558-3588　　　　www.sullcrom.com

Engaged in international law.

Sullivan & Cromwell, Nine Queen's Rd., 28/F, Central, Hong Kong PRC

SUN MICROSYSTEMS, INC.

901 San Antonio Road, Palo Alto, CA, 94303

Tel: (650) 960-1300　　　　Fax: (650) 961-9131　　　　www.sun.com

Computer peripherals and programming services.

Sun Microsystems, 22/F, Shui on Center, 8 Harbour Road, Wanchai, Hong Kong PRC

SUNBEAM CORPORATION

2381 Executive Center Dr., Boca Raton, FL, 33431

Tel: (561) 912-4100　　　　Fax: (561) 912-4567　　　　www.sunbeam.com

Mfr. household and personal grooming appliances; Sunbeam, Mr. Coffee, First Alert, Mixmaster and Oster.

Orient Fair Development Ltd., Rm.1018, 21-33 Tai Lin Pai Rd., Kwai Chung N.T., Hong Kong PRC

SUNKIST GROWERS INC.

14130 Riverside Drive, Van Nuys, CA, 91423

Tel: (818) 986-4800　　　　Fax: (818) 379-7405　　　　www.sunkist.com

Citrus marketing cooperative; fruits and vegetables.

Sunkist c/o Reliance Commercial Enterprises HK Ltd., Rm. 705, 7/F, Central Plaza, 18 Harbor Rd., 1 Wan Chai, Hong Kong PRC

Tel: 852-2525-2236

SYBASE, INC.

5000 Hacienda Dr., Dublin, CA, 94568

Tel: (925) 236-5000　　　　Fax: (925) 236-4321　　　　www.sybase.com

Design/mfg/distribution of database management systems, software development tools, connectivity products, consulting and technical support services..

Sybase Hong Kong Ltd., 33/F, Natwest Tower, Times Square, I Matheson St., Causeway Bay, Hong Kong PRC

Tel: 852-2506-8900　Fax: 852-2506-6050

SYMANTEC CORPORATION

20330 Stevens Creek Blvd., Cupertino, CA, 95014-2132

Tel: (408) 253-9600   Fax: (408) 253-3968   www.symantec.com

Designs and produces PC network security and network management software and hardware.

Symantec Ltd., Unit 1101-1102, Onfem Tower, No. 29 Wyndham St., Central, Hong Kong PRC

Tel: 852-2528-6206 Fax: 852-2861-3420

SYMMETRICOM, INC.

2300 Orchard Pkwy., San Jose, CA, 95131-1017

Tel: (408) 433-0910   Fax: (408) 428-7999   www.symmetricom.com

Mfr. synchronization and timing equipment for telephones and broadband networks.

Symmetricom Hong Kong Ltd., Unit 1005, Jubilee Centre, 42 - 46 Gloucester Road, Wan Chai, Hong Kong PRC

SYNOPSYS, INC.

700 East Middlefield Road, Mountain View, CA, 94043

Tel: (650) 962-5000   Fax: (650) 965-8637   www.synopsys.com

Mfr. electronic design automation software.

Synopsys Hong Kong, Unit 903, Asia Orient Tower, 33 Lockhart Road, Wan Chai, Hong Kong PRC

Tel: 852-2369-8156

TBWA WORLDWIDE

488 Madison Avenue, 6th Floor, New York, NY, 10022

Tel: (212) 804-1000   Fax: (212) 804-1200   www.tbwachiat.com

International full service advertising agency.

TBWA Lee Davis, Hong Kong PRC

TBWA Thompson, Hong Kong PRC

THE TCW GROUP

865 S. Figueroa St., Ste. 1800, Los Angeles, CA, 90017

Tel: (213) 244-0000   Fax: (213) 244-0000   www.tcwgroup.com

Engaged in managing pension and profit sharing funds, retirement/health and welfare funds, insurance company funds, endowments and foundations.

TCW Group, Hong Kong PRC

TEKTRONIX INC.

14200 SW Karl Braun Dr., PO Box 500, Beaverton, OR, 97077

Tel: (503) 627-7111   Fax: (503) 627-2406   www.tek.com

Mfr. test and measure, visual systems/color printing and communications/video and networking products.

Tektronix Hong Kong Ltd., 65/F, The Lee Gardens, 3 Hysan Ave., Causeway Bay, Hong Kong PRC

Tel: 852-2585-6688 Fax: 852-2598-6260

TELETECH HOLDINGS, INC.

9197 South Peoria Street, Englewood, CO, 80112-5833

Tel: (303) 397-8100   Fax: (303) 397-8668   www.teletech.com

Provider of teleservices.

TeleTech Holdings, Inc., 8th Floor, Tower I, The Millennium City, 388 Kwun Tong Road, Hong Kong PRC

Tel: 852-2882-9933 Fax: 852-2882-9922

TELEX COMMUNICATIONS INC.

12000 Portland Ave. South, Burnsville, MN, 55337

Tel: (952) 884-4051   Fax: (952) 884-0043   www.telexcommunications.com

Mfr. communications, audio-visual and professional audio products.

EVI Audio (Hong Kong) Ltd., Unit E/F, 21F, Luk Hop Industrial Bldg., 8 Luk Hop Street, San Po Kong, Kowloon, Hong Kong PRC

TELLABS INC.

1415 W. Diehl Rd., Naperville, IL, 60563

Tel: (630) 378-8800   Fax: (630) 852-7346   www.tellabs.com

Design/mfr./service voice/data transport and network access systems.

Tellabs Ltd., Suite 1702-4, 1111 King's Road, Taikoo Shing, Hong Kong PRC

TERADYNE INC.

321 Harrison Ave., Boston, MA, 02118

Tel: (617) 482-2700   Fax: (617) 422-2910   www.teradyne.com

Mfr. electronic test equipment and blackplane connection systems.

Teradyne (Hong Kong) Ltd., 33 Canton Rd., #1018, Kowloon, Hong Kong PRC

TERAYON COMMUNICATION SYSTEMS, INC..

2952 Bunker Hill Lane, Santa Clara, CA, 95054

Tel: (408) 727-4400   Fax: (408) 727-6205   www.terayon.com

Mfr. cable modem systems and broadband communication services.

Terayon Communication Systems Hong Kong, Suite 2604-06, The Gateway, 25 Canton Road, Kowloon, Hong Kong PRC

Tel: 852 2111 5988   Contact: Andrew A. Bigbee

TEXAS INSTRUMENTS INC.

12500 TI Blvd., Dallas, TX, 75266

Tel: (972) 995-3773   Fax: (972) 995-4360   www.ti.com

Mfr. semiconductor devices, electronic electro-mechanical systems, instruments and controls.

Texas Instruments Hong Kong, Hong Kong PRC

Tel: 800-96-1111-800-800-

TEXTRON INC.

40 Westminster Street, Providence, RI, 02903

Tel: (401) 421-2800   Fax: (401) 421-2878   www.textron.com

Mfr. Aerospace (Bell Helicopter and Cessna Aircraft), industry and consumer products, fasteners and financial services.

Avdel China Ltd., Room 1708 Nanyang Plaza, 57 Hungto Road Kwun Tong, Kowloon, Hong Kong PRC

Tel: 852-2950-0630   Fax: 852-2950-0022   Contact: Johnny Tam

THE MARMON GROUP, INC.

200 West Adams, Ste. 2211, Chicago, IL, 60606

Tel: (312) 372-9500   Fax: (312) 845-5305   www.marmon.com

Holding company for diversified manufacturing and service firms.

Asia Cardiovascular Products, 8/F, Wyler Center, 200 Tai Lin Pai Rd., Kwai Chung NT, Hong Kong PRC

Tel: 852-2484-9759   Fax: 852-2484-9616   Contact: Paul Rieff, President   Emp: 10

Getz Bros. & Co. (Hong Kong) Ltd., 8/F, Wyler Centre, 200 Tai Lin Pai Rd., Kwai Chung NT, Hong Kong PRC

Tel: 852-2429-1292   Fax: 852-2480-4691   Contact: Stephen Lee, Gen. Mgr.   Emp: 135

Getz Bros. & Co. Inc., 12/F, Baskerville House, 22 Ice House St., Central, Hong Kong PRC

THERMADYNE HOLDINGS CORPORATION

101 South Hanley Road, Suite 300, St. Louis, MO, 63105

Tel: (314) 746-2197   Fax: (314) 746-2349   www.thermadyne.com

Mfr. welding, cutting, and safety products.

Thermadyne Hong Kong Ltd., 3/F, Block G, Marigold Garden, 12-14 Marigold Road,, Kowloon, Hong Kong PRC

Tel: 852-2791-9404   Contact: Ivan Moo

THERMO ORION, INC.

500 Cummings Court, Beverly, MA, 01915

Tel: (978) 922-4400   Fax: (978) 922-6015   www.thermoorion.com

Mfr. laboratory and industrial products, measure and display instruments.

Orion Research Far East Inc., Federal Bldg., #904, 369 Lockhart Rd., Wanchai, Hong Kong PRC

Tel: 852-283-60981   Fax: 852-283-45160

THERM-O-DISC, INC.

1320 S. Main Street, Mansfield, OH, 44907-0538

Tel: (419) 525-8300   Fax: (419) 525-8344   www.thermodisc.com

Mfr. thermostats, controls, sensor and thermal cutoffs, switches.

Therm-O-Disc, 3904, Central Plaza, 18 Harbour Rd., Wanchai, Hong Kong PRC

THOMAS GROUP, INC.

5221 N. O'Connor Blvd., Ste. 500, Irving, TX, 75039-3714

Tel: (972) 869-3400   Fax: (972) 443-1701   www.thomasgroup.com

Engaged in management consulting services.

Thomas Group, Tower 6 The Gateway, 9 Canton Road, Ste. 2801, Tsimshatsui Kowloon, Hong Kong PRC

THOMAS INDUSTRIES INC.

4360 Brownsboro Road, Ste. 300, Louisville, KY, 40232

Tel: (502) 893-4600   Fax: (502) 893-4685   www.thomasind.com

Mfr. lighting fixtures and specialty pumps and compressors for global OEM applications.

T.I. Asia Pacific Ltd., Units 1-5, 25/F, Metropole Square, No. 2 On Yiu Street, Siu Lek Yuen, Shatin New Territories, Hong Kong PRC

Tel: 852-2690-3502   Fax: 852-2792-4598

THOMAS PUBLISHING COMPANY

5 Penn Plaza, New York, NY, 10007

Tel: (212) 695-0500   Fax: (212) 290-7362   www.thomaspublishing.com

Publishing magazines and directories.

Interasia Publications Ltd., 200 Lockhart Rd., Victoria, Hong Kong PRC

TIFFANY & COMPANY

727 Fifth Ave., New York, NY, 10022

Tel: (212) 755-8000   Fax: (212) 605-4465   www.tiffany.com

Mfr./retail fine jewelry, silverware, china, crystal, leather goods, etc.

Tiffany & Co. Hong Kong, The Landmark Shop, 17, G/F, Pedder St., Central, Hong Kong PRC

Tel: 852-2845-9853

Tiffany & Co. Hong Kong, The Peninsula Hote, Shop E1, G/F Salisbury Rd., Hong Kong PRC

Tel: 852-2722-7691

TOMMY HILFIGER CORPORATION

25 West 39th Street, 13th Fl., New York, NY, 10018

Tel: (212) 840-8888   Fax: (212) 302-8718   www.tommy.com

Clothing manufacturer and chain stores. (JV with Tommy Hilfiger Corp., Hong Kong)

Tommy Hilfiger Corp., 11/F Novel Industrial Building, 850-870 Lai Chi Kok Road, Cheung Sha Wan, Kowloon, Hong Kong PRC

Tel: 852-2216-0668   Fax: v   Contact: Silas K. F. Chou, Co-Chair

TOOTSIE ROLL INDUSTRIES INC.

7401 S. Cicero Ave., Chicago, IL, 60629

Tel: (773) 838-3400   Fax: (773) 838-3534   www.tootsie.com

Mfr. candies and chocolate products.

Tootsie Roll Worldwide Ltd., Room 1501, Eight Plaza, 8 Sunning Rd., Causeway Bay, Hong Kong PRC

TOTES ISOTONER CORPORATION

9655 International Blvd., PO Box 465658, Cincinnati, OH, 45246

Tel: (513) 682-8200   Fax: (513) 682-8602   www.totes.com

Mfr. rubber and plastic footwear, slippers, umbrellas.

Totes Asia, Hong Kong PRC

TOWERS PERRIN

335 Madison Ave., New York, NY, 10017-4605

Tel: (212) 309-3400   Fax: (212) 309-0975   www.towers.com

Management consulting services.

Towers Perrin, Central Plaza, Ste. 3001-2, 18 Harbour Rd., Wanchai, Hong Kong PRC

Tel: 852-2593-4588   Fax: 852-2868-1517

TOYS R US INC.

461 From Road, Paramus, NJ, 07652

Tel: (201) 262-7800   Fax: (201) 845-0973   www.toysrus.com

Retail stores: toys and games, sporting goods, computer software, books, records.

Toys R Us Lifung Ltd., Yen Sheng Centre, 11/F, 64 Hoi Yuen Rd., Kwun Tong, Kowloon, Hong Kong PRC

THE TRANE COMPANY

3600 Pammel Creek Road, La Crosse, WI, 54601

Tel: (608) 787-2000   Fax: (608) 787-4990   www.trane.com

Mfr. distribution and service of A/C systems and equipment.

Jardine Trane Air Conditioning, Jardine Engineering House, 15/F, 260 King's Rd., North Point, Hong Kong PRC

Trane Asia Pacific (Reg. HQ), St. John's Bldg., 16/F, 33 Garden Rd., Hong Kong PRC

TRANSATLANTIC HOLDINGS, INC.

80 Pine Street, New York, NY, 10005

Tel: (212) 770-2000   Fax: (212) 289-6801   www.transre.com

Engaged in reinsurance.

TRC Reinsurance, 3303 The Lee Gardens, 33 Hysan Avenue, Causeway Bay, Hong Kong PRC

TRANSISTOR DEVICES, INC.

85 Horsehill Road, Cedar Knolls, NJ, 07927

Tel: (973) 267-1900   Fax: (973) 267-2047   www.tdipower.com

Mfr. electronic power supplies and equipment.

TDI China, Garden City Plaza 9/F, Tsuen Wan, Hong Kong PRC

Tel: 852-2417-7051

TRICON GLOBAL RESTAURANTS INC.

1441 Gardner Lane, Louisville, KY, 40213

Tel: (502) 874-1000   Fax: (502) 874-8315   www.triconglobal.com

Owns and operates KFC, Taco Bell and Pizza Hut restaurant food chains.

Tricon Global Greater China, 33 Hysin Avenue, Rm. 1602, Causeway Bay, Hong Kong PRC

Tel: 852-2834-8330   Fax: 852-2831-1879

TRIDENT MICROSYSTEMS, INC.

1090 E. Arques Ave, Sunnyvale, CA, 94085

Tel: (408) 991-8800   Fax: (408) 733-1438   www.tridentmicro.com

Mfr. computer components.

Trident Microsystems Far East Ltd., Tower III, 18/F, Enterprise Square, 9 Sheung Yuet Road, Kowloon Bay Kowloon, Hong Kong PRC

TROPICANA PRODUCTS, INC.

1001 13th Avenue East, Bradenton, FL, 34208

Tel: (941) 747-4461   Fax: (941) 665-5330   www.tropicana.com

Marketer and producer of branded juices, including Tropicana, Dole, Looza and Copella.

Tropicana Beverages Greater China Limited, 1111 King's Road, Ste 1203-6, Taikoo Shing, Hong Kong PRC

Tel: 852-2121-8200   Fax: 852-2121-8201

TROUTMAN SANDERS LLP

999 Peachtree Street NE, Atlanta, GA, 30309-3915

Tel: (404) 885-3651   Fax: (404) 885-3900   www.troutmansanders.com

International law firm.

Troutman Sanders LLP, 2 Exchange Square, 8 Connaught Place, Ste. 3503, Central, Hong Kong PRC

Tel: 852-2533-7888   Contact: Roger D. Williams

TYCO CAPITAL

1211 Avenue of the Americas, New York, NY, 10036

Tel: (212) 536-1390   Fax: (212) 536-1912   www.citgroup.com

Engaged in commercial finance.

Newcourt Credit, Div. Tyco Capital, 20 Des Voeux Road, Rm. 1402 Takshing House, Central, Hong Kong PRC

Tel: 852-2869-0790   Fax: 852-2537-1612

TYSON FOODS INC.

2210 W. Oaklawn Dr., Springdale, AR, 72762-6999

Tel: (501) 290-4000   Fax: (501) 290-4061   www.tyson.com

Production/mfr./distributor poultry, beef, pork and seafood products.

Tyson Hong Kong, Rm. 3204-5, 32/F, Great Eagle Centre, 23 Harbour Rd., Wanchai, Hong Kong PRC

Tel: 852-2878-1038   Fax: 852-2537-8316   Contact: Kenneth Shum, Reg. Dir.   Emp: 21

UAL CORPORATION

1200 E. Algonquin Rd., Chicago, IL, 60007

Tel: (847) 700-4000   Fax: (847) 700-4081   www.ual.com

Air transportation, passenger and freight services.

United Airlines, Hong Kong PRC

UBS PAINEWEBBER

1285 Ave. of the Americas, New York, NY, 10019

Tel: (212) 713-2000   Fax: (212) 713-4889   www.ubspainewebber.com

Engaged in stock brokerage and investment services.

UBS PaineWebber Intl., Ste. 3204-05, Citibank Towe, Citibank Plaza, 3 Garden Rd., Hong Kong PRC

Tel: 852-2842-0600

UNION CARBIDE CORPORATION

39 Old Ridgebury Road, Danbury, CT, 06817

Tel: (203) 794-2000   Fax: (203) 794-6269   www.unioncarbide.com

Mfr. industrial chemicals, plastics and resins.

Union Carbide Asia Ltd., Metroplaza, Tower 1, 26/F, Rm. 2612-2624, 223 High Fong Rd., Kwai Fong NT, Hong Kong PRC

UNISYS CORPORATION.

PO Box 500, Union Meeting Road, Blue Bell, PA, 19424

Tel: (215) 986-4011   Fax: (215) 986-6850   www.unisys.com

Mfr./marketing/servicing electronic information systems.

Unisys Asia Ltd., Sun Hung Kai Centre, 30 Harbour Rd., Wan Chai 1015, Hong Kong PRC
Unisys Hong Kong Ltd., Sun Hung Kai Centre, 30 Harbour Rd., Wan Chai 1015, Hong Kong PRC

UNITED PARCEL SERVICE, INC.

55 Glenlake Parkway, NE, Atlanta, GA, 30328

Tel: (404) 828-6000   Fax: (404) 828-6593   www.ups.com

International package-delivery service.

UPS Parcel Delivery Service Ltd., Ste. 602-610, North Tower, World Finance Centre, Harbour City Tsimshatsui, Kowloon, Hong Kong PRC

Tel: 852-2735-3535   Fax: 852-2738-5071

UNIVERSAL CORPORATION

1501 N. Hamilton Street, Richmond, VA, 23230

Tel: (804) 359-9311   Fax: (804) 254-3582   www.universalcorp.com

Holding company for tobacco and commodities.

Universal Leaf Far-East Ltd., 1435, Central Bldg., Queens Rd., Central, Hong Kong PRC

UNIVERSAL SECURITY INSTRUMENTS, INC.

PO Box 825, Binghamton, NY, 13902-0825

Tel: (607) 779-7689   Fax: (607) 779-7301   www.uic.com

Provider of innovative electronic circuit assembly technology and equipment, integrated system solutions, and process expertise.

Universal Instruments Ltd., Tsimshatsui Kowloon, Hong Kong PRC

Tel: 852-2723-2800   Fax: 852-2739-2698

UOP LLC

25 East Algonquin Road, Des Plaines, IL, 60017

Tel: (847) 391-2000   Fax: (847) 391-2253   www.uop.com

Engaged in developing and commercializing technology for license to the oil refining, petrochemical and gas processing industries.

Norplex Pacific Div. UOP Hong Kong Ltd., Kowloon, Hong Kong PRC

URS CORPORATION

100 California Street, Ste. 500, San Francisco, CA, 94111

Tel: (415) 774-2700   Fax: (415) 398-1905   www.urscorp.com

Engineering, environmental and construction management services.

O'Brien-Kreitzberg, 1801, Yue Xiu Bldg., 160-174 Lockhart Rd., Wanchai, Hong Kong PRC

USF WORLDWIDE INC.

1100 Arlington Heights Road, Ste. 600, Itasca, IL, 60143

Tel: (630) 919-4800   Fax: (630) 773-9179   www.usfreightways.com

Provides shipping and transport support services.

USF Asia Group, Room 1013, 10/F Phase I, MTL Warehouse Bldg., Berth One, Container Port Road, Kwai Chung, Kowloon, Hong Kong PRC

Tel: 852-2735-8882

UUNET

22001 Loudoun County Pkwy., Ashburn, VA, 20147

Tel: (703) 206-5600   Fax: (703) 206-5601   www.uu.net

World's largest Internet service provider; World Wide Web hosting services, security products and consulting services to businesses, professionals, and on-line service providers.

UUNET Hong Kong, 18 Harbour Road, Suite 3601, Central Plaza, Wanchai, Hong Kong PRC

VALSPAR CORPORATION

1101 South Third Street, Minneapolis, MN, 55415-1259

Tel: (612) 332-7371   Fax: (612) 375-7723   www.valspar.com

Mfr. paints and coatings.

Valspar (H.K.) Corporation Ltd., Valspar Hai Hong Company, Limited, 2101-02, 21/F., Vicwood Plaza, 199 Des Voeux Road, Central, Hong Kong PRC

VARIAN MEDICAL SYSTEMS, INC.

3050 Hansen Way, Palo Alto, CA, 94304-100

Tel: (650) 493-4000   Fax: (650) 424-5358   www.varian.com

Mfr. microwave tubes and devices, analytical instruments, semiconductor process and medical equipment, vacuum systems.

Varian Medical Systems Pacific, Inc., Room 1018-20, Tower A, Mandarin Plaza, 14 Science Museum Rd., Tsimshatsui East Kowloon, Hong Kong PRC

VARIAN SEMICONDUCTOR EQUIPMENT ASSOCIATES, INC. (VSEA)

35 Dory Road, Gloucester, MA, 01930

Tel: (978) 281-2000   Fax: (978) 283-5391   www.vsea.com

Mfr. semiconductors and ion implantation systems.

Varian Semiconductor Equipment Assocates, Room 1018-20, Tower A, Mandarin Plaza, 14 Science Museum Road, Tsimshatsui East Kowloon, Hong Kong PRC

Tel: 852-2724-2836

VEECO INSTRUMENTS INC.

100 Sunnyside Blvd., Woodbury, NY, 11797

Tel: (516) 677-0200   Fax: (516) 677-9125   www.veeco.com

Mfr. surface profiler, atomic force microscopes, leak and plating thickness detectors and semiconductor products.

Veeco Hong Kong Support Center, Ste. 2207-9, Peregrine Tower, Lippo Ctr., Admiralty, Hong Kong PRC

Tel: 852-2530-8863   Fax: 852-2530-8123

VELCRO USA INC.

406 Brown Avenue, Manchester, NH, 03108

Tel: (603) 669-4892   Fax: (603) 669-9271   www.velcro.com

Mfr./sales of Velcro brand hook and loop fasteners, plastic buckles and metal hardware and cable control straps.

Velcro Hong Kong Ltd., Rm.1103A, Seaview Estate, Blk. B, 2-8 Watson Road, North Point, Hong Kong PRC

Tel: 852-2570-3698   Fax: 852-2807-0285

VERIFONE, INC.

4988 Great America Pkwy., Santa Clara, CA, 94054-1200

Tel: (408) 496-0444   Fax: (408) 919-5105   www.verifone.com

Mfr. electronic payment software and hardware.

VeriFone North Asia Limited, Suite 1208 Central Plaza, 18 Harbour Road, Wanchai, Hong Kong PRC

VERINT SYSTEMS INC.

234 Crossways Park Drive, Woodbury, NY, 11797

Tel: (516) 677-7300   Fax: (516) 677-7197   www.verintsystems.com

Mfr. and sales of analytic software.

Verint Systems Hong Kong, Central Plaza 17/F, 18 Harbour Road, Wanchai, Hong Kong PRC

Tel: 852-2863-7126

VERITAS SOFTWARE INC.

350 Ellis Street, Mountain View, CA, 94043

Tel: (650) 527-8000   Fax: (650) 527-8050   www.veritas.com

Mfr. of storage management software for data protection, application availability, and disaster recovery.

VERITAS Software, 19 Harbour Road, Ste. 1801, Wanchai, Hong Kong PRC

Tel: 852-2507-2233   Fax: 852-2598-7788

VF CORPORATION

628 Green Valley Road, Suite 500, Greensboro, NC, 27408

Tel: (336) 547-6000   Fax: (336) 547-7630   www.vfc.com

Mfr./marketing apparel including Lee and Wrangler jeans, Jansport backpacks and Healthtex.

VF Asia/Pacific Ltd., Flat B, Kader Bldg., 10/F, 22 Kai Cheung Rd., Kowloon Bay, Hong Kong PRC

VIASYS HEALTHCARE INC.

227 Washington Street, Ste. 200, Conshohocken, PA, 19428

Tel: (610) 862-0800   Fax: (610) 862-0836   www.viasyshealthcare.com

Mfr. medical instruments and devices.

Nicolet Far East Service Company, Ltd, Room 1601, Ritz Building, 625 Nathan Road, Kowloon, Hong Kong PRC

Contact: Benjamin, S.C. So

VIEWLOCITY, INC.

3475 Piedmont Road, Ste. 1700, Atlanta, GA, 30305

Tel: (404) 267-6400   Fax: (404) 267-6500   www.viewlocity.com

Mfr. supply chain management software.

Viewlocity, 2 Queen's Road, 16/F, Central, Hong Kong PRC

Tel: 852-2297-2214

THE VIKING CORPORATION

210 N. Industrial Park Rd., Hastings, MI, 49058

Tel: (616) 945-9501   Fax: (616) 945-9599   www.vikingcorp.com

Mfr. fire extinguishing equipment.

Viking Holding (HK) Limited, Room 905A, New Kowloon Plaza, 38 Tai Kok Tsui Road, Tai Kok Tsui Kowloon, Hong Kong PRC

Tel: 852-2391-1078

VISHAY SILICONIX INC.

2201 Laurelwood Drive, Santa Clara, CA, 95054

Tel: (408) 988-8000   Fax: (408) 970-3950   www.siliconix.com

Mfr. power IC's and analog signal processing devices for computers, cell phones, fixed communications networks, automobiles, and other electronic systems.

Vishay Siliconix Hong Kong Ltd., 5-6-7/F, Liven House, 61-63 King Yip St., Kowloon, Hong Kong PRC

VISHAY VITRAMON INC.

PO Box 544, Bridgeport, CT, 06601

Tel: (203) 268-6261   Fax: (203) 261-4446   www.vitramon.com

Ceramic capacitors.

Vishay Vitramon Hong Kong Ltd., The Gateway, Harbour City, Suite 3301, 33/F, Tower 1, Tsimshatsui, Kowloon, Hong Kong PRC

VIVITAR CORPORATION

1280 Rancho Conejo Blvd, Newbury Park, CA, 91320

Tel: (805) 498-7008   Fax: (805) 498-5086   www.vivitar.com

Mfr. photographic equipment, electronic supplies.

Vivitar (Asia) Limited, Units 1004-1005, Conic Investment Building, 13 Hok Yuen Street, Hunghom, Kowloon, Hong Kong PRC

Tel: 852-2363-6313

VSOURCE, INC.

16875 w. Bernardo Drive, Ste. 250, San Diego, CA, 92127

Tel: (858) 618-5884   Fax: (858) 618-5904   www.vsource.com

Engaged in outsourcing services.

Vsource, 5th Floor, AXA Center, 151 Gloucester Road, Wanchai, Hong Kong PRC

THE WACKENHUT CORPORATION

4200 Wackenhut Dr., Ste. 100, Palm Beach Gardens, FL, 33410

Tel: (561) 622-5656   Fax: (561) 691-6736   www.wackenhut.com

Security systems and services.

Wackenhut Security (HK) Ltd., 1404A, Argyle Centre 1, 688 Nathan Rd., Kowloon, Hong Kong PRC

Tel: 852-2390-3456   Fax: 852-2789-8311

WARNER ELECTRIC COMPANY

449 Gardner St., South Beloit, IL, 61080

Tel: (815) 389-3771   Fax: (815) 389-2582   www.warnernet.com

Global supplier of Power Transmission and Motion Control Solution Systems; automotive, industry brakes, and clutches.

Dana Asia c/o Shui Hing Mfg. Co. Ltd., Block B, Marvel Industrial Building, 4/F, 17 Kwai Fung Crescent, Hong Kong PRC

Tel: 852-2422-0057   Fax: 852-2480-4450

THE WASHINGTON POST COMPANY

1150 15th St. NW, Washington, DC, 20071

Tel: (202) 334-6000   Fax: (202) 334-4536   www.washpostco.com

Engaged in magazine publishing, cable and television broadcasting, educational services and the Internet.

International Herald Tribune, 1201, K. Wah Centre, 191 Java Road, North Point, Hong Kong PRC

Newsweek Inc., Suite 2007, Realty Bldg., 71 Des Voeux Rd., Hong Kong PRC

WASTE MANAGEMENT, INC.

1001 Fannin Street, Ste. 4000, Houston, TX, 77002

Tel: (713) 512-6200   Fax: (713) 512-6299   www.wastemanagement.com

Environmental services and disposal company; collection, processing, transfer and disposal facilities.

Pacific Waste Management Ltd., Room 4114-19, Sun Hung Kai Center, 30 Harbour Rd., Wanchai, Hong Kong PRC

TD WATERHOUSE GROUP, INC.

100 Wall Street, New York, NY, 10005

Tel: (212) 806-3500   Fax: (212) 361-6656   www.tdwaterhousegroup.com

Engaged in online brokerage.

TD Waterhouse Group, Inc., Suite 3413-3422, Two Pacific Place, 88 Queensway, Hong Kong PRC

Tel: 852-2801-1112

WATSON WYATT & COMPANY HOLDINGS

1717 H Street NW, Washington, DC, 20006-3807

Tel: (202) 715-7000   Fax: (202) 715-7700   www.watsonwyatt.com

Creates compensation and benefits programs for major corporations.

Watson Wyatt & Co., 27/F, Sun Hung Kai Center, 30 Harbour Rd., Hong Kong PRC

Tel: 852-2827-8833   Fax: 852-2827-8899   Contact: Karen Nip

WEATHERFORD INTERNATIONAL, INC.

515 Post Oak Blvd. Ste. 600, Houston, TX, 77027-3415

Tel: (713) 287-8400   Fax: (713) 963-9785   www.weatherford.com

Oilfield services, products and equipment; mfr. marine cranes for oil and gas industry.

Weatherford Intl., 2803 Admiralty Centre, Tower 1, 18 Harcourt Rd., Hong Kong PRC

WEBMETHODS, INC.

3930 Pender Drive, Fairfax, VA, 22030

Tel: (703) 460-2500   Fax: (703) 460-2599   www.webmethods.com

Mfr. automated business software.

WebMethods, 2/F, Shui On Center, 8 Harbour Road, Wanchai, Hong Kong PRC

WEIGHT WATCHERS INTERNATIONAL, INC.

175 Crossways Park Dr., Woodbury, NY, 11797

Tel: (516) 390-1400   Fax: (516) 390-1763   www.weightwatchers.com

Weight loss programs.

Weight Watchers Hong Kong, c/o Union Church, 22a Kennedy Road Mid-Levels, Hong Kong PRC

WELCH ALLYN INC.

4341 State Street Road, Skaneateles Falls, NY, 13153

Tel: (315) 685-4100   Fax: (315) 685-4091   www.welchallyn.com

Mfr. fiber optic products and medical diagnostic equipment.

Welch Allyn Hong Kong, #1 Kornhill Road, Off. 601, Quarry Bay, Hong Kong PRC

Tel: 852-2886-8980

WELLS FARGO & COMPANY

420 Montgomery Street, San Francisco, CA, 94163

Tel: (415) 396-0855   Fax: (415) 788-7404   www.wellsfargo.com

Mortgage and general banking and financial services.

Wells Fargo HSBC Trade Bank, Peninsula Office Tower, 9th Floor, 18 Middle Road, Tsimshatsui, Central, Hong Kong PRC

Tel: 852-2822-1111   Contact: David Eldon

WELLS LAMONT CORPORATION

6640 W. Touhy Avenue, Niles, IL, 60714

Tel: (847) 647-8200   Fax: (847) 647-6943   www.wellslamontindustry.com

Mfr. industrial protective work gloves and industrial rainwear.

Austins Marmon LTD · AML, 29th Floor, Nanyang Plaza, 57 Hung To Road, Kwun Tong, Kowloon, Hong Kong PRC

Tel: 852-2858-0388   Fax: 852-2858-5450

WESTERN DIGITAL CORPORATION

20511 Lake Forest Dr., Lake Forest, CA, 92630-7741

Tel: (949) 672-7000   Fax: (949) 672-5408   www.westerndigital.com

Mfr. hard disk drives, video graphics boards, VLSI.

Western Digital Hong Kong, 807-809, Tower 3, 33 Canton Rd., Tsim Shat Sui, Hong Kong PRC

WEYERHAEUSER COMPANY

33663 Weyerhaeuser Way South, Federal Way, WA, 98003

Tel: (253) 924-2345   Fax: (253) 924-2685   www.weyerhaeuser.com

Wood and wood fiber products.

Weyerhaeuser Far East Ltd., GPO Box 3818, Hong Kong PRC

WHIRLPOOL CORPORATION

2000 N. M-63, Benton Harbor, MI, 49022-2692

Tel: (616) 923-5000   Fax: (616) 923-5443   www.whirlpoolcorp.com

Mfr., market home appliances: Whirlpool, Roper, KitchenAid, Estate, and Inglis.

Whirlpool Asia Appliance Group, 16/F, Paliburg Plaza, 68 Yee Wo St., Causeway Bay, Hong Kong PRC

WHITE & CASE LLP

1155 Ave. of the Americas, New York, NY, 10036-2767

Tel: (212) 819-8200   Fax: (212) 354-8113   www.whitecase.com

Engaged in international law.

White & Case Solicitors, 9/F, Glouster Tower, The Landmark, 11 Pedder St., Hong Kong PRC

Tel: 852-2822-8700   Fax: 852-2845-9070   Contact: George K. Crozer

W. A. WHITNEY COMPANY

650 Race Street, PO Box 1206, Rockford, IL, 61105-1206

Tel: (815) 964-6771   Fax: (815) 964-3175   www.wawhitney.com

Mfr. thermal cutting (plasma and laser), punching, and punch/plasma equipment systems and tooling.

W.A. Whitney Esterline Technologies Ltd., 2502-3, Railway Plaza, 39 Chatham Rd. S., T.S.T., Kowloon, Hong Kong PRC

Tel: 852-2311-9339

WILBUR-ELLIS COMPANY

345 California St., 27th Fl., San Francisco, CA, 94120

Tel: (415) 772-4000   Fax: (415) 772-4011   www.wilburellis.com

Marketing, distribution, formulation of agricultural products and industrial specialty chemicals and raw materials.

Connell Bros. Co. Ltd., 601 Stanhope House, 738 King's Rd., North Point, Hong Kong PRC

WORLD COURIER INC.

45 Southfield Avenue, Ste. 3450, Stamford, CT, 06902-7210

Tel: (203) 975-9333   Fax: (203) 316-9455   www.worldcourier.com

International courier service.

World Courier Hong Kong, 404 Air Cargo Terminal Office Bldg., Kaitak Intl. Airport, Hong Kong PRC

WORLD MINERALS INC.

130 Castilian Drive, Santa Barbara, CA, 93117

Tel: (805) 562-0200   Fax: (805) 562-0298   www.worldminerals.com

Mfr. premium quality diatomite and perlite products.

World Minerals Hong Kong, Ste. 3715, Sun Hung Kai Ctr., 37/F, 30 Harbour Rd., Wanchai, Hong Kong PRC

WORLDCOM, INC.

500 Clinton Center Drive, Clinton, MS, 39060

Tel: (601) 360-8600   Fax: (601) 360-8616   www.wcom.com

*Telecommunications; serving local, long distance and Internet customers domestically and internationally. **Corporation under worldwide reorganization under Chapter 11 Bankruptcy; new data unavailable for this edition.*

WorldCom International, 10/F, Sino Faovour Centre, 1 Yip Street, Chai Wan, Hong Kong PRC

Tel: 852-2110-8899   Fax: 852-2505-0308   Contact: Fred Moss, Reg. Ops. Mgr.

WorldCom International, 24/F, Central Tower, 28 Queen's Road, Central, Hong Kong PRC

Tel: 852-2110-8800   Fax: 852-2521-6933   Contact: Magdala Hoi, Gen. Mgr.

WM WRIGLEY JR. COMPANY

410 N. Michigan Ave., Chicago, IL, 60611-4287

Tel: (312) 644-2121   Fax: (312) 644-0353   www.wrigley.com

Mfr. chewing gum.

The Wrigley Co. (HK) Ltd., 186-191 Connaught Rd. West, Hong Kong PRC

WYETH

5 Giralda Farms, Madison, NJ, 07940-0874

Tel: (973) 660-5000   Fax: (973) 660-7026   www.wyeth.com

Mfr. consumer healthcare products.

Fort Dodge Animal Health, Div. Wyeth, 8A On Kui Street, On Lok Tsuen, Fanling, N.T., Hong Kong PRC

Tel: 852-2682-0613

Whitehall International (H.K.), Room 1401-3, C.C. Wu Bldg., 302-308 Hennessy Road, Wanchai, Hong Kong PRC

Tel: 852-2573-5661   Fax: 852-2891-0962

WYETH PHARMACEUTICALS

555 E. Lancaster Ave., Wayne, PA, 19087-5109

Tel: (610) 971-5400   Fax: (610) 995-4668   www.wyeth.com

Mfr. antibiotics and pharmaceutical products.

Wyeth (Hong Kong) Ltd., 22/F., Oxford House, 979 King's Road, Taikoo Place, Island East, Hong Kong PRC

Tel: 852-2599-8888   Fax: 852-2599-8999

XEROX CORPORATION

800 Long Ridge Road, PO Box 1600, Stamford, CT, 06904

Tel: (203) 968-3000   Fax: (203) 968-4312   www.xerox.com

Mfr. document processing equipment, systems and supplies.

Xerox (China) Ltd.., 1308, Harcourt House 39, Glouster Rd., Manchai, Hong Kong PRC

Tel: 852-2861-5333

XILINX INC.

2100 Logic Drive, San Jose, CA, 95124-3400

Tel: (408) 559-7778   Fax: (408) 559-7114   www.xilinx.com

Programmable logic and related development systems software.

Xilinx Asia Pacific, Unit No. 4312, Tower 2, Metroplaza, Hing Fong Rd., Kwai Fong NT, Hong Kong PRC

Tel: 852-2424-5200

XIRCOM, INC.

2300 Corporate Center Drive, Thousand Oaks, CA, 91320

Tel: (805) 376-9300   Fax: (805) 376-9311   www.xircom.com

Mfr. PC card network adapters and modems.

Xircom Asia Limited, Central Building, 11/F, 1 Pedder Street, Central, Hong Kong PRC

Tel: 852-2841-7813

X-RITE, INC.

3100 44th Street SW, Grandville, MI, 49418

Tel: (616) 534-7663   Fax: (616) 534-9215   www.xrite.com

Mfr. precision measurement devices, systems and processes that enhance the measurement of color, light and shape.

X-Rite Asia Pacific Ltd., Room 808-10, Kornhill Metro Tower, 1 Kornhill Road, Quarry Bay, Hong Kong PRC

Tel: 852-2-568-6283   Fax: 852-2-885-8610

XTRA CORPORATION

200 Nyala Farms Rd., Westport, CT, 06880

Tel: (203) 221-1005   Fax: (203) 221-9024   www.xtracorp.com

Holding company: leasing.

XTRA International, Hong Kong PRC

XTRA International, Centre Point, 20/F, 185 Gloucester Rd., Wanchai, Hong Kong PRC

YAHOO! INC.

701 First Avenue, Sunnyvale, CA, 94089

Tel: (408) 439-3300   Fax: (408) 439-3301   www.yahoo-inc.com

Internet media company providing specialized content, free electronic mail and community offerings and commerce.

Yahoo! Inc., Hong Kong PRC

YORK INTERNATIONAL CORPORATION

631 South Richland Ave., York, PA, 17403

Tel: (717) 771-7890   Fax: (717) 771-6212   www.york.com

Mfr. heating, ventilating, air conditioning and refrigeration equipment.

York Air Conditioning & Refrig. Inc., Unit 5A, Sime Darby Ind. Centre, 420-424 Kwun Tong Rd., Kowloon, Hong Kong PRC

York International Corporation, Unit 1008, 10/F, Tower II, 123 Hoi Bun Road, Kwun Tong, Kowloon, Hong Kong PRC

Tel: 852-2331-9286   Fax: 852-2331-9840

YOUNG & RUBICAM INC.

285 Madison Ave., New York, NY, 10017

Tel: (212) 210-3000   Fax: (212) 370-3796   www.yr.com

Advertising, public relations, direct marketing and sales promotion, corporate and product ID management.

Dentsu Young & Rubicam Brand Communications, Suite 418, Mount Parker House, 1111 King's Rd., Hong Kong PRC

Tel: 852-2884-6668   Fax: 852-2885-3208

YSI INC.

1700-1725 Brannum Lane, Yellow Springs, OH, 45387

Tel: (937) 767-7241   Fax: (937) 767-9353   www.ysi.com

Mfr. analyzers, measure instruments and electrical components.

YSI Hong Kong, Flat B 16/F Regency Center, 39 Wong Chuk Hang Road, Aberdeen, Hong Kong PRC

ZEBRA TECHNOLOGIES CORPORATION

333 Corporate Woods Pkwy., Vernon Hills, IL, 60061-3109

Tel: (847) 634-6700   Fax: (847) 913-8766   www.zebracorporation.com

Mfr. bar code systems.

Zebra Technologies Hong Kong, Rm 2903, Admiralty Centre Tower 1, No.18 Harcourt Road, Hong Kong PRC

Tel: 852-2111-0210   Fax: 852-2235-9098

ZILOG, INC.

532 Race Street, San Jose, CA, 95126

Tel: (408) 558-8500   Fax: (408) 558-8300   www.zilog.com

Mfr. integrated circuits.

ZILOG Hong Kong, Miramar Tower, Until 608, 132 Nathan Road, Tsimshatsui, Kowloon, Hong Kong PRC

ZIMMER HOLDINGS, INC.

345 East Main St., Warsaw, IN, 46580

Tel: (574) 267-6131   Fax: (574) 372-4988   www.zimmer.com

Engaged in design and manufacture of orthopedic products.

Zimmer Hong Kong, 15/B, Will Strong Development Bldg., 57-59 Parkes Street, Jordan, Kowloon, Hong Kong PRC

Tel: 852-2992-0968   Fax: 852-2992-0982

ZORAN CORPORATION

3112 Scott Boulevard, Santa Clara, CA, 95054

Tel: (408) 919-4111   Fax: (408) 919-4122   www.zoran.com

Mfr. specialized integrated circuits and software.

Zoran Asia Pacific Limited, North Tower, Concordia Plaza, 7/F, No. 1 Science Museum Road, TST East Kowloon, Hong Kong PRC

Tel: 852-2620-5838

Hungary

3COM CORPORATION

5400 Bayfront Plaza, Santa Clara, CA, 95052-8145

Tel: (408) 326-5000   Fax: (408) 326-5001   www.3com.com

Engaged in the development and manufacture of computer networking products and systems.

3Com Magyarorszag, Lajos utca 48-66, H-1036 Budapest, Hungary

Tel: 36-1-250-83-41   Fax: 36-1-250-83-47

3M (MINNESOTA MINING & MFG.)

3M Center, St. Paul, MN, 55144-1000

Tel: (651) 733-1110   Fax: (651) 733-9973   www.mmm.com

Mfr. diversified products for industry, consumer, health care, imaging, communications, transport, safety, etc.

3M Hungaria Kft., Vaci ut 110, H-1133 Budapest, Hungary

Tel: 36-1-270-7777   Fax: 36-1-267-1803

ABBOTT LABORATORIES

100 Abbott Park Rd., Abbott Park, IL, 60064

Tel: (847) 937-6100   Fax: (847) 937-1511   www.abbott.com

Development, manufacture and sale of diversified health care products and services.

Abbott Laboratories Ltd., Varosligeti Fasor 47-49, H-1071 Budapest, Hungary

ACCENTURE LTD.

1345 Avenue of the Americas, New York, NY, 10105

Tel: (917) 452-4400   Fax: (917) 527-9915   www.accenture.com

Provides management and technology consulting services.

Accenture, East-West Business Ctr., Rákóczi ú 1-3, H-1088 Budapest, Hungary

Tel: 36-1-327-3700   Fax: 36-1-266-7709

THE AES CORPORATION

1001 North 19th Street, Arlington, VA, 22209

Tel: (703) 522-1315   Fax: (703) 528-4510   www.aesc.com

Gas and electric utility.

AES Borsodi Energetika Kft., Budapest, Hungary

AIG AMERICAN INTERNATIONAL GROUP INC.

70 Pine Street, New York, NY, 10270

Tel: (212) 770-7000   Fax: (212) 509-9705   www.aig.com

Worldwide insurance and financial services.

AIG Central Europe, Infopark Research Centre, Neumann János u. 1, H-1117 Budapest, Hungary

Tel: 36-1-382-5100 Fax: 36-1-382-5101

AIG Hungary, Szigelvari Utca 7, H-1083 Budapest, Hungary

ALCOA INC.

Alcoa Center, 201 Isabella Street at 7th Street Bridge, Pittsburgh, PA, 15212-5858

Tel: (412) 553-4545   Fax: (412) 553-4498   www.alcoa.com

World's leading producer of aluminum and alumina; mining, refining, smelting, fabricating and recycling.

AFL/Michels GmbH, Enying, Hungary

AFL/Stribel GmbH, Mor, Hungary

Alcoa-Köföém KFT, Székesfehérvöár, Hungary

CSI Hungary Mfg. and Trading, L.L.C., Székesfehérvöár, Hungary

AMERICAN APPRAISAL ASSOCIATES INC.

411 E. Wisconsin Ave., Ste. 1900, Milwaukee, WI, 53202

Tel: (414) 271-7240   Fax: (414) 271-1041   www.american-appraisal.com

Valuation consulting services.

American Appraisal Hungary Co. Ltd., Bécsi út 120., H-1034 Budapest, Hungary

Tel: 36-1-388-9903   Contact: Ferenc Tordai

AMERICAN EXPRESS COMPANY

90 Hudson Street, Jersey City, NJ, 07302

Tel: (212) 640-2000   Fax: (212) 619-9802   www.americanexpress.com

Engaged in travel, travelers cheques, charge card and financial services.

American Express Hungary Ltd., Deák Ferenc u. 10, H-1052 Budapest, Hungary

Tel: 36-1-235-4300

AMWAY CORPORATION

7575 Fulton Street East, Ada, MI, 49355-0001

Tel: (616) 787-6000   Fax: (616) 787-6177   www.amway.com

Mfr./sale home care, personal care, nutrition and houseware products.

Amway Hungaria Marketing Kft., Kalvaria ter 7, H-1089 Budapest, Hungary

ANDERSEN

33 West Monroe Street, Chicago, IL, 60603

Tel: (312) 580-0033   Fax: (312) 507-6748   www.andersen.com

*Accounting and audit, tax and management consulting services. **Firm under worldwide reorganization; new data unavailable for this edition.*

Andersen Worldwide, Váci út 35, H-1134 Budapest, Hungary

Tel: 36-1-451-7100

ANIXTER INTERNATIONAL INC..

4711 Golf Road, Skokie, IL, 60076

Tel: (847) 677-2600   Fax: (847) 677-8557   www.anixter.com

Distributor wiring systems/products for voice, video, data and power applications.

Anixter Hungary, Terra Park D8, H-2040 Budaors, Hungary

AON CORPORATION

200 East Randolph, Chicago, IL, 60601

Tel: (312) 381-1000   Fax: (312) 381-6032   www.aon.com

Insurance brokers worldwide; underwrites accident and health insurance, specialty and professional insurance; and provides risk management consultation.

AON Hungary Ltd., Pest Ctr., H-1071 Budapest, Hungary

Tel: 36-1-351-7644   Fax: 36-1-351-7649   Contact: George Csik

APOGENT TECHNOLOGIES INC.

48 Congress Street, Portsmouth, NH, 03801

Tel: (603) 433-6131   Fax: (603) 431-0860   www.apogent.com

Design, mfr. & sell products for laboratories, clinical research, industrial markets & analytical products.

Erie Scientific Hungary Kft., Koerberki u. 36, 1502 Budapest Pf. 56, H-1112 Budapest, Hungary

APPLERA CORPORATION

301 Merritt 7, Norwalk, CT, 06851

Tel: (203) 840-2000   Fax: (203) 840-2312   www.applera.com

Leading supplier of systems for life science research and related applications.

Analytical Instruments, Szegedi ut 35-37, H-1135 Budapest, Hungary

ARBOR ACRES FARM INC.

439 Marlborough Road, Glastonbury, CT, 06033

Tel: (860) 633-4681   Fax: (860) 633-2433   www.aaf.com

Producers of male and female broiler breeders, commercial egg layers.

Babolna Breeding Farms, 2943 Babolna, H-PF25 Budapest, Hungary

Contact: Robert Jakus

ARENT FOX KINTNER PLOTKIN & KAHN, PLC

1050 Connecticut Ave., N.W., Washington, DC, 20036-5339

Tel: (202) 857-6000   Fax: (202) 857-6395   www.arentfox.com

International law firm.

Arent Fox Kintner Plotkin & Kahn, PLLC, Nagymezo Ut 44, H-1065 Budapest, Hungary

ARROW ELECTRONICS INC.

25 Hub Drive, Melville, NY, 11747

Tel: (516) 391-1300   Fax: (516) 391-1640   www.arrow.com

Distributor of electronic components and computer products.

Spoerle Electronic Budapest, Vaci ut 45, H-1134 Budapest, Hungary

AT&T BROADBAND, LLC

188 Inverness Dr. West, Englewood, CO, 80112

Tel: (303) 875-5500   Fax: (303) 875-4984   www.broadband.att.com

Provides broadband technology services; digital TV, digital telephone and high-speed cable internet services.

Westel 450/900, Budapest, Hungary

AUTODESK INC.

111 McInnis Parkway, San Rafael, CA, 94903

Tel: (415) 507-5000   Fax: (415) 507-6112   www.autodesk.com

Develop/marketing/support computer-aided design, engineering, scientific and multimedia software products.

Autodesk Ltd., Arpad Ctr., Arboc u.6., H-1134 Budapest, Hungary
Tel: 36-1-359-9882   Fax: 36-1-359-9884

AUTOMATIC SWITCH CO. (ASCO)

50-60 Hanover Rd., Florham Park, NJ, 07932

Tel: (973) 966-2000   Fax: (973) 966-2628   www.asco.com

Mfr. solenoid valves, emergency power controls, pressure and temperature switches.

ASCO Magnesszelep Kft., Mikovinyi S. U. 2-4, H-1037 Budapest, Hungary
Tel: 36-1-387-4811   Fax: 36-1-250-2383   Contact: L. Malmos

AVERY DENNISON CORPORATION

150 N. Orange Grove Blvd., Pasadena, CA, 91103

Tel: (626) 304-2000   Fax: (626) 792-7312   www.averydennison.com

Mfr. pressure-sensitive adhesives and materials, office products, labels, tags, retail systems, Carter's Ink and specialty chemicals.

Dennison/WW Office Products, Mogyorodi ut 32, H-1149 Budapest, Hungary
Tel: 36-1-252-7864   Fax: 36-1-383-2394

AVNET INC.

2211 South 47th Street, Phoenix, AZ, 85034

Tel: (480) 643-2000   Fax: (480) 643-4670   www.avnet.com

Distributor electronic components, computers and peripherals.

Avnet Elektronika KFT, Taboz u. 6, H-1037 Budapest, Hungary
Tel: 36-1436-7210   Fax: 36-1250-7647

AVON PRODUCTS, INC.

1345 Avenue of the Americas, New York, NY, 10105-0196

Tel: (212) 282-5000   Fax: (212) 282-6049   www.avon.com

Mfr. direct seller of cosmetics and beauty-related items.

Avon Cosmetics Hungary KFT, Kosma u.4, H-1108 Budapest, Hungary
Tel: 36-1-262-5555   Fax: 36-1-262-3374   Contact: Erika Nagy

AZON CORPORATION

2204 Ravine Road, Kalamazoo, MI, 49004-3506

Tel: (616) 385-5942   Fax: (616) 385-5937   www.azonintl.com

Designs and manufactures special multi-component chemical metering, mixing and dispensing machines.

Azon Hungary Ltd., Azon Repro Centre, Belgrad rpk 1315, H1056 Budapest, Hungary

BAKER & McKENZIE

130 East Randolph Drive, Ste. 2500, Chicago, IL, 60601

Tel: (312) 861-8000   Fax: (312) 861-2899   www.bakerinfo.com

International legal services.

Baker & McKenzie, Andrassy-ut 125, H-1062 Budapest, Hungary

Tel: 36-1- 251-5777   Fax: 36-1- 342-0513

BATES WORLDWIDE INC.

498 Seventh Avenue, New York, NY, 10018

Tel: (212) 297-7000   Fax: (212) 986-0270   www.batesww.com

Advertising, marketing, public relations and media consulting.

Bates Saatchi & Saatchi Advertising, Alvinci ut 16, H-1022 Budapest, Hungary

Tel: 36-1-212-4039   Fax: 36-1-212-5506   Contact: Neil Hardwick, Dir.

BAXTER INTERNATIONAL INC.

One Baxter Parkway, Deerfield, IL, 60015

Tel: (847) 948-2000   Fax: (847) 948-3948   www.baxter.com

Mfr. products and provide services in the field of the administration of medication and bioscience.

Baxter Kft., Dozsa Gy. u.44, H-1076 Budapest, Hungary

BBDO WORLDWIDE

1285 Ave. of the Americas, New York, NY, 10019

Tel: (212) 459-5000   Fax: (212) 459-6645   www.bbdo.com

Multinational group of advertising agencies.

BBDO Budapest, Bajza u. 40, H-1062 Budapest, Hungary

Tel: 36-1-462-2400

BDO SEIDMAN, LLP   BELGIUM

130 East Randolph Street, Chicago, IL, 60601

Tel: (312) 856-9100   Fax: (312) 856-1379   www.bdo.com

International accounting and financial consulting firm.

BDO Kontroll KFT, Belgrád rkp 13-15, H-1056 Budapest, Hungary

Tel: 36-1-266-6445   Fax: 36-1-266-6438   Contact: Zaltán Gerendy

BECKMAN COULTER, INC.

4300 N. Harbor Boulevard, Fullerton, CA, 92834

Tel: (714) 871-4848   Fax: (714) 773-8898   www.beckmancoulter.com

Develop/mfr./marketing automated systems and supplies for biological analysis.

Diagon Kft. (Diagnostics), 1325 Ujpest 1. Pf. 41, Baross u. 52, H-1047 Budapest, Hungary

BELDEN, INC.

7701 Forsyth Blvd., Ste. 800, St. Louis, MO, 63015

Tel: (314) 854-8000   Fax: (314) 854-8001   www.belden.com

Mfr. electronic wire and cable products.

Belden Dunákabel, Hengermalom Straße 43, H-1116 Budapest, Hungary

LOUIS BERGER INTERNATIONAL INC.

100 Halsted Street, East Orange, NJ, 07019

Tel: (201) 678-1960   Fax: (201) 672-4284   www.louisberger.com

Consulting engineers, engaged in architecture, environmental and advisory services.

Louis Berger SA, Batthyany u. 46 II./4, H-1015 Budapest, Hungary

Tel: 36-1-214-1281   Fax: 36-1-214-1281

BEST WESTERN INTERNATIONAL

6201 North 24th Place, Phoenix, AZ, 85106

Tel: (602) 957-4200   Fax: (602) 957-5740   www.bestwestern.com

International hotel chain.

Grand Hotel Hungaria, Budapest, Hungary

BMC INDUSTRIES INC.

One Meridian Crossings, Ste. 850, Minneapolis, MN, 55423

Tel: (612) 851-6000   Fax: (612) 851-6065   www.bmcind.com

Design/mfr./marketing precision etched products, electroformed components, special printed circuits, ophthalmic devices.

BMC Hungary, Tauaszmezo U-6, H-2800 Tatabanya, Hungary

Tel: 36-34-512-242   Fax: 36-34-512-267   Contact: John Springer   Emp: 250

BORLAND SOFTWARE CORPORATION

100 Enterprise Way, Scotts Valley, CA, 95066

Tel: (831) 431-1000   Fax: (831) 431-4141   www.borland.com

Mfr. development software.

Borland Hungary, Hungaria krt. 79-81, H-1143 Budapest, Hungary

Tel: 36-1-252-8145   Fax: 36-1-252-8773   Contact: Jozsef Hizo

THE BOSTON CONSULTING GROUP

Exchange Place, 31st Fl., Boston, MA, 02109

Tel: (617) 973-1200   Fax: (617) 973-1339   www.bcg.com

Management consulting company.

The Boston Consulting Group, Madach Trade Center, Madach Imre Ut. 13-14, H-1075 Budapest, Hungary

Tel: 36-1-328-5020

BOZELL GROUP

40 West 23rd Street, New York, NY, 10010

Tel: (212) 727-5000   Fax: (212) 645-9173   www.bozell.com

Advertising, marketing, public relations and media consulting.

Bozell Hungary, Kft, Dereglye u. 5/B, H-1036 Budapest, Hungary

Tel: 36-1-367-3747   Fax: 36-1-387-7696   Contact: Martin Hoffman, Mng. Dir.

BRANSON ULTRASONICS CORPORATION

41 Eagle Road, Danbury, CT, 06813-1961

Tel: (203) 796-0400   Fax: (203) 796-2285   www.branson-plasticsjoin.com

Engaged in design, development, manufacture and marketing of plastics joining, precision cleaning and processing equipment.

Wittmann, Div. Branson Ultrasonics, u. 32 Eperjesl, H-2509 Esziergom-Kertvaros, Hungary

BRISTOL-MYERS SQUIBB COMPANY

345 Park Ave., New York, NY, 10154-0037

Tel: (212) 546-4000   Fax: (212) 546-4020   www.bms.com

Pharmaceutical and food preparations, medical and surgical instruments.

ConvaTec KFT Budapest, Kis Buda Ctr. Irodahaz, Frankel Leo U 30-34, H-1023 Budapest, Hungary

Pharmavit, Div. Bristol-Myers Squibb, Levai utca 5, H-2112 Veresegyhaz, Hungary

LEO BURNETT, DIV. B-COM 3 GROUP

35 West Wacker Drive, Chicago, IL, 60601

Tel: (312) 220-5959   Fax: (312) 220-6533   www.leoburnett.com

Engaged in advertising, marketing, media buying and planning, and public relations.

Leo Burnett Budapest, Ltd., Budapest, Hungary

BURSON-MARSTELLER

230 Park Avenue South, New York, NY, 10003-1566

Tel: (212) 614-4000   Fax: (212) 614-4262   www.bm.com

Public relations/public affairs consultants.

Golden Burson-Marsteller, Lajos u. 46-66, Fifth Fl., H-1036 Budapest, Hungary

Tel: 36-1-250-8560   Fax: 36-1-250-8535

CADENCE DESIGN SYSTEMS, INC.

2655 Seely Ave., Bldg. 5, San Jose, CA, 95134

Tel: (408) 943-1234   Fax: (408) 943-0513   www.cadence.com

Mfr. electronic design automation software.

Cadence Design Systems, Kalman Imre U 1, H-1054 Budapest 1054, Hungary

Tel: 36-1-475-1332

CANBERRA INDUSTRIES, INC.

800 Research Parkway, Meriden, CT, 06450

Tel: (203) 238-2351   Fax: (203) 235-1347   www.canberra.com

Mfr. instruments for nuclear research.

Canberra-Packard Kft., Filler u. 6, H-1024 Budapest, Hungary

Tel: 36-1-3450550

CARGILL, INC.

15407 McGinty Road West, Minnetonka, MN, 55440-5625

Tel: (612) 742-7575   Fax: (612) 742-7393   www.cargill.com

Food products, feeds, animal products.

Cargill Kft., Vaci ut 37, Budapest, Hungary

Tel: 36-1-236-1417   Contact: Dean Warras

CATERPILLAR INC.

100 NE Adams Street, Peoria, IL, 61629-6105

Tel: (309) 675-1000   Fax: (309) 675-1182   www.cat.com

Mfr. earth/material-handling and construction machinery and equipment and engines.

Caterpillar Hungary Ltd., Isaszegi út, H-2100 Gödöllö, Hungary

Tel: 36-28-432-186

CB RICHARD ELLIS SERVICES

200 N. Sepulveda Blvd., Ste. 300, El Segundo, CA, 90245-4380

Tel: (310) 563-8600   Fax: (310) 563-8670   www.cbrichardellis.com

Commercial real estate services.

CB Richard Ellis Kft, Lajos utca 48-66, H-1036 Budapest, Hungary

CHARLES RIVER LABORATORIES INTERNATIONAL, INC.

251 Ballardvale Street, Wilmington, MA, 01887-1000

Tel: (978) 658-6000   Fax: (978) 658-7132   www.criver.com

Engaged in sales of pathogen-free, fertilized chicken eggs for drug testing.

Charles River, Istvan u. 11.1/2, H-1078 Budapest, Hungary

CHECKPOINT SYSTEMS, INC.

101 Wolf Drive, Thorofare, NJ, 08086

Tel: (856) 848-1800   Fax: (856) 848-0937   www.checkpointsystems.com

Mfr. test, measurement and closed-circuit television systems.

Checkpoint Systems Hungary Kft., Dembinzky ul., H-1115 Budapest, Hungary

Tel: 36-1-3050-100   Fax: 36-1-3050-101   Contact: Gabor Kekesi, Gen. Mgr.

CHESTERTON BLUMENAUER BINSWANGER

Two Logan Square, 4th Floor, Philadelphia, PA, 19103-2759

Tel: (215) 448-6000   Fax: (215) 448-6238   www.cbbi.com

Real estate and related services.

Binswanger Hungary, Vigado ter 3., H-1051 Budapest, Hungary

Chesterdon International plc., Utca 52, H-1082 Budapest Futo, Hungary

A.W. CHESTERTON COMPANY

225 Fallon Road, Stoneham, MA, 02180

Tel: (781) 438-7000   Fax: (781) 438-8971   www.chesterton.com

Mfr. of industrial fluid sealing, hydraulic, pneumatic and maintenance products.

Chesterton Hungary Kft., Gödölloi ut 115, H-2146 Mogyorod, Hungary

CISCO SYSTEMS, INC.
170 West Tasman Drive, San Jose, CA, 95134-1706
Tel: (408) 526-4000   Fax: (408) 526-4100   www.cisco.com
Develop/mfr./market computer hardware and software networking systems.

Cisco Systems Hungary, Cisco Systems Magyarorszag KFT., Vaci utca 81, H-1056 Budapest, Hungary
Tel: 36-1-235-1100   Fax: 36-1-235-1111

CITIGROUP, INC.
399 Park Avenue, New York, NY, 10022
Tel: (212) 559-1000   Fax: (212) 559-3646   www.citigroup.com
Provides insurance and financial services worldwide.

Citigroup, Citibank Tower, Bank Ctr., Szabadsag ter 7, H-1052 Budapest, Hungary
Contact: Richard D. Jackson

CNA FINANCIAL CORPORATION
CNA Plaza, Chicago, IL, 60685
Tel: (312) 822-5000   Fax: (312) 822-6419   www.cna.com
Commercial property/casualty insurance policies.

CNA Hungary, Budapest, Hungary

THE COCA-COLA COMPANY
1 Coca Cola Plaza, Atlanta, GA, 30313
Tel: (404) 676-2121   Fax: (404) 676-6792   www.coca-cola.com
Mfr./marketing/distributor soft drinks, syrups and concentrates, juice and juice-drink products.

Coca-Cola Hungary Services KFT, Némedi út 104, H-2330 Dunaharaszti, Hungary
Tel: 36 24 500-100

THE COLEMAN COMPANY, INC.
3600 N. Hydraulic, Wichita, KS, 67219
Tel: (316) 832-2700   Fax: (316) 832-2794   www.colemanoutdoors.com
Mfr. distributor and sales of camping and outdoor recreation products.

Camping Gaz Hungaria, Dugonics UTCA 11, H-1043 Budapest, Hungary

COLGATE-PALMOLIVE COMPANY
300 Park Ave., New York, NY, 10022
Tel: (212) 310-2000   Fax: (212) 310-2919   www.colgate.com
Mfr. pharmaceuticals, cosmetics, toiletries and detergents.

Colgate-Palmolive, Daróci út 82., H-1113 Budapest, Hungary

COLLIERS INTERNATIONAL PROPERTY CONSULTANTS INC.
84 State Street, 3rd Fl., Boston, MA, 02109
Tel: (617) 722-0221   Fax: (617) 722-0224   www.colliers.com
Engaged in commercial real estate.

Colliers International, Mammut II, 5/F, Margit Korut 87-89, H-0124 Budapest, Hungary
Tel: 36-1-336-4200   Fax: 36-1-336-4201

COUDERT BROTHERS LLP
1114 Ave. of the Americas, New York, NY, 10036-7794
Tel: (212) 626-4400   Fax: (212) 626-4120   www.coudert.com
Engaged in international law.

Coudert Brothers Associated Office,, Nagy É Trócsányi Ügyrédi Iroda, Pálya u. 9, H-1012 Budapest, Hungary
Tel: 36-1-212-0444   Fax: 36-1-212-0443

CUSHMAN & WAKEFIELD INC.
51 West 52nd Street, New York, NY, 10019
Tel: (212) 841-7500   Fax: (212) 841-7867   www.cushwake.com
Engaged in commercial real estate services.

Cushman & Wakefield, Rakoczi ut 42, H-1072 Budapest, Hungary
Tel: 36-1-268-1288

D&B (DUN & BRADSTREET CORPORATION))

1 Diamond Hill Road, Murray Hill, NJ, 07974

Tel: (908) 665-5000   Fax: (908) 665-5524   www.dnb.com

Provides corporate credit, marketing and accounts-receivable management services and publishes financial information.

D&B Hungaria Kft., Varmegye u.3-5, H-1052 Budapest, Hungary

Tel: 36-1-267-4190

DANZAS AEI, INC.

120 Tokeneke Road, PO Box 1231, Darien, CT, 06820

Tel: (203) 655-7900   Fax: (203) 655-5779   www.aeilogistics.com

International air freight forwarder.

Danzas AEI, c/o Cargoplan Ferihegy Terminal 1 LR1,, Air Cargo Terminal 1, LR1 Air Cargo Terminal, H-1675 Budapest, Hungary

Tel: 36-1-296-6756   Fax: 36-1-296-8621

D'ARCY MASIUS BENTON & BOWLES INC. (DMB&B)

1675 Broadway, New York, NY, 10019

Tel: (212) 468-3622   Fax: (212) 468-2987   www.darcyww.com

Full service international advertising and communications group.

DMB&B Europe, Iranyl Utca 1, 11em 3, H-1056 Budapest, Hungary

DDB WORLDWIDE COMMUNICATIONS GROUP

437 Madison Ave., New York, NY, 10022

Tel: (212) 415-2000   Fax: (212) 415-3417   www.ddbn.com

Advertising agency.

DDB/Hungary, Budapest, Hungary

DEBEVOISE & PLIMPTON

919 Third Avenue, New York, NY, 10022

Tel: (212) 909-6000   Fax: (212) 909-6836   www.debevoise.com

Engaged in international law.

Debevoise & Plimpton, Revay, Köz 2 III/I, H-1065 Budapest, Hungary

Tel: 36-1-312-8067   Fax: 36-1-332-7995   Contact: Eva Tamasi, Office Mgr.   Emp: 4

DELCO REMY INTERNATIONAL, INC.

2902 Enterprise Drive, Anderson, IN, 46013

Tel: (765) 778-6499   Fax: (765) 778-6404   www.delcoremy.com

Mfr. electrical components for heavy-duty vehicles.

Delco Remy Hungary Kft., Bajnok u. 13., H-1063 Budapest, Hungary

Tel: 36-1-302-3390

DELOITTE TOUCHE TOHMATSU INTERNATIONAL

1633 Broadway, New York, NY, 10019

Tel: (212) 492-4000   Fax: (212) 392-4154   www.deloitte.com

Accounting, audit, tax and management consulting services.

Deloitte & Touche, Varmegye u. 3-5, H-1052 Budapest, Hungary

DEWEY BALLANTINE LLP

1301 Avenue of the Americas, New York, NY, 10019

Tel: (212) 259-8000   Fax: (212) 259-6333   www.deweyballantine.com

International law firm.

Dewey Ballantine LLP, Andrassy ut 60, H-1062 Budapest, Hungary

Tel: 36-1-374-2660   Fax: 36-1-374-2661

DHL WORLDWIDE EXPRESS

50 California Avenue, San Francisco, CA, 94111

Tel: (415) 677-6100   Fax: (415) 824-9700   www.dhl.com

Worldwide air express carrier.

DHL Worldwide Express, Rakoczi Ut 1-3, H-1088 Budapest, Hungary

Tel: 36-1-266-7777

DIAGNOSTIC PRODUCTS CORPORATION

5700 West 96th Street, Los Angeles, CA, 90045

Tel: (310) 645-8200   Fax: (310) 645-9999   www.dpcweb.com

Mfr. diagnostic products.

Diatron Ltd., Pomázi út 15, H-1037 Budapest, Hungary

Tel: 36-1-436-0640   Fax: 36-1-436-0649

DIEBOLD INC.

5995 Mayfair Road, North Canton, OH, 44720-8077

Tel: (330) 490-4000   Fax: (330) 490-3794   www.diebold.com

Mfr. automated banking systems; security services for banking industrial and related fields.

Deibold Hungary, Budaorsi ut 46, H-1112 Budapest, Hungary

DIONEX CORPORATION

1228 Titan Way, PO Box 3603, Sunnyvale, CA, 94086-3603

Tel: (408) 737-0700   Fax: (408) 730-9403   www.dionex.com

Develop/mfr./market chromatography systems and related products.

CP-Analitika Kft., Zsolnay Vilmos u. 6, Telepes u. 113-115 a/1., H-1147 Budapest, Hungary

EASTMAN CHEMICAL COMPANY

100 North Eastman Road, Kingsport, TN, 37662-5075

Tel: (423) 229-2000   Fax: (423) 229-1351   www.eastman.com

Mfr. plastics, chemicals, fibers.

Eastman Chemical B.V., Buda Busines Ctr., Off. 601, Kapas u. 11-15/601, H-1027 Budapest, Hungary

Tel: 36-1-202-4615   Fax: 36-1-202-4642   Contact: Laszlo Siroki

EASTMAN KODAK COMPANY

343 State Street, Rochester, NY, 14650

Tel: (716) 724-4000   Fax: (716) 724-1089   www.kodak.com

Develop/mfr. photo and chemicals products, information management/video/copier systems, fibers/plastics for various industry.

Kodak Kft. Hungary, Tartsay Vilmos u. 14 3.em, H-1126 Budapest XII, Hungary

ECOLAB INC.

370 N. Wabasha Street, St. Paul, MN, 55102

Tel: (651) 293-2233   Fax: (651) 293-2379   www.ecolab.com

Develop/mfr. premium cleaning, sanitizing and maintenance products and services for the hospitality, institutional, and residential markets.

Ecolab Ltd., Bucharest, Hungary

Tel: 36-1-372-5555

ECOLOGY AND ENVIRONMENT INC.

368 Pleasant View Drive, Lancaster, NY, 14086-1397

Tel: (716) 684-8060   Fax: (716) 684-0844   www.ecolen.com

Environmental, scientific and engineering consulting.

E&E Budapest Environmental Ltd., Toboz u. 19, H-1037 Budapest, Hungary

J.D. EDWARDS & COMPANY

One Technology Way, Denver, CO, 80237

Tel: (303) 334-4000   Fax: (303) 334-4970   www.jdedwards.com

Computer software products.

Synergon Informatika Rt., Vaci ut 168/A, H-1138 Budapest, Hungary

Tel: 36-1-270-5120   Fax: 36-1-270-5132

EGL INC. (EAGLE GLOBAL LOGISTICS)

15350 Vickery Drive, Houston, TX, 77032

Tel: (281) 618-3100   Fax: (281) 618-3223   www.eagleusa.com

Ocean/air freight forwarding, customs brokerage, packing and wholesale, logistics management and insurance.

EGL Eagle Global Logistics, Ferihegyi Airport Term 1, H-1185 Budapest, Hungary

Tel: 36-1-157-8086 Fax: 36-1-157-7487

EL PASO ENERGY PARTNERS, LP

1001 Louisiana Street, Houston, TX, 77252-2511

Tel: (713) 420-2131   Fax: (713) 420-4266   www.epenergy.com

Energy and gas.

El Paso Energy Hungary, Dunaujvaros, Hungary

ELECTRONIC DATA SYSTEMS, INC. (EDS)

5400 Legacy Dr., Plano, TX, 75024

Tel: (972) 604-6000   Fax: (972) 605-2643   www.eds.com

Engaged in systems integration, network and systems operations and management consulting.

EDS Hungary, Egressy u. 20, H-1149 Budapest, Hungary

Tel: 36-1-460-1100 Fax: 36-1-251-2762

EMERSON PROCESS MANAGEMENT

8301Cameron Road, Austin, TX, 78754

Tel: (512) 834-7689   Fax: (512) 832-3232   www.frco.com

Mfr. industrial process control equipment.

Emerson Process Management, Erzsébet királyné útja 1/c, H-1146 Budapest, Hungary

EMERY FORWARDING

One Lagoon Drive, Ste. 400, Redwood City, CA, 94065

Tel: (650) 596-9600   Fax: (650) 596-7901   www.emeryworld.com

Freight transport, global logistics and air cargo.

Emery Forwarding, Terminal 1, LRI Cargo Bldg., 1st Fl., H-1675 Budapest-Ferihegy Airport, Hungary

ENRON CORPORATION

1400 Smith Street, Houston, TX, 77002-7369

Tel: (713) 853-6161   Fax: (713) 853-3129   www.enron.com

Exploration, production, transportation and distribution of integrated natural gas and electricity. **Corporation under worldwide reorganization; new data unavailable for this edition.

Energovill, Raday Ut 42-44, H-1092 Budapest, Hungary

Tel: 36-1-456-4300

ERICO PRODUCTS INC.

34600 Solon Road, Cleveland, OH, 44139

Tel: (440) 248-0100   Fax: (440) 248-0723   www.erico.com

Mfr. electric welding apparatus and hardware, metal stampings, specialty fasteners.

Erico Products, Ceglédi út 1-3, H-1107 Budapest, Hungary

Tel: 36-1-4313-464

ERNST & YOUNG INTERNATIONAL

5 Times Square, New York, NY, 10036

Tel: (212) 773-3000   Fax: (212) 773-6350   www.eyi.com

Engaged in assurance and advisory business services, tax, law and corporate finance.

Ernst & Young, Váci út 20, H-1132 Budapest, Hungary

Ernst & Young International, Hermina ut 17, H-1146 Budapest, Hungary

Tel: 36-1-252-8333 Fax: 36-1-251-8778   Contact: Csaba Repassy

EURO RSCG WORLDWIDE

350 Hudson Street, New York, NY, 10014

Tel: (212) 886-2000 Fax: (212) 886-2016 www.eurorscg.com

International advertising agency group.

EURO RSCG Budapest, Daru utca 2/b, H-1023 Budapest, Hungary

EXXON MOBIL CORPORATION

5959 Las Colinas Blvd., Irving, TX, 75039-2298

Tel: (972) 444-1000 Fax: (972) 444-1882 www.exxonmobil.com

Petroleum exploration, production, refining; mfr. petroleum and chemicals products; coal and minerals.

Exxon Mobil, Inc., Budapest, Hungary

FRITZ COMPANIES, INC., DIV. UPS

706 Mission Street, Ste. 900, San Francisco, CA, 94103

Tel: (415) 904-8360 Fax: (415) 904-8661 www.fritz.com

Integrated transportation, sourcing, distribution and customs brokerage services.

Fritz Companies Inc., Budapest, Hungary

GENERAL ELECTRIC CAPITAL CORPORATION

260 Long Ridge Road, Stamford, CT, 06927

Tel: (203) 357-4000 Fax: (203) 357-6489 www.gecapital.com

Financial, property, casualty insurance, computer sales and trailer leasing services.

ERC Group, Div. GE Capital, Visegrádi utca 47, HU-1132 Budapest, Hungary

GENERAL ELECTRIC COMPANY

3135 Easton Turnpike, Fairfield, CT, 06431

Tel: (203) 373-2211 Fax: (203) 373-3131 www.ge.com

Diversified manufacturing, technology and services.

GE Hungary, Ipari és Kereskedelmi Rt., Váci út 77, Budapest, Hungary, H-1340
Tel: 36-1-399-1100

GENERAL MOTORS ACCEPTANCE CORPORATION

3044 W. Grand Blvd., Detroit, MI, 48202

Tel: (313) 556-5000 Fax: (313) 556-5108 www.gmac.com

Automobile financing.

GMAC Hungary Financial Services Ltd., Marvany utca 17, H-1012 Budapest, Hungary

GENERAL MOTORS CORPORATION

300 Renaissance Center, Detroit, MI, 48285

Tel: (313) 556-5000 Fax: (313) 556-5108 www.gm.com

Mfr. full line vehicles, automotive electronics, commercial technologies, telecommunications, space, finance.

AC Bakony, Verszprem, Hungary

GENICOM CORPORATION

4500 Daly Drive, Ste. 100, Chantilly, VA, 20151

Tel: (703) 633-8700 Fax: (703) 222-7629 www.genicom.com

Supplier of network systems, service and printer solutions.

Printer Service KFT, Palotai Ut. 62, H-8000 Szekesfehervar, Hungary

THE GILLETTE COMPANY

Prudential Tower Building, Boston, MA, 02199

Tel: (617) 421-7000 Fax: (617) 421-7123 www.gillette.com

Develop/mfr. personal care/use products: blades and razors, toiletries, cosmetics, stationery.

Gillette Hungary, c/o Braun B.T, Frankel Leo U 30-34, H-1023 Budapest, Hungary

GILSON INC.

3000 W. Beltline Hwy, PO Box 620027, Middleton, WI, 53562-0027

Tel: (608) 836-1551 Fax: (608) 831-4451 www.gilson.com

Mfr. analytical/biomedical instruments.

Allegro Ltd., Szent Laszlo U. 95, H-1135 Budapest, Hungary

GRANT THORNTON INTERNATIONAL

800 One Prudential Plaza, 130 E. Randolph Drive, Chicago, IL, 60601-6050

Tel: (312) 856-0001   Fax: (312) 616-7052   www.grantthornton.com

Accounting, audit, tax and management consulting services.

Grant Thornton Consulting Kft., Vamhaz krt 13, H-1093 Budapest, Hungary

Tel: 36-1-455-2000   Contact: Dr. Dipl. Oec. Anna Kuti

GREY GLOBAL GROUP

777 Third Ave., New York, NY, 10017

Tel: (212) 546-2000   Fax: (212) 546-1495   www.grey.com

International advertising agency.

Grey Budapest, Belgrad rkp 26 II em, BP 1395, Pf. 431, H-1056 Budapest, Hungary

GUARDIAN INDUSTRIES CORPORATION

2300 Harmon Road, Auburn Hills, MI, 48326-1714

Tel: (248) 340-1800   Fax: (248) 340-9988   www.guardian.com

Mfr. and fabricate flat glass products and insulation materials.

Hunguard Float Glass Co., Csorvasi U .31, Oroshaza, Hungary

Tel: 36-68-411366

HARRIS CORPORATION

1025 West NASA Blvd., Melbourne, FL, 32919

Tel: (407) 727-9100   Fax: (407) 727-9344   www.harris.com

Mfr. communications and information-handling equipment, including copying and fax systems.

Avnet EMG, Setron Electronika Kft., Toboz u.6., H-1037 Budapest, Hungary

Tel: 36-1-250-4618   Fax: 36-1-250-7646

H.J. HEINZ COMPANY

600 Grant Street, Pittsburgh, PA, 15219

Tel: (412) 456-5700   Fax: (412) 456-6128   www.heinz.com

Processed food products and nutritional services.

Magyar Foods Ltd., Kecskemet, Hungary

HEWITT ASSOCIATES LLC

100 Half Day Road, Lincolnshire, IL, 60069

Tel: (847) 295-5000   Fax: (847) 295-7634   www.hewitt.com

Employee benefits consulting firm.

Hewitt Associates, Bajcsy-Zsilinszky út 57., H-1065 Budapest, Hungary

Tel: 36-1-475-6020

HEWLETT-PACKARD COMPANY

3000 Hanover Street, Palo Alto, CA, 94304-1185

Tel: (650) 857-1501   Fax: (650) 857-5518   www.hp.com

Mfr. computing, communications and measurement products and services.

Hewlett-Packard Magyarorszag Kft., Erzebet kiralyne utja 1/c, 11th/12th fl., H-1146 Budapest, Hungary

HILTON HOTELS CORPORATION

9336 Civic Center Drive, Beverly Hills, CA, 90210

Tel: (310) 278-4321   Fax: (310) 205-7880   www.hiltonhotels.com

International hotel chain: Hilton International, Vista Hotels and Hilton National Hotels.

Hilton International Hotels, Hess András tèr 1-3, H-1014 Budapest, Hungary

Tel: 36-1-488-6600

HOGAN & HARTSON LLP

555 13th Street NW, Washington, DC, 20004-1109

Tel: (202) 637-5600   Fax: (202) 637-5910   www.hhlaw.com

Engaged in international law.

Hogan & Hartson, Granite Tower 9/F, Budapest V. Szabadsag ter 7-9, H-1054 Budapest, Hungary

Tel: 36-1-302-9050   Contact: Kornelia nagy-Koppany

HONEYWELL INTERNATIONAL INC.

Honeywell Plaza, Minneapolis, MN, 55408

Tel: (612) 951-1000   Fax: (612) 951-8537   www.honeywell.com

Develop/mfr. controls for home and building, industry, space and aviation, burglar and fire alarm systems.

Honeywell Kft., Gogol u. 13, H-1133 Budapest, Hungary

Tel: 36-1-451-4300   Fax: 36-1-451-4343

HORWATH INTERNATIONAL ASSOCIATION

420 Lexington Avenue, Suite 526, New York, NY, 10170-0526

Tel: (212) 808-2000   Fax: (212) 808-2020   www.horwath.com

Public accountants and auditors.

Horwath Consulting Hungary, Paulay Ede u.13, H-1061 Budapest, Hungary

SALDO Penzugyi Szervezoe ee, Tanaacsado Vaallalat Bartok Beela Ut120-122, Budapest, Hungary

HYATT CORPORATION

200 West Madison Street, Chicago, IL, 60606

Tel: (312) 750-1234   Fax: (312) 750-8578   www.hyatt.com

International hotel management.

Atrium Hyatt Budapest Hotel, Roosevelt Tér 2, H-1051 Budapest, Hungary

Tel: 36-1-266-1234   Fax: 36-1-266-9101

HYPERCOM CORPORATION

2851 West Kathleen Road, Phoenix, AZ, 85053

Tel: (602) 504-5000   Fax: (602) 504-4578   www.hypercom.com

Mfr. point-of-sale systems.

Hypercom Hungary, Hajogyari Sziget 131, H-1033 Budapest, Hungary

Tel: 36-1-437-9044   Fax: 36-1-437-9045   Contact: Jeno Hato

IBM CORPORATION

1133 Westchester Avenue, White Plains, NY, 10604

Tel: (914) 765-1900   Fax: (914) 765-7382   www.ibm.com

Information products, technology and services.

IBM Hungary Ltd., Menesi ut. 22, H-1118 Budapest, Hungary

Tel: 36-1-372-1111   Fax: 36-1-372-1199

ICC INDUSTRIES INC.

460 Park Ave., New York, NY, 10022

Tel: (212) 521-1700   Fax: (212) 521-1794   www.iccchem.com

Manufacturing and trading of chemicals, plastics and pharmaceuticals.

ICC Chemol Kft., Vaci Ut. 19, H-1134 Budapest, Hungary

Tel: 36-1-238-9200   Fax: 36-1-238-9210

ICN PHARMACEUTICALS, INC.

3300 Hyland Ave., Costa Mesa, CA, 92626

Tel: (714) 545-0100   Fax: (714) 641-7268   www.icnpharm.com

Mfr. and distribution of pharmaceuticals.

ICN Pharmaceuticals, Inc., Czararka u. 82-84, H-1025 Budapest II District, Hungary

Tel: 36-1-345-5900

IMI NORGREN GROUP

5400 South Delaware Street, Littleton, CO, 80120-1663

Tel: (303) 794-2611   Fax: (303) 795-9487   www.usa.norgren.com

Mfr. pneumatic filters, regulators, lubricators, valves, automation systems, dryers, push-in fittings.

IMI Norgren Kft, Bathory utca 130, H-1196 Budapest, Hungary

Tel: 36-1-2811-182   Fax: 36-1-2823-788

INFONET SERVICES CORPORATION

2160 East Grand Ave., El Segundo, CA, 90245-1022

Tel: (310) 335-2600   Fax: (310) 335-4507   www.infonet.com

Provider of Internet services and electronic messaging services.

Infonet Hungary, Naphegy ter.8, H-1016 Budapest, Hungary

Tel: 36-1-1202-6246   Fax: 36-1-375-8064

INTER-CONTINENTAL HOTELS

3 Ravinia Drive, Suite 2900, Atlanta, GA, 30346-2149

Tel: (770) 604-2000   Fax: (770) 604-5403   www.interconti.com

Worldwide hotel and resort accommodations.

Hotel Inter-Continental Budapest, Budapest V, Apaczal Csere J.U. 12-14, H-1368 Budapest, Hungary

Tel: 36-1-32-6333   Fax: 36-1-327-6357

INTERGRAPH CORPORATION

One Madison Industrial Park, Huntsville, AL, 35894-0001

Tel: (256) 730-2000   Fax: (256) 730-7898   www.intergraph.com

Develop/mfr. interactive computer graphic systems.

Intergraph Hungary Ltd., Istenhegyi Ut. 40/A, H-1126 Budapest, Hungary

Tel: 36-1-214-2007   Fax: 36-1-214-9588

INTERNATIONAL FLAVORS & FRAGRANCES INC.

521 West 57th Street, New York, NY, 10019-2960

Tel: (212) 765-5500   Fax: (212) 708-7132   www.iff.com

Design/mfr. flavors, fragrances and aroma chemicals.

International Flavors & Fragrances, Amerikai Ut. 11, H-1145 Budapest, Hungary

Tel: 36-1-363-7491   Fax: 36-1-252-5090

INTERNATIONAL MANAGEMENT GROUP (IMG)

1360 East Ninth Street, Ste. 100, Cleveland, OH, 44114

Tel: (216) 522-1200   Fax: (216) 522-1145   www.imgworld.com

Manages athletes, sports academies and real estate facilities worldwide.

IMG Hungary, Andrassy ut. 97, H-1062 Budapest, Hungary

Tel: 36-1-352-2406   Fax: 36-1-352-2410

INTERNATIONAL SPECIALTY PRODUCTS, INC.

1361 Alps Rd., Wayne, NJ, 07470

Tel: (973) 389-3083   Fax: (973) 628-4117   www.ispcorp.com

Mfr. specialty chemical products.

ISP Hungaria, Kenese u.8. 11, H-1113 Budapest XI, Hungary

Tel: 36-1-385-8288   Fax: 36-1-466-2550

J. WALTER THOMPSON COMPANY

466 Lexington Ave., New York, NY, 10017

Tel: (212) 210-7000   Fax: (212) 210-6944   www.jwt.com

International advertising and marketing services.

Partners/J. Walter Thompson Co., Budapest, Hungary

JABIL CIRCUIT, INC.

10560 Ninth St. North, St. Petersburg, FL, 33716

Tel: (727) 557-9749   Fax: (727) 579-8529   www.jabil.com

Mfr. printed circuit boards, electronic components and systems.

Jabil Circuit Hungary, Huszar Andor ut 1, Tiszaujvarosi Ipari Park, H-3580 Tiszaujvaros Budapest, Hungary

Tel: 36-49-54-8500

JOHNSON & JOHNSON

One Johnson & Johnson Plaza, New Brunswick, NJ, 08933

Tel: (732) 524-0400   Fax: (732) 214-0334   www.jnj.com

Mfr./distributor/R&D pharmaceutical, health care and cosmetic products.

Johnson & Johnson Kft., Hun u.2., H-1135 Budapest, Hungary

SC JOHNSON

1525 Howe St., Racine, WI, 53403

Tel: (262) 260-2000   Fax: (262) 260-2133   www.scjohnsonwax.com

Home, auto, commercial and personal care products and specialty chemicals.

SC Johnson, Apor Vilmos tér 6, H-1124 Budapest, Hungary

Tel: 36-1-224-8400

JOHNSON CONTROLS INC.

5757 N. Green Bay Ave., PO Box 591, Milwaukee, WI, 53201-0591

Tel: (414) 228-1200   Fax: (414) 228-2077   www.johnsoncontrols.com

Mfr. facility management and control systems and auto seating.

Johnson Controls International Kft., Fertö u I/D, H-1107 Budapest, Hungary

Tel: 36-1-263-3033   Fax: 36-30-263-1317   Contact: Istvan Dombovari, Branch Mgr.

JONES LANG LASALLE

153 East 53rd Street, New York, NY, 10022

Tel: (212) 812-5700   Fax: (212) 421-3544   www.am.joneslanglasalle.com

International marketing consultants, leasing agents and property management advisors.

Jones Lang Wootton, Budapest, Hungary

A.T. KEARNEY INC.

5400 Legacy Dr., Plano, TX, 75201

Tel: (972) 604-4600   Fax: (972) 543-7680   www.atkearney.com

Management consultants and executive search.

A. T. Kearney, Honvéd u. 20/a, H-1055 Budapest, Hungary

Tel: 36-1-301-2300

KENNAMETAL INC.

1600 Technology Way, PO Box 231, Latrobe, PA, 15650

Tel: (724) 539-5000   Fax: (724) 539-4710   www.kennametal.com

Tools, hard carbide and tungsten alloys for metalworking industry.

Hardt Gepforgalmazo Bt., Serhaz U. 3, H-4027 Debrecen, Hungary

Tel: 36-52-431060   Fax: 36-52-431060

KIMBERLY-CLARK CORPORATION

351 Phelps Drive, Irving, TX, 75038

Tel: (972) 281-1200   Fax: (972) 281-1435   www.kimberly-clark.com

Mfr./sales/distribution of consumer tissue, household and personal care products.

Kimberly-Clark Corp., Budapest, Hungary

KORN/FERRY INTERNATIONAL

1800 Century Park East, Los Angeles, CA, 90067

Tel: (310) 843-4100   Fax: (310) 553-6452   www.kornferry.com

Engaged in executive search and management consulting.

Korn/Ferry International, Chazar Andras U.9, H-1146 Budapest, Hungary

Tel: 36-1-352-0027   Fax: 36-1-352-0026

KPMG CONSULTING INC.

1676 International Dr., McLean, VA, 22102

Tel: (703) 747-3000   Fax: (703) 747-8500   www.kpmg.com

Accounting and audit, tax and management consulting services.

KPMG Hungária KFT, XIII Váci út 99, H-1139 Budapest, Hungary

Tel: 36-1-270-7100   Fax: 36-1-270-7101   Contact: Michael Kevehazi, Sr. Ptnr.

KV PHARMACEUTICAL COMPANY

2503 South Hanley Road, St. Louis, MO, 63144

Tel: (314) 645-6600   Fax: (314) 567-1096   www.kvpharma.com

Mfr. branded and generic drugs.

Gedeon Richter Ltd., X. Gyomri Út 19-21, PO Box 27, H-1457 Budapest 10, Hungary

Tel: 36-1-431-4000   Fax: 36-1-260-6650

LANCER CORPORATION

6655 Lancer Blvd., San Antonio, TX, 78219

Tel: (210) 310-7000   Fax: (210) 310-7252   www.lancercorp.com

Mfr. beverage dispensing equipment.

Lancer Hungary, Isaszegi út 67, H-2100 Gödöllő, Hungary

Tel: 36-28-417-179   Fax: 36-28416-881

LEVI STRAUSS & COMPANY

1155 Battery St., San Francisco, CA, 94111-1230

Tel: (415) 544-6000   Fax: (415) 501-3939   www.levistrauss.com

Mfr. and distributor of casual wearing apparel, including jeans and sportswear.

Levi Strauss Trading Kft., Rakoczi Str. 42, Emke Bldg., H-1072 Budapest, Hungary

Tel: 36-1-327-7600   Fax: 36-1-267-9937

ELI LILLY & COMPANY

Lilly Corporate Center, Indianapolis, IN, 46285

Tel: (317) 276-2000   Fax: (317) 277-6579   www.lilly.com

Mfr. pharmaceuticals and animal health products.

Lilly Hungaria KFT, Madach I.U 13-14, 7th Fl., H-1075 Budapest, Hungary

Tel: 36-1-328-5100   Fax: 36-1-328-5101

LOCKHEED MARTIN CORPORATION

6801 Rockledge Drive, Bethesda, MD, 20817

Tel: (301) 897-6000   Fax: (301) 897-6652   www.imco.com

Design/mfr./management systems in fields of space, defense, energy, electronics and technical services.

Aeroplex of Central Europe, Ltd., PO Box 186, H-1675 Budapest, Hungary

Aeroplex of Central Europe, Ltd., Ferihegy International Airport, Technical Base Gate oDo, Bldg. A, 3rd Fl., H-1185 Budapest, Hungary

Tel: 36-1-157-7007   Fax: 36-1-167-6787

LUCENT TECHNOLOGIES, INC.

600 Mountain Ave., Murray Hill, NJ, 07974-0636

Tel: (908) 582-3000   Fax: (908) 582-2576   www.lucent.com

Design/mfr. wide range of public and private networks, communication systems and software, data networking systems, business telephone systems and microelectronics components.

Lucent Technologies Hungary Ltd., Vaci ut 168, H-1138 Budapest, Hungary

Tel: 36-1-270-9500

M/A-COM INC.

1011 Pawtucket Boulevard, Lowell, MA, 01853-3295

Tel: (978) 442-5000   Fax: (978) 442-5354   www.macom.com

Mfr. radio frequency (RF) and microwave integrated circuits and IP Networks to the wireless telecommunications and defense-related industries.

Tavkozlest Innovations Co., Ungvar U-6466, H-1142 Budapest, Hungary

MAGNETEK

10900 Wilshire Blvd., Suite 850, Los Angeles, CA, 90024

Tel: (310) 208-1980   Fax: (310) 208-6133   www.magnetek.com

Mfr. fractional horsepower electric motors.

MagneTek Power, Pomaz, Hungary

MANPOWER INTERNATIONAL INC.

5301 N. Ironwood Rd., PO Box 2053, Milwaukee, WI, 53201-2053

Tel: (414) 961-1000   Fax: (414) 961-7081   www.manpower.com

Temporary help, contract service, training and testing.

Manpower, Hungaria KFT, H-1146 Budapest, Hungary

Tel: 36-1-252-1578   Fax: 36-1-251-7014

MARRIOTT INTERNATIONAL INC.

10400 Fernwood Rd., Bethesda, MD, 20817

Tel: (301) 380-3000   Fax: (301) 380-5181   www.marriott.com

Hotel services.

Budapest Marriott Hotel, Budapest, Hungary

MARSH & McLENNAN COS INC.

1166 Ave. of the Americas, New York, NY, 10036-2774

Tel: (212) 345-5000   Fax: (212) 345-4808   www.marshmac.com

Insurance agents/brokers, pension and investment management consulting services.

J&H Marsh & McLennan Budapest Kft., Vaci ut. 110, H-1133 Budapest, Hungary

Tel: 36-1-465-4200   Fax: 36-1-465-4280   Contact: Jozef Klinger

McCANN-ERICKSON WORLDGROUP

750 Third Ave., New York, NY, 10017

Tel: (212) 697-6000   Fax: (212) 984-3575   www.mccann.com

International advertising and marketing services.

McCann-Erickson Budapest, Benczúr u. 29., H-1086 Budapest, Hungary

Tel: 36-1-462-4100

McDONALD'S CORPORATION

McDonald's Plaza, Oak Brook, IL, 60523

Tel: (630) 623-3000   Fax: (630) 623-7409   www.mcdonalds.com

Fast food chain stores.

McDonald's Corp., Budapest, Hungary

McKINSEY & COMPANY

55 East 52nd Street, New York, NY, 10022

Tel: (212) 446-7000   Fax: (212) 446-8575   www.mckinsey.com

Management and business consulting services.

McKinsey & Company, Alexander Court, Nagysandor Jozsef u.6., H-1054 Budapest, Hungary

Tel: 36-1-248-2000   Fax: 36-1-248-2001

MECHANICAL DYNAMICS, INC.

2300 Traverwood Drive, Ann Arbor, MI, 48105

Tel: (734) 994-3800   Fax: (734) 994-6418   www.adams.com

Mfr. Adams prototyping software for functional virtual prototyping solutions.

Tarok Mernokiroda BT, Karinthy F ut. 44 IX. e., H-1111 Budapest, Hungary

Tel: 36-1-165-4377   Fax: 36-1-165-4495

MICRO AGE, INC.

1330 West Southern Avenue, Tempe, AZ, 85282-1896

Tel: (480) 366-2000   Fax: (480) 966-7339   www.microage.com

Computer systems integrator, software products and telecommunications equipment.

MicroAge, Inc., Budapest, Hungary

MICROSOFT CORPORATION

One Microsoft Way, Redmond, WA, 98052-6399

Tel: (425) 882-8080   Fax: (425) 936-7329   www.microsoft.com

Computer software, peripherals and services.

Microsoft Hungary Kft, Madach Imre 13-14, H-1075 Budapest, Hungary

Tel: 36-1-268-1668   Fax: 36-1-268-1558

MILLIPORE CORPORATION

80 Ashby Road, PO Box 9125, Bedford, MA, 01730

Tel: (781) 533-6000   Fax: (781) 533-3110   www.millipore.com

Mfr. flow and pressure measurement and control components; precision filters, hi-performance liquid chromatography instruments.

Millipore Kft., Ménesi út 23/a, H-1118 Budapest, Hungary

MODINE MANUFACTURING COMPANY

1500 DeKoven Ave., Racine, WI, 53403

Tel: (262) 636-1200   Fax: (262) 636-1424   www.modine.com

Mfr. heat-transfer products.

Modine Manufacturing Co., Mezőkövesd, Hungary

MONSANTO

800 N. Lindbergh Boulevard, St. Louis, MO, 63167

Tel: (314) 694-1000   Fax: (314) 694-7625   www.monsanto.com

Life sciences company focusing on agriculture, nutrition, pharmaceuticals, health and wellness and sustainable development.

Monsanto Kereskedilmi Kft, Verhalm Utca 12-16, H-1023 Budapest, Hungary

Tel: 36-1-345-0671   Fax: 36-1-345-0679

MOTOROLA, INC.

1303 East Algonquin Road, Schaumburg, IL, 60196

Tel: (847) 576-5000   Fax: (847) 538-5191   www.motorola.com

Mfr. communications equipment, semiconductors and cellular phones.

Motorola Hungary, Lajos UT. 48-66, Bii Fl., H-1036 Budapest, Hungary

Tel: 36-1-250-8329   Fax: 36-1-250-8328

NATIONAL STARCH AND CHEMICAL COMPANY

10 Finderne Ave., Bridgewater, NJ, 08807-3300

Tel: (908) 685-5000   Fax: (908) 685-5005   www.nationalstarch.com

Mfr. adhesives and sealants, resins and specialty chemicals, electronic materials and adhesives, food products, industry starch.

National Starch & Chemical Ltd., Batthyany Utca. 28-11-8, H-1195 Budapest, Hungary

Tel: 36-1-282-2226   Fax: 36-1-281-2954

AC NIELSEN COMPANY

177 Broad Street, Stamford, CT, 06901

Tel: (203) 961-3000   Fax: (203) 961-3190   www.acnielsen.com

Engaged in market and consumer research.

ACNielsen, Nyat Utca 32, 4/F, H-1075 Budapest, Hungary

NORDSON CORPORATION

28601 Clemens Road, Westlake, OH, 44145-4551

Tel: (440) 892-1580   Fax: (440) 892-9507   www.nordson.com

Mfr. industry application equipment, sealants and packaging machinery.

Spett GmbH, Postyen u.13, H-1141 Budapest, Hungary

Tel: 36-1-222-1951

NOVELL WORLDWIDE

1800 S. Novell Place, Provo, UT, 84606

Tel: (801) 861-7000   Fax: (801) 861-5555   www.novell.com

Develop/mfr. networking software and related equipment.

Novell Hungary, East West Business Centre, Rákóczi ut 1-3, H-1088 Budapest, Hungary

NYPRO INC.

101 Union Street, Clinton, MA, 01510

Tel: (978) 365-9721   Fax: (978) 368-0236   www.nypro.com

Mfr. plastic parts for telecommunications industry.

Nypro Hungary, Basco Bela ut 41, H-2890 Tata, Hungary

OFFICE DEPOT, INC.

2200 Old Germantown Road, Delray Beach, FL, 33445

Tel: (561) 278-4800   Fax: (561) 265-4406   www.officedepot.com

Discount office product retailer with warehouse-style superstores.

Elso Iroda Superstore Kft., Polus Center, Szentmihalyi UT.131, H-1152 Budapest, Hungary

Tel: 36-1-419-4151   Fax: 36-1-461-419-4220   Contact: Istvan Miholec, Gen. Mgr.

OHAUS CORPORATION

PO Bpx 2033,19a Chapin Road, Pine Brook, NJ, 07058

Tel: (973) 377-9000   Fax: (973) 593-0359   www.ohaus.com

Mfr. balances and scales for laboratories, industry and education.

Ohaus, Hatarhalom u 4, H-1173 Budapest, Hungary

OTIS ELEVATOR COMPANY

One Farm Springs Road, Farmington, CT, 06032

Tel: (860) 676-6000   Fax: (860) 676-5111   www.otis.com

Mfr. elevators and escalators.

Otis Felvono Kft., Hustzi ut 34, H-1033 Budapest, Hungary

OWENS-ILLINOIS, INC.

One SeaGate, PO Box 1035, Toledo, OH, 43666

Tel: (419) 247-5000   Fax: (419) 247-2839   www.o-i.com

Mfr. glass containers and packaging products.

Continental PET Technologies, Inc., Gyor, Hungary

Oroshaza Glass Manufacturing and Trading, Kft., Oroshaza, Hungary

PAREXEL INTERNATIONAL CORPORATION

195 West Street, Waltham, MA, 02154

Tel: (781) 487-9900   Fax: (781) 487-0525   www.parexel.com

Provides contract medical, biotechnology, and pharmaceutical research and consulting services.

PAREXEL International, Pest Ctr., Peterdy Utca 15, H-1071 Budapest, Hungary

Tel: 36-1-351-7659

PFIZER INC.

235 East 42nd Street, New York, NY, 10017-5755

Tel: (212) 573-2323   Fax: (212) 573-7851   www.pfizer.com

Research-based, global health care company.

Pfizer Biogal LLC, Budapest, Hungary

PHARMACIA CORPORATION

100 Route 206 North, Peapack, NJ, 07977

Tel: (908) 901-8000   Fax: (908) 901-8379   www.pharmacia.com

Mfr. pharmaceuticals, agricultural products, industry chemicals.

Pharmacia & Upjohn Kft, Istenhegyi ut 18, H-1126 Budapest, Hungary

Tel: 36-1-488-0960   Fax: 36-1-214-1755

PHELPS DODGE CORPORATION

2600 North Central Ave., Phoenix, AZ, 85004-3089

Tel: (602) 234-8100   Fax: (602) 234-8337   www.phelpsdodge.com

Copper, minerals, metals and special engineered products for transportation and electrical markets.

Columbian Chemicals Co., Budapest, Hungary

Columbian Tiszai Carbon, Tiszaujvaros, Hungary

PIC GROUP

2929 Seventh Avenue, Ste. 130, Berkeley, CA, 94710

Tel: (510) 848-8266   Fax: (510) 848-0324   www.pic.com

Engaged in biotechnology.

PIC Hungary, Foldvary ul. 4, H-1097 Budapest, Hungary

PIONEER HI-BRED INTERNATIONAL INC.

400 Locust Street, Ste. 800, Des Moines, IA, 50309

Tel: (515) 248-4800   Fax: (515) 248-4999   www.pioneer.com

Agricultural chemicals, farm supplies, biological products, research.

Pioneer Hi-Bred, Magyarország Rt. Távíró köz 4, H-2040 Budaörs Budapest, Hungary

PIONEER-STANDARD ELECTRONICS, INC.

6065 Parkland Blvd., Cleveland, OH, 44124

Tel: (440) 720-8500   Fax: (440) 720-8501   www.pios.com

Mfr. and distribution of electronic parts for computers and networking equipment.

Eurodis Microdis Electronics Kft., Vaci ut 19, H-1134 Budapest, Hungary

POGO PRODUCING COMPANY

5 Greenway Plaza, Houston, TX, 77252

Tel: (713) 297-5000   Fax: (713) 297-5100   www.pogoproducing.com

Engaged in oil and gas exploration.

Pogo Producing Company, ul. Kalman Imre, H-1054 Budapest, Hungary

Tel: 36-1-475-1390

POLYONE CORPORATION

200 Public Square, Cleveland, OH, 44114-2304

Tel: (216) 589-4000   Fax: (216) 589-4077   www.polyone.com

Mfr. custom made compounded plastics, including polymer, elastomer, colorant and additive products.

PolyOne Magyarország Kft., Budapest, Hungary

PRICEWATERHOUSECOOPERS LLP

1301 Ave. of the Americas, New York, NY, 10019

Tel: (212) 596-7000   Fax: (212) 259-1301   www.pwcglobal.com

Accounting and auditing, tax and management, and human resource consulting services.

PriceWaterhouseCoopers, Rumbach Center, Rumbach Sebestyen utca 21, H-1075 Budapest, Hungary

Tel: 36-1-269-6910   Fax: 36-1-269-6936

PROCTER & GAMBLE COMPANY

One Procter & Gamble Plaza, Cincinnati, OH, 45202

Tel: (513) 983-1100   Fax: (513) 562-4500   www.pg.com

Personal care, food, laundry, cleaning and industry products.

Procter & Gamble KTT, Pf.243, H-1391 Budapest 62, Hungary

Tel: 36-1-451-1100   Fax: 36-1-451-1391

PSI NET (PERFORMANCE SYSTEMS INTERNATIONAL INC.)

44983 Knoll Square, Ashburn, VA, 20147

Tel: (703) 726-4100   Fax: (703) 726-4200   www.psinet.com

Internet service provider.

PSINet Hungary, Elender Informatikai, Rt. Bp. 1134 Vaci ut 37, Budapest, Hungary

QWEST COMMUNICATIONS INTERNATIONAL INC.

1801 California Street, Ste. 5200, Denver, CO, 80202

Tel: (303) 896-2020   Fax: (303) 793-6654   www.uswest.com

Tele-communications provider; integrated communications services.

Kablekom, Budapest, Hungary

Tel: 36-1-165-2466   Fax: 36-1-181-2377

RADISSON HOTELS INTERNATIONAL

Carlson Pkwy., PO Box 59159, Minneapolis, MN, 55459-8204

Tel: (612) 540-5526   Fax: (612) 449-3400   www.radisson.com

Operates, manages and franchises full-service hotels and resorts worldwide.

Radisson Beke Hotel, Terez Korut 43, H-1067 Budapest, Hungary

Radisson SAS Beke Hotel, Terez Korut 43, H-1067 Budapest, Hungary

Tel: 36-1-30-11600   Fax: 36-1-30-11615

RAY & BERNDTSON, INC.

301 Commerce, Ste. 2300, Fort Worth, TX, 76102

Tel: (817) 334-0500   Fax: (817) 334-0779   www.prb.com

Executive search, management audit and management consulting firm.

Ray & Berndtson, Rakoczi ut 42, H-1072 Budapest, Hungary

Tel: 36-1-327-4598   Fax: 36-1-267-9100   Contact: Joachim Zyla, Mng. Ptnr.

C. H. ROBINSON WORLDWIDE, INC. (CHR)

8100 Mitchell Road, Eden Prairie, MN, 55344

Tel: (612) 937-8500   Fax: (612) 937-6714   www.chrobinson.com

Global door-to-door freight forwarding services, including flexible transportation solutions and global logistics.

C.H. Robinson Hungary, Budafoki ut 60, H-1117 Budapest, Hungary

RUDDICK CORPORATION

301 S. Tryon St., Ste. 1800, Charlotte, NC, 28202

Tel: (704) 372-5404   Fax: (704) 372-6409   www.amefird.com

Mfr. industrial sewing thread for worldwide industrial and consumer markets.

Ruddick Corp Budapest Ltd., Jozsef Krt 29, II EM 20, H-1206 Budapest, Hungary

SARA LEE CORPORATION

3 First National Plaza, Chicago, IL, 60602-4260

Tel: (312) 726-2600   Fax: (312) 558-4995   www.saralee.com

Mfr./distributor food and consumer packaged goods, intimate apparel and knitwear.

Compack Douwe Egberts Rt., Landler Jeno u. 23-25, H-1078 Budapest, Hungary

SAS INSTITUTE INC.

SAS Campus Drive, Cary, NC, 27513

Tel: (919) 677-8000   Fax: (919) 677-4444   www.sas.com

Mfr. and distribution of decision support software.

SAS Institute (Hungary) Ltd., Határor út 36, H-1122 Budapest, Hungary

Tel: 36-1-202-6247   Fax: 36-1-202-5847

SCANSOFT, INC.

9 Centennial Dr., Peabody, MA, 01960

Tel: (978) 977-2000   Fax: (978) 977-2436   www.scansoft.com

Mfr. digital imaging software for speech and language solutions.

ScanSoft Hungary Corp., Budapest, Hungary

Tel: 36-1-452-3700   Contact: Akos Reszler

SCHLUMBERGER LIMITED

153 East 53rd St., 57th Fl., New York, NY, 10022-4624

Tel: (212) 350-9400   Fax: (212) 350-9457   www.slb.com

Engaged in oil and gas services, metering and payment systems, and produces semiconductor testing equipment and smart cards.

Schlumberger Measurements, Rezsõ u. 5-7, H-1089 Budapest, Hungary

SHEARMAN & STERLING

599 Lexington Ave., New York, NY, 10022-6069

Tel: (212) 848-4000   Fax: (212) 848-7179   www.shearman.com

Law firm engaged in general American and international financial and commercial practice.

Shearman & Sterling, Szerb Utca 17-19, H-1056 Budapest, Hungary

SIEGMUND AND ASSOCIATES, INC.

49 Pavilion Avenue, Providence, RI, 02905

Tel: (401) 785-2600   Fax: (401) 785-3110   www.siegmundgroup.com

Engaged in civil engineering services, including design of infrastructure elements, water supply and wastewater collection systems and transportation projects.

Marlett Kft., Nagyfuvaros u. 6, H-1084 Budapest, Hungary

Tel: 36-1-314-0082 Fax: 36-1-314-0082   Contact: Tibor Bekenyi

NOVIA Ltd., Rakoczi u.11, H-3535 Miskolc, Hungary
Tel: 36-46-327-924   Fax: 36-46-411-764

SILICON GRAPHICS INC.

1600 Amphitheatre Pkwy., Mountain View, CA, 94043-1351

Tel: (650) 960-1980   Fax: (650) 932-0661   www.sgi.com

Design/mfr. special-effects computer graphic systems and software.

Silicon Graphics, Budapest, Hungary

A.O. SMITH CORPORATION

11270 West Park Place, PO Box 23972, Milwaukee, WI, 53224

Tel: (414) 359-4000   Fax: (414) 359-4064   www.aosmith.com

Auto and truck frames, motors, water heaters, storage/handling systems, plastics, railroad products.

A. O. Smith Corporation, Budapest, Hungary
Contact: Gordon A. Davis

SPENCER STUART MANAGEMENT CONSULTANTS

401 North Michigan Ave., Ste. 3400, Chicago, IL, 60611

Tel: (312) 822-0080   Fax: (312) 822-0116   www.spencerstuart.com

Executive recruitment firm.

Spencer Stuart & Associates Inc., Riadó u. 12, H-1026 Budapest, Hungary
Tel: 36-1-200-0850   Fax: 36-1-394-1097   Contact: Richard Kohlmann

SPRAYING SYSTEMS COMPANY

PO Box 7900, Wheaton, IL, 60189-7900

Tel: (630) 665-5000   Fax: (630) 260-0842   www.spray.com

Designs and manufactures industrial spray products.

Spraying Systems GmbH, Lova u. 10.ll. Em.3, H-9028 Gyor, Hungary

SQUIRE, SANDERS & DEMPSEY

4900 Key Tower, 127 Public Square, Cleveland, OH, 44114-1304

Tel: (216) 479-8500   Fax: (216) 479-8780   www.ssd.com

Engaged in international law.

Squire, Sanders & Dempsey, Andrássy út 64, H-1062 Budapest, Hungary
Tel: 36-1-312-7654   Fax: 36-1-312-7682   Contact: Blaise Pasztory

THE ST. PAUL COMPANIES, INC.

385 Washington Street, St. Paul, MN, 55102

Tel: (651) 310-7911   Fax: (651) 310-8294   www.stpaul.com

Provides investment, insurance and reinsurance services.

ÁB-Aegon Általanos Biztosito Rt., Üllöi únit 1, H-1091 Budapest, Hungary

THE STANLEY WORKS

1000 Stanley Drive, PO Box 7000, New Britain, CT, 06053

Tel: (860) 225-5111   Fax: (860) 827-3987   www.stanleyworks.com

Mfr. hand tools and hardware.

Stanley Works, Hatar u 56, H-1205 Budapest, Hungary

STARKEY LABORATORIES, INC.

6700 Washington Avenue South, Eden Prairie, MN, 55344

Tel: (952) 941-6401   Fax: (952) 947-4787   www.starkey.com

Mfr. custom in-the-ear hearing aids.

Starkey Hungary, Laboratorium Kft., Bajza utca 24, H-1062 Budapest, Hungary

SUN MICROSYSTEMS, INC.

901 San Antonio Road, Palo Alto, CA, 94303

Tel: (650) 960-1300   Fax: (650) 961-9131   www.sun.com

Computer peripherals and programming services.

Sun Microsystems Magyarorszag Kft., Kapa's u 11-15, H-1027 Budapest, Hungary

SYKES ENTERPRISES, INC.

100 N. Tampa Street, Ste. 3900, Tampa, FL, 33602

Tel: (813) 274-1000   Fax: (813) 273-0148   www.sykes.com

Provides information technology outsourcing services.

Sykes, Fehérvári út 79, H-1119 Budapest, Hungary

TBWA WORLDWIDE

488 Madison Avenue, 6th Floor, New York, NY, 10022

Tel: (212) 804-1000   Fax: (212) 804-1200   www.tbwachiat.com

International full service advertising agency.

Fokusz TBWA, Budapest, Hungary

TELLABS INC.

1415 W. Diehl Rd., Naperville, IL, 60563

Tel: (630) 378-8800   Fax: (630) 852-7346   www.tellabs.com

Design/mfr./service voice/data transport and network access systems.

Tellabs Hungary, EMKE Building, Rakoczi Ut. 42, H-1072 Budapest, Hungary

TERADATA

1700 South Patterson Blvd., Dayton, OH, 45479

Tel: (937) 445-5000   Fax: (937) 445-1682   www.teradata.com

Mfr. software to store information.

Teradata Div. NCR, Hermina ut 17, H-1146 Budapest, Hungary

TEXAS INSTRUMENTS INC.

12500 TI Blvd., Dallas, TX, 75266

Tel: (972) 995-3773   Fax: (972) 995-4360   www.ti.com

Mfr. semiconductor devices, electronic electro-mechanical systems, instruments and controls.

Texas Instruments, Budapest, Hungary

THE MARMON GROUP, INC.

200 West Adams, Ste. 2211, Chicago, IL, 60606

Tel: (312) 372-9500   Fax: (312) 845-5305   www.marmon.com

Holding company for diversified manufacturing and service firms.

Getz Bros. & Co. Inc., PO Box 136, H-1431 Budapest, Hungary

Getz Intl. Travel, Nephadsereg u.5, H-1055 Budapest, Hungary

THETFORD CORPORATION

7101 Jackson Road, PO Box 1285, Ann Arbor, MI, 48106

Tel: (734) 769-6000   Fax: (734) 769-2023   www.thetford.com

Mfr. sanitation products and chemicals.

Thetford Hungary (Rep), Bartók Béla út 138, H-1224 Budapest, Hungary

THE TRANE COMPANY

3600 Pammel Creek Road, La Crosse, WI, 54601

Tel: (608) 787-2000   Fax: (608) 787-4990   www.trane.com

Mfr. distribution and service of A/C systems and equipment.

Trane Hungaria Kft., Rubin Center Office N-305, Dayka Gabor u. 3, H-118 Budapest, Hungary

TRANTER PHE, INC.

PO Box 2289, Wichita Falls, TX, 76306

Tel: (940) 723-7125   Fax: (940) 723-1131   www.tranter.com

Mfr. heat exchangers.

SWEP Hungary Kft., Nagyszombat u. 1, HU-1036 Budapest, Hungary

TREDEGAR CORPORATION

1100 Boulders Pkwy., Richmond, VA, 23225

Tel: (804) 330-1000   Fax: (804) 330-1177   www.tredegar.com

Engaged in oil and gas production and manufacture of plastics and aluminum products.

Tredegar Film Products, Ipari út 2, H-2651 Rétság, Hungary

TYCO CAPITAL

1211 Avenue of the Americas, New York, NY, 10036

Tel: (212) 536-1390   Fax: (212) 536-1912   www.citgroup.com

Engaged in commercial finance.

Newcourt, Div. Tyco Capital, Zazlos u. 18, H-1443 Budapest, Hungary

Tel: 36-1-223-1202

UNITED PARCEL SERVICE, INC.

55 Glenlake Parkway, NE, Atlanta, GA, 30328

Tel: (404) 828-6000   Fax: (404) 828-6593   www.ups.com

International package-delivery service.

UPS Hungary Ltd., Kozma utca 4, H-1108 Budapest, Hungary

Tel: 36-1-262-0000

UUNET

22001 Loudoun County Pkwy., Ashburn, VA, 20147

Tel: (703) 206-5600   Fax: (703) 206-5601   www.uu.net

World's largest Internet service provider; World Wide Web hosting services, security products and consulting services to businesses, professionals, and on-line service providers.

UUNET Magyarország, Bank Center City Bank Tower, H-1054 Budapest, Hungary

VISHAY INTERTECHNOLOGY INC.

63 Lincoln Hwy., Malvern, PA, 19355

Tel: (610) 644-1300   Fax: (610) 296-0657   www.vishay.com

Mfr. resistors, strain gages, capacitors, inductors, printed circuit boards.

Vishay Electronic, Foti ut. 56., H-1047 Budapest, Hungary

Tel: 36-1-233-2236   Fax: 36-1-233-2263

WAHL CLIPPER CORPORATION

2902 N. Locust Street, Sterling, IL, 61081

Tel: (815) 625-6525   Fax: (815) 625-1193   www.wahlclipper.com

Mfr. hair clippers, beard and mustache trimmers, shavers, pet clippers and soldering irons.

Kuno Moser Kft., Mosonmagyaróvár, Hungary

WALBRO ENGINE MANAGEMENT

7400 N. Oracle Road, Ste. 310, Tucson, AZ, 85704

Tel: (520) 877-3000   Fax: (520) 877-3006   www.walbro.com

Mfr. motor vehicle accessories and parts, automotive fluid carrying systems.

TI Group Automotive Systems, Ipari ut 1, Postafiok 18, H-5123 Jaszarokszallas, Hungary

Tel: 36-57-531-800

WEIL, GOTSHAL & MANGES LLP

767 Fifth Ave., New York, NY, 10153

Tel: (212) 310-8000   Fax: (212) 310-8007   www.weil.com

Engaged in international law.

Weil, Gotshal & Manges LLP, Bank Centre Granite Tower, Szabadság tér 7, H-1944 Budapest, Hungary

Tel: 36-1-302-9100   Fax: 36-1-302-9110   Contact: Anita Monus

WENDY'S INTERNATIONAL, INC.

4288 West Dublin Granville Roads, Dublin, OH, 43017-0256

Tel: (614) 764-3100   Fax: (614) 764-3459   www.wendysintl.com

Fast food restaurant chain.

Wendy's International, Budapest, Hungary

WHIRLPOOL CORPORATION

2000 N. M-63, Benton Harbor, MI, 49022-2692

Tel: (616) 923-5000   Fax: (616) 923-5443   www.whirlpoolcorp.com

Mfr., market home appliances: Whirlpool, Roper, KitchenAid, Estate, and Inglis.

Whirlpool Hungary, Fehérvári út 79, B lépcs ház, II. Em, H-1119 Budapest, Hungary

Tel: 36-1-382-7500

WHITE & CASE LLP

1155 Ave. of the Americas, New York, NY, 10036-2767

Tel: (212) 819-8200   Fax: (212) 354-8113   www.whitecase.com

Engaged in international law.

White & Case LLP, Süba Ctr., Nagymezo utca 44, H-1065 Budapest, Hungary

Tel: 36-1-269-0550   Fax: 36-1-269-1199   Contact: Duncan G. Calder III

WM WRIGLEY JR. COMPANY

410 N. Michigan Ave., Chicago, IL, 60611-4287

Tel: (312) 644-2121   Fax: (312) 644-0353   www.wrigley.com

Mfr. chewing gum.

Wrigley Hungaria, KFT., Cseppk köz 3, H-1025 Budapest, Hungary

Tel: 36-1-345-7900   Fax: 36-1-325-6590

WYETH

5 Giralda Farms, Madison, NJ, 07940-0874

Tel: (973) 660-5000   Fax: (973) 660-7026   www.wyeth.com

Mfr. consumer healthcare products.

Wyeth Whitehall Hungary Kft., Lajos u. 78, H-1036 Budapest, Hungary

Tel: 36-1-240-4625

WYETH PHARMACEUTICALS

555 E. Lancaster Ave., Wayne, PA, 19087-5109

Tel: (610) 971-5400   Fax: (610) 995-4668   www.wyeth.com

Mfr. antibiotics and pharmaceutical products.

Wyeth-Lederle Hungary, Vaci ut 110, H-1133 Budapest, Hungary

Tel: 36-1-35-00-292

XEROX CORPORATION

800 Long Ridge Road, PO Box 1600, Stamford, CT, 06904

Tel: (203) 968-3000   Fax: (203) 968-4312   www.xerox.com

Mfr. document processing equipment, systems and supplies.

Xerox Hungary, Szépvölgyi Business Park, Szépvölgyi út 35-37, H-1037 Budapest, Hungary

Tel: 36-1-436-8800

YELLOW CORPORATION

10990 Roe Ave., PO Box 7270, Overland Park, KS, 66207

Tel: (913) 696-6100   Fax: (913) 696-6116   www.yellowcorp.com

Commodity transportation.

FM Hungaria Kft., Akadaly u. 15, H-1183 Budapest, Hungary

YORK INTERNATIONAL CORPORATION

631 South Richland Ave., York, PA, 17403

Tel: (717) 771-7890   Fax: (717) 771-6212   www.york.com

Mfr. heating, ventilating, air conditioning and refrigeration equipment.

York International Kft., York Magyaroszag, Vaci ut 206, H-1138 Budapest, Hungary

Tel: 36-1-465-7060

YOUNG & RUBICAM INC.

285 Madison Ave., New York, NY, 10017

Tel: (212) 210-3000   Fax: (212) 370-3796   www.yr.com

Advertising, public relations, direct marketing and sales promotion, corporate and product ID management.

Young & Rubicam Hungary, Szilágyi E. Fasor 22/b, H-1125 Budapest, Hungary

Tel: 36-1-275-2480

ZIMMER HOLDINGS, INC.

345 East Main St., Warsaw, IN, 46580

Tel: (574) 267-6131   Fax: (574) 372-4988   www.zimmer.com

Engaged in design and manufacture of orthopedic products.

Zimmer, Pharmavit RT/BMS, Veresegyhaz, H-2112 Levai Utca 5, Hungary

Tel: 36-28-385960   Fax: 36-28-387930

ZOLTEK COMPANIES, INC.

3101 McKelvey Road, St. Louis, MO, 63044

Tel: (314) 291-5110   Fax: (314) 291-8536   www.zoltek.com

Engaged in production and manufacture of carbon fibers.

Zoltek Hungary, Varga József tér 1, H-2537 Nyergesujfalu, Hungary

Iceland

ABBOTT LABORATORIES

100 Abbott Park Rd., Abbott Park, IL, 60064

Tel: (847) 937-6100   Fax: (847) 937-1511   www.abbott.com

Development, manufacture and sale of diversified health care products and services.

Pharmaco HF, Horgatuni 2, PO Box 200, IS-210 Gardabaer, Iceland

Tel: 354-565-8111

BDO SEIDMAN, LLP   BELGIUM

130 East Randolph Street, Chicago, IL, 60601

Tel: (312) 856-9100   Fax: (312) 856-1379   www.bdo.com

International accounting and financial consulting firm.

BDO SamEnd ehf, Ármúli 10, IS-108 Reykjavik, Iceland

Tel: 354-568-7210   Fax: 354-568-8352   Contact: Sigurður B. Amporsson

BOZELL GROUP

40 West 23rd Street, New York, NY, 10010

Tel: (212) 727-5000   Fax: (212) 645-9173   www.bozell.com

Advertising, marketing, public relations and media consulting.

YDDA Advertising Agency, Grjotagota 7, IS-101 Reykjavik, Iceland

Tel: 354-562-2992   Fax: 354-551-7829   Contact: Hallur Baldursson, Mng. Dir.

BRISTOL-MYERS SQUIBB COMPANY

345 Park Ave., New York, NY, 10154-0037

Tel: (212) 546-4000   Fax: (212) 546-4020   www.bms.com

Pharmaceutical and food preparations, medical and surgical instruments.

Pharmaco, Div. Bristol-Myers Squibb, Horgatuni 2, PO Box 200, IS-212 Gardabaer, Iceland

Tel: 354-56-58-111

DANZAS AEI, INC.

120 Tokeneke Road, PO Box 1231, Darien, CT, 06820

Tel: (203) 655-7900   Fax: (203) 655-5779   www.aeilogistics.com

International air freight forwarder.

Danzas AEI, Hotabakki V/Holtaveg, IS-104 Reykjavik, Iceland

Tel: 354-569-8050   Fax: 354-569-8001

DELOITTE TOUCHE TOHMATSU INTERNATIONAL

1633 Broadway, New York, NY, 10019

Tel: (212) 492-4000   Fax: (212) 392-4154   www.deloitte.com

Accounting, audit, tax and management consulting services.

Deloitte & Touche, Armula 40, PO Box 8736, IS-108 Reykjavik, Iceland

DHL WORLDWIDE EXPRESS

50 California Avenue, San Francisco, CA, 94111

Tel: (415) 677-6100   Fax: (415) 824-9700   www.dhl.com

Worldwide air express carrier.

DHL Worldwide Express, Faxafen 9, IS-108 Reykjavik, Iceland

Tel: 354-535-1100   Fax: 354-535-1111

ERNST & YOUNG INTERNATIONAL

5 Times Square, New York, NY, 10036

Tel: (212) 773-3000   Fax: (212) 773-6350   www.eyi.com

Engaged in assurance and advisory business services, tax, law and corporate finance.

Endurskodun & Radgjof HF/Ernst & Young International, Skeifan 11 A, PO Box 8693, IS-108 Reykjavik, Iceland

Tel: 354-568-55-11   Fax: 568-96-95-85   Contact: Erna Bryndis Halldorsdottir

GILSON INC.

3000 W. Beltline Hwy, PO Box 620027, Middleton, WI, 53562-0027

Tel: (608) 836-1551   Fax: (608) 831-4451   www.gilson.com

Mfr. analytical/biomedical instruments.

Groco Hf, PO Box 83-64, Sudurlandsbraut 6, IS-128 Reykjavik, Iceland

GRANT THORNTON INTERNATIONAL

800 One Prudential Plaza, 130 E. Randolph Drive, Chicago, IL, 60601-6050

Tel: (312) 856-0001   Fax: (312) 616-7052   www.grantthornton.com

Accounting, audit, tax and management consulting services.

Thema ehf., endurskodunarstofa, Sudurlandsbraut 20, IS-108 Reykjavik, Iceland

Contact: Olafur Sigurdsson

HENRY SCHEIN, INC.

135 Duryea Rd., Melville, NY, 11747

Tel: (516) 843-5500   Fax: (516) 843-5658   www.henryschein.com

Mfr. and supply dental equipment.

Henry Schein Fides Inc., Laufasgata 9, IS-600 Akureyri, Iceland

Tel: 354-461-1129

IBM CORPORATION

1133 Westchester Avenue, White Plains, NY, 10604

Tel: (914) 765-1900   Fax: (914) 765-7382   www.ibm.com

Information products, technology and services.

IBM Iceland, Nyherji, Skaftahlid 24, IS-105 Reykjavik, Iceland

Tel: 354-5697-700

INTERMEC TECHNOLOGIES CORPORATION

6001 36th Avenue West, PO Box 4280, Everett, WA, 98203-9280

Tel: (425) 348-2600   Fax: (425) 355-9551   www.intermec.com

Mfr. and distributor automated data collection systems.

Intermec Iceland, Bildshofda 12, PO Box 8589, IS-128 Reykjavik, Iceland

INTERNATIONAL GAME TECHNOLOGY INC. (IGT)

9295 Prototype Drive, Reno, NV, 89511

Tel: (702) 448-0100   Fax: (702) 448-1488   www.igtonline.com

Mfr. slot machines, video gaming machines and gaming terminals.

IGT Iceland, Ltd., c/o Deloitte & Touche, Armula 40, IS-108 Reykjavik, Iceland

Tel: 354-588-7622   Fax: 354-588-7632

KPMG CONSULTING INC.

1676 International Dr., McLean, VA, 22102

Tel: (703) 747-3000   Fax: (703) 747-8500   www.kpmg.com

Accounting and audit, tax and management consulting services.

KPMG Endurskodun hf., Vegmuli 3, IS-108 Reykjavik, Iceland

Tel: 354-533-5555   Fax: 354-533-5550   Contact: Tryggvi Jonsson, Ptnr.

McCANN-ERICKSON WORLDGROUP

750 Third Ave., New York, NY, 10017

Tel: (212) 697-6000   Fax: (212) 984-3575   www.mccann.com

International advertising and marketing services.

Gott Folk McCann Erickson, Síðumúli 24, PO Box 8680, 108 Reykjavik, Iceland

PAPA JOHN'S INTERNATIONAL, INC.

2002 Papa John's Blvd., Louisville, KY, 40299-2334

Tel: (502) 266-5200   Fax: (502) 266-2925   www.papajohns.com

Retailer and pizza franchiser.

Papa John's International Inc., Grensasvegur 3, IS-108 Reykjavik, Iceland
Tel: 354-567-8678

SCHENKER USA INC.

150 Albany Ave., Freeport, NY, 11520

Tel: (516) 403-5416   Fax: (516) 377-3092   www.schenkerusa.com

Freight forwarders.

BM Transport HF, Holtabakka v/Holtaveg, PO Box 904, Reykjavik, Iceland
Tel: 354-588-9977   Fax: 354-588-9949

SCIENCE APPLICATIONS INTL. CORPORATION (SAIC)

10260 Campus Point Dr., San Diego, CA, 92121

Tel: (858) 826-6000   Fax: (858) 535-7589   www.saic.com

Engaged in research and engineering.

US Naval Hosp Keflavik/Chcs, SAIC/J Falconieri, Keflavikurflugvollur, IS-235 Keflavik, Iceland
Tel: 354-425-3380   Fax: 354-425-3203

THE ST. PAUL COMPANIES, INC.

385 Washington Street, St. Paul, MN, 55102

Tel: (651) 310-7911   Fax: (651) 310-8294   www.stpaul.com

Provides investment, insurance and reinsurance services.

Sjova-Almennar tryggingar hg, Kringlan 5, PO Box 5300, IS-103 Reykjavik, Iceland

WESTERN WIRELESS CORPORATION

3650 131st Avenue SE, Ste. 400, Bellevue, WA, 98006

Tel: (425) 586-8700   Fax: (425) 586-8666   www.wwireless.com

Provides wireless communication services.

TAL, Ltd., Div. Western Wireless, 28 Sidumuli, Reykjavik, Iceland

WORLD MINERALS INC.

130 Castilian Drive, Santa Barbara, CA, 93117

Tel: (805) 562-0200   Fax: (805) 562-0298   www.worldminerals.com

Mfr. premium quality diatomite and perlite products.

World Minerals Iceland, Höfða 2, IS-640 Húsavík, Iceland
Tel: 354-464-1288   Fax: 354-464-1041

India

3COM CORPORATION

5400 Bayfront Plaza, Santa Clara, CA, 95052-8145

Tel: (408) 326-5000   Fax: (408) 326-5001   www.3com.com

Engaged in the development and manufacture of computer networking products and systems.

3Com Asia Ltd., Ste. 702, 7th Fl. International Trade Tower, Nehru Place, New Delhi 110 019, India

Tel: 91-11-644-3974 Fax: 91-11-623-6509

3M (MINNESOTA MINING & MFG.)

3M Center, St. Paul, MN, 55144-1000

Tel: (651) 733-1110   Fax: (651) 733-9973   www.mmm.com

Mfr. diversified products for industry, consumer, health care, imaging, communications, transport, safety, etc.

Birla 3M Limited, Prince Chambers, 3rd Fl., Prince Complex, Hazratgani, Lucknow, India

Tel: 522-281650

Birla 3M Limited, 43-A Weston House, Okhla Industrial Estate, New Delhi 110-020, India

Tel: 91-40-241-130

Birla 3M Limited, Raheja Paramount, 13 Residency Road, Bangalore 560 025, India

Tel: 91-80-558-8881 Fax: 91-80-558-5612

Birla 3M Limited Calcutta, 4C, Shivan Chambers, 53 Syed Amir Ali Avenue, Calcutta 700 020, India

Tel: 91-33-28000621

ABBOTT LABORATORIES

100 Abbott Park Rd., Abbott Park, IL, 60064

Tel: (847) 937-6100   Fax: (847) 937-1511   www.abbott.com

Development, manufacture and sale of diversified health care products and services.

Abbott Laboratories, Ltd., United No. 131, Ashish Industrial Estate, Adkhale Road South, Bombay 400 025, India

Tel: 91-22-2430-0560

ACCENTURE LTD.

1345 Avenue of the Americas, New York, NY, 10105

Tel: (917) 452-4400   Fax: (917) 527-9915   www.accenture.com

Provides management and technology consulting services.

Accenture, 17th Fl., Express Towers, Nariman Point, Mumbai 400 021, India

Tel: 91-22-282-5000 Fax: 91-22-2282-6000

ADVANCED MICRO DEVICES INC.

1 AMD Place, Sunnyvale, CA, 94086

Tel: (408) 732-2400   Fax: (408) 982-6164   www.amd.com

Mfr. integrated circuits for communications and computation industry.

Advanced Micro Devices Far East Ltd., Ste. 205 Chintels Business Centre, Chintels House, A-11 Kailash Colony, New Dehli 110 048, India

AIRGAS, INC.

259 N. Radnor Chester Rd., Ste. 100, Radnor, PA, 19087-5283

Tel: (610) 687-5253   Fax: (610) 687-1052   www.airgas.com

Engaged in distribution of specialty, industrial, and medical gases.

Airgas Management India Pvt. Ltd., Raheja Vihar Evening Star A-303, 119 Tungwa Chandivali Farm Rd., Powai Bombay 400 072, India

Contact: Neil Amber

Bhoruka Gases Ltd., Whitefield Road, Mahadevapura, Bangalore 560-048, India

Tel: 91-80-851-0288 Fax: 91-80-851-0365 Contact: M. Gururaj

Superior Air Products Ltd., B1/J-3 Extension, Mohan Co-Op Industrial Estate, Mathura Road, Badarpur New Delhi 110 044, India

Tel: 91-11-694-8725   Fax: 91-11-694-2505   Contact: Ashok Chandra

ALCOA INC.

Alcoa Center, 201 Isabella Street at 7th Street Bridge, Pittsburgh, PA, 15212-5858

Tel: (412) 553-4545   Fax: (412) 553-4498   www.alcoa.com

World's leading producer of aluminum and alumina; mining, refining, smelting, fabricating and recycling.

Alcoa-ACC Industrial Chemicals Ltd., Falta, India

ALLEGHENY LUDLUM CORPORATION

1000 Six PPG Place, Pittsburgh, PA, 15222

Tel: (412) 394-2805   Fax: (412) 394-2800   www.alleghenyludlum.com

Mfr. steel and alloys.

Allegheny Ludlum, India

Tel: 91-22-283-6366   Fax: 91-22-283-7288

ALLEN TELECOM

25101 Chagrin Boulevard, Beachwood, OH, 44122-5619

Tel: (216) 765-5818   Fax: (216) 765-0410   www.allentele.com

Mfr. communications equipment, automotive bodies and parts, electronic components.

Allen Telecom Inc., F-1 Adarshini Plaza, 93 Adchini, Sri Aurobindo Road, New Delhi 110 017, India

Tel: 91-11-696-9990   Fax: 91-11-653-2120   Contact: Rajiv Gupta

ALLEN-BRADLEY COMPANY, INC.

1201 South Second Street, Milwaukee, WI, 53204

Tel: (414) 382-2000   Fax: (414) 382-4444   www.ab.com

Mfr. electrical controls and information devices.

Allen-Bradley India Ltd., C-11 Industrial Area, Site 4, Sahibabad Dist., Ghaziabad 201 010, India

ALLERGAN INC.

2525 Dupont Drive, Irvine, CA, 92612

Tel: (714) 246-4500   Fax: (714) 246-6987   www.allergan.com

Mfr. therapeutic eye care products and skin care pharmaceuticals.

Alergan India Limited, North Block, Rear Wing, 9th Fl., Manipal Centre, 47 Dickenson Rd., Bangalore 560 042, India

Tel: 91-80-555-0476   Fax: 91-80-555-0474

ALLIANCE CAPITAL MANAGEMENT HOLDING LP

1345 Ave. of the Americas, New York, NY, 10105

Tel: (212) 969-1000   Fax: (212) 969-2229   www.alliancecapital.com

Engaged in fund management for large corporations.

Alliance Capital Management, Indage House, 82 Dr. Annie Besant Road, Worli Mumbai 400 018, India

Tel: 91-22-497-8000

ALLIANCE SEMICONDUCTOR CORPORATION

2675 Augustine Drive, Santa Clara, CA, 95054

Tel: (408) 855-4900   Fax: (408) 855-4999   www.alsc.com

Mfr. semi-conductors and related chips.

Alliance India, 39 Langford Road, Bangalore 560 025, India

Tel: 91-80-224-6452   Fax: 91-80-224-6453

ALLTEL CORPORATION

1 Allied Drive, Little Rock, AR, 72202

Tel: (501) 905-8000   Fax: (501) 905-6444   www.alltel.com

Full range outsourcing services.

ALLTEL Systems Ltd., India

AMERICAN LOCKER GROUP INC.

608 Allen Street, Jamestown, NY, 14701-3966

Tel: (716) 664-9600   Fax: (716) 483-2822   www.americanlocker.com

Mfr. coin-operated locks and office furniture.

Barnhardt International (India) Ltd., Chennai, Madras 6000034, India

Tel: 91-44-8272732

AMF BOWLING WORLDWIDE, INC.

8100 AMF Drive, Richmond, VA, 23111

Tel: (804) 730-4000   Fax: (804) 559-6276   www.amf.com

Operates bowling alleys.

AMF Bowling India Ltd., C-13, 1/F Community Centre, Safdarjung Development Area, New Delhi 110 016, India

Tel: 91-11-652-5457

AMPHENOL CORPORATION

358 Hall Ave., Wallingford, CT, 06492-7530

Tel: (203) 265-8900   Fax: (203) 265-8793   www.amphenol.com

Mfr. electronic interconnect penetrate systems and assemblies.

Amphetronix Ltd., 105 Bhosari Ind. Area, Pune 411 026, India

Tel: 91-20-790-363   Fax: 91-20-790-581

ANALOG DEVICES INC.

1 Technology Way, Norwood, MA, 02062

Tel: (781) 329-4700   Fax: (781) 326-8703   www.analog.com

Mfr. integrated circuits and related devices.

Analog Devices Asian Sales Inc., Corporate Towers C & D, 7th Floor, Diamond District, Airport Road,, Bangalore 560 008, India

Tel: 91-80-5208090   Fax: 91-80-5216532

ANDERSEN

33 West Monroe Street, Chicago, IL, 60603

Tel: (312) 580-0033   Fax: (312) 507-6748   www.andersen.com

*Accounting and audit, tax and management consulting services. **Firm under worldwide reorganization; new data unavailable for this edition.*

Andersen Worldwide, 11th Fl., Du Parc Trinity, 17 M.G. Rd., Bangalore 560 001, India

Tel: 91-80-559-6262

Andersen Worldwide, 66 Maker Towers, F, Cuffe Parade, PO Box 16093 Colaba, Mumbai 400 005, India

Tel: 91-22-218-2929

Andersen Worldwide, 426, World Trade Ctr., Barakhamba Lane, New Delhi 110 001, India

ANSYS, INC.

275 Technology Drive, Canonsburg, PA, 15317

Tel: (724) 746-3304   Fax: (724) 514-9494   www.ansys.com

Mfr. CAD and CAE software.

ANSYS Software Ltd., 80 Feet Road, No. 248, Defence Colony, Indiranagar, Bangalore 560 038, India

Contact: Venkatesh Natajaran

AON CORPORATION

200 East Randolph, Chicago, IL, 60601

Tel: (312) 381-1000   Fax: (312) 381-6032   www.aon.com

Insurance brokers worldwide; underwrites accident and health insurance, specialty and professional insurance; and provides risk management consultation.

AON Worldwide / Global Insurance Services Pvt. Ltd., Gresham Assurance House, 4th Fl., Sir P.M. Rd., Mumbai 400 001, India

Tel: 91-22-266-1387   Fax: 91-22-266-3649   Contact: Prabhat Thakker

APAR INFOTECH CORPORATION

160 Technology Drive, Canonsburg, PA, 15317

Tel: (724) 745-7100   Fax: (724) 745-6494   www.apar.com

Provides software development.

Apar Infotech Limited, Corporate Park Bldg. No. 6, Sion Trombay Road, Chembur Mumbai 400 071, India

Apar Technologies, 7 Suryodai Complex, Airport Road Kodihalli, Bangalore 560 008, India

APL LOGISTICS

1111 Broadway, Oakland, CA, 94607

Tel: (510) 272-8000   Fax: (510) 272-7421   www.apllogistics.com

Provides ocean container shipping and logistics services.

APL India, Technopark, Mumbai, India

APPLE COMPUTER, INC.

One Infinite Loop, Cupertino, CA, 95014

Tel: (408) 996-1010   Fax: (408) 974-2113   www.apple.com

Personal computers, peripherals and software.

Apple Computer International Inc., 5/F, Du Parc Trinity, 17 MG Rd., Bangalore 560 001, India

Tel: 91-80-555-0575 Fax: 91-80-555-0660   Contact: Samit Roy, Gen. Mgr.

APPLERA CORPORATION

301 Merritt 7, Norwalk, CT, 06851

Tel: (203) 840-2000   Fax: (203) 840-2312   www.applera.com

Leading supplier of systems for life science research and related applications.

Labindia Instruments, Vaitalik USO Road, A-8 Qutab Institutional Area, New Delhi 110 067, India

APW, INC.

N22 W23685 Ridgeview Parkway West, Waukesha, WI, 53188-1013

Tel: (262) 523-7600   Fax: (262) 523-7624   www.apw1.com

Mfr. hi-pressure tools, vibration control products, consumables, technical furniture and enclosures.

APW India, 303 New India Industrial Estate, Andheri East, Mumbai 400093, India

Tel: 91-22-6938080   Fax: 91-22-6938181

AQUENT

711 Boylston Street, Boston, MA, 02116

Tel: (617) 535-5000   Fax: (617) 535-6001   www.aquent.com

Engaged in temporary, specialized employment.

AQUENT, 271, Solitair Corporate Park, 7/F, Andheri-Kurla Link Road, Andheri-Kurla Link Road, Bombay 400 093, India

Tel: 91-22-693-5282   Fax: 91-22-693-5291

ARBOR ACRES FARM INC.

439 Marlborough Road, Glastonbury, CT, 06033

Tel: (860) 633-4681   Fax: (860) 633-2433   www.aaf.com

Producers of male and female broiler breeders, commercial egg layers.

Arbor Acres Farm India Ltd., PO Box 73, Raipur Rd., Dehra Dun, Uttar Pradesh 248 001, India

ARGO INTERNATIONAL CORPORATION

140 Franklin Street, New York, NY, 10013

Tel: (212) 431-1700   Fax: (212) 431-2206   www.argointl.com

Distribution of quality electrical and mechanical equipment, components, renewal spare parts for the worldwide industrial, marine, metal mining, oil well drilling, utility, refineries and petroleum industries.

Argo International India, Judges Colony, 1/F, R.T. Nagar, Bangalore, India

ARIBA, INC.

1565 Charleston Rd., Mountain View, CA, 94043

Tel: (650) 930-6200   Fax: (650) 930-6300   www.ariba.com

Mfr. software.

Ariba Technologies India, 20 Prestige Center Point, No. 7 Edward Road, Bangalore 560 052, India

ARMSTRONG HOLDINGS, INC.

2500 Columbia Avenue, Lancaster, PA, 17604-3001

Tel: (717) 397-0611 Fax: (717) 396-2787 www.armstrong.com

Mfr. and marketing interior furnishings and specialty products for building, auto and textile industry.

Inarco Ltd., Armstrong House, 2 Pokhran Road, Thane Bombay 400 601, India

Tel: 91-22-536-2903 Fax: 91-22-534-8448

ARROW ELECTRONICS INC.

25 Hub Drive, Melville, NY, 11747

Tel: (516) 391-1300 Fax: (516) 391-1640 www.arrow.com

Distributor of electronic components and computer products.

Arrow Elecronics India Ltd., 34/4 Meanee Ave., Tank Road, Bangalore 560 042, India

Arrow Elecronics India Ltd., Shere-E-Punjab Co-op, Mahakali Caves Road, Andheri E, Bombay 400 093, India

ARVIN MERITOR INC

2135 W. Maple Rd., Troy, MI, 48084-7186

Tel: (248) 435-1000 Fax: (248) 435-1393 www.arvinmeritor.com

Mfr. of automotive exhaust systems and ride control products, axles and power-steering pumps.

Meritor HVS, Jakarta, India

ASSOCIATED MERCHANDISING CORPORATION

500 Seventh Ave., 2nd Fl., New York, NY, 10018

Tel: (212) 819-6600 Fax: (212) 819-6701 www.theamc.com

Retail service organization; apparel, shoes and accessories.

Associated Merchandising Corp., 2/F, World Trade Tower, Barakhamba Rd., New Delhi 110 001, India

Associated Merchandising Corp., 220 Backbay Reclamation, Nariman Point, Mumbai 400 021, India

ASSOCIATED PRESS INC.

50 Rockefeller Plaza, New York, NY, 10020-1605

Tel: (212) 621-1500 Fax: (212) 621-5447 www.ap.com

News gathering agency.

The Associated Press, New Delhi, India

Tel: 91-11-462-8506

AT&T BROADBAND, LLC

188 Inverness Dr. West, Englewood, CO, 80112

Tel: (303) 875-5500 Fax: (303) 875-4984 www.broadband.att.com

Provides broadband technology services; digital TV, digital telephone and high-speed cable internet services.

BPL/US West Cellular Ltd., Delhi, India

AUTODESK INC.

111 McInnis Parkway, San Rafael, CA, 94903

Tel: (415) 507-5000 Fax: (415) 507-6112 www.autodesk.com

Develop/marketing/support computer-aided design, engineering, scientific and multimedia software products.

Autodesk, SAARC, 206, Raheja Plaza, 17 Commissariat Rd., Shoolay Tank Bed Area, Bangalore 560 025, India

Tel: 91-80-556-4939 Fax: 91-80-556-4897

AUTOMATIC SWITCH CO. (ASCO)

50-60 Hanover Rd., Florham Park, NJ, 07932

Tel: (973) 966-2000 Fax: (973) 966-2628 www.asco.com

Mfr. solenoid valves, emergency power controls, pressure and temperature switches.

ASCO Power Technologies India, 407-412 Swastik Chambers, 4th Floor, Sion Trombay Rd., Chembur Mumbai 400 071, India

Tel: 91-22-5229639 Fax: 91-22-5229646 Contact: M. N. Radhakrishnan

AVERY DENNISON CORPORATION

150 N. Orange Grove Blvd., Pasadena, CA, 91103

Tel: (626) 304-2000   Fax: (626) 792-7312   www.averydennison.com

Mfr. pressure-sensitive adhesives and materials, office products, labels, tags, retail systems, Carter's Ink and specialty chemicals.

APG Avery Dennison India, Narsinghpur Ind Area, Six Kilometre Stone, Delhi Jaipur Highway, Haryana New Delhi 122 001, India

Tel: 91-124-371-602   Fax: 91-124-371-601

AVON PRODUCTS, INC.

1345 Avenue of the Americas, New York, NY, 10105-0196

Tel: (212) 282-5000   Fax: (212) 282-6049   www.avon.com

Mfr. direct seller of cosmetics and beauty-related items.

Avon Beauty Products India Pvt. Ltd., M38 Commercial Complex, Greater Kailash II, New Delhi 110 048, India

Tel: 91-11-623-3920   Fax: 91-11-623-3923   Contact: Mansoor Abdullah, VP

BANDAG INCORPORATED

2905 North Highway 61, Muscatine, IA, 52761

Tel: (319) 262-1400   Fax: (319) 262-1252   www.bandag.com

Mfr. and sale retread tires.

Indag Rubber Ltd., Khemka House, 11 Community Centre, Saket New Delhi 110-017, India

BANK OF AMERICA CORPORATION

Bank of America Corporate Center, Charlotte, NC, 28255

Tel: (415) 622-3530   Fax: (704) 386-6699   www.bankofamerica.com

Financial services.

Bank of America NT & SA, DCM Bldg., 6/F, 15 Barakhamba Rd., New Delhi 110 001, India

Tel: 91-11-371-5565   Fax: 91-11-371-5554   Contact: Ambi Venkateswaran, SVP

THE BANK OF NEW YORK

One Wall Street, New York, NY, 10286

Tel: (212) 495-1784   Fax: (212) 495-2546   www.bankofny.com

Banking services.

The Bank of New York, Express Towers, 13th Fl., Nariman Point, Mumbai 400 021, India

Tel: 91-22-202-2936   Fax: 91-22-204-4941

C. R. BARD, INC.

730 Central Ave., Murray Hill, NJ, 07974

Tel: (908) 277-8000   Fax: (908) 277-8078   www.crbard.com

Mfr. health care products.

Bard International, 53 Free Press House, 215 Nariman Point, Mumbai 400 021, India

BARRY-WEHMILLER COMPANIES, INC.

8020 Forsyth Boulevard, St. Louis, MO, 63105

Tel: (314) 862-8000   Fax: (314) 862-8858   www.barry-wehmillerco.com

Mfr. of packaging automation equipment for filling, closing, conveying, cartoning, shrink wrapping and case packing plus systems integration.

Barry-Wehmiller India, Y-50 Ninth Street, Annanagar West, Chennai 600 040, India

Tel: 91-44-628-5035

BATES WORLDWIDE INC.

498 Seventh Avenue, New York, NY, 10018

Tel: (212) 297-7000   Fax: (212) 986-0270   www.batesww.com

Advertising, marketing, public relations and media consulting.

Bates Clarion Bangalore, Ganash Towers, 111 Infantry Rd., Bangalore 560 001, India

Tel: 91-80-559-9925   Fax: 91-80-559-5727

Bates Clarion Corporate, 55B Mirza Ghalib St., Calcutta 700 016, India

Tel: 91-33-295-270   Fax: 91-33-249-5290   Contact: Sudipio Sarkar, Chmn.

Bates Clarion Corporate, Merchant Chambers, New Marine Lines, Mumbai (Bombay) 400 020, India

Tel: 91-22-203-9702   Contact: K. Khalap, CEO

Bates Clarion Delhi, Milap Naketan, Bahadurshah Zalar Marg, Delhi 110 002, India

Tel: 91-11-331-9908   Fax: 91-11-331-9682   Contact: S. Sinha, SVP

BAUSCH & LOMB INC.

One Bausch & Lomb Place, Rochester, NY, 14604-2701

Tel: (716) 338-6000   Fax: (716) 338-6007   www.bausch.com

Mfr. vision care products and accessories.

Bausch & Lomb India, Ltd., Piccadilly Place, 3/F, Capt. Gaur Marg Srinivaspuri, Okhla New Delhi 110 065, India

BAX GLOBAL INC.

16808 Armstrong Ave., PO Box 19571, Irvine, CA, 92623

Tel: (949) 752-4000   Fax: (949) 260-3182   www.baxworld.com

Air freight forwarder.

BAX Global - Reg. Office, 4G & H, 4th Fl., Hansalaya Bldg., 15 Barakhamba Rd., New Delhi 110 001, India

Tel: 91-11-331-3972   Fax: 91-11-332-9665

BAX Global India Pvt. Ltd., 2nd Fl., Perstige Terminus 1, Airport Exit Rd., Konena Agrahara, Bangalore 560 017, India

Tel: 91-80-526-8646   Fax: 91-80-527-3384

BAXTER INTERNATIONAL INC.

One Baxter Parkway, Deerfield, IL, 60015

Tel: (847) 948-2000   Fax: (847) 948-3948   www.baxter.com

Mfr. products and provide services in the field of the administration of medication and bioscience.

Baxter India Pvt. Ltd., Baxter House, E-2 Udyog Nagar, Rohtak Road, New Delhi 110 041, India

Tel: 91-11-518-7970

BBDO WORLDWIDE

1285 Ave. of the Americas, New York, NY, 10019

Tel: (212) 459-5000   Fax: (212) 459-6645   www.bbdo.com

Multinational group of advertising agencies.

R K Swamy/BBDO, Madras, India

BDO SEIDMAN, LLP   BELGIUM

130 East Randolph Street, Chicago, IL, 60601

Tel: (312) 856-9100   Fax: (312) 856-1379   www.bdo.com

International accounting and financial consulting firm.

Lodha & Co., 14 Government Place East, Calcutta 69, India

Tel: 91-33-248-7102   Fax: 91-33-248-6960   Contact: Rajendra S. Lodha

BECHTEL GROUP INC.

50 Beale Street, PO Box 3965, San Francisco, CA, 94105-1895

Tel: (415) 768-1234   Fax: (415) 768-9038   www.bechtel.com

General contractors in engineering, construction and project management.

Bechtel India Private Limited, 249 A Udyog Vihar Phase IV, Haryana, Gurgaon 122 015, India

Tel: 91-124-343-107   Fax: 91-124-343-110

BELLSOUTH CORPORATION LATIN AMERICA

1155 Peachtree Street NE, Ste. 400, Atlanta, GA, 30367

Tel: (404) 249-4800   Fax: (404) 249-4880   www.bellsouth.com

Mobile communications, telecommunications network systems.

SkyCell Communications, Paramount Plaza, No. 22 Mahatma Gandhi Road, Nungambakkam, Madras 600 034, India

Tel: 91-44-822-4595   Fax: 91-44-855-4503

TBL, 7th Fl., Mercantile House, 15 Kasturba Gandhi Marg, New Delhi 110 001, India

Tel: 91-11-371-7207   Fax: 91-11-371-7214

BENTLY NEVADA CORPORATION

1631 Bently Parkway South, Minden, NV, 89423

Tel: (775) 782-3611   Fax: (775) 782-9259   www.bently.com

Provides hardware, software, and services for machinery information and management systems.

Sherman Intl. Pvt. Ltd., Himalaya House H-88, 23 Kasturba Gandhi Marg., New Delhi 110 001, India

Sherman Intl. Pvt. Ltd., 711 Maker Chamber V, 221 Nariman Pt., Mumbai 400 021, India

LOUIS BERGER INTERNATIONAL INC.

100 Halsted Street, East Orange, NJ, 07019

Tel: (201) 678-1960   Fax: (201) 672-4284   www.louisberger.com

Consulting engineers, engaged in architecture, environmental and advisory services.

Louis Berger International Inc., M-122 Greater Kailash Part-1, New Delhi 110 048, India

Louis Berger International Inc., 1/F, KUIDP, 38/1 Coles Road, Cross Frazer Town, Bangalore 560 005, India
Tel: 91-80-563-866   Fax: 91-80-563-867

BEST WESTERN INTERNATIONAL

6201 North 24th Place, Phoenix, AZ, 85106

Tel: (602) 957-4200   Fax: (602) 957-5740   www.bestwestern.com

International hotel chain.

Surya Hotel, New Friends Colony, New Delhi 110 065, India

BHA GROUP HOLDINGS, INC.

8800 East 63rd Street, Kansas City, MO, 64133

Tel: (816) 356-8400   Fax: (816) 353-1873   www.bha.com

Mfr. air pollution control replacement parts.

BHA Group International, Lohia Jain Business Center 2/F, Friends Park Co-op Society, Senepati Bapat Marg, Shivaji Nagar Pune 411 053, India

BLACK & VEATCH LLP

8400 Ward Pkwy., PO Box 8405, Kansas City, MO, 64114

Tel: (816) 339-2000   Fax: (816) 339-2934   www.bv.com

Engaged in engineering, construction and consulting, specializing in infrastructure development in the fields of energy, water and information.

Black & Veatch India, Ltd., 1006, Bhikaji Cama Place, 10th Fl., Bhikaji Cama Bhawan, New Delhi 110 066, India
Tel: 91-11-616-7375 Fax: 91-11-616-7250   Contact: Pradeep Jain, Dir.

THE BLACKSTONE GROUP INC.

345 Park Ave., New York, NY, 10154

Tel: (212) 583-5000   Fax: (212) 583-5712   www.bgglobal.com

Marketing research, business consulting, engineering design and software.

Blackstone Market Facts, 201, Arunkiran Residency, Gagan Vihar Colony Begumpet, Hyderabad 560 016, India

Blackstone Market Facts, 2/F, 6/J Keyatala Road, Calcutta 700 029, India

Blackstone Market Facts, 315 Ground, Indira Nagar, 1st stage, Bangalore 38, India

Blackstone Market Facts, G/3, Heera House 1st Road, Khar (West), Mumbai 400 052, India

Blackstone Market Facts, D-109, LBR Complex, 1/F, 1 Main Road, Anna Nagar (East) Chennai 600 102, India

The Blackstone Group of India, AA 25 Anna Nagar, Madras 600 040, India
Tel: 91-44-6442976   Fax: 91-44-644-2983

The Blackstone Group of India, 68/A, First Fl., Kunj Society, Alkapuri, Baroda 390 005, India
Tel: 91-265-339563   Fax: 91-265-339583

The Blackstone Group of India, F-14, Upper Ground Fl., East of Kailash, New Delhi 110 065, India
Tel: 91-11-622-162525   Fax: 91-11-622-1191

BLOOM ENGINEERING CO., INC.

5460 Horning Rd., Pittsburgh, PA, 15236

Tel: (412) 653-3500   Fax: (412) 653-2253   www.bloomeng.com

Mfr. custom engineered burners and combustion systems.

Thermax Ltd., Burner Development Group, Chinchwad, Pune 411 019, India
Tel: 91-212-770436   Fax: 91-212-774640

BOOZ-ALLEN & HAMILTON INC.

8283 Greensboro Drive, McLean, VA, 22102

Tel: (703) 902-5000   Fax: (703) 902-3333   www.bah.com

International management and technology consultants.

Booz Allen & Hamilton (India) Ltd. Co. KG, Bajaj Bhavan, 2nd Fl., Nariman Point, Mumbai 400 021, India

Tel: 91-22-282-8286 Fax: 91-22-282-8330

THE BOSTON CONSULTING GROUP

Exchange Place, 31st Fl., Boston, MA, 02109

Tel: (617) 973-1200   Fax: (617) 973-1339   www.bcg.com

Management consulting company.

The Boston Consulting Group Pte. Ltd., 55/56 Free Press House, 215 Free Press Journal Marg, Nariman Point, Mumbai 400 021, India

Tel: 91-22-283-7451

BOYDEN CONSULTING CORPORATION

364 Elwood Ave., Hawthorne, NY, 10502

Tel: (914) 747-0093   Fax: (914) 980-6147   www.boyden.com

International executive search firm.

Boyden Associates Ltd., 2-11 Phoenix Mills Compound, Senapati Bapat Mang, Lower Parel, Mumbai 400 013, India

Tel: 91-22-494-3521

Boyden Associates Ltd., 23 Gold Fields Plaza, 45 Sassoon Rd., Pune 411 001, India

Tel: 91-212-639-264

Boyden Associates Ltd., Hug 'S' S-24-25, 2nd Fl., 80 Feet Main Rd., Koramangala, Bangalore 560 095, India

Tel: 91-80-553-5825

BOZELL GROUP

40 West 23rd Street, New York, NY, 10010

Tel: (212) 727-5000   Fax: (212) 645-9173   www.bozell.com

Advertising, marketing, public relations and media consulting.

MAA Communications Bozell, Hdqtrs., MAA House, 6 Service Rd., I Stage, Domlur Layout, Bangalore 560 071, India

Tel: 91-80-556-8910   Fax: 91-80-554-3891   Contact: Bunty Peerbhoy, Mng. Dir.

MAA Communications Bozell, Ltd., 3rd Fl., David Sasoon Bldg., 143 Mahatma Gandhi Rd., Mumbai 400 023, India

Tel: 91-22-267-7374   Fax: 91-22-267-7547   Contact: Ram Kumar Seshu, EVP

MAA Communications Bozell, Ltd. (Chennai), 79 C P Ramaswamy Rd., Alawarpet, Chennai 600 018, India

Tel: 91-44-499-1353   Fax: 91-44-499-2035   Contact: Amrita Chugh

MAA Communications Bozell, Ltd. (Cochin), Door No. 41/615, Ground Fl., Krishnaswamy Rd., Cochin 682 035, India

Tel: 91-484-354-609   Fax: 91-484-354-614   Contact: P. Ravindranath, Mgr.

MAA Communications Bozell, Ltd. (Coimbatore), 4th Fl., 'Vyshnax', 95-A Race Course, Coimbatore 641 018, India

Tel: 91-422-211-183   Fax: 91-422-317-479   Contact: P. Ramskrishnan, Mgr.

MAA Communications Bozell, Ltd. (Delhi), K-77 Lajpat Nagar II, New Delhi 110 024, India

Tel: 91-11-691-4640   Fax: 91-11-691-4670   Contact: Shankar Narayan J. Alva, EVP

MAA Communications Bozell, Ltd. (Pune), 3015/8, Sri Nidhi Chambers, MHT Bldg., 4th Fl., Senapathi Bapat Rd., Pune 411 016, India

Tel: 91-212-353-632   Contact: Vishwas Shrikhande, Mgr.

BRANSON ULTRASONICS CORPORATION

41 Eagle Road, Danbury, CT, 06813-1961

Tel: (203) 796-0400   Fax: (203) 796-2285   www.branson-plasticsjoin.com

Engaged in design, development, manufacture and marketing of plastics joining, precision cleaning and processing equipment.

Branson Ultrasonics, PO Box 6840, Santa Cruz East, Mumbai 400 055, India

Tel: 91-22-850-5570   Fax: 91-22-850-8681

BRISTOL-MYERS SQUIBB COMPANY

345 Park Ave., New York, NY, 10154-0037

Tel: (212) 546-4000   Fax: (212) 546-4020   www.bms.com

Pharmaceutical and food preparations, medical and surgical instruments.

ConvaTec, Div. Bristol-Myers Squibb, Marol Naka, Sir MV Road, Andheri, East Bombay 400 059, India

Tel: 91-22-852-2629

BROADVISION, INC.

585 Broadway, Redwood City, CA, 94063

Tel: (650) 261-5100   Fax: (650) 261-5900   www.broadvision.com

Develops and delivers an integrated suite of packaged applications for personalized enterprise portals.

BroadVision India
c/o DBS Corporate Club, Raheja Chambers, 213 Nariman Point, Mumbai 400 021, India

BRY-AIR INC.

10793 Street, Rt. 37 West, Sunbury, OH, 43074

Tel: (740) 965-2974   Fax: (740) 965-5470   www.bry-air.com

Mfr. industrial dehumidifiers/auxiliary equipment for plastics industrial.

Bry-Air Asia Pvt. Ltd., 20 Rajpur Road, Delhi 110 054, India

Tel: 91-11-291-2800   Fax: 91-11-291-5127   Contact: Deepak Pahwa

BUCYRUS INTERNATIONAL, INC.

1100 Milwaukee Avenue, South Milwaukee, WI, 53172

Tel: (414) 768-4000   Fax: (414) 768-4474   www.bucyrus.com

Mfr. of surface mining equipment, primarily walking draglines, electric mining shovels and blast hole drills.

Bacyrus India Pvt. Ltd., B-1 Marble Arch, 9 Prithvi Raj Rd., New Delhi 110 011, India

Tel: 91-11-462-5572   Fax: 91-11-462-5561   Contact: David Lee, Mng. Dir.

BUDGET GROUP, INC.

125 Basin St., Ste. 210, Daytona Beach, FL, 32114

Tel: (904) 238-7035   Fax: (904) 238-7461   www.budgetrentacar.com

Car and truck rental system.

Budget Rent A Car, G-3 Arunachal, Barakginba, Read, New Delhi, India

Tel: 91-11-3318600

LEO BURNETT, DIV. B-COM 3 GROUP

35 West Wacker Drive, Chicago, IL, 60601

Tel: (312) 220-5959   Fax: (312) 220-6533   www.leoburnett.com

Engaged in advertising, marketing, media buying and planning, and public relations.

Chiatra Leo Burnett, Mumbai, India

BURSON-MARSTELLER

230 Park Avenue South, New York, NY, 10003-1566

Tel: (212) 614-4000   Fax: (212) 614-4262   www.bm.com

Public relations/public affairs consultants.

Burson-Marsteller Rogers Pereira Communications Pvt. Ltd., 306 NILGIRI, 9 Barakhamba Rd., New Delhi 110 001, India

Tel: 91-11-335-4821   Fax: 91-11-335-4871   Emp: 35

Burson-Marsteller Rogers Pereira Communications Pvt. Ltd., Whitehall, 143 A.K.Marg. Kemp's Corner, Mumbai 400 036, India

Tel: 91-22-363-0398   Fax: 91-22-364-3597

BUTLER INTERNATIONAL

110 Summit Ave., Montvale, NJ, 07645

Tel: (201) 573-8000   Fax: (201) 573-9723   www.butler.com

Leading supplier of skilled technical personnel.

Butler Technical Group, Suite 408, Diamond Block, Rockdale Compound, Somajiguda 500082, India

Contact: Praveen Reddy

CADENCE DESIGN SYSTEMS, INC.

2655 Seely Ave., Bldg. 5, San Jose, CA, 95134

Tel: (408) 943-1234   Fax: (408) 943-0513   www.cadence.com

Mfr. electronic design automation software.

Cadence Design Systems (India) PVT Ltd., "Embassy Classic", 1/F, No. 11, Vittal Mallya Road, Bangalore 560001, India

Tel: 91-80-2122028   Fax: 91-80-2122043

CALDERA INTERNATIONAL

355 South 520 West, Ste. 100, Linden, UT, 84057

Tel: (801) 765-4999   Fax: (801) 765-1313   www.caldera.com

Provides integrated solutions for small-to-medium businesses, retail operations, telecommunications and other vertical markets.

Caldera India, 56, Janpath, 2/F, New Delhi 110001, India

Contact: Srikant Acharya

CAMBREX CORPORATION

1 Meadowlands Plaza, East Rutherford, NJ, 07063

Tel: (201) 804-3000   Fax: (201) 804-9852   www.cambrex.com

human health, animal health/agriculture and Mfr. biotechnology products and produce specialty chemicals.

Cambrex India, 316, Vardhaman Chambers, Sector 17, Vashi, New Bombay 400 705, India

Tel: 91-22-767-1472   Fax: 91-22-768-7204

Osmic India, 124-B Sanjeeva, Reedy Nagar, Hyderabad 500 038, India

CAPITAL CONTROLS COMPANY, INC.

3000 Advance Lane, PO Box 211, Colmar, PA, 18915-0211

Tel: (215) 997-4000   Fax: (215) 997-4062   www.capitalcontrols.com

Mfr./services water disinfecting products and systems.

Capital Controls Pvt. Ltd., 15/AJ Laxmi Industrial Estate, Link Road Andheri, West Mumbai 400 053, India

CARBOLINE COMPANY

350 Hanley Industrial Court, St. Louis, MO, 63144

Tel: (314) 644-1000   Fax: (314) 644-4617   www.carboline.com

Mfr. coatings and sealants.

CDC Carboline (India) Pvt. Ltd., 162 A Greams Rd., Tamil Nadu, Madras 600 006, India

CARLSON COMPANIES, INC.

PO Box 59159, Minneapolis, MN, 55459

Tel: (612) 550-4520   Fax: (612) 550-4580   www.cmg.carlson.com

Marketing services agency.

Direm Marketing Services Pvt. Ltd., 83-C Dr E Moses Road, Worli Mumbai 400 018, India

Tel: 91- 22-495-4944   Fax: 91- 22-493-5575

THE CARLYLE GROUP L.P.

1001 Pennsylvania Avenue, NW, Washington, DC, 20004-2505

Tel: (202) 347-2626   Fax: (202) 347-1818   www.thecarlylegroup.com

Global investor in defense contracts.

The Carlyle Group, Bangalore, India

CARPENTER TECHNOLOGY CORPORATION

PO Box 14662, Reading, PA, 19612-4662

Tel: (610) 208-2000   Fax: (610) 208-3214   www.cartech.com

Mfr. specialty steels and structural ceramics for casting industrial.

Kalyani Carpenter Special Steels Ltd. (JV), Pune, India

CARRIER CORPORATION

One Carrier Place, Farmington, CT, 06034-4015

Tel: (860) 674-3000   Fax: (860) 679-3010   www.carrier.com

Mfr./distributor/services A/C, heating and refrigeration equipment.

Carrier Aircon Ltd., Narsingpur, Kherki dhaula Post, Gurgaon Haryana 120 001, India

Tel: 91-124-323231   Fax: 91-124-323241

CATERPILLAR INC.

100 NE Adams Street, Peoria, IL, 61629-6105

Tel: (309) 675-1000   Fax: (309) 675-1182   www.cat.com

Mfr. earth/material-handling and construction machinery and equipment and engines.

Hindustan Powerplus Ltd., Saki-Vihar Rd., Powai, Mumbai 400 072, India

CB RICHARD ELLIS SERVICES

200 N. Sepulveda Blvd., Ste. 300, El Segundo, CA, 90245-4380

Tel: (310) 563-8600   Fax: (310) 563-8670   www.cbrichardellis.com

Commercial real estate services.

CB Richard Ellis Ltd., 207 Embassy Square, 148 Infantry Rd., Bangalore 560 001, India

CB Richard Ellis Ltd., 113C Mittal Tower, Nariman Point, Mumbai 400 021, India

CB Richard Ellis Ltd., 1/F, E-1 Connaught Place, New Delhi 110 001, India

CB Richard Ellis Ltd., 2H Gee Emerald, 151 Village Road, Nungambakkam, Chennai 600 034, India

CDM INTERNATIONAL INC.

50 Hampshire Street, Cambridge, MA, 02139

Tel: (617) 452-6000   Fax: (617) 452-8000   www.cdm.com

Consulting engineers.

CDM Camp Dresser & McKee International Inc., 1M Prince Arcade, 22A Cathedral Road, Channai 600 086, India

Tel: 91-44-827-3755

CENDANT CORPORATION

9 West 57th Street, New York, NY, 10019

Tel: (212) 413-1800   Fax: (212) 413-1918   www.cendant.com

Membership-based, direct marketer offering shopping/travel/insurance and dining discount programs

Delhi Express Travels, Private Ltd., P-13 Connaught Circus, New Delhi 110 001, India

Tel: 91-11-3365952   Fax: 91-11-3363718

CHEMCENTRAL CORPORATION

7050 West 71st Street, Bedford Park, IL, 60499

Tel: (708) 594-7000   Fax: (708) 594-6382   www.chemcentral.com

Engaged in chemicals distribution.

RishiChem Distributors Pvt. Ltd., 65 Atlanta, Nariman Point, Mumbai 400 021, India

Tel: 91-22-282 -5200

THE CHEMITHON CORPORATION

5430 West Marginal Way Southwest, Seattle, WA, 98106

Tel: (206) 937-9954   Fax: (206) 932-3786   www.chemithon.com.

Chemicals process equipment manufacturing for detergent, specialty chemicals and power generation industries.

Chemithon Engineers (P) Ltd., 372/374 S.V. Road, 1st Floor, Shiv Anand-A Goregaon (West), Mumbai 400 104, India

Tel: 91-22-8741188   Fax: 91-22-8741366

CHEMTEX INTERNATIONAL INC.

1979 Eastwood Rd., Wilmington, NC, 28403

Tel: (910) 509-4400   Fax: (910) 509-4567   www.chemtex.com

Mfr. fibers and petrochemicals; engineering, procurement, construction, construction management.

Chemtex Consulting of India Ltd, First Fl., B-1, Tower Corporate Block, Golden Enclave, Airport Rd., Bangalore 560 017, India

Tel: 91-80-526-5627   Fax: 91-80-526 9659

Chemtex Engineering of India Ltd., B-3/51, 1/F, Commercial Complex, Safdarjung Enclave, New Delhi 110 029, India

Tel: 91-11-616-2441   Fax: 91-11-616-1226

Chemtex Engineering of India Ltd., Chemtex House, Main Street, Sector 12, Hiranandani Gardens, Powai Mumbai 400 076, India

Tel: 91-22-570-4491   Fax: 91-22-570-1998   Contact: R. K. Dasgupta, Pres.

THE CHERRY CORPORATION

3600 Sunset Ave., PO Box 718, Waukegan, IL, 60087

Tel: (847) 662-9200   Fax: (847) 662-2990   www.cherrycorp.com

Mfr. electrical switches, electronic keyboards, controls and displays.

TVS Cherry Pvt. Ltd., 205 Madhava Building, Bandra-Kurla Complex, Bandra East IND-Bombay 400 051, India

Tel: 91-22-6452582   Fax: 91-22-6452582

CHESTERTON BLUMENAUER BINSWANGER

Two Logan Square, 4th Floor, Philadelphia, PA, 19103-2759

Tel: (215) 448-6000   Fax: (215) 448-6238   www.cbbi.com

Real estate and related services.

Chesterton Meghraj Property Consultants Pvt. Ltd., 1109-10, Ashoka Estate, Barakhamba Road, Connaught Place, New Delhi 110 001, India

CHICAGO RAWHIDE INDUSTRIES (CRI)

735 Tollgate Road, Elgin, IL, 60123

Tel: (847) 742-7840   Fax: (847) 742-7845   www.chicago-rawhide.com

Mfr. shaft and face seals.

CR Seals India Pvt. Ltd., 13/5, Singasandra, 13 KM Hosur Road, Bangalore 560 068, India

Tel: 91-22-600-1489   Fax: 91-22-600-1541

CHILD CUSTODY CONSULTANTS

400 West Tenth Street, Suite 204, Santa Ana, CA, 92701

Tel: (714) 285-1104   Fax: (714) 285-1136   www.laislaw.com

Facilitators in child custody and visitation issues.

Child Custody Consultants, Vidya Rattan Associates, 183/31, Ashok Vihar, Sonepat 131001, India

Child Custody Consultants, Ronald E. Lais, Inc., 1230 Sector , Pocket 1, Vasant Kung, New Delhi 110070, India

Tel: 91-11-6899515

THE CHUBB CORPORATION

15 Mountain View Road, Warren, NJ, 07061-1615

Tel: (908) 580-2000   Fax: (908) 580-3606   www.chubb.com

Holding company for property and casualty insurance and liability insurance for corporate executives.

Federal Insurance Company/Chubb Group, Ste. 323, Hyatt Regency Delhi, Bhikaiji Cama Place, Ring Rd., New Delhi 110 066, India

Tel: 91-11-619-6754   Fax: 91-11-616-5110

CIGNA COMPANIES

One Liberty Place, Philadelphia, PA, 19192

Tel: (215) 761-1000   Fax: (215) 761-5511   www.cigna.com

Insurance, invest, health care and other financial services.

CIGNA HealthCare Management Company Pvt. Limited, Ste. 301-305, Prestige Terminus II, No. 22 Airport Exit Road, Bangalore 560 017, India

Tel: 91-80-527-8398   Fax: 91-80-527-8402

CINCINNATI INCORPORATED

PO Box 11111, Cincinnati, OH, 45211

Tel: (513) 367-7100   Fax: (513) 367-7552   www.e-ci.com

Mfr. metal fabricating equipment.

Heatly & Gresham India, Ltd., E-47/4, Okhla Industrial Area Phase II, New Delhi, India

Tel: 91-11-683-6293   Fax: 91-11-6847-171

CINCOM SYSTEMS INC.

55 Merchant Street, Cincinnati, OH, 45446

Tel: (513) 612-2300   Fax: (513) 481-8332   www.cincom.com

Develop/distributor computer software.

Cincom Systems India Inc., 914-915, Arunachal Bldg., 19 Barakhamba Road, New Delhi 110 001, India

CISCO SYSTEMS, INC.

170 West Tasman Drive, San Jose, CA, 95134-1706

Tel: (408) 526-4000   Fax: (408) 526-4100   www.cisco.com

Develop/mfr./market computer hardware and software networking systems.

Cisco Systems (HK) Ltd., New Delhi Office, M-6 GK II Market, New Delhi 110 048, India

Tel: 91-11-623-3201   Fax: 91-11-623-3207

CITIGROUP, INC.

399 Park Avenue, New York, NY, 10022

Tel: (212) 559-1000   Fax: (212) 559-3646   www.citigroup.com

Provides insurance and financial services worldwide.

Citigroup, Sakhar Bhavan, 10th Fl., 230 Backbay Reclamation, Nairman Point, Bombay 400 021, India

Contact: David P. Conner

CITRIX SYSTEMS, INC.

6400 NW 6th Way, Fort Lauderdale, FL, 33309

Tel: (954) 267-3000   Fax: (954) 267-9319   www.citrix.com

Developer of computer software.

Citrix Software India Limited, 212, I Main Road, Domlur II Stage, Bangalore 560071, India

Tel: 91-80-5352911   Fax: 91-80-5352916

CLEAR CHANNEL COMMUNICATIONS

200 East Basse Road, San Antonio, TX, 78209

Tel: (210) 822-2828   Fax: (210) 822-2299   www.clearchannel.com

Owns, manages, promotes and produces concerts and shows; programs and sells airtime for radio stations, owns and places outdoor advertising displays and provides agent services to athletes and broadcasters.

More Group, Maker Chambers 3, 6/F, Nariman Point, Mumbai 400 021, India

Tel: 91-22-287-5141   Fax: 91-22-284-5763   Contact: Sandy Nandwani, Mgr.

CNH (CASE NEW HOLLAND) GLOBAL

100 South Saunders Road, Lake Forest, IL, 60045

Tel: (847) 955-3821   Fax: (847) 955-3961   www.casecorp.com

Mfr. and sale of agricultural and construction equipment.

CNH India Limited, 103, Askoka Estate, 24 Barakhamba Road, New Delhi 110 001, India

Tel: 91-11-373-1589   Fax: 91-11-335-2306

CNH Pvt. Ltd., 210, Okhla Industrial Area III, New Delhi 110 020, India

Tel: 91-11-693-220-07

THE COCA-COLA COMPANY

1 Coca Cola Plaza, Atlanta, GA, 30313

Tel: (404) 676-2121   Fax: (404) 676-6792   www.coca-cola.com

Mfr./marketing/distributor soft drinks, syrups and concentrates, juice and juice-drink products.

Coca-Cola Ltd., India

Contact: Donald W. Short

COEN COMPANY, INC.

1510 Rollins Road, Burlingame, CA, 94010

Tel: (650) 697-0440   Fax: (650) 686-5655   www.coen.com

Mfr. industrial burners.

Coen Bharat, Ltd., 302, Delta, Hiranandani Gardens, Powai, Mumbai 400 076, India

Tel: 91-22-570-2501   Fax: 91-22-570-2504

COGNIZANT TECHNOLOGY SOLUTIONS CORPORATION

500 Glenpointe Centre West, Teaneck, NJ, 07666

Tel: (201) 801-0233   Fax: (201) 801-0243   www.cognizant.com

Provides software development , application management, computer date corrections, and currency conversion.

Cognizant Technology Solutions, 1/1 to 1/5, Silver Jubilee Block, 3rd Cross, Mission Road, Bangalore 560 027, India

Cognizant Technology Solutions, Karunai Kudil, 226 Cathedral Road, Chennai 600 086, India

COLGATE-PALMOLIVE COMPANY

300 Park Ave., New York, NY, 10022

Tel: (212) 310-2000   Fax: (212) 310-2919   www.colgate.com

Mfr. pharmaceuticals, cosmetics, toiletries and detergents.

Colgate-Palmolive (India) Pvt. Ltd., Steelcrete House, 3 Dinshaw Vacha Rd., Mumbai 400 020, India

COMPUTER ASSOCIATES INTERNATIONAL INC.

One Computer Associates Plaza, Islandia, NY, 11788

Tel: (516) 342-5224   Fax: (516) 342-5329   www.cai.com

Integrated business software for enterprise computing and information management, application development, manufacturing, financial applications and professional services.

Computer Associates Pte. Ltd., 511/512 Merchant Chambers, 98A Hill Rd., Bandra West Mumbai 400 050, India

Tel: 91-22-643-4681

CONAGRA FOODS, INC.

One ConAgra Drive, Omaha, NE, 68102-5001

Tel: (402) 595-4000   Fax: (402) 595-4707   www.conagra.com

Prepared/frozen foods, grains, flour, animal feeds, agro chemicals, poultry, meat, dairy products, including Healthy Choice, Butterball and Hunt's.

ConAgra Inc., Nepal, India

CONEXANT SYSTEMS, INC.

4311 Jamboree Road, PO Box C, Newport Beach, CA, 92658-8902

Tel: (949) 483-4600   Fax: (949) 483-4078   www.conexant.com

Provides semiconductor products for communications electronics.

Conexant Systems Worldwide, Inc., 47 Community Centre, Friends Colony, New Delhi 110 065, India

Tel: 91-11-692-4780   Fax: 91-11-692-4712

COOPER BUSSMANN

PO Box 14460, St. Louis, MO, 63178-4460

Tel: (636) 394-2877   Fax: (636) 527-1405   www.bussmann.com

Mfr. and markets circuit protection products for the electrical, electronic, and automotive industries.

Bussmann India, White House, Unit #5, 2/F, 23-29 St. Marks Road, Bangalore 560 001, India

Tel: 91 80 227 0893   Fax: 91 80 224 0124

COOPER INDUSTRIES INC.

6600 Travis Street, Ste. 5800, Houston, TX, 77002

Tel: (713) 209-8400   Fax: (713) 209-8995   www.cooperindustries.com

Mfr./distributor electrical products, tools, hardware and automotive products, fuses and accessories for electronic applications and circuit boards.

Bussmann India, Div. Cooper Industries, 2nd Fl., Unit # 5, White House, 23-29 St. Marks Rd., Bangalore 560 001, India

Tel: 91-80-227-0893   Fax: 91-80-224-0124

COOPER-STANDARD AUTOMOTIVE GROUP

2401 South Gulley Road, Dearborn, MI, 48124

Tel: (313) 561-1100   Fax: (313) 561-6526   www.cooperstandard.com

Mfr. molded and extruded rubber and plastic products for automotive and appliance industry, retread tire industry.

Cooper Standard Automotive, 3 Bishen Udhyog Premises, Opp. Raja Industrial Estate, P.K. Road, Mulung W Mumbai 400 080, India

Tel: 91-22-564-5313   Fax: 91-22-564-2577

COPELAND CORPORATION

1675 West Campbell Road, Sidney, OH, 45365-0669

Tel: (937) 498-3011   Fax: (937) 498-3334   www.copeland-corp.com

Producer of compressors and condensing units for commercial and residential air conditioning and refrigeration equipment.

Kirloskar Copeland Limited, 1202/1 Ghole Road, Shivajinagar, Pune 411 005, India

CORNING INC.

One Riverfront Plaza, Corning, NY, 14831-0001

Tel: (607) 974-9000   Fax: (607) 974-8091   www.corning.com

Mfr. glass and specialty materials, consumer products; communications, laboratory services.

Corning India, World Trade Tower, 3rd Fl., Barakhamba Lane, New Delhi 110 001, India

Tel: 91-11-332-7391   Fax: 91-11-372-1520

CORRPRO COMPANIES, INC.

1090 Enterprise Drive, Medina, OH, 44256

Tel: (330) 725-6681   Fax: (330) 723-0244   www.corrpro.com

Engaged in full-services corrosion engineering and cathodic protection.

Corrpro Companies India, Flat No. 51, Charkop Happy Home C.H.S., Plot No. 210, Road No. RDP-5, Sector 4, Charkop Kandivli West, Mumbai 400 067, India

Tel: 91-22-8690343   Fax: 91-22-8690343   Contact: Madhav Joshi

CRAWFORD & COMPANY

5620 Glenridge Drive NE, Atlanta, GA, 30342

Tel: (404) 256-0830   Fax: (404) 847-4025   www.crawfordandcompany.com

Provides international insurance services engaged in risk management and claims adjustment.

Anuj Puri & Associates, 1109-1110 Ashoka Estate, Barakhamba Road, Connaught Place, New Delhi 110 001, India

CUMMINS, INC.

500 Jackson Street, PO Box 3005, Columbus, IN, 47202-3005

Tel: (812) 377-5000   Fax: (812) 377-4937   www.cummins.com

Mfr. diesel engines.

Kirldskar Cummins Ltd., Kothrun, Pune 411 029, India

CUSHMAN & WAKEFIELD INC.

51 West 52nd Street, New York, NY, 10019

Tel: (212) 841-7500   Fax: (212) 841-7867   www.cushwake.com

Engaged in commercial real estate services.

Cushman & Wakefield, 578 Syndicate Bank Road, Indiranagar 1st Stage, Bangalore 560 038, India

Cushman & Wakefield, Mafatlal House, Backbay Redamation, Churchate, Mumbai 400 020, India

CYLINK CORPORATION

3131 Jay Street, Santa Clara, CA, 95054

Tel: (408) 855-6000   Fax: (408) 855-6100   www.cyllink.com

Develop and manufactures encryption software.

Cylink India, A27/4 DLF Quatab Enclave, I, Gurgoan 122 002, India

Tel: 91-124 6346-14   Contact: Mash Khan

CYPRESS SEMICONDUCTOR CORPORATION

3901 N. First Street, San Jose, CA, 95134-1599

Tel: (408) 943-2600   Fax: (408) 943-2796   www.cypress.com

Mfr. integrated circuits.

Cypress Semiconductor, Sharda Towers, 1/F, 56 Nandiurg Road, Benson Town Bangalore 560 046, India

Tel: 91-80-3530132   Fax: 91-80-3438679

DANA CORPORATION

4500 Dorr Street, Toledo, OH, 43615

Tel: (419) 535-4500   Fax: (419) 535-4643   www.dana.com

Mfr./sales of automotive, heavy truck, off-highway, fluid and mechanical power components and engine parts, filters and gaskets.

Perfect Circle Victor Limited, 20 Midc Estate, Satpur Nasik 422 007, India

Perfect Circle Victor Ltd., Magnet House, Narottan Mararjee Mrg, Ballard Estate, Bombay 400 038, India

Spicer India, 29 Milestone Pune-Nasik Hwy., Kuruli Khed, Pune 410 501, India

Tel: 91-212-798713

DANZAS AEI, INC.

120 Tokeneke Road, PO Box 1231, Darien, CT, 06820

Tel: (203) 655-7900   Fax: (203) 655-5779   www.aeilogistics.com

International air freight forwarder.

Danzas AEI, c/o Lemuir Air Express, Head Office, 12 K. Dubash Marg, Fort Bombay Mumbai 400 023, India

Tel: 91-22-284-4420   Fax: 91-22-204-0806

D'ARCY MASIUS BENTON & BOWLES INC. (DMB&B)

1675 Broadway, New York, NY, 10019

Tel: (212) 468-3622   Fax: (212) 468-2987   www.darcyww.com

Full service international advertising and communications group.

Enterprise Advertising Pvt. Ltd., 4/F, Pharma Search House, BG Kher Rd., Worli Mumbai 400 081, India

DAZEL CORPORATION

301 Congress Ave., Ste. 1100, Austin, TX, 78701

Tel: (512) 494-7300   Fax: (512) 494-7394   www.dazel.com

Mfr. software for information delivery solutions on documents and reports.

Dazel HP India Ltd., Innovator Building, Unit No. 2, Level 8 ITPL, Whitefield Road, Bangalor, India

DDB WORLDWIDE COMMUNICATIONS GROUP

437 Madison Ave., New York, NY, 10022

Tel: (212) 415-2000   Fax: (212) 415-3417   www.ddbn.com

Advertising agency.

Mudra Communications(DDB), Ahmedabad, India

DELL COMPUTER CORPORATION

One Dell Way, Round Rock, TX, 78682-2222

Tel: (512) 338-4400   Fax: (512) 728-3653   www.dell.com

Direct marketer and supplier of computer systems.

Dell Asia Pacific Sdn., India Liaison Office, 1 & 11 Fl., J. S. Towers, Brigade Rd., Bangalore 560 001, India

Tel: 91-80-565842 Fax: 91-80-5544738   Contact: Naren Ayyar, Gen. Mgr.

DELOITTE TOUCHE TOHMATSU INTERNATIONAL

1633 Broadway, New York, NY, 10019

Tel: (212) 492-4000   Fax: (212) 392-4154   www.deloitte.com

Accounting, audit, tax and management consulting services.

C.C. Chokshi & Company, Mafalal House, Backbay Reclamation, Mumbai Bombay 400 020, India

Deloitte Haskins & Sells, Jehangir Wadia Bldg., 3rd Fl., 51 Mahatma Gandhi Rd., Mumbai Bombay 400 023, India

Deloitte Haskins & Sells, 2/2A Ho Chi Minh Sarani, Calcutta 700 071, India

Fraser & Company, 169 North Usman Rd., T Nagar, Madras 600 017, India

DELTA AIR LINES INC.

Hartsfield International Airport, 1030 Delta Blvd., Atlanta, GA, 30320-6001

Tel: (404) 715-2600   Fax: (404) 715-5494   www.delta-air.com

Major worldwide airline; international air transport services.

Delta Air Lines Inc., Mumbai, India

DELUXE CORPORATION

3680 Victoria Street North, Shoreview, MN, 55126-2966

Tel: (612) 483-7111   Fax: (612) 481-4163   www.deluxe.com

Leading U.S. check printer and provider of electronic payment services.

HCL Deluxe Corp., A-10-11, Sector III, Noida UP 201 301, India

Tel: 91-11-9154-3256   Fax: 91-11-9154-0775

DENTSPLY INTERNATIONAL

570 West College Ave., PO Box 872, York, PA, 17405-0872

Tel: (717) 845-7511   Fax: (717) 843-6357   www.dentsply.com

Mfr. and distribution of dental supplies and equipment.

Dentsply India, 7th Main Fourth Cross, HAL 11nd Stage, Indiranagar Bangalore 560 008, India

Tel: 91-80-526-2735

Dentsply India, Flat #201, Tej Mahan Apartments, J.B.Nagar, Andheri East, Mumbai 400 059, India

Tel: 91-22-820-3285

Dentsply India, D-21 Saket, New Delhi 110 017, India

Tel: 91-11-696-1714

Dentsply India Plant, Plot #294, Udyog Vihar, Phase II, Gurgaon Haryana 122 016, India

Tel: 91-124-345-333

DHL WORLDWIDE EXPRESS

50 California Avenue, San Francisco, CA, 94111

Tel: (415) 677-6100   Fax: (415) 824-9700   www.dhl.com

Worldwide air express carrier.

DHL Worldwide Express, Lok Bharati Complex, Marol Maroshi Rd., Andheri East, Mumbai 400 059, India

Tel: 91-22-851-5151

DIAMOND CHAIN COMPANY

402 Kentucky Ave., Indianapolis, IN, 46225

Tel: (317) 638-6431   Fax: (317) 633-2243   www.diamondchain.com

Mfr. roller chains.

T.I. Diamond Chain Ltd., 11/12 North Beach Rd., Madras 600 001, India

DIEBOLD INC.

5995 Mayfair Road, North Canton, OH, 44720-8077

Tel: (330) 490-4000   Fax: (330) 490-3794   www.diebold.com

Mfr. automated banking systems; security services for banking industrial and related fields.

Diebold HMA, No. 1 - 2/F, Ceebros Centre, 45 Montieth Road, Egmore Chennai 600 008, India

Tel: 91-44-855-3139

DIMON INCORPORATED

512 Bridge Street, PO Box 681, Danville, VA, 24543-0681

Tel: (804) 792-7511   Fax: (804) 791-0377   www.dimon.com

One of world's largest importer and exporters of leaf tobacco.

DIMON International Services Limited, Door 3-30-15 Ring Road, Guntur Andhra Pradesh 522006, India

Tel: 91-863-351-187   Fax: 91-863-350-199

DIONEX CORPORATION

1228 Titan Way, PO Box 3603, Sunnyvale, CA, 94086-3603

Tel: (408) 737-0700   Fax: (408) 730-9403   www.dionex.com

Develop/mfr./market chromatography systems and related products.

Indtech Analytical, K-227 Ansa Industrial Estate, Saki-Vihar Road, Saki-Naka, Bombay 400 072, India

Tel: 91-22-852-4809

DISCOVERY COMMUNICATIONS, INC.
7700 Wisconsin Avenue, Bethesda, MD, 20814

Tel: (301) 986-0444   Fax: (301) 771-4064   www.discovery.com

Owns and operates cable networks.

Discovery Communications, N 606 North Block, Rear Wing, 47 Manipal Centre, Dickenson Road, Bangalore Bangalore, India

Tel: 91-80-558-3453

Discovery Communications, 9/1 B Qutab Institution Area, Aruna Asaf Ali Marg, New Delhi 110 067, India

Tel: 91-11-686-1909

DIVINE
1301 N. Elston Ave., Chicago, IL, 60622

Tel: (773) 394-6600   Fax: (773) 394-6601   www.divine.com

Software and services provider.

Divine, Inc., 8-3-229/34,Tahirville, Yousufguda Check Post, Hyderabad 500 045, India

DMC STRATEX NETWORKS, INC.
170 Rose Orchard Way, San Jose, CA, 95134

Tel: (408) 943-0777   Fax: (408) 944-1648   www.dmcstratexnetworks.com

Designs, manufactures, and markets advanced wireless solutions for wireless broadband access.

DMC Stratex Networks, 1/F, 114 Jor Bagh, New Delhi 110 003, India

Tel: 91-11-465-2860

D-M-E COMPANY
29111 Stephenson Highway, Madison Heights, MI, 48071

Tel: (248) 398-6000   Fax: (248) 544-5705   www.dmeco.com

Manufacture and distribution of mold tooling, mold components, hot runner systems, and electronic controls for the plastics industry.

D-M-E Company (India) Ltd., 203, Turf Estate Shakti Mill Lane, Mahalakshmi Mumbai 400 001, India

DONALDSON COMPANY, INC.
PO Box 1299, Minneapolis, MN, 55431

Tel: (952) 887-3131   Fax: (952) 887-3155   www.donaldson.com

Mfr. filtration systems and replacement parts.

D. I. Filter Systems Pvt. Ltd., C-94, 1st Fl., Shivalik, Near Malviya Nagar, New Delhi 110 017, India

R.R. DONNELLEY & SONS COMPANY
77 West Wacker Drive, Chicago, IL, 60601-1696

Tel: (312) 326-8000   Fax: (312) 326-8543   www.rrdonnelley.com

Engaged in commercial printing and allied communication services.

R. R. Donnelley Financial, c/o Tata Donnelley Ltd., Birya House, Prin Naiman St., Fort Mumbai 400 001, India

Tel: 91-22-265-5737

Tata Donnelley Ltd., 414 Veer Savarkar Marg, Prabhadevi, Mumbai 400 025, India

Tel: 91-22-768-2430

DOUBLECLICK, INC.
450 West 33rd Street, New York, NY, 10001

Tel: (212) 683-0001   Fax: (212) 889-0062   www.doubleclick.net

Engaged in online advertising and e-mail marketing.

Doubleclick, Apeejay House, 3 Dinshaw Vachha Road, Mumbai 400 020, India

THE DOW CHEMICAL COMPANY
2030 Dow Center, Midland, MI, 48674

Tel: (989) 636-1000   Fax: (989) 636-3228   www.dow.com

Mfr. chemicals, plastics, pharmaceuticals, agricultural products, consumer products.

Dow Chemical NV, PO Box 109, New Delhi 110 001, India

IDL Chemicals Ltd., Kukatpally, Sanatnagar (I.E.), PO Box, Hyderabad 500 018, India

Polychem Ltd., 7 Jamshedji Tata Rd., Churchgate Reclamation, Mumbai 400 020, India

DRAFT WORLDWIDE

633 North St. Clair Street, Chicago, IL, 60611-3211

Tel: (312) 944-3500   Fax: (312) 944-3566   www.draftworldwide.com

Full service international advertising agency, engaged in brand building, direct and promotional marketing.

Corvo DraftWorldwide PVT Ltd., 52-57 Grants Bldg., 1st Fl., 19A Arthur Bunder Rd., Colaba Mumbai 400 005, India

Tel: 91-22-285-2208   Fax: 91-22-285-2289

DraftWorldwide, H-28 Basement Masjid Moth., Greater Kailash-II, New Delhi 110 048, India

Tel: 91-11-641-4632   Fax: 91-11-621-6964

DRESSER-RAND COMPANY

PO Box 560, Paul Clark Drive, Olean, NY, 14760

Tel: (716) 375-3000   Fax: (716) 375-3178   www.dresser-rand.com

Mfr. generators, centrifugal compressors, turbines and control systems.

Dresser-Rand India Pvt. Ltd., Rhone-Poulenc House, 2/F, S K Ahire Marg, Prabhadevi PO Box 9123, Mumbai 400 025, India

Tel: 91-22-460-8600

DREVER COMPANY

PO Box 98, 380 Red Lion Road, Huntingdon, PA, 19006-0098

Tel: (215) 947-3400   Fax: (215) 947-7934   www.drever.com

Mfr. industrial furnaces and heat processing equipment.

Nirvan Industrial Furnaces, G-6, Gitanjali, Near Radio Club, Colaba, Mumbai 400005, India

E.I. DUPONT DE NEMOURS & COMPANY

1007 Market Street, Wilmington, DE, 19898

Tel: (302) 774-1000   Fax: (302) 774-7321   www.dupont.com

Mfr. and sales of diversified chemicals, plastics, specialty products and fibers.

E.I. DuPont India Ltd., 701-724 Bonanza, B Wing, Sahar Plaza Complex 7/F, Andheri-Kurla Road, Andheri (E), Mumbai 4000059, India

Tel: 91 22 839 0770

EASTMAN CHEMICAL COMPANY

100 North Eastman Road, Kingsport, TN, 37662-5075

Tel: (423) 229-2000   Fax: (423) 229-1351   www.eastman.com

Mfr. plastics, chemicals, fibers.

Eastman Chemical Ltd., 1301, Raheja Centre, Nariman Point, Mumbai 400 021, India

Tel: 91-22-287-6568   Fax: 91-22-284-3220   Contact: Harish Davey

EASTMAN KODAK COMPANY

343 State Street, Rochester, NY, 14650

Tel: (716) 724-4000   Fax: (716) 724-1089   www.kodak.com

Develop/mfr. photo and chemicals products, information management/video/copier systems, fibers/plastics for various industry.

India Photographic Co. Ltd., Kodak House, Dr. Dadabhai Naoroji Rd., PO Box 343, Mumbai 400 001, India

J.D. EDWARDS & COMPANY

One Technology Way, Denver, CO, 80237

Tel: (303) 334-4000   Fax: (303) 334-4970   www.jdedwards.com

Computer software products.

Systime Computer Systems Ltd., Steepz, Andheri (E), Mumbai 400 096, India

Tel: 91-22-832-0051   Fax: 91-22-836-4126

EDWARDS LIFESCIENCES CORPORATION

1 Edwards Way, Irvine, CA, 92614

Tel: (949) 250-2500   Fax: (949) 250-2525   www.edwards.com

Mfr. instruments for cardiovascular patients.

Edwards Lifesciences, Shah Ind. Estate, Plot No: 9, Veera Desai Road Andheri West, Mumbai 400053, India

EG&G INC.

900 Clopper Road, Ste. 200, Gaithersburg, MD, 20878

Tel: (301) 840-3000   Fax: (301) 590-0502   www.egginc.com

Diversified R/D, mfr. and services.

EG&G Sealol Hindustan Ltd., Survey, 212/2, Sholapur Rd., Hadapsar, Pune 411 028, India

EG&G Sealol Hindustan Ltd., Bhupati Chambers, 4/F, 13 Mathew Rd., Opera House, Mumbai 400 004, India

EGL INC. (EAGLE GLOBAL LOGISTICS)

15350 Vickery Drive, Houston, TX, 77032

Tel: (281) 618-3100   Fax: (281) 618-3223   www.eagleusa.com

Ocean/air freight forwarding, customs brokerage, packing and wholesale, logistics management and insurance.

EGL Eagle Global Logistics, 315, Siddarth Complex, R.C. Dutt Rd., Alakapuri, Baroda 390 005, India
Tel: 91-265-322-838   Fax: 91-265-339-336

EGL Eagle Global Logistics, Cheran Towers 81/10, 2nd Fl., 78 Arts College Rd., Coimbatore 641 018, India
Tel: 91-422-213-864   Fax: 91-422-213-864

EGL Eagle Global Logistics, 1-10-72/2B Cheekoti Gardens, Begumpet Hyderabad 500 016, India
Tel: 91-842-811-346   Fax: 91-842-811-346

EGL Eagle Global Logistics, 38-80 Feet Rd., Hall III Stage, Bangalore 560 075, India
Tel: 91-80-528-9202   Fax: 91-812-528-1796

EGL Eagle Global Logistics, 1/B Vaspujya Chambers, Ashram Rd., Ahmedabad 380 014, India
Tel: 91-79-447-158   Fax: 91-272-655-8744

EGL Eagle Global Logistics, Atlanta Tower, 4th Fl., Sahar Rd., Sahar Bombay Mumbai 400 099, India
Tel: 91-22-837-5724   Fax: 91-22-836-7488

EGL Eagle Global Logistics, 24/1592 Subramaniam Rd., 1st Fl., Wet Island, Cochin 682 003, India
Tel: 91-484-666-453   Fax: 91-484-667-677

EGL Eagle Global Logistics, 6F, Everest Bldg., 46C Jawaharl Nehru Rd., Calcutta 700 071, India
Tel: 91-33-242-2033   Fax: 91-33-242-2529

EGL Eagle Global Logistics, 2-A, First Fl., Wellingdon Estate, 24 Commander In Chief Rd., Madras 600 015, India
Tel: 91-44-827-8767   Fax: 91-44-825-1604

EGL Eagle Global Logistics, SCP Towers 1st Fl., Model School Junction, Thampanoor, Trivandru 695 001, India
Tel: 91-471-659-31   Fax: 91-471-659-31

EGL Eagle Global Logistics, Flat #1215/1216, 12th Fl., Ansal Towers, 38 Nehru Place, New Delhi 110 018, India
Tel: 91-11-646-6330   Fax: 91-11-646-5698

EGL Eagle Global Logistics, 309 ,MPJ Chambers, 3rd Fl., Wakadewadi, Bombay-Pune Rd., Pune 411 003, India
Tel: 91-212-312-637   Fax: 91-212-313-264

EMERSON ELECTRIC COMPANY

8000 W. Florissant Ave., PO Box 4100, St. Louis, MO, 63136

Tel: (314) 553-2000   Fax: (314) 553-3527   www.emersonelectric.com

Electrical and electronic products, industrial components and systems, consumer, government and defense products.

Emerson Co., 1108, Maker Chambers V, Nariman Point, Bombay 400 002, India
Tel: 91-22-285-2808

Emerson Company, 406, Metro House, 7 Mangaldas Road, Pune 411 001, India
Tel: 91-20-639-590

EMERSON PROCESS MANAGEMENT

8301Cameron Road, Austin, TX, 78754

Tel: (512) 834-7689   Fax: (512) 832-3232   www.frco.com

Mfr. industrial process control equipment.

Emerson Process Management, 147 Karapakkam Village, Madras 600 096, India
Tel: 91-44-492-5455   Fax: 91-44-492-6114

ENERPAC

6101 N. Baker Road, PO Box 3241, Milwaukee, WI, 53201-3241

Tel: (414) 781-6600   Fax: (414) 781-1049   www.enerpac.com

Mfr. hydraulic cylinders, pumps, valves, presses, tools, accessories and system components.

EMERPAC Pvt Ltd., Plot No. A-571, MIDC TTC Industrial Area, Mahape Navi Mumbai 400 701, India

ENGELHARD CORPORATION

101 Wood Avenue South, Iselin, NJ, 08830

Tel: (732) 205-5000   Fax: (732) 632-9253   www.engelhard.com

Mfr. pigments, additives, catalysts, chemicals, engineered materials.

Engelhard Environmental Systems (India) Ltd., Maramalai Nagar, India

ENRON CORPORATION

1400 Smith Street, Houston, TX, 77002-7369

Tel: (713) 853-6161   Fax: (713) 853-3129   www.enron.com

*Exploration, production, transportation and distribution of integrated natural gas and electricity. **Corporation under worldwide reorganization; new data unavailable for this edition.*

Dabhol Power Company, 517-518, Meridian West Tower, Raisina Rd., New Delhi 110 001, India
Tel: 91-11-335-4182

Dabhol Power Company, 611, Midas Sahar Plaza, Mathurdas Vassanji Road, Andheri (East) Mumbai 400 059, India

Enron India Pvt Ltd., 15/F, Nariman Point, Mumbai 400 021, India

ERIEZ MAGNETICS

2200 Asbury Road, Erie, PA, 16506

Tel: (814) 835-6000   Fax: (814) 838-4960   www.eriez.com

Mfr. magnets, vibratory feeders, metal detectors, screeners/sizers, mining equipment, current separators.

Eriez MBI India Limited (EMIL), Whitefield Bangalore, India
Tel: 91-80-845-5381   Fax: 91-80-845-5380   Contact: Vinod Kochat

ERNST & YOUNG INTERNATIONAL

5 Times Square, New York, NY, 10036

Tel: (212) 773-3000   Fax: (212) 773-6350   www.eyi.com

Engaged in assurance and advisory business services, tax, law and corporate finance.

S.R.Batliboi & Company, Himalaya House, 7th Fl., 23 Kasturba Gandhi Marg, New Delhi 110 001, India
Tel: 91-11-371-4387   Fax: 91-11-331-4802   Contact: Kashi Nath Memani

ETHYL CORPORATION

330 South 4th Street, PO Box 2189, Richmond, VA, 23219

Tel: (804) 788-5000   Fax: (804) 788-5688   www.ethyl.com

Provide additive chemistry solutions to enhance the performance of petroleum products.

Ethyl Corporation (India), G1, Sangeet Plaza, Marol Maroshi Road, Andheri-East Mumbai 770 060, India
Tel: 91-22-8597415   Fax: 91-22-8597417

EURO RSCG WORLDWIDE

350 Hudson Street, New York, NY, 10014

Tel: (212) 886-2000   Fax: (212) 886-2016   www.eurorscg.com

International advertising agency group.

EURO RSCG, PO Box 23937, The Pyramid Centre, #307, Umm Hurair Road (Zabeel Road), Dubai, India

EXCELLON AUTOMATION

24751 Crenshaw Boulevard, Torrance, CA, 90505

Tel: (310) 534-6300   Fax: (310) 534-6777   www.excellon.com

PCB drilling and routing machines; optical inspection equipment.

Max Atotech Ltd., 66 KM Stone NH Delhi Jaipur Hwy., Sidhrawali Village Gurgaon Haryana, 123 413, India
Tel: 91-1274-42115   Fax: 91-1274-42116

EXPEDITORS INTERNATIONAL OF WASHINGTON INC.

1015 Third Avenue, 12th Fl., Seattle, WA, 98104-1182

Tel: (206) 674-3400   Fax: (206) 682-9777   www.expd.com

Air/ocean freight forwarding, customs brokerage, international logistics solutions.

Expeditors International (India) Pvt. Ltd., Salzburg Square, 2/F, 107 Harrington Road, Chetpet Chennai 600 031, India

Tel: 91-44-8237647   Fax: 91-44-8238691

Expeditors International Service Center, Khasta 411, 50B, Sainik Farms, Village Khirki Tehsil-Mehrauli, New Delhi 110 062, India

EXXON MOBIL CORPORATION

5959 Las Colinas Blvd., Irving, TX, 75039-2298

Tel: (972) 444-1000   Fax: (972) 444-1882   www.exxonmobil.com

Petroleum exploration, production, refining; mfr. petroleum and chemicals products; coal and minerals.

Exxon Mobil, Inc., Plot No. 5, Road No. 8, Export Promo Ind. Park, Whitefield Bangalore 560 006, India

Exxon Mobil, Inc., 92 Marker Chambers VI, 220 Backbay Reclamation, Nariman Point Mumbai 400 021, India

FIRESTONE POLYMERS

381 W. Wilbeth Road, Akron, OH, 44301

Tel: (330) 379-7864   Fax: (330) 379-7875   www.firesyn.com

Mfr. polymers; rubber, plastics and adhesives

Empire Chemicals, 414 Senapati Bapat Marg., Lower Parel, Mumbai 400 013, India

Tel: 91-22-496-4203   Fax: 91-22-493-1150   Contact: Niraj Shah

FLEETBOSTON FINANCIAL CORPORATION

100 Federal Street, Boston, MA, 02110

Tel: (617) 434-2400   Fax: (617) 434-6943   www.fleet.com

Banking and insurance services.

FleetBoston - Bombay, 1114-1115, Maker Chambers, 11th Fl., Nariman Point, Mumbai 400 021, India

Tel: 91-22-202-1141   Fax: 91-22-282-6108

FLOWSERVE CORPORATION

222 W. Los Colinas Blvd., Irving, TX, 75039

Tel: (972) 443-6500   Fax: (972) 443-6858   www.flowserve.com

Mfr. chemicals equipment, pumps, valves, filters, fans and heat exchangers.

Durametallic India Ltd., 147 Karapakkam Village, Mahabalipuram Road, Sholinganallur, Madras 600 096, India

Virgo Engineers Limited, J/517 MIDC Industrial Area, Off Telco Road, Bhosari Pune 411 026, India

FLUOR CORPORATION

One Enterprise Drive, Aliso Viejo, CA, 92656-2606

Tel: (949) 349-2000   Fax: (949) 349-5271   www.flour.com

Engineering and construction services.

Fluor Daniel India Private Limited, DLF Square, 14th Floor, Jacaranda Marg, DLF City, Phase - II Gurgaon 122002, India

Tel: 91-124-656-0651

FMC CORPORATION

1735 Market St., Philadelphia, PA, 19103

Tel: (215) 299-6000   Fax: (215) 299-6618   www.fmc.com

Mfr. specialty chemicals, including alginate, carrageenan and microcrystalline cellulose.

FMC India, Krislon House 1/F, Saki Vihar Road, Mumbai Maharashtra, India

FOSTER WHEELER LTD.

Perryville Corporate Park, Clinton, NJ, 08809-4000

Tel: (908) 730-4000   Fax: (908) 730-4100   www.fwc.com

Manufacturing, engineering and construction.

Foster Wheeler India Pvt. Ltd., Prakash Presidium, 1/F, 110 Mahatma Gandhi Road, Nungambakkam, Chennai 600 034, India

Tel: 91-44-822-7341   Fax: 91-44-822-7340

FRANKLIN COVEY COMPANY

2200 W. Parkway Blvd., Salt Lake City, UT, 84119-2331

Tel: (801) 975-1776   Fax: (801) 977-1431   www.franklincovey.com

Provides productivity and time management products and seminars.

Leadership Resources Pte., 301-B, Eden -3, Hiranandani Gardens, Powai Mumbai 400 076, India

Tel: 91-22-570-0005   Fax: 91-22-570-1383

FRANKLIN RESOURCES, INC.

1 Franklin Pkwy., Bldg. 970, 1st Fl., San Mateo, CA, 94404

Tel: (415) 312-2000   Fax: (415) 312-5606   www.frk.com

Global and domestic investment advisory and portfolio management.

Templeton Asset Management (India) Pvt. Ltd., Mumbai, India

FRITZ COMPANIES, INC., DIV. UPS

706 Mission Street, Ste. 900, San Francisco, CA, 94103

Tel: (415) 904-8360   Fax: (415) 904-8661   www.fritz.com

Integrated transportation, sourcing, distribution and customs brokerage services.

Fritz Companies Inc., Bangalore, India

FSI INTERNATIONAL INC.

3455 Lyman Boulevard, Chaska, MN, 55318-3052

Tel: (952) 448-5440   Fax: (952) 448-2825   www.fsi-intl.com

Manufacturing equipment for computer silicon wafers.

Fabteq, Div. FSI, No. 100 4th Cross, 2nd Block, Koramangala, Bangalore 560 034, India

THE GATES RUBBER COMPANY

990 S. Broadway, PO Box 5887, Denver, CO, 80217-5887

Tel: (303) 744-1911   Fax: (303) 744-4000   www.gatesrubber.com

Mfr. automotive and industrial belts and hoses.

Gates Rubber India, Chandigarh Ambala Highway, District of Patiala Punjab 140 501, India

Tel: 91-171-79050   Fax: 91-171-79151   Contact: Keshav Sachdev

GE BETZ, DIV. GE SPECIALTY MATERIALS

4636 Somerton Road, PO Box 3002, Trevose, PA, 19053-6783

Tel: (215) 355-3300   Fax: (215) 953-5524   www.gebetz.com

Engaged in engineered chemical treatment of water and process systems in industrial, commercial and institutional facilities

GE Betz, Div. GE Specialty Materials, 5th Fl., Vayudhooth-Chambers, 15/16 Mahatma Gandhi Rd., Bangalore 560 001, India

GENERAL BINDING CORPORATION

One GBC Plaza, Northbrook, IL, 60062

Tel: (847) 272-3700   Fax: (847) 272-1369   www.gbc.com

Engaged in the design, manufacture and distribution of branded office equipment, related supplies and thermal laminating films.

GBC Modi Limited, F-41, Sector-6, Distt. Guatam Budh Nagar, Noida UP 201301, India

Tel: 91-11-8454-9600   Fax: 91-11-8454-9961   Contact: Sutendra Kumar

GENERAL ELECTRIC COMPANY

3135 Easton Turnpike, Fairfield, CT, 06431

Tel: (203) 373-2211   Fax: (203) 373-3131   www.ge.com

Diversified manufacturing, technology and services.

GE Automation, 10 Haddows Rd., Madras 600 006, India

Tel: 91-44-826-7741   Fax: 91-44-825-7340

GE Fanuc Systems, 308 Swastik Chamber, Sion Trombay Road, Chembur, Mumbai 400 071, India

Tel: 91-22 527-5684   Fax: 91-22 527-5690   Contact: Ashwin Kamat

GE Fanuc Systems, 1110 Indra Prakash Building, 21 Barakhamba Road, New Delhi 110 001, India

Tel: 91-11-335-0410   Fax: 91-11-335-0344   Contact: Piyush Pandey

GE Fanuc Systems, c/o ATB Business Centre, 35, First Main Rd, Gandhi Nagar, Adyar, Chennai 600020, India
Tel: 91-44-490-8640   Fax: 91-44-491-7490   Contact: Anoop Pereira

GE Fanuc Systems, 211 Lake Terrace Extension,, Calcutta 700029, India
Tel: 91-33-464-6784   Fax: 91-33-464-7049   Contact: Piyush Pandey

GE Fanuc Systems, East Wing, Combatta Building 4/F, 101 Maharishi Karve Road, Churchgate, Mumbai 400 020, India

GE Fanuc Systems, 12 Rachana Trade Estate. CTS No.105, FP No.84, Law College Road, Pune 411004, India
Tel: 91-20-544-8366   Fax: 91-20-400-2119   Contact: Sachin Sandikar

GE Fanuc Systems, 90/B, Electronics City, Hosur Road,, Bangalore 561 229, India
Tel: 91-80-8528337   Contact: Hemant Joshi

GEO LOGISTICS CORPORATION

1521 E. Dyer Rd., Santa Ana, CA, 92705
Tel: (714) 513-3000   Fax: (714) 513-3120   www.geo-logistics.com
Engaged in freight forwarding, warehousing and distribution services, specializing in heavy cargo.

GeoLogistics Ltd., 2/F, Chitrakoot Building 230A, AJC Bose Rd., Calcutta 700 020, India
Tel: 91-33-240-2140   Fax: 91-33-240-2140

GeoLogistics Ltd., Navkar Chambers, Wing A, 5th Floor, Andheri-Kurla Road, Andheri (E), Mumbai 400 059, India
Tel: 91-22-859-6640   Fax: 91-22-859-7510

GeoLogistics Ltd., 303, 1st Fl, Ashok Terrace, 100 Feet Rd, Indiranagar, I stage, Bangalore 560 038, India
Tel: 91-80-527-4724   Fax: 91-80-527-4725

GERBER SCIENTIFIC, INC.

83 Gerber Road West, South Windsor, CT, 06074
Tel: (860) 644-1551   Fax: (860) 644-5547   www.gerberscientific.com
Mfr. computer-based automated manufacturing and design systems for signs and graphics.

Gerber Technology, Springdale No. 51, Residency Road, 1st Cross, Bangalore 560025, India

THE GILLETTE COMPANY

Prudential Tower Building, Boston, MA, 02199
Tel: (617) 421-7000   Fax: (617) 421-7123   www.gillette.com
Develop/mfr. personal care/use products: blades and razors, toiletries, cosmetics, stationery.

Indian Shaving Products Ltd., 34 Okhla Industrial Estate, New Delhi 110 020, India

GILSON INC.

3000 W. Beltline Hwy, PO Box 620027, Middleton, WI, 53562-0027
Tel: (608) 836-1551   Fax: (608) 831-4451   www.gilson.com
Mfr. analytical/biomedical instruments.

ASR Instruments, 1/F, Baba Chambers, 73 Richmond Road, Bangalore 560 025, India

GIW INDUSTRIES, INC.

5000 Wrightsboro Rd., Grovetown, GA, 30813
Tel: (706) 863-1011   Fax: (706) 860-5897   www.giwindustries.com
Mfr. slurry pumps.

KSB Pumps Limited, Bombay-Pune Road, Pune 411 018, India

GLEASON CORPORATION

1000 University Ave., Rochester, NY, 14692
Tel: (716) 473-1000   Fax: (716) 461-4348   www.gleasoncorp.com
Mfr. gear making machine tools; tooling and services.

Gleason Works (India) Pvt. Ltd., Plot No. 37, Doddenakundi Industrial Area, Whitefield Rd., Mahadevapura Bangalore 560 048, India
Tel: 91-80-851-6177   Fax: 91-80-851-6178

GLENAYRE ELECTRONICS LTD.

11360 Lakefield Drive, Duluth, GA, 30097

Tel: (770) 283-1000   Fax: (770) 497-3982   www.glenayre.com

Mfr. infrastructure components and pagers.

Glenayre Electronics India Pvt. Ltd., c/o Continental Business Center, Flat No. 912, International Trade Tower, New Delhi 110 019, India

Tel: 91-11-623-3635   Fax: 91-11-628-6173

THE GOODYEAR TIRE & RUBBER COMPANY

1144 East Market Street, Akron, OH, 44316

Tel: (330) 796-2121   Fax: (330) 796-1817   www.goodyear.com

Mfr. tires, automotive belts and hose, conveyor belts, chemicals; oil pipeline transmission.

Goodyear India Ltd., 3/F, Godreg Bhavan, Mathura Rd., New Delhi 110 065, India

W. R. GRACE & COMPANY

7500 Grace Drive, Columbia, MD, 21044

Tel: (410) 531-4000   Fax: (410) 531-4367   www.grace.com

Mfr. specialty chemicals and materials: packaging, health care, catalysts, construction, water treatment/process.

W.R. Grace & Co. (India), Suite 420, 3A Cross, 3rd Block, 16th Main Koramangala, Bangalore 560 034, India

Tel: 91-80-552-0316   Fax: 91-80-553-4500

GRANT THORNTON INTERNATIONAL

800 One Prudential Plaza, 130 E. Randolph Drive, Chicago, IL, 60601-6050

Tel: (312) 856-0001   Fax: (312) 616-7052   www.grantthornton.com

Accounting, audit, tax and management consulting services.

K.S. Aiyar & Co., East & West Bldg., 49-55 Mumbai Samachar Marg, Mumbai 400 023, India

GREFCO MINERALS, INC.

23705 Crenshaw Blvd., Ste. 101, Torrance, CA, 90505

Tel: (310) 517-0700   Fax: (310) 517-0794   www.grefco.com

Mfr. diatomite and perlite products, and exclusive distributor of Dicaflock cellulose fibers.

Amoi Dicalite Ltd., Behind Haldervas Octroi Naka, Raknial Rd., Ahmedahad 380 023, India

GREY GLOBAL GROUP

777 Third Ave., New York, NY, 10017

Tel: (212) 546-2000   Fax: (212) 546-1495   www.grey.com

International advertising agency.

Trikaya Grey, Phoenix Estate, Block 2-D, 3rd fl., 462 Tulsi Pipe Road, Mumbai 400 013, India

GUARDIAN INDUSTRIES CORPORATION

2300 Harmon Road, Auburn Hills, MI, 48326-1714

Tel: (248) 340-1800   Fax: (248) 340-9988   www.guardian.com

Mfr. and fabricate flat glass products and insulation materials.

Gujarat Guardian Limited, State Highway 13, Village Kondh, Taluka Valia Dist. of Bharuch, Gujarat PIN 393 011, India

Tel: 91-2643-75106   Fax: 91-2643-75105

HALLIBURTON COMPANY

500 North Akard Street, Ste. 3600, Dallas, TX, 75201-3391

Tel: (214) 978-2600   Fax: (214) 978-2685   www.halliburton.com

Engaged in diversified energy services, engineering and construction.

Halliburton Ltd., Gintanjali Tubes Compound, 1/1 Poonamallee High Rd., Nerkundram Madras 600 107, India

Tel: 91-44-487-1345   Fax: 91-44-487-1346

HARCOURT GENERAL, INC.

27 Boylston St., Chestnut Hill, MA, 02467

Tel: (617) 232-8200   Fax: (617) 739-1395   www.harcourt.com

Publisher of educational materials.

Harcourt General Asia Pte.Ltd., 27 M-Block Market, Great Kailash II, New Delhi 110 048, India

Tel: 91-11-646-4550   Fax: 91-11-647-5065   Contact: Sanjay Banerjee, Mgr.

HARRIS CORPORATION

1025 West NASA Blvd., Melbourne, FL, 32919

Tel: (407) 727-9100   Fax: (407) 727-9344   www.harris.com

Mfr. communications and information-handling equipment, including copying and fax systems.

Intersil Pvt. Ltd., Plot 54, SEEPZ, Marol Industrial Area, Anderi (E), Mumbai 400 096, India

Tel: 91-22-832-3097   Fax: 91-22-836-6682

HAWORTH INC.

1 Haworth Center, Holland, MI, 49423-9576

Tel: (616) 393-3000   Fax: (616) 393-1570   www.haworth.com

Mfr. office furniture.

Haworth India Pvt Ltd., 704 Carlton Towers, 1 Airport Road, Bangalore 560008, India

HEIDRICK & STRUGGLES INTERNATIONAL, INC.

233 South Wacker Drive, Chicago, IL, 60606

Tel: (312) 496-1200   Fax: (312) 496-1290   www.heidrick.com

Executive search firm.

Heidrick & Struggles Intl. Inc., 505 International Trade Tower, Nehru Place, New Delhi 110 019, India

H.J. HEINZ COMPANY

600 Grant Street, Pittsburgh, PA, 15219

Tel: (412) 456-5700   Fax: (412) 456-6128   www.heinz.com

Processed food products and nutritional services.

Heinz India Pvt. Ltd., Mumbai, India

HERCULES INC.

Hercules Plaza, 1313 N. Market Street, Wilmington, DE, 19894-0001

Tel: (302) 594-5000   Fax: (302) 594-5400   www.herc.com

Mfr. specialty chemicals, plastics, film and fibers, coatings, resins and food ingredients.

Herdillia Chemicals Ltd., Air India Bldg., Post Bag 9962, Nariman Point, Mumbai 400 021, India

HEWITT ASSOCIATES LLC

100 Half Day Road, Lincolnshire, IL, 60069

Tel: (847) 295-5000   Fax: (847) 295-7634   www.hewitt.com

Employee benefits consulting firm.

Nobel & Hewitt, Z-1 First Floor, Hauz Khas, New Delhi 110 016, India

Tel: 91-11-686-1594   Fax: 91-11-651-5501

Nobel & Hewitt, Getta Building Ground Floor, Dr. Pandita Ramaabai Road, Gamdevi Mumbai 400 007, India

Tel: 91-22-369-7676

Nobel & Hewitt, Ste. 810-81, Wing B, 8th Fl., Mittal Tower, 6 M.G. Road, Bangalore 560 001, India

Tel: 91-80-559-4592

HEWLETT-PACKARD COMPANY

3000 Hanover Street, Palo Alto, CA, 94304-1185

Tel: (650) 857-1501   Fax: (650) 857-5518   www.hp.com

Mfr. computing, communications and measurement products and services.

Hewlett-Packard India Ltd., Chandiwala Estate, Maa Ananadmai Marg Kalkaji, New Delhi 110 019, India

Tel: 91-11-682-6030

HOLIDAY INN (BASS RESORTS) WORLDWIDE, INC.

3 Ravinia Drive, Ste. 2900, Atlanta, GA, 30346-2149

Tel: (770) 604-2000   Fax: (770) 604-5403   www.holidayinn.com

Hotels, restaurants and casinos.

Holiday Inn Inc., Juhu Beach, Mumbai 400 049, India

Holiday Inn Inc. - India, Fatehabab Rd., Taj Ganj, Agra, India

HOLLINGSWORTH & VOSE COMPANY

112 Washington Street, East Walpole, MA, 02032

Tel: (508) 668-0295   Fax: (508) 668-3557   www.hollingsworth-vose.com

Mfr. technical and industrial papers and non-woven fabrics.

Hollingsworth & Vose, Summer Garden, Flat No. 5, South Main Road, Koregaon Park, Pune 411 001, India

HONEYWELL INTERNATIONAL INC.

Honeywell Plaza, Minneapolis, MN, 55408

Tel: (612) 951-1000   Fax: (612) 951-8537   www.honeywell.com

Develop/mfr. controls for home and building, industry, space and aviation, burglar and fire alarm systems.

Honeywell Europe Inc., 403/404, "Madhava", Bandra Kurla Complex, Bundra East, Bombay, India

Tel: 91-22-204-5827   Fax: 91-22-640-9513

Tata Honeywell Ltd., 55-1, 8&89 Hadapsar, Industrial Estate, Pune 411 013, India

Tel: 91-212-670-445   Fax: 91-212-672-205

HORWATH INTERNATIONAL ASSOCIATION

420 Lexington Avenue, Suite 526, New York, NY, 10170-0526

Tel: (212) 808-2000   Fax: (212) 808-2020   www.horwath.com

Public accountants and auditors.

N.M. Raiji Co., Universal Insurance Bldg., Pherozeshaha Mehta Rd., Mumbai 400 001, India

P.K. Chopra & Co., N Block, Mumbai Life Bldg., Connaught Place, New Delhi 110 001, India

HOUGHTON INTERNATIONAL INC.

PO Box 930, Madison & Van Buren Avenues, Valley Forge, PA, 19482-0930

Tel: (610) 666-4000   Fax: (610) 666-1376   www.houghtonintl.com

Mfr. specialty chemicals, hydraulic fluids and lubricants.

Houghton Hardcastle India Ltd., Brabourne Stadium, 87 Veer Nariman Rd., Mumbai 400 020, India

HOWMEDICA OSTEONICS, INC.

59 Route 17 South, Allendale, NJ, 07401

Tel: (201) 507-7300   Fax: (201) 935-4873   www.howmedica.com

Mfr. of maxillofacial products (orthopedic implants).

Howmedica India, Mumbai, India

Tel: 91-22-6783-432

J.M. HUBER CORPORATION

333 Thornall Street, Edison, NJ, 08818

Tel: (732) 549-8600   Fax: (732) 549-2239   www.huber.com

Diversified, multinational supplier of engineered materials, natural resources and technology-based services to customers spanning many industries, from paper and energy to plastics and construction.

Huber Chemicals India Pvt Ltd, 4014-4019, Oberoi Estate, Chandivli Farms Road, Andheri E, Mumbai 400 072., India

HUNTSMAN CORPORATION

500 Huntsman Way, Salt Lake City, UT, 84108

Tel: (801) 532-5200   Fax: (801) 536-1581   www.huntsman.com

Mfr. and sales of specialty chemicals, industrial chemicals and petrochemicals.

ICI India Limited C/O Huntsman Polyurethanes, Thane Belapur Road, PO Box 87, Thane Maharashtra 400 601, India

Tel: 91-22-761-9835   Contact: A. Khetan

HUSSMANN INTERNATIONAL

12999 St. Charles Rock Road, Bridgeton, MO, 63044

Tel: (314) 291-2000   Fax: (314) 291-5144   www.hussmann.com

Mfr. refrigeration and environmental control systems for food industrial.

Ingersoll Rand (India) Ltd., Phase 1, Peenya, Bangalore 560 058, India

Tel: 91-80-8395791

i2 TECHNOLOGIES, INC.

11701 Luna Road, Dallas, TX, 75234

Tel: (214) 860-6106   Fax: (214) 860-6060   www.i2.com

Engaged in supply chain management; solutions to help companies collaborate on decision-making processes.

i2 Technologies India Pvt. Ltd., No. 1 Primrose Road, Bangalore 560 025, India

IBM CORPORATION

1133 Westchester Avenue, White Plains, NY, 10604

Tel: (914) 765-1900   Fax: (914) 765-7382   www.ibm.com

Information products, technology and services.

IBM Global Services India Ltd., TISL Tower Golden Enclave, Airport Road, Bangalore 560 017, India

Tel: 91-80-526-7117   Fax: 91-80-527-7991

ICC INDUSTRIES INC.

460 Park Ave., New York, NY, 10022

Tel: (212) 521-1700   Fax: (212) 521-1794   www.iccchem.com

Manufacturing and trading of chemicals, plastics and pharmaceuticals.

Lexicon Chemicals, Manorama, Lt. Dilip Gupte Road, Mahim Mumbai 400 016, India

Tel: 91-22-445-7984   Fax: 91-22-446-3844

IGATE CORPORATION

680 Andersen Drive, Foster Plaza 10, Pittsburgh, PA, 15220

Tel: (412) 503-4450   Fax: (412) 503-4490   www.igatecorp.com

Provides IT services.

iGate, Mascot Systems Divison, No 1, Main Road, Jakkasandra, Bangalore 560 034, India

IKOS SYSTEMS, INC.

79 Great Oaks Blvd., San Jose, CA, 95119

Tel: (408) 284-0400   Fax: (408) 284-0401   www.ikos.com

Mfr. hardware and software.

IKOS India Private Limited, A-4, Sector 10, Noida UP 201 301, India

Tel: 91-118-4551466   Fax: 91-118-4538259

ILLINOIS TOOL WORKS (ITW)

3600 West Lake Ave., Glenview, IL, 60025-5811

Tel: (847) 724-7500   Fax: (847) 657-4268   www.itw.com

Mfr. gears, tools, fasteners, sealants, plastic and metal components for industrial, medical, etc.

HMA Systems, 1F3, SS Plaza North, Kamala Nagar, Hyderabad 500 062, India

IMATION CORPORATION

One Imation Place, Oakdale, MN, 55128

Tel: (612) 704-4000   Fax: (612) 704-3444   www.imation.com

Dry laser-imaging film systems.

Imation India, 46 Sidharta Enclave, New Delhi 110 014, India

Tel: 91-11-373-0755

IMI NORGREN GROUP

5400 South Delaware Street, Littleton, CO, 80120-1663

Tel: (303) 794-2611   Fax: (303) 795-9487   www.usa.norgren.com

Mfr. pneumatic filters, regulators, lubricators, valves, automation systems, dryers, push-in fittings.

Shavo Norgren India Pvt. Ltd., 78 Mittal Chambers, Nariman Point, Mumbai 400 021, India

INDUCTOTHERM INDUSTRIES

10 Indel Ave., PO Box 157, Rancocas, NJ, 08073-0157

Tel: (609) 267-9000   Fax: (609) 267-5705   www.inductotherm.com

Mfr. induction melting furnaces, induction power supplies, charging and preheating systems, automatic pouring systems and computer control systems.

Athena Controls, Ambli-Bopal Road, Ahhmedabad 380054, India

Inductotherm (India) Ltd., Ambli-Bopal Rd., Bopal, Ahmedabad 380 054, India

Tel: 91-2717-31961   Contact: Bharat Sheth

Inductotherm India, Bopal, Ahmedabad, Gujarat 380 058, India

INFORMATION RESOURCES, INC. (IRI)

150 N. Clinton St., Chicago, IL, 60661

Tel: (312) 726-1221   Fax: (312) 726-0360   www.infores.com

Provides bar code scanner services for retail sales organizations; processes, analyzes and sells data from the huge database created from these services.

Operations Research Group, 222, A.J.C. Bose Rd., 3rd Fl., Calcutta 700 017, India

Tel: 91-33-240-48441   Fax: 91-33-240-6908

INGERSOLL-RAND COMPANY

200 Chestnut Ridge Road, Woodcliff Lake, NJ, 07675

Tel: (201) 573-0123   Fax: (201) 573-3172   www.irco.com

Leading innovation and solutions provider for the major global markets of Security and Safety, Climate Control, Industrial Solutions and Infrastructure.

Ingersoll-Rand (India) Ltd., Rhone-Poulenc House, S.K. Ahire Marg., PO Box 9138, Mumbai 400 025, India

Tel: 91-22-4936765   Fax: 91-22-4950516

Ingersoll-Rand India, 22/29 GIDC Estate, Naroda, Ahmedabad 382 330, India

INGRAM MICRO INC.

1600 E. St. Andrew Place, Santa Ana, CA, 92799

Tel: (714) 566-1000   Fax: (714) 566-7940   www.ingrammicro.com

Engaged in wholesale distribution of microcomputer products.

Ingram Micro India Ltd., MF 7 Cipet Hostel Road, Thiru-Vi-Ka Nagar, Ekkatuthangal Chennai 600 097, India

INTEL CORPORATION

2200 Mission College Blvd., Santa Clara, CA, 95052-8119

Tel: (408) 765-8080   Fax: (408) 765-1739   www.intel.com

Mfr. semiconductor, microprocessor and micro-communications components and systems.

Intel Asia Electronics Inc., DuParc Trinity, 17, Mahatma Gandhi Road, Bangalore 560001, India

INTELLIGROUP, INC.

499 Thornall Street, Edison, NJ, 08837

Tel: (732) 590-1600   Fax: (732) 362-2100   www.intelligroup.com

Provides systems integration, customer software and Internet application development.

Intelligroup Asia Limited, 5-9-22, Mana Sarovar Complex, Secretariat Road, Hyderabad Andhra Pradesh 500 063, India

Tel: 91-40-329-7487

INTER-CONTINENTAL HOTELS

3 Ravinia Drive, Suite 2900, Atlanta, GA, 30346-2149

Tel: (770) 604-2000   Fax: (770) 604-5403   www.interconti.com

Worldwide hotel and resort accommodations.

Taj Palace Inter-Continental New Delhi, 2 Sardar Patel Marg, Diplomatic Enclave, New Delhi 110 021, India

Tel: 91-11-611-0202   Fax: 91-11-611-0808

INTERGRAPH CORPORATION

One Madison Industrial Park, Huntsville, AL, 35894-0001

Tel: (256) 730-2000   Fax: (256) 730-7898   www.intergraph.com

Develop/mfr. interactive computer graphic systems.

Intergraph (India) Pvt. Ltd., 1-8-446 & 447 Begumpet, Hyderabad, Andhra Pradesh 500 016, India

Tel: 91-40-815378   Fax: 91-40-815379

INTERNATIONAL COMPONENTS CORPORATION

420 N. May Street, Chicago, IL, 60622

Tel: (312) 829-2525   Fax: (312) 829-0213   www.icc-charge.com

Mfr. portable, rechargeable power, control and accessory products.

International Components Corp. (India) Ltd., 3-A Kodambakkam High Rd., Nungambakkam, Madras 600 034, India

INTERNATIONAL FLAVORS & FRAGRANCES INC.

521 West 57th Street, New York, NY, 10019-2960

Tel: (212) 765-5500   Fax: (212) 708-7132   www.iff.com

Design/mfr. flavors, fragrances and aroma chemicals.

International Flavors & Fragrances, Floral Deck Plaza, 3rd Floor, Off. Midc Central Road, Andheri (East), Mumbai 400 096, India

Tel: 91-22-8236677   Fax: 91-22-8203834

INTERNATIONAL MANAGEMENT GROUP (IMG)

1360 East Ninth Street, Ste. 100, Cleveland, OH, 44114

Tel: (216) 522-1200   Fax: (216) 522-1145   www.imgworld.com

Manages athletes, sports academies and real estate facilities worldwide.

IMG, Unit 15, Upper Phoenix Centre, The Phoenix Mills Compound, 462 Senapati Bapat Marg, Lower Parel Mumbai 400 013, India

Tel: 91-22-498-3811   Fax: 91-22-491-8621

IMG, 268 Masjid Moth, 4/F, Uday Park, New Delhi 100 049, India

Tel: 91-11-625-5864   Fax: 91-11-625-8583

INTERNATIONAL RECTIFIER CORPORATION

233 Kansas Street, El Segundo, CA, 90245

Tel: (310) 322-3331   Fax: (310) 322-3332   www.irf.com

Mfr. power semiconductor components.

International Rectifier Corp., c/o Semiconductor Electronics Ltd., SDF #23, Seepz Post Office, Andheri East, Mumbai 400 096, India

Tel: 91-22-829-1055   Fax: 91-22-829-0473

INTERNATIONAL SPECIALTY PRODUCTS, INC.

1361 Alps Rd., Wayne, NJ, 07470

Tel: (973) 389-3083   Fax: (973) 628-4117   www.ispcorp.com

Mfr. specialty chemical products.

ISP International Inc., C-211 Floral Deck Plaza, Opp: Seepz M.I.D.C. Andheri (East), Mumbai 400 093, India

Tel: 91-22-837-0472   Fax: 91-22-837-0449

INVITROGEN CORPORATION

1600 Faraday Avenue, Carlsbad, CA, 92008

Tel: (760) 603-7200   Fax: (760) 602-6500   www.invitrogen.com

Mfr. products and kits for gene analysis.

Invitrogen India Pvt., 4/F Gopala Tower, 25 Rajendra Place, New Delhi 110008, India

IPSEN INDUSTRIES INC.

894 Ipsen Rd., Cherry Valley, IL, 61016

Tel: (815) 332-4941   Fax: (815) 332-7625   www.ipsen-intl.com

Heat treating equipment.

Wesman Ipsen Furnaces Pvt., Diamond Harbour Road, Bhasa West Bengal 743503, India

IRIDIUM LLC

1600 Wilson Boulevard, Suite 1000, Washington, DC, 20009

Tel: (202) 408-3800   Fax: (202) 408-3801   www.iridium.com

Consortium of companies sharing the construction and implementation of a global satellite communications system.

Iridium India Telecom Ltd. (South Asia Reg. HQ), 2nd Fl., c/8 St. No 22 M.I.D.C., Marol Andheri East Mumbai 400 093, India

Tel: 91-22-821-4248   Fax: 91-22-821-4248   Contact: Moosa Raza, Chmn.

J. WALTER THOMPSON COMPANY

466 Lexington Ave., New York, NY, 10017

Tel: (212) 210-7000   Fax: (212) 210-6944   www.jwt.com

International advertising and marketing services.

Contract Advertising(JWT), Mumbai, India

Hindustan Thompson Associates, Mumbai, India

JACOBS ENGINEERING GROUP INC.

1111 S. Arroyo Parkway, Pasadena, CA, 91105

Tel: (626) 578-3500   Fax: (626) 578-6916   www.jacobs.com

Engineering, design and consulting; construction and construction management; process plant maintenance.

Humphreys & Glasgow Consultants, H&G House, Sector II, Plot No. 12, DBD Belapur, Mumbai 400 614, India

Tel: 91-22-757-3046   Fax: 91-22-757-3049

Humphreys & Glasgow Consultants, Corporate Hdqrts., Gammon House, Scrarker Marq, Prabhadevi, Mumbei 400 025, India

Tel: 91-22-430-2481   Fax: 91-22-422-2494   Contact: Dr. Arun N. Bravid, Dir.

Humphreys & Glasgow Consultants Ltd., Natubhai Centre, 11 Fl., Race Course, Gotri Rd., Vadodara 390 007, India

Tel: 91-265-339-638   Fax: 91-265-341-522   Contact: S. N. Deshpande, Dir.   Emp: 43

Humphreys & Glasgow Consultants Ltd., 2nd Fl., No. 3 Dacres Lane, West Bengal, Calcutta 708 069, India

Tel: 91-33-221-4967   Fax: 91-33-221-4969   Contact: S. K. Sengupta, Mgr.   Emp: 54

Jacobs Engineering Group, 242 Okhla Industrial Estate, Phase-III, New Delhi 110 020, India

Tel: 91-11-631-1584   Fax: 91-11-631-1767   Contact: S. N. Deshponde, Dir.

JLG INDUSTRIES INC.

One JLG Drive, McConnellsburg, PA, 17233-9533

Tel: (717) 485-5161   Fax: (717) 485-6417   www.jlg.com

Mfr. aerial work platforms and vertical personnel lifts.

JLG Industries, G-62 Saket, New Delhi 110 017, India

Tel: 91-11652-5507   Fax: 91-11652-5751

JOHNSON & JOHNSON

One Johnson & Johnson Plaza, New Brunswick, NJ, 08933

Tel: (732) 524-0400   Fax: (732) 214-0334   www.jnj.com

Mfr./distributor/R&D pharmaceutical, health care and cosmetic products.

Janssen-Cilag Pharmaceutica, Mumbai, India

Johnson & Johnson Ltd., 30 Forjett St., Post Box 9301, Mumbai 400 036, India

Johnson & Johnson Professional, Mumbai, India

SC JOHNSON

1525 Howe St., Racine, WI, 53403

Tel: (262) 260-2000   Fax: (262) 260-2133   www.scjohnsonwax.com

Home, auto, commercial and personal care products and specialty chemicals.

SC Johnson, Muttha Chambers IV, Senapati Bapat Marg, Pune 411 016, India

JOHNSON CONTROLS INC.

5757 N. Green Bay Ave., PO Box 591, Milwaukee, WI, 53201-0591

Tel: (414) 228-1200   Fax: (414) 228-2077   www.johnsoncontrols.com

Mfr. facility management and control systems and auto seating.

Johnson Controls / India, RV House, B-37 Veera Desai Rd., Off Link Rd., Andheri West Mumbai 400 053, India

Tel: 91-22-6261734   Fax: 91-22-6261801   Contact: Karkal Pramoda, Branch Mgr.

THE JOHNSON CORPORATION

805 Wood Street, Three Rivers, MI, 49093

Tel: (269) 278-1715   Fax: (269) 273-2230   www.joco.com

Mfr. rotary joints and siphon systems.

Johnson India, 3, Abirami Nagar, G.N. Mills Post, Coimbatore 641029, India

JONES, DAY, REAVIS & POGUE

North Point, 901 Lakeside Ave., Cleveland, OH, 44114

Tel: (216) 586-3939   Fax: (216) 579-0212   www.jonesday.com

International law firm.

Pathak & Associates, 13th Fl., Dr. Gopal Das Bhavan, 28 Barakhamba Rd., New Delhi 110 001, India

Tel: 91-11-373-8793   Fax: 91-11-335-3761   Contact: Jai S. Pathak, Res. Prtn   Emp: 10

JOY GLOBAL

100 East Wisconsin Avenue Suite 2780, Milwaukee, WI, 53202

Tel: (414) 779-4500   Fax: (414) 779-4507   www.joyglobal.com

Mfr. of underground mining equipment.

Joy Global, 1A Janki Shah Road, Calcutta 700 022, India

JUKI UNION SPECIAL CORPORATION

8500 N.W. 17th St., Miami, FL, 33126

Tel: (305) 594-0059   Fax: (305) 594-0720   www.unionspecial.com

Mfr. sewing machines.

JUKI Machineries India Pvt. Ltd., 1st Fl., Fazal Manor, No. 89, Richmond Rd., Bangalore 560 025, India

Tel: 91-80-224-0957   Fax: 91-80-221-2442

JUKI Machineries India Pvt. Ltd., A-215/B, Okhla Industrial Area Phase-1, New Delhi 110 020, India

Tel: 91-80-224-0957   Fax: 91-80-221-2442

A.T. KEARNEY INC.

5400 Legacy Dr., Plano, TX, 75201

Tel: (972) 604-4600   Fax: (972) 543-7680   www.atkearney.com

Management consultants and executive search.

A. T. Kearney Ltd., Taj Mahal Business Centre, One Mansingh Rd., Ste. 1001, New Delhi 110 011, India

Tel: 91-11-301-6162

THE KENDALL COMPANY TYCO HEALTHCARE

15 Hampshire Street, Mansfield, MA, 02048

Tel: (508) 261-8000   Fax: (508) 261-8542   www.kendallhq.com

Mfr. and markets a broad range of wound care, needles and syringes, electrodes, specialized paper, vascular therapy, urological care, incontinence care, and nursing care products.

Kendall South Asia, #22 Mirza Hyuder Ali Khan St., Royapettah, Madras 600 014, India

Tel: 91-44-854-4981   Fax: 91-44-854-4981

KENNAMETAL INC.

1600 Technology Way, PO Box 231, Latrobe, PA, 15650

Tel: (724) 539-5000   Fax: (724) 539-4710   www.kennametal.com

Tools, hard carbide and tungsten alloys for metalworking industry.

Birla Kennametal Ltd., B-15/4 MIDC Industrial Area, Waluj, Aurangabad 431 133, India

Tel: 91-240-554300   Fax: 91-240-554302

Drillco Hertel Ltd., Motwani Chambers, 1187/59, J.M. Rd., Shivaji Nagar Pune 411 005, India

Tel: 91-212-325-8292   Fax: 91-212-323225

KIMBERLY-CLARK CORPORATION

351 Phelps Drive, Irving, TX, 75038

Tel: (972) 281-1200   Fax: (972) 281-1435   www.kimberly-clark.com

Mfr./sales/distribution of consumer tissue, household and personal care products.

Kimberly-Clark Corp., India

KOCH-GLITSCH, INC.

4111 E. 37th Street North, Wichita, KS, 67220

Tel: (316) 828-5110   Fax: (316) 828-5263   www.koch-glitsch.com

Engaged in mass transfer, mist elimination, and motionless mixer technology.

Koch-Glitsch India Ltd., 42, Kalpataru Court, Dr. C. Gidwani Marg, Chembur, Mumbai 400 074, India

Tel: 91-22-520-2050   Fax: 91-22-520-2040

KORN/FERRY INTERNATIONAL

1800 Century Park East, Los Angeles, CA, 90067

Tel: (310) 843-4100   Fax: (310) 553-6452   www.kornferry.com

Engaged in executive search and management consulting.

Korn/Ferry International, New Delhi, India

Tel: 91-11-652-2455   Fax: 91-11-652-2458

KPMG CONSULTING INC.

1676 International Dr., McLean, VA, 22102

Tel: (703) 747-3000   Fax: (703) 747-8500   www.kpmg.com

Accounting and audit, tax and management consulting services.

KPMG Barat S. Raut & Co., 511, World Trade Centre, Barbar Rd., New Delhi 110 001, India

Tel: 91-11-3355-1222   Fax: 91-11-332-3632   Contact: Rajesh Jain, Ptnr.

KPMG International, 2A Century Plaza, Fl. 2, 560 Anna Salai, Madras 600 018, India

KPMG International, 5th Fl., Shariff Chambers 14, Cunningham Rd., Bangalore 560 052, India

KPMG International, The Metropolitan, West Wing, Fl. 3, Bandra-Kurla Complex, E-Block, Mumbai 400 051, India

Tel: 91-22-643-8110   Fax: 91-22-645-6930   Contact: Sridar A. Lyengar, Ptnr.

KPMG International, World Trade Centre Central, 11th Fl., #5&6 Cuffe Parade, Mumbai 400 005, India

KROLL INC.

9023 Columbine Road, Eden Prairie, MN, 55347

Tel: (952) 937-1107   Fax: (952) 937-5815   www.knollworldwide.com

Mfr. of software and engaged in data recovery services.

Kroll Inc., 84 Maker Chambers VI, 220 Nariman Point, Mumbai 400021, India

Tel: 91-22-281-8560   Fax: 91-22-281-8561

THE KULJIAN CORPORATION

3700 Science Center, Philadelphia, PA, 19104

Tel: (215) 243-1900   Fax: (215) 243-1909

Studies, design, engineering, construction management and site supervision.

Development Consultants Pvt. Ltd., 24-B Park St., Calcutta 700 016, India

Development Consultants Pvt. Ltd., Hamed Bldg., 193 Anna Salai, Madras 600 006, India

The Kuljian Corp., 307-309, Sahyog, 58 Nehru Place, New Delhi 110 019, India

KURT SALMON ASSOCIATES (KSA)

1355 Peachtree Street NE, Atlanta, GA, 30309

Tel: (404) 892-0321   Fax: (404) 898-9590   www.kurtsalmon.com

Management consulting: consumer products, retailing.

KSA Technopak (India) Pvt. Ltd., A-5, Pamposh Enclave, New Delhi 110 048, India

LANCER CORPORATION

6655 Lancer Blvd., San Antonio, TX, 78219

Tel: (210) 310-7000   Fax: (210) 310-7252   www.lancercorp.com

Mfr. beverage dispensing equipment.

Lancer India, Dr. Annie Besant Road, Worli Mumbai 400 018, India

Tel: 91-22-283-0862

LANDOR ASSOCIATES

Klamath House, 1001 Front Street, San Francisco, CA, 94111-1424

Tel: (415) 955-1400   Fax: (415) 365-3190   www.landor.com

International marketing consulting firm, engaged in brand strategy, design, naming, digital branding, print literature design and research services.

Landor Associates, c/o SNR Associates, D5 Hari Chambers, 3/F, RB Centre 58-64 S.B. Road, Fort Bombay 400 023, India

Tel: 91-22-266-2339   Fax: 91-22-265-4763   Contact: Swapnesh Patel

LEAR CORPORATION

21557 Telegraph Road, Southfield, MI, 48086-5008

Tel: (248) 746-1500   Fax: (248) 746-1722   www.lear.com

Mfr. and distribute automotive materials and car seats.

Lear Corporation (Opel Division), Halol, India

LEGATO SYSTEMS, INC.

2350 West El Camino Real, Mountain View, CA, 94040

Tel: (650) 210-7000   Fax: (650) 210-7032   www.legato.com

Mfr. storage management software.

Legato Systems, PDTC Okhla Industrial Estate, New Delhi 110 020, India

LEHMAN BROTHERS HOLDINGS INC.

*101 Hudson Street, Jersey City, NJ, 07302

Tel: (201) 524-2000   Fax: (201) 524-2000   www.lehman.com

Financial services, securities and merchant banking services.

Lehman Brothers, Dr. Gopal Das Bhavan Bldg., 28 Barakhamba Road, 15th Fl., New Delhi 110 001, India

Tel: 91-11-373-6559

LEXMARK INTERNATIONAL

740 W. New Circle Rd., Lexington, KY, 40550

Tel: (859) 232-2000   Fax: (859) 232-1886   www.lexmark.com

Develop, manufacture, supply of printing solutions and products, including laser, inkjet, and dot matrix printers.

Lexmark Representative Office, Room 207, Apeejay Business Centre, Haddows Road, Chennai 600 006, India

Tel: 91-44-822-4949   Fax: 91-44-826-2447

ELI LILLY & COMPANY

Lilly Corporate Center, Indianapolis, IN, 46285

Tel: (317) 276-2000   Fax: (317) 277-6579   www.lilly.com

Mfr. pharmaceuticals and animal health products.

Eli Lilly Ranbaxy JV, 8 Balaji Estate, Guru Ravi Dass Marg. Kalkaji, New Delhi 110 019, India

Tel: 91-11-621-0084   Fax: 91-11-621-0075

LINCOLN ELECTRIC HOLDINGS

22801 St. Clair Ave., Cleveland, OH, 44117-1199

Tel: (216) 481-8100   Fax: (216) 486-8385   www.lincolnelectric.com

Mfr. arc welding and welding related products, oxy-fuel and thermal cutting equipment and integral AC motors.

Lincoln Electric Company, India, 309 Solaris-II, Third Fl., Saki Vihar Road, OPP. L&T Powai, Gate No. 6, Andheri East Mumbai 400 072, India

Tel: 91-22-851-4290   Fax: 91-22-852-4260   Contact: G. Gurushankar, Mng. Dir.

LNP ENGINEERING PLASTICS

475 Creamery Way, Exton, PA, 19341

Tel: (610) 363-4500   Fax: (610) 363-4749   www.geplastics.com

Mfr. thermoplastic composites.

General Electric Plastics UK, Plastic Avenue, PO Jawaharnagar, Baroda Gujarat 391320, India

LOCKHEED MARTIN CORPORATION

6801 Rockledge Drive, Bethesda, MD, 20817

Tel: (301) 897-6000   Fax: (301) 897-6652   www.imco.com

Design/mfr./management systems in fields of space, defense, energy, electronics and technical services.

Lockheed Martin Global, Inc., Rm. 1462, Maurya Sheraton, Diplomatic Enclave, New Delhi 110 021, India

Tel: 91-11-302-3273   Fax: 91-11-302-3275   Contact: Jaggi B. Malhotra

Lockheed Martin Intl. Ltd., 9 Jor Bagh, 1st Fl., New Delhi 110 003, India

Tel: 91-11-464-1915   Fax: 91-11-464-1916   Contact: J. Malhotra, VP

LORAL SPACE & COMMUNICATIONS LTD.

600 Third Ave., New York, NY, 10016

Tel: (212) 697-1105   Fax: (212) 338-5662   www.loral.com

Marketing coordination: defense electronics, communications systems.

Loral CyberStar, 203-204, Prestige Meridian 1, MG Road, Bangalore 560 001, India

Tel: 91-80-509-5858   Fax: 91-80-509-5857

LORD CORPORATION

2000 West Grandview Blvd, Erie, PA, 16514

Tel: (814) 868-0924   Fax: (814) 486-4345   www.lordcorp.com

Mfg. adhesives, coatings, chemicals, film products.

Lord India, 601, Tulsani Chambers, 212 Backbay Reclamation, Nariman Point, Mumbai 400 021, India

Tel: 91-22-232-5321   Fax: 91-22-232-5330

THE LUBRIZOL CORPORATION

29400 Lakeland Blvd., Wickliffe, OH, 44092-2298

Tel: (440) 943-4200   Fax: (440) 943-5337   www.lubrizol.com

Mfr. chemicals additives for lubricants and fuels.

Lubrizol India Ltd., Leo House, 4/F, 88-C Old Prabhadevi Rd., Mumbai 400 025, India

Tel: 91-22-430-0672

LUCENT TECHNOLOGIES, INC.

600 Mountain Ave., Murray Hill, NJ, 07974-0636

Tel: (908) 582-3000   Fax: (908) 582-2576   www.lucent.com

Design/mfr. wide range of public and private networks, communication systems and software, data networking systems, business telephone systems and microelectronics components.

Lucent Finolex Fiber Optic Cables, Ltd., Plot No. 344 Village Urse, Taluka Maval, Dist. Pune, India

Tel: 91-212-1423711   Fax: 91-212-1423762   Contact: Subrata Paul, Location Head

Lucent Technologies India Pvt. Ltd., Dr. Gopal Dass Bhawan, 3rd Floor, 28 Barakhamba Road, New Delhi 110 001, India

Tel: 91-11-335-3233   Fax: 91-11-335-3198   Contact: Ragini Maheshwari, PR Mgr.

M/A-COM INC.

1011 Pawtucket Boulevard, Lowell, MA, 01853-3295

Tel: (978) 442-5000   Fax: (978) 442-5354   www.macom.com

Mfr. radio frequency (RF) and microwave integrated circuits and IP Networks to the wireless telecommunications and defense-related industries.

AMP India Pvt. Ltd., Maruthi Industrial Estate, Hoody Rajapalya, Whitefield Main Road, Mahadevapura Post, Bangalore 560 048, India

Tel: 91-80-841-0200   Fax: 91-80-841-0210

MARATHON LE TOURNEAU COMPANY

PO Box 2307, Longview, TX, 75606

Tel: (903) 237-7000   Fax: (903) 236-6533   www.letourneau-inc.com

Mfr. heavy construction and mining machinery equipment.

General Marketing & Mfg. Co. Ltd., Birla Bldg., 14/F, 9/I R. N. Mukherjee Rd, Calcutta 700 001, India

MARK IV INDUSTRIES INC.

501 John James Audubon Pkwy., PO Box 810, Amherst, NY, 14226-0810

Tel: (716) 689-4972   Fax: (716) 689-1529   www.mark-iv.com

Mfr. of engineered systems and components utilizing mechanical and fluid power transmission, fluid transfer, and power systems and components.

Purolator India Ltd. J.V. Mark IV Auto, Sarojini Nagar, New Dehli 110 023, India

Tel: 91-11-688-5137   Fax: 91-11-688-5225

MARKET FACTS INC.

3040 Salt Creek Lane, Arlington Heights, IL, 60005

Tel: (847) 590-7000   Fax: (847) 590-7010   www.marketfacts.com

Market research services.

Blackstone Market Facts India Pvt. Ltd., Hotel Avion, Opp Domestic Airport, Nehru Road, Vile Parle (E), Mumbai 400 057, India

MARLEY COOLING TOWER COMPANY

7401 West 129th Street, Overland Park, KS, 66213

Tel: (913) 664-7400   Fax: (913) 664-7641   www.marleyct.com

Cooling and heating towers and waste treatment systems.

Marley Cooling Tower Co., India Liaison Office, 1067/017, Prestige Centre Point, No. 7 Edward Road, Bangalore 560 052, India

Tel: 91-80-228-5357   Fax: 91-80-228-4694

MASTERCARD INTERNATIONAL INC.

200 Purchase Street, Purchase, NY, 10577

Tel: (914) 249-2000   Fax: (914) 249-5475   www.mastercard.com

Provides financial payment systems globally.

MasterCard International Inc., 12 Upper, Ground Floor, Antriksh Bhawan, Kasturba Gandhi Marg, New Delhi 110 001, India

MAYFRAN INTERNATIONAL, INC.

PO Box 43038, Cleveland, OH, 44143

Tel: (440) 461-4100   Fax: (440) 461-5565   www.mayfran.com

Mfr. conveying systems, filtration equipment and separators that facilitate material handling and coolant recovery for automobile manufacturers and machine tool builders.

Miven Mayfran, PO Box 59, Karwar Road, Hubli 580 024, India

Tel: 91-836-303246 Fax: 91-836-303265

McCANN-ERICKSON WORLDGROUP

750 Third Ave., New York, NY, 10017

Tel: (212) 697-6000   Fax: (212) 984-3575   www.mccann.com

International advertising and marketing services.

Tara Sinha McCann-Erickson Pvt. Ltd., 15 Green Park Ext., New Delhi 110 016, India

McDERMOTT INTERNATIONAL INC.

1450 Poydras Street, PO Box 60035, New Orleans, LA, 70160-0035

Tel: (504) 587-5400   Fax: (504) 587-6153   www.mcdermott.com

Provides energy, engineering and construction services for industrial, utility, and hydrocarbon processing facilities, and to the offshore oil and natural gas industries.

Thermax Babcock & Wilcox, LTD., Sagar Complex, Mumbai Pune Rd., Near Nasik Phata, Kasarwadi, Pune 411 034, India

Tel: 91-21-279-5745   Fax: 91-21-279-5533   Contact: Jack Treier, Mng. Dir.

McDONALD'S CORPORATION

McDonald's Plaza, Oak Brook, IL, 60523

Tel: (630) 623-3000   Fax: (630) 623-7409   www.mcdonalds.com

Fast food chain stores.

McDonald's Corp., India

THE McGRAW-HILL COMPANIES

1221 Avenue of the Americas, New York, NY, 10020

Tel: (212) 512-2000   Fax: (212) 512-2703   www.mccgraw-hill.com

Books, magazines, information systems, financial service, publishing and broadcast operations.

Tata McGraw-Hill Publishing Co. Ltd., No. 7 West Patel Nagar, New Delhi 110 008, India
Tel: 91-11-573-2841

Tata McGraw-Hill Publishing Co. Ltd., 12/4 Asaf Ali Rd., New Delhi 110 002, India

McKINSEY & COMPANY

55 East 52nd Street, New York, NY, 10022

Tel: (212) 446-7000   Fax: (212) 446-8575   www.mckinsey.com

Management and business consulting services.

McKinsey & Company, Express Towers, 21st Fl., Nariman Point, Mumbai 400 021, India
Tel: 91-22-285-5532   Fax: 91-22-285-5531

McKinsey & Company, TAJ Palace Hotel, 2 Sardar Patel Marg, Diplomatic Enclave, New Delhi 110 021, India
Tel: 91-11-302-3580   Fax: 91-11-687-3227

MECHANICAL DYNAMICS, INC.

2300 Traverwood Drive, Ann Arbor, MI, 48105

Tel: (734) 994-3800   Fax: (734) 994-6418   www.adams.com

Mfr. Adams prototyping software for functional virtual prototyping solutions.

EDS Technlogies Pvt. Ltd., 153 II Cross, Promenade Road Frazier Town, Bangalore 560 005, India
Tel: 91-80551-4338

Mechanical Dynamics India, W19 Greater Kailash II, New Delhi 110 048, India
Tel: 91-11628-6596

NIIt Ltd., NIIT House, C-125, Okhla Phase-I, New Delhi 110 020, India

MENASHA CORPORATION

1645 Bergstrom Road, Neenah, WI, 54957-0367

Tel: (920) 751-1000   Fax: (920) 751-1236   www.menasha.com

Mfr. packaging and paperboard products.

Poly Hi Solidur India, Sub. Menasha, Plot Nos. 160 C/D & 161 C/D, Cherlapally IDA Phase II, Hyderabad 500 051, India

THE MENTHOLATUM COMPANY, INC.

707 Sterling Drive, Orchard Park, NY, 14127-1587

Tel: (716) 677-2500   Fax: (716) 674-3696   www.mentholatum.com

Mfr. of non-prescription pharmaceuticals, healthcare and cosmeceutical products and medical devices.

Mentholatum Pharmaceuticals India Pvt. Ltd., Sion-Trombay Road, Deonar, Mumbai 400 088, India
Tel: 91-22-558-5037   Fax: 91-22-588-5054   Contact: Anil Nadkarni

MERCK & COMPANY, INC.

One Merck Drive, PO Box 100, Whitehouse Station, NJ, 08889-0100

Tel: (908) 423-1000   Fax: (908) 423-2592   www.merck.com

Pharmaceuticals, chemicals and biologicals.

Merck, Sharp & Dohme of India Ltd., New India Centre, 17 Cooperage, Mumbai 400 039, India

MERRILL LYNCH & COMPANY, INC.

World Financial Center, 250 Vesey Street, New York, NY, 10281-1332

Tel: (212) 236-1000   Fax: (212) 449-2892   www.ml.com

Security brokers and dealers, investment and business services.

DSP Merrill Lynch Limited, Mafatlal Centre, 10/F, Nariman Road, Mumbai 400 021, India
Tel: 91-22-288-2550   Fax: 91-22-287-2093

METRON TECHNOLOGY

1350 Old Bayshore Highway, Ste. 210, Burlingame, CA, 94010

Tel: (650) 401-4600 Fax: (650) 373-1135 www.metrontech.com

Global provider of marketing, sales, service and support solutions to semiconductor materials and equipment suppliers and semiconductor manufacturers.

Metron Technology/FABTEQ, No. 100, 4th Cross, 2nd Block, Koramangala, Bangalore 560 034, India

Tel: 91-80-55 34 067 Fax: 91-80-55 22 947

METROPOLITAN LIFE INSURANCE COMPANY

1 Madison Ave., New York, NY, 10010-3603

Tel: (212) 578-3818 Fax: (212) 252-7294 www.metlife.com

Insurance and retirement savings products and services.

MetLife India Limited, Brigade Seshamahal, No. 5 Vani Vilas Road, Basavanagudi, Bangalore 560 004, India

Tel: 91-80-667-8617

M-I

PO Box 48242, Houston, TX, 77242-2842

Tel: (713) 739-0222 Fax: (713) 308-9503 www.midf.com

Developer, manufacturer and marketer of drilling and completion fluids and services.

IONA, Flat #31, Moulana Azad Road, Juhu Koliwada, Mumbai 400 049, India

Tel: 91-22-660-1763

MICRO ABRASIVES CORPORATION

720 Southampton Rd., Westfield, MA, 01086-0669

Tel: (413) 562-3641 Fax: (413) 562-7409 www.microgrit.com

Precision abrasive powders and slurries.

Micro Abrasives (India) Ltd., 65 Jor Bagh, New Delhi 110 003, India

MICROCHIP TECHNOLOGY INCORPORATED

2355 West Chandler Boulevard, Chandler, AZ, 85224

Tel: (602) 786-7200 Fax: (602) 899-9210 www.microchip.com

Mfr. electronic subassemblies and components.

Microchip Technology, Inc., No. 6 Legacy, Convent Road, Bangalore 560 025, India

Tel: 91-80-229-0061 Fax: 91-80-229-0062

MICROSEMI CORPORATION

2830 South Fairview St., Santa Ana, CA, 92704

Tel: (714) 979-8220 Fax: (714) 557-5989 www.microsemi.com

Design, manufacture and market analog, mixed-signal and discrete semiconductors.

Microsemi Corp. India, Unit 13 & 16, SDF Bldg.#1, SEEPZ, Andheri (East), Bombay 400 096, India

Tel: 91-22-8291210

MICROSOFT CORPORATION

One Microsoft Way, Redmond, WA, 98052-6399

Tel: (425) 882-8080 Fax: (425) 936-7329 www.microsoft.com

Computer software, peripherals and services.

Microsoft Corporation (India) Pvt. Ltd., Peharpur Business Centre, 21 Nehru Place, New Delhi 110 019, India

Tel: 91-11-646-0694 Fax: 91-11-647-4714

MILACRON INC.

2090 Florence Ave., Cincinnati, OH, 45206

Tel: (513) 487-5000 Fax: (513) 487-5057 www.milacron.com

Metalworking and plastics technologies.

Milacron Inc. Private Ltd., Factory: Plot No. 14/16, Phase-I, GIDC Vatva Ahmedabad 382 445, India

Tel: 91-79-5830112 Fax: 91-79-5830125 Contact: Mahendra N. Patel

MILLER ELECTRIC MFG. COMPANY

1635 W. Spencer Street, Appleton, WI, 54912-1079

Tel: (920) 734-9821   Fax: (920) 735-4125   www.millerwelds.com

Mfr. arc welding machines.

ITW Welding Products, H-No: 1-2-365/26, 2/A R.K. Mutt Road, Domalguda Hyderabad, Andhra Pradesh 500 029, India

Tel: 91-40-760-4541   Fax: 91-40-374-0191

MILLIPORE CORPORATION

80 Ashby Road, PO Box 9125, Bedford, MA, 01730

Tel: (781) 533-6000   Fax: (781) 533-3110   www.millipore.com

Mfr. flow and pressure measurement and control components; precision filters, hi-performance liquid chromatography instruments.

Millipore (India) Pvt. Ltd., 50A, 2nd Phase Ring Rd., Peenya, Bangalore 560 058, India

MILTON ROY COMPANY

201 Ivyland Road, Ivylan, PA, 18974

Tel: (215) 441-0800   Fax: (215) 293-0468   www.miltonroy.com

Mfr. medical and industry equipment and process control instruments.

Milton Roy Asia, 4 Rajarajan St., Visaiakshi Nagar Ekkaduthangal, Madras 600 097, India

Tel: 91-44-234-4200   Fax: 91-44-234-6294   Contact: Dr. G. Nallakrishnan

MINE SAFETY APPLIANCES COMPANY

121 Gamma Drive, PO Box 426, Pittsburgh, PA, 15230

Tel: (412) 967-3000   Fax: (412) 967-3452   www.msa.net

Safety equipment, industry filters.

Mine Safety Appliances Ltd., P-25 Transport Depot Rd., Calcutta 700 088, India

MISYS HEALTHCARE SYSTEMS

8529 Six Forks Road, Raleigh, NC, 27615

Tel: (919) 847-8102   Fax: (919) 846-1555   www.misyhealthcare.com

Mfr. practice management software.

Misys Healthcare India, Unit 2/3, Level 4, Innovator Block, International Technology ark, Whitefield Road, Bangalore 560 066, India

MOLEX INC.

2222 Wellington Court, Lisle, IL, 60532

Tel: (630) 969-4550   Fax: (630) 969-1352   www.molex.com

Mfr. electronic, electrical and fiber optic interconnection products and systems, switches, application tooling.

Molex (India) Ltd., Plot No. 6(A) Sada Industrial Area, Kadugodi Bangalore 560 067, India

Tel: 91-80-845-2911   Fax: 91-80-845-2922

MONSANTO

800 N. Lindbergh Boulevard, St. Louis, MO, 63167

Tel: (314) 694-1000   Fax: (314) 694-7625   www.monsanto.com

Life sciences company focusing on agriculture, nutrition, pharmaceuticals, health and wellness and sustainable development.

Cargill Seeds India Ltd., 808, Sophia's Choice #7, St, Marks Road, Bangolore 580 001, India

Monsanto (India) Ltd., Ahura Centre, 5/F, 96 Mahakali Caves Road, Andheri (East) Mumbai 400 093, India

Tel: 91-22-824-6450   Fax: 91-22-690-2111

Monsanto Bangolore, INDRI, 1st Floor, 18th Cross Road Malleswaram, Bangalore 560 003, India

Monsanto Enterprise Ltd., Vishal Towers, Flat # 1016-1018, New Delhi, India

Monsanto Enterprises Ltd., 5 F&G, 5th floor, Gee Gee Emerald Building, Chennai, India

MOOG INC.

300 Jamison Road, East Aurora, NY, 14052-0018

Tel: (716) 652-2000   Fax: (716) 687-4471   www.moog.com

Mfr. precision control components and systems.

Moog Controls (India) Pvt. Ltd., Plot 1-2-3, Electric City, Bangalore, India

J. P. MORGAN CHASE & CO. INC.

270 Park Ave., New York, NY, 10017

Tel: (212) 270-6000   Fax: (212) 622-9030   www.jpmorganchase.com

Provides integrated financial solutions for institutions and individuals worldwide, including asset management, investment banking and commercial banking.

J. P. Morgan Chase & Co., Maker Chambers VI, 7/F, Nariman Point, Mumbai 400 021, India

Tel: 91-22-285-5666   Fax: 91-2-202-7772

MORGAN STANLEY DEAN WITTER & CO.

1585 Broadway, New York, NY, 10036

Tel: (212) 761-4000   Fax: (212) 761-0086   www.msdw.com

Securities and commodities brokerage, investment banking, money management, personal trusts.

Morgan Stanley Asset Managemen/India PVT Ltd., 4th Fl., Charanjit Rai Marg, Mumbai 400 001, India

MOTOROLA, INC.

1303 East Algonquin Road, Schaumburg, IL, 60196

Tel: (847) 576-5000   Fax: (847) 538-5191   www.motorola.com

Mfr. communications equipment, semiconductors and cellular phones.

Motorola Singapore Pte. Ltd., Meridien Commercial Towers, 8th Fl., Windson Place, New Delhi 110 001, India

Tel: 91-11-371-0080   Fax: 91-11-371-8086

MRO SOFTWARE, INC.

100 Crosby Drive, Bedford, MA, 01730

Tel: (781) 280-2000   Fax: (781) 280-0207   www.mrosoftware.com

Design/sales of enterprise asset maintenance software.

MRO Software, 410, Mercantile House, 15, Kasturba Handhi Marg, New Delhi 110001, India

NATIONAL INSTRUMENTS CORPORATION

11550 N. Mopac Expwy., Austin, TX, 78759-3504

Tel: (512) 338-9119   Fax: (512) 794-5794   www.ni.com

Mfr. hardware and graphical software.

National Instruments India, 100 Feet Road, HAL 2nd Stage Indiranagar, Bangalore 560 008, India

NATIONAL MACHINERY COMPANY

161 Greenfield St., Tiffin, OH, 44883-2471

Tel: (419) 447-5211   Fax: (419) 447-5299   www.nationalmachinery.com

Mfr. high-speed metal parts forming machines.

National Machinery Company, New Delhi, India

Tel: 91-11-686-7282

National Machinery Company, Calcutta, India

Tel: 91-33-220-4621

NATIONAL STARCH AND CHEMICAL COMPANY

10 Finderne Ave., Bridgewater, NJ, 08807-3300

Tel: (908) 685-5000   Fax: (908) 685-5005   www.nationalstarch.com

Mfr. adhesives and sealants, resins and specialty chemicals, electronic materials and adhesives, food products, industry starch.

National Starch & Chemical, Plot No. 1/1 TTC Industrial Area, Thane Belpur Road, Post Box 12, Koparkhaime, New Mumbai 400709, India

NORDSON CORPORATION

28601 Clemens Road, Westlake, OH, 44145-4551

Tel: (440) 892-1580   Fax: (440) 892-9507   www.nordson.com

Mfr. industry application equipment, sealants and packaging machinery.

Nordson Corp. South Asia Reg. Office, #3 Ground Fl., Maya Apartments, Rd. #15, Chembur Mumbai 400 071, India

Tel: 91-22-528-4800   Fax: 91-22-528-1334

Nordson India Pvt. Ltd. (Hdqtrs.), 143-A Bommasandra, Industrial Area, Bangalore 562 158, India

Tel: 91-8110-34915   Fax: 91-8110-34920

Nordson India Pvt. Ltd. New Delhi Branch, B-4, Greater Kailash Enclave Part II, New Delhi 110 048, India
Tel: 91-11-628-7581

NORTON ABRASIVES COMPANY

1 New Bond Street, Worcester, MA, 01606

Tel: (508) 795-5000   Fax: (508) 795-5741   www.nortonabrasives.com

Mfr. abrasives for industrial manufacturing.

Grindwell Norton Ltd., Devanahalli Rd., off Old Madras Rd., Bangalore, India

Grindwell Norton Ltd., Army & Navy Bldg., 148 Mahatma Gandhi Rd., Mumbai 400 023, India

NOVELL WORLDWIDE

1800 S. Novell Place, Provo, UT, 84606

Tel: (801) 861-7000   Fax: (801) 861-5555   www.novell.com

Develop/mfr. networking software and related equipment.

Onward Novell Software (India) Ltd., 62, M.I.D.C. 13th Street, Andheri (East), Mumbai 400 093, India

NOVEON INTERNATIONAL

9911 Brecksville Road, Cleveland, OH, 44141-3427

Tel: (216) 447-5000   Fax: (216) 447-5669   www.noveoninc.com

Mfr. specialty chemicals.

Noveon Diamalt Private Limited, Plot No. B5 & B6, MEPZ, Tambaram, Chennai 600 045, India
Tel: 91-44-262-6261

NYPRO INC.

101 Union Street, Clinton, MA, 01510

Tel: (978) 365-9721   Fax: (978) 368-0236   www.nypro.com

Mfr. plastic parts for telecommunications industry.

Nypro Forbes Product Ltd., Sub. Division Plot No. 52, Sipcot Industrial Complex, Hosur, Tamil Nadin 635 126, India

OCCIDENTAL PETROLEUM CORPORATION

10889 Wilshire Blvd., Los Angeles, CA, 90024

Tel: (310) 208-8800   Fax: (310) 443-6690   www.oxy.com

Petroleum and petroleum products, chemicals, plastics.

Intl. Ore & Fertilizer India Pvt. Ltd., 5/F, 71 Nehru Place, Guru Angad Bhavan, New Delhi 110 019, India

OCEANEERING INTERNATIONAL INC.

11911 FM 529, Houston, TX, 77041

Tel: (713) 329-4500   Fax: (713) 329-4951   www.oceaneering.com

Transportation equipment, underwater service to offshore oil and gas industry.

Oceaneering International, Mumbai, India

OFFSHORE LOGISTICS, INC.

224 Rue de Jean, Lafayette, LA, 70505

Tel: (337) 233-1221   Fax: (337) 235-6678   www.olog.com

Engaged in helicopter transportation services for offshore oil and gas companies.

Bristow/Deccan Aviation Ltd., c/o Cairn Energy India, Uppataguptan Mandal, Challipalli, East Godavari, Surasari Yanan 533212, India

THE O'GARA COMPANY

1250 24th Street, NW, Suite 300, Washington, DC, 20037

Tel: (202) 835-1680   Fax: (202) 835-1685   www.ogara.com

Security and consulting services and vehicles.

Kroll Associates (Asia) Ltd. (India Liasion Office), 208 Barakhamba Rd., New Delhi 110 001, India
Tel: 91-11-373-6355   Fax: 91-11-373-6356

OGILVY & MATHER WORLDWIDE

309 West 49th Street, New York, NY, 10017-7399

Tel: (212) 237-4000   Fax: (212) 237-5123   www.ogilvypr.com

Engaged in public relations and communications.

Ogilvy Public Relations Worldwide, Kamala Mills Compound, Senapati Bapat Marg Lower Parel, Mumbai 400 013, India

Tel: 91-22-491-3914   Contact: Mahnaz Curmally

Ogilvy Public Relations Worldwide, Motijug House, 1 Auckland Place, Calcutta 700 017, India

Tel: 91-33-281-0658   Fax: 91-33-247-1663   Contact: Simky Barua

Ogilvy Public Relations Worldwide, 139/140 Marshalls Road, 3/F, Egmore Chennai 600 008, India

Tel: 91-44-852-9471   Contact: Arup Kavan

Ogilvy Public Relations Worldwide, Mahalaxmi Chambers, 2/F, 29 Mahatma Gandhi Road, Bangalore 560 001, India

Tel: 91-80-506-5046   Fax: 91-80-506-5049   Contact: Mahnaz Curmally

Ogilvy Public Relations Worldwide, Mahavir House, Basheer Bagh Cross Roads, Hyderabad 500 029, India

Tel: 91-40-322-7316   Contact: Bhavani Giddu

THE OILGEAR COMPANY

2300 S. 51st Street, Milwaukee, WI, 53219

Tel: (414) 327-1700   Fax: (414) 327-0532   www.oilgear.com

Mfr. hydraulic power transmission machinery.

Oilgear Pvt. Ltd., Harman House, #482, 80 Feet Rd., Ganganagar, Bangalore 560 032, India

Oilgear Towler Polyhydron Pvt. Ltd., Plot #4, R.S. #680/2, Belgaum Mfrs. Co-op Industrial Estate Ltd., Udyambag Belgaum 590 008, India

ONDEO NALCO COMPANY

Ondeo Nalco Center, 1601 W. Diehl Road, Naperville, IL, 60563-1198

Tel: (630) 305-1000   Fax: (630) 305-2900   www.ondeo-nalco.com

Mfr. specialty chemicals for water and waste water treatment, oil products and refining, industry processes; water and energy management service.

ONDEO Nalco Chemicals India Ltd., Ste. 6, 20-A Park St., Calcutta 700 016, India

Tel: 91-33-249-4883   Fax: 91-33-249-3999

OPW FUELING COMPONENTS

PO Box 405003, Cincinnati, OH, 45240-5003

Tel: (513) 870-3100   Fax: (513) 874-1231   www.opw-fc.com

Mfr. fueling and vapor recovery nozzles, service station equipment, aboveground storage tank equipment.

Dover India Pvt. Ltd., 36 Marol Co-Op. Ind. Estate Ltd., Mathuradas Vasanji Road, 2/F, Marol, Andheri Mumbai 400 059, India

Tel: 91-22-695-2473   Fax: 91-22-695-2474

ORACLE CORPORATION

500 Oracle Parkway, Redwood Shores, CA, 94065

Tel: (650) 506-7000   Fax: (650) 506-7200   www.oracle.com

Develop/manufacture software.

Oracle India, Bangalore, India

OTIS ELEVATOR COMPANY

One Farm Springs Road, Farmington, CT, 06032

Tel: (860) 676-6000   Fax: (860) 676-5111   www.otis.com

Mfr. elevators and escalators.

Otis Elevator Co. Ltd., Gateway Bldg., Apollo Bunder, Mumbai 400 039, India

Otis Elevator Co. Ltd., Akurli Rd., Kandivli East, Mumbai 400 101, India

OWENS-CORNING CORPORATION

One Owens Corning Pkwy., Toledo, OH, 43659

Tel: (419) 248-8000   Fax: (419) 248-8445   www.owenscorning.com

Mfr. building materials systems and composites systems.

Owens Corning Building Materials Systems, 10/1-B Graphite India Road, Hoodi Village, KR Puram Hobli, Bangalore 560 048, India

Tel: 91-80-852-4380

Owens Corning India, 301-10, Sahar Plaza Complex, Bonanza MV Road, Andheri East, Mumbai (Bombay) 400 059, India

Tel: 91-22-839-8250   Contact: Rajeev Moudgil

OWENS-ILLINOIS, INC.

One SeaGate, PO Box 1035, Toledo, OH, 43666

Tel: (419) 247-5000   Fax: (419) 247-2839   www.o-i.com

Mfr. glass containers and packaging products.

Owens-Brockway (India) Ltd., New Delhi, India

PALL CORPORATION

2200 Northern Boulevard, East Hills, NY, 11548-1289

Tel: (516) 484-5400   Fax: (516) 484-5228   www.pall.com

Specialty materials and engineering; filters and related fluid clarification equipment.

Pall Pharmalab Filtration PVT, Ltd., Star Metal Compoundm, LBS Marg, Vikhoroli, Bombay 400 083, India

Tel: 91-22-5783-368   Fax: 91-22-5785-329

PANDUIT CORPORATION

17301 Ridgeland Ave., Tinley Park, IL, 60477-0981

Tel: (708) 532-1800   Fax: (708) 532-1811   www.panduit.com

Mfr. of network connectivity and electrical products.

Panduit Asia Pacific Pte. Ltd. Bombay, 203, J.B. Nagar Andheri (E), Bombay 400 059, India

PARAMETRIC TECHNOLOGY CORPORATION

140 Kendrick St., Needham, MA, 02494

Tel: (781) 370-5000   Fax: (781) 370-6000   www.ptc.com

Supplier of mechanical design automation and product data management software and services.

Parametric Technology India, Office # 506-509, Pahparpur Business Center, 21 Nehru Place, New Delhi 110 019, India

Tel: 91-11-647-4701   Fax: 91-11-647-4718

Parametric Technology India, DBS Corporate Club, 26 Cunningham Road, Bangalore 560 052, India

Tel: 91-80-226-7272   Fax: 91-80-228-1092

Parametric Technology India Pvt. Ltd., TCI Business Center, 170 Dhole Patil Road, Pune 411 001, India

Tel: 91-212-625156   Fax: 91-212-625156

Parametric Technology India Pvt. Ltd., DBS Corporate Services, 31A Catheral Garden Road, Madras 600 034, India

Tel: 91-44-822-2008x302   Fax: 91-44-825-7258

Parametric Technology India Pvt. Ltd., #402 A.N. Chambers, Guru Nanak Road, Bandra Bombay 400 050, India

Tel: 91-22-645-4427   Fax: 91-22-645-4428

PATNI COMPUTER SYSTEMS (PCS) DATA CONVERSION

238 Main Street, Cambridge, MA, 02142

Tel: (617) 354-7424   Fax: (617) 876-4711   www.patni.com

Software consulting and contract programming services.

Patni Computer Systems Ltd., 54/55, SDF-II, Seepz, Andheri (E), Mumbai 400 096, India

P-COM, INC.

3175 South Winchester Blvd., Campbell, CA, 95008

Tel: (408) 866-3666   Fax: (408) 866-3655   www.p-com.com

Mfr. microwave radio transmission equipment.

P-Com India, A27/4, Qutub Enclave, DLF Phase-1, Gurgaon 122002, India

J.C. PENNEY COMPANY, INC.

6501 Legacy Drive, Plano, TX, 75024-3698

Tel: (972) 431-1000   Fax: (972) 431-1977   www.jcpenney.com

Markets family apparel, shoes, home furnishings, jewelry, and offers credit cards.

J. C. Penney Purchasing Corp., 139/T Juhu Rd., Santacruz W., Mumbai 400 049, India

PEOPLESOFT INC.

4460 Hacienda Drive, Pleasanton, CA, 94588-8618

Tel: (925) 225-3000   Fax: (925) 694-4444   www.peoplesoft.com

Mfr. applications to manage business operations across computer networks.

PeopleSoft India Pvt. Ltd., 26 Cunningham Road, Bangalore 560 052, India

PEPSiCO INC.

700 Anderson Hill Road, Purchase, NY, 10577-1444

Tel: (914) 253-2000   Fax: (914) 253-2070   www.pepsico.com

Beverages and snack foods.

PepsiCo Ltd., India

PEROT SYSTEMS CORPORATION

12404 Park Central Drive, Dallas, TX, 75251

Tel: (972) 340-5000   Fax: (972) 455-4100   www.perotsystems.com

Provides technology and business solutions.

HCL Perot Systems, A-10-11, Sector 3, Noida UP 201301, India

Tel: 91-120-4547671

PFAUDLER, INC.

1000 West Ave., PO Box 23600, Rochester, NY, 14692-3600

Tel: (716) 235-1000   Fax: (716) 436-9644   www.pfaudler.com

Mfr. glass lined reactors, storage vessels and reglassing services.

GMM Pfaudler, Karamsad, India

Tel: 91-26-923-0416   Fax: 91-26-924-6467

GMM Pfaudler, Churchgate House, 32-34 Veer Nariman Rd., Fort Bombay 400 001, India

PFIZER INC.

235 East 42nd Street, New York, NY, 10017-5755

Tel: (212) 573-2323   Fax: (212) 573-7851   www.pfizer.com

Research-based, global health care company.

Duchem Laboratories Ltd., Madras, India

Dumex Ltd., Madras, India

Pfizer Ltd., Madras, India

PHARMACIA CORPORATION

100 Route 206 North, Peapack, NJ, 07977

Tel: (908) 901-8000   Fax: (908) 901-8379   www.pharmacia.com

Mfr. pharmaceuticals, agricultural products, industry chemicals.

Pharmacia & Upjohn India Pvt. Ltd., S.C.O. 27, Sector 14, Gurgaon Haryana 122 001, India

Tel: 91-124-6308252   Fax: 91-124-6308249

PHELPS DODGE CORPORATION

2600 North Central Ave., Phoenix, AZ, 85004-3089

Tel: (602) 234-8100   Fax: (602) 234-8337   www.phelpsdodge.com

Copper, minerals, metals and special engineered products for transportation and electrical markets.

Asian Cables Ltd., Great Mahal, 463 Dr. Annie Senant Road, Worit Mumbai 400 025, India

PHILLIPS PETROLEUM COMPANY

Phillips Building, 411 S. Keeler Ave., Bartlesville, OK, 74004

Tel: (918) 661-6600   Fax: (918) 661-7636   www.phillips66.com

Crude oil, natural gas, liquefied petroleum gas, gasoline and petro-chemicals.

Cochin Refineries Ltd., Post Bag 2, PO Ambalamugal, Ernakulam Dist., Kerala 632 302, India

Gujarat Carbon Ltd., Harikripa, Alkapuri, Baroda, Gujarat 390 005, India

Phillips Carbon Black Ltd., Duncan House, 31 Netaji Subhas Rd., Calcutta 700 001, India

Phillips Petroleum Intl. Corp., 1-A Vandhana Blvd., 11 Tolstov Marg, New Delhi 110 001, India

PILLAR INDUSTRIES INC.

21905 Gateway Road, Brookfield, WI, 53045

Tel: (262) 317-5300   Fax: (262) 317-5353   www.pillar.com

Mfr. induction heating and melting equipment.

Pillar Induction (India) Pvt. Ltd., 2nd Avenue, Block A-13, Anna Nagar, Madras 600 102, India

PIONEER HI-BRED INTERNATIONAL INC.

400 Locust Street, Ste. 800, Des Moines, IA, 50309

Tel: (515) 248-4800   Fax: (515) 248-4999   www.pioneer.com

Agricultural chemicals, farm supplies, biological products, research.

Pioneer Hi-Bred, 401/402, Suneja Towers, District Centre II, Janakpuri 110 058, India

PRAXAIR, INC.

39 Old Ridgebury Road, Danbury, CT, 06810-5113

Tel: (203) 837-2000   Fax: (203) 837-2450   www.praxair.com

Produces and distributes industrial and specialty gases.

Praxair India Pvt., Ltd., Praxair House, No.8 Ulsoor Rd., Bangalore 560 042, India

Tel: 91-80-555-9841   Fax: 91-80-559-5925

PRECISION VALVE & TRIM, INC.

11923 Cloverland Ave, Baton Rouge, LA, 70809

Tel: (225) 752-5600   Fax: (225) 752-5400   www.precisionvalve.com

Mfr. aerosol valves.

Precision Valve (India) Pvt. Ltd., 228 Pragti (TODI) Ind. Estate, N.M. Joshi Marg, Lower Parel, Mumbai 400 011, India

PRICEWATERHOUSECOOPERS LLP

1301 Ave. of the Americas, New York, NY, 10019

Tel: (212) 596-7000   Fax: (212) 259-1301   www.pwcglobal.com

Accounting and auditing, tax and management, and human resource consulting services.

PriceWaterhouseCoopers, Suite No. B, 3rd Fl, 20-A Park St., Calcutta 700 016, India

Tel: 91-33-2494680 Fax: 91-33-2434980

PriceWaterhouseCoopers, B-102 Himalaya House, 23 Kasturba Gandhi Marg, PO Box 466, New Delhi 110 001, India

Tel: 91-11-3319856 Fax: 91-11-3323183

PriceWaterhouseCoopers, B3/1 Gillander House, Netaji Subhas Road, PO Box 2238, Calcutta 700 001, India

Tel: 91-33-2209001 Fax: 91-33-2202420

PriceWaterhouseCoopers, 305-307, Century Arcade, 8/3 Narangi Baug Road, Off. Boat Club Road, Pune 411 001, India

Tel: 91-212-663271

PriceWaterhouseCoopers, St. Patrick's Business Complex, 21 Museum Road, PO Box 2544, Bangalore 560 025, India

Tel: 91-80-558-7239   Fax: 91-80-558-8751

PriceWaterhouseCoopers, 1002/1107, Raheja Chambers, Nariman Point, Mumbai 400 021, India

Tel: 91-22-2835190 Fax: 91-22-2045592

PriceWaterhouseCoopers, 610, Anna Salai, PO Box 743, Madras 600 006, India

Tel: 91-44-827-1597   Fax: 91-44-8260787

PRIDE INTERNATIONAL, INC.

5847 San Felipe, Ste. 3300, Houston, TX, 77057

Tel: (713) 789-1400   Fax: (713) 789-1430   www.prde.com

Provides drilling services.

Pride Foramerl, Darvesh Chambers #401, 743 PD Hinduja Road Khar (West), Mumbai 400 052, India

PROCTER & GAMBLE COMPANY

One Procter & Gamble Plaza, Cincinnati, OH, 45202

Tel: (513) 983-1100   Fax: (513) 562-4500   www.pg.com

Personal care, food, laundry, cleaning and industry products.

Procter & Gamble Hygiene & Health Care Ltd., Tiecicon House, Dr. E. Moses Road, Mumbai Bombay 400 011, India

PSC INC.

111 SW Fifth Avenue, Ste. 4100, Portland, OR, 97204-3644

Tel: (503) 553-3920   Fax: (503) 553-3940   www.pscnet.com

Mfr. and sales of bar code scanners.

PSC Inc., F-41, South Extension, Part-I Ring Road, U&I Center, New Delhi - 110 049 New Delhi - 110 049, India

Tel: 91-11-4621586   Fax: 91-11-4623305

PUBLIC SERVICE ENTERPRISE GROUP (PSEG)

80 Park Plaza, Newark, NJ, 07101

Tel: (973) 430-7000   Fax: (973) 623-5389   www.pseg.com

Electric and gas utility.

PSEG India Inc., Prakash Presidium, II Floor, 110 Mahatma Gandhi Road, Nungambakkam, Chennai 600 034, India

Tel: 91-44-821-0100   Fax: 91-44-822-3166   Contact: B. Vanchi

QUAKER CHEMICAL CORPORATION

1 Quaker Park, 901 Hector St., Conshohocken, PA, 19428-0809

Tel: (610) 832-4000   Fax: (610) 832-8682   www.quakerchem.com

Mfr. developer, producer, and marketer of custom-formulated chemical specialty products.

Quaker Chemical India Ltd. (JV), 7B Pretoria St., Calcutta 700 071, India

Tel: 91-33-282-5414   Contact: G. Kumar Sachdev, Mng. Dir.

QUALCOMM INC.

5775 Morehouse Dr., San Diego, CA, 92121-1714

Tel: (858) 587-1121   Fax: (858) 658-2100   www.qualcomm.com

Digital wireless telecommunications systems.

QUALCOMM India, DBS Corporate Centre, 1/F, World Trade Tower, Rms.15-16, Barakhamba Lane, New Delhi 110 001, India

QUINTILES TRANSNATIONAL CORPORATION

4709 Creekstone Dr., Durham, NC, 27703

Tel: (919) 998-2000   Fax: (919) 998-9113   www.quintiles.com

Mfr. pharmaceuticals.

Quintiles Spectral Limited, 3 Ashoknagar Bungalows Behind Sundarvan, Satellite Road, Ahmedabad 380 015, India

QWEST COMMUNICATIONS INTERNATIONAL INC.

1801 California Street, Ste. 5200, Denver, CO, 80202

Tel: (303) 896-2020   Fax: (303) 793-6654   www.uswest.com

Tele-communications provider; integrated communications services.

BPL/USW - India, Maharashtra, India

Tel: 91-11-301-0101x1110   Fax: 91-11-302-3153

RADISSON HOTELS INTERNATIONAL

Carlson Pkwy., PO Box 59159, Minneapolis, MN, 55459-8204

Tel: (612) 540-5526   Fax: (612) 449-3400   www.radisson.com

Operates, manages and franchises full-service hotels and resorts worldwide.

Radisson Hotel Delhi, National Highway 8, New Delhi 110 037, India

Tel: 91-11-613-7373   Fax: 91-11-689-8540

Radisson Hotel St. Thomas Mount, Chennai, 355C GST Rd., St. Thomas Mount, Chennai 600 016, India

Tel: 91-44-4322382   Fax: 91-44-4323380

RATIONAL SOFTWARE CORPORATION

18880 Homestead Road, Cupertino, CA, 95014-0721

Tel: (408) 863-9900   Fax: (408) 863-4120   www.rationale.com

Mfr. application development software.

Rational Software, N. 40, 100 Feet Road, 4th Block, Koramangala, Bangalore 560 034, India

RAY & BERNDTSON, INC.

301 Commerce, Ste. 2300, Fort Worth, TX, 76102

Tel: (817) 334-0500   Fax: (817) 334-0779   www.prb.com

Executive search, management audit and management consulting firm.

Ray & Berndtson, 208 Richmond Tower, 12 Richmond Rd., Bangalore 560, India

Tel: 91-80-227-8296   Fax: 91-80-227-8297   Contact: Charence Lobo, Mng. Ptnr.

Ray & Berndtson, 606 Prabhadevi Estate, Veer Savakar Marg, Prabhadevi, Mumbai 400 025, India

Tel: 91-22-437-7272   Fax: 91-22-436-2644   Contact: Mari & Clarence Lobo, Mng. Prtns.

RAYMOND JAMES FINANCIAL, INC.

880 Carillon Parkway, St. Petersburg, FL, 33716

Tel: (813) 573-3800   Fax: (813) 573-8244   www.rjf.com

Financial services; securities brokerage, asset management, and investment banking services.

ASK-Raymond James Securities India Ltd., Bandbox House, Rear 2/F, 254-D Dr. Annie Besant Road, Worli Mumbai 400 025, India

Tel: 91-22-498-5670 Fax: 91-22-5665

RAYTHEON COMPANY

141 Spring Street, Lexington, MA, 02173

Tel: (781) 862-6600   Fax: (781) 860-2172   www.raytheon.com

Mfr. diversified electronics, appliances, energy and environmental products; publishing, industry and construction services.

Raytheon International, DOOR Training India, Sandeep Budhiraja, Lavleen Raheja Yogesh Sood, New Delhi, India

Tel: 91-11-462-5017 Fax: 91-11-463-8899

REEBOK INTERNATIONAL LTD.

1895 J. W. Foster Blvd., Canton, MA, 02021

Tel: (781) 401-5000   Fax: (781) 401-7402   www.reebok.com

Mfr. athletic shoes including casual, dress golf and walking shoes.

Planet Reebok, 6/D, Brigade Road, Bangalore 560 01, India

REFCO GROUP LTD.

200 Liberty Street Tower A, New York, NY, 10281

Tel: (212) 693-7700   Fax: (212) 693-7856   www.refco.com

Commodity and security brokers engaged in the execution and clearing of futures and options and institutional asset management services.

Refco-Sify Securities India Pvt. Ltd. (JV), Mumbai, India

RELIANT ENERGY, INC.

1111 Louisiana Street, Houston, TX, 77002

Tel: (713) 207-3000   Fax: (713) 207-0206   www.houind.com

Provides gas and electric services.

Rain Calcining Limited, India

RENAISSANCE HOTELS AND RESORTS

10400 Fernwood Road, Bethesda, MD, 20817

Tel: (301) 380-3000   Fax: (301) 380-5181   www.renaissancehotels.com

upscale, full-service hotel and resort chain under Marriott International, Inc.

Renaissance Goa Resort, Goa, India

Tel: 91-834-74-5208

ROBBINS & MYERS INC.

1400 Kettering Tower, Dayton, OH, 45423-1400

Tel: (937) 222-2610   Fax: (937) 225-3355   www.robn.com

Mfr. progressing cavity pumps, valves and agitators.

R&M Energy Systems, New Delhi, India

ROCKWELL AUTOMATION, INC.

777 East Wisconsin Ave., Ste. 1400, Milwaukee, WI, 53202

Tel: (414) 212-5200   Fax: (414) 212-5201   www.rockwellautomation.com

Products and service for aerospace and defense, automotive, electronics, graphics and automation industry.

Rockwell Automation, 131 Industrial Area, Patparganj Delhi 110 092, India

Tel: 91-11-214-5605

Rockwell Automation/Allen-Bradley India Ltd., C-8&9 Minoo Minar, Veera Desai Rd., Andheri West, Mumbai 400 053, India

Tel: 91-22-67-0400   Fax: 91-22-626-7127

Rockwell International Overseas Corp., A-5 Kailash Colony, New Delhi 110 048, India

Tel: 91-11-621-5374   Fax: 91-11-647-5138

Rockwell Intl. (Asia Pacific) Ltd., C-11, Site IV Industrial Area, Dist. Ghaziabad, Sahibabad 201 010, India

Tel: 91-575-771113   Fax: 91-575-770822

Rockwell Semiconductor Systems, Capital Trust House, 47 Community Centre, Friends Colony, New Delhi 110 065, India

Tel: 91-11-692-4780   Fax: 91-11-647-5138

ROHM AND HAAS COMPANY

100 Independence Mall West, Philadelphia, PA, 19106

Tel: (215) 592-3000   Fax: (215) 592-3377   www.rohmhaas.com

Mfr. specialty chemicals.

Rohm and Haas (India) Pvt. Ltd., Maks Commercial Centre, A/14 Veera Industrial Estate, Off Veera Desai Rd., Andheri West Mumbai 400 053, India

Rohm and Haas (India) Pvt. Ltd., 114 Jorgagh, New Delhi 110 003, India

Tel: 91-11-464-7682

RYERSON TULL

2621 W. 15th Place, Chicago, IL, 60608

Tel: (773) 762-2121   Fax: (773) 762-0179   www.ryersontull.com

Engaged in metal distribution.

Ryerson Tull (JV), 43, Chowringhee Road, Tata Center, Kolkata 700 071, India

SAPIENT CORPORATION

1 Memorial Drive, Cambridge, MA, 02142

Tel: (617) 621-0200   Fax: (617) 621-1300   www.sapient.com

Engaged in information technology and consulting services.

Sapient Corporation Private Limited, Videocon Tower, 12/F, Jhandewalan Extension, Rani Jhansi Marg, New Delhi 110 055, India

SCHENECTADY INTERNATIONAL INC.

PO Box 1046, Schenectady, NY, 12301

Tel: (518) 370-4200   Fax: (518) 382-8129   www.siigroup.com

Mfr. electrical insulating varnishes, enamels, phenolic resins, alkylphenols.

Schenectady (Beck) India, Beck House, Damle Path, Law College Road, Pune 411 004, India

Tel: 91-20-543-8540   Fax: 91-20-543-9048   Contact: Manu Tandon

Schenectady India Ltd., 195 Nariman Point, Mumbai 400 021, India

Schenectady Specialities Asia Ltd. (JV), Janki Niwas N.C., Kelkar Road - Dadar, Mumbai 400 028, India

Tel: 91-22-430-1454

SCHENKER USA INC.

150 Albany Ave., Freeport, NY, 11520

Tel: (516) 403-5416   Fax: (516) 377-3092   www.schenkerusa.com

Freight forwarders.

Schenker International Pvt Ltd., MKM Chambers, 5th Fl., 154-155, Kodambakkam High Rd., Nungambakkam Madras 600 034, India

Tel: 91-44-823-1187   Fax: 91-44-823-0995

Schenker International Pvt Ltd., 22 Community Center, Basant Lok Vasant Vihar, New Delhi 110 057, India

Tel: 91-80-823-4151   Fax: 91-22-835-5137

SCHERING-PLOUGH CORPORATION

One Giralda Farms, Madison, NJ, 07940-1000

Tel: (973) 822-7000   Fax: (973) 822-7048   www.sch-plough.com

Proprietary drug and cosmetic products.

C. E. Fulford (India) Pvt. Ltd., Oxford House, Apollo Bunder, Mumbai 400 039, India

SCHLUMBERGER LIMITED

153 East 53rd St., 57th Fl., New York, NY, 10022-4624

Tel: (212) 350-9400   Fax: (212) 350-9457   www.slb.com

Engaged in oil and gas services, metering and payment systems, and produces semiconductor testing equipment and smart cards.

Schlumberger India, 12-13/F, Mohan Dev Building, Tolstoy Marg, New Delhi 110 001, India

SCHOLASTIC CORPORATION

555 Broadway, New York, NY, 10012

Tel: (212) 343-6100   Fax: (212) 343-6934   www.scholastic.com

Publishing/distribution educational and children's magazines, books, software.

Scholastic India Pvt. Ltd., 29 Udyog Vihar, Phase-1, Gurgaon, Haryana 122 016, India

Tel: 91-124-346-824   Contact: Arvind Kumar, Mng. Dir.

SCIENTIFIC-ATLANTA, INC.

5030 Sugarloaf Pkwy., Lawrenceville, GA, 30044

Tel: (770) 903-5000   Fax: (770) 236-6777   www.sciatl.com

Mfr. cable set-top boxes, modems, transmission and distribution equipment.

Scientific-Atlanta, Inc., U&I Centre, F-41, South Extension Part-1, Ring Road, New Delhi 110 049, India

SCM MICROSYSTEMS, INC.

47211 Bayside Pkwy., Fremont, CA, 94538

Tel: (510) 360-2300   Fax: (510) 360-0211   www.scmmicro.com

Mfr. computer hardware for digital cameras.

SCM Microsystems, Module Nos. 0506/7/8, Tidel Park 4, Canal Bank Board, Taramany, Chennai 600 113, India

Tel: 91-44-2540020   Fax: 91-44-2540029

SEALED AIR CORPORATION

Park 80 East, Saddle Brook, NJ, 07663

Tel: (201) 791-7600   Fax: (201) 703-4205   www.sealedaircorp.com

Mfr. protective and specialty packaging solutions for industrial, food and consumer products.

Sealed Air (Singapore) Pte. Ltd., 4/1, 122 Chord Rd., Industrial Suburb, Rajajinagar, Bangalore 560 010, India

Tel: 91-80-3432528   Fax: 91-80-3432528

G.D. SEARLE & COMPANY

5200 Old Orchard Road, Skokie, IL, 60077

Tel: (847) 982-7000   Fax: (847) 470-1480   www.searlehealthnet.com

Mfr. pharmaceuticals, health care, optical products and specialty chemicals.

Searle (India) Ltd., Ralli House, 21 Damodardas Sukhadvala Marg, PO Box 233, Mumbai 400 001, India

SEMINIS, INC.

2700 Camino del Sol, Oxnard, CA, 93030-7967

Tel: (805) 647-1572   Fax: (805) 918-2545   www.seminis.com

Produces fruit and vegetable seeds.

Seminis Vegetable Seeds India, Gut No. 4, Chitegoan, Paithan Road, Aurangabad, Maharashtra 431 005, India

SHIPLEY COMPANY, LLC

455 Forest Street, Marlborough, MA, 01752

Tel: (508) 481-7950   Fax: (508) 485-9113   www.shipley.com

Supplier of materials and processes technology to the microelectronics and printed wiring board industries.

LeaRonal India, 114, Ansal Bhawan, 16 KG Marg, New Delhi 110 001, India

Tel: 91-11-3711123   Fax: 91-11-3713141

SIG DOBOY INC.

869 South Knowles Ave., New Richmond, WI, 54017-1797

Tel: (715) 246-6511   Fax: (715) 246-6539   www.doboy.com

Mfr. packaging machinery.

SIG Simonazzi India Pvt. Ltd., B-30, Greater Kailash - 1, New Delhi 110 0048, India

SIGMA-ALDRICH CORPORATION

3050 Spruce Street, St. Louis, MO, 63103

Tel: (314) 771-5765   Fax: (314) 771-5757   www.sigma-aldrich.com

Chemicals and biochemical's, aluminum and structural steel components.

Sigma-Aldrich India Limited, Survey #31/1 Sitharamapalaya, Mahadevapura, Bangalore 560 048, India

SIGNODE PACKAGING SYSTEMS

3610 West Lake Ave., Glenview, IL, 60025

Tel: (847) 724-6100   Fax: (847) 657-4392   www.signode.com

Mfr. industrial tools and machinery for packaging and strapping.

ITW Signode India Limited, III Floor Merchant Towers, No. 8-2-472, Plot No. 5, Road No. 4, Banjara Hills, Hyderabad 500 034, India

SIMON & SCHUSTER INC.

1230 Avenue of the Americas, New York, NY, 10020

Tel: (212) 698-7000   Fax: (212) 698-7007   www.simonandschuster.com

Publishes and distributes hardcover and paperback books, audiobooks and software.

Prentice-Hall of India Pvt. Ltd., 14-97 Connaught Circus, New Delhi 110 001, India

SITEL CORPORATION

111 South Calver Street, Ste. 1900, Baltimore, MD, 21202

Tel: (410) 246-1505   Fax: (410) 246-0200   www.sitel.com

Provides outsourced customer management services.

SITEL India, 4-A, Parke-Davis Complex, Andheri-Kurla Road, Saki-Naka, Andheri, Mumbai 400 072, India

WILBUR SMITH ASSOCIATES (WSA)

PO Box 92, Columbia, SC, 29202

Tel: (803) 758-4500   Fax: (803) 251-2064   www.wilbursmith.com

Consulting engineers.

Wilbur Smith Associates Inc., #75, 2nd Floor, 14th Cross, 1st Block, R. T. Nagar, Bangalore 560032, India

Tel: 91-22-644-1599   Fax: 91-22-644-1347   Contact: Rajendra K. Mehta

SOLUTIA INC.

575 Maryville Center Dr, St. Louis, MO, 63141

Tel: (314) 674-1000   Fax: (314) 694-8686   www.solutia.com

Mfr. specialty chemical based products.

Solutia Chemical India Private Ltd., 205-220, Midas Sahar Plaza Complex, Andheri-Kurla Road, Andheri (East) Mumbai 400 059, India

Tel: 91-22-830-2860

Solutia Chemical India Private Ltd., PO Box No. 7034, New Delhi 110 002, India
Tel: 91-11-327-7651

SPERRY-SUN DRILLING SERVICES

PO Box 60070, Houston, TX, 77205

Tel: (281) 871-5100   Fax: (281) 871-5742   www.sperry-sun.com

Provides drilling services to the oil and gas drilling industry.

Sperry-Sun, Inc., Sanghi Oxygen Compound, Mahakali Caves Road, Andheri (East) Mumbai 400 049, India

SPS TECHNOLOGIES INC.

165 Township Line Rd., Two Pitcairn Place, Jenkintown, PA, 19046

Tel: (215) 517-2000   Fax: (215) 517-2032   www.spstech.com

Mfr. aerospace and industry fasteners, tightening systems, magnetic materials, super alloys.

Avitrade SPS Technologies, G02, #10 Haudin Road, Ussoor, Bangalore 560 042, India
Contact: Lt. Col. Ashok K. Soti

Precision Fasteners Ltd., New India Centre, 17 Cooperage Rd., Marahashtra, Mumbai 400 039, India

SPSS INC.

233 S. Wacker Dr., 11th Fl., Chicago, IL, 60606

Tel: (312) 651-6000   Fax: (312) 329-3668   www.spss.com

Mfr. statistical software.

SPSS UK Ltd., Ashok Hotel, #223, 50B, Chanakyapuri, New Delhi 110 021, India

THE ST. PAUL COMPANIES, INC.

385 Washington Street, St. Paul, MN, 55102

Tel: (651) 310-7911   Fax: (651) 310-8294   www.stpaul.com

Provides investment, insurance and reinsurance services.

The New India Assurance Company Ltd., 87 Mahatma Gandhi Road, Fort Mumbai 400 001, India

STANDARD COMMERCIAL CORPORATION

2201 Miller Rd., PO Box 450, Wilson, NC, 27894

Tel: (252) 291-5507   Fax: (252) 237-1109   www.sccgroup.com

Leaf tobacco dealers and processors and wool processors.

Trans-Continental Tobacco, PO Box 400, Andhra Pradesh Guntur 522 007, India

STA-RITE INDUSTRIES INC.

293 Wright Street, Delavan, WI, 53115

Tel: (262) 728-5551   Fax: (262) 728-7323   www.sta-rite.com

Mfr. water pumps, filters and systems.

Chansuba Pumps Ltd., 125 Rajaji Road, Rannagar, Coimbatore 641 009, India

STARWOOD HOTELS & RESORTS WORLDWIDE

777 Westchester Avenue, White Plains, NY, 10604

Tel: (914) 640-8100   Fax: (914) 640-8316   www.starwoodhotels.com

Hotel operations including Sheraton, Westin, St. Regis, Four Points and Caesars.

Chola Sheraton, 10 Cathedral Rd., Madras 600 086, India

Maurya Sheraton Hotel & Towers, Diplomatic Enclave, Sardar Patel Marg 110 021, India

Mughal Sheraton, Fatehabad Rd., Agra 282 001, India

STORAGE TECHNOLOGY CORPORATION

One Storagetech Dr., Louisville, CO, 80028-4377

Tel: (303) 673-5151   Fax: (303) 673-5019   www.stortek.com

Mfr., market, service information, storage and retrieval systems.

StorageTek International Corporation, C/o DBS Business Center, 26, Cunningham Road, Bangalore 560052, India
Tel: 91-80-2267272   Contact: Vijay Pradhan

STRYKER CORPORATION

2725 Fairfield Rd., Kalamazoo, MI, 49002

Tel: (616) 385-2600   Fax: (616) 385-1062   www.strykercorp.com

Develops, manufactures and markets specialty surgical and medical products worldwide.

Stryker Far East, D86 Gulmohar Park, Lower Ground Floor, New Dehli 110 006, India

Tel: 91-11-686-2567   Fax: 91-11-667-545   Contact: Vikram Singh

SYBASE, INC.

5000 Hacienda Dr., Dublin, CA, 94568

Tel: (925) 236-5000   Fax: (925) 236-4321   www.sybase.com

Design/mfg/distribution of database management systems, software development tools, connectivity products, consulting and technical support services..

Sybase India Ltd. (Liason Office), 302, 3rd Fl., Embassy Square, 148 Infantry Rd., Bangalore 560 001, India

Tel: 91-80-228-3850   Fax: 91-20-228-3851

SYMBOL TECHNOLOGIES, INC.

One Symbol Plaza, Holtsville, NY, 11742-1300

Tel: (631) 738-2400   Fax: (631) 738-5990   www.symbol.com

Mfr. Bar code-driven data management systems, wireless LAN's, and Portable Shopping System™.

Symbol Technologies of India, A-29 Ghamshyam Industrial Estate, Veera Desai Road Andheri W, Bombay 400 053, India

Tel: 91-22-623-7152

SYNOPSYS, INC.

700 East Middlefield Road, Mountain View, CA, 94043

Tel: (650) 962-5000   Fax: (650) 965-8637   www.synopsys.com

Mfr. electronic design automation software.

Synopsys India Office, 131/82/2C, 3rd A Cross, 18th Main, 6th Block, Koramangala, Bangalore 560 095, India

Tel: 91-80-552-2201   Fax: 91-80-553-0865

SYNPLICITY, INC.

935 Stewart Drive, Sunnyvale, CA, 94085

Tel: (408) 215-6000   Fax: (408) 990-0290   www.synplicity.com

Mfr. software.

Synplicity India, Unit-2, 3rd Floor, Innovator, International Tech Park, Whitefield Road, Bangalore 560 066, India

Tel: 91-80-841-0825/26   Fax: 91-80-84-123-67

TALISMA CORPORATION

4600 Carillon Point, Kirkland, WA, 98033

Tel: (425) 897-2900   Fax: (425) 828-9587   www.talisma.com

Mfr. customer relationship management software.

Talisma Coporation, Prestige Terminus 2, 9/1 Airport Exit Road, Bangalore 560 017, India

THE TCW GROUP

865 S. Figueroa St., Ste. 1800, Los Angeles, CA, 90017

Tel: (213) 244-0000   Fax: (213) 244-0000   www.tcwgroup.com

Engaged in managing pension and profit sharing funds, retirement/health and welfare funds, insurance company funds, endowments and foundations.

TCW Group (JV), Bangalore, India

TEKTRONIX INC.

14200 SW Karl Braun Dr., PO Box 500, Beaverton, OR, 97077

Tel: (503) 627-7111   Fax: (503) 627-2406   www.tek.com

Mfr. test and measure, visual systems/color printing and communications/video and networking products.

Tektronix (India) Ltd., Tek Tower, Hayes Rd., Bangalore 560 025, India

Tel: 91-80-227-5577   Fax: 91-80-227-5588

TELEFLEX INC.

630 W. Germantown Pike, Ste. 450, Plymouth Meeting, PA, 19462

Tel: (610) 834-6301   Fax: (610) 834-8307   www.teleflex.com

Design, manufacture and marketing of mechanical and electro-mechanical systems, control systems and surgical devices.

Rusch AVT Medical Limited, Chennai, India

TELLABS INC.

1415 W. Diehl Rd., Naperville, IL, 60563

Tel: (630) 378-8800   Fax: (630) 852-7346   www.tellabs.com

Design/mfr./service voice/data transport and network access systems.

Tellabs Bangalore, No. 45 Race Course Road, 6/F, Bangalore 560 001, India

Tellabs New Delhi, U-1 Green Park, New Delhi 110 016, India

TENNECO AUTOMOTIVE INC.

500 North Field Drive, Lake Forest, IL, 60045

Tel: (847) 482-5241   Fax: (847) 482-5295   www.tenneco-automotive.com

Mfr. automotive parts, exhaust systems and service equipment.

Monroe, c/o Hydraulics Ltd., 38A+B, Morrison St., Alandur, Madras 600 016, India

Tel: 91-44-234-1942   Fax: 91-44-234-3690   Contact: N.N. Neelakantan, Mgr.   Emp: 389

Monroe, c/o Renowned Auto Products Mfs, Ltd., Hosur, India

Tel: 91-4344-76413   Fax: 91-4344-76414   Contact: K.A. Padmanabhan, Mgr.   Emp: 125

Monroe Hydraulics, Ltd., No. B80 Pipdic Industrial Estate, Mettupalayan Pondicherry 605 009, India

Tel: 91-413-71348   Fax: 91-413-71739   Contact: T. Krishnamurthy, Mgr.   Emp: 162

TETRA TECH, INC.

670 N. Rosemead Blvd., Pasadena, CA, 91107

Tel: (626) 351-4664   Fax: (626) 351-1188   www.tetratech.com

Environmental engineering and consulting services.

Tetra Tech Inc., Plot No. 5, Sector 27C, Mathura Rd., Faridabad 121 003, India

Tel: 91-129-27-2490   Fax: 91-129-27-0201   Contact: Dr. N. Sriram

TEXAS INSTRUMENTS INC.

12500 TI Blvd., Dallas, TX, 75266

Tel: (972) 995-3773   Fax: (972) 995-4360   www.ti.com

Mfr. semiconductor devices, electronic electro-mechanical systems, instruments and controls.

Texas Instruments India, Delhi, India

Tel: 91-17-800-800-1450

THE MARMON GROUP, INC.

200 West Adams, Ste. 2211, Chicago, IL, 60606

Tel: (312) 372-9500   Fax: (312) 845-5305   www.marmon.com

Holding company for diversified manufacturing and service firms.

Muller & Phipps (India) Ltd., Queen's Mansion, Amrit Keshav Naik Marg, Fort Mumbai 400 001, India

Tel: 91-22-204-2544   Fax: 91-22-207-1097   Contact: U. Dhupelia   Emp: 35

THERMO ORION, INC.

500 Cummings Court, Beverly, MA, 01915

Tel: (978) 922-4400   Fax: (978) 922-6015   www.thermoorion.com

Mfr. laboratory and industrial products, measure and display instruments.

Thermo Orion India, 105 Ashoka Apartments, 1/F, Ranjit Nagar Commercial Complex, New Dehli 110 008, India

Tel: 91-11-5705775

THERMON MANUFACTURING COMPANY

100 Thermon Drive, PO Box 609, San Marcos, TX, 78667-0609

Tel: (512) 396-5801   Fax: (512) 396-3627   www.thermon.com

Mfr. steam and electric heat tracing systems, components and accessories.

Thermon Heat Tracers Ltd., B-3086, Oberoi Garden Estates, Off Saki Vihar Road, Chandivali Andreri, East Mumbai 400 072, India

Thermon India, 20-P Ballygunge Terrace, Calcutta 700029, India

THE TORRINGTON COMPANY

59 Field St., PO Box 1008, Torrington, CT, 06790

Tel: (860) 626-2000   Fax: (860) 496-3625   www.torrington.com

Mfr. precision bearings, motion control components and automotive steering assemblies.

NRB Torrington Pvt. Ltd., New Delhi, India

THE TRANE COMPANY

3600 Pammel Creek Road, La Crosse, WI, 54601

Tel: (608) 787-2000   Fax: (608) 787-4990   www.trane.com

Mfr. distribution and service of A/C systems and equipment.

Trane India Ltd., 604, Dalamal House, 206 Jamnal Bajaj Rd., Nariman Point Mumbai 400 021, India

TRANSOCEAN INC.

4 Greenway Plaza, Houston, TX, 77046

Tel: (713) 232-7500   Fax: (713) 232-7027   www.deepwater.com

Engaged in oil and gas offshore drilling.

Transocean Inc., 501 Balarama, Bandra Kurla Complex 5/F, Bandra East Mumbai 400 051, India

TRANTER PHE, INC.

PO Box 2289, Wichita Falls, TX, 76306

Tel: (940) 723-7125   Fax: (940) 723-1131   www.tranter.com

Mfr. heat exchangers.

Dover India Pvt Ltd, SWEP Div., 1, Gulmohar Kubera Ind. Complex 1/F, Salunke Vihar Road, Poona-411040 Poona-411040, India

Tel: 91-20-683-0576   Fax: 91-20-683-1151

TRILOGY

5001 Plaza on the Lake, Austin, TX, 78746

Tel: (512) 874-3100   Fax: (512) 874-8900   www.trilogy.com

Mfr. and sales of purchasing software.

Trilogy E-Business Software, #96 Patton House, 4th B Cross, 5th Block, Koramangala Bangalore 560 095, India

TRIVIUM SYSTEMS, INC.

3305 NW Aloclek Drive, Ste. 200, Hillsboro, OR, 97124

Tel: (503) 439-9338   Fax: (503) 439-1526   www.triviumsys.com

Mfr. software.

Trivium India Software Ltd., 138/6, 6-A Cross, 10th Main RMV Extension, Sadashivnagar, Bangalore 560 080, India

Tel: 91-80-33-66071   Fax: 91-80-33-66071

U.S. WHEAT ASSOCIATES

1620 "I" Street NW, Ste. 801, Washington, DC, 20006-4005

Tel: (202) 463-0999   Fax: (202) 785-1052   www.uswheat.org

Market development for wheat products.

U.S. Wheat Associates Inc., 902 New Delhi House, 27 Barakhamba Rd., New Delhi 110 001, India

UNITED PARCEL SERVICE, INC.

55 Glenlake Parkway, NE, Atlanta, GA, 30328

Tel: (404) 828-6000   Fax: (404) 828-6593   www.ups.com

International package-delivery service.

UPS - Elbee Services Ltd., S.M. House, 11 Sahakar Rd., Vile Parle East, Mumbai 400 057, India

Tel: 91-22-859-2200

UNIVERSAL SECURITY INSTRUMENTS, INC.

PO Box 825, Binghamton, NY, 13902-0825

Tel: (607) 779-7689   Fax: (607) 779-7301   www.uic.com

Provider of innovative electronic circuit assembly technology and equipment, integrated system solutions, and process expertise.

International Marketing Corporation, Bangalore, India
Tel: 91-80-223-7147   Fax: 91-80-223-147

International Marketing Corporation, Mumbai, India
Tel: 91-22-269-7253   Fax: 91-22-269-1096

International Marketing Corporation, New Delhi, India
Tel: 91-11-623-5523   Fax: 91-11-623-5523

UOP LLC

25 East Algonquin Road, Des Plaines, IL, 60017

Tel: (847) 391-2000   Fax: (847) 391-2253   www.uop.com

Engaged in developing and commercializing technology for license to the oil refining, petrochemical and gas processing industries.

UOP India Pvt. Ltd./UOP Asia Ltd., Industrial Park, Sector-36, Pace City II Gurgaon Haryana 122 004, India
Tel: 91-124-373288-91   Fax: 91-124-373283-84

UTSTARCOM, INC.

1275 Harbor Bay Pkwy., Alameda, CA, 94502

Tel: (510) 864-8800   Fax: (510) 864-8802   www.utstar.com

Mfr. and sales of wireless telecommunications access systems and software products.

UTStarcom Inc., 805 Signature Towers II, South City I, Gurgaon, Haryana 122001, India
Tel: 91-124-6805045   Fax: 91-124-6380842

VARIAN MEDICAL SYSTEMS, INC.

3050 Hansen Way, Palo Alto, CA, 94304-100

Tel: (650) 493-4000   Fax: (650) 424-5358   www.varian.com

Mfr. microwave tubes and devices, analytical instruments, semiconductor process and medical equipment, vacuum systems.

Varian Intl. AG, 7 Community Centre, Basant Lok, Vasant Vihar, New Delhi 110 057, India

VERIFONE, INC.

4988 Great America Pkwy., Santa Clara, CA, 94054-1200

Tel: (408) 496-0444   Fax: (408) 919-5105   www.verifone.com

Mfr. electronic payment software and hardware.

VeriFone North Asia Limited, Suite # 330, The Atria Hotel, No.1, Palace Road, Bangalore 560 001, India

VERINT SYSTEMS INC.

234 Crossways Park Drive, Woodbury, NY, 11797

Tel: (516) 677-7300   Fax: (516) 677-7197   www.verintsystems.com

Mfr. and sales of analytic software.

Verint Systems, Paharpur Business Center, 21, Nehru Place Greens, New Delhi 110 019, India
Tel: 91-11-620-0694   Fax: 91-11-620-7103

VERITAS SOFTWARE INC.

350 Ellis Street, Mountain View, CA, 94043

Tel: (650) 527-8000   Fax: (650) 527-8050   www.veritas.com

Mfr. of storage management software for data protection, application availability, and disaster recovery.

VERITAS Software, Unit No. 217, "Bonanza", Sahar Plaza Complex, M.V. Road, Andheri (East) Mumbai, Mumbai 400 059, India
Tel: 91-22-830-3025   Fax: 91-22-830-3043

VERIZON COMMUNICATIONS INC.

1095 Ave. of the Americas, New York, NY, 10036

Tel: (212) 395-2121   Fax: (212) 395-1285   www.verizon.com

Telecommunications.

Reliance Telecom, New Delhi, India

VIRAGE LOGIC CORPORATION

46501 Landing Pkwy., Fremont, CA, 94538

Tel: (510) 360-8000   Fax: (510) 360-8099   www.viragelogic.com

Mfr. software.

Virage Logic Corporation, A-75, Sector - 57, Noida UP 20130, India

WABTEC CORPORATION

1001 Air Brake Ave., Wilmerding, PA, 15148

Tel: (412) 825-1000   Fax: (412) 825-1501   www.wabtec.com

Mfr. equipment for locomotives, railway freight cars, and passenger transit vehicles

Pioneer Friction Products, Calcutta, India

THE WACKENHUT CORPORATION

4200 Wackenhut Dr., Ste. 100, Palm Beach Gardens, FL, 33410

Tel: (561) 622-5656   Fax: (561) 691-6736   www.wackenhut.com

Security systems and services.

Wackenhut & Lancers (India) Pvt. Ltd., B6/4, Commercial Complex, Safarjung Enclave, New Delhi 110 029, India

Tel: 91-11-617-4562   Fax: 91-11-618-7462

WALBRO ENGINE MANAGEMENT

7400 N. Oracle Road, Ste. 310, Tucson, AZ, 85704

Tel: (520) 877-3000   Fax: (520) 877-3006   www.walbro.com

Mfr. motor vehicle accessories and parts, automotive fluid carrying systems.

TI Group Automotive Systems, 2 GIDC Estate - Makarpura, PO Box 70, Baroda Gujarat 390 010, India

WARNER ELECTRIC COMPANY

449 Gardner St., South Beloit, IL, 61080

Tel: (815) 389-3771   Fax: (815) 389-2582   www.warnernet.com

Global supplier of Power Transmission and Motion Control Solution Systems; automotive, industry brakes, and clutches.

Stieber Precision Ltd., B. 48 M.I.D.C., Ind-Satara 415 004, India

Tel: 91-216-244454   Fax: 91-216-244204

TD WATERHOUSE GROUP, INC.

100 Wall Street, New York, NY, 10005

Tel: (212) 806-3500   Fax: (212) 361-6656   www.tdwaterhousegroup.com

Engaged in online brokerage.

Tata TD Waterhouse Securities Ltd., Bombay, India

WATSON WYATT & COMPANY HOLDINGS

1717 H Street NW, Washington, DC, 20006-3807

Tel: (202) 715-7000   Fax: (202) 715-7700   www.watsonwyatt.com

Creates compensation and benefits programs for major corporations.

Watson Wyatt India Pvt. Ltd., 209 Meghdott Building, 94 Nehru Place, New Delhi 110 019, India

Tel: 91-11-622-9174   Fax: 91-11-622-9784   Contact: Shailesh Shah

Watson Wyatt India Pvt. Ltd., Solitaire CorporatePark, Building No. 5, 1st Floor, Andheri-Kurla Road, Mumbai 400 093, India

Tel: 91-22-690-4400   Fax: 91-22-690-4401   Contact: Shailesh Shah

WEATHERFORD INTERNATIONAL, INC.

515 Post Oak Blvd. Ste. 600, Houston, TX, 77027-3415

Tel: (713) 287-8400   Fax: (713) 963-9785   www.weatherford.com

Oilfield services, products and equipment; mfr. marine cranes for oil and gas industry.

Oilfield Eqmt. & Services Pvt. Ltd., Vaswani Mansions, Dinshaw Vachha Rd., Mumbai 400 020, India

Tel: 91-22-820-3279   Fax: 91-22-822-2803

JERVIS B. WEBB COMPANY

34375 W.Twelve Mile Rd., Farmington Hills, MI, 48331

Tel: (248) 553-1220   Fax: (248) 553-1237   www.jervisbwebb.com

Mfr. integrators of material handling systems solutions.

Webb India Ltd., Khaleel Plaza, 32/1 RV Rd., Basavanagudi, Bangalore 560 004, India

WHIRLPOOL CORPORATION

2000 N. M-63, Benton Harbor, MI, 49022-2692

Tel: (616) 923-5000   Fax: (616) 923-5443   www.whirlpoolcorp.com

Mfr., market home appliances: Whirlpool, Roper, KitchenAid, Estate, and Inglis.

TVS Whirlpool Ltd., Madras, India

Emp: 5,700

Whirlpool Asia Manufacturing, New Delhi, India

WHITE & CASE LLP

1155 Ave. of the Americas, New York, NY, 10036-2767

Tel: (212) 819-8200   Fax: (212) 354-8113   www.whitecase.com

Engaged in international law.

White & Case LLP, Nirmal Building, 17th Fl., Nariman Point, Mumbai 400 021, India

Tel: 91-22-282-6300   Fax: 91-22-282-6305   Contact: Raj Pande, Ptnr.

WIDIA VALENITE INC

31700 Research Park Dr., Madison Heights, MI, 48071-4627

Tel: (248) 589-1000   Fax: (248) 597-4820   www.valenite.com

Cemented carbide, high speed steel, ceramic and diamond cutting tool products, etc.

Widia (India) Limited, 8/9th Mile, Tumkur Road, Bangalore 560 073, India

Tel: 91-80-8394321   Fax: 91-80-8394494

T.D. WILLIAMSON INC.

6801 S. 65th West Avenue, Tulsa, OK, 74131-2444

Tel: (918) 447-5100   Fax: (918) 446-6327   www.tdwilliamson.com

Mfr. equipment and provide service for pipeline maintenance.

TDW, Ltd., Vadodara Baroda, India

WIND RIVER SYSTEMS, INC.

500 Wind River Way, Alameda, CA, 94501

Tel: (510) 748-4100   Fax: (510) 749-2010   www.isi.com

Develops and markets computer software products and services.

Wind River Systems, Inc., U & I Business Centre, F-41 South Extension Part-I, New Delhi 110 049, India

Tel: 91-11-464-9421   Fax: 91-11-462-3305   Contact: Sanjay Raina

Wind River Systems, Inc., 4/1 Millers Road, High Grounds, Bangalore 560 052, India

Tel: 91-80-2283920   Contact: Ajit Edlabadkar

WIRELESS FACILITIES, INC. (WFI).

4810 Eastgate Mall, San Diego, CA, 92121

Tel: (858) 228-2000   Fax: (858) 228-2001   www.wfinet.com

Engaged in the management of wireless networks.

WFI India Pvt. Ltd., DBS Corporate Centre, 1st Floor, World Trade Tower, Barakhamba Lane, New Delhi 110001, India

WOODWARD GOVERNOR COMPANY

5001 N. Second Street, PO Box 7001, Rockford, IL, 61125-7001

Tel: (815) 877-7441   Fax: (815) 639-6033   www.woodward.com

Mfr./service speed control devices and systems for aircraft turbines, industrial engines and turbines.

Woodward Governor India Pvt. Ltd., 23/6 Mathura Rd., Ballabgarh, Haryana 121 004, India

Tel: 91-129-232-8040   Fax: 91-129-230-418   Contact: Ken Axelson   Emp: 50

WM WRIGLEY JR. COMPANY

410 N. Michigan Ave., Chicago, IL, 60611-4287

Tel: (312) 644-2121   Fax: (312) 644-0353   www.wrigley.com

Mfr. chewing gum.

Wrigley India Pvt. Ltd., Bangalore, India

WYETH

5 Giralda Farms, Madison, NJ, 07940-0874

Tel: (973) 660-5000   Fax: (973) 660-7026   www.wyeth.com

Mfr. consumer healthcare products.

Fort Dodge Animal Health, Div. Wyeth, No. 40, Landons Road, Kilpauk Madras 600 010, India

Tel: 91-44-532-9005

Geoffrey Manners & Co. Ltd., Div. Wyeth Consumer Healthcare, Post Box 976, Mumbai 400 001, India

Tel: 91-22-261-6991   Fax: 91-22-261-6995

WYETH PHARMACEUTICALS

555 E. Lancaster Ave., Wayne, PA, 19087-5109

Tel: (610) 971-5400   Fax: (610) 995-4668   www.wyeth.com

Mfr. antibiotics and pharmaceutical products.

Wyeth Lederle Ltd., Nyloc House, 254-D2, Dr. Annie Besant Rd., Mumbai 400 025, India

Tel: 91-22-493-5211

WYNN OIL COMPANY

1050 West Fifth Street, PO Box 9510, Azusa, CA, 91702-9510

Tel: (626) 334-0231   Fax: (626) 334-6463   www.wynnusa.com

Mfr. of specialty chemicals, equipment and related service programs for automotive and industrial markets.

Wynn's Mekuba India Pvt, Ltd., 4D/2, Third Main Road, Industrial Estate, Ambattur, Chennai 600 058, India

Tel: 91-44-6250917   Fax: 91-44-6359193

XEROX CORPORATION

800 Long Ridge Road, PO Box 1600, Stamford, CT, 06904

Tel: (203) 968-3000   Fax: (203) 968-4312   www.xerox.com

Mfr. document processing equipment, systems and supplies.

Modi Xerox Ltd., 98 Nahru Place, Ground Fl., New Delhi 110 019, India

Tel: 91-11-643-4544   Fax: 91-11-644-4652

Xerox Corp., Modipur, Bareilly Rd., Rampur, India

XTRA CORPORATION

200 Nyala Farms Rd., Westport, CT, 06880

Tel: (203) 221-1005   Fax: (203) 221-9024   www.xtracorp.com

Holding company: leasing.

XTRA International, Mumbai, India

YORK INTERNATIONAL CORPORATION

631 South Richland Ave., York, PA, 17403

Tel: (717) 771-7890   Fax: (717) 771-6212   www.york.com

Mfr. heating, ventilating, air conditioning and refrigeration equipment.

York Air Conditioning & Refrigeration, Inc., Greater Kallash II, New Delhi 110 001, India

Tel: 91-11-623-5246   Fax: 91-11-623-5246

YOUNG & RUBICAM INC.

285 Madison Ave., New York, NY, 10017

Tel: (212) 210-3000   Fax: (212) 370-3796   www.yr.com

Advertising, public relations, direct marketing and sales promotion, corporate and product ID management.

DY&R/Rediffusion/Bombay, Prabhadevi Mumbai, India

JOHN ZINK COMPANY

11920 East Apache, Tulsa, OK, 74121-1220

Tel: (918) 234-1800   Fax: (918) 234-2700   www.johnzink.com

Engaged in the development and manufacture of next-generation combustion products, technologies and clean-air solutions that power global industry.

John Zink Company, Div. Koch, 42, Kalpataru Court, C. Gidwani Marg, Mumbai 400 074, India

Contact: S. V. Chipalkatti

Indonesia

3COM CORPORATION

5400 Bayfront Plaza, Santa Clara, CA, 95052-8145

Tel: (408) 326-5000   Fax: (408) 326-5001   www.3com.com

Engaged in the development and manufacture of computer networking products and systems.

3Com Asia Ltd., Level 7, Wisma 46, KOTA BNI, JL. Jend. Sudirman Kav. 1, Jakarta 10220, Indonesia

Tel: 62-21-572-2088 Fax: 62-21-572-2089

3M (MINNESOTA MINING & MFG.)

3M Center, St. Paul, MN, 55144-1000

Tel: (651) 733-1110   Fax: (651) 733-9973   www.mmm.com

Mfr. diversified products for industry, consumer, health care, imaging, communications, transport, safety, etc.

3M Indonesia, Jl. Raya Diponegoro Km 39, Tambun, Bekasi 17510, Indonesia

Tel: 62-21-883-46059 Fax: 62-21-883-46108

3M Surbaya Customer Service, Graha Bumi Modern, 6th Fl., Jl. Basuki Rachmat 106-128, Surabaya 60271, Indonesia

Tel: 62-31-566-2300

ABBOTT LABORATORIES

100 Abbott Park Rd., Abbott Park, IL, 60064

Tel: (847) 937-6100   Fax: (847) 937-1511   www.abbott.com

Development, manufacture and sale of diversified health care products and services.

Abbott Laboratories, Ltd., Jl. Raya Jakarta-Bogor Km. 37, Cimanggis Desa Sukamaju Bogor, Indonesia

ACCELRYS INC.

9685 Scranton Road, San Diego, CA, 92121-3752

Tel: (858) 799-5000   Fax: (858) 799-5100   www.accelrys.com

Mfr. software for drug research.

Accelrys Indonesia, 16, 3rd Cross, 13th 'H' Main, Doopanhalli, HAL 2nd Stage, Bangalore-560008 Bangalore-560008, Indonesia

Tel: 91-80-5216561 Fax: 91-80-5253135

ACCENTURE LTD.

1345 Avenue of the Americas, New York, NY, 10105

Tel: (917) 452-4400   Fax: (917) 527-9915   www.accenture.com

Provides management and technology consulting services.

Accenture, Wisma 46, Kota BNI, 18th Fl., Jl. Jend. Sudirman Kav. 1, Jakarta 10220, Indonesia

Tel: 62-21-574-6575 Fax: 62-21-574-6576

AETNA INC.

151 Farmington Avenue, Hartford, CT, 06156

Tel: (860) 273-0123   Fax: (860) 275-2677   www.aetna.com

Managed health care, annuities, individual retirement and group pension services, and asset management products worldwide.

Aetna Life Indonesia, Jakarta, Indonesia

AIG AMERICAN INTERNATIONAL GROUP INC.

70 Pine Street, New York, NY, 10270

Tel: (212) 770-7000   Fax: (212) 509-9705   www.aig.com

Worldwide insurance and financial services.

P.T. Asuransi AIU Indonesia, Jl.K.H. Hasyin Ashari 35, Jakarta 10130, Indonesia

AIRBORNE INC.

3101 Western Ave., PO Box 662, Seattle, WA, 98121

Tel: (206) 285-4600   Fax: (206) 281-1444   www.airborne.com

Air transport services.

Airborne Express, Jl. Wijayai No 2a, Jakarta Selatan 12170, Indonesia

Tel: 62-21-723-3364   Fax: 62-21-723-3368

AMWAY CORPORATION

7575 Fulton Street East, Ada, MI, 49355-0001

Tel: (616) 787-6000   Fax: (616) 787-6177   www.amway.com

Mfr./sale home care, personal care, nutrition and houseware products.

PT Jasa Manajemen Amway, Wisma SSK, Jl. Daan Mogot KM 11, Jakarta Barat, Indonesia

ANDERSEN

33 West Monroe Street, Chicago, IL, 60603

Tel: (312) 580-0033   Fax: (312) 507-6748   www.andersen.com

*Accounting and audit, tax and management consulting services. **Firm under worldwide reorganization; new data unavailable for this edition.*

Drs. Gunawan, Prijohandojo, Utomo & Co., Wisma Batamindo, Level D3, Jl. Rasamala No. 1, Muka Kuning Batam 29433, Indonesia

Tel: 62-778-611163

Kautor Akuntan Publik, Prasetio, Utomo & Co., Wisma 46 Kota BNI, Jl. Jend. Sudirman Kav. 1, PO Box 2134, Jakarta 10001, Indonesia

Tel: 62-21-575-7999

Prasetio, Utomo & Co., Jl. Sulanjana No. 4, PO Box 1339, Badung 40013, Indonesia

Tel: 62-22-420-4464

Prasetio, Utomo & Co., Jl. Imam Bonjol No. 16A, PO Box 1994, Medan 20001, Indonesia

Tel: 62-61-326075

Prasetio, Utomo & Co., Jl. Raya Dr. Sutomo No. 77, PO Box 1172, Surabaya 60264, Indonesia

Tel: 62-31-574471

ANDREW CORPORATION

10500 West 153rd Street, Orland Park, IL, 60462

Tel: (708) 349-3300   Fax: (708) 349-5410   www.andrew.com

Designer, manufacturer, and supplier of communications equipment, services, and systems.

Andrew Jakarta, Benchmark, The Ascot Jakarta, #2 Jl. Kebon Kacang Raya, Jakarta 10230, Indonesia

Tel: 62-21-318-5821   Fax: 62-21-318-5820

AON CORPORATION

200 East Randolph, Chicago, IL, 60601

Tel: (312) 381-1000   Fax: (312) 381-6032   www.aon.com

Insurance brokers worldwide; underwrites accident and health insurance, specialty and professional insurance; and provides risk management consultation.

P.T. AON Lippo Indonesia, Menara Sudirman, Lantai 3 and 5 Jl. Jend. Sudirman KAV. 60, Jakarta 12190, Indonesia

Tel: 62-21-522-0123   Fax: 62-21-522-0111   Contact: Junaedy Ganie

APPLERA CORPORATION

301 Merritt 7, Norwalk, CT, 06851

Tel: (203) 840-2000   Fax: (203) 840-2312   www.applera.com

Leading supplier of systems for life science research and related applications.

PT Laborindo Savaria, Ruko Permata, Kevayoran Plaza, BN 11, Jl. Jiban No. 2, Kebayoran Lama, Jakarta 12220, Indonesia

ARBOR ACRES FARM INC.

439 Marlborough Road, Glastonbury, CT, 06033

Tel: (860) 633-4681   Fax: (860) 633-2433   www.aaf.com

Producers of male and female broiler breeders, commercial egg layers.

PT Arbor Acres Indonesia, Jl. Karang Bolong Raya, Blok 12 No. 9-10, Ancol-Jakarta 14430, Indonesia

AT&T BROADBAND, LLC

188 Inverness Dr. West, Englewood, CO, 80112

Tel: (303) 875-5500   Fax: (303) 875-4984   www.broadband.att.com

Provides broadband technology services; digital TV, digital telephone and high-speed cable internet services.

AriaWest, Jakarta, Indonesia

AUTODESK INC.

111 McInnis Parkway, San Rafael, CA, 94903

Tel: (415) 507-5000   Fax: (415) 507-6112   www.autodesk.com

Develop/marketing/support computer-aided design, engineering, scientific and multimedia software products.

Autodesk Asia Pte. Ltd., c/o Servcorp, Level 43, Wisma 46, Jln. Jenderal Sudirman Kav. 1, Jakarta Selatan 10220, Indonesia

AUTOMATIC SWITCH CO. (ASCO)

50-60 Hanover Rd., Florham Park, NJ, 07932

Tel: (973) 966-2000   Fax: (973) 966-2628   www.asco.com

Mfr. solenoid valves, emergency power controls, pressure and temperature switches.

ASCO Asia, Indonesia, c/o Emerson Electric South Asia, Jl. Cikini II No. 4, Jakarta 10330, Indonesia

Tel: 62-21-315-6134   Fax: 62-21-314-0861   Contact: Djohan Gunawan

AVERY DENNISON CORPORATION

150 N. Orange Grove Blvd., Pasadena, CA, 91103

Tel: (626) 304-2000   Fax: (626) 792-7312   www.averydennison.com

Mfr. pressure-sensitive adhesives and materials, office products, labels, tags, retail systems, Carter's Ink and specialty chemicals.

Avery Dennison Asia Pacific Group, Blk V, 81D, JI Jababeka V, Cikarang Ind Estate-Jababeka, Bekasi West Java 17550, Indonesia

Tel: 62-21-893-6033   Fax: 62-21-93-6031

AVIS GROUP HOLDINGS, INC.

6 Sylvan Way, Parsippany, NJ, 07054

Tel: (973) 222-3000   Fax: (973) 222-4381   www.avis.com

Car rental services.

Avis Group Holdings Ltd., Jl. Diponegoro 25, Jakarta, Indonesia

AVON PRODUCTS, INC.

1345 Avenue of the Americas, New York, NY, 10105-0196

Tel: (212) 282-5000   Fax: (212) 282-6049   www.avon.com

Mfr. direct seller of cosmetics and beauty-related items.

P.T. Avon Indonesia, Bldg. 208, Cilandak Commercial Estate, Cilandak Djakarta 12560, Indonesia

Tel: 62-21-780-1200   Fax: 62-21-780-1712   Contact: Agung Sardjono, Mgr.

BAKER & McKENZIE

130 East Randolph Drive, Ste. 2500, Chicago, IL, 60601

Tel: (312) 861-8000   Fax: (312) 861-2899   www.bakerinfo.com

International legal services.

B & M Consultants, Jakarta Stock Exchange Bldg., Tower II 21/F, Sudirman Central Business District, Jl. Jend. Sudirman Kav. 52-53, Jakarta 12190, Indonesia

Tel: 62-21-515-5090   Fax: 62-21-515-4840

BAKER HUGHES INCORPORATED

3900 Essex Lane, Ste. 1200, Houston, TX, 77027

Tel: (713) 439-8600   Fax: (713) 439-8699   www.bakerhughes.com

Develop and apply technology to drill, complete and produce oil and natural gas wells; provide separation systems to petroleum, municipal, continuous process and mining industries.

Baker Oil Tools, c/o PT DWI Sentana Prima, JL Mulawarman KM 16, Balikpapan East Kalimantan 76115, Indonesia

Tel: 62-542-64391   Fax: 62-542-65068

Baker Oil Tools, c/o PT Imeco Inter Sarana, JL Ampera Raya Kav. 10, 4th Fl., Cilandak Jakarta 12550, Indonesia

Tel: 62-21-780-5432   Fax: 62-21-780885

PT Milchem Indonesia, D-5 Setiabudi Bldg., Jl. H.R. Rasuna Said 62, Kuningan, Jakarta Selatan, Indonesia

BAKER PETROLITE CORPORATION

3900 Essex Lane, Houston, TX, 77027

Tel: (713) 599-7400   Fax: (713) 599-7592   www.bakerhughes.com

Mfr. specialty chemical treating programs, performance-enhancing additives and related equipment and services.

PT Petrolite Indonesia Pratama, Batu Ampar, Pulua Batam, Indonesia

BANK OF AMERICA CORPORATION

Bank of America Corporate Center, Charlotte, NC, 28255

Tel: (415) 622-3530   Fax: (704) 386-6699   www.bankofamerica.com

Financial services.

Bank of America NT & SA, 22/F, Jakarta Stock Exchange Bldg., Jl. Jend. Sudirman Kav. 52-53, Jakarta 12190, Indonesia

Tel: 62-21-515-1392   Fax: 62-21-515-1407   Contact: K.C. Gan, SVP

THE BANK OF NEW YORK

One Wall Street, New York, NY, 10286

Tel: (212) 495-1784   Fax: (212) 495-2546   www.bankofny.com

Banking services.

The Bank of New York, Mashi Plaza, #18-09 Jl. Jend. Sudirman Kav. 25, Jakarta 12920, Indonesia

Tel: 62-21-526-7806

BARRY CONTROLS INC.

40 Guest Street, PO Box 9105, Brighton, MA, 02135-9105

Tel: (617) 787-1555   Fax: (617) 254-7381   www.barrymounts.com

Mfr./sale vibration isolation mounting devices.

Androjaya Satryatama p.t., 2/F, Jl. Rajawali Barat No. 61, Bandung West Java 40184, Indonesia

BATES WORLDWIDE INC.

498 Seventh Avenue, New York, NY, 10018

Tel: (212) 297-7000   Fax: (212) 986-0270   www.batesww.com

Advertising, marketing, public relations and media consulting.

Bates 141 Indonesia, Jl. Iskandarsyah Raya No. 97, Blok M. Jakarta 12160, Indonesia

Tel: 62-21-723-2383   Fax: 62-21-723-2407   Contact: Linda Rustram

Bates Indonesia, Jl. Iskandarsyah Raya No. 97, Blok M. Jakarta 12160, Indonesia

Tel: 62-21-723-2383   Fax: 62-21-723-2407   Contact: Geoff Seebeck, CEO

BBDO WORLDWIDE

1285 Ave. of the Americas, New York, NY, 10019

Tel: (212) 459-5000   Fax: (212) 459-6645   www.bbdo.com

Multinational group of advertising agencies.

BBDO (Malaysia), Kuala Lumpur, Indonesia

BDO SEIDMAN, LLP   BELGIUM

130 East Randolph Street, Chicago, IL, 60601

Tel: (312) 856-9100   Fax: (312) 856-1379   www.bdo.com

International accounting and financial consulting firm.

RB Tanubrata & Rekan, Bukit duri Permai Estate, Blok 8/1, Jl. Jatinegara Barat 54E, Jakarta 13320, Indonesia

Tel: 62-21-819-9189 Fax: 62-21-819-9949 Contact: Richard B. Tanubrata

BECHTEL GROUP INC.

50 Beale Street, PO Box 3965, San Francisco, CA, 94105-1895

Tel: (415) 768-1234   Fax: (415) 768-9038   www.bechtel.com

General contractors in engineering, construction and project management.

Bechtel Inc., Bursa Efek Jakarta Bldg., 11th Fl., Jl.Jend. Sudirman Kav. 52, Jakarta 12190, Indonesia

Tel: 62-21-515-7000 Fax: 62-21-515-3477

Pacific Bechtel Corp., Jl. Menteng Raya 8, PO Box 467, Jakarta, Indonesia

LOUIS BERGER INTERNATIONAL INC.

100 Halsted Street, East Orange, NJ, 07019

Tel: (201) 678-1960   Fax: (201) 672-4284   www.louisberger.com

Consulting engineers, engaged in architecture, environmental and advisory services.

Louis Berger International Inc., PO Box 4312, Kelurahan Mampang, Jakarta 12043, Indonesia

Tel: 62-21-720-5774 Fax: 62-21-720-5775

Louis Berger International Inc., PO Box 195, Jl. Moh. Yamin #11, Maumere Flores, Nusa Tenggara Timur 86111, Indonesia

Louis Berger International Inc., Kabupaten Road Master Training Plan, Haery I Building Lt.2, Jl.Kemanh Selatan #151, Kebayoran Baru Jakarta Selatan, Indonesia

Tel: 62-21-789-1923 Fax: 62-21-789-1925

BEST WESTERN INTERNATIONAL

6201 North 24th Place, Phoenix, AZ, 85106

Tel: (602) 957-4200   Fax: (602) 957-5740   www.bestwestern.com

International hotel chain.

Asean International, Jl. H. Adama Malik No. 5, Sumatera 20114, Indonesia

SAMUEL BINGHAM ENTERPRISES INC.

9529 South Main Street, Jonesboro, GA, 30236

Tel: (770) 477-7503   Fax: (770) 477-9532   www.binghamrollers.com

Mfr. rubber covered rolls, chemicals and supplies for the printing industry.

PT Kahardjaja, PO Box 2189, Jakarta, Indonesia

BLACK & VEATCH LLP

8400 Ward Pkwy., PO Box 8405, Kansas City, MO, 64114

Tel: (816) 339-2000   Fax: (816) 339-2934   www.bv.com

Engaged in engineering, construction and consulting, specializing in infrastructure development in the fields of energy, water and information.

Binnie Black & Veatch, Kemang Business Centre, 2/F, Building II, Jl. Kemang Raya No. 2, Kemang Jakarta Selatan 12730, Indonesia

Tel: 62-21-572-2380 Fax: 62-21-572-2371 Contact: Ted Burgess

Black & Veatch International, Menara Batavia 29/F, Jl. K.H. Mas Mansyur Kav. 126, Jakarta Pusat 10220, Indonesia

Tel: 62-21-572-2380 Fax: 62-21-572-2385 Contact: John M. Gustke

BMC SOFTWARE, INC.

2101 City West Blvd., Houston, TX, 77042-2827

Tel: (713) 918-8800   Fax: (713) 918-8000   www.bmc.com

Engaged in mainframe-related utilities software and services.

BMC Software Ltd., Wisma GKBI, Ste. 3901, Jl. Jend. Sudirman No. 28, Jakarta 10210, Indonesia

Tel: 62-21-5799-8131 Fax: 62-21-5799-8080

BOOZ-ALLEN & HAMILTON INC.

8283 Greensboro Drive, McLean, VA, 22102

Tel: (703) 902-5000   Fax: (703) 902-3333   www.bah.com

International management and technology consultants.

PT Booz Allen & Hamilton Indonesia, 25th Fl. Wisma Danamon Aetna Tower, Jl. Jend. Sudirman Kav. 45-46, Jakarta 12930, Indonesia

Tel: 62-21-577-0077   Fax: 62-21-577-1760

THE BOSTON CONSULTING GROUP

Exchange Place, 31st Fl., Boston, MA, 02109

Tel: (617) 973-1200   Fax: (617) 973-1339   www.bcg.com

Management consulting company.

The Boston Consulting Group, Level 11, Mashill Tower, J1. Jend. Sudirman Kav. 25, Jakarta Selantan 12920, Indonesia

Tel: 62-21-526-7775

BOWNE & COMPANY, INC.

345 Hudson Street, New York, NY, 10014

Tel: (212) 924-5500   Fax: (212) 229-3420   www.bowne.com

Financial printing and foreign language translation, localization (software), internet design and maintenance and facilities management.

Bowne Global Solutions, Jakarta Stock Exch. Bldg., 23/F, Ste.2302, Jl.Jend Sudirman, Jakarta 12190, Indonesia

Tel: 62-21-515-3210   Fax: 62-21-515-3211   Contact: Chui Peng Au, Mgr.

BOYDEN CONSULTING CORPORATION

364 Elwood Ave., Hawthorne, NY, 10502

Tel: (914) 747-0093   Fax: (914) 980-6147   www.boyden.com

International executive search firm.

Boyden Associates Ltd., Wisma Bank Dharmala, #1801 B, Jl. Jend. Sudirman Kav. 28, Jakarta 12910, Indonesia

Tel: 62-21-522-9652

BOZELL GROUP

40 West 23rd Street, New York, NY, 10010

Tel: (212) 727-5000   Fax: (212) 645-9173   www.bozell.com

Advertising, marketing, public relations and media consulting.

PT Dian Mentari Pratama Bozell, Jl. Permuda No. 715, Jakarta Timur, Indonesia

Tel: 62-21-471-3738   Fax: 62-21-471-3739   Contact: Maria Indriani, Pres.

BRISTOL-MYERS SQUIBB COMPANY

345 Park Ave., New York, NY, 10154-0037

Tel: (212) 546-4000   Fax: (212) 546-4020   www.bms.com

Pharmaceutical and food preparations, medical and surgical instruments.

BMS (Indonesia), Tamara Cntra, 10th Fl., Jl Jend. Sudirman Kav 24, Indonesia

ConvaTec Indonesia, c/o PT Enseval, 4/F, Jl. Jetjen, Suprapto, Jakarta, Indonesia

Tel: 62-21-424-3908

BROWN SHOE COMPANY, INC.

8300 Maryland Avenue, St. Louis, MO, 63105

Tel: (314) 854-4000   Fax: (314) 854-4274   www.brownshoe.com

Markets branded and private label footwear, including Dr. Scholl's, Air Step and Buster Brown.

Brown Shoe International, Jakarta, Indonesia

BRY-AIR INC.

10793 Street, Rt. 37 West, Sunbury, OH, 43074

Tel: (740) 965-2974   Fax: (740) 965-5470   www.bry-air.com

Mfr. industrial dehumidifiers/auxiliary equipment for plastics industrial.

Bry-Air (Indonesia, Jl. Gading Kirana Utara, Blok H10/No. 11, Kelapa Gading Barat, Jakarta 14240, Indonesia

Tel: 62-21-4533526   Fax: 62-21-45846578

LEO BURNETT, DIV. B-COM 3 GROUP

35 West Wacker Drive, Chicago, IL, 60601

Tel: (312) 220-5959   Fax: (312) 220-6533   www.leoburnett.com

Engaged in advertising, marketing, media buying and planning, and public relations.

Kreasindo Advertising & Marketing Consultants, Jakarta, Indonesia

BURSON-MARSTELLER

230 Park Avenue South, New York, NY, 10003-1566

Tel: (212) 614-4000   Fax: (212) 614-4262   www.bm.com

Public relations/public affairs consultants.

Burson-Marsteller Jakarta, PT Binamitra Indocipta, 16th Fl., Mid Plaza 2 Bldg., Jl. Jend. Sudirman KAV 10-11, Jakarta 10220, Indonesia

Tel: 62-21-573-9646   Fax: 62-21-573-9647

CALTEX CORPORATION

PO Box 619500, Dallas, TX, 75261-9500

Tel: (972) 830-1000   Fax: (972) 830-1081   www.caltex.com

Petroleum products.

Caltex Pacific Indonesia, Jakarta, Indonesia

CARBOLINE COMPANY

350 Hanley Industrial Court, St. Louis, MO, 63144

Tel: (314) 644-1000   Fax: (314) 644-4617   www.carboline.com

Mfr. coatings and sealants.

PT Pacific Paint, Jl. Gunung Sahari XI, 291, Jakarta 10720, Indonesia

PT Tirtajaya Segara, Jl. Hayam Wuruk 3T, PO Box 4228, Jakarta 10120, Indonesia

CARGILL, INC.

15407 McGinty Road West, Minnetonka, MN, 55440-5625

Tel: (612) 742-7575   Fax: (612) 742-7393   www.cargill.com

Food products, feeds, animal products.

Cargill Indonesia, PO Box 4345, Jakarta 1001, Indonesia

CATERPILLAR INC.

100 NE Adams Street, Peoria, IL, 61629-6105

Tel: (309) 675-1000   Fax: (309) 675-1182   www.cat.com

Mfr. earth/material-handling and construction machinery and equipment and engines.

P. T. Solar Services Indonesia, Jakarta, Indonesia

CB RICHARD ELLIS SERVICES

200 N. Sepulveda Blvd., Ste. 300, El Segundo, CA, 90245-4380

Tel: (310) 563-8600   Fax: (310) 563-8670   www.cbrichardellis.com

Commercial real estate services.

PT Urbana Daya Perkasa, 7/FJalan Jenderal Sadirman Kav 27, Jakarta 12920, Indonesia

CENTRAL NATIONAL-GOTTESMAN INC.

3 Manhattanville Road, Purchase, NY, 10577-2110

Tel: (914) 696-9000   Fax: (914) 696-1066   www.cng-inc.com

Distribution of pulp and paper products.

PT Intersentral Nugraha, Wijaya Graha Centre, Block H-18, Jl. Wijaya II Kebayron Baru, Jakarta 12160, Indonesia

Tel: 62-21-725-4144   Fax: 62-21-725-7274   Contact: Benny Pranata

CENTURY 21 REAL ESTATE CORPORATION

One Campus Drive, Parsippany, NJ, 07054-3826

Tel: (973) 496-5722   Fax: (973) 496-5527   www.century21.com

Engaged in real estate sales.

Century 21 Indonesia, Gedung Mall Ciputra Lantai P1, Jl. Arteri S. Parman, Grogol Jakarta 11470, Indonesia

Tel: 62-21-566-2121

CHESTERTON BLUMENAUER BINSWANGER

Two Logan Square, 4th Floor, Philadelphia, PA, 19103-2759

Tel: (215) 448-6000   Fax: (215) 448-6238   www.cbbi.com

Real estate and related services.

Pt. Chesterton Nusantara, Chase Plaza, level 3, Jl. Jend. Sudirman Kav. 21, Jakarta 12910, Indonesia
Contact: Santhosh Kumar

CHEVRON TEXACO CORPORATION

575 Market Street, San Francisco, CA, 94105-2856

Tel: (415) 894-7700   Fax: (415) 894-2248   www.chevrontexaco.com

Oil exploration, production and petroleum products.

ChevronTexaco, Jl. Thamrin, PO Box 158, Jakarta, Indonesia

CHICAGO BRIDGE & IRON COMPANY (CBI)

10200 Grogan's Mill Road, Suite 300, The Woodlands, TX, 77380

Tel: (281) 774-2200   Fax: (281) 774-2202   www.chicago-bridge.com

Holding company: engaged in metal plate fabricating, construction and oil and gas drilling.

PT CBI Indonesia, PO Box 6924, Jakarta 12069, Indonesia

CIGNA COMPANIES

One Liberty Place, Philadelphia, PA, 19192

Tel: (215) 761-1000   Fax: (215) 761-5511   www.cigna.com

Insurance, invest, health care and other financial services.

PT Asuransi Cigna Indonesia, The Landmark Centre, 9/F, #901, Jl. Jen Sudirman Kav. 70-A, Jakarta 12910, Indonesia

PT Asuransi Niaga CIGNA Life, Menara Kadin Indonesia, 15th Fl., Jl. HR. Rasuna Said, Blk X-5, Kav. 02-03, Jakarta 12950, Indonesia
Tel: 62-21-250-5313   Fax: 62-21-250-5310   Contact: Steve Novkov

CINCOM SYSTEMS INC.

55 Merchant Street, Cincinnati, OH, 45446

Tel: (513) 612-2300   Fax: (513) 481-8332   www.cincom.com

Develop/distributor computer software.

Cincom PT Mitra Integrasi, Wisma Metropolitan I - 6/F, Jalan Jend. Sudirman Kav. 29-31, Jakarta 12920, Indonesia

CISCO SYSTEMS, INC.

170 West Tasman Drive, San Jose, CA, 95134-1706

Tel: (408) 526-4000   Fax: (408) 526-4100   www.cisco.com

Develop/mfr./market computer hardware and software networking systems.

Cisco Systems (HK), Indonesia, Level 12A Menara BCD, Jl. Jend. Sudirman Kav. 26, Jakarta 12920, Indonesia
Tel: 62-21-250-6533   Fax: 62-21-250-6532

CITIGROUP, INC.

399 Park Avenue, New York, NY, 10022

Tel: (212) 559-1000   Fax: (212) 559-3646   www.citigroup.com

Provides insurance and financial services worldwide.

Citigroup, Landmark Centre, 5th Fl., Jl. Jend Sudirman No 1, Jakarta 12910, Indonesia
Contact: Pijush Gupta

THE COCA-COLA COMPANY

1 Coca Cola Plaza, Atlanta, GA, 30313

Tel: (404) 676-2121   Fax: (404) 676-6792   www.coca-cola.com

Mfr./marketing/distributor soft drinks, syrups and concentrates, juice and juice-drink products.

Jakarta Coca-Cola Bottler, Jakarta, Indonesia

COMPUTER ASSOCIATES INTERNATIONAL INC.

One Computer Associates Plaza, Islandia, NY, 11788

Tel: (516) 342-5224   Fax: (516) 342-5329   www.cai.com

Integrated business software for enterprise computing and information management, application development, manufacturing, financial applications and professional services.

Computer Associates Indonesia, Wisma 46, Kota BNI, Level 34-05/06, Jl. Jend Sudirman Kav. 1, Jakarta 10220, Indonesia

Tel: 62-21-251-5030

CONOCO INC.

600 N. Dairy Ashford, Houston, TX, 77252

Tel: (281) 293-1000   Fax: (281) 293-1440   www.conoco.com

Oil, gas, coal, chemicals and minerals.

Conoco Irian Jaya Co., PO Box 367, Jakarta, Indonesia

Continental Oil Co./ Pertamina, Five Pillars Office Park, Jl. Let. Jen. M.T. Haryono 58, Jakarta, Indonesia

CORE LABORATORIES

6316 Windfern, Houston, TX, 77040

Tel: (713) 328-2673   Fax: (713) 328-2150   www.corelab.com

Petroleum testing and analysis, analytical chemicals, laboratory and octane analysis instrumentation.

PT Corlab Indonesia, Bldg. 303, Cilandak Commercial Estate, JL Cilandak KKO, Jakarta Selantan 12560, Indonesia

CORRPRO COMPANIES, INC.

1090 Enterprise Drive, Medina, OH, 44256

Tel: (330) 725-6681   Fax: (330) 723-0244   www.corrpro.com

Engaged in full-services corrosion engineering and cathodic protection.

Rohrback Cosasco Systems, Jl. Haji Agus Salim No. 128, Menteng, Jakarta 10310, Indonesia

Tel: 62-21-392-8989   Fax: 62-21-392-8990   Contact: M. Edgar Lewis

COUDERT BROTHERS LLP

1114 Ave. of the Americas, New York, NY, 10036-7794

Tel: (212) 626-4400   Fax: (212) 626-4120   www.coudert.com

Engaged in international law.

Coudert Brothers Indonesian Practice, CB Indonesia 16th Fl. Central Plaza, Jl. Jend. Sudirman Kav. 47, Jakarta 12930, Indonesia

Tel: 62-21-525-1985   Fax: 62-21-525-0734   Contact: Michael S. Horn, Ptnr.

CRAWFORD & COMPANY

5620 Glenridge Drive NE, Atlanta, GA, 30342

Tel: (404) 256-0830   Fax: (404) 847-4025   www.crawfordandcompany.com

Provides international insurance services engaged in risk management and claims adjustment.

Crawford & Company, Jl. Jend. Sudirman 3-4, Jakarta 10220, Indonesia

CROWLEY MARITIME CORPORATION

155 Grand Ave., Oakland, CA, 94612

Tel: (510) 251-7500   Fax: (510) 251-7788   www.crowley.com

Engaged in marine transportation and logistics.

Crowley Liner Services, Inc., Jl. Banka Raya 59, Jakarta Selatan 12730, Indonesia

CROWN CORK & SEAL COMPANY, INC.

One Crown Way, Philadelphia, PA, 19154-4599

Tel: (215) 698-5100   Fax: (215) 698-5201   www.crowncork.com

Mfr. metal and plastic packaging, including steel and aluminum cans for food, beverage and household products.

PT Crown Cork & Seal Indonesia, PO Box 3420/JKT, Jakarta, Indonesia

DANA CORPORATION

4500 Dorr Street, Toledo, OH, 43615

Tel: (419) 535-4500   Fax: (419) 535-4643   www.dana.com

Mfr./sales of automotive, heavy truck, off-highway, fluid and mechanical power components and engine parts, filters and gaskets.

P.T International Ganda Perdana, Jl. Pegangsaan Dua, Blok A1 Km. 1-6, Pulogadung Jakarta, Indonesia
Tel: 62-21-460-2755 Fax: 62-21-460-2765

DANZAS AEI, INC.

120 Tokeneke Road, PO Box 1231, Darien, CT, 06820

Tel: (203) 655-7900   Fax: (203) 655-5779   www.aeilogistics.com

International air freight forwarder.

Danzas AEI P.T. Angkutan Expressindo International, Jl. Ir H Juanda III/26 A-B, Jakarta Pusat 10120, Indonesia
Tel: 62-21-380-1239 Fax: 62-21-384-6700

D'ARCY MASIUS BENTON & BOWLES INC. (DMB&B)

1675 Broadway, New York, NY, 10019

Tel: (212) 468-3622   Fax: (212) 468-2987   www.darcyww.com

Full service international advertising and communications group.

DMB&B Asia Pacific, Jl. Buncit Raya Penaten 28, Pasar Minggu, Jakarta 12510, Indonesia

DELOITTE TOUCHE TOHMATSU INTERNATIONAL

1633 Broadway, New York, NY, 10019

Tel: (212) 492-4000   Fax: (212) 392-4154   www.deloitte.com

Accounting, audit, tax and management consulting services.

Hans Tuanakotta & Mustofa, Wisma Antara Bldg., 12th Fl., Jl. Medan Merdeka Selatan No. 17, Jakarta 10110, Indonesia

DETROIT DIESEL CORPORATION

13400 Outer Drive West, Detroit, MI, 48239

Tel: (313) 592-5000   Fax: (313) 592-5058   www.detroitdiesel.com

Mfr. diesel and aircraft engines and heavy-duty transmissions.

PT Mabua Detroit Diesel, Bldg #109, Cilandak Comm EST, Jakarta 12560, Indonesia

DHL WORLDWIDE EXPRESS

50 California Avenue, San Francisco, CA, 94111

Tel: (415) 677-6100   Fax: (415) 824-9700   www.dhl.com

Worldwide air express carrier.

DHL Worldwide Express, Jakarta, Indonesia
Tel: 62-21-830-6677

DIEBOLD INC.

5995 Mayfair Road, North Canton, OH, 44720-8077

Tel: (330) 490-4000   Fax: (330) 490-3794   www.diebold.com

Mfr. automated banking systems; security services for banking industrial and related fields.

Diebold Indonesia, Kompleks Bahan Bangunan, Blok F2/19, Jl. Mangga Due Raya, Jakarta 10730, Indonesia

DIMON INCORPORATED

512 Bridge Street, PO Box 681, Danville, VA, 24543-0681

Tel: (804) 792-7511   Fax: (804) 791-0377   www.dimon.com

One of world's largest importer and exporters of leaf tobacco.

DIMON Indonesia, Ruko Surya Inti Permata II, JL H.R. Muhammad, Blok B-12B, Surabaya, Indonesia
Tel: 62-31-734-3485 Fax: 62-31-734-3486

DIONEX CORPORATION

1228 Titan Way, PO Box 3603, Sunnyvale, CA, 94086-3603

Tel: (408) 737-0700   Fax: (408) 730-9403   www.dionex.com

Develop/mfr./market chromatography systems and related products.

Omega Indonesia, The Garden Center #04-0, Cilandak Commercial Estate, Cilandak Jakarta 12560, Indonesia

DMC STRATEX NETWORKS, INC.

170 Rose Orchard Way, San Jose, CA, 95134

Tel: (408) 943-0777   Fax: (408) 944-1648   www.dmcstratexnetworks.com

Designs, manufactures, and markets advanced wireless solutions for wireless broadband access.

DMC Stratex Networks, Masindo, Perkantoran Hijau Arkadia, Block A, 5/F, Jl. Letjen T.B. Simatupang No. 88, Jakarta 12520, Indonesia

DONALDSON COMPANY, INC.

PO Box 1299, Minneapolis, MN, 55431

Tel: (952) 887-3131   Fax: (952) 887-3155   www.donaldson.com

Mfr. filtration systems and replacement parts.

PT Panata Jaya Mandiri, Jl Pluit Selatan No. 1A, Jakarta 14440, Indonesia

DOVER CORPORATION

280 Park Ave., New York, NY, 10017-1292

Tel: (212) 922-1640   Fax: (212) 922-1656   www.dovercorporation.com

Holding company for varied industries; assembly and testing equipment, oil-well gear and other industrial products.

Pt. Karya Intertek Kencana, Jl. Daan Mogot 35 D-E, Jakarta 11470, Indonesia

Tel: 62-21-566-5115   Fax: 62-21-568-2084

THE DOW CHEMICAL COMPANY

2030 Dow Center, Midland, MI, 48674

Tel: (989) 636-1000   Fax: (989) 636-3228   www.dow.com

Mfr. chemicals, plastics, pharmaceuticals, agricultural products, consumer products.

Pacific Chemicals Indonesia PT, Jl. M.H. Thamrin 59, Jakarta, Indonesia

E.I. DUPONT DE NEMOURS & COMPANY

1007 Market Street, Wilmington, DE, 19898

Tel: (302) 774-1000   Fax: (302) 774-7321   www.dupont.com

Mfr. and sales of diversified chemicals, plastics, specialty products and fibers.

P.T. Indonesia Teijin DuPont Films, Mid Plaza 5/F, Jalan Jend. Sudiram Kav. 10-11, Jakarta 10220, Indonesia

EASTMAN CHEMICAL COMPANY

100 North Eastman Road, Kingsport, TN, 37662-5075

Tel: (423) 229-2000   Fax: (423) 229-1351   www.eastman.com

Mfr. plastics, chemicals, fibers.

Eastman Chemical Ltd., 9th Fl, S. Widjojo Centre, Jl. Jend. Sudirman 71, Jakarta 12190, Indonesia

Tel: 62-21-522-3102   Fax: 62-21-522-3101   Contact: Chen Yeow Wai

ECOLAB INC.

370 N. Wabasha Street, St. Paul, MN, 55102

Tel: (651) 293-2233   Fax: (651) 293-2379   www.ecolab.com

Develop/mfr. premium cleaning, sanitizing and maintenance products and services for the hospitality, institutional, and residential markets.

Ecolab Ltd., Jakarta, Indonesia

Tel: 62-21-570-7557

EDISON INTERNATIONAL

2244 Walnut Grove Avenue, Rosemead, CA, 91770

Tel: (626) 302-2222   Fax: (626) 302-2517   www.edison.com

Utility holding company.

Edison Mission Energy, Jakarta, Indonesia

J.D. EDWARDS & COMPANY

One Technology Way, Denver, CO, 80237

Tel: (303) 334-4000   Fax: (303) 334-4970   www.jdedwards.com

Computer software products.

PT Infotech Global Distribusi, Mashill Tower 14th Floor, Jl. Jend Sundirman Kav. 125, Jakarta 12920, Indonesia

Tel: 62-21-522-9828   Fax: 62-21-522-5538

EGL INC. (EAGLE GLOBAL LOGISTICS)

15350 Vickery Drive, Houston, TX, 77032

Tel: (281) 618-3100   Fax: (281) 618-3223   www.eagleusa.com

Ocean/air freight forwarding, customs brokerage, packing and wholesale, logistics management and insurance.

EGL Eagle Global Logistics, PT Hartapersada Interfreight, 4th Fl., Ayu Mas Bldg., Jl Kwitang aya 24, Jakarta 10150, Indonesia

Tel: 62-21-390-3033   Fax: 62-21-390-3031

EL PASO ENERGY PARTNERS, LP

1001 Louisiana Street, Houston, TX, 77252-2511

Tel: (713) 420-2131   Fax: (713) 420-4266   www.epenergy.com

Energy and gas.

El Paso Energy International, Sulawesi, Indonesia

EMERSON ELECTRIC COMPANY

8000 W. Florissant Ave., PO Box 4100, St. Louis, MO, 63136

Tel: (314) 553-2000   Fax: (314) 553-3527   www.emersonelectric.com

Electrical and electronic products, industrial components and systems, consumer, government and defense products.

Emerson Pte. Ltd., Wisma Danamon Aetna Life - 19/F, Jl. Jend. Sudirman Kav. 45-46, Jakarta 12930, Indonesia

EMERSON PROCESS MANAGEMENT

8301Cameron Road, Austin, TX, 78754

Tel: (512) 834-7689   Fax: (512) 832-3232   www.frco.com

Mfr. industrial process control equipment.

Emerson Process Management, Jl. Ampera Raya No. 10, 3rd Fl., Cilandak, Jakarta Selatan 12560, Indonesia

Tel: 62-21-780-7881 Fax: 62-21-780-7879

ENRON CORPORATION

1400 Smith Street, Houston, TX, 77002-7369

Tel: (713) 853-6161   Fax: (713) 853-3129   www.enron.com

Exploration, production, transportation and distribution of integrated natural gas and electricity. **Corporation under worldwide reorganization; new data unavailable for this edition.

Enron International, 19/F, Jakarta Stock Exch. Bldg., Jl.Jend Sudirman KAV. 52-63, Jakarta 12910, Indonesia

Tel: 62-21-515-0744

ERICO PRODUCTS INC.

34600 Solon Road, Cleveland, OH, 44139

Tel: (440) 248-0100   Fax: (440) 248-0723   www.erico.com

Mfr. electric welding apparatus and hardware, metal stampings, specialty fasteners.

Erico Products, Danamon Aetna Life - 19/F, Jalan Jend Sudirman -Kav. 45-46, Jakarta 12930, Indonesia

Tel: 62-21-575-0941

ERNST & YOUNG INTERNATIONAL

5 Times Square, New York, NY, 10036

Tel: (212) 773-3000   Fax: (212) 773-6350   www.eyi.com

Engaged in assurance and advisory business services, tax, law and corporate finance.

Kantor Akuntan/Drs, Santoso Harsokusumo & Rekan, PO Box 2333, Jakarta 10001, Indonesia

Tel: 62-21-522-0358   Fax: 62-21-520-1136   Contact: Jaja Zakaria

EURO RSCG WORLDWIDE

350 Hudson Street, New York, NY, 10014

Tel: (212) 886-2000   Fax: (212) 886-2016   www.eurorscg.com

International advertising agency group.

AdWork! EURO RSCG Partnership, Jl. Guntur 48, Jakarta, Indonesia

EXE TECHNOLOGIES, INC.

8787 N. Stemmons Fwy., Dallas, TX, 75247-3702

Tel: (214) 775-6000 Fax: (214) 775-0911 www.exe.com

Provides a complete line of supply chain management execution software for WMS.

EXE Technologies, Inc. Indonesia, c/o PT. Belmanda Lestari, Wijaya Grand Centre Blok C-17-18, Jakarta 12160, Indonesia

Tel: 62-21-724-6212 Fax: 62-21-720-6625

EXPEDITORS INTERNATIONAL OF WASHINGTON INC.

1015 Third Avenue, 12th Fl., Seattle, WA, 98104-1182

Tel: (206) 674-3400 Fax: (206) 682-9777 www.expd.com

Air/ocean freight forwarding, customs brokerage, international logistics solutions.

Expeditors Cargo Management Systems, c/o Pt. Segara Pacific, Maju Jl. Muara Karang Raya 163-165, Jakarta Utara 14450, Indonesia

Tel: 62-21-660-3301 Fax: 62-21-661-0474

Expeditors/PT Lancar Utama Tatanusa, Jl. Let. Jend. Soeprato 86A-B, Jakarta 10540, Indonesia

Tel: 62-21-421-2328 Fax: 62-21-421-4431

EXXON MOBIL CORPORATION

5959 Las Colinas Blvd., Irving, TX, 75039-2298

Tel: (972) 444-1000 Fax: (972) 444-1882 www.exxonmobil.com

Petroleum exploration, production, refining; mfr. petroleum and chemicals products; coal and minerals.

Exxon Mobil, Inc., Jl. H.R. Rasuna Said, Sampoerna Plaza, Jakarta, Indonesia

FERRO CORPORATION

1000 Lakeside Ave., Cleveland, OH, 44114-7000

Tel: (216) 641-8580 Fax: (216) 696-5784 www.ferro.com

Mfr. Specialty chemicals, coatings, plastics, colors, refractories.

P.T. Chandra Silamas Company, Jl. Intan No. 70, Cilandak Barat, Cilandak Jakarta, Selatan 12430, Indonesia

Tel: 62-21-750-8426 Fax: 62-21-750-3524 Contact: W.M.W. Silalahi

P.T. Ferro Mas Dinamika, Jl. Raya Cikarang, Ds. Pasir Sari Kp. Tegal Gede, Kec. Lemah Abang, Cibarusah Bekasi, Indonesia

Tel: 62-82-136920 Fax: 62-82-136580 Contact: Victor B. Buenconsejo, Mng. Dir.

FLEETBOSTON FINANCIAL CORPORATION

100 Federal Street, Boston, MA, 02110

Tel: (617) 434-2400 Fax: (617) 434-6943 www.fleet.com

Banking and insurance services.

FleetBoston - Jakarta, S. Widjojo Centre, 10th Fl., Jl. Jend, Sudirman 71, Jakarta 12190, Indonesia

Tel: 62-21-252-4111 Fax: 62-21-252-4113

FLUOR CORPORATION

One Enterprise Drive, Aliso Viejo, CA, 92656-2606

Tel: (949) 349-2000 Fax: (949) 349-5271 www.flour.com

Engineering and construction services.

Fluor Daniel Eastern Inc., Plaza 89, Suite 1101, PO Box 4569, Jakarta 12045, Indonesia

Tel: 62-21-520-5663 Fax: 62-21-522-2745

FMC CORPORATION

1735 Market St., Philadelphia, PA, 19103

Tel: (215) 299-6000 Fax: (215) 299-6618 www.fmc.com

Mfr. specialty chemicals, including alginate, carrageenan and microcrystalline cellulose.

FMC Indonesia, PO Box 146, Ungaran, Jawa Tengah, Indonesia

FMC Indonesia, Wisma Kodel, 10/F, Jl. Hr Rasuna Said Kav. B-4, Kuningan, Jakarta 12920, Indonesia

Tel: 62-21-522-2350

FMC TECHNOLOGIES, INC.

200 E. Randolph Dr., Chicago, IL, 60601

Tel: (312) 861-6000   Fax: (312) 861-6176   www.fmctechnologies.com

Mfr. bulk material handling and automation equipment and cargo loaders.

FMC Santana Petroleum, Jl. Jend Sudirman No. 487, Balikpapan 76114, Indonesia

FOSTER WHEELER LTD.

Perryville Corporate Park, Clinton, NJ, 08809-4000

Tel: (908) 730-4000   Fax: (908) 730-4100   www.fwc.com

Manufacturing, engineering and construction.

Foster Wheeler Intercontinental Corporation, Graha Simatupang Menara, Jl. Simatupang Kav. 38, Jakarta 12540, Indonesia

Tel: 62-21-782-9416

FRANKLIN COVEY COMPANY

2200 W. Parkway Blvd., Salt Lake City, UT, 84119-2331

Tel: (801) 975-1776   Fax: (801) 977-1431   www.franklincovey.com

Provides productivity and time management products and seminars.

Franklin Covey Indonesia, Jl. Bendungan Jatiluhur 56, Bendungan Hilir, Jakarta 10210, Indonesia

Tel: 62-21-572-0761   Fax: 62-21-572-0762

FREEPORT-McMoRAN COPPER & GOLD INC.

1615 Poydras Street, New Orleans, LA, 70112

Tel: (504) 582-4000   Fax: (504) 582-4899   www.fcx.com

Natural resources exploration and processing.

PT Freeport Indonesia Co., Plaza 89, 5/F, Jl. H.R. Rasuna Said Kav. X-7 No. 6, Jakarta 12940, Indonesia

Tel: 62-21-522-5666   Fax: 62-21-526-1874

PT Smelting (Gresik), Plaza 89, 6/F, S-602, Jl. H. R. Rasuna Said Kav. X-7 No. 6, Jakarta 12940, Indonesia

Tel: 62-21-522-9616   Fax: 62-21-522-9615

PT-FI IRIAN JAYA (Papua), Tembagapura Timika, Kuala Kencana, Indonesia

Contact: Adrianto Machribie

FRITZ COMPANIES, INC., DIV. UPS

706 Mission Street, Ste. 900, San Francisco, CA, 94103

Tel: (415) 904-8360   Fax: (415) 904-8661   www.fritz.com

Integrated transportation, sourcing, distribution and customs brokerage services.

PT Fritz Ritra Intl. Transportation, Ritra Bldg., 3/F, J. Warung Buncit Raya 6, Jakarta 12740, Indonesia

H.B. FULLER COMPANY

1200 Willow Lake Blvd., Vadnais Heights, MN, 55110

Tel: (651) 236-5900   Fax: (651) 236-5898   www.hbfuller.com

Mfr./distributor adhesives, sealants, coatings, paints, waxes, sanitation chemicals.

H.B. Fuller Company, Wisma Bisnis Indonesia, 10th Floor, Jl. Let. Jend. S. Parman Kav. 12, Jakarta 11480, Indonesia

Tel: 62-21-530-7232   Fax: 62-21-530-7235

GE BETZ, DIV. GE SPECIALTY MATERIALS

4636 Somerton Road, PO Box 3002, Trevose, PA, 19053-6783

Tel: (215) 355-3300   Fax: (215) 953-5524   www.gebetz.com

Engaged in engineered chemical treatment of water and process systems in industrial, commercial and institutional facilities

GE Betz, Div. GE Specialty Materials, Gedung Bank Bali 6th Fl., Jl. Jend. Sudirman Kav 27, Jakarta 12920, Indonesia

GENERAL ELECTRIC COMPANY

3135 Easton Turnpike, Fairfield, CT, 06431

Tel: (203) 373-2211   Fax: (203) 373-3131   www.ge.com

Diversified manufacturing, technology and services.

GE Fanuc Systems, Jl. Jend. Gatot Subroto No 517, Komp PT Pindad, Bandung 40284, Indonesia
Tel: 62-21-573-0500 Fax: 62-21-574-7089

GE International, Menara Batavia, 5th Fl., Jl. KH Mas Mansyur Kav. 126, Jakarta 10220, Indonesia
Tel: 62-21-574-7123

GEPS Global Power Generation, Menara Batagvia, 5th Fl., Jl. KH Mas Mansyur Kav. 126, Jakarta 10220, Indonesia
Tel: 62-21-574-7123

THE GILLETTE COMPANY

Prudential Tower Building, Boston, MA, 02199

Tel: (617) 421-7000   Fax: (617) 421-7123   www.gillette.com

Develop/mfr. personal care/use products: blades and razors, toiletries, cosmetics, stationery.

PT Gillette Indonesia, Jl. Raya Pondok Cabe, Ciputat 15418, Tangerang, Jakarta, Indonesia

GILSON INC.

3000 W. Beltline Hwy, PO Box 620027, Middleton, WI, 53562-0027

Tel: (608) 836-1551   Fax: (608) 831-4451   www.gilson.com

Mfr. analytical/biomedical instruments.

PT Siberhegindo Teknik, Gedung Gajah, Unit AJ, Jl. Dr. Saharjo Raya No. 11 Tebet, Jakarta 12810, Indonesia

GLOBAL INDUSTRIES, LTD.

8000 Global Drive, Caryss, LA, 70665

Tel: (337) 583-5000   Fax: (337) 583-5100   www.globalind.com

Engaged in the construction and dismantling of offshore drilling platforms.

Global Offshore International, Jl Brigien Katamso KM 6:5, Tanjung Uncang, Batam 29421, Indonesia

GLOBAL SANTA FE CORPORATION

777 North Eldridge Pkwy., Houston, TX, 77079

Tel: (281) 496-8000   Fax: (281) 531-1260   www.gsfdrill.com

Offshore contract drilling, turnkey drilling, oil and gas exploration and production.

Global SantaFe, Jakarta, Indonesia

GLOBAL SILVERHAWK INTERNATIONAL MOVING

1000 Burnett Avenue, Concord, CA, 94520

Tel: (510) 609-7080   Fax: (510) 609-7081   www.globalsilverhawk.com

International moving and forwarding.

Global Silverhawk, Mampang Plaza, First Fl., Jl. Mampang Prapatan Raya No.100, Jakarta 12760, Indonesia
Tel: 62-21-800-4966   Contact: Jeff Offutt, Gen. Mgr.

THE GOODYEAR TIRE & RUBBER COMPANY

1144 East Market Street, Akron, OH, 44316

Tel: (330) 796-2121   Fax: (330) 796-1817   www.goodyear.com

Mfr. tires, automotive belts and hose, conveyor belts, chemicals; oil pipeline transmission.

PT Goodyear Indonesia, PO Box 5, Jl. Pemuda 27, Bogor West Java 16161, Indonesia

W. R. GRACE & COMPANY

7500 Grace Drive, Columbia, MD, 21044

Tel: (410) 531-4000   Fax: (410) 531-4367   www.grace.com

Mfr. specialty chemicals and materials: packaging, health care, catalysts, construction, water treatment/process.

P.T. Grace Specialty Chemicals Indonesia, Cikarang Industrial Estate, Kav C-32, Cikarang Bekasi 17530, Indonesia
Tel: 62-21-893-4260   Fax: 62-21-893-4315

GREY GLOBAL GROUP

777 Third Ave., New York, NY, 10017

Tel: (212) 546-2000   Fax: (212) 546-1495   www.grey.com

International advertising agency.

Rama & Grey Advertising, J. Sultan Hasanuddin 72, Jakarta 12160, Indonesia

HALLIBURTON COMPANY

500 North Akard Street, Ste. 3600, Dallas, TX, 75201-3391

Tel: (214) 978-2600   Fax: (214) 978-2685   www.halliburton.com

Engaged in diversified energy services, engineering and construction.

Halliburton India Ltd., Tower 1, 21st Floor Suite 2102, Jl. Jendral Sudirman Kav 52-53, Jakarta 12920, Indonesia

HARRIS CORPORATION

1025 West NASA Blvd., Melbourne, FL, 32919

Tel: (407) 727-9100   Fax: (407) 727-9344   www.harris.com

Mfr. communications and information-handling equipment, including copying and fax systems.

P. T. Silicontama Jaya, Jl. A.M. Sangaji No. 15 B4, Jakarta Pusat, Indonesia

Tel: 62-21-345-4050   Fax: 62-21-345-4427

H.J. HEINZ COMPANY

600 Grant Street, Pittsburgh, PA, 15219

Tel: (412) 456-5700   Fax: (412) 456-6128   www.heinz.com

Processed food products and nutritional services.

Heinz ABC Indonesia (JV), Jakarta, Indonesia

Contact: Kogan Mandala, Pres.

HERCULES INC.

Hercules Plaza, 1313 N. Market Street, Wilmington, DE, 19894-0001

Tel: (302) 594-5000   Fax: (302) 594-5400   www.herc.com

Mfr. specialty chemicals, plastics, film and fibers, coatings, resins and food ingredients.

Hercules Chemicals, Pandan, Indonesia

HEWITT ASSOCIATES LLC

100 Half Day Road, Lincolnshire, IL, 60069

Tel: (847) 295-5000   Fax: (847) 295-7634   www.hewitt.com

Employee benefits consulting firm.

PT Hewitt Konsultan Indonesia, Suite 34-09, Level 34, Wisma BNI 46, Jl. Jend. Sudirman Kav. 1, Jakarta, Indonesia

HILTON HOTELS CORPORATION

9336 Civic Center Drive, Beverly Hills, CA, 90210

Tel: (310) 278-4321   Fax: (310) 205-7880   www.hiltonhotels.com

International hotel chain: Hilton International, Vista Hotels and Hilton National Hotels.

Hilton International Company, PO Box 3315, Jl Jend Gatot Subroto, Senayan, Jakarta 10002, Indonesia

HONEYWELL INTERNATIONAL INC.

Honeywell Plaza, Minneapolis, MN, 55408

Tel: (612) 951-1000   Fax: (612) 951-8537   www.honeywell.com

Develop/mfr. controls for home and building, industry, space and aviation, burglar and fire alarm systems.

PT Honeywell Indonesia, Wisma Budi, 4th Fl., Ste. 405, J.I.H.R. Rasuna Said Kav. C-6, Jakarta 12940, Indonesia

Tel: 62-21-521-3330   Fax: 62-21-521-3735

HORIZON OFFSHORE, INC.

2500 City West Blvd., Ste. 2200, Houston, TX, 77042-3097

Tel: (713) 361-2600   Fax: (713) 361-2690   www.horizonoffshore.com

Provides offshore marine construction services.

PT Armandi Pranaupaya, JR Woler Mongonsidi 9, Kebayoran Baru, Jakarta 12110, Indonesia

HORWATH INTERNATIONAL ASSOCIATION

420 Lexington Avenue, Suite 526, New York, NY, 10170-0526

Tel: (212) 808-2000   Fax: (212) 808-2020   www.horwath.com

Public accountants and auditors.

Drs. Pamintori & Rekan, Wisma Sejahtera, #1C, #1E Jl.Let. Jend.S.Parman Kav.75, Jakarta Barat 11410, Indonesia

HOWMEDICA OSTEONICS, INC.

59 Route 17 South, Allendale, NJ, 07401

Tel: (201) 507-7300   Fax: (201) 935-4873   www.howmedica.com

Mfr. of maxillofacial products (orthopedic implants).

Howmedica Indionesia - Atra Widiya Agung, Jakarta, Indonesia

Tel: 62-21-750-7707

HQ GLOBAL WORKPLACES INC.

15305 Dallas Parkway, Ste. 1400, Addison, TX, 75001

Tel: (972) 361-8221   Fax: (972) 361-8221   www.hq.com

Provides office outsourcing, officing solutions, including internet access, telecommunications, meeting rooms, furnished offices and team rooms, state-of-the-art videoconferencing, and trained on-site administrative support teams -

HQ Global Workplaces, Ariobimo Central, 4/F, Blok X-2, No. 5, Jakarta 12950, Indonesia

Tel: 62-21-252-5725

HUGHES ELECTRONICS CORPORATION

200 N. Sepulveda Blvd., PO Box 956, El Segundo, CA, 90245-0956

Tel: (310) 662-9821   Fax: (310) 647-6213   www.hughes.com

Provides digital television entertainment, satellite services, and satellite-based private business networks.

Hughes Space, Mid Plaza II Building, 22nd Floor, Jl. Jend. Sudirman Kav 10-11, Jakarta Pusat 10220, Indonesia

Tel: 62-21-573-4161   Fax: 62-21-573-4162

HYATT CORPORATION

200 West Madison Street, Chicago, IL, 60606

Tel: (312) 750-1234   Fax: (312) 750-8578   www.hyatt.com

International hotel management.

Grand Hyatt Bali Resort, PO Box 53, Nusa Dua, Bali, Indonesia

Tel: 62-361-77-1234   Fax: 62-361-772038

Grand Hyatt Jakarta Hotel, Jl. M.H. Thamrin, Jakarta 10230, Indonesia

Tel: 62-21-290-1234   Fax: 62-21-334-321

Hyatt Regency Yogyakarta, Jl. Palagan Tentara Pelajar, Yogyakarta 55581, Indonesia

Tel: 62-274-869-123   Fax: 62-274-869-588

IBM CORPORATION

1133 Westchester Avenue, White Plains, NY, 10604

Tel: (914) 765-1900   Fax: (914) 765-7382   www.ibm.com

Information products, technology and services.

IBM Indonesia PT, 5 Jim H. Thamrin, Jakarta, Indonesia

IBM World Trade Corp., Landmark Center One, 31th Floor, Jl. Jend. Sudiman No.1, Jakarta 12910, Indonesia

Tel: 62-21-251-2922   Fax: 62-21-251-2933

INFONET SERVICES CORPORATION

2160 East Grand Ave., El Segundo, CA, 90245-1022

Tel: (310) 335-2600   Fax: (310) 335-4507   www.infonet.com

Provider of Internet services and electronic messaging services.

Infonet Indonesia, WITEL IV, GRHA CITRA CARAKA Lantai III, Jl. Gatot Subroto No. 52, Jakarta 12710, Indonesia

Tel: 62-21-521-2996   Fax: 62-21-522-2296

INTELLIGROUP, INC.

499 Thornall Street, Edison, NJ, 08837

Tel: (732) 590-1600   Fax: (732) 362-2100   www.intelligroup.com

Provides systems integration, customer software and Internet application development.

Intelligroup Indonesia, C/O - SDI Technologies, Wisma Danamon Aetna Life, 25/F, Jl. Jend, Sudirman. Kav. 45-46, Jakarta 12930, Indonesia

Tel: 62-21-577-1570

INTER-CONTINENTAL HOTELS

3 Ravinia Drive, Suite 2900, Atlanta, GA, 30346-2149

Tel: (770) 604-2000   Fax: (770) 604-5403   www.interconti.com

Worldwide hotel and resort accommodations.

Borobudur Inter-Continental Jakarta, Jl. Lapangan Banteng Selatan, PO Box 1329, Jakarta, Indonesia

Tel: 62-21-380-5555   Fax: 62-21-380-9595

INTERGRAPH CORPORATION

One Madison Industrial Park, Huntsville, AL, 35894-0001

Tel: (256) 730-2000   Fax: (256) 730-7898   www.intergraph.com

Develop/mfr. interactive computer graphic systems.

PT Indograf Teknotama, Menara Mulia 24th Fl. Ste. 2407, Jl. Jenderal Gatot Subroto Kavs 9-11, Jakarta 12930, Indonesia

Tel: 62-21-5257488   Fax: 62-21-5204064

INTERNATIONAL FLAVORS & FRAGRANCES INC.

521 West 57th Street, New York, NY, 10019-2960

Tel: (212) 765-5500   Fax: (212) 708-7132   www.iff.com

Design/mfr. flavors, fragrances and aroma chemicals.

Essence Indonesia PT, Jl. Oto Iskandardinata 74, PO Box 3008/DKT, Jakarta, Indonesia

INTERNATIONAL MANAGEMENT GROUP (IMG)

1360 East Ninth Street, Ste. 100, Cleveland, OH, 44114

Tel: (216) 522-1200   Fax: (216) 522-1145   www.imgworld.com

Manages athletes, sports academies and real estate facilities worldwide.

IMG Senayan Golf Club, Plaza Lippo, 10/F, Jalen Jend. Sudtman Kav. 25, Jakarta 12920, Indonesia

Tel: 62-21-526-8038   Fax: 62-21-526-80339

INTERNATIONAL SPECIALTY PRODUCTS, INC.

1361 Alps Rd., Wayne, NJ, 07470

Tel: (973) 389-3083   Fax: (973) 628-4117   www.ispcorp.com

Mfr. specialty chemical products.

ISP (Singapore) Pte. Ltd., Indonesia Representative Office, Wisma Bisnis Indonesia, 8th Fl., Jl. Let. Jend. S. Parman Kav 12, Jakarta 11480, Indonesia

Tel: 62-21-530-7181   Fax: 62-21-530-7183

J. WALTER THOMPSON COMPANY

466 Lexington Ave., New York, NY, 10017

Tel: (212) 210-7000   Fax: (212) 210-6944   www.jwt.com

International advertising and marketing services.

AdForce/JWT, Jakarta, Indonesia

JLM INDUSTRIES, INC.

8675 Hidden River Pkwy., Tampa, FL, 33637

Tel: (813) 632-3300   Fax: (813) 632-3301   www.jlmgroup.com

Mfr. and distribution of performance chemicals.

JLM Chemicals Indonesia, Wisma Sejahtera 204A, JL. Letjen S. Parman Kav 75, Jakarta 11410, Indonesia

JOHN HANCOCK FINANCIAL SERVICES, INC.

200 Clarendon Street, Boston, MA, 02117

Tel: (617) 572-6000   Fax: (617) 572-9799   www.johnhancock.com

Life insurance services.

P.T. Asuransi Jiwa Bumiputera John Hancock, Jakarta, Indonesia

JOHNSON & JOHNSON

One Johnson & Johnson Plaza, New Brunswick, NJ, 08933

Tel: (732) 524-0400   Fax: (732) 214-0334   www.jnj.com

Mfr./distributor/R&D pharmaceutical, health care and cosmetic products.

Janssen-Cilag Pharmaceutica, Jakarta, Indonesia

PT Johnson & Johnson Indonesia, PO Box 3200, Jakarta, Indonesia

SC JOHNSON

1525 Howe St., Racine, WI, 53403

Tel: (262) 260-2000   Fax: (262) 260-2133   www.scjohnsonwax.com

Home, auto, commercial and personal care products and specialty chemicals.

SC Johnson, PO Box 1345/JAT, Jakarta Timur, Indonesia

THE JOHNSON CORPORATION

805 Wood Street, Three Rivers, MI, 49093

Tel: (269) 278-1715   Fax: (269) 273-2230   www.joco.com

Mfr. rotary joints and siphon systems.

Johnson Corporation Asia Pacific, J1. Alam Hijau, Blok E XI No. 14, Citra Raya Surabaya 60219, Indonesia

Tel: 62-31-7407950

JOHNSON OUTDOORS, INC.

555 Main Street, Racine, WI, 53177

Tel: (262) 631-6600   Fax: (262) 631-6601   www.johnsonoutdoors.com

Mfr. diving, fishing, boating and camping sports equipment.

P.T. Uwatec Batam, Lot 258, Jl Kenanga, BIP, Muka Kuning, Batam 29433, Indonesia

Tel: 62-778-611694   Fax: 62-778-611693

JONES LANG LASALLE

153 East 53rd Street, New York, NY, 10022

Tel: (212) 812-5700   Fax: (212) 421-3544   www.am.joneslanglasalle.com

International marketing consultants, leasing agents and property management advisors.

Jones Lang Wootton, Indonesia

JUKI UNION SPECIAL CORPORATION

8500 N.W. 17th St., Miami, FL, 33126

Tel: (305) 594-0059   Fax: (305) 594-0720   www.unionspecial.com

Mfr. sewing machines.

JUKI Singapore Ptd., Wisma Abadi ,2nd Fl., C-3 Jl Kyaj Caringin No. 29-31, Jakarta 10160, Indonesia

Tel: 62-21-384-8768   Fax: 62-21-386-5449

A.T. KEARNEY INC.

5400 Legacy Dr., Plano, TX, 75201

Tel: (972) 604-4600   Fax: (972) 543-7680   www.atkearney.com

Management consultants and executive search.

A. T. Kearney, Sudirman Central Business District, 18/F, Jl. Jend. Sudirman Kav. 52-53, Jakarta 12190, Indonesia

Tel: 62-21-523-9130   Fax: 62-21-523-9193

KELLOGG BROWN & ROOT INC.

PO Box 4557, Houston, TX, 77210-4557

Tel: (713) 676-3011   Fax: (713) 676-8695   www.halliburton.com

Engaged in technology-based engineering and construction.

Kellogg Brown & Root, Bldgs.106/107, Cilandak Commercial Estate, Jl. Cilandak KKO, Jakarta Selantan 12560, Indonesia

Tel: 62-21-780-1100

Kellogg Brown & Root, Ratu Plaza Office Tower, 10/F, Jl Jend Budirman 9, Jakarta 10270, Indonesia

KENNAMETAL INC.

1600 Technology Way, PO Box 231, Latrobe, PA, 15650

Tel: (724) 539-5000   Fax: (724) 539-4710   www.kennametal.com

Tools, hard carbide and tungsten alloys for metalworking industry.

C.V. MultiTeknik, Gajkah Mada Tower, 19th Fl., Ste. 1909, Jln. Gajah Mada 9-26, Jakarta 10130, Indonesia

Tel: 62-21-6339151   Fax: 62-21-600-9150

P.T. Germantara Toolindo Sistema, Jl. Permuda 44, Jakarta 13220, Indonesia

Tel: 62-21489-3952   Fax: 62-21-471-3628

KIMBERLY-CLARK CORPORATION

351 Phelps Drive, Irving, TX, 75038

Tel: (972) 281-1200   Fax: (972) 281-1435   www.kimberly-clark.com

Mfr./sales/distribution of consumer tissue, household and personal care products.

PT Kimsari Paper Indonesia, Medan, Indonesia

KOCH INDUSTRIES INC.

4111 East 37th Street North, Wichita, KS, 67220-3203

Tel: (316) 828-5500   Fax: (316) 828-5950   www.kochind.com

Oil, financial services, agriculture and Purina Mills animal feed.

Koch Membrane Systems, Inc., Jakarta Barat, Indonesia

Tel: 62-21-584-6202

KPMG CONSULTING INC.

1676 International Dr., McLean, VA, 22102

Tel: (703) 747-3000   Fax: (703) 747-8500   www.kpmg.com

Accounting and audit, tax and management consulting services.

Hanadi Sudjendro & Rekan, Jl Palang Merah 40, PO Box 506, Medan 20111, Indonesia

Hanadi Sudjendro & Rekan, 301 A Batam Industrial Park, Muka Kuning, Batam, Indonesia

Hanadi Sudjendro & Rekan, Wisma BII, 7th Fl., Jl Pemuda 60-70, Surabaya 60271, Indonesia

Hanadi Sudjendro & Rekan, Jl Ir H Juanda 49, Bandung, Indonesia

PT Sudjendro Soesanto Management Consultants, Wisma Dharmala Sakti, Jl. Jend. Sudirman 32, Jakarta 10220, Indonesia

Tel: 62-21-570-6111   Fax: 62-21-573-3003   Contact: Kanaka Puradiredja, Ptnr.

LANDOR ASSOCIATES

Klamath House, 1001 Front Street, San Francisco, CA, 94111-1424

Tel: (415) 955-1400   Fax: (415) 365-3190   www.landor.com

International marketing consulting firm, engaged in brand strategy, design, naming, digital branding, print literature design and research services.

Landor Associates, Menara Estro, 3/F, Tanah Abang 3 No. 31, Jakarta 10160, Indonesia

Tel: 62-21-3483-0458   Fax: 62-21-3483-0459   Contact: Daniel Surya

LEHMAN BROTHERS HOLDINGS INC.

*101 Hudson Street, Jersey City, NJ, 07302

Tel: (201) 524-2000   Fax: (201) 524-2000   www.lehman.com

Financial services, securities and merchant banking services.

Lehman Brothers, Bapindo Plaza, Tower 2, (\19/F, Jl. Jend Sudirman, Kav 54-55, Jakarta 12190, Indonesia

Tel: 62-21-521-0715

ELI LILLY & COMPANY

Lilly Corporate Center, Indianapolis, IN, 46285

Tel: (317) 276-2000   Fax: (317) 277-6579   www.lilly.com

Mfr. pharmaceuticals and animal health products.

P.T. Tempo Scan Pacific, Bina Mulia II, 7th Fl., Jl. H.R. Said Kav 11, Rasuna Jakarta 12950, Indonesia

Tel: 62-21-520-1919   Fax: 62-21-520-1194

LINCOLN ELECTRIC HOLDINGS

22801 St. Clair Ave., Cleveland, OH, 44117-1199

Tel: (216) 481-8100   Fax: (216) 486-8385   www.lincolnelectric.com

Mfr. arc welding and welding related products, oxy-fuel and thermal cutting equipment and integral AC motors.

Lincoln Electric Company, Indonesia, Persona Bahari Apt. Blok Jade No. 26-D, Jl. Mangga Dua Abdad, Mangga Dua Jakarta Pusat 10730, Indonesia

Tel: 62-21-612-9358   Fax: 62-21-612-9358   Contact: Richard Lane, Mgr.

PT Lincoln Austenite Indonesia, Bekasi International Industrial Estate, Block C-10, No 12A, Lippo Cikarang Bekasis 17550, Indonesia

Tel: 62-21-8990-7629   Fax: 62-21-8990-76309   Contact: Dyonisius Soeprihandono, Plant Mgr.

LOCKHEED MARTIN CORPORATION

6801 Rockledge Drive, Bethesda, MD, 20817

Tel: (301) 897-6000   Fax: (301) 897-6652   www.imco.com

Design/mfr./management systems in fields of space, defense, energy, electronics and technical services.

Aircraft Systems International, Bandung, Indonesia

Tel: 62-22-2500303   Fax: 62-22-613935

Lockheed Martin Global, Inc., Wisma Danamon Aetna 14/F, Jl. Jend Sudirman Kav. 45-46, Jakarta 12930, Indonesia

Tel: 62-21-738-7533   Fax: 62-21-738-8861

THE LUBRIZOL CORPORATION

29400 Lakeland Blvd., Wickliffe, OH, 44092-2298

Tel: (440) 943-4200   Fax: (440) 943-5337   www.lubrizol.com

Mfr. chemicals additives for lubricants and fuels.

Lubrizol Indonesia, Jakarta, Indonesia

LUCENT TECHNOLOGIES, INC.

600 Mountain Ave., Murray Hill, NJ, 07974-0636

Tel: (908) 582-3000   Fax: (908) 582-2576   www.lucent.com

Design/mfr. wide range of public and private networks, communication systems and software, data networking systems, business telephone systems and microelectronics components.

P.T. Lucent Technologies Network Systems, MM2100 Industrial Town, Block B-3, Cibitung Bekasi 17520, Indonesia

Tel: 62-21-898-0840   Fax: 62-21-8978-0808   Contact: Jonnie Oden, PR Mgr.

P.T. Lucent Technologies Network Systems, Wisma Danamon Aetna Life, 7th Floor JL. Jend. Sudiriman Kav 45-60, Jakarta 12930, Indonesia

Tel: 62-21-577-1677   Fax: 62-21-577-1676   Contact: Jonnie Oden, PR Mgr.

MARATHON OIL COMPANY

5555 San Felipe Road, Houston, TX, 77056

Tel: (713) 629-6600   Fax: (713) 296-2952   www.marathon.com

Oil and gas exploration.

Marathon Petroleum Indonesia Ltd., Jl. H.R. Rasuna Said, Kav. B-10, Lippo Life Bldg., Jakarta, Indonesia

MARLEY COOLING TOWER COMPANY

7401 West 129th Street, Overland Park, KS, 66213

Tel: (913) 664-7400   Fax: (913) 664-7641   www.marleyct.com

Cooling and heating towers and waste treatment systems.

P. T. Tasan Megah, Rep. Office, Komplek Grogol Permai, Blok A, 20-21, Jl. Prof. Dr. Latumeten, Jakarta Barat 11460, Indonesia

MARSH & McLENNAN COS INC.

1166 Ave. of the Americas, New York, NY, 10036-2774

Tel: (212) 345-5000 Fax: (212) 345-4808 www.marshmac.com

Insurance agents/brokers, pension and investment management consulting services.

P.T. Peranas Agung, Multika Bldg., JIN Mampang Prapatan Raya 71-73, Ste. 303, Jakarta 12790, Indonesia

Tel: 62-21-797-5201 Fax: 62-21-797-5202 Contact: Adri G. Sinaulan

MATTEL INC.

333 Continental Blvd., El Segundo, CA, 90245-5012

Tel: (310) 252-2000 Fax: (310) 252-2179 www.mattel.com

Mfr. toys, dolls, games, crafts and hobbies.

Mattel, Jakarta, Indonesia

McCANN-ERICKSON WORLDGROUP

750 Third Ave., New York, NY, 10017

Tel: (212) 697-6000 Fax: (212) 984-3575 www.mccann.com

International advertising and marketing services.

Grafik McCann-Erickson, Jl. Riau 17, Jakarta, Indonesia

McDERMOTT INTERNATIONAL INC.

1450 Poydras Street, PO Box 60035, New Orleans, LA, 70160-0035

Tel: (504) 587-5400 Fax: (504) 587-6153 www.mcdermott.com

Provides energy, engineering and construction services for industrial, utility, and hydrocarbon processing facilities, and to the offshore oil and natural gas industries.

P.T. Babcock & Wilcox, Wisma Tugu II, 4th Fl, PO Box 737/JKTM 12701, Jl. H.R. Rasuna said Kav. C 7-9, Kuningan, Jakarta 12940, Indonesia

Tel: 62-21-520-8630 Fax: 62-21-520-8631 Contact: Nick Carter, Mgr.

McDONALD'S CORPORATION

McDonald's Plaza, Oak Brook, IL, 60523

Tel: (630) 623-3000 Fax: (630) 623-7409 www.mcdonalds.com

Fast food chain stores.

McDonald's Corp., Jakarta, Indonesia

THE McGRAW-HILL COMPANIES

1221 Avenue of the Americas, New York, NY, 10020

Tel: (212) 512-2000 Fax: (212) 512-2703 www.mccgraw-hill.com

Books, magazines, information systems, financial service, publishing and broadcast operations.

McGraw-Hill Grand Boutique Centre, Block D 65JI Mangga Due Raya, Jakarta 11430, Indonesia

McKINSEY & COMPANY

55 East 52nd Street, New York, NY, 10022

Tel: (212) 446-7000 Fax: (212) 446-8575 www.mckinsey.com

Management and business consulting services.

McKinsey & Company, MidPlaza, 2 Bldg., Lt. 19, Jl. Jend. Sudirman Kav. 10-11, Jakarta 10220, Indonesia

Tel: 62-21-573-5950 Fax: 62-21-573-5951

THE MENTHOLATUM COMPANY, INC.

707 Sterling Drive, Orchard Park, NY, 14127-1587

Tel: (716) 677-2500 Fax: (716) 674-3696 www.mentholatum.com

Mfr. of non-prescription pharmaceuticals, healthcare and cosmeceutical products and medical devices.

P.T. Rohto Laboratories Indonesia, JL. Tanah Abang 11/37, Jakarta 10160, Indonesia

Tel: 62-21-350-897981 Fax: 62-21-386-1847

MERRILL LYNCH & COMPANY, INC.

World Financial Center, 250 Vesey Street, New York, NY, 10281-1332

Tel: (212) 236-1000   Fax: (212) 449-2892   www.ml.com

Security brokers and dealers, investment and business services.

P.T. Merrill Lynch Indonesia, 18th Fl., Jakarta Stock Exchange Bldg., Jl Jend. Sudirman Kav 52-53, Jakarta 12190, Indonesia

Tel: 62-21-515-0888   Fax: 62-21-515-8819

METROPOLITAN LIFE INSURANCE COMPANY

1 Madison Ave., New York, NY, 10010-3603

Tel: (212) 578-3818   Fax: (212) 252-7294   www.metlife.com

Insurance and retirement savings products and services.

PT Metlife Sejahtera, Menara Mulia, 3rd Floor, Jl. Jend. gatot Subroto Kav. 9, Jakarta Selatan 12930, Indonesia

Tel: 62-21-527-7608   Fax: 62-21-527-7620   Contact: Leonard Logan, Pres. & Dir.

M-I

PO Box 48242, Houston, TX, 77242-2842

Tel: (713) 739-0222   Fax: (713) 308-9503   www.midf.com

Developer, manufacturer and marketer of drilling and completion fluids and services.

IMCO Services Indonesia PT, Setiabudi Bldg. 1, H.R. Rasuma Said 62, PO Box 3033, Jakarta, Indonesia

PT M-I Indonesia, Annex Building, 2nd Floor, JL Ampera Raya Kav 9-10, Jakarta 12550, Indonesia

Tel: 62-21-780-6578

MICROSOFT CORPORATION

One Microsoft Way, Redmond, WA, 98052-6399

Tel: (425) 882-8080   Fax: (425) 936-7329   www.microsoft.com

Computer software, peripherals and services.

Microsoft Indonesia P.T., 17th Floor, Plaza Chase, Jl. Jend. Sudirman, Kav 21, Jakarta 12920, Indonesia

Tel: 62-21-520-8111   Fax: 61-21-520-8122

MILBANK, TWEED, HADLEY & McCLOY LLP

1 Chase Manhattan Plaza, New York, NY, 10005-1413

Tel: (212) 530-5000   Fax: (212) 530-5219   www.milbank.com

International law practice.

Makarim & Taira S., 17th Fl., Summitmas Tower, J1. Jend. Sudirman 61, Jakarta, Indonesia

Tel: 62-21-252-1272   Fax: 62-21-252-2751

MONSANTO

800 N. Lindbergh Boulevard, St. Louis, MO, 63167

Tel: (314) 694-1000   Fax: (314) 694-7625   www.monsanto.com

Life sciences company focusing on agriculture, nutrition, pharmaceuticals, health and wellness and sustainable development.

Monsanto Co. Chemical Group, P T Monagro Kimia Permata Plaza, 9/F, Jaian M H Thamrin 57, Jakarta 10350, Indonesia

Tel: 62-21-390-3141   Fax: 62-21-390-146

Monsanto Indonesia, Menera Mulia Building, 22/F, Suite 2201, Jakarta 12950, Indonesia

J. P. MORGAN CHASE & CO. INC.

270 Park Ave., New York, NY, 10017

Tel: (212) 270-6000   Fax: (212) 622-9030   www.jpmorganchase.com

Provides integrated financial solutions for institutions and individuals worldwide, including asset management, investment banking and commercial banking.

J. P. Morgan Chase & Co., 4/F Chase Plaza, Jl. Jend Sudirman Kav. 21, Jakarta 12920, Indonesia

Tel: 62-21-571-0088   Fax: 62-21-570-3690

MOTOROLA, INC.

1303 East Algonquin Road, Schaumburg, IL, 60196

Tel: (847) 576-5000   Fax: (847) 538-5191   www.motorola.com

Mfr. communications equipment, semiconductors and cellular phones.

PT. Motorola Indonesia, BRI II., Ste. 3001, Jl. Jend. Sudirman Kav. 44-46, Jakarta 10210, Indonesia

Tel: 62-21-251-3050   Fax: 62-21-571-3646

NATIONAL STARCH AND CHEMICAL COMPANY

10 Finderne Ave., Bridgewater, NJ, 08807-3300

Tel: (908) 685-5000   Fax: (908) 685-5005   www.nationalstarch.com

Mfr. adhesives and sealants, resins and specialty chemicals, electronic materials and adhesives, food products, industry starch.

National Starch & Chemical, 26 Jl. Rembang Industri Raya, PIER Pasuruan, East Java 67152, Indonesia

Tel: 62-34-374-4060   Fax: 62-34-374-4059

NEW BALANCE ATHLETIC SHOE, INC.

Brighton Landing, 20 Guest Street, Boston, MA, 02135-2088

Tel: (617) 783-4000   Fax: (617) 787-9355   www.newbalance.com

Mfr. men's and women's athletic shoes.

New Balance Indonesia, Level 9, Tamara Centre, J1 Jend Sudirman, Jakarta KAV 24, Indonesia

NEW YORK LIFE INSURANCE COMPANY

51 Madison Ave., New York, NY, 10010

Tel: (212) 576-7000   Fax: (212) 576-4291   www.newyorklife.com

Insurance services.

New York Life Insurance Co. Indonesia, Jakarta, Indonesia

NEWMONT MINING CORPORATION

1700 Lincoln Street, Denver, CO, 80203

Tel: (303) 863-7414   Fax: (303) 837-5837   www.newmont.corp

Gold mining.

PT Newmont Minahasa Raya & Nusa Tenggara, Atria Square, 14th Fl., Jl. Jend. Sudirman Kav. 33A, Jakarta 10220, Indonesia

NORTON ABRASIVES COMPANY

1 New Bond Street, Worcester, MA, 01606

Tel: (508) 795-5000   Fax: (508) 795-5741   www.nortonabrasives.com

Mfr. abrasives for industrial manufacturing.

PT Norton Hamplas Industries, Surabaya, Indonesia

OCCIDENTAL PETROLEUM CORPORATION

10889 Wilshire Blvd., Los Angeles, CA, 90024

Tel: (310) 208-8800   Fax: (310) 443-6690   www.oxy.com

Petroleum and petroleum products, chemicals, plastics.

Occidental of Indonesia Inc, Indonesia

OCEANEERING INTERNATIONAL INC.

11911 FM 529, Houston, TX, 77041

Tel: (713) 329-4500   Fax: (713) 329-4951   www.oceaneering.com

Transportation equipment, underwater service to offshore oil and gas industry.

P.T. Calmarine, Div. Engineering, Imeco Building 10, 1/F, Jl. Ampera Raya 9-10, Cilandak Jakarta 12550, Indonesia

P.T. Calmarine, Div. Oceaneering, Miramar Utama Complex, Jalan M Taher Handil III, Muara Jawa, Samarinda, Indonesia

P.T. Calmarine, Div. Oceaneering, Jalan Jendral Sudirman RT ll No. 237, Markoni, Balikpapan East Kalimantan, Indonesia

OGILVY & MATHER WORLDWIDE

309 West 49th Street, New York, NY, 10017-7399

Tel: (212) 237-4000   Fax: (212) 237-5123   www.ogilvypr.com

Engaged in public relations and communications.

Ogilvy Public Relations Worldwide, Bapindo Plaza, Menara 1, Lantai 25 Jalan Jendral Sudirman Kav. 54-55, Jakarta 12190, Indonesia

Tel: 62-21-526-6261   Contact: Ong Hock Chuan

ONDEO NALCO COMPANY

Ondeo Nalco Center, 1601 W. Diehl Road, Naperville, IL, 60563-1198

Tel: (630) 305-1000   Fax: (630) 305-2900   www.ondeo-nalco.com

Mfr. specialty chemicals for water and waste water treatment, oil products and refining, industry processes; water and energy management service.

PT ONDEO Nalco Perkasa, c/o P.T. Astenia-Napan, Wisma Indocement, Jl. Jend Sudirman Kav. 70-71, Jakarta 12910, Indonesia

Tel: 62-21-573-2188   Fax: 62-21-573-1870

ORACLE CORPORATION

500 Oracle Parkway, Redwood Shores, CA, 94065

Tel: (650) 506-7000   Fax: (650) 506-7200   www.oracle.com

Develop/manufacture software.

Oracle Indonesia, Jakarta, Indonesia

OSMONICS INC.

5951 Clearwater Drive, Minnetonka, MN, 55343-8995

Tel: (952) 933-2277   Fax: (952) 933-0141   www.osmonics.com

Mfr. equipment, controls and components for the filtration and water-treatment industries.

Osmonics Indonesia, c/o PT Sembada Perdana Insan, Jl. Taman Tanah Abang 111, #19, Jakarta 10160, Indonesia

OTIS ELEVATOR COMPANY

One Farm Springs Road, Farmington, CT, 06032

Tel: (860) 676-6000   Fax: (860) 676-5111   www.otis.com

Mfr. elevators and escalators.

P.T. Citas Otis Elevator, Jl. Sultan Hasanuddin 56, Jakarta 12160, Indonesia

OWENS-ILLINOIS, INC.

One SeaGate, PO Box 1035, Toledo, OH, 43666

Tel: (419) 247-5000   Fax: (419) 247-2839   www.o-i.com

Mfr. glass containers and packaging products.

PT Kangar Consolidated Industries, Jakarta, Indonesia

PACCAR INC.

777 106th Ave. NE, Bellevue, WA, 98004

Tel: (425) 468-7400   Fax: (425) 468-8216   www.pacar.com

Heavy duty dump trucks, military vehicles.

PACCAR International, 2/F - Jl. Raya Bekasi Km. 22, Jakarta 13910, Indonesia

Tel: 62-21-460-3932

PACCAR International, Jl. Zamrud VII, Block E-45, Permata Hijau Jakarta, Indonesia

Tel: 62-21-535-5801   Fax: 62-21-535-5801

PACIFIC ARCHITECTS & ENGINEERS INC. (PAE)

888 South Figueroa Street, 17th Fl., Los Angeles, CA, 90017

Tel: (213) 481-2311   Fax: (213) 481-7189   www.paechl.com

Technical engineering services.

P.T. Paranda Ekaysa, Papan Sejahtera Building 6th Fl., Jl. H.R. Rasuna Said Kav. C-1, Kuningan Jakarta, Indonesia

Tel: 62-21-252-6188   Fax: 62-21-520-7724   Contact: Herman Sudjono, Pres. & Dir.

PANDUIT CORPORATION

17301 Ridgeland Ave., Tinley Park, IL, 60477-0981

Tel: (708) 532-1800   Fax: (708) 532-1811   www.panduit.com

Mfr. of network connectivity and electrical products.

Wisma Danamon Aetna Life, Jalan Jendral Ste. 29, Surdirman Kav. 45-46, Jakarta 12930, Indonesia

PARAMETRIC TECHNOLOGY CORPORATION

140 Kendrick St., Needham, MA, 02494

Tel: (781) 370-5000   Fax: (781) 370-6000   www.ptc.com

Supplier of mechanical design automation and product data management software and services.

Parametric Technology Indonesia, Wisma Danamon Aetna Life 19th Fl., Jl. Jend. Sudirman Kav. 45-46, Jakarta 12930, Indonesia

Tel: 62-21-575-0909   Fax: 62-21-575-0916

PARKER DRILLING COMPANY

1401 Enclave Pkwy., Ste. 600, Houston, TX, 77077

Tel: (281) 406-2000   Fax: (281) 406-2001   www.parkerdrilling.com

Provides land contract drilling services to firms in the oil and gas industry.

Parker Drilling Co. of Indonesia-PT Dati, Jl. Sultan Hasanuddin 28, Kebayoran Bara, Jakarta 12160, Indonesia

Parker Drilling Co. of Indonesia-PT Sebina, Griya Ampera Bldg., Jl. Ampera Raya 18, Kemang Jakarta, Indonesia

PARSONS BRINCKERHOFF INC.

One Penn Plaza, New York, NY, 10119-0061

Tel: (212) 465-5000   Fax: (212) 465-5096   www.pbworld.com

Provides planning, engineering, construction management and operations and maintenance services.

Parsons Brinckerhoff, Jalan Ciasem IV/No. 1, Kebayoran Baru, Jakarta Selatan 12180, Indonesia

Tel: 62-21-724-8371   Fax: 62-21-724-8373

PARSONS CORPORATION

100 West Walnut Street, Pasadena, CA, 91124

Tel: (626) 440-2000   Fax: (626) 440-4919   www.parsons.com

Engaged in engineering, procurement, and construction management services.

Parsons Engineering Science Inc., Jl Prapen Indah II/F2, Surabaya 60299, Indonesia

PERKIN ELMER, INC.

45 William Street, Wellesley, MA, 02481

Tel: (781) 237-5100   Fax: (781) 431-4255   www.perkinelmer.com

Mfr. equipment and devices to detect explosives and bombs on airline carriers.

PerkinElmer Life Sciences, Blok 207, Lantai 2, Jalan Beringin Kawasan, Industri Batamindo, Muka Kuning-Batam 29433, Indonesia

Tel: 62-778-611084

PFIZER INC.

235 East 42nd Street, New York, NY, 10017-5755

Tel: (212) 573-2323   Fax: (212) 573-7851   www.pfizer.com

Research-based, global health care company.

Pfizer International, Indonesia

PHARMACIA CORPORATION

100 Route 206 North, Peapack, NJ, 07977

Tel: (908) 901-8000   Fax: (908) 901-8379   www.pharmacia.com

Mfr. pharmaceuticals, agricultural products, industry chemicals.

PT Upjohn Indonesia, Jl Raya Jakarta Bogor km 38.1, Cilangkap Cimanggis, Kotamadya Depok, Indonesia

Tel: 6221-875-2819   Fax: 6221-875-2859

PT Upjohn Indonesia, Menera Mulia Bldg. 22Fl Suite 2201, Jl. Gatot Subroto Kav 9-11, Jakarta 12930, Indonesia

Tel: 62-21-527-8551   Fax: 62-21-527-8501

PHILLIPS PETROLEUM COMPANY

Phillips Building, 411 S. Keeler Ave., Bartlesville, OK, 74004

Tel: (918) 661-6600   Fax: (918) 661-7636   www.phillips66.com

Crude oil, natural gas, liquefied petroleum gas, gasoline and petro-chemicals.

Phillips Petroleum Co. Indonesia, Jl. Melawai Raya No. 16, Keb. Baru, Jakarta, Indonesia

PIONEER HI-BRED INTERNATIONAL INC.

400 Locust Street, Ste. 800, Des Moines, IA, 50309

Tel: (515) 248-4800   Fax: (515) 248-4999   www.pioneer.com

Agricultural chemicals, farm supplies, biological products, research.

PT Pioneer Hibrida Indonesia, Jl. Imam Bonjol 80, 8/F, Jakarta 10310, Indonesia

PLANET HOLLYWOOD INTERNATIONAL, INC.

8669 Commodity Circle, Orlando, FL, 32819

Tel: (407) 363-7827   Fax: (407) 363-4862   www.planethollywood.com

Theme-dining restaurant chain and merchandise retail stores.

Planet Hollywood International, Inc., Jakarta, Indonesia

PRICEWATERHOUSECOOPERS LLP

1301 Ave. of the Americas, New York, NY, 10019

Tel: (212) 596-7000   Fax: (212) 259-1301   www.pwcglobal.com

Accounting and auditing, tax and management, and human resource consulting services.

PriceWaterhouseCoopers, Price Waterhouse Center, Jl. HR Rasuna Said Kav. C-3, PO Box 2169/2473, Jakarta 10001, Indonesia

Tel: 62-21-521-2941   Fax: 62-21-521-2950

THE PRINCIPAL FINANCIAL GROUP

711 High Street, Des Moines, IA, 50392-9950

Tel: (515) 248-8288   Fax: (515) 248-8049   www.principal.com

Insurance and investment services.

Dana Pensiun Lembaga Keuangan (DPLK), Jl. Tanah Abang II No. 15, Jakarta 10160, Indonesia

Tel: 62-21-344-0238 Fax: 62-21-344-3191   Contact: Wartini Johan

PT. Asuransi Jiwa Principal Egalita, Jl. Tanah Abang II No. 15, Jakarta 10160, Indonesia

Tel: 62-21-344-0238 Fax: 62-21-344-0216   Contact: Doug Rasmussen, Mng. Dir.

PROCTER & GAMBLE COMPANY

One Procter & Gamble Plaza, Cincinnati, OH, 45202

Tel: (513) 983-1100   Fax: (513) 562-4500   www.pg.com

Personal care, food, laundry, cleaning and industry products.

PT Procter & Gamble Indonesia, Tifa Building, 8th Fl., Jl. Kuningan Barat 26, Jakarta 12710, Indonesia

QUIKSILVER, INC.

15202 Graham Sreet, Huntington Beach, CA, 92649

Tel: (714) 889-2200   Fax: (714) 889-2315   www.quiksilver.com

Mfr. sportswear and activewear.

Quiksilver Indonesia, JL.Kubu Anyar 69X, Kuta-Bali 80361, Indonesia

QWEST COMMUNICATIONS INTERNATIONAL INC.

1801 California Street, Ste. 5200, Denver, CO, 80202

Tel: (303) 896-2020   Fax: (303) 793-6654   www.uswest.com

Tele-communications provider; integrated communications services.

Ariawest International, Jakarta, Indonesia

Tel: 62-21-7398-222 Fax: 62-21-7243-371   Contact: Lawrence Tjandra, PR Mgr.

RADISSON HOTELS INTERNATIONAL

Carlson Pkwy., PO Box 59159, Minneapolis, MN, 55459-8204

Tel: (612) 540-5526   Fax: (612) 449-3400   www.radisson.com

Operates, manages and franchises full-service hotels and resorts worldwide.

Radisson Jakarta, Jl. Peconongan 72, Jakarta 10120, Indonesia

Tel: 62-21-35-000-77   Fax: 62-21-35-000-55

RAYTHEON COMPANY

141 Spring Street, Lexington, MA, 02173

Tel: (781) 862-6600   Fax: (781) 860-2172   www.raytheon.com

Mfr. diversified electronics, appliances, energy and environmental products; publishing, industry and construction services.

Raytheon International, Jakarta, Indonesia

THE RENDON GROUP INC.

1875 Connecticut Ave., NE, Washington, DC, 20009

Tel: (202) 745-4900   Fax: (202) 745-0215   www.rendon.com

Public relations, print and video production, strategic communications.

PT TRG, Plaza 89, 4th fl., Suite 407, Jl. H.R. Rasuna Said 4-7, Jakarta 12940, Indonesia

THE RITZ-CARLTON HOTEL COMPANY, L.L.C.

3414 Peachtree Road NE, Ste. 300, Atlanta, GA, 30326

Tel: (404) 237-5500   Fax: (404) 365-9643   www.ritzcarlton.com

5-star hotel and restaurant chain.

The Ritz-Carlton Bali, Jl. Karang Mas Sejahtera, Jimbaran Bali 80364, Indonesia

Tel: 62-361-702-222

THE ROCKPORT COMPANY

1895 J.W. Foster Boulevard, Canton, MA, 02021

Tel: (508) 485-2090   Fax: (508) 480-0012   www.rockport.com

Mfr./import dress and casual footwear.

Rockport Indonesia, Jl, Kapten Tendean 1, 4/F, Jakarta 12710, Indonesia

Emp: 21

ROCKWELL AUTOMATION, INC.

777 East Wisconsin Ave., Ste. 1400, Milwaukee, WI, 53202

Tel: (414) 212-5200   Fax: (414) 212-5201   www.rockwellautomation.com

Products and service for aerospace and defense, automotive, electronics, graphics and automation industry.

Rockwell Automation Southeast Asia Pte. Ltd., Ste. 2301, Gedung BRI II ,23rd Fl., Jl. Jend. Sudirman Kav 44-46, Jakarta 10210, Indonesia

Tel: 62-21-571-906   Fax: 61-21-571-9065

ROHM AND HAAS COMPANY

100 Independence Mall West, Philadelphia, PA, 19106

Tel: (215) 592-3000   Fax: (215) 592-3377   www.rohmhaas.com

Mfr. specialty chemicals.

PT Rohm and Haas Indonesia, Cilegon Plant Krakatau Industrial Estate, Kavling M-2 Jl. Raya Anyer, Cilegon 42401, Indonesia

Tel: 62-254-380631

Rohm and Haas Asia Inc., Jakarta Office, Summitas I, 20th Fl., Jl. Jend. Sudirman Kav 61-62, Jakarta 12069, Indonesia

Tel: 62-21-252-0535

ROWAN COMPANIES INC.

2800 Post Oak Boulevard, Houston, TX, 77056-6196

Tel: (713) 621-7800   Fax: (713) 960-7560   www.rowancompanies.com

leading turnkey provider of large mobile equipment for forestry, intermodal, marine and mining markets, worldwide.

Rowan Intl. Inc., Jl. Letjen M.T. Haryono 58, Pancoran, Jakarta, Indonesia

SARA LEE CORPORATION

3 First National Plaza, Chicago, IL, 60602-4260

Tel: (312) 726-2600   Fax: (312) 558-4995   www.saralee.com

Mfr./distributor food and consumer packaged goods, intimate apparel and knitwear.

House of Sara Lee, Jakarta, Indonesia

SAS INSTITUTE INC.

SAS Campus Drive, Cary, NC, 27513

Tel: (919) 677-8000   Fax: (919) 677-4444   www.sas.com

Mfr. and distribution of decision support software.

SAS Institute (Indonesia) Pte., Wisma Bank Dharmala 18th Fl, Suite 04, Jl. Jend. Sudirman Kav 28, Jakarta 12920, Indonesia

Tel: 62-21-3901761   Fax: 62-21-3902582

SCHERING-PLOUGH CORPORATION

One Giralda Farms, Madison, NJ, 07940-1000

Tel: (973) 822-7000   Fax: (973) 822-7048   www.sch-plough.com

Proprietary drug and cosmetic products.

P.T. Pimaimas Citra, PO Box 2981/JKT, Jakarta 12810, Indonesia

SCHLUMBERGER LIMITED

153 East 53rd St., 57th Fl., New York, NY, 10022-4624

Tel: (212) 350-9400   Fax: (212) 350-9457   www.slb.com

Engaged in oil and gas services, metering and payment systems, and produces semiconductor testing equipment and smart cards.

Schlumberger Ltd., 214 Melawai Raya 18, Keb. Baru, Indonesia

Schlumberger Ltd., PT Mecoindo, Sentra Mulia, 16/F, Ste. 1603 Jl. HR Rasuna Said Kav. X-6, Jakarta 12940, Indonesia

SCIENCE APPLICATIONS INTL. CORPORATION (SAIC)

10260 Campus Point Dr., San Diego, CA, 92121

Tel: (858) 826-6000   Fax: (858) 535-7589   www.saic.com

Engaged in research and engineering.

SAIC C/O BP Expl. Oper. Co. Ltd., Kuningan Plaza South, Ste. 401, J1 H. R. Rasuna Said Kav C 11-14, Jakarta 12940, Indonesia

Tel: 62-21-5201515   Contact: J. Espinosa

SEAGATE TECHNOLOGY, INC.

920 Disc Dr., Scotts Valley, CA, 95066

Tel: (408) 438-6550   Fax: (408) 438-7205   www.seagate.com

Develop computer technology, software and hardware.

Seagate Technology, Lot 19, Batamindo Industrial Park, Muka Kuning, Batam Island, Indonesia

Tel: 62-778-61564   Fax: 62-778-611942   Contact: Hamzah Bin Sulong, Dir.   Emp: 700

G.D. SEARLE & COMPANY

5200 Old Orchard Road, Skokie, IL, 60077

Tel: (847) 982-7000   Fax: (847) 470-1480   www.searlehealthnet.com

Mfr. pharmaceuticals, health care, optical products and specialty chemicals.

Searle, Division of P.T. Soho Industri Pharmasi, Jl. Pulo Gadung No. 6, Jakarta 13920, Indonesia

Tel: 62-21-461-0421   Fax: 62-21-461-0474

SENSIENT TECHNOLOGIES CORPORATION

777 E. Wisconsin Ave., Milwaukee, WI, 53202

Tel: (414) 271-6755   Fax: (414) 347-4783   www.sensient.com

Mfr. flavor applications for the beverage, bakery, confection, dairy, snack and savory markets.

Sensient Technologies, PT .Suryana Jalan Majapahit 34 / 8, Jakarta 10160, Indonesia

THE SERVICEMASTER COMPANY

2300 Warrenville Road, Downers Grove, IL, 60515-1700

Tel: (630) 271-1300   Fax: (630) 271-2710   www.svm.com

Provides residential consumer services, including lawn care and landscape maintenance, termite and pest control, plumbing, heating and air conditioning maintenance and repair.

Terminix, Jarkarta, Indonesia

SILICON GRAPHICS INC.

1600 Amphitheatre Pkwy., Mountain View, CA, 94043-1351

Tel: (650) 960-1980   Fax: (650) 932-0661   www.sgi.com

Design/mfr. special-effects computer graphic systems and software.

Silicon Graphics Pte. Ltd. Indonesia, Level 27 Wisma Danamon Aetna Life Tower II, Jl. Jend Sudirman Kav 45-46, Jakarta 12930, Indonesia

Tel: 62-21-251-2828   Fax: 62-21-251-0868   Contact: Rene Widjaja, Mgr.

SONOCO PRODUCTS COMPANY

North Second Street, PO Box 160, Hartsville, SC, 29550

Tel: (843) 383-7000   Fax: (843) 383-7008   www.sonoco.com

Mfr. packaging for consumer and industrial market and recycled paperboard.

PT Tritunggal Sejahtera (Factory), Jl. Raya Cicadas Km 9 Gunung Putri Bogor, PO Box 18 Citeureup, Bogor Jawa Barat West Java, Indonesia

Tel: 62-21-867-0417   Fax: 62-21-867-2927

PT Tritunggal Sejahtera (Office), Jakarta Stock Exchange Bldg., Ste. 1709, Jl. Jend. Sudirman Kav 52-53, Jakarta 12190, Indonesia

Tel: 62-21-515-0830   Fax: 62-21-515-0831

SOTHEBY'S HOLDINGS, INC.

1334 York Avenue, New York, NY, 10021

Tel: (212) 606-7000   Fax: (212) 606-7027   www.sothebys.com

Auction house specializing in fine art and jewelry.

Sotheby's Holdings, Inc., 31 Gatot Subroto, Kav. 21, Jakarta 12930, Indonesia

SPERRY-SUN DRILLING SERVICES

PO Box 60070, Houston, TX, 77205

Tel: (281) 871-5100   Fax: (281) 871-5742   www.sperry-sun.com

Provides drilling services to the oil and gas drilling industry.

P.T. Indokor Sperry-Sun, Jl. Letjen S. Parman, RT 04, RW 01, No. 41, Balikpapan Tengah, East Kalimantan, Indonesia

Tel: 62-21-780-1100

SPS TECHNOLOGIES INC.

165 Township Line Rd., Two Pitcairn Place, Jenkintown, PA, 19046

Tel: (215) 517-2000   Fax: (215) 517-2032   www.spstech.com

Mfr. aerospace and industry fasteners, tightening systems, magnetic materials, super alloys.

Triple Mandiri Sentosa SPS, 14A Jalan Rawa Kemiri, Kebayoran Lama, Jakarta 12220, Indonesia

Contact: Grace Santosa

SPSS INC.

233 S. Wacker Dr., 11th Fl., Chicago, IL, 60606

Tel: (312) 651-6000   Fax: (312) 329-3668   www.spss.com

Mfr. statistical software.

SPSS, Jl. Alam Asri V/7, Pondok Indah Jakarta 12310, Indonesia

THE ST. PAUL COMPANIES, INC.

385 Washington Street, St. Paul, MN, 55102

Tel: (651) 310-7911   Fax: (651) 310-8294   www.stpaul.com

Provides investment, insurance and reinsurance services.

PT Asuransi Central Asia, Komplek Duta Merlin Blok A No. 4-5, Jl. Gajah Mada No. 3-5, Jakarta 10130, Indonesia

STARWOOD HOTELS & RESORTS WORLDWIDE

777 Westchester Avenue, White Plains, NY, 10604

Tel: (914) 640-8100   Fax: (914) 640-8316   www.starwoodhotels.com

Hotel operations including Sheraton, Westin, St. Regis, Four Points and Caesars.

Sheraton Bandara, Bandara Soekarno-Hatta Jakarta, 19110, PO Box 1198, Jakarta 19100, Indonesia

Tel: 62-21-559-7777   Fax: 62-21-559-7700

STIEFEL LABORATORIES INC.

255 Alhambra Circle, Ste. 1000, Coral Gables, FL, 33134

Tel: (305) 443-3807   Fax: (305) 443-3467   www.stiefel.com

Mfr. pharmaceuticals, dermatological specialties.

Stiefel Laboratories Limited, Graha Darya-Varia, 3/F, Jl. Melawai Raya No. 93, Kebayoran Baru, Jakarta 12130, Indonesia

SUNBEAM CORPORATION

2381 Executive Center Dr., Boca Raton, FL, 33431

Tel: (561) 912-4100   Fax: (561) 912-4567   www.sunbeam.com

Mfr. household and personal grooming appliances; Sunbeam, Mr. Coffee, First Alert, Mixmaster and Oster.

Pt. Pelita Unggul Pratama, Permata Building, 3/F, Jalan Ciputat Raya No. 30, Tanah Kusir, Jakarta Selatan 12240, Indonesia

SYBASE, INC.

5000 Hacienda Dr., Dublin, CA, 94568

Tel: (925) 236-5000   Fax: (925) 236-4321   www.sybase.com

Design/mfg/distribution of database management systems, software development tools, connectivity products, consulting and technical support services..

PT Sybase Informatindo Indonesia, Menara 2, Plaza Bapindo, 23rd Fl., Jl. Jend. Sudirman Kav. 54-55, Jakarta 12190, Indonesia

Tel: 62-21-526-6520   Fax: 62-21-526-6523

THE TCW GROUP

865 S. Figueroa St., Ste. 1800, Los Angeles, CA, 90017

Tel: (213) 244-0000   Fax: (213) 244-0000   www.tcwgroup.com

Engaged in managing pension and profit sharing funds, retirement/health and welfare funds, insurance company funds, endowments and foundations.

TCW Group (JV), Jakarta, Indonesia

TEKTRONIX INC.

14200 SW Karl Braun Dr., PO Box 500, Beaverton, OR, 97077

Tel: (503) 627-7111   Fax: (503) 627-2406   www.tek.com

Mfr. test and measure, visual systems/color printing and communications/video and networking products.

P.T. Cosmotec Sarana Elektronika Indonesia, Jl. Jembatan Dua, Komplek Ruko Harmoni Mas, Blok A, 15, Jakarta Utara 14450, Indonesia

Tel: 62-21-667-0011   Fax: 62-21-667-0020

TETRA TECH, INC.

670 N. Rosemead Blvd., Pasadena, CA, 91107

Tel: (626) 351-4664   Fax: (626) 351-1188   www.tetratech.com

Environmental engineering and consulting services.

Tetra Tech Inc., First City Complex Blok 2 Nos. 30-32, PO Box 160 Batam Centre, Batam 29400, Indonesia

Tel: 62-778-462-049   Fax: 62-778-462-127   Contact: Shannon B. Lumbanotobing

TEXAS INSTRUMENTS INC.

12500 TI Blvd., Dallas, TX, 75266

Tel: (972) 995-3773   Fax: (972) 995-4360   www.ti.com

Mfr. semiconductor devices, electronic electro-mechanical systems, instruments and controls.

Texas Instruments Indonesia, Jakarta, Indonesia

Tel: 801-10-800-800-1450

THERMADYNE HOLDINGS CORPORATION

101 South Hanley Road, Suite 300, St. Louis, MO, 63105

Tel: (314) 746-2197   Fax: (314) 746-2349   www.thermadyne.com

Mfr. welding, cutting, and safety products.

P T Comweld Indonesia, Kawasan Industri Jababeka, JI Jababeka VI Blok P No. 3, Cikarang Bekasi 17550, Indonesia

Tel: 62-21-425-6243

TIDEWATER INC.

601 Poydras Street, Ste.1900, New Orleans, LA, 70130

Tel: (504) 568-1010   Fax: (504) 566-4582   www.tdw.com

Marine service and equipment to companies engaged in exploration, development and production of oil, gas and minerals.

Tidewater Marine International, Inc., Jalan Tegal Parang Utara 32, Tegal Parang Jakarta Selatan 12790, Indonesia

Tel: 62-21-7993637   Fax: 62-21-7982330

THE TRANE COMPANY

3600 Pammel Creek Road, La Crosse, WI, 54601

Tel: (608) 787-2000   Fax: (608) 787-4990   www.trane.com

Mfr. distribution and service of A/C systems and equipment.

PT Tatasol Pratama, Jl. Abdul Muis 24-26, Jakarta Pusat 10160, Indonesia

PT Tatasol USI Pratama, 42-44 Jl. Kayoon, Surabaya 60270, Indonesia

TRANSOCEAN INC.

4 Greenway Plaza, Houston, TX, 77046

Tel: (713) 232-7500   Fax: (713) 232-7027   www.deepwater.com

Engaged in oil and gas offshore drilling.

Transocean Inc., Sentra Mulia Bldg., Suite 1801, J I H.R. Rasuna Said Kav. X-6 No. 8, Kuningan-Jakarta 12940 12940, Indonesia

UNION CARBIDE CORPORATION

39 Old Ridgebury Road, Danbury, CT, 06817

Tel: (203) 794-2000   Fax: (203) 794-6269   www.unioncarbide.com

Mfr. industrial chemicals, plastics and resins.

PT Union Carbide Indonesia, Wisma Metropolitan II, Jl. Jend. Sudiman, PO Box 2677, Jakarta 12920, Indonesia

UNITED PARCEL SERVICE, INC.

55 Glenlake Parkway, NE, Atlanta, GA, 30328

Tel: (404) 828-6000   Fax: (404) 828-6593   www.ups.com

International package-delivery service.

UPS - Pt. Cardig Citra Primajasa, Halim Perdanakusuma Airport, Jakarta 13610, Indonesia

Tel: 62-21-800-7066   Fax: 62-21-809-1934

UNOCAL CORPORATION

2141 Rosecrans Ave., Ste. 4000, El Segundo, CA, 90245

Tel: (310) 726-7600   Fax: (310) 726-7817   www.unocal.com

Engaged in oil and gas exploration and production.

Unocal Makassar, Ltd., Jakarta, Indonesia

UOP LLC

25 East Algonquin Road, Des Plaines, IL, 60017

Tel: (847) 391-2000   Fax: (847) 391-2253   www.uop.com

Engaged in developing and commercializing technology for license to the oil refining, petrochemical and gas processing industries.

UOP Processes International, Inc., Wisma Rajawali, 15/F, Jalan Jendral Sudirman, Kav 34, Jakarta 10220, Indonesia

Tel: 62-21-573-6368   Fax: 62-21-573-8532

URS CORPORATION

100 California Street, Ste. 500, San Francisco, CA, 94111

Tel: (415) 774-2700   Fax: (415) 398-1905   www.urscorp.com

Engineering, environmental and construction management services.

PT Dames & Moore Indonesia, Jl. Kusuma Atmaja No. 75, Jakarta 10310, Indonesia

VALSPAR CORPORATION

1101 South Third Street, Minneapolis, MN, 55415-1259

Tel: (612) 332-7371   Fax: (612) 375-7723   www.valspar.com

Mfr. paints and coatings.

PT Valspar Indonesia, Jl. H. Baping 108, Ciracas, Jakarta 13740, Indonesia

VARCO INTERNATIONAL INC.

2000 W. Sam Houston Pkwy S., Ste. 1700, Houston, TX, 77042

Tel: (281) 953-2200   Fax: (281) 953-2400   www.varco.com

Mfr. oilfield and industry weight and measure systems.

Varco BJ, c/o P. T. Inti Jatam Pura, JL. Warung Buncit Raya No. 75, Jakarta 12790, Indonesia

VERIZON COMMUNICATIONS INC.

1095 Ave. of the Americas, New York, NY, 10036

Tel: (212) 395-2121   Fax: (212) 395-1285   www.verizon.com

Telecommunications.

Excelcomindo, Jakarta, Indonesia

WAL-MART STORES INC.

702 SW 8th Street, Bentonville, AR, 72716-8611

Tel: (501) 273-4000   Fax: (501) 273-1917   www.wal-mart.com

Retailer.

Wal-Mart Stores Inc., Jakarta, Indonesia

WASTE MANAGEMENT, INC.

1001 Fannin Street, Ste. 4000, Houston, TX, 77002

Tel: (713) 512-6200   Fax: (713) 512-6299   www.wastemanagement.com

Environmental services and disposal company; collection, processing, transfer and disposal facilities.

PT Waste Management Indonesia, Bimantara Building, 17th Floor, Jl. Kebon Sirih, Kav. 17-19, Jakarta 10304, Indonesia

PT Waste management Indonesia, Jl Raya Narogong Desa Nambo, PO Box 18 Cileungsi, Bogor 16820, Indonesia

Contact: Nizar Mansur, Mgr.

WATSON WYATT & COMPANY HOLDINGS

1717 H Street NW, Washington, DC, 20006-3807

Tel: (202) 715-7000   Fax: (202) 715-7700   www.watsonwyatt.com

Creates compensation and benefits programs for major corporations.

Watson Wyatt & Co., Menara Dea Building 2nd Floor, Jl. Mega Kuningan Barat Kav., E.4.3 No. 1 Kawasan Mega Kuningan, Jakarta Selatan 12950, Indonesia

Tel: 62-21-576-2635   Fax: 62-21-520-7467   Contact: Lisbeth Simbolon

WEATHERFORD INTERNATIONAL, INC.

515 Post Oak Blvd. Ste. 600, Houston, TX, 77027-3415

Tel: (713) 287-8400   Fax: (713) 963-9785   www.weatherford.com

Oilfield services, products and equipment; mfr. marine cranes for oil and gas industry.

Weatherford Oil Tool Pte. Ltd., Cilandak Commercial Estate, Unit 105, Raya, Cilandak KKO, Jakarta 12560, Indonesia

Tel: 62-21-780-7801   Fax: 62-21-780-7796

WENDY'S INTERNATIONAL, INC.

4288 West Dublin Granville Roads, Dublin, OH, 43017-0256

Tel: (614) 764-3100   Fax: (614) 764-3459   www.wendysintl.com

Fast food restaurant chain.

Wendy's International, Jakarta, Indonesia

WHITE & CASE LLP

1155 Ave. of the Americas, New York, NY, 10036-2767

Tel: (212) 819-8200   Fax: (212) 354-8113   www.whitecase.com

Engaged in international law.

PT WCI Konsultan, Wisma Danamon Aetna Life 27th Fl., Jl. Jend. Sudirman Kav. 45-46, Jakarta 12930, Indonesia
Tel: 62-21-577-1527   Fax: 62-21-577-1535   Contact: Wendell C. Maddrey

WILBUR-ELLIS COMPANY

345 California St., 27th Fl., San Francisco, CA, 94120

Tel: (415) 772-4000   Fax: (415) 772-4011   www.wilburellis.com

Marketing, distribution, formulation of agricultural products and industrial specialty chemicals and raw materials.

Connell Bros. Co. Ltd., Lippo Centre 504, Jl. Gatot Subroto Kav. 35-36, Jakarta 12950, Indonesia
Tel: 62-21-522-4460   Fax: 62-21-520-1138   Contact: Yosef Herwanto

WYETH PHARMACEUTICALS

555 E. Lancaster Ave., Wayne, PA, 19087-5109

Tel: (610) 971-5400   Fax: (610) 995-4668   www.wyeth.com

Mfr. antibiotics and pharmaceutical products.

Wyeth Pharmaceuticals, PT Wirayuda Estithama, Graha Paramita Bldg. 3/F, J1 Denpasar D-2, Kuningan, Jakarta 12940, Indonesia
Tel: 62-21-526-5688

XEROX CORPORATION

800 Long Ridge Road, PO Box 1600, Stamford, CT, 06904

Tel: (203) 968-3000   Fax: (203) 968-4312   www.xerox.com

Mfr. document processing equipment, systems and supplies.

PT Astra Graphia, Jl Kramat Raya 43, Jakarta 10450, Indonesia
Tel: 62-21-3909190   Fax: 62-21-3909181

YORK INTERNATIONAL CORPORATION

631 South Richland Ave., York, PA, 17403

Tel: (717) 771-7890   Fax: (717) 771-6212   www.york.com

Mfr. heating, ventilating, air conditioning and refrigeration equipment.

York Air Conditioning & Refrigeration, Inc., Jalan Kyai Caringin No. 2B, Jakarta, Indonesia
Tel: 62-21-385-9227

YOUNG & RUBICAM INC.

285 Madison Ave., New York, NY, 10017

Tel: (212) 210-3000   Fax: (212) 370-3796   www.yr.com

Advertising, public relations, direct marketing and sales promotion, corporate and product ID management.

PT Dentsu Young & Rubicam Pte. Ltd., Jakarta, Indonesia

Iran

DHL WORLDWIDE EXPRESS

50 California Avenue, San Francisco, CA, 94111

Tel: (415) 677-6100   Fax: (415) 824-9700   www.dhl.com

Worldwide air express carrier.

DHL Worldwide Express, No. 353 Dr. Beheshti Ave., Tehran 15166, Iran

Tel: 98-21-871-7985

GENERAL ELECTRIC COMPANY

3135 Easton Turnpike, Fairfield, CT, 06431

Tel: (203) 373-2211   Fax: (203) 373-3131   www.ge.com

Diversified manufacturing, technology and services.

GE Appliances, 1137 Vali Asr Ave., 6th Floor, Tehran 15119, Iran

Tel: 98-21-801-6329

GE International, 1137 Vali Asr Ave., 6th Floor, Tehran 15119, Iran

Tel: 98-21-801-6708   Fax: 98-21-801-6965

Nuovo Pignone, Mirzaye Shirazi Ave. 225, Tehran, Iran

Tel: 98-21-872-5084   Fax: 98-21-872-5083

KPMG CONSULTING INC.

1676 International Dr., McLean, VA, 22102

Tel: (703) 747-3000   Fax: (703) 747-8500   www.kpmg.com

Accounting and audit, tax and management consulting services.

Bayat Rayan, 227 Ave. Iranshahr, Tehran 15847, Iran

Tel: 98-21-882-6684   Fax: 98-21-837927   Contact: M. Bayat, Sr. Ptnr.

PANAMETRICS

221 Crescent Street, Waltham, MA, 02154

Tel: (781) 899-2719   Fax: (781) 899-1552   www.panametrics.com

Engaged in manufacture and distribution of ultrasonic testing equipment and process control instrumentation.

Kavosh Azmoon Company, 141 Kheradmand Shomali, 3rd Fl., Tehran, Iran

Tel: 98-21-835954   Fax: 98-21-837535

SCHENKER USA INC.

150 Albany Ave., Freeport, NY, 11520

Tel: (516) 403-5416   Fax: (516) 377-3092   www.schenkerusa.com

Freight forwarders.

Delta Bar Co. Ltd., PO Box 15745-181, Tehran 15745, Iran

Tel: 98-21-882-0118   Fax: 98-21-882-0183

XEROX CORPORATION

800 Long Ridge Road, PO Box 1600, Stamford, CT, 06904

Tel: (203) 968-3000   Fax: (203) 968-4312   www.xerox.com

Mfr. document processing equipment, systems and supplies.

Balli Group, 19 Kalantari St., Qarani Ave., PO Box 15815-3445, Tehran, Iran

Ireland

3COM CORPORATION

5400 Bayfront Plaza, Santa Clara, CA, 95052-8145

Tel: (408) 326-5000   Fax: (408) 326-5001   www.3com.com

Engaged in the development and manufacture of computer networking products and systems.

3Com Ireland, Ballycoolin Business Park, Blanchardstown, Dublin 15, Ireland

Tel: 353-1-823-5000   Fax: 353-1-823-5001

3M (MINNESOTA MINING & MFG.)

3M Center, St. Paul, MN, 55144-1000

Tel: (651) 733-1110   Fax: (651) 733-9973   www.mmm.com

Mfr. diversified products for industry, consumer, health care, imaging, communications, transport, safety, etc.

3M Ireland Ltd., 3M House, Adelphi Centre, Upper Georges St., Dun Laoghaire Dublin, Ireland

Tel: 353-280-3555   Fax: 353-280-3555   Contact: Wayne W. Brown

ABBOTT LABORATORIES

100 Abbott Park Rd., Abbott Park, IL, 60064

Tel: (847) 937-6100   Fax: (847) 937-1511   www.abbott.com

Development, manufacture and sale of diversified health care products and services.

Abbott Laboratories Ltd., Finisklin Industrial Estate, Sligo, Ireland

Tel: 353-71-71708

ACCENTURE LTD.

1345 Avenue of the Americas, New York, NY, 10105

Tel: (917) 452-4400   Fax: (917) 527-9915   www.accenture.com

Provides management and technology consulting services.

Accenture, Andersen House, Harbourwater Place, Dublin 1, Ireland

Tel: 353-1-670-1000   Fax: 353-1-670-1010

ACCO WORLD CORPORATION

300 Tower Parkway, Lincolnshire, IL, 60069

Tel: (847) 541-9500   Fax: (847) 541-5750   www.accobrands.com

Provides services in the office and computer markets and manufactures paper fasteners, clips, metal fasteners, binders and staplers.

ACCO-Rexel Ireland, Clonshaugh Industrial Estate, Dublin 17, Ireland

ACT MANUFACTURING, INC.

2 Cabot Road, Hudson, MA, 01749

Tel: (978) 567-4000   Fax: (978) 568-1904   www.actmfg.com

Mfr. printed circuit boards.

ACT Manufacturing Ireland, Citywest Business Campus, Unit 2008, Naas Road, Dublin 24, Ireland

Tel: 353-1-403-5200   Fax: 353-1-403-5299

ACTERNA CORPORATION

20400 Observation Drive, Germantown, MD, 20876

Tel: (301) 353-1550   Fax: (301) 353-1536   www.acterna.com

Develop, manufacture and market communications test instruments, systems, software and services.

Ireland Butler Technologies, Unit 10, Northwest Centre, Northwest Business Park, Blanchardstown, Dublin 15, Ireland

ADVANCED MATERIALS GROUP, INC.

20211 S. Susana Road, Rancho Dominguez, CA, 90221

Tel: (310) 537-5444   Fax: (310) 537-4557   www.advmatl.com

Mfr. and fabricator of specialty foams, foils, films and pressure-sensitive adhesive components.

Advanced Materials Group Ireland, Toughers Industrial Park, Newhall, Nass, County Kildare, Ireland

Tel: 353-45-438-477

AIG AMERICAN INTERNATIONAL GROUP INC.

70 Pine Street, New York, NY, 10270

Tel: (212) 770-7000   Fax: (212) 509-9705   www.aig.com

Worldwide insurance and financial services.

AIG Europe Ltd., AIG House, Merrion Road, Dublin 4, Ireland

AIR PRODUCTS AND CHEMICALS, INC.

7201 Hamilton Boulevard, Allentown, PA, 18195-1501

Tel: (610) 481-4911   Fax: (610) 481-5900   www.airproducts.com

Mfr. industry gases and related equipment, specialty chemicals, environmental/energy systems.

Air Products Ireland Ltd., Unit 950, Western Industrial Estate 2, Killeen Rd., Naasroad, Dublin, Ireland

ALCOA INC.

Alcoa Center, 201 Isabella Street at 7th Street Bridge, Pittsburgh, PA, 15212-5858

Tel: (412) 553-4545   Fax: (412) 553-4498   www.alcoa.com

World's leading producer of aluminum and alumina; mining, refining, smelting, fabricating and recycling.

AFL Ireland Ltd., Dundalk, Ireland

ALCOA FUJIKURA LTD.

800 Crescent Centre Drive, Ste. 600, Franklin, TN, 37067

Tel: (615) 778-6000   Fax: (615) 778-5927   www.alcoa-fujikura.com

Mfr. optical ground wire, tube cable, fiber optic connectors and automotive wiring harnesses. (JV of Alcoa USA).

Alcoa Fujikura Ireland Ltd., Dundalk, Ireland

ALLERGAN INC.

2525 Dupont Drive, Irvine, CA, 92612

Tel: (714) 246-4500   Fax: (714) 246-6987   www.allergan.com

Mfr. therapeutic eye care products and skin care pharmaceuticals.

Allergan Ireland Ltd., Sweepstakes Centre, Ballsbridge, Dublin 4, Ireland

Tel: 353-1-614-2000   Fax: 353-1-614-2099

AMERICAN EXPRESS COMPANY

90 Hudson Street, Jersey City, NJ, 07302

Tel: (212) 640-2000   Fax: (212) 619-9802   www.americanexpress.com

Engaged in travel, travelers cheques, charge card and financial services.

American Express Foreign Exchange Service, c/o Dublin Tourism Centre, Suffolk Street, Dublin, Ireland

Tel: 353-1-605-7709

AMETEK POWER INSTRUMENTS, INC.

255 North Union Street, Rochester, NY, 14605

Tel: (716) 263-7700   Fax: (716) 262-4777   www.rochester.com

Mfr. transient recorders, microprocessor-based relays, calibrators, annunciators, and signal conditioners.

AMETEK Power Instruments, 27 Cragside, Sedgefield, Stockton-on-Tees, County Durham, Ireland

Contact: Norman Midgley

ANALOG DEVICES INC.

1 Technology Way, Norwood, MA, 02062

Tel: (781) 329-4700   Fax: (781) 326-8703   www.analog.com

Mfr. integrated circuits and related devices.

Analog Devices BV, Bay F-1, Raheen Industrial Estate, Limerick, Ireland

Fax: 353-61-302263   Contact: Helen Kearney

ANC RENTAL CORPORATION

200 S. Andrews Ave., Ft. Lauderdale, FL, 33301

Tel: (954) 320-4000   Fax: (954) 320-4077   www.ancrental.com

Engaged in car rental services, including National Car Rental and Alamo Rent A Car.

National Car Rental, Baggott St. Bridge, Dublin 4, Ireland

ANDERSEN

33 West Monroe Street, Chicago, IL, 60603

Tel: (312) 580-0033   Fax: (312) 507-6748   www.andersen.com

Accounting and audit, tax and management consulting services. **Firm under worldwide reorganization; new data unavailable for this edition.

Arthur Andersen & Co., Andersen House, Int'l Financial Service Centre, Dublin 1, Ireland

Tel: 353-1-670-1000

ANIXTER INTERNATIONAL INC..

4711 Golf Road, Skokie, IL, 60076

Tel: (847) 677-2600   Fax: (847) 677-8557   www.anixter.com

Distributor wiring systems/products for voice, video, data and power applications.

Anixter Ireland, Unit16, Westlink Ind. Estate, Kylemore Road, Dublin 10, Ireland

Tel: 353-1-6244-68

AON CORPORATION

200 East Randolph, Chicago, IL, 60601

Tel: (312) 381-1000   Fax: (312) 381-6032   www.aon.com

Insurance brokers worldwide; underwrites accident and health insurance, specialty and professional insurance; and provides risk management consultation.

AON Alexander, Haddington Court, Haddington Rd., Dublin 4, Ireland

Tel: 353-1-605-9400   Fax: 353-1-660-5831   Contact: Ken D. Reid

AON Consulting, 94, St. Stephens Green, Dublin 2, Ireland

Tel: 353-1-677-3100   Contact: Gerry Herbert

AON MacDonald Boland, 9 Lr. Cecil St., Limerick, Ireland

Tel: 353-61-417633   Fax: 353-61-310726   Contact: Ken D. Reid

APPLE COMPUTER, INC.

One Infinite Loop, Cupertino, CA, 95014

Tel: (408) 996-1010   Fax: (408) 974-2113   www.apple.com

Personal computers, peripherals and software.

Apple Computer Ltd., Holly Hill Ind. Estate, Holly Hill, Cork, Ireland

APPLIED MATERIALS, INC.

3050 Bowers Ave., Santa Clara, CA, 95054-3299

Tel: (408) 727-5555   Fax: (408) 727-9943   www.appliedmaterials.com

Supplies manufacturing systems and services to the semiconductor industry.

Applied Materials, Ireland, 14 Collinstown Industrial Park, Leixlip County Kildare IR2, Ireland

Tel: 353-1-606-6305   Fax: 353-1-606-8006

APW, INC.

N22 W23685 Ridgeview Parkway West, Waukesha, WI, 53188-1013

Tel: (262) 523-7600   Fax: (262) 523-7624   www.apw1.com

Mfr. hi-pressure tools, vibration control products, consumables, technical furniture and enclosures.

APW Custom Systems, Mahon Industrial Estate, Blackrock, Cork, Ireland

Tel: 353-21-4357201

AQUENT

711 Boylston Street, Boston, MA, 02116

Tel: (617) 535-5000   Fax: (617) 535-6001   www.aquent.com

Engaged in temporary, specialized employment.

AQUENT, Lower Fitzwilliam Street, Dublin 2, Ireland

ARROW ELECTRONICS INC.

25 Hub Drive, Melville, NY, 11747

Tel: (516) 391-1300   Fax: (516) 391-1640   www.arrow.com

Distributor of electronic components and computer products.

Arrow Dublin, 37A Barrow Road, Dublin Industrial Estate, Glasnevin Dublin 11, Ireland

Tel: 353-1-830-7522

AT&T CORPORATION

295 N. Maple Ave., Basking Ridge, NJ, 07920-1002

Tel: (908) 221-2000   Fax: (908) 221-2528   www.att.com

Engaged in long distance telecommunications.

AT&T Ireland, Corke Abbey, Bray, Dublin, Ireland

ATTACHMATE CORPORATION

3617 131st Avenue SE, Bellevue, WA, 98006-1332

Tel: (425) 644-4010   Fax: (425) 747-9924   www.attachmate.com

Mfr. connectivity software.

Attachmate Ireland, Bay 4 AD, Shannon Industrial Estate, Shannon County Clare, Ireland

Tel: 353-61-474-666   Fax: 353-61-472-733

AUTODESK INC.

111 McInnis Parkway, San Rafael, CA, 94903

Tel: (415) 507-5000   Fax: (415) 507-6112   www.autodesk.com

Develop/marketing/support computer-aided design, engineering, scientific and multimedia software products.

Autodesk Ireland ltd., East Point Business Park, Alfie Byrne Road, Clontarf IRL-Dublin 3, Ireland

Tel: 353-1-805-4400   Fax: 353-1-805-4401

AVERY DENNISON CORPORATION

150 N. Orange Grove Blvd., Pasadena, CA, 91103

Tel: (626) 304-2000   Fax: (626) 792-7312   www.averydennison.com

Mfr. pressure-sensitive adhesives and materials, office products, labels, tags, retail systems, Carter's Ink and specialty chemicals.

Fasson Ireland Ltd., Unit 5, Ballymount Bus. Park, Dublin 12, Ireland

Tel: 353-1-456-9733   Fax: 353-1-456-9742

AVID TECHNOLOGY, INC.

1 Park West, Tewksbury, MA, 01876

Tel: (978) 640-6789   Fax: (978) 640-1366   www.avid.com

Mfr. animation design software and digital and audio systems.

Avid Technology BV, Carmanhall Road, Unit 38, Sandyford Industrial Estate, Dublin 18, Ireland

Tel: 353-1-207-8200   Fax: 353-1-295-0079

AVNET INC.

2211 South 47th Street, Phoenix, AZ, 85034

Tel: (480) 643-2000   Fax: (480) 643-4670   www.avnet.com

Distributor electronic components, computers and peripherals.

Avnet EMG, Unit 7, Swords Business Park, Swords County, Dublin, Ireland

Tel: 353-1-890-1000   Fax: 353-1-890-1010

AVOCENT CORPORATION

4991 Corporate Drive, Huntsville, AL, 35805

Tel: (256) 430-4000   Fax: (250) 430-4030   www.avocent.com

Mfr. computer hardware.

Avocent European Headquarters, Avocent House, Shannon Free Zone, Shannon, County Clare, Ireland

AVON PRODUCTS, INC.
1345 Avenue of the Americas, New York, NY, 10105-0196

Tel: (212) 282-5000   Fax: (212) 282-6049   www.avon.com

Mfr. direct seller of cosmetics and beauty-related items.

Arlington Ltd., Cooltedexry, Port Arlington, County Laois, Ireland

B/E AEROSPACE
1400 Corporate Center Way, Wellington, FL, 33414

Tel: (561) 791-5000   Fax: (561) 791-7900   www.bek.com

Mfr. commercial aircraft interiors.

B/E Aerospace, 2 Moor Road, County Down, Kilkeel, Ireland

BALDWIN TECHNOLOGY COMPANY, INC.
12 Commerce Drive, Shelton, CT, 06484

Tel: (203) 402-1000   Fax: (203) 402-5500   www.baldwintech.com

Mfr./services material handling, accessories, control and prepress equipment for print industry.

Graphics Financing Ireland Ltd.(Baldwin Europe Consolidated), Altoste, Ireland

BANK OF AMERICA CORPORATION
Bank of America Corporate Center, Charlotte, NC, 28255

Tel: (415) 622-3530   Fax: (704) 386-6699   www.bankofamerica.com

Financial services.

Bank of America NT & SA, Russell Ct., St. Stephen's Green, Dublin 2, Ireland
Tel: 353-1-407-2100   Fax: 353-1-407-2199   Contact: Adrian E. Wrafter, VP

THE BANK OF NEW YORK
One Wall Street, New York, NY, 10286

Tel: (212) 495-1784   Fax: (212) 495-2546   www.bankofny.com

Banking services.

AIB/BNY Fund Management (Ireland) Ltd., AIB International Centre, Dublin 1, Ireland
Tel: 353-1-670-1158   Fax: 353-1-670-1168

BANTA CORPORATION
225 Main St., Menasha, WI, 54952-8003

Tel: (920) 751-7777   Fax: (920) 751-7790   www.banta.com

Provides printing, electronic media and packaging services.

Banta Global Turnkey Group, Hollyhill Industrial Estate, Hollyhill Cork, Ireland
Tel: 353-21-397515

Banta Global Turnkey Group, Woodford Business Park, Santry, Dublin 17, Ireland
Tel: 353-1-816-3400

Banta Global Turnkey Group, Raheen Industrial Estate, Raheen Limerick, Ireland
Tel: 353-61-303888

C. R. BARD, INC.
730 Central Ave., Murray Hill, NJ, 07974

Tel: (908) 277-8000   Fax: (908) 277-8078   www.crbard.com

Mfr. health care products.

C.R. Bard Ireland Ltd., Parkmore Industrial Estate, Galway, Ireland

BATES WORLDWIDE INC.
498 Seventh Avenue, New York, NY, 10018

Tel: (212) 297-7000   Fax: (212) 986-0270   www.batesww.com

Advertising, marketing, public relations and media consulting.

Bates Healthcom, 9 Upper Pembroke St., Dublin 1, Ireland
Tel: 353-1-676-0221   Fax: 353-1-676-5201   Contact: Joe Clancy, CEO

Bates Ireland, 9 Upper Pembroke St., Dublin 2, Ireland
Tel: 353-1-676-0221   Fax: 353-1-676-5201   Contact: Joe Clancy, CEO

BAX GLOBAL INC.

16808 Armstrong Ave., PO Box 19571, Irvine, CA, 92623

Tel: (949) 752-4000   Fax: (949) 260-3182   www.baxworld.com

Air freight forwarder.

BAX Global, Unit 6-7, Franksfield Rd. Industrial Estate, Franksfield Rd., Cork, Ireland

Tel: 353-21-319222   Fax: 353-21-319233

BAX Global, Smithstown, Shannon Country, Clare, Ireland

Tel: 353-61-363200

BAX Global, No. 29 The Mall, Waterford, Ireland

Tel: 353-51-858238

BAX Global, Unit 16 Airways Industrial Estate, Dublin 17, Ireland

Tel: 353-1-862-1044   Fax: 353-1-862-0134

BAXTER INTERNATIONAL INC.

One Baxter Parkway, Deerfield, IL, 60015

Tel: (847) 948-2000   Fax: (847) 948-3948   www.baxter.com

Mfr. products and provide services in the field of the administration of medication and bioscience.

Baxter Healthcare Ltd., Unit 7, Deansgrange Ind. Estate, Blackrock, Co. Dublin, Ireland

BCOM 3 GROUP

35 W. Wacker Dr., Chicago, IL, 60601

Tel: (312) 220-1000   Fax: (312) 220-3299   www.bcom3group.com

Advertising agency and marketing services. (JV with Dentsu)

QMP D'Arcy, 16, Sir John Rogerson's Quay, Dublin 2, Ireland

Contact: Jeremy Crisp

BDO SEIDMAN, LLP   BELGIUM

130 East Randolph Street, Chicago, IL, 60601

Tel: (312) 856-9100   Fax: (312) 856-1379   www.bdo.com

International accounting and financial consulting firm.

BDO Simpson Xavier, Simpson Xavier Court, Merchants Quay, Dublin 8, Ireland

Tel: 353-1-617-0100   Fax: 353-1-679-0111   Contact: Liam Dowdall

THE BEAR STEARNS & COMPANIES., INC.

245 Park Ave., New York, NY, 10167

Tel: (212) 272-2000   Fax: (212) 272-3092   www.bearstearns.com

Investment banking, securities broker/dealer and investment advisory services.

Bear Stearns Bank plc, Blk 8 Harcourt Center, Fl. 3, Charlotte Way, Dublin 2, Ireland

Tel: 353-1-402-6200   Fax: 353-1-402-6222

BECKMAN COULTER, INC.

4300 N. Harbor Boulevard, Fullerton, CA, 92834

Tel: (714) 871-4848   Fax: (714) 773-8898   www.beckmancoulter.com

Develop/mfr./marketing automated systems and supplies for biological analysis.

Labplan (Bioresearch), Allenwood Enterprise Park, Naas, Kildare, Ireland

BENCHMARK ELECTRONICS, INC.

3000 Technology Drive, Angleton, TX, 77515

Tel: (979) 849-6550   Fax: (979) 848-5270   www.bench.com

Mfr. printed circuit boards.

Benchmark Electronics, Cork Business & Tech Park, Model Farm Road, Cork, Ireland

Tel: 353-214-801-800 Fax: 353-214-801-800   Contact: Malachy McElroy

Benchmark Electronics, Blanchardstown Business Park, Blanchardstown, Dublin 15, Ireland

BERLITZ CROSS-CULTURAL TRAINING INC.

400 Alexander Park, Princeton, NJ, 08540

Tel: (609) 514-9650   Fax: (609) 514-9689   www.berlitz.com

Consulting and management training services to bridge cultural gaps for international travelers as well as for business transferees and families.

Berlitz Language Centre, 3 West Pier Business Campus, Dun Laoghaire, County Dublin, Ireland

BEST WESTERN INTERNATIONAL

6201 North 24th Place, Phoenix, AZ, 85106

Tel: (602) 957-4200   Fax: (602) 957-5740   www.bestwestern.com

International hotel chain.

Howth Lodge Hotel, Dublin, Ireland

BIJUR LUBRICATING CORPORATION

50 Kocher Dr., Bennington, VT, 05201-1994

Tel: (802) 447-2174   Fax: (802) 447-1365   www.bijur.com

Design and manufacture of grease and oil pumps.

Bijur Ireland Ltd., Gort Road, Ennis, County Clare, Ireland

Tel: 353 65-68-21543   Fax: 353 65-68-20327   Contact: Martin Egan, Operations Mgr.   Emp: 80

BIOWHITTAKER INC.

8830 Biggs Ford Road, Walkersville, MD, 21793

Tel: (301) 898-7025   Fax: (301) 845-6099   www.biowhittaker.com

Mfr. cell culture products, endotoxin detection assays.

Irotec Laboratories Ltd., Little Island, County Cork, Ireland

Tel. 353-21-353-706

BISSELL INC.

2345 Walker Road, NW, Grand Rapids, MI, 49504

Tel: (616) 453-4451   Fax: (616) 453-1383   www.bissell.com

Mfr. home care products.

Bissell Ireland, Donroe Rd., County Louth, Drogheda, Ireland

Tel: 353-41-36491

BLACK & VEATCH LLP

8400 Ward Pkwy., PO Box 8405, Kansas City, MO, 64114

Tel: (816) 339-2000   Fax: (816) 339-2934   www.bv.com

Engaged in engineering, construction and consulting, specializing in infrastructure development in the fields of energy, water and information.

Paterson Candy Ltd., Fitzwilliam Business Centre, 26/27 Upper Pembroke St., Dublin 2, Ireland

Tel: 353-1-662-0448   Fax: 353-1-662-0365   Contact: John Devlin

BOSE CORPORATION

The Mountain, Framingham, MA, 01701-9168

Tel: (508) 879-7330   Fax: (508) 766-7543   www.bose.com

Mfr. quality audio equipment and speakers.

BOSE Ireland, Castleblayney Rd., Carrickmacross, County Monaghan, Ireland

BOSTON SCIENTIFIC CORPORATION (BSC)

One Scientific Place, Natick, MA, 01760-1537

Tel: (508) 650-8000   Fax: (508) 650-8923   www.bostonscientific.com

Developer, manufacturer and marketer of medical devices.

Boston Scientific Ireland Ltd., Ballybrit Business Park, Galway, Ireland

Tel: 353-91-756300   Fax: 353-91-757398

BOURNS INC.

1200 Columbia Avenue, Riverside, CA, 92507

Tel: (909) 781-5500   Fax: (909) 781-5006   www.bourns.com

Mfr. resistive components and networks, precision potentiometers, panel controls, switches, transducers and surge protectors..

Bourns Electronics (Ireland), Mahon Industrial Estate, Blackrock, Cork, Ireland

BOWNE & COMPANY, INC.

345 Hudson Street, New York, NY, 10014

Tel: (212) 924-5500   Fax: (212) 229-3420   www.bowne.com

Financial printing and foreign language translation, localization (software), internet design and maintenance and facilities management.

Bowne Global Solutions, 65/66 Lower Mount Street, Dublin 2, Ireland

Tel: 353-1-614-6300   Fax: 353-1-614-6333

BRIGHTPOINT, INC.

600 East 96th Street, Ste. 575, Indianapolis, IN, 46240

Tel: (317) 805-4100   Fax: (317) 805-4101   www.brightpoint.com

Provider of outsourced services in the global wireless telecommunications and data industry; distribution of wireless voice and data products.

Brightpoint Ireland Ltd., Unit 6, Oak Court, Western Business Park, Dublin 12, Ireland

Tel: 353-1-460-3300   Fax: 353-1-460-3330

BRINK'S INC.

Thorndal Circle, Darien, CT, 06820

Tel: (203) 662-7800   Fax: (203) 662-7968   www.brinks.com

Security transportation.

Brink's Allied Limited, Dublin, Ireland

BRISTOL-MYERS SQUIBB COMPANY

345 Park Ave., New York, NY, 10154-0037

Tel: (212) 546-4000   Fax: (212) 546-4020   www.bms.com

Pharmaceutical and food preparations, medical and surgical instruments.

ConvaTec Ireland (Eire), 2 St. John's Court, Santry, Eire, Dublin 9, Ireland

Irish Plant - Linson, Ltd., Swords, County Dublin, Ireland

BROWN BROTHERS HARRIMAN & COMPANY

140 Broadway, New York, NY, 10005

Tel: (212) 483-1818   Fax: (212) 493-8526   www.bbh.com

Leading provider of mergers and acquisition advisory services and private equity capital to private and closely held public companies.

Brown Brothers Harriman, 80 Harcourt Street, Dublin 2, Ireland

BROWN RUDNICK BERLACK ISRAELS

One Financial Ctr., 745 Atlantic Avenue, Boston, MA, 02111

Tel: (617) 856-8200   Fax: (617) 856-8201   www.brownrudnick.com

Engaged in international law.

Brown Rudnick Berlack Israels, The Sweepstakes, Ballsbridge, Dublin 4, Ireland

Tel: 353-1-664-1738

BROWN-FORMAN CORPORATION

PO Box 1080, 850 Dixie Hwy., Louisville, KY, 40201-1080

Tel: (502) 585-1100   Fax: (502) 774-7876   www.brown-forman.com

Mfr./distributor distilled spirits, wine, china, crystal, silverware and luggage.

Clintock Ltd., Fox & Geese, Robinhood Rd., Clondalkin Dublin 22, Ireland

BUCHANAN INGERSOLL PROFESSIONAL CORPORATION

301 Grant Street, Ste. 20, Pittsburgh, PA, 15219-1408

Tel: (412) 562-8800   Fax: (412) 562-1041   www.buchananingersoll.com

Engaged in international law.

Buchanan Ingersoll UK, 4 Custom House Plaza, level 1, Dublin 1, Ireland

BUCK CONSULTANTS INC.

One Penn Plaza, New York, NY, 10119

Tel: (212) 330-1000   Fax: (212) 695-4184   www.buckconsultants.com

Employee benefit, actuarial and compensation consulting services.

Buck Consultants (Ireland) Ltd., 12 Northumberland Avenue, Dun Laoghaire, Dublin, Ireland

Tel: 353-1-280-0257   Fax: 353-1-280-1893   Contact: Derek McNamee

BUCKEYE TECHNOLOGIES, INC.

1001 Tillman St., Memphis, TN, 38108-0407

Tel: (901) 320-8100   Fax: (901) 320-8131   www.bkitech.com

Mfr. specialty cellulose and absorbency products.

Buckeye Technologies UK, Cork, Ireland

BUDGET GROUP, INC.

125 Basin St., Ste. 210, Daytona Beach, FL, 32114

Tel: (904) 238-7035   Fax: (904) 238-7461   www.budgetrentacar.com

Car and truck rental system.

Budget Rent A Car, International Hotel, Kenmare St., Killarney, Ireland

Tel: 353-64-34341

Budget Rent A Car, Cork Airport, Cork, Ireland

Budget Rent A Car, Ferry Port, 151 Lower Drumcondra Rd., Dublin, Ireland

Tel: 353-1-837-9611

Budget Rent A Car, Galway Airport, Ireland

Tel: 353-91-566-376

LEO BURNETT, DIV. B-COM 3 GROUP

35 West Wacker Drive, Chicago, IL, 60601

Tel: (312) 220-5959   Fax: (312) 220-6533   www.leoburnett.com

Engaged in advertising, marketing, media buying and planning, and public relations.

Young Advertising, Dublin, Ireland

C&D TECHNOLOGIES

1400 Union Meeting Road, Blue Bell, PA, 19422

Tel: (215) 619-2700   Fax: (215) 619-7840   www.cdtechno.com

Mfr./produce electrical power storage and conversion products and industrial batteries.

C&D Technologies, Inc., Bay 132, County Clare, Shannon Free Zone, Ireland

Tel: 353-61-474-133 Fax: 353-61-474-141

CADENCE DESIGN SYSTEMS, INC.

2655 Seely Ave., Bldg. 5, San Jose, CA, 95134

Tel: (408) 943-1234   Fax: (408) 943-0513   www.cadence.com

Mfr. electronic design automation software.

Cadence Design Systems, Filenet House, Ground Floor, Block U, Eastpoint Business Park, Fairview, Dublin 3, Ireland

Tel: 353-1-805-4300   Fax: 353-1-805-4310

CAMBREX CORPORATION

1 Meadowlands Plaza, East Rutherford, NJ, 07063

Tel: (201) 804-3000   Fax: (201) 804-9852   www.cambrex.com

human health, animal health/agriculture and Mfr. biotechnology products and produce specialty chemicals.

Irotec Laboratories Limited, Little Island, Cork, Ireland

Irotec Laboratories Limited, Little Island, Cork, Ireland

CATERPILLAR INC.
100 NE Adams Street, Peoria, IL, 61629-6105
Tel: (309) 675-1000   Fax: (309) 675-1182   www.cat.com
Mfr. earth/material-handling and construction machinery and equipment and engines.

Caterpillar International Finance plc., Wicklow, Ireland
Servtech Ltd., Dublin, Ireland

CBS TELEVISION NETWORK
51 West 52nd Street, New York, NY, 10019
Tel: (212) 975-4321   Fax: (212) 975-9387   www.cbs.com
TV/radio broadcasting, mfr. electronic systems for industry/defense, financial and environmental services.

Thermo King Europe, Monivea Rd., Mervue, Galway, Ireland

CCITRIAD
804 Las Cimas Pkwy., Ste. 200, Austin, TX, 78746
Tel: (512) 328-2300   Fax: (512) 328-8209   www.cci-triad.com
Technology solutions for the automotive aftermarket and hardlines and lumber industries.

Tridex Systems Ireland Ltd., Templemichael Ballinalee Road, County Longford, Ireland
Tel: 353-43-41857   Fax: 353-43-41858

CDI CORPORATION
1717 Arch Street, 35th Fl., Philadelphia, PA, 19103
Tel: (215) 569-2200   Fax: (215) 569-1300   www.cdicorp.com
Engineering, technical and temporary personnel services.

Anders Elite, 63 Lower Mount Street, Dublin, Ireland

CH2M HILL INC.
6060 South Willow Drive, Greenwood Village, CO, 80111
Tel: (303) 771-0900   Fax: (303) 770-2616   www.ch2m.com
Consulting engineers, planners, economists and scientists.

CH2M Hill, High Street, Tallaght, Dublin 24, Ireland

CHEMFAB CORPORATION
701 Daniel Webster Hwy., PO Box 1137, Merrimack, NH, 03054
Tel: (603) 424-9000   Fax: (603) 424-9028   www.chemfab.com
Mfr. advanced polymer materials.

Chemfab Europe, Fergus Lodge, Clonroad Bridge Ennis, County Clare, Ireland
Tel: 353-65-20988   Fax: 353-65-20993

CHEVRON TEXACO CORPORATION
575 Market Street, San Francisco, CA, 94105-2856
Tel: (415) 894-7700   Fax: (415) 894-2248   www.chevrontexaco.com
Oil exploration, production and petroleum products.

ChevronTexaco, Texaco House, Ballsbridge, Dublin 4, Ireland
Contact: Dr. John Lynn

CHOICE HOTELS INTERNATIONAL, INC.
10750 Columbia Pike, Silver Springs, MD, 20902
Tel: (301) 592-5000   Fax: (301) 592-6227   www.choicehotels.com
Hotel franchises, including Comfort Inn, Econo Lodge, Roadway Inn and Quality.

Choice Hotels International, 32 South Terrace, Cork C. Cork, Ireland

THE CHUBB CORPORATION
15 Mountain View Road, Warren, NJ, 07061-1615
Tel: (908) 580-2000   Fax: (908) 580-3606   www.chubb.com
Holding company for property and casualty insurance and liability insurance for corporate executives.

Chubb Insurance Co. of Europe, SA, 50 Dawson St., Dublin 2, Ireland
Tel: 353-1-670-7070   Fax: 353-1-670-7271

CISCO SYSTEMS, INC.

170 West Tasman Drive, San Jose, CA, 95134-1706

Tel: (408) 526-4000   Fax: (408) 526-4100   www.cisco.com

Develop/mfr./market computer hardware and software networking systems.

Cisco Systems, Dunluce House, Eastpoint, Dublin 3, Ireland

Tel: 353-1-819-2700   Fax: 353-1-819-2701

Cisco Systems Ltd., Europa House, 4th Fl., Harcourt St., Dublin 2, Ireland

Tel: 353-1-475-4244   Fax: 353-1-475-4778

CITIGROUP, INC.

399 Park Avenue, New York, NY, 10022

Tel: (212) 559-1000   Fax: (212) 559-3646   www.citigroup.com

Provides insurance and financial services worldwide.

Citigroup, IFSC House, Custom House Quay, Dublin 1, Ireland

Contact: Aidan M. Brady, Mgr.

CITRIX SYSTEMS, INC.

6400 NW 6th Way, Fort Lauderdale, FL, 33309

Tel: (954) 267-3000   Fax: (954) 267-9319   www.citrix.com

Developer of computer software.

Citrix Systems International, Block A-1, 2nd Floor, East Point Business Park Fairview, Dublin 3, Ireland

CLEAR CHANNEL COMMUNICATIONS

200 East Basse Road, San Antonio, TX, 78209

Tel: (210) 822-2828   Fax: (210) 822-2299   www.clearchannel.com

Owns, manages, promotes and produces concerts and shows; programs and sells airtime for radio stations, owns and places outdoor advertising displays and provides agent services to athletes and broadcasters.

More Group, Beech House, Beech Hill Road, Donnybrook, Dublin 4, Ireland

Tel: 353-1-478-4500   Fax: 353-1-478-4582   Contact: Terry Buckley, Mgr.

CNA FINANCIAL CORPORATION

CNA Plaza, Chicago, IL, 60685

Tel: (312) 822-5000   Fax: (312) 822-6419   www.cna.com

Commercial property/casualty insurance policies.

Galway Insurance Company, Galway, Ireland

COLGATE-PALMOLIVE COMPANY

300 Park Ave., New York, NY, 10022

Tel: (212) 310-2000   Fax: (212) 310-2919   www.colgate.com

Mfr. pharmaceuticals, cosmetics, toiletries and detergents.

Colgate-Palmolive Ireland Ltd., Unit C, Airport Industrial Estate, Swords Rd., Santry Dublin 9, Ireland

COLLIERS INTERNATIONAL PROPERTY CONSULTANTS INC.

84 State Street, 3rd Fl., Boston, MA, 02109

Tel: (617) 722-0221   Fax: (617) 722-0224   www.colliers.com

Engaged in commercial real estate.

Colliers International, 51 Dawson Street, Dublin 2, Ireland

Tel: 353-1-671-5156

COM21, INC.

750 Tasman Drive, Milpitas, CA, 95035

Tel: (408) 953-9100   Fax: (408) 953-9299   www.com21.com

Mfr. cable modems and software.

COM21, Inc., 4400 Cork Airport Business Park, Kinsdale Road, Cork, Ireland

Tel: 353-21-7305-800

COMPUTER ASSOCIATES INTERNATIONAL INC.

One Computer Associates Plaza, Islandia, NY, 11788

Tel: (516) 342-5224   Fax: (516) 342-5329   www.cai.com

Integrated business software for enterprise computing and information management, application development, manufacturing, financial applications and professional services.

Computer Associates Plc, Europa House, 2nd Fl., Harcourt St., Dublin 2, Ireland

Tel: 353-1-478-0800

CONCURRENT COMPUTER CORPORATION

4375 River Green Pkwy., Duluth, GA, 30096

Tel: (678) 258-4000   Fax: (678) 258-4300   www.ccur.com

Mfr. computer systems and software.

Concurrent Computers (Ireland) Ltd., 30 Green Mount Office Park, Harolds Cross, Dublin 6, Ireland

CONOCO INC.

600 N. Dairy Ashford, Houston, TX, 77252

Tel: (281) 293-1000   Fax: (281) 293-1440   www.conoco.com

Oil, gas, coal, chemicals and minerals.

Conoco Ireland Ltd., Conoco House, Deansgrange, Blackrock, Dublin, Ireland

COOPER CAMERON CORPORATION

515 Post Oak Blvd., Ste.1200, Houston, TX, 77027

Tel: (713) 513-3300   Fax: (713) 513-3355   www.coopercameron.com

Mfr. oil and gas industry equipment.

Cooper Cameron Ireland, Aghafad, Longford, Ireland

Tel: 353-43-45301

COOPER INDUSTRIES INC.

6600 Travis Street, Ste. 5800, Houston, TX, 77002

Tel: (713) 209-8400   Fax: (713) 209-8995   www.cooperindustries.com

Mfr./distributor electrical products, tools, hardware and automotive products, fuses and accessories for electronic applications and circuit boards.

Cooper Automotive, Naas Kildare, Ireland

COOPERATIVE COMPUTING, INC.

804 Las Cimas Parkway, Ste. 200, Austin, TX, 78746

Tel: (512) 328-2300   Fax: (512) 326-6461   www.cci-triad.com

Mfr. information management software.

Ireland Triad Systems, Ltd., Ballinalee Road, Longford County 14001, Ireland

Tel: 353-43-41857

CRAWFORD & COMPANY

5620 Glenridge Drive NE, Atlanta, GA, 30342

Tel: (404) 256-0830   Fax: (404) 847-4025   www.crawfordandcompany.com

Provides international insurance services engaged in risk management and claims adjustment.

Crawford & Company, 112 Oliver Plunkett Street, Cork, Ireland

A.T. CROSS COMPANY

One Albion Road, Lincoln, RI, 02865

Tel: (401) 333-1200   Fax: (401) 334-2861   www.cross.com

Mfr. writing instruments, leads, erasers and ink refills.

A.T. Cross Ltd., One Cleaghmore, Ballinasloe, County Galway, Ireland

Tel: 353-905-31400

CROWN CORK & SEAL COMPANY, INC.

One Crown Way, Philadelphia, PA, 19154-4599

Tel: (215) 698-5100   Fax: (215) 698-5201   www.crowncork.com

Mfr. metal and plastic packaging, including steel and aluminum cans for food, beverage and household products.

The Irish Crown Cork Co. Ltd., Church Field Industrial Estate, Cork, Ireland

CROWN EQUIPMENT CORPORATION

40 South Washington Street, New Bremen, OH, 45869

Tel: (419) 629-2311   Fax: (419) 629-2900   www.crownlift.com

Mfr. and sales of forklift trucks and stackers.

Crown Equipment, Galway, Ireland

D&B (DUN & BRADSTREET CORPORATION))

1 Diamond Hill Road, Murray Hill, NJ, 07974

Tel: (908) 665-5000   Fax: (908) 665-5524   www.dnb.com

Provides corporate credit, marketing and accounts-receivable management services and publishes financial information.

D&B Ireland Ltd., Holbrook House, Holles St., Dublin 2, Ireland
Tel: 353-1-764-230

DANAHER CORPORATION

1250 24th St. NW, Ste. 800, Washington, DC, 20037

Tel: (202) 828-0850   Fax: (202) 828-0860   www.danaher.com

Mfr. hand tools and motion controls.

Danaher (Ireland) Ltd., Gort Rd., Ennis, County Clare, Ireland

DANZAS AEI, INC.

120 Tokeneke Road, PO Box 1231, Darien, CT, 06820

Tel: (203) 655-7900   Fax: (203) 655-5779   www.aeilogistics.com

International air freight forwarder.

Danzas AEI, Unit 6, New Cargo Building, Belfast International Airport, Belfast BT29 4GB, Ireland
Tel: 353-2894-4546-47

D'ARCY MASIUS BENTON & BOWLES INC. (DMB&B)

1675 Broadway, New York, NY, 10019

Tel: (212) 468-3622   Fax: (212) 468-2987   www.darcyww.com

Full service international advertising and communications group.

DMB&B Europe, Stephens House, 7/8 Upper Mount St., Dublin 2, Ireland

DDB WORLDWIDE COMMUNICATIONS GROUP

437 Madison Ave., New York, NY, 10022

Tel: (212) 415-2000   Fax: (212) 415-3417   www.ddbn.com

Advertising agency.

Peter Owens DDB Worldwide, Dublin, Ireland

DELL COMPUTER CORPORATION

One Dell Way, Round Rock, TX, 78682-2222

Tel: (512) 338-4400   Fax: (512) 728-3653   www.dell.com

Direct marketer and supplier of computer systems.

Dell Computer Corporation, Bogdall Rd., Bray County, Wickow, Ireland
Tel: 353-1-286-0500   Fax: 353-1-286-2020   Contact: Philip Van Houtte, Mng. Dir.
Dell Products Europe BV, Raheen Industrial Estate, Limerick, Ireland
Tel: 353-61-304091   Fax: 353-61-304090   Contact: Phil Hubble, Mng. Dir.

DELOITTE TOUCHE TOHMATSU INTERNATIONAL

1633 Broadway, New York, NY, 10019

Tel: (212) 492-4000   Fax: (212) 392-4154   www.deloitte.com

Accounting, audit, tax and management consulting services.

Deloitte & Touche, Deloitte & Touche House, Earlsfort Terrace, Dublin 2, Ireland
Deloitte & Touche, 25 Stephen St., Sligo, Ireland

DELTA AIR LINES INC.

Hartsfield International Airport, 1030 Delta Blvd., Atlanta, GA, 30320-6001

Tel: (404) 715-2600   Fax: (404) 715-5494   www.delta-air.com

Major worldwide airline; international air transport services.

Delta Air Lines Inc., Dublin, Ireland

DeMATTEIS ORGANIZATION

820 Elmont Road, Elmont, NY, 11003

Tel: (516) 285-5500   Fax: (516) 285-6950

Real estate development and construction services.

DeMatteis Ireland Ltd., 21 Fitzwilliam Place, Dublin 2, Ireland

Tel: 353-1-662-1188   Fax: 353-1-662-1191   Contact: Fergus J. Rainey, Mng. Dir.

DHL WORLDWIDE EXPRESS

50 California Avenue, San Francisco, CA, 94111

Tel: (415) 677-6100   Fax: (415) 824-9700   www.dhl.com

Worldwide air express carrier.

DHL Worldwide Express, Dublin Airport Col., Dublin, Ireland

Tel: 353-1-844-4111

DICTAPHONE CORPORATION

3191 Broadbridge Ave., Stratford, CT, 06497-2559

Tel: (203) 381-7000   Fax: (203) 381-7100   www.dictaphone.com

Mfr./sale dictation, telephone answering and multi-channel voice communications recording systems.

Dictaphone Company Ltd., Loughlinstown Drive, Dun Laoghaire, Dublin, Ireland

Tel: 353-1-282-5222

R.R. DONNELLEY & SONS COMPANY

77 West Wacker Drive, Chicago, IL, 60601-1696

Tel: (312) 326-8000   Fax: (312) 326-8543   www.rrdonnelley.com

Engaged in commercial printing and allied communication services.

Irish Printers (Holdings) Ltd., Clonshaugh Industrial Estate, Clonshaugh, Dublin 17, Ireland

DONNELLY CORPORATION

49 West Third Street, Holland, MI, 49423-2813

Tel: (616) 786-7000   Fax: (616) 786-6034   www.donnelly.com

Mfr. fabricated, molded and coated glass products for the automotive and electronics industries.

Donnelly Electronics Ireland, IDA Industrial Estate, Ballinalee Road, Longford, Ireland

Tel: 353-45-897101   Fax: 353-45-897157   Contact: David Watson, Mgr.

Donnelly Mirrors Limited/, County Kildare, Naas, Ireland

Tel: 353-725-5350   Contact: David Watson

DOUBLECLICK, INC.

450 West 33rd Street, New York, NY, 10001

Tel: (212) 683-0001   Fax: (212) 889-0062   www.doubleclick.net

Engaged in online advertising and e-mail marketing.

Doubleclick, Ltd., The Riverside Centre, 8-11 Sir John Rogersons Quay, Dublin 2, Ireland

DRAKE BEAM MORIN INC.

100 Park Avenue, 11th Fl., New York, NY, 10017

Tel: (212) 692-7700   Fax: (212) 297-0426   www.dbm.com

Human resource management consulting and training.

DBM Ireland, 3 Argos House, Greenmount Office Park, Dublin 6W, Ireland

Tel: 353-1-4533-591   Fax: 353-1-4533-640

DRIVER-HARRIS COMPANY

600 Essex St, Harrison, NJ, 07029

Tel: (973) 483-4802   Fax: (973) 483-4806   www.driver-harris.com

Mfr. non-ferrous alloys.

Irish Driver-Harris Co. Ltd., 5A Ballymount Trading Estate, Lower Ballymount Rd., Walkinstown, Dublin 12, Ireland

Tel: 353-1-450-6935   Fax: 353-1-450-6330   Contact: Jim Kinsella

E.I. DUPONT DE NEMOURS & COMPANY

1007 Market Street, Wilmington, DE, 19898

Tel: (302) 774-1000   Fax: (302) 774-7321   www.dupont.com

Mfr. and sales of diversified chemicals, plastics, specialty products and fibers.

Conoco Ireland Ltd., Dublin, Ireland

EASTMAN CHEMICAL COMPANY

100 North Eastman Road, Kingsport, TN, 37662-5075

Tel: (423) 229-2000   Fax: (423) 229-1351   www.eastman.com

Mfr. plastics, chemicals, fibers.

Lawter International, Luxembourg Sarl, Grannagh, Waterford, Ireland

Tel: 353-51-87-6616   Fax: 353-51-87-9399   Contact: Maurice Parker

EASTMAN KODAK COMPANY

343 State Street, Rochester, NY, 14650

Tel: (716) 724-4000   Fax: (716) 724-1089   www.kodak.com

Develop/mfr. photo and chemicals products, information management/video/copier systems, fibers/plastics for various industry.

Kodak Ireland Ltd., Kodak House, Pottery Rd., Dun Laoghaire County Dublin, Ireland

ECOLAB INC.

370 N. Wabasha Street, St. Paul, MN, 55102

Tel: (651) 293-2233   Fax: (651) 293-2379   www.ecolab.com

Develop/mfr. premium cleaning, sanitizing and maintenance products and services for the hospitality, institutional, and residential markets.

Ecolab Ltd., Dublin, Ireland

Tel: 353-1-286-8225

ECOLOGY AND ENVIRONMENT INC.

368 Pleasant View Drive, Lancaster, NY, 14086-1397

Tel: (716) 684-8060   Fax: (716) 684-0844   www.ecolen.com

Environmental, scientific and engineering consulting.

Ecology and Environment Ltd., Poulgorm, Maryboto 11, Douglas, Cork, Ireland

EDELMAN PUBLIC RELATIONS WORLDWIDE

200 East Randolph Drive, 62nd Fl., Chicago, IL, 60601

Tel: (312) 240-3000   Fax: (312) 240-0596   www.edelman.com

International independent public relations firm.

Edelman PR Worldwide, Huguenot House, 5th Fl., 35/38 Stephens Green, Dublin 2, Ireland

Tel: 353-1-678-9333   Fax: 353-1-661-4408   Contact: John Mahony, Mng. Dir.

J.D. EDWARDS & COMPANY

One Technology Way, Denver, CO, 80237

Tel: (303) 334-4000   Fax: (303) 334-4970   www.jdedwards.com

Computer software products.

Software Resources, 7 South Leinster Street, Dublin, Ireland

Tel: 353-1-678-9299   Fax: 353-1-678-9544

EFCO

1800 NE Broadway Ave., Des Moines, IA, 50316-0386

Tel: (515) 266-1141   Fax: (515) 266-7970   www.efco-usa.com

Mfr. systems for concrete construction.

EFCO, 2B Crofton Ct., Naas, Co. Kildare, Ireland

EG&G INC.

900 Clopper Road, Ste. 200, Gaithersburg, MD, 20878

Tel: (301) 840-3000   Fax: (301) 590-0502   www.egginc.com

Diversified R/D, mfr. and services.

EG&G Intl./Sealol Div., Shannon Free Airport, County Clare, Ireland

EG&G Ireland/Instruments Div., Blanchardstown Industrial Park, Blanchardstown, Dublin 15, Ireland

EGL INC. (EAGLE GLOBAL LOGISTICS)

15350 Vickery Drive, Houston, TX, 77032

Tel: (281) 618-3100   Fax: (281) 618-3223   www.eagleusa.com

Ocean/air freight forwarding, customs brokerage, packing and wholesale, logistics management and insurance.

EGL Eagle Global Logistics, 4/5 Citylink Park, Forge Hill, Cork, Ireland
Tel: 353-21-965-422   Fax: 353-21-314-140

EGL Eagle Global Logistics, Cargo Terminal, Dublin Airport, Dublin, Ireland
Tel: 353-1-844-5171   Fax: 353-1-842-7882

EGL Eagle Global Logistics, John F. Kennedy Rd., Naas Rd., Dublin 12, Ireland
Tel: 353-1-450-9444   Fax: 353-1-450-9468

EGL Eagle Global Logistics, Smithstown Ind. Est., County Clare, Shannon, Ireland
Tel: 353-61-362766   Fax: 353-61-362-732

ELECTRONIC DATA SYSTEMS, INC. (EDS)

5400 Legacy Dr., Plano, TX, 75024

Tel: (972) 604-6000   Fax: (972) 605-2643   www.eds.com

Engaged in systems integration, network and systems operations and management consulting.

EDS Ireland Ltd., Lower Grand Canal Street, Dublin 2, Ireland

EMERSON PROCESS MANAGEMENT

8301Cameron Road, Austin, TX, 78754

Tel: (512) 834-7689   Fax: (512) 832-3232   www.frco.com

Mfr. industrial process control equipment.

Emerson Process Management, 2200 Cork Airport Business Park, Kinsale Road, County Cork, Ireland

ENERGIZER HOLDINGS, INC.

533 Maryville University Dr., St. Louis, MO, 63141

Tel: (314) 985-2000   Fax: (214) 985-2205   www.energizer.com

Mfr. Eveready and Energizer brand batteries and lighting products.

Eveready Ltd., PO Box 373A, 17 Portobello Harbour, Dublin 8, Ireland
Tel: 353-1-478-3764   Fax: 353-1-475-2327

EPICOR SOFTWARE CORPORATION

195 Technology Drive, Irvine, CA, 92618

Tel: (949) 585-4000   Fax: (949) 450-4419   www.epicor.com

Mfr. software for e-business.

Epicor Ireland, Park House - North Circular Road, Dublin 7, Ireland
Tel: 353-1-868-1250   Fax: 353-1-868-1255

ERNST & YOUNG INTERNATIONAL

5 Times Square, New York, NY, 10036

Tel: (212) 773-3000   Fax: (212) 773-6350   www.eyi.com

Engaged in assurance and advisory business services, tax, law and corporate finance.

Ernst & Young International, Ernst & Young Bldg., Harcourt Centre, Harcourt St., Dublin 2, Ireland
Tel: 353-1-4750555 Fax: 353-1-4750555 Contact: Jim Ryan

Ernst & Young International, Bedford House, 16 Bedford Street, Belfast BT2 7DT, Ireland

ESCO TECHNOLOGIES INC.

8888 Ladue Road, Ste. 200, St. Louis, MO, 63124-2090

Tel: (314) 213-7200   Fax: (314) 213-7250   www.escostl.com

Electronic subassemblies and components.

Filtertek, B.V., Div. ESCO, Industrial Estate Newcastle West, County Limerick, Ireland
Tel: 353-69-62666   Fax: 353-69-62575

EXPEDITORS INTERNATIONAL OF WASHINGTON INC.

1015 Third Avenue, 12th Fl., Seattle, WA, 98104-1182

Tel: (206) 674-3400   Fax: (206) 682-9777   www.expd.com

Air/ocean freight forwarding, customs brokerage, international logistics solutions.

Expeditors Sea Sky Limited, Unit 9, Boeing Road, Airways Industrial Estate, Cloghran Dublin 17, Ireland

Tel: 353-1-816-1800

Expeditors Sea Sky Limited, Units 1-3, University Hall Industrial Park, Sarsfield Road, Doughcloyne County Cork, Ireland

Tel: 353-21-346111   Fax: 353-21-346112

E-Z-EM INC.

717 Main Street, Westbury, NY, 11590

Tel: (516) 333-8230   Fax: (516) 333-8278   www.ezem.com

Engaged in the design, manufacture and marketing of contrast media for gastrointestinal tract radiography.

AngioDynamics Ltd., Enniscorthy, County Wexford, Ireland

FileNET CORPORATION

3565 Harbor Boulevard, Costa Mesa, CA, 92626

Tel: (714) 966-3400   Fax: (714) 966-3490   www.filenet.com

Provides integrated document management (IDM) software and services for internet and client server-based imaging, workflow, cold and electronic document management solutions.

FileNET Co. Ltd., FileNet House, Blk. W, East Point Business Park, Faiview, Dublin 3, Ireland

Tel: 353-1-819-0100

FLINT INK CORPORATION

4600 Arrowhead Drive, Ann Arbor, MI, 48105

Tel: (734) 622-6000   Fax: (734) 622-6060   www.flintink.com

Manufacturer of printing inks and pigments.

Flint Ink Europe, Dunsinea Works, Ashtown, Dublin 15, Ireland

Tel: 353-1-838-7300   Fax: 353-1-838-7382   Contact: Jim Mahony, Pres. Europe

FLOWSERVE CORPORATION

222 W. Los Colinas Blvd., Irving, TX, 75039

Tel: (972) 443-6500   Fax: (972) 443-6858   www.flowserve.com

Mfr. chemicals equipment, pumps, valves, filters, fans and heat exchangers.

Durco Ireland, Shannon Town Ctr. #2, Shannon, County Clare, Ireland

FMC CORPORATION

1735 Market St., Philadelphia, PA, 19103

Tel: (215) 299-6000   Fax: (215) 299-6618   www.fmc.com

Mfr. specialty chemicals, including alginate, carrageenan and microcrystalline cellulose.

FMC Ireland, Wallingstown, Little Island, Cork, Ireland

Tel: 353-214-435-4133

FORD MOTOR COMPANY

One American Road, Dearborn, MI, 48126

Tel: (313) 322-3000   Fax: (313) 322-9600   www.ford.com

Mfr./sales motor vehicles.

Ford Motor Co., Marina, Cork, Ireland

FOREST LABORATORIES INC.

909 Third Ave., 23rd Fl., New York, NY, 10022

Tel: (212) 421-7850   Fax: (212) 750-9152   www.frx.com

Mfr. name-brand and generic pharmaceutical products.

Forest Laboratories Ireland Limited, Clonshaugh Industrial Estate, Dublin 17, Ireland

Tel: 353-1-8670477

Tosara Products Limited, Baldoyle Industrial Estate, Grange Road, Dublin 13, Ireland

FORMICA CORPORATION

10155 Reading Road, Cincinnati, OH, 45241-4805

Tel: (513) 786-3400   Fax: (513) 786-3082   www.formica.com

Mfr. decorative laminate, adhesives and solvents.

Formica Ireland, Block B, Arran Court, Arran Quay, Dublin 7, Ireland

FRANKLIN COVEY COMPANY

2200 W. Parkway Blvd., Salt Lake City, UT, 84119-2331

Tel: (801) 975-1776   Fax: (801) 977-1431   www.franklincovey.com

Provides productivity and time management products and seminars.

Franklin Covey Ireland, 5 Argyle Street, Donybrook, Dublin 4, Ireland

Tel: 353-1-668-1422   Fax: 353-1-668-1459

FRITZ COMPANIES, INC., DIV. UPS

706 Mission Street, Ste. 900, San Francisco, CA, 94103

Tel: (415) 904-8360   Fax: (415) 904-8661   www.fritz.com

Integrated transportation, sourcing, distribution and customs brokerage services.

Fritz Companies Inc., Cork, Ireland

GATEWAY INC.

4545 Towne Centre Ct., San Diego, CA, 92121

Tel: (858) 799-3401   Fax: (858) 779-3459   www.gateway.com

Computers manufacture, sales and services.

Gateway Ireland, Clonshaugh Industrial Estate, Dublin 17, Ireland

GE BETZ, DIV. GE SPECIALTY MATERIALS

4636 Somerton Road, PO Box 3002, Trevose, PA, 19053-6783

Tel: (215) 355-3300   Fax: (215) 953-5524   www.gebetz.com

Engaged in engineered chemical treatment of water and process systems in industrial, commercial and institutional facilities

GE Betz, Div. GE Specialty Materials, 34 Greenmount Office Park, Harolds Cross Bridge, Dublin 6W, Ireland

GE CAPITAL FLEET SERVICES

3 Capital Drive, Eden Prairie, MN, 55344

Tel: (612) 828-1000   Fax: (612) 828-2010   www.gefleet.com

Corporate vehicle leasing and services.

GE Capital, Woodchester House, Golden Lane, Dublin 8, Ireland

Tel: 353-1-478-0000

GE POLYMERSHAPES INC.

11515 Vanstory Drive, Huntersville, NC, 28078

Tel: (704) 205-3100   Fax: (704) 583-4715   www.gepolymershapes.com

Distributor of plastic sheet, rod, tube, and films.

GE Polymershapes, Stillorgan Park Industrial Estate, Unite 36 - Spruce Avenue, Blackrock Dublin, Ireland

GEN RE INTERMEDIARIES CORPORATION

PO Box 10216, Stamford, CT, 06904-2216

Tel: (203) 357-8883   Fax: (203) 328-6408   www.genre.com

Provides reinsurance services worldwide.

Cologne Reinsurance Company (Dublin) Ltd., 1 George's Dock, I.F.S.C., Dublin 1, Ireland

Tel: 353-1-670-2060 Fax: 353-1-670-2066   Contact: John B. Houldsworth, Mgr.

GENCORP INC.

Hwy. 50 and Aerojet Rd., Ranchero Cordova, CA, 95853

Tel: (916) 355-4000   Fax: (916) 355-2459   www.gencorp.com

Mfr. aerospace, defense and automotive products.

GenCorp Henniges, Crossmolina Road - Ballina, County Mayo, Ireland

GENERAL ELECTRIC CAPITAL CORPORATION

260 Long Ridge Road, Stamford, CT, 06927

Tel: (203) 357-4000   Fax: (203) 357-6489   www.gecapital.com

Financial, property, casualty insurance, computer sales and trailer leasing services.

GE Capital Global Consumer Finance, Woodchester House, Golden Lane, Dublin 8, Ireland

Tel: 353-1-478-0000   Fax: 353-1-475-2165

GENERAL ELECTRIC COMPANY

3135 Easton Turnpike, Fairfield, CT, 06431

Tel: (203) 373-2211   Fax: (203) 373-3131   www.ge.com

Diversified manufacturing, technology and services.

GE Insurance Holdings, 133-137 Shannon Industrial Estate, Shannon, County Clare, Ireland

Tel: 353-61-714-500

GE Lighting, Unit 280, Western Industrial Estate, Naas Road, Dublin 12, Ireland

Tel: 353-1-456-5591

GE Superabrasives, Clonshaugh Industrial Estate, 17, Ireland, Dublin

Tel: 353-1-803 7700

GENERAL MOTORS CORPORATION

300 Renaissance Center, Detroit, MI, 48285

Tel: (313) 556-5000   Fax: (313) 556-5108   www.gm.com

Mfr. full line vehicles, automotive electronics, commercial technologies, telecommunications, space, finance.

General Motors Distribution Ireland Ltd., Belgard Rd., Tallaght, Dublin, Ireland

Packard Electric Ireland Ltd., Airton Rd., Tallaght, Dublin, Ireland

GENUITY, INC.

225 Presidential Way, Woburn, MA, 01801

Tel: (781) 865-2000   Fax: (781) 865-3936   www.genuity.com

R/D computer, communications, acoustics technologies and internetworking services.

Genuity Ireland, Alexandra House, Ballsbridge, Dublin 4, Ireland

Tel: 353-1-664-1710

GENZYME CORPORATION

1 Kendall Square, Cambridge, MA, 02139-1562

Tel: (617) 252-7500   Fax: (617) 252-7600   www.genzyme.com

Mfr. healthcare products for enzyme deficient diseases.

Genzyme Ireland Ltd., IDA Industrial Park, Old Kilmeaden Road, Waterford, Ireland

GILEAD SCIENCES, INC.

333 Lakeside Dr, Foster City, CA, 94404

Tel: (650) 574-3000   Fax: (650) 578-9264   www.gilead.com

Engaged in healthcare research and development; biotech treatments for viruses.

NeXstar Pharmaceuticals, Ltd., Unit 13, Stillorgan Industrial Park, Blackrock County Dublin, Ireland

Tel: 353-1-295-2729   Fax: 353-1-295-2449

THE GILLETTE COMPANY

Prudential Tower Building, Boston, MA, 02199

Tel: (617) 421-7000   Fax: (617) 421-7123   www.gillette.com

Develop/mfr. personal care/use products: blades and razors, toiletries, cosmetics, stationery.

Jafra Cosmetics Intl. Ltd., Foxrock Dublin, Ireland

Contact: Roger Murphy, Gen. Mgr.

Oral-B Laboratories, Green Road, Newbridge, Kildare, Ireland

Contact: Roger Murphy, Gen. Mgr.

Rethgil Properties Ltd., Dublin, Ireland

Contact: Roger Murphy, Gen. Mgr.

THE GORMAN-RUPP COMPANY

PO Box 1217, 305 Bowman St., Mansfield, OH, 44901-1217

Tel: (419) 755-1011   Fax: (419) 755-1266   www.gormanrupp.com

Mfr. of pumps and pumping systems for the municipal, water, wastewater, sewage, industrial, construction, petroleum, fire and OEM markets.

Patterson Pump Ireland Limited, Newbrook, Mulingar, County Westmeath, Ireland

GOW-MAC INSTRUMENT COMPANY

277 Brodhead Rd., Bethlehem, PA, 18017

Tel: (610) 954-9000   Fax: (610) 954-0599   www.gow-mac.com

Mfr. analytical instruments

GOW-MAC Instrument Co., Bay K 14a, Industrial Estate, Shannon County Clare, Ireland

Tel: 353-61-471632   Fax: 353-61-471042

W. R. GRACE & COMPANY

7500 Grace Drive, Columbia, MD, 21044

Tel: (410) 531-4000   Fax: (410) 531-4367   www.grace.com

Mfr. specialty chemicals and materials: packaging, health care, catalysts, construction, water treatment/process.

Grace Construction Products, Unit 200, Holly Road, Western Industrial Estate, Naas Road, Dublin 12, Ireland

Tel: 353-1-456-960   Fax: 353-1-4569-604

GRANT THORNTON INTERNATIONAL

800 One Prudential Plaza, 130 E. Randolph Drive, Chicago, IL, 60601-6050

Tel: (312) 856-0001   Fax: (312) 616-7052   www.grantthornton.com

Accounting, audit, tax and management consulting services.

Grant Thornton International, Ashford House, Tara St., Dublin 2, Ireland

Tel: 353-1-671-4677   Fax: 353-1-671-7209   Contact: James Murphy

GREY GLOBAL GROUP

777 Third Ave., New York, NY, 10017

Tel: (212) 546-2000   Fax: (212) 546-1495   www.grey.com

International advertising agency.

Campbell Grey & Associates, 6 Adelaide Ct., Adelaide Road, Dublin 2, Ireland

GRIFFITH LABORATORIES INC.

One Griffith Center, Alsip, IL, 60658

Tel: (708) 371-0900   Fax: (708) 597-3294   www.griffithlabs.com

Mfr. industrial food ingredients and equipment.

Griffith Labs Ltd., Dublin, Ireland

Tel: 353-1-493-6000   Fax: 353-1-493-6151

GUY CARPENTER & COMPANY, INC.

114 West 47th Street, New York, NY, 10036

Tel: (212) 323-1000   Fax: (212) 345-2494   www.guycarp.com

Engaged in global reinsurance and risk management.

Guy Carpenter & Company, Ltd., 25-28 Adelaide Road, 5th Floor, Dublin 2, Ireland

Tel: 353-1605-3000   Fax: 353-1605-3010   Contact: Michael Dicker

THE GYMBOREE CORPORATION

700 Airport Boulevard, Ste. 200, Burlingame, CA, 94010-1912

Tel: (650) 579-0600   Fax: (650) 696-2920   www.gymboree.com

Mfr. and sales of children's apparel and on-site play programs.

Gymboree Corporation, 75 Grafton Street, Dublin, Ireland

Tel: 353-1-670-3331

HAMILTON SUNSTRAND

One Hamilton Rd., Windsor Locks, CT, 06096-1010

Tel: (860) 654-6000   Fax: (860) 654-3469   www.hamiltonsunstrandcorp.com

Design/mfr. aerospace systems for commercial, regional, corporate and military aircraft.

Hamilton Sunstrand Corp., Shannon, Ireland

HARRIS CALORIFIC COMPANY

2345 Murphy Boulevard, Gainesville, GA, 30501

Tel: (770) 536-8801   Fax: (770) 536-0544   www.harriscal.com

Mfr./sales of gas welding and cutting equipment.

Harris Calorific Ireland,, Harris House, Charvey Lane, Rathnew, Wicklow, Ireland

H.J. HEINZ COMPANY

600 Grant Street, Pittsburgh, PA, 15219

Tel: (412) 456-5700   Fax: (412) 456-6128   www.heinz.com

Processed food products and nutritional services.

Custom Foods Ltd., Dundalk, Ireland

H.J. Heinz Co. (Ireland) Ltd., Dublin, Ireland

HENRY SCHEIN, INC.

135 Duryea Rd., Melville, NY, 11747

Tel: (516) 843-5500   Fax: (516) 843-5658   www.henryschein.com

Mfr. and supply dental equipment.

Henry Schein Ireland Ltd., Unit 61A, Longmile Centre, Longmile Road, Dublin 12, Ireland

THE HERTZ CORPORATION

225 Brae Boulevard, Park Ridge, NJ, 07656-0713

Tel: (201) 307-2000   Fax: (201) 307-2644   www.hertz.com

Worldwide headquarters office for car rental, car leasing and equipment rental.

Hertz Rental Car, Dublin, Ireland

HEWITT ASSOCIATES LLC

100 Half Day Road, Lincolnshire, IL, 60069

Tel: (847) 295-5000   Fax: (847) 295-7634   www.hewitt.com

Employee benefits consulting firm.

Hewitt Associates, Iveagh Court, 6 Harcourt Rd., Dublin 2, Ireland
Tel: 353-1-418-9130

HEWLETT-PACKARD COMPANY

3000 Hanover Street, Palo Alto, CA, 94304-1185

Tel: (650) 857-1501   Fax: (650) 857-5518   www.hp.com

Mfr. computing, communications and measurement products and services.

Hewlett-Packard Ireland Ltd., Hewlett-Packard House, Stradbrook Rd., Black Rock, County Dublin, Ireland

HIGH VOLTAGE ENGINEERING CORPORATION

401 Edgewater Place, Ste. 680, Wakefield, MA, 01880

Tel: (781) 224-1001   Fax: (781) 224-1011   www.highvolteng.com

Holding company: owner and operator of a diversified group of middle market industrial and technology-based manufacturing businesses.

HIVEC-Ireland, Rathealy Rd., Fermoy, Co. Cork, Ireland

HOOD SAILMAKERS INC.

23 Johnny Cake Hill, Middletown, RI, 02842

Tel: (401) 849-9400   Fax: (401) 849-9700   www.hood-sails.com

Mfr. furling genoas, jibs, easy stow mainsails, and spinnakers.

Hood Textiles Ltd., McCurtain Hill, Clonakilty, County Cork, Ireland

HORWATH INTERNATIONAL ASSOCIATION

420 Lexington Avenue, Suite 526, New York, NY, 10170-0526

Tel: (212) 808-2000   Fax: (212) 808-2020   www.horwath.com

Public accountants and auditors.

Simpson Xavier, Simpson Xavier Court, Merchants Quay, Dublin 8, Ireland

Simpson Xavier, 4 Michael St., Limerick, Ireland

HOSKINS MFG. COMPANY

10776 Hall Road, PO Box 218, Hamburg, MI, 48139-0218

Tel: (810) 231-1900   Fax: (810) 231-4311   www.hoskinsmfgco.com

Engaged in the development and manufacture of resistance, heating, temperature measurement and electrical control alloys.

Hoskins Alloys Intl., Kildare Enterprise Centre, Melitta Rd., Kildare Town, Co. Kildare, Ireland

HOUGHTON INTERNATIONAL INC.

PO Box 930, Madison & Van Buren Avenues, Valley Forge, PA, 19482-0930

Tel: (610) 666-4000   Fax: (610) 666-1376   www.houghtonintl.com

Mfr. specialty chemicals, hydraulic fluids and lubricants.

Houghton Oils & Chemicals (Ireland) Ltd., Dunboyne Industrial Park, Dunboyne, County Meath, Ireland

HOWMEDICA OSTEONICS, INC.

59 Route 17 South, Allendale, NJ, 07401

Tel: (201) 507-7300   Fax: (201) 935-4873   www.howmedica.com

Mfr. of maxillofacial products (orthopedic implants).

Howmedica Ireland, Limerick, Ireland

Tel: 353-61-471866

HUNT SCREW & MFG. COMPANY

4117 North Kilpatrick Ave., Chicago, IL, 60641

Tel: (773) 283-6900   Fax: (773) 283-6068   www.huntscrew.com

Engaged in manufacture of custom screw machine products.

Hunt Associates Ltd., Leislip, Kildare, Ireland

HYPERION SOLUTIONS CORPORATION

1344 Crossman Avenue, Sunnyvale, CA, 94089

Tel: (408) 744-9500   Fax: (408) 744-0400   www.hyperion.com

Mfr. data analysis software tools.

Niederlassung Ireland, Regus Business Centre, Block C, The Sweep Stakes Balls Bridge, Dublin 4, Ireland

Tel: 35-31-631-9096

IBM CORPORATION

1133 Westchester Avenue, White Plains, NY, 10604

Tel: (914) 765-1900   Fax: (914) 765-7382   www.ibm.com

Information products, technology and services.

IBM Ireland Ltd., 2 Burlington Rd., Ballsbrige, Dublin 4, Ireland

Tel: 353-1-660-3744   Fax: 353-1-850-401601

IBP FOODS COMPANY INC.

PO Box 515, Dakota City, NE, 68731

Tel: (402) 494-2061   Fax: (402) 241-2068   www.ibpinc.com

Produce beef and pork, hides and associated products, animal feeds, pharmaceuticals.

Foodbrands America, Inc., Naas, County Kildare, Ireland

IDEX CORPORATION

630 Dundee Road, Ste. 400, Northbrook, IL, 60062

Tel: (847) 498-7070   Fax: (847) 498-3940   www.idexcorp.com

Mfr. industrial pumps, lubrication systems, metal fabrication equipment, bending and clamping devices.

Viking Pump (Europe) Ltd., R-79 Shannon Industrial Estate, Shannon, County Clare, Ireland

IKON OFFICE SOLUTIONS

70 Valley Stream Parkway, Malvern, PA, 19355

Tel: (610) 296-8000　　Fax: (610) 408-7022　　www.ikon.com

Sales of office equipment, including fax machines, copiers and printers.

IKON Europe International, Unit 4 Parkwest Drive, Nangor Road, Dublin 22, Ireland

Tel: 353-1-623-9000　Fax: 353-1-623-0166

ILLINOIS TOOL WORKS (ITW)

3600 West Lake Ave., Glenview, IL, 60025-5811

Tel: (847) 724-7500　　Fax: (847) 657-4268　　www.itw.com

Mfr. gears, tools, fasteners, sealants, plastic and metal components for industrial, medical, etc.

ITW Hi-Cone Ltd., Newbridge Business Park, Green Road, Kildare, Ireland

IMI NORGREN GROUP

5400 South Delaware Street, Littleton, CO, 80120-1663

Tel: (303) 794-2611　　Fax: (303) 795-9487　　www.usa.norgren.com

Mfr. pneumatic filters, regulators, lubricators, valves, automation systems, dryers, push-in fittings.

IMI Norgren Ltd., Unit 137, Slaney Close, Dublin Industrial Estate, Glasnevin, Dublin 11, Ireland

Tel: 353-1-830-0288　Fax: 353-1-830-0082

INFONET SERVICES CORPORATION

2160 East Grand Ave., El Segundo, CA, 90245-1022

Tel: (310) 335-2600　　Fax: (310) 335-4507　　www.infonet.com

Provider of Internet services and electronic messaging services.

Infonet Ireland, Alexandra House, Earlsfort Centre, Dublin 2, Ireland

Tel: 353-1-602-4999　Fax: 353-1-676-8745

INGERSOLL-RAND COMPANY

200 Chestnut Ridge Road, Woodcliff Lake, NJ, 07675

Tel: (201) 573-0123　　Fax: (201) 573-3172　　www.irco.com

Leading innovation and solutions provider for the major global markets of Security and Safety, Climate Control, Industrial Solutions and Infrastructure.

CPM Europe Ltd., Whitemill Industrial Estate, Wexford, Ireland

Ingersoll-Rand Co. Ireland Ltd., John F. Kennedy Dr., Bluebell, Dublin 12, Ireland

INTERGRAPH CORPORATION

One Madison Industrial Park, Huntsville, AL, 35894-0001

Tel: (256) 730-2000　　Fax: (256) 730-7898　　www.intergraph.com

Develop/mfr. interactive computer graphic systems.

Intergraph Ireland Ltd., Stradbrook House, Stradbrook Rd., Blackrock Dublin, Ireland

Tel: 353-1-2801366　Fax: 353-1-2801116

INTERMEC TECHNOLOGIES CORPORATION

6001 36th Avenue West, PO Box 4280, Everett, WA, 98203-9280

Tel: (425) 348-2600　　Fax: (425) 355-9551　　www.intermec.com

Mfr. and distributor automated data collection systems.

Intermec Ireland Ltd., 19-20 York Road, Dunlaoire, County Dublin, Ireland

INTERNATIONAL FLAVORS & FRAGRANCES INC.

521 West 57th Street, New York, NY, 10019-2960

Tel: (212) 765-5500　　Fax: (212) 708-7132　　www.iff.com

Design/mfr. flavors, fragrances and aroma chemicals.

International Flavors & Fragrances, Industrial Estate, Donore Road, Drogheda County. Louth, Ireland

Tel: 353-41-983-1031　Fax: 353-41-983-5119

INTERNATIONAL MANAGEMENT GROUP (IMG)

1360 East Ninth Street, Ste. 100, Cleveland, OH, 44114

Tel: (216) 522-1200   Fax: (216) 522-1145   www.imgworld.com

Manages athletes, sports academies and real estate facilities worldwide.

IMG, 5 Clare Street, Dublin 2, Ireland

Tel: 353-1-661-7420   Fax: 353-1-661-7425

IONICS INC.

65 Grove Street, Watertown, MA, 02172

Tel: (617) 926-2500   Fax: (617) 926-4304   www.ionics.com

Mfr. desalination equipment.

Ionics Ireland, Ballybane Galway, Ireland

IRON MOUNTAIN INCORPORATED

745 Atlantic Avenue, Boston, MA, 02111

Tel: (617) 535-4766   Fax: (617) 350-7881   www.ironmountain.com

Engaged in records and information management.

Iron Mountain Incorporated, 13-17 Newmarket, Dublin 8, Ireland

Iron Mountain Incorporated, Docklands Business Park Unit 3, Dock Road, Limerick, Ireland

Iron Mountain Incorporated, Monahan Road, County Cork, Ireland

ITT-GOULDS PUMPS INC.

2881 East Bayard Street, Seneca Falls, NY, 13148

Tel: (315) 568-2811   Fax: (315) 568-7651   www.gouldspumps.com

Mfr. industrial and water systems pumps.

ESI Technologies Limited, Crawford Commercial Park, Bishop Street, Cork, Ireland

ITW DEVCON PLEXUS

30 Endicott Street, Danvers, MA, 01923

Tel: (978) 777-1100   Fax: (978) 774-0516   www.devcon-equip.com

Engaged in technology and products for OEM assembly, and maintenance/repair applications.

Devcon Ltd., Shannon Ind. Estate, Shannon Free Airport, County Clare, Ireland

IVAX CORPORATION

4400 Biscayne Blvd., Miami, FL, 33137

Tel: (305) 575-6000   Fax: (305) 575-6055   www.ivax.com

Mfr. pharmaceuticals.

IVAX Ireland, Waterford Industrial Estate, Unit 301, Waterford, Ireland

J. WALTER THOMPSON COMPANY

466 Lexington Ave., New York, NY, 10017

Tel: (212) 210-7000   Fax: (212) 210-6944   www.jwt.com

International advertising and marketing services.

DDFH&B Advertising(JWT), Dublin, Ireland

JABIL CIRCUIT, INC.

10560 Ninth St. North, St. Petersburg, FL, 33716

Tel: (727) 557-9749   Fax: (727) 579-8529   www.jabil.com

Mfr. printed circuit boards, electronic components and systems.

Jabil Global Services, Clonshaugh Industrial Estate, Dublin 17, Ireland

JACOBS ENGINEERING GROUP INC.

1111 S. Arroyo Parkway, Pasadena, CA, 91105

Tel: (626) 578-3500   Fax: (626) 578-6916   www.jacobs.com

Engineering, design and consulting; construction and construction management; process plant maintenance.

Jacobs Engineering Inc., Merrion House, Merrion Rd., Dublin 4, Ireland

Tel: 353-1-269-5666 Fax: 353-1-269-5497   Contact: James R. Thomas, Dir.   Emp: 214

Jacobs Engineering Inc., Mahon Industrial Estate, Blackrock, County Cork, Ireland

Tel: 353-21-515-777 Fax: 353-21-358-977   Contact: Thomas G. Concannon, Mgr.   Emp: 233

JOHN HANCOCK FINANCIAL SERVICES, INC.

200 Clarendon Street, Boston, MA, 02117

Tel: (617) 572-6000   Fax: (617) 572-9799   www.johnhancock.com

Life insurance services.

John Hancock Advisors International (Ireland) Ltd., Dublin, Ireland

JOHNSON & JOHNSON

One Johnson & Johnson Plaza, New Brunswick, NJ, 08933

Tel: (732) 524-0400   Fax: (732) 214-0334   www.jnj.com

Mfr./distributor/R&D pharmaceutical, health care and cosmetic products.

Janssen-Cilag Pharmaceutical Ltd., Little Island, Cork, Ireland

Johnson & Johnson (Ireland) Ltd., Belgard Rd., IRL Tallaght, Dublin 24, Ireland

Tel: 353-1-4621089   Fax: 353-1-4510954

Vistakon, Limerick, Ireland

SC JOHNSON

1525 Howe St., Racine, WI, 53403

Tel: (262) 260-2000   Fax: (262) 260-2133   www.scjohnsonwax.com

Home, auto, commercial and personal care products and specialty chemicals.

SC Johnson, Robinhood Industrial Estate, Clon Dalkin Co., Dublin, Ireland

JONES LANG LASALLE

153 East 53rd Street, New York, NY, 10022

Tel: (212) 812-5700   Fax: (212) 421-3544   www.am.joneslanglasalle.com

International marketing consultants, leasing agents and property management advisors.

Jones Lang Wootton, Dublin, Ireland

JUNIPER NETWORKS, INC.

1194 North Mathilda Ave., Sunnyvale, CA, 94089

Tel: (408) 745-2000   Fax: (408) 745-2100   www.juniper.net

Engaged in the design and sales of Internet Protocol routers for access networks.

Juniper Networks Ireland, Airside Business Park, Swords, County Dublin, Ireland

KELLOGG COMPANY

One Kellogg Square, PO Box 3599, Battle Creek, MI, 49016-3599

Tel: (616) 961-2000   Fax: (616) 961-2871   www.kelloggs.com

Mfr. ready-to-eat cereals and convenience foods.

Kellogg Co. of Ireland Ltd., Attn: Ireland Office, One Kellogg Square, PO Box 3599, Battle Creek, MI, 49016-3599

KELLY SERVICES, INC.

999 W. Big Beaver Road, Troy, MI, 48084

Tel: (248) 362-4444   Fax: (248) 244-4154   www.kellyservices.com

Temporary help placement.

Kelly Services (Ireland) Ltd., 21-22 Grafton, Dublin 2, Ireland

Tel: 353-1-679-3111   Fax: 353-1-677-3048

KEPNER-TREGOE INC.

PO Box 704, Princeton, NJ, 08542-0740

Tel: (609) 921-2806   Fax: (609) 497-0130   www.kepner-tregoe.com

Management consulting; specializing in strategy formulation, problem solving, decision making, project management, and cost reduction.

Kepner-Tregoe Ireland, Alexandra House The Sweepstakes, Ballsbridge Dublin 4, Ireland

Tel: 353-1-283-4030   Fax: 353-1-283-6230

KEY TRONIC CORPORATION

4424 N. Sullivan Rd., PO Box 14687, Spokane, WA, 99214-0687

Tel: (509) 928-8000   Fax: (509) 927-5555   www.keytronic.com

Mfr. computer keyboards and peripherals.

Key Tronic Corporation Europe, Finnabair Industrial Park, Dundalk County Louth, Ireland

Tel: 353-4238-100   Fax: 353-4238-309   Contact: Tony McVeigh

KIMBERLY-CLARK CORPORATION

351 Phelps Drive, Irving, TX, 75038

Tel: (972) 281-1200   Fax: (972) 281-1435   www.kimberly-clark.com

Mfr./sales/distribution of consumer tissue, household and personal care products.

Kimberly-Clark Corp., Dublin, Ireland

KINETIC CONCEPTS, INC.

8023 Vantage Drive, San Antonio, TX, 78230-4728

Tel: (210) 524-9000   Fax: (210) 255-4524   www.KCI1.com

Mfr. specialized medical beds.

KCI Ethos Medical Group, Monksland Industrial Estate, Summerhill Business Park, Athlone C. Westmeath, Ireland

Tel: 353-902-94412

KPMG CONSULTING INC.

1676 International Dr., McLean, VA, 22102

Tel: (703) 747-3000   Fax: (703) 747-8500   www.kpmg.com

Accounting and audit, tax and management consulting services.

KPMG International, One Stokes Place, St. Stephen's Green, Dublin, Ireland

Tel: 353-1-708-1000   Fax: 353-1-708-1122   Contact: Jerome Kennedy, Sr. Ptnr.

KWIK LOK CORPORATION

PO Box 9548, Yakima, WA, 98909

Tel: (509) 248-4770   Fax: (509) 457-6531   www.kwiklok.com

Mfr. bag closing machinery.

Kwik Lok Ireland, Bay 72, Industrial Estate, Shannon Airport, Shannon, Ireland

Tel: 353-6147-1193   Fax: 353-6147-2683

LAM RESEARCH CORPORATION

4650 Cushing Pkwy., Fremont, CA, 94538

Tel: (510) 659-0200   Fax: (510) 572-6454   www.lamrc.com

Mfr. semiconductor processing equipment.

Lam Research/Intel SSP, Unit 6, The Courtyard, Kilcarbery Business Park, New Nangor Road, Dublin 2, Ireland

Tel: 353-1-4579-186   Fax: 353-1-4611-068

LEVI STRAUSS & COMPANY

1155 Battery St., San Francisco, CA, 94111-1230

Tel: (415) 544-6000   Fax: (415) 501-3939   www.levistrauss.com

Mfr. and distributor of casual wearing apparel, including jeans and sportswear.

Levi Strauss Ireland, 12 Duke Lane, Dublin 2, Ireland

Tel: 353-1-671-8300   Fax: 353-1-671-8061

LIBERTY MUTUAL GROUP

175 Berkeley Street, Boston, MA, 02117

Tel: (617) 357-9500   Fax: (617) 350-7648   www.libertymutual. com

Provides workers' compensation insurance and operates physical rehabilitation centers and provides risk prevention management.

Liberty Underwriters, 35-38 St. Stephen's Green, Huguenot House, Dublin 2, Ireland

ELI LILLY & COMPANY

Lilly Corporate Center, Indianapolis, IN, 46285

Tel: (317) 276-2000   Fax: (317) 277-6579   www.lilly.com

Mfr. pharmaceuticals and animal health products.

Eli Lilly and Company Ireland Ltd., 44 Fitzwilliam Place, Dublin 2, Ireland

Tel: 353-21-661-4377

LIONBRIDGE TECHNOLOGIES, INC.

950 Winter St., Waltham, MA, 02451

Tel: (781) 434-6000   Fax: (781) 434-6034   www.lionbridge.com

Provides solutions for worldwide deployment of technology and content.

Lionbridge Dublin, Grattan House, Temple Road, Blackrock, County Dublin, Ireland

VeriTest - Lionbridge, Emmet Street, Ballina, County Mayo, Ireland

LOCKHEED MARTIN CORPORATION

6801 Rockledge Drive, Bethesda, MD, 20817

Tel: (301) 897-6000   Fax: (301) 897-6652   www.imco.com

Design/mfr./management systems in fields of space, defense, energy, electronics and technical services.

MountainGate Data Systems International, St. Joseph's Road, Portumna, County Galway, Ireland

Contact: W. Burke, Gen. Mgr.

LOST ARROW CORPORATION

259 West Santa Clara Street, Ventura, CA, 93001

Tel: (805) 643-8616   Fax: (805) 653-6355   www.patagonia.com

Mfr. high-end outdoor sportswear, via catalogues and specialty retailers, including Patagonia stores.

Patagonia Ireland, 24/26 Exchequer Street, Dublin 2, Ireland

LUCENT TECHNOLOGIES, INC.

600 Mountain Ave., Murray Hill, NJ, 07974-0636

Tel: (908) 582-3000   Fax: (908) 582-2576   www.lucent.com

Design/mfr. wide range of public and private networks, communication systems and software, data networking systems, business telephone systems and microelectronics components.

Bell Labs Network Products, Cork Abbey, Bray County, County Wicklow, Ireland

Tel: 353-1-2882-333   Fax: 353-1-2822-864   Contact: Sam Baxter, PR Mgr.

Lucent/Bell Labs, Lucent House, Ste. Stephens Green, Dublin 2, Ireland

MAIDENFORM WORLDWIDE INC.

154 Avenue E, Bayonne, NJ, 07002

Tel: (201) 436-9200   Fax: (201) 436-9009   www.maidenform.com

Mfr. intimate apparel.

Maidenform Intl. Ltd., Shannon Industrial Estate, Shannon, Co. Clare, Ireland

MALLINCKRODT PHARMACUTICALS, INC.

675 McDonnell Blvd., Hazelwood, MO, 63042

Tel: (314) 654-2000   Fax: (314) 654-5380   www.mallinckrodt.com

Mfr. products for respiratory care.

Mallinckrodt Ireland, Cornamaddy, Athlone, County Westmeath, Ireland

Tel: 353-902-75210

Mallinckrodt Ireland, New Mervue Industrial Park, Michael Collins Road, Mervue Galway, Ireland

Tel: 353-91-753771

MANPOWER INTERNATIONAL INC.

5301 N. Ironwood Rd., PO Box 2053, Milwaukee, WI, 53201-2053

Tel: (414) 961-1000   Fax: (414) 961-7081   www.manpower.com

Temporary help, contract service, training and testing.

Manpower Ireland Ltd., 54 Grafton Street, Dublin 2, Ireland

Tel: 44-1353-1677-7321

MANUFACTURER'S SERVICES LTD. (MSL)

300 Baker Ave., Concord, MA, 01742-2125

Tel: (978) 287-5630   Fax: (978) 287-5635   www.manserve.com

Provides electronic manufacturing services to the medical, computer and peripherals industries.

MSL Ireland, Parkmore Business Park, Ballybrit Galway, Ireland

Tel: 353-91-705000

MSL Ireland, Garrycastle Athlone, County Westmeath, Ireland

Tel: 353-902-20800   Fax: 353-902-20801

MARATHON OIL COMPANY

5555 San Felipe Road, Houston, TX, 77056

Tel: (713) 629-6600   Fax: (713) 296-2952   www.marathon.com

Oil and gas exploration.

Marathon Petroleum Ireland Ltd., Mahon Industrial Estate, Blackrock, Cork, Ireland

MARCONI DATA SYSTEMS INC.

1500 Mittel Blvd., Wood Dale, IL, 60191

Tel: (630) 860-7300   Fax: (630) 616-3657   www.videojet.com

Mfr. computer peripherals and hardware, state-of-the-art industrial ink jet marking and coding products.

Videojet, Div. Marconi Data Systems, Unit 1, Chestnut Rd., Western Industrial Estate, Dublin 12, Ireland

Tel: 353-1-450-2833   Fax: 353-1-450-2941   Contact: Paul Walker

MARSH & McLENNAN COS INC.

1166 Ave. of the Americas, New York, NY, 10036-2774

Tel: (212) 345-5000   Fax: (212) 345-4808   www.marshmac.com

Insurance agents/brokers, pension and investment management consulting services.

J&H Marsh & McLennan Ireland Ltd., 12 South Mall, Cork, Ireland

Tel: 353-21-27-6743   Fax: 353-21-27-2555   Contact: Gerard O'Donovn

J&H Marsh & McLennan Ireland Ltd., 10-11 South Leinster St, Dublin 2, Ireland

Tel: 353-1-618-2720   Fax: 353-1-678-5839   Contact: David Caird

J&H Marsh & McLennan Ireland Ltd., Crescent House, Upper Hartstonge St., Limerick, Ireland

Tel: 353-61-319155   Fax: 353-61-317598   Contact: David Bermington

J&H Marsh & McLennan Management Services (Dublin) Ltd., Level 2, Treasury Bldg., Lr Grand Canal St., Dublin 2, Ireland

Tel: 353-1-676-2748   Fax: 353-1-678-9636   Contact: Ian J. Clancy

MASONITE CORPORATION

One South Wacker Drive, Chicago, IL, 60606

Tel: (312) 750-0900   Fax: (312) 750-0958   www.masonite.com

Mfr. hardboard, softboard and molded products.

Masonite Europe, Segrave House, 19/29 Earlsfort Terrace, Dublin 2, Ireland

Contact: Claire Devine

Masonite Ireland, Dublin Rd., ICA Industrial Estate, Carrick-on-Shannon, Co. Leitrim, Ireland

MAXTOR CORPORATION

500 McCarthy Blvd., Milpitas, CA, 95035

Tel: (408) 894-5000   Fax: (408) 432-4510   www.maxtor.com

Mfr. develops and markets hard disk drives for desktop computer systems.

Maxtor Ireland Ltd., Bray County Wicklow, Ireland

MBNA CORPORATION

1100 N. King Street, Wilmington, DE, 19801

Tel: (302) 453-9930   Fax: (302) 432-3614   www.mbna.com

Credit card issuer dealing primarily with VISA and MasterCard, home equity loans and property and casualty insurance.

MBNA Ireland, 46 St. Stephen's Green, Dublin 2, UK

McCANN-ERICKSON WORLDGROUP

750 Third Ave., New York, NY, 10017

Tel: (212) 697-6000   Fax: (212) 984-3575   www.mccann.com

International advertising and marketing services.

McCann-Erickson (Ireland), Dublin, Ireland

McDONALD'S CORPORATION

McDonald's Plaza, Oak Brook, IL, 60523

Tel: (630) 623-3000   Fax: (630) 623-7409   www.mcdonalds.com

Fast food chain stores.

McDonald's Corp., Tralee, Ireland

McKINSEY & COMPANY

55 East 52nd Street, New York, NY, 10022

Tel: (212) 446-7000   Fax: (212) 446-8575   www.mckinsey.com

Management and business consulting services.

McKinsey & Company, Canada House, 65-68 St. Stephen's Green, Dublin 2, Ireland
Tel: 353-1-478-5500   Fax: 353-1-478-5512

MELLON FINANCIAL CORPORATION

One Mellon Bank Center, Pittsburgh, PA, 15258-0001

Tel: (412) 234-5000   Fax: (412) 236-1662   www.mellon.com

Commercial and trade banking and foreign exchange.

Mellon Fund Administration, Dublin, Ireland
Premier Financial Services (Ireland) Ltd., 20-22 Lower Hatch St., Dublin 2, Ireland
Tel: 353-1-790-5000

MEMOREX CORPORATION

10100 Pioneer Blvd., Ste. 110, Santa Fe Springs, CA, 90670

Tel: (562) 906-2800   Fax: (562) 906-2848   www.memorex.com

Magnetic recording tapes, etc.

Memorex Ireland Ltd., Kestral House, Clanwilliam House, Clanwilliam Place, Lower Mount St., Dublin 2, Ireland

MERRILL LYNCH & COMPANY, INC.

World Financial Center, 250 Vesey Street, New York, NY, 10281-1332

Tel: (212) 236-1000   Fax: (212) 449-2892   www.ml.com

Security brokers and dealers, investment and business services.

Merrill Lynch Capital Markets Bank, Treasury Building, Lower Grand Canal Street, Dublin 2, Ireland
Tel: 353-1-605-8500   Fax: 353-1-605-8510

METHODE ELECTRONICS INC.

7401 W. Wilson Ave., Chicago, IL, 60656

Tel: (708) 867-6777   Fax: (708) 867-6999   www.methode.com

Mfr. electronic components.

Methode Electronics Ireland Ltd, Annacotty Industrial Estate, Annacotty, County Limerick, Ireland
Tel: 353-61-330-013   Contact: Michael O'Donnell

METROMEDIA FIBER NETWORK, INC.

360 Hamilton Avenue, White Plains, NY, 10601

Tel: (914) 421-6700   Fax: (914) 421-6777   www.mfn.com

Mfr. urban fiber-optic networks for telecommunications providers.

Metromedia Fiber Network Ireland Ltd, 4033 Citywest Avenue, Citywest Business Campus, Dublin 24, Ireland

MICROSEMI CORPORATION

2830 South Fairview St., Santa Ana, CA, 92704

Tel: (714) 979-8220   Fax: (714) 557-5989   www.microsemi.com

Design, manufacture and market analog, mixed-signal and discrete semiconductors.

Microsemi Corp. Ireland, Gort Rd., Ennis, Co. Clare, Ireland
Tel: 353-65-68-40044

MICROSOFT CORPORATION

One Microsoft Way, Redmond, WA, 98052-6399

Tel: (425) 882-8080 Fax: (425) 936-7329 www.microsoft.com

Computer software, peripherals and services.

Microsoft Ireland Operations Ltd., Blackthorn Rd., Sandyford Ind. Estates, Dublin 18, Ireland

MILACRON INC.

2090 Florence Ave., Cincinnati, OH, 45206

Tel: (513) 487-5000 Fax: (513) 487-5057 www.milacron.com

Metalworking and plastics technologies.

Plas-Tech Equipment Limited, 83 New Muirhevna Dublin Road, Dundalk County Louth, Ireland

Tel: 353-42-9330900 Fax: 353-42-9326466 Contact: Bernhard Gründemann

MILLIPORE CORPORATION

80 Ashby Road, PO Box 9125, Bedford, MA, 01730

Tel: (781) 533-6000 Fax: (781) 533-3110 www.millipore.com

Mfr. flow and pressure measurement and control components; precision filters, hi-performance liquid chromatography instruments.

Millipore Ireland B.V., Tullagreen, Carrigtwohill County, Ireland

MILTON ROY COMPANY

201 Ivyland Road, Ivylan, PA, 18974

Tel: (215) 441-0800 Fax: (215) 293-0468 www.miltonroy.com

Mfr. medical and industry equipment and process control instruments.

LDC-Shannon, Shannon Industrial Estate, Bldg. 89, Clare, Ireland

MINTEQ INTERNATIONAL INC.

395 Grove City Road, Slippery Rock, PA, 16057

Tel: (724) 794-3000 Fax: (724) 794-4455 www.mineralstech.com

Mfr./market specialty refractory and metallurgical products and application systems.

MINTEQ Europe Ltd., Box 105, Tivoli Industrial Estate, Cork, Ireland

Tel: 353-21-503-241 Fax: 353-21-506-352 Contact: David Rosenberg, VP Emp: 45

MODUS MEDIA, INC.

690 Canton Street, Westwood, MA, 02090

Tel: (781) 407-2000 Fax: (781) 407-3800 www.modusmedia.com

Engaged in outsourced manufacturing, fulfillment and distribution services.

Modus Media International, Unit 180 189, Lakeshore Drive, Airside Business Park, Swords, Co. Dublin, Ireland

Tel: 353-1-816-2300 Fax: 353-1-816-2340

MOLEX INC.

2222 Wellington Court, Lisle, IL, 60532

Tel: (630) 969-4550 Fax: (630) 969-1352 www.molex.com

Mfr. electronic, electrical and fiber optic interconnection products and systems, switches, application tooling.

Molex Inc., 62 Pembroke Road, Dublin 4, Ireland

MOOG INC.

300 Jamison Road, East Aurora, NY, 14052-0018

Tel: (716) 652-2000 Fax: (716) 687-4471 www.moog.com

Mfr. precision control components and systems.

Moog Ltd. (Ireland), Ringeskiddy, County Cork, Ireland

Tel: 353-21-4519000

J. P. MORGAN CHASE & CO. INC.

270 Park Ave., New York, NY, 10017

Tel: (212) 270-6000 Fax: (212) 622-9030 www.jpmorganchase.com

Provides integrated financial solutions for institutions and individuals worldwide, including asset management, investment banking and commercial banking.

J. P. Morgan Chase & Co., Chase Manhattan House, International Financial Services Centre, Dublin 1, Ireland

Tel: 353-1-612-3000 Fax: 353-1-612-3123

MOTOROLA, INC.

1303 East Algonquin Road, Schaumburg, IL, 60196

Tel: (847) 576-5000　　　Fax: (847) 538-5191　　　www.motorola.com

Mfr. communications equipment, semiconductors and cellular phones.

Motorola Ireland Ltd., LMPS Bldg, Newtown Park, Holybanks, County Dublin, Ireland

Tel: 353-1-840-8866　Fax: 353-1-840-0920

MTI TECHNOLOGY CORPORATION

4905 East LaPalma Avenue, Anaheim, CA, 92807

Tel: (714) 970-0300　　　Fax: (714) 693-2202　　　www.mti.com

Mfr. data storage systems software.

MTI Technology Ireland, Blanchardstown Corporate Park #5, Ballycoolin, Dublin 15, Ireland

Tel: 353-1-885-0500　Fax: 353-1-885-0555

MTS, INCORPORATED

2500 Del Monte Street, West Sacramento, CA, 95691

Tel: (916) 373-2500　　　Fax: (916) 373-2535　　　www.towerrecords.com

Specialty retailer of music and video stores.

Tower Records, 6-8 Wicklow Street, Dublin 2, Ireland

NCR (NATIONAL CASH REGISTER)

1700 South Patterson Blvd., Dayton, OH, 45479

Tel: (937) 445-5000　　　Fax: (937) 445-7042　　　www.ncr.com

Mfr. automated teller machines and high-performance stationary bar code scanners.

NCR, Dublin, Ireland

NETMANAGE, INC.

10725 N. De Anza Blvd., Cupertino, CA, 95014

Tel: (408) 973-7171　　　Fax: (408) 257-6405　　　www.netmanage.com

Develop and manufacture computer software applications and tools.

NetManage UK, Unit C18, Wicklow Enterprise Centre, The Murrough, Wicklow Town, Ireland

Tel: 353-404-66444

NEWAY MANUFACTURING INC.

1013 N. Shiawassee Street, PO Box 188, Corunna, MI, 48817-0188

Tel: (517) 743-3458　　　Fax: (517) 743-5764　　　www.newaymfg.com

Mfr. valve and valve seat reconditioning tools and equipment.

Neway Manufacturing Ltd., Unit 2, IDA Cluster Devel., Spollanstown Tullamore, County Offaly, Ireland

AC NIELSEN COMPANY

177 Broad Street, Stamford, CT, 06901

Tel: (203) 961-3000　　　Fax: (203) 961-3190　　　www.acnielsen.com

Engaged in market and consumer research.

ACNielsen, 36 Merrion Sq., Dublin 2, Ireland

NORTHERN TRUST CORPORATION

50 South LaSalle Street, Chicago, IL, 60675

Tel: (312) 630-6000　　　Fax: (312) 630-1512　　　www.ntrs.com

Engaged in banking and financial services.

Northern Trust Fund Managers (Ireland) Ltd., George's Quay House, 43 Townsend Street, Dublin 2, Ireland

Tel: 353-1-434-5000

NORTHROP GRUMMAN CORPORATION

1840 Century Park East, Los Angeles, CA, 90067-2199

Tel: (310) 553-6262　　　Fax: (310) 201-3023　　　www.northgrum.com

Advanced technology for aircraft, electronics, and technical support services.

Wescan Europe Ltd., Blanchardstown Industrial Park, Blanchardstown, Dublin 15, Ireland

Tel: 353-1-820-0322　Fax: 353-1-820-0388

NORTON ABRASIVES COMPANY

1 New Bond Street, Worcester, MA, 01606

Tel: (508) 795-5000 Fax: (508) 795-5741 www.nortonabrasives.com

Mfr. abrasives for industrial manufacturing.

Drill Tools Ireland Ltd., Shannon Industrial Estate, Shannon, County Clare, Ireland

NOVA INFORMATION SYSTEMS, INC.

1 Concourse Pkwy. Ste. 300, Atlanta, GA, 30328

Tel: (770) 396-1456 Fax: (770) 396-2117 www.novacorp.net

Engaged in processing of credit card transactions.

EuroConex Customer Support Centre, PO Box 56, Arklow Business Park, Arklow, County Wicklow, Ireland

EuroConex Ireland, Arena House, Arena Road, Sandyford Industrial Estate, Dublin 18, Ireland

NOVELL WORLDWIDE

1800 S. Novell Place, Provo, UT, 84606

Tel: (801) 861-7000 Fax: (801) 861-5555 www.novell.com

Develop/mfr. networking software and related equipment.

Novell Ireland Software Ltd., Treasury Buildings, Lower Grand Canal Street, Dublin 2, Ireland

Tel: 353-1-6058000

NOVELLUS SYSTEMS INC.

4000 North First Street, San Jose, CA, 95134

Tel: (408) 943-9700 Fax: (408) 943-3422 www.novellus.com

Mfr. chemical vapor deposition (CVD), physical vapor deposition (PVD) and copper electrofill systems.

Novellus Systems Ireland Ltd., IR4-1-10, Colinstown Industrial Park, Leixlip, County Kildare, Ireland

Tel: 353-1-606-5247 Fax: 353-1-606-5180

NTL INCORPORATED

110 East 59th Street, New York, NY, 10022

Tel: (212) 906-8440 Fax: (212) 752-1157 www.ntl.com

Provides cable TV and Internet services.

NTL, Building P2, East Point Business Park, Dublin 3, Ireland

Tel: 353-1-245-8419 Fax: 353-1-245-8534 Contact: Anna-Marie Barry

NYPRO INC.

101 Union Street, Clinton, MA, 01510

Tel: (978) 365-9721 Fax: (978) 368-0236 www.nypro.com

Mfr. plastic parts for telecommunications industry.

Nypro Ireland, Corke Abbey, Bray, County Dublin, Ireland

C.M. OFFRAY & SON INC.

360 Rt. 24, Box 601, Chester, NJ, 07930-0601

Tel: (908) 879-4700 Fax: (908) 879-8588 www.offray.com

Mfr. ribbons and narrow fabrics.

Offray Ribbon Ltd., Ashbury Rd., Roscrea, County Tipperary, Ireland

OGILVY & MATHER WORLDWIDE

309 West 49th Street, New York, NY, 10017-7399

Tel: (212) 237-4000 Fax: (212) 237-5123 www.ogilvypr.com

Engaged in public relations and communications.

Wilson Hartnell PR/Ogilvy, 14 Leeson Park, Dublin 6, Ireland

Tel: 353-1-496-0244 Fax: 353-1-497-5163 Contact: Mary Finan

OPENWAVE SYSTEMS INC.

1400 Seaport Blvd., Redwood City, CA, 94063

Tel: (650) 480-8000 Fax: (650) 480-8100 www.openwave.com

Mfr. software for wireless telephones.

Openwave Systems, Charles House, 103/111 Donegall Street, Belfast BT1 2FJ, Ireland

OTIS ELEVATOR COMPANY

One Farm Springs Road, Farmington, CT, 06032

Tel: (860) 676-6000   Fax: (860) 676-5111   www.otis.com

Mfr. elevators and escalators.

Otis Elevator Co. UK, Unit 21, Naas Road Business Park, Muirfield Drive, Dublin 12, Ireland

PACIFIC SCIENTIFIC COMPANY

4301 Kishwaukee Street, PO Box 106, Rockford, IL, 61105-0106

Tel: (815) 226-3100   Fax: (815) 226-3148   www.pacsci.com

Mfr. high performance motors and drives.

Pacific Scientific Ltd., Ennis, Ireland

PALL CORPORATION

2200 Northern Boulevard, East Hills, NY, 11548-1289

Tel: (516) 484-5400   Fax: (516) 484-5228   www.pall.com

Specialty materials and engineering; filters and related fluid clarification equipment.

Pall Gelman Sciences, 24 Kill Avenue, Dun Laoire, Dublin, Ireland

Tel: 353-1-284-6177   Fax: 353-1-280-7739

Pall Ireland (Div. Pall Netherlands), Rosanna Road, Tipperary Town, County Tipperary, Ireland

Tel: 353-62-82600   Fax: 353-62-82680

PALM, INC.

5470 Great American Pkwy., Santa Clara, CA, 95054

Tel: (408) 878-9000   Fax: (408) 878-2750   www.palm.com

Mfr. handheld computers, Palm Pilot.

Palm Ireland, 43B Park West Business Park, Nangor Road, Dublin 12, Ireland

Tel: 353-1-439-6700

PANAMETRICS

221 Crescent Street, Waltham, MA, 02154

Tel: (781) 899-2719   Fax: (781) 899-1552   www.panametrics.com

Engaged in manufacture and distribution of ultrasonic testing equipment and process control instrumentation.

Panametrics Ltd., Bay 148 Shannon Airport, Shannon, Co. Clare, Ireland

Tel: 353-61-471377   Fax: 353-61-471359   Contact: Jim Gibson

PARAMETRIC TECHNOLOGY CORPORATION

140 Kendrick St., Needham, MA, 02494

Tel: (781) 370-5000   Fax: (781) 370-6000   www.ptc.com

Supplier of mechanical design automation and product data management software and services.

Parametric Technology (IRL) Ltd., Regus House, Hartcourt Centre, Hartcourt Road, Dublin 2, Ireland

Tel: 353-1-4029575   Fax: 353-1-4029568

PARSONS BRINCKERHOFF INC.

One Penn Plaza, New York, NY, 10119-0061

Tel: (212) 465-5000   Fax: (212) 465-5096   www.pbworld.com

Provides planning, engineering, construction management and operations and maintenance services.

Parsons Brinckerhoff, 42 St. Stephen's Green, Dublin 2, Ireland

Tel: 353-1647-0300

PAYSYS INTERNATIONAL,INC.

900 Winderley Place, Ste. 140, Maitland, FL, 32751

Tel: (407) 660-0343   Fax: (407) 875-8246   www.paysys.com

Mfr. credit card management software.

PaySys International Ltd., Orwell SC Orwell Park, Templeogue, Dublin 6, Ireland

PEPSiCO INC.

700 Anderson Hill Road, Purchase, NY, 10577-1444

Tel: (914) 253-2000   Fax: (914) 253-2070   www.pepsico.com

Beverages and snack foods.

PepsiCo (Ireland) Ltd., Dublin, Ireland

PepsiCo Mfg. (Ireland), Little Island Cork, Ireland

Tel: 353-21-353921   Fax: 353-21-353926   Contact: Frank O'Mahony

Seven-Up Ireland Ltd., Dublin, Ireland

The Concentrate Mfg. Co. of Ireland, Dublin, Ireland

PEREGRINE SYSTEMS, INC.

3611 Valley Centre Drive, San Diego, CA, 92130

Tel: (858) 481-5000   Fax: (858) 481-1751   www.peregrine.com

Mfr. resource planning software.

Peregrine Systems Global Limited, Unit 3094, National Digital Park, Citywest, Dublin 24, Ireland

PEROT SYSTEMS CORPORATION

12404 Park Central Drive, Dallas, TX, 75251

Tel: (972) 340-5000   Fax: (972) 455-4100   www.perotsystems.com

Provides technology and business solutions.

Perot Systems, Mespil House, Dublin 4, Ireland

Tel: 353-1-285-1211

PFIZER INC.

235 East 42nd Street, New York, NY, 10017-5755

Tel: (212) 573-2323   Fax: (212) 573-7851   www.pfizer.com

Research-based, global health care company.

NAMIC Eireann BV, Tullamore, Ireland

Pfizer Ireland Ltd., Dublin, Ireland

Pfizer Pharmaceutical Production, Ringaskiddy, Ireland

PHARMACIA CORPORATION

100 Route 206 North, Peapack, NJ, 07977

Tel: (908) 901-8000   Fax: (908) 901-8379   www.pharmacia.com

Mfr. pharmaceuticals, agricultural products, industry chemicals.

Pharmacia & Upjohn Gaeleo Ltd., Little Island, Cork, Ireland

Pharmacia & Upjohn Letterkenny Ltd., High Road, Letterkenny, Counrty Donegal, Ireland

Pharmacia Ireland, Boeing Rd., Airways Industrial Estate, Dublin 17, Ireland

Tel: 353-1-8428733   Fax: 353-1-8428936

PHH ARVAL VEHICLE MANAGEMENT

307 International Circle, Hunt Valley, MD, 21030

Tel: (410) 771-3600   Fax: (410) 771-2841   www.phh.com

Provides fleet leasing and fleet management services to corporate and government clients with sales, service, delivery, executive or specialized trucks fleets.

PHH Vehicle Management Services, Merchants House, 27-30A Merchants Quay, Dublin 8, Ireland

Tel: 353-1-671-0022

PHILLIPS PETROLEUM COMPANY

Phillips Building, 411 S. Keeler Ave., Bartlesville, OK, 74004

Tel: (918) 661-6600   Fax: (918) 661-7636   www.phillips66.com

Crude oil, natural gas, liquefied petroleum gas, gasoline and petro-chemicals.

O'Brien Plastics Ltd., Bishopstown Cork, Ireland

Star Plastics Co. Ltd., Ballyconnell Cavan, Ireland

PIC GROUP

2929 Seventh Avenue, Ste. 130, Berkeley, CA, 94710

Tel: (510) 848-8266   Fax: (510) 848-0324   www.pic.com

Engaged in biotechnology.

PIC Ireland, Orchardstown, Lisronagh Clonmel, County Tipperary, Ireland

PITNEY BOWES INC.

1 Elmcroft Road, Stamford, CT, 06926-0700

Tel: (203) 356-5000   Fax: (203) 351-6835   www.pitneybowes.com

Mfr. postage meters, mailroom equipment, copiers, bus supplies, bus services, facsimile systems and financial services.

Pitney Bowes Ireland Ltd., Unit 4, Parkmore Industrial Estate, Long Mile Road, Dublin 12, Ireland

Tel: 353-1-4502-252   Fax: 3531-4505-493

PLANTRONICS

345 Encinal Street, Santa Cruz, CA, 95060

Tel: (831) 426-5858   Fax: (831) 425-5198   www.plantronics.com

Mfr. lightweight headsets and communications equipment and electrical and electronic appliances.

Plantronics, Darina Mangan (C/O Eircom), Naas Road Industrial Park, Old Naas Rd., Dublin 12, Ireland

THE PNC FINANCIAL SERVICES GROUP

249 Fifth Ave., Pittsburgh, PA, 15222

Tel: (412) 762-2000   Fax: (412) 762-7829   www.pncbank.com

Engaged in financial and asset management.

PFPC International (Dublin) Ltd., Abbey Court, Block C, Irish Life Centre, Lower Abbey Street, Dublin 1, Ireland

Tel: 353-1-790-3500   Contact: Fergus McKeon

PPG INDUSTRIES

One PPG Place, Pittsburgh, PA, 15272

Tel: (412) 434-3131   Fax: (412) 434-2190   www.ppg.com

Mfr. coatings, flat glass, fiber glass, chemicals.

Transitions Optical Ltd., IDA Industrial Estate, Dunmore Rd., Tuam, County Golway, Ireland

PRICEWATERHOUSECOOPERS LLP

1301 Ave. of the Americas, New York, NY, 10019

Tel: (212) 596-7000   Fax: (212) 259-1301   www.pwcglobal.com

Accounting and auditing, tax and management, and human resource consulting services.

PriceWaterhouseCoopers, Gardner House, 1 South Mall, Cork, Ireland

Tel: 353 21 276631   Fax: 353-21-276630

PriceWaterhouseCoopers, Gardner House, Wilton Place, Dublin 2, Ireland

Tel: 353-1-6626000   Fax: 353-1-6626200

PriceWaterhouseCoopers, Gardner House, Bank Place, Limerick, Ireland

Tel: 353-61-416644   Fax: 353-61-416331

PROCTER & GAMBLE COMPANY

One Procter & Gamble Plaza, Cincinnati, OH, 45202

Tel: (513) 983-1100   Fax: (513) 562-4500   www.pg.com

Personal care, food, laundry, cleaning and industry products.

Procter & Gamble ., Nenagh, Ireland

QAD INC.

6450 Via Real, Carpinteria, CA, 93013

Tel: (805) 684-6614   Fax: (805) 566-4479   www.qad.com

Mfr. software.

QAD Ireland, Hamilton House, National Tech Park, Limerick, Ireland

QUINTILES TRANSNATIONAL CORPORATION

4709 Creekstone Dr., Durham, NC, 27703

Tel: (919) 998-2000   Fax: (919) 998-9113   www.quintiles.com

Mfr. pharmaceuticals.

Innovex Ireland, Quintiles Building East, Point Business Park, Fairview Dublin 3, Ireland

RADISYS CORPORATION

5445 NE Dawson Creek Drive, Hillsboro, OR, 97124

Tel: (503) 615-1100   Fax: (503) 615-1121   www.radisys.com

Mfr. embedded computer systems.

RadiSys Ireland, 2nd Floor Mardyke House, Mardyke Street, Athlone, Co. Westmeath, Ireland

RAINHANDLER, INC.

2710 North Avenue, Bridgeport, CT, 06604

Tel: (203) 382-2991   Fax: (203) 382-2995   www.rainhandler.com

RainhandleR is a state-of-the-art rain dispersal system for home gutter replacement.

Rainhandler Europe, 11 Ravenhill Road, Belfast BT6 8DS, Ireland

RAYONIER INC.

50 N. Laura Street, Jacksonville, FL, 32202

Tel: (904) 357-9100   Fax: (904) 357-9155   www.rayonier.com

Engaged in logging and manufacture of paper pulp, chemicals and cellulose.

Rayonier Ireland, Dublin, Ireland

REFLEXITE TECHNOLOGY

120 Darling Drive, Avon, CT, 06001

Tel: (860) 676-7100   Fax: (860) 676-7199   www.reflexite.com

Mfr. plastic film, sheet, materials and shapes, optical lenses.

Reflexite Ireland Ltd., Unit 4, Industrial Estate, Cork Road, Waterford, Ireland

Tel: 353-51-358132   Fax: 353-51-35825   Contact: Declan Cunningham

REMINGTON PRODUCTS COMPANY, L.L.C.

60 Main Street, Bridgeport, CT, 06604

Tel: (203) 367-4400   Fax: (203) 332-4848   www.remington-products.com

Mfr. home appliances, electric shavers.

Remington Consumer Products Limited, Unit 7C, Riverview Bus Park, New Magnor Road - Clondalkin, Dublin 12, Ireland

Tel: 353-4604711

REVLON INC.

625 Madison Ave., New York, NY, 10022

Tel: (212) 527-4000   Fax: (212) 527-4995   www.revlon.com

Mfr. cosmetics, fragrances, toiletries and beauty care products.

Hydrocurve Ltd., Ireland

Reheis Chemical Ltd., Ireland

Revlon Ireland, Harmonstown Rd., Artane, Dublin 5, Ireland

Technicon Ireland Ltd., Ireland

RIDGE TOOL COMPANY

400 Clark Street, Elyria, OH, 44035

Tel: (440) 323-5581   Fax: (440) 329-4853   www.ridgid.com

Mfr. hand and power tools for working pipe, drain cleaning equipment, etc.

The Ridge Tool Co., Div. of Emerson Electric Ireland Ltd., Cork, Ireland

ROCHESTER MIDLAND CORPORATION (RML)

PO Box 31515, 333 Hollenbeck St., Rochester, NY, 14603-1515

Tel: (716) 336-2200   Fax: (716) 467-4406   www.rochestermidland.com

Mfr. specialty chemicals for industry cleaning and maintenance, water treatment and personal hygiene.

Rochester Midland Ireland, Raheens East, Ringaskiddy, Cork, Ireland

Tel: 353-21-378689

ROCKWELL AUTOMATION, INC.

777 East Wisconsin Ave., Ste. 1400, Milwaukee, WI, 53202

Tel: (414) 212-5200   Fax: (414) 212-5201   www.rockwellautomation.com

Products and service for aerospace and defense, automotive, electronics, graphics and automation industry.

Rockwell Automation (Ireland) Ltd., Naas Rd. Industrial Park, Dublin 12, Ireland

Tel: 353-1-450-8164   Fax: 353-1-456-5474

S1 CORPORATION

3500 Lenox Road, Ste. 200, Atlanta, GA, 30326-1108

Tel: (404) 923-3500   Fax: (404) 923-6727   www.s1.com

Mfr. on-line banking software.

S1 Dublin, Embassy House, Ballsbridge, Dublin 4, Ireland

SABRE INC.

3150 Sabre Drive, Southlake, TX, 76092

Tel: (682) 605-1000   Fax: (682) 605-8267   www.sabre.com

Computerized travel reservation system.

Gradient Solutions Limited, Ormonde House, 12 Lower Leeson Street, Dublin 2, Ireland

Tel: 353-1-2400500

SALESFORCE.COM

1 Market Street, Ste. 300, San Francisco, CA, 94105

Tel: (415) 901-7000   Fax: (415) 901-7040   www.salesforce.com

Mfr. software to manage customer information.

Salesforce.com, Powerscourt House, Enniskerry, County Wicklow, Ireland

Tel: 353-1-2723-502

SANMINA-SCI CORPORATION

2700 North First Street, San Jose, CA, 95134

Tel: (408) 964-3500   Fax: (408) 964-3799   www.sanmina-sci.com

Engaged in electronics contract manufacturing.

Sanmina Corporation, Blanchardstown Industrial Park, Dublin 15, Ireland

Tel: 353-1-802-5400   Fax: 353-1-882-2365

Sanmina-SCI Ireland, Holland Rd - Nat. Tech Park, Limerick, Ireland

Tel: 353-61-50330

SARA LEE CORPORATION

3 First National Plaza, Chicago, IL, 60602-4260

Tel: (312) 726-2600   Fax: (312) 558-4995   www.saralee.com

Mfr./distributor food and consumer packaged goods, intimate apparel and knitwear.

Pretty Polly Ltd., Park Rd., Killarney County Kerry, Ireland

SAS INSTITUTE INC.

SAS Campus Drive, Cary, NC, 27513

Tel: (919) 677-8000   Fax: (919) 677-4444   www.sas.com

Mfr. and distribution of decision support software.

SAS Institute, 50 Northumberland Road, Dublin 4, Ireland

SCHENKER USA INC.

150 Albany Ave., Freeport, NY, 11520

Tel: (516) 403-5416   Fax: (516) 377-3092   www.schenkerusa.com

Freight forwarders.

Inter Continental Cargo Ltd, Unit 3B, Santry Industrial Estate, Santry, Dublin, Ireland

Tel: 353-1-842-9955   Fax: 353-1-842-9708

SCHERING-PLOUGH CORPORATION

One Giralda Farms, Madison, NJ, 07940-1000

Tel: (973) 822-7000   Fax: (973) 822-7048   www.sch-plough.com

Proprietary drug and cosmetic products.

Schering-Plough Ireland AG, 4 Dartmouth Square, Dublin 6, Ireland

Tel: 353-1-668-8566

SCHIFF HARDIN & WAITE

233 South Wacker Drive, Ste. 7200, Chicago, IL, 60606-6349

Tel: (312) 876-1000   Fax: (312) 258-5700   www.schiffhardin.com

Engaged in international law.

Schiff Hardin & Waite, 3 Burlington Road, Dublin 4, Ireland

Tel: 353-1-202-6555   Fax: 353-1-668-1212

SCHLEGEL SYSTEMS

1555 Jefferson Road, PO Box 23197, Rochester, NY, 14692-3197

Tel: (716) 427-7200   Fax: (716) 427-9993   www.schlegel.com

Mfr. engineered perimeter sealing systems for residential and commercial construction; fibers; rubber product.

Schlegel Ireland Ltd., Dublin Rd., Loughrea, Co. Galway, Ireland

SCHOLASTIC CORPORATION

555 Broadway, New York, NY, 10012

Tel: (212) 343-6100   Fax: (212) 343-6934   www.scholastic.com

Publishing/distribution educational and children's magazines, books, software.

School Book Fairs Ltd., Dublin, Ireland

SEAGATE TECHNOLOGY, INC.

920 Disc Dr., Scotts Valley, CA, 95066

Tel: (408) 438-6550   Fax: (408) 438-7205   www.seagate.com

Develop computer technology, software and hardware.

Seagate Technology, Victoria Cross, Cork, Ireland

Tel: 353-21-856-620   Fax: 353-21-347-180   Contact: Kevin O'Dwyer, Mgr.   Emp: 10

G.D. SEARLE & COMPANY

5200 Old Orchard Road, Skokie, IL, 60077

Tel: (847) 982-7000   Fax: (847) 470-1480   www.searlehealthnet.com

Mfr. pharmaceuticals, health care, optical products and specialty chemicals.

Serale & Company Ltd., Bray Industrial Estate, Pinewood Close Bray, County Wicklow, Ireland

Tel: 353-1-286-7412   Fax: 353-1-282-5894

SENSORMATIC ELECTRONICS CORPORATION

951 Yamato Road, Boca Raton, FL, 33431-0700

Tel: (561) 989-7000   Fax: (561) 989-7774   www.sensormatic.com

Electronic article surveillance equipment.

Sensormatic Electronics Corporation, Melbourne Road, Bishopstown, County Cork, Ireland

Tel: 353-21-801000   Fax: 353-21-801050

SERVICE CORPORATION INTERNATIONAL

1929 Allen Parkway, Houston, TX, 77019

Tel: (713) 522-5141   Fax: (713) 525-5586   www.sci-corp.com

Operates funeral homes, cemeteries and crematoriums and sells caskets, burial vaults and cremation receptacles.

SCI Ireland, Dublin, Ireland

THE SERVICEMASTER COMPANY

2300 Warrenville Road, Downers Grove, IL, 60515-1700

Tel: (630) 271-1300   Fax: (630) 271-2710   www.svm.com

Provides residential consumer services, including lawn care and landscape maintenance, termite and pest control, plumbing, heating and air conditioning maintenance and repair.

Merry Maids, Dublin, Ireland

ServiceMaster, Dublin, Ireland

SIEBEL SYSTEMS, INC.

2207 Bridgepointe Pkwy., San Mateo, CA, 94404

Tel: (650) 295-5000   Fax: (650) 295-5111   www.siebel.com

Provider of e-Business applications software.

Siebel Systems Ireland Limited, IDA Business Park, Dangan Galway, Ireland

Tel: 353-91-518-400

SITEL CORPORATION

111 South Calver Street, Ste. 1900, Baltimore, MD, 21202

Tel: (410) 246-1505   Fax: (410) 246-0200   www.sitel.com

Provides outsourced customer management services.

SITEL, 8 Park West Business Park, Nangor Road, Dubline 12, Ireland

Contact: William Carson

SKILLSOFT INC.

20 Industrial Park Drive, Nashua, NH, 03062

Tel: (603) 324-3000   Fax: (603) 324-3000   www.smartforce.com

Provides strategic learning solutions that help enterprises achieve tangible business results, such as increasing speed and effectiveness of business execution, driving revenues and reducing costs.

SmartCertify Direct, Div. SkillSoft, Glendenning House, 6-8 Wicklow Street, Dublin 2, Ireland

Tel: 353-1-670-3177   Fax: 353-1-670-3211

A.O. SMITH CORPORATION

11270 West Park Place, PO Box 23972, Milwaukee, WI, 53224

Tel: (414) 359-4000   Fax: (414) 359-4064   www.aosmith.com

Auto and truck frames, motors, water heaters, storage/handling systems, plastics, railroad products.

A.O. Smith Electric Motors (Ireland) Ltd., Boghall Rd., Bray, Wicklow, Ireland

Tel: 353-12-868-234   Fax: 353-12-868-237   Contact: Edward Smythe, Gen. Mgr.

SMURFIT-STONE CONTAINER CORPORATION

150 N. Michigan Ave., Chicago, IL, 60601-7568

Tel: (312) 346-6600   Fax: (312) 580-3486   www.smurfit-stone.net

Mfr. paper and paper packaging.

Smurfit-Stone Container Corporation, Dublin, Ireland

SNAP-TITE INC.

8325 Hessinger Road, Erie, PA, 16509

Tel: (814) 838-5700   Fax: (814) 838-6382   www.snap-tite.com

Engaged in the development and manufacture of laboratory, scientific and research instrumentation.

Snap-Tite Europe B.V., Industrial Estate, Whitemill, Wesford, Ireland

Tel: 353-534-1566

SOFTWARE SPECTRUM, INC.

2140 Merritt Drive, Garland, TX, 75041

Tel: (972) 840-6600   Fax: (972) 864-7878   www.softwarespectrum.com

Engaged in software resale.

Software Spectrum Ireland, Merrion House, Merrion Road, Dublin 4, Ireland

Tel: 353-1-260-1788

SOLA INTERNATIONAL INC.

10690 W. Ocean Air Drive, Ste. 300, San Diego, CA, 92130

Tel: (858) 509-9899   Fax: (858) 509-9898   www.sola.com

Mfr. and sales of plastic and glass eyeglasses.

SOLA Ophthalmic Products, Grantham House, 56A Camden Street, Dublin 2, Ireland

SOLECTRON CORPORATION

777 Gibraltar Drive, Milpitas, CA, 95035

Tel: (408) 957-8500   Fax: (408) 956-6075   www.solectron.com

Provides contract manufacturing services to equipment manufacturers.

Solectron Corporation, Clonshaugh Industrial Estate, Dublin 17, Ireland

Tel: 353-1-8484222   Fax: 353-1-8484900

SOTHEBY'S HOLDINGS, INC.

1334 York Avenue, New York, NY, 10021

Tel: (212) 606-7000   Fax: (212) 606-7027   www.sothebys.com

Auction house specializing in fine art and jewelry.

Sotheby's Holdings, Inc., 16 Molesworth Street, Dublin 2, Ireland

Tel: 353-1-671-1786

SPECTRUM CONTROL, INC.

8031 Avonia Road, Fairview, PA, 16415

Tel: (814) 835-1650   Fax: (814) 835-1651   www.spectrumcontrol.com

Mfr. control systems for telecommunications equipment.

Spectrum Control, PO Box 34, Ludham, Great Yarmouth, Norfolk NR29 5RA, Ireland

Tel: 44-1692-678041

SPEEDFAM-IPEC INC.

305 N. 54th Street, Chandler, AZ, 85226-2416

Tel: (480) 961-1600   Fax: (480) 705-2793   www.sfamipec.com

Mfr. semiconductors.

SpeedFam-IPEC, Unit 23, Hills Industrial Estate, Liffey Bridge, Lucan County, Ireland

Tel: 353-1-621-9459   Contact: Henry Cooke

SPS TECHNOLOGIES INC.

165 Township Line Rd., Two Pitcairn Place, Jenkintown, PA, 19046

Tel: (215) 517-2000   Fax: (215) 517-2032   www.spstech.com

Mfr. aerospace and industry fasteners, tightening systems, magnetic materials, super alloys.

High Life Tools, Sub. SPS, Shannon Industrial Estate, Shannon County Clare, Ireland

Tel: 353-61-716500   Fax: 353-61-716584

SPSS INC.

233 S. Wacker Dr., 11th Fl., Chicago, IL, 60606

Tel: (312) 651-6000   Fax: (312) 329-3668   www.spss.com

Mfr. statistical software.

SPSS Ireland Ltd., Data House, 79 Old Kilmainham, Dublin 8, Ireland

SQUIRE, SANDERS & DEMPSEY

4900 Key Tower, 127 Public Square, Cleveland, OH, 44114-1304

Tel: (216) 479-8500   Fax: (216) 479-8780   www.ssd.com

Engaged in international law.

Brian O'Donnell & Partners, 62 Merrion Square, Dublin 2, Ireland

THE ST. PAUL COMPANIES, INC.

385 Washington Street, St. Paul, MN, 55102

Tel: (651) 310-7911   Fax: (651) 310-8294   www.stpaul.com

Provides investment, insurance and reinsurance services.

Hibernian Insurance Company Ltd., Hibernian House, Haddington Road, Dublin 4, Ireland

St. Paul International Insurance Company Ltd., Longphort House, Earlsfort Centre, Lower Leeson St., Dublin 2, Ireland

Tel: 353-1-609-5600   Fax: 353-1-662-4945   Contact: Pala Hodson

STANDEX INTERNATIONAL CORPORATION

6 Manor Parkway, Salem, NH, 03079

Tel: (603) 893-9701   Fax: (603) 893-7324   www.standex.com

Mfr. diversified graphics, institutional, industry, electronic and consumer products.

Standex (Ireland) Ltd., Acragar Road, Mountmellick, County Laois, Ireland

Tel: 353-502-24350 Fax: 353-502-24744   Contact: Patrick McCormack, Mgr.

STATE STREET CORPORATION

225 Franklin Street, Boston, MA, 02101

Tel: (617) 786-3000   Fax: (617) 654-3386   www.statestreet.com

Engaged in investment management and institutional investor services.

Bank of Ireland Securities, New Century House, International Financial Services Centre, Mayor Street Lower Dublin 1, Ireland

STIEFEL LABORATORIES INC.

255 Alhambra Circle, Ste. 1000, Coral Gables, FL, 33134

Tel: (305) 443-3807   Fax: (305) 443-3467   www.stiefel.com

Mfr. pharmaceuticals, dermatological specialties.

Stiefel Laboratories Ltd., Finisklin Industrial Estate, Sligo, Ireland

Stiefel Laboratories Ltd., 15/16 Stillorgan Industrial Park, Blackrock, Co. Dublin, Ireland

STORAGE TECHNOLOGY CORPORATION

One Storagetech Dr., Louisville, CO, 80028-4377

Tel: (303) 673-5151   Fax: (303) 673-5019   www.stortek.com

Mfr., market, service information, storage and retrieval systems.

StorageTek Ireland Limited, 2/F, Temple House, Temple Road, Blackrock, Dublin, Ireland

Contact: Sean Jackman

THE STRUCTURE TONE ORGANIZATION

15 East 26th Street, New York, NY, 10010-1589

Tel: (212) 481-6100   Fax: (212) 685-9267   www.structuretone.com

Provides general contracting and construction management.

Structure Tone Organization, 25 Denzille Lane, Dublin 2, Ireland

SUN MICROSYSTEMS, INC.

901 San Antonio Road, Palo Alto, CA, 94303

Tel: (650) 960-1300   Fax: (650) 961-9131   www.sun.com

Computer peripherals and programming services.

Sun Microsystems, Hamilton House, East Point Business Park, Dublin 3, Ireland

SYBASE, INC.

5000 Hacienda Dr., Dublin, CA, 94568

Tel: (925) 236-5000   Fax: (925) 236-4321   www.sybase.com

Design/mfg/distribution of database management systems, software development tools, connectivity products, consulting and technical support services..

Sybase Products Ltd., 7 Inns Court Winetavern St., Dublin 8, Ireland

Tel: 353-1-677-6777 Fax: 353-1-677-6614

SYKES ENTERPRISES, INC.

100 N. Tampa Street, Ste. 3900, Tampa, FL, 33602

Tel: (813) 274-1000   Fax: (813) 273-0148   www.sykes.com

Provides information technology outsourcing services.

Sykes Enterprises, D1 Industrial Estate, Shannon Co. Clare, Ireland

SYMANTEC CORPORATION

20330 Stevens Creek Blvd., Cupertino, CA, 95014-2132

Tel: (408) 253-9600 Fax: (408) 253-3968 www.symantec.com

Designs and produces PC network security and network management software and hardware.

Symantec Ltd. Ireland, Ballycoolin Business Park, Blanchardstown, Dublin 15, Ireland

Tel: 353-1-820-5060 Fax: 353-1-820-4055

SYNOPSYS, INC.

700 East Middlefield Road, Mountain View, CA, 94043

Tel: (650) 962-5000 Fax: (650) 965-8637 www.synopsys.com

Mfr. electronic design automation software.

Synopsys International Limited, Unit 4B-1, Blanchardstown Corporate Park, Blanchardstown Dublin 15, Ireland

Tel: 353-1-808-9180

TACONIC LTD.

PO Box 69, 136 Coon Brook Road, Petersburg, NY, 12138

Tel: (518) 658-3202 Fax: (518) 658-3204 www.4taconic.com

Mfr. Teflon/silicone-coated fiberglass fabrics, tapes and belts; specialty tapes and circuit board substrates.

Taconic International, Ltd., Mullingar Business Park, Mullingar, County Westmeath, Ireland

Tel: 353-44-40477 Fax: 353-44-44369

TECHNITROL INC.

1210 Northbrook Drive, #385, Trevose, PA, 19053

Tel: (215) 355-2900 Fax: (215) 355-7397 www.technitrol.com

Mfr. of electronic components, electrical contacts, and other parts/materials.

Pulse Engineering Electronic Components, Tuam, Ireland

TELCORDIA TECHNOLOGIES, INC.

445 South Street, Morristown, NJ, 07960-6438

Tel: (973) 829-2000 Fax: (973) 829-3172 www.telecordia.com

Mfr. telecom software.

Telcordia Technologies International, 44 Nortumberland Road, Off. 4, Ballsbridge Dublin 4, Ireland

TELLABS INC.

1415 W. Diehl Rd., Naperville, IL, 60563

Tel: (630) 378-8800 Fax: (630) 852-7346 www.tellabs.com

Design/mfr./service voice/data transport and network access systems.

Tellabs Drogheda, Donore Industrial Site, Droghed, County Louth, Ireland

Tellabs Sandyford, Unit 1B, Bracken Business Park, Sandyford Industrial Estate, Sandyford Dublin, Ireland

TERADYNE INC.

321 Harrison Ave., Boston, MA, 02118

Tel: (617) 482-2700 Fax: (617) 422-2910 www.teradyne.com

Mfr. electronic test equipment and blackplane connection systems.

Teradyne Connection Systems (TCS), Snugboro Industrial Park, Blanchardstown, Dublin 15, Ireland

Tel: 353-1-820-2299 Fax: 353-1-820-3586

TEREX CORPORATION

500 Post Road East, Ste. 320, Westport, CT, 06880

Tel: (203) 222-7170 Fax: (203) 222-7976 www.terex.com

Mfr. lifting and earthmoving equipment.

Powerscreen Ireland Ltd., No. 4, 90 Main Street, Portlaoise, County Laoise, Ireland

Tel: 353-502-22978

Powerscreen Ltd., Lower Main Street, Kilbeggan, County Westmeath, Ireland

Tel: 353-506-32178

TEXAS INSTRUMENTS INC.

12500 TI Blvd., Dallas, TX, 75266

Tel: (972) 995-3773   Fax: (972) 995-4360   www.ti.com

Mfr. semiconductor devices, electronic electro-mechanical systems, instruments and controls.

Texas Instruments Ltd., Dublin, Ireland

THERMA-TRU CORPORATION

1687 Woodlands Drive, Maumee, OH, 43537

Tel: (419) 891-7400   Fax: (419) 891-7411   www.thermatru.com

Mfr. fiberglass doors.

Artic Doors/Therma-Tru, Killanne, Enniscorthy Co., Wexford, Ireland

Tel: 44-353-54-55479   Fax: 44-353-55480

THERM-O-DISC, INC.

1320 S. Main Street, Mansfield, OH, 44907-0538

Tel: (419) 525-8300   Fax: (419) 525-8344   www.thermodisc.com

Mfr. thermostats, controls, sensor and thermal cutoffs, switches.

Therm-O-Disc, Raheen Estate, Limerick, Ireland

TJX COMPANIES INC.

770 Cochituate Road, Framingham, MA, 01701

Tel: (508) 390-1000   Fax: (508) 390-2828   www.tjx.com

Retail stores, catalog and mail order houses.

T. J. Maxx, Dublin, Ireland

TMP WORLDWIDE, INC.

622 Third Ave., New York, NY, 10017

Tel: (212) 351-7000   Fax: (212) 658-0540   www.tmpw.com

#1 Yellow Pages agency and a leader in the recruitment and interactive advertising fields.

TMP Worldwide, 10 Lower Mount Street, 2/F, Dublin 2, Ireland

TMP Worldwide Advertising & Communications, 15 D Gilford Road, Sandymount, Dublin 4, Ireland

TOKHEIM CORPORATION

PO Box 360, 10501 Corporate Drive, Fort Wayne, IN, 46845

Tel: (219) 470-4600   Fax: (219) 482-2677   www.tokheim.com

Engaged in design, manufacture and service of electronic and mechanical petroleum marketing systems.

Tokheim Ireland, Western Parkway, Ballymount Road, Dublin 12, Ireland

Tel: 353-1-4500575   Fax: 353-1-4500597

THE TOPPS COMPANY, INC.

1 Whitehall Street, New York, NY, 10004-2108

Tel: (212) 376-0300   Fax: (212) 376-0573   www.topps.com

Mfr. entertainment products, principally collectible trading cards, confections, sticker collections, and comic books.

Topps Ireland Ltd., Innishmore, Ballincollig, County Cork, Ireland

Tel: 353-21-871005   Fax: 353-21-870512

THE TRANE COMPANY

3600 Pammel Creek Road, La Crosse, WI, 54601

Tel: (608) 787-2000   Fax: (608) 787-4990   www.trane.com

Mfr. distribution and service of A/C systems and equipment.

Trane (UK) Ltd., 8 The Mall, Lucan, Co. Dublin, Ireland

TRANSISTOR DEVICES, INC.

85 Horsehill Road, Cedar Knolls, NJ, 07927

Tel: (973) 267-1900   Fax: (973) 267-2047   www.tdipower.com

Mfr. electronic power supplies and equipment.

TDI Ireland, Carrigtwohill Industrial Estate, Carrigtwohill, County Cork, Ireland

UNIFI INC.

7201 West Friendly Ave., Greensboro, NC, 27410-6237

Tel: (336) 294-4410   Fax: (336) 316-5422   www.unifi-inc.com

Yarn spinning mills, throwing/winding mills.

Unifi Textured Yarns Europe Ltd., Ballyraine, Letterkenny, Donegal, Ireland

UNITED PARCEL SERVICE, INC.

55 Glenlake Parkway, NE, Atlanta, GA, 30328

Tel: (404) 828-6000   Fax: (404) 828-6593   www.ups.com

International package-delivery service.

UPS Ireland Ltd., Unit 134, Slaney Close, Dublin Industrial Estate, Glasnevin, Dublin 11, Ireland

Tel: 800-575757

UNIVERSAL SECURITY INSTRUMENTS, INC.

PO Box 825, Binghamton, NY, 13902-0825

Tel: (607) 779-7689   Fax: (607) 779-7301   www.uic.com

Provider of innovative electronic circuit assembly technology and equipment, integrated system solutions, and process expertise.

Universal Instruments Elecronics Ltd., Dublin, Ireland

Tel: 353-1-492-3766   Fax: 353-1-492-3766

UOP LLC

25 East Algonquin Road, Des Plaines, IL, 60017

Tel: (847) 391-2000   Fax: (847) 391-2253   www.uop.com

Engaged in developing and commercializing technology for license to the oil refining, petrochemical and gas processing industries.

UOP Johnson Well Screens (Ireland) Ltd., Leixlip, Ireland

UPRIGHT INC.

1775 Park Street, Selma, CA, 93662

Tel: (209) 891-5200   Fax: (209) 896-9012   www.upright.com

Mfr. aerial work platforms and telescopic handlers.

UpRight Ireland Ltd., Industrial Estate, Pottery Rd., Dun Laoire, Dublin, Ireland

URS CORPORATION

100 California Street, Ste. 500, San Francisco, CA, 94111

Tel: (415) 774-2700   Fax: (415) 398-1905   www.urscorp.com

Engineering, environmental and construction management services.

Dames & Moore, 2214 Richmond Business Campus, North Brunswick St., Dublin 7, Ireland

USINTERNETWORKING, INC.

1 USI Plaza, Annapolis, MD, 21401-7478

Tel: (410) 897-4400   Fax: (410) 573-1906   www.usi-net

Mfr. software.

USI-Net Ireland, Clonshaugh Industrial Estate, Coolock, Dublin, Ireland

UUNET

22001 Loudoun County Pkwy., Ashburn, VA, 20147

Tel: (703) 206-5600   Fax: (703) 206-5601   www.uu.net

World's largest Internet service provider; World Wide Web hosting services, security products and consulting services to businesses, professionals, and on-line service providers.

UUNET Ireland, Erne Street, Dublin 2, Ireland

VALSPAR CORPORATION

1101 South Third Street, Minneapolis, MN, 55415-1259

Tel: (612) 332-7371   Fax: (612) 375-7723   www.valspar.com

Mfr. paints and coatings.

Valspar/Lilly Industries, Willowfield Road, Ballinamore, County Leitrim, Ireland

VARIAN SEMICONDUCTOR EQUIPMENT ASSOCIATES, INC. (VSEA)

35 Dory Road, Gloucester, MA, 01930

Tel: (978) 281-2000   Fax: (978) 283-5391   www.vsea.com

Mfr. semiconductors and ion implantation systems.

VSEA Ireland, M/S IR2-14, Colinstown Industrial Park, Leixlip, County Kildare, Ireland

Tel: 353-1-606-6504

VASTERA, INC.

45025 Aviation Drive, Ste. 300, Dulles, VA, 20166

Tel: (703) 661-9006   Fax: (703) 742-4580   www.vastera.com

Helps companies to define and deploy best business processes for trade and manages their global trade operations.

Vastera Ireland, 17 Hazel Lane, Drogheda, County Louth, Ireland

VERIZON COMMUNICATIONS INC.

1095 Ave. of the Americas, New York, NY, 10036

Tel: (212) 395-2121   Fax: (212) 395-1285   www.verizon.com

Telecommunications.

Cable & Wireless Ireland, 1 Airton Road, Tallaght, Dublin 24, Ireland

VERIZON WIRELESS, INC.

180 Washington Valley Rd., Bedminster, NJ, 07921

Tel: (908) 306-7000   Fax: (908) 306-6927   www.verizonwireless.com

Engaged in mobile phone operations.

Vodafone Ireland, Unit 9 Richview Business Park, Clonskeagh, Dublin 14, Ireland

VERTEX INTERACTIVE, INC.

22 Audrey Place, Fairfield, NJ, 07004

Tel: (973) 777-3500   Fax: (973) 472-0814   www.vertexinteractive.com

Mfr. software.

Vertex Interactive, 31-33 The Triangle, Ranelagh, Dublin 6, Ireland

THE WARNACO GROUP INC.

90 Park Ave., New York, NY, 10016

Tel: (212) 661-1300   Fax: (212) 687-0480   www.warnaco.com

Mfr./sales intimate apparel and men's and women's sportswear.

Warnaco, Dublin, Ireland

WASHINGTON GROUP INTERNATIONAL, INC.

720 Park Blvd., PO Box 73, Boise, ID, 83729

Tel: (208) 386-5000   Fax: (208) 386-7186   www.wgint.com

Engaged in engineering and construction.

Washington Group International, Inc., 12 South Mall, Cork, Ireland

Tel: 353-21-906800   Fax: 353-21-906801

WEBER MARKING SYSTEMS INC.

711 West Algonquin Road, Arlington Heights, IL, 60005-4457

Tel: (847) 364-8500   Fax: (847) 364-8575   www.webermarking.com

Mfr. label printing systems and custom labels.

Weber Marking Systems Ireland, 61 Irish Street, Enniscorthy, County Wexford, Ireland

Tel: 353-54-33-778

WELCH ALLYN INC.

4341 State Street Road, Skaneateles Falls, NY, 13153

Tel: (315) 685-4100   Fax: (315) 685-4091   www.welchallyn.com

Mfr. fiber optic products and medical diagnostic equipment.

Welch Allyn Ireland Ltd., Kells Road, Navan, County Meath, Ireland

Tel: 353-46-79060

Welch Allyn Ltd. (Data Collection Division), 21 Sandyford Office Park, Sandyford, Dublin 18, Ireland

WELLMAN INC.

595 Shrewsbury Avenue, Shrewsbury, NJ, 07702

Tel: (732) 212-3300   Fax: (732) 212-3344   www.wellmaninc.com

Mfr. and sale of polyester products, including Fortrel brand polyester textile fibers, polyester fibers made from recycled raw materials and PermaClear PET (polyethylene terephthalate) resins.

Wellman International Ltd., Mullagh, Kells, Meath, Ireland

WESTERN WIRELESS CORPORATION

3650 131st Avenue SE, Ste. 400, Bellevue, WA, 98006

Tel: (425) 586-8700   Fax: (425) 586-8666   www.wwireless.com

Provides wireless communication services.

Meteor Mobile Communications Ltd., 4030 Kingswood Avenue, Citywest Business Park Naas Road, Dublin 24, Ireland

WHIRLPOOL CORPORATION

2000 N. M-63, Benton Harbor, MI, 49022-2692

Tel: (616) 923-5000   Fax: (616) 923-5443   www.whirlpoolcorp.com

Mfr., market home appliances: Whirlpool, Roper, KitchenAid, Estate, and Inglis.

Whirlpool Europe B.V., Dublin, Ireland

WILLAMETTE INDUSTRIES, INC.

1300 SW Fifth Ave., Ste. 3800, Portland, OR, 97201

Tel: (503) 227-5581   Fax: (503) 273-5603   www.wii.com

Mfr./sales and distribution of paper and wood products.

Willamette Europe, Redmondstown, Clonmel, County Tipperrary, Ireland

Tel: 353-52-21166   Fax: 353-52-21815   Contact: Rory Kirwan, Mng. Dir.   Emp: 200

HARRY WINSTON INC.

718 Fifth Ave., New York, NY, 10019

Tel: (212) 245-2000   Fax: (212) 245-2000   www.harry-winston.com

Diamonds and lapidary work.

Harry Winston Irish Rough Diamonds Ltd., Hermitage, Ennis, Clare, Ireland

WORLDCOM, INC.

500 Clinton Center Drive, Clinton, MS, 39060

Tel: (601) 360-8600   Fax: (601) 360-8616   www.wcom.com

*Telecommunications; serving local, long distance and Internet customers domestically and internationally. **Corporation under worldwide reorganization under Chapter 11 Bankruptcy; new data unavailable for this edition.*

WorldCom International, International Business Centre, National Technological Park, Limerick, Ireland

WorldCom International, MCI WorldCom House, Ballybrit Business Park, Galway, Ireland

WorldCom International, Embassy House, Ballsbridge, Dublin 4, Ireland

WorldCom International, Versyss Building, Mahon Industrial Estate, Blackrock County Cork, Ireland

WYETH

5 Giralda Farms, Madison, NJ, 07940-0874

Tel: (973) 660-5000   Fax: (973) 660-7026   www.wyeth.com

Mfr. consumer healthcare products.

Whitehall Laboratories Limited, 765 South Circular Road, Islandbridge, Dublin, Ireland

Tel: 353-16-772-669   Fax: 353-16-797-278

WYETH PHARMACEUTICALS

555 E. Lancaster Ave., Wayne, PA, 19087-5109

Tel: (610) 971-5400   Fax: (610) 995-4668   www.wyeth.com

Mfr. antibiotics and pharmaceutical products.

Wyeth Laboratories, 765 South Circular Road, Islandbridge, Dublin 8, Ireland

Tel: 353-1-6709200

XEROX CORPORATION

800 Long Ridge Road, PO Box 1600, Stamford, CT, 06904

Tel: (203) 968-3000   Fax: (203) 968-4312   www.xerox.com

Mfr. document processing equipment, systems and supplies.

Xerox Ltd., Glasnevin Industrial Estate, Finglas Rd., Dublin 11, Ireland

Tel: 353-1-661-6322   Fax: 353-1-806-2581

XILINX INC.

2100 Logic Drive, San Jose, CA, 95124-3400

Tel: (408) 559-7778   Fax: (408) 559-7114   www.xilinx.com

Programmable logic and related development systems software.

Xilinx Ireland, 1 Logic Dr., Citywest Business Campus, Saggart County, Dublin, Ireland

Tel: 353-1-464-0311

XL REINSURANCE AMERICA INC.

70 Seaview Ave., Stamford, CT, 06902-6040

Tel: (203) 964-5200   Fax: (203) 964-0763   www.xlcapital.com

Provides reinsurance products.

XL Europe Ltd., La Touche House, International Financial Services Centre, Dublin 1, Ireland

YAHOO! INC.

701 First Avenue, Sunnyvale, CA, 94089

Tel: (408) 439-3300   Fax: (408) 439-3301   www.yahoo-inc.com

Internet media company providing specialized content, free electronic mail and community offerings and commerce.

Yahoo! Inc., Ireland -c/o 80/81 St. Martin's Lane, London WC2N 4AA, UK

YELLOW CORPORATION

10990 Roe Ave., PO Box 7270, Overland Park, KS, 66207

Tel: (913) 696-6100   Fax: (913) 696-6116   www.yellowcorp.com

Commodity transportation.

Frans Maas Ireland Ltd., Swords Business Park, Swords, County Dublin, Ireland

Frans Maas Ireland ltd., Newmarket on Fergus, Shannon, Count Cuare, Ireland

YORK INTERNATIONAL CORPORATION

631 South Richland Ave., York, PA, 17403

Tel: (717) 771-7890   Fax: (717) 771-6212   www.york.com

Mfr. heating, ventilating, air conditioning and refrigeration equipment.

York Ireland, Unit 19, University Hale Ind. Estate, Sarsfield Road, Wilton Cork, Ireland

Tel: 353-21-346-580

York Ireland, Unit 2004/3, City West Business Campus, Naas Road, Dublin 22, Ireland

Tel: 353-1-466-0177

ZOMAX INCORPORATED

5353 Nathan Lane, Plymouth, MN, 55442

Tel: (763) 553-9300   Fax: (763) 519-3710   www.zomax.com

Engaged in outsourcing services.

Zomax Limited, Carrisbrook House, 122 Pembroke Road, Ballsbridge, Dublin 4, Ireland

Tel: 353-1-405-6350   Fax: 353-1-457-7675

Zomax Limited, Unit 1, Cloverhill Industrial Estate, Clondalkin, Dublin 22, Ireland

Tel: 353-1-405-6218   Fax: 353-1-457-7675   Contact: Mike Murphy

Isle of Man

AON CORPORATION

200 East Randolph, Chicago, IL, 60601

Tel: (312) 381-1000   Fax: (312) 381-6032   www.aon.com

Insurance brokers worldwide; underwrites accident and health insurance, specialty and professional insurance; and provides risk management consultation.

AON Insurance Managers (Isle of Man) Ltd., Post Office Chambers, Douglas IM11 2EA, UK

Tel: 44-1634-689-400   Fax: 44-1624-673-242   Contact: Geoll Hunk

AON Risk Services Ltd., 28 Athol St., Douglas 1M1 1QE, UK

Tel: 44-1624-673-325   Fax: 44-1624-623-664   Contact: Mike Henthorn

BDO SEIDMAN, LLP   BELGIUM

130 East Randolph Street, Chicago, IL, 60601

Tel: (312) 856-9100   Fax: (312) 856-1379   www.bdo.com

International accounting and financial consulting firm.

BDO Binder, Ragnall House, 18 Peel Road, Douglas IM1 4LZ, UK

Tel: 44-1624-620711   Fax: 44-1624-672446   Contact: John D. Clarke

DHL WORLDWIDE EXPRESS

50 California Avenue, San Francisco, CA, 94111

Tel: (415) 677-6100   Fax: (415) 824-9700   www.dhl.com

Worldwide air express carrier.

DHL Worldwide Express, Island Express, Unit 27, Spring Valley Industrial Estate, Bradden IM2 2QT, UK

Tel: 44-1624-661122   Fax: 44-1624-661394

ERNST & YOUNG INTERNATIONAL

5 Times Square, New York, NY, 10036

Tel: (212) 773-3000   Fax: (212) 773-6350   www.eyi.com

Engaged in assurance and advisory business services, tax, law and corporate finance.

Ernst & Young International, Derby Housem Athol St., Douglas, UK

Tel: 44-1624-626661   Fax: 44-1624-626375   Contact: Larry A. Kearns

ICC INDUSTRIES INC.

460 Park Ave., New York, NY, 10022

Tel: (212) 521-1700   Fax: (212) 521-1794   www.iccchem.com

Manufacturing and trading of chemicals, plastics and pharmaceuticals.

Dover Chemical Ltd., 1 Athol St., Douglas 1M1 1LD, UK

Tel: 44-1624-626-573   Fax: 44-1624-616-350   Contact: Dwain Colvin

KPMG CONSULTING INC.

1676 International Dr., McLean, VA, 22102

Tel: (703) 747-3000   Fax: (703) 747-8500   www.kpmg.com

Accounting and audit, tax and management consulting services.

KPMG International, Heritage Court, 41 Athol Street, Douglas 1M99 1HN, UK

Tel: 44-1624-681000   Fax: 44-1624-681098   Contact: Peter F. Pell-Hiley, Sr. Ptnr.

MERRILL LYNCH & COMPANY, INC.

World Financial Center, 250 Vesey Street, New York, NY, 10281-1332

Tel: (212) 236-1000   Fax: (212) 449-2892   www.ml.com

Security brokers and dealers, investment and business services.

Merrill Lynch International - Trust Services, Atlantic House, Circular Road, Douglas 1M1 1QW, UK

Tel: 44-1624-688600   Fax: 44-1624-688601

Merrill Lynch Investment Managers, Belgravia House, 34/44 Circular Road, Douglas IM1 1QW, Isle of Man

PRICEWATERHOUSECOOPERS LLP

1301 Ave. of the Americas, New York, NY, 10019

Tel:　(212) 596-7000　　　　Fax:　(212) 259-1301　　　　　www.pwcglobal.com

Accounting and auditing, tax and management, and human resource consulting services.

PriceWaterhouseCoopers, 1-3 Upper Church St., Douglas, UK

Tel: 44-1624-662550　　Fax: 44-1624-673113

Israel

3COM CORPORATION

5400 Bayfront Plaza, Santa Clara, CA, 95052-8145

Tel: (408) 326-5000   Fax: (408) 326-5001   www.3com.com

Engaged in the development and manufacture of computer networking products and systems.

3Com Israel, 6 H'Baal Shem Tov Street, PO Box 867, LOD 71100, Israel

Tel: 972-8-920-6373

3M (MINNESOTA MINING & MFG.)

3M Center, St. Paul, MN, 55144-1000

Tel: (651) 733-1110   Fax: (651) 733-9973   www.mmm.com

Mfr. diversified products for industry, consumer, health care, imaging, communications, transport, safety, etc.

3M Israel Ltd., 91 Medinat H'yehudim Street, Herzilya 46120, Israel

Tel: 972-9-561-490   Fax: 972-9-561676

AAR CORPORATION

1100 North Wood Dale Road, Wood Dale, IL, 60191

Tel: (630) 227-2000   Fax: (630) 227-2019   www.aarcorp.com

Provides aviation repair and supply provisioning; aircraft sales and leasing.

AAR International, Local: 9, Hamachtarot Street, Ra'anana 4335, Israel

Tel: 972-977-16581

AAVID THERMAL TECHNOLOGIES, INC.

1 Eagle Square, Ste. 509, Concord, NH, 03301

Tel: (603) 224-1117   Fax: (603) 224-6673   www.aatt.com

Mfr. fluid dynamics software.

Aavid Thermalloy Srl, Via XXV Aprile 32, Cadriano Bologna 40138, Israel

Tel: 39-051-764002

ABBOTT LABORATORIES

100 Abbott Park Rd., Abbott Park, IL, 60064

Tel: (847) 937-6100   Fax: (847) 937-1511   www.abbott.com

Development, manufacture and sale of diversified health care products and services.

Abbott Pharmaceuticals ProMedico Ltd., PO Box 29031, Tel Aviv 61292, Israel

ADC TELECOMMUNICATIONS INC.

13625 Technology Drive, Eden Prairie, MN, 55344

Tel: (952) 938-8080   Fax: (952) 946-3292   www.adc.com

Mfr. telecommunications equipment.

ADC Telecommunications, 10 Ha'Sadnaot St., P.O. Box 2003, Herzliya 49520, Israel

Tel: 972-9-959-1818   Fax: 972-9-959-1888

ADE CORPORATION

80 Wilson Way, Westwood, MA, 02090

Tel: (781) 467-3500   Fax: (781) 467-0500   www.ade.com

Mfr. semiconductor wafers and computer disks.

G-Electronics, 3 Tefutsot Israel Street, Industrial Center, Givatayim 53583, Israel

Tel: 972-35-14333   Fax: 972-35-13958

AGILENT TECHNOLOGIES, INC.

395 Page Mill Road, PO Box 10395, Palo Alto, CA, 94303

Tel: (650) 752-5000   Fax: (650) 752-5633   www.agilent.com

Mfr. communications components.

Agilent Technologies Israel Ltd., 2 Hashlosh Street, Building B3, Tel Aviv 67060, Israel

ALLEGHENY TECHNOLOGIES INC.

1000 Six PPG Place, Pittsburgh, PA, 15222

Tel: (412) 394-2800   Fax: (412) 394-2805   www.alleghenytechnologies.com

Diversified mfr. aviation and electronics, specialty metals, industrial and consumer products.

Allegheny Technologies, America House, 35 Shaul Hamelech Blvd., Tel Aviv 64927, Israel

Composite Ltd., 12 Ha-Gat Street, #27, Rishon Le Ziyyon 75498, Israel

ALPHA WIRE COMPANY

711 Lidgerwood Ave., Elizabeth, NJ, 07207

Tel: (908) 925-8000   Fax: (908) 925-6923   www.alphawire.com

Mfr. wire, cable and tubing products.

Gilad Yalon, 5 Hazoran Street, PO Box 8849, Netanya 42504, Israel

Tel: 972-892-4444   Fax: 972-892-4455

AMDOCS LIMITED

1390 Timberlake Manor Pkwy., Chesterfield, MO, 63017

Tel: (314) 212-7000   Fax: (314) 212-7500   www.amdocs.com

Mfr. telecommunications software.

Amdocs Israel, 8 Hapnina Street, Ra'anana 43000, Israel

AMERICAN EXPRESS COMPANY

90 Hudson Street, Jersey City, NJ, 07302

Tel: (212) 640-2000   Fax: (212) 619-9802   www.americanexpress.com

Engaged in travel, travelers cheques, charge card and financial services.

American Express Travel Service, El Al Building, 32 Ben Yehuda Street, Tel Aviv, Israel

AMERICAN LOCKER GROUP INC.

608 Allen Street, Jamestown, NY, 14701-3966

Tel: (716) 664-9600   Fax: (716) 483-2822   www.americanlocker.com

Mfr. coin-operated locks and office furniture.

Safe Locker Secure Storage Systems, 50 Dizengoff Street, Tel Aviv, Israel

Tel: 972-3-621-2401   Fax: 972 3 621 240

AMERICAN SAFETY RAZOR COMPANY

240 Cedar Knolls Rd., Ste. 401, Cedar Knolls, NJ, 07927

Tel: (973) 753-3000   Fax: (973) 326-9004   www.asrco.com

Mfr. private-label and branded shaving razors and blades and cotton swabs.

Personna Israel, 1 Derech Hachativot Street, Upper Nazareth 17000, Israel

ANALOG DEVICES INC.

1 Technology Way, Norwood, MA, 02062

Tel: (781) 329-4700   Fax: (781) 326-8703   www.analog.com

Mfr. integrated circuits and related devices.

Analog Devices (Israel) Ltd., Giron Ctr., 3-5 Jabolinsky St., Ra'anana 43363, Israel

ANC RENTAL CORPORATION

200 S. Andrews Ave., Ft. Lauderdale, FL, 33301

Tel: (954) 320-4000   Fax: (954) 320-4077   www.ancrental.com

Engaged in car rental services, including National Car Rental and Alamo Rent A Car.

National Car Rental, Box 26113, Tel Aviv, Israel

ANDERSEN

33 West Monroe Street, Chicago, IL, 60603

Tel: (312) 580-0033   Fax: (312) 507-6748   www.andersen.com

*Accounting and audit, tax and management consulting services. **Firm under worldwide reorganization; new data unavailable for this edition.*

Luboshitz, Kasierer & Co., 9 Achad Ha'am St., Shalom Tower, PO Box 29452, Tel-Aviv 61293, Israel

Tel: 972-3-511-8222

ANDREA ELECTRONICS CORPORATION

45 Melville Park Road, Melville, NY, 11747

Tel: (631) 719-1800   Fax: (631) 719-1950   www.andreaelectronics.com

Mfr. noise reduction electronic headsets, handsets and microphones.

Lamar Signal Processing, Ltd., PO Box 273, Yoqneam Ilit 20692, Israel

APPLIED MATERIALS, INC.

3050 Bowers Ave., Santa Clara, CA, 95054-3299

Tel: (408) 727-5555   Fax: (408) 727-9943   www.appliedmaterials.com

Supplies manufacturing systems and services to the semiconductor industry.

Applied Materials Israel, Ltd., SB Industry Campus Har Hotzvim, 5 Kiryat-Mada St., Luz Bldg., PO Box 45141, Jerusalem 91450, Israel

Tel: 972-2-58-70750   Fax: 972-2-58-70757

Applied Materials, Ltd., Atidim Industrial Park, Bldg. 2, PO Box 58152, Tel Aviv 61581, Israel

Tel: 972-3-645-0201   Fax: 972-3-645-0280

APPLIED MICRO CIRCUITS CORPORATION

6290 Sequence Drive, San Diego, CA, 92121

Tel: (858) 450-9333   Fax: (858) 535-6500   www.amcc.com

Mfr. voice and data transmissions software.

AMCC Israel Ltd., 10B Giborei Israel Street, PO Box 8402, Netanya 42504, Israel

ASSOCIATED MERCHANDISING CORPORATION

500 Seventh Ave., 2nd Fl., New York, NY, 10018

Tel: (212) 819-6600   Fax: (212) 819-6701   www.theamc.com

Retail service organization; apparel, shoes and accessories.

Associated Merchandising Corp., Migdalel Vaiv Bldg., 6th Fl., 48A Petach Tikva Rd., Tel Aviv 66184, Israel

ASTEA INTERNATIONAL, INC.

455 Business Center Drive, Horsham, PA, 19044

Tel: (215) 682-2500   Fax: (215) 682-2515   www.astea.com

Produces computer software that assists to automate and manage field service, sales and customer support operations.

Astea-Israel Ltd., PO Box 7, Industrial Park Tefen, Migdal, Tefen 24959, Israel

Tel: 972-4-987-2519   Fax: 972-4-987-2031

ASTRONAUTICS CORPORATION OF AMERICA

4115 N. Teutonia Ave., Milwaukee, WI, 53209-6731

Tel: (414) 447-8200   Fax: (414) 447-8231   www.astronautics.com

Design/development/mfr. aircraft instruments, avionics, electronics systems, vehicle electronics and computer maintenance service.

Astronautics C.A. Ltd., 23 Hayarkon St., PO Box 882, Bnei-Brak, Israel

AUTODESK INC.

111 McInnis Parkway, San Rafael, CA, 94903

Tel: (415) 507-5000   Fax: (415) 507-6112   www.autodesk.com

Develop/marketing/support computer-aided design, engineering, scientific and multimedia software products.

Audodesk Israel Ltd., 11 Galgalei Haplada St., PO Box 12590, Herzliya 46733, Israel

Tel: 972-9-950-4610   Fax: 972-9-950-3726

AVX CORPORATION

801 17th Ave. South, Myrtle Beach, SC, 29577

Tel: (843) 448-9411   Fax: (843) 448-7139   www.avxcorp.com

Mfr. multilayer ceramic capacitors.

AVX Israel Ltd., PO Box 3108, Jerusalem 91030, Israel

AXEDA SYSTEMS INC.

257 Great Valley Pkwy., Malvern, PA, 19355

Tel: (610) 251-9999   Fax: (610) 695-2592   www.axeda.com

Mfr. software.

Axeda Systems, Basel 16, PO Box 10151, Petach Tikva 49002, Israel

BARNWELL INDUSTRIES INC.

1100 Alakea Street, Ste. 2900, Honolulu, HI, 96813-2833

Tel: (808) 531-8400   Fax: (808) 531-7181   www.brninc.con

Holding company: exploration/development gas and oil, drill water systems, farming/marketing papayas.

Barnwell of Israel Ltd., PO Box 3005, Tel Aviv 61030, Israel

BARRY CONTROLS INC.

40 Guest Street, PO Box 9105, Brighton, MA, 02135-9105

Tel: (617) 787-1555   Fax: (617) 254-7381   www.barrymounts.com

Mfr./sale vibration isolation mounting devices.

Mono Electronics Ltd., PO Box 8198, New Industrial Zone, Netanya 422943, Israel

BATES WORLDWIDE INC.

498 Seventh Avenue, New York, NY, 10018

Tel: (212) 297-7000   Fax: (212) 986-0270   www.batesww.com

Advertising, marketing, public relations and media consulting.

Bates Armoni, 22 Seadia Gaon St., Tel-Aviv 67135, Israel

Tel: 972-3-5650565   Fax: 972-3-5650555   Contact: Yoran Baumann, Pres.

BBDO WORLDWIDE

1285 Ave. of the Americas, New York, NY, 10019

Tel: (212) 459-5000   Fax: (212) 459-6645   www.bbdo.com

Multinational group of advertising agencies.

Gitam BBDO, 3 Abba Hillel Silver Street, Ramat-Gan 52522, Israel

Tel: 972-3-5765757   Fax: 972-3-7525564

BDO SEIDMAN, LLP   BELGIUM

130 East Randolph Street, Chicago, IL, 60601

Tel: (312) 856-9100   Fax: (312) 856-1379   www.bdo.com

International accounting and financial consulting firm.

BDO Almgor & Company, Silver House, 12th Floor, 7 Habba Hillel Rd., Ramat-Gan 52134, Israel

Tel: 972-3-576-0606   Fax: 972-3-575-4671   Contact: Yali Sheffi

THE BEAR STEARNS & COMPANIES., INC.

245 Park Ave., New York, NY, 10167

Tel: (212) 272-2000   Fax: (212) 272-3092   www.bearstearns.com

Investment banking, securities broker/dealer and investment advisory services.

Bear, Stearns & Co. Inc.
Representative Office, Ackerstein Towers - East Wing, 11 Hamenofim Street, 9th Floor, Herzliya 46725, Israel

BEBE STORES, INC.

380 Valley Drive, Brisbane, CA, 94005

Tel: (415) 715-3900   Fax: (415) 715-3939   www.bebe.com

Mfr. contemporary clothes for young women.

Bebe Stores, Inc., Emporium, Herod Hotel Walkway, Eilat City, Israel

BELLSOUTH CORPORATION LATIN AMERICA

1155 Peachtree Street NE, Ste. 400, Atlanta, GA, 30367

Tel: (404) 249-4800   Fax: (404) 249-4880   www.bellsouth.com

Mobile communications, telecommunications network systems.

Cellcom, 2001 Merkazim Building, 29 Maskit Street, Herzliya Pituach 46733, Israel

Tel: 972-9-959-9599

BEN & JERRY'S HOMEMADE INC.

30 Community Drive, South Burlington, VT, 05403-6828

Tel: (802) 651-9600   Fax: (802) 651-9647   www.benjerry.com

Mfr. premium ice cream.

Ben & Jerry's International, Yavne, Israel

Ben & Jerry's International, Jerusalem, Israel

Ben & Jerry's International, 1 Hameisav St., Yavne 70600, Israel

Tel: 972-8-943-7474   Fax: 972-8-943-7475

BERLITZ CROSS-CULTURAL TRAINING INC.

400 Alexander Park, Princeton, NJ, 08540

Tel: (609) 514-9650   Fax: (609) 514-9689   www.berlitz.com

Consulting and management training services to bridge cultural gaps for international travelers as well as for business transferees and families.

Berlitz (Israel) Ltd., 37 Shaul Hamelech Avenue, Tel Aviv 64982, Israel

BEST WESTERN INTERNATIONAL

6201 North 24th Place, Phoenix, AZ, 85106

Tel: (602) 957-4200   Fax: (602) 957-5740   www.bestwestern.com

International hotel chain.

Nof Hotel, 101 Hanassi Ave., Haifa, Israel

SAMUEL BINGHAM ENTERPRISES INC.

9529 South Main Street, Jonesboro, GA, 30236

Tel: (770) 477-7503   Fax: (770) 477-9532   www.binghamrollers.com

Mfr. rubber covered rolls, chemicals and supplies for the printing industry.

Haglil Ltd., PO Box 862, Ashdod 77107, Israel

BIO-RAD LABORATORIES INC.

1000 Alfred Nobel Drive, Hercules, CA, 94547

Tel: (510) 724-7000   Fax: (510) 724-3167   www.bio-rad.com

Mfr. life science research products, clinical diagnostics, analytical instruments.

Bio-Rad Laboratories, New Industrial Area, 12 Homa Street, Rishon Le Zion 75150, Israel

BIO-TECHNOLOGY GENERAL CORP.

70 Wood Avenue South, Iselin, NJ, 08830

Tel: (732) 632-8800   Fax: (732) 632-8844   www.btgc.com

Engaged in research, development and marketing of genetically engineered pharmaceuticals.

BTG Israel Ltd. (Bio-Technology General Ltd.), Kiryat Weizmann, Rehovot 76326, Israel

Contact: Dr. Dov Kanner   Emp: 200

BMC SOFTWARE, INC.

2101 City West Blvd., Houston, TX, 77042-2827

Tel: (713) 918-8800   Fax: (713) 918-8000   www.bmc.com

Engaged in mainframe-related utilities software and services.

BMC Software, ATIDIM, Bldg. 7, PO Box 58168, Tel Aviv 61581, Israel

BOZELL GROUP

40 West 23rd Street, New York, NY, 10010

Tel: (212) 727-5000   Fax: (212) 645-9173   www.bozell.com

Advertising, marketing, public relations and media consulting.

Dahaf Group, 2-Ben-TZVI Blvd., Jaffa, Tel-Aviv 68181, Israel

Tel: 972-3-512-7788   Fax: 972-3-683-5413   Contact: Oren Zurabin, CEO & Gen. Mgr.

BRANSON ULTRASONICS CORPORATION

41 Eagle Road, Danbury, CT, 06813-1961

Tel: (203) 796-0400   Fax: (203) 796-2285   www.branson-plasticsjoin.com

Engaged in design, development, manufacture and marketing of plastics joining, precision cleaning and processing equipment.

Elina Ltd., PO Box 11439, Bet-Dagan 58001, Israel

Tel: 972-3-559-0337   Fax: 972-3-556-0952

BRINK'S INC.

Thorndal Circle, Darien, CT, 06820

Tel: (203) 662-7800   Fax: (203) 662-7968   www.brinks.com

Security transportation.

Brink's Israel Ltd., Migdal Shalom Mayer Bldg, 9 Ahad-Haam St., PO Box 29785, Tel Aviv, Israel

BRISTOL-MYERS SQUIBB COMPANY

345 Park Ave., New York, NY, 10154-0037

Tel: (212) 546-4000   Fax: (212) 546-4020   www.bms.com

Pharmaceutical and food preparations, medical and surgical instruments.

Bristol-Myer Squibb - Israel - Habinim, Pharmabest Beith Habonim, 2 Habonim St., Ramat-Gan 52462, Israel

Philtel Ltd., 14 Shenkar str. Kiryat Arie, 49513, PO Box 3918, Petach Tikva 49130, Israel

BUDGET GROUP, INC.

125 Basin St., Ste. 210, Daytona Beach, FL, 32114

Tel: (904) 238-7035   Fax: (904) 238-7461   www.budgetrentacar.com

Car and truck rental system.

Budget Rent A Car, 46 Hahistadrut Blvd., Check Post, Haifa, Israel

Tel: 972-4-842-4004

Budget Rent A Car, 8 King David St., Jerusalem, Israel

Tel: 972-2-624=8991

Budget Rent A Car, Rival St 34, Tel Aviv at Ben Gurion Airport, Israel

Tel: 972-3-688-5777

LEO BURNETT, DIV. B-COM 3 GROUP

35 West Wacker Drive, Chicago, IL, 60601

Tel: (312) 220-5959   Fax: (312) 220-6533   www.leoburnett.com

Engaged in advertising, marketing, media buying and planning, and public relations.

Reuveni Pridan Adertising, Tel Aviv, Israel

CADENCE DESIGN SYSTEMS, INC.

2655 Seely Ave., Bldg. 5, San Jose, CA, 95134

Tel: (408) 943-1234   Fax: (408) 943-0513   www.cadence.com

Mfr. electronic design automation software.

Cadence Design Systems, 85 Medinat Hayehudim Street, 5/F, Herzelia 46766 Herzelia 46766, Israel

Tel: 972-9-9511-799   Fax: 972-9-9511-796

CALDERA INTERNATIONAL

355 South 520 West, Ste. 100, Linden, UT, 84057

Tel: (801) 765-4999   Fax: (801) 765-1313   www.caldera.com

Provides integrated solutions for small-to-medium businesses, retail operations, telecommunications and other vertical markets.

Caldera Israel, Bell House, 20, Hata's Street, PB 60, Keffar-Sava 44425, Israel

Contact: Felix Eisenberg

CAMBREX CORPORATION

1 Meadowlands Plaza, East Rutherford, NJ, 07063

Tel: (201) 804-3000   Fax: (201) 804-9852   www.cambrex.com

human health, animal health/agriculture and Mfr. biotechnology products and produce specialty chemicals.

Dexmor Ltd., PO Box 13141, Tel Aviv 61131, Israel

Tel: 972-3-498503

CENTURY 21 REAL ESTATE CORPORATION

One Campus Drive, Parsippany, NJ, 07054-3826

Tel: (973) 496-5722   Fax: (973) 496-5527   www.century21.com

Engaged in real estate sales.

Century 21 Israel, Ltd., 20 Ben Gurion St., City Gate 1, Herzelia, Israel

Tel: 972-9-957-7222   Fax: 972-9-957-7221

CH2M HILL INC.

6060 South Willow Drive, Greenwood Village, CO, 80111

Tel: (303) 771-0900   Fax: (303) 770-2616   www.ch2m.com

Consulting engineers, planners, economists and scientists.

CH2M Hill, Qiryat Gat, #628, Ha'ashiagan Street 10, PO Box 8617, Qiryat Gat 82109, Israel

CHECKPOINT SYSTEMS, INC.

101 Wolf Drive, Thorofare, NJ, 08086

Tel: (856) 848-1800   Fax: (856) 848-0937   www.checkpointsystems.com

Mfr. test, measurement and closed-circuit television systems.

Checkpoint Systems Israel, PO Box 8301, 8 Ha'argaman St., New Industrial Zone K. Nordau, Netanya 42504, Israel

Tel: 972-9-885-3332   Fax: 972-9-885-3155   Contact: Israel Elran

THE CHERRY CORPORATION

3600 Sunset Ave., PO Box 718, Waukegan, IL, 60087

Tel: (847) 662-9200   Fax: (847) 662-2990   www.cherrycorp.com

Mfr. electrical switches, electronic keyboards, controls and displays.

Astragal Ltd., 3 Hashikma Street, PO Box 906, IL-Tel Aviv 61008, Israel

Tel: 972-3-5591660   Fax: 972-3-5592340

CHESTERTON BLUMENAUER BINSWANGER

Two Logan Square, 4th Floor, Philadelphia, PA, 19103-2759

Tel: (215) 448-6000   Fax: (215) 448-6238   www.cbbi.com

Real estate and related services.

Dashkad Binswanger, 2 Habarzel Street, 3/F, Tel Aviv, Israel

Contact: Dubi Weiss

THE CHRISTIAN SCIENCE PUBLISHING SOCIETY

1 Norway Street, Boston, MA, 02115

Tel: (617) 450-2000   Fax: (617) 450-7575   www.christianscience.com

Publishing company.

The Christian Science Monitor Publication, Beit Agron, Box 3, 37 Hillel St., Jerusalem 93503, Israel

CIGNA COMPANIES

One Liberty Place, Philadelphia, PA, 19192

Tel: (215) 761-1000   Fax: (215) 761-5511   www.cigna.com

Insurance, invest, health care and other financial services.

CIGNA Insurance Co., c/o Tocatly & Sons, Migdal Shalom Mayer, PO Box 1025, Tel Aviv, Israel

CIGNA Insurance Co. of Europe SA/NV (Securitas Ins. Ltd.), 38 Rothschild Bldg., PO Box 1791, Tel Aviv, Israel

CINCINNATI INCORPORATED

PO Box 11111, Cincinnati, OH, 45211

Tel: (513) 367-7100   Fax: (513) 367-7552   www.e-ci.com

Mfr. metal fabricating equipment.

Josef Rosenthaler Co. Ltd., PO Box 791, Haifa 31007, Israel

Tel: 972-4-852-2676   Fax: 972-4-85-8824

CISCO SYSTEMS, INC.

170 West Tasman Drive, San Jose, CA, 95134-1706

Tel: (408) 526-4000   Fax: (408) 526-4100   www.cisco.com

Develop/mfr./market computer hardware and software networking systems.

Cisco Systems Israel, 3 Hayezira St., Natanya 42160, Israel

Tel: 972-9-863-2000   Fax: 972-9-658518

CITIGROUP, INC.

399 Park Avenue, New York, NY, 10022

Tel: (212) 559-1000   Fax: (212) 559-3646   www.citigroup.com

Provides insurance and financial services worldwide.

Citigroup, 76 Rothschild Blvd., Beit Mozes, 7th Fl., Tel Aviv 65785, Israel

Tel: 972-3-566-5567   Fax: 972-3-566-5565   Contact: Ron Braverman

THE COCA-COLA COMPANY

1 Coca Cola Plaza, Atlanta, GA, 30313

Tel: (404) 676-2121   Fax: (404) 676-6792   www.coca-cola.com

Mfr./marketing/distributor soft drinks, syrups and concentrates, juice and juice-drink products.

Coca-Cola Bottlers Israel, Israel Office c/o Zamberly Place, 107/111 Peascod St., Windsor Berks SL4 1PE, UK

COLFAX PUMP GROUP, DIV. COLFAX INC.

1710 Airport Road, PO Box 5020, Monroe, NC, 28111-5020

Tel: (704) 289-6511   Fax: (704) 289-4839   www.colfaxpump.com

Mfr. rotary and centrifugal pumps.

I.Ettner Rep IMO Colfax, 51, Ir Shemesh Street, Tel Aviv 69086, Israel

Tel: 972-3-648-5141

COMMWORKS CORPORATION

3800 Golf Road, Rolling Meadows, IL, 60008

Tel: (847) 262-5000   Fax: (847) 262-0327   www.commworks.com

Provides Internet protocol-based network access software and equipment.

Commworks Israel, PO Box 867, 6 Baal Shem Tov Street, Lod 71100, Israel

COMPUTER ASSOCIATES INTERNATIONAL INC.

One Computer Associates Plaza, Islandia, NY, 11788

Tel: (516) 342-5224   Fax: (516) 342-5329   www.cai.com

Integrated business software for enterprise computing and information management, application development, manufacturing, financial applications and professional services.

Computer Associates Israel Ltd., Deborah Hanevia St., Neva Sharet, Atidim, PO Box 58160, Tel Aviv 61580, Israel

Tel: 972-3-648-1120

COMVERSE, INC.

100 Quannapowitt Parkway, Wakefield, MA, 01880

Tel: (781) 246-9000   Fax: (781) 224-8143   www.comverse.com

Provides communications solutions.

Comverse Infosys Ltd., 23 Habarzel Street, Tel Aviv 69710, Israel

Tel: 972-3-766-5888   Fax: 972-3-766-5889

CONEXANT SYSTEMS, INC.

4311 Jamboree Road, PO Box C, Newport Beach, CA, 92658-8902

Tel: (949) 483-4600   Fax: (949) 483-4078   www.conexant.com

Provides semiconductor products for communications electronics.

Conexant Systems Israel Ltd., 11 Galgalei Ha Plada Street, PO Box 12660, Herzlia 46733, Israel

Tel: 972-9-952-4000   Fax: 972-9-957-3732

CONVERGYS CORPORATION

201 E. 4th St., Cincinnati, OH, 45202

Tel: (513) 723-7000   Fax: (513) 421-8624   www.convergys.com

Engaged in data bill processing, telemarketing and customer services representation for major corporations.

Convergys Corporation, 8 Maskit Street, Herzlia 46766, Israel

Tel: 31-153-606060

COPELAND CORPORATION

1675 West Campbell Road, Sidney, OH, 45365-0669

Tel: (937) 498-3011   Fax: (937) 498-3334   www.copeland-corp.com

Producer of compressors and condensing units for commercial and residential air conditioning and refrigeration equipment.

Scharf/Copeland Israel, 25 Hamerkava Street, Holon 58851, Israel

Tel: 972-3-5595239   Fax: 972-3-5595243

CRAWFORD & COMPANY

5620 Glenridge Drive NE, Atlanta, GA, 30342

Tel: (404) 256-0830   Fax: (404) 847-4025   www.crawfordandcompany.com

Provides international insurance services engaged in risk management and claims adjustment.

Crawford & Company, Tossman-Shambit Assessors, 107 Hashmonaim Street, Tel Aviv 67011, Israel

CROMPTON CORPORATION

One American Lane, Greenwich, CT, 06831

Tel: (203) 552-2000   Fax: (203) 552-2870   www.cromptoncorp.com

Mfr. dyes, colors, flavors, fragrances, specialty chemicals and industrial products.

Crompton Chemical Ltd., PO Box 975, Haifa 31000, Israel

CYLINK CORPORATION

3131 Jay Street, Santa Clara, CA, 95054

Tel: (408) 855-6000   Fax: (408) 855-6100   www.cyllink.com

Develop and manufactures encryption software.

Cylink Israel/Algorithmic Research, 10 Nevatim Street, Kiryat Matalon, Petach Tikva 49561, Israel

Tel: 972- 3-927-9500   Fax: 972- 3-923-0864

CYPRESS SEMICONDUCTOR CORPORATION

3901 N. First Street, San Jose, CA, 95134-1599

Tel: (408) 943-2600   Fax: (408) 943-2796   www.cypress.com

Mfr. integrated circuits.

Cypress Semiconductor, Pakris 2, Rehovot 76703, Israel

Tel: 972-894-664-06   Fax: 972-894-664-05

D&B (DUN & BRADSTREET CORPORATION))

1 Diamond Hill Road, Murray Hill, NJ, 07974

Tel: (908) 665-5000   Fax: (908) 665-5524   www.dnb.com

Provides corporate credit, marketing and accounts-receivable management services and publishes financial information.

D&B (Israel) Ltd., 27 Hamered St., Fl. C-2, Tel Aviv 68125, Israel

Tel: 972-3-510-3355

DANZAS AEI, INC.

120 Tokeneke Road, PO Box 1231, Darien, CT, 06820

Tel: (203) 655-7900   Fax: (203) 655-5779   www.aeilogistics.com

International air freight forwarder.

Danzas AEI, c/o Flying Cargo Ltd., 11 Hachilazon St., Ramat-Gan Tel Aviv 52522, Israel

Tel: 972-3-576-3939   Fax: 972-3-575-9123

Danzas AEI c/o Flying Cargo Logistics Services, 79 Hayarok St., Bldg. 121, Kanot Industrial Park, Maar, Israel

Tel: 972-8-869-2430   Fax: 972-8-869-2429

D'ARCY MASIUS BENTON & BOWLES INC. (DMB&B)

1675 Broadway, New York, NY, 10019

Tel: (212) 468-3622   Fax: (212) 468-2987   www.darcyww.com

Full service international advertising and communications group.

Geller-Nesis D'Arcy, 20 Lincoln St., Tel Aviv 67137, Israel

DATA SYSTEMS & SOFTWARE INC.

200 Rte. 17, Mahwah, NJ, 07430

Tel: (201) 529-2026   Fax: (201) 529-3163   www.dssiinc.com

Engaged in technology software consulting and development.

DSI Decision Systems Israel Ltd., 11 Ben Gurion Street, Giv'at Shmuel 54017, Israel

Tel: 972-3-531-3333   Fax: 972-3-531-3322   Contact: Yacov Kaufman, VP

DDB WORLDWIDE COMMUNICATIONS GROUP

437 Madison Ave., New York, NY, 10022

Tel: (212) 415-2000   Fax: (212) 415-3417   www.ddbn.com

Advertising agency.

Linial DDB, 14 Kreminizki Street, Tel Aviv 67899, Israel

Tel: 972-3-5616116   Fax: 972-3-5624212

DELOITTE TOUCHE TOHMATSU INTERNATIONAL

1633 Broadway, New York, NY, 10019

Tel: (212) 492-4000   Fax: (212) 392-4154   www.deloitte.com

Accounting, audit, tax and management consulting services.

Igal Brightman & Co., PO Box 16593, Tel Aviv 61164, Israel

Igal Brightman & Co., PO Box 5648, Haifa 31055, Israel

Igal Brightman & Co., New Clal Ctr., 42 Agrippas St., Jerusalem 94301, Israel

DHL WORLDWIDE EXPRESS

50 California Avenue, San Francisco, CA, 94111

Tel: (415) 677-6100   Fax: (415) 824-9700   www.dhl.com

Worldwide air express carrier.

DHL Worldwide Express, 5 Hapardes St., Azur 58001, Israel

Tel: 972-3-557-3850

DIONEX CORPORATION

1228 Titan Way, PO Box 3603, Sunnyvale, CA, 94086-3603

Tel: (408) 737-0700   Fax: (408) 730-9403   www.dionex.com

Develop/mfr./market chromatography systems and related products.

Manbar Tech, 17a Lazarov Street, PO Box 797, Rishon Le-Zion 75106, Israel

DIVINE

1301 N. Elston Ave., Chicago, IL, 60622

Tel: (773) 394-6600   Fax: (773) 394-6601   www.divine.com

Software and services provider.

Divine, Inc., 3 Hayetzira Street, Ramat-Gan 52521, Israel

D-M-E COMPANY

29111 Stephenson Highway, Madison Heights, MI, 48071

Tel: (248) 398-6000   Fax: (248) 544-5705   www.dmeco.com

Manufacture and distribution of mold tooling, mold components, hot runner systems, and electronic controls for the plastics industry.

R.M. Industrial Services Ltd., 27 Schocken Street, Tel Aviv 66532, Israel

Tel: 972-3-6824242

R.R. DONNELLEY & SONS COMPANY

77 West Wacker Drive, Chicago, IL, 60601-1696

Tel: (312) 326-8000   Fax: (312) 326-8543   www.rrdonnelley.com

Engaged in commercial printing and allied communication services.

R. R. Donnelley Financial, Elnit Financial Printing Ltd., Sharbat House, 4 Kaufman St., Tel Aviv 68012, Israel

Tel: 972-3-510-7818

DRAFT WORLDWIDE

633 North St. Clair Street, Chicago, IL, 60611-3211

Tel: (312) 944-3500   Fax: (312) 944-3566   www.draftworldwide.com

Full service international advertising agency, engaged in brand building, direct and promotional marketing.

DraftWorldwide, PO Box 16419, Jerusalem 91163, Israel

Tel: 972-2-656-3008   Fax: 972-2-585-5851   Contact: Douglas Greener, Co-Mng. Dir.

MediawiSe - DraftWorldwide, c/o Greener, 16/5 Gdud Hermesh Street, Jerusalem 97545, Israel

Tel: 972-2-656-3008   Fax: 972-2-585-5851

DRAKE BEAM MORIN INC.

100 Park Avenue, 11th Fl., New York, NY, 10017

Tel: (212) 692-7700   Fax: (212) 297-0426   www.dbm.com

Human resource management consulting and training.

DBM Israel, 18 Hashoftim St., POB 3643, Ramat Hasharon 47134, Israel

DSP GROUP, INC.

3120 Scott Blvd., Santa Clara, CA, 95054

Tel: (408) 986-4300   Fax: (408) 986-4323   www.dspg.com

Mfr. speech compressor software.

DSP Group, Ltd., 5, Shenkar Street, Herzelia Pituach 46120, Israel

Tel: 972-9-9529696   Fax: 972-9-9541234

EASTMAN CHEMICAL COMPANY

100 North Eastman Road, Kingsport, TN, 37662-5075

Tel: (423) 229-2000   Fax: (423) 229-1351   www.eastman.com

Mfr. plastics, chemicals, fibers.

Eastman Chemical B.V., PO Box 11304, Yuhud 56450, Israel

Tel: 972-3-632-0741   Fax: 972-3-632-0740   Contact: Wolf Lobato

EATON CORPORATION

Eaton Center, 1111 Superior Ave., Cleveland, OH, 44114-2584

Tel: (216) 523-5000   Fax: (216) 479-7068   www.eaton.com

Advanced technical products for transportation and industrial markets.

Automotive Equipment Ltd., 74 Petach Tikva Rd., PO Box 20205, Tel Aviv, Israel

EGL INC. (EAGLE GLOBAL LOGISTICS)

15350 Vickery Drive, Houston, TX, 77032

Tel: (281) 618-3100   Fax: (281) 618-3223   www.eagleusa.com

Ocean/air freight forwarding, customs brokerage, packing and wholesale, logistics management and insurance.

EGL Eagle Global Logistics, Albany Agents & Forwarders, 19 Hatzfira St., Tel Aviv 67779, Israel

Tel: 972-3-537-6022   Fax: 972-3-537-6025

ELECTRO SCIENTIFIC INDUSTRIES, INC.

13900 NW Science Park Drive, Portland, OR, 97229

Tel: (503) 641-4141   Fax: (503) 643-4873   www.esi.com

Mfg. production and testing equipment used in manufacture of electronic components in pagers and cellular communication devices.

EMMTECH Advanced Packaging Group (Rep), PO Box 221, Gedera 70700, Israel

Tel: 972-8-859-4361

ELECTRONIC DATA SYSTEMS, INC. (EDS)

5400 Legacy Dr., Plano, TX, 75024

Tel: (972) 604-6000   Fax: (972) 605-2643   www.eds.com

Engaged in systems integration, network and systems operations and management consulting.

EDS Israel, Ackerstein House, 103 Medinat Hayehudim, Herzliya 46766, Israel

EMC CORPORATION

35 Parkwood Drive, Hopkinton, MA, 01748-9103

Tel: (508) 435-1000   Fax: (508) 435-8884   www.emc.com

Designs/supplies intelligent enterprise storage and retrieval technology for open systems, mainframes and midrange environments.

EMC Computer Systems Israel, Atidim Industrial Park, Bldg. 7, PO Box 58061, Tel Aviv 61280, Israel

Tel: 972-3-645-4220

A. EPSTEIN AND SONS INTERNATIONAL, INC.

600 West Fulton Street, Chicago, IL, 60606-1199

Tel: (312) 454-9100   Fax: (312) 559-1217   www.epstein-isi.com

Engaged in architecture, engineering, planning, construction and interior design.

A. Epstein & Sons (UK) Ltd., 3 Nirim Street, PO Box 9084, Tel Aviv 61090, Israel

Tel: 972-3-636-1636   Fax: 972-3-646-2876

ERNST & YOUNG INTERNATIONAL

5 Times Square, New York, NY, 10036

Tel: (212) 773-3000   Fax: (212) 773-6350   www.eyi.com

Engaged in assurance and advisory business services, tax, law and corporate finance.

Kost Forer & Gabbay E&Y, 3 Aminadav Street, Tel Aviv 67067, Israel

Luboshitz Kasierer E&Y, 9 Ahad Ha'am Street, Tel Aviv 61293, Israel

Tel: 972-3-511-8222   Fax: 972-3-510-1667   Contact: Itshak Forer

EURO RSCG WORLDWIDE

350 Hudson Street, New York, NY, 10014

Tel: (212) 886-2000   Fax: (212) 886-2016   www.eurorscg.com

International advertising agency group.

EURO RSCG Zarfatti Sternschuss Zamir, 12 Yad Harutzim Street, Tel Aviv, Israel

EXCELLON AUTOMATION

24751 Crenshaw Boulevard, Torrance, CA, 90505

Tel: (310) 534-6300   Fax: (310) 534-6777   www.excellon.com

PCB drilling and routing machines; optical inspection equipment.

E&M Engineering Ltd., 5 Jabotinsky Street, PO Box 3191, Ramaat-Gan 52520, Israel

Tel: 972-3-751-2929   Fax: 972-3-751-3201

FRITZ COMPANIES, INC., DIV. UPS

706 Mission Street, Ste. 900, San Francisco, CA, 94103

Tel: (415) 904-8360   Fax: (415) 904-8661   www.fritz.com

Integrated transportation, sourcing, distribution and customs brokerage services.

Fritz Companies Israel Ltd., 34 Beit Hillel St., Tel Aviv 67017, Israel

FSI INTERNATIONAL INC.

3455 Lyman Boulevard, Chaska, MN, 55318-3052

Tel: (952) 448-5440   Fax: (952) 448-2825   www.fsi-intl.com

Manufacturing equipment for computer silicon wafers.

Metron Technology Ltd., 10 Haharootsim Street, PO Box 8226, Netanya 82293, Israel

FUNDTECH LTD.

30 Montgomery Street, Ste. 501, Jersey City, NJ, 07302

Tel: (201) 946-1100   Fax: (201) 946-1313   www.fundtech.com

Mfr. electronic funds transfer software.

Fundtech Ltd., 12 Ha'hilazon Street, 5/F, Ramat-Gan 52522, Israel

GENERAL DYNAMICS CORPORATION

3190 Fairview Park Drive, Falls Church, VA, 22042-4523

Tel: (703) 876-3000   Fax: (703) 876-3125   www.gendyn.com

Mfr. aerospace equipment, submarines, strategic systems, armored vehicles, defense support systems.

General Dynamics Corp., Attn: Israel Office, Embassy of the USA/Israel, Peace Marble, APO, USA, 09672-0008

GENERAL ELECTRIC COMPANY

3135 Easton Turnpike, Fairfield, CT, 06431

Tel: (203) 373-2211   Fax: (203) 373-3131   www.ge.com

Diversified manufacturing, technology and services.

General Electric Co. - General Engineers, 1 Maskit St., Herzliya 46105, Israel

Tel: 972-9-959-2233   Fax: 972-9-955-5122

GENZYME CORPORATION

1 Kendall Square, Cambridge, MA, 02139-1562

Tel: (617) 252-7500   Fax: (617) 252-7600   www.genzyme.com

Mfr. healthcare products for enzyme deficient diseases.

Genzyme Israel Ltd., Beit-Hapaamon, 20 Hataas Street, Kfar-Saba-Industrial Zone 44111, Israel

Tel: 972-9-7-666640   Fax: 92-9-7-666631

GLEASON CORPORATION

1000 University Ave., Rochester, NY, 14692

Tel: (716) 473-1000   Fax: (716) 461-4348   www.gleasoncorp.com

Mfr. gear making machine tools; tooling and services.

Josef Rosenthaler Co. Ltd., 17 Neemanim Street, PO Box 791, Haifa 31007, Israel

Tel: 97-248-522-676   Fax: 97-248-528-824

GREY GLOBAL GROUP

777 Third Ave., New York, NY, 10017

Tel: (212) 546-2000   Fax: (212) 546-1495   www.grey.com

International advertising agency.

Adler Chomski Warshavsky Grey, 154 Derekh Petach Tikva St, Tel Aviv 64921, Israel

Tel: 972-3-6088888   Fax: 972-3-6088861

GRIFFITH LABORATORIES INC.

One Griffith Center, Alsip, IL, 60658

Tel: (708) 371-0900   Fax: (708) 597-3294   www.griffithlabs.com

Mfr. industrial food ingredients and equipment.

Griffith/Ein-Bar, Kibbutz Einat, Israel

Tel: 972-3-938-5167   Fax: 972-3-938-5176

HARRIS CORPORATION

1025 West NASA Blvd., Melbourne, FL, 32919

Tel: (407) 727-9100   Fax: (407) 727-9344   www.harris.com

Mfr. communications and information-handling equipment, including copying and fax systems.

Aviv Electronics, PO Box 2433, Ra'anana 43100, Israel

Tel: 972-9-748-3232   Fax: 972-9741-6510

HEIDRICK & STRUGGLES INTERNATIONAL, INC.

233 South Wacker Drive, Chicago, IL, 60606

Tel: (312) 496-1200   Fax: (312) 496-1290   www.heidrick.com

Executive search firm.

Heidrick & Struggles Intl. Inc., 3 Hayezira Street, SH.A.P House, Ramat-Gan, Israel

Tel: 972-3-613-7210

HENRY SCHEIN, INC.

135 Duryea Rd., Melville, NY, 11747

Tel: (516) 843-5500   Fax: (516) 843-5658   www.henryschein.com

Mfr. and supply dental equipment.

Henry Schein Israel, Beit Hashinhav, Beit Hadfuss 12, Givat Shaul Jerusalem 95483, Israel

Tel: 972-2-651-0701

HEWLETT-PACKARD COMPANY

3000 Hanover Street, Palo Alto, CA, 94304-1185

Tel: (650) 857-1501   Fax: (650) 857-5518   www.hp.com

Mfr. computing, communications and measurement products and services.

Hewlett-Packard Israel Ltd., 11 Hashiosha Street, Tel Aviv 67060, Israel

Tel: 972-3-538-0301

HILTON HOTELS CORPORATION

9336 Civic Center Drive, Beverly Hills, CA, 90210

Tel: (310) 278-4321   Fax: (310) 205-7880   www.hiltonhotels.com

International hotel chain: Hilton International, Vista Hotels and Hilton National Hotels.

Tel Aviv Hilton, Independence Park, Tel Aviv 63405, Israel

HOLLAND & KNIGHT LLP

400 North Ashley Dr., Ste. 2300, Tampa, FL, 33602

Tel: (813) 227-8500   Fax: (813) 229-0134   www.hklaw.com

Engaged in international law.

Holland & Knight, Haim Samet, Steinmetz, Haring & Co., 23 Begin Road, Tel Aviv 66814, Israel

Tel: 972-3-5670100

HORWATH INTERNATIONAL ASSOCIATION

420 Lexington Avenue, Suite 526, New York, NY, 10170-0526

Tel: (212) 808-2000   Fax: (212) 808-2020   www.horwath.com

Public accountants and auditors.

Horwath, Bawly, Millner & Co., PO Box 50025, 27 Hamered Street, Tel Aviv 68125, Israel

Horwath, Bawly, Millner & Co., PO Box 33777, 5 Habankim Street, Haifa 31337, Israel

Zitnitski Weinstein & Co., 65 Yigal Allon Street, Tel-Aviv 67443, Israel

Tel: 972-3-625-1111   Contact: Shimon Zitnitski

HOUGHTON INTERNATIONAL INC.

PO Box 930, Madison & Van Buren Avenues, Valley Forge, PA, 19482-0930

Tel: (610) 666-4000   Fax: (610) 666-1376   www.houghtonintl.com

Mfr. specialty chemicals, hydraulic fluids and lubricants.

Delkol Ltd., PO Box 31, Lod 71100, Israel

i2 TECHNOLOGIES, INC.

11701 Luna Road, Dallas, TX, 75234

Tel: (214) 860-6106   Fax: (214) 860-6060   www.i2.com

Engaged in supply chain management; solutions to help companies collaborate on decision-making processes.

i2 Technologies, PO Box 12109, Herzliya Pituach Industrial Zone 46733, Israel

Tel: 972-9-9554971   Fax: 972-9-9565085

IBM CORPORATION

1133 Westchester Avenue, White Plains, NY, 10604

Tel: (914) 765-1900   Fax: (914) 765-7382   www.ibm.com

Information products, technology and services.

IBM Israel Ltd., IBM House, 2 Weizmann Street, PO Box 33666, Tel Aviv 61336, Israel

Tel: 972-3-697-8500   Fax: 972-3-695-9985

ICC INDUSTRIES INC.

460 Park Ave., New York, NY, 10022

Tel: (212) 521-1700   Fax: (212) 521-1794   www.iccchem.com

Manufacturing and trading of chemicals, plastics and pharmaceuticals.

ICC (Israel) Chemicals Ltd., 135 Dizengoff St., Tel Aviv 56461, Israel

Tel: 972-3-522-5072   Fax: 972-3-524-9265   Contact: Yaakov Aviram

IKOS SYSTEMS, INC.

79 Great Oaks Blvd., San Jose, CA, 95119

Tel: (408) 284-0400   Fax: (408) 284-0401   www.ikos.com

Mfr. hardware and software.

IES Electronics Agencies Ltd, 32 Ben Gurion Street, Ramat-Gan 52573, Israel

Tel: 972-3-753-0776

INFOGRAMES, INC.

417 Fifth Avenue, New York, NY, 10016

Tel: (212) 726-6500   Fax: (212) 679-3224   www.infogrames.com

Mfr. video games.

Infogrames Israel, 21 Atir Yeda Street, PO Box 2358, Kefar Saba 44641, Israel

Tel: 972-9-7679777

INFONET SERVICES CORPORATION

2160 East Grand Ave., El Segundo, CA, 90245-1022

Tel: (310) 335-2600   Fax: (310) 335-4507   www.infonet.com

Provider of Internet services and electronic messaging services.

Infonet Israel, Ltd., 9 Hasivim Street, PO Box 7106, Petach-Tikva 49170, Israel

Tel: 972-3-921-3663   Fax: 972-3-921-3665

INTEGRATED DEVICE TECHNOLOGY, INC. (IDT)

2975 Stender Way, Santa Clara, CA, 95054

Tel: (408) 727-6116   Fax: (408) 492-8674   www.idt.com

Mfr. high-performance semiconductors and modules.

Integrated Device Technology (IDT), Derech Petah-Tikva 48, Aviv Tower, Bldg A, 12th Fl., Tel Aviv 66184, Israel

Tel: 972-3-6885492   Fax: 972-3-6885370

INTEL CORPORATION

2200 Mission College Blvd., Santa Clara, CA, 95052-8119

Tel: (408) 765-8080   Fax: (408) 765-1739   www.intel.com

Mfr. semiconductor, microprocessor and micro-communications components and systems.

Intel Semiconductor (Israel), Ltd., 100 Hachashmonaim Street, POB 52638, Tel Aviv 67133, Israel

Tel: 972-2-589-7111

INTER-CONTINENTAL HOTELS

3 Ravinia Drive, Suite 2900, Atlanta, GA, 30346-2149

Tel: (770) 604-2000   Fax: (770) 604-5403   www.interconti.com

Worldwide hotel and resort accommodations.

Inter-Continental Hotels, 5 Yoni Netanyahu Street, Tel Aviv 60250, Israel

Tel: 972-3-538-8444   Fax: 972-3-533-5986

INTERGRAPH CORPORATION

One Madison Industrial Park, Huntsville, AL, 35894-0001

Tel: (256) 730-2000   Fax: (256) 730-7898   www.intergraph.com

Develop/mfr. interactive computer graphic systems.

Intergraph Israel, 20 Galgaley Haplada Industrial Area, PO Box 708, Herzlia 46106, Israel

Tel: 972-9-954-3101   Fax: 972-9-954-3972

INTERMEC TECHNOLOGIES CORPORATION

6001 36th Avenue West, PO Box 4280, Everett, WA, 98203-9280

Tel: (425) 348-2600   Fax: (425) 355-9551   www.intermec.com

Mfr. and distributor automated data collection systems.

Intermec Bar Code Ltd., Bnei Moshe Street, PO Box 8161, Ramat-Gan 52181, Israel

Tel: 972-3-926-9666   Fax: 972-3-924-7666

INTERNATIONAL FLAVORS & FRAGRANCES INC.

521 West 57th Street, New York, NY, 10019-2960

Tel: (212) 765-5500   Fax: (212) 708-7132   www.iff.com

Design/mfr. flavors, fragrances and aroma chemicals.

International Flavors & Fragrances, 4 Ha Taas Street, Ramat-Gan 52512, Israel

Tel: 972-3-6138454   Fax: 972-3-6136644

INTERNATIONAL PAPER COMPANY

400 Atlantic Street, Stamford, CT, 06921

Tel: (203) 541-8000   Fax: (203) 358-6444   www.ipaper.com

Mfr./distributor container board, paper and wood products.

International Paper USA Ltd., Starco Bldg., PO Box 34056, Haifa, Israel

IONICS INC.

65 Grove Street, Watertown, MA, 02172

Tel: (617) 926-2500   Fax: (617) 926-4304   www.ionics.com

Mfr. desalination equipment.

Ionics Environmental, Herzlia, Israel

Tel: 972-9-9509650

ISM FASTENING SYSTEMS CORPORATION

PO Box 629, Butler, PA, 16003

Tel: (800) 378-3430   Fax: (800) 827-4762   www.ismsys.com

Mfr. industrial stapling machines and supplies.

Packaging & Printing Systems (Dvikol) Ltd., 53 Petach Tikva Rd., PO Box 20122, Tel Aviv, Israel

IVC INDUSTRIES, INC.

500 Halls Mill Road, Freehold, NJ, 07728

Tel: (732) 308-3000   Fax: (732) 308-9793   www.ivcinc.com

Mfr. and distributor of vitamins and dietary supplements.

IVC Industries, Inc., 32 Hazohar, Tel Aviv, Israel

J. WALTER THOMPSON COMPANY

466 Lexington Ave., New York, NY, 10017

Tel: (212) 210-7000   Fax: (212) 210-6944   www.jwt.com

International advertising and marketing services.

Tamir Cohen, 6 Kreminitski St, Tel Aviv 67899, Israel

Tel: 972-3-6231111   Fax: 972-3-6231100

JDS UNIPHASE CORPORATION

210 Baypoint Pkwy., San Jose, CA, 95134

Tel: (408) 434-1800   Fax: (408) 954-0760   www.jdsunph.com

Mfr. advanced fiber optic products for the cable television and telecommunications industries.

JDS Uniphase (Israel) Ltd., Harel House, Suite 8-18 3, Abba Hillel Silver Street, Ramat-Gan 52522, Israel

Tel: 972-3-7541149

JOHNSON & JOHNSON

One Johnson & Johnson Plaza, New Brunswick, NJ, 08933

Tel: (732) 524-0400   Fax: (732) 214-0334   www.jnj.com

Mfr./distributor/R&D pharmaceutical, health care and cosmetic products.

Biosense Europe, Haifa, Israel

Janssen-Cilag, Kibbutz Shefayim 60990, Israel

Tel: 972-9-9591109   Fax: 972-9-9503002

JONES LANG LASALLE

153 East 53rd Street, New York, NY, 10022

Tel: (212) 812-5700   Fax: (212) 421-3544   www.am.joneslanglasalle.com

International marketing consultants, leasing agents and property management advisors.

Jones Lang Wootton, Israel

KIMBERLY-CLARK CORPORATION

351 Phelps Drive, Irving, TX, 75038

Tel: (972) 281-1200   Fax: (972) 281-1435   www.kimberly-clark.com

Mfr./sales/distribution of consumer tissue, household and personal care products.

Hogla-Kimberly, Tel Aviv, Israel

Contact: Avi Brener, Gen.Mgr.

Kimberly-Clark Corp., Hadera, Israel

Kimberly-Clark Corporation, Afula, Israel

KLA-TENCOR CORPORATION

160 Rio Robles, San Jose, CA, 95134

Tel: (408) 875-6000   Fax: (408) 875-3030   www.kia-tencor.ocm

Mfr. software and equipment.

KLA-Tencor Israel, 4, Haticshoret Street, Migdal Ha'emek 23100, Israel

Tel: 972-4-644-9449   Fax: 972-4-644-9450

KOCH-GLITSCH, INC.

4111 E. 37th Street North, Wichita, KS, 67220

Tel: (316) 828-5110   Fax: (316) 828-5263   www.koch-glitsch.com

Engaged in mass transfer, mist elimination, and motionless mixer technology.

Koch-Glitsch, Inc., 17 Modin St., PO Box 6111, Bnei Brak, Israel

KPMG CONSULTING INC.

1676 International Dr., McLean, VA, 22102

Tel: (703) 747-3000   Fax: (703) 747-8500   www.kpmg.com

Accounting and audit, tax and management consulting services.

KPMG Braude Bavly, 65 Ha'atzmaut Rd., Haifa 31338, Israel

KPMG Braude Bavly, 33 Jaffa Rd., Jerusalem 91002, Israel

KPMG Braude Bavly, 29 Hamered St., Tel-Aviv 68125, Israel

Tel: 972-3-51408   Fax: 972-3-510-1918   Contact: Itzahk Rotman, Sr. Ptnr.

KULICKE & SOFFA INDUSTRIES INC.

2101 Blair Mill Road, Willow Grove, PA, 19090

Tel: (215) 784-6000   Fax: (215) 659-7588   www.kns.com

Semiconductor assembly systems and services.

Kulicke & Soffa (Israel) Ltd., Advanced Technology Center, PO Box 875, Haifa 31008, Israel

Tel: 972-4-854-5222   Fax: 972-4-855-0007   Contact: Avner Hermoni, VP & Mng. Dir.

Ortec Marketing Equipment & Supply Ltd.l, 11 Hasadna Street, Ra'anana 43650, Israel

TRIGON Trading & Engineering Ltd, 9 Timna Street, PO Box 1970, Holon 58117 I, Israel

Tel: 972-4-993-9444   Fax: 972-4-959-1234

LAM RESEARCH CORPORATION

4650 Cushing Pkwy., Fremont, CA, 94538

Tel: (510) 659-0200   Fax: (510) 572-6454   www.lamrc.com

Mfr. semiconductor processing equipment.

Lam Research, 71 Hamelacha Street, K. Nordau Industrial Park, Box 8249, Natanya, Israel

Tel: 972-9-8-659-08   Fax: 972-9-8-659-086

LEHMAN BROTHERS HOLDINGS INC.

*101 Hudson Street, Jersey City, NJ, 07302

Tel: (201) 524-2000   Fax: (201) 524-2000   www.lehman.com

Financial services, securities and merchant banking services.

Lehman Brothers, Asia House, 4 Weizmann Street, 4/F, Tel Aviv, Israel

Tel: 972-3-696-6122

ELI LILLY & COMPANY

Lilly Corporate Center, Indianapolis, IN, 46285

Tel: (317) 276-2000   Fax: (317) 277-6579   www.lilly.com

Mfr. pharmaceuticals and animal health products.

Eli Lilly Israel LTC, 4 Kaufman St., Bet Sharbaat, Tel Aviv 68012, Israel

Tel: 972-3-510-0840   Fax: 942-3-516-2643

LOCKHEED MARTIN CORPORATION

6801 Rockledge Drive, Bethesda, MD, 20817

Tel: (301) 897-6000   Fax: (301) 897-6652   www.imco.com

Design/mfr./management systems in fields of space, defense, energy, electronics and technical services.

Lockheed Fort Worth Intl. Corp., L.R.O. Cyclone, Carmiel, Israel

Tel: 972-967-058   Fax: 972-4-967-057

Lockheed Fort Worth Intl. Corp., Beit Ackerstein, 103 Medinat Hayehudim, Herzliya Pituach 46766, Israel

Tel: 972-9-580621   Fax: 972-9-581189

Lockheed Fort Worth Intl. Corp., Technical Pubs, Peace Marble, Pitah Tikva, Israel

Tel: 972-3-934-7629   Fax: 972-3-390-1326

Lockheed Martin International S.A., Asia House, 4 Weizman Street, Tel Aviv, Israel

Tel: 972-3-695-8343   Fax: 972-3-695-9627

Lockheed Martin Technical Operations, Beit-Eliahu, Tel Aviv 64077, Israel

Tel: 972-3-430040   Fax: 972-3-695-2059

LORD CORPORATION

2000 West Grandview Blvd, Erie, PA, 16514

Tel: (814) 868-0924   Fax: (814) 486-4345   www.lordcorp.com

Mfg. adhesives, coatings, chemicals, film products.

Lord Corporation Metech Israel, PO Box 3028, Omer Industrial Park, Omer 84965, Israel

Tel: 972-8-6900801   Fax: 972-8-6900803

LSI LOGIC CORPORATION

1551 McCarthy Blvd., Milpitas, CA, 95035

Tel: (408) 433-8000   Fax: (408) 954-3220   www.lsilogic.com

Develop and manufacture semiconductors.

LSI Logic Ramat Hashron, 40 Sokolov Street, PO Box 1311, Ramat Hashron 47235, Israel

Tel: 972-3-5-480480   Fax: 972-3-5-403747

LTX CORPORATION

LTX Park, University Ave., Westwood, MA, 02090

Tel: (617) 461-1000   Fax: (617) 326-4883   www.ltx.com

Design/mfr. computer-controlled semiconductor test systems.

LTX Israel Ltd., Saharov, 17 Rishon Lezion, PO Box 5053, 75105, Israel

Tel: 972-50-3368-92   Fax: 972-3-5598606

LUCENT TECHNOLOGIES, INC.

600 Mountain Ave., Murray Hill, NJ, 07974-0636

Tel: (908) 582-3000   Fax: (908) 582-2576   www.lucent.com

Design/mfr. wide range of public and private networks, communication systems and software, data networking systems, business telephone systems and microelectronics components.

WaveAccess Ltd., Re'anana, Israel

M/A-COM INC.

1011 Pawtucket Boulevard, Lowell, MA, 01853-3295

Tel: (978) 442-5000   Fax: (978) 442-5354   www.macom.com

Mfr. radio frequency (RF) and microwave integrated circuits and IP Networks to the wireless telecommunications and defense-related industries.

M/A-COM Ltd., Div. Tyco, Twin Towers II, Rm. 911, 35 Zabotinski Road, Ramat-Gan 52517, Israel
Tel: 972-3-7518421   Fax: 972-3-7510498

MacDERMID INC.

245 Freight Street, Waterbury, CT, 06702-0671

Tel: (203) 575-5700   Fax: (203) 575-7900   www.macdermid.com

Chemicals processing for metal industrial, plastics, electronics cleaners, strippers.

MacDermid Israel Ltd., PO Box 13011, Tel Aviv 61130, Israel

MANPOWER INTERNATIONAL INC.

5301 N. Ironwood Rd., PO Box 2053, Milwaukee, WI, 53201-2053

Tel: (414) 961-1000   Fax: (414) 961-7081   www.manpower.com

Temporary help, contract service, training and testing.

Manpower Israel Ltd., 90-92 Yigal Alon Street, Tel Aviv 67891, Israel
Tel: 972-3-563-9999   Fax: 972-3-562-5702

MARRIOTT INTERNATIONAL INC.

10400 Fernwood Rd., Bethesda, MD, 20817

Tel: (301) 380-3000   Fax: (301) 380-5181   www.marriott.com

Hotel services.

Nazareth Marriott Hotel, Nazareth, Israel
Tel: 972-2-628-4724

MARSH & McLENNAN COS INC.

1166 Ave. of the Americas, New York, NY, 10036-2774

Tel: (212) 345-5000   Fax: (212) 345-4808   www.marshmac.com

Insurance agents/brokers, pension and investment management consulting services.

Lowenthal Sagiv Ben-Zur Ltd., 12 Yad Harutzim St., Tel Aviv 67778, Israel
Tel: 972-3-638-3030   Fax: 972-3-639-2866   Contact: Elhanan Lowenthal

McCANN-ERICKSON WORLDGROUP

750 Third Ave., New York, NY, 10017

Tel: (212) 697-6000   Fax: (212) 984-3575   www.mccann.com

International advertising and marketing services.

Kesher Barel & Associates, 159 Yigal Alon Street, Tel Aviv 67443, Israel
Tel: 972-3-6939393   Fax: 972-3-6959142

MECHANICAL DYNAMICS, INC.

2300 Traverwood Drive, Ann Arbor, MI, 48105

Tel: (734) 994-3800   Fax: (734) 994-6418   www.adams.com

Mfr. Adams prototyping software for functional virtual prototyping solutions.

Matrix Engineering Ltd., PO Box 3021, Even Yeuda 40500, Israel
Tel: 972-9-899-9862

MERCURY INTERACTIVE CORPORATION

1325 Borregas Ave., Sunnyvale, CA, 94089

Tel: (408) 822-5200　　　Fax: (408) 822-5300　　　www.merc-int.com

Mfr. computer software to decipher and eliminate "bugs" from systems.

Mercury Interactive (Israel) Ltd., Ottobrunner Strasse 43, Or-ehuda 82008, Israel

Tel: 972-3-575-9301

MERRILL LYNCH & COMPANY, INC.

World Financial Center, 250 Vesey Street, New York, NY, 10281-1332

Tel: (212) 236-1000　　　Fax: (212) 449-2892　　　www.ml.com

Security brokers and dealers, investment and business services.

Merrill Lynch Private Client Group, 1 Azrieli Centre, 37/F Round Tower, Tel Aviv 67021, Israel

Tel: 972-3-607-2000

META GROUP, INC.

208 Harbor Drive, PO Box 120061, Stamford, CT, 06912-0061

Tel: (203) 973-6700　　　Fax: (203) 359-8066　　　www.metagroup.com

Engaged in research and consulting, focusing on information technology and business transformation strategies.

META Group, Meshek Schwarzkopf, PO Box 151, Zion, Moshav Bnei 60910, Israel

METRON TECHNOLOGY

1350 Old Bayshore Highway, Ste. 210, Burlingame, CA, 94010

Tel: (650) 401-4600　　　Fax: (650) 373-1135　　　www.metrontech.com

Global provider of marketing, sales, service and support solutions to semiconductor materials and equipment suppliers and semiconductor manufacturers.

Metron Technology (Israel) Ltd., Park SEE-IM 2000, 10 Haharootsim Street, Netanya 82293, Israel

MICROSOFT CORPORATION

One Microsoft Way, Redmond, WA, 98052-6399

Tel: (425) 882-8080　　　Fax: (425) 936-7329　　　www.microsoft.com

Computer software, peripherals and services.

Microsoft Israel Ltd., Business Park, 6 Maskit Street, Industrial Area, Herzelia Pituach, Israel

Tel: 972-9-525-353　Fax: 972-9-525-333

MILACRON INC.

2090 Florence Ave., Cincinnati, OH, 45206

Tel: (513) 487-5000　　　Fax: (513) 487-5057　　　www.milacron.com

Metalworking and plastics technologies.

Azur Technology and Marketing Ltd., PO Box 248, Moshav Bazra IL 60944, Israel

Tel: 972-9-7443111　Fax: 972-9-7440338　Contact: Pablo Yanovsky

MINDSPEED TECHNOLOGIES

4000 MacArthur, Newport Beach, CA, 92660-3095

Tel: (949) 579-3000　　　Fax: (945) 579-3020　　　www.mindspeed.com

Mfr. integrated circuits.

Mindspeed Technologies, Box 12660, 11 GalGaley HaPlada Street, Herzlia 46733, Israel

MOLEX INC.

2222 Wellington Court, Lisle, IL, 60532

Tel: (630) 969-4550　　　Fax: (630) 969-1352　　　www.molex.com

Mfr. electronic, electrical and fiber optic interconnection products and systems, switches, application tooling.

Telsys Ltd., Div. Molex, Atidim, Bldg 3, Dvora Hanevia Str., Neve Sharet, Tel Aviv 61431, Israel

MOTOROLA, INC.

1303 East Algonquin Road, Schaumburg, IL, 60196

Tel: (847) 576-5000　　　Fax: (847) 538-5191　　　www.motorola.com

Mfr. communications equipment, semiconductors and cellular phones.

Motorola Israel Ltd., 3 Kremenetski St., PO Box 25016, Tel Aviv 67899, Israel

Tel: 972-3-565-8888　Fax: 972-3-562-4925

MSC.SOFTWARE CORPORATION

2 MacArthur Place, Santa Ana, CA, 92707

Tel: (714) 540-8900   Fax: (714) 784-4056   www.mscsoftware.com

Develop finite element analysis software used in the field of computer-aided engineering.

MSC.Software/EMAS, PO Box 998, 29a Jerusalem Blvd., Kiriat Yam 29011, Israel

MULTILINK TECHOLOGY CORPORATION

300 Atrium Drive, 2nd Fl., Somerset, NJ, 08873-4105

Tel: (732) 537-3700   Fax: (732) 805-9177   www.mltc.com

Mfr. high-band, mixed-signal integrated circuits.

MLTC Israel, 13 Gan Raveh Blvd., Yavne 81222, Israel

NATIONAL INSTRUMENTS CORPORATION

11550 N. Mopac Expwy., Austin, TX, 78759-3504

Tel: (512) 338-9119   Fax: (512) 794-5794   www.ni.com

Mfr. hardware and graphical software.

National Instruments, PO Box 184, Givatayim 53101, Israel

NATIONAL SEMICONDUCTOR CORPORATION

2900 Semiconductor Dr., PO Box 58090, Santa Clara, CA, 95052-8090

Tel: (408) 721-5000   Fax: (408) 739-9803   www.national.com

Engaged in producing computer-on-a-chip solutions for the information highway.

National Semiconductor Israel Ltd., 8 Hasadnaot Street, Box 3007, Herzlia B46130, Israel

NATURE'S SUNSHINE PRODUCTS, INC.

75 East 1700 South, Provo, UT, 84605

Tel: (801) 342-4300   Fax: (801) 342-4305   www.naturessunshine.com

Mfr. and sales of holistic health products.

Nature's Sunshine Products, PO Box 12839, Herzeliya Pituah 46722, Israel

NETMANAGE, INC.

10725 N. De Anza Blvd., Cupertino, CA, 95014

Tel: (408) 973-7171   Fax: (408) 257-6405   www.netmanage.com

Develop and manufacture computer software applications and tools.

NetManage Ltd., Matam-Advanced Tech Ctr., Bldg. 9m, Haifa 31905, Israel
Tel: 972-4-855-0234   Fax: 972-4-855-0122

NETWORK APPLIANCE, INC.

495 E. Java Drive, Sunnyvale, CA, 94089

Tel: (408) 822-6000   Fax: (408) 822-4501   www.netapp.com

Engaged in data storage market equipment.

NetApp Israel, 25 Bazel Street, Kiryat Arie, Petah Tikva 49001, Israel

NEW HORIZONS WORLDWIDE, INC.

1900 S. State College Blvd., Anaheim, CA, 92806-6135

Tel: (714) 940-8000   Fax: www.newhorizons.com

Provides customer-focused computer training choices, through computer training centers.

New Horizons Worldwide, 30 Yitzchak Sade' Street, Tel Aviv 67212, Israel
Tel: 972-3-6894000   Fax: 972-3-6889550

NOVELL WORLDWIDE

1800 S. Novell Place, Provo, UT, 84606

Tel: (801) 861-7000   Fax: (801) 861-5555   www.novell.com

Develop/mfr. networking software and related equipment.

Novell Israel Ltd., Ackerstein Building, Medinat Hayehudim St 103, Herzliyya 46776, Israel

NOVELLUS SYSTEMS INC.

4000 North First Street, San Jose, CA, 95134

Tel: (408) 943-9700   Fax: (408) 943-3422   www.novellus.com

Mfr. chemical vapor deposition (CVD), physical vapor deposition (PVD) and copper electrofill systems.

Novellus Systems Israel Ltd., Zohar Tal #11, Herzlia Petuach 56741, Israel

Tel: 972-9-957-1951   Fax: 972-9-957-1951

OFFICE DEPOT, INC.

2200 Old Germantown Road, Delray Beach, FL, 33445

Tel: (561) 278-4800   Fax: (561) 265-4406   www.officedepot.com

Discount office product retailer with warehouse-style superstores.

Office Depot Israel Ltd., 76 Yigal St. Alon St., PO Box 9048, Tel Aviv 67067, Israel

Tel: 972-3-565-4416   Fax: 972-3-561-7877

Office Depot Israel Ltd., Ha'Haroshet, Atar Hutzot-Hamifratz, PO Box 12007, Haifa 26119, Israel

Tel: 972-4-842-0290 Fax: 972-4-842-0380

Office Depot Israel Ltd. - Corporate Office, 11 Ben-Gurion Rd., B'nei-Brak 51260, Israel

Tel: 972-3-617-6431   Fax: 972-3-578-8199   Contact: Zach Fishbein, Pres.

OGILVY & MATHER WORLDWIDE

309 West 49th Street, New York, NY, 10017-7399

Tel: (212) 237-4000   Fax: (212) 237-5123   www.ogilvypr.com

Engaged in public relations and communications.

Fogel-Levin Ogilvy & Mather, 40 Namal St., Tel Aviv 63506, Israel

Tel: 972-3-5442110   Fax: 972-3-5442148

OPLINK COMMUNICATIONS, INC.

3469 N. First Street, San Jose, CA, 95134

Tel: (408) 433-0606   Fax: (408) 433-0608   www.oplink.com

Mfr. fiber optic components.

Appeltronics Ltd., Buliding 101, POB 101, Tirat-Yehuda 73175, Israel

Tel: 972-39027344   Fax: 972-39027345   Contact: Baruch Appel

PANAMETRICS

221 Crescent Street, Waltham, MA, 02154

Tel: (781) 899-2719   Fax: (781) 899-1552   www.panametrics.com

Engaged in manufacture and distribution of ultrasonic testing equipment and process control instrumentation.

Dectal Advanced Technologies, PO Box 8043, 19 Ben Gurion St., Ramat-Gan 52180, Israel

Tel: 972-3-5795001   Fax: 972-3-5795003

PARAMETRIC TECHNOLOGY CORPORATION

140 Kendrick St., Needham, MA, 02494

Tel: (781) 370-5000   Fax: (781) 370-6000   www.ptc.com

Supplier of mechanical design automation and product data management software and services.

Parametric Technology Israel Ltd., MATAM, Bldg. 23, Haifa 31905, Israel

Tel: 972-4-855-0035 Fax: 972-4-855-0036

PAREXEL INTERNATIONAL CORPORATION

195 West Street, Waltham, MA, 02154

Tel: (781) 487-9900   Fax: (781) 487-0525   www.parexel.com

Provides contract medical, biotechnology, and pharmaceutical research and consulting services.

PAREXEL Lansal Ltd., Herzelia Business Park, 6 Maskit St., Bldg. B, 2nd Fl., Herzelia, Israel

Tel: 972-9-941-5411   Fax: 972-9-951-5313

PHARMOS CORPORATION

99 Wood Avenue South, Ste. 301, Iselin, NJ, 08830

Tel: (732) 452-9556   Fax: (732) 452-9557   www.pharmoscorp.com

Mfr. drug products for neurological conditions.

Pharmos Ltd., Kiryat Weizmann, Rehobot 76326, Israel

Tel: 972-8-940-9679

PHILIPP BROTHERS CHEMICALS INC.

1 Parker Plaza, 400 Kelby Street, Fort Lee, NJ, 07029

Tel: (201) 944-6020   Fax: (201) 944-7916   www.philipp-brothers.com

Mfr. industry and agricultural chemicals.

Koffolk, Box 1098, Tel Aviv 61010,, Israel

Tel: 972-3-9273100   Fax: 972-3-9230341

PLANET HOLLYWOOD INTERNATIONAL, INC.

8669 Commodity Circle, Orlando, FL, 32819

Tel: (407) 363-7827   Fax: (407) 363-4862   www.planethollywood.com

Theme-dining restaurant chain and merchandise retail stores.

Planet Hollywood International, Inc., Tel Aviv, Israel

PLEXUS CORPORATION

55 Jewelers Park Drive, Neenah, WI, 54957-0677

Tel: (920) 722-3451   Fax: (920) 751-5395   www.plexus.com

Mfr. electronic products for companies in the telecommunications and computer markets.

Plexus Corporation, 21D Yegea Kapaym, 1st Fl., PO Box 3691, Petach-Tikva 49130, Israel

Tel: 972-3-921-5877   Fax: 972-3-921-5882

POLARIS INDUSTRIES INC.

2100 Highway 55, Medina, MN, 55440

Tel: (612) 542-0500   Fax: (612) 542-0599   www.polarisindustries.com

Mfr. snowmobiles and all-terrain recreational and utility vehicles.

Polaris Machinery Importers, PO Box 304, Industrial Zone, Ashkelon 78102, Israel

Tel: 972-7-675-0734   Fax: 972-7-675-1181

PR NEWSWIRE ASSOCIATION INC.

810 Seventh Avenue, 35th Fl., New York, NY, 10019

Tel: (212) 596-1500   Fax: (212) 541-6114   www.prnewswire.com

Distribution of news releases and photos to media organizations.

PR Newswire Israel, Box 10260, Ramat-Gan 52002, Israel

PRAXAIR, INC.

39 Old Ridgebury Road, Danbury, CT, 06810-5113

Tel: (203) 837-2000   Fax: (203) 837-2450   www.praxair.com

Produces and distributes industrial and specialty gases.

Maxima Air Separation Center Ltd., Silver House, 7 Abba Hillel Rd., IL-Ramat-Gan 52522, Israel

Tel: 972-3-575-5130   Fax: 972-3-575-5120

PRICEWATERHOUSECOOPERS LLP

1301 Ave. of the Americas, New York, NY, 10019

Tel: (212) 596-7000   Fax: (212) 259-1301   www.pwcglobal.com

Accounting and auditing, tax and management, and human resource consulting services.

PriceWaterhouseCoopers, PO Box 609, Tel Aviv 61006, Israel

Tel: 972-3-517-44-44   Fax: 972-3-517-44-40

PriceWaterhouseCoopers, PO Box 212, Jerusalem 91001, Israel

Tel: 972-2-253291   Fax: 972-2-353292

PriceWaterhouseCoopers, PO Box 240, Tirat HaCarmel Haifa 39101, Israel

Tel: 972-4-857-9888   Fax: 972-4-857-9857

QUALCOMM INC.

5775 Morehouse Dr., San Diego, CA, 92121-1714

Tel: (858) 587-1121 Fax: (858) 658-2100 www.qualcomm.com

Digital wireless telecommunications systems.

QUALCOMM Israel, Omega Center, 4/F, Nahum Het Street, Tyrat Hacarmel, Haifa 31905, Israel

Tel: 972-4-850-6506

QUINTILES TRANSNATIONAL CORPORATION

4709 Creekstone Dr., Durham, NC, 27703

Tel: (919) 998-2000 Fax: (919) 998-9113 www.quintiles.com

Mfr. pharmaceuticals.

Quintiles Israel Ltd., Kibutz Shefayim, Tel Aviv 60990, Israel

QUIVER, INC.

1065 Folsom Street, San Francisco, CA, 94103

Tel: (415) 863-9945 Fax: (415) 863-9946 www.quiver.com

Mfr. content management software.

Quiver, Ltd., 2 Ha-Bonim Street, Ha-Bonim House, 2/F, Ramat-Gan 52522, Israel

Tel: 972-3-752-0178 Fax: 972-3-752-4169

RADISSON HOTELS INTERNATIONAL

Carlson Pkwy., PO Box 59159, Minneapolis, MN, 55459-8204

Tel: (612) 540-5526 Fax: (612) 449-3400 www.radisson.com

Operates, manages and franchises full-service hotels and resorts worldwide.

Colony's Beach Resort, Attn: Israel Office, Carlson Parkway, PO Box 59159, Minneapolis, MN, 55459-8204

Colony's Mandarin Resort, Attn: Israel Office, Carlson Parkway, PO Box 59159, Minneapolis, MN, 55459-8204

RADISYS CORPORATION

5445 NE Dawson Creek Drive, Hillsboro, OR, 97124

Tel: (503) 615-1100 Fax: (503) 615-1121 www.radisys.com

Mfr. embedded computer systems.

RadiSys Israel, Bergman 2 Street, Park Rabin, Rehovot 76705, Israel

RATIONAL SOFTWARE CORPORATION

18880 Homestead Road, Cupertino, CA, 95014-0721

Tel: (408) 863-9900 Fax: (408) 863-4120 www.rationale.com

Mfr. application development software.

Rational Software Israel, 16 Galgaly Hapelada Street, PO Box 12689, Herzliya 46733, Israel

RENAISSANCE HOTELS AND RESORTS

10400 Fernwood Road, Bethesda, MD, 20817

Tel: (301) 380-3000 Fax: (301) 380-5181 www.renaissancehotels.com

upscale, full-service hotel and resort chain under Marriott International, Inc.

Renaissance Jerusalem Hotel, Jerusalem, Israel

Tel: 972-2-6528111

REVLON INC.

625 Madison Ave., New York, NY, 10022

Tel: (212) 527-4000 Fax: (212) 527-4995 www.revlon.com

Mfr. cosmetics, fragrances, toiletries and beauty care products.

Revlon (Israel) Ltd., Industrial Zone, PO Box 131, Ashdod, Israel

Contact: Moshe Vidam, Gen. Mgr.

RICHARDSON ELECTRONICS, LTD.

40 W 267 Keslinger Road, LaFox, IL, 60147-0393

Tel: (630) 208-2200 Fax: (630) 208-2550 www.rell.com

Mfr. and distribution of electron tubes and related equipment.

AvivRichardson Electronics, 4 Hayetzira Street, Ra'anana 43100, Israel

ROBERT HALF INTERNATIONAL INC.

2884 Sand Hill Road, Ste. 200, Menlo Park, CA, 94025

Tel: (650) 234-6000   Fax: (650) 234-6999   www.rhii.com

World leader in personnel and specialized staffing services.

Robert Half Intl. Inc., Hatachana 4, Jerusalem, Israel

ROCKWELL AUTOMATION, INC.

777 East Wisconsin Ave., Ste. 1400, Milwaukee, WI, 53202

Tel: (414) 212-5200   Fax: (414) 212-5201   www.rockwellautomation.com

Products and service for aerospace and defense, automotive, electronics, graphics and automation industry.

Rockwell Semiconductor Systems (Israel) Ltd., 11 Galgaley Haplada St., PO Box 12660, Herzlia 46733, Israel

Tel: 972-9-9524-000   Fax: 972-9-9573-732

SAATCHI & SAATCHI

375 Hudson St., New York, NY, 10014

Tel: (212) 463-2000   Fax: (212) 463-9855   www.saatchi-saatchi.com

Provides advertising and marketing services.

Bauman Ber Rivnay Saatchi & Saatchi, 6 Hachilazon Street, Ramat-Gan 52522, Israel

Tel: 972-3-7552626   Fax: 972-3-7552727

SANMINA-SCI CORPORATION

2700 North First Street, San Jose, CA, 95134

Tel: (408) 964-3500   Fax: (408) 964-3799   www.sanmina-sci.com

Engaged in electronics contract manufacturing.

Sanmina-SCI Maalot Plant, Hamelacha Street, Box 155, Maalot Industrial Zone 24952, Israel

SBC COMMUNICATIONS INC.

175 East Houston, San Antonio, TX, 78205

Tel: (210) 821-4105   Fax: (210) 351-5034   www.sbc.com

Engaged in telecommunications.

Amdocs Ltd., Tel Aviv, Israel

Aurec Group, Tel Aviv, Israel

SIGMA-ALDRICH CORPORATION

3050 Spruce Street, St. Louis, MO, 63103

Tel: (314) 771-5765   Fax: (314) 771-5757   www.sigma-aldrich.com

Chemicals and biochemical's, aluminum and structural steel components.

Makor Chemical Ltd., PO Box 25469, Jerusalem 91060, Israel

Sigma Israel Chemical Ltd., PO Box 37673, Tel Aviv, Israel

Sigma-Aldrich Israel, 3 Menahem Plaut Street, Park Rabin, Rehovot 76326, Israel

SILICON GRAPHICS INC.

1600 Amphitheatre Pkwy., Mountain View, CA, 94043-1351

Tel: (650) 960-1980   Fax: (650) 932-0661   www.sgi.com

Design/mfr. special-effects computer graphic systems and software.

Silicon Graphics Israel, Dori Building, 1 Hamenofim Street, PO Box 2010, Herzilya 46120, Israel

Tel: 972-9-970-6666   Fax: 972-9-954-7779

SL INDUSTRIES, INC.

520 Fellowship Road, Ste. A-114,, Mount Laurel, NJ, 08054

Tel: (609) 727-1500   Fax: (609) 727-1683   www.slindustries.com

Mfr./design electronic protection and power fluctuation devices.

Abiry Technologies - SL-MTI, PO Box 53051 Tel-Aviv, Tel-Aviv 61530, Israel

SLANT/FIN CORPORATION

100 Forest Drive, Greenvale, NY, 11548

Tel: (516) 484-2600   Fax: (516) 484-2694   www.slantfin.com

Mfr. baseboard heating systems and a leading maker of cast-iron boilers and portable electric heaters.

Slant/Fin Hidron Ltd., 7 Ben Zion St., Tel Aviv 61322, Israel

SOTHEBY'S HOLDINGS, INC.

1334 York Avenue, New York, NY, 10021

Tel: (212) 606-7000   Fax: (212) 606-7027   www.sothebys.com

Auction house specializing in fine art and jewelry.

Sotheby's Holdings, Inc., 46 Rothschild Boulevard, Tel Aviv 66883, Israel

Tel: 972-3-560-1666   Fax: 972-3-560-8111   Contact: Rivka Saker

SPSS INC.

233 S. Wacker Dr., 11th Fl., Chicago, IL, 60606

Tel: (312) 651-6000   Fax: (312) 329-3668   www.spss.com

Mfr. statistical software.

Genius Systems Ltd., 28 Hida Street, Bnei Brak 51371, Israel

THE STANLEY WORKS

1000 Stanley Drive, PO Box 7000, New Britain, CT, 06053

Tel: (860) 225-5111   Fax: (860) 827-3987   www.stanleyworks.com

Mfr. hand tools and hardware.

Stanley Works, Via Parco 47, Biassono (Mi) 20046, Israel

ZAG Ltd., 19 Ha'Melacha Street, New Industrial Zone, Rosh Ha'Ayin 48091, Israel

STARWOOD HOTELS & RESORTS WORLDWIDE

777 Westchester Avenue, White Plains, NY, 10604

Tel: (914) 640-8100   Fax: (914) 640-8316   www.starwoodhotels.com

Hotel operations including Sheraton, Westin, St. Regis, Four Points and Caesars.

Sheraton Jerusalem Plaza, 47 King George St., Jerusalem 91076, Israel

Tel Aviv Sheraton Hotel & Towers, 115 Hayarkon St., Tel Aviv 61034, Israel

Tel: 972-3-521-1111   Fax: 972-3-523-3322

SUN MICROSYSTEMS, INC.

901 San Antonio Road, Palo Alto, CA, 94303

Tel: (650) 960-1300   Fax: (650) 961-9131   www.sun.com

Computer peripherals and programming services.

Sun Microsystems, Sun Israel Development Center, 10 Ha Sadnaot, Herzliya Pituach 46733, Israel

SUPERIOR TELECOM INC.

One Meadowlands Plaza, Suite 200, East Rutherford, NJ, 30339

Tel: (201) 549-4400   Fax: (201) 549-4428   www.superioressex.com

Mfr. wire and cable products.

Superior Essex Israel, PO Box 400, Kiriat Bialik 27103, Israel

Tel: 972-4-8466222

SYNCOR INTERNATIONAL CORPORATION

6464 Canoga Avenue, Woodland Hills, CA, 91367-2407

Tel: (818) 737-4000   Fax: (818) 737-4468   www.syncor.com

Mfr. and distribution of radio pharmaceutical products.

SYNCOR Worldwide, PO Box 239, Tel Aviv 81100, Israel

SYNOPSYS, INC.

700 East Middlefield Road, Mountain View, CA, 94043

Tel: (650) 962-5000   Fax: (650) 965-8637   www.synopsys.com

Mfr. electronic design automation software.

Synopsys Israel, Herzelia Business Park, 4 Maskit Street, Bldg. C, Box 12323, Herzelia 46733, Israel

Tel: 972-9-951-13771   Fax: 972-9-951-13772

SYNPLICITY, INC.

935 Stewart Drive, Sunnyvale, CA, 94085

Tel: (408) 215-6000   Fax: (408) 990-0290   www.synplicity.com

Mfr. software.

Synplicity, Inc., 9 Ha'omanut St., PO Box 8636, New Industrial Zone, Netanya 42504, Israel

TBWA WORLDWIDE

488 Madison Avenue, 6th Floor, New York, NY, 10022

Tel: (212) 804-1000   Fax: (212) 804-1200   www.tbwachiat.com

International full service advertising agency.

Yehoshua TBWA, 1 Nirim Street, Tel Aviv 67060, Israel

Tel: 972-3-6361818   Fax: 972-3-6361800

TEKTRONIX INC.

14200 SW Karl Braun Dr., PO Box 500, Beaverton, OR, 97077

Tel: (503) 627-7111   Fax: (503) 627-2406   www.tek.com

Mfr. test and measure, visual systems/color printing and communications/video and networking products.

Eastronics Ltd., 11 Rozanis St. Tel Branch, PO Box 39300, Tel Aviv 61392, Israel

Tel: 972-3-645-8777   Fax: 972-3-645-8666

TERAYON COMMUNICATION SYSTEMS, INC..

2952 Bunker Hill Lane, Santa Clara, CA, 95054

Tel: (408) 727-4400   Fax: (408) 727-6205   www.terayon.com

Mfr. cable modem systems and broadband communication services.

Terayon Communication Systems, 132 Petah Tikva Road, Tel Aviv 67021, Israel

Tel: 972-3645-8500   Fax: 972-3645-8517

THE MARMON GROUP, INC.

200 West Adams, Ste. 2211, Chicago, IL, 60606

Tel: (312) 372-9500   Fax: (312) 845-5305   www.marmon.com

Holding company for diversified manufacturing and service firms.

ScanMaster Systems (IRT) Ltd., 5 B Ha'Nagar Street, Neve Ne'Eman, Hod Ha'Sharon B-45800, Israel

TIMKEN SUPER PRECISION

PO Box 547 Precision Park, Keene, NH, 03431-0547

Tel: (603) 352-0310   Fax: (603) 355-4553   www.timken.com

Mfr., sales and distribution of bearings, tape guides and systems for missiles, etc.

RDT Components Ltd., PO Box 58013, Tel Aviv 61580, Israel

Tel: 972-3645-0707

TW METALS INC.

760 Constitution Drive, Ste. 204, Exton, PA, 19341

Tel: (610) 458-1300   Fax: (610) 458-1399   www.twmetals.com

Engaged in metals distribution and processing.

Romis International, Div. TW Metals, 19/8 Shazar Street, Haifa 34861, Israel

Tel: 972-4821-4560   Fax: 972-4821-4030

UNITED PARCEL SERVICE, INC.

55 Glenlake Parkway, NE, Atlanta, GA, 30328

Tel: (404) 828-6000   Fax: (404) 828-6593   www.ups.com

International package-delivery service.

UPS Israel, 21 Bar Kochva St., Industrial Zone, Bnei Brak 51260, Israel

Tel: 972-3-577-0101   Fax: 972-3-618-4048

UNIVERSAL SECURITY INSTRUMENTS, INC.

PO Box 825, Binghamton, NY, 13902-0825

Tel: (607) 779-7689   Fax: (607) 779-7301   www.uic.com

Provider of innovative electronic circuit assembly technology and equipment, integrated system solutions, and process expertise.

E&M Engineering (Y.G.R.) Ltd., Iramat-Gan, Israel

Tel: 972-3-751-2929   Fax: 972-3-751-3201

UTSTARCOM, INC.

1275 Harbor Bay Pkwy., Alameda, CA, 94502

Tel: (510) 864-8800   Fax: (510) 864-8802   www.utstar.com

Mfr. and sales of wireless telecommunications access systems and software products.

UTStarcom Inc., 15 Hagalim Avenue, PO Box 12262, Herzliya 46733, Israel

Tel: 972-9-9502320   Fax: 972-9-9502421

VERINT SYSTEMS INC.

234 Crossways Park Drive, Woodbury, NY, 11797

Tel: (516) 677-7300   Fax: (516) 677-7197   www.verintsystems.com

Mfr. and sales of analytic software.

Verint Systems, 23 Habarzel Street, Tel-Aviv 69710, Israel

Tel: 972-3-766-2323   Fax: 972-3-766-2333

VERNAY LABORATORIES INC.

120 East South College St., Box 310, Yellow Springs, OH, 45387

Tel: (937) 767-7261   Fax: (937) 767-1208   www.vernay.com

Mfr. precision fluid handling products.

Vernay Israel, Rotem Park, Mishor Yamin, D.N. Arava 86800, Israel

THE VIKING CORPORATION

210 N. Industrial Park Rd., Hastings, MI, 49058

Tel: (616) 945-9501   Fax: (616) 945-9599   www.vikingcorp.com

Mfr. fire extinguishing equipment.

H.R.R. Marketing & Distribution Limited, 6 Rozanski Street, New Industrial Zone, Zone IL Rishon Le Zion 75706, Israel

VIRAGE LOGIC CORPORATION

46501 Landing Pkwy., Fremont, CA, 94538

Tel: (510) 360-8000   Fax: (510) 360-8099   www.viragelogic.com

Mfr. software.

Virage Logic Corporation, 3/3 Barqan Street, Kfar Saba 44288, Israel

Tel: 972-9-745-2595   Fax: 972-9-741-3088

VISHAY INTERTECHNOLOGY INC.

63 Lincoln Hwy., Malvern, PA, 19355

Tel: (610) 644-1300   Fax: (610) 296-0657   www.vishay.com

Mfr. resistors, strain gages, capacitors, inductors, printed circuit boards.

Dale Israel Electronics Ltd., Industrial Park, PO Box 87, Dimona 86100, Israel

Vishay Israel Ltd., 2 Haofan St., Holon 58125, Israel

VISHAY SILICONIX INC.

2201 Laurelwood Drive, Santa Clara, CA, 95054

Tel: (408) 988-8000   Fax: (408) 970-3950   www.siliconix.com

Mfr. power IC's and analog signal processing devices for computers, cell phones, fixed communications networks, automobiles, and other electronic systems.

Talviton Electronics Ltd., 9 Biltmore St., PO Box 21104, Tel Aviv, Israel

VOLT INFORMATION SCIENCES, INC.

560 Lexington Avenue, 16th Fl., New York, NY, 10022-6828

Tel: (212) 704-2400   Fax: (212) 704-2417   www.volt.com

Staffing services and telecommunication services.

Volt Autologic Ltd., 6 Ahallay St., Ramat-Gan 52522, Israel

WARNER BROS.

4000 Warner Boulevard, Bldg.170, 3rd Fl., Burbank, CA, 91522

Tel: (818) 954-6000   Fax: (818) 977-4040   www.wbitv.com

Distributor TV programming and theatrical features.

Warner Bros., Attn: Israel Office, 135 Wardour St., London W1V 4AP, UK

Tel: 44-207-494-3710   Fax: 44-207-465-4207   Contact: Richard Milnes, VP Israel

WASTE MANAGEMENT, INC.

1001 Fannin Street, Ste. 4000, Houston, TX, 77002

Tel: (713) 512-6200   Fax: (713) 512-6299   www.wastemanagement.com

Environmental services and disposal company; collection, processing, transfer and disposal facilities.

Waste Management Israel Ltd., 3 Daniel Frish Street, Tel Aviv 64731, Israel

WATERS CORPORATION

34 Maple Street, Milford, MA, 01757

Tel: (508) 478-2000   Fax: (508) 872-1990   www.waters.com

Mfr./distribute liquid chromatographic instruments and test and measurement equipment.

Medtechnica Ltd., 5 Efal St. Kiriat Arie, P.O.Box 3359, Petach Tikva 49511, Israel

WIND RIVER SYSTEMS, INC.

500 Wind River Way, Alameda, CA, 94501

Tel: (510) 748-4100   Fax: (510) 749-2010   www.isi.com

Develops and markets computer software products and services.

Wind River Systems Israel, Corex Building, 10 Zarchin St., PO Box 2535, Ra'anana 43663, Israel

Tel: 972-9-741-9561   Fax: 972-9-746-0867

WOLFE AXELROD WEINBERGER

317 Madison Avenue, Suite 515, New York, NY, 10017

Tel: (212) 370-4500   Fax: (212) 370-4505   www.wolfeaxelrod.com

Financial public relations, investor relations.

Wolfe Axelrod Associates, c/o Stephen J. Kohn, 42 Brenner St., Ranana, Israel

WM WRIGLEY JR. COMPANY

410 N. Michigan Ave., Chicago, IL, 60611-4287

Tel: (312) 644-2121   Fax: (312) 644-0353   www.wrigley.com

Mfr. chewing gum.

Wrigley Israel Ltd., Herzeliya-Pituach, Israel

XEROX CORPORATION

800 Long Ridge Road, PO Box 1600, Stamford, CT, 06904

Tel: (203) 968-3000   Fax: (203) 968-4312   www.xerox.com

Mfr. document processing equipment, systems and supplies.

ELDAF Ltd., 10 Kehilat Venezia St., Neot Afeka, Tel Aviv, Israel

Tel: 972-3-645 6350   Fax: 972-3-647 4364

YOUNG & RUBICAM INC.

285 Madison Ave., New York, NY, 10017

Tel: (212) 210-3000   Fax: (212) 370-3796   www.yr.com

Advertising, public relations, direct marketing and sales promotion, corporate and product ID management.

Shalmor-Avnon-Amichay Y & R, 13 Rozanis Street, Tel Aviv 69018, Israel

Tel: 972-3-6493311   Fax: 972-3-6493334

ZORAN CORPORATION

3112 Scott Boulevard, Santa Clara, CA, 95054

Tel: (408) 919-4111   Fax: (408) 919-4122   www.zoran.com

Mfr. specialized integrated circuits and software.

Zoran Microelectronics Ltd., Advanced Technology Center, PO Box 2495, Haifa 31024, Israel

Tel: 972-4-854-5777

ZYGO CORPORATION

Laurel Brook Road, Middlefield, CT, 06455

Tel: (860) 347-8506   Fax: (860) 347-8372   www.zygo.com

Mfr. high-precision, electro-optical measuring equipment.

Lahat Technologies Ltd., Teradion Ind. Zone, D.N. Misgav 20179, Israel

Italy

24/7 REAL MEDIA, INC.

1250 Broadway, New York, NY, 10001-3701

Tel: (212) 231-7100   Fax: (212) 760-1774   www.247media.com

Provides global online advertising, sponsorships, e-commerce and direct marketing solutions to advertisers and Web publishers.

24/7 Media Italia, Via San Maurilio 16, I-20123 Milan, Italy

Tel: 39-02-8699-7060

3COM CORPORATION

5400 Bayfront Plaza, Santa Clara, CA, 95052-8145

Tel: (408) 326-5000   Fax: (408) 326-5001   www.3com.com

Engaged in the development and manufacture of computer networking products and systems.

3Com Italia, Via Michelengelo Buonarroti 1, I-24093 Cologno Monzese Milan, Italy

Tel: 39-02-253-011   Fax: 39-02-273-04244

3Com Italy, Ufficio di Roma, Viale Citt d'Europa 681, I-00144 Rome, Italy

3D SYSTEMS CORPORATION

26081 Avenue Hall, Valencia, CA, 91355

Tel: (805) 295-5600   Fax: (805) 294-8406   www.3dsystems.com

Mfr. computer lasers.

3D Systems, Via Archimede 42, I-20041 Agrate Brianza (MI), Italy

THE 3DO COMPANY

100 Cardinal Way, Ste. 425, Redwood City, CA, 94063

Tel: (650) 385-3000   Fax: (650) 385-3184   www.3do.com

Mfr. entertainment software.

Leader Distribuzione S.p.a.S, Via Adua 22, Gazzada Schianno, I-21045, Italy

3M (MINNESOTA MINING & MFG.)

3M Center, St. Paul, MN, 55144-1000

Tel: (651) 733-1110   Fax: (651) 733-9973   www.mmm.com

Mfr. diversified products for industry, consumer, health care, imaging, communications, transport, safety, etc.

3M Italia SpA, Strada per Ozzero - Fraz. Soria, Via San Bovio 3, I-20080 Milan, Italy

Tel: 39-01-67-802145   Fax: 39-02-7035-2007   Contact: James B. Stake

3M TOUCH SYSTEMS, INC.

300 Griffin Brook Park Drive, Methuen, MA, 01844

Tel: (978) 659-9000   Fax: (978) 659-9100   www.microtouch.com

Mfr. Touchscreen Sensors, Touch Monitors, and Industrial Computer Products.

3M Touch Systems Srl, C.so Milano 19, I-20052 Monza (MI), Italy

Tel: 39-39-230-2230

AAF INTERNATIONAL (AMERICAN AIR FILTER)

10300 Ormsby Park Place, Ste. 600, Louisville, KY, 40232-5690

Tel: (502) 637-0011   Fax: (502) 637-0321   www.aafintl.com

Mfr. air filtration and pollution control and noise control equipment.

AAF International, Via Valassina 24, I-20159 Milan, Italy

Tel: 39-2-607-0251

AAR CORPORATION

1100 North Wood Dale Road, Wood Dale, IL, 60191

Tel: (630) 227-2000   Fax: (630) 227-2019   www.aarcorp.com

Provides aviation repair and supply provisioning; aircraft sales and leasing.

AAR Aircraft Component Services, Via F. Cavalli, 12, I-20050 Zoccorino (MI), Italy

ABBOTT LABORATORIES

100 Abbott Park Rd., Abbott Park, IL, 60064

Tel: (847) 937-6100   Fax: (847) 937-1511   www.abbott.com

Development, manufacture and sale of diversified health care products and services.

Abbott SpA, Via Mar della Cina 262, I-00144 Rome, Italy

Tel: 39-6-529911

ABS (AMERICAN BUREAU OF SHIPPING)

ABS Plaza, 16855 Northchase Drive, Houston, TX, 77060

Tel: (281) 877-6000   Fax: (281) 877-6344   www.eagle.org

Classification and certification of ships and offshore structures, development and technical assistance.

ABS Italy SRL, Bergamo Station, Via Aldo Moro 26/26, Canonica d'Adda, I-24040 Bergamo, Italy

ABS Italy SRL, Via Varese, 6, Pregnana Milanese (MI), I-20 010 Milan, Italy

ACCENTURE LTD.

1345 Avenue of the Americas, New York, NY, 10105

Tel: (917) 452-4400   Fax: (917) 527-9915   www.accenture.com

Provides management and technology consulting services.

Accenture, Largo Donegani 2, I-20121 Milan, Italy

Tel: 39-02-290381   Fax: 39-02-6598644

ACCO WORLD CORPORATION

300 Tower Parkway, Lincolnshire, IL, 60069

Tel: (847) 541-9500   Fax: (847) 541-5750   www.accobrands.com

Provides services in the office and computer markets and manufactures paper fasteners, clips, metal fasteners, binders and staplers.

ACCO Italia Spa, Via Regio Parco, PO Box 183, I-10036 Settimo Torinese, Italy

ACCURIDE INTERNATIONAL, INC.

12311 Shoemaker Ave., Santa Fe Springs, CA, 90670-4721

Tel: (562) 903-0200   Fax: (562) 903-0208   www.accuride.com

Mfr. drawer slides.

Accuride International, Via Melano 70, I-20013 Magenta (MI), Italy

Tel: 39-02-972-92-103   Fax: 39-02-972-92-094

ACTEL CORPORATION

955 East Arquest Avenue, Sunnyvale, CA, 94086-4533

Tel: (408) 739-1010   Fax: (408) 739-1540   www.actel.com

Mfr. integrated circuits.

Actel Italy, Via dei Garibaldini, 5, I-20019 Settimo Milanese Milan, Italy

ACTERNA CORPORATION

20400 Observation Drive, Germantown, MD, 20876

Tel: (301) 353-1550   Fax: (301) 353-1536   www.acterna.com

Develop, manufacture and market communications test instruments, systems, software and services.

Acterna Italia Srl, Via Pio Emanuelli, I-00143 Rome, Italy

ADAC LABORATORIES, INC.

540 Alder Drive, Milpitas, CA, 95035

Tel: (408) 321-9100   Fax: (408) 321-9536   www.adaclabs.com

Mfr. cameras and equipment for nuclear medicine.

ADAC Laboratories SRL, Via Torquato Tasso 29, I-20099 Sesto San Giovanni, Italy

ADEMCO INTERNATIONAL

1769 N.W. 79th Avenue, Miami, FL, 33126

Tel: (305) 477-5204   Fax: (305) 477-5404   www.ademcoint.com

Mfr. security, fire and burglary systems and products.

ADEMCO Italia SpA, Via Cristoforo Colombo 1, I-20090 Corsico Milan, Italy

Tel: 39-02-458-0750   Fax: 39-02-458-0762

ADEPT TECHNOLOGY, INC.

150 Rose Orchard Way, San Jose, CA, 95134

Tel: (408) 432-0888   Fax: (408) 434-6267   www.adept.com

Mfr. robots for industries.

Adept Technology, Via Don Luigi Sturzo N. 39/41, I-52100 Arezzo, Italy

ADOBE SYSTEMS INCORPORATED

345 Park Avenue, San Jose, CA, 95110

Tel: (408) 536-6000   Fax: (408) 537-6000   www.adobe.com

Engaged in print technology and distributor of Acrobat Reader.

Adobe Systems Italia Srl, Viale Colleoni, 5 Centro Direzionale, Palazzo Taurus A3, I-20041 Agrate Brianza Milan, Italy

ADVANCED DIGITAL INFORMATION CORPORATION

11431 Willows Rd. NE, PO Box 97057, Redmond, WA, 98073

Tel: (425) 881-8004   Fax: (425) 881-2296   www.adic.com

Mfr. computer storage systems.

ADIC Italy, Viale Fulvio Testi 11, I-20092 Cinisello B. Milan, Italy

ADVANCED MICRO DEVICES INC.

1 AMD Place, Sunnyvale, CA, 94086

Tel: (408) 732-2400   Fax: (408) 982-6164   www.amd.com

Mfr. integrated circuits for communications and computation industry.

Advanced Micro Devices SpA, Via Novara, 570, I-20153 Milan, Italy

Tel: 39-03-381-961

AGCO CORPORATION

4205 River Green Parkway, Duluth, GA, 30096-2568

Tel: (770) 813-9200   Fax: (770) 813-6038   www.agcocorp.com

Mfr. farm equipment and machinery.

Agrinova SNC, Via Strade per Porzano 9, I-25025 Manerbio BS, Italy

Tel: 39-30-993-8823

Massey Ferguson Distribution, Div. AGCO, Via Mateotti 7, I-42042 Fabbrico Reggio Emilia, Italy

Tel: 39-522-665-951

AGILENT TECHNOLOGIES, INC.

395 Page Mill Road, PO Box 10395, Palo Alto, CA, 94303

Tel: (650) 752-5000   Fax: (650) 752-5633   www.agilent.com

Mfr. communications components.

Agilent Technologies Italy S.p.A, Via Giuseppe Di Vittorio 9, I-20063 Cernusco S/N (MI), Italy

Tel: 32-2-92-121

AIG AMERICAN INTERNATIONAL GROUP INC.

70 Pine Street, New York, NY, 10270

Tel: (212) 770-7000   Fax: (212) 509-9705   www.aig.com

Worldwide insurance and financial services.

AIG Europe S.A., Via Valcava 6, I-20155 Milan, Italy

AIRBORNE INC.

3101 Western Ave., PO Box 662, Seattle, WA, 98121

Tel: (206) 285-4600   Fax: (206) 281-1444   www.airborne.com

Air transport services.

Airborne Express, Via Novegro 3, I-20090 Novegro Di Segrate Milan, Italy

Tel: 39-55-435666   Fax: 39-55-435701

ALBANY INTERNATIONAL CORPORATION

1373 Broadway, Albany, NY, 12204

Tel: (518) 445-2200   Fax: (518) 445-2265   www.albint.com

Mfr. broadwoven and engineered fabrics, plastic products, filtration media.

Albany Intl. Italiana SpA, Viale Lombardi 68, I-20010 Inveruno, Italy

ALBERTO-CULVER COMPANY

2525 Armitage Ave., Melrose Park, IL, 60160

Tel: (708) 450-3000   Fax: (708) 450-3354   www.alberto.com

Mfr./marketing personal care and household brand products.

Alberto-Culver Products SRL, Viale Brenta 18, I-20139 Milan, Italy

ALCOA INC.

Alcoa Center, 201 Isabella Street at 7th Street Bridge, Pittsburgh, PA, 15212-5858

Tel: (412) 553-4545   Fax: (412) 553-4498   www.alcoa.com

World's leading producer of aluminum and alumina; mining, refining, smelting, fabricating and recycling.

Alcoa Italia S.p.A, Milan, Italy

Contact: Giuseppe Toia, Mng. Dir.

ALCOA FUJIKURA LTD.

800 Crescent Centre Drive, Ste. 600, Franklin, TN, 37067

Tel: (615) 778-6000   Fax: (615) 778-5927   www.alcoa-fujikura.com

Mfr. optical ground wire, tube cable, fiber optic connectors and automotive wiring harnesses. (JV of Alcoa USA).

Alcoa Italia S.p.A., Modena, Italy

ALLEGHENY TECHNOLOGIES INC.

1000 Six PPG Place, Pittsburgh, PA, 15222

Tel: (412) 394-2800   Fax: (412) 394-2805   www.alleghenytechnologies.com

Diversified mfr. aviation and electronics, specialty metals, industrial and consumer products.

Allegheny Technologies, Corso de Porta Romana 2, I-20122 Milan, Italy

ALLEGIANCE HEALTHCARE CORPORATION

1430 Waukegan Road, McGaw Park, IL, 60085

Tel: (847) 689-8410   Fax: (847) 578-4437   www.allegiance.net

Manufactures and distributes medical, surgical, respiratory therapy and laboratory products.

Allegiance Medica srl, Viale Tiziano 25, I-00196 Rome, Italy

Tel: 39-06-32-4911   Fax: 39-06-32-491204   Contact: Sandro Lombardi, Bus. Dir.

ALLEN TELECOM

25101 Chagrin Boulevard, Beachwood, OH, 44122-5619

Tel: (216) 765-5818   Fax: (216) 765-0410   www.allentele.com

Mfr. communications equipment, automotive bodies and parts, electronic components.

Forem Italy, Via Archimede 22/24, I-20041 Agrate Brianza, Italy

Tel: 39-039-60541   Fax: 39-039-6054477

ALLEN-BRADLEY COMPANY, INC.

1201 South Second Street, Milwaukee, WI, 53204

Tel: (414) 382-2000   Fax: (414) 382-4444   www.ab.com

Mfr. electrical controls and information devices.

Allen-Bradley Italia SRL, Via Tortona 33, I-20144 Milan, Italy

Nuova OSAI SRL, Allen-Bradley Motion Control Div., Stradale Torino 603, I-10015 Ivrea, Italy

ALLERGAN INC.

2525 Dupont Drive, Irvine, CA, 92612

Tel: (714) 246-4500   Fax: (714) 246-6987   www.allergan.com

Mfr. therapeutic eye care products and skin care pharmaceuticals.

Allergan S.p.A., Via Salvatore Quasimodo N. 134/138, I-00144 Rome, Italy

Tel: 39-6-509561   Fax: 39-6-50956410

ALTERA CORPORATION

101 Innovation Drive, San Jose, CA, 95134

Tel: (408) 544-7000   Fax: (408) 544-8303   www.altera.com

Mfr. high-density programmable chips for semi-conductor industry.

Altera Italia S.R.L., Corso Lombardia 75, Autoporto Pescarito, I-10099 San Mauro Torinese (Torino), Italy

Tel: 39-11-223-8588

AMDOCS LIMITED

1390 Timberlake Manor Pkwy., Chesterfield, MO, 63017

Tel: (314) 212-7000   Fax: (314) 212-7500   www.amdocs.com

Mfr. telecommunications software.

Amdocs Italy, Via di Vigna, Murata, 40, I-00143 Rome, Italy

Tel: 39-06-548-32015

AMERICAN APPRAISAL ASSOCIATES INC.

411 E. Wisconsin Ave., Ste. 1900, Milwaukee, WI, 53202

Tel: (414) 271-7240   Fax: (414) 271-1041   www.american-appraisal.com

Valuation consulting services.

American Appraisal Italia SRL, Centro Direzionale Colleoni, Viale Colleoni 21, Edif. Pegaso 1, I-20041 Agrate Milan, Italy

Tel: 39-39-605-6226   Fax: 39-39-65-4443   Contact: Caterina Biondi

AMERICAN EXPRESS COMPANY

90 Hudson Street, Jersey City, NJ, 07302

Tel: (212) 640-2000   Fax: (212) 619-9802   www.americanexpress.com

Engaged in travel, travelers cheques, charge card and financial services.

American Express Services, Via Dante Alighieri 22 R, I-50122 Florence, Italy

AMERICAN MANAGEMENT SYSTEMS, INC. (AMS)

4050 Legato Road, 10th Fl., Fairfax, VA, 22033

Tel: (703) 267-8000   Fax: (703) 267-5073   www.amsinc.com

Provides integrated IT solutions, outsourcing, and transformation services.

AMS Management Systems Italia, SPA, Via Monte Rosa 60, I-20121 Milan, Italy

Tel: 39-02-669-6452

AMERICAN SOFTWARE, INC.

470 East Paces Ferry Road, NE, Atlanta, GA, 30305

Tel: (404) 261-4381   Fax: (404) 264-5514   www.amsoftware.com

Mfr./sales of financial control software and systems.

Information Technology Italia, Strada 4, Palazzo Q7, I-20089 Assago (MI) Milanfiori, Italy

Tel: 39-2-5750-1440   Fax: 39-2-5750-1461

AMERICAN STANDARD COMPANIES, INC.

One Centennial Avenue, Piscataway, NJ, 08855-6820

Tel: (732) 980-3000   Fax: (732) 980-6118   www.americanstandard.com

Mfr. automotive, plumbing, heating, air conditioning products and medical diagnostics systems.

DiaSorin s.r.l., Via Crescentino, I-1340 Saluggia VC, Italy

Tel: 39-01-61-487-087   Fax: 390-161-487-396

WABCO Compagnia Italiana Segnali SpA, Via Volvera 51, I-10045 Piossasco Turin, Italy

WABCO SpA, Via Pier Carlo Boggio 20, I-10138 Turin, Italy

AMETEK INC.

37 N. Valley Road, PO Box 1764, Paoli, PA, 19301-0801

Tel: (610) 647-2121   Fax: (610) 296-3412   www.ametek.com

Mfr. instruments, electric motors and engineered materials.

AMETEK Italia S.r.l., Vacuum Products, Via De Gasperi 18/A, I-26010 Ripalta Cremasca, Italy

Tel: 39-0373-2101   Fax: 39-0373-268200

AMETEK Italia Srl, Via de Barzi, Robecco Sul Naviglio, I-20087 Milan, Italy

Tel: 39-02-94-6931   Fax: 39-02-94-71179

AMGEN INC.

One Amgen Center Drive, Thousand Oaks, CA, 91320-1799

Tel: (805) 447-1000   Fax: (805) 499-2694   www.amgen.com

Biotechnology research and pharmaceuticals.

Amgen S.p.A., Via Vitruvio 38, I-20124 Milan, Italy

Tel: 39-02-6698-4125

AMPEX CORPORATION

1228 Douglas Avenue, Redwood City, CA, 94063-3199

Tel: (650) 367-2011   Fax: (650) 367-4669   www.ampex.com

Mfr. extremely high-performance digital data storage, data retrieval and image processing systems for a broad range of corporate scientific and government applications.

Ampex Italiana SpA, Via Cristoforo Colombo 40, I-20090 Trezzano sul Naviglio Milan, Italy

AMPHENOL CORPORATION

358 Hall Ave., Wallingford, CT, 06492-7530

Tel: (203) 265-8900   Fax: (203) 265-8793   www.amphenol.com

Mfr. electronic interconnect penetrate systems and assemblies.

Ampheno Italia, S.P.A., Galleria Ghandi 2/27, I-20017 Mazzo di Rho Milan, Italy

Tel: 39-02-9390-4192   Fax: 39-02-9390-1030

AMR CORPORATION (AMERICAN AIRLINES)

4333 Amon Carter Boulevard, Ft. Worth, TX, 76155

Tel: (817) 963-1234   Fax: (817) 967-9641   www.amrcorp.com

Air transport services.

American Airlines Inc., Via Sicilia 50, I-00187 Rome, Italy

AMSTED INDUSTRIES INC.

205 North Michigan Ave., Chicago, IL, 60601

Tel: (312) 645-1700   Fax: (312) 819-8523   www.amsted.com

Privately-held, diversified manufacturer of products for the construction and building markets, general industry and the railroads.

Baltimore Aircoil Italia S.r.l., Div. Amsted, I-23030 Chiuro Sondrio, Italy

Tel: 39-0342-482-882   Fax: 39-0342-83-022   Contact: Massimo Moltoni, Gen. Mgr.   Emp: 22

AMWAY CORPORATION

7575 Fulton Street East, Ada, MI, 49355-0001

Tel: (616) 787-6000   Fax: (616) 787-6177   www.amway.com

Mfr./sale home care, personal care, nutrition and houseware products.

Amway Italia SRL, Via G. di Vittorio 10, I-20094 Corsico Milan, Italy

ANALOG DEVICES INC.

1 Technology Way, Norwood, MA, 02062

Tel: (781) 329-4700   Fax: (781) 326-8703   www.analog.com

Mfr. integrated circuits and related devices.

Analog Devices SRL, Via Galileo Galilei 2, I-20091 Bresso, Italy

ANDERSEN

33 West Monroe Street, Chicago, IL, 60603

Tel: (312) 580-0033   Fax: (312) 507-6748   www.andersen.com

Accounting and audit, tax and management consulting services. **Firm under worldwide reorganization; new data unavailable for this edition.

Andersen Worldwide, Via Della Moscova 3, I-20121 Milan, Italy

Tel: 39-02-290371

Studio di Consulenza Legale e Tributaria, Largo Donegani 2, I-20121 Milan, Italy

Tel: 39-02-62401

Studio di Consulenza Legale e Tributaria, Via XX Settembre 1, I-00187 Rome, Italy

Tel: 39-06-489901

Studio di Consulenza Legale e Tributaria, Via M. D'Azeglio 19, I-40123 Bologna, Italy

Tel: 39-051-237539

ANDREW CORPORATION

10500 West 153rd Street, Orland Park, IL, 60462

Tel: (708) 349-3300   Fax: (708) 349-5410   www.andrew.com

Designer, manufacturer, and supplier of communications equipment, services, and systems.

Andrew SRL, Via Rombon 11, I-20134 Milan, Italy

Tel: 39-02-215611   Fax: 39-02-215-0490

ANHEUSER-BUSCH INTERNATIONAL INC.

One Busch Place, St. Louis, MO, 63118-1852

Tel: (314) 577-2000   Fax: (314) 577-2900   www.anheuser-busch.com

Malt production, aluminum beverage containers, rice milling, real estate development, metalized and paper label printing, railcar repair and theme-park facilities.

S.P.A. Birra Peroni Industriale, Milan, Italy

ANIXTER INTERNATIONAL INC..

4711 Golf Road, Skokie, IL, 60076

Tel: (847) 677-2600   Fax: (847) 677-8557   www.anixter.com

Distributor wiring systems/products for voice, video, data and power applications.

Anixter Italy, Via Walter Tobagi 24, I-20068 Peschiera Borromeo, Italy

Tel: 39-02-54-7491   Fax: 39-02-55-301777

Anixter Italy, Via Della Grande Muraglia 284, I-00144 Rome, Italy

Tel: 39-06-526-201   Fax: 39-05-522-05-250

ANSYS, INC.

275 Technology Drive, Canonsburg, PA, 15317

Tel: (724) 746-3304   Fax: (724) 514-9494   www.ansys.com

Mfr. CAD and CAE software.

ANSYS Italy, Via Guido d'Arezzo, 4, I-20145 Milan, Italy

AOL TIME WARNER

75 Rockefeller Plaza, New York, NY, 10019

Tel: (212) 484-8000   Fax: (212) 275-3046   www.aoltimewarner.com

Engaged in media and communications; provides internet services, communications, publishing and entertainment.

Time-Life Intl. SARL, Via Turati 29, Milan, Italy

AON CORPORATION

200 East Randolph, Chicago, IL, 60601

Tel: (312) 381-1000   Fax: (312) 381-6032   www.aon.com

Insurance brokers worldwide; underwrites accident and health insurance, specialty and professional insurance; and provides risk management consultation.

AON Italia SpA, Piazza della Repubblica 32, Milan, Italy

Tel: 39-02-678-481   Fax: 39-02-678-48200   Contact: Raffaele Bozzano

Manzitti Howden Beck SpA, Via XX Settembre 33, Genoa, Italy

Tel: 39-010-541-951   Fax: 39-010-582-825   Contact: Beppe Manzitti

APOGENT TECHNOLOGIES INC.

48 Congress Street, Portsmouth, NH, 03801

Tel: (603) 433-6131   Fax: (603) 431-0860   www.apogent.com

Design, mfr. & sell products for laboratories, clinical research, industrial markets & analytical products.

Kerr Italia SpA, Via Passanti 332, Casella Postale 46, I-84018 Scafati Salerno, Italy

APPLE COMPUTER, INC.

One Infinite Loop, Cupertino, CA, 95014

Tel: (408) 996-1010   Fax: (408) 974-2113   www.apple.com

Personal computers, peripherals and software.

Apple Computer SpA, Via Bovio 5, Zona Ind. di Mancasale, I-42100 Reggio Emilia, Italy

APPLERA CORPORATION

301 Merritt 7, Norwalk, CT, 06851

Tel: (203) 840-2000   Fax: (203) 840-2312   www.applera.com

Leading supplier of systems for life science research and related applications.

Applied Biosystems, Via Tiepolo 18, I-20052 Monza (MI), Italy

Tel: 39-0-39-838-9492

APPLIED MATERIALS, INC.

3050 Bowers Ave., Santa Clara, CA, 95054-3299

Tel: (408) 727-5555   Fax: (408) 727-9943   www.appliedmaterials.com

Supplies manufacturing systems and services to the semiconductor industry.

Applied Materials S.A.R.L., Centro Direaionale Colleoni, Viale Colleoni 15, Palazzo Orione, I-20041 Agrate Brianza Milan, Italy

Tel: 39-039-605-8111   Fax: 39-039-605-6446

APW, INC.

N22 W23685 Ridgeview Parkway West, Waukesha, WI, 53188-1013

Tel: (262) 523-7600   Fax: (262) 523-7624   www.apw1.com

Mfr. hi-pressure tools, vibration control products, consumables, technical furniture and enclosures.

APW Enclosure Products, Corso Lombardia, 52 Regione Pescarito, I-10099 S. Mauro Torinese, Italy

ARBOR ACRES FARM INC.

439 Marlborough Road, Glastonbury, CT, 06033

Tel: (860) 633-4681   Fax: (860) 633-2433   www.aaf.com

Producers of male and female broiler breeders, commercial egg layers.

Arbor Acres Italia SpA, Localita Mojentina, I-20070 San Rocco Al Porto Milan, Italy

ARGO INTERNATIONAL CORPORATION

140 Franklin Street, New York, NY, 10013

Tel: (212) 431-1700   Fax: (212) 431-2206   www.argointl.com

Distribution of quality electrical and mechanical equipment, components, renewal spare parts for the worldwide industrial, marine, metal mining, oil well drilling, utility, refineries and petroleum industries.

Argo International Europe Ltd., Viale Dei Mille 74, Florence, Italy

Argo International Italy, Via Bassa 33B, I-50018 Scandicci Firenze, Italy

ARIBA, INC.

1565 Charleston Rd., Mountain View, CA, 94043

Tel: (650) 930-6200   Fax: (650) 930-6300   www.ariba.com

Mfr. software.

Ariba Italia, Largo Richini 6, I-20122 Milan, Italy

ARMSTRONG HOLDINGS, INC.

2500 Columbia Avenue, Lancaster, PA, 17604-3001

Tel: (717) 397-0611   Fax: (717) 396-2787   www.armstrong.com

Mfr. and marketing interior furnishings and specialty products for building, auto and textile industry.

Armstrong World Industries Italia SRL, Milan, Italy

ARROW ELECTRONICS INC.

25 Hub Drive, Melville, NY, 11747

Tel: (516) 391-1300   Fax: (516) 391-1640   www.arrow.com

Distributor of electronic components and computer products.

Arrow Italia, Via Collamarini 22, I-40138 Bologna, Italy

Arrow Italia, Via Crocillo 69, I-80010 Naples, Italy

Arrow Italia, Viale Delle Industrie 13, I-35101 Padova, Italy

Arrow Italia, Via Bille 26, I-63023 Ascoli Piceno, Italy

Arrow Italia, Via Giunio Antonio Resti 63, I-00143 Rome, Italy

Arrow Italia, Via A da Noli 6, I-50127 Firenze, Italy

Arrow Italia, Via Fulvio Testi 280, I-20126 Milan, Italy

Arrow Italia, Corso Svizzera 185 bis, Centro Piero della Francesca, I-10149 Torino, Italy

Arrow Italia, Via A. da Noli 6, I-50127 Firenze, Italy

Silverstar, Viale Fulvio Testi 280, I-20126 Milan, Italy

Tel: 39-02-66-12-51   Fax: 39-02-66-10-42-79   Contact: Germano Fanelli, Mng. Dir.

ART TECHNOLOGY GROUP, INC.

25 First Street, Cambridge, MA, 02141

Tel: (617) 386-1000   Fax: (617) 386-1111   www.atg.com

Mfr. application service software.

Art Technology Group, Piazzale Biancamano, 8, I-20121 Milan, Italy

ASG (ALLEN SYSTEMS GROUP)

1333 Third Avenue South, Naples, FL, 34102

Tel: (941) 435-2200   Fax: (941) 263-3692   www.asg.com

Mainframe computer software, specializing in OnMark 2000 software.

ASG Italy, Via Ludovico il Moro 4/b, Palazzo Pitagora, I-20080 Basiglio MI, Italy

Tel: 39-02-904-5001

ASHLAND OIL INC.

50 E. RiverCenter Blvd., Box 391, Covington, KY, 41012-0391

Tel: (859) 815-3333   Fax: (859) 815-5053   www.ashland.com

Petroleum exploration, refining and transportation; mfr. chemicals, oils and lubricants.

Ashland Chemical Italiana SpA, Via Giacomo Watt 42, I-20143 Milan, Italy

ASSOCIATED MERCHANDISING CORPORATION

500 Seventh Ave., 2nd Fl., New York, NY, 10018

Tel: (212) 819-6600   Fax: (212) 819-6701   www.theamc.com

Retail service organization; apparel, shoes and accessories.

Amcrest Corp., Piazza della Republica 32, I-20124 Milan, Italy

Amcrest Corp., Via Guicciardini 13, I-50125 Florence, Italy

ASSOCIATED PRESS INC.

50 Rockefeller Plaza, New York, NY, 10020-1605

Tel: (212) 621-1500   Fax: (212) 621-5447   www.ap.com

News gathering agency.

The Associated Press, Piazza Grazioli 5, Rome, Italy

Tel: 39-06-678-9936

AT&T CORPORATION

295 N. Maple Ave., Basking Ridge, NJ, 07920-1002

Tel: (908) 221-2000   Fax: (908) 221-2528   www.att.com

Engaged in long distance telecommunications.

AT&T Italia SpA, Via Cristoforo Colombo 153, I-00147 Rome, Italy

ATMEL CORPORATION

2325 Orchard Pkwy., San Jose, CA, 95131

Tel: (408) 441-0311   Fax: (408) 436-4200   www.atmel.com

Design, manufacture and marketing of advanced semiconductors.

Atmel Italy, Uff di Milano Centro Dierzionale, Colleoni Palazzo Andromeda 3, I-20041 Agrate Brianza, Italy

Tel: 39-39-605-6955   Fax: 39-39-605-6969

ATTACHMATE CORPORATION

3617 131st Avenue SE, Bellevue, WA, 98006-1332

Tel: (425) 644-4010   Fax: (425) 747-9924   www.attachmate.com

Mfr. connectivity software.

Attachmate Italy, Via Vitruvio 38, I-20124 Milan, Italy

Tel: 39-02-671-3101   Fax: 39-02-669-1113

Attachmate Italy, Via Cristoforo Colombo 440, I-00145 Rome, Italy

Tel: 39-06-542-3281   Fax: 39-06-540-8851

AUTODESK INC.

111 McInnis Parkway, San Rafael, CA, 94903

Tel: (415) 507-5000   Fax: (415) 507-6112   www.autodesk.com

Develop/marketing/support computer-aided design, engineering, scientific and multimedia software products.

Autodesk SpA, Milanofiori, Strada4 Palazzo A5, 1-20090 Milan, Italy

Tel: 39-02-57-5511   Fax: 39-01-57-510-105

AUTOMATIC DATA PROCESSING INC.

One ADP Blvd., Roseland, NJ, 07068

Tel: (973) 994-5000   Fax: (973) 994-5387   www.adp.com

Data processing services.

ADP-GSI S.p.A., Via Natale Battaglia 8, I-20127 Milan, Italy

Tel: 39-02-261651   Fax: 39-02-282-7639   Contact: Lina Gallo

AUTOMATIC SWITCH CO. (ASCO)

50-60 Hanover Rd., Florham Park, NJ, 07932

Tel: (973) 966-2000   Fax: (973) 966-2628   www.asco.com

Mfr. solenoid valves, emergency power controls, pressure and temperature switches.

ASCO/Joucomatic S.P.A., Via Inverigo 14, I-20151 Milan, Italy

Tel: 39-02-380411   Fax: 39-02-334-00409   Contact: D. Ferrari

AUTOSPLICE INC.

10121 Barnes Canyon Road, San Diego, CA, 92121

Tel: (858) 535-0077   Fax: (858) 535-0130   www.autosplice.com

Mfr. electronic components.

Autosplice Italia, Via Sicilia 19, I-20040 Carnate (MI), Italy

Fax: 39-39-6705-30   Contact: Dr. Laura Camisasca

AVERY DENNISON CORPORATION

150 N. Orange Grove Blvd., Pasadena, CA, 91103

Tel: (626) 304-2000   Fax: (626) 792-7312   www.averydennison.com

Mfr. pressure-sensitive adhesives and materials, office products, labels, tags, retail systems, Carter's Ink and specialty chemicals.

Avery Dennison Italia SpA, Via Honduras 15, Pomezia, Italy

Tel: 39-69-160-0311

Fasson Italia SpA, Corso Italia 2, I-21040 Origgio Varese, Italy

AVID TECHNOLOGY, INC.

1 Park West, Tewksbury, MA, 01876

Tel: (978) 640-6789   Fax: (978) 640-1366   www.avid.com

Mfr. animation design software and digital and audio systems.

Avid Technology Srl, Palazzo E-1, I-20090 AssagoMilanofiori (MI) Milan, Italy

Tel: 39-02-5778-971

AVNET INC.

2211 South 47th Street, Phoenix, AZ, 85034

Tel: (480) 643-2000   Fax: (480) 643-4670   www.avnet.com

Distributor electronic components, computers and peripherals.

Avnet EMG SRL Adelsy, Centro Direzionale, Via Novara 780, I-20153 Milan MI, Italy

Tel: 39-238-1901   Fax: 39-238-2988

BFI Ibexsa S.p.A., 18 Via Massena, Milan, Italy

Tel: 39-233-100535   Fax: 39-233-611603

AVON PRODUCTS, INC.

1345 Avenue of the Americas, New York, NY, 10105-0196

Tel: (212) 282-5000   Fax: (212) 282-6049   www.avon.com

Mfr. direct seller of cosmetics and beauty-related items.

Avon Cosmetics SpA, Via XXV Aprile 15, I-22077 Olgiate Comasco Como, Italy

Tel: 39-031-998111   Fax: 39-031-998312   Contact: Fabio Stillitano, Field Dir.

AXCELIS TECHNOLOGIES, INC.

55 Cherry Hill Drive, Beverly, MA, 01915

Tel: (978) 787-4000   Fax: (978) 787-4200   www.axcelis.com

Mfr. implantation devices.

Axcelis Technologies Italy, Via Archimede, 31 Agrate, I-20041 Brianza, Italy

Tel: 39-039-656-1524

BAIN & COMPANY, INC.

Two Copley Place, Boston, MA, 02116

Tel: (617) 572-2000   Fax: (617) 572-2427   www.bain.com

Strategic management consulting services.

Bain, Cuneo e Associati, Via Lutezia 8, I-00198 Rome, Italy

Bain, Cuneo e Associati, Via Crocefisso 10/12, I-20122 Milan, Italy

Tel: 39-02-582-881   Fax: 39-02-583-14070

BAKER & McKENZIE

130 East Randolph Drive, Ste. 2500, Chicago, IL, 60601

Tel: (312) 861-8000   Fax: (312) 861-2899   www.bakerinfo.com

International legal services.

Studio Avvocati Associati, Via degli Scipioni 288, I-00192 Rome, Italy

Tel: 39-06-3225162   Fax: 39-06-3203502

Studio Legale de Libero Camilli Boniello Bartolo Di Garbo, 3 Piazza Meda, I-20121 Milan, Italy

Tel: 39-02-76013921   Fax: 39-02-76008322

BAKER HUGHES INCORPORATED

3900 Essex Lane, Ste. 1200, Houston, TX, 77027

Tel: (713) 439-8600   Fax: (713) 439-8699   www.bakerhughes.com

Develop and apply technology to drill, complete and produce oil and natural gas wells; provide separation systems to petroleum, municipal, continuous process and mining industries.

Baker Oil Tools (Italia), SRL, Via Monti 2 Zona Bassette, I-48100 Ravenna, Italy

Tel: 39-544-453-339

Baker Oil Tools (Italia), SRL, Via Monti 2, Zona Bassette, I-48101 Ravenna, Italy

Tel: 39-054-445-6229   Fax: 39-054-445-4816

Baker Oil Tools (Italia), SRL, Strada Statale 602, Km 5 + 170, Santa Teresa, I-65010 Spoltore Pescara, Italy

Tel: 39-085-497-1190   Fax: 39-085-497-1224

BAKER PETROLITE CORPORATION

3900 Essex Lane, Houston, TX, 77027

Tel: (713) 599-7400   Fax: (713) 599-7592   www.bakerhughes.com

Mfr. specialty chemical treating programs, performance-enhancing additives and related equipment and services.

Petrolite Italiana SpA, Via Sasari 86, I-95127 Catania, Italy

BALDOR ELECTRIC COMPANY

5711 R.S. Boreham Jr. Street, Fort Smith, AR, 72908

Tel: (501) 646-4711   Fax: (501) 648-5792   www.baldor.com

Mfr. electric motors.

Baldor Italia SRL, Via Galileo Galilel 17, I-22070 Guanzate Como, Italy

BALTIMORE AIRCOIL CO., INC.

PO Box 7322, Baltimore, MD, 21227

Tel: (410) 799-6200   Fax: (410) 799-6416   www.baltimoreaircoil.com

Mfr. evaporative heat transfer and ice thermal storage products.

Baltimore Aircoil Italia s.r.l., I-23030 Chiuro Sondrio, Italy

BANFI VINTNERS

1111 Cedar Swamp Road, Old Brookville, NY, 11545

Tel: (516) 626-9200   Fax: (516) 626-9218   www.banfivintners.com

Engaged in wine import.

Castello Banfi, I-53024 Montalcini (SI), Italy

BANK OF AMERICA CORPORATION

Bank of America Corporate Center, Charlotte, NC, 28255

Tel: (415) 622-3530   Fax: (704) 386-6699   www.bankofamerica.com

Financial services.

Bank of America - Southern Europe, Corso Matteotti 10, I-20121 Milan, Italy

Tel: 39-02-760-691   Fax: 39-02-760-69200   Contact: Pier Giorgio Rota Baldini, EVP

THE BANK OF NEW YORK

One Wall Street, New York, NY, 10286

Tel: (212) 495-1784   Fax: (212) 495-2546   www.bankofny.com

Banking services.

The Bank of New York, Piazzale Cadorna 4, I-20123 Milan, Italy

Tel: 39-02-720-10333   Fax: 39-02-720-10325

C. R. BARD, INC.

730 Central Ave., Murray Hill, NJ, 07974

Tel: (908) 277-8000   Fax: (908) 277-8078   www.crbard.com

Mfr. health care products.

Bard SpA, Via Cina 444, I-00144 Rome, Italy

BARRY CONTROLS INC.

40 Guest Street, PO Box 9105, Brighton, MA, 02135-9105

Tel: (617) 787-1555   Fax: (617) 254-7381   www.barrymounts.com

Mfr./sale vibration isolation mounting devices.

UVIT il Cingolo, Via F Busoni, I-20137 Milan, Italy

BATES WORLDWIDE INC.

498 Seventh Avenue, New York, NY, 10018

Tel: (212) 297-7000   Fax: (212) 986-0270   www.batesww.com

Advertising, marketing, public relations and media consulting.

Bates Italia, Via Paleocapa 7, I-20121 Milan, Italy

Tel: 39-02-805-2283   Fax: 39-02-864-54305   Contact: Giordano Spagllardi, Mgr.

Bates Italia, Via Panama 12, I-00195 Rome, Italy

Tel: 39-06-844-0381   Fax: 39-06-853-55607   Contact: S. Pazzagli, Mgr.

Bates Medical/Healthcom, Via Paleocapa 7, I-20121 Milan, Italy

Tel: 39-02-72-2231   Fax: 39-02-72-010811   Contact: Leonardo Vinci, CEO

BAUSCH & LOMB INC.

One Bausch & Lomb Place, Rochester, NY, 14604-2701

Tel: (716) 338-6000   Fax: (716) 338-6007   www.bausch.com

Mfr. vision care products and accessories.

Bausch & Lomb, Via Pasubio, 34, I-20050 Milan, Italy

BAX GLOBAL INC.

16808 Armstrong Ave., PO Box 19571, Irvine, CA, 92623

Tel: (949) 752-4000   Fax: (949) 260-3182   www.baxworld.com

Air freight forwarder.

BAX Global, Blocco 2/3, I-40010 Interporto Bologna, Italy

Tel: 39-051-665-1001   Fax: 39-051-665-0643

BAX Global - Reg. Office, Via Salomone 43, I-20138 Milan, Italy

Tel: 39-02-506761   Fax: 39-02-5801-0619

BAX Global - Rome, Via Fulco Ruffo di Calabria 3/5 - 7/9, I-00054 Fiumicino Paese Rome, Italy

Tel: 39-06-6504-7551   Fax: 39-06-650-5546

BAXTER INTERNATIONAL INC.

One Baxter Parkway, Deerfield, IL, 60015

Tel: (847) 948-2000   Fax: (847) 948-3948   www.baxter.com

Mfr. products and provide services in the field of the administration of medication and bioscience.

Baxter SpA, Viale Tiziano 25, I-00196 Rome, Italy

Laboratori Don Baxter SpA, Via Flavia 122, I-34146 Trieste, Italy

BBDO WORLDWIDE

1285 Ave. of the Americas, New York, NY, 10019

Tel: (212) 459-5000   Fax: (212) 459-6645   www.bbdo.com

Multinational group of advertising agencies.

BBDO Italy, Milan, Italy

BDO SEIDMAN, LLP   BELGIUM

130 East Randolph Street, Chicago, IL, 60601

Tel: (312) 856-9100   Fax: (312) 856-1379   www.bdo.com

International accounting and financial consulting firm.

Sala Scelsi, Farina BDO, Piazza del Liberty 4, I-20121 Milan, Italy

Tel: 39-02-784563   Fax: 39-02-784567   Contact: Girogio Farina

BEA SYSTEMS, INC.

2315 North First Street, St. Jose, CA, 95131

Tel: (408) 570-8000   Fax: (408) 570-8091   www.beasys.com

Develops communications management software and provider of software consulting services.

BEA Systems Italia Spa, Via Giorgio Stephenson, 11th Fl., I-20157 Milan, Italy

Tel: 39-02-773-000   Fax: 39-02-773-001

THE BEAR STEARNS & COMPANIES., INC.

245 Park Ave., New York, NY, 10167

Tel: (212) 272-2000   Fax: (212) 272-3092   www.bearstearns.com

Investment banking, securities broker/dealer and investment advisory services.

Bear, Stearns International Limited, Via Pietro Verri 6, I-20121 Milan, Italy

Tel: 39-02-3030-1730   Fax: 39-02-3030-1700

BECKMAN COULTER, INC.

4300 N. Harbor Boulevard, Fullerton, CA, 92834

Tel: (714) 871-4848　　　Fax: (714) 773-8898　　　www.beckmancoulter.com

Develop/mfr./marketing automated systems and supplies for biological analysis.

Beckman-Analytical SpA, Centro Direzionale Lombardo, Palazzo F/1, Via Roma 108, I-20060 Cassina de Pecchi Milan, Italy

BELDEN, INC.

7701 Forsyth Blvd., Ste. 800, St. Louis, MO, 63015

Tel: (314) 854-8000　　　Fax: (314) 854-8001　　　www.belden.com

Mfr. electronic wire and cable products.

Belden International Inc., Via Paracelso 26, Centro Direzionale Colleoni, Palazzo Cassiopea Ingr. 3, I-20041 Agrate Brianza MI, Italy

BELL MICROPRODUCTS INC.

1941 Ringwood Avenue, San Jose, CA, 95131

Tel: (408) 451-9400　　　Fax: (408) 451-1600　　　www.bellmicro.com

Distributes semiconductor and computer products from manufacturers.

Rorke Data, Div. Bell Microproducts, Via Angelo Carrara 210, I-16147 Genoa, Italy

Tel: 39-10-373-3126

BERLITZ CROSS-CULTURAL TRAINING INC.

400 Alexander Park, Princeton, NJ, 08540

Tel: (609) 514-9650　　　Fax: (609) 514-9689　　　www.berlitz.com

Consulting and management training services to bridge cultural gaps for international travelers as well as for business transferees and families.

Berlitz Language Centers, Via Larga, 8, I-20122 Milan, Italy

BEST WESTERN INTERNATIONAL

6201 North 24th Place, Phoenix, AZ, 85106

Tel: (602) 957-4200　　　Fax: (602) 957-5740　　　www.bestwestern.com

International hotel chain.

Hotel Syrene, Via Camerelle 51, Capri, Italy

BICC GENERAL

4 Tesseneer Drive, Highland Heights, KY, 41076

Tel: (859) 572-8000　　　Fax: (859) 572-8444　　　www.generalcable.com

Mfr., marketing and distribution of copper, aluminum and fiber optic wire and cable products for the communications, energy and electrical markets.

BICC General, 16Via Brescia 16, I-10036 Settimo Torinese Turin, Italy

BIO-RAD LABORATORIES INC.

1000 Alfred Nobel Drive, Hercules, CA, 94547

Tel: (510) 724-7000　　　Fax: (510) 724-3167　　　www.bio-rad.com

Mfr. life science research products, clinical diagnostics, analytical instruments.

Bio-Rad Laboratories SRL, Via Peroglio, 23, I-00144 Rome, Italy

BIOWHITTAKER INC.

8830 Biggs Ford Road, Walkersville, MD, 21793

Tel: (301) 898-7025　　　Fax: (301) 845-6099　　　www.biowhittaker.com

Mfr. cell culture products, endotoxin detection assays.

Profarmaco, Via Cucchiari, 1, I-20155 Milan, Italy

Tel: 39-02-3310-5520　Fax: 39-02-3310-5730

BLACK & DECKER CORPORATION

701 E. Joppa Road, Towson, MD, 21286

Tel: (410) 716-3900　　　Fax: (410) 716-2933　　　www.blackanddecker.com

Mfr. power tools and accessories, security hardware, small appliances, fasteners, information systems and services.

Black & Decker Italy, Attn: Italy Office, 701 East Joppa Road, Towson, MD, 21286

BLACK BOX CORPORATION

1000 Park Dr., Lawrence, PA, 15055

Tel: (724) 746-5500   Fax: (724) 746-0746   www.blackbox.com

Direct marketer and technical service provider of communications, networking and related computer connectivity products.

Black Box Italia SpA, Viale Delle Industrie 11, I-20090 Vimodrone Milan, Italy

Tel: 39-02-2740-0815 Fax: 39-02-2740-0219 Contact: Giancarlo Mauri, Gen. Mgr.

BLOOM ENGINEERING CO., INC.

5460 Horning Rd., Pittsburgh, PA, 15236

Tel: (412) 653-3500   Fax: (412) 653-2253   www.bloomeng.com

Mfr. custom engineered burners and combustion systems.

Bloom Engineering (Europa) S.r.l., Via Bottego, 2/30, I-16149 Genoa, Italy

Tel: 390-10-466772   Fax: 390-10-6468473

BMC SOFTWARE, INC.

2101 City West Blvd., Houston, TX, 77042-2827

Tel: (713) 918-8800   Fax: (713) 918-8000   www.bmc.com

Engaged in mainframe-related utilities software and services.

BMC Software, Via M. Bianchini 51, I-00142 Rome, Italy

BMC Software S.r.l., Via Ugo Bassi 8/A, I-20159 Milan, Italy

THE BOEING COMPANY

100 N. Riverside Plaza, Chicago, IL, 60606

Tel: (312) 544-2000   Fax: (312) 544-2082   www.boeing.com.

World's largest aerospace company; mfr. military and commercial aircraft, missiles and satellite launch vehicles.

The Boeing Company, Rome, Italy

BOISE CASCADE CORPORATION

1111 West Jefferson Street, PO Box 50, Boise, ID, 83728-0001

Tel: (208) 384-6161   Fax: (208) 384-7189   www.bc.com

Mfr./distributor paper and paper products, building products, office products.

Carlos Proto Agencies, Rome, Italy

Tel: 39-06-321-6565

BONTEX INC.

One Bondex Drive, Buena Vista, VA, 24416

Tel: (540) 261-2181   Fax: (540) 261-3784   www.bontex.com

Engaged in development and distribution of advanced materials, systems for a broad range of applications.

Bontex Italia SRL, Via Francia N. 1, I-37069 Villafranc, Italy

Tel: 39-45 630 34 12   Fax: 39-0-630 35 88

BOOZ-ALLEN & HAMILTON INC.

8283 Greensboro Drive, McLean, VA, 22102

Tel: (703) 902-5000   Fax: (703) 902-3333   www.bah.com

International management and technology consultants.

Booz, Allen & Hamilton Italia Ltd., Via dei Bossi 4, I-20121 Milan, Italy

Tel: 39-02-725091   Fax: 39-02-72-50-9400

BORG-WARNER AUTOMOTIVE INC.

200 S. Michigan Ave., Chicago, IL, 60604

Tel: (312) 322-8500   Fax: (312) 461-0507   www.bwauto.com

Mfr. automotive components; provider of security services.

Regina-Warner SpA, Via Monza 90, I-22052 Cernusco Lombardone, Italy

BOSE CORPORATION

The Mountain, Framingham, MA, 01701-9168

Tel: (508) 879-7330   Fax: (508) 766-7543   www.bose.com

Mfr. quality audio equipment and speakers.

BOSE S.p.A, Via Della Magliana 876, I-00148 Rome, Italy

Tel: 39-066-567-0802

THE BOSTON CONSULTING GROUP

Exchange Place, 31st Fl., Boston, MA, 02109

Tel: (617) 973-1200   Fax: (617) 973-1339   www.bcg.com

Management consulting company.

The Boston Consulting Group, Via della Moscova 18, I-20121 Milan, Italy

Tel: 39-02-65-5991

BOSTON SCIENTIFIC CORPORATION (BSC)

One Scientific Place, Natick, MA, 01760-1537

Tel: (508) 650-8000   Fax: (508) 650-8923   www.bostonscientific.com

Developer, manufacturer and marketer of medical devices.

Boston Scientific SpA, World Trade Ctr., 10th Fl., Via Dei Marini, I-16149 Genoa, Italy

Tel: 39-010-60601   Fax: 39-010-6060200

Boston Scientific SpA, Corso Mateotti 1, Scala A, 2nd piano, I-20121 Milan, Italy

Tel: 39-02-783-890   Fax: 39-02-783-910

BOWNE & COMPANY, INC.

345 Hudson Street, New York, NY, 10014

Tel: (212) 924-5500   Fax: (212) 229-3420   www.bowne.com

Financial printing and foreign language translation, localization (software), internet design and maintenance and facilities management.

Bowne Global Solutions, Via Senato 12, I-20121 Milan, Italy

Tel: 39-02-763623-09   Fax: 39-02-764097-27

BOYDEN CONSULTING CORPORATION

364 Elwood Ave., Hawthorne, NY, 10502

Tel: (914) 747-0093   Fax: (914) 980-6147   www.boyden.com

International executive search firm.

Boyden International. SRL, Via G.B. Martini 13, I-00198 Rome, Italy

Tel: 39-06-841-3400

Boyden International. SRL, Via G. Carducci 32, I-20123 Milan, Italy

Tel: 39-02-805-5352

BOZELL GROUP

40 West 23rd Street, New York, NY, 10010

Tel: (212) 727-5000   Fax: (212) 645-9173   www.bozell.com

Advertising, marketing, public relations and media consulting.

Bozell Italia S.p.A., Corso Europa 2, I-20122 Milan, Italy

Tel: 39-02-77411   Fax: 39-02-781263   Contact: Marco Vecchia, Pres.

BRADY CORPORATION

6555 W. Good Hope Road, Milwaukee, WI, 53223

Tel: (414) 358-6600   Fax: (414) 358-6600   www.whbrady.com

Mfr. industrial ID for wire marking, circuit boards; facility ID, signage, printing systems and software.

Brady Italia Srl, Via Lazzaroni 7, I-21047 Saronno, Italy

Tel: 39-02-96-700-507   Fax: 39-02-96-703-644   Contact: Giancarlo Prosdotti, Gen. Mgr.

Seton Italia Srl, Casella Postale 51, I-20037 Paderno Dugnano Milan, Italy

Tel: 39-02-96-703-198   Fax: 39-02-96-703-644   Contact: Giancarlo Prosdotti, Gen. Mgr.

BRANSON ULTRASONICS CORPORATION

41 Eagle Road, Danbury, CT, 06813-1961

Tel: (203) 796-0400   Fax: (203) 796-2285   www.branson-plasticsjoin.com

Engaged in design, development, manufacture and marketing of plastics joining, precision cleaning and processing equipment.

Branson Ultrasuoni SpA, Via Dei Lavoratori 25, I-20092 Cinisello Balsamo Milan, Italy

Tel: 39-02-660-10479   Fax: 39-02-660-10480

BRINK'S INC.

Thorndal Circle, Darien, CT, 06820

Tel: (203) 662-7800   Fax: (203) 662-7968   www.brinks.com

Security transportation.

Brink's Securmark SpA, Florence, Italy

BRISTOL-MYERS SQUIBB COMPANY

345 Park Ave., New York, NY, 10154-0037

Tel: (212) 546-4000   Fax: (212) 546-4020   www.bms.com

Pharmaceutical and food preparations, medical and surgical instruments.

Bristol Italiana (SUD) S.p.A., Largo Carlo Salinari N. 18, I-00142 Rome, Italy

Clairol Italiana S.p.A., Via Boccaccio 15, I-20123 Milan, Italy

ConvaTec, Div. Bristol-Myers Squibb Co., Via Paolo di Dono 73, I-00143 Rome, Italy

Laboratori Guieu Italia, Via Lomellina 10, I-20133 Milan, Italy

Laboratori Guieu Italia, Via Robbio 35, I-26030 Confienza Pavia, Italy

Matrix Essentials Italia, S.p.A, Via Bruno Pontacorvo SNC, Via Tiburtina KM. 18700, I-00012 Guidonia Montecello Rome, Italy

Squibb S.p.A, Latina Plant, Vua del Murillo, Sermonet Latina, Italy

Squibb S.p.A., Via Virgilio Maroso 50, I-00142 Rome, Italy

UPSAMedica S.p.A., Via Agnello 18, I-20121 Milan, Italy

Zimmer S.r.L., Via Tolstoi 86, I-20098 San Giuliano Milanese, Italy

BROADVISION, INC.

585 Broadway, Redwood City, CA, 94063

Tel: (650) 261-5100   Fax: (650) 261-5900   www.broadvision.com

Develops and delivers an integrated suite of packaged applications for personalized enterprise portals.

BroadVision Italy, Centro Direzionale Milanofiori, Strada 6, Palazzo N2, I-20089 Rozzano (Milan), Italy

Tel: 39-02-89200539

BROWN SHOE COMPANY, INC.

8300 Maryland Avenue, St. Louis, MO, 63105

Tel: (314) 854-4000   Fax: (314) 854-4274   www.brownshoe.com

Markets branded and private label footwear, including Dr. Scholl's, Air Step and Buster Brown.

Pagoda Italia, Via Garibaldi 8, I-50123 Florence, Italy

BROWNING

1 Browning Place, Morgan, UT, 84050

Tel: (801) 876-2711   Fax: (801) 876-3331   www.browning.com

Sales and distribution of port firearms, fishing rods, etc.

Browning Sports Italia, S.r.l., Via Enrico Mattei 8, I-25046 Cazzago S. Martino (Brescia), Italy

BUCKMAN LABORATORIES INTERNATIONAL, INC.

1258 N. McLean Blvd., Memphis, TN, 38108-0308

Tel: (901) 278-0330   Fax: (901) 276-5343   www.buckman.com

Mfr. specialty chemicals.

Buckman Laboratories Italiana S.r.l., Via Verdi, 3, I-20080 Zibido San Giacomo, Italy

BUNGE LIMITED

50 Main St., 6th Fl., White Plains, NY, 10606

Tel: (914) 684-2800   Fax: (914) 684-3499   www.bunge.com

Engaged in agribusiness; oilseed and grain processing, fertilizer, wheat and corn milling, food ingredients, and commercial and branded food product markets.

Bunge International Trading, Rome, Italy

BURLINGTON INDUSTRIES INC.

3330 W. Friendly Ave., PO Box 21207, Greensboro, NC, 27420

Tel: (336) 379-2000   Fax: (336) 379-4943   www.burlington-ind.com

Manufacturer and developer of textiles for apparel and interior furnishing.

Marzotto Italy, Milan, Italy

LEO BURNETT, DIV. B-COM 3 GROUP

35 West Wacker Drive, Chicago, IL, 60601

Tel: (312) 220-5959   Fax: (312) 220-6533   www.leoburnett.com

Engaged in advertising, marketing, media buying and planning, and public relations.

Leo Burnett Co. SRL, Via Fatebenefratelli 14, I-20138 Milan, Italy

BURSON-MARSTELLER

230 Park Avenue South, New York, NY, 10003-1566

Tel: (212) 614-4000   Fax: (212) 614-4262   www.bm.com

Public relations/public affairs consultants.

Burson-Marsteller S.r.l., Via Beatrice Cenci 7/a, I-00186 Rome, Italy
Tel: 39-06-688-9631   Fax: 39-06-668-96368   Emp: 14

Burson-Marsteller SRL, Palazzo Recalcati, Via Amedei 8, I-20123 Milan, Italy
Tel: 39-02-721-431   Fax: 39-02-878-960   Emp: 50

BUTTERICK COMPANY, INC.

161 Avenue of the Americas, New York, NY, 10013

Tel: (212) 620-2500   Fax: (212) 620-2746   www.butterick.com

Prints sewing patterns and related magazines.

Vla G.A. Boltraffio, Via Cola Montano 10, I-20159 Milan, Italy

CABLE DESIGN TECHNOLOGIES CORPORATION

661 Andersen Drive, Plaza 7, Pittsburgh, PA, 15220

Tel: (412) 937-2300   Fax: (412) 937-9690   www.cdtc.com

Mfr. computer connector copper, fiber optic and composite cables.

Industria Tecnica/DCT, Via Bora 4, I-48012 Bagnacavallo, Italy
Tel: 39-0-545-60470

CABOT CORPORATION

2 Seaport Lane, Ste. 1300, Boston, MA, 02210-2019

Tel: (617) 345-0100   Fax: (617) 342-6103   www.cabot-corp.com

Mfr. carbon blacks, plastics; oil and gas, information systems.

Cabot Italiana SpA, Casella Postale 444, Via Senistra Canate Candiano, I-48100 Ravenna, Italy

CADENCE DESIGN SYSTEMS, INC.

2655 Seely Ave., Bldg. 5, San Jose, CA, 95134

Tel: (408) 943-1234   Fax: (408) 943-0513   www.cadence.com

Mfr. electronic design automation software.

Cadence Design Systems, Palazzo Bonadies, Via di San Pantaleo 66, I-00186 Rome, Italy

Cadence Design Systems, Milanofiori, Strada 7 Palazzo R/3, I-20089 Rossano, Milan, Italy

CALDERA INTERNATIONAL

355 South 520 West, Ste. 100, Linden, UT, 84057

Tel: (801) 765-4999   Fax: (801) 765-1313   www.caldera.com

Provides integrated solutions for small-to-medium businesses, retail operations, telecommunications and other vertical markets.

Caldera Systems Italia Srl, Centro Direzionale Lombardo, Via Roma 108, I-20060 Cassina de Pecchi (MI), Italy

Tel: 39-02-9510231   Fax: 39-02-9516394   Contact: Orlando Zanni

CALED CHEMICAL

26 Hanes Drive, Wayne, NJ, 07470

Tel: (973) 696-7575   Fax: (973) 696-4790   www.caledchemical.com

Mfr. dry cleaning chemicals and machine filters, laundry detergents, fabric protectors, flame retardants.

CALED International of Italy, Milan, Italy

CALVIN KLEIN, INC.

205 West 39th Street, 4th Fl., New York, NY, 10018

Tel: (212) 719-2600   Fax: (212) 768-8922   www.calvinklein.com

Mfr. of high quality clothing and accessories

Calvin Klein Ltd., Milan, Italy

CAMBREX CORPORATION

1 Meadowlands Plaza, East Rutherford, NJ, 07063

Tel: (201) 804-3000   Fax: (201) 804-9852   www.cambrex.com

human health, animal health/agriculture and Mfr. biotechnology products and produce specialty chemicals.

Bio Whittaker Italia s.r.l., Via D. Cucchiari 17, I-20155 Milan, Italy

Tel: 39-02-33-105601   Fax: 39-02-33-105606

Cambrex Corp. Profarmaco S.r.l., Via Cucchiari 17, I-20155 Milan, Italy

Tel: 39-02-3310-5520   Fax: 39-02-3310-5730

Profarmaco S.r.l., Via Cucchiari 17, I-20155 Milan, Italy

Tel: 39-02-3310-5520

CANBERRA INDUSTRIES, INC.

800 Research Parkway, Meriden, CT, 06450

Tel: (203) 238-2351   Fax: (203) 235-1347   www.canberra.com

Mfr. instruments for nuclear research.

Canberra-Packard SRL, Via della Circonvallazione Nomentana 514, I-00162 Rome, Italy

Canberra-Packard SRL, Via Vincenzo Monti 23, I-20016 Pero Milan, Italy

CANDLE CORPORATION

201 N. Douglas Street, El Segundo, CA, 90245

Tel: (310) 535-3600   Fax: (310) 727-4287   www.candle.com

Mfr. management software.

Candle Southern Europe, Vai Cavriana, 3, I-20134 Milan, Italy

CAPITAL CONTROLS COMPANY, INC.

3000 Advance Lane, PO Box 211, Colmar, PA, 18915-0211

Tel: (215) 997-4000   Fax: (215) 997-4062   www.capitalcontrols.com

Mfr./services water disinfecting products and systems.

Capital Controls SpA, Via Isola Guarnieri 13, I-20063 Cernusco S/N, Italy

Tel: Gabriele Perazzo

CAPTURA, INC.

6710 108th Avenue NE, Kirkland, WA, 98033

Tel: (425) 803-6000   Fax: (425) 803-6100   www.captura.com

Mfr. automated payment software.

Captura International Italy, Via Feltrina Nord, 62, I-31044 Montebulluna, Treviso, Italy

CARBOLINE COMPANY
350 Hanley Industrial Court, St. Louis, MO, 63144

Tel: (314) 644-1000   Fax: (314) 644-4617   www.carboline.com

Mfr. coatings and sealants.

APSA SpA, Via Pirelli 30, I-20124 Milan, Italy

CARGILL, INC.
15407 McGinty Road West, Minnetonka, MN, 55440-5625

Tel: (612) 742-7575   Fax: (612) 742-7393   www.cargill.com

Food products, feeds, animal products.

Cargill Srl, Via Rombon 11, I-20134 Milan, Italy

CARLSON COMPANIES, INC.
PO Box 59159, Minneapolis, MN, 55459

Tel: (612) 550-4520   Fax: (612) 550-4580   www.cmg.carlson.com

Marketing services agency.

SitCap, Via San Francesco da Paola, I-10123 Torino, Italy
Tel: 39-11-810-6511   Fax: 39-11-810-6565

THE CARLYLE GROUP L.P.
1001 Pennsylvania Avenue, NW, Washington, DC, 20004-2505

Tel: (202) 347-2626   Fax: (202) 347-1818   www.thecarlylegroup.com

Global investor in defense contracts.

CEP Advisors Srl, Via dell'Arcivescovado 1, I-20122 Milan, Italy
Tel: 39-02-8901-2107   Fax: 39-02-8699-1301

CARPENTER TECHNOLOGY CORPORATION
PO Box 14662, Reading, PA, 19612-4662

Tel: (610) 208-2000   Fax: (610) 208-3214   www.cartech.com

Mfr. specialty steels and structural ceramics for casting industrial.

Carpenter Technology (Italy) SRL, Via Monte Rosa 60, I-20149 Milan, Italy

CARRIER CORPORATION
One Carrier Place, Farmington, CT, 06034-4015

Tel: (860) 674-3000   Fax: (860) 679-3010   www.carrier.com

Mfr./distributor/services A/C, heating and refrigeration equipment.

Delchi Carrier SpA, Via Raffaello Sanzio 9, I-20058 Villasanta Milan, Italy
Tel: 39-039-3636   Fax: 39-039-3636-252

CASCADE CORPORATION
2201 NE 201st Ave., Fairview, OR, 97024-9718

Tel: (503) 669-6300   Fax: (503) 669-6321   www.cascor.com

Mfr. hydraulic forklift truck attachments.

Assistance Italy Mecoil s.r.l., Via del Mandorlo 28, I-59100 Prato, Italy
Nuova SAR s.r.l., Brescia, Via L. Ariosto 7, I-25080 Molinetto di Mazzano, Italy

CATERPILLAR INC.
100 NE Adams Street, Peoria, IL, 61629-6105

Tel: (309) 675-1000   Fax: (309) 675-1182   www.cat.com

Mfr. earth/material-handling and construction machinery and equipment and engines.

Caterpillar, Inc., Milan, Italy

CB RICHARD ELLIS SERVICES
200 N. Sepulveda Blvd., Ste. 300, El Segundo, CA, 90245-4380

Tel: (310) 563-8600   Fax: (310) 563-8670   www.cbrichardellis.com

Commercial real estate services.

CB Richard Ellis SpA, 4 Via dei Giardini, I-20121 Milan, Italy
CB Richard Ellis SpA, Piazza Del Popolo 18, I-00187 Rome, Italy

CENTRAL NATIONAL-GOTTESMAN INC.

3 Manhattanville Road, Purchase, NY, 10577-2110

Tel: (914) 696-9000   Fax: (914) 696-1066   www.cng-inc.com

Distribution of pulp and paper products.

Central National Italia SRL, Via Antonio da Recante 4, I-20124 Milan, Italy

Tel: 39-02-670-3162   Fax: 39-02-670-2895   Contact: Manuel Polo

CH2M HILL INC.

6060 South Willow Drive, Greenwood Village, CO, 80111

Tel: (303) 771-0900   Fax: (303) 770-2616   www.ch2m.com

Consulting engineers, planners, economists and scientists.

CH2M Hill, Via Alserio 22, I-20159 Milan, Italy

CHECKPOINT SYSTEMS, INC.

101 Wolf Drive, Thorofare, NJ, 08086

Tel: (856) 848-1800   Fax: (856) 848-0937   www.checkpointsystems.com

Mfr. test, measurement and closed-circuit television systems.

Checkpoint Systems Italia s.r.l., Via Senigallia 18/2, I-20161 Bruzzano Milano, Italy

Tel: 39-2-6622-4097   Fax: 39-2-645-8136   Contact: Alfredo Maggi, Gen. Mgr.

THE CHEMITHON CORPORATION

5430 West Marginal Way Southwest, Seattle, WA, 98106

Tel: (206) 937-9954   Fax: (206) 932-3786   www.chemithon.com.

Chemicals process equipment manufacturing for detergent, specialty chemicals and power generation industries.

Chemithon Corporation, Via Alba, 18, I-21052 Busto Arsizio (VA), Italy

THE CHERRY CORPORATION

3600 Sunset Ave., PO Box 718, Waukegan, IL, 60087

Tel: (847) 662-9200   Fax: (847) 662-2990   www.cherrycorp.com

Mfr. electrical switches, electronic keyboards, controls and displays.

Silverstar Ltd. S.p.A., Viale Fulvio Testi 280, I-20126 Milan, Italy

Tel: 39-2-661251   Fax: 39-2-66101359

CHESTERTON BLUMENAUER BINSWANGER

Two Logan Square, 4th Floor, Philadelphia, PA, 19103-2759

Tel: (215) 448-6000   Fax: (215) 448-6238   www.cbbi.com

Real estate and related services.

Redilco SpA, 115 Via XX Settembre, I-24100 Bergamo, Italy

Redilco SpA, Via dell' Arcivescovado 1, I-20122 Milan, Italy

Redilco SpA, Corte lambruschini, 8 C.so Buenos Aires, I-16121 Genoa, Italy

CHICAGO RAWHIDE INDUSTRIES (CRI)

735 Tollgate Road, Elgin, IL, 60123

Tel: (847) 742-7840   Fax: (847) 742-7845   www.chicago-rawhide.com

Mfr. shaft and face seals.

RFT SpA, Strada per Poirino 41, I-14019 Villanova d'Asti, Italy

CHIQUITA BRANDS INTERNATIONAL INC.

250 East Fifth Street, Cincinnati, OH, 45202

Tel: (513) 784-8000   Fax: (513) 784-8030   www.chiquita.com

Sale and distribution of bananas, fresh fruits and processed foods.

Chiquita Italia SpA, Via Tempio del Ciela 3, I-00144 Rome, Italy

CHIRON CORPORATION

4560 Horton Street, Emeryville, CA, 94608-2916

Tel: (510) 655-8730   Fax: (510) 655-9910   www.chiron.com

Engaged in biotechnology; biopharmaceuticals, blood testing and vaccines.

Chiron Biocine SpA, Via Fiorentina 1, I-53100 Siena, Italy

Tel: 39-57-724-3111   Fax: 39-57-724- 3085

CHOICE HOTELS INTERNATIONAL, INC.

10750 Columbia Pike, Silver Springs, MD, 20902

Tel: (301) 592-5000   Fax: (301) 592-6227   www.choicehotels.com

Hotel franchises, including Comfort Inn, Econo Lodge, Roadway Inn and Quality.

Choice Hotels Europe, Via Bramante 39, I-20154 Milan, Italy

THE CHUBB CORPORATION

15 Mountain View Road, Warren, NJ, 07061-1615

Tel: (908) 580-2000   Fax: (908) 580-3606   www.chubb.com

Holding company for property and casualty insurance and liability insurance for corporate executives.

Chubb Insurance Co. of Europe, SA, Piazzetta Pattari 1, I-20122 Milan, Italy

Tel: 39-01-806-7101   Fax: 39-02-805-7236

Chubb Insurance Company of Europe, S.., Via San Vitale 4, I-40125 Bologna, Italy

Tel: 39-051-273-271   Fax: 39-051-227-453

Chubb Insurance Company of Europe, S.A., Corso Milano 74, I-35139 Padova, Italy

Tel: 39-049-872-6033   Fax: 39-049-871-0206

CIGNA COMPANIES

One Liberty Place, Philadelphia, PA, 19192

Tel: (215) 761-1000   Fax: (215) 761-5511   www.cigna.com

Insurance, invest, health care and other financial services.

CIGNA Insurance Co. of Europe SA/NV, Viale Maresciallo Pilsudski 124, I-00197 Rome, Italy

CIGNA Italy-Societa A Responsabilita Limitada, Viale Maresciallo Pilsudski 124, I-00197 Rome, Italy

Esis Intl. Inc., Via della Moscova 3, I-20120 Milan, Italy

CINCOM SYSTEMS INC.

55 Merchant Street, Cincinnati, OH, 45446

Tel: (513) 612-2300   Fax: (513) 481-8332   www.cincom.com

Develop/distributor computer software.

Cincom Italia S.r.l., Via Botero 18, I-10122 Torino, Italy

Cincom Italia S.r.l., 1 Via San Clemente, I-20122 Milan, Italy

CISCO SYSTEMS, INC.

170 West Tasman Drive, San Jose, CA, 95134-1706

Tel: (408) 526-4000   Fax: (408) 526-4100   www.cisco.com

Develop/mfr./market computer hardware and software networking systems.

Cisco Systems Italy Srl, Viale della Grande Muraglia 284, I-00114 Rome, Italy

Tel: 39-06-527-9971   Fax: 39-06-5220-9952

Cisco Systems Italy Srl, Via Torri Bianche 7, Palazzo Faggio, I-20059 Vimercate Milan, Italy

Tel: 39-039-62951   Fax: 39-039-6295-299

CITIGROUP, INC.

399 Park Avenue, New York, NY, 10022

Tel: (212) 559-1000   Fax: (212) 559-3646   www.citigroup.com

Provides insurance and financial services worldwide.

Citigroup, Trade/Capital Markets 16, I-20121 Foro Buonaparte Milan, Italy

Contact: Sergio Ungaro

CITRIX SYSTEMS, INC.

6400 NW 6th Way, Fort Lauderdale, FL, 33309

Tel: (954) 267-3000   Fax: (954) 267-9319   www.citrix.com

Developer of computer software.

Citrix Systems Italia, Via Giovanni da Udine, 34, I-20156 Milan, Italy

CLARCOR INC.

2323 Sixth Street, PO Box 7007, Rockford, IL, 61125

Tel: (815) 962-8867   Fax: (815) 962-0417   www.clarcor.com

Mfr. filtration products and consumer packaging products.

Facet Italiana S.p.A., Div. CLARCOR, Via IV Novembre 58, I-10070 Cafasse Torino, Italy

CLEAR CHANNEL COMMUNICATIONS

200 East Basse Road, San Antonio, TX, 78209

Tel: (210) 822-2828   Fax: (210) 822-2299   www.clearchannel.com

Owns, manages, promotes and produces concerts and shows; programs and sells airtime for radio stations, owns and places outdoor advertising displays and provides agent services to athletes and broadcasters.

AAF Italy, Via Giulini 2, I-20123 Milan, Italy

Tel: 39-02-806651   Contact: Francesco Celentano, Mgr.

Jolly Pubblicita Advertising, Via B. Cellini 66, I-35027 Noventa Padovana, Italy

Tel: 39-0490625699   Contact: Francesco Celentano, Mgr.

CLEARY GOTTLIEB STEEN & HAMILTON

One Liberty Plaza, New York, NY, 10006

Tel: (212) 225-2000   Fax: (212) 225-3999   www.cgsh.com

Engaged in international law.

Cleary, Gottlieb, Steen & Hamilton, Rome, Italy

CNA FINANCIAL CORPORATION

CNA Plaza, Chicago, IL, 60685

Tel: (312) 822-5000   Fax: (312) 822-6419   www.cna.com

Commercial property/casualty insurance policies.

CNA Insurance Company (Europe) Limited (CIE), Corso Matteotti #22, I-20121 Milan, Italy

COACH LEATHERWEAR COMPANY

516 West 34th Street, New York, NY, 10001

Tel: (212) 594-1850   Fax: (212) 594-1682   www.coach.com

Mfr. and sales of high-quality leather products, including handbags, wallets and shoes.

Coach at Mitsukoshi Rome, Via Nazionale 259, Via Torino 29, I-00184 Rome, Italy

THE COCA-COLA COMPANY

1 Coca Cola Plaza, Atlanta, GA, 30313

Tel: (404) 676-2121   Fax: (404) 676-6792   www.coca-cola.com

Mfr./marketing/distributor soft drinks, syrups and concentrates, juice and juice-drink products.

Coca-Cola Italia S.r.l., Via Nazario Sauro, 38, Sesto S. Giovanni, I-20099 Milan, Italy

Contact: Roberto Farina

COGNEX CORPORATION

1 Vision Drive, Natick, MA, 01760

Tel: (508) 650-3000   Fax: (508) 650-3333   www.cognex.com

Mfr. machine vision systems.

Cognex Italy, Via Gasparotto 1, I-20124 Milan, Italy

Tel: 39-02-6747-1200   Fax: 39-02-6747-1300

THE COLEMAN COMPANY, INC.

3600 N. Hydraulic, Wichita, KS, 67219

Tel: (316) 832-2700   Fax: (316) 832-2794   www.colemanoutdoors.com

Mfr. distributor and sales of camping and outdoor recreation products.

Coleman SVB (Italy), Via Canova 11, I-25010 Centenaro-Lonato Brescia, Italy

COLFAX CORPORATION

9211 Forest Hill Avenue, Ste. 109, Richmond, VA, 23235

Tel: (804) 560-4070   Fax: (804) 560-4076   www.colfaxcorp.com

Mfr. industrial clutches and brakes and motion control products and components.

Colfax Pumps, Via R. Luxenburg 49, I-20065 Locate di Triulzi (M), Italy

COLFAX PUMP GROUP, DIV. COLFAX INC.

1710 Airport Road, PO Box 5020, Monroe, NC, 28111-5020

Tel: (704) 289-6511   Fax: (704) 289-4839   www.colfaxpump.com

Mfr. rotary and centrifugal pumps.

Colfax Pumps, Via Correggio 19, I-20149 Milan, Italy

COLGATE-PALMOLIVE COMPANY

300 Park Ave., New York, NY, 10022

Tel: (212) 310-2000   Fax: (212) 310-2919   www.colgate.com

Mfr. pharmaceuticals, cosmetics, toiletries and detergents.

Colgate-Palmolive SpA, Via Georgione 59/63, I-00147 Rome, Italy

COLLIERS INTERNATIONAL PROPERTY CONSULTANTS INC.

84 State Street, 3rd Fl., Boston, MA, 02109

Tel: (617) 722-0221   Fax: (617) 722-0224   www.colliers.com

Engaged in commercial real estate.

Colliers International, Via Tronto, 16, I-00198 Rome, Italy

COMMWORKS CORPORATION

3800 Golf Road, Rolling Meadows, IL, 60008

Tel: (847) 262-5000   Fax: (847) 262-0327   www.commworks.com

Provides Internet protocol-based network access software and equipment.

Commworks Corporation, Ufficio de Roma, Viale Citta d'Europa 681, I-00144 Rome, Italy

COMPUTER ASSOCIATES INTERNATIONAL INC.

One Computer Associates Plaza, Islandia, NY, 11788

Tel: (516) 342-5224   Fax: (516) 342-5329   www.cai.com

Integrated business software for enterprise computing and information management, application development, manufacturing, financial applications and professional services.

Computer Associates S.p.A., Palazzo Leonardo da Vinci, Via Francisco Storza 3, I-20080 Basiglio Milan 3, Italy
Tel: 39-01-90-4641

COMPUWARE CORPORATION

31440 Northwestern Hwy., Farmington Hills, MI, 48334-2564

Tel: (248) 737-7300   Fax: (248) 737-7108   www.compuware.com

Develop and market software for enterprise and e-commerce solutions.

Compuware S.p.A., Via Della Nocetta 109, I-00164 Rome, Italy
Tel: 39-06-6613-001

CONEXANT SYSTEMS, INC.

4311 Jamboree Road, PO Box C, Newport Beach, CA, 92658-8902

Tel: (949) 483-4600   Fax: (949) 483-4078   www.conexant.com

Provides semiconductor products for communications electronics.

Conexant Systems Italia, Via G. DiVittorio 1, I-20017 Mazzo Di Rho, Italy
Tel: 39-02-9317-9911   Fax: 39-02-9317-9913

CONOCO INC.

600 N. Dairy Ashford, Houston, TX, 77252

Tel: (281) 293-1000   Fax: (281) 293-1440   www.conoco.com

Oil, gas, coal, chemicals and minerals.

Conoco Idrocarburi SpA, Via Vittorio Veneto 116, I-00187 Rome, Italy
Continental Oil Co. of Italy, c/o Studio Dott. Rag. Sergio Pagani, Via G. Frua 24, I-20146 Milan, Italy

CONTINENTAL AIRLINES INC.

1600 Smith St., Houston, TX, 77002

Tel: (713) 324-5000   Fax: (713) 324-2637   www.continental.com

International airline carrier.

Continental Airlines Inc., Rome, Italy

CONVERGYS CORPORATION

201 E. 4th St., Cincinnati, OH, 45202

Tel: (513) 723-7000   Fax: (513) 421-8624   www.convergys.com

Engaged in data bill processing, telemarketing and customer services representation for major corporations.

Convergys Corporation, Viale Fulvia Testi 280, I-20100 Milan, Italy

COOPER INDUSTRIES INC.

6600 Travis Street, Ste. 5800, Houston, TX, 77002

Tel: (713) 209-8400   Fax: (713) 209-8995   www.cooperindustries.com

Mfr./distributor electrical products, tools, hardware and automotive products, fuses and accessories for electronic applications and circuit boards.

Cooper Automotive, Capri, Italy

Kirsch Division, Milan, Italy

CORDIS CORPORATION

PO Box 25700, Miami, FL, 33102-5700

Tel: (305) 824-2000   Fax: (305) 824-2747   www.cordis.com

Mfr. medical devices and systems.

Cordis Italia, Piazza Don Enrico Mapelli 1, I-20099 Sesto San Giovanni, Italy

CORECHANGE, INC.

260 Franklin Street, Ste. 1890, Boston, MA, 02110

Tel: (617) 204-3300   Fax: (617) 204-3333   www.corechange.com

Mfr. software.

Corechange Italy, Via Solferino 82, I-20035 Lissone, Italy

CORNING INC.

One Riverfront Plaza, Corning, NY, 14831-0001

Tel: (607) 974-9000   Fax: (607) 974-8091   www.corning.com

Mfr. glass and specialty materials, consumer products; communications, laboratory services.

Corning International Italy, Via Cappelletti 1, I-20091 Bresso Milan, Italy

Tel: 39-2-6650-5091   Fax: 39-2-66-50-5088

CORPORATE SOFTWARE (CORPSOFT INC.)

2 Edgewater Drive, Norwood, MA, 02062

Tel: (781) 440-1000   Fax: (781) 440-7070   www.corpsoft.com

Mfr. asset management software.

Corporate Software, Viale Monza No. 1, I-20125 Milan, Italy

Tel: 39-02-2804-0188

CPAC, INC.

2364 Leicester Road, Leicester, NY, 14481

Tel: (716) 382-3223   Fax: (716) 382-3031   www.cpao-fuller.com

Mfr. and sales of consumer industrial products.

CPAC Italy, Via C. Porta, 49/56, I-2064 Gorgonzola, Italy

Contact: Chimifoto Omano

CRAWFORD & COMPANY

5620 Glenridge Drive NE, Atlanta, GA, 30342

Tel: (404) 256-0830   Fax: (404) 847-4025   www.crawfordandcompany.com

Provides international insurance services engaged in risk management and claims adjustment.

Crawford & Company, Via Olmetto 5, I-20123 Milan, Italy

CREDENCE SYSTEMS CORPORATION

215 Fourier Avenue, Fremont, CA, 94539

Tel: (510) 657-7400   Fax: (510) 623-2560   www.credence.com

Mfr. software for semiconductor production.

Credence Systems Italy, Piazza Danta n.2, I-20050 Ronco Briantino (MI), Italy

Tel: 39-039-681-7153

CROMPTON CORPORATION

One American Lane, Greenwich, CT, 06831

Tel: (203) 552-2000   Fax: (203) 552-2870   www.cromptoncorp.com

Mfr. dyes, colors, flavors, fragrances, specialty chemicals and industrial products.

Crompton Chemical Italiana SRL, Via Vincenzo Monti 79/2, I-20145 Milan, Italy

Crompton Italy SRL, Div. SITECH, Via Roccavecchia 9, I-27029 Vigevano, Italy

A.T. CROSS COMPANY

One Albion Road, Lincoln, RI, 02865

Tel: (401) 333-1200   Fax: (401) 334-2861   www.cross.com

Mfr. writing instruments, leads, erasers and ink refills.

A.T. Cross Italia S.r.l., Via R. Franchetti 1, I-20124 Milan, Italy
Tel: 39-02-636114

CULLIGAN INTERNATIONAL COMPANY

One Culligan Parkway, Northbrook, IL, 60062

Tel: (847) 205-6000   Fax: (847) 205-6030   www.culligan-man.com

Water treatment products and services.

Culligan Italiana SpA, Via Gandolfi 6, Cadriano di Granarolo, I-40057 Emilia Bologna, Italy
Tel: 39-051-601-7111   Fax: 39-051-601-7215

CUMMINS, INC.

500 Jackson Street, PO Box 3005, Columbus, IN, 47202-3005

Tel: (812) 377-5000   Fax: (812) 377-4937   www.cummins.com

Mfr. diesel engines.

Cummins Diesel Italia SpA, Piazza Locatelli 8, Zona Industriale, I-20098 San Guiliano Milan, Italy

CUNO INCORPORATED

400 Research Pkwy., Meriden, CT, 06450

Tel: (203) 237-5541   Fax: (203) 238-8977   www.cuno.com

Mfr. water filtration products.

CUNO Srl, Via Zara, 38, I-20032 Cormano (MI), Italy
Tel: 39-2-615-516 1

CUSHMAN & WAKEFIELD INC.

51 West 52nd Street, New York, NY, 10019

Tel: (212) 841-7500   Fax: (212) 841-7867   www.cushwake.com

Engaged in commercial real estate services.

Cushman & Wakefield, Via Vittorio Veneto 54b, I-00187 Rome, Italy

Cushman & Wakefield, Via Augusto Righi 19, I-40126 Bologna, Italy

Cushman & Wakefield, Via Turati 25, I-20121 Milan, Italy

CYPRESS SEMICONDUCTOR CORPORATION

3901 N. First Street, San Jose, CA, 95134-1599

Tel: (408) 943-2600   Fax: (408) 943-2796   www.cypress.com

Mfr. integrated circuits.

Cypress Semiconductor, Centro Colleoni, Palazzo Liocorno, Via Paracelso 4-6, Piano Int 6 5/6, I-20041 AB Milan, Italy
Tel: 39-039-60-74-200   Fax: 39-039-60-74-222

CYTEC INDUSTRIES, INC.

5 Garret Mountain Plaza, West Paterson, NJ, 07424

Tel: (973) 357-3100   Fax: (973) 357-3054   www.cytec.com

Mfr. specialty chemicals and materials.

Cytec Industries Italia s.r.l., Via Sporting Mirasole 4, I-20090 Noverasco Di Opera Milan, Italy
Tel: 39-2-576-06175

D&B (DUN & BRADSTREET CORPORATION))

1 Diamond Hill Road, Murray Hill, NJ, 07974

Tel: (908) 665-5000   Fax: (908) 665-5524   www.dnb.com

Provides corporate credit, marketing and accounts-receivable management services and publishes financial information.

D&B, 48 Via dei Valtorta, I-20127 Milan, Italy

Tel: 39-02-284-551

DANA CORPORATION

4500 Dorr Street, Toledo, OH, 43615

Tel: (419) 535-4500   Fax: (419) 535-4643   www.dana.com

Mfr./sales of automotive, heavy truck, off-highway, fluid and mechanical power components and engine parts, filters and gaskets.

Ofira Italiano, Div. Dana, Via Eritrea 20F, I-26126 Brescia, Italy

Spicer Agricultural Axie Div., Via P Paoli 9/A, I-22100 Como Co, Italy

Tel: 39-31-523-515

Spicer Italia, Via Prov. Lucchese 181, I-50019 Sesto F. Ro. Firenze, Italy

Tel: 39-55-341031

Spicer Off-Highway Axle Div., Zona Industriale, I-38062 Arco, Italy

Tel: 39-4640-580-111

DANAHER CORPORATION

1250 24th St. NW, Ste. 800, Washington, DC, 20037

Tel: (202) 828-0850   Fax: (202) 828-0860   www.danaher.com

Mfr. hand tools and motion controls.

Danaher Motion Srl, Via Brughetti Zr, IT-20030 Bivisio Masciago (MI), Italy

Contact: Alberto Favalessa

DANZAS AEI, INC.

120 Tokeneke Road, PO Box 1231, Darien, CT, 06820

Tel: (203) 655-7900   Fax: (203) 655-5779   www.aeilogistics.com

International air freight forwarder.

Danzas AEI, c/o Coimexco S.p.A.,, Alitalia Cargo Bldg., Rm. 219, Aeroporto Leonardo da Vinci, Rome, Italy

Danzas AEI, Via E. Montale 14/24, I-20090 Novegro di Segrate Milan, Italy

Tel: 39-02-75271   Fax: 39-02-7527-454

D'ARCY MASIUS BENTON & BOWLES INC. (DMB&B)

1675 Broadway, New York, NY, 10019

Tel: (212) 468-3622   Fax: (212) 468-2987   www.darcyww.com

Full service international advertising and communications group.

DMB&B Europe, I-10121 Torino, Italy

DMB&B Europe, Via Correggio 18, I-20149 Milan, Italy

DARDEN RESTAURANTS, INC.

5900 Lake Ellenor Drive, Orlando, FL, 32809

Tel: (407) 245-4000   Fax: (407) 245-5114   www.darden.com

Operates casual dining, full-service restaurants, including Red Lobster and Olive Garden

Olive Garden Riserva di Fizzano, Tuscany, Italy

DATASCOPE CORPORATION

14 Phillips Pkwy., Montvale, NJ, 07645

Tel: (201) 391-8100   Fax: (201) 307-5400   www.datascope.com

Mfr. medical devices.

Datascope Italia S.r.l., Via Siusi n. 20, I-20132 Milan, Italy

DDB WORLDWIDE COMMUNICATIONS GROUP

437 Madison Ave., New York, NY, 10022

Tel: (212) 415-2000   Fax: (212) 415-3417   www.ddbn.com

Advertising agency.

Broucc/Verba DDB Needham SRL, Galleria Passarella 2, I-20122 Milan, Italy

Verba DDB SRL, Via Solari 11, I-20144 Milan, Italy

DECISION STRATEGIES FAIRFAX INTERNATIONAL

33 East 33rd Street, New York, NY, 10016

Tel: (212) 935-4040   Fax: (212) 935-4046   www.dsfx.com

Provides discreet consulting, investigative, business intelligence and security services to corporations, financial and investment institutions, law firms and governments worldwide.

Decision Strategies, Via Sacchi 4, I-20121 Milan, Italy

Tel: 39-02-8699-6834   Fax: 39-02-8909-7579

DEERE & COMPANY

One John Deere Place, Moline, IL, 61265

Tel: (309) 765-8000   Fax: (309) 765-5772   www.deere.com

Mfr./sale agricultural, construction, utility, forestry and lawn, grounds care equipment.

John Deere Italy, Casella Postale, I-20060 Vignate Milan, Italy

Tel: 39-2-95458-1   Fax: 39-2-95604-82

DELOITTE TOUCHE TOHMATSU INTERNATIONAL

1633 Broadway, New York, NY, 10019

Tel: (212) 492-4000   Fax: (212) 392-4154   www.deloitte.com

Accounting, audit, tax and management consulting services.

Deloitte & Touche, Palazzo Carducci, Via Olona 2, I-20123 Milan, Italy

Deloitte & Touche Consulting, Via Vittor Pisani 22, I-20124 Milan, Italy

DELTA AIR LINES INC.

Hartsfield International Airport, 1030 Delta Blvd., Atlanta, GA, 30320-6001

Tel: (404) 715-2600   Fax: (404) 715-5494   www.delta-air.com

Major worldwide airline; international air transport services.

Delta Air Lines Inc., Milan, Italy

DENTSPLY INTERNATIONAL

570 West College Ave., PO Box 872, York, PA, 17405-0872

Tel: (717) 845-7511   Fax: (717) 843-6357   www.dentsply.com

Mfr. and distribution of dental supplies and equipment.

De Art SRL, Via Rimini 22, I-20142 Milan, Italy

Dentsply Gendex, Via Capelli 12, I-20126 Milan, Italy

Tel: 39-02-270-82600

Dentsply Italia, Via A. Cavaglieri 26, I-00173 Rome, Italy

Tel: 39-06-723-3626

DETROIT DIESEL CORPORATION

13400 Outer Drive West, Detroit, MI, 48239

Tel: (313) 592-5000   Fax: (313) 592-5058   www.detroitdiesel.com

Mfr. diesel and aircraft engines and heavy-duty transmissions.

MDC-Detroit Diesel Italia SpA, Corso Aurelio Saffi 29/1-2, I-16128 Genoa, Italy

Tel: 39-1056-4979   Fax: 39-1053-2759

DHL WORLDWIDE EXPRESS

50 California Avenue, San Francisco, CA, 94111

Tel: (415) 677-6100   Fax: (415) 824-9700   www.dhl.com

Worldwide air express carrier.

DHL Worldwide Express, Viale Milanofiori, Strada 5, Palazzo U3, I-20089 Rozzano Milan, Italy

Tel: 39-02-57571

DIAGNOSTIC PRODUCTS CORPORATION

5700 West 96th Street, Los Angeles, CA, 90045

Tel: (310) 645-8200   Fax: (310) 645-9999   www.dpcweb.com

Mfr. diagnostic products.

Medical Systems S.p.A., Via Rio Torbido N. 40, I-16165 Struppa Genoa, Italy

Tel: 39-010-834-01   Fax: 39-010-808-007

DIMON INCORPORATED

512 Bridge Street, PO Box 681, Danville, VA, 24543-0681

Tel: (804) 792-7511   Fax: (804) 791-0377   www.dimon.com

One of world's largest importer and exporters of leaf tobacco.

DIMON Italia S.r.l., 3 Via Nazioni Unite, I-00046 Grottaferrata Rome, Italy

Tel: 39-06-9454-9033   Fax: 390-6-9454-7408

DIONEX CORPORATION

1228 Titan Way, PO Box 3603, Sunnyvale, CA, 94086-3603

Tel: (408) 737-0700   Fax: (408) 730-9403   www.dionex.com

Develop/mfr./market chromatography systems and related products.

Dionex S.r.l., 5 Via Tulipani, I-20090 Pieve Emanuele Milan, Italy

Dionex S.r.l., Via della Maglianella 65R, I-00166 Roma RM, Italy

WALT DISNEY COMPANY

500 South Buena Vista Street, Burbank, CA, 91521

Tel: (818) 560-1000   Fax: (818) 560-1930   www.disney.com

Film/TV production, theme parks, resorts, publishing, recording and retail stores.

Creazioni Walt Disney SpAI, Via Hoepli 3, I-20121 Milan, Italy

DIVINE

1301 N. Elston Ave., Chicago, IL, 60622

Tel: (773) 394-6600   Fax: (773) 394-6601   www.divine.com

Software and services provider.

Divine, Inc., Via Leonardo da Vinci 43, I-20090 Trezzano sul Naviglio, Milan, Italy

D-M-E COMPANY

29111 Stephenson Highway, Madison Heights, MI, 48071

Tel: (248) 398-6000   Fax: (248) 544-5705   www.dmeco.com

Manufacture and distribution of mold tooling, mold components, hot runner systems, and electronic controls for the plastics industry.

COMAT-DME SpA, Via Desiderio 24, I-20131 Milan, Italy

Tel: 39-02-7064981

DO ALL COMPANY

254 North Laurel Ave., Des Plaines, IL, 60016

Tel: (847) 803-7380   Fax: (847) 699-7524   www.doall.com

Distributors of machinery tools, metal cutting tools, instruments and industrial supplies for metalworking industry.

DoALL Center, Via L. Perosi 5, I-20146 Milan, Italy

Tel: 39-2-4236086   Fax: 39-2-48953828

DONNELLY CORPORATION

49 West Third Street, Holland, MI, 49423-2813

Tel: (616) 786-7000   Fax: (616) 786-6034   www.donnelly.com

Mfr. fabricated, molded and coated glass products for the automotive and electronics industries.

Donnelly Italy, Corso Orbassano 336, I-10137 Torino, Italy

DOONEY & BOURKE

1 Regent Street, Norwalk, CT, 06855

Tel: (203) 853-7754   Fax: (203) 838-7515   www.dooney.com

Mfr., sales and distribution of fine leather handbags, wallets, belts and accessories.

Dooney & Bourke, Rome, Italy

DOUBLECLICK, INC.

450 West 33rd Street, New York, NY, 10001

Tel: (212) 683-0001   Fax: (212) 889-0062   www.doubleclick.net

Engaged in online advertising and e-mail marketing.

Doubleclick, Ltd., Piazza Bertarelli, I-20122 Milan, Italy

Tel: 39-02-855011-1

DRAFT WORLDWIDE

633 North St. Clair Street, Chicago, IL, 60611-3211

Tel: (312) 944-3500   Fax: (312) 944-3566   www.draftworldwide.com

Full service international advertising agency, engaged in brand building, direct and promotional marketing.

DraftWorldwide, Via Ariosto 23, I-20145 Milan, Italy

Tel: 39-02-48-19-480   Fax: 39-02-48-19-836

DRAKE BEAM MORIN INC.

100 Park Avenue, 11th Fl., New York, NY, 10017

Tel: (212) 692-7700   Fax: (212) 297-0426   www.dbm.com

Human resource management consulting and training.

DBM Italy, Via Anfiteatro 15, I-20121 Milan, Italy

Tel: 39-02-86-2717   Fax: 39-02-72-00-4296

DRESSER INSTRUMENT DIVISION

250 East Main Street, Stratford, CT, 06614-5145

Tel: (203) 378-8281   Fax: (203) 385-0357   www.dresserinstruments.com

Mfr. pressure gauges and temperature instruments.

Dresser Energy Valve, Via Italo Betto 11, I-27058 Voghera, Italy

Tel: 39-0383-6911   Fax: 39-0383-367-166   Contact: Salvatore Ruggeri, Pres.

DREVER COMPANY

PO Box 98, 380 Red Lion Road, Huntingdon, PA, 19006-0098

Tel: (215) 947-3400   Fax: (215) 947-7934   www.drever.com

Mfr. industrial furnaces and heat processing equipment.

Drever Italy, Ferre Milanofiori, Strada 6, Palazzo NI, I-20089 Rozzano Milan, Italy

DUO-FAST CORPORATION

2400 Galvin Dr., Elgin, IL, 60123

Tel: (847) 783-5500   Fax: (847) 669-7301   www.duofast.com

Mfr. staplers, tackers and nailers.

Eco-Fast Italy, Via Dell"artigianato, 66 Z.I., I-20046 Usmate Velate Milan, Italy

Tel: 39-039-6829240

E.I. DUPONT DE NEMOURS & COMPANY

1007 Market Street, Wilmington, DE, 19898

Tel: (302) 774-1000   Fax: (302) 774-7321   www.dupont.com

Mfr. and sales of diversified chemicals, plastics, specialty products and fibers.

DuPont Italiana SpA, Via W. Tobagi, I-46040 Casaloldo (MN), Italy

Tel: 39-376-778650

DVI, INC.

2500 york Road, Jamison, PA, 18929

Tel: (215) 488-5000   Fax: (215) 488-5010   www.dvifs.com

Engaged in financing of medical equipment.

DVI Italy, Via Locatelli n. 4, I-20124 Milan, Italy

EASTMAN CHEMICAL COMPANY

100 North Eastman Road, Kingsport, TN, 37662-5075

Tel: (423) 229-2000   Fax: (423) 229-1351   www.eastman.com

Mfr. plastics, chemicals, fibers.

Eastman Chemical, Via Rosellini 12, I-20124 Milan, Italy

Fax: 39-02-6991-1532   Contact: Franco Galli, Mgr.

Eastman Chemical Italia S.r.l, Localta Confine, I-37010 Cola'DiLazise (VR), Italy

Tel: 39-45-644-5511   Fax: 39-45-6450   Contact: Alberto Cinelli, Plant Mgr.

EASTMAN KODAK COMPANY

343 State Street, Rochester, NY, 14650

Tel: (716) 724-4000   Fax: (716) 724-1089   www.kodak.com

Develop/mfr. photo and chemicals products, information management/video/copier systems, fibers/plastics for various industry.

Kodak SpA, Casella Postale 11057, I-20110 Milan, Italy

EASTMAN RESINS, INC.

1 Terra Way, 8601 95th St., Pleasant Prairie, WI, 53158

Tel: (262) 947-7300   Fax: (262) 947-7328   www.lawter.com

Resins, pigments and coatings.

Eastman Resins Lawter International, Via A. Volta n 13, I-20050 Mezzago (MI), Italy

Tel: 39-039-602-0760   Fax: 39-039-602-0691

EATON CORPORATION

Eaton Center, 1111 Superior Ave., Cleveland, OH, 44114-2584

Tel: (216) 523-5000   Fax: (216) 479-7068   www.eaton.com

Advanced technical products for transportation and industrial markets.

Eaton SpA, Strada Lombardore, Km. 15.300, I-10040 Leini, Italy

ECOLAB INC.

370 N. Wabasha Street, St. Paul, MN, 55102

Tel: (651) 293-2233   Fax: (651) 293-2379   www.ecolab.com

Develop/mfr. premium cleaning, sanitizing and maintenance products and services for the hospitality, institutional, and residential markets.

Ecolab Ltd., Milan, Italy

Tel: 39-039-60501

EDELMAN PUBLIC RELATIONS WORLDWIDE

200 East Randolph Drive, 62nd Fl., Chicago, IL, 60601

Tel: (312) 240-3000   Fax: (312) 240-0596   www.edelman.com

International independent public relations firm.

Edelman PR Worldwide, Via Telesio 25, I-20145 Milan, Italy

Tel: 39-02-467141   Fax: 39-02-4671-4467   Contact: Rasanna D'antona, Mng. Dir.

EDISON INTERNATIONAL

2244 Walnut Grove Avenue, Rosemead, CA, 91770

Tel: (626) 302-2222   Fax: (626) 302-2517   www.edison.com

Utility holding company.

Edison Mission Energy, Milan, Italy

J.D. EDWARDS & COMPANY

One Technology Way, Denver, CO, 80237

Tel: (303) 334-4000   Fax: (303) 334-4970   www.jdedwards.com

Computer software products.

Consor, S.r.l., Via Plinio 11, I-20129 Milan, Italy

Tel: 39-02-2940-5859   Fax: 39-02-2940-1800

J. D. Edwards Segrate, Via Cassenese 224, Palazzo Tiziano, I-20090 Segrate Milan, Italy

Tel: 39-02-26967-1   Fax: 39-02-26967-200

Proxima Informatica Aziendale, Via P. Costa 2, I-48100 Ravenna, Italy
Tel: 39-054-212-912   Fax: 39-054-421-2916

Sirio Informatica, spa, Viale Fulvio Testi 126, I-20092 Cinisello Balsamo Milan, Italy
Tel: 39-02-262-421   Fax: 39-02-425-5557

EG&G INC.

900 Clopper Road, Ste. 200, Gaithersburg, MD, 20878
Tel: (301) 840-3000   Fax: (301) 590-0502   www.egginc.com
Diversified R/D, mfr. and services.

EG&G SpA/Instruments Div., Via Bernardo Rucellai 23, I-20126 Milan, Italy
EG&G SpA/Sealol Div., Via Bernardo Rucellai 23, I-20126 Milan, Italy

EGL INC. (EAGLE GLOBAL LOGISTICS)

15350 Vickery Drive, Houston, TX, 77032
Tel: (281) 618-3100   Fax: (281) 618-3223   www.eagleusa.com
Ocean/air freight forwarding, customs brokerage, packing and wholesale, logistics management and insurance.

EGL Eagle Global Logistics, Cargo Bldg. AZ, Stamza 210, I-00050 Fiumicino Aeroporto Rome, Italy
Tel: 39-06-652-9242 Fax: 39-06-652-9243

EGL Eagle Global Logistics, Via Darsena 7, I-56122 Pisa, Italy
Tel: 39-050-502-522 Fax: 39-050-502-294

EGL Eagle Global Logistics, Via J. F. Kennedy 3, Frazione Millepini, I-10090 Rodano Milan, Italy
Tel: 39-02-953-2116-6 Fax: 39-01-953-2810-6

EGL Eagle Global Logistics, Via F. Righi 52, Loc. Osmannoro, I-50019 Sesto Florento Florence, Italy
Tel: 39-055-311062 Fax: 39-055-310-474

EGL Eagle Global Logistics, Palazzina Spedizionieri, Aeroporto Malpensa, I-21010 Malpensa Milan, Italy
Tel: 39-02-400-9933-5 Fax: 39-02-400-9939-6

EGL Eagle Global Logistics, Aeroporto Cristoforo Colombo, I-16154 Genoa, Italy
Tel: 39-010-650-8431   Fax: 39-010-651-6378

EGL Eagle Global Logistics, Palazzina Spedizionieri, Aeroporto Caselle, Caselle Torinese, Italy
Tel: 39-011-567-8151   Fax: 39-011-567-8153

ELANCO ANIMAL HEALTH

500 East 96th Street, Ste. 125, Indianapolis, IN, 46240
Tel: (317) 276-3000   Fax: (317) 276-6116   www.elanco.com
Antibiotics and fine chemicals.

Elanco Animal Health, Caselle Postali 193-177, I-50019 Sesto Fiorentino Florence, Italy
Tel: 39-55-42571

ELECTRO SCIENTIFIC INDUSTRIES, INC.

13900 NW Science Park Drive, Portland, OR, 97229
Tel: (503) 641-4141   Fax: (503) 643-4873   www.esi.com
Mfg. production and testing equipment used in manufacture of electronic components in pagers and cellular communication devices.

Factum Italia s.r.l., Trim, Via Lombardia 10, I-20064 Gorgonzola, Italy
Tel: 39-02-9530-1791 Fax: 39-02-9530-1436   Contact: Roger Goldenberg

ELECTRONICS FOR IMAGING, INC. (EFI)

303 Velocity Way, Foster City, CA, 94404
Tel: (650) 357-3500   Fax: (650) 357-3907   www.efi.com
Design/mfr. computer software and hardware for color desktop publishing.

EFI Italy, Centro Direzionale Milano Fiori, Strada 6, Palazzo E1, I-20090 Assago (Milano), Italy
Tel: 39 028 228 1219

EMC CORPORATION

35 Parkwood Drive, Hopkinton, MA, 01748-9103

Tel: (508) 435-1000   Fax: (508) 435-8884   www.emc.com

Designs/supplies intelligent enterprise storage and retrieval technology for open systems, mainframes and midrange environments.

EMC Computer Systems Italia SpA, Via Cefalonia 24, I-25125 Brescia, Italy

Tel: 39-030-242-1791

EMC Computer Systems Italia SpA, Via Caldera 21, Palazzo D, Ala 3, I-20153 Milan, Italy

Tel: 39-02-409081

EMC Computer Systems Italia SpA, Via Savonarola 217, I-35153 Padova, Italy

Tel: 39-049-823-5853

EMC Computer Systems Italia SpA, Piazza Marconi 25, I-00144 Rome, Italy

Tel: 39-06-545041

EMC Computer Systems Italia SpA, Corso Svizzera 185/Bis, I-10149 Torino, Italy

Tel: 39-011-746527

EMC Computer Systems Italia SpA, Via A Saffi 15, I-40131 Bologna, Italy

Tel: 39-051-522579

EMERSON & CUMING COMPOSITE MATERIALS, INC.

59 Walpole Street, Canton, MA, 02021

Tel: (781) 821-4250   Fax: (781) 821-0737   www.emersoncuming.com

Mfr. high performance encapsulants, adhesives and coatings for the automotive, telecommunications and electronic industries.

Emerson & Cuming Italia, Via Roma 29, I-20050 Mezzago (Milan), Italy

Tel: 39-039-6092246

EMERSON PROCESS MANAGEMENT

8301Cameron Road, Austin, TX, 78754

Tel: (512) 834-7689   Fax: (512) 832-3232   www.frco.com

Mfr. industrial process control equipment.

Emerson Process Management, Via Vittore Carpaccio 60, I-00147 Rome, Italy

Emerson Process Management, Via Pavia 21, I-20053 Muggio Milan, Italy

EMERY FORWARDING

One Lagoon Drive, Ste. 400, Redwood City, CA, 94065

Tel: (650) 596-9600   Fax: (650) 596-7901   www.emeryworld.com

Freight transport, global logistics and air cargo.

Emery Forwarding, Off Airport Office, Linate, Via Degli Alpini 26, I-10900 Segrate Milan, Italy

ENCYCLOPAEDIA BRITANNICA INC.

310 S. Michigan Ave., Chicago, IL, 60604

Tel: (312) 427-9700   Fax: (312) 294-2176   www.eb.com

Publishing; books.

Encyclopaedia Britannica (Italy) Ltd., Via Angelo Bargoni 28, I-00153 Rome, Italy

ENERGIZER HOLDINGS, INC.

533 Maryville University Dr., St. Louis, MO, 63141

Tel: (314) 985-2000   Fax: (214) 985-2205   www.energizer.com

Mfr. Eveready and Energizer brand batteries and lighting products.

Ralston Energy Systems S.p.A., Via di Vittorio 10, I-20094 Corsico Milan, Italy

Tel: 39-2-45-178-205   Fax: 39-2-45-178-1

ENERPAC

6101 N. Baker Road, PO Box 3241, Milwaukee, WI, 53201-3241

Tel: (414) 781-6600   Fax: (414) 781-1049   www.enerpac.com

Mfr. hydraulic cylinders, pumps, valves, presses, tools, accessories and system components.

ENERPAC S.p.A., Via Canova 4, I-20094 Corsico (Milan), Italy

ENGELHARD CORPORATION

101 Wood Avenue South, Iselin, NJ, 08830

Tel: (732) 205-5000   Fax: (732) 632-9253   www.engelhard.com

Mfr. pigments, additives, catalysts, chemicals, engineered materials.

Engelhard-Clal Italy, Via de Salone 245, I-00131 Rome, Italy
Tel: 39-641-9921   Fax: 39-641992-338

Engelhard-Clal Italy, 17 Via Ronchi, I-20134 Milan, Italy

Engelhard-Clal Italy, Via Ronchi 17, I-20134 Milan, Italy
Tel: 39-226-4251   Fax: 39-221-57-167

ENRON CORPORATION

1400 Smith Street, Houston, TX, 77002-7369

Tel: (713) 853-6161   Fax: (713) 853-3129   www.enron.com

Exploration, production, transportation and distribution of integrated natural gas and electricity. **Corporation under worldwide reorganization; new data unavailable for this edition.

Enron International, Via Torina 2, I-20123 Milan, Italy
Tel: 39-02-725-464-00

Sarlux, S.r.l., 8 Galleria De Cristoforis, I-20122 Milan, Italy
Tel: 39-02-773-7224

EQUIFAX INC.

1550 Peachtree St. NW, Atlanta, GA, 30309

Tel: (404) 885-8000   Fax: (404) 888-5452   www.equifax.com

Provides information and knowledge-based solutions on consumers and businesses around the world.

Equifax Florence, Via della Fortezza, 7/9 r, I-50129 Florence, Italy

Equifax Milan, Viale Marche, 37, I-20125 Milan, Italy

Equifax Rome, Via C. Colombo, 440, I-00145 Rome, Italy

ERICO PRODUCTS INC.

34600 Solon Road, Cleveland, OH, 44139

Tel: (440) 248-0100   Fax: (440) 248-0723   www.erico.com

Mfr. electric welding apparatus and hardware, metal stampings, specialty fasteners.

Erico Italia SpA, Via Edison Nr. 50, I-20019 Settimo Milan, Italy
Tel: 39-2-3350-1178

ERNST & YOUNG INTERNATIONAL

5 Times Square, New York, NY, 10036

Tel: (212) 773-3000   Fax. (212) 773-6350   www.cyi.com

Engaged in assurance and advisory business services, tax, law and corporate finance.

Cap Gemini Ernst & Young, Via di Torre Spaccata 140, I-00169 Rome, Italy

Cap Gemini Ernst & Young, Via Rainaldi 5, I-40139 Bologna, Italy

Cap Gemini Ernst & Young, via XX Settembre, 42, I-16121 Geneva, Italy

Cap Gemini Ernst & Young, Viale Fulvio Testi 280/6, I-20126 Milan, Italy
Tel: 39-02-661-341   Contact: Fabio Greco

ESTERLINE TECHNOLOGIES

10800 NE 8th Street, Ste. 600, Bellevue, WA, 98004

Tel: (425) 453-9400   Fax: (425) 453-2916   www.esterline.com

Mfr. equipment and instruments for industrial automation, precision measure, data acquisition.

International Precision Products BV, Casella Postale, Novara Ferrovia AD, I-28100 Novara, Italy
Tel: 39-0321-36461   Fax: 39-0321-398012

EURO RSCG WORLDWIDE

350 Hudson Street, New York, NY, 10014

Tel: (212) 886-2000   Fax: (212) 886-2016   www.eurorscg.com

International advertising agency group.

Agenpress, Via Filelfo 10, Milan, Italy

Equipe, Via Crocefisso 12, Milan, Italy

EURO RSCG Mezzano Costantini Mignani srl, Via Dante 7, Milan, Italy

EXCELLON AUTOMATION

24751 Crenshaw Boulevard, Torrance, CA, 90505

Tel: (310) 534-6300 Fax: (310) 534-6777 www.excellon.com

PCB drilling and routing machines; optical inspection equipment.

Excellon Italia Srl. c/o Centre Direzionale Colleoni, Via Paracelso 16, Palazzo Andromeda 1, Piano 5, Interno 3, I-20041 Agrate Brianza, Italy

Tel: 39-39-652-446 Fax: 39-39-652-447

EXCELON INC.

25 Mall Road, Burlington, MA, 01803

Tel: (781) 674-5000 Fax: (781) 674-5010 www.exceloncorp.com

Developer of object-oriented database management systems software.

eXcelon Software SRL, Via C. Esterle 9, I-20132 Milan, Italy

EXIDE TECHNOLOGIES

210 Carnegie Center, Ste. 500, Princeton, NJ, 08540

Tel: (609) 627-7200 Fax: (609) 627-7217 www.exideworld.com

Mfr. lead-acid automotive and industrial batteries.

Exide Italia, Romano, Italy

EXPEDITORS INTERNATIONAL OF WASHINGTON INC.

1015 Third Avenue, 12th Fl., Seattle, WA, 98104-1182

Tel: (206) 674-3400 Fax: (206) 682-9777 www.expd.com

Air/ocean freight forwarding, customs brokerage, international logistics solutions.

Expeditors International Italia SRL, Via Leonardo da Vinci 13, I-20090 Segrate Milan, Italy

Tel: 39-045-855-0433 Fax: 39-045-855-0450

EXXON MOBIL CORPORATION

5959 Las Colinas Blvd., Irving, TX, 75039-2298

Tel: (972) 444-1000 Fax: (972) 444-1882 www.exxonmobil.com

Petroleum exploration, production, refining; mfr. petroleum and chemicals products; coal and minerals.

Exxon Mobil Italy, Stabilimento di Vado Ligure, Strada di Scorrimento 2, CP 204, I-17047 Vado Ligure Savona, Italy

Exxon Mobil S.p.A., Via Vigevano 43, I-28069 San Martino di Trecate Novara, Italy

Exxon Mobil, Inc., C.P. 101, I-96011 Augusta Siracusa, Italy

Exxon Mobil, Inc., Via Paleocapa 7, I-20121 Milan, Italy

Tel: 39-02-880-31

Exxon Mobil, Inc., Viale Castello della Magliana, I-00148 Rome, Italy

FAIR, ISAAC AND COMPANY, INC.

200 Smith Ranch Road, San Rafael, CA, 94903

Tel: (415) 472-2211 Fax: (415) 492-5691 www.fairisaac.com

Mfr. automated systems for credit and loan approvals.

Fair, Isaac and Co., Via Dogana 3, I-10123 Milan, Italy

Tel: 39-02-86-7141

FAIRCHILD PUBLICATIONS INC.

7 West 34th Street, New York, NY, 10001

Tel: (212) 630-4000 Fax: (212) 630-3563 www.fairchildpub.com

Magazine publishers: Women's Wear Daily, Supermarket News, Brand Marketing, Executive Technology, Footwear News, Salon News.

Fairchild Publications, 2 Piazza Cavour, I-20121 Milan, Italy

Tel: 39-02-76-00-50-78 Fax: 39-02-78-34-89

FEDERAL-MOGUL CORPORATION

26555 Northwestern Highway, PO Box 1966, Southfield, MI, 48034

Tel: (248) 354-7700   Fax: (248) 354-8983   www.federal-mogul.com

Mfr./distributor precision parts for automobiles, trucks, farm and construction vehicles.

Federal-Mogul Aftermarket Italia Srl, Via E. Fermi 8, I-37135 Verona, Italy

Tel: 39-045-8281311

FELLOWES, INC.

1789 Norwood Avenue, Itasca, IL, 60143-109

Tel: (630) 893-1600   Fax: (630) 893-1648   www.fellowes.com

Mfr. of office products and accessories.

Fellowes Italy, Via D. Alighieri, 43, I-60021 Camerano, Italy

Tel: 39-071-730041   Contact: Paolo Leonardi

FERRO CORPORATION

1000 Lakeside Ave., Cleveland, OH, 44114-7000

Tel: (216) 641-8580   Fax: (216) 696-5784   www.ferro.com

Mfr. Specialty chemicals, coatings, plastics, colors, refractories.

Ecotech Italia SpA, Via Dell'Elettronica 15, I-28040 Verbania-Fondotoce, Italy

Tel: 39-0323-586984   Fax: 39-0323-586977   Contact: Roberto Codecasa

Ferro ICC Laboratory, Via Radici in Piano 312, I-41041 Casinalbo, Italy

Tel: 39-059-559111   Fax: 39-059-462067

Ferro SRL, Via Radici in Piano 312, I-41041 Casinalbo, Italy

Tel: 39-059-1559111   Fax: 39-059-551109   Contact: P. Bencivenni, Gen. Mgr.

Ferro SRL - Colour Division, Via Trentino 9, I-41049 Sassuolo, Italy

Tel: 39-053-6806912   Fax: 39-053-6811641

Ferro SRL Cannara Plant, Localita' Isola, I-06033 Cannara, Italy

Tel: 39-0742-3311   Fax: 39-0742-72144

FERROTEC CORPORATION

40 Simon Street, Nashua, NH, 03061

Tel: (603) 883-9800   Fax: (603) 883-2308   www.ferrofluidics.com

Mfr. rotary feedthrough designs, emission seals, automated crystal-growing systems, bearings, ferrofluids.

Ferrotec S.r.l., Via Medici 15, I-20123 Milan, Italy

Tel: 39-02-86-46-7082

FileNET CORPORATION

3565 Harbor Boulevard, Costa Mesa, CA, 92626

Tel: (714) 966-3400   Fax: (714) 966-3490   www.filenet.com

Provides integrated document management (IDM) software and services for internet and client server-based imaging, workflow, cold and electronic document management solutions.

FileNET Italy, Via Visconti di Modrone 33, I-20122 Milan, Italy

Tel: 39-02-7733-051   Fax: 39-02-7729-40

C.B. FLEET COMPANY, INC.

4615 Murray Place, PO Box 11349, Lynchburg, VA, 24506

Tel: (804) 528-4000   Fax: (804) 847-4219   www.cbfleet.com

Mfr. pharmaceutical, health and beauty aids.

Bergamon, S.r.l., Via Farini 5, I-00185 Rome, Italy

Tel: 39-06-462-0211   Fax: 39-06-462-02199

FLINT INK CORPORATION

4600 Arrowhead Drive, Ann Arbor, MI, 48105

Tel: (734) 622-6000   Fax: (734) 622-6060   www.flintink.com

Manufacturer of printing inks and pigments.

Flint Ink Europe, Via Michelozzo da Forli 2/4i, I-10096 Pioltello Milana, Italy

Tel: 39-02-921-60503   Fax: 39-02-9267309   Contact: Jim Mahony, Pres. Europe

FLOW INTERNATIONAL CORPORATION

23500 64th Avenue S., PO Box 97040, Kent, WA, 98064-9740

Tel: (253) 872-4900   Fax: (253) 813-3285   www.flowcorp.com

Mfr. high-pressure water jet cutting/cleaning equipment, powered scaffolding; concrete cleaning/removal.

Flow Italy, Strada per Turbigo 64, I-20010 Arluno (MI), Italy

FLOWSERVE CORPORATION

222 W. Los Colinas Blvd., Irving, TX, 75039

Tel: (972) 443-6500   Fax: (972) 443-6858   www.flowserve.com

Mfr. chemicals equipment, pumps, valves, filters, fans and heat exchangers.

Durco Europe SA, Cotrada Costa Pisone, I-96011 Augusta, Italy

Flowserve Italy, Via Prealp. 30, I-20032 Cormano Milan, Italy

FM GLOBAL INC.

1301 Atwood Avenue, Johnston, RI, 02919

Tel: (401) 275-3000   Fax: (401) 275-3029   www.fmglobal.com

Engaged in commercial and industrial property insurance and risk management, specializing in engineering-driven property protection.

FM Global, Factory Mutual International Italia SrL, Corso Unione Sovietica 612/3/C, I-10135 Torino, Italy

Tel: 39-011-39-76-011

FOOT LOCKER INC.

112 West 34th Street, New York, NY, 10020

Tel: (212) 720-3700   Fax: (212) 553-2042   www.venatorgroup.com

Mfr./sales shoes and sneakers.

Foot Locker International, Via Sestri 220, I-16039 Genoa, Italy

Tel: 39-010-6049392

Foot Locker International, Via Aldo Moro 1, I-21100 Varese, Italy

Tel: 39-02-831005

Foot Locker International, Via Rome 306, I-10121 Torino, Italy

Tel: 39-011-537176

Foot Locker International, Via Crea 10, I-10095 Grugliasco Torino, Italy

Tel: 39-011-7708646

Foot Locker International, Via Xx Settembre 101/103/105r, I-16021 Genoa, Italy

Tel: 39-010-586906

Foot Locker International, Via Martiri Della Liberta 33, I-15100 Alessandria, Italy

Tel: 39-01-31-254921

FORD MOTOR COMPANY

One American Road, Dearborn, MI, 48126

Tel: (313) 322-3000   Fax: (313) 322-9600   www.ford.com

Mfr./sales motor vehicles.

Ford Italiana SpA, Viale Pasteur 8/10, Casella Postale 10058, I-00144 Rome, Italy

FORMICA CORPORATION

10155 Reading Road, Cincinnati, OH, 45241-4805

Tel: (513) 786-3400   Fax: (513) 786-3082   www.formica.com

Mfr. decorative laminate, adhesives and solvents.

Formica Italia Srl, Via Sardegna 24, M1, I-20090 Pieve Emmanuele Milan, Italy

FOSSIL, INC.

2280 N. Greenville Avenue, Richardson, TX, 75082

Tel: (972) 234-2525   Fax: (972) 234-4669   www.fossil.com

Mfr. fashion watches

Fossil Italy, Via Vecchia Ferriera, 4, I-36100 Vicenza, Italy

FOSTER WHEELER LTD.

Perryville Corporate Park, Clinton, NJ, 08809-4000

Tel: (908) 730-4000   Fax: (908) 730-4100   www.fwc.com

Manufacturing, engineering and construction.

Foster Wheeler Energia Italiana S.p.A, Via Sebastiano Caboto 1, I-20094 Corsico Milan, Italy

Tel: 39-2-4486-1   Fax: 39-2-4486-3473

FRANKLIN RESOURCES, INC.

1 Franklin Pkwy., Bldg. 970, 1st Fl., San Mateo, CA, 94404

Tel: (415) 312-2000   Fax: (415) 312-5606   www.frk.com

Global and domestic investment advisory and portfolio management.

Templeton Italia SRL, Via Quintino Sella 4, I-20121 Milan, Italy

Tel: 39-02-723021   Fax: 39-02-80-9394

FRITZ COMPANIES, INC., DIV. UPS

706 Mission Street, Ste. 900, San Francisco, CA, 94103

Tel: (415) 904-8360   Fax: (415) 904-8661   www.fritz.com

Integrated transportation, sourcing, distribution and customs brokerage services.

Fritz Companies Inc., Florence, Italy

FRONTRANGE SOLUTIONS INC.

1125 Kelly Johnson Blvd., Colorado Springs, CO, 80820

Tel: (719) 531-5007   Fax: (719) 536-0620   www.frontrange.com

Mfr. customer support software.

FrontRange Solutions Italy, Via Conservatorio 22, I-20122 Milan, Italy

FRONTSTEP, INC.

2800 Corporate Exchange Drive, Ste. 400, Columbus, OH, 43231

Tel: (614) 523-7000   Fax: (614) 895-2504   www.frontstep.com

Mfr. management software.

Frontstep Italy, Via Larga, 13, I-20122 Milan, Italy

Tel: 39-02-5843-0177

FSI INTERNATIONAL INC.

3455 Lyman Boulevard, Chaska, MN, 55318-3052

Tel: (952) 448-5440   Fax: (952) 448-2825   www.fsi-intl.com

Manufacturing equipment for computer silicon wafers.

Metron Technology (Italia) S.r.l., Filiale Italiana, Via per Ornago, I-20040 Bellusco Milan, Italy

H.B. FULLER COMPANY

1200 Willow Lake Blvd., Vadnais Heights, MN, 55110

Tel: (651) 236-5900   Fax: (651) 236-5898   www.hbfuller.com

Mfr./distributor adhesives, sealants, coatings, paints, waxes, sanitation chemicals.

H.B. Fuller Italia s.r.l., S.S. 211 Della Lomellina, Km. 63.233, I-28071 Borgolavezzaro, Italy

Tel: 39-0321-888-800   Fax: 39-0321-888-802

GARTNER, INC.

56 Top Gallant Road, Stamford, CT, 06904-2212

Tel: (203) 316-1111   Fax: (203) 316-1100   www.gartner.com

Engaged in information technology consulting.

Gartner Group Italy, Milan, Italy

Tel: 39-02-482891   Fax: 39-02-48289389

GE BETZ, DIV. GE SPECIALTY MATERIALS

4636 Somerton Road, PO Box 3002, Trevose, PA, 19053-6783

Tel: (215) 355-3300   Fax: (215) 953-5524   www.gebetz.com

Engaged in engineered chemical treatment of water and process systems in industrial, commercial and institutional facilities

GE Betz, Div. GE Specialty Materials, Viale Gino Cervi 6, I-00139 Rome, Italy

Tel: 39-06-8727-1326   Contact: Fabio Ceccacci

GEN RE INTERMEDIARIES CORPORATION

PO Box 10216, Stamford, CT, 06904-2216

Tel: (203) 357-8883   Fax: (203) 328-6408   www.genre.com

Provides reinsurance services worldwide.

General Re Europe Ltd. - Milan, Ufficio de Rappresentanza di Milan, Largo Augusto 7, I-20122 Milan, Italy

Tel: 39-02-762-11852   Fax: 39-02-760-02667   Contact: Angelo Garbelli, VP

HartRe Company, Via Soperga 2, 6/F, Milan, Italy

Tel: 39-02-673-34311   Fax: 39-02-673-34321

La Kölnische Italia, Servzi Riassicurativi s.r.l., Largo Augusto 7, I-20122 Milan, Italy

Tel: 39-02-762-1181   Fax: 39-02-7600-1577   Contact: Massimo Apolloni, Gen. Mgr.

GENERAL BINDING CORPORATION

One GBC Plaza, Northbrook, IL, 60062

Tel: (847) 272-3700   Fax: (847) 272-1369   www.gbc.com

Engaged in the design, manufacture and distribution of branded office equipment, related supplies and thermal laminating films.

General Binding Corp. SpA, Milanofiori Palazzo F10, I-20090 Assago Milan, Italy

Contact: Robert Baci

GENERAL DATACOMM INC.

6 Rubber Avenue, Naugatuck, CT, 06770

Tel: (203) 729-0271   Fax: (203) 729-2883   www.gdc.com

Mfr., sales and service of transportation equipment for communications networks.

General DataComm, Via Leone XIII 95, I-00100 Rome, Italy

GENERAL ELECTRIC CAPITAL CORPORATION

260 Long Ridge Road, Stamford, CT, 06927

Tel: (203) 357-4000   Fax: (203) 357-6489   www.gecapital.com

Financial, property, casualty insurance, computer sales and trailer leasing services.

ERC Group, Div. GE Capital, Via Gasparotto 1, I-20124 Milan, Italy

Tel: 39-02-66-711-260   Fax: 39-02-66-711-906

ERC Group, Div. GE Capital, Via Ettore de Sonnaz 3, I-10121 Torino, Italy

Tel: 39-011-56-12205   Fax: 39-011-56-12230

GENERAL ELECTRIC COMPANY

3135 Easton Turnpike, Fairfield, CT, 06431

Tel: (203) 373-2211   Fax: (203) 373-3131   www.ge.com

Diversified manufacturing, technology and services.

GE FANUC Automation, Piazza Tirana 24/4B, I-20147 Milan, Italy

Tel: 39-02-417176   Fax: 39-02-49669

GE International, Viale Farngosta 75, I-20142 Milan, Italy

Tel: 39-02-8950-4755   Fax: 39-02-8953-1652

GE SeaCo Italia Srl, Via de Marini, 53, Genoa, Italy, I-16149

Tel: 39-010-659-241   Contact: F. delle Piane

Nuovo Pignone, Via Felice Matteucci 2, I-50127 Florence, Italy

Tel: 39-055-423-2710   Fax: 39-055-423-2709

GENERAL MOTORS ACCEPTANCE CORPORATION

3044 W. Grand Blvd., Detroit, MI, 48202

Tel: (313) 556-5000   Fax: (313) 556-5108   www.gmac.com

Automobile financing.

GMAC Italia SpA, Via Rivoltana 13, Milan San Felice, I-20090 Segrato, Italy

GMAC Italia SpA, Piazzale dell Industria 40, I-00144 Rome, Italy

GENERAL MOTORS CORPORATION

300 Renaissance Center, Detroit, MI, 48285

Tel: (313) 556-5000   Fax: (313) 556-5108   www.gm.com

Mfr. full line vehicles, automotive electronics, commercial technologies, telecommunications, space, finance.

General Motors Italia SpA, Piazza dell' Industria, I-00144 Rome, Italy

GENUITY, INC.

225 Presidential Way, Woburn, MA, 01801

Tel: (781) 865-2000   Fax: (781) 865-3936   www.genuity.com

R/D computer, communications, acoustics technologies and internetworking services.

Genuity Italy, Palazzo Tintoretto Centro Milano Oltre, Via Cassanese 224, I-20090 Segrate Milan, Italy

Tel: 39-02-2692-6142   Contact: Pia Boitano

GENZYME CORPORATION

1 Kendall Square, Cambridge, MA, 02139-1562

Tel: (617) 252-7500   Fax: (617) 252-7600   www.genzyme.com

Mfr. healthcare products for enzyme deficient diseases.

Genzyme SRL, Via Scaglia Est. 144, I-41100 Modena, Italy

Tel: 39-059-349811

GEORGIA-PACIFIC GROUP

133 Peachtree Street NE, 41st Floor, Atlanta, GA, 30303

Tel: (404) 652-4000   Fax: (404) 230-7008   www.gp.com

Mfr. and distribution of tissue, pulp, paper and building products and related chemicals.

Chem-Plast Specialties SPA, Div. Georgia-Pacific, Piazza Vetra, 21, I-20123 Milan, Italy

G-I HOLDINGS, INC.

1361 Alps Road, Wayne, NJ, 07470

Tel: (973) 628-3000   Fax: (973) 628-3326   www.gaf.com

Mfr. roofing and building materials.

G-I Holdings, Inc., Via Pipamonti 66, I-20141 Milan, Italy

GILEAD SCIENCES, INC.

333 Lakeside Dr, Foster City, CA, 94404

Tel: (650) 574-3000   Fax: (650) 578-9264   www.gilead.com

Engaged in healthcare research and development; biotech treatments for viruses.

NeXstar Pharmaceuticals, Via G. Frua 16, I-20146 Milan, Italy

Tel: 39-02-4802-1500   Fax: 39-02-4802-2578

THE GILLETTE COMPANY

Prudential Tower Building, Boston, MA, 02199

Tel: (617) 421-7000   Fax: (617) 421-7123   www.gillette.com

Develop/mfr. personal care/use products: blades and razors, toiletries, cosmetics, stationery.

Gillette Group Italy SpA, via Pirelli 18, I-21024 Milan, Italy

Contact: Domenico Ottavis, Gen. Mgr.

Oral-B Laboratories, via Pirelli 18, I-21024 Milan, Italy

GILSON INC.

3000 W. Beltline Hwy, PO Box 620027, Middleton, WI, 53562-0027

Tel: (608) 836-1551   Fax: (608) 831-4451   www.gilson.com

Mfr. analytical/biomedical instruments.

Gilson Italia Srl., Via Alserio 5, I-20159 Milan, Italy

GLEASON CORPORATION
1000 University Ave., Rochester, NY, 14692
Tel: (716) 473-1000   Fax: (716) 461-4348   www.gleasoncorp.com
Mfr. gear making machine tools; tooling and services.
Gleason Milano, Via Caldera 21/B3, I-20153 Milan, Italy
Tel: 39-024828571   Fax: 39-0248204698

GLOBAL SILVERHAWK INTERNATIONAL MOVING
1000 Burnett Avenue, Concord, CA, 94520
Tel: (510) 609-7080   Fax: (510) 609-7081   www.globalsilverhawk.com
International moving and forwarding.
Global Silverhawk, Via F. Iii Beltrami 61, I-20026 Novate Milanese Milan, Italy
Tel: 39-2-356-0925   Contact: Gilberto Tumietto, Gen. Mgr.

THE GOLDMAN SACHS GROUP
85 Broad Street, New York, NY, 10004
Tel: (212) 902-1000   Fax: (212) 902-3000   www.gs.com
Investment bankers; securities broker dealers.
Goldman Sachs Group, Passaggio Centrale 2, I-20123 Milan, Italy
Tel: 39-02-8022-1000

THE GOODYEAR TIRE & RUBBER COMPANY
1144 East Market Street, Akron, OH, 44316
Tel: (330) 796-2121   Fax: (330) 796-1817   www.goodyear.com
Mfr. tires, automotive belts and hose, conveyor belts, chemicals; oil pipeline transmission.
Goodyear Italiana SpA, Piazza G. Marconi 25, Casella Postale 10768, I-10100 Rome, Italy

W. R. GRACE & COMPANY
7500 Grace Drive, Columbia, MD, 21044
Tel: (410) 531-4000   Fax: (410) 531-4367   www.grace.com
Mfr. specialty chemicals and materials: packaging, health care, catalysts, construction, water treatment/process.
Grace Italiana SpA, Via Trento 7, 1-20017 Passirana di Rho Milan, Italy
Tel: 39-02-935371   Fax: 39-02-93537-555

GRAFTECH INTERNATIONAL LTD.
1521 Concord Pike, Ste. 301, Wilmington, DE, 19803
Tel: (302) 778-8277   Fax: (302) 778-8237   www.graftechinternational.com
Mfr. graphite electrodes for electrical products.
UCAR S.P.A., Via G. Garibaldi 43, I-21047 Saronno (VA), Italy
Tel: 39-02-9617081   Fax: 39-02-9670-1496

GRANITE SYSTEMS, INC.
1228 Elm Street, Manchester, NH, 03101
Tel: (603) 625-0100   Fax: (603) 625-4812   www.granitesystems.com
Mfr. service resource management software.
Granite Systems, Inc., Via di Vigna Murata 40, I-00143 Rome, Italy
Tel: 39-06-5483-2138

GRANT THORNTON INTERNATIONAL
800 One Prudential Plaza, 130 E. Randolph Drive, Chicago, IL, 60601-6050
Tel: (312) 856-0001   Fax: (312) 616-7052   www.grantthornton.com
Accounting, audit, tax and management consulting services.
Grant Thornton Italia S.p.A., Viale Brigate Partigiane 12, I-16129 Genoa, Italy
Tel: 39-010-587948   Fax: 39-010-587948
Grant Thornton Italia S.p.A., Via Sparano 115, I-70121 Bari, Italy
Tel: 39-080-587948   Fax: 39-080-521-4688
Grant Thornton Italia S.p.A., Via Santa Brigida 51, I-80133 Napoli, Italy
Tel: 39-08-1552-9052   Fax: 39-08-1055-19055   Contact: Licio Duca

Grant Thornton Italia S.p.A., Via G. Zanellato 5, I-35121 Padova, Italy

Tel: 39-049-870-3019   Fax: 39-049-870-2275   Contact: Beretta Giorgio

Grant Thornton Italia S.p.A., Via Colli 20, I-10129 Torino, Italy

Tel: 39-02-2561-1185   Fax: 39-011-561-1815

Grant Thornton Italia S.p.A., Via Nizza 45, I-00198 Rome, Italy

Tel: 39-06-854-0056   Fax: 39-06-855-7469

Grant Thornton S.p.A., Largo Augusto 7, I-20122 Milan, Italy

Tel: 39-02-762970   Fax: 39-02-781498   Contact: Lorenzo Penca

GREAT LAKES CHEMICAL CORPORATION

500 East 96th Street, Ste. 500, Indianapolis, IN, 46240

Tel: (317) 715-3000   Fax: (317) 715-3050   www.greatlakeschem.com

Mfr. innovative specialty chemical solutions, including flame retardants and other polymer additives, water treatment chemicals, performance and fine chemicals, fire extinguishers.

Great Lakes Chemical Italia SRL, Via Mazzini N. 11, I-24066 Pedrengo, Italy

Tel: 39-03-565-3111

GREG MANNING AUCTIONS, INC.

775 Passaic Avenue, West Caldwell, NJ, 07006

Tel: (973) 882-0004   Fax: (973) 882-3499   www.gregmanning.com

Specialty auction house; dealing primarily in stamps.

GMAI Europe, Via Privata Maria Teresa 11, I-20123 Milan, Italy

GREY GLOBAL GROUP

777 Third Ave., New York, NY, 10017

Tel: (212) 546-2000   Fax: (212) 546-1495   www.grey.com

International advertising agency.

Milano & Grey, Via Bertani 6, I-20154 Milan, Italy

GRIFFITH LABORATORIES INC.

One Griffith Center, Alsip, IL, 60658

Tel: (708) 371-0900   Fax: (708) 597-3294   www.griffithlabs.com

Mfr. industrial food ingredients and equipment.

Griffith Labs, Rome, Italy

Tel: 39-06-3031-0632   Fax: 39-06-3031-0885

GROUP 1 SOFTWARE, INC.

4200 parliament Place, Ste. 600, Lanham, MD, 20706-1860

Tel: (301) 918-0400   Fax: (301) 918-0735   www.g1.com

Mfr. management software.

Group 1 Software Italy, Piazza Quattro Novembre, 4, I-20124 Milan, Italy

GUY CARPENTER & COMPANY, INC.

114 West 47th Street, New York, NY, 10036

Tel: (212) 323-1000   Fax: (212) 345-2494   www.guycarp.com

Engaged in global reinsurance and risk management.

Guy Carpenter & Company, S.r.l., Corso Magenta 27, I-20123 Milan, Italy

Tel: 39-02-854-2141   Fax: 39-02-8699-7994   Contact: Andrea Manzitti

HAEMONETICS CORPORATION

400 Wood Road, Braintree, MA, 02184-9114

Tel: (781) 848-7100   Fax: (781) 848-5106   www.haemonetics.com

Mfr. automated blood processing systems and blood products.

Haemonetics Italia S.R.L., Via Donizetti 30, I-20020 Lainate Milan, Italy

Tel: 39-02-935-70113   Fax: 39-02-935-72132

THE HAIN CELESTIAL GROUP, INC.

50 Charles Lindbergh Blvd., Uniondale, NY, 11553

Tel: (516) 237-6200   Fax: (516) 237-6240   www.hain-celestial.com

Mfr. specialty foods, including health foods and teas.

Euro Food Spa, Via Privata Tacito 12, I-20094 Corsico, Milan, Italy

HALLIBURTON COMPANY

500 North Akard Street, Ste. 3600, Dallas, TX, 75201-3391

Tel: (214) 978-2600   Fax: (214) 978-2685   www.halliburton.com

Engaged in diversified energy services, engineering and construction.

Halliburton Ltd., Via del Marchhesato, I-48023 Marina di Ravenna, Italy

Tel: 39-0383-691557   Fax: 39-0383-640529

Halliburton Ltd., Via Tolstoi 86, San Gluliano, I-10098 Milanese Milan, Italy

Tel: 39-02-9849-1451   Fax: 39-02-9824-0488

Halliburton Ltd., Ufficio Postale Succursale 6, I-29110 Piacenza, Italy

Tel: 39-052-3540401   Fax: 39-052-3593610

Halliburton Ltd., Via Elorina, Contrada Pantanelli, I-96100 Siracusa Sicily, Italy

Tel: 39-093-146-3882   Fax: 39-093-146-3883

Halliburton Ltd., CP 59, I-48023 Marina di Ravenna, Italy

Tel: 39-054-453-0709   Fax: 39-054-453-1042

HA-LO INDUSTRIES, INC.

5800 West Touhy Avenue, Niles, IL, 60714

Tel: (847) 600-3000   Fax: (847) 600-4000   www.halo.com

Engaged in distribution of brand-awareness, promotional products.

HA-LO Italy, Via Della Massa 32, I-500112 Candeli, Italy

Parsons International, Viale FT Marineti 221, I-00143 Rome, Italy

HAMILTON SUNSTRAND

One Hamilton Rd., Windsor Locks, CT, 06096-1010

Tel: (860) 654-6000   Fax: (860) 654-3469   www.hamiltonsunstrandcorp.com

Design/mfr. aerospace systems for commercial, regional, corporate and military aircraft.

Hamilton Sunstrand Corp., Torino, Italy

HARRIS CALORIFIC COMPANY

2345 Murphy Boulevard, Gainesville, GA, 30501

Tel: (770) 536-8801   Fax: (770) 536-0544   www.harriscal.com

Mfr./sales of gas welding and cutting equipment.

Harris Europa SpA, Via Nazionale 79, I-40065 Pianoro Bologna, Italy

HARRIS CORPORATION

1025 West NASA Blvd., Melbourne, FL, 32919

Tel: (407) 727-9100   Fax: (407) 727-9344   www.harris.com

Mfr. communications and information-handling equipment, including copying and fax systems.

Harris Semiconductor, Viale Fulvio Testi 126, I-20092 Cinisello Balsamo Milan, Italy

Tel: 39-02-262-222131

HASBRO INDUSTRIES INC.

1027 Newport Ave., Pawtucket, RI, 02861

Tel: (401) 725-8697   Fax: (401) 727-5099   www.hasbro.com

Mfr. toy products, including games and puzzles, dolls and plush products.

Hasbro Iberia, S.L., Poligono Industrial, Sec. 13, Calle 17, I-46190 Ribarraja del Turia, Italy

Tel: 96-271-9400

Wizards, Div. Hasbro Industries, Via Giovanni da Udine 3, I-20156 Milan, Italy

Tel: 44-1628-780-530

HAUPPAUGE DIGITAL, INC.

91 Cabot Court, Hauppauge, NY, 11788

Tel: (631) 434-1600   Fax: (631) 434-3198   www.hauppauge.com

Mfr. circuit boards.

Hauppauge Computer Works Italy, Via Treccani degli Alfier 14, I-20141 Milan, Italy

Tel: 39-02-84800286

HAWORTH INC.

1 Haworth Center, Holland, MI, 49423-9576

Tel: (616) 393-3000   Fax: (616) 393-1570   www.haworth.com

Mfr. office furniture.

Haworth Furniture, Via Olmatello, 21, I-40064 Delli Emilia Bologna, Italy

HAYES LEMMERZ INTERNATIONAL

15300 Centennial Dr., Northville, MI, 48167

Tel: (734) 737-5000   Fax: (734) 737-2003   www.hayes-lemmerz.com

Mfr. steel and aluminum car wheels.

Hayes Lemmerz S.p.A., Via Cavour 26, I-10060 Camiglione Fenile, Italy

Hayes Lemmerz S.p.A., Via Roma 200, I-25020 Dello, Italy

HAYNES INTERNATIONAL INC.

1020 W. Park Ave., PO Box 9013, Kokomo, IN, 46904-9013

Tel: (765) 456-6000   Fax: (765) 456-6905   www.haynesintl.com

Development and manufacture of high-performance nickel and cobalt based alloys for service in severe corrosion and high-temperature applications.

Haynes International, S.R.L., Viale Brianza 8, I-20127 Milan, Italy

Tel: 39-2-2614-1331   Fax: 39-2-282-8273

HEIDRICK & STRUGGLES INTERNATIONAL, INC.

233 South Wacker Drive, Chicago, IL, 60606

Tel: (312) 496-1200   Fax: (312) 496-1290   www.heidrick.com

Executive search firm.

Heidrick & Struggles Intl. Inc., Corso Venezia 16, I-20122 Milan, Italy

Tel: 39-02-76-000-393   Fax: 39-02-76-000-801

Heidrick & Struggles Intl. Inc., Via XXIV Maggio 43, I-00187 Rome, Italy

HEIN-WERNER CORPORATION

2110 A Pewaukee Rd., PO Box 1606, Waukesha, WI, 53188

Tel: (262) 542-6611   Fax: (262) 542-7890   www.blackhawk kj.com

Mfr. auto body repair equipment, engine rebuilding and brake repair equipment, hydraulic cylinders.

Blackhawk Italia SRL, Via dell'Industria 5, I-37066 Sommacampagna Verona, Italy

H.J. HEINZ COMPANY

600 Grant Street, Pittsburgh, PA, 15219

Tel: (412) 456-5700   Fax: (412) 456-6128   www.heinz.com

Processed food products and nutritional services.

AIAL (Arimpex SRL Industrie Alimentari), Commessaggio, Italy

Dega SRL, Mori, Italy

Heinz Italia SpA, Milan, Italy

PLADA SpA (Plasmon Dietetici Alimentari SpA), Milan, Italy

HERCULES INC.

Hercules Plaza, 1313 N. Market Street, Wilmington, DE, 19894-0001

Tel: (302) 594-5000   Fax: (302) 594-5400   www.herc.com

Mfr. specialty chemicals, plastics, film and fibers, coatings, resins and food ingredients.

Hercules Italia SpA, Via Rosellini 2, I-20124 Milan, Italy

Hercules Italia SpA, Bologna, Italy

HERMAN MILLER INC.

855 East Main, Zeeland, MI, 49464

Tel: (616) 654-3000   Fax: (616) 654-5385   www.hermanmiller.com

Mfr. office furnishings.

Herman Miller Italia, Via Gran Sasso 6, I-20030 Lentate sul Seveso, Italy

HERSHEY FOODS CORPORATION

100 Crystal A Drive, Hershey, PA, 17033

Tel: (717) 534-6799   Fax: (717) 534-6760   www.hersheys.com

Mfr. chocolate, mints, gum, food and confectionery products.

Sperlari SRL, Via Milan 16, I-26100 Cremona, Italy

HEWITT ASSOCIATES LLC

100 Half Day Road, Lincolnshire, IL, 60069

Tel: (847) 295-5000   Fax: (847) 295-7634   www.hewitt.com

Employee benefits consulting firm.

Hewitt Associates, Via Alessandro Volta 16, Scala H, I-20093 Cologno Monzese Milan, Italy

Tel: 39-02-254-0794

HEWLETT-PACKARD COMPANY

3000 Hanover Street, Palo Alto, CA, 94304-1185

Tel: (650) 857-1501   Fax: (650) 857-5518   www.hp.com

Mfr. computing, communications and measurement products and services.

Hewlett-Packard Italiana SpA, Via Giuseppe di Vittorio 9, I-20063 Cernusco sul Naviglio Milan, Italy

HIGH VOLTAGE ENGINEERING CORPORATION

401 Edgewater Place, Ste. 680, Wakefield, MA, 01880

Tel: (781) 224-1001   Fax: (781) 224-1011   www.highvolteng.com

Holding company: owner and operator of a diversified group of middle market industrial and technology-based manufacturing businesses.

ASI, Div. High Voltage (HVE), Viale Sarca 336, I-20126 Milan, Italy

HILLENBRAND INDUSTRIES, INC.

700 State Route 46 East, Batesville, IN, 47006

Tel: (812) 934-7000   Fax: (812) 934-1963   www.hillenbrand.com

Holding company: mfr. hospital beds, incubators and caskets.

Hill-Rom SpA, Via Ambrosoli Nr. 6, I-20090 Rodano Milan, Italy

Tel: 39-02-950-541   Fax: 39-02-953-28578   Contact: Angelo Lugrini

HILTON HOTELS CORPORATION

9336 Civic Center Drive, Beverly Hills, CA, 90210

Tel: (310) 278-4321   Fax: (310) 205-7880   www.hiltonhotels.com

International hotel chain: Hilton International, Vista Hotels and Hilton National Hotels.

Hilton International Hotels, Via Galvani 12, I-20124 Milan, Italy

HLW INTERNATIONAL, LLP

115 Fifth Ave., New York, NY, 10003

Tel: (212) 353-4600   Fax: (212) 353-4666   www.hlw.com

Architecture, engineering, planning and interior design.

HLW International LLP, Milan, Italy

HOLIDAY INN (BASS RESORTS) WORLDWIDE, INC.

3 Ravinia Drive, Ste. 2900, Atlanta, GA, 30346-2149

Tel: (770) 604-2000   Fax: (770) 604-5403   www.holidayinn.com

Hotels, restaurants and casinos.

Holiday Inn, Viale Castello della Magliana 65, I-10210 Parco Dei Medici Rome, Italy

HOLLINGSWORTH & VOSE COMPANY

112 Washington Street, East Walpole, MA, 02032

Tel: (508) 668-0295   Fax: (508) 668-3557   www.hollingsworth-vose.com

Mfr. technical and industrial papers and non-woven fabrics.

Hollingsworth & Vose Company, SRL, Via Bodina 41, I-12100 Cuneo, Italy

HONEYWELL INTERNATIONAL INC.

Honeywell Plaza, Minneapolis, MN, 55408

Tel: (612) 951-1000   Fax: (612) 951-8537   www.honeywell.com

Develop/mfr. controls for home and building, industry, space and aviation, burglar and fire alarm systems.

Honeywell S.p.A., Via P. Gobetti - 2/b, I-20063 Cemusco sul Naviglio, Italy

Tel: 39-02-921-461   Fax: 39-02-921-46888

HORWATH INTERNATIONAL ASSOCIATION

420 Lexington Avenue, Suite 526, New York, NY, 10170-0526

Tel: (212) 808-2000   Fax: (212) 808-2020   www.horwath.com

Public accountants and auditors.

Horwath & Horwath Italia, Via Calabria 7, I-00187 Rome, Italy

Polandri Horwath, Piazza Navona 49, I-00186 Rome, Italy

HOUGHTON INTERNATIONAL INC.

PO Box 930, Madison & Van Buren Avenues, Valley Forge, PA, 19482-0930

Tel: (610) 666-4000   Fax: (610) 666-1376   www.houghtonintl.com

Mfr. specialty chemicals, hydraulic fluids and lubricants.

Houghton Italia SpA, Casella Postale 6069, I-16100 Genoa, Italy

Tel: 39-010-745-01-51

HOWMEDICA OSTEONICS, INC.

59 Route 17 South, Allendale, NJ, 07401

Tel: (201) 507-7300   Fax: (201) 935-4873   www.howmedica.com

Mfr. of maxillofacial products (orthopedic implants).

Howmedica Italy, Rome, Italy

Tel: 39-06-33182

HOWMET CASTINGS

9 Old Kings Hwy. South, Darien, CT, 06820

Tel: (203) 857-3120   Fax: (203) 857-3158   www.howmet.com

Mfr. precision investment castings, alloys, engineering and refurbishment for jet aircraft and industrial gas turbine (IGT) engine components.

Ciral IT, Via P.G.A. Filippino 119, I-00144 Rome, Italy

HUNTSMAN CORPORATION

500 Huntsman Way, Salt Lake City, UT, 84108

Tel: (801) 532-5200   Fax: (801) 536-1581   www.huntsman.com

Mfr. and sales of specialty chemicals, industrial chemicals and petrochemicals.

Huntsman Polyurethanes, Via Mazzini 58, I-21020 Ternate, Italy

Tel: 39-332-941-111   Contact: A. Lettieri

Tioxide Europe Srl, Stablimento di Scarlino, Contrada Casone CP113, I-58022 Follonica, Italy

Tel: 39-566-71111

HUSSMANN INTERNATIONAL

12999 St. Charles Rock Road, Bridgeton, MO, 63044

Tel: (314) 291-2000   Fax: (314) 291-5144   www.hussmann.com

Mfr. refrigeration and environmental control systems for food industrial.

Hussmann Koxka, Via Marco Polo n.4, I-35035 Mestrino, Italy

Tel: 39-049-9004680   Fax: 39-049-9005072

HYPERION SOLUTIONS CORPORATION

1344 Crossman Avenue, Sunnyvale, CA, 94089

Tel: (408) 744-9500   Fax: (408) 744-0400   www.hyperion.com

Mfr. data analysis software tools.

Niederlassung Italy, Via Giorgione 18, I-00147 Rome, Italy

Tel: 39-06-542491 Fax: 39-06-5422-5821

Niederlassung Italy, Via Margignoni 25, I-20124 Milan, Italy

Tel: 39-02-698131 Fax: 39-0-688-6567

i2 TECHNOLOGIES, INC.

11701 Luna Road, Dallas, TX, 75234

Tel: (214) 860-6106   Fax: (214) 860-6060   www.i2.com

Engaged in supply chain management; solutions to help companies collaborate on decision-making processes.

i2 Technologies Italy S.r.l., Via Albani 21, 4/F, 4 Piano, I-20149 Milan, Italy

IBM CORPORATION

1133 Westchester Avenue, White Plains, NY, 10604

Tel: (914) 765-1900   Fax: (914) 765-7382   www.ibm.com

Information products, technology and services.

IBM Italia SpA, Via Lecco 61, I-20090 Vimercate Milan, Italy

Tel: 39-039-600-7666 Fax: 39-039-600-7150

ICC INDUSTRIES INC.

460 Park Ave., New York, NY, 10022

Tel: (212) 521-1700   Fax: (212) 521-1794   www.iccchem.com

Manufacturing and trading of chemicals, plastics and pharmaceuticals.

ICC Talia S.R.L., Via G. Cardano 8, I-20124 Milan, Italy

Tel: 39-02-670-1406 Fax: 39-02-670-0477 Contact: Francesco Minervino

ICN PHARMACEUTICALS, INC.

3300 Hyland Ave., Costa Mesa, CA, 92626

Tel: (714) 545-0100   Fax: (714) 641-7268   www.icnpharm.com

Mfr. and distribution of pharmaceuticals.

ICN Pharmaceuticals, Inc., Via Labor 23/25, I-20090 Opera MI, Italy

Tel: 39-2-57601041 Fax: 39-2-57601610

IDEXX LABORATORIES, INC.

1 IDEXX Dr., Westbrook, ME, 04092-2041

Tel: (207) 856-0300   Fax: (207) 856-0346   www.idexx.com

Mfr. and sales of veterinary products.

IDEXX Laboratories Italia S.r.l., Via Canova, 27, I-20145 Milan, Italy

Tel: 39-2-319-2031

ILLINOIS TOOL WORKS (ITW)

3600 West Lake Ave., Glenview, IL, 60025-5811

Tel: (847) 724-7500   Fax: (847) 657-4268   www.itw.com

Mfr. gears, tools, fasteners, sealants, plastic and metal components for industrial, medical, etc.

ITW Hi-Cone, S.P.A., Galleria Ugo Bassi. 1 (1° Piano), I-40121 Bologna, Italy

Tel: 39-051-269190 Fax: 39-051-229531 Contact: Felice Guerriero

IMATION CORPORATION

One Imation Place, Oakdale, MN, 55128

Tel: (612) 704-4000   Fax: (612) 704-3444   www.imation.com

Dry laser-imaging film systems.

Imation Corp., Milan, Italy

IMI NORGREN GROUP

5400 South Delaware Street, Littleton, CO, 80120-1663

Tel: (303) 794-2611　　　Fax: (303) 795-9487　　　www.usa.norgren.com

Mfr. pneumatic filters, regulators, lubricators, valves, automation systems, dryers, push-in fittings.

IMI Norgren S.p.A., Via Marzabotto 2, I-20059 Vimercate Milan, Italy

Tel: 39-06-0631　Fax: 39-06-063-301

INDUCTOTHERM INDUSTRIES

10 Indel Ave., PO Box 157, Rancocas, NJ, 08073-0157

Tel: (609) 267-9000　　　Fax: (609) 267-5705　　　www.inductotherm.com

Mfr. induction melting furnaces, induction power supplies, charging and preheating systems, automatic pouring systems and computer control systems.

Grein Guardscan, Via SGB DeLaSalle, 4/A, I-20132 Milan, Italy

INFONET SERVICES CORPORATION

2160 East Grand Ave., El Segundo, CA, 90245-1022

Tel: (310) 335-2600　　　Fax: (310) 335-4507　　　www.infonet.com

Provider of Internet services and electronic messaging services.

Infonet Italia, Via Rombon 11, I-20134 Milan, Italy

Tel: 39-02-217131　Fax: 39-02-21713-203

INFORMATION RESOURCES, INC. (IRI)

150 N. Clinton St., Chicago, IL, 60661

Tel: (312) 726-1221　　　Fax: (312) 726-0360　　　www.infores.com

Provides bar code scanner services for retail sales organizations; processes, analyzes and sells data from the huge database created from these services.

IRI InfoScan, Viale Brenta 18, I-20139 Milan, Italy

Tel: 39-02-525-79651　Fax: 39-02-569-5767　Contact: Marco Cuppini

INGERSOLL INTERNATIONAL INC.

707 Fulton Ave., Rockford, IL, 61103

Tel: (815) 987-6000　　　Fax: (815) 987-6725　　　www.ingersoll.com

Multinational supplier of special machine tools and services for the metalworking industries.

Ingersoll Italy, Vai J.F. Kennedy 19, I-20090 Rodano Millepini (MI), Italy

Tel: 39-02-9532-0794　Fax: 39-02-9532-0801

INGERSOLL-RAND COMPANY

200 Chestnut Ridge Road, Woodcliff Lake, NJ, 07675

Tel: (201) 573-0123　　　Fax: (201) 573-3172　　　www.irco.com

Leading innovation and solutions provider for the major global markets of Security and Safety, Climate Control, Industrial Solutions and Infrastructure.

Ingersoll-Rand Italiana SpA, Strada Prov. Cassamese 108, I-20060 Vignate Milan, Italy

Tel: 39-02-95056-537　Fax: 39-02-9560194

Worthington SpA, Via Rossini 90-92, I-20033 Desio Milan, Italy

INGRAM MICRO INC.

1600 E. St. Andrew Place, Santa Ana, CA, 92799

Tel: (714) 566-1000　　　Fax: (714) 566-7940　　　www.ingrammicro.com

Engaged in wholesale distribution of microcomputer products.

Ingram Micro Inc., Milan, Italy

INSTRON CORPORATION

100 Royal Street, Canton, MA, 02021-1089

Tel: (781) 575-5000　　　Fax: (781) 575-5751　　　www.instron.com

Mfr., markets and services materials testing instruments, systems and accessories.

Instron Intl. Ltd., Via del Cignoli, Milan, Italy

Tel: 39-2-380-00003

INTEGRATED DEVICE TECHNOLOGY, INC. (IDT)

2975 Stender Way, Santa Clara, CA, 95054

Tel: (408) 727-6116   Fax: (408) 492-8674   www.idt.com

Mfr. high-performance semiconductors and modules.

Integrated Device Technology (IDT), Centro Direzionale Colleoni, Palazzo Astrolabio, Via Cardano 2, I-20041 Agrate Brianza, Italy

Tel: 39-39-6899987   Fax: 39-39-6899986

INTEL CORPORATION

2200 Mission College Blvd., Santa Clara, CA, 95052-8119

Tel: (408) 765-8080   Fax: (408) 765-1739   www.intel.com

Mfr. semiconductor, microprocessor and micro-communications components and systems.

Intel Semiconductor (Italy) SpA, Via Fermi, 20, I-20090 Assago, Italy

Tel: 39-02-575-441

INTER-CONTINENTAL HOTELS

3 Ravinia Drive, Suite 2900, Atlanta, GA, 30346-2149

Tel: (770) 604-2000   Fax: (770) 604-5403   www.interconti.com

Worldwide hotel and resort accommodations.

De La Ville Inter-Continental Roma, Via Sistina 6769, I-00018 Rome, Italy

Tel: 39-06-67331   Fax: 39-06-678-4213

Inter-Continental Hotels, Via Vittor Pisani 12, I-20124 Milan, Italy

Tel: 39-02-669-2542

INTERGRAPH CORPORATION

One Madison Industrial Park, Huntsville, AL, 35894-0001

Tel: (256) 730-2000   Fax: (256) 730-7898   www.intergraph.com

Develop/mfr. interactive computer graphic systems.

Intergraph Italia LLC, Centrp Direzionale Milanofiori, Strada 7, Palazzo R, I-20089 Rozzano Milan, Italy

Tel: 39-02-575451   Fax: 39-02-5751-2470

Intergraph Rome, Via Dino Frescobaldi 7, Rome, Italy

Tel: 39-06-8689-7200   Fax: 39-06-8689-7195

INTERMEC TECHNOLOGIES CORPORATION

6001 36th Avenue West, PO Box 4280, Everett, WA, 98203-9280

Tel: (425) 348-2600   Fax: (425) 355-9551   www.intermec.com

Mfr. and distributor automated data collection systems.

Intermec Technologies S.r.l., Via Enrico Cialdini 37, I-20161 Milan, Italy

Tel: 39-02-662-4051   Fax: 39-02-662-40558

INTERNATIONAL FLAVORS & FRAGRANCES INC.

521 West 57th Street, New York, NY, 10019-2960

Tel: (212) 765-5500   Fax: (212) 708-7132   www.iff.com

Design/mfr. flavors, fragrances and aroma chemicals.

International Flavors & Fragrances, Via Fratelli Cervi, I-20090 Trezzano sul Naviglio Milan, Italy

Tel: 39-02-48-472-1   Fax: 39-02-484-03953

INTERNATIONAL MANAGEMENT GROUP (IMG)

1360 East Ninth Street, Ste. 100, Cleveland, OH, 44114

Tel: (216) 522-1200   Fax: (216) 522-1145   www.imgworld.com

Manages athletes, sports academies and real estate facilities worldwide.

IMG Srl, Viale Beatrice D'Este 1, I-20122 Milan, Italy

Tel: 39-02-583-13364   Fax: 39-02-583-13095

INTERNATIONAL PAPER COMPANY

400 Atlantic Street, Stamford, CT, 06921

Tel: (203) 541-8000   Fax: (203) 358-6444   www.ipaper.com

Mfr./distributor container board, paper and wood products.

Anitec Image Italia SRL, S.S. 233 Km. 20.5, I-21040 Origgio, Italy

Aussedat Rey Italia SRL, Viale Milanfiori, Palazzo F1, I-20090 Assago, Italy

Cartiera di Valtaggio SRL, Loc. Pian Maxina, I-15060 Voltaggio, Italy

Horsell Italia Industrie Grafiche SRL, Viale del Lavoro, I-37036 S. Martino Buon Albergo, Italy

Ilford Photo SpA, S.S. 233 Km. 20.5, I-21040 Origgio, Italy

International Paper Italia SpA, Via Omago 55, I-20040 Bellusco Milan, Italy

INTERNATIONAL RECTIFIER CORPORATION

233 Kansas Street, El Segundo, CA, 90245

Tel: (310) 322-3331   Fax: (310) 322-3332   www.irf.com

Mfr. power semiconductor components.

International Rectifier Corp., Via Privata Liguria 49, I-10071 Borgaro-Torino, Italy

Tel: 39-011-451-0111   Fax: 39-011-4510-374

INTERNATIONAL SPECIALTY PRODUCTS, INC.

1361 Alps Rd., Wayne, NJ, 07470

Tel: (973) 389-3083   Fax: (973) 628-4117   www.ispcorp.com

Mfr. specialty chemical products.

ISP (Italia) Srl, Via Dei Gracchi, 30, I-20146 Milan, Italy

Tel: 39-02-75-419-642   Fax: 39-02-52-75419-644

INTERVOICE-BRITE INC.

17811 Waterview Pkwy., Dallas, TX, 75206

Tel: (972) 454-8000   Fax: (972) 454-8707   www.intervoice.com

Mfr. telecom network hardware and software systems.

InterVoice-Brite SpA, Via Flaminia 173, I-00196 Rome, Italy

Tel: 39-06-320-0450   Fax: 39-06-320-8467

INVITROGEN CORPORATION

1600 Faraday Avenue, Carlsbad, CA, 92008

Tel: (760) 603-7200   Fax: (760) 602-6500   www.invitrogen.com

Mfr. products and kits for gene analysis.

Invitrogen Italia Srl, Via Tolstoj 86, San Giuliano Milanese (MI), Italy

IONICS INC.

65 Grove Street, Watertown, MA, 02172

Tel: (617) 926-2500   Fax: (617) 926-4304   www.ionics.com

Mfr. desalination equipment.

Ionics Italba, Via Livraghi 1/B, I-21026 Milan, Italy

IRIDIUM LLC

1600 Wilson Boulevard, Suite 1000, Washington, DC, 20009

Tel: (202) 408-3800   Fax: (202) 408-3801   www.iridium.com

Consortium of companies sharing the construction and implementation of a global satellite communications system.

Iridium South Europe Reg. HQ / Iridium Italia S.p.A., Via Leofreni 4, I-00131 Rome, Italy

Tel: 39-6-417281   Fax: 39-6-4172-8296   Contact: Paolo Torresani, Chmn.

ITT INDUSTRIES, INC.

4 West Red Oak Lane, White Plains, NY, 10604

Tel: (914) 641-2000   Fax: (914) 696-2950   www.ittind.com

Mfr. pumps, systems and services to move and control water/fluids and produces connectors, switches, keypads and cabling used in computing, telecommunications, aerospace and industrial applications, as well as network services.

Galfer, Via San Maratino 87, I-12032 Barge (CN), Italy

Tel: 39-01-75-34-7228

ITT Automotive Italy S.p.A., Via San Maratino 87, I-12032 Barge(CN), Italy
Tel: 39-01-75-347228

Lowara S.p.A., Via Dott Lombardi 14, I-36075 Montecchio Maggiore, Italy
Tel: 39-444-70-7111   Fax: 39-444-49-2109

IVAX CORPORATION
4400 Biscayne Blvd., Miami, FL, 33137
Tel: (305) 575-6000   Fax: (305) 575-6055   www.ivax.com
Mfr. pharmaceuticals.

Delta Biologicals, V. Costarica 14, I-00040 Pomezia, Rome, Italy

J. WALTER THOMPSON COMPANY
466 Lexington Ave., New York, NY, 10017
Tel: (212) 210-7000   Fax: (212) 210-6944   www.jwt.com
International advertising and marketing services.

J. Walter Thompson Italia, Milan, Italy

JABIL CIRCUIT, INC.
10560 Ninth St. North, St. Petersburg, FL, 33716
Tel: (727) 557-9749   Fax: (727) 579-8529   www.jabil.com
Mfr. printed circuit boards, electronic components and systems.

Jabil Circuit Italy, Viale Europe 2, I-24040 Stezzano Bergamo, Italy
Tel: 39-035-4542-111

JACOBS ENGINEERING GROUP INC.
1111 S. Arroyo Parkway, Pasadena, CA, 91105
Tel: (626) 578-3500   Fax: (626) 578-6916   www.jacobs.com
Engineering, design and consulting; construction and construction management; process plant maintenance.

Serete Italia, Via Alessondro Volta No. 16, I-20093 Cologno Monzese Milan, Italy
Tel: 39-02-250-981   Fax: 39-02-253-90-973   Contact: Alfredo Radeplia, Chmn. & CEO   Emp: 116

JDS UNIPHASE CORPORATION
210 Baypoint Pkwy., San Jose, CA, 95134
Tel: (408) 434-1800   Fax: (408) 954-0760   www.jdsunph.com
Mfr. advanced fiber optic products for the cable television and telecommunications industries.

JDS Uniphase S.r.L, Via Cernuschi 8, Palazzina B2, III Piano, I-20052 Monza (MI), Italy
Tel: 39-039-2315889

JLG INDUSTRIES INC.
One JLG Drive, McConnellsburg, PA, 17233-9533
Tel: (717) 485-5161   Fax: (717) 485-6417   www.jlg.com
Mfr. aerial work platforms and vertical personnel lifts.

JLG Industries (Italia) s.r.l., Via Po. 2.2, I-20010 Pregnana Milanese Milan, Italy
Tel: 39-02-935-95210   Fax: 39-02-935-95845

JOHNSON & JOHNSON
One Johnson & Johnson Plaza, New Brunswick, NJ, 08933
Tel: (732) 524-0400   Fax: (732) 214-0334   www.jnj.com
Mfr./distributor/R&D pharmaceutical, health care and cosmetic products.

DePuy Italy SRL, Milan, Italy

Ethicon SpA/ Ethicon Endo-Surgery SpA, Rome, Italy

Janssen-Cilag SpA, Milan, Italy

Johnson & Johnson SpA, Casella Postale 10742, I-00144 Rome, Italy

LifeScan SpA, Milan, Italy

Ortho-Clinical Diagnostics SpA, Casella Postale 17171, I-20170 Milan, Italy

SC JOHNSON

1525 Howe St., Racine, WI, 53403

Tel: (262) 260-2000   Fax: (262) 260-2133   www.scjohnsonwax.com

Home, auto, commercial and personal care products and specialty chemicals.

SC Johnson, Casella Postale 18, I-20020 Arese Milan, Italy

JOHNSON CONTROLS INC.

5757 N. Green Bay Ave., PO Box 591, Milwaukee, WI, 53201-0591

Tel: (414) 228-1200   Fax: (414) 228-2077   www.johnsoncontrols.com

Mfr. facility management and control systems and auto seating.

Johnson Controls SpA, Via Monfalcone 15, I-20132 Milan, Italy

Tel: 39-02-280421 Fax: 39-02-28042230   Contact: Giovanni Frangi, Branch Mgr.

THE JOHNSON CORPORATION

805 Wood Street, Three Rivers, MI, 49093

Tel: (269) 278-1715   Fax: (269) 273-2230   www.joco.com

Mfr. rotary joints and siphon systems.

Johnson Corporation Italia, S.r.l., Corso Piemonte, 25, San Mauro Torinese, I-10099 Torino, Italy

Johnson Montaggi Srl, Uffici Tecnici e Officina, Via Renco, 73bis, I-28059 Verbania VB, Italy

JOHNSON OUTDOORS, INC.

555 Main Street, Racine, WI, 53177

Tel: (262) 631-6600   Fax: (262) 631-6601   www.johnsonoutdoors.com

Mfr. diving, fishing, boating and camping sports equipment.

Scubapro Italy s.r.l., Via Latino 21/C, I-16039 Sestri-Levante Genova, Italy

Tel: 39-0185-482321   Fax: 39-0185-459122

JONES, DAY, REAVIS & POGUE

North Point, 901 Lakeside Ave., Cleveland, OH, 44114

Tel: (216) 586-3939   Fax: (216) 579-0212   www.jonesday.com

International law firm.

Jones, Day, Reavis & Pogue, Via Conservatorio, 17, 20122 Milan, Italy

Tel: 39-02-7645-4001

JPMORGAN PRIVATE BANK

345 Park Avenue, New York, NY, 10154-1002

Tel: (212) 483-2323   Fax: (212) 464-1120   www.jpmorgan.com

Engaged in private banking services.

JPMorgan Private Bank, Via Catena, 4, I-20121 Milan, Italy

JUKI UNION SPECIAL CORPORATION

8500 N.W. 17th St., Miami, FL, 33126

Tel: (305) 594-0059   Fax: (305) 594-0720   www.unionspecial.com

Mfr. sewing machines.

Union Special Italia SpA, Via Bergamo 4, I-20020 Lainate Milan, Italy

Tel: 39-02-937-2142   Fax: 39-02-935-70164

KAHLE ENGINEERING COMPANY

25 DeForest Avenue, Summit, NJ, 07901

Tel: (908) 598-1140   Fax: (908) 598-1160   www.kahleengineering.com

Mfr. state of the art assembly equipment for the Health Care Industry.

Kahle SpA, Via Artigiani 1, I-24043 Caravaggio, Italy

Tel: 39-363-350351   Fax: 39-363-54458

KAYDON CORPORATION

315 E. Eisenhower Pkwy., Ste. 300, Ann Arbor, MI, 48108-3330

Tel: (734) 747-7025 Fax: (734) 747-6565 www.kaydon.com

Design/mfr. custom engineered products: bearings, rings, seals, etc.

Magi S.R.L, Milan, Italy

Tel: 39-02-551-94708

A.T. KEARNEY INC.

5400 Legacy Dr., Plano, TX, 75201

Tel: (972) 604-4600 Fax: (972) 543-7680 www.atkearney.com

Management consultants and executive search.

A. T. Kearney SpA, Corso Venezia 34/36, I-20121 Milan, Italy

Tel: 39-02-76-2951

KEITHLEY INSTRUMENTS INC.

28775 Aurora Road, Cleveland, OH, 44139

Tel: (440) 248-0400 Fax: (440) 248-6168 www.keithley.com

Mfr. electronic test/measure instruments, PC-based data acquisition hardware/software.

Keithley Instruments SRL, Viale S. Gimignano 38, I-20146 Milan, Italy

KELLOGG BROWN & ROOT INC.

PO Box 4557, Houston, TX, 77210-4557

Tel: (713) 676-3011 Fax: (713) 676-8695 www.halliburton.com

Engaged in technology-based engineering and construction.

Kellogg Brown & Root/QGPC Project Italy, c/o Snamprogetti, Viale Aleide De Gasperi 16, San Donata, I-20097 Milano, Italy

KELLOGG COMPANY

One Kellogg Square, PO Box 3599, Battle Creek, MI, 49016-3599

Tel: (616) 961-2000 Fax: (616) 961-2871 www.kelloggs.com

Mfr. ready-to-eat cereals and convenience foods.

Kellogg Italia SpA, Attn: Italian Office, One Kellogg Square, PO Box 3599, Battle Creek, MI, 49016-3599

KELLY SERVICES, INC.

999 W. Big Beaver Road, Troy, MI, 48084

Tel: (248) 362-4444 Fax: (248) 244-4154 www.kellyservices.com

Temporary help placement.

Kelly Services Italia S.R.L., Corso Vittorio Emanuele II 30, I-20122 Milan, Italy

Tel: 39-02-762-351 Fax: 39-02-762-3551

THE KENDALL COMPANY TYCO HEALTHCARE

15 Hampshire Street, Mansfield, MA, 02048

Tel: (508) 261-8000 Fax: (508) 261-8542 www.kendallhq.com

Mfr. and markets a broad range of wound care, needles and syringes, electrodes, specialized paper, vascular therapy, urological care, incontinence care, and nursing care products.

Meditec-Kendall Italia, Via Michelli 16, I-43056 San Polo di Torrile, Italy

Tel: 39-052-1813-488 Fax: 39-052-1813-842

KENDLE INTERNATIONAL INC.

1200 Carew Tower, 441 Vine Street, Cincinnati, OH, 45202

Tel: (513) 381-5550 Fax: (513) 381-5870 www.kendle.com

Provides contract research and development services.

Kendle International, Vicolo del Caldo 36, I-21047 Saronno, Italy

Tel: 39-02-961-9921 Fax: 39-02-96-707-422

KENNAMETAL INC.

1600 Technology Way, PO Box 231, Latrobe, PA, 15650

Tel: (724) 539-5000   Fax: (724) 539-4710   www.kennametal.com

Tools, hard carbide and tungsten alloys for metalworking industry.

Kennametal Ca. Me. S. S.p.A., I-20141 Milan, Italy

Tel: 39-02-8951-1508   Fax: 39-02-832-1456

Kennametal Hertel S.p.A., Via Corrado 11 Salico 50, I-20141 Milan, Italy

Tel: 39-02-895961   Fax: 39-02-500672

KIMBERLY-CLARK CORPORATION

351 Phelps Drive, Irving, TX, 75038

Tel: (972) 281-1200   Fax: (972) 281-1435   www.kimberly-clark.com

Mfr./sales/distribution of consumer tissue, household and personal care products.

Kimberly-Clark SpA, Villanovetta, Italy

KINETIC CONCEPTS, INC.

8023 Vantage Drive, San Antonio, TX, 78230-4728

Tel: (210) 524-9000   Fax: (210) 255-4524   www.KCI1.com

Mfr. specialized medical beds.

KCI Medical, Via Albert Einstein, 6, I-20090 Assagd Milan, Italy

KLA-TENCOR CORPORATION

160 Rio Robles, San Jose, CA, 95134

Tel: (408) 875-6000   Fax: (408) 875-3030   www.kia-tencor.ocm

Mfr. software and equipment.

KLA-Tencor Italy SRL, S.S. Padana Superiore 2 B, Cernusco sul Naviglio, I-20036 Milan, Italy

Tel: 39-02-9244301

KOCH-GLITSCH, INC.

4111 E. 37th Street North, Wichita, KS, 67220

Tel: (316) 828-5110   Fax: (316) 828-5263   www.koch-glitsch.com

Engaged in mass transfer, mist elimination, and motionless mixer technology.

Koch-Glitsch Italy, SS 148 Pontina KM 52, Casella Postale 7, I-04010 Campoverde di Aprilia, Italy

Tel: 39-06-928-911   Fax: 39-06-925-3134

Koch-Glitsch Italy, Via Tonale 50, Casella Postale 3, Albano S., I-24061 Alessandro Bergamo, Italy

Tel: 39-035-328-611   Fax: 39-035-328-600   Contact: Urban Monsch, Pres.

Koch-Glitsch Italy, Piazza Duca d'Aosta 14, I-20124 Milan, Italy

Tel: 39-02-6698-1623   Fax: 39-06-925-3134

KORN/FERRY INTERNATIONAL

1800 Century Park East, Los Angeles, CA, 90067

Tel: (310) 843-4100   Fax: (310) 553-6452   www.kornferry.com

Engaged in executive search and management consulting.

Korn/Ferry International, Sala dei Longobardi 2, I-20121 Milan, Italy

Tel: 39-02-806001   Fax: 39-02-80600-500

Korn/Ferry International, Via Nicolo Tartaglia 11, I-00197 Rome, Italy

Tel: 39-06-80-68-7090   Fax: 39-06-807-3380

KPMG CONSULTING INC.

1676 International Dr., McLean, VA, 22102

Tel: (703) 747-3000   Fax: (703) 747-8500   www.kpmg.com

Accounting and audit, tax and management consulting services.

KPMG Consulting SpA, Via Carlo Alberto 65, I-10123 Turin, Italy

KPMG Fides Fiduciaria SpA, Via Ettore Petrolini 2, I-00197 Rome, Italy

KPMG International, Via G. Porzio, Edif. F.10, I-80143 Centro Direzionale Napoli, Italy

KPMG International, Piazza della Repubblica 15, I-60121 Ancona, Italy

Tel: 39-07-12070-374   Fax: 39-07-12070-378   Contact: Stefano Bandini, Sr. Ptnr.

KPMG International, Piazza della Vittoria 10/7, Genoa, Italy

KPMG International, Piazza Castelnuovo 12, I-90141 Palermo, Italy

KPMG International, Corsa Italia 2, I-50123 Florence, Italy

KPMG International, Viale Aldo Moro 64, I-40127 Bologna, Italy

KPMG International, Via Abate Gemma 30, I-70121 Bari, Italy

KPMG International, Via Vittor Pisani 25, I-20124 Milan, Italy

Tel: 39-02-67631   Fax: 39-02-6763-2445   Contact: Giorgio Loli, Ptnr.

Studio Associato, Corso Cavour 39, I-37121 Verona, Italy

KROLL INC.

9023 Columbine Road, Eden Prairie, MN, 55347

Tel: (952) 937-1107   Fax: (952) 937-5815   www.knollworldwide.com

Mfr. of software and engaged in data recovery services.

Kroll Inc., Fiori Oscuri 11, I-20121 Milan, Italy

Tel: 39-02-8699-8088 Fax: 39-02-890-0138

KULICKE & SOFFA INDUSTRIES INC.

2101 Blair Mill Road, Willow Grove, PA, 19090

Tel: (215) 784-6000   Fax: (215) 659-7588   www.kns.com

Semiconductor assembly systems and services.

Electron Mec, S.r.l., Via Negroli 51, I-20133 Milan, Italy

KURT SALMON ASSOCIATES (KSA)

1355 Peachtree Street NE, Atlanta, GA, 30309

Tel: (404) 892-0321   Fax: (404) 898-9590   www.kurtsalmon.com

Management consulting: consumer products, retailing.

Kurt Salmon Associates SRL, Via Sporting Mirasole 2, Noverasco di Opera, I-20090 Milan, Italy

LAM RESEARCH CORPORATION

4650 Cushing Pkwy., Fremont, CA, 94538

Tel: (510) 659-0200   Fax: (510) 572-6454   www.lamrc.com

Mfr. semiconductor processing equipment.

Lam Research Srl, c/o BIC Sicilia, Zona Industriale Pantano d'Arci, Contrada Torre Allegra, I-95030 Catania, Italy

Tel: 39-095-7357303 Fax: 39-095-7357328

LANDOR ASSOCIATES

Klamath House, 1001 Front Street, San Francisco, CA, 94111-1424

Tel: (415) 955-1400   Fax: (415) 365-3190   www.landor.com

International marketing consulting firm, engaged in brand strategy, design, naming, digital branding, print literature design and research services.

Landor Associates, Piazza Eleonora Duse 2, I-20122 Milan, Italy

Tel: 39-02-7601-2601   Fax: 39-02-7601-2596   Contact: Antonio Marazza

LANIER WORLDWIDE, INC.

2300 Parklake Drive, N.E., Atlanta, GA, 30345

Tel: (770) 496-9500   Fax: (770) 938-1020   www.lanier.com

Specialize in digital copiers and multi-functional systems.

Lanier Italia S.p.A., Via E. Vittorini 129, I-00144 Rome, Italy

Tel: 39-06-501-4304   Fax: 39-06-501-7703

Lanier Italia S.p.A., Via Cassanese 100, I-20090 Segrate Milan, Italy

Tel: 39-02-216-041   Fax: 39-02-216-04444

Lanier Italia S.p.A., Via Posillipo 203-Parco Ruffo, I-80122 Napoli, Italy

Tel: 39-08-1575-1692   Fax: 39-08-1575-1917

LEAR CORPORATION

21557 Telegraph Road, Southfield, MI, 48086-5008

Tel: (248) 746-1500   Fax: (248) 746-1722   www.lear.com

Mfr. and distribute automotive materials and car seats.

Lear Corporation, Torino, Italy

LECROY CORPORATION

700 Chestnut Ridge Road, Chestnut Ridge, NY, 10977

Tel: (845) 425-2000   Fax: (845) 425-8967   www.lecroy.com

Mfr. signal analyzers and electronic measurement systems.

LeCroy S.A., Centro Direzionale, Valecenter Office Via E Mattei 1/102, I-30020 Marcon Venice, Italy

LEGATO SYSTEMS, INC.

2350 West El Camino Real, Mountain View, CA, 94040

Tel: (650) 210-7000   Fax: (650) 210-7032   www.legato.com

Mfr. storage management software.

Legato Systems, Via Colleoni, Palazzo Pegaso Entrance 3, Agrate Brianza, Milan, Italy

LEHMAN BROTHERS HOLDINGS INC.

*101 Hudson Street, Jersey City, NJ, 07302

Tel: (201) 524-2000   Fax: (201) 524-2000   www.lehman.com

Financial services, securities and merchant banking services.

Lehman Brothers, Piazza Del Carmine 4, I-20121 Milan, Italy

Tel: 39-02-721581

LEVI STRAUSS & COMPANY

1155 Battery St., San Francisco, CA, 94111-1230

Tel: (415) 544-6000   Fax: (415) 501-3939   www.levistrauss.com

Mfr. and distributor of casual wearing apparel, including jeans and sportswear.

Levi Strauss Italia SpA, Corso Como Nr. 15, I-20154 Milan, Italy

Tel: 39-02-290231   Fax: 39-02-290-3681

LEVOLOR KIRSCH, DIV. LEVOLOR HARDWARE

4110 Premier Drive, High Point, NC, 27265

Tel: (336) 812-8181   Fax: (336) 659-5614   www.kirsch.com

Mfr. drapery hardware and accessories, wood shelving, woven wood shades, etc.

Cooper Industries Italia, Via Roma 108, Centro Direzional Lombardo, Palazo B/1, I-20060 Cassina de Pecchi Milan, Italy

ELI LILLY & COMPANY

Lilly Corporate Center, Indianapolis, IN, 46285

Tel: (317) 276-2000   Fax: (317) 277-6579   www.lilly.com

Mfr. pharmaceuticals and animal health products.

Eli Lilly Italia SpA, Via Gramsci 731-733, Sesto Fiorentino, I-50019 Florence, Italy

Tel: 39-055-42571   Fax: 39-055-4257-707

LINCOLN ELECTRIC HOLDINGS

22801 St. Clair Ave., Cleveland, OH, 44117-1199

Tel: (216) 481-8100   Fax: (216) 486-8385   www.lincolnelectric.com

Mfr. arc welding and welding related products, oxy-fuel and thermal cutting equipment and integral AC motors.

Lincoln Electric - EWS, Via Degh Artigram, I-17015 Celle Ligure Genoa, Italy

Tel: 39-010-998981   Fax: 39-019-9910978   Contact: Giovanni Pedrazzo, Mng. Dir.

Lincoln Electric - Sacit, Via Carlo Torre 23/27, I-20143 Milan, Italy

Tel: 39-02-832-3741   Fax: 39-02-832-2688   Contact: Roberto Tavecchio, Mng. Dir.

Lincoln Electric Italia SRL, Via Gelasio Adamoli 239 b/c, I-16141 Genoa, Italy

Tel: 39-010-835-5507   Fax: 39-010-835-5050   Contact: Giovanni Pedrazzo, Mng. Dir.

LNP ENGINEERING PLASTICS

475 Creamery Way, Exton, PA, 19341

Tel: (610) 363-4500   Fax: (610) 363-4749   www.geplastics.com

Mfr. thermoplastic composites.

General Electric Plastics, Viale Brianza, 181, I-20092 Cinisello Balsamo, Milan, Italy

LOCKHEED MARTIN CORPORATION

6801 Rockledge Drive, Bethesda, MD, 20817

Tel: (301) 897-6000   Fax: (301) 897-6652   www.imco.com

Design/mfr./management systems in fields of space, defense, energy, electronics and technical services.

CalComp S.p.A., Viale Masini 20, I-40126 Bologna, Italy

Tel: 39-051-352-540   Fax: 39-051-369-711

CalComp S.p.A., Via del Tulipani 5, I-20090 Pieve Emanuele Milan, Italy

Tel: 39-02-907-81519   Fax: 39-02-268-62616

CalComp S.p.A., Via Thailandia, I-00144 Rome, Italy

Tel: 39-06-591-4402   Fax: 39-06-591-2768

Lockheed Martin Intl., Via Fillungo 107, I-55100 Lucca, Italy

LORAL SPACE & COMMUNICATIONS LTD.

600 Third Ave., New York, NY, 10016

Tel: (212) 697-1105   Fax: (212) 338-5662   www.loral.com

Marketing coordination: defense electronics, communications systems.

Loral CyberStar, Via Conservatorio 22, I-20122 Milan, Italy

Tel: 39-02-77-29293

LORD CORPORATION

2000 West Grandview Blvd, Erie, PA, 16514

Tel: (814) 868-0924   Fax: (814) 486-4345   www.lordcorp.com

Mfg. adhesives, coatings, chemicals, film products.

Lord Metal Gomma, Via Moscatello 64 - Fraz., I-46040 Castellaro di Monzambano, Italy

Tel: 39-0376-88819   Fax: 39-0376-88919

LSB INDUSTRIES INC.

16 S. Pennsylvania Ave., Oklahoma City, OK, 73107

Tel: (405) 235-4546   Fax: (405) 235-5067   www.lsbindustries.com

Mfr. sells chemicals and climate control products.

LSB Europe Ltd., Via Vittor Pisani 14, I-20124 Milan, Italy

Tel: 39-02-6698-4785   Fax: 39-02-6698-2082

LSI LOGIC CORPORATION

1551 McCarthy Blvd., Milpitas, CA, 95035

Tel: (408) 433-8000   Fax: (408) 954-3220   www.lsilogic.com

Develop and manufacture semiconductors.

LSI Logic S.p.A., Centro Direzionale Colleoni Palazzo Orione, Ingresso 1, I-20041 Agrate Brianza Milan, Italy

Tel: 39-039-687371   Fax: 39-039-605-7867

LTX CORPORATION

LTX Park, University Ave., Westwood, MA, 02090

Tel: (617) 461-1000   Fax: (617) 326-4883   www.ltx.com

Design/mfr. computer-controlled semiconductor test systems.

LTX (Italia) SRL, Centro Colleoni, Palazzo Cassiopea-Scala 1, Italy

Tel: 39-605-8080   Fax: 39-605-6416

THE LUBRIZOL CORPORATION

29400 Lakeland Blvd., Wickliffe, OH, 44092-2298

Tel: (440) 943-4200   Fax: (440) 943-5337   www.lubrizol.com

Mfr. chemicals additives for lubricants and fuels.

Lubrizol Italiana SpA, Milan, Italy

Tel: 39-02-269761

LUCENT TECHNOLOGIES, INC.

600 Mountain Ave., Murray Hill, NJ, 07974-0636

Tel: (908) 582-3000   Fax: (908) 582-2576   www.lucent.com

Design/mfr. wide range of public and private networks, communication systems and software, data networking systems, business telephone systems and microelectronics components.

Lucent Technologies Italia S.p.A., Viale Fulvio Testi 117, I-20092 Cinisell Balsamo, Italy

Tel: 39-02-660-8131   Fax: 39-02-612-7005

Lucent Technologies Italia S.p.A., 56 Via Tucidide, Torre 2, I-20134 Milan, Italy

Tel: 39-02-754-1161

Lucent Technologies Italia S.p.A., Via Aurelia 866, I-00165 Rome, Italy

Tel: 39-06-664961

Lucent Technologies Italia S.p.A., Via Nazario Sauro 38, I-20099 Sesto S. Giovanno Milan, Italy

Tel: 39-02-262931

LYONDELL CHEMICAL COMPANY

1221 McKinney St., Houston, TX, 77010

Tel: (713) 652-7200   Fax: (713) 309-2074   www.lyondell.com

Mfr. polymers and petrochemicals.

Lyondell Chemcial Italia S.r.l., Via Torino 2, I-20123 Milan, Italy

M/A-COM INC.

1011 Pawtucket Boulevard, Lowell, MA, 01853-3295

Tel: (978) 442-5000   Fax: (978) 442-5354   www.macom.com

Mfr. radio frequency (RF) and microwave integrated circuits and IP Networks to the wireless telecommunications and defense-related industries.

M/A-COM Ltd., Div. Tyco, Centro Direzionale Colleoni, Palazzo Taurus, Scala 2, Viale Colleoni N. 3, I-20041 Agrate Brianza Milan, Italy

Tel: 39-039-6091436   Fax: 39-039-6091502

M/A-COM Ltd., Div. Tyco, Via Dei Luxardo 37, I-00156 Rome, Italy

Tel: 39-06-412-10242   Fax: 39-06-412-10227

MacDERMID INC.

245 Freight Street, Waterbury, CT, 06702-0671

Tel: (203) 575-5700   Fax: (203) 575-7900   www.macdermid.com

Chemicals processing for metal industrial, plastics, electronics cleaners, strippers.

MacDermid Italiana SRL, Via. A. Machieraldo 21, I-13042 Cavaglia Vercelli, Italy

Tel: 39-01-61-966721   Fax: 39-0161-966740

MAGNETEK

10900 Wilshire Blvd., Suite 850, Los Angeles, CA, 90024

Tel: (310) 208-1980   Fax: (310) 208-6133   www.magnetek.com

Mfr. fractional horsepower electric motors.

MagneTek Power, Valdarno, Italy

MAGNETROL INTERNATIONAL

5300 Belmont Road, Downers Grove, IL, 60515-4499

Tel: (630) 969-4000   Fax: (630) 969-9489   www.magnetrol.com

Mfr. level and flow instrumentation.

Magnetrol International, Via Arese 12, I-20159 Milan, Italy

Tel: 39-02-607-2298   Fax: 39-02-27001960   Contact: Carlo Mariani, Sales Mgr.

MALLINCKRODT BAKER, INC.

222 Red School Lane, Phillipsburg, NJ, 08865

Tel: (908) 859-2151   Fax: (908) 859-9318   www.mallbaker.com

Mfr. of high purity chemicals and related products and services.

Mallinckrodt Baker Italia, Via P. Portaluppi 11/2, I-20138 Milan, Italy

Tel: 39-02-580891   Fax: 39-02-58019264

MALLINCKRODT PHARMACUTICALS, INC.

675 McDonnell Blvd., Hazelwood, MO, 63042

Tel: (314) 654-2000 Fax: (314) 654-5380 www.mallinckrodt.com

Mfr. products for respiratory care.

Mallinckrodt Italia SRL, Via Edison 6, I-20090 Assago Milan, Italy

Tel: 39-02-4577161 Fax: 39-02-45706239

MANPOWER INTERNATIONAL INC.

5301 N. Ironwood Rd., PO Box 2053, Milwaukee, WI, 53201-2053

Tel: (414) 961-1000 Fax: (414) 961-7081 www.manpower.com

Temporary help, contract service, training and testing.

Manpower Italia SRL, Via Baracchini 9, I-20123 Milan, Italy

Tel: 39-02-7200-1663 Fax: 39-02-7200-1666

MARK IV INDUSTRIES INC.

501 John James Audubon Pkwy., PO Box 810, Amherst, NY, 14226-0810

Tel: (716) 689-4972 Fax: (716) 689-1529 www.mark-iv.com

Mfr. of engineered systems and components utilizing mechanical and fluid power transmission, fluid transfer, and power systems and components.

Dayco Europe SpA, Strade Cebrosa 70, I-10036 Settimo Torinese, Italy

Tel: 39-011-816-2311

Dayco Europe SpA, Via Torino 71, 1-10060 Airasca, Italy

Tel: 39-011-986-861 Fax: 39-011-986-8723

MARKEM CORPORATION

150 Congress Street, Keene, NH, 03431

Tel: (603) 352-1130 Fax: (603) 357-1835 www.markem.com.

Mfr. and sales of industrial marking, print machinery and hot stamping foils.

Markem SRL, Frazione Venina 7, I-20090 Assago Milan, Italy

Tel: 39-02-892-2041 Fax: 39-02-895-1159

MARLEY COOLING TOWER COMPANY

7401 West 129th Street, Overland Park, KS, 66213

Tel: (913) 664-7400 Fax: (913) 664-7641 www.marleyct.com

Cooling and heating towers and waste treatment systems.

SPIG International S.P.A., Piazza San Graziano 2, I-28041 Arona, Italy

Tel: 39-0322-233456 Fax: 39-0322-233458

MARSH & McLENNAN COS INC.

1166 Ave. of the Americas, New York, NY, 10036-2774

Tel: (212) 345-5000 Fax: (212) 345-4808 www.marshmac.com

Insurance agents/brokers, pension and investment management consulting services.

J&H Marsh & McLennan Italia & Co. SpA, Via Turazza 30, I-35128 Padova, Italy

Tel: 39-049-828-5411 Fax: 39-049-828-5430 Contact: Loris Fasolato

J&H Marsh & McLennan Italia & Co. SpA, Via Cavour1, I-10123 Torino, Italy

Tel: 39-011-156-5471 Fax: 39-011-154-2215 Contact: Emanuele Cordero di Vonzo

J&H Marsh & McLennan Italia & Co. SpA, Via Del Porto 1, I-40122 Bologna, Italy

Tel: 39-051-124-9900 Fax: 39-051-124-8657 Contact: Maurizio Vaghi

J&H Marsh & McLennan Italia & Co. SpA, Viale della Liberazione 18, I-20124 Milan, Italy

Tel: 39-02-669-9981 Fax: 39-02-669-6333 Contact: Irelio Offman

J&H Marsh & McLennan Italia & Co. SpA, Piazza G. Marconi 25, I-00144 Rome, Italy

Tel: 39-06-654-5161 Fax: 39-06-591-9718 Contact: Vincenzo Albini

MASCO CORPORATION

21001 Van Born Road, Taylor, MI, 48180

Tel: (313) 274-7400 Fax: (313) 374-6666 www.masco.com

Mfr. faucets, cabinets, locks and numerous home improvement, building and home furnishings products.

Keoma SRL, Z.I. Sant' Andrea, I-34170 Gorizia, Italy

Rubinetterie Mariani SpA, Via Berlino 2/4, I-24040 Zingonia Bergamo, Italy

S.T.S.R. (Studio Tecnico Sviluppoee Ricerche), Via Delli Artigianato N. 3, I-20084 Lacchiarella Milan, Italy
Tel: 39-02-9007-6832

Systema S.r.l., Via S. Martino, 17/23, I- S. Giustina in Colle (PD), Italy

MATRIXONE, INC.

210 Littleton Road, Westford, MA, 01886

Tel: (978) 589-4000   Fax: (978) 589-5700   www.matrixone.com

Mfr. software.

MatrixOne, Via Grosio 10/10, I-20151 Milan, Italy

MATTEL INC.

333 Continental Blvd., El Segundo, CA, 90245-5012

Tel: (310) 252-2000   Fax: (310) 252-2179   www.mattel.com

Mfr. toys, dolls, games, crafts and hobbies.

Fisher-Price SRL, Via Cassanese 224, I-20090 Segrate, Italy

Mattel Mfg. Europe SRL, Via Vittorio Veneto 119, I-28040 Oleggio Castello Piemonte, Italy

GEORGE S. MAY INTERNATIONAL COMPANY

303 S Northwest Hwy., Park Ridge, IL, 60068-4255

Tel: (847) 825-8806   Fax: (847) 825-7937   www.georgesmay.com

Engaged in management consulting.

George S. May International, Centro Direzionale Colleoni, Palazzo Orio 1, I-20041 Agrate Brianza Milan, Italy
Contact: Daniel Hostetler, Mng. Dir.

McCANN-ERICKSON WORLDGROUP

750 Third Ave., New York, NY, 10017

Tel: (212) 697-6000   Fax: (212) 984-3575   www.mccann.com

International advertising and marketing services.

McCann-Erickson Italiana SpA, Via Meravegli 2, I-20123 Milan, Italy

McCann-Erickson Italiana SpA, La Ferratella, Via Elio Vittorini 129, I-00144 Rome, Italy

Universal McCann SRL, Via Bassano Parrone 6, I-20123 Milan, Italy

McDONALD'S CORPORATION

McDonald's Plaza, Oak Brook, IL, 60523

Tel: (630) 623-3000   Fax: (630) 623-7409   www.mcdonalds.com

Fast food chain stores.

McDonald's Corp., Milan, Italy

THE McGRAW-HILL COMPANIES

1221 Avenue of the Americas, New York, NY, 10020

Tel: (212) 512-2000   Fax: (212) 512-2703   www.mccgraw-hill.com

Books, magazines, information systems, financial service, publishing and broadcast operations.

McGraw-Hill Libri Italia, s.r.l., Piazza Emila 5, I-20129 Milan, Italy

McKINSEY & COMPANY

55 East 52nd Street, New York, NY, 10022

Tel: (212) 446-7000   Fax: (212) 446-8575   www.mckinsey.com

Management and business consulting services.

McKinsey & Company, Piazza del Duomo 31, I-20122 Milan, Italy
Tel: 39-02-724-061   Fax: 39-02-7200-1440

McKinsey & Company, Viale Liegi 44, I-00198 Rome, Italy
Tel: 39-06-85-7981   Fax: 39-06-841-5287

MECHANICAL DYNAMICS, INC.

2300 Traverwood Drive, Ann Arbor, MI, 48105

Tel: (734) 994-3800   Fax: (734) 994-6418   www.adams.com

Mfr. Adams prototyping software for functional virtual prototyping solutions.

Mechanical Dynamics Italy Srl, Via Onorato Vigliani 25/4, I-10137 Torino, Italy

Tel: 39-011-316-1412

Mechanical Dynamics Italy Srl, Via Palladio 98, I-33010 Tavagnacco, Italy

Tel: 39-0432-573942

MEDIA 100 INC.

450 Donald Lynch Blvd., Marlborough, MA, 01752

Tel: (508) 460-1600   Fax: (508) 481-8627   www.media100.com

Mfr. digital editing software and hardware.

Media 100 S.r.L, Brescia, Italy

MEDICUS GROUP INTERNATIONAL

1675 Broadway, New York, NY, 10019

Tel: (212) 468-3100   Fax: (212) 468-3222   www.medicusgroup.com

Healthcare communications company engaged in professional advertising, sales promotion, global branding and launch planning.

Medicus Intercon S.r.L., Via Correggio 18, I-20149 Milan, Italy

Tel: 39-02-480-611   Contact: Mario Ammirati

Medicus Intercon S.r.L., Viale di Val Fiorita 88, I-00144 Rome, Italy

Tel: 39-02-480-611   Contact: Mario Ammirati

MEDTRONIC, INC.

7000 Central Ave. N.E., Minneapolis, MN, 55432-5604

Tel: (763) 514-4000   Fax: (763) 514-4879   www.medtronic.com

Mfr., sales and service of electrotherapeutic medical devices, specializing in implantable and invasive therapies.

Medtronic Italia SpA, Piazza Duca d'Aosta 12, I-20124 Milan, Italy

MEMC ELECTRONIC MATERIALS, INC.

501 Pearl Drive, St. Peters, MO, 63376

Tel: (636) 474-5500   Fax: (636) 474-5161   www.memc.com

Mfg. and distribution of silicon wafers.

MEMC Electronic Materials, SpA, Viale Gherzi 31, I-28100 Novara, Italy

Tel: 39-0321-334-444   Fax: 39-0321-691-000

MEMC Electronic Materials, SpA, Via Nazionale 59, I-39012 Merano Bolzano, Italy

Tel: 39-0472-333-333   Fax: 39-0473-333-270

MENTOR CORPORATION

201 Mentor Drive, Santa Barbara, CA, 93111

Tel: (805) 879-6000   Fax: (805) 967-7108   www.mentorcorp.com

Mfr. medical devices including breast implants.

Mentor Medical Systems Iberica, S.L., Via Olmetto 7, E-20123 Milan, Italy

Tel: 39-02-880-7761

MERCK & COMPANY, INC.

One Merck Drive, PO Box 100, Whitehouse Station, NJ, 08889-0100

Tel: (908) 423-1000   Fax: (908) 423-2592   www.merck.com

Pharmaceuticals, chemicals and biologicals.

Merck, Sharp & Dohme Italia SpA, Via G. Fabbroni 6, I-00191 Rome, Italy

MERCURY INTERACTIVE CORPORATION

1325 Borregas Ave., Sunnyvale, CA, 94089

Tel: (408) 822-5200   Fax: (408) 822-5300   www.merc-int.com

Mfr. computer software to decipher and eliminate "bugs" from systems.

Mercury Interactive S.r.L., Milanofiori Strada 4, Palazzo A/4, I-20090 Assago, Italy

MERIDIAN BIOSCIENCE INC

3471 River Hills Drive, Cincinnati, OH, 45244

Tel: (513) 271-3700   Fax: (513) 271-3762   www.meridiandiagnostics.com

Develops, manufactures and markets a broad range of disposable diagnostic test kits and related diagnostic products used for the rapid diagnosis of infectious diseases

Meridian Bioscience Europe SRL, Via Del Industrial, 7, Villa Cortese, I-20020 Milan, Italy

Tel: 39-0331-433-636   Contact: Antonio Interno

MERRILL LYNCH & COMPANY, INC.

World Financial Center, 250 Vesey Street, New York, NY, 10281-1332

Tel: (212) 236-1000   Fax: (212) 449-2892   www.ml.com

Security brokers and dealers, investment and business services.

Merrill Lynch Global Markets, Palazzo Borghese, Largo Fontanella di Borghese, 19, I-00186 Rome, Italy

Tel: 39-06-683-931

Merrill Lynch International Bank, Via Manzoni 31, I-20121 Milan, Italy

Tel: 39-02-290-02663   Fax: 39-02-290-00384

META GROUP, INC.

208 Harbor Drive, PO Box 120061, Stamford, CT, 06912-0061

Tel: (203) 973-6700   Fax: (203) 359-8066   www.metagroup.com

Engaged in research and consulting, focusing on information technology and business transformation strategies.

META Group, Via Melchiorre Gioia 64, I-20125 Milan, Italy

METROLOGIC INSTRUMENTS, INC.

90 Coles Road, Blackwood, NJ, 08012

Tel: (856) 225-8100   Fax: (856) 228-6673   www.metrologic.com

Mfr. and sales of hologram based, bar code scanner systems.

Metrologic Instruments Italia SRL, Via Emilia 70, I-40064 Ozzano dell'Emilia (BO), Italy

METRON TECHNOLOGY

1350 Old Bayshore Highway, Ste. 210, Burlingame, CA, 94010

Tel: (650) 401-4600   Fax: (650) 373-1135   www.metrontech.com

Global provider of marketing, sales, service and support solutions to semiconductor materials and equipment suppliers and semiconductor manufacturers.

Metron Technology, Via per Ornago, I-20040 Bellusco, Milan, Italy

Tel: 39-039-627 41-1   Fax: 39-039-627 41-200

M-I

PO Box 48242, Houston, TX, 77242-2842

Tel: (713) 739-0222   Fax: (713) 308-9503   www.midf.com

Developer, manufacturer and marketer of drilling and completion fluids and services.

M-I Italliana, S.p.A., Viale Famagosta 75, I-20142 Milan, Italy

Tel: 39-02-89515401   Fax: 39-02-89516993

MICROCHIP TECHNOLOGY INCORPORATED

2355 West Chandler Boulevard, Chandler, AZ, 85224

Tel: (602) 786-7200   Fax: (602) 899-9210   www.microchip.com

Mfr. electronic subassemblies and components.

Arizona Microchip Technology SRL, Centro Direzionale Colleoni, Palazzo Tauru 1, I-20041 Agrate Brianza Milan, Italy

Tel: 39-039-689-9939   Fax: 39-039-689-9883

MICROMERITICS INSTRUMENT CORPORATION

One Micromeritics Drive, Norcross, GA, 30093-1877

Tel: (770) 662-3620   Fax: (770) 662-3696   www.micromeritics.com

Mfr. analytical instruments.

Micromeritics SRL, Via W. Tibagi 26/7, I-20068 Peschiera Borromeo Milan, Italy

Tel: 39-2-553-02833

MICROMUSE INC.
139 Townsend Street, San Francisco, CA, 94107
Tel: (415) 538-9090   Fax: (415) 538-9091   www.micromuse.com
Mfr. software for information technology.
Micromuse Ltd., Via Giovanni da Udine, 34, I-20156 Milan, Italy

MICRON TECHNOLOGY, INC.
8000 S. Federal Way, Boise, ID, 83707-0006
Tel: (208) 368-4000   Fax: (208) 368-4435   www.micron.com
Mfr. random-access memory chips and semi-conductor memory components.
Micron Technology Italy, S.R.L., Via Antonia Pacinotti 5/7, Nuclco Industrial, AQ , Building #2, I-67051 Avezzano (AQ), Italy
Tel: 39-0863-4231   Fax: 39-0863-4231

MICROSOFT CORPORATION
One Microsoft Way, Redmond, WA, 98052-6399
Tel: (425) 882-8080   Fax: (425) 936-7329   www.microsoft.com
Computer software, peripherals and services.
Microsoft Italy SpA, Centro Direzionale San Felice, Via Rivoltana 13m, Palazzo A, I-20090 Segrate Milan, Italy
Tel: 39-02-703921   Fax: 39-02-703-92020

MICROSTRATEGY INCORPORATED
1861 International Drive, McLean, VA, 22102
Tel: (703) 848-8600   Fax: (703) 848-8610   www.microstrategy.com
Mfr. business intelligence software.
MicroStrategy Italy, Piazza Pio XI, 5, I-20123 Milan, Italy

MILACRON INC.
2090 Florence Ave., Cincinnati, OH, 45206
Tel: (513) 487-5000   Fax: (513) 487-5057   www.milacron.com
Metalworking and plastics technologies.
Gallazzi Macchine S.r.l., Via Tonso 100I, I-15100 Alessandria, Italy
Tel: 39-131-265433   Fax: 39-131-68101   Contact: Dr. Ricardo Gallazzi

MILLER ELECTRIC MFG. COMPANY
1635 W. Spencer Street, Appleton, WI, 54912-1079
Tel: (920) 734-9821   Fax: (920) 735-4125   www.millerwelds.com
Mfr. arc welding machines.
Miller Europe S.R.L, Via Privata Iseo 6/E, I-20098 San Giuliano Milan, Italy
Tel: 39-02-9829-01   Fax: 39-02-9829-0203

MILTON ROY COMPANY
201 Ivyland Road, Ivylan, PA, 18974
Tel: (215) 441-0800   Fax: (215) 293-0468   www.miltonroy.com
Mfr. medical and industry equipment and process control instruments.
Milton Roy, Centro Direzionale Colleoni, Via Paraceiso 16 Ing., 1 Palazzo Andromeda, I-20041 AB Milan, Italy
Tel: 39-3960-56891   Fax: 39-3960-56906   Contact: Enrico Andreoli

MINE SAFETY APPLIANCES COMPANY
121 Gamma Drive, PO Box 426, Pittsburgh, PA, 15230
Tel: (412) 967-3000   Fax: (412) 967-3452   www.msa.net
Safety equipment, industry filters.
MSA Italiana SpA, Caselle Postale 1719, I-20101 Milan, Italy

MINOLTA-QMS INC.

One Magnum Pass, PO Box 81250, Mobile, AL, 36618

Tel: (205) 633-4300   Fax: (205) 633-4866   www.qms.com

Mfr. of high-performance color and monochrome document printing solutions for office automation, electronic publishing, graphic design, and advanced imaging applications.

Minolta-QMS Italy, Via Stephenson 37, I-20157 Milan, Italy

MINTEQ INTERNATIONAL INC.

395 Grove City Road, Slippery Rock, PA, 16057

Tel: (724) 794-3000   Fax: (724) 794-4455   www.mineralstech.com

Mfr./market specialty refractory and metallurgical products and application systems.

MINTEQ Italiana S.p.A., Via Creta 8, I-25124 Brescia, Italy

Tel: 39-030-24-566-1   Fax: 39-030-24-555-20   Contact: D. Rosenberg & G. Felchilcher, Pres. & Mgr.   Emp: 18

MIRANT CORPORATION

1155 Perimeter Center West, Ste. 100, Atlanta, GA, 30338

Tel: (678) 579-5000   Fax: (678) 579-5754   www.mirant.com

Engaged in natural gas and electricity.

Mirant Italia S.r.l., Via Pontaccio 10, I-20120 Milan, Italy

MODINE MANUFACTURING COMPANY

1500 DeKoven Ave., Racine, WI, 53403

Tel: (262) 636-1200   Fax: (262) 636-1424   www.modine.com

Mfr. heat-transfer products.

Modine Manufacturing Co., Milan, Italy

MOLEX INC.

2222 Wellington Court, Lisle, IL, 60532

Tel: (630) 969-4550   Fax: (630) 969-1352   www.molex.com

Mfr. electronic, electrical and fiber optic interconnection products and systems, switches, application tooling.

Molex Inc., Centro Direzionale Lombardo, Palazzo CD1, I-108-20060 Rome, Italy

MONSANTO

800 N. Lindbergh Boulevard, St. Louis, MO, 63167

Tel: (314) 694-1000   Fax: (314) 694-7625   www.monsanto.com

Life sciences company focusing on agriculture, nutrition, pharmaceuticals, health and wellness and sustainable development.

Monsanto Italiana SpA, Via Walter Tobagi 8, I-20068 Peschiera Borromeo Milan, Italy

Tel: 39-02-54-7411   Fax: 39-02-5474-1500

MOODY'S INVESTOR SERVICES, INC.

99 Church St., New York, NY, 10007

Tel: (212) 553-1658   Fax: (212) 553-0462   www.moodys.com

Publishes credit ratings.

Moody's Italia S.r.l., Via Monte di Pieta 21, I-20121 Milan, Italy

Tel: 39-02-86-337-470

MOOG INC.

300 Jamison Road, East Aurora, NY, 14052-0018

Tel: (716) 652-2000   Fax: (716) 687-4471   www.moog.com

Mfr. precision control components and systems.

Moog Italiana SRL, Via dei Tre Corsi, Zona Industriale Sud-D1, I-21046 Malnate, Italy

Moog Microset Srl, Via GB Cacciamali 71, I-25125 Brescia, Italy

J. P. MORGAN CHASE & CO. INC.

270 Park Ave., New York, NY, 10017

Tel: (212) 270-6000   Fax: (212) 622-9030   www.jpmorganchase.com

Provides integrated financial solutions for institutions and individuals worldwide, including asset management, investment banking and commercial banking.

J. P. Morgan Chase & Co., Viale Bertoloni 26B, I-00197 Rome, Italy

Tel: 39-06-808-5655   Fax: 39-06-808-8766

J. P. Morgan Chase & Co., Via Catena 4, I-20121 Milan, Italy

J. P. Morgan Chase & Co., Piazzale Accursio 18, I-20156 Milan, Italy

J. P. Morgan Chase & Co., Piazza Meda 1, I-20121 Milan, Italy

J. P. Morgan Chase & Co., Via Catena 4, I-20121 Milan, Italy

Tel: 39-02-8895-1   Fax: 39-02-8895-2218

MORGAN STANLEY DEAN WITTER & CO.

1585 Broadway, New York, NY, 10036

Tel: (212) 761-4000   Fax: (212) 761-0086   www.msdw.com

Securities and commodities brokerage, investment banking, money management, personal trusts.

Banca Morgan Stanley S.p.A., Corso Venezia 16, I-20121 Milan, Italy

Contact: Carlo Pagliani

MOTION PICTURE ASSN. OF AMERICA

1600 Eye Street, NW, Washington, DC, 20006

Tel: (202) 293-1966   Fax: (202) 293-7674   www.mpaa.org

Motion picture trade association.

Motion Picture Export Assn. of Rome, Via del Tritone 61, Scala D Int. 12, I-00187 Rome, Italy

Tel: 39-06-679-8842   Fax: 39-06-678-8834   Contact: Marc M. Spiegel

MOTOROLA, INC.

1303 East Algonquin Road, Schaumburg, IL, 60196

Tel: (847) 576-5000   Fax: (847) 538-5191   www.motorola.com

Mfr. communications equipment, semiconductors and cellular phones.

Motorola SpA, Centro Milanofiori, Stabile C-2, I-20090 Assago Milan, Italy

Tel: 39-02-82-20-329   Fax: 39-02-82-20350

MRO SOFTWARE, INC.

100 Crosby Drive, Bedford, MA, 01730

Tel: (781) 280-2000   Fax: (781) 280-0207   www.mrosoftware.com

Design/sales of enterprise asset maintenance software.

MRO Software Italia, Via Paolo Veronese 250, I-10148 Torino, Italy

MSC.SOFTWARE CORPORATION

2 MacArthur Place, Santa Ana, CA, 92707

Tel: (714) 540-8900   Fax: (714) 784-4056   www.mscsoftware.com

Develop finite element analysis software used in the field of computer-aided engineering.

MSC.Software, Viale Brigata Bisagno 2/10, I-16129 Geneva, Italy

MSC.Software, Via Emilia, 83, I-20093 Cologno Monzese, Italy

MSC.Software, Via Giannone, 10, I-10121 Torino, Italy

MTS SYSTEMS CORPORATION

14000 Technology Drive, Eden Prairie, MN, 55344-2290

Tel: (612) 937-4000   Fax: (612) 937-4515   www.mts.com

Develop/mfr. mechanical testing and simulation products and services, industry measure and automation instrumentation.

MTS Systems SRL, Corso Cincinnato, 228/b, I-10151 Turin, Italy

Tel: 39-011-4517511   Contact: Adriano Coisson

NATIONAL GYPSUM COMPANY

2001 Rexford Road, Charlotte, NC, 28211

Tel: (704) 365-7300   Fax: (704) 365-7276   www.national-gypsum.com

Mfr. building products and services.

Austin Italia SpA, Milan, Italy

NATIONAL INSTRUMENTS CORPORATION

11550 N. Mopac Expwy., Austin, TX, 78759-3504

Tel: (512) 338-9119   Fax: (512) 794-5794   www.ni.com

Mfr. hardware and graphical software.

National Instruments, Via Anna Kuliscioff, 22, I-20152 Milan, Italy

NATIONAL MACHINERY COMPANY

161 Greenfield St., Tiffin, OH, 44883-2471

Tel: (419) 447-5211   Fax: (419) 447-5299   www.nationalmachinery.com

Mfr. high-speed metal parts forming machines.

National Machinery Company, Bolzano, Italy

Tel: 34-93-301-9510

NATIONAL SERVICE INDUSTRIES INC.

1420 Peachtree Street NE, Atlanta, GA, 30309

Tel: (404) 853-1000   Fax: (404) 853-1211   www.nationalservice.com

Mfr. envelopes and engaged in linen rentals.

Zep Europe, Rome, Italy

NATIONAL STARCH AND CHEMICAL COMPANY

10 Finderne Ave., Bridgewater, NJ, 08807-3300

Tel: (908) 685-5000   Fax: (908) 685-5005   www.nationalstarch.com

Mfr. adhesives and sealants, resins and specialty chemicals, electronic materials and adhesives, food products, industry starch.

National Starch & Chemical SpA, Via Roma 29, Mezzago Milan, Italy

Tel: 39-039-60921   Fax: 39-039-3092201

NAVIGATION TECHNOLOGIES CORPORATION

The Merchandise Mart, Ste. 900, Chicago, IL, 60654

Tel: (312) 894-7000   Fax: (312) 894-7050   www.navtech.com

Mfr. navigation systems for automobiles.

Navigation Technologies S.r.l., Largo Luigi Antonelli 30, I-00145 Rome, Italy

NCR (NATIONAL CASH REGISTER)

1700 South Patterson Blvd., Dayton, OH, 45479

Tel: (937) 445-5000   Fax: (937) 445-7042   www.ncr.com

Mfr. automated teller machines and high-performance stationary bar code scanners.

NCR Milan, Viale Cassala 150/4, I-20153 Milan, Italy

Tel: 39-01-479-04448   Fax: 39-01-479-04011   Contact: Carmelo Leornadis, VP

THE NDP GROUP, INC.

900 West Shore Road, Port Washington, NY, 11050

Tel: (516) 625-0700   Fax: (516) 625-2347   www.npd.com

Engaged in consumer buying research.

NDP Group, Via Bigna, 6, I-20123 Milan, Italy

NETIQ CORPORATION

3553 North First Street, San Jose, CA, 95134

Tel: (408) 856-3000   Fax: (408) 273-0578   www.netiq.com

Mfr. performance management software.

NetIQ, Via Senigallia, 18, I-20161 Milan, Italy

NETMANAGE, INC.

10725 N. De Anza Blvd., Cupertino, CA, 95014

Tel: (408) 973-7171   Fax: (408) 257-6405   www.netmanage.com

Develop and manufacture computer software applications and tools.

NetManage Italia, Via Bisceglie n. 76, I-20152 Milan, Italy

Tel: 39-02-412-5105   Fax: 39-02-412-5121

NETWORK APPLIANCE, INC.

495 E. Java Drive, Sunnyvale, CA, 94089

Tel: (408) 822-6000   Fax: (408) 822-4501   www.netapp.com

Engaged in data storage market equipment.

Network Appliance Italy, Centro Direzionale Torri Bianche, Palazzo Larice, I-20059 Vimercate MI, Italy

Tel: 39-396-858-483

NETWORK ASSOCIATES, INC.

3965 Freedom Circle, Santa Clara, CA, 95054

Tel: (408) 988-3832   Fax: (408) 970-9727   www.networkassociates.com

Designs and produces network security and network management software and hardware.

Network Associates Italia S.r.l., Centro Direzionale Summit, Via Brescia 28, Palazzo D/1, I-20063 Cernusco sul Naviglio Milan, Italy

Tel: 39-02-926-501

NEW HAMPSHIRE BALL BEARINGS INC. (NHBB)

9700 Independence Ave., Chatsworth, CA, 91311-4323

Tel: (818) 407-9300   Fax: (818) 407-9300   www.nhbb.com

Mfr. bearings and bearing assemblies.

NHBB, c/o NMB Italia s.r.l., Via A.Grandi, 39/41, I-20017 Mazzo di Rho (MI), Italy

THE NEW YORK TIMES COMPANY

229 West 43rd Street, New York, NY, 10036-3959

Tel: (212) 556-1234   Fax: (212) 556-7389   www.nytimes.com

Diversified media company including newspapers, magazines, television and radio stations, and electronic information and publishing.

International Herald Tribune (IHT), Via Mecenate 91, I-20138 Milan, Italy

Tel: 39-2-5095-6545

The New York Times Rome Bureau SRL, Corso Victorio Emanuel 2, 154, I-00186 Rome, Italy

NEWELL RUBBERMAID

29 East Stephenson Street, Freeport, IL, 61032-0943

Tel: (815) 235-4171   Fax: (815) 489-8212   www.newellco.com

Mfr. hardware, housewares, and office products.

The Newell Company, Milan, Italy

NEWPORT CORPORATION

1791 Deere Ave., PO Box 19607, Irvine, CA, 92606

Tel: (949) 863-3144   Fax: (949) 253-1800   www.newport.com

Engaged in the design, manufacture and marketing of high-precision components, instruments and integrated systems to the fiber optic communications, semiconductor equipment and aerospace and research markets.

Newport-Micro-Controle, Via G. Pascoli 19, I-20063 Cernusco Sul Naviglio Milan, Italy

Tel: 39-02-924-5518   Fax: 39-02-923-2448   Contact: Franco Pepe, Mgr.

AC NIELSEN COMPANY

177 Broad Street, Stamford, CT, 06901

Tel: (203) 961-3000   Fax: (203) 961-3190   www.acnielsen.com

Engaged in market and consumer research.

D&B Marketing Information Services SpA, Via G. DiVittorio 10, I-20094 Corsico Milan, Italy

NORDSON CORPORATION

28601 Clemens Road, Westlake, OH, 44145-4551

Tel: (440) 892-1580   Fax: (440) 892-9507   www.nordson.com

Mfr. industry application equipment, sealants and packaging machinery.

Nordson Italia S.p.A., Via Dei Gigli 3/b, I-20090 Pieve Emanuele Milan, Italy

Tel: 39-02-90-4691   Fax: 39-02-90782485

NORTEK INC.

50 Kennedy Plaza, Providence, RI, 02903

Tel: (401) 751-1600   Fax: (401) 751-4610   www.nortek-inc.com

Mfr. residential and commercial building products.

Best S.p.A, Fabriano, Italy

Elektromec S.p.A, Montefano, Italy

NORTON ABRASIVES COMPANY

1 New Bond Street, Worcester, MA, 01606

Tel: (508) 795-5000   Fax: (508) 795-5741   www.nortonabrasives.com

Mfr. abrasives for industrial manufacturing.

Christensen Diamond Product Co. SpA, Via Flaminia 160, I-00196 Rome, Italy

Norton SpA, Via per Cesano Boscone 4, I-20094 Corsico Milan, Italy

NOVELL WORLDWIDE

1800 S. Novell Place, Provo, UT, 84606

Tel: (801) 861-7000   Fax: (801) 861-5555   www.novell.com

Develop/mfr. networking software and related equipment.

Novell Italy, Piazza don Mapelli, 75, Edificio U3, Sesto San Giovanni, I-20099 Milan, Italy

NOVEON INTERNATIONAL

9911 Brecksville Road, Cleveland, OH, 44141-3427

Tel: (216) 447-5000   Fax: (216) 447-5669   www.noveoninc.com

Mfr. specialty chemicals.

Noveon Italia S.R.L., Viale Gian Galeazzo, 25, I-20136 Milan, Italy

Tel: 39-02-584-7941

NU SKIN ENTERPRISES, INC.

75 West Center St., Provo, UT, 84601

Tel: (801) 345-6100   Fax: (801) 345-5999   www.nuskin.com

Develops and distributes premium-quality personal care and nutritional products.

NuSkin Italy, Via E. Fermi 44, I-20090 Assago, Italy

OAO TECHNOLOGY SOLUTIONS, INC.

7500 Greenway Center Drive, 16th Fl., Greenbelt, MD, 20770

Tel: (301) 486-0400   Fax: (301) 486-0415   www.oaot.com

Provides information technology services.

OAO Technology Solutions, c/o LaNaia and Partners, Via Aurelio Saffi, 29, I-20123 Milan, Italy

OEO Consorzio, Via Lecco, 6, I-20124 Milan, Italy

THE O'GARA COMPANY

1250 24th Street, NW, Suite 300, Washington, DC, 20037

Tel: (202) 835-1680   Fax: (202) 835-1685   www.ogara.com

Security and consulting services and vehicles.

Kroll-O'Gara, Torino Facility, P. le Principessa Clotilde 8, I-20121 Milan, Italy

Tel: 39-0172-89434   Fax: 39-0172-89434

OGILVY & MATHER WORLDWIDE

309 West 49th Street, New York, NY, 10017-7399

Tel: (212) 237-4000   Fax: (212) 237-5123   www.ogilvypr.com

Engaged in public relations and communications.

Ogilvy One Worldwide S.P.A., Via Lancetti 29, I-20158 Milan, Italy

Tel: 39-02-60789   Contact: Nick May, Pres.

OHAUS CORPORATION

PO Bpx 2033,19a Chapin Road, Pine Brook, NJ, 07058

Tel: (973) 377-9000   Fax: (973) 593-0359   www.ohaus.com

Mfr. balances and scales for laboratories, industry and education.

Ohaus Italian Representative Office, Via Vialba 42, I-20026 Novate Milanese Milan, Italy

Tel: 39-02-33332297

THE OILGEAR COMPANY

2300 S. 51st Street, Milwaukee, WI, 53219

Tel: (414) 327-1700   Fax: (414) 327-0532   www.oilgear.com

Mfr. hydraulic power transmission machinery.

Oilgear Towler SRL, Via Artigianale 23, I-25010 Montirone Brescia, Italy

ONDEO NALCO COMPANY

Ondeo Nalco Center, 1601 W. Diehl Road, Naperville, IL, 60563-1198

Tel: (630) 305-1000   Fax: (630) 305-2900   www.ondeo-nalco.com

Mfr. specialty chemicals for water and waste water treatment, oil products and refining, industry processes; water and energy management service.

ONDEO Nalco Diversified Technologies, Via G. de Notaris 51.5, I-20128 Milan, Italy

Tel: 39-01-158-0322   Fax: 39-01-158-0322

ONDEO Nalco Italiana SpA, Viale dell Esperanto 71, I-00144 Rome, Italy

Tel: 39-06-542-971   Fax: 39-06-542-97300

OPEN MARKET, INC.

1 Wayside Road, Burlington, MA, 01803

Tel: (781) 359-3000   Fax: (781) 359-8111   www.openmarket.com

Mfr. catalog management software.

Open Market Italy Srl, Via Leonardo da Vinci 43, I-20090 Trezzano sul Naviglio Milan, Italy

Tel: 39-02-48409866

OPENWAVE SYSTEMS INC.

1400 Seaport Blvd., Redwood City, CA, 94063

Tel: (650) 480-8000   Fax: (650) 480-8100   www.openwave.com

Mfr. software for wireless telephones.

Openwave Systems, Via della Mercede, No. 37 - First Floor, I-00100 Rome, Italy

OPLINK COMMUNICATIONS, INC.

3469 N. First Street, San Jose, CA, 95134

Tel: (408) 433-0606   Fax: (408) 433-0608   www.oplink.com

Mfr. fiber optic components.

Ligh Tech SRL, Via Angelo Biffi, 3, Trezzo S/Adda, I-20056 Milan, Italy

Tel: 39-2-9096-3287   Fax:
Email   Contact: Carlo Marchesi

ORACLE CORPORATION

500 Oracle Parkway, Redwood Shores, CA, 94065

Tel: (650) 506-7000   Fax: (650) 506-7200   www.oracle.com

Develop/manufacture software.

Oracle Italia/Datamat SpA, Via Laurentina 756, I-00143 Rome, Italy

OSHKOSH TRUCK CORPORATION

2307 Oregon St., Oshkosh, WI, 54902

Tel: (920) 235-9151   Fax: (920) 233-9314   www.oshkoshtruck.com

Mfr. heavy-duty vehicles for commercial industries and defense.

Geesink BV, Centro dir Colleoni, Palazzo Cassiopea, Via Paracelso 22, I-20041 Agrate Brianza (MI), Italy

Contact: R.W Braghieri

OSMONICS INC.

5951 Clearwater Drive, Minnetonka, MN, 55343-8995

Tel: (952) 933-2277   Fax: (952) 933-0141   www.osmonics.com

Mfr. equipment, controls and components for the filtration and water-treatment industries.

Osmonics, Milan, Italy

OTIS ELEVATOR COMPANY

One Farm Springs Road, Farmington, CT, 06032

Tel: (860) 676-6000   Fax: (860) 676-5111   www.otis.com

Mfr. elevators and escalators.

Otis SpA, Via Firenze 11, I-20063 Cernusco sul Naviglio Milan, Italy

OWENS-CORNING CORPORATION

One Owens Corning Pkwy., Toledo, OH, 43659

Tel: (419) 248-8000   Fax: (419) 248-8445   www.owenscorning.com

Mfr. building materials systems and composites systems.

Owens-Corning Alcopor, Strada Settimo 399/11, I-10156 Torino, Italy

Tel: 39-011-223-4411

OWENS-ILLINOIS, INC.

One SeaGate, PO Box 1035, Toledo, OH, 43666

Tel: (419) 247-5000   Fax: (419) 247-2839   www.o-i.com

Mfr. glass containers and packaging products.

AVIR S.p.A., Bari, Italy

Owens-Illinois Inc., Via Montelungo 4, Casella Postale 243, I-56100 Pisa, Italy

PALL CORPORATION

2200 Northern Boulevard, East Hills, NY, 11548-1289

Tel: (516) 484-5400   Fax: (516) 484-5228   www.pall.com

Specialty materials and engineering; filters and related fluid clarification equipment.

Pall Gelman Sciences, Via Gioacchino Murat 84, I-10159 Milan, Italy

Tel: 39-01-690-06109   Fax: 39-02-69-006110

Pall Italia s.r.l., Via G. Bruzzesi 38/40, I-20146 Milan, Italy

Tel: 39-02-47-7961   Fax: 39-02-412-2985

PANAMETRICS

221 Crescent Street, Waltham, MA, 02154

Tel: (781) 899-2719   Fax: (781) 899-1552   www.panametrics.com

Engaged in manufacture and distribution of ultrasonic testing equipment and process control instrumentation.

Panametrics S.r.l., Via Feltre 19/A, I-20132 Milan, Italy

Tel: 39-02-264-2131   Fax: 39-02-26414454   Contact: Emilio Elzi

PANDUIT CORPORATION

17301 Ridgeland Ave., Tinley Park, IL, 60477-0981

Tel: (708) 532-1800   Fax: (708) 532-1811   www.panduit.com

Mfr. of network connectivity and electrical products.

Panduit SAS, Via Como 10, I-20020 Lainate Milan, Italy

PARAMETRIC TECHNOLOGY CORPORATION

140 Kendrick St., Needham, MA, 02494

Tel: (781) 370-5000 Fax: (781) 370-6000 www.ptc.com

Supplier of mechanical design automation and product data management software and services.

Parametric Technology Italy, S.r.l., Viala Colleoni 5, Palazzo Taurus 3, I-20041 Agrate Brianza Milan, Italy

Tel: 39-02-605-7942 Fax: 39-02-605-7931

Parametric Technology Italy, S.r.l., Viale Della Costituzione, Isola E/1, I-80043 Napoli, Italy

Tel: 39-08-15-628535 Fax: 39-08-15-628538

Parametric Technology Italy, S.r.l., Via Grandi 46/C, I-60131 Ancona, Italy

Tel: 39-07-12-901073 Fax: 39-07-12-901137

Parametric Technology Italy, S.r.l., Via Aperanza N. 35/A, I-40068 S. Lazzaro di Savena Bologna, Italy

Tel: 39-051-6279411 Fax: 39-051-453172

Parametric Technology Italy, S.r.l., Brixia Business Ctr. S.R.L., Via Cipro 1, I-25024 Brescia, Italy

Tel: 39-030-295601 Fax: 39-030-295535

Parametric Technology Italy, S.r.l., Via Lisbona 7, I-35135 Padova, Italy

Tel: 39-049-870-1481 Fax: 39-049-870-1479

Parametric Technology Italy, S.r.l., Bat. C-445, Ave. Andre Ampere BP 267000, F-13797 Aix-en-Provence Cedex, France

Tel: 39-04-42-970000 Fax: 39-04-42-970001

Parametric Technology Italy, S.r.l., Centro Polifunzionale Lingotto, Via Nizza 262/42 Torre Sud, I-10126 Torino, Italy

Tel: 39-011-6643211 Fax: 39-011-664-3258

Parametric Technology Italy, S.r.l., Via Filippo Tommaso Marinetti 221, I-00143 Rome, Italy

Tel: 39-06-5028-1229 Fax: 39-06-502-0016

PAREXEL INTERNATIONAL CORPORATION

195 West Street, Waltham, MA, 02154

Tel: (781) 487-9900 Fax: (781) 487-0525 www.parexel.com

Provides contract medical, biotechnology, and pharmaceutical research and consulting services.

PAREXEL International s.r.l., Via Filippo Turati 28, I-20121 Milan, Italy

Tel: 39-02-624-1111 Fax: 39-02-624-11150

PARKER HANNIFIN CORPORATION

6035 Parkland Blvd., Cleveland, OH, 44124-4141

Tel: (216) 896-3000 Fax: (216) 896-4000 www.parker.com

Mfr. motion-control products.

Parker Hannifin SpA, Viale Lombardia 87, I-25031 Capriolo, Italy

Parker Hannifin SpA, Via Privata Archimede 1, I-20094 Corsico Milan, Italy

Parker Hannifin SpA, Cylinder & Pneumatics, Via Carducci 11, I-21010 Arsago Seprio, Italy

Parker Hannifin SpA, Div. SCEM RCD, Via E. Fermi 5, I-20060 Gessate Milan, Italy

P-COM, INC.

3175 South Winchester Blvd., Campbell, CA, 95008

Tel: (408) 866-3666 Fax: (408) 866-3655 www.p-com.com

Mfr. microwave radio transmission equipment.

P-Com Italy, S.S. Per Voghera, Regione Villoria, I-15057 Tortona (AL), Italy

PENTAIR, INC.

1500 County Road, B2 West, St. Paul, MN, 55113-3105

Tel: (612) 636-7920 Fax: (612) 636-5508 www.pentair.com

Diversified manufacturer operating in electrical and electronic enclosures, professional tools/equipment and water products.

SIATA S.r.l., Via Virginio, 370-372, Montespertoli, I-50025 Florence, Italy

Tel: 39-0571-6301

PEOPLESOFT INC.

4460 Hacienda Drive, Pleasanton, CA, 94588-8618

Tel: (925) 225-3000　　Fax: (925) 694-4444　　www.peoplesoft.com

Mfr. applications to manage business operations across computer networks.

PeopleSoft S.r.L., Via Amonte de Pieta 21, I-20121 Milan, Italy

Tel: 39-2-8633-7313

PEREGRINE SYSTEMS, INC.

3611 Valley Centre Drive, San Diego, CA, 92130

Tel: (858) 481-5000　　Fax: (858) 481-1751　　www.peregrine.com

Mfr. resource planning software.

Peregrine Systems S.r.l., Via Mario Bianchini, 47, I-00142 00142, Italy

PFIZER INC.

235 East 42nd Street, New York, NY, 10017-5755

Tel: (212) 573-2323　　Fax: (212) 573-7851　　www.pfizer.com

Research-based, global health care company.

Pfizer Italiana SpA, Via Valbondione 113, I-10018 Rome, Italy

Tel: 39-06-33-182

Roerig Farmaceutici Italiana SRL, Milan, Italy

SudFarma SRL, Milan, Italy

PHARMACIA CORPORATION

100 Route 206 North, Peapack, NJ, 07977

Tel: (908) 901-8000　　Fax: (908) 901-8379　　www.pharmacia.com

Mfr. pharmaceuticals, agricultural products, industry chemicals.

Pharmacia & Upjohn SpA, Via Robert Koch 1 2, I-20152 Milan, Italy

Tel: 39-02-4838-1　Fax: 39-02-4838-2734

PHELPS DODGE CORPORATION

2600 North Central Ave., Phoenix, AZ, 85004-3089

Tel: (602) 234-8100　　Fax: (602) 234-8337　　www.phelpsdodge.com

Copper, minerals, metals and special engineered products for transportation and electrical markets.

Columbia Carbon Europa, San Martino Di Trecate, Italy

Columbian Carbon Europe SRL, 10 Via P. Verri, I-20121 Milan, Italy

PHH ARVAL VEHICLE MANAGEMENT

307 International Circle, Hunt Valley, MD, 21030

Tel: (410) 771-3600　　Fax: (410) 771-2841　　www.phh.com

Provides fleet leasing and fleet management services to corporate and government clients with sales, service, delivery, executive or specialized trucks fleets.

Arvil Service Lease Italia SpA, Milanfiori, Strada 4, Palazzo A2, I-20090 Assago Milan, Italy

Tel: 39-02-892-2071

PHILLIPS PETROLEUM COMPANY

Phillips Building, 411 S. Keeler Ave., Bartlesville, OK, 74004

Tel: (918) 661-6600　　Fax: (918) 661-7636　　www.phillips66.com

Crude oil, natural gas, liquefied petroleum gas, gasoline and petro-chemicals.

Phillips Petroleum Intl. SRL, Via Cavallotti 13, I-20122 Milan, Italy

PIC GROUP

2929 Seventh Avenue, Ste. 130, Berkeley, CA, 94710

Tel: (510) 848-8266　　Fax: (510) 848-0324　　www.pic.com

Engaged in biotechnology.

PIC Italy, Strada dei Loggi 22, I-06087 Ponte San Giovanni Perugia, Italy

PINNACLE WORLDWIDE, INC.

1201 Marquette Ave., Ste. 300, Minneapolis, MN, 55403

Tel: (612) 338-2215 Fax: (612) 338-2572 www.pinnacleww.com

International network of independent public relations firms.

Noesis S.R.L, Via Savona 19/a, I-20144 Milan, Italy

Tel: 39-02-83-1051 Fax: 39-02-83-201161 Contact: Martin Slater, Pres.

PIONEER HI-BRED INTERNATIONAL INC.

400 Locust Street, Ste. 800, Des Moines, IA, 50309

Tel: (515) 248-4800 Fax: (515) 248-4999 www.pioneer.com

Agricultural chemicals, farm supplies, biological products, research.

Pioneer Hi-Bred Italia SpA, Via Provinciale 42/44, I-43018 Sissa, Italy

PIONEER-STANDARD ELECTRONICS, INC.

6065 Parkland Blvd., Cleveland, OH, 44124

Tel: (440) 720-8500 Fax: (440) 720-8501 www.pios.com

Mfr. and distribution of electronic parts for computers and networking equipment.

Eurodis Fanton, Via Melegnano 22, I-20019 Settimo M Milan, Italy

PITNEY BOWES INC.

1 Elmcroft Road, Stamford, CT, 06926-0700

Tel: (203) 356-5000 Fax: (203) 351-6835 www.pitneybowes.com

Mfr. postage meters, mailroom equipment, copiers, bus supplies, bus services, facsimile systems and financial services.

Pitney Bowes Italia Srl., Via Martiri Della Liberta 46, I-20060 Liscate Milan, Italy

Tel: 39-01-9535-1110 Fax: 39-02-9535-1210 Contact: Oscar Parigi, Mng. Dir. Emp: 60

PLANET HOLLYWOOD INTERNATIONAL, INC.

8669 Commodity Circle, Orlando, FL, 32819

Tel: (407) 363-7827 Fax: (407) 363-4862 www.planethollywood.com

Theme-dining restaurant chain and merchandise retail stores.

Planet Hollywood International, Inc., Rome, Italy

PLANTRONICS

345 Encinal Street, Santa Cruz, CA, 95060

Tel: (831) 426-5858 Fax: (831) 425-5198 www.plantronics.com

Mfr. lightweight headsets and communications equipment and electrical and electronic appliances.

Plantronics Acoustics Italia SRL, Palazzo G Via Rome 108, I-20060 Cassina De'Pecchi Milan, Italy

Tel: 39-02-951-1900 Fax: 39-02-951-1903 Contact: Gian Carlo Degortes

PLAYTEX APPAREL INC.

3330 Healy Drive, Winston Salem, NC, 27106

Tel: (336) 519-8688 Fax: (336) 519-6053 www.playtexbras.com

Mfr. intimate apparel.

Playtex Italia SpA, Piazza L. Sturzo 31, I-00144 Rome, Italy

POLAROID CORPORATION

784 Memorial Drive, Cambridge, MA, 02139

Tel: (781) 386-2000 Fax: (781) 386-3924 www.polaroid.com

Photographic equipment and supplies, optical products.

Polaroid Italy, Via Piave, 11, I-21051 Arcisate (Varese), Italy

POLYCOM, INC.

1565 Barber Lane, Milpitas, CA, 95035

Tel: (408) 526-9000 Fax: (408) 526-9100 www.polycom.com

Mfr. video conferencing systems, network bridging and multiplexing products, system peripherals.

Polycom, Inc., Via Cavriana 3, I-20134 Milan, Italy

Tel: 39-02-7391-214 Fax: 39-02-7391-410

POLYONE CORPORATION

200 Public Square, Cleveland, OH, 44114-2304

Tel: (216) 589-4000   Fax: (216) 589-4077   www.polyone.com

Mfr. custom made compounded plastics, including polymer, elastomer, colorant and additive products.

SO.F.TER. SpA (JV), Via Mastro Georgio, 2, I-47100 Forli, Italy
Tel: 39-0943-790411

PORTAL SOFTWARE, INC.

10200 S. De Anza Bolevard, Cupertino, CA, 95014

Tel: (408) 572-2000   Fax: (408) 572-2001   www.portal.com

Mfr. customer management and billing software.

Portal Software, Via Torino 2, Ste. 506, I-20123 Milan, Italy
Portal Software, Largo Tartini 3/4, I-00198 Rome, Italy
Tel: 390-685-203-239   Fax: 390-685-203-622

PPG INDUSTRIES

One PPG Place, Pittsburgh, PA, 15272

Tel: (412) 434-3131   Fax: (412) 434-2190   www.ppg.com

Mfr. coatings, flat glass, fiber glass, chemicals.

Ampaspace SRL, Via Montello 40, I-26010 Casaletto Vaprio Cremona, Italy
PPG Industries Italia SRLe SpA, Via Sera 1, I-15028 Quattoraio, Italy

PRAXAIR, INC.

39 Old Ridgebury Road, Danbury, CT, 06810-5113

Tel: (203) 837-2000   Fax: (203) 837-2450   www.praxair.com

Produces and distributes industrial and specialty gases.

Praxair S.p.A., Via Durini 7, I-20122 Milan, Italy
Tel: 39-02-7600-9110

Rivoira S.p.A., Via Durini 7, I-20122 Milan, Italy
Tel: 39-02-771191   Fax: 39-02-77119600

SAID S.p.A., Via S. Bernardino 92, I-24126 Bergamo, Italy
Tel: 39-035-328-111   Fax: 39-035-315-486

PRECISION VALVE & TRIM, INC.

11923 Cloverland Ave, Baton Rouge, LA, 70809

Tel: (225) 752-5600   Fax: (225) 752-5400   www.precisionvalve.com

Mfr. aerosol valves.

Precision Valve Italia SpA, Via Ravello 1/3, I-20081 Vermezzo Milan, Italy

PRICEWATERHOUSECOOPERS LLP

1301 Ave. of the Americas, New York, NY, 10019

Tel: (212) 596-7000   Fax: (212) 259-1301   www.pwcglobal.com

Accounting and auditing, tax and management, and human resource consulting services.

PriceWaterhouseCoopers, Via Bogino 23, I-10123 Turin, Italy
Tel: 39-011-88081   Fax: 39-011-8395613

PriceWaterhouseCoopers, Via Trieste 31/A, I-35121 Padova, Italy
Tel: 39-049-655222   Fax: 39-049-657814

PriceWaterhouseCoopers, Via Fieschi 3/14, I-16121 Genoa, Italy
Tel: 39-010-530061   Fax: 39-010-593996

PriceWaterhouseCoopers, Via Corridoni 2, I-60123 Ancona, Italy
Tel: 39-07-136881   Fax: 39-07-136623

PriceWaterhouseCoopers, Via Antonio Bosio 22, I-00161 Rome, Italy
Tel: 39-06-44240373   Fax: 39-06-44242098

PriceWaterhouseCoopers, Viale Tanara 20/A, I-43100 Parma, Italy
Tel: 39-052-1242848   Fax: 39-052-1781844

PriceWaterhouseCoopers, Via Del Rione Sirignano 7, I-80121 Naples, Italy
Tel: 39-08-17614100   Fax: 39-08-1667802

PriceWaterhouseCoopers, Corso Europa 2, I-20122 Milan, Italy
Tel: 39-02-77851   Fax: 39-02-7785240

PriceWaterhouseCoopers, Largo Augusto 1/3, I-20122 Milan, Italy
Tel: 39-02-77851   Fax: 39-02-7785402

PriceWaterhouseCoopers, Via Bonifacio Lupi 11, I-50129 Florence, Italy
Tel: 39-055-471747   Fax: 39-055-470779

PriceWaterhouseCoopers, Corso Italia 191, I-70123 Bari, Italy
Tel: 39-080-5793139   Fax: 39-080-5797088

PriceWaterhouseCoopers, Via Vallescura 2, I-40136 Bologna, Italy
Tel: 39-051-334893   Fax: 39-051-330756

PriceWaterhouseCoopers, Via Giovanni Battista de Rossi 32/B, I-00161 Rome, Italy
Tel: 39-06-441921   Fax: 39-06-44244890

PROCTER & GAMBLE COMPANY
One Procter & Gamble Plaza, Cincinnati, OH, 45202
Tel: (513) 983-1100   Fax: (513) 562-4500   www.pg.com
Personal care, food, laundry, cleaning and industry products.

Procter & Gamble Italia SpA, Via Cesare Pavese 385, I-00144 Rome, Italy

PROCTER & GAMBLE PHARMACEUTICALS (P&GP)
17 Eaton Ave., Norwich, NY, 13815-1799
Tel: (607) 335-2111   Fax: (607) 335-2798   www.pg.com
Engaged in research dedicated to creating and delivering solutions that improve the health and well-being of people around the world.

Procter & Gamble SpA, Via Cesare Pavese 385, I-00144 Rome, Italy

PSC INC.
111 SW Fifth Avenue, Ste. 4100, Portland, OR, 97204-3644
Tel: (503) 553-3920   Fax: (503) 553-3940   www.pscnet.com
Mfr. and sales of bar code scanners.

PSC Italy, Centro Torri Bianche, Torre "F" - Palazzo Quercia, Via Torri Bianche, 9, I-20059 Vimercate, Italy

PSI NET (PERFORMANCE SYSTEMS INTERNATIONAL INC.)
44983 Knoll Square, Ashburn, VA, 20147
Tel: (703) 726-4100   Fax: (703) 726-4200   www.psinet.com
Internet service provider.

PSINet Italy, S Giovanni Bosco 15/B, I-25125 Brescia, Italy

PUBLIC SERVICE ENTERPRISE GROUP (PSEG)
80 Park Plaza, Newark, NJ, 07101
Tel: (973) 430-7000   Fax: (973) 623-5389   www.pseg.com
Electric and gas utility.

PSEG Global, c/o Office Point Sr 1, Via Guido D'Arezzo 4, I-20145 Milan, Italy
Tel: 39-02-4855-9415   Fax: 39-02-4855-9307

QAD INC.
6450 Via Real, Carpinteria, CA, 93013
Tel: (805) 684-6614   Fax: (805) 566-4479   www.qad.com
Mfr. software.

QAD Italy, Via Milanese, 20, I-20099 Sesto S. Giovanni (MI), Italy

THE QUAKER OATS COMPANY
Quaker Tower, 321 North Clark Street, Chicago, IL, 60610-4714
Tel: (312) 222-7111   Fax: (312) 222-8323   www.quakeroats.com
Mfr. foods and beverages.

Chiari & Forti, Via Cendon 20, I-31057 Silea Treviso, Italy

Quaker Chiari & Forti SpA, Viale Monterosa 21, I-20149 Milan, Italy

QUINTILES TRANSNATIONAL CORPORATION

4709 Creekstone Dr., Durham, NC, 27703

Tel: (919) 998-2000 Fax: (919) 998-9113 www.quintiles.com

Mfr. pharmaceuticals.

Innovex S.r.l., Centro Direzionale Colleoni, Palazzo Taurus Viale Colleoni 3, I-20041 Agrate Brianza MI, Italy

Quintiles S.r.l., Via Clemente Prudenzio 16, I-20138 Milan, Italy

RADISSON HOTELS INTERNATIONAL

Carlson Pkwy., PO Box 59159, Minneapolis, MN, 55459-8204

Tel: (612) 540-5526 Fax: (612) 449-3400 www.radisson.com

Operates, manages and franchises full-service hotels and resorts worldwide.

Radisson SAS Hotels Italy, Milan, Italy

Tel: 39-0371-410461 Fax: 39-0371-410464

RATIONAL SOFTWARE CORPORATION

18880 Homestead Road, Cupertino, CA, 95014-0721

Tel: (408) 863-9900 Fax: (408) 863-4120 www.rationale.com

Mfr. application development software.

Rational Software, Palazzo Pitagora M13 City, I-20080 Basiglio MI, Italy

RAY & BERNDTSON, INC.

301 Commerce, Ste. 2300, Fort Worth, TX, 76102

Tel: (817) 334-0500 Fax: (817) 334-0779 www.prb.com

Executive search, management audit and management consulting firm.

Ray & Berndtson, Piazza Erculea 11, I-20122 Milan, Italy

Tel: 39-02-72000404 Fax: 39-02-72000389 Contact: Catherine B. Nelson, Mng. Ptnr.

RAYMOND JAMES FINANCIAL, INC.

880 Carillon Parkway, St. Petersburg, FL, 33716

Tel: (813) 573-3800 Fax: (813) 573-8244 www.rjf.com

Financial services; securities brokerage, asset management, and investment banking services.

Raymond James Milan, Via Cerva 25, I-20122 Milan, Italy

Tel: 39-02-76-00-22-31 Fax: 39-02-76-01-44-15 Contact: L. Biasi

RAYOVAC CORPORATION

601 Rayovac Drive, Madison, WI, 53711-2497

Tel: (608) 275-3340 Fax: (608) 275-4577 www.rayovac.com

Mfr. batteries and lighting devices.

Rayovac Italy, Milan, Italy

RAYTHEON COMPANY

141 Spring Street, Lexington, MA, 02173

Tel: (781) 862-6600 Fax: (781) 860-2172 www.raytheon.com

Mfr. diversified electronics, appliances, energy and environmental products; publishing, industry and construction services.

Badger Italiana SRL, Via Vincenzo Monti 51, I-20123 Milan, Italy

READER'S DIGEST ASSOCIATION, INC.

Reader's Digest Rd., Pleasantville, NY, 10570

Tel: (914) 238-1000 Fax: (914) 238-4559 www.readersdigest.com

Publisher of magazines and books and direct mail marketer.

Selezione dal Reader's Digest SpA, Via Alserio 10, I-20159 Milan, Italy

RECOTON CORPORATION

2950 Lake Emma Road, Lake Mary, FL, 32746

Tel: (407) 333-8900 Fax: (407) 333-8903 www.recoton.com

Mfr. electronic accessories and aftermarket products for computers and office equipment.

Recoton Corporation, V.1 Maggio N 18, Quarto Inferiore, Bologna, Italy

Tel: 39-051-768-576 Fax: 39-051-768-366

REEBOK INTERNATIONAL LTD.

1895 J. W. Foster Blvd., Canton, MA, 02021

Tel: (781) 401-5000   Fax: (781) 401-7402   www.reebok.com

Mfr. athletic shoes including casual, dress golf and walking shoes.

Reebok Italia SRL, Viale Enrico Fermi 17, I-20052 Monza Milan, Italy

REFCO GROUP LTD.

200 Liberty Street Tower A, New York, NY, 10281

Tel: (212) 693-7700   Fax: (212) 693-7856   www.refco.com

Commodity and security brokers engaged in the execution and clearing of futures and options and institutional asset management services.

Refco Futures Ltd., Rome, Italy

REFLEXITE TECHNOLOGY

120 Darling Drive, Avon, CT, 06001

Tel: (860) 676-7100   Fax: (860) 676-7199   www.reflexite.com

Mfr. plastic film, sheet, materials and shapes, optical lenses.

Reflexite Italia, Via Giovanni da Udine 34, I-20156 Milan, Italy

Tel: 39-02-380-93415   Fax: 39-02380-93418

REGAL-BELOIT CORPORATION

200 State Street, Beloit, WI, 53512-0298

Tel: (608) 364-8800   Fax: (608) 364-8818   www.regal-beloit.com

Mfr. power transmission equipment, perishable cutting tools.

Costruzioni Meccaniche Legnanesi SRL (CML), Via Del Brugo 5, I-20025 Legnano Milan, Italy

Tel: 39-331-548-847   Fax: 39-331-592-800

REMINGTON PRODUCTS COMPANY, L.L.C.

60 Main Street, Bridgeport, CT, 06604

Tel: (203) 367-4400   Fax: (203) 332-4848   www.remington-products.com

Mfr. home appliances, electric shavers.

Remington Italia S.r.l., Largo Guido Novello, 1/F, I-50126 Firenze, Italy

Tel: 39-055-6800506

REVLON INC.

625 Madison Ave., New York, NY, 10022

Tel: (212) 527-4000   Fax: (212) 527-4995   www.revlon.com

Mfr. cosmetics, fragrances, toiletries and beauty care products.

Revlon SpA, Casella Postale 4128, Via Appia Nuova Km. 17.850, I-00100 Rome, Italy

Contact: Maria Rosario Montiroli, Gen. Mgr.

REXNORD CORPORATION

4701 West Greenfield Ave., Milwaukee, WI, 53214

Tel: (414) 643-3000   Fax: (414) 643-3078   www.rexnord.com

Mfr. power transmission and conveying components.

Rexnord Harbett, S.p.A., Via Della Costituzione 45, I-42015 Correggio, Italy

RICHARDSON ELECTRONICS, LTD.

40 W 267 Keslinger Road, LaFox, IL, 60147-0393

Tel: (630) 208-2200   Fax: (630) 208-2550   www.rell.com

Mfr. and distribution of electron tubes and related equipment.

Richardson Electronics, Viale L. Ariosto, 492/G, I-50019 Florence, Italy

RICHCO, INC.

5825 N. Tripp Ave., PO Box 804238, Chicago, IL, 60680

Tel: (773) 539-4060   Fax: (773) 539-6770   www.richco.com

Mfr. quality plastic fasteners, wire management devices, circuit board hardware, and custom components.

Richco Italia SRL, Via G. Masserenti 1, Loc. 1 Maggio, I-40013 Castelmaggiore Bologna, Italy

Tel: 39-51-6325266

RIDGE TOOL COMPANY

400 Clark Street, Elyria, OH, 44035

Tel: (440) 323-5581   Fax: (440) 329-4853   www.ridgid.com

Mfr. hand and power tools for working pipe, drain cleaning equipment, etc.

Ridge Tool Div. Emerson Electric SRL, Milan, Italy

C. H. ROBINSON WORLDWIDE, INC. (CHR)

8100 Mitchell Road, Eden Prairie, MN, 55344

Tel: (612) 937-8500   Fax: (612) 937-6714   www.chrobinson.com

Global door-to-door freight forwarding services, including flexible transportation solutions and global logistics.

C. H. Robinson (CHR), Via W. Tobagi, 3-A, Paderno, I-20037 Milan, Italy

Tel: 39-29-101-381

THE ROCKPORT COMPANY

1895 J.W. Foster Boulevard, Canton, MA, 02021

Tel: (508) 485-2090   Fax: (508) 480-0012   www.rockport.com

Mfr./import dress and casual footwear.

Rockport International Trading Co., Via Don Lorenzo Peroso 14, I-50018 Scandicci, Italy

ROCKWELL AUTOMATION, INC.

777 East Wisconsin Ave., Ste. 1400, Milwaukee, WI, 53202

Tel: (414) 212-5200   Fax: (414) 212-5201   www.rockwellautomation.com

Products and service for aerospace and defense, automotive, electronics, graphics and automation industry.

Rockwell Automation S.r.L., Viale de Gasperi 126, I-20017 Mazzo di Rho Milan, Italy

Tel: 39-02-939721   Fax: 39-02-93972-201

Rockwell Automation S.r.l., Via Persicetana 12, I-40012 Calderara di Reno BO, Italy

Tel: 39-051-6464-111   Fax: 39-051-728-670

ROFIN-SINAR TECHNOLOGIES, INC.

45701 Mast St., Plymouth, MI, 48170

Tel: (734) 455-5400   Fax: (734) 455-2741   www.rofin-sinar.com

Mfr. industrial lasers.

ROFIN-SINAR Italy, Via Galilei, 1, I-30090 Rovagnasco, Italy

Tel: 39-02-2169511

ROHM AND HAAS COMPANY

100 Independence Mall West, Philadelphia, PA, 19106

Tel: (215) 592-3000   Fax: (215) 592-3377   www.rohmhaas.com

Mfr. specialty chemicals.

Morton International Spa, Via Trieste 25, I-22076 Mozzate, Italy

Rohm and Haas Italia Srl, Via 3 Giugno, 14, I-20020 Robecchetto (MI), Italy

Rohm and Haas Italia Srl, 7 Strada Marziana, I-27020 Arona Lomellina PV, Italy

Rohm and Haas Italia SRL, Shipley Chemicals Italia Srl, Viale Lombardia 52, I-21040 Castronno (Varese), Italy

Rohm and Haas Italia Srl, Strada Statale 11, Kilometro 190 200, I-24050 Mozzanica, Italy

Rohm and Haas Italia Srl, Via Borgo S. Siro 63, I-27026 Garlasco (PV), Italy

Rohm and Haas Italia Srl, Via della Filanda 2, I-20060 Gessate Milan, Italy

Tel: 39-02-952501

Rohm and Haas Italia Srl, Divisione Pulverlac, Via Monte Tomba 10, I-36060 Romano d'Ezzelino, Italy

RPM INC.

PO Box 777, 2628 Pearl Road, Medina, OH, 44258

Tel: (330) 273-5090   Fax: (330) 225-8743   www.rpminc.com

Mfr. protective coatings and paints.

APSA SpA, Milan, Italy

RUDDICK CORPORATION

301 S. Tryon St., Ste. 1800, Charlotte, NC, 28202

Tel: (704) 372-5404   Fax: (704) 372-6409   www.amefird.com

Mfr. industrial sewing thread for worldwide industrial and consumer markets.

American & Efird (Italia) S.p.A, Via Salicchi 758, I-55100 Acquacalda Lucca, Italy

RUSSELL REYNOLDS ASSOCIATES INC.

200 Park Avenue, New York, NY, 10166-0002

Tel: (212) 351-2000   Fax: (212) 370-0896   www.russreyn.com

Executive recruiting services.

Russell Reynolds Associates Inc., Via Andrea Appiani 7, I-20121 Milan, Italy

Tel: 39-02-6231-121   Fax: 39-02-6552-837   Contact: Alberto Gavazzi

SAMSONITE CORPORATION

11200 East 45th Ave., Denver, CO, 80239-3018

Tel: (303) 373-2000   Fax: (303) 373-6300   www.samsonite.com

Mfr. luggage and leather goods.

Samsonite Italy, Via Enrico de Nicola 18, I-20090 Cesano Boscone, Italy

SANFORD CORPORATION

2711 Washington Boulevard, Bellwood, IL, 60104

Tel: (708) 547-6650   Fax: (708) 547-6719   www.sanfordcorp.com

Mfr. inks, writing, drawing and drafting instruments.

Sanford Italia s.r.l., Via Ugo Bassi, 21, I-20159 Milan, Italy

SAPIENT CORPORATION

1 Memorial Drive, Cambridge, MA, 02142

Tel: (617) 621-0200   Fax: (617) 621-1300   www.sapient.com

Engaged in information technology and consulting services.

Sapient SpA, Via Crocefisso 19, I-20122 Milan, Italy

Tel: 39-02-5821-71

SARA LEE CORPORATION

3 First National Plaza, Chicago, IL, 60602-4260

Tel: (312) 726-2600   Fax: (312) 558-4995   www.saralee.com

Mfr./distributor food and consumer packaged goods, intimate apparel and knitwear.

Filodoro Calze S.p.A., Via Brescia, 6, I-46040 Casalmore (MN), Italy

Maglificio Bellia SpA, Via C. Bellia 34, I-13050 Pettinengo, Italy

SAS INSTITUTE INC.

SAS Campus Drive, Cary, NC, 27513

Tel: (919) 677-8000   Fax: (919) 677-4444   www.sas.com

Mfr. and distribution of decision support software.

SAS Institute (Italia) SpA, Via San Martino 17, I-20122 Milan, Italy

Tel: 39-02-5830-1686   Fax: 39-02-5830-0602

SBS TECHNOLOGIES, INC.

2400 Louisiana Blvd. NE, Ste. 600, Albuquerque, NM, 87110

Tel: (505) 875-0600   Fax: (505) 875-0400   www.sbs.com

Mfr. high-tech computer components.

SBS Technologies Italy, Via Giovanni da Udine 34, I-20156 Milan, Italy

Tel: 39-02-38093281   Contact: Alessandro Becca

SCHENKER USA INC.

150 Albany Ave., Freeport, NY, 11520

Tel: (516) 403-5416   Fax: (516) 377-3092   www.schenkerusa.com

Freight forwarders.

Schenker Italiana S.P.A., Via S. Romano In Carfagnana 45, I-00148 Rome, Italy

Tel: 39-06-657-0741   Fax: 39-06-653-2820

Schenker Italiana S.P.A., Via Fratelli Bandiera 27, I-20068 Peschiera Borromeo Milan, Italy
Tel: 39-01-51666-398   Fax: 39-01-51666-50`

Schenker Italiana S.P.A., Via Don L. Sturzo 3, I-24020 Gorle Bergamo, Italy
Tel: 39-035-299451   Fax: 39-035-296984

R. P. SCHERER CORPORATION

645 Martinsville Rd., Ste. 200, Basking Ridge, NJ, 07920
Tel: (908) 580-1500   Fax: (908) 580-9220   www.rpscherer.com
Mfr. pharmaceuticals; soft gelatin and two-piece hard shell capsules.

R.P. Scherer SpA, Via Nettunense, km 20 100, I-04011 Aprilia Latina, Italy
Tel: 39-06-927141   Fax: 39-06-92727890   Contact: Dr. Giuliane Bide, Gen. Mgr.   Emp: 128

SCHERING-PLOUGH CORPORATION

One Giralda Farms, Madison, NJ, 07940-1000
Tel: (973) 822-7000   Fax: (973) 822-7048   www.sch-plough.com
Proprietary drug and cosmetic products.

Schering-Plough Animal Health, Centro Dir Milano Due, Palazzo Borromini, I-20090 Segrate Milan, Italy
Tel: 39-02-210-181

SCHLEGEL SYSTEMS

1555 Jefferson Road, PO Box 23197, Rochester, NY, 14692-3197
Tel: (716) 427-7200   Fax: (716) 427-9993   www.schlegel.com
Mfr. engineered perimeter sealing systems for residential and commercial construction; fibers; rubber product.

Schlegel SRL, Via Miglioli 9, I-20090 Segrate Milan, Italy

SCHLUMBERGER LIMITED

153 East 53rd St., 57th Fl., New York, NY, 10022-4624
Tel: (212) 350-9400   Fax: (212) 350-9457   www.slb.com
Engaged in oil and gas services, metering and payment systems, and produces semiconductor testing equipment and smart cards.

Schlumberger Sema, Via Riccardo Morandi 36, I-00050 Rome, Italy

Schlumberger Test & Transactions, Cards Div., Via Cornelio Celso 22/A, I-00161 Rome, Italy

SCIENCE APPLICATIONS INTL. CORPORATION (SAIC)

10260 Campus Point Dr., San Diego, CA, 92121
Tel: (858) 826-6000   Fax: (858) 535-7589   www.saic.com
Engaged in research and engineering.

US Naval Hospital, Via Eduardo Scarfogolio, I-80125 Agano, Italy
Tel: 39-81-7243699   Fax: 39-81-7243665   Contact: Ronald Freeman

SCIENTECH, INC.

2650 McCormick Drive, Suite 300, Clearwater, FL, 33759
Tel: (727) 669-3003   Fax: (727) 669-3100   www.scientech.com
worldwide provider of expert services to the energy and telecommunication markets

Scientech Italy, Via Deruta 20, I-20132 Milan, Italy

SCIENTIFIC-ATLANTA, INC.

5030 Sugarloaf Pkwy., Lawrenceville, GA, 30044
Tel: (770) 903-5000   Fax: (770) 236-6777   www.sciatl.com
Mfr. cable set-top boxes, modems, transmission and distribution equipment.

Scientific-Atlanta Mediterranean, Inc., Via Fosso Centroni 4, I-00040 Morena, Italy
Tel: 39-06-7489-011   Fax: 39-06-7984-0034

SEAGATE TECHNOLOGY, INC.

920 Disc Dr., Scotts Valley, CA, 95066
Tel: (408) 438-6550   Fax: (408) 438-7205   www.seagate.com
Develop computer technology, software and hardware.

Seagate Technology SRL, Via Litta Modignani 7, I-20161 Milan, Italy
Tel: 39-02-662-01515   Fax: 39-02-662-02530   Contact: Walter Fontana   Emp: 1

SEALED AIR CORPORATION

Park 80 East, Saddle Brook, NJ, 07663

Tel: (201) 791-7600 Fax: (201) 703-4205 www.sealedaircorp.com

Mfr. protective and specialty packaging solutions for industrial, food and consumer products.

Instapak Italia SpA, Via Belvedere 18, I-20043 Arcore Milan, Italy

Sealed Air S.p.A., Via per Ornago, I-20040 Bellusco Milan, Italy

Tel: 39-039-6835-1 Fax: 39-039-6835-350

G.D. SEARLE & COMPANY

5200 Old Orchard Road, Skokie, IL, 60077

Tel: (847) 982-7000 Fax: (847) 470-1480 www.searlehealthnet.com

Mfr. pharmaceuticals, health care, optical products and specialty chemicals.

Searle Framaceutici S.p.A., Via Walter Tobagi 8, I-20068 Peschiera Borromeo Milan, Italy

Tel: 39-02-516-611 Fax: 39-02-516-61203

SEEBEYOND TECHNOLOGY CORPORATION

404 East Huntington Drive, Monrovia, CA, 91016

Tel: (626) 471-6000 Fax: (626) 471-6104 www.seebeyond.com

Mfr. business software.

SeeBeyond Italy, Largo Richini, 6, I-20122 Milan, Italy

Tel: 39-02-5821-5521

SELAS CORPORATION OF AMERICA

2034 S. Limekiln Pike, Dresher, PA, 19025

Tel: (215) 646-6600 Fax: (215) 646-3536 www.selas.com

Mfr. heat treating equipment for metal, glass, ceramic and chemical industry.

Selas Italiana SRL, Via delle Tuberose 14, I-20146 Milan, Italy

SEMITOOL, INC.

655 West Reserve Drive, Kalispell, MT, 59901

Tel: (406) 752-2107 Fax: (406) 752-5522 www.semitool.com

Mfr. semiconductor manufacturing equipment.

Semitool Italia SRL, Centro Colleoni Taurus A3, I-20041 Agrate Brianza (MI), Italy

SENSIENT TECHNOLOGIES CORPORATION

777 E. Wisconsin Ave., Milwaukee, WI, 53202

Tel: (414) 271-6755 Fax: (414) 347-4783 www.sensient.com

Mfr. flavor applications for the beverage, bakery, confection, dairy, snack and savory markets.

Curt Georgi Imes SpA, Milan, Italy

SENSORMATIC ELECTRONICS CORPORATION

951 Yamato Road, Boca Raton, FL, 33431-0700

Tel: (561) 989-7000 Fax: (561) 989-7774 www.sensormatic.com

Electronic article surveillance equipment.

Sensormatic Italy, Via Teocrito 54, I-20128 Milan, Italy

SERVICE CORPORATION INTERNATIONAL

1929 Allen Parkway, Houston, TX, 77019

Tel: (713) 522-5141 Fax: (713) 525-5586 www.sci-corp.com

Operates funeral homes, cemeteries and crematoriums and sells caskets, burial vaults and cremation receptacles.

Pompes Funereraves Geneacuterales (PFG), Milan, Italy

THE SHAW GROUP INC.

4171 Essen Lane, Baton Rouge, LA, 70809

Tel: (225) 932-2500 Fax: (225) 932-2661 www.shawgrp.com

Vertically-integrated provider of complete piping systems, and comprehensive engineering, procurement and construction services.

IT Infrastructure & Environmental, Piazza Duca D'Aosta No. 12, I-20124 Milan, Italy

SHC, INC.

425 Meadow Street, Chicopee, MA, 01013

Tel: (413) 536-1200   Fax: (413) 322-2216   www.spalding.com

Mfr. athletic products, including golf balls, footballs, basketballs and volleyballs.

Spalding, Div. SHC, Paizza Parigi, 12, I-31044 Montebelluna, Italy

SHIPLEY COMPANY, LLC

455 Forest Street, Marlborough, MA, 01752

Tel: (508) 481-7950   Fax: (508) 485-9113   www.shipley.com

Supplier of materials and processes technology to the microelectronics and printed wiring board industries.

Shipley Italy, Viale Lombardia 52, I-21040 Castronno Varese, Italy

Tel: 39-033-289-6311   Fax: 39-033-289-6398

SHOOK, HARDY & BACON L.L.P.

1200 Main Street, Ste. 3100, Kansas City, MO, 64105-2118

Tel: (816) 474-6550   Fax: (816) 421-5547   www.shb.com

International law firm.

Shook, Hardy & Bacon, Via Meravigli 3, I-20123 Milan, Italy

SICOR INC.

19 Hughes, Irvine, CA, 92618

Tel: (949) 455-4700   Fax: (949) 855-8210   www.gensiasicor.com

Mfr. and sales oncology drugs.

SICOR Inc., Via Terrazzano 77, I-20017 Rho Milan, Italy

SICOR Inc., 13048 Santhia, Vercelli, Italy

SIEBEL SYSTEMS, INC.

2207 Bridgepointe Pkwy., San Mateo, CA, 94404

Tel: (650) 295-5000   Fax: (650) 295-5111   www.siebel.com

Provider of e-Business applications software.

Siebel Systems Italia S.r.l, Piazzale Biancamano 8, I-20121 Milan, Italy

Tel: 39-02-62033004

SIG DOBOY INC.

869 South Knowles Ave., New Richmond, WI, 54017-1797

Tel: (715) 246-6511   Fax: (715) 246-6539   www.doboy.com

Mfr. packaging machinery.

SIG Simonazzi S.p.A., Via dell'Elettronica, 9, I-37139 Verona, Italy

SILICON GRAPHICS INC.

1600 Amphitheatre Pkwy., Mountain View, CA, 94043-1351

Tel: (650) 960-1980   Fax: (650) 932-0661   www.sgi.com

Design/mfr. special-effects computer graphic systems and software.

Silicon Graphics, Via Montecassiano 155, I-01156 Rome, Italy

Silicon Graphics, Centro Dir. Piero della Francesca, Corso Svizzera 185, I-10149 Torino, Italy

Silicon Graphics, Centro Dir. Milanofiori, Strada 6 Palazzo N3, I-20089 Rozzano Milan, Italy

SMITH INTERNATIONAL, INC.

PO Box 60068, Houston, TX, 77205-0068

Tel: (713) 443-3370   Fax: (713) 233-5996   www.smith.com

Mfr. drilling tools and equipment and provides related services for the drilling, completion and production sectors of the petroleum and mining industries.

Smith International Italia SpA, Via Grandi 1, Castle Maggiore, I-40013 Bologna, Italy

Tel: 39-051-713-401   Contact: Luciano Bernardini, Area Mgr.

SMURFIT-STONE CONTAINER CORPORATION

150 N. Michigan Ave., Chicago, IL, 60601-7568

Tel: (312) 346-6600   Fax: (312) 580-3486   www.smurfit-stone.net

Mfr. paper and paper packaging.

Smurfit-Stone Container Corporation, Milan, Italy

SOLA INTERNATIONAL INC.

10690 W. Ocean Air Drive, Ste. 300, San Diego, CA, 92130

Tel: (858) 509-9899   Fax: (858) 509-9898   www.sola.com

Mfr. and sales of plastic and glass eyeglasses.

SOLA Optical Italia, Via S.e.P. Mazzucchelli No. 17, 21043, I- Castiglione Olona, Varese, Italy

Tel: 39-331-851111   Fax: 39-331-850720

SONESTA INTERNATIONAL HOTELS CORPORATION

200 Clarendon Street, Boston, MA, 02116

Tel: (617) 421-5400   Fax: (617) 421-5402   www.sonesta.com

Own/manage hotels, resorts, and Nile cruises.

Sonesta Resort & Country Club, Tuscany, Italy

SONOCO PRODUCTS COMPANY

North Second Street, PO Box 160, Hartsville, SC, 29550

Tel: (843) 383-7000   Fax: (843) 383-7008   www.sonoco.com

Mfr. packaging for consumer and industrial market and recycled paperboard.

Sonoco L.P.D. Italia, s.r.l., S.S. 87 Sannitica Km 21500, Via Delle Industrie, I-81020 S. Marco Evangelista Caserta, Italy

Tel: 39-0823-424388

SOTHEBY'S HOLDINGS, INC.

1334 York Avenue, New York, NY, 10021

Tel: (212) 606-7000   Fax: (212) 606-7027   www.sothebys.com

Auction house specializing in fine art and jewelry.

Sotheby's Holdings, Inc., Palazzo Broggi, Via Broggi 19, I-20129 Milan, Italy

Tel: 39-02-295-001   Fax: 39-02-295-18595   Contact: Paul Mack

SPARKLER FILTERS INC.

PO Box 19, Conroe, TX, 77305-0019

Tel: (936) 756-4471   Fax: (936) 539-1165   www.sparklerfilters.com

Mfr. chemical process filtration industry.

Sparkler Italy, Corso di Porta Ticinese 87, I-20123 Milan, Italy

Tel: 39-02-58100920   Fax: 39-02-58-101400

SPENCER STUART MANAGEMENT CONSULTANTS

401 North Michigan Ave., Ste. 3400, Chicago, IL, 60611

Tel: (312) 822-0080   Fax: (312) 822-0116   www.spencerstuart.com

Executive recruitment firm.

Spencer Stuart & Associates Inc., 7 Via A. Kircher, I-00198 Rome, Italy

Tel: 39-06-802071   Fax: 39-06-8020-7200   Contact: Luca Pacces

Spencer Stuart & Associates Inc., 36 Corso Monforte, I-20122 Milan, Italy

Tel: 39-02-771251   Fax: 39-02-782452   Contact: Luca Pacces

SPHERION CORPORATION

2050 Spectrum Boulevard, Fort Lauderdale, FL, 33309

Tel: (954) 938-7600   Fax: (954) 938-7666   www.spherion.com

Provides temporary personnel placement and staffing.

Michael Page Finance, Via Meravigli 3, I-20123 Milan, Italy

Tel: 39-02-806-8001

SPIGADORO, INC.

70 East 55th Street, 24th Fl., New York, NY, 10022

Tel: (212) 754-4271　　　　Fax: (212) 754-4044　　　　www.spigadoro.com

Engaged in food services, including sales of pasta products.

Spigadoro, via IV Novembre, 2/4, I-06083 Bastia Umbra Perugia, Italy

SPRINT CORPORATION

2330 Shawnee Mission Parkway, Westwood, KS, 66205

Tel: (913) 624-3000　　　　Fax: (913) 624-3281　　　　www.sprint.com

Telecommunications equipment and services.

Sprint Corporation, Centro Direzionale Lombardo, Via Roma 108, Palazzo CD, I-20060 Cassina de'Pecchi Milan, Italy

SPS TECHNOLOGIES INC.

165 Township Line Rd., Two Pitcairn Place, Jenkintown, PA, 19046

Tel: (215) 517-2000　　　　Fax: (215) 517-2032　　　　www.spstech.com

Mfr. aerospace and industry fasteners, tightening systems, magnetic materials, super alloys.

Asti Aircraft Services, Via Balme No. 5, I-10143 Torino, Italy

Tel: 39-011-74-5517　　Contact: Gian Piero Garbarino

SPX CORPORATION

700 Terrace Point Drive, PO Box 3301, Muskegon, MI, 49443-3301

Tel: (231) 724-5000　　　　Fax: (231) 724-5720　　　　www.spx.com

Mfr. auto parts, special service tools, engine and drive-train parts.

Bear Italiana SRL, Via dei Confini 201, I-50010 Capalle Florence, Italy

SQUIRE, SANDERS & DEMPSEY

4900 Key Tower, 127 Public Square, Cleveland, OH, 44114-1304

Tel: (216) 479-8500　　　　Fax: (216) 479-8780　　　　www.ssd.com

Engaged in international law.

Studio Legale Bernascone & Soci, Squire, Sanders & Dempsey L.L.P., Piazza San Babila, 3, I-20122 Milan, Italy

SRI INTERNATIONAL

333 Ravenswood Ave., Menlo Park, CA, 94025-3493

Tel: (650) 859-2000　　　　Fax: (650) 326-5512　　　　www.sri.com

Engaged in international consulting and research.

SRI Italy, Via Lanzone 6, I-20123 Milan, Italy

THE ST. PAUL COMPANIES, INC.

385 Washington Street, St. Paul, MN, 55102

Tel: (651) 310-7911　　　　Fax: (651) 310-8294　　　　www.stpaul.com

Provides investment, insurance and reinsurance services.

Toro Assicuraziona S.A., Via Arcivescovado 16, I-10121 Turin, Italy

STANDARD COMMERCIAL CORPORATION

2201 Miller Rd., PO Box 450, Wilson, NC, 27894

Tel: (252) 291-5507　　　　Fax: (252) 237-1109　　　　www.sccgroup.com

Leaf tobacco dealers and processors and wool processors.

Transcatab, SpA, Via Provinciale Appia, I-81020 San Nicola La Strada Caserta, Italy

STANDEX INTERNATIONAL CORPORATION

6 Manor Parkway, Salem, NH, 03079

Tel: (603) 893-9701　　　　Fax: (603) 893-7324　　　　www.standex.com

Mfr. diversified graphics, institutional, industry, electronic and consumer products.

Standex International S.R.L., Via 1 Maggio 20, I-20064 Gorgonzola Milan, Italy

Tel: 39-02-95-740-951　Fax: 39-02-95-740-713　Contact: Giorgio Mazza, Mgr.

STANLEY BOSTITCH FASTENING SYSTEMS

815 Briggs Street, East Greenwich, RI, 02818

Tel: (401) 884-2500   Fax: (401) 885-6511   www.stanleybostich.com

Mfr. stapling machines, stapling supplies, fastening systems and wire.

Stanley Bostitch Atro Italy, Via Parco 47, I-20046 Biassono (Mi), Italy

THE STANLEY WORKS

1000 Stanley Drive, PO Box 7000, New Britain, CT, 06053

Tel: (860) 225-5111   Fax: (860) 827-3987   www.stanleyworks.com

Mfr. hand tools and hardware.

Stanley Mediterranea SpA, Via Motolense Supino, Frosinone, Italy

Stanley Tools SpA, Via Trieste 1, I-22060 Figino Serenza Como, Italy

Stanley Works (Italia) SRL, Via Leopardi 9, I-22060 Figino Serenza Como, Italy

STA-RITE INDUSTRIES INC.

293 Wright Street, Delavan, WI, 53115

Tel: (262) 728-5551   Fax: (262) 728-7323   www.sta-rite.com

Mfr. water pumps, filters and systems.

Nocchi Pompe SPA, Via Masaccio 13, I-56010 Lugnano Pisa, Italy

Tel: 39-050-71-6111   Fax: 39-050-70-3137   Contact: Georgio Nocchi   Emp: 228

STARKEY LABORATORIES, INC.

6700 Washington Avenue South, Eden Prairie, MN, 55344

Tel: (952) 941-6401   Fax: (952) 947-4787   www.starkey.com

Mfr. custom in-the-ear hearing aids.

Starkey Italy, 20063 Cernusco sul Naviglio, Via Torino 51, Milan, Italy

Tel: 39-02-92-72181

STARWOOD HOTELS & RESORTS WORLDWIDE

777 Westchester Avenue, White Plains, NY, 10604

Tel: (914) 640-8100   Fax: (914) 640-8316   www.starwoodhotels.com

Hotel operations including Sheraton, Westin, St. Regis, Four Points and Caesars.

Sheraton Sales Center, Via Vittor Pisani 7, I-20124 Milan, Italy

STEINER CORPORATION

505 E. South Temple, Salt Lake City, UT, 84102

Tel: (801) 328-8831   Fax: (801) 363-5680   www.alsco.com

Mfr. soap and towel dispensers and uniforms.

Steiner Company International SA, Piazza De Angeli 3, I-20146 Milan, Italy

STIEFEL LABORATORIES INC.

255 Alhambra Circle, Ste. 1000, Coral Gables, FL, 33134

Tel: (305) 443-3807   Fax: (305) 443-3467   www.stiefel.com

Mfr. pharmaceuticals, dermatological specialties.

Stiefel Laboratories SRL, Via Calabria 15, I-20090 Redecesio Di Segrate Milan, Italy

STORAGE TECHNOLOGY CORPORATION

One Storagetech Dr., Louisville, CO, 80028-4377

Tel: (303) 673-5151   Fax: (303) 673-5019   www.stortek.com

Mfr., market, service information, storage and retrieval systems.

StorageTek Italy, Palazzo Congressor WPC, Milanofiori, Assago, I-20090 Milan, Italy

STOWE WOODWARD MOUNT HOPE

One Technology Drive, Westborough, MA, 01581

Tel: (508) 616-9458   Fax: (508) 616-9479   www.stowewoodward.com

Mfr. roll covering and bowed roll technologies for the web handling industries.

Stowe Woodward IRGA Italy, Via A. Volta 73, I-21010 Cardano al Campo, Italy

Tel: 39-3-3126-1514

THE STRUCTURE TONE ORGANIZATION

15 East 26th Street, New York, NY, 10010-1589

Tel: (212) 481-6100   Fax: (212) 685-9267   www.structuretone.com

Provides general contracting and construction management.

Structure Tone Organization, Via Balzaretti 17, I-20133 Milan, Italy

SUDLER & HENNESSEY

230 Park Avenue South, New York, NY, 10003-1566

Tel: (212) 614-4100   Fax: (212) 598-6933   www.sudler.com

Engaged in healthcare products advertising.

IntraMed Communications/S&H, Via M.V. Traiano 7, I-20149 Milan, Italy

Tel: 39-02-349-721   Fax: 39-01-349-1698   Contact: Massimo Vergnano

SUN MICROSYSTEMS, INC.

901 San Antonio Road, Palo Alto, CA, 94303

Tel: (650) 960-1300   Fax: (650) 961-9131   www.sun.com

Computer peripherals and programming services.

Sun Microsystems, Centro Direzionale Colleoni, Palazzo Andromeda 1, Via Paracelso 16, I-20041 Agrate Brianza, Italy

Tel: 39-0167-874-707

SUNRISE MEDICAL INC.

7477 East Dry Creek Parkway, Longmont, CO, 80503

Tel: (303) 218-4500   Fax: (303) 218-4590   www.sunrisemedical.com

Designs, manufactures and markets rehabilitation products and assistive technology devices for people with disabilities, and patient care products used in nursing homes, hospitals and homecare settings.

Sunrise Medical Italy, Via Riva 20, Montale, I-29100 Piacenza (PC), Italy

SUPERIOR GRAPHITE COMPANY

10 South Riverside Plaza, Chicago, IL, 60606

Tel: (312) 559-2999   Fax: (312) 559-9064   www.graphitesgc.com

Mfr. natural and synthetic graphites, electrodes, lubricants, suspensions, carbide and carbon.

Tesi S.p.A, Via Manzoni 20, I-20052 Monza (MI), Italy

SYBASE, INC.

5000 Hacienda Dr., Dublin, CA, 94568

Tel: (925) 236-5000   Fax: (925) 236-4321   www.sybase.com

Design/mfg/distribution of database management systems, software development tools, connectivity products, consulting and technical support services..

Sybase Italia, Via del Poggio Laurentino 118, I-00144 Rome, Italy

Tel: 39-06-592-6324   Fax: 39-06-593-2924

Sybase Italia, Via Anna Kuliscioff 35, I-20152 Milan, Italy

Tel: 39-02-483-241   Fax: 39-02-483-0660

SYBRON DENTAL SPECIALTIES, INC.

1717 West Collins, Orange, CA, 92867

Tel: (714) 516-7400   Fax: (714) 516-7904   www.sybrondental.com

Mfr. consumable dental products, light curing instruments and plastics for dental use.

Kerr International, Div. Sybron Dental, PO Box 46, Via Passanti 332, I-84018 Salerno, Italy

Tel: 39-0-81-850-8311   Fax: 39-0-81-863-7076

Kerr International, Div. Sybron Dental, Via Tiziano 20, I-10126 Torino, Italy

SYKES ENTERPRISES, INC.

100 N. Tampa Street, Ste. 3900, Tampa, FL, 33602

Tel: (813) 274-1000   Fax: (813) 273-0148   www.sykes.com

Provides information technology outsourcing services.

Sykes, via E. Barsanti, 24, I-59100 Prato, Italy

SYMANTEC CORPORATION

20330 Stevens Creek Blvd., Cupertino, CA, 95014-2132

Tel: (408) 253-9600   Fax: (408) 253-3968   www.symantec.com

Designs and produces PC network security and network management software and hardware.

Symantec Srl, Voa Abbadesse 40, I-20124 Milan, Italy

Tel: 39-02-695521   Fax: 39-02-5501-2270

SYMBOL TECHNOLOGIES, INC.

One Symbol Plaza, Holtsville, NY, 11742-1300

Tel: (631) 738-2400   Fax: (631) 738-5990   www.symbol.com

Mfr. Bar code-driven data management systems, wireless LAN's, and Portable Shopping System™.

Symbol Technologies Italy S.r.l., Via Cristoforo Colombo 49, I-20090 Trezzano S/N Milan, Italy

Tel: 39-02-44-84441   Fax: 39-02-44-54385

SYNAVANT INC.

3445 Peachtree Road NE, Ste. 1400, Atlanta, GA, 30326

Tel: (404) 841-4000   Fax: (404) 841-4115   www.synavant.com

Mfr. support software for pharmaceutical industry.

Synavant, Viale F. Restelli 1/A, I-20124 Milan, Italy

SYNOPSYS, INC.

700 East Middlefield Road, Mountain View, CA, 94043

Tel: (650) 962-5000   Fax: (650) 965-8637   www.synopsys.com

Mfr. electronic design automation software.

Synopsys Srl, Centro Direzionale Colleoni, Viale Colleoni 11, Palazzo Sirio 3, I-20041 Agrate Brianza-Mi, Italy

Tel: 39-039-657-981   Fax: 39-039-657-98300

SYNTEGRA

4201 Lexington Avenue North, Arden Hills, MN, 55126-6198

Tel: (651) 415-2999   Fax: (651) 415-4891   www.cdc.com

Engaged in consulting and systems integration.

Syntegra Italy S.p.A., Palazzo Verrocchio, Centro Diezionale, Milan 2, I-20090 Segrate Milan, Italy

Tel: 39-02-21741   Fax: 39-02-2641-4187

SYSTEMAX INC.

22 Harbor Park Dr., Port Washington, NY, 11050

Tel: (516) 608-7000   Fax: (516) 608-7111   www.systemax.com

Direct marketer of computers and related products to businesses.

Misco Italy Computer Supplies S.p.A., Il Girasole UDV 2.01, I-20084 Lacchiarella Milan, Italy

Tel: 39-02-900-90977

TALISMA CORPORATION

4600 Carillon Point, Kirkland, WA, 98033

Tel: (425) 897-2900   Fax: (425) 828-9587   www.talisma.com

Mfr. customer relationship management software.

Talisma Corporation, Notramo Venture, Via Dello Studio 8, I-50122 Firenze, Italy

TARANTELLA, INC.

425 Encinal Street, Santa Cruz, CA, 95060

Tel: (831) 425-7222   Fax: (831) 427-5400   www.tarantella.com

Mfr. server software.

Tarantella Italy, Via Bergamo 6, Cassina de' Pecchi, I-20060 Cassina de' Pecchi Milan, Italy

TBWA WORLDWIDE

488 Madison Avenue, 6th Floor, New York, NY, 10022

Tel: (212) 804-1000   Fax: (212) 804-1200   www.tbwachiat.com

International full service advertising agency.

TBWA Italia, Milan, Italy

TECHNITROL INC.

1210 Northbrook Drive, #385, Trevose, PA, 19053

Tel: (215) 355-2900   Fax: (215) 355-7397   www.technitrol.com

Mfr. of electronic components, electrical contacts, and other parts/materials.

Mec Betras Italia s.r.l. Contatti Elettrici, Lentate Seveso, Italy

TECUMSEH PRODUCTS COMPANY

100 E. Patterson Street, Tecumseh, MI, 49286-1899

Tel: (517) 423-8411   Fax: (517) 423-8526   www.tecumseh.com

Mfr. of hermetic compressors for air conditioning and refrigeration products, gasoline engines and power train components for lawn and garden applications, and pumps.

Tecnamotor SRL, Casella Postale 1221, I-10100 Torino, Italy

TEKELEC

26580 West Agoura Road, Calabasas, CA, 91302

Tel: (818) 880-5656   Fax: (818) 880-6993   www.tekelec.com

Mfr. telecommunications testing equipment.

Tekelec Europe S.r.L, Via Zante 14, I-20128 Milan, Italy

Tel: 39-2-580-3951

TEKTRONIX INC.

14200 SW Karl Braun Dr., PO Box 500, Beaverton, OR, 97077

Tel: (503) 627-7111   Fax: (503) 627-2406   www.tek.com

Mfr. test and measure, visual systems/color printing and communications/video and networking products.

Tektronix SpA, Via XI Febbraio 99, I-20090 Vimodrome Milan, Italy

Tel: 39-02-25086-501   Fax: 39-02-25086-500

TELCORDIA TECHNOLOGIES, INC.

445 South Street, Morristown, NJ, 07960-6438

Tel: (973) 829-2000   Fax: (973) 829-3172   www.telecordia.com

Mfr. telecom software.

Telcordia Technologies International, Via Mar della Cina 199, I-00144 Rome, Italy

TELEFLEX INC.

630 W. Germantown Pike, Ste. 450, Plymouth Meeting, PA, 19462

Tel: (610) 834-6301   Fax: (610) 834-8307   www.teleflex.com

Design, manufacture and marketing of mechanical and electro-mechanical systems, control systems and surgical devices.

Rüsch S.r.l., Varedo (MI), Italy

TFX Marine European Sales Office, Varedo (MI), Italy

TELLABS INC.

1415 W. Diehl Rd., Naperville, IL, 60563

Tel: (630) 378-8800   Fax: (630) 852-7346   www.tellabs.com

Design/mfr./service voice/data transport and network access systems.

Tellabs Italy, Palazzo Valadier, Piazza del Popolo 18, I-00187 Rome, Italy

TENNECO AUTOMOTIVE INC.

500 North Field Drive, Lake Forest, IL, 60045

Tel: (847) 482-5241   Fax: (847) 482-5295   www.tenneco-automotive.com

Mfr. automotive parts, exhaust systems and service equipment.

Monroe Italia SRL, Via Plinio 43, I-20129 Milan, Italy

TERADATA

1700 South Patterson Blvd., Dayton, OH, 45479

Tel: (937) 445-5000   Fax: (937) 445-1682   www.teradata.com

Mfr. software to store information.

Teradata Div., NCR, Via Cusago 150.4, I-20153 Milan, Italy

TERADYNE INC.

321 Harrison Ave., Boston, MA, 02118

Tel: (617) 482-2700   Fax: (617) 422-2910   www.teradyne.com

Mfr. electronic test equipment and blackplane connection systems.

Teradyne Italia SRL, Via Modigliani 27, I-20090 Segrate, Italy

TEXAS INSTRUMENTS INC.

12500 TI Blvd., Dallas, TX, 75266

Tel: (972) 995-3773   Fax: (972) 995-4360   www.ti.com

Mfr. semiconductor devices, electronic electro-mechanical systems, instruments and controls.

Texas Instruments Italia SpA, Avezzano, Italy

Texas Instruments Italia SpA, Via John F. Kennedy 141, Aversa, Italy

TEXTRON INC.

40 Westminster Street, Providence, RI, 02903

Tel: (401) 421-2800   Fax: (401) 421-2878   www.textron.com

Mfr. Aerospace (Bell Helicopter and Cessna Aircraft), industry and consumer products, fasteners and financial services.

Maag Italia S.p.A., Viale Romagna 7, I-20089 Rozzano, Italy

Tel: 39-02-824-71310

Textron Fastening Systems, Via Manin 350/21, I-20099 Sesto San Giovanni (MI), Italy

Tel: 39-02-262-9171   Fax: 39-02-2424956   Contact: Gian-Paolo Bellagamba

THERMADYNE HOLDINGS CORPORATION

101 South Hanley Road, Suite 300, St. Louis, MO, 63105

Tel: (314) 746-2197   Fax: (314) 746-2349   www.thermadyne.com

Mfr. welding, cutting, and safety products.

OCIM, S.r.L., Via Benaco, 3, I-20098 Milan, Italy

TEC.MO. S.r.l., Via Rio Fabianni, Rastignano, I-40067 Rastignano Bologna, Italy

Thermadyne Europe, Via Stazione, 5, Villanova d' Ardenghi, I-27030 Pavia, Italy

THERMO FINNIGAN CORPORATION

355 River Oaks Parkway, San Jose, CA, 95134-1991

Tel: (408) 433-4800   Fax: (408) 433-4823   www.thermo.com

Mfr. mass spectrometers.

CE Instruments Div., Thermo Finnigan, Strada Rivoltana, I-20090 Rodano Milan, Italy

THERMO NICOLET CORPORATION

5225 Verona Road, Madison, WI, 53711-4495

Tel: (608) 276-6100   Fax: (608) 276-6222   www.nicolet.com

Mfr. infrared spectrometers and oscilloscopes and medical electro-diagnostic equipment.

Thermo Optek Italia SpA, Via Fl lli Gracchi 27, Cinisello Balsamo, I-20092 Milan, Italy

Tel: 39-02-6601-6362   Fax: 39-02-6128429

THERMO RAMSEY INC.

501 90th Avenue NW, Minneapolis, MN, 55433

Tel: (763) 783-2500   Fax: (763) 780-2525   www.thermoramsey.com

Mfr. of industrial control products.

Thermo Ramsey Srl, Via Cesare Cantù 5, I-20092 Cinisello Balsamo (MI), Italy

Tel: 39-02-660-8151

THERMON MANUFACTURING COMPANY

100 Thermon Drive, PO Box 609, San Marcos, TX, 78667-0609

Tel: (512) 396-5801   Fax: (512) 396-3627   www.thermon.com

Mfr. steam and electric heat tracing systems, components and accessories.

Thermon Italia SpA, Viale Lomellina 12A, ang. Via Piemonte, I-20090 Buccinasco Milan, Italy

THETFORD CORPORATION

7101 Jackson Road, PO Box 1285, Ann Arbor, MI, 48106

Tel: (734) 769-6000   Fax: (734) 769-2023   www.thetford.com

Mfr. sanitation products and chemicals.

Thetford Italia, Via 28 Luglio n.180, I-47893 Borgo Maggiore, Italy

Contact: Gianni Minzoni

THOMAS & BETTS CORPORATION

8155 T&B Blvd., Memphis, TN, 38125

Tel: (901) 252-5000   Fax: (901) 685-1988   www.tnb.com

Mfr. elect/electronic connectors and accessories.

Thomas & Betts SpA, Via Archimede Angola Piazzale Labriola, I-20092 Balsamo, Italy

TIBCO SOFTWARE INC.

3165 Porter Drive, Palo Alto, CA, 94304

Tel: (650) 846-5000   Fax: (650) 846-1005   www.tibco.com

Mfr. software and provides e-commerce, consulting, and support services. (JV of Reuters UK)

TIBCO Software Inc., Via del Casale Solaro 119, Rome, Italy

TIDEWATER INC.

601 Poydras Street, Ste.1900, New Orleans, LA, 70130

Tel: (504) 568-1010   Fax: (504) 566-4582   www.tdw.com

Marine service and equipment to companies engaged in exploration, development and production of oil, gas and minerals.

Tidewater Marine, Inc./o Petromed Ltd., Via Angelo Moro 119, I-20097 San Donato Milanese, Italy

Tel: 39-02-516-4031   Fax: 39-02-5164-0343

TIFFANY & COMPANY

727 Fifth Ave., New York, NY, 10022

Tel: (212) 755-8000   Fax: (212) 605-4465   www.tiffany.com

Mfr./retail fine jewelry, silverware, china, crystal, leather goods, etc.

Tiffany & Co. Florence, At Faraone S.p.A., Via Tornabuoni 25/R, I-50123 Florence, Italy

Tel: 39-055-215506

Tiffany & Co. Milan, At Faraone S.p.A., Via Montenapoleone 7A, I-20121 Milan, Italy

Tel: 39-02-7601-3656

THE TIMBERLAND COMPANY

200 Domain Drive, Stratham, NH, 03885

Tel: (603) 772-9500   Fax: (603) 773-1640   www.timberland.com

Design/mfr. footwear, apparel and accessories for men and women.

Timberland Europe Inc., Centro Direczionale Colleoni, Palazzo Orione, Viale Colleoni, I-20041 Agrate Brianza, Italy

TIMKEN SUPER PRECISION

PO Box 547 Precision Park, Keene, NH, 03431-0547

Tel: (603) 352-0310   Fax: (603) 355-4553   www.timken.com

Mfr., sales and distribution of bearings, tape guides and systems for missiles, etc.

GIMAR di D.F. eM. Giordano, Via Busoni 7a, I-20137 Milan, Italy

Tel: 39-2-5516918

TMP WORLDWIDE, INC.

622 Third Ave., New York, NY, 10017

Tel: (212) 351-7000   Fax: (212) 658-0540   www.tmpw.com

#1 Yellow Pages agency and a leader in the recruitment and interactive advertising fields.

TMP Worldwide Executive Search, Via Emilia 65, I-00187 Rome, Italy

TMP Worldwide Executive Search, Via Agnello 18, I-20121 Milan, Italy

TMP Worldwide/SMET, Via P. Colletta 59, I-20137 Milan, Italy

Tel: 39-02-546-5168

TOGETHERSOFT CORPORATION

900 Main Campus Drive, Ste. 500, Raleigh, NC, 27606

Tel: (919) 833-5550   Fax: (919) 833-5533   www.togethersoft.com

Mfr. software.

TogetherSoft Italy, Nadim Center, C. So Orbassano 336, I-10137 Torino, Italy

TOKHEIM CORPORATION

PO Box 360, 10501 Corporate Drive, Fort Wayne, IN, 46845

Tel: (219) 470-4600   Fax: (219) 482-2677   www.tokheim.com

Engaged in design, manufacture and service of electronic and mechanical petroleum marketing systems.

Tokheim, Quattordio Km 10800 SP 26, I-14030 Scurzolengo, Italy

Tokheim Sofitam, Quattordio KM 10800, S.P. 26, I-14030 Scurzolengo (AT), Italy

TOPFLIGHT CORPORATION

277 Commerce Dr., Glen Rock, PA, 17327

Tel: (717) 227-5400   Fax: (717) 227-1415   www.topflight.com

Commercial printing and service paper.

Topflight Italia, Via C. Colombo, 5, I-27018 Vidigulfo, Italy

THE TOPPS COMPANY, INC.

1 Whitehall Street, New York, NY, 10004-2108

Tel: (212) 376-0300   Fax: (212) 376-0573   www.topps.com

Mfr. entertainment products, principally collectible trading cards, confections, sticker collections, and comic books.

Topps Italia SRL, Via Villoresi 13, I-20143 Milan, Italy

Tel: 39-02-58-100100   Fax: 39-02-58-101122

TOWERS PERRIN

335 Madison Ave., New York, NY, 10017-4605

Tel: (212) 309-3400   Fax: (212) 309-0975   www.towers.com

Management consulting services.

Tillinghast Towers Perrin, Via Pontaccio 10, I-20121 Milan, Italy

Tel: 39-02-863-921   Fax: 39-02-809-753

TOWNSEND ENGINEERING COMPANY, INC.

2425 Hubbell Ave., Des Moines, IA, 50317

Tel: (515) 265-8181   Fax: (515) 263-3355   www.townsendeng.com

Mfr. machinery for food industry.

Townsend Engineering Company, S.S. 33 del Sempione no. 30, I-20014 Nerviano (Milan), Italy

Tel: 39-033-155-5846

THE TRANE COMPANY

3600 Pammel Creek Road, La Crosse, WI, 54601

Tel: (608) 787-2000   Fax: (608) 787-4990   www.trane.com

Mfr. distribution and service of A/C systems and equipment.

Trane Italia SRL, Via Enrico Fermi 21/23, I-20090 Assago, Italy

TRANTER PHE, INC.

PO Box 2289, Wichita Falls, TX, 76306

Tel: (940) 723-7125   Fax: (940) 723-1131   www.tranter.com

Mfr. heat exchangers.

SWEP Italia SRL, Via Ercolano, 24, I-20052 Monza, Italy

Tel: 39-039-282821   Fax: 39-039-834315

TREIBACHER SCHLEIFMITTEL CORPORATION

2000 College Ave., Niagara Falls, NY, 14305

Tel: (716) 286-1234   Fax: (716) 286-1224   www.treibacher-schleifm.com

Mfr. abrasives.

Treibacher Schleifmittel, Via Derna, 32-34, I-20132 Milan, Italy

TRIMBLE NAVIGATION LIMITED

645 N. Mary Ave., Sunnyvale, CA, 94086

Tel: (408) 481-8000   Fax: (408) 481-2000   www.trimble.com

Design/mfr. electronic geographic instrumentation.

Trimble Navigation Italia s.r.l., Largo T. Solera 7, Ed. 1, Sc.B, I-00199 Rome, Italy

Tel: 39-06-8621-6070   Fax: 39-06-8621-7970

TRUSERV CORPORATION

8600 West Bryn Mawr, Chicago, IL, 60631-3505

Tel: (773) 695-5000   Fax: (773) 695-6541   www.truserv.com

Dealer-owned, independent, hardware store cooperative.

TruServ Corporation, Milan, Italy

TRW INC.

1900 Richmond Road, Cleveland, OH, 44124-2760

Tel: (216) 291-7000   Fax: (216) 291-7932   www.trw.com

Electric and energy-related products, automotive and aerospace products, tools and fasteners.

TRW Italia SpA, Via Valtrompia 87, I-25063 Gardone Valtrompia Brescial, Italy

TTI, INC.

2441 Northeast Pkwy., Fort Worth, TX, 76106-1896

Tel: (817) 740-9000   Fax: (817) 740-9898   www.ttiinc.com

Distribution of resistors and capacitors, including cables and sockets.

TTI, Inc., Centro Direzional Milanofiori, Strada 1 Palazzo E1, I-20090 Assago, Italy

TUPPERWARE CORPORATION

14901 S. Orange Blossom Trail, Orlando, FL, 32837

Tel: (407) 826-5050   Fax: (407) 826-8268   www.tupperware.com

Engaged in direct selling of plastic household products.

Tuperware Italy, Milan, Italy

TWIN DISC INCORPORATED

1328 Racine Street, Racine, WI, 53403-1758

Tel: (262) 638-4000   Fax: (262) 638-4482   www.twindisc.com

Mfr. industry clutches, reduction gears and transmissions.

Twin Disc Italia SRL, Via dei Calzolai 92, Z.I. Le Bocchette, I-55040 Capezzano Pianore (Lu), Italy

Twin Disc Technodrive, via S. Cristoforo 131, I-40010 Matteo Decima (BO), Italy

TYCO CAPITAL

1211 Avenue of the Americas, New York, NY, 10036

Tel: (212) 536-1390   Fax: (212) 536-1912   www.citgroup.com

Engaged in commercial finance.

Newcourt, Div. Tyco Capital, Via Alto Vannucci 13, I-20135 Milan, Italy

Tel: 39-258-20310   Fax: 39-258-20380

UNION CARBIDE CORPORATION

39 Old Ridgebury Road, Danbury, CT, 06817

Tel: (203) 794-2000   Fax: (203) 794-6269   www.unioncarbide.com

Mfr. industrial chemicals, plastics and resins.

Union Carbide Chemicals SpA, Milan, Italy

UNISYS CORPORATION.

PO Box 500, Union Meeting Road, Blue Bell, PA, 19424

Tel: (215) 986-4011   Fax: (215) 986-6850   www.unisys.com

Mfr./marketing/servicing electronic information systems.

Unisys Italia SpA, Via B. Crespi 57, I-20159 Milan, Italy

UNITED PARCEL SERVICE, INC.

55 Glenlake Parkway, NE, Atlanta, GA, 30328

Tel: (404) 828-6000   Fax: (404) 828-6593   www.ups.com

International package-delivery service.

UPS Italy s.r.l., Via G. Fantoli 15/2, I-20138 Milan, Italy

Tel: 39-02-167-822054   Fax: 39-02-554-00180

UNITED STATES SURGICAL CORPORATION

150 Glover Ave., Norwalk, CT, 06856

Tel: (203) 845-1000   Fax: (203) 847-0635   www.ussurg.com

Mfr./development/market surgical staplers, laparoscopic instruments and sutures.

U.S. Surgical, Tyco Healthcare Italia SPA, Via Rivoltana 2/d, Palazzina B, I-20090 Segrate Milan, Italy

Tel: 39-02-703171   Fax: 39-02-70317317

UNITED TECHNOLOGIES CORPORATION

One Financial Plaza, Hartford, CT, 06103

Tel: (860) 728-7000   Fax: (860) 728-7979   www.utc.com

Mfr. aircraft engines, elevators, A/C, auto equipment, space and military electronic and rocket propulsion systems. Products include Pratt and Whitney, Otis elevators, Carrier heating and air conditioning and Sikorsky helicopters.

Carrier Italia SpA, Via Boccaccio 35, I-20090 Trezzano Sul Naviglio Milan, Italy

Marlo SpA, Via Vincenzo Monti 23, I-20016 Pero Milan, Italy

S.P. Elettronica, Via Carlo Pisacane 7, I-20016 Pero Milan, Italy

UNIVERSAL CORPORATION

1501 N. Hamilton Street, Richmond, VA, 23230

Tel: (804) 359-9311   Fax: (804) 254-3582   www.universalcorp.com

Holding company for tobacco and commodities.

Deltafina SpA, Via Donizetti 10, I-00198 Rome, Italy

UNIVERSAL SECURITY INSTRUMENTS, INC.

PO Box 825, Binghamton, NY, 13902-0825

Tel: (607) 779-7689   Fax: (607) 779-7301   www.uic.com

Provider of innovative electronic circuit assembly technology and equipment, integrated system solutions, and process expertise.

Laser Optronic SRL, Milan, Italy

Tel: 39-02-57-46-51   Fax: 39-01-57-4101-27

UNIVERSAL WEATHER & AVIATION INC.

8787 Tallyho Road, Houston, TX, 77061

Tel: (713) 944-1622   Fax: (713) 943-4650   www.univ-wea.com

Provides service management, and worldwide weather and communications to the corporate aviation community.

Universal Aviation Italy SRL, Aereoporto Malpensa, I-21013 Gallarte, Italy

UOP LLC

25 East Algonquin Road, Des Plaines, IL, 60017

Tel: (847) 391-2000   Fax: (847) 391-2253   www.uop.com

Engaged in developing and commercializing technology for license to the oil refining, petrochemical and gas processing industries.

UOP M.S., S.p.A., Viale Milano Fiori, Strada 1, Palazzo E1, I-20090 Assago Mi Milan, Italy

Tel: 39-02-57540-1   Fax: 39-02-5750-0145

URS CORPORATION

100 California Street, Ste. 500, San Francisco, CA, 94111

Tel: (415) 774-2700   Fax: (415) 398-1905   www.urscorp.com

Engineering, environmental and construction management services.

Dames & Moore, Via Caldera 21, I-20153 Milan, Italy

UUNET

22001 Loudoun County Pkwy., Ashburn, VA, 20147

Tel: (703) 206-5600   Fax: (703) 206-5601   www.uu.net

World's largest Internet service provider; World Wide Web hosting services, security products and consulting services to businesses, professionals, and on-line service providers.

UUNET Italy, Via Vasto 1, I-20121 Milan, Italy

VALSPAR CORPORATION

1101 South Third Street, Minneapolis, MN, 55415-1259

Tel: (612) 332-7371   Fax: (612) 375-7723   www.valspar.com

Mfr. paints and coatings.

Valspar (Italy) Corporation S.R.l., Via Buzzi No. 4, Mazzo di Rho, I-20017 Milan, Italy

VAPOR BUS INTERNATIONAL

6420 West Howard Street, Niles, IL, 60714-3395

Tel: (847) 967-8300   Fax: (847) 965-9874   www.vapordoors.com

Mfr. bus and rail transit automatic door systems, railcar/locomotive relays and contractors, vehicle ID systems.

HP S.r.l., Viale Regina Pacis 298, I-41049 Sassuolo Modena, Italy

Tel: 39-0536-806-441 Fax: 39-0536-801-789   Contact: Luigi Camellini, Mng. Dir.

VARIAN MEDICAL SYSTEMS, INC.

3050 Hansen Way, Palo Alto, CA, 94304-100

Tel: (650) 493-4000   Fax: (650) 424-5358   www.varian.com

Mfr. microwave tubes and devices, analytical instruments, semiconductor process and medical equipment, vacuum systems.

Varian Medical System Italia SpA, Via Varian 54, I-10040 Lenini Turin, Italy

Varian Medical System Italia SpA, Via Brescia 28 D1, I-20063 Cernusco Sul Naviglio Milan, Italy

VELCRO USA INC.

406 Brown Avenue, Manchester, NH, 03108

Tel: (603) 669-4892   Fax: (603) 669-9271   www.velcro.com

Mfr./sales of Velcro brand hook and loop fasteners, plastic buckles and metal hardware and cable control straps.

Velcro Italia, S.R.L., Via Nazario Sauro 12, I-20043 Arcore Milan, Italy

Tel: 39-39-688-2004   Fax: 39-39-601-5518

VERIFONE, INC.

4988 Great America Pkwy., Santa Clara, CA, 94054-1200

Tel: (408) 496-0444   Fax: (408) 919-5105   www.verifone.com

Mfr. electronic payment software and hardware.

VeriFone SRL, Via Cesare Cantu, 19, I-20092 Cinisello Balsamo (MI), Italy

VERISIGN, INC.

1350 Charleston Rd., Mountain View, CA, 94043

Tel: (650) 961-7500   Fax: (650) 961-7300   www.verisign.com

Mfr. software.

Trust Italy, Via Caradosso, 17, I-20123 Milan, Italy

Contact: Ernesto Pascale

VERIZON COMMUNICATIONS INC.

1095 Ave. of the Americas, New York, NY, 10036

Tel: (212) 395-2121   Fax: (212) 395-1285   www.verizon.com

Telecommunications.

Omnitel Pronto Italia S.p.A., Via Caboto 15, I-20094 Corsico, Italy

Tel: 39-02-41431   Fax: 39-02-4143-3610   Contact: Carlo Peretti, Chmn.

VERNAY LABORATORIES INC.

120 East South College St., Box 310, Yellow Springs, OH, 45387

Tel: (937) 767-7261   Fax: (937) 767-1208   www.vernay.com

Mfr. precision fluid handling products.

Vernay Italia SRL, Localita Rilate 21, I-14100 Asti Piemonte, Italy

VERTEX INTERACTIVE, INC.

22 Audrey Place, Fairfield, NJ, 07004

Tel: (973) 777-3500   Fax: (973) 472-0814   www.vertexinteractive.com

Mfr. software.

Vertex Interactive Italia s.r.l., Via Ponchielli, 1, I-20063 Cernusco, Italy

Tel: 39-02-9290971

VESTAR CAPITAL PARTNERS

245 Park Avenue, 41st Fl., New York, NY, 10167

Tel: (212) 949-6500   Fax: (212) 808-4922   www.vestarcapital.com

Engaged in management buyouts, recapitalizations and growth capital investments.

Vestar Capital Partners Europe, Foro Buonaparte, 67, I-20121 Milan, Italy

Tel: 39-02-8635911   Contact: Giorgio Gandini

VIASYSTEMS GROUP, INC.

101 South Hanley Road, Ste. 40, St. Louis, MO, 63105

Tel: (314) 727-2087   Fax: (314) 719-2255   www.viasystems.com

Engaged in contract manufacturing of printed circuit boards.

Viasystems EMS, Strada Maratta Bassa KM 3,695, I-05100 Terni, Italy

VICOR CORPORATION

25 Frontage Rd., Andover, MA, 01810-5413

Tel: (978) 470-2900   Fax: (978) 749-3536   www.vicr.com

Designs, manufactures, and markets modular power components and complete configurable and custom power systems.

Vicor Italy, Via Milanese 20, I-20099 Sesto S. Giovanni Milan, Italy

VIEWSONIC CORPORATION

381 Brea Canyon Road, Walnut, CA, 91789

Tel: (909) 444-8888   Fax: (909) 869-7958   www.viewsonic.com

Mfr. displays.

ViewSonic Italy, Via Torino 24/2, I-20060 Gessate, Milan, Italy

VIGNETTE CORPORATION

1601 South Mopac Expwy., Bldg. 3, Austin, TX, 78746-5776

Tel: (512) 741-4300   Fax: (512) 741-4500   www.vignette.com

Mfr. software.

Vignette Italy, Via Torino, 2, I-20123 Milan, Italy

THE VIKING CORPORATION

210 N. Industrial Park Rd., Hastings, MI, 49058

Tel: (616) 945-9501   Fax: (616) 945-9599   www.vikingcorp.com

Mfr. fire extinguishing equipment.

Viking Italia SRL, Via Leonardo da Vinci 46/B, I-20030 Senago (Milan), Italy

VISHAY INTERTECHNOLOGY INC.

63 Lincoln Hwy., Malvern, PA, 19355

Tel: (610) 644-1300   Fax: (610) 296-0657   www.vishay.com

Mfr. resistors, strain gages, capacitors, inductors, printed circuit boards.

Vishay S.r.l., Via Gadames 128, I-20151 Milan, Italy

Tel: 39-02-30011911   Fax: 39-02-30011999

VITESSE SEMICONDUCTOR CORPORATION

741 Calle Plano, Camarillo, CA, 93012

Tel: (805) 388-3700   Fax: (805) 389-7188   www.vitesse.com

Mfr. integrated circuits.

Vitesse Semiconductor S.r.L., Via F. Ferruccio 2, I-20145 Milan, Italy

Tel: 39-02-3453-8747   Fax: 39-02-3453-5611   Contact: Guido Carasso

WALBRO ENGINE MANAGEMENT

7400 N. Oracle Road, Ste. 310, Tucson, AZ, 85704

Tel: (520) 877-3000   Fax: (520) 877-3006   www.walbro.com

Mfr. motor vehicle accessories and parts, automotive fluid carrying systems.

TI Group Automotive Systems, Viale Arno 11, PO Box 248, I-72100 Brindisi, Italy

TI Group Automotive Systems, Strada Farnese 9, I-43100 Parma, Italy

TI Group Automotive Systems/Bundy Refrig, Via Giacomo Ponassi 11, Loc La Palazzina, PO Box 9, I-15060 Borghetto Borbera (AL), Italy

Walbro Italy, Via Caduti di Melissa, 12, Casalecchio di Reno, I-40033 Bologna, Italy

Walbro TDD, Via Caduti di Melissa, 12, I-40033 Casalecchio di Reno, Italy

Tel: 39-051-613-2113

THE WARNACO GROUP INC.

90 Park Ave., New York, NY, 10016

Tel: (212) 661-1300   Fax: (212) 687-0480   www.warnaco.com

Mfr./sales intimate apparel and men's and women's sportswear.

Warnaco, Milan, Italy

WARNER BROS.

4000 Warner Boulevard, Bldg.170, 3rd Fl., Burbank, CA, 91522

Tel: (818) 954-6000   Fax: (818) 977-4040   www.wbitv.com

Distributor TV programming and theatrical features.

Warner Bros., Via Giuseppe Avezzana 51, I-00195 Rome, Italy

Tel: 39-06-321-7779   Fax: 39-06-321-7278   Contact: Rosario Ponzio, Mng. Dir.

WARNER ELECTRIC COMPANY

449 Gardner St., South Beloit, IL, 61080

Tel: (815) 389-3771   Fax: (815) 389-2582   www.warnernet.com

Global supplier of Power Transmission and Motion Control Solution Systems; automotive, industry brakes, and clutches.

Dana Italia S.p.A., Via Bernardina Vero 90, I-20141 Milan, Italy

Tel: 39-02-582-1761   Fax: 39-02-5696318

WASHINGTON GROUP INTERNATIONAL, INC.

720 Park Blvd., PO Box 73, Boise, ID, 83729

Tel: (208) 386-5000   Fax: (208) 386-7186   www.wgint.com

Engaged in engineering and construction.

Washington Group International, Inc., Via C. Boncompagni 60, I-20139 Milan, Italy

Tel: 39-02-5220-2661   Fax: 39-02-5220-2665

THE WASHINGTON POST COMPANY

1150 15th St. NW, Washington, DC, 20071

Tel: (202) 334-6000   Fax: (202) 334-4536   www.washpostco.com

Engaged in magazine publishing, cable and television broadcasting, educational services and the Internet.

International Herald Tribune, Via Mecenate 91, I-20138 Milan, Italy

Tel: 39-2-5095-6545

WASTE MANAGEMENT, INC.

1001 Fannin Street, Ste. 4000, Houston, TX, 77002

Tel: (713) 512-6200   Fax: (713) 512-6299   www.wastemanagement.com

Environmental services and disposal company; collection, processing, transfer and disposal facilities.

Waste Management Italia SRL, Via XXV Aprile 59, I-22070 Guanzate, Italy

WATERS CORPORATION

34 Maple Street, Milford, MA, 01757

Tel: (508) 478-2000   Fax: (508) 872-1990   www.waters.com

Mfr./distribute liquid chromatographic instruments and test and measurement equipment.

Waters SpA, Via Achille Grandi, 27, I-20090 Vimodrone Milan, Italy

WATLOW ELECTRIC MFG. COMPANY

12001 Lackland Rd., St. Louis, MO, 63146-4039

Tel: (314) 878-4600   Fax: (314) 434-1020   www.watlow.com

Mfr. electrical heating units, electronic controls, thermocouple wire, metal-sheathed cable, infrared sensors.

Watlow Italy SRL, Via Adige 13, I-20135 Milan, Italy

Tel: 39-02-541-6941   Fax: 39-02-5519-1596

WATSON WYATT & COMPANY HOLDINGS

1717 H Street NW, Washington, DC, 20006-3807

Tel: (202) 715-7000   Fax: (202) 715-7700   www.watsonwyatt.com

Creates compensation and benefits programs for major corporations.

Watson Wyatt S.r.l., Via XX Settembre 98/E, I-00187 Rome, Italy

Tel: 39-06-320-2026   Fax: 39-06-320-2028   Contact: Sandro Catani

WATTS INDUSTRIES, INC.

815 Chestnut Street, North Andover, MA, 01845-6098

Tel: (978) 688-1811   Fax: (978) 688-5841   www.wattsind.com

Designs/mfr./sales of industry valves and safety control products.

Intermes SpA, Via Bellini 30, I-20095 Cusano Milanino Milan, Italy

Intermes SpA, Zona Industriale, I-39052 Caldaro, Italy

ISI Industria Saracinesche Idrauliche SpA, Zona Industriale, Localita Ischiello, I-38015 Lavis, Italy

WD-40 COMPANY

1061 Cudahy Place, San Diego, CA, 92110-3998

Tel: (619) 275-1400   Fax: (619) 275-5823   www.wd40.com

Mfr. branded multiple-purpose lubrication, protection and general maintenance products.

WD-40 Company Ltd., Strada Maggiore 49, I-40125 Bologna, Italy

Tel: 39-51-636-0252   Fax: 39 51 342 80

WEATHERFORD INTERNATIONAL, INC.

515 Post Oak Blvd. Ste. 600, Houston, TX, 77027-3415

Tel: (713) 287-8400   Fax: (713) 963-9785   www.weatherford.com

Oilfield services, products and equipment; mfr. marine cranes for oil and gas industry.

Weatherford Intl. Inc., Via Stabbio 90, I-24044 Bergamo Dalmine, Italy

Tel: 39-353-70573   Fax: 39-353-70584

Weatherford Italiana SpA, Via Pirano 19, I-48100 Ravenna, Italy

Tel: 39-054-443-5911   Fax: 39-054-4436-519

JERVIS B. WEBB COMPANY

34375 W.Twelve Mile Rd., Farmington Hills, MI, 48331

Tel: (248) 553-1220   Fax: (248) 553-1237   www.jervisbwebb.com

Mfr. integrators of material handling systems solutions.

CoMeCar (Representative), Torino, Italy

Tel: 39-011-358-2982   Fax: 39-011-358-1937

WELCH ALLYN INC.

4341 State Street Road, Skaneateles Falls, NY, 13153

Tel: (315) 685-4100   Fax: (315) 685-4091   www.welchallyn.com

Mfr. fiber optic products and medical diagnostic equipment.

Welch Allyn Italy, Napo Torriani 29, I-20124 Milan, Italy

Fax: 39-2-6671-3599

WENDY'S INTERNATIONAL, INC.

4288 West Dublin Granville Roads, Dublin, OH, 43017-0256

Tel: (614) 764-3100   Fax: (614) 764-3459   www.wendysintl.com

Fast food restaurant chain.

Wendy's International, Rome, Italy

WENNER MEDIA LLC

1290 Ave. of the Americas, New York, NY, 10104

Tel: (212) 484-1616   Fax: (212) 484-1713   www.usmagazine.com

Publishes entertainment magazines, including Rolling Stone, US Weekly and Men's Journal.

Rolling Stone Magazine, Via G. Compagnoni 24, I-20129 Milan, Italy

Tel: 39-02-7000-3528

WEYERHAEUSER COMPANY

33663 Weyerhaeuser Way South, Federal Way, WA, 98003

Tel: (253) 924-2345   Fax: (253) 924-2685   www.weyerhaeuser.com

Wood and wood fiber products.

Weyerhaeuser Italia SRL, Viale Tunisia 38, I-20124 Milan, Italy

WHIRLPOOL CORPORATION

2000 N. M-63, Benton Harbor, MI, 49022-2692

Tel: (616) 923-5000   Fax: (616) 923-5443   www.whirlpoolcorp.com

Mfr., market home appliances: Whirlpool, Roper, KitchenAid, Estate, and Inglis.

Whirlpool Europe BV, Viale G. Borghi 27, I-21025 Comerio, Italy

W. A. WHITNEY COMPANY

650 Race Street, PO Box 1206, Rockford, IL, 61105-1206

Tel: (815) 964-6771   Fax: (815) 964-3175   www.wawhitney.com

Mfr. thermal cutting (plasma and laser), punching, and punch/plasma equipment systems and tooling.

W.A. Whitney Italia SpA, Strade del Francese 132/9, I-10156 Torino, Italy

Tel: 39-011-470-2702

WIDIA VALENITE INC

31700 Research Park Dr., Madison Heights, MI, 48071-4627

Tel: (248) 589-1000   Fax: (248) 597-4820   www.valenite.com

Cemented carbide, high speed steel, ceramic and diamond cutting tool products, etc.

Widia Valenite Italia SPA, Via Milano, 42, I-20090 Cesano Boscone, Italy

WILLKIE FARR & GALLAGHER

787 Seventh Avenue, New York, NY, 10019-6099

Tel: (212) 821-8000   Fax: (212) 821-8111   www.willkie.com

International law firm.

Willkie Farr & Gallagher, Via di Ripetta 142, I-00186 Rome, Italy

Willkie Farr & Gallagher, Via Michele Barozzi 2, I-20122 Milan, Italy

WIND RIVER SYSTEMS, INC.

500 Wind River Way, Alameda, CA, 94501

Tel: (510) 748-4100   Fax: (510) 749-2010   www.isi.com

Develops and markets computer software products and services.

Wind River Systems Italia s.r.l., Piazza Don Enrico Mapelli 60, Sestet San Giovanni, I-20099 Milan, Italy

Wind River Systems Italia s.r.l., Centro Direzionale, Piero della Francesca, Corso Svizzera 185, I-10149 Torino, Italy

Tel: 39-011-750-1511

WOODHEAD INDUSTRIES INC.

Three Parkway North, Ste. 550, Deerfield, IL, 60015

Tel: (847) 236-9300   Fax: (847) 236-0503   www.woodhead.com

Develop/mfr./sale/distributor elect/electronic, fiber optic and ergonomic special-function, non-commodity products.

mPm S.p.A., Via Zucchi 39, int. G, I-20095 Cusano Milanino Milan, Italy

WORLD COURIER INC.

45 Southfield Avenue, Ste. 3450, Stamford, CT, 06902-7210

Tel: (203) 975-9333   Fax: (203) 316-9455   www.worldcourier.com

International courier service.

World Courier Italia SRL, Via Mecenate 30, 6, Milan, Italy

WORLD MINERALS INC.

130 Castilian Drive, Santa Barbara, CA, 93117

Tel: (805) 562-0200   Fax: (805) 562-0298   www.worldminerals.com

Mfr. premium quality diatomite and perlite products.

World Minerals Italiana SRL, Alzaia Trento 6, I-20094 Corsico, Italy

Tel: 39-02-451-741   Fax: 39-02-440-9451

WORLDCOM, INC.

500 Clinton Center Drive, Clinton, MS, 39060

Tel: (601) 360-8600   Fax: (601) 360-8616   www.wcom.com

Telecommunications; serving local, long distance and Internet customers domestically and internationally. **Corporation under worldwide reorganization under Chapter 11 Bankruptcy; new data unavailable for this edition.

WorldCom International, Via San Simpliciano 1, Corso Garibaldi 86, I-20121 Milano, Italy

WRIGHT MEDICAL GROUP, INC.

5677 Airline Road, Arlington, TN, 38002

Tel: (901) 867-9971   Fax: (901) 867-9534   www.wmt.com

Mfr. orthopedic reconstructive implants.

Wright Cremascoli Ortho SpA, Via Clemente Prudenzio 14/16, I-20138 Milan, Italy

WYETH

5 Giralda Farms, Madison, NJ, 07940-0874

Tel: (973) 660-5000   Fax: (973) 660-7026   www.wyeth.com

Mfr. consumer healthcare products.

Fort Dodge Animal Health, Viale Masini, I-12-40126 Bologna, Italy

Tel: 39-051-421-5312

Whitehall Italia S.p.A., Via G. Puccini, 3, I-20121 Milan, Italy

Tel: 39-02-806918-1

WYETH PHARMACEUTICALS

555 E. Lancaster Ave., Wayne, PA, 19087-5109

Tel: (610) 971-5400   Fax: (610) 995-4668   www.wyeth.com

Mfr. antibiotics and pharmaceutical products.

Wyeth-Lederle SpA, Via Nettunense 90, I-04011 Aprilia Latina, Italy

Tel: 39-06-927-151   Fax: 39-06-927-15-700

Wyeth-Lederle SpA, Via Franco Gorgone, Zone Industriale, I-95030 Catania, Italy

Tel: 39-95-59-8111

XEROX CORPORATION

800 Long Ridge Road, PO Box 1600, Stamford, CT, 06904

Tel: (203) 968-3000   Fax: (203) 968-4312   www.xerox.com

Mfr. document processing equipment, systems and supplies.

Xerox Italy, Strada Padana Superiore 28, I-20063 Cernusco S/N (MI), Italy

Xerox, S.p.A, Strada Padana Superiore 28, I-20063 Cernusco SN Milan, Italy

Tel: 39-02-92-1881   Fax: 39-02-9236-8209

XIRCOM, INC.

2300 Corporate Center Drive, Thousand Oaks, CA, 91320

Tel: (805) 376-9300   Fax: (805) 376-9311   www.xircom.com

Mfr. PC card network adapters and modems.

Xircom France Srl, Via Giovanni da Udine 34, I-20156 Milan, Italy

XTRA CORPORATION

200 Nyala Farms Rd., Westport, CT, 06880

Tel: (203) 221-1005   Fax: (203) 221-9024   www.xtracorp.com

Holding company: leasing.

XTRA International, Milan, Italy

YAHOO! INC.

701 First Avenue, Sunnyvale, CA, 94089

Tel: (408) 439-3300   Fax: (408) 439-3301   www.yahoo-inc.com

Internet media company providing specialized content, free electronic mail and community offerings and commerce.

Yahoo! Inc., Regus Milan, Via Torino 2, I-20122 Milan, Italy

Tel: 39-02-7254-6207   Fax: 39-02-7254-6400

YORK INTERNATIONAL CORPORATION

631 South Richland Ave., York, PA, 17403

Tel: (717) 771-7890   Fax: (717) 771-6212   www.york.com

Mfr. heating, ventilating, air conditioning and refrigeration equipment.

York International S.p.A, 29 Via XXV Aprile, I-20030 Barlassina Milan, Italy

Tel: 39-362-5381

YOUNG & RUBICAM INC.

285 Madison Ave., New York, NY, 10017

Tel: (212) 210-3000   Fax: (212) 370-3796   www.yr.com

Advertising, public relations, direct marketing and sales promotion, corporate and product ID management.

Young & Rubicam Italia SpA, Piazza Eleonora Duse 2, I-20122 Milan, Italy

ZEBRA TECHNOLOGIES CORPORATION

333 Corporate Woods Pkwy., Vernon Hills, IL, 60061-3109

Tel: (847) 634-6700   Fax: (847) 913-8766   www.zebracorporation.com

Mfr. bar code systems.

Zebra Technologies Europe Limited, Via Dell'Arcoveggio 41/5, I-40100 Bologna, Italy

Tel: 33-1-552-09393

ZIMMER HOLDINGS, INC.

345 East Main St., Warsaw, IN, 46580

Tel: (574) 267-6131   Fax: (574) 372-4988   www.zimmer.com

Engaged in design and manufacture of orthopedic products.

Zimmer Italy, Via Milano 6, I-20097 San Donato Milanese, Italy

Tel: 39-02-98-2121   Fax: 39-02-9842-6460

JOHN ZINK COMPANY

11920 East Apache, Tulsa, OK, 74121-1220

Tel: (918) 234-1800   Fax: (918) 234-2700   www.johnzink.com

Engaged in the development and manufacture of next-generation combustion products, technologies and clean-air solutions that power global industry.

John Zink Srl, Via F. Casati 32, I-20124 Milan, Italy

Tel: 39-02-6698-1232   Contact: Daniel Civardi

Ivory Coast

AIG AMERICAN INTERNATIONAL GROUP INC.

70 Pine Street, New York, NY, 10270

Tel: (212) 770-7000   Fax: (212) 509-9705   www.aig.com

Worldwide insurance and financial services.

American Intl. Assurance Co. Ltd., 08 Boite Postale 873, Abidjan, Ivory Coast

LOUIS BERGER INTERNATIONAL INC.

100 Halsted Street, East Orange, NJ, 07019

Tel: (201) 678-1960   Fax: (201) 672-4284   www.louisberger.com

Consulting engineers, engaged in architecture, environmental and advisory services.

Louis Berger International Inc., Residence Sainte Anne, 04 Boite Postale 295, Cocody Abidjan, Ivory Coast

Tel: 225-210-079   Fax: 225-211-058

Louis Berger International Inc., Route de Facobly, Boite Postale 346, Man, Ivory Coast

BJ SERVICES COMPANY

5500 NW Central Drive, Houston, TX, 77092

Tel: (713) 462-4239   Fax: (713) 895-5898   www.bjservices.com

Provides pressure pumping services to the petroleum and oil businesses.

BJ Services, Abidjan, Ivory Coast

Tel: 225-2127-3280

CITIGROUP, INC.

399 Park Avenue, New York, NY, 10022

Tel: (212) 559-1000   Fax: (212) 559-3646   www.citigroup.com

Provides insurance and financial services worldwide.

Citigroup, Immeuble Botreau-Roussel, 18 Ave. Delafosse, 01 Boite Postale 3698, Abidjan, Ivory Coast

Contact: Mark H. Wiessing

COLGATE-PALMOLIVE COMPANY

300 Park Ave., New York, NY, 10022

Tel: (212) 310-2000   Fax: (212) 310-2919   www.colgate.com

Mfr. pharmaceuticals, cosmetics, toiletries and detergents.

Colgate-Palmolive Cote d'Ivoire, Blvd. Giscard d'Estaing, 01 Boite Postale 1283, Abidjan, Ivory Coast

DELOITTE TOUCHE TOHMATSU INTERNATIONAL

1633 Broadway, New York, NY, 10019

Tel: (212) 492-4000   Fax: (212) 392-4154   www.deloitte.com

Accounting, audit, tax and management consulting services.

Deloitte & Touche, Immeuble Alpha 2000, 14e Etag, rue Gourgas, Plateau, (B.P. 224), Abidjan 01, Ivory Coast

DHL WORLDWIDE EXPRESS

50 California Avenue, San Francisco, CA, 94111

Tel: (415) 677-6100   Fax: (415) 824-9700   www.dhl.com

Worldwide air express carrier.

DHL Worldwide Express, Ivory Coast

Tel: 225-249999

THE DOW CHEMICAL COMPANY

2030 Dow Center, Midland, MI, 48674

Tel: (989) 636-1000   Fax: (989) 636-3228   www.dow.com

Mfr. chemicals, plastics, pharmaceuticals, agricultural products, consumer products.

Dow Chemical Co., Boite Postale 1521, Abidjan, Ivory Coast

ERNST & YOUNG INTERNATIONAL

5 Times Square, New York, NY, 10036

Tel: (212) 773-3000   Fax: (212) 773-6350   www.eyi.com

Engaged in assurance and advisory business services, tax, law and corporate finance.

Ernst & Young International, 5 Ave. Marchand, 01 Boite Postale 2715, Abidjan, Ivory Coast

FFA Ernst & Young, 5 Ave. Marchand, 01 Boite Postale 1222, Abidjan, Ivory Coast

Tel: 225-21-11-15   Fax: 225-21-12-59   Contact: Leon Dakouri

FMC CORPORATION

1735 Market St., Philadelphia, PA, 19103

Tel: (215) 299-6000   Fax: (215) 299-6618   www.fmc.com

Mfr. specialty chemicals, including alginate, carrageenan and microcrystalline cellulose.

FMC Corp., 2, rue de la Canebiere, OB BP 723, Abidjon 8, Ivory Coast

FRITZ COMPANIES, INC., DIV. UPS

706 Mission Street, Ste. 900, San Francisco, CA, 94103

Tel: (415) 904-8360   Fax: (415) 904-8661   www.fritz.com

Integrated transportation, sourcing, distribution and customs brokerage services.

Fritz Companies Inc., Ivory Coast

H.J. HEINZ COMPANY

600 Grant Street, Pittsburgh, PA, 15219

Tel: (412) 456-5700   Fax: (412) 456-6128   www.heinz.com

Processed food products and nutritional services.

Star-Kist Foods Inc., Abidjan, Ivory Coast

SC JOHNSON

1525 Howe St., Racine, WI, 53403

Tel: (262) 260-2000   Fax: (262) 260-2133   www.scjohnsonwax.com

Home, auto, commercial and personal care products and specialty chemicals.

SC Johnson, c/o CFCI Div. Technique, Boite Postale 1844, Abidjan, Ivory Coast

LEXMARK INTERNATIONAL

740 W. New Circle Rd., Lexington, KY, 40550

Tel: (859) 232-2000   Fax: (859) 232-1886   www.lexmark.com

Develop, manufacture, supply of printing solutions and products, including laser, inkjet, and dot matrix printers.

Revendeur Lexmark, BP 2292, Abidjan 11, Ivory Coast

ELI LILLY & COMPANY

Lilly Corporate Center, Indianapolis, IN, 46285

Tel: (317) 276-2000   Fax: (317) 277-6579   www.lilly.com

Mfr. pharmaceuticals and animal health products.

Eli Lilly - Bureau d'Informations, 01 Boite Postale 8615, Abidjan, Ivory Coast

Tel: 225-22-36-18   Fax: 225-22-36-14

McCANN-ERICKSON WORLDGROUP

750 Third Ave., New York, NY, 10017

Tel: (212) 697-6000   Fax: (212) 984-3575   www.mccann.com

International advertising and marketing services.

Nelson McCann-Ivory Coast, Ave. Giscard d'Estaing face a "La Galerie", 01 Boite Postale 3420, Abidjan, Ivory Coast

J. P. MORGAN CHASE & CO. INC.

270 Park Ave., New York, NY, 10017

Tel: (212) 270-6000   Fax: (212) 622-9030   www.jpmorganchase.com

Provides integrated financial solutions for institutions and individuals worldwide, including asset management, investment banking and commercial banking.

J. P. Morgan Chase & Co., 01 Boite Postale 4107, Abidjan, Ivory Coast

PHILLIPS PETROLEUM COMPANY

Phillips Building, 411 S. Keeler Ave., Bartlesville, OK, 74004

Tel: (918) 661-6600   Fax: (918) 661-7636   www.phillips66.com

Crude oil, natural gas, liquefied petroleum gas, gasoline and petro-chemicals.

Phillips Petroleum, Boite Postale 20947, Abidjan, Ivory Coast

PRICEWATERHOUSECOOPERS LLP

1301 Ave. of the Americas, New York, NY, 10019

Tel: (212) 596-7000   Fax: (212) 259-1301   www.pwcglobal.com

Accounting and auditing, tax and management, and human resource consulting services.

PriceWaterhouseCoopers, Boite Postale 2921, Abidjan 01, Ivory Coast

Tel: 225-22-22-89   Fax: 225-22-87-02

PRIDE INTERNATIONAL, INC.

5847 San Felipe, Ste. 3300, Houston, TX, 77057

Tel: (713) 789-1400   Fax: (713) 789-1430   www.prde.com

Provides drilling services.

Pride Foramer, Angle de l'avenue Nogues et du Bd, Botreau, Le Plateau 17 BP 458, Ivory Coast

TIDEWATER INC.

601 Poydras Street, Ste.1900, New Orleans, LA, 70130

Tel: (504) 568-1010   Fax: (504) 566-4582   www.tdw.com

Marine service and equipment to companies engaged in exploration, development and production of oil, gas and minerals.

Tidewater Marine International, Inc., Apt. 38A, 57/F, Immeuble Longchamp Plateau, Abidjan 01, Ivory Coast

Tel: 225-22-69-58   Fax: 225-21-72-00

TRANSOCEAN INC.

4 Greenway Plaza, Houston, TX, 77046

Tel: (713) 232-7500   Fax: (713) 232-7027   www.deepwater.com

Engaged in oil and gas offshore drilling.

Transocean Inc., Avenue Houdaille, Immeuble Ranger Oil, 01 BP 8707 Abidjan 01, Ivory Coast

UNITED PARCEL SERVICE, INC.

55 Glenlake Parkway, NE, Atlanta, GA, 30328

Tel: (404) 828-6000   Fax: (404) 828-6593   www.ups.com

International package-delivery service.

UPS, Treichville Immeuble Nanan Yamousso, Esc I, Apt. 141, 1 er étage, 05 Boite Postale 2877, Abidjan, Ivory Coast

Tel: 225-25-97-40   Fax: 225-25-97-40

THE WACKENHUT CORPORATION

4200 Wackenhut Dr., Ste. 100, Palm Beach Gardens, FL, 33410

Tel: (561) 622-5656   Fax: (561) 691-6736   www.wackenhut.com

Security systems and services.

Wackenhut Seges, 2 Plateaux rue des Jardins, Boite Postale 2159, Abidjan, Ivory Coast

Tel: 225-425926   Fax: 225-425141

HARRY WINSTON INC.

718 Fifth Ave., New York, NY, 10019

Tel: (212) 245-2000   Fax: (212) 245-2000   www.harry-winston.com

Diamonds and lapidary work.

Societe Wharton, Boite Postale 2816, Abidjan, Ivory Coast

XEROX CORPORATION

800 Long Ridge Road, PO Box 1600, Stamford, CT, 06904

Tel: (203) 968-3000   Fax: (203) 968-4312   www.xerox.com

Mfr. document processing equipment, systems and supplies.

Ivoire Document Systems, Immeuble Carville Bd, Giscard d'Estaing, 01 Boite Postale 402, Abdijan, Ivory Coast

Tel: 225-256-060   Fax: 225-255-950

YORK INTERNATIONAL CORPORATION

631 South Richland Ave., York, PA, 17403

Tel: (717) 771-7890   Fax: (717) 771-6212   www.york.com

Mfr. heating, ventilating, air conditioning and refrigeration equipment.

AFRIC Refrigeration, rue de Chimistes, I. Vridi, 15 BP 1111, Abidjan 15-RC I, Ivory Coast

Tel: 225-27-3448

Jamaica

3M (MINNESOTA MINING & MFG.)

3M Center, St. Paul, MN, 55144-1000

Tel: (651) 733-1110   Fax: (651) 733-9973   www.mmm.com

Mfr. diversified products for industry, consumer, health care, imaging, communications, transport, safety, etc.

3M Interamerica Inc., 218 Marcus Garvey Lane, Kingston 11, Jamaica

Tel: 809-937-3859   Fax: 809-937-4369

AIG AMERICAN INTERNATIONAL GROUP INC.

70 Pine Street, New York, NY, 10270

Tel: (212) 770-7000   Fax: (212) 509-9705   www.aig.com

Worldwide insurance and financial services.

American Intl. Underwriters (Jamaica) Ltd., 25 Dominica Drive, 5th Fl., Kingston, Jamaica

ALCOA INC.

Alcoa Center, 201 Isabella Street at 7th Street Bridge, Pittsburgh, PA, 15212-5858

Tel: (412) 553-4545   Fax: (412) 553-4498   www.alcoa.com

World's leading producer of aluminum and alumina; mining, refining, smelting, fabricating and recycling.

Alcoa Minerals of Jamaica L.L.C., PO Box 241, Kingston 6, Jamaica

ALCOA FUJIKURA LTD.

800 Crescent Centre Drive, Ste. 600, Franklin, TN, 37067

Tel: (615) 778-6000   Fax: (615) 778-5927   www.alcoa-fujikura.com

Mfr. optical ground wire, tube cable, fiber optic connectors and automotive wiring harnesses. (JV of Alcoa USA).

Alcoa Minerals of Jamaica, L.L.C., Clarendon, Jamaica

AMR CORPORATION (AMERICAN AIRLINES)

4333 Amon Carter Boulevard, Ft. Worth, TX, 76155

Tel: (817) 963-1234   Fax: (817) 967-9641   www.amrcorp.com

Air transport services.

American Airlines Inc., PO Box 159, Windward Rd. Station, Kingston 2, Jamaica

ANC RENTAL CORPORATION

200 S. Andrews Ave., Ft. Lauderdale, FL, 33301

Tel: (954) 320-4000   Fax: (954) 320-4077   www.ancrental.com

Engaged in car rental services, including National Car Rental and Alamo Rent A Car.

National Car Rental, 16 Beechwood Ave., Kingston 5, Jamaica

AVIS GROUP HOLDINGS, INC.

6 Sylvan Way, Parsippany, NJ, 07054

Tel: (973) 222-3000   Fax: (973) 222-4381   www.avis.com

Car rental services.

Avis Group Holdings Ltd., 3 Oxford Rd., New Kingston, Jamaica

D. D. BEAN & SONS COMPANY

Peterborough Road, PO Box 348, Jaffrey, NH, 03452

Tel: (603) 532-8311   Fax: (603) 532-7361   www.ddbean.com

Mfr. paper book and wooden stick matches.

Jamaica Match Holdings Ltd., DD Bean & Sons, PO Box 370, Kingston 11, Jamaica

LOUIS BERGER INTERNATIONAL INC.

100 Halsted Street, East Orange, NJ, 07019

Tel: (201) 678-1960   Fax: (201) 672-4284   www.louisberger.com

Consulting engineers, engaged in architecture, environmental and advisory services.

Louis Berger International Inc., Office Center UDC Building, 12 Ocean Boulevard, 7th Floor, Kingston, Jamaica

SAMUEL BINGHAM ENTERPRISES INC.

9529 South Main Street, Jonesboro, GA, 30236

Tel: (770) 477-7503   Fax: (770) 477-9532   www.binghamrollers.com

Mfr. rubber covered rolls, chemicals and supplies for the printing industry.

Coates Bros. (Jamaica) Ltd., PO Box 317, Kingston 11, Jamaica

Tel: 876-923-6028

BLUE CROSS AND BLUE SHIELD ASSOC.

225 N. Michigan Ave., Chicago, IL, 60601-7680

Tel: (312) 297-6000   Fax: (312) 297-6609   www.blueshield.com

Provides health care coverage through indemnity insurance, HMO's and Medicare programs.

The University Hospital West Indies, Mona, St. Andrew, Kingston 7, Jamaica

BRISTOL-MYERS SQUIBB COMPANY

345 Park Ave., New York, NY, 10154-0037

Tel: (212) 546-4000   Fax: (212) 546-4020   www.bms.com

Pharmaceutical and food preparations, medical and surgical instruments.

Mead Johnson Jamaica Ltd., 16 Half Way Tree Rd., Kingston 5, Jamaica

Mead Johnson Jamaica Ltd., 8 Carvalho Drive, Kingston 10, Jamaica

Media-Grace, 33 1/2 Eastwood Park Road, Kingston, Jamaica

CARBOLINE COMPANY

350 Hanley Industrial Court, St. Louis, MO, 63144

Tel: (314) 644-1000   Fax: (314) 644-4617   www.carboline.com

Mfr. coatings and sealants.

Berger Paints Jamaica Ltd., PO Box 8, 256 Spanish Town Rd., Kingston 11, Jamaica

CHEVRON TEXACO CORPORATION

575 Market Street, San Francisco, CA, 94105-2856

Tel: (415) 894-7700   Fax: (415) 894-2248   www.chevrontexaco.com

Oil exploration, production and petroleum products.

ChevronTexaco Caribbean Inc., Mutual Life Centre, 2 Oxford Street, Kingston 5, Jamaica

CHOICE HOTELS INTERNATIONAL, INC.

10750 Columbia Pike, Silver Springs, MD, 20902

Tel: (301) 592-5000   Fax: (301) 592-6227   www.choicehotels.com

Hotel franchises, including Comfort Inn, Econo Lodge, Roadway Inn and Quality.

Comfort Suites Crane Ridge, 17 La Costa Drive, Ocho Rios, Jamaica

CIGNA COMPANIES

One Liberty Place, Philadelphia, PA, 19192

Tel: (215) 761-1000   Fax: (215) 761-5511   www.cigna.com

Insurance, invest, health care and other financial services.

Insurance Co. of North America, 21 Constant Spring Rd., Kingston, Jamaica

CITIGROUP, INC.

399 Park Avenue, New York, NY, 10022

Tel: (212) 559-1000   Fax: (212) 559-3646   www.citigroup.com

Provides insurance and financial services worldwide.

Citigroup, 63-67 Knutsford Blvd., PO Box 286, Kingston 5, Jamaica

Contact: Peter H. Moses

COLGATE-PALMOLIVE COMPANY

300 Park Ave., New York, NY, 10022

Tel: (212) 310-2000   Fax: (212) 310-2919   www.colgate.com

Mfr. pharmaceuticals, cosmetics, toiletries and detergents.

Colgate-Palmolive (Jamaica) Ltd., 26 Marcus Garvey Dr., Kingston 11, Jamaica

CUNA MUTUAL BUSINESS SERVICES

5910 Mineral Point Rd., PO Box 391, Madison, WI, 53701

Tel: (608) 238-5851   Fax: (608) 238-0830   www.cunamutual.com

Insurance services.

CUNA Mutual Insurance, 2A Manhattan Rd., PO Box 396, Kingston 5, Jamaica

DANZAS AEI, INC.

120 Tokeneke Road, PO Box 1231, Darien, CT, 06820

Tel: (203) 655-7900   Fax: (203) 655-5779   www.aeilogistics.com

International air freight forwarder.

Danzas AEI, 89 East St., Kingston, Jamaica

Tel: 809-922-2537   Fax: 809-967-2773

DELOITTE TOUCHE TOHMATSU INTERNATIONAL

1633 Broadway, New York, NY, 10019

Tel: (212) 492-4000   Fax: (212) 392-4154   www.deloitte.com

Accounting, audit, tax and management consulting services.

Deloitte & Touche, 7 West Ave., PO Box 13, Kingston Gardens Kingston 4, Jamaica

Deloitte & Touche, 42B & 42C Union St., PO Box 60, Montego Bay, Jamaica

DHL WORLDWIDE EXPRESS

50 California Avenue, San Francisco, CA, 94111

Tel: (415) 677-6100   Fax: (415) 824-9700   www.dhl.com

Worldwide air express carrier.

DHL Worldwide Express, 54 Duke St., Kingston, Jamaica

Tel: 876-922-7333

DOVER CORPORATION

280 Park Ave., New York, NY, 10017-1292

Tel: (212) 922-1640   Fax: (212) 922-1656   www.dovercorporation.com

Holding company for varied industries; assembly and testing equipment, oil-well gear and other industrial products.

Multi-Tec Engineering Services, Ltd., 4 Balmoral Ave., Kingston, Jamaica

Tel: 876-926-4663   Fax: 876-929-9119

ECOLAB INC.

370 N. Wabasha Street, St. Paul, MN, 55102

Tel: (651) 293-2233   Fax: (651) 293-2379   www.ecolab.com

Develop/mfr. premium cleaning, sanitizing and maintenance products and services for the hospitality, institutional, and residential markets.

Ecolab Ltd., Kingston, Jamaica

Tel: 876-926-0750

EGL INC. (EAGLE GLOBAL LOGISTICS)

15350 Vickery Drive, Houston, TX, 77032

Tel: (281) 618-3100   Fax: (281) 618-3223   www.eagleusa.com

Ocean/air freight forwarding, customs brokerage, packing and wholesale, logistics management and insurance.

EGL Eagle Global Logistics, 105 Second St., Newport West, PO Box 113, Kingston 15, Jamaica

Tel: 809-923-6562   Fax: 809-923-3139

ENRON CORPORATION

1400 Smith Street, Houston, TX, 77002-7369

Tel: (713) 853-6161   Fax: (713) 853-3129   www.enron.com

Exploration, production, transportation and distribution of integrated natural gas and electricity. **Corporation under worldwide reorganization; new data unavailable for this edition.

Industrial Gases Ltd., 595 Spanish Town Road, PO Box 224, Kingston, Jamaica

Tel: 809-923-8434   Fax: 809-923-4058

ERNST & YOUNG INTERNATIONAL

5 Times Square, New York, NY, 10036

Tel: (212) 773-3000   Fax: (212) 773-6350   www.eyi.com

Engaged in assurance and advisory business services, tax, law and corporate finance.

Ernst & Young International, 28 Beechwood Ave., PO Box 351, Kingston 5, Jamaica

Tel: 809-929-1616   Fax: 809-926-7580   Contact: Vilma Wallen

FRITZ COMPANIES, INC., DIV. UPS

706 Mission Street, Ste. 900, San Francisco, CA, 94103

Tel: (415) 904-8360   Fax: (415) 904-8661   www.fritz.com

Integrated transportation, sourcing, distribution and customs brokerage services.

Fritz Companies Inc., Kingston, Jamaica

THE GILLETTE COMPANY

Prudential Tower Building, Boston, MA, 02199

Tel: (617) 421-7000   Fax: (617) 421-7123   www.gillette.com

Develop/mfr. personal care/use products: blades and razors, toiletries, cosmetics, stationery.

Gillette Caribbean Ltd., Kingston, Jamaica

Contact: Práxedes M. Rivera-Ferrer, Gen. Mgr.

Gillette Foreign Sales Corp. Ltd., Kingston, Jamaica

Contact: Práxedes M. Rivera-Ferrer, Gen. Mgr.

THE GOODYEAR TIRE & RUBBER COMPANY

1144 East Market Street, Akron, OH, 44316

Tel: (330) 796-2121   Fax: (330) 796-1817   www.goodyear.com

Mfr. tires, automotive belts and hose, conveyor belts, chemicals; oil pipeline transmission.

Goodyear (Jamaica) Ltd., 29 Tobago Ave., Kingston 10, Jamaica

GREY GLOBAL GROUP

777 Third Ave., New York, NY, 10017

Tel: (212) 546-2000   Fax: (212) 546-1495   www.grey.com

International advertising agency.

Grimax Advertising, Kingston, Jamaica

HOLIDAY INN (BASS RESORTS) WORLDWIDE, INC.

3 Ravinia Drive, Ste. 2900, Atlanta, GA, 30346-2149

Tel: (770) 604-2000   Fax: (770) 604-5403   www.holidayinn.com

Hotels, restaurants and casinos.

Rose Hall, PO Box 480, Montego Bay, Jamaica

IBM CORPORATION

1133 Westchester Avenue, White Plains, NY, 10604

Tel: (914) 765-1900   Fax: (914) 765-7382   www.ibm.com

Information products, technology and services.

IBM World Trade Corporation, 52-56 Knutsford Blvd., PO Box 391, New Kingston, Kingston 5, Jamaica

Tel: 876-926-3200

J. WALTER THOMPSON COMPANY

466 Lexington Ave., New York, NY, 10017

Tel: (212) 210-7000   Fax: (212) 210-6944   www.jwt.com

International advertising and marketing services.

Dunlop Corbin Communications, Kingston, Jamaica

JOHNSON & JOHNSON

One Johnson & Johnson Plaza, New Brunswick, NJ, 08933

Tel: (732) 524-0400   Fax: (732) 214-0334   www.jnj.com

Mfr./distributor/R&D pharmaceutical, health care and cosmetic products.

Johnson & Johnson Ltd., PO Box 8103, Kingston 11, Jamaica

KAISER ALUMINUM CORPORATION

5847 San Felipe, Ste. 2600, Houston, TX, 77057-3010

Tel: (713) 267-3777   Fax: (713) 267-3701   www.kaiseral.com

Aluminum refining and manufacturing.

Alumina Partners of Jamaica (Alpart), Nain, Jamaica
Kaiser Jamaica Bauxite Company (KJBC), Jamaica

KOPPERS INDUSTRIES INC.

436 Seventh Ave., Pittsburgh, PA, 15219-1800

Tel: (412) 227-2000   Fax: (412) 227-2333   www.koppers.com

Construction materials and services; chemicals and building products.

Wood Preservation Ltd., Kingston, Jamaica

KPMG CONSULTING INC.

1676 International Dr., McLean, VA, 22102

Tel: (703) 747-3000   Fax: (703) 747-8500   www.kpmg.com

Accounting and audit, tax and management consulting services.

KPMG International, The Victoria Mutual Bldg., 6 Duke St., Kingston, Jamaica
Tel: 809-922-6640   Fax: 809-922-7198   Contact: Rolf Lanigan, Sr. Ptnr.

LAND O' LAKES, INC.

4001 Lexington Ave. North, Arden Hills, MN, 55126

Tel: (612) 481-2222   Fax: (612) 481-2022   www.landolakes.com

Produces butter, margarine, packaged milk, sour cream, snack dips and Alpine Lace cheeses and crop protection products.

Land O' Lakes, Inc., Jamaica

MAIDENFORM WORLDWIDE INC.

154 Avenue E, Bayonne, NJ, 07002

Tel: (201) 436-9200   Fax: (201) 436-9009   www.maidenform.com

Mfr. intimate apparel.

Jamaica Needlecraft Ltd., PO Box 28, Kingston 15, Jamaica

MARSH & McLENNAN COS INC.

1166 Ave. of the Americas, New York, NY, 10036-2774

Tel: (212) 345-5000   Fax: (212) 345-4808   www.marshmac.com

Insurance agents/brokers, pension and investment management consulting services.

Allied Insurance Brokers Ltd., 26 Belmont Rd., Kingston 5, Jamaica
Tel: 876-926-6784   Fax: 876-929-9391   Contact: Paul A. Bitter

MAXXAM INC.

5847 San Felipe, Ste. 2600, Houston, TX, 77057

Tel: (713) 975-7600   Fax: (713) 267-3701

Holding company for aluminum and timber products and real estate industries.

Kaiser Bauxite Co., Div. MAXXAM, 60 Knutsford Boulevard, 5, Jamaica
Tel: 876-926-4723

McCANN-ERICKSON WORLDGROUP

750 Third Ave., New York, NY, 10017

Tel: (212) 697-6000   Fax: (212) 984-3575   www.mccann.com

International advertising and marketing services.

McCann-Erickson (Jamaica) Ltd., 7 Knutsford Street, PO Box 168, Kingston 5, Jamaica

McDONALD'S CORPORATION

McDonald's Plaza, Oak Brook, IL, 60523

Tel: (630) 623-3000   Fax: (630) 623-7409   www.mcdonalds.com

Fast food chain stores.

McDonald's Corp., Montego Bay, Jamaica

ONDEO NALCO COMPANY

Ondeo Nalco Center, 1601 W. Diehl Road, Naperville, IL, 60563-1198

Tel: (630) 305-1000   Fax: (630) 305-2900   www.ondeo-nalco.com

Mfr. specialty chemicals for water and waste water treatment, oil products and refining, industry processes; water and energy management service.

ONDEO Nalco Chemical Jamaica, Kingston, Jamaica

Tel: 809-968-8165   Fax: 809-929-2848

PIONEER HI-BRED INTERNATIONAL INC.

400 Locust Street, Ste. 800, Des Moines, IA, 50309

Tel: (515) 248-4800   Fax: (515) 248-4999   www.pioneer.com

Agricultural chemicals, farm supplies, biological products, research.

Pioneer Hi-Bred/Tropical Research Station, PO Box 197, Kingston 11, Jamaica

Tel: 876-984-3234

PRICEWATERHOUSECOOPERS LLP

1301 Ave. of the Americas, New York, NY, 10019

Tel: (212) 596-7000   Fax: (212) 259-1301   www.pwcglobal.com

Accounting and auditing, tax and management, and human resource consulting services.

PriceWaterhouseCoopers, 32 Market St., PO Box 180, Montego Bay, Jamaica

Tel: 809-952-5065   Fax: 809-952-1273

PriceWaterhouseCoopers, Scotiabank Centre, Duke St., PO Box 372, Kingston, Jamaica

Tel: 809-922-6230   Fax: 809-922-7581

RADISSON HOTELS INTERNATIONAL

Carlson Pkwy., PO Box 59159, Minneapolis, MN, 55459-8204

Tel: (612) 540-5526   Fax: (612) 449-3400   www.radisson.com

Operates, manages and franchises full-service hotels and resorts worldwide.

Ciboney, Ocho Rios, PO Box 728, Ocho Rios, Jamaica

Poinciana Beach Resort, Negril, Jamaica

RENAISSANCE HOTELS AND RESORTS

10400 Fernwood Road, Bethesda, MD, 20817

Tel: (301) 380-3000   Fax: (301) 380-5181   www.renaissancehotels.com

upscale, full-service hotel and resort chain under Marriott International, Inc.

Renaissance Hotel, Ocho Rios, Jamaica

Tel: 809-974-2201

THE SHERWIN-WILLIAMS COMPANY

101 Prospect Ave., N.W., Cleveland, OH, 44115-1075

Tel: (216) 566-2000   Fax: (216) 566-2947   www.sherwin-williams.com

Mfr. paint, wall coverings and related products.

Sherwin-Williams West Indies Ltd., PO Box 35, Spanish Town, St. Catherine, Jamaica

SITEL CORPORATION

111 South Calver Street, Ste. 1900, Baltimore, MD, 21202

Tel: (410) 246-1505   Fax: (410) 246-0200   www.sitel.com

Provides outsourced customer management services.

SITEL Caribbean, The Freezone, Montego Bay, Jamaica

STANLEY CONSULTANTS, INC.

Stanley Building, 225 Iowa Ave., Muscatine, IA, 52761-3764

Tel: (563) 264-6600   Fax: (563) 264-6658   www.stanleygroup.com

Engaged in engineering, architectural, planning and management services.

Stanley Consultants, Inc., Apt. C201, Baypointe, Freeport, Montego Bay, Jamaica
Tel: 876-956-3698   Fax: 876-956-3641

Stanley Consultants, Inc., Ocean Palm, Lot 40, PO Box 2, Duncans, Trelawny, Jamaica
Tel: 876-926-4820   Fax: 876-926-2656

UNITED PARCEL SERVICE, INC.

55 Glenlake Parkway, NE, Atlanta, GA, 30328

Tel: (404) 828-6000   Fax: (404) 828-6593   www.ups.com

International package-delivery service.

UPS / Airpak Express, Tinson Pen Aerodrome, PO Box 50, Kingston 11, Jamaica
Tel: 876-923-0371   Fax: 876-923-5089

WYNDHAM INTERNATIONAL, INC.

1950 Stemmons Fwy., Ste. 6001, Dallas, TX, 75207

Tel: (214) 863-1000   Fax: (214) 863-1527   www.wyndhamintl.com

Hotel operator.

Wyndham Rose Hall Resort and Country Club, PO Box 599, Mnontego Bay, Jamaica
Tel: 876-953-2650   Fax: 876-953-2617

XEROX CORPORATION

800 Long Ridge Road, PO Box 1600, Stamford, CT, 06904

Tel: (203) 968-3000   Fax: (203) 968-4312   www.xerox.com

Mfr. document processing equipment, systems and supplies.

Xerox (Jamaica) Ltd., L.O.J. Centre, Ground Fl., PO Box 226, Kingston 5, Jamaica
Tel: 809-926-5630   Fax: 809-929-5372

Japan

3COM CORPORATION

5400 Bayfront Plaza, Santa Clara, CA, 95052-8145

Tel: (408) 326-5000   Fax: (408) 326-5001   www.3com.com

Engaged in the development and manufacture of computer networking products and systems.

3Com Japan, Shinjuku Sumitomo Bldg., 23F, 2-6-1 Nishi Shinjuku, Shinjuku-ku, Tokyo 163-02, Japan
Tel: 81-3-3345-7251 Fax: 81-3-3345-7261

3Com Japan, Nishi Honmaci Mitsui Bldg., 3F, 1-3-15 Awaza Nishi-ku, Oska-shi, Osaka 550, Japan
Tel: 81-6-536-3303 Fax: 81-6-536-3304

3Com KK, Bunkyo Green Court Center Office, 2-28-8 Honkomagome, Bunkyo-ku, Tokyo 105, Japan
Tel: 81-3-5977-3266 Fax: 81-3-5977-3370

3D LABS INC., LTD.

480 Potrero Avenue, Sunnyvale, CA, 94086

Tel: (408) 530-4700   Fax: (408) 530-4701   www.3dlabs.com

Produces 3D graphics accelerators chips for the PC computer platform.

3D Labs KK, Level 16, Shiroyama Hills, 4-3-1 Toranomon, Minato-ku, Tokyo 105, Japan
Tel: 81-3-5403-4653 Fax: 81-3-5403-4654

3D SYSTEMS CORPORATION

26081 Avenue Hall, Valencia, CA, 91355

Tel: (805) 295-5600   Fax: (805) 294-8406   www.3dsystems.com

Mfr. computer lasers.

3D Systems Japan, AIG Building, 9/Fl., 1-1-3 Marunouchi, Chiyoda-ku Tokyo 100-0005, Japan

3M (MINNESOTA MINING & MFG.)

3M Center, St. Paul, MN, 55144-1000

Tel: (651) 733-1110   Fax: (651) 733-9973   www.mmm.com

Mfr. diversified products for industry, consumer, health care, imaging, communications, transport, safety, etc.

Sumitomo 3M Ltd., PO Box 43, 33-1 Tamagawa-dai 2-chome, Setagaya-ku, Tokyo 158, Japan
Tel: 81-3-3709-8170 Fax: 81-3-3709-8751 Contact: William G. Allen

3M TOUCH SYSTEMS, INC.

300 Griffin Brook Park Drive, Methuen, MA, 01844

Tel: (978) 659-9000   Fax: (978) 659-9100   www.microtouch.com

Mfr. Touchscreen Sensors, Touch Monitors, and Industrial Computer Products.

3M Touch Systems K.K., Bellevue Mizonokuchi Building, 3/F, 3-2-3 Hisamoto, Takatsu-ku Kawasaki-shi, Kanagawa 213, Japan
Tel: 81-4-4811-1133

AAVID THERMAL TECHNOLOGIES, INC.

1 Eagle Square, Ste. 509, Concord, NH, 03301

Tel: (603) 224-1117   Fax: (603) 224-6673   www.aatt.com

Mfr. fluid dynamics software.

Aavid Thermalloy, Sun Court Yotsuya No.303, 1 Suga-Cho Shinjyuku-Ku, Tokyo 160-0018, Japan
Tel: 81-3-5366-8401

ABBOTT LABORATORIES

100 Abbott Park Rd., Abbott Park, IL, 60064

Tel: (847) 937-6100   Fax: (847) 937-1511   www.abbott.com

Development, manufacture and sale of diversified health care products and services.

Abbott/Dainabot Co., Osaka Tokio Marine Bldg., 2-53 Shiromi 2- chome, Chuo-ku, Osaka 540-001, Japan

ABS (AMERICAN BUREAU OF SHIPPING)

ABS Plaza, 16855 Northchase Drive, Houston, TX, 77060

Tel: (281) 877-6000   Fax: (281) 877-6344   www.eagle.org

Classification and certification of ships and offshore structures, development and technical assistance.

ABS Pacific, Urban Square Yokohama, 4/F, 1-1 Sakai-Cho Kanagawa-Ku, Yokohama 221-0052, Japan

Tel: 81-45-441-1000

ACCELRYS INC.

9685 Scranton Road, San Diego, CA, 92121-3752

Tel: (858) 799-5000   Fax: (858) 799-5100   www.accelrys.com

Mfr. software for drug research.

Accelrys Japan KK, Nakarin-Auto Bldg. 5/F, 2-8-4 Shinkawa, Chuo-ku Tokyo 104-0033, Japan

Tel: 81-3-3206-3575   Fax: 81-3-3206-3572   Contact: Noriaki (Ray) Tsunoda

ACCENTURE LTD.

1345 Avenue of the Americas, New York, NY, 10105

Tel: (917) 452-4400   Fax: (917) 527-9915   www.accenture.com

Provides management and technology consulting services.

Accenture, Nihon Seimei Akasaka, Daini Bldg., 7-1-16 Akasaka, Minato-ku, Tokyo 107, Japan

Tel: 81-3-3470-9241   Fax: 81-3-3423-2544

ACCLAIM ENTERTAINMENT, INC.

One Acclaim Plaza, Glen Cove, NY, 11542

Tel: (516) 656-5000   Fax: (516) 656-2040   www.acclaim.com

Mfr. video games.

Acclaim Japan, Ltd., 210 Nomora Bldg., 6/F, 2-10-9 Shibuya, Shibuyaku Tokyo 150-0002, Japan

ACCO WORLD CORPORATION

300 Tower Parkway, Lincolnshire, IL, 60069

Tel: (847) 541-9500   Fax: (847) 541-5750   www.accobrands.com

Provides services in the office and computer markets and manufactures paper fasteners, clips, metal fasteners, binders and staplers.

ACCO Japan, Ste. 513, 2-1-15 Takanawa, Minato-ku, Tokyo 108, Japan

Contact: Mark Miller

ACCURIDE INTERNATIONAL, INC.

12311 Shoemaker Ave., Santa Fe Springs, CA, 90670-4721

Tel: (562) 903-0200   Fax: (562) 903-0208   www.accuride.com

Mfr. drawer slides.

Accuride International, 2-5-13 Nihonbashi Muromachi, Chuo-ku, Tokyo 103, Japan

ACE CONTROLS INC.

23435 Industrial Park Drive, Farmington Hills, MI, 48024

Tel: (248) 476-0213   Fax: (248) 276-2470   www.acecontrols.com

Industry hydraulic shock absorbers, cylinders, valves and automation controls.

ACE Controls Japan Ltd., 261-1-102 Tamasaki, Ichihara City Chiba Pref. 290, Japan

Tel: 81-436-246711   Fax: 81-436-246712

ACHESON COLLOIDS INDUSTRIES, INC.

1600 Washington Avenue, Port Huron, MI, 48060

Tel: (810) 984-5581   Fax: (810) 984-1446   www.nationalstarch.com

Chemicals, chemical preparations, paints and lubricating oils.

Acheson Colloids Industries KK, Box 538, Kobe Port, Kobe 651-0191, Japan

Tel: 81-78-332-3601   Fax: 81-78-391-5903

Acheson Japan Ltd., 6-B Kakogawa, Kogyo Danchi, Kakogawa 675-0011, Japan

Tel: 81-79-426-2188   Fax: 81-79-421-8006

ACTEL CORPORATION

955 East Arquest Avenue, Sunnyvale, CA, 94086-4533

Tel: (408) 739-1010   Fax: (408) 739-1540   www.actel.com

Mfr. integrated circuits.

Actel Japan, EXOS Ebisu Bldg., 4/F, 1-24-14 Ebisu Shibuya-ku, Tokyo 150, Japan

Tel: 81-3-3445-7671

ACTERNA CORPORATION

20400 Observation Drive, Germantown, MD, 20876

Tel: (301) 353-1550   Fax: (301) 353-1536   www.acterna.com

Develop, manufacture and market communications test instruments, systems, software and services.

Acterna KK, Kyoritsu Shin-Yokohama, 4/F, 2-15-12 Shin-Yokohama, Kouhoku-ku, Yokohama 222-0033, Japan

ACTIVISION

3100 Ocean Park Boulevard, Santa Monica, CA, 90405

Tel: (310) 255-2000   Fax: (310) 255-2100   www.activision.com

Development and manufacture of entertainment software and video games.

Activision Japan, Aobadai Tower, Annex SF, 3-1-18 Aobadai, Meguro-ku, Tokyo 153, Japan

Tel: 81-3-5458-6561   Fax: 81-3-5458-6562   Emp: 10

ACTUATE CORPORATION

701 Gateway Boulevard, South San Francisco, CA, 94080

Tel: (650) 837-2000   Fax: (650) 827-1560   www.actuate.com

Develops software.

Actuate Japan, 2-2-8 Roppongi, Minato-ku, Tokyo 106, Japan

Tel: 81-03-3584-0970

ADAPTEC INC.

691 South Milpitas Boulevard, Milpitas, CA, 95035

Tel: (408) 945-8600   Fax: (408) 262-2533   www.adaptec.com

Design/mfr./marketing hardware and software solutions.

Adaptec Japan Ltd., Harmony Tower, 3/F, 1-32-2 Honcho Nakano-ku, Tokyo 164, Japan

Tel: 81-3-5365-6700   Fax: 81-3-5365-6950

ADC TELECOMMUNICATIONS INC.

13625 Technology Drive, Eden Prairie, MN, 55344

Tel: (952) 938-8080   Fax: (952) 946-3292   www.adc.com

Mfr. telecommunications equipment.

ADC Telecommunications, Yaesu-Ishizuka Bldg.10F, 1-5-20 Yaesu, Chuo-ku, Tokyo 103-0028, Japan

ADE CORPORATION

80 Wilson Way, Westwood, MA, 02090

Tel: (781) 467-3500   Fax: (781) 467-0500   www.ade.com

Mfr. semiconductor wafers and computer disks.

Japan ADE Ltd., 16-1 Minami Kamata 2-Chome, Ohta-Ku, Tokyo 144, Japan

Tel: 81-35703-5611   Fax: 81-35703-5600

ADEPT TECHNOLOGY, INC.

150 Rose Orchard Way, San Jose, CA, 95134

Tel: (408) 432-0888   Fax: (408) 434-6267   www.adept.com

Mfr. robots for industries.

Adept Japan Co. Ltd., 6/F, Yokohama World Porters, 2-1-1 shinkou, Yokohama, Kanagawa 231-0001, Japan

Tel: 81-45-222-2985

ADOBE SYSTEMS INCORPORATED

345 Park Avenue, San Jose, CA, 95110

Tel: (408) 536-6000   Fax: (408) 537-6000   www.adobe.com

Engaged in print technology and distributor of Acrobat Reader.

Adobe Systems Co., Ltd., Gate City Osaki East Tower, 1-11-2 Osaki, Shinagawa-ku, Tokyo 141-0032, Japan

Tel: 81-3-5740-2400   Fax: 81-3-5423-8209

ADVANCED ENERGY INDUSTRIES, INC.

1625 Sharp Point Drive, Fort Collins, CO, 80525

Tel: (970) 221-4670   Fax: (970) 221-5583   www.advanced-energy.com

Mfr. semiconductors.

Advanced Energy Japan KK, TOWA Edogawabashi Bldg. 347, Yamabuki-cho Shinjuku-ku, Tokyo 162-0801, Japan

ADVANCED MICRO DEVICES INC.

1 AMD Place, Sunnyvale, CA, 94086

Tel: (408) 732-2400   Fax: (408) 982-6164   www.amd.com

Mfr. integrated circuits for communications and computation industry.

Advanced Micro Devices Asia, Shinjuku Nissel, Sumitomo Bldg., 5/F, 2-4-1 Nishi Shinjuku, Tokyo 163-0839, Japan

Tel: 81-3-3346-7550   Fax: 81-3-3342-8958

AFLAC INCORPORATED

1932 Wynnton Rd., Columbus, GA, 31999

Tel: (706) 323-3431   Fax: (706) 324-6330   www.aflac.com

Provides supplemental medical insurance policies for cancer care intensive care and nursing home care, accident and disability coverage.

AFLAC - Japan, Shinjuku Mitsui Bldg., 10F, 1-1 Nishishinjuku 2-chome, Shinjuku-ku, Tokyo 163, Japan

Contact: Hidefumi Matsui

AFLAC Japan, 1 Kioi-cho, Chiyoda-ku, Tokyo 102-8578, Japan

Contact: Hidefumi Matsui

AGILE SOFTWARE CORPORATION

1 Almaden Blvd., San Jose, CA, 95113-2253

Tel: (408) 975-3900   Fax: (408) 271-4862   www.agilesoft.com

Mfr. software for supply chain management.

Agile Software KK, Level 19, Sumitomo Nakano-Sakaue Bldg., 1-38-1 Chuo, Nakano-ku, Tokyo 164-0011, Japan

Tel: 81-3-5338-9771

AIG AMERICAN INTERNATIONAL GROUP INC.

70 Pine Street, New York, NY, 10270

Tel: (212) 770-7000   Fax: (212) 509-9705   www.aig.com

Worldwide insurance and financial services.

American Home Assurance Co., AIG Tower, 1-2-4 Kinshi, Surnida-Ku, Tokyo 130-8562, Japan

AIR PRODUCTS AND CHEMICALS, INC.

7201 Hamilton Boulevard, Allentown, PA, 18195-1501

Tel: (610) 481-4911   Fax: (610) 481-5900   www.airproducts.com

Mfr. industry gases and related equipment, specialty chemicals, environmental/energy systems.

Air Products Asia Inc., Shuwa 2, Kamiyacho Bldg., 3-18-19 Toranomon, Minato-ku, Tokyo 105, Japan

Contact: Wayne A. Hinman, Pres.

AJAX MAGNETHERMIC CORPORATION

1745 Overland Ave. NE, PO Box 991, Warren, OH, 44482

Tel: (330) 372-8511   Fax: (330) 372-8644   www.ajaxcan.com

Mfr. induction heating and melting equipment.

Japan Ajax Magnethermic Co. Ltd., 1-6-35 Shinsuna Koto-ku, N-Building, 7/F, Tokyo 136-0075, Japan

Tel: 81-3-3647-7661   Fax: 81-3-3647-7662   Contact: Chris Imai

ALBANY INTERNATIONAL CORPORATION

1373 Broadway, Albany, NY, 12204

Tel: (518) 445-2200   Fax: (518) 445-2265   www.albint.com

Mfr. broadwoven and engineered fabrics, plastic products, filtration media.

Albany Intl. of Japan Ltd., 3/F,Akasaka Sanno Bldg., 5-11 Akasaka 2-chome, Minato-ku, Tokyo 107, Japan

ALBEMARLE CORPORATION

PO Box 1335, 330 S. 4th Street, Richmond, VA, 23218-1335

Tel: (804) 788-6000   Fax: (804) 788-5688   www.albemarle.com

Mfr. of specialty chemicals used in agriculture, photography, water treatment and petroleum products; mfr. phosphates used in beverages and detergents.

Albemarle Asano Corp., 2-2 Uchisaiwaicho, 16/F, 2-Chome Chiyoda-ku, Tokyo 100, Japan

Tel: 81-3-5251-0791   Fax: 81-3-3500-5623

ALCOA INC.

Alcoa Center, 201 Isabella Street at 7th Street Bridge, Pittsburgh, PA, 15212-5858

Tel: (412) 553-4545   Fax: (412) 553-4498   www.alcoa.com

World's leading producer of aluminum and alumina; mining, refining, smelting, fabricating and recycling.

Alcoa Fujikura Ltd., Tokyo, Japan

Contact: Timothy J. Leveque, Pres.

KSL Alcoa Aluminum Company, Ltd., Moka, Japan

Moralco Ltd., wakuni City, Japan

ALCOA FUJIKURA LTD.

800 Crescent Centre Drive, Ste. 600, Franklin, TN, 37067

Tel: (615) 778-6000   Fax: (615) 778-5927   www.alcoa-fujikura.com

Mfr. optical ground wire, tube cable, fiber optic connectors and automotive wiring harnesses. (JV of Alcoa USA).

Alcoa Fujikura Ltd., Shishiny Toho Bldg., IO/F, 3-17 Fukumachi, Naka-ku, Hiroshima City 730, Japan

ALLEGHENY LUDLUM CORPORATION

1000 Six PPG Place, Pittsburgh, PA, 15222

Tel: (412) 394-2805   Fax: (412) 394-2800   www.alleghenyludlum.com

Mfr. steel and alloys.

Allegheny Ludlum, Tokyo, Japan

Tel: 81-3-3239-9080   Fax: 813-3239-9021

ALLEGHENY TECHNOLOGIES INC.

1000 Six PPG Place, Pittsburgh, PA, 15222

Tel: (412) 394-2800   Fax: (412) 394-2805   www.alleghenytechnologies.com

Diversified mfr. aviation and electronics, specialty metals, industrial and consumer products.

Allegheny Technologies, Nihon Seimei Akasaka Bldg., 3/F, 8-1-19 Akasaka, Minato-ku, Tokyo 107, Japan

ALLEGIANCE HEALTHCARE CORPORATION

1430 Waukegan Road, McGaw Park, IL, 60085

Tel: (847) 689-8410   Fax: (847) 578-4437   www.allegiance.net

Manufactures and distributes medical, surgical, respiratory therapy and laboratory products.

Allegiance Healthcare KK, 6, Rokubancho, Chiyoda-ku, Tokyo 102-0085, Japan

Tel: 81-3521-35639

ALLEN-BRADLEY COMPANY, INC.

1201 South Second Street, Milwaukee, WI, 53204

Tel: (414) 382-2000   Fax: (414) 382-4444   www.ab.com

Mfr. electrical controls and information devices.

Allen-Bradley Japan Co. Ltd., Shinkawa Sanko Bldg., 3-17 Shinkawa 1-chome, Tokyo 104, Japan

ALLERGAN INC.

2525 Dupont Drive, Irvine, CA, 92612

Tel: (714) 246-4500   Fax: (714) 246-6987   www.allergan.com

Mfr. therapeutic eye care products and skin care pharmaceuticals.

Allergan K.K., Toranomon 40 Mori Bldg., 13-1 Toranomon 5-Chome, Minato-ku, Tokyo 105, Japan

Tel: 81-3-5402-8900   Fax: 81-3-5402-8970

ALLIANCE CAPITAL MANAGEMENT HOLDING LP

1345 Ave. of the Americas, New York, NY, 10105

Tel: (212) 969-1000   Fax: (212) 969-2229   www.alliancecapital.com

Engaged in fund management for large corporations.

Alliance Capital Management, Otemaci First Square West Tower, 12/F, 1-5-1- Otemachi Chiyoda-ku, Tokyo 100-0004, Japan

Tel: 81-3-3240-8410

ALLIANCE SEMICONDUCTOR CORPORATION

2675 Augustine Drive, Santa Clara, CA, 95054

Tel: (408) 855-4900   Fax: (408) 855-4999   www.alsc.com

Mfr. semi-conductors and related chips.

Alliance Semiconductor, Level, 11 Park West Bldg., 6-12-1 Nishi Shinjuku, Shinjuku-ku, Tokyo 160-0023, Japan

Tel: 81-3-5325-3155

ALTERA CORPORATION

101 Innovation Drive, San Jose, CA, 95134

Tel: (408) 544-7000   Fax: (408) 544-8303   www.altera.com

Mfr. high-density programmable chips for semi-conductor industry.

Altera Japan, Ltd., Shinjukui, Land Tower, 32/F, 5-1 Nishi Shinjuku 6-Chome, Shinjuku-ku, Tokyo 163-1332, Japan

Tel: 81-3-3340-9480

AMAZON.COM, INC.

1200 12th Ave. South, Ste. 1200, Seattle, WA, 98144-2734

Tel: (206) 266-1000   Fax: (206) 266-4206   www.amazon.com

Computer site that offers books, CDs, DVDS, videos, toys, tools, and electronics.

Amazon.Com KK, Tokyo, Japan

AMC ENTERTAINMENT INC.

106 West 14th Street, Kansas City, MO, 64121-9615

Tel: (816) 221-4000   Fax: (816) 480-4617   www.amctheatres.com

Operates movie theater chains.

AMC Ikspiari at Tokyo Disney Resort, 2-11, Maihama Urayasu-shi, Chiba-ken 809-0013, Japan

AMC Nakama 16, 3-11-1 Kamirengeji, Nakama City 809-0013, Japan

Tel: 81-93-245-6880

AMDOCS LIMITED

1390 Timberlake Manor Pkwy., Chesterfield, MO, 63017

Tel: (314) 212-7000   Fax: (314) 212-7500   www.amdocs.com

Mfr. telecommunications software.

Amdocs KK, Akasakamitsuke Bldge. 6/F, 3-9-18 Akasaka, Tokyo 107-0052, Japan

AMEREX ENERGY

One Sugar Creek Center Blvd., Suite 700, Sugar Land, TX, 77478

Tel: (281) 340-5200   Fax: (281) 634-8883   www.amerexenergy.com

energy broker, providing voice brokerage, market liquidity, price discovery and data services.

Amerex Petroleum Tokyo, Komatsu Building, 2nd Floor, 1-11-4 Shiba Daimon, Minato-Ku, Tokyo 105-0012, Japan

AMERICAN APPRAISAL ASSOCIATES INC.
411 E. Wisconsin Ave., Ste. 1900, Milwaukee, WI, 53202

Tel: (414) 271-7240   Fax: (414) 271-1041   www.american-appraisal.com

Valuation consulting services.

American Appraisal Japan Co. Ltd., Kabutocho Yachiyo Bldg., 20-5 Kabotocho, Nihonbashi, Chuo-ku, Tokyo 103, Japan

Tel: 81-3-3-639-5803   Fax: 81-3-3-639-5927   Contact: Kinji Yasu

AMERICAN AXLE & MANUFACTURING HOLDINGS, INC.
1840 Holbrook Ave., Detroit, MI, 48212

Tel: (313) 974-2000   Fax: (313) 974-3090   www.aam.com

Mfr. axles, propeller shafts and chassis components.

American Axle & Manufacturing, Minato Kirimura Bldg., 7/F, 3-6-1 Minato Chuo-Ku, Tokyo 104-0043, Japan
Contact: James M. Uyeno, Dir.

ABC, INC.
77 West 66th Street, 13th Fl., New York, NY, 10023

Tel: (212) 456-7777   Fax: (212) 456-6384   www.abc.com

Radio/TV production and broadcasting.

ABC News, Rokugo-ku Bldg., 6-5-9 Roppongi, Minato-ku, Tokyo 106, Japan

AMGEN INC.
One Amgen Center Drive, Thousand Oaks, CA, 91320-1799

Tel: (805) 447-1000   Fax: (805) 499-2694   www.amgen.com

Biotechnology research and pharmaceuticals.

Amgen KK, Hamacho Center Building, 8F, 31-1 Nihonbashi Hamacho 2-chome, Chuo-ku, Tokyo 103, Japan
Tel: 81-3-5641-9954

AMKOR TECHNOLOGY, INC.
1345 Enterprise Dr., West Chester, PA, 19380

Tel: (610) 431-9600   Fax: (610) 431-1988   www.amkor.com

Microchip technology engaged in semiconductor packaging and test services.

Amkor Technology Japan, KK, Ebisu Prime Square Tower, 4/F, 1-1-39 Hiroo, Shibuya-ku, Tokyo 150-0012, Japan
Tel: 81-3-5469-6215   Contact: Paul B. Grant, Mgr.

AMPEX CORPORATION
1228 Douglas Avenue, Redwood City, CA, 94063-3199

Tel: (650) 367-2011   Fax: (650) 367-4669   www.ampex.com

Mfr. extremely high-performance digital data storage, data retrieval and image processing systems for a broad range of corporate scientific and government applications.

Ampex Japan Ltd.., PO Box 15, Tokyo Ryutsu Ctr., 6-1-1 Heiwajima, Ota-ku, Tokyo 143, Japan
Tel: 81-3-3767-4521   Fax: 81-3-3767-8523   Contact: Hiroshi Okochi   Emp: 9

AMPHENOL CORPORATION
358 Hall Ave., Wallingford, CT, 06492-7530

Tel: (203) 265-8900   Fax: (203) 265-8793   www.amphenol.com

Mfr. electronic interconnect penetrate systems and assemblies.

Amphenol Japan K.K., 2-3-27 Kudan Minami, Chiyoda-Ku, Tokyo 102-0074, Japan
Tel: 81-3-3263-5611   Fax: 81-3-5276-7059

AMR CORPORATION (AMERICAN AIRLINES)
4333 Amon Carter Boulevard, Ft. Worth, TX, 76155

Tel: (817) 963-1234   Fax: (817) 967-9641   www.amrcorp.com

Air transport services.

American Airlines Inc., KAL Bldg. 12-1 Honmachi 3-chome, Higashi-ku, Osaka 541, Japan

American Airlines Inc., Rm. 203 Kokusai Bldg., 1-1 Marunouchi 3-chome, Chiyoda-ku, Tokyo 100, Japan
Tel: 81-3-3248 -2011

AMSTED INDUSTRIES INC.

205 North Michigan Ave., Chicago, IL, 60601

Tel: (312) 645-1700   Fax: (312) 819-8523   www.amsted.com

Privately-held, diversified manufacturer of products for the construction and building markets, general industry and the railroads.

BAC-Japan Co., Ltd., 2-27-4 Shin-Machi, Setagaya-ku, Tokyo 154, Japan

Tel: 81-3-5450-6161   Fax: 81-3-5450-6166   Contact: Tatsuro Nishimura, Pres.

AMWAY CORPORATION

7575 Fulton Street East, Ada, MI, 49355-0001

Tel: (616) 787-6000   Fax: (616) 787-6177   www.amway.com

Mfr./sale home care, personal care, nutrition and houseware products.

Amway (Japan) Ltd., Arco Tower, 1-8-1 Shimomeguro, Meguro-ku, Tokyo 153, Japan

ANALOG DEVICES INC.

1 Technology Way, Norwood, MA, 02062

Tel: (781) 329-4700   Fax: (781) 326-8703   www.analog.com

Mfr. integrated circuits and related devices.

Analog Devices of Japan Inc., Jibiki Bldg., 7-8 Kojimachi 4-chome, Chiyoda-ku, Tokyo 102, Japan

ANDERSEN

33 West Monroe Street, Chicago, IL, 60603

Tel: (312) 580-0033   Fax: (312) 507-6748   www.andersen.com

Accounting and audit, tax and management consulting services. **Firm under worldwide reorganization; new data unavailable for this edition.

Asahi & Co., Asahi Ctr. Bldg., 1-2 Tsukudo-cho, Shinjuku-ku, Tokyo 162, Japan

Tel: 81-3-3266-7507

Asahi & Co., Hankyu Grand Bldg., 18F, 8-47 Kakuta-cho, Kita-ku, Osaka 530, Japan

Tel: 81-6-311-1425

Asahi & Co., Nissei Bldg., 1-18 Ageba-cho, Shinjuku-ku, Tokyo 162, Japan

Tel: 81-52-571-5471

Asahi & Co., Ohasi Bldg., 3-25-3 Meiki, Nakaamura-ku, Nagoya Aichi 450, Japan

Uno Tax Accountant Office, Chuo Bldg., 2-17 Kagurazaka, Shinjuku-ku, Tokyo 162, Japan

Tel: 81-3-5228-1600

ANDREW CORPORATION

10500 West 153rd Street, Orland Park, IL, 60462

Tel: (708) 349-3300   Fax: (708) 349-5410   www.andrew.com

Designer, manufacturer, and supplier of communications equipment, services, and systems.

Andrew International Corp., Room 305, Nagatacho TBR Bldg., 2-10-1 Nagata-cho, Chiyoda-ku, Tokyo 100, Japan

Tel: 81-3-3581-0221 Fax: 81-3-3581-0222

ANHEUSER-BUSCH INTERNATIONAL INC.

One Busch Place, St. Louis, MO, 63118-1852

Tel: (314) 577-2000   Fax: (314) 577-2900   www.anheuser-busch.com

Malt production, aluminum beverage containers, rice milling, real estate development, metalized and paper label printing, railcar repair and theme-park facilities.

Anheuser-Busch Asia Inc., Akasalee Twin Tower, 17-22 Akasalee 2-chome, Minato-ku, Tokyo 107, Japan

ANSYS, INC.

275 Technology Drive, Canonsburg, PA, 15317

Tel: (724) 746-3304   Fax: (724) 514-9494   www.ansys.com

Mfr. CAD and CAE software.

ANSYS Japan Ltd., Nisi Shinjuku Forest Building 1/F, 32-12 Nishi-Shinjuku 4-chome, Shinjuku-ku, Tokyo 160-0023, Japan

Contact: Yoichi Nagashima

AOL TIME WARNER

75 Rockefeller Plaza, New York, NY, 10019

Tel: (212) 484-8000   Fax: (212) 275-3046   www.aoltimewarner.com

Engaged in media and communications; provides internet services, communications, publishing and entertainment.

AOL Time Warner Asia, Tokyo, Japan

Time-Life International KK, Tokyo, Japan

AON CORPORATION

200 East Randolph, Chicago, IL, 60601

Tel: (312) 381-1000   Fax: (312) 381-6032   www.aon.com

Insurance brokers worldwide; underwrites accident and health insurance, specialty and professional insurance; and provides risk management consultation.

AON Risk Services Japan Ltd., Bancho Kaikan 5F, 12-1 Gobancho, Chiyoda-ku, Tokyo 102-0076, Japan

Tel: 81-3-3449-5503   Fax: 81-3-3449-9121   Contact: Akio Tanaguchi

API MOTION INC.

45 Hazelwood Dr., Amherst, NY, 14228

Tel: (716) 691-9100   Fax: (716) 691-9181   www.apimotion.com

Engaged in motion control solutions using motors and drives, motor gear heads, resolver and encoder feedback devices.

API Motion Japan Ltd., 7-10 Nihombashi-Honcho 4-chome, Chuo-ku, Tokyo, Japan

APL LOGISTICS

1111 Broadway, Oakland, CA, 94607

Tel: (510) 272-8000   Fax: (510) 272-7421   www.apllogistics.com

Provides ocean container shipping and logistics services.

APL Logistics, Pier D-4, 1-10 Honmoko Futo, Naka-Ku, Yokohama 231-0811, Japan

APOGENT TECHNOLOGIES INC.

48 Congress Street, Portsmouth, NH, 03801

Tel: (603) 433-6131   Fax: (603) 431-0860   www.apogent.com

Design, mfr. & sell products for laboratories, clinical research, industrial markets & analytical products.

Sybron Dental Specialties Japan Inc., Onarimon #2 Bldg., 2/F, 16-12 Shimbashi 6-chome, Minato-ku, Tokyo 107, Japan

APPLE COMPUTER, INC.

One Infinite Loop, Cupertino, CA, 95014

Tel: (408) 996-1010   Fax: (408) 974-2113   www.apple.com

Personal computers, peripherals and software.

Apple Computer Japan Inc., Akasaka Twin Tower, Main Bldg., 16/F, 2-17-22 Akasaka, Minato-ku, Tokyo 107, Japan

APPLERA CORPORATION

301 Merritt 7, Norwalk, CT, 06851

Tel: (203) 840-2000   Fax: (203) 840-2312   www.applera.com

Leading supplier of systems for life science research and related applications.

Applied Biosystems Japan KK, 4-5-4 Hatchobori, Chuo-Ku, Tokyo 104-0032, Japan

APPLIED MATERIALS, INC.

3050 Bowers Ave., Santa Clara, CA, 95054-3299

Tel: (408) 727-5555   Fax: (408) 727-9943   www.appliedmaterials.com

Supplies manufacturing systems and services to the semiconductor industry.

Applied Materials Japan, Nogedaria Ind.Par, 14-3 Shinizumi, Narita-shi, Chiba-ken 286-8516, Japan

Tel: 81-476-362181   Fax: 81-476-361095

APPLIX, INC.

289 Turnpike Rd., Westboro, MA, 01581

Tel: (508) 870-0300   Fax: (508) 366-4873   www.applix.com

Engaged in business productivity application software.

APPLIX KK, 2-35-F214, Oyaguchi, Itabashi-Ku, Tokyo 173 0036, Japan

APW, INC.

N22 W23685 Ridgeview Parkway West, Waukesha, WI, 53188-1013

Tel: (262) 523-7600   Fax: (262) 523-7624   www.apw1.com

Mfr. hi-pressure tools, vibration control products, consumables, technical furniture and enclosures.

APW Japan Ltd., Win Nishi-Waseda Building, SF, 2-20-9, Nichi-Waseda, Shinjuku-ku, Tokyo 169-0051, Japan

APW-WRIGHT LINE INC.

160 Gold Star Blvd., Worcester, MA, 01606

Tel: (508) 852-4300   Fax: (508) 853-8904   www.wrightline.com

Provides technical environment solutions for productive, space-effective, and reconfigurable work environments.

APW-Wright Line LLC, Win Nishi-Waseda Building, SF, 2-20-9, Nishi-Waseda, Shinjuku-Ku, Tokyo 169-0051, Japan

Tel: 81-3-5273-6100   Fax: 81-3-5273-6055

AQUENT

711 Boylston Street, Boston, MA, 02116

Tel: (617) 535-5000   Fax: (617) 535-6001   www.aquent.com

Engaged in temporary, specialized employment.

AQUENT, 5-4 Kojimachi, Chiyoda-ku, Tokyo 102-0083, Japan

Tel: 81-3-5214-3242

AQUENT, 1-3-3 Kyomachibori, 4/F, Nishiku, Osaka-si 550-0003, Japan

Tel: 81-6-6459-3303   Fax: 81-6-6459-3304

ARBOR ACRES FARM INC.

439 Marlborough Road, Glastonbury, CT, 06033

Tel: (860) 633-4681   Fax: (860) 633-2433   www.aaf.com

Producers of male and female broiler breeders, commercial egg layers.

Arbor Acres Japan Co. Ltd., 880 Ueno, Kitamatsuno, Fujikawa-Cho, Ihara-Gun, Shizwoka Pref. MZ 421-33, Japan

Tel: 81-545-85-2111   Fax: 81-545-85-2871

ARCH CHEMICALS

501 Merritt Seven, Norwalk, CT, 06856

Tel: (203) 229-2900   Fax: (203) 229-3213   www.archchemicals.com

Mfr. specialty chemicals.

FUJIFILM Arch, 15th Arai-Bldg, 19-20 Jingumae 6-chome, Shibuya-ku, Tokyo 150, Japan

Tel: 81-3-3406 6911   Fax: 81-3-3498 0567

ARCHER DANIELS MIDLAND COMPANY (ADM)

4666 Faries Parkway, Decatur, IL, 62526

Tel: (217) 424-5200   Fax: (217) 424-6196   www.admworld.com

Grain processing: flours, grains, oils and flax fiber.

ADM Far East Ltd., Tokyo, Japan

ARGO TECH CORPORATION

23555 Euclid Avenue, Cleveland, OH, 44117

Tel: (216) 692-6000   Fax: (216) 692-5293   www.jccarter.com

Mfr. aerospace valves and pumps, cryogenic pumps and fuel delivery systems.

Nippon Carter, Rokko Atelier House, 1-15 Yamadacho 3-chome, Nada-ku, Kobe 657, Japan

ARIBA, INC.

1565 Charleston Rd., Mountain View, CA, 94043

Tel: (650) 930-6200   Fax: (650) 930-6300   www.ariba.com

Mfr. software.

Nihon Ariba KK, Shinjuku Park Towerk, 30/F, 3-7-1 Nishi-Shinjuku, Shinjuku-ku, Tokyo 163-1030, Japan

Tel: 81-3-5326-3091

ARMSTRONG HOLDINGS, INC.

2500 Columbia Avenue, Lancaster, PA, 17604-3001

Tel: (717) 397-0611   Fax: (717) 396-2787   www.armstrong.com

Mfr. and marketing interior furnishings and specialty products for building, auto and textile industry.

Armstrong (Japan) KK, Onarimon Yusen Bldg., 5-Nishi-Shinbashi, 3-Chome Minato-ku, Tokyo 105, Japan

Tel: 813-343-344473

ARMSTRONG INTERNATIONAL INC.

816 Maple Street, Three Rivers, MI, 49093

Tel: (616) 273-1415   Fax: (616) 278-6555   www.armintl.com

Mfr. steam specialty products: traps, air vents, liquid drainers, strainers, valves, etc.

Yoshitake-Armstrong, Inc., 955-5 Miyamae Irukadesinden, Komaki, Aichi, 485, Japan

Tel: 81-568-75-7551

Yoshitake-Armstrong, Inc., 955-5 Miyamae irukadesinden, Komaki, Aichi 485, Japan

Tel: 81-568-75-7551

ARROW ELECTRONICS INC.

25 Hub Drive, Melville, NY, 11747

Tel: (516) 391-1300   Fax: (516) 391-1640   www.arrow.com

Distributor of electronic components and computer products.

Marubun Arrow Asia, Ltd., Marubun Daiya Bldg., 8-1 Nihonbashi Odenmacho, Chuo-ku, Tokyo 103-8577, Japan

ARROW INTERNATIONAL, INC.

2400 Bernville Rd., Reading, PA, 19605

Tel: (610) 378-0131   Fax: (610) 374-5360   www.arrowintl.com

Develop, manufacture, and marketing of medical devices.

Arrow Japan, Ltd., 4F, Shin Osaka Kita Bldg., 4-1-46 Miyahara 4-chome, Yodagawa-ku, Osaka 532, Japan

Contact: Kanji Kurisawa

Arrow Japan, Ltd., Nagaoka Bldg., 16-3 Kita-Otasuka 3-chome, Toshima-ku, Tokyo 170, Japan

Contact: Kanji Kurisawa

ART TECHNOLOGY GROUP, INC.

25 First Street, Cambridge, MA, 02141

Tel: (617) 386-1000   Fax: (617) 386-1111   www.atg.com

Mfr. application service software.

Art Technology Group, KK Imperial Tower 15/F, 1 Uchisaiwaicho, Chiyoda-Ku, Tokyo 100-0011, Japan

ARVIN MERITOR INC

2135 W. Maple Rd., Troy, MI, 48084-7186

Tel: (248) 435-1000   Fax: (248) 435-1393   www.arvinmeritor.com

Mfr. of automotive exhaust systems and ride control products, axles and power-steering pumps.

ArvinMeritor International Inc., Halifax Bldg., 6F, 1-1 Asakusabashi 3-chome, Tailo-ku, Tokyo 111-0053, Japan

Tel: 81-3-3862-4408   Fax: 81-3-3862-4498   Contact: Hiro Nakamura, Mng. Dir.   Emp: 5

ArvinMeritor Intl. Inc., Kaneko Bldg., 3-25 Koraku 2-chome, Bunkyo-ku, Tokyo 112, Japan

ASHLAND OIL INC.

50 E. RiverCenter Blvd., Box 391, Covington, KY, 41012-0391

Tel: (859) 815-3333   Fax: (859) 815-5053   www.ashland.com

Petroleum exploration, refining and transportation; mfr. chemicals, oils and lubricants.

Hodogaya Ashland Co. Ltd., 4-2 Toranomon 1-chome, Minato-ku, Tokyo 105, Japan

ASPECT COMMUNICATIONS CORPORATION

1310 Ridder Park Dr., San Jose, CA, 95131-2312

Tel: (408) 325-2200   Fax: (408) 325-2260   www.aspect.com

Mfr. software and related equipment.

Aspect Communications Japan KK, 6F Daini Taihei Building, 7-20-3, Nishi-Shinjuku, Shinjuku-ku 160-0023, Japan

Contact: Kazuo Imai

ASPEN TECHNOLOGY, INC.

10 Canal Park, Cambridge, MA, 02141

Tel: (617) 949-1000   Fax: (617) 949-1030   www.aspentec.com

Mfr. software for chemists and refineries.

AspenTech Japan Co. Ltd., Atlas Bldg., 5 Ichibancho, Chiyoda-Ku, Tokyo 102, Japan

Tel: 81-3-3262-1710   Fax: 81-3-3264-5425

ASSOCIATED MERCHANDISING CORPORATION

500 Seventh Ave., 2nd Fl., New York, NY, 10018

Tel: (212) 819-6600   Fax: (212) 819-6701   www.theamc.com

Retail service organization; apparel, shoes and accessories.

Associated Merchandising Corp., Nakanoshima Ctr. Bldg., 2-27 Nakanoshima 6-chome, Kita-ku, Osaka 530, Japan

ASSOCIATED PRESS INC.

50 Rockefeller Plaza, New York, NY, 10020-1605

Tel: (212) 621-1500   Fax: (212) 621-5447   www.ap.com

News gathering agency.

The Associated Press, CPO Box 607, Tokyo 100-91, Japan

Tel: 81-3-3545-5902

ASYST TECHNOLOGIES, INC.

48761 Kato Road, Fremont, CA, 94538

Tel: (510) 661-5000   Fax: (510) 661-5166   www.asyst.com

Produces wafer handling equipment.

Asyst Kabushiki Kaisha K.K., Kaneko Dai 2 Bldg., 7/F, 2-6-23 Shin-Yokohama, Kohoku-ku Yokohama-shi, Kanagawa-ken 222-0033, Japan

AT&T BROADBAND, LLC

188 Inverness Dr. West, Englewood, CO, 80112

Tel: (303) 875-5500   Fax: (303) 875-4984   www.broadband.att.com

Provides broadband technology services; digital TV, digital telephone and high-speed cable internet services.

Chofu, Tokyo, Japan

TITUS, Tokyo, Japan

AT&T CORPORATION

295 N. Maple Ave., Basking Ridge, NJ, 07920-1002

Tel: (908) 221-2000   Fax: (908) 221-2528   www.att.com

Engaged in long distance telecommunications.

AT&T Japan Ltd., 25 Mori Bldg., 1-4-30 Roppongi, Minato-ku, Tokyo 106, Japan

ATMEL CORPORATION

2325 Orchard Pkwy., San Jose, CA, 95131

Tel: (408) 441-0311   Fax: (408) 436-4200   www.atmel.com

Design, manufacture and marketing of advanced semiconductors.

Atmel Japan KK, Tonetsu Shinkawa Bldg., 9/F, 1-24-8 Shinkawa, Chuo-ku, Tokyo 104-0033, Japan

Tel: 81-3-3523-3551   Fax: 81-3-3523-7581

ATTACHMATE CORPORATION

3617 131st Avenue SE, Bellevue, WA, 98006-1332

Tel: (425) 644-4010   Fax: (425) 747-9924   www.attachmate.com

Mfr. connectivity software.

Attachmate Japan, Pier West Square, 1-11-8 Tsukuda Chuo-ku, Tokyo 104, Japan

Tel: 81-3-5560-8970

AUSPEX SYSTEMS, INC.

2800 Scott Blvd., Santa Clara, CA, 95050

Tel: (408) 566-2000   Fax: (408) 566-2020   www.auspex.com

Mfr. data management and file sharing software.

Auspex KK, ATT Shinkan 6/F, 2-11-7 Akasaka, Minato-ku, Tokyo 107-0052, Japan

Tel: 81-3-3586-1751

AUTODESK INC.

111 McInnis Parkway, San Rafael, CA, 94903

Tel: (415) 507-5000   Fax: (415) 507-6112   www.autodesk.com

Develop/marketing/support computer-aided design, engineering, scientific and multimedia software products.

Autodesk Fukuoka Sales, Hakata Mitsui Bldg. No. 2, 7F, 1-35 Tenyamachi, Hakata-ku, Fukuoka 812, Japan

Tel: 81-92-282-0781   Fax: 81-92-282-0720

Autodesk Ltd. Japan, Yebisu Garden Place Tower, 24F, 4-20-3 Ebisu, Shibuya-ku, Tokyo 150, Japan

Tel: 81-33-473-9511   Fax: 81-33-473-9642

Autodesk Nagoya Sales, 12/F, Nishiki Park Bldg. 2-4-3, Nishiki, Naka-ku, Nagoya 460, Japan

Tel: 81-52-232-7891   Fax: 81-52-232-7894

Autodesk Osaka Sales, Shin Osaka Daini Mori Bldg., 14F, 3-5-36 Miyahara, Yodogawa-ku, Osaka 532, Japan

Tel: 81-6-350-5221   Fax: 81-6-350-5222

AUTOMATIC SWITCH CO. (ASCO)

50-60 Hanover Rd., Florham Park, NJ, 07932

Tel: (973) 966-2000   Fax: (973) 966-2628   www.asco.com

Mfr. solenoid valves, emergency power controls, pressure and temperature switches.

ASCO (Japan) Ltd., 1-20 Takahata-cho, Nishinomiya, Hyogo 663-8202, Japan

Tel: 81-798-65-6361   Fax: 81-798-63-4443   Contact: M. Kato

AUTOSPLICE INC.

10121 Barnes Canyon Road, San Diego, CA, 92121

Tel: (858) 535-0077   Fax: (858) 535-0130   www.autosplice.com

Mfr. electronic components.

Autosplice Japan, 3-7-39 Minami-cho, Higashi Kurume-shi, Tokyo 203, Japan

Tel: 81-424-62-8481   Fax: 81-424-62-8513   Contact: Koichi Itoh

AVERY DENNISON CORPORATION

150 N. Orange Grove Blvd., Pasadena, CA, 91103

Tel: (626) 304-2000   Fax: (626) 792-7312   www.averydennison.com

Mfr. pressure-sensitive adhesives and materials, office products, labels, tags, retail systems, Carter's Ink and specialty chemicals.

Fasson-Avery Dennison/Sanyo, 3F, Asahi Seimei Suginami Bldg., 2-3-9 Amanuma, Suginami-ku, Tokyo 167-0032, Japan

Tel: 813-5347-2720   Fax: 813-5347-2725

AVID TECHNOLOGY, INC.

1 Park West, Tewksbury, MA, 01876

Tel: (978) 640-6789   Fax: (978) 640-1366   www.avid.com

Mfr. animation design software and digital and audio systems.

Avid Japan KK, ATT New Tower, 4/F, 2-11-7 Akasaka, Minato-ku, Tokyo 107-0052, Japan

Tel: 81-3-3505-7937   Fax: 81-3-3505-7938

Avid Japan KK, Sausuhoresuto Bldg., 1-14-19 Minamimorimachi, Kita-Ku Osaka 530-0054, Japan

Tel: 81-6-6314-3132   Fax: 81-6-6314-2624

AVON PRODUCTS, INC.

1345 Avenue of the Americas, New York, NY, 10105-0196

Tel: (212) 282-5000   Fax: (212) 282-6049   www.avon.com

Mfr. direct seller of cosmetics and beauty-related items.

Avon Products Co. Ltd., Totate Int. Bldg., 12-19 Shibuya 2-chome, Shibuya-ku, Tokyo 150, Japan

Tel: 81-3-3797-8224   Fax: 81-3-3400-6930   Contact: Wendy Allen, Sales Dir.

AXEDA SYSTEMS INC.

257 Great Valley Pkwy., Malvern, PA, 19355

Tel: (610) 251-9999   Fax: (610) 695-2592   www.axeda.com

Mfr. software.

Axeda Systems KK, Izumi Nishiazabu Bldg., 4-3-11 Nishiazabu, Minato-ku, Tokyo 106-0031, Japan

BAIN & COMPANY, INC.

Two Copley Place, Boston, MA, 02116

Tel: (617) 572-2000   Fax: (617) 572-2427   www.bain.com

Strategic management consulting services.

Bain & Company Japan Inc., Hibiya Kokusai Bldg., 14/F, 2-2-3 Uchisaiwai-cho, Chiyoda-ku, Tokyo 100, Japan
Tel: 81-3-3502-6401   Fax: 81-3-3592-4960

BAKER & McKENZIE

130 East Randolph Drive, Ste. 2500, Chicago, IL, 60601

Tel: (312) 861-8000   Fax: (312) 861-2899   www.bakerinfo.com

International legal services.

Baker & McKenzie (Tokyo Aoyama Law Office), 2-3 Kita-Aoyama 1-chome, Minato-ku, Tokyo 107, Japan
Tel: 81-3-3403-5281   Fax: 81-3-3470-3152

BAKER & TAYLOR CORPORATION

2709 Water Ridge Pkwy., Charlotte, NC, 28217

Tel: (704) 357-3500   Fax: (704) 329-9105   www.btol.com

Book wholesaler; supplies books and audio books, calendars and information services to public and university libraries.

Baker & Taylor Corporation, c/o Kinokuniya, 38-1 Sakuragaoka 5-chome, Setagaya-ku, Tokyo 156, Japan
Tel: 81-3-3439-0115   Fax: 81-3-3439-0123

BAKER PETROLITE CORPORATION

3900 Essex Lane, Houston, TX, 77027

Tel: (713) 599-7400   Fax: (713) 599-7592   www.bakerhughes.com

Mfr. specialty chemical treating programs, performance-enhancing additives and related equipment and services.

Tokyo-Petrolite Co., Toin Bldg., 12-15 Shinkawa 2-chome, Chuo-ku, Tokyo 104, Japan

BALDWIN TECHNOLOGY COMPANY, INC.

12 Commerce Drive, Shelton, CT, 06484

Tel: (203) 402-1000   Fax: (203) 402-5500   www.baldwintech.com

Mfr./services material handling, accessories, control and prepress equipment for print industry.

Baldwin Japan Ltd., 2-4-34 Toyo 2-chome, Kohtok-ku, Tokyo 135, Japan
Tel: 81-3-5606-2771   Fax: 81-3-5606-2779   Contact: Y. Yano, Mng. Dir.

BALTEK CORPORATION

10 Fairway Court, PO Box 195, Northvale, NJ, 07647

Tel: (201) 767-1400   Fax: (201) 387-6631   www.baltek.com

Mfr. light lumber, balsa wood and PVC foam.

Baltek International Corporation, 1-10-1 Yurakucho Chiyoda-ku, 11/F, Tokyo 1000-0006, Japan

BALTIMORE AIRCOIL CO., INC.

PO Box 7322, Baltimore, MD, 21227

Tel: (410) 799-6200   Fax: (410) 799-6416   www.baltimoreaircoil.com

Mfr. evaporative heat transfer and ice thermal storage products.

BAC-Japan Co. Ltd., 2-27-4 Shin-Machi, Setagaya-Ku, Tokyo 154, Japan

BANDAG INCORPORATED

2905 North Highway 61, Muscatine, IA, 52761

Tel: (319) 262-1400   Fax: (319) 262-1252   www.bandag.com

Mfr. and sale retread tires.

Bandag Japan KK, Elshin Bldg. 5/F, 3-6-1 Kanda Ogawamachi, Chiyoda-ku, Tokyo 101, Japan

BANK OF AMERICA CORPORATION

Bank of America Corporate Center, Charlotte, NC, 28255

Tel: (415) 622-3530   Fax: (704) 386-6699   www.bankofamerica.com

Financial services.

Bank of America NT & SA, ARK Mori Bldg., 34/F, 1-12-32 Akasaka Minato-ku, PO Box 511, Tokyo 107, Japan

Tel: 81-3-3587-3155 Fax: 81-3-3587-3460   Contact: Arun Duggal, SVP

BANK OF HAWAII CORPORATION

130 Merchant Street, Honolulu, HI, 96813

Tel: (808) 643-3888   Fax: (808) 537-8440   www.boh.com

Engaged in commercial and consumer banking services.

Bank of Hawaii Corporation, 41st Floor, Shinjuku Center Building, 1-25-1, Nishi-Shinjuku, Tokyo 163-0641, Japan

Tel: 81-3-5909-3670

THE BANK OF NEW YORK

One Wall Street, New York, NY, 10286

Tel: (212) 495-1784   Fax: (212) 495-2546   www.bankofny.com

Banking services.

The Bank of New York, Fukoku Seimei Bldg., 6th Fl., 2-2-2 Uchisaiwai-cho, Chiyoda-ku, Tokyo 100, Japan

The Bank of New York, Osaka Bldg., 8th Fl., 8-15 Azuchimachi 1- chome Chuo-ku, Osaka 541, Japan

BANK ONE CORPORATION

One Bank One Plaza, Chicago, IL, 60670

Tel: (312) 732-4000   Fax: (312) 732-3366   www.fcnbd.com

Provides financial products and services.

Bank One, NA, Hibiya Central Building, 7F, 2-9 Hishi-Shimbashi, 1-chome Minato-ku, Tokyo 105, Japan

Tel: 81-3-3596-8757 Fax: 81-3-3596-8745   Contact: Yoshio Kitazawa, Gen. Mgr.

C. R. BARD, INC.

730 Central Ave., Murray Hill, NJ, 07974

Tel: (908) 277-8000   Fax: (908) 277-8078   www.crbard.com

Mfr. health care products.

Medicon, Inc., Hiranomachi Century Building, 8F, 2-5-8 Hiranomachi, Chou-ku, Osaka 541-0046, Japan

Tel: 81-66-203-6541 Fax: 81-66-203-1516

BARRA, INC.

2100 Milvia Street, Berkeley, CA, 94704

Tel: (510) 548-5442   Fax: (510) 548-4374   www.barra.com

Mfr. analytical software for private investors and portfolio managers.

BARRA International, Ltd., Sumitomo Hamamatsucho Bldg., 7/F, 1-18-16 Hamamatsucho, Minato-ku, Tokyo 105-013, Japan

Tel: 81-3-5402-4153 Fax: 81-3-5402-4154

BATES WORLDWIDE INC.

498 Seventh Avenue, New York, NY, 10018

Tel: (212) 297-7000   Fax: (212) 986-0270   www.batesww.com

Advertising, marketing, public relations and media consulting.

Bates 141 Japan, Shibaur Square Bldg., 3/F, 4-9-25 Shibaura, Minato-ku, Tokyo 108, Japan

Tel: 81-3-3455-5181 Fax: 81-3-3455-6970   Contact: Naotaki Okuno, Dir.

Saatchi & Saatchi Bates Yomiko, Shibaura Square Bldg., 4-9-25 Shibaura, Minato-ku, Tokyo 108, Japan

Tel: 81-3-3455-4123 Fax: 81-3-3455-4110   Contact: David Meredith, Pres.

BAUSCH & LOMB INC.

One Bausch & Lomb Place, Rochester, NY, 14604-2701

Tel: (716) 338-6000   Fax: (716) 338-6007   www.bausch.com

Mfr. vision care products and accessories.

B.L.J. Company Ltd., Tower B Omori Bellport, 7/F, 6-26-2 Minami-Oi, Shinagawa-ku, Tokyo 140-0013, Japan

Charles River Japan, Inc., Atsugi, Japan

Contact: Hino, Tskuba, and Yokohama

BAX GLOBAL INC.

16808 Armstrong Ave., PO Box 19571, Irvine, CA, 92623

Tel: (949) 752-4000   Fax: (949) 260-3182   www.baxworld.com

Air freight forwarder.

BAX Global Japan K.K., G1, Higashi Nihonbashi Bldg., 9-7 Higashi Nihonbashi, 1-chome Chuo-ku, Tokyo 103-0004, Japan

Tel: 81-3-5820-6851   Fax: 81-3-5820-6855

BAXTER INTERNATIONAL INC.

One Baxter Parkway, Deerfield, IL, 60015

Tel: (847) 948-2000   Fax: (847) 948-3948   www.baxter.com

Mfr. products and provide services in the field of the administration of medication and bioscience.

Baxter Ltd., 4 Rokubancho, Chiyoda-ku, Tokyo 102, Japan

BDO SEIDMAN, LLP   BELGIUM

130 East Randolph Street, Chicago, IL, 60601

Tel: (312) 856-9100   Fax: (312) 856-1379   www.bdo.com

International accounting and financial consulting firm.

BDO Binder & Company, Nissei Bldg., 5F, 1-18 Ageba-cho, Shinjuku-ku, Tokyo 162, Japan

Tel: 81-3-3266-7679   Fax: 81-3-3266-7699   Contact: Masayuki Takase

BDO Sanyu & Company, STEC, 22F, 1-24-1 Nishi-Shinjuku, Shinjuku-ku, Tokyo 160, Japan

Tel: 81-3-5322-3531   Fax: 81-3-5322-3593   Contact: Jum Sugita

BEA SYSTEMS, INC.

2315 North First Street, St. Jose, CA, 95131

Tel: (408) 570-8000   Fax: (408) 570-8091   www.beasys.com

Develops communications management software and provider of software consulting services.

BEA Systems Japan Ltd., Shin-Nikko Building, East Tower 14F, 2-10-1 Toranomon, Minato-ku, Tokyo 105-0001, Japan

THE BEAR STEARNS & COMPANIES., INC.

245 Park Ave., New York, NY, 10167

Tel: (212) 272-2000   Fax: (212) 272-3092   www.bearstearns.com

Investment banking, securities broker/dealer and investment advisory services.

Bear Stearns Japan Ltd., Shiroyama Hills, 3-1 Toranomon 4-chome, Minato-ku, Tokyo 105, Japan

Tel: 81-3-3437-7800   Fax: 81-3-3437-7880

BECHTEL GROUP INC.

50 Beale Street, PO Box 3965, San Francisco, CA, 94105-1895

Tel: (415) 768-1234   Fax: (415) 768-9038   www.bechtel.com

General contractors in engineering, construction and project management.

Bechtel International Corp., Fuji Bldg., Room 310, 2-3 Marunouchi, 3-Chrome, Chiyoda-ku, Tokyo 100-0005, Japan

Tel: 81-3-3214-4481   Fax: 81-3-3214-2596

BECKMAN COULTER, INC.

4300 N. Harbor Boulevard, Fullerton, CA, 92834

Tel: (714) 871-4848   Fax: (714) 773-8898   www.beckmancoulter.com

Develop/mfr./marketing automated systems and supplies for biological analysis.

Beckman Coulter KK, Toranomon 37 Mori Building, 3-5-1 Toranomon, Minato-ku, Tokyo 105-0001, Japan

Tel: 81-3-5404-8359   Fax: 81-3-5404-8436

BECTON DICKINSON AND COMPANY

One Becton Drive, Franklin Lakes, NJ, 07417-1880

Tel: (201) 847-6800   Fax: (201) 847-6475   www.bd.com

Mfr./sale medical supplies, devices and diagnostic systems.

Nippon Becton Dickinson, Shimato Bldg., 5-34 Akasaka 8-chome, Minato-ku, Tokyo 107, Japan

BENTLY NEVADA CORPORATION

1631 Bently Parkway South, Minden, NV, 89423

Tel: (775) 782-3611   Fax: (775) 782-9259   www.bently.com

Provides hardware, software, and services for machinery information and management systems.

Rikei Corp., Nichimen Bldg., 4/F, 2-2-3 Nakanoshima, Kita-ku, Osaka 530, Japan

Rikei Corp., Shinjuku Normura Bldg., 1-26-2 Nishi-Shinjuku, Shinjuku-ku, Tokyo 160, Japan

LOUIS BERGER INTERNATIONAL INC.

100 Halsted Street, East Orange, NJ, 07019

Tel: (201) 678-1960   Fax: (201) 672-4284   www.louisberger.com

Consulting engineers, engaged in architecture, environmental and advisory services.

Louis Berger International Inc., Watase Building, 2/F, 5-8-3 Nishi-Shimbashi, Minato-ku, Tokyo 105-0003, Japan

Tel: 81-3-3437-1999   Fax: 81-3-3578-9581

BERLITZ CROSS-CULTURAL TRAINING INC.

400 Alexander Park, Princeton, NJ, 08540

Tel: (609) 514-9650   Fax: (609) 514-9689   www.berlitz.com

Consulting and management training services to bridge cultural gaps for international travelers as well as for business transferees and families.

Berlitz Japan, Inc., Mitsui Seimei Kitasenju Building, 3F, 41-1 Senju-Nakacho, Adachi-ku, Tokyo 120-0036, Japan

Berlitz Japan, Inc., Mitsui Seimei Kitasenju Building, 3/F, 41-1 Senju-Nakacho, Adachi-ku, Tokyo 120-0036, Japan

BEST WESTERN INTERNATIONAL

6201 North 24th Place, Phoenix, AZ, 85106

Tel: (602) 957-4200   Fax: (602) 957-5740   www.bestwestern.com

International hotel chain.

The Richmond Hotel, 3-5-14 Meijiro, Toshima-ku, Tokyo 171, Japan

BEVERLY ENTERPRISES INC.

1200 South Waldron Road, Ft. Smith, AR, 72903

Tel: (501) 452-6712   Fax: (501) 452-5131   www.beverlycares.com

Nursing homes, retirement living centers, pharmacies.

Beverly Japan Corp. (JV), Tohgeki Bldg., 1-1 Tsukiji 4-chome, Chuo-ku, Tokyo, Japan

BIOGEN, INC.

14 Cambridge Center, Cambridge, MA, 02142

Tel: (617) 679-2000   Fax: (617) 679-2617   www.biogen.com

Engaged in medical research and development of autoimmune diseases.

Biogen Japan KK, AIG Bldg. 9/F, 1-1-3 Marunouchi, Chiyoda-Ku, Tokyo 100-005, Japan

Tel: 81-3-5288-5201   Contact: Toshio Nakata

BIO-RAD LABORATORIES INC.

1000 Alfred Nobel Drive, Hercules, CA, 94547

Tel: (510) 724-7000   Fax: (510) 724-3167   www.bio-rad.com

Mfr. life science research products, clinical diagnostics, analytical instruments.

Nippon Bio-Rad Laboratories KK, Cosmo Park Bldg. 7-18, Higashi-Nippori 5-chome, Arakawa-Ku, Tokyo 116-0014, Japan

Tel: 81-03-5811-6287   Fax: 81-03-5811-6273

BLACK & DECKER CORPORATION

701 E. Joppa Road, Towson, MD, 21286

Tel: (410) 716-3900   Fax: (410) 716-2933   www.blackanddecker.com

Mfr. power tools and accessories, security hardware, small appliances, fasteners, information systems and services.

Black & Decker Japan, Attn: Japan Office, 701 East Joppa Road, Towson, MD, 21286

BLACK & VEATCH LLP

8400 Ward Pkwy., PO Box 8405, Kansas City, MO, 64114

Tel: (816) 339-2000   Fax: (816) 339-2934   www.bv.com

Engaged in engineering, construction and consulting, specializing in infrastructure development in the fields of energy, water and information.

M&B Engineering Co. Ltd., 1-2 Uchikanda 2-chome, Chiyoda-ku, Tokyo 101, Japan

BLACK BOX CORPORATION

1000 Park Dr., Lawrence, PA, 15055

Tel: (724) 746-5500   Fax: (724) 746-0746   www.blackbox.com

Direct marketer and technical service provider of communications, networking and related computer connectivity products.

Black Box Japan, Nec Eitai Bldg., 16-10 Fuyuki, Koto-ku, Tokyo 135, Japan

Tel: 81-3-3820-5011   Fax: 81-3-3820-5036   Contact: Frances Wertheimber, Gen. Mgr.

BLACKROCK, INC.

345 Park Avenue, New York, NY, 10154

Tel: (212) 754-5560   Fax: (212) 409-3123   www.blackrock.com

Engaged in investment management services.

BlackRock Japan KK, Nihonbashi-Muromaci 2-1-1, Chuo-ku, Tokyo 103-0022, Japan

Tel: 81-3-3241-9980   Fax: 81-3-3241-9713

BLOOM ENGINEERING CO., INC.

5460 Horning Rd., Pittsburgh, PA, 15236

Tel: (412) 653-3500   Fax: (412) 653-2253   www.bloomeng.com

Mfr. custom engineered burners and combustion systems.

Nippon Herr Company Ltd., Daiichi Choujiya Bldg., 1-2-13 Shibadaimon, Minato-ku, Tokyo 105-0012, Japan

Tel: 81-3-5425-6461   Fax: 81-3-5425-6433

BLOOMBERG L.P.

499 Park Ave., New York, NY, 10022

Tel: (212) 318-2000   Fax: (212) 940-1954   www.bloomberg.com

Publishes magazines and provides TV, radio and newspaper wire services.

Bloomberg L.P., Tokyo, Japan

BLOUNT INTERNATIONAL, INC

4520 Executive Park Dr., Montgomery, AL, 36116-1602

Tel: (334) 244-4000   Fax: (334) 271-8130   www.blount.com

Mfr. cutting chain and equipment, timber harvest and handling equipment and riding mowers.

Blount Japan Ltd., Toranomon Kotohira Kaika, 2-8 Toranomon 1-chome, Minato-ku, Tokyo, Japan

Tel: 81-3-3503-6716   Fax: 81-3-3504-1334   Contact: Toshio Suzuki, Mgr.

BLUE CROSS AND BLUE SHIELD ASSOC.

225 N. Michigan Ave., Chicago, IL, 60601-7680

Tel: (312) 297-6000   Fax: (312) 297-6609   www.blueshield.com

Provides health care coverage through indemnity insurance, HMO's and Medicare programs.

BlueCare Worldwide, Tokyo, Japan

BMC SOFTWARE, INC.

2101 City West Blvd., Houston, TX, 77042-2827

Tel: (713) 918-8800   Fax: (713) 918-8000   www.bmc.com

Engaged in mainframe-related utilities software and services.

BMC Software, Nishi-Shinjuku Mitsui Bldg., 10F, 6-24-1 Nishi-Shinjuku, Shinjuku-ku, Tokyo 160-0023, Japan

BOBCAT COMPANY

250 E. Beaton Drive, PO Box 6000, West Fargo, ND, 58078-8700

Tel: (701) 241-8700   Fax: (701) 241-8704   www.melroe.com

Mfr. heavy equipment.

Bobcat Corporation Japan, 636 Morooka-chi, Kouhoku-ku, Yokohama-shi, Kanagawa-ken 222, Japan

Tel: 81-45-532-0151

BOOZ-ALLEN & HAMILTON INC.

8283 Greensboro Drive, McLean, VA, 22102

Tel: (703) 902-5000　　Fax: (703) 902-3333　　www.bah.com

International management and technology consultants.

Booz Allen & Hamilton (Japan) Inc., Shiroyama Hills, 18F, 4-3-1 Toranoman, Minato-ku, Tokyo 105, Japan

Tel: 81-3-3436-8600　Fax: 81-3-3436-8668

BORG-WARNER AUTOMOTIVE INC.

200 S. Michigan Ave., Chicago, IL, 60604

Tel: (312) 322-8500　　Fax: (312) 461-0507　　www.bwauto.com

Mfr. automotive components; provider of security services.

Borg-Warner Automotive KK, 1300-50 Yabata, Nabari City, Nabari 518-04, Japan

NSK-Warner KK, 2345 Aino, Fikuroi City, Shizuoka 437, Japan

BOSE CORPORATION

The Mountain, Framingham, MA, 01701-9168

Tel: (508) 879-7330　　Fax: (508) 766-7543　　www.bose.com

Mfr. quality audio equipment and speakers.

BOSE KK, Shibuya YT Bldg., 28-3 Maruyamacho, Shibuya-ku, Tokyo, Japan

THE BOSTON CONSULTING GROUP

Exchange Place, 31st Fl., Boston, MA, 02109

Tel: (617) 973-1200　　Fax: (617) 973-1339　　www.bcg.com

Management consulting company.

The Boston Consulting Group, The New Otani Garden Court, 4-1 Kioi-cho, Chiyoda-ku, Tokyo 102, Japan

Tel: 81-3-5211-0300

BOSTON SCIENTIFIC CORPORATION (BSC)

One Scientific Place, Natick, MA, 01760-1537

Tel: (508) 650-8000　　Fax: (508) 650-8923　　www.bostonscientific.com

Developer, manufacturer and marketer of medical devices.

Boston Scientific Japan, KK, STEC JYOHO Bldg., 23F, 1-24-1 Nishi-Shinjuku, Shinjuku-ku, Tokyo 160, Japan

Tel: 81-3-5322-3720　Fax: 81-3-5322-3700

BOWNE & COMPANY, INC.

345 Hudson Street, New York, NY, 10014

Tel: (212) 924-5500　　Fax: (212) 229-3420　　www.bowne.com

Financial printing and foreign language translation, localization (software), internet design and maintenance and facilities management.

Bowne Global Solutions, Tomoecho Annex No. 2, 8/F, 3-8-27 Toranomon, Minato-ku, Tokyo 105-0001, Japan

Tel: 81-3-5425-6600　Fax: 81-3-5425-6605

Bowne Global Solutions, Yokohama Landmark Tower, 42F, 2-2-1-1 Minato-Mirai, Nishi-ku, Yokohama 220-8142, Japan

Tel: 81-45-640-4250　Fax: 81-45-6404206

BOYDEN CONSULTING CORPORATION

364 Elwood Ave., Hawthorne, NY, 10502

Tel: (914) 747-0093　　Fax: (914) 980-6147　　www.boyden.com

International executive search firm.

Boyden Assoc. (Japan) Ltd., #308, 1-3-28 Motoazabu, Minato-ku, Tokyo 106, Japan

Tel: 81-3-5232-1872

BOZELL GROUP

40 West 23rd Street, New York, NY, 10010

Tel: (212) 727-5000　　Fax: (212) 645-9173　　www.bozell.com

Advertising, marketing, public relations and media consulting.

Bozell Worldwide, Japan, Nisseki Shibuya Bldg., 3F, 2-16-1 Shibuya, Shibuya-ku, Tokyo 150, Japan

Tel: 81-3-3797-6262　Fax: 81-3-3797-6261　Contact: Robert Jenkins, Pres.

BRADY CORPORATION

6555 W. Good Hope Road, Milwaukee, WI, 53223

Tel: (414) 358-6600   Fax: (414) 358-6600   www.whbrady.com

Mfr. industrial ID for wire marking, circuit boards; facility ID, signage, printing systems and software.

Nippon Brady KK, Sumitomo Fudosan Shin, Yokahama Building, 8F, 2-5-5 Shin Yokahama, Kohoku-ku, Yokohama Kanagawa 222, Japan

Tel: 81-45-474-2800   Fax: 81-45-474-6701   Contact: Tsutomo Matsumoto, Mng. Dir.

BRANSON ULTRASONICS CORPORATION

41 Eagle Road, Danbury, CT, 06813-1961

Tel: (203) 796-0400   Fax: (203) 796-2285   www.branson-plasticsjoin.com

Engaged in design, development, manufacture and marketing of plastics joining, precision cleaning and processing equipment.

Branson Ultrasonics, 4-3-14 Okada, Atsugi-shi, Kanagawa 243, Japan

Tel: 81-462-28-2881   Fax: 81-462-28-8992

BRINK'S INC.

Thorndal Circle, Darien, CT, 06820

Tel: (203) 662-7800   Fax: (203) 662-7968   www.brinks.com

Security transportation.

Brink's Japan KK, Tokyo, Japan

BRISTOL-MYERS SQUIBB COMPANY

345 Park Ave., New York, NY, 10154-0037

Tel: (212) 546-4000   Fax: (212) 546-4020   www.bms.com

Pharmaceutical and food preparations, medical and surgical instruments.

Bristol-Myers Lion Ltd., Nihon Seimei Akasaka, 7-1-16 Akasaka Minato-ku, Japan

ConvaTec Japan, EBISU, MF Bldg. 6F, Tokyo 150, Japan

ConvaTec, Div. Bristol-Myers Squibb, 27/Fk Shinjuku I-Land Tower, 6-5-1 Nishi-Shinjuku 6-chome, Shinjuku-ku, Tokyo 163-13, Japan

Japan Toda Labs, 1-34-17 Naka-Cho, Toda City, Saitama Pref. 335, Japan

Zimmer, Japan K.K., Mita 43 Mori Bldg., Minato-ku, Tokyo, Japan

Zimmer, Japan K.K., 1656, 1Nakabata, Gotemba City 108, Japan

BROADCOM CORPORATION INTERNATIONAL

16215 Alton Pkwy., Irvine, CA, 92619-7013

Tel: (949) 450-8700   Fax: (949) 450-8710   www.broadcom.com

Designs, develops and supplies integrated circuits and high density communication processors.

Broadcom Corporation, Shinjyuku Nomura Bldg. 32F, 1-26-2 Nishi-Shinjyuku, Shinjuku-ku, Tokyo 163-0532, Japan

Tel: 81-3-5322-1391   Fax: 81-3-5322-1393

BROADVISION, INC.

585 Broadway, Redwood City, CA, 94063

Tel: (650) 261-5100   Fax: (650) 261-5900   www.broadvision.com

Develops and delivers an integrated suite of packaged applications for personalized enterprise portals.

BroadVision Japan, Tennoz Parkside Bldg., 12/F, 2-5-8 Higashi-Shinagawa, Shinagawa-ku, Tokyo 140-0002, Japan

Tel: 81-3-5461-8810   Fax: 81-3-5461-8833

BROCADE COMMUNICATIONS SYSTEMS, INC.

1745 Technology Drive, San Jose, CA, 95110

Tel: (408) 487-8000   Fax: (408) 487-8101   www.brocade.com

Mfr. software.

Brocade Communications KK, 1-1-1 Uchisaiwaicho Chiyoda-ku, Imperial Tower 15/F, Tokyo 100-0011, Japan

Tel: 81-3-3507-5900   Fax: 81-3-3507-5802

BROOKS-PRI AUTOMATION, INC.

15 Elizabeth Drive, Chelmsford, MA, 01824

Tel: (978) 262-2400   Fax: (978) 262-2500   www.brooks.com

Mfr. tool automation products.

Brooks Automation Japan, K.K., KSP R&D Business Park Bldg., 9/F, 3-2-1 Sakado Takatsu-ku, Kawasaki Kanagawa 213, Japan

Tel: 81-44-850-2900   Fax: 81-44-850-2901

Brooks Automation Japan, K.K., 1500 Komakihara-Shinden, Komaki City - Aichi Pref. 485-8653, Japan

Tel: 81-568-74-1511   Fax: 81-568-74-1602

BROWN BROTHERS HARRIMAN & COMPANY

140 Broadway, New York, NY, 10005

Tel: (212) 483-1818   Fax: (212) 493-8526   www.bbh.com

Leading provider of mergers and acquisition advisory services and private equity capital to private and closely held public companies.

Brown Brothers Harriman & Co., Banzai Building, 5/F, 2-31-19, Shiba, Minato-ku, Tokyo 105-0014, Japan

Tel: 813-5427-2211

BRUNSWICK CORPORATION

1 Northfield Court, Lake Forest, IL, 60045-4811

Tel: (847) 735-4700   Fax: (847) 735-4765   www.brunswickcorp.com

Mfr. recreational boats, marine engines, bowling centers and equipment, fishing equipment, defense/aerospace.

Nippon Brunswick KK, Nippon Brunswick Bldg., 27-7 Sendagaya 5-chome, Skibuya-ku, Tokyo, Japan

BRUSH WELLMAN ENGINEERED MATERIALS INC.

17876 St. Clair Ave., Cleveland, OH, 44110

Tel: (216) 486-4200   Fax: (216) 383-4091   www.beminc.com

Mfr. beryllium, beryllium alloys and ceramics, specialty metal systems and precious metal products.

Brush Wellman (Japan) Ltd., Dai-Ichi Marusan Bldg, 9 Kanda Jimbocho 3-chome, Chiyoda-ku, Tokyo 101, Japan

Tel: 81-3-3230-2961   Fax: 81-3-3230-2908

BUCKMAN LABORATORIES INTERNATIONAL, INC.

1258 N. McLean Blvd., Memphis, TN, 38108-0308

Tel: (901) 278-0330   Fax: (901) 276-5343   www.buckman.com

Mfr. specialty chemicals.

Buckman Labs KK, Kyodo Bldg. 7/F, 16-8 Nihonbashi Kodenniacho Chuo-ku, Tokyo 103-0001, Japan

BUDGET GROUP, INC.

125 Basin St., Ste. 210, Daytona Beach, FL, 32114

Tel: (904) 238-7035   Fax: (904) 238-7461   www.budgetrentacar.com

Car and truck rental system.

Budget Rent A Car, 3-255 Kukomae, Hakata-ku 812, Tokyo, Japan

Tel: 81-92-2810543

LEO BURNETT, DIV. B-COM 3 GROUP

35 West Wacker Drive, Chicago, IL, 60601

Tel: (312) 220-5959   Fax: (312) 220-6533   www.leoburnett.com

Engaged in advertising, marketing, media buying and planning, and public relations.

Leo Burnett-Kyodo Co. Ltd., 18F, Akasaka Twin Tower, 17-22 Akasaka 2-chome, Minato-ku, Tokyo 107, Japan

BURSON-MARSTELLER

230 Park Avenue South, New York, NY, 10003-1566

Tel: (212) 614-4000   Fax: (212) 614-4262   www.bm.com

Public relations/public affairs consultants.

Dentsu Burson-Marsteller Co. Ltd., Sogo 3 Bldg., 6 Kojimachi 1-chome, Chiyoda-ku, Tokyo 102, Japan

Tel: 81-3-3264-6701   Fax: 81-3-3234-9647

BUTLER AUTOMATIC, INC.

41 Leona Drive, Middleborough, MA, 02346

Tel: (508) 923-0544   Fax: (508) 923-0885   www.butlerautomatic.com

Mfr. web splicing equipment.

Isowa-Hooperswift Ltd., 66, Nishiya-Cho, Kasugai 486 0908, Aichi, Japan

Tel: 81-568-33-6010

CABOT CORPORATION

2 Seaport Lane, Ste. 1300, Boston, MA, 02210-2019

Tel: (617) 345-0100   Fax: (617) 342-6103   www.cabot-corp.com

Mfr. carbon blacks, plastics; oil and gas, information systems.

Cabot Far East Inc., 8-15 Akasaka 4-chome, Minato-ku, Tokyo 107, Japan

CABOT MICROELECTRONICS

870 Commons Drive, Aurora, IL, 60504

Tel: (630) 375-6631   Fax: (630) 375-5582   www.cabot-corp.com

Mfr. polishing compounds and polishing pads used in the manufacture of advanced semiconductors (chips) and rigid disks-critical components.

Cabot Microelectronics KK, 1287-19 Oazo-Kitakoyama, Geino-Cho, Age-Gun, Mie-Ken, Japan

Tel: 81-59-266-0120   Contact: Hiroyuki Nishiya

CADENCE DESIGN SYSTEMS, INC.

2655 Seely Ave., Bldg. 5, San Jose, CA, 95134

Tel: (408) 943-1234   Fax: (408) 943-0513   www.cadence.com

Mfr. electronic design automation software.

Cadence Design Systems KK, Fudosan Yotsubashi Bldg., 14/F, 1-4-4 Awaza, Nishi-ku, Osaka 550-0011, Japan

Tel: 81-6-4390-7371   Fax: 81-6-4390-7372

Cadence Design Systems KK, 3-17-6 Shin-Yokohama, Kohoku-ku, Yokohama Kanagawa 222-0033, Japan

Tel: 81-45-475-6330   Fax: 81-45-475-6331

CALDERA INTERNATIONAL

355 South 520 West, Ste. 100, Linden, UT, 84057

Tel: (801) 765-4999   Fax: (801) 765-1313   www.caldera.com

Provides integrated solutions for small-to-medium businesses, retail operations, telecommunications and other vertical markets.

Caldera KK, Nakamura Bldg., 2-24-3 Ohashi Meguro-ku, Tokyo 153-0044, Japan

Tel: 81-3-5486-3905   Fax: 81-3-5486-3918   Contact: Makoto Asoh

CALGON CARBON CORPORATION

400 Calgon Carbon Drive, Pittsburgh, PA, 15230-0717

Tel: (412) 787-6700   Fax: (412) 787-4541   www.calgoncarbon.com

Mfr. activated carbon, related systems and services.

Calgon Far East Co., Ltd., Tokyo, Japan

CALIFORNIA CEDAR PRODUCTS COMPANY

400 Fresno Ave., Stockton, CA, 95201

Tel: (209) 944-5800   Fax: (209) 944-9072   www.calcedar.com

Mfr. Duraframe-brand matches and fireplace logs, and incense-cedar products.

California Cedar Products Co., Shuttle Bldg. Rm. 303, 1-17 3-chome, Ohji-Dai Sakura-Shi, Chiba-Ken, Japan

CALLAWAY GOLF COMPANY

2180 Rutherford Rd., Carlsbad, CA, 92008-8815

Tel: (760) 931-1771   Fax: (760) 931-8013   www.callawaygolf.com

Mfr. and sales of golf clubs.

Callaway Golf KK Japan, Shin-Onarimon Bldg., 1F, 6-17-19 Shinbashi, Minato-Ku, Tokyo 105-0004, Japan

Tel: 81-3-5405-4500   Fax: 81-3-5472-0405

CALTEX CORPORATION

PO Box 619500, Dallas, TX, 75261-9500

Tel: (972) 830-1000   Fax: (972) 830-1081   www.caltex.com

Petroleum products.

Caltex Oil Japan KK, Hisseki Honkan, 9F, 3-12 Nishi Shinbashi 1-chome, Minato-ku, Tokyo 105, Japan

Caltraport (Far East) Co., 703 Uschisaiwaicho Osaka Bldg., 3-3 Uchisaiwai-cho 1-chome, Chiyoda-ku, Tokyo 100, Japan

Koa Oil Company, Tokyo, Japan

CALVIN KLEIN, INC.

205 West 39th Street, 4th Fl., New York, NY, 10018

Tel: (212) 719-2600   Fax: (212) 768-8922   www.calvinklein.com

Mfr. of high quality clothing and accessories

Calvin Klein Ltd., Tokyo, Japan

CAMPBELL SOUP COMPANY

Campbell Place, Camden, NJ, 08103-1799

Tel: (856) 342-4800   Fax: (856) 342-3878   www.campbellsoup.com

Mfr. food products.

Campbell Japan Inc., Tokyo, Japan

CANBERRA INDUSTRIES, INC.

800 Research Parkway, Meriden, CT, 06450

Tel: (203) 238-2351   Fax: (203) 235-1347   www.canberra.com

Mfr. instruments for nuclear research.

Packard Japan KK, Kansai Iwamotocho Bldg., 19-8 Iwamoto-cho 2-chome, Chiyoda-ku, Tokyo 101, Japan

CANDELA LASER CORPORATION

530 Boston Post Road, Wayland, MA, 01778

Tel: (508) 358-7400   Fax: (508) 358-5602   www.clzr.com

Mfr./services medical laser systems.

Candela Japan, 3/F, Tokyo Knit Bldg., 9-5 Ryogoku 2-chome, Sumida-ku, Tokyo 130, Japan

CANDLE CORPORATION

201 N. Douglas Street, El Segundo, CA, 90245

Tel: (310) 535-3600   Fax: (310) 727-4287   www.candle.com

Mfr. management software.

Candle Corporation, 2-14-3 Nagatacho, 9/F, Chiyoda-ku, Tokyo 100-0014, Japan

CANNONDALE CORPORATION

16 Trowbridge Drive, Bethel, CT, 06829

Tel: (203) 749-7000   Fax: (203) 748-4012   www.cannondale.com

Mfr. bicycles.

Cannondale Japan KK, 12-5 Harayamadai, 5-Cho Sakai City, Osaka 590-132, Japan
Tel: 81-722-99-9399

CANTOR FITZGERALD LP

299 Park Avenue, New York, NY, 10171

Tel: (212) 821-6710   Fax: (212) 821-6710   www.cantor.com

Engaged in fixed income securities and stocks.

Cantor Fitzgerald Japan KK, 14F 3-8-1 Kasumigaseki, Chiyoda-ku, Tokyo 100-0013, Japan
Tel: 81-3-3519-9100 Fax: 81-3-3519-9157

THE CAPITAL GROUP COS INC.

333 South Hope Street, Los Angeles, CA, 90071

Tel: (213) 486-9200   Fax: (213) 486-9557   www.capgroup.com

Investment management.

Capital Group Companies, Hibiya Kokusai Bldg., 19/F, 2-2-3 Uchisaiuaicho Chiyoda-ky, Tokyo 100-0011, Japan
Tel: 81-3-3595-3362 Fax: 81-3-3595-1703

CARBOLINE COMPANY

350 Hanley Industrial Court, St. Louis, MO, 63144

Tel: (314) 644-1000   Fax: (314) 644-4617   www.carboline.com

Mfr. coatings and sealants.

Japan Carboline Co. Ltd., Wakura Bldg., 1-5 Fukagawa 1-chome, Koto-ku, Tokyo, Japan

CARGILL, INC.

15407 McGinty Road West, Minnetonka, MN, 55440-5625

Tel: (612) 742-7575   Fax: (612) 742-7393   www.cargill.com

Food products, feeds, animal products.

Cargill Japan, Fugi Bldg., 3-2-3 Marunouchi, Chiyoda-ku, Tokyo 100, Japan

CARLISLE COMPANIES INC.

13925 Ballantyne Corporate Place, Ste. 400, Charlotte, NC, 28277

Tel: (704) 501-1100   Fax: (704) 501-1190   www.carlisle.com

Engaged in rubber, plastics and friction technologies.

Japan Power Brake (JV), 2453-9 Aza-dainooka, Liyama, Atsugi-shi, Kanagawa-ken 243-02, Japan
Tel: 81-46-247-7564   Fax: 81-46-247-0582

CARRIER CORPORATION

One Carrier Place, Farmington, CT, 06034-4015

Tel: (860) 674-3000   Fax: (860) 679-3010   www.carrier.com

Mfr./distributor/services A/C, heating and refrigeration equipment.

Carrier Higashi-Chugoku Co. Ltd., Okayama, Japan

Carrier Nishi Chugoku Co. Ltd., Hiroshima, Japan

Carrier Transicold Japan Ltd., Yokohama, Japan

Ebara Carrier Co. Ltd., Tokyo, Japan

General Aircon Tecnica Inc., Tokyo, Japan

Keihin Sobi Co. Ltd., Tokyo, Japan

Nippon Building Systems Co. (NBS), Tokyo, Japan

NIT Intelligent Planning & Development Co. Ltd., Tokyo, Japan

Tokyo Carrier Engineering Co. Ltd., Mitshui Annex Bldg. #2, 4-4-20 Nihonbashi-Hongoku-cho, Chuo-ku, Tokyo 103, Japan
Tel: 81-3-3270-9414   Fax: 81-3-3270-3779

United Technologies Building Systems Co., Tokyo, Japan

CASCADE CORPORATION

2201 NE 201st Ave., Fairview, OR, 97024-9718

Tel: (503) 669-6300   Fax: (503) 669-6321   www.cascor.com

Mfr. hydraulic forklift truck attachments.

Cascade (Japan) Ltd., 5-5-41 Torikai Kami Settsu, Osaka 566, Japan
Tel: 81-726-53-3490   Fax: 81-726-53-3497

CATAPULT COMMUNICATIONS CORPORATION

160 South Whisman Road, Mountain View, CA, 94041

Tel: (650) 960-1025   Fax: (650) 960-1029   www.catapult.com

Mfr. test systems for telecommunications service providers.

Catapult Communications Corp., Int's Nakano Bldg., 8/F, 3-33-3 Nakano Nakano-ku, Tokyo 164-0001, Japan
Tel: 81-3-3384-7661

CATERPILLAR INC.

100 NE Adams Street, Peoria, IL, 61629-6105

Tel: (309) 675-1000   Fax: (309) 675-1182   www.cat.com

Mfr. earth/material-handling and construction machinery and equipment and engines.

Akashi GS Co., Ltd., Okyo, Japan

Shin Caterpillar Mitsubishi Ltd., 3700 Tana, Sagamihara-shi, Kanagawaken 229, Japan

CB RICHARD ELLIS SERVICES

200 N. Sepulveda Blvd., Ste. 300, El Segundo, CA, 90245-4380

Tel: (310) 563-8600   Fax: (310) 563-8670   www.cbrichardellis.com

Commercial real estate services.

CB Richard Ellis KK, 4F Nishi Shimbashi JK Building, 3-15-12 Nishi Shimbashi, Minato-ku, Tokyo 105-0013, Japan

Ikoma/CB Richard Ellis, 9/F Tokyo Shintaku Bldg., 1-8-19 Chuo Aoba-ku, Sendai-shi 980-0021, Japan

Ikoma/CB Richard Ellis, 7/F Nihon Dantai Seimei Kagoshima Bldg., Kagoshima-shi 892-0847, Japan

Ikoma/CB Richard Ellis, 10/F, Chiba TN Bldg., 3-13 Shinmachi, Chuo-ku, Chiba-shi 260-0028, Japan

Ikoma/CB Richard Ellis, 6/F, Asahi Seimei Takamatsu Daini Bldg., 1-2-5 Kobobuki-cho, Takamatsu-shi, 760-0023, Japan

Ikoma/CB Richard Ellis, 8/F, Nihon Seimei Shinjuku Bldg., 1-17-1 Nishi-Shinjuku, Shinjuku-ku, Tokyo 160-0023, Japan

Ikoma/CB Richard Ellis, 2/F, Kyoto Karasuma Dai-ichi Seimei Bldg., 646 Nijo, Bukkoji-agaru Karasuma-dori, Shimogyo-ku Kyoto-shi 600-8412, Japan

Ikoma/CB Richard Ellis, 8/F, Meiji Seimei Omiya Bldg., 3-1 Miyacho, Omiya-shi, Japan

Ikoma/CB Richard Ellis, 11/F, Fukuoka Center Bldg., 2-2-1 Hakata-ekimae, Hakata-ku, Fukuoka-shi 812-0011, Japan

Ikoma/CB Richard Ellis, 3-4/F, Marunouchi ia Bldg., 3-17-29 Marunouchi, Naka-ku, Nagoya-shi, 460-0002, Japan

Ikoma/CB Richard Ellis, 2/F, Mitsui Seimei Yokohama Bldg., 2-25-2 Tsuruyacho, Kanagawa-ku, Yokohama-shi 221-0835, Japan

Ikoma/CB Richard Ellis, 5/F, Asahi Seimei Sannomiya Bldg., 1-3-11 Sannomiya-cho Chuo-ku, Kobe-shi 650-0021, Japan

Ikoma/CB Richard Ellis, 5/F, Tachikawa Mitsubishi Bldg., 2-13-3 Akebonocho, Tachikawa-shi, Tokyo 190-0012, Japan

Ikoma/CB Richard Ellis, 8/F, Sumitomo Seimei Niigata, Higashi-Odori Bldg., 2-5-1 Higashi-Odori, Nigata-shi 950-0087, Japan

Ikoma/CB Richard Ellis, 9/F, Daini Yuraku Bldg., 4-1-7 Honcho Chuo-ku, Osaka 541-0053, Japan

Ikoma/CB Richard Ellis, 2/F, KE Bldg., 2-1-10, Shimoishii Okayama-shi 700-0907, Japan

Ikoma/CB Richard Ellis, 4-5/F, Dai-ichi Building, Shuwa Hamamatsucho 2-2-12 Hamamatsucho, Minato-ku, Tokyo 105-0013, Japan

Ikoma/CB Richard Ellis, 6/F Daiwa Bank Sapporo Bldg., 3-2 Nishi, Kita-ichijo Chuo-ku, Sapporo-shi 060-0001, Japan

Ikoma/CB Richard Ellis, 8/F, Yasuda Seimei Horishima Bldg., Naka-hu, Hiroshima-shi 730-0035, Japan

Ikoma/CB Richard Ellis, 2/F Meiji Seimei Matsuyama Ichibancho Bldg., 4-1-3 Ichibancho, Matsuyama-shi 790-0001, Japan

Ikoma/CB Richard Ellis, 9/F, Nakaya Mitsui Bldg., 2-17 Oyama-cho, Kanazawa-shi 920-0918, Japan

Ikoma/CB Richard Ellis, 5/F, Shizuoka Meiji Seimeikan Bldg., 1-4 Tokiwa-cho, Shizuoka-shi, 420-0034, Japan

CCH INCORPORATED

2700 Lake Cook Road, Riverwoods, IL, 60015

Tel: (847) 267-7000   Fax: (800) 224-8299   www.cch.com

Provides tax and business law information and software for accounting, legal, human resources, securities and health care professionals.

CCH Japan Ltd., Ginza TK Bldg., 3/F, 1-1-7 Shintomi, Chuo-ku, Tokyo 104, Japan

CDM INTERNATIONAL INC.

50 Hampshire Street, Cambridge, MA, 02139

Tel: (617) 452-6000   Fax: (617) 452-8000   www.cdm.com

Consulting engineers.

CDM Camp Dresser & McKee Internaitonal Inc., New Erimo Bldge, 7/F, 2-2-1 Senba Nishi, Minoh Cit, Osaka 562-0036, Japan

Tel: 81-727-27-3181

CENDANT CORPORATION

9 West 57th Street, New York, NY, 10019

Tel: (212) 413-1800   Fax: (212) 413-1918   www.cendant.com

Membership-based, direct marketer offering shopping/travel/insurance and dining discount programs

Tax Free Shopping, Japan K.K., Uchida Bldg., 4F, 2-13-11 Shin Kawa, Tokyo 124-0033, Japan

Tel: 81-3-5541-6718   Fax: 81-3-5541-6719

CENTILLIUM COMMUNICATIONS, INC.

47211 Lakeview Blvd., Fremont, CA, 94538

Tel: (510) 771-3700   Fax: (510) 771-3500   www.centillium.com

Mfr. integrated circuits for networking equipment.

Centillium Japan, Landmark Shiba-koen Bldg., 3/F, Shiba-koen 1-2-6, Minato-ku, Tokyo 105-0011, Japan

Tel: 81-3-5733-8502   Fax: 81-3-5401-3660

CENTOCOR INC.

200 Great Valley Parkway, Malvern, PA, 19355-1307

Tel: (610) 651-6000   Fax: (610) 651-6100   www.centocor.com

Develop/mfr./marketing diagnostic and therapeutic products for human health care.

Nippon Centocor KK, 2-8-3 Higashi-Nihonbashi Chuo-ku, Tokyo 103-0004, Japan

Tel: 81-3-5823-6565

CENTRAL NATIONAL-GOTTESMAN INC.

3 Manhattanville Road, Purchase, NY, 10577-2110

Tel: (914) 696-9000   Fax: (914) 696-1066   www.cng-inc.com

Distribution of pulp and paper products.

Central National Pacific Ltd., Ginza Sunny Bldg., 4-16 Ginza 3-chome, Chuo-ku, Tokyo 104, Japan

Tel: 81-3-3562-3701   Fax: 81-3-3562-3705   Contact: Taijiu Hatakeyama

CENTURY 21 REAL ESTATE CORPORATION

One Campus Drive, Parsippany, NJ, 07054-3826

Tel: (973) 496-5722   Fax: (973) 496-5527   www.century21.com

Engaged in real estate sales.

Century 21 Real Estate of Japan Ltd., Kita-Aoyama Yoshikawa Bldg., 7F, 2-12-16 Kita Aoyama, Minato-ku, Tokyo 107, Japan

Tel: 81-3-3497-0021

CH2M HILL INC.

6060 South Willow Drive, Greenwood Village, CO, 80111

Tel: (303) 771-0900   Fax: (303) 770-2616   www.ch2m.com

Consulting engineers, planners, economists and scientists.

CH2M Hill, Nishiki-cho 320, Yasuda Building 3/F, Chiyoda-ku, Tokyo 101, Japan

Tel: 81-3-5259-1641

CHADBOURNE & PARKE LLP

30 Rockefeller Plaza, New York, NY, 10112-0127

Tel: (212) 408-5100   Fax: (212) 541-5369   www.chadbourne.com

Engaged in international law.

Chadbourne & Parke Gaikokuho Jimu Bengoshi Jimusho, Aoyama Building No. 924, 1-2-3 Kita-Aoyama, Minato-Ku, Tokyo 107-0061, Japan

Tel: 81-3-3478-6120

Watanabe, Nakamori, Nishida & Sugiura, Aoyama Building No. 924, 1-2-3 Kita-Aoyama, Minato-Ku, Tokyo 107-0061, Japan

Tel: 813-3470-0271   Contact: Yaeji Wantanabe

CHECKPOINT SYSTEMS, INC.

101 Wolf Drive, Thorofare, NJ, 08086

Tel: (856) 848-1800   Fax: (856) 848-0937   www.checkpointsystems.com

Mfr. test, measurement and closed-circuit television systems.

Checkpoint Systems Japan, 8F, Marusho Bldg., 1-1-8 Asakusabashi, Taito-ku, Tokyo, Japan

Tel: 81-3-3864-1774 Fax: 81-3-3864-4130 Contact: Katsutoshi Ono, Pres.

CHEMFAB CORPORATION

701 Daniel Webster Hwy., PO Box 1137, Merrimack, NH, 03054

Tel: (603) 424-9000   Fax: (603) 424-9028   www.chemfab.com

Mfr. advanced polymer materials.

Chemfab Japan KK, Sanko Bldg. No. 2, 1/F, 2-23 Ichigaya-Tamachi, Shinjuku-ku, Tokyo 162-0843, Japan

Tel: 81-3-3235-7193 Fax: 81-3-3235-3737

CHEMFIRST INC.

700 North Street, Jackson, MS, 39202

Tel: (601) 948-7550   Fax: (601) 960-6813   www.chemfirst.com

Mfr. specialty chemicals.

EKC Technology, Inc., 3-2-1 Sakado, Takatsu-Ku, Kawasaki Karrawaga 213-0012, Japan

Contact: Sakado Kumasata

THE CHERRY CORPORATION

3600 Sunset Ave., PO Box 718, Waukegan, IL, 60087

Tel: (847) 662-9200   Fax: (847) 662-2990   www.cherrycorp.com

Mfr. electrical switches, electronic keyboards, controls and displays.

Cherry Automotive-Japan, 20-20 Hiradai, Midori-ku, Yokohama-shi, Japan

Hirose Cherry Precision Co. Ltd., 8/F, Kaneko No. 2 Building, No.2-6-23 Shin-Yokohama, Kohoku-Ku Yokohama, Kanagawa 222, Japan

Hirose Cherry Precision Co. Ltd., 5-30-11 Shukugawara, Tama-ku, Kawasaki, Kanagawa 214, Japan

CHESTERTON BLUMENAUER BINSWANGER

Two Logan Square, 4th Floor, Philadelphia, PA, 19103-2759

Tel: (215) 448-6000   Fax: (215) 448-6238   www.cbbi.com

Real estate and related services.

Sotsu Binswanger, 69 Waseda-machi, Shinjuku-ku, Tokyo 162, Japan

Sotsu Binswanger, 1-3 Honcho, Naka-Ku, Yokohama-Shi Kanagawa 231, Japan

CHEVRON PHILLIPS CHEMICAL COMPANY LP

1301 McKinney Street, Houston, TX, 77010

Tel: (713) 754-2000   Fax: (713) 754-2016   www.chevron.com

Mfr. petro chemicals.

Oronite Japan Ltd., Landmark Plaza, 7/F, 1-6-7 Shiba-Koen, Minato-ku, Tokyo 105, Japan

CHEVRON TEXACO CORPORATION

575 Market Street, San Francisco, CA, 94105-2856

Tel: (415) 894-7700   Fax: (415) 894-2248   www.chevrontexaco.com

Oil exploration, production and petroleum products.

ChevronTexaco, c/o NOEC Producing Japan, 18-1 Shingashi 1-chome, Minato-ku, Tokyo 105, Japan

CHICAGO BRIDGE & IRON COMPANY (CBI)

10200 Grogan's Mill Road, Suite 300, The Woodlands, TX, 77380

Tel: (281) 774-2200   Fax: (281) 774-2202   www.chicago-bridge.com

Holding company: engaged in metal plate fabricating, construction and oil and gas drilling.

Chicago Bridge & Iron Company, Kamiyacho Square Building, 5/F, 1-7-3 Azabudai, Minato-ku, Tokyo 106, Japan

Tel: 81-33-224-3981 Fax: 81-33-224-3986

CHICAGO RAWHIDE INDUSTRIES (CRI)

735 Tollgate Road, Elgin, IL, 60123

Tel: (847) 742-7840   Fax: (847) 742-7845   www.chicago-rawhide.com

Mfr. shaft and face seals.

Chicago Rawhide Asia-Pacific, 3-2 Shin Yokohama, 10/F, Kouhoku-ku Yokohama, Kanagawa 222-0033, Japan

Tel: 81-45-473-4823

Koyo Chicago Rawhide Co. Ltd., Aizumi, Itanogun, Tokushima 771-12, Japan

CHIPPAC, INC.

47400 Kato Road, Fremont, CA, 94538

Tel: (510) 979-8000   Fax: (510) 979-8001   www.chippac.com

Mfr. packaging for circuit boards.

ChipPAC, Yurakucho Denki, 1-7-1 Yurakucho, 9/F, Chiyoda-Ku, Tokyo 100-0006, Japan

CHIQUITA BRANDS INTERNATIONAL INC.

250 East Fifth Street, Cincinnati, OH, 45202

Tel: (513) 784-8000   Fax: (513) 784-8030   www.chiquita.com

Sale and distribution of bananas, fresh fruits and processed foods.

United Brands Japan Ltd., Shichijo Bldg., 7/F, 2-20-10 Higashi Nihonbashi, Chuo-ku, Tokyo 103, Japan

THE CHRISTIAN SCIENCE PUBLISHING SOCIETY

1 Norway Street, Boston, MA, 02115

Tel: (617) 450-2000   Fax: (617) 450-7575   www.christianscience.com

Publishing company.

The Christian Science Monitor, 6-14-18 Shimouma, Setagaya-ku, Tokyo 157, Japan

Tel: 81-3-5722-4536   Emp: 2

THE CHUBB CORPORATION

15 Mountain View Road, Warren, NJ, 07061-1615

Tel: (908) 580-2000   Fax: (908) 580-3606   www.chubb.com

Holding company for property and casualty insurance and liability insurance for corporate executives.

Federal Insurance Co., 9F, Sumitomo Ichigaya Bldg., 1-1 Ichigaya Honmura-cho, Shinjuku-ku, Tokyo 162, Japan

Tel: 81-3-3266-1051   Fax: 81-3-3266-1060

CIENA CORPORATION

1201 Winterson Road, Linthicum, MD, 21090-2205

Tel: (410) 865-8500   Fax: (410) 694-5750   www.ciena.com

Mfr. optical network switching hardware.

CIENA Ltd., St. Luke's Tower, 32/F, Akashicho, Chuo-ku, Tokyo 104-0040, Japan

CIGNA COMPANIES

One Liberty Place, Philadelphia, PA, 19192

Tel: (215) 761-1000   Fax: (215) 761-5511   www.cigna.com

Insurance, invest, health care and other financial services.

CIGNA Insurance Co., Akasaka Eight-One Bldg., 7F, 13-5 Mayata-cho 2-chome, Chiyoda-ku, Tokyo 100, Japan

CIGNA Intl. Investment Advisors KK, Tobaya Bldg., 9-22 Akasaka 4-chome, Minato-ku, Tokyo, Japan

Esis Intl. Inc., Akasaka 81 Bldg., 13-5 Nagata-Cho 2-chome, Chiyoda-ku, Tokyo 100, Japan

INA Himawari Life Insurance Company, Ltd., Shinjuku Mitsui Bldg., 35F, 1-1 Nishi Shinjuku 2-Chome, Shinjuku-ku, Tokyo 163-04, Japan

Tel: 81-3-3344-7696   Fax: 81-3-3346-9415   Contact: Mike Clowes

INA Life Insurance Co. Ltd., Shinjuku Ctr. Bldg., 48F, 1-25 Nishi-Shinjuku 1-chome, Shinjuku-ku, Tokyo 160, Japan

Yasuda Kasia CIGNA Securities, Shinjuku Center Building, 50/F, 25-1 Nishi-shinjuku 1-chome, Shinjuku-ku, Tokyo 163-0650, Japan

Tel: 81-3-5326-1407   Fax: 81-3-5326-1432   Contact: Akimasa Oshima

CINCINNATI INCORPORATED

PO Box 11111, Cincinnati, OH, 45211

Tel: (513) 367-7100   Fax: (513) 367-7552   www.e-ci.com

Mfr. metal fabricating equipment.

Cincinnati Japan Ltd., CPO Box 1643, Tokyo, Japan

Tel: 81-33-861-2662   Fax: 81-22-861-2665   Contact: Matt Kubotera, Pres.

Cincinnati Japan, Ltd., Central PO Box 1643, Tokyo, Japan

Tel: 81-33-861-2262   Fax: 81-33-861-2665

CINCOM SYSTEMS INC.

55 Merchant Street, Cincinnati, OH, 45446

Tel: (513) 612-2300   Fax: (513) 481-8332   www.cincom.com

Develop/distributor computer software.

Cincom Systems Inc., Osaka, Japan

Cincom Systems Inc., Masonic 39 Mori Bldg., 2-4-6, Azabudai, Minato-Ku, Tokyo, Japan

CIRRUS LOGIC, INC.

4210 South industrial Drive, Austin, TX, 78744

Tel: (512) 445-7222   Fax: (512) 445-7581   www.cirrus.com

Engaged in manufacture of semiconductors and integrated circuits for entertainment devices.

Cirrus Logic KK, Aioi Sonpo Bldg. 6/F, 5-6 Niban-cho, Chiyoda-ku, Tokyo 102-0084, Japan

Tel: 81-3-5226-7390

CISCO SYSTEMS, INC.

170 West Tasman Drive, San Jose, CA, 95134-1706

Tel: (408) 526-4000   Fax: (408) 526-4100   www.cisco.com

Develop/mfr./market computer hardware and software networking systems.

Cisco Nihon Systems K.K., Fuji Bldg., 3-2-3 Fl. 9 Marunouchi, Chiyoda-ku, Tokyo 100, Japan

Tel: 81-3-5219-6370   Fax: 81-3-5219-6028

CITIGROUP, INC.

399 Park Avenue, New York, NY, 10022

Tel: (212) 559-1000   Fax: (212) 559-3646   www.citigroup.com

Provides insurance and financial services worldwide.

Citigroup, Kanese Bldg., 1F, 3-5-5 Honmachi Chuo-ku, Osaka 541-0053, Japan

Citigroup, Citicorp Centre, 19F, 2-3-14 Higashi-Shinagawa, Shinagawa-ku, Tokyo 140, Japan

Contact: Arthur M. de Graffenried III

CITRIX SYSTEMS, INC.

6400 NW 6th Way, Fort Lauderdale, FL, 33309

Tel: (954) 267-3000   Fax: (954) 267-9319   www.citrix.com

Developer of computer software.

Citrix Systems Japan, Arco Tower 16F, 1-8-1 Shimomeguro, Meguro-ku, Tokyo 153-0064, Japan

Tel: 81-3-5434-0992

CLEARY GOTTLIEB STEEN & HAMILTON

One Liberty Plaza, New York, NY, 10006

Tel: (212) 225-2000   Fax: (212) 225-3999   www.cgsh.com

Engaged in international law.

Cleary, Gottlieb, Steen & Hamilton, Shin Kasumigaseki Bldg., 20/F, 3-2 Kasumigaseki 3-Chome Chiyoda-Ku,, Tokyo 100-0013, Japan

Cleary, Gottlieb, Steen & Hamilton Gaikokuho Jimubengoshi, 20/F, 3-2 Kasumigaseki 3-chome, Chiyoda-ku, Tokyo 100, Japan

CNA FINANCIAL CORPORATION

CNA Plaza, Chicago, IL, 60685

Tel: (312) 822-5000   Fax: (312) 822-6419   www.cna.com

Commercial property/casualty insurance policies.

CNA Insurance KK, Tokio Kaijo Bldg., 6F, 2-1 Marunouchi 1-chome, Chiyoda-ku, Tokyo 100, Japan

CNH (CASE NEW HOLLAND) GLOBAL

100 South Saunders Road, Lake Forest, IL, 60045

Tel: (847) 955-3821   Fax: (847) 955-3961   www.casecorp.com

Mfr. and sale of agricultural and construction equipment.

CNH Hft Japan Inc., No. 2-2-1-7 Nishi 25, Chrome Kita 7 Chuo-Ku, Sapporo 060, Japan

Tel: 81-11-643-2151   Fax: 81-11-644-6173

COACH LEATHERWEAR COMPANY

516 West 34th Street, New York, NY, 10001

Tel: (212) 594-1850   Fax: (212) 594-1682   www.coach.com

Mfr. and sales of high-quality leather products, including handbags, wallets and shoes.

Coach Hibiya Shop, Toho Twin Tower Building, 1F, 1-5-2 Yurakucho, Chiyoda-ku, Tokyo 100-0006, Japan

THE COCA-COLA COMPANY

1 Coca Cola Plaza, Atlanta, GA, 30313

Tel: (404) 676-2121   Fax: (404) 676-6792   www.coca-cola.com

Mfr./marketing/distributor soft drinks, syrups and concentrates, juice and juice-drink products.

Coca-Cola West Japan Co. Ltd., PO Box 10, Shibuya-ku, Tokyo 150, Japan

Contact: Michael W. Hall

COGNEX CORPORATION

1 Vision Drive, Natick, MA, 01760

Tel: (508) 650-3000   Fax: (508) 650-3333   www.cognex.com

Mfr. machine vision systems.

Cognex KK, Bunkyo Green Court, 23/F, 2-28-8 Honkomagome, Bunkyo-ku, Tokyo 113-6591, Japan

Tel: 81-3-5977-5400   Fax: 81-3-5977-5401

Cognex KK, IT Meieki Building, 4/F, 3-11-22 Meieki Nakamura-ku, Nagoya-shi Aichi-ken 451-0045, Japan

Tel: 81-52-569-5900   Fax: 81-52-581-7760

Cognex KK, 5/F, Hakata Kaisei Bldg., 1-18-25 Hakataeki-Higashi, Hakata-ku Fukuoka-shi, Fukuoka-ken 812-0013, Japan

Tel: 81-92-432-7741   Fax: 81-92-412-3590

Cognex KK, Central Shin-Osaka Building, 302, 4-5-36 Miyahara Yodogawa-ku, Osaka-shi 532-0003, Japan

Tel: 81-6-4807-8201   Fax: 81-6-4807-8202

Cognex KK, Musashiya Bldg., 4/F, 3-1-4 Kokubun-cho, Aoba-ku Sendai-shi, Miyagi-ken 980-0803, Japan

Tel: 81-22-222-6393   Fax: 81-22-723-2887

COHERENT INC.

5100 Patrick Henry Drive, PO Box 54980, Santa Clara, CA, 95056

Tel: (408) 764-4000   Fax: (408) 764-4800   www.cohr.com

Mfr. lasers for science, industrial and medical.

Coherent Japan Inc., 2 Asanuma Bldg., 6F, 21-10 Hongo 3-chome, Bunkyo-ku, Tokyo 113, Japan

lambda Physik Japan Co. Ltd., German Industry Ctr., 1-18-2 Hakusan, Midori-ku, Yokohama 226, Japan

Tel: 81-45-939-7848

COHU, INC.

12367 Crosthwaite Circle, Poway, CA, 92064

Tel: (858) 848-8100   Fax: (858) 848-8185   www.cohu.com

Mfr. semiconductor test handling systems.

Kan Electronics Co., Ltd, Kirokoji Bldg., 1/F, 1-17-6 Ueno, Taito-ku, Tokyo 110, Japan

Tel: 81-33-836-2800   Fax: 81-33-836-2266

THE COLEMAN COMPANY, INC.

3600 N. Hydraulic, Wichita, KS, 67219

Tel: (316) 832-2700   Fax: (316) 832-2794   www.colemanoutdoors.com

Mfr. distributor and sales of camping and outdoor recreation products.

Coleman Japan Ltd., JBP Hakozaki Bldg., 2/F, 5-14 Nihonbashi Hakozakicho, Chuo-ku, Tokyo 103, Japan

COLFAX PUMP GROUP, DIV. COLFAX INC.

1710 Airport Road, PO Box 5020, Monroe, NC, 28111-5020

Tel: (704) 289-6511   Fax: (704) 289-4839   www.colfaxpump.com

Mfr. rotary and centrifugal pumps.

NHK Morse Co. Ltd., 3-21-10 Shin-Yokohama, Kohoku-ku, Yokohama 222, Japan

COLGATE-PALMOLIVE COMPANY

300 Park Ave., New York, NY, 10022

Tel: (212) 310-2000   Fax: (212) 310-2919   www.colgate.com

Mfr. pharmaceuticals, cosmetics, toiletries and detergents.

CKR (Japan) Co. Ltd., Kakihara Asahi Eitai Bldg., 7/F, 3-7-13 Toyo, Koto-ku, Tokyo 135, Japan

COMDISCO HOLDING COMPANY

6111 N. River Road, Rosemont, IL, 60018

Tel: (847) 698-3000   Fax: (847) 518-5440   www.comdisco.com

Hi-tech asset and facility management and equipment leasing.

Comdisco Japan Inc., 3-1-1 Marunouchi, Kokusai Bldg., 9/F, Chiyoda-Ku, Tokyo 100-005, Japan

COMMERCIAL METALS COMPANY (CMC)

7800 Stemmons Fwy., Dallas, TX, 75247

Tel: (214) 689-4300   Fax: (214) 689-4320   www.commercialmetals.com

Metal collecting/processing, steel mills and metal trading.

Cometals Far East Inc., Daiichi Seimei Sogo-kan, 7-1 Kyobashi 3-chome, Chuo-ku, Tokyo 104, Japan

COMMWORKS CORPORATION

3800 Golf Road, Rolling Meadows, IL, 60008

Tel: (847) 262-5000   Fax: (847) 262-0327   www.commworks.com

Provides Internet protocol-based network access software and equipment.

Commworks Japan KK, 2-28-8, Honkomagome, 21/F, Bunkyo-ku, Tokyo 113-6591, Japan

COMPUTER ASSOCIATES INTERNATIONAL INC.

One Computer Associates Plaza, Islandia, NY, 11788

Tel: (516) 342-5224   Fax: (516) 342-5329   www.cai.com

Integrated business software for enterprise computing and information management, application development, manufacturing, financial applications and professional services.

Computer Associates Japan Ltd., Shinjuku Mitsui Bldg., 2-1-1 Nishi-Shinjuku, Shinjuku-ku, Tokyo 163-0439, Japan
Tel: 81-3-5320-8080

COMPUTER NETWORK TECHNOLOGY CORPORATION

6000 Nathan Lane, Plymouth, MN, 55442

Tel: (763) 268-6000   Fax: (763) 268-6800   www.cnt.com

Engaged in the sale of storage networking products for creating and connecting storage area networks.

CNT Japan KK, Shiroyama JT Mori Bldg., 16/F, 4-3-1, Toranomon, Minato-ku, Tokyo 105, Japan

COMPUWARE CORPORATION

31440 Northwestern Hwy., Farmington Hills, MI, 48334-2564

Tel: (248) 737-7300   Fax: (248) 737-7108   www.compuware.com

Develop and market software for enterprise and e-commerce solutions.

Compuware Japan Corporation, 2-4-27 Dojima - 13/F, Kita-Ku, Osaka 530-0003, Japan
Tel: 81-6-6345-2816   Fax: 81-6-6345-2818

Compuware Japan Corporation, Tanakayama Bldg. 10/F, 4-1-20 Toranomon, Minato-ku, Tokyo 105-0001, Japan
Tel: 81-3-5473-4540

COMVERSE, INC.

100 Quannapowitt Parkway, Wakefield, MA, 01880

Tel: (781) 246-9000   Fax: (781) 224-8143   www.comverse.com

Provides communications solutions.

Comverse Japan Limited, Meiho Bldg., 8/F, 1-21-1 Nishi-shinjuku, Shinjuku-ku, Tokyo 160-0023, Japan
Tel: 81-3-5324-9171   Fax: 81-3-5324-9121

CONAGRA FOODS, INC.

One ConAgra Drive, Omaha, NE, 68102-5001

Tel: (402) 595-4000   Fax: (402) 595-4707   www.conagra.com

Prepared/frozen foods, grains, flour, animal feeds, agro chemicals, poultry, meat, dairy products, including Healthy Choice, Butterball and Hunt's.

ConAgra Inc., Tokyo, Japan

CONCURRENT COMPUTER CORPORATION

4375 River Green Pkwy., Duluth, GA, 30096

Tel: (678) 258-4000   Fax: (678) 258-4300   www.ccur.com

Mfr. computer systems and software.

Concurrent Nippon Corporation, Shuwa Yanagibashi Bldg., 5F, 19-6 2-chome, Taito-ku, Tokyo 111, Japan
Tel: 81-3-3864-5711   Fax: 81-3-3864-0898

CONE MILLS CORPORATION

3101 N. Elm Street, PO Box 26540, Greensboro, NC, 27415-6540

Tel: (336) 379-6220   Fax: (336) 379-6287   www.cone.com

Mfr. denims, flannels, chamois and other fabrics.

Sugi Enterprise, Tamaya Bldg., 5F, 2-chome, 3-11 Minami Honmachi, Chuo-0ku, Osaka 541, Japan
Tel: 81-6-262-5481   Fax: 81-6-262-5483   Contact: H. Sugiyama

CONEXANT SYSTEMS, INC.

4311 Jamboree Road, PO Box C, Newport Beach, CA, 92658-8902

Tel: (949) 483-4600   Fax: (949) 483-4078   www.conexant.com

Provides semiconductor products for communications electronics.

Conexant Systems Japan Company Limited, 1-46-3 Hatsudai, Shibuya-ku, Tokyo 151, Japan
Tel: 81-3-5371-1520   Fax: 81-3-5371-1501

CONOCO INC.

600 N. Dairy Ashford, Houston, TX, 77252

Tel: (281) 293-1000   Fax: (281) 293-1440   www.conoco.com

Oil, gas, coal, chemicals and minerals.

Conoco Chemical Far East Inc., PO Box 110, Kasumigaseki Bldg., 25F, Tokyo, Japan

COOPER-STANDARD AUTOMOTIVE GROUP

2401 South Gulley Road, Dearborn, MI, 48124

Tel: (313) 561-1100   Fax: (313) 561-6526   www.cooperstandard.com

Mfr. molded and extruded rubber and plastic products for automotive and appliance industry, retread tire industry.

Nishikawa Rubber Co., Ltd., 2-2-8 Misasa-cho, Nishi Ward, Hiroshima-shi 733, Japan
Tel: 81-82-237-9372   Fax: 81-82-230-0403

COPELAND CORPORATION

1675 West Campbell Road, Sidney, OH, 45365-0669

Tel: (937) 498-3011   Fax: (937) 498-3334   www.copeland-corp.com

Producer of compressors and condensing units for commercial and residential air conditioning and refrigeration equipment.

Copeland Japan KK, No. 8 Tenko Building, 2-5-19 Shin-Yokohama, Kohoku-Ku, Yokohama 222-0033, Japan

CORBIS CORPORATION

15395 SE 30th Place, Ste. 300, Bellevue, WA, 98007

Tel: (425) 641-4505   Fax: (425) 643-9740   www.corbis.com

Provides digital photograph imagery to creative professionals in magazine, book and newspaper publishing, advertising and graphic design and Internet and new media publishing.

Corbis Japan, 2-2 Kanda-Jimbocho, 8/F, Chiyoda-ku, Tokyo 101-0051, Japan
Tel: 81-3-3511-3600

CORECHANGE, INC.

260 Franklin Street, Ste. 1890, Boston, MA, 02110

Tel: (617) 204-3300   Fax: (617) 204-3333   www.corechange.com

Mfr. software.

Corechange KK, Cerulean Tower, 15/F, 26-1 Sakuragaoka-chu, Shibuya-Ku, Tokyo 150-0031, Japan

Tel: 81-3-5456-5422

CORN PRODUCTS INTERNATIONAL, INC.

6500 South Archer Ave., Bedford Park, IL, 60501-1933

Tel: (708) 563-2400   Fax: (708) 563-6852   www.cornproducts.com

Produces corn products for ingredients corn starch corn oil and corn syrups.

Corn Products Japan Ltd., 11 Kanda-Higashi-Matsushitacho, Chiyoda-ku, Tokyo 101-0042, Japan

Tel: 81-03-5297-2717   Fax: 81-03-5297-2718

CORNING INC.

One Riverfront Plaza, Corning, NY, 14831-0001

Tel: (607) 974-9000   Fax: (607) 974-8091   www.corning.com

Mfr. glass and specialty materials, consumer products; communications, laboratory services.

Corning International K.K., No. 35 Kowa Bldg., 3F, 14-14 Akasaka 1-chome, Minato-ku, Tokyo 107-0052, Japan

Tel: 81-3-3586-1052   Fax: 81-3-3587-0906   Contact: Satoshi Furuyama

COSTCO WHOLESALE CORPORATION

999 Lake Dr., Issaquah, WA, 98027

Tel: (425) 313-8100   Fax: (425) 313-8103   www.costco.com

Operates wholesale, membership warehouse stores.

Costco Wholesale Corp., Torium Value Centre, 1152-1 Aza Takayanagi, Oaza-Yamada, Fukuoka, Japan

COUDERT BROTHERS LLP

1114 Ave. of the Americas, New York, NY, 10036-7794

Tel: (212) 626-4400   Fax: (212) 626-4120   www.coudert.com

Engaged in international law.

Coudert Brothers, Daini Okamotoya Bldg., 10F, 1-22-16 Toranomon, Minato-ku, Tokyo 105, Japan

Tel: 81-3-3580-2290   Fax: 81-3-3580-2301

CRAIN COMMUNICATIONS INC.

1155 Gratiot Avenue, Detroit, MI, 48207-2997

Tel: (313) 446-6000   Fax: (313) 446-6100   www.crain.com

Publishes business and trade journals.

Crain Communications Automobile, c/o FCCJ, Yurakucho Denki Bldg., 1-7-1 Yurakucho, Chiyoda-ku, Tokyo 100, Japan

CRAWFORD & COMPANY

5620 Glenridge Drive NE, Atlanta, GA, 30342

Tel: (404) 256-0830   Fax: (404) 847-4025   www.crawfordandcompany.com

Provides international insurance services engaged in risk management and claims adjustment.

Crawford & Company, 4-2-2 Hachobori Chuo-ku, Tokyo 104-0032, Japan

CRC PRESS LLC

2000 NW Corporate Blvd., Boca Raton, FL, 33431

Tel: (561) 994-0555   Fax: (561) 997-0949   www.crcpress.com

Publishing: science, technical and medical books and journals.

CRC Press, Misuzu Bldg., 2/F, 2-42-14 Matsubara, Setagaya-ku, Tokyo 156, Japan

CRITICARE SYSTEMS INC.

20925 Crossroads Circle, Waukesha, WI, 53186

Tel: (262) 798-8282   Fax: (262) 798-8491   www.csiusa.com

Develop/mfr. diagnostic and therapeutic products and patient monitoring systems..

Criticare Systems Inc. Japan, Maruki Bldg., 3-6-11 Hongo, Bunkyo-ku, Tokyo 113, Japan

A.T. CROSS COMPANY

One Albion Road, Lincoln, RI, 02865

Tel: (401) 333-1200   Fax: (401) 334-2861   www.cross.com

Mfr. writing instruments, leads, erasers and ink refills.

Cross Company of Japan Ltd., Kando Grow Bldg., 6F, 1-34-4 Kando Sudacho, Chiyoda-ku, Tokyo 101, Japan

Tel: 81-3-5294-1781

CTS CORPORATION

905 Northwest Boulevard, Elkhart, IN, 46514

Tel: (219) 293-7511   Fax: (219) 293-6146   www.ctscorp.com

Mfr. designs, produces and sells passive, electro-mechanical, hybrid and interconnect components for OEMs.

CTS Japan Inc., TVP Building, 2F, 3-9-13, Moriya-cho, Kanagawa-Ku, Yokohama 221-0022, Japan

CUMMINS, INC.

500 Jackson Street, PO Box 3005, Columbus, IN, 47202-3005

Tel: (812) 377-5000   Fax: (812) 377-4937   www.cummins.com

Mfr. diesel engines.

Cummins Diesel Japan Ltd., Ark Mori Bldg., 17/F, PO Box 525, 12-32 Akasaka 1-chome, Minato-ku, Tokyo 107, Japan

Cummins Diesel Sales Corp., 1-12-10 Shintomi, Chuo-ku, Tokyo 104, Japan

CUNO INCORPORATED

400 Research Pkwy., Meriden, CT, 06450

Tel: (203) 237-5541   Fax: (203) 238-8977   www.cuno.com

Mfr. water filtration products.

CUNO K.K., Hodogaya Station Building 6/F, 1-7 Iwai-cho, Hodogaya-ku, Yokohama 240, Japan

Tel: 81-55-337-1820

CUSHMAN & WAKEFIELD INC.

51 West 52nd Street, New York, NY, 10019

Tel: (212) 841-7500   Fax: (212) 841-7867   www.cushwake.com

Engaged in commercial real estate services.

Cushman & Wakefield KK, Toranomon 5-12-13, Minato-ku, Tokyo 105-001, Japan

Tel: 81-3-3431-2500   Fax: 81-3-3431-2560

CUTTER & BUCK INC.

2701 First Avenue, Ste. 500, Seattle, WA, 98121

Tel: (206) 622-4191   Fax: (206) 448-0589   www.cutterbuck.com

Engaged in the sales and distribution of golf and sports apparel to golf pro shops.

The Seibu Department Stores, Ltd., Cutter & Buck, 1-16-15 Minami-Ikebukuro, Toshima-ku, Tokyo 171-8530, Japan

Tel: 81-3-3455-0124   Fax: 81-3-3455-6119   Contact: Yukihiro Saito

CYMER, INC.

16750 Via del Campo Court, San Diego, CA, 92127

Tel: (858) 385-7300   Fax: (858) 385-7100   www.cymer.com

Mfr. excimer lasers.

Cymer Japan KK, Cosmos Motoyawata Building, 4-17-8 Minamiyawata, Ichikawa-shi, Chiba 272-0023, Japan

Tel: 81-47-393-5668

CYPRESS SEMICONDUCTOR CORPORATION

3901 N. First Street, San Jose, CA, 95134-1599

Tel: (408) 943-2600   Fax: (408) 943-2796   www.cypress.com

Mfr. integrated circuits.

Cypress Semiconductor, Harmony Tower, 17/F, 1-32-2 Hon-cho Nakano-ku, Tokyo 164-0012, Japan

Tel: 81-3-5371-1921

CYTEC INDUSTRIES, INC.

5 Garret Mountain Plaza, West Paterson, NJ, 07424

Tel: (973) 357-3100   Fax: (973) 357-3054   www.cytec.com

Mfr. specialty chemicals and materials.

Mitsui Cytec Ltd., Torii Nihonbashi Bldg., 6/F, 3-4-1 Nihonbashi Honcho, Chou-Ku, Tokyo 103, Japan
Tel: 81-3-3231-6072

DADE BEHRING INC.

1717 Deerfield Road, Deerfield, IL, 60015-0778

Tel: (847) 267-5300   Fax: (847) 267-5408   www.dadebehring.com

Mfr. diagnostic equipment.

Dade Behring KK, 1-32-2 Honcho, Nakano-ku, Tokyo 164-8721, Japan
Tel: 81-3-5365-8210

DANA CORPORATION

4500 Dorr Street, Toledo, OH, 43615

Tel: (419) 535-4500   Fax: (419) 535-4643   www.dana.com

Mfr./sales of automotive, heavy truck, off-highway, fluid and mechanical power components and engine parts, filters and gaskets.

Daido-Sprag Ltd., Central Bldg., 6/F, 19-10 Toranomon 1-chome, Minato-ku, Tokyo 105, Japan
Koshin-Racine, 1-12 Shin-Sayama 1 chome, Sayama-shi, Saitama-ken 350-115, Japan
Najico Spicer Co. Ltd., 1010 3-chrome Tsukiji, Chuo-ku, Tokyo 104-0045, Japan
Tel: 81-03-5566-6781

DANZAS AEI, INC.

120 Tokeneke Road, PO Box 1231, Darien, CT, 06820

Tel: (203) 655-7900   Fax: (203) 655-5779   www.aeilogistics.com

International air freight forwarder.

Danzas AEI Maruzen Ltd. - Reg. Hdqtrs., 3-6 Nohonbashi- Hamacho, 1-chome, Chuo-ku, Tokyo 103, Japan
Tel: 81-3-5821-5851   Fax: 81-3-5821-5850

D'ARCY MASIUS BENTON & BOWLES INC. (DMB&B)

1675 Broadway, New York, NY, 10019

Tel: (212) 468-3622   Fax: (212) 468-2987   www.darcyww.com

Full service international advertising and communications group.

DMB&B Asia Pacific, Akasaka Daiichi Bldg., 4-9-17 Akasaka, Minato-ku, Tokyo 107, Japan

DATA I/O CORPORATION

10525 Willows Road NE, Redmond, WA, 98073-9746

Tel: (425) 881-6444   Fax: (425) 882-1043   www.dataio.com

Mfr. computer testing devices.

Data I/O Japan, Sumitumoseimei Higashishinbashi Bldg. 8/F, 2-1-7 Higashi-Shinbashi, Minato-ku, Tokyo 105, Japan

DATASTREAM SYSTEMS, INC.

50 Datastream Plaza, Greenville, SC, 29605

Tel: (864) 422-5001   Fax: (864) 422-5000   www.datastream.net

Mfr. asset management software.

Datastream Systems KK, Mita Maruhachi Bldg., 6/F, 3-1-10 Mita Minato-ku, Tokyo 108-0073, Japan

DAVIS POLK & WARDWELL

450 Lexington Ave., New York, NY, 10017

Tel: (212) 450-4000   Fax: (212) 450-4800   www.dpw.com

Engaged in international law.

Davis Polk & Wardwell, Akasaka Twin Tower East, 13F, 17-22 Akasaka 2-chome, Minato-ku, Tokyo 107, Japan
Tel: 81-3-5561-4421   Fax: 81-3-5561-4425

DAYTON PROGRESS CORPORATION

500 Progress Road, Dayton, OH, 45449

Tel: (937) 859-5111   Fax: (937) 859-5353   www.daytonprogress.com

Engaged in the production of catalog and special punches, punch blanks and metal stamping tools.

Dayton Progress Corporation of Japan, 2-7-35 Hashimotodai, Sagamihara-Shi Kanagawa-Ken 229-1132, Japan

DDB WORLDWIDE COMMUNICATIONS GROUP

437 Madison Ave., New York, NY, 10022

Tel: (212) 415-2000   Fax: (212) 415-3417   www.ddbn.com

Advertising agency.

DDB Worldwide, Hibiya Kokusai Bldg., 2-3 Uchisaiwai-cho 2-chome, Chiyoda-ku, Tokyo 100, Japan

DDI CORPORATION

1220 Simon Circle, Anaheim, CA, 92806

Tel: (714) 688-7200   Fax: (714) 688-7400   www.ddiglobal.com

Engaged in software development tools contract manufacturing.

DDI Design Services, 1-2-1 Shiba-Daimon, Minato-ku, Kishimoto Bldg., 3/F, Tokyo 105-0012, Japan

Tel: 81-3-5733-7567

DELL COMPUTER CORPORATION

One Dell Way, Round Rock, TX, 78682-2222

Tel: (512) 338-4400   Fax: (512) 728-3653   www.dell.com

Direct marketer and supplier of computer systems.

Dell Computer K.K., Solid Square East Tower 20F, 580 Horikawa-cho, Saiwai-ku, Kawasaki Kanagawa 210-0913, Japan

Tel: 81-44-556-4300   Fax: 81-44-556-3205   Contact: Charles (Chip) H. Saunders, Mng. Dir.

DELOITTE TOUCHE TOHMATSU INTERNATIONAL

1633 Broadway, New York, NY, 10019

Tel: (212) 492-4000   Fax: (212) 392-4154   www.deloitte.com

Accounting, audit, tax and management consulting services.

Tohmatsu & Co., Sapporo Daiichikaikei Bldg., 1-10, Kita Nijo, Nishi 13-chome Chuo-ku, Sapporo 060, Japan

Tohmatsu & Co., Osaka Kokusai Bldg. 3-13, Azuchi-machi 2-chome, Chuo-ku, Osaka 541, Japan

Tohmatsu & Co., Nagoya Daiya Bldg. 2-Gukan, 15-1-Meieki 3-chome, Nakamura-ku, Nagoya 450, Japan

Tohmatsu & Co., M S Shibaur Bldg., 13-3 Shibaura 4-chome, Minato-ku, Tokyo 108, Japan

DELTA AIR LINES INC.

Hartsfield International Airport, 1030 Delta Blvd., Atlanta, GA, 30320-6001

Tel: (404) 715-2600   Fax: (404) 715-5494   www.delta-air.com

Major worldwide airline; international air transport services.

Delta Air Lines Inc., Kioicho Bldg., 9/F, 3-12 Kioicho, Chiyoda-ku, Tokyo-Narita 102, Japan

Tel: 81-3-5275-7510   Fax: 81-3-5275-7505

DENTSPLY INTERNATIONAL

570 West College Ave., PO Box 872, York, PA, 17405-0872

Tel: (717) 845-7511   Fax: (717) 843-6357   www.dentsply.com

Mfr. and distribution of dental supplies and equipment.

Dentsply Japan, Tsunashima No. 2 Bldg., 20-12 Yushima 3-chome, Bunkyo-ku, Toyko 113, Japan

Tel: 81-3-3836-9911

DHL WORLDWIDE EXPRESS

50 California Avenue, San Francisco, CA, 94111

Tel: (415) 677-6100   Fax: (415) 824-9700   www.dhl.com

Worldwide air express carrier.

DHL Worldwide Express, 37-8 Higashi-Shinagawa 1-chome, Shinagawa-ku, Tokyo 140-002, Japan

Tel: 81-3-54792580

DIONEX CORPORATION

1228 Titan Way, PO Box 3603, Sunnyvale, CA, 94086-3603

Tel: (408) 737-0700   Fax: (408) 730-9403   www.dionex.com

Develop/mfr./market chromatography systems and related products.

Nippon Dionex KK, Shin-Osaka GH Bldg., #205, 9-20 Nishi-Nakajima 6-chome, Yodogawa-ku, Osaka 532, Japan

DISCOVERY COMMUNICATIONS, INC.

7700 Wisconsin Avenue, Bethesda, MD, 20814

Tel: (301) 986-0444   Fax: (301) 771-4064   www.discovery.com

Owns and operates cable networks.

Discovery Communications, Tokyo Opera City Tower-35th Floor, 3-20-2 Nishi Shinjuku, Shinjuku-ku, Tokyo 163-1462, Japan

Tel: 81-3-5353-7038

WALT DISNEY COMPANY

500 South Buena Vista Street, Burbank, CA, 91521

Tel: (818) 560-1000   Fax: (818) 560-1930   www.disney.com

Film/TV production, theme parks, resorts, publishing, recording and retail stores.

Walt Disney Enterprises of Japan Ltd., Kanesaka Bldg., 5-4 Shimbashi 2-chome, Minato-ku, Tokyo 105, Japan

D-M-E COMPANY

29111 Stephenson Highway, Madison Heights, MI, 48071

Tel: (248) 398-6000   Fax: (248) 544-5705   www.dmeco.com

Manufacture and distribution of mold tooling, mold components, hot runner systems, and electronic controls for the plastics industry.

Japan D-M-E Corporation, Toyo-Cho SH Bldg. 2/F, 10-4, Toyo 4-Chome Koto-Ku, Tokyo 135-0016, Japan

Tel: 81-3-56832331 Fax: 81-3-56832330

DOCUMENTUM, INC.

6801 Koll Center Pkwy., Pleasanton, CA, 94566

Tel: (925) 600-6800   Fax: (925) 600-6850   www.documentum.com

Mfr. content management software.

Nihon Documentum K.K., TE Building, 3/F, 4-5-16 Yoga, Setagaya-ku, Tokyo 158-0097, Japan

DONALDSON COMPANY, INC.

PO Box 1299, Minneapolis, MN, 55431

Tel: (952) 887-3131   Fax: (952) 887-3155   www.donaldson.com

Mfr. filtration systems and replacement parts.

Nippon Donaldson, Ltd., 13-2, 5 chome Imadera, Ome City, Tokyo 198, Japan

Tel: 81-428-31-4111 Fax: 81-428-31-9074 Contact: Hideki Inahara

R.R. DONNELLEY & SONS COMPANY

77 West Wacker Drive, Chicago, IL, 60601-1696

Tel: (312) 326-8000   Fax: (312) 326-8543   www.rrdonnelley.com

Engaged in commercial printing and allied communication services.

R. R. Donnelley Japan K.K., Donnelley Bldg., 4th Fl., 2-28-7 Kami-Ochiai 2-chome, Shinjuku-ku, Tokyo 161, Japan

Tel: 81-3-3227-5211

DONNELLY CORPORATION

49 West Third Street, Holland, MI, 49423-2813

Tel: (616) 786-7000   Fax: (616) 786-6034   www.donnelly.com

Mfr. fabricated, molded and coated glass products for the automotive and electronics industries.

Donnelly Corporation, 10F, 101, Takanawa Empire Bldg., 3-24-18 Takanawa Minato-Ku, Tokyo 104-0074, Japan

Tel: 81-33-447-5911 Fax: 81-33-447-8595

DOONEY & BOURKE

1 Regent Street, Norwalk, CT, 06855

Tel: (203) 853-7754   Fax: (203) 838-7515   www.dooney.com

Mfr., sales and distribution of fine leather handbags, wallets, belts and accessories.

Dooney & Bourke, Shin-Yokohama Prince Hotel, 3-4 Shin-Yokohama, Kohoku-ku, Yokohama 222-0033, Japan

DORSEY & WHITNEY LLP

50 South Sixth Street, Ste. 1500, Minneapolis, MN, 55402

Tel: (612) 340-2600   Fax: (612) 340-2868   www.dorseylaw.com

International law firm.

Dorsey & Whitney LLP, Shiroyama JT Mori Building, 16F, 4-3-1 Toranomon, Tokyo 105-6016, Japan

Tel: 81-3-5403-4876

DOUBLECLICK, INC.

450 West 33rd Street, New York, NY, 10001

Tel: (212) 683-0001   Fax: (212) 889-0062   www.doubleclick.net

Engaged in online advertising and e-mail marketing.

Doubleclick, Ltd., Step-Roppongi Bldg. West, 1/F, 6-8-10 Roppongi, Minato-ku, Tokyo 106-0032, Japan

Tel: 81-3-5770-4109   Fax: 81-3-5770-4112

Doubleclick, Ltd., Step Roppongi 1F, Roppongi 6-8-10 Minato-ku, Tokyo 106-0032, Japan

THE DOW CHEMICAL COMPANY

2030 Dow Center, Midland, MI, 48674

Tel: (989) 636-1000   Fax: (989) 636-3228   www.dow.com

Mfr. chemicals, plastics, pharmaceuticals, agricultural products, consumer products.

Dow Chemical Japan Ltd., Osaka, Japan

Dow Chemical Japan Ltd., Hibiya Chunichi Bldg., 6F, 2-1-4 Uchisaiwai-cho, Chiyoda-ku, Tokyo 100, Japan

DRAFT WORLDWIDE

633 North St. Clair Street, Chicago, IL, 60611-3211

Tel: (312) 944-3500   Fax: (312) 944-3566   www.draftworldwide.com

Full service international advertising agency, engaged in brand building, direct and promotional marketing.

DraftWorldwide, Div. of Yomiko, 1-8-14 Ginza, 1-chome, Chuo-ku, Tokyo 104, Japan

Tel: 81-3-3563-7889   Fax: 81-3-3562-2594

DRAKE BEAM MORIN INC.

100 Park Avenue, 11th Fl., New York, NY, 10017

Tel: (212) 692-7700   Fax: (212) 297-0426   www.dbm.com

Human resource management consulting and training.

DBM Japan KK, MS Bldg., 9/F, 11-5 Shiba 4-chome, Minato-ku, Tokyo 108, Japan

Tel: 81-3-3452-1461   Fax: 81-3-3452-4904

DRESSER INSTRUMENT DIVISION

250 East Main Street, Stratford, CT, 06614-5145

Tel: (203) 378-8281   Fax: (203) 385-0357   www.dresserinstruments.com

Mfr. pressure gauges and temperature instruments.

Dresser Japan Ltd., Room 818 Shin Tokyo Building, 3-3-1 Tokyo, Tokyo 100, Japan

Tel: 81-3-3201-1501   Fax: 81-3-3213-6673

DREVER COMPANY

PO Box 98, 380 Red Lion Road, Huntingdon, PA, 19006-0098

Tel: (215) 947-3400   Fax: (215) 947-7934   www.drever.com

Mfr. industrial furnaces and heat processing equipment.

Drever Japan, 71-4, 3-chome Mutsukawa, Minami-ku, Yokohama 232-0066, Japan

Tel: 81-45 713-1460

DSP GROUP, INC.

3120 Scott Blvd., Santa Clara, CA, 95054

Tel: (408) 986-4300   Fax: (408) 986-4323   www.dspg.com

Mfr. speech compressor software.

Nihon DSP Group K.K., Koizumi Bldg., 9/F, 1-29-1 Nishi Gotanda, Shinagawa-ku, Tokyo 141-0031, Japan

DUO-FAST CORPORATION

2400 Galvin Dr., Elgin, IL, 60123

Tel: (847) 783-5500   Fax: (847) 669-7301   www.duofast.com

Mfr. staplers, tackers and nailers.

Duo-Fast Japan, 1937-3 Nurumizu, Atsugi City 243 Kanagawa, Japan

E.I. DUPONT DE NEMOURS & COMPANY

1007 Market Street, Wilmington, DE, 19898

Tel: (302) 774-1000   Fax: (302) 774-7321   www.dupont.com

Mfr. and sales of diversified chemicals, plastics, specialty products and fibers.

DuPont Asia Pacific, Arco Tower, 8-1, Shimomeguro 1-chome, Meguro-ku, Tokyo 153-0064, Japan
Tel: 81-3-5434-5984

DuPont Far East Inc., Kowa Bldg., 11-39 Akasaka 1-chome, Minato-ku, Tokyo 107, Japan
Contact: Masatoshi Yamamoto, Pres.

Teijin DuPont Films Japan Limited, Lino Bldg, 1-1, Uchisaiwai-Cho, 2-Chome, Chiyoda-Ku, Tokyo 100-8585, Japan

DUPONT PHOTOMASKS, INC. (DPI)

131 Old Settlers Blvd., Round Rock, TX, 78664

Tel: (512) 310-6500   Fax: (512) 255-9627   www.photomask.com

Mfr. photo masks for semiconductors.

DuPont Photomasks Japan KK, Arco Tower 12/F, 8-1, Shimomeguro 1-chome, Meguro-ku, Tokyo 153-0064, Japan

DURACELL INTERNATIONAL INC.

8 Research Drive, Bethel, CT, 06801

Tel: (203) 796-4000   Fax: (203) 796-4745   www.duracell.com

Mfr. batteries.

Duracell Battery Japan Ltd., Masudaya Bldg., 8/F, 2-6-4 Kuramae, Taito-ku, Tokyo 111, Japan

EASTMAN & BEAUDINE INC.

5700 West Plano Parkway, Ste. 2800, Plano, TX, 75093

Tel: (972) 267-8891   Fax: (972) 267-8891   www.beaudine.com

Engaged in retained executive search and selection.

Eastman & Beaudine Inc., 401 Akasaka Heights Bldg., 5-26 Akasaka 9-chome, Minato-ku, Tokyo 107, Japan

EASTMAN CHEMICAL COMPANY

100 North Eastman Road, Kingsport, TN, 37662-5075

Tel: (423) 229-2000   Fax: (423) 229-1351   www.eastman.com

Mfr. plastics, chemicals, fibers.

Eastman Chemical Japan Ltd., Yebisu Garden Place Tower, 32F, 4-20-3-Ebisu, Shibuya-ku, Tokyo 150, Japan
Tel: 81-3-5424-1551 Fax: 81-3-5424-1590 Contact: Joe Imaizumi, Pres.

EASTMAN KODAK COMPANY

343 State Street, Rochester, NY, 14650

Tel: (716) 724-4000   Fax: (716) 724-1089   www.kodak.com

Develop/mfr. photo and chemicals products, information management/video/copier systems, fibers/plastics for various industry.

Eastman Kodak Asia-Pacific Ltd., Gotenyama Mori Bldg., 4-7-35 Kita-Shinagawa, Shinagawa-ku, Tokyo 140, Japan
Kodak Imagica KK, Gotenyama Mori Bldg., 4-7-35 Kita-Shinagawa, Shinagawa-ku, Tokyo 140, Japan
Kodak Japan Industries Ltd., 18-2 Hakusan 1-chome, Midori-ku, Kanagawa 226, Japan
Kodak Japan Ltd., Gotenyama Mori Bldg., 4-7-35 Kita-Shinagawa, Shinagawa-ku, Tokyo 140, Japan

EASTMAN RESINS, INC.

1 Terra Way, 8601 95th St., Pleasant Prairie, WI, 53158

Tel: (262) 947-7300   Fax: (262) 947-7328   www.lawter.com

Resins, pigments and coatings.

Eastman Resins Japan KK, Maison Emerald #106, 683-1 Niizo, Toda-Shi, Saitama 335-0021, Japan

EATON CORPORATION

Eaton Center, 1111 Superior Ave., Cleveland, OH, 44114-2584

Tel: (216) 523-5000   Fax: (216) 479-7068   www.eaton.com

Advanced technical products for transportation and industrial markets.

Eaton Japan Co. Ltd., Ohno Bldg., 1-19-8 Kyobashi, Chuo-ku, Tokyo 104, Japan

Nitta-Moore Co. Ltd., Osaka, Japan

ECOLAB INC.

370 N. Wabasha Street, St. Paul, MN, 55102

Tel: (651) 293-2233   Fax: (651) 293-2379   www.ecolab.com

Develop/mfr. premium cleaning, sanitizing and maintenance products and services for the hospitality, institutional, and residential markets.

Ecolab Ltd., Tokyo, Japan

Tel: 81-3-5285-2653

EDDIE BAUER INC.

15010 NE 36th Street, Redmond, WA, 98073

Tel: (425) 882-6100   Fax: (425) 882-6383   www.eddiebauer.com

Clothing retailer and mail order catalog company.

Eddie Bauer Inc., Tokyo, Japan

J.D. EDWARDS & COMPANY

One Technology Way, Denver, CO, 80237

Tel: (303) 334-4000   Fax: (303) 334-4970   www.jdedwards.com

Computer software products.

IBM Japan General Business Solution Company, Minato-ku Tokyo 106, Japan

Tel: 81-3-5563-5328   Fax: 81-3-5563-7755

J. D. Edwards, Sanbancho UF Building, 3F, 6-3 Sanbancho, Chiyoda-ku, Tokyo 102, Japan

Tel: 81-3-3265-7141   Fax: 81-3-3265-7145

EDWARDS LIFESCIENCES CORPORATION

1 Edwards Way, Irvine, CA, 92614

Tel: (949) 250-2500   Fax: (949) 250-2525   www.edwards.com

Mfr. instruments for cardiovascular patients.

Edwards Lifesciences, 2-8 Rokubancho Chiyoda-ku, Tokyo 102-0085, Japan

EG&G INC.

900 Clopper Road, Ste. 200, Gaithersburg, MD, 20878

Tel: (301) 840-3000   Fax: (301) 590-0502   www.egginc.com

Diversified R/D, mfr. and services.

Eagle EG&G Aerospace Co. Ltd., 1-12-15 Shiba-Daimon, Minato-ku, Tokyo 105, Japan

Eagle Industry Co. Ltd., 1-12-15 Shiba-Daimon, Minato-ku, Tokyo 105, Japan

EG&G Japan, Shuwa Kioicho TBR #1223, 7 Kojimachi 5-chome, Chiyoda-ku, Tokyo 102, Japan

Nok EG&G Optoelectronics Corp., 4-3-1 Tsujido-Shinmachi, Fujisawa-shi, Kanagawa-ken 251, Japan

Seiko EG&G Co. Ltd., 31-1 Kameido 6-chome, Koto-ku, Tokyo 136, Japan

EGL INC. (EAGLE GLOBAL LOGISTICS)

15350 Vickery Drive, Houston, TX, 77032

Tel: (281) 618-3100   Fax: (281) 618-3223   www.eagleusa.com

Ocean/air freight forwarding, customs brokerage, packing and wholesale, logistics management and insurance.

EGL Eagle Global Logistics, NACT, Room No. 202, 11-43 Nanko-Higashi 4-chome, Suminoe-ku, Osaka-Shi 559, Japan

Tel: 81-6-614-0820   Fax: 81-6-614-7176

EGL Eagle Global Logistics, 1 International Cargo Agent Bldg. Rm. 207, Sensyu Kuko Minami No.1, Sennan-Shi, Osaka 549, Japan

Tel: 81-724-565-850   Fax: 81-724-565-851

EGL Eagle Global Logistics, Araya Bldg., 9-13 Hatsudai 1-chome, Shibuya-ku, Tokyo 151, Japan

Tel: 81-3-3337-30851   Fax: 81-3-337-30860

EGL Eagle Global Logistics, New Tokyo International Airport, No.1 Cargo Bldg., Rm. 322, 154-4 Aza-Komamae Furugome Narita-Shi, Chiba Tokyo 282, Japan

Tel: 81-476-328-201   Fax: 81-476-328-204

EGL Eagle Global Logistics, Air Export Gateway, 4-10 Nihonbashi-Nakasu, Chuo-ku, Tokyo 103, Japan

Tel: 81-3-324-90571   Fax: 81-3-324-9185-4

EGL Eagle Global Logistics, Air Import Gateway, Tokyo Aircargo City Terminal C, 2526 Baraki, Ichikawa-Shi, Chiba 272, Japan

Tel: 81-473-282-685   Fax: 81-473-274-152

ELECTRO SCIENTIFIC INDUSTRIES, INC.

13900 NW Science Park Drive, Portland, OR, 97229

Tel: (503) 641-4141   Fax: (503) 643-4873   www.esi.com

Mfg. production and testing equipment used in manufacture of electronic components in pagers and cellular communication devices.

Electro Scientific Industries Japan Co., Ltd.(KK), Denpa Bldg., 1-11-15 Higashi Gotanda, Shinagawa-ku, Tokyo 141, Japan

Tel: 81-3-3440-5081   Fax: 81-3-3440-5029   Contact: Ted Hasegawa

ELECTROGLAS INC.

6042 Silver Creek Valley Road, San Jose, CA, 95138

Tel: (408) 528-3000   Fax: (408) 528-3542   www.electroglas.com

Mfr. semi-conductor test equipment, automatic wafer probes.

Electroglas KK, 8-3 Funado 1-chome, Itabashi-ku, Tokyo 174, Japan

ELECTRONIC DATA SYSTEMS, INC. (EDS)

5400 Legacy Dr., Plano, TX, 75024

Tel: (972) 604-6000   Fax: (972) 605-2643   www.eds.com

Engaged in systems integration, network and systems operations and management consulting.

EDS Japan, 4-2-12 Shibuya, Shibuya-ku, Tokyo 150-0002, Japan

ELECTRONICS FOR IMAGING, INC. (EFI)

303 Velocity Way, Foster City, CA, 94404

Tel: (650) 357-3500   Fax: (650) 357-3907   www.efi.com

Design/mfr. computer software and hardware for color desktop publishing.

EFI KK, Shinjuku I, Land Wing, 13/F, 3-1 Nishi-Shinjuku 6-chome, Shinjuku-ku, Tokyo 160-0023, Japan

Tel: 81-3-3344 3123

ELECTRO-SCIENCE LABORATORIES, INC.

416 East Church Road, King of Prussia, PA, 19406

Tel: (610) 272-8000   Fax: (610) 272-6759   www.electroscience.com

Mfr. advanced thick film materials for hybrid microcircuits and other electronic packaging and component applications.

ESL-Nippon Company, Ltd., Sukegawa Building, 6/F, 3-4 Yanagibashi 1-chome, Taito-ku, Tokyo 111-0052, Japan

Tel: 81-3-3864-8521   Fax: 03-3864-852   Contact: Takeshi Wada

EMC CORPORATION

35 Parkwood Drive, Hopkinton, MA, 01748-9103

Tel: (508) 435-1000   Fax: (508) 435-8884   www.emc.com

Designs/supplies intelligent enterprise storage and retrieval technology for open systems, mainframes and midrange environments.

EMC Japan KK, Shinjuku-Miksui Bldg., 55F, 2-1 Nishi-Shinjuku 2-chome, Shinjuku-ku, Tokyo 163-0466, Japan

Tel: 81-3-3345-3211

EMC Japan KK, Umeda Ctr. Bldg., 6F, 4-12 Nakazaki-Nishi 2-chome, Kita-ku Osaka-shi, Osaka 530-0015, Japan

Tel: 81-6-373-8300

EMC Japan KK, Shizuoka, Japan

Tel: 81-54-203-2425

EMC Japan KK, Nagoya Kokusai Ctr. Bldg., 18F, 47-1 Nagono 1-chome, Nakamura-ku, Nagoya 450-0001, Japan

Tel: 81-52-562-0571

EMERSON & CUMING COMPOSITE MATERIALS, INC.

59 Walpole Street, Canton, MA, 02021

Tel: (781) 821-4250   Fax: (781) 821-0737   www.emersoncuming.com

Mfr. high performance encapsulants, adhesives and coatings for the automotive, telecommunications and electronic industries.

Grace Specialty Polymers, Div. Emerson & Cuming, Grace Atsugi Ctr., 100 Kaneda, Atsugi-shi, Kanagawa-ken 243, Japan

EMERSON ELECTRIC COMPANY

8000 W. Florissant Ave., PO Box 4100, St. Louis, MO, 63136

Tel: (314) 553-2000   Fax: (314) 553-3527   www.emersonelectric.com

Electrical and electronic products, industrial components and systems, consumer, government and defense products.

Emerson Japan Ltd., New Pier South Tower 7F, 1-16-1 Kaigan, Minato-ku, Tokyo 105-0022, Japan

Tel: 81-3-5403-2900

EMERSON PROCESS MANAGEMENT

8301Cameron Road, Austin, TX, 78754

Tel: (512) 834-7689   Fax: (512) 832-3232   www.frco.com

Mfr. industrial process control equipment.

Emerson Process Management, Empire Bldg., 10F, 23-1 Hatchobori 2-chome, Chuo-ku, Tokyo 104, Japan

Tel: 81-3-3552-5751   Fax: 81-3-3555-0735

EMERY FORWARDING

One Lagoon Drive, Ste. 400, Redwood City, CA, 94065

Tel: (650) 596-9600   Fax: (650) 596-7901   www.emeryworld.com

Freight transport, global logistics and air cargo.

Emery Forwarding, No. 2 Shuwa Nihombashi, Honcho Bldg., 3-2 Nihombashi Ohdemmacho, Tokyo 103, Japan

Tel: 81-33-669-9088   Fax: 81-33-669-3462

ENCYCLOPAEDIA BRITANNICA INC.

310 S. Michigan Ave., Chicago, IL, 60604

Tel: (312) 427-9700   Fax: (312) 294-2176   www.eb.com

Publishing; books.

Encyclopaedia Britannica (Japan) Inc., Meiho Bldg., 1-21-1 Nishi Shinjuku, Shinjuku-ku, Tokyo 160, Japan

TBS-Britannica Ltd., Shuwa Sanbancho Bldg., 28-1 Sanbancho, Chiyoda-ku, Tokyo 102, Japan

ENERPAC

6101 N. Baker Road, PO Box 3241, Milwaukee, WI, 53201-3241

Tel: (414) 781-6600   Fax: (414) 781-1049   www.enerpac.com

Mfr. hydraulic cylinders, pumps, valves, presses, tools, accessories and system components.

Applied Power Japan Ltd., 1-1-11 Shimomae, Toda-shi, Saitama 335-0016, Japan

Tel: 81-048-421-2311

ENGELHARD CORPORATION

101 Wood Avenue South, Iselin, NJ, 08830

Tel: (732) 205-5000   Fax: (732) 632-9253   www.engelhard.com

Mfr. pigments, additives, catalysts, chemicals, engineered materials.

Engelhard Corporation, Masonic 39 Mori Bldg., 5/F, 245 Azabudai, Minato-ku, Tokyo 106-0041, Japan

A. EPSTEIN AND SONS INTERNATIONAL, INC.

600 West Fulton Street, Chicago, IL, 60606-1199

Tel: (312) 454-9100   Fax: (312) 559-1217   www.epstein-isi.com

Engaged in architecture, engineering, planning, construction and interior design.

A. Epstein and Sons Japan, Inc., Akasaka Tokyo Building, 12/F, 2-14-3 Nagatacho Chiyoda-Ku, Tokyo 100-0014, Japan

Tel: 81-3-3595-0363

ERIEZ MAGNETICS

2200 Asbury Road, Erie, PA, 16506

Tel: (814) 835-6000   Fax: (814) 838-4960   www.eriez.com

Mfr. magnets, vibratory feeders, metal detectors, screeners/sizers, mining equipment, current separators.

Eriez Magnetics Japan Co. Ltd., Shinkawa Ohara Bldg., 4F, 27-8 Chinkawa 1-chome, Chuo-ku, Tokyo 104, Japan

Tel: 81-473-546381   Fax: 81-473-547643   Contact: T. Homma

ERNST & YOUNG INTERNATIONAL

5 Times Square, New York, NY, 10036

Tel: (212) 773-3000   Fax: (212) 773-6350   www.eyi.com

Engaged in assurance and advisory business services, tax, law and corporate finance.

Sowa Ota / Ernst & Young Co., Ltd., Hitotsubashi Bldg., 2-6-3 Hitotsubashi, Chiyoda-ku, Tokyo 101, Japan

Tel: 81-3-3288-2120   Fax: 3-3288-6389   Contact: Yoji Ishizaka

ESTEE LAUDER COMPANIES INC.

767 Fifth Ave., New York, NY, 10153

Tel: (212) 572-4200   Fax: (212) 572-3941   www.esteelauder.com

Cosmetics, perfumes and Aveda hair care products.

Estee Lauder Cosmetics (Japan) Ltd., Nihon Seimei Akasaka Bldg., 1-19 Akasaka 8-chome, Minato-ku, Tokyo 107, Japan

ETHAN ALLEN INTERIORS INC.

Ethan Allen Drive, Danbury, CT, 06811

Tel: (203) 743-8000   Fax: (203) 743-8298   www.ethanallen.com

Mfr. and sale of premium-priced furniture and home furnishings.

Ethan Allen Home Interiors, 1-17-28 Minami Horie, Nishi-Ku, Osaka Shi, Japan

Tel: 61-6-539-4321   Fax: 61-6-539-4322

Ethan Allen Home Interiors, IDC TFT Bldg., 4/F, 3-1 Ariake Koto-Ku, Tokyo, Japan

Tel: 81-3-5530-5555   Fax: 81-3-5530-5556

ETHYL CORPORATION

330 South 4th Street, PO Box 2189, Richmond, VA, 23219

Tel: (804) 788-5000   Fax: (804) 788-5688   www.ethyl.com

Provide additive chemistry solutions to enhance the performance of petroleum products.

Ethyl Japan, 19/F, Shiroyama Hills, 4-3-1 Toranomon, Minato-ku, Tokyo 105-6019, Japan

Tel: 81-3-5401-2901   Fax: 81-3-5401-3368

Ethyl Japan Tsukuba Technical Center, 5-5 Toukoudai, Tsukuba Ibaraki 300-2635, Japan

Tel: 81-298-47-1061   Fax: 81-298-47-1063

EURO RSCG WORLDWIDE

350 Hudson Street, New York, NY, 10014

Tel: (212) 886-2000   Fax: (212) 886-2016   www.eurorscg.com

International advertising agency group.

EURO RSCG Partnership, 2-3-11 Hirakawa-cho, Chiyoda-ku, Tokyo, Japan

EXABYTE CORPORATION

1635 38th Street, Boulder, CO, 80301

Tel: (303) 442-4333   Fax: (303) 417-7170   www.exabyte.com

Mfr. computer hardware, including tape drives and cartridges.

Nihon Exabyte, Kioicho TBR Building 1214, 5-7 Koujimachi, Chiyoda-ku, Tokyo 102-0083, Japan

EXCELLON AUTOMATION

24751 Crenshaw Boulevard, Torrance, CA, 90505

Tel: (310) 534-6300   Fax: (310) 534-6777   www.excellon.com

PCB drilling and routing machines; optical inspection equipment.

Excellon Japan, 2-15-22 Hirakawa-Cho, Chiyoda-Ku, Tokyo 102, Japan

Tel: 81-3-5275-7473   Fax: 81-3-5275-6609

EXCELON INC.

25 Mall Road, Burlington, MA, 01803

Tel: (781) 674-5000   Fax: (781) 674-5010   www.exceloncorp.com

Developer of object-oriented database management systems software.

eXcelon Japan Co., Ltd., Kawakita Memorial Bldg., 18 Ichibancho, Chiyoda-ku, Tokyo 102-0082, Japan

Tel: 81-33-556-7612   Fax: 81-33-556-7642

EXE TECHNOLOGIES, INC.

8787 N. Stemmons Fwy., Dallas, TX, 75247-3702

Tel: (214) 775-6000   Fax: (214) 775-0911   www.exe.com

Provides a complete line of supply chain management execution software for WMS.

EXE Technologies, Inc. Japan, Akasaka Twin Tower, 2-17-22 Akasaka, Minato-ku, Tokyo 107, Japan

Tel: 81-3-5562-3106   Fax: 81-3-5562-3146   Contact: Kenichi Tsumura, Pres

EXPEDITORS INTERNATIONAL OF WASHINGTON INC.

1015 Third Avenue, 12th Fl., Seattle, WA, 98104-1182

Tel: (206) 674-3400   Fax: (206) 682-9777   www.expd.com

Air/ocean freight forwarding, customs brokerage, international logistics solutions.

Tokyo Expeditors (Japan) Ltd., 1-2-11 Minami-Shinagawa, Shinagawa-ku, Tokyo 140-0004, Japan

EXXON MOBIL CORPORATION

5959 Las Colinas Blvd., Irving, TX, 75039-2298

Tel: (972) 444-1000   Fax: (972) 444-1882   www.exxonmobil.com

Petroleum exploration, production, refining; mfr. petroleum and chemicals products; coal and minerals.

Exxon Mobil KK, Kawasaki Chemical Plant, 7-1 Ukishima-Cho, Kawasaki-ku Kawasaki-Shi, Kanagawa-Ken 210, Japan

Exxon Mobil KK, 34-1 Towada, Kamisu-Cho, Kashima-Gun, Ibaraki-Ken 314-02, Japan

Exxon Mobil KK, TBS Kaikan Bldg., 3-3 Akasaka 5-chome, Minato-ku, Tokyo 107, Japan

Exxon Mobil KK, Palace Side Bldg., 1-1 Hitotsubashi 1-chome, Chiyoda-ku, Tokyo 100, Japan

Exxon Mobil KK, New Pier Takeshiba, 16-1 Kaigan 1-Chome, Minato-ku, Tokyo 105-8572, Japan

E-Z-EM INC.

717 Main Street, Westbury, NY, 11590

Tel: (516) 333-8230   Fax: (516) 333-8278   www.ezem.com

Engaged in the design, manufacture and marketing of contrast media for gastrointestinal tract radiography.

Toho Kagaku Kenkyusho Co. Inc., 3-11-11 Tatekawa, Sumida-ku, Tokyo 130-0023, Japan

Tel: 81-3-3634-0831   Fax: 81-3-3634-0955   Contact: Tohru Nagami, Pres   Emp: 35

FACTSET RESEARCH SYSTEMS, INC.

1 Greenwich Plaza, Greenwich, CT, 06830

Tel: (203) 863-1599   Fax: (203) 863-1501   www.factset.com

Provides on-line investment research services to financial institutions.

FactSet Limited, Daini Okamotoya Bldg., 8/F, 1-22-16 Toranomon.-ku, Minato-ku, Tokyo 105-0001, Japan

Tel: 81-3-5512-7700

FAIR, ISAAC AND COMPANY, INC.

200 Smith Ranch Road, San Rafael, CA, 94903

Tel: (415) 472-2211   Fax: (415) 492-5691   www.fairisaac.com

Mfr. automated systems for credit and loan approvals.

Fair, Isaac and Co., Kioi-cho TBR Bldg., #1200, 5-7 Kojimachi, Chiyoda-ku, Tokyo 102-0083, Japan

Tel: 81-3-5213-3425

FAIRCHILD SEMICONDUCTOR INTERNATIONAL, INC.

82 Running Hill Road, South Portland, ME, 04106

Tel: (207) 775-8100   Fax: (207) 761-0392   www.fairchildsemi.com

Mfr. semiconductor chips.

Fairchild Semiconductor Japan Ltd., 6F, Bancho-Kaikan, 12-1 Gobancho, Chiyoda-ku, Tokyo 102-0076, Japan

FEDERAL-MOGUL CORPORATION

26555 Northwestern Highway, PO Box 1966, Southfield, MI, 48034

Tel: (248) 354-7700   Fax: (248) 354-8983   www.federal-mogul.com

Mfr./distributor precision parts for automobiles, trucks, farm and construction vehicles.

Federal-Mogul Japan KK, Osaka, Japan

FEDEX CORPORATION

942 South Shady Grove Rd., Memphis, TN, 38120

Tel: (901) 369-3600   Fax: (901) 395-2000   www.fdxcorp.com

Package express delivery service.

Federal Express (Japan) KK, Akaishi Bldg., 9-3 Higashi Azabu 1-chome, Minato-ku, Tokyo, Japan

FEI CORPORATION

7451 NW Evergreen Pkwy., Hillsboro, OR, 97124-5830

Tel: (503) 640-7500   Fax: (503) 640-7509   www.feicompany.com

Design and mfr. of charged particle beam systems serving the research, development and production needs of customers in semiconductor, data storage, and industry/institute markets.

Micrion Japan K.K., Faret Tachikawa Center Square Bldg.11F, 36-2-2-Chome, Akebono-cho,, Tachikawa, Tokyo 190-0012, Japan

Tel: 81-42-523-1776   Fax: 81-42-526-5456

FELLOWES, INC.

1789 Norwood Avenue, Itasca, IL, 60143-109

Tel: (630) 893-1600   Fax: (630) 893-1648   www.fellowes.com

Mfr. of office products and accessories.

Fellowes Japan KK, Helios Bldg., 9/F, 5-1-3 Nishi-Gotanda, Shinagawa-ku, Tokyo 141-0031, Japan

Tel: 81-3-5496-2401

FERRO CORPORATION

1000 Lakeside Ave., Cleveland, OH, 44114-7000

Tel: (216) 641-8580   Fax: (216) 696-5784   www.ferro.com

Mfr. Specialty chemicals, coatings, plastics, colors, refractories.

Ferro Enamels, Ltd. - Main Office, 1-27 Oyodo Kita 2-chome, Kita-ku, Osaka, Japan

Tel: 81-6-458-3551   Fax: 81-6-458-8911   Contact: Hirofumi Miki, Chmn.

Ferro Enamels, Ltd. Agricultural R&D Center, 1152 Tsurumi Okuyamada, Beppu City, Oita Pref., Japan

Tel: 81-977-67-7917

Ferro Enamels, Ltd. Kyushu Plant, 997 Aza Gotanda, Oaza Kamisokoino, Nakama City Fukuoka Pref., Japan

Tel: 81-93-245-3031

Nissan Ferro Organic Chemical Co. Ltd., Nissan Edobashi Bldg., 10-5 Nihonbashi Honcho 1-chome, Chuo-ku, Tokyo 103, Japan

Tel: 81-3-3245-0661   Fax: 81-3-3231-7810   Contact: H. Akabayashi, Pres.

FERROTEC CORPORATION

40 Simon Street, Nashua, NH, 03061

Tel: (603) 883-9800   Fax: (603) 883-2308   www.ferrofluidics.com

Mfr. rotary feedthrough designs, emission seals, automated crystal-growing systems, bearings, ferrofluids.

Ferrotec Corporation, 1-14-4 Kyobashi, Chuo-ku, Tokyo 150, Japan

Tel: 81-3-3845-1021

FIDUCIARY TRUST COMPANY INTERNATIONAL

175 Federal Street, Boston, MA, 02110

Tel: (617) 482-5270   Fax: (617) 482-5270   www.ftc.com

Banking services.

Fiduciary Trust (Intl.) SA, Tokyo, Japan

FileNET CORPORATION

3565 Harbor Boulevard, Costa Mesa, CA, 92626

Tel: (714) 966-3400   Fax: (714) 966-3490   www.filenet.com

Provides integrated document management (IDM) software and services for internet and client server-based imaging, workflow, cold and electronic document management solutions.

Nihon FileNET, Shiroyama-JT-Mori Bldg., 15F, 4-3-1 Toranomon, Minato-ku, Tokyo 105, Japan

Tel: 81-3-3436-8781   Fax: 81-3-3436-8793   Contact: Naoki Sudoh, Mng. Dir.

FINANCIAL GUARANTY INSURANCE COMPANY

115 Broadway, New York, NY, 10006

Tel: (212) 312-3000   Fax: (212) 312-3093   www.fgic.com

Engaged in insuring debt securities and investment, operation, and information services to state and local governments

Financial Guaranty Insurance Co. (Tokyo), Tokyo Sumitomo Twin Bldg., Sumitomo Marine Bldg.,14/F, 27-2 Shinkawa #2-chome, Tokyo, Japan

FINNEGAN, HENDERSON LLP

1300 "I" Street NW, Ste. 700, Washington, DC, 20005-3314

Tel: (202) 408-4000   Fax: (202) 408-4400   www.finnegan.com

Engaged in international law.

Finnegan Henserson, Toranomon No. 45 Mori Building, 1-5, Toranomon 5-Chome, Minato-ku, Tokyo 105-0001, Japan

Tel: 813-3431-6943   Fax: 813-3431-6945

FIREPOND, INC.

890 Winter Stret, Waltham, MA, 02451

Tel: (781) 487-8400   Fax: (781) 487-8450   www.firepond.com

Mfr. enterprise software.

Firepond Japan KK, Fuerte Kojimachi Building, 6/F, 1-7-25 Kojimachi, Chiyoda-ku Tokyo 102-0083, Japan

Tel: 81-3-5213-0330   Fax: 81-3-5213-0335

FISHER SCIENTIFIC INTERNATIONAL INC.

1 Liberty Lane, Hampton, NH, 03842

Tel: (603) 929-5911   Fax: (603) 929-0222   www.fisherscientific.com

Mfr. and distribution of science equipment, instruments, and supplies.

Fisher Scientific Japan, Mita-Kokusai Bldg. Annex, Room 111, 1-4-28 Mita, Minato-ku, Tokyo 108-0073, Japan

Tel: 81-3-5484-4731   Fax: 81-3-5485-4736

FLEETBOSTON FINANCIAL CORPORATION

100 Federal Street, Boston, MA, 02110

Tel: (617) 434-2400   Fax: (617) 434-6943   www.fleet.com

Banking and insurance services.

FleetBoston Financial, AIG Bldg., 7F, 1-3 Marunochi 1-chome, Chiyoda-ku, Tokyo 100, Japan

Tel: 81-3-3211-2611   Fax: 81-3-3201-6879

FLOW INTERNATIONAL CORPORATION

23500 64th Avenue S., PO Box 97040, Kent, WA, 98064-9740

Tel: (253) 872-4900   Fax: (253) 813-3285   www.flowcorp.com

Mfr. high-pressure water jet cutting/cleaning equipment, powered scaffolding; concrete cleaning/removal.

Flow Japan, Tokyo, Japan

FLOWSERVE CORPORATION

222 W. Los Colinas Blvd., Irving, TX, 75039

Tel: (972) 443-6500   Fax: (972) 443-6858   www.flowserve.com

Mfr. chemicals equipment, pumps, valves, filters, fans and heat exchangers.

Flowserve FCD Japan Business Development, Sandensha Building, 5F, 2-7-15 Hamamatsu-cho, Minato-ku, Tokyo 105-0013, Japan

FLUOR CORPORATION

One Enterprise Drive, Aliso Viejo, CA, 92656-2606

Tel: (949) 349-2000   Fax: (949) 349-5271   www.flour.com

Engineering and construction services.

Fluor Daniel Japan, 303-7-10 Moto-Akasaka, 1 Chome, Miuato-Ku, Tokyo 107-0051, Japan

FM GLOBAL INC.

1301 Atwood Avenue, Johnston, RI, 02919

Tel: (401) 275-3000   Fax: (401) 275-3029   www.fmglobal.com

Engaged in commercial and industrial property insurance and risk management, specializing in engineering-driven property protection.

FM Global, Queen's Tower A, Section 809, 2-3-1 Minato Mirai, Nishi-ku, Yokohama Kanagawa 220-6008, Japan

FMC CORPORATION

1735 Market St., Philadelphia, PA, 19103

Tel: (215) 299-6000   Fax: (215) 299-6618   www.fmc.com

Mfr. specialty chemicals, including alginate, carrageenan and microcrystalline cellulose.

FMC Japan, Kyodo Bldg., 7/F, Chuo-ku, Tokyo, Japan

Tel: 81-3-3660-8990

FMC Japan KK, 5-24 Miyahara 3-chome, 11/F, Yodogawa-ku, Osaka 532, Japan

FMC Japan KK (Plant), 4089-1, Naoshima-cho, Kagawa-gun, Kagawa-ken, Naoshima, Japan

Tel: 81-87-892-3801

FMR (FIDELITY INVESTMENTS)

82 Devonshire Street, Boston, MA, 02109

Tel: (617) 563-7000   Fax: (617) 476-6105   www.fidelity.com

Diversified financial services company offering investment management, retirement, brokerage, and shareholder services directly to individuals and institutions and through financial intermediaries.

Fidelity Brokerage Services, Japan, LLC, Across Shinkawa Bldg., 4th Fl., 1-8-8 Shinkawa, Chuo-ku, Tokyo 104-0333, Japan

Tel: 81-3-5543-8902   Fax: 81-3-5543-1041   Contact: Roger T. Servison, Pres.

FOOT LOCKER INC.

112 West 34th Street, New York, NY, 10020

Tel: (212) 720-3700   Fax: (212) 553-2042   www.venatorgroup.com

Mfr./sales shoes and sneakers.

Foot Locker International, Funabashi/Sogo 1-1, Hamamachi 2-chome Funabashi-Shi, Chiba, Japan

Tel: 81-4-7432-6750

Foot Locker International, Shin Yuri 1-1 Asi-ku, Kawasaki-Shi 1-2, Kanagawa K, Japan

Foot Locker International, Parco Sr 6 15-1, Uchidagawa-Cho Shibya-ku Tokyo, Japan

FORD MOTOR COMPANY

One American Road, Dearborn, MI, 48126

Tel: (313) 322-3000   Fax: (313) 322-9600   www.ford.com

Mfr./sales motor vehicles.

Ford Motor Co. (Japan) Ltd., Mori Bldg., 5-1 Toranomon 3-chome, Minato-ku, Tokyo 105, Japan

FORRESTER RESEARCH, INC.

400 Technology Square, Cambridge, MA, 02139

Tel: (617) 497-7090   Fax: (617) 868-0577   www.forrester.com

Provides clients an analysis of the effect of changing technologies on their operations.

Forrester Research, Level 9, AIG Building, 1-1-3 Marunouchi, Chiyoda-Ku, Tokyo 100-0005, Japan

FORTUNE BRANDS

300 Tower Parkway, Lincolnshire, IL, 60069

Tel: (847) 484-4400   Fax: (800) 310-5960   www.fortunebrands.com

Mfr. diversified consumer products including Masterbrand, Acco office products, Jim Bean distillery products, Footjoy and Titleist golf products and Moen bath products.

Fortune Brands International Corporation, Ichigaya K-T Bldg. #2, 6/F, 7-16 Kudan Minami 4-chome, Ciyoda-ku, Tokyo 102-0074, Japan

Tel: 8133-556-6263

FOSTER WHEELER LTD.

Perryville Corporate Park, Clinton, NJ, 08809-4000

Tel: (908) 730-4000   Fax: (908) 730-4100   www.fwc.com

Manufacturing, engineering and construction.

Foster Wheeler K.K., 4-1 Hamamatsu-cho, 2-Chome Manato-ku, Tokyo 105-6137, Japan

Tel: 81-3-3434-8600

FRANK RUSSELL COMPANY

909 A Street, Tacoma, WA, 98402

Tel: (253) 572-9500   Fax: (253) 591-3495   www.russell.com

Investment management and asset strategy consulting.

Frank Russell Japan, 49-13 Nishihara 3-chome, Shibuya-ku, Tokyo 151, Japan

Tel: 81-3-3467-9800   Fax: 81-3-3467-9808   Contact: Masanori Tsuno, President   Emp: 36

FRANKLIN COVEY COMPANY

2200 W. Parkway Blvd., Salt Lake City, UT, 84119-2331

Tel: (801) 975-1776   Fax: (801) 977-1431   www.franklincovey.com

Provides productivity and time management products and seminars.

Franklin Covey Japan, Marumasu Kojimachi Building, 6 7F, 3-3 Kojimachi, Chiyoda-ku, Tokyo 102-0083, Japan

Tel: 81-3-3237-7711   Fax: 81-3-3237-7722

FRANKLIN ELECTRIC COMPANY, INC.

400 East Spring Street, Bluffton, IN, 46714-3798

Tel: (219) 824-2900   Fax: (219) 824-2909   www.fele.com

Mfr./distribute electric motors, submersible motors and controls.

Franklin Electric International Japan, Inc., Room 402 Y Building, 5-6-15, Otsuka, Bunkyo-Ku 112-0002, Japan

Contact: Masao Hotchi

THE FRANKLIN MINT

US Route 1, Media, PA, 19091-0001

Tel: (610) 459-6000   Fax: (610) 459-6880   www.franklinmint.com

Design/marketing collectibles and luxury items.

Franklin Mint Co. Ltd., Recruit Kachidoki Bldg., 2-11-9 Kachidoki, Chuo-ku, Tokyo 104, Japan

FRANKLIN RESOURCES, INC.

1 Franklin Pkwy., Bldg. 970, 1st Fl., San Mateo, CA, 94404

Tel: (415) 312-2000   Fax: (415) 312-5606   www.frk.com

Global and domestic investment advisory and portfolio management.

Templeton Investment Management Co., Ltd., Tokyo, Japan

FRITO-LAY COMPANY

7701 Legacy Drive, Plano, TX, 75024

Tel: (972) 334-7000   Fax: (972) 334-2019   www.fritolay.com

Mfr. snack food products.

Japan Frito-Lay Ltd., Tokyo, Japan

FRITZ COMPANIES, INC., DIV. UPS

706 Mission Street, Ste. 900, San Francisco, CA, 94103

Tel: (415) 904-8360   Fax: (415) 904-8661   www.fritz.com

Integrated transportation, sourcing, distribution and customs brokerage services.

Suzuyo/Fritz Ltd., Suzuyo Tokyo Building, 3/F, 1-2-12 Shibakoen, Minato-ku, Tokyo 105, Japan

FRONTSTEP, INC.

2800 Corporate Exchange Drive, Ste. 400, Columbus, OH, 43231

Tel: (614) 523-7000   Fax: (614) 895-2504   www.frontstep.com

Mfr. management software.

Frontstep Japan, 2/F Yushimadai-Bldg., 2-31-27 Yushima, Bunkyo-ku, Tokyo 113-0034, Japan
Tel: 81-3-5802-7540-1

FSI INTERNATIONAL INC.

3455 Lyman Boulevard, Chaska, MN, 55318-3052

Tel: (952) 448-5440   Fax: (952) 448-2825   www.fsi-intl.com

Manufacturing equipment for computer silicon wafers.

FSI Metron Japan, Okayama Technology Center, Okayama Research Park, 5311, Haga, Okayama 701-1221, Japan
FSI Metron Japan, Kyohan Kudan Bldg., 4F, 5-10 Iidabashi 1-chome, Chiyoda-ku, Tokyo 102, Japan
Tel: 81-3-3265-9171   Fax: 81-3-3265-9179

H.B. FULLER COMPANY

1200 Willow Lake Blvd., Vadnais Heights, MN, 55110

Tel: (651) 236-5900   Fax: (651) 236-5898   www.hbfuller.com

Mfr./distributor adhesives, sealants, coatings, paints, waxes, sanitation chemicals.

H.B. Fuller Japan Co. Ltd., 700 Matsushimacho Hamamatsu City, Shizuoka 430-0834, Japan
H.B. Fuller Japan Co. Ltd., Kudan Nikkana Building, 3-9-12 Kudanminami, Chiyoda-ku, Tokyo 102, Japan
Tel: 81-3-5275-5831   Fax: 81-3-5275-2391

THE GAP

2 Folsom St., San Francisco, CA, 94105

Tel: (650) 952-4400   Fax: (650) 952-5884   www.gap.com

Clothing store chain.

The Gap, Tokyo, Japan

GARTNER, INC.

56 Top Gallant Road, Stamford, CT, 06904-2212

Tel: (203) 316-1111   Fax: (203) 316-1100   www.gartner.com

Engaged in information technology consulting.

Gartner Group Japan, Aobadai Hills 6F, 7-7 Aobadai 4-chome, Meguro-ku, Tokyo 153-0042, Japan
Tel: 81-3-3481-3670   Fax: 81-3-3481-3644

THE GATES RUBBER COMPANY

990 S. Broadway, PO Box 5887, Denver, CO, 80217-5887

Tel: (303) 744-1911   Fax: (303) 744-4000   www.gatesrubber.com

Mfr. automotive and industrial belts and hoses.

Gates Rubber Company Japan, Matsura Building, 5/F, 1-9-6 Shiba, Minato-ku Sumida-ku, Tokyo 105-0014, Japan
Tel: 81-3-5439-5188   Fax: 81-3-5439-5189   Contact: Tadashi Namiki
GNAPCO Pte. Ltd., 4-26 Sakuragawa 4-Chome, Naniwa-Ku, Osaka 556-0022, Japan
Tel: 81-6-6563-1266   Fax: 81-6-6563-1267

GE BETZ, DIV. GE SPECIALTY MATERIALS

4636 Somerton Road, PO Box 3002, Trevose, PA, 19053-6783

Tel: (215) 355-3300   Fax: (215) 953-5524   www.gebetz.com

Engaged in engineered chemical treatment of water and process systems in industrial, commercial and institutional facilities

GE Betz, Div. GE Specialty Materials, R Bldg., 7F, 8-12 Kita-Shinagawa 1-chome, Shinagawa-ku, Tokyo 140, Japan

GE CAPITAL FLEET SERVICES

3 Capital Drive, Eden Prairie, MN, 55344

Tel: (612) 828-1000   Fax: (612) 828-2010   www.gefleet.com

Corporate vehicle leasing and services.

Japan Leasing Auto./GE Capital Fleet, 3-2-10 Shirokanedai, Minato-ku, Tokyo, Japan

Tel: 81-3-5442-6666

GEMSTAR-TV GUIDE INTERNATIONAL, INC.

135 North Los Robles Avenue, Ste. 800, Pasadena, CA, 91101

Tel: (626) 792-5700   Fax: (626) 792-0257   www.gemstar.com

Mfr. technology for VCR programming.

Gemstar Japan KK, 2-29-18 Nishi-Ikebukuro, Toshima-ku, Tokyo 171, Japan

Tel: 81-3-5950-7777   Fax: 81-3-5950-7770

GEN RE INTERMEDIARIES CORPORATION

PO Box 10216, Stamford, CT, 06904-2216

Tel: (203) 357-8883   Fax: (203) 328-6408   www.genre.com

Provides reinsurance services worldwide.

Cologne Reinsurance Company - Far East Liaison Office, TT-2 Bldg., 11F, 8-1 Nihonbashi Ningyocho, 3-chome Chuo-ku, Tokyo 103, Japan

Tel: 81-3-3663-7447   Fax: 81-3-3663-7450   Contact: Rainer Schürmann, Gen. Mgr.

General Re Financial Products (Japan) Inc. - Tokyo, Toranomon Waiko Bldg., 9F, 5-12-1 Toranomon, Minato-ku, Tokyo 105, Japan

Tel: 81-3-5473-6655   Fax: 81-3-5473-6650

General Reinsurance Corporation, TT-2 Bldg., 11F, 8-1 Nihonbashi Ningyocho, 3-chome Chuo-ku, Tokyo 103, Japan

Tel: 81-3-3663-7449   Fax: 81-3-3663-7450   Contact: Elizabeth S. King

GENERAL BINDING CORPORATION

One GBC Plaza, Northbrook, IL, 60062

Tel: (847) 272-3700   Fax: (847) 272-1369   www.gbc.com

Engaged in the design, manufacture and distribution of branded office equipment, related supplies and thermal laminating films.

GBC Japan K.K., 14F Harmony Tower, 14/F, 1-32-2, Honcho Nakano-Ku, Tokyo 164-0012, Japan

GENERAL DYNAMICS CORPORATION

3190 Fairview Park Drive, Falls Church, VA, 22042-4523

Tel: (703) 876-3000   Fax: (703) 876-3125   www.gendyn.com

Mfr. aerospace equipment, submarines, strategic systems, armored vehicles, defense support systems.

General Dynamics Intl. Corp., 30 Mori Bldg., 2-2 Toranomon 3-chome, Minato-ku, Tokyo 105, Japan

GENERAL ELECTRIC CAPITAL CORPORATION

260 Long Ridge Road, Stamford, CT, 06927

Tel: (203) 357-4000   Fax: (203) 357-6489   www.gecapital.com

Financial, property, casualty insurance, computer sales and trailer leasing services.

ERC Group, Div. GE Capital, Kowa 35 Bldg., 14-14 Akasaka 1-chome, Minato-ku, Tokyo 107, Japan

Tel: 81-3-3588-1821   Fax: 81-3-3588-1822

ERC Group, Div. GE Capital, Tokyo, Japan

GE Capital/Japan Leasing Corp., Tokyo, Japan

GE Edison Life Insurance, No. 35 Kowa Bldg., Minato-ku, Tokyo 107, Japan

GENERAL ELECTRIC COMPANY

3135 Easton Turnpike, Fairfield, CT, 06431

Tel: (203) 373-2211   Fax: (203) 373-3131   www.ge.com

Diversified manufacturing, technology and services.

GE Aircraft Engines, 8-2 Haneda-kuko 1-choe, Tokyo 144, Japan

Tel: 81-3-3747-8250

GE Appliances, Bldg. 3-3 Kojamacki Chiyoda-ku, Tokyo 102, Japan
Tel: 81-3-3264-1140

GE Capital Services GENSTAR container, 7-F, Tomoecho Annex II, Tokyo, Japan
Tel: 81-3433-8661

GE Fanuc Automation, 589-12 Aza Ochiai, Motosoujamachi, Maebashi 371, Japan
Tel: 81-2-7251-8431   Fax: 81-2-7251-8330

GE Fanuc Automation, c/o Dataviews International Inc., 16 Parale Mitsui., 8 Higashida-cho, Kawasaki-ku, Kawasaki, Kanagawa 210-0005, Japan
Contact: Mamoru Fujinaka

GE SeaCo Japan Ltd, Shibaura 2-Chome Building, 5/F, 7-5 Shibaura 2-Chome, Minato-ku, Tokyo 108-0023, Japan
Contact: George Koyama

GE Silicones Japan, Rm 1008, Tower 1, Tokyo 106-8550, Japan

GE Toshiba Silicon, Roppongi 6-2-31, Mir Ku, Tokyo 106-8550, Japan
Tel: 81-3-3479-3918

General Electric Japan Ltd., No. 35 Kowa Bldg., Minato-ku, Tokyo 107, Japan
Tel: 81-3-3588-5190   Fax: 81-3-3588-5288   Contact: Jay F. Lapin, Pres.

GEPS Global Power Generation, No. 35 Kowa Bldg., Minato-ku, Tokyo 107, Japan
Tel: 81-3-3588-5176   Fax: 81-3-3588-3372

GENERAL MOTORS CORPORATION

300 Renaissance Center, Detroit, MI, 48285

Tel: (313) 556-5000   Fax: (313) 556-5108   www.gm.com

Mfr. full line vehicles, automotive electronics, commercial technologies, telecommunications, space, finance.

Isuzu Motors Ltd., Tokyo, Japan

Suzuki Motor Co. Ltd., Hamamatsu, Japan

GENOMIC SOLUTIONS INC.

4355 Varsity Drive, Ste. E, Ann Arbor, MI, 48108

Tel: (734) 975-4800   Fax: (734) 975-4808   www.genomicsolutions.com

Mfr. software for gene research.

Genomic Solutions KK, Gotanda Chuo Bldg. 2/F, 3-5, Higashigotanda 2-chome, Shinagawa-Ku, Tokyo 141-0022, Japan
Tel: 81-33-280-0990   Fax: 81-33-280-0991

GENUITY, INC.

225 Presidential Way, Woburn, MA, 01801

Tel: (781) 865-2000   Fax: (781) 865-3936   www.genuity.com

R/D computer, communications, acoustics technologies and internetworking services.

Genuity Japan KK, Bldg. 22 Fl., 2-4-1 Nishishinjuku, Shinjuku-ku, Tokyo, Japan
Tel: 81-3-5339-6021

GENZYME CORPORATION

1 Kendall Square, Cambridge, MA, 02139-1562

Tel: (617) 252-7500   Fax: (617) 252-7600   www.genzyme.com

Mfr. healthcare products for enzyme deficient diseases.

Idenics, Div. Genzyme, Izumiyamabuki-Cho Bldg., 333 Yamabuki-Cho, Shinjuku-ku, Tokyo 162-0801, Japan
Tel: 81-3-5228-6464   Fax: 81-3-5228-5933

GEO LOGISTICS CORPORATION

1521 E. Dyer Rd., Santa Ana, CA, 92705

Tel: (714) 513-3000   Fax: (714) 513-3120   www.geo-logistics.com

Engaged in freight forwarding, warehousing and distribution services, specializing in heavy cargo.

GeoLogistics Ltd., Kasen Building, 5/F, 6-8 Kawara-machi 4-chome, Chuo-Ku, Osaka 541-0048, Japan
Tel: 81-6-201-5461   Fax: 81-6-227-5230

GEORGIA-PACIFIC GROUP

133 Peachtree Street NE, 41st Floor, Atlanta, GA, 30303

Tel: (404) 652-4000   Fax: (404) 230-7008   www.gp.com

Mfr. and distribution of tissue, pulp, paper and building products and related chemicals.

Canfor/Georgia-Pacific Japan Corp, Tokyo, Japan

G-I HOLDINGS, INC.

1361 Alps Road, Wayne, NJ, 07470

Tel: (973) 628-3000   Fax: (973) 628-3326   www.gaf.com

Mfr. roofing and building materials.

G-I Holdings, Inc., Kogen Bldg., 17-2 Shinbashi 6-chome, Minato-ku, Tokyo, Japan

THE GILLETTE COMPANY

Prudential Tower Building, Boston, MA, 02199

Tel: (617) 421-7000   Fax: (617) 421-7123   www.gillette.com

Develop/mfr. personal care/use products: blades and razors, toiletries, cosmetics, stationery.

Braun Japan KK, Yokohama, Japan

Contact: Hans Th. Pauli, Mgr.

Gillette (Japan) Inc., Tokyo, Japan

Contact: Richard L. Guilfoile, Mgr.

GILSON INC.

3000 W. Beltline Hwy, PO Box 620027, Middleton, WI, 53562-0027

Tel: (608) 836-1551   Fax: (608) 831-4451   www.gilson.com

Mfr. analytical/biomedical instruments.

M&S Instruments Trading Inc., 12-4 Mikuni-Hommachi 2-Chome, Yodogawa-ku, Osaka 532-0005, Japan

GLEASON CORPORATION

1000 University Ave., Rochester, NY, 14692

Tel: (716) 473-1000   Fax: (716) 461-4348   www.gleasoncorp.com

Mfr. gear making machine tools; tooling and services.

OGA Corporation, 8-3 Tsukishima 1-Chome, Chuo-Ku, Tokyo 104, Japan

GLENAYRE ELECTRONICS LTD.

11360 Lakefield Drive, Duluth, GA, 30097

Tel: (770) 283-1000   Fax: (770) 497-3982   www.glenayre.com

Mfr. infrastructure components and pagers.

Nihon Glenayre Electronics K.K., 19-8 Annex Bldg., 4F, Akasaka 2-chome, Minato-ku, Tokyo 107, Japan

Tel: 81-3-5545-7811   Fax: 81-3-5545-7812

GLOBAL SILVERHAWK INTERNATIONAL MOVING

1000 Burnett Avenue, Concord, CA, 94520

Tel: (510) 609-7080   Fax: (510) 609-7081   www.globalsilverhawk.com

International moving and forwarding.

Global Silverhawk, No. 2 AB Building, 6F, 1-17 Roppongi 3-chome, Minato-ku, Tokyo 106, Japan

Tel: 81-3-3589-6666   Contact: Lance Allen, Gen. Mgr.

THE GOLDMAN SACHS GROUP

85 Broad Street, New York, NY, 10004

Tel: (212) 902-1000   Fax: (212) 902-3000   www.gs.com

Investment bankers; securities broker dealers.

Goldman Sachs Group, ARK Mori Building, 12-32 Akasaka 1-chome, Minato-ku, Tokyo 107-6005, Japan

Tel: 81-3-3589-7000

Goldman Sachs Group, K&K Shinsaibashi Building, 12-21 Nishi-Shinsaibashi 1-chome, Chuo-ku, Osaka 542-0086, Japan

Tel: 81-6-253-1333

THE GOODYEAR TIRE & RUBBER COMPANY

1144 East Market Street, Akron, OH, 44316

Tel: (330) 796-2121   Fax: (330) 796-1817   www.goodyear.com

Mfr. tires, automotive belts and hose, conveyor belts, chemicals; oil pipeline transmission.

Nippon Goodyear KK, Sankaido Building, 9-13 Akasaka 1-chome, Minato-ku, Tokyo 107, Japan

W. L. GORE & ASSOCIATES, INC.

555 Paper Mill Road, Newark, DE, 19711

Tel: (302) 738-4880   Fax: (302) 738-7710   www.gorefabrics.com

Mfr. electronic, industrial filtration, medical and fabric products.

Japan Gore-Tex, Inc., 1-42-5 Akazutumi Setagaya-ku, Tokyo 156-8505, Japan

Tel: 81-3-3327-0011   Fax: 81-3-3327-1853

GOSS INTERNATIONAL CORPORATION

700 Oakmont Lane, Westmont, IL, 60559-5546

Tel: (630) 850-5600   Fax: (630) 850-6310   www.gossgraphic.com

Engaged in the design and manufacture of advanced technology web offset press systems for the newspaper and commercial printing industries.

Goss Graphic Systems Japan, Mitsuya Toranomon Building, 22-14 Toranomon 1-Chome, Minato-Ku Tokyo 105, Japan

Tel: 81-3-3503-3901   Contact: Seiji Kato, VP

GP STRATEGIES CORPORATION

9 West 57th Street, New York, NY, 10019

Tel: (212) 230-9500   Fax: (212) 230-9545   www.genphysics.com

Mfr./distributor medical, health care and specialty products.

Hydron Japan KK, 1-14-18 Shironganedai, Minato-ku, Tokyo 108, Japan

W. R. GRACE & COMPANY

7500 Grace Drive, Columbia, MD, 21044

Tel: (410) 531-4000   Fax: (410) 531-4367   www.grace.com

Mfr. specialty chemicals and materials: packaging, health care, catalysts, construction, water treatment/process.

Fuji-Davison Chemical Ltd., 1846 Kozoji-cho 2-chome, Kusagai-shi, Aichi-ken 487, Japan

Grace Japan KK, 100 Kaneda, Atsugi-shi 243, Japan

Tel: 81-462-25-8800   Fax: 81-462-24-9254

Grace Japan KK, Tomita Building, 9F, 2-2 Ushijima-cho, Nishi-ku, Nagoya 451, Japan

Tel: 81-52-586-9630   Fax: 81-52-586-9616

GRACO INC.

88 - 11th Avenue NE, PO Box 1441, Minneapolis, MN, 55440-1441

Tel: (612) 623-6000   Fax: (612) 623-6777   www.graco.com

Mfr. systems and equipment to service fluid handling systems and automotive equipment.

Graco KK, 1-27-12 Hayabuchi, Tsuzuki-ku, Yokohama City 224-0025, Japan

GRANT THORNTON INTERNATIONAL

800 One Prudential Plaza, 130 E. Randolph Drive, Chicago, IL, 60601-6050

Tel: (312) 856-0001   Fax: (312) 616-7052   www.grantthornton.com

Accounting, audit, tax and management consulting services.

Grant Thornton Shinko, Nikko Ichibancho Bldg., 7F, 13-3 Ichibancho, Chiyoda-ku, Tokyo 102, Japan

Tel: 81-3-5210-9055   Fax: 81-3-5210-9050

GRAYBAR ELECTRIC CO., INC.

34 N. Meramec Ave., Clayton, MO, 63105

Tel: (314) 512-9200   Fax: (314) 512-9453   www.graybar.com

Electrical communications components distributor.

Konishi Electric Co., Ltd., 2-16-6 Minami Shinagawa, Shinagawa-Ku, Tokyo 140, Japan

Tel: 81-35-479-5505   Fax: 81-35-479-5558   Contact: Jun Konishi, Pres.

GREAT LAKES CHEMICAL CORPORATION

500 East 96th Street, Ste. 500, Indianapolis, IN, 46240

Tel: (317) 715-3000　　Fax: (317) 715-3050　　www.greatlakeschem.com

Mfr. innovative specialty chemical solutions, including flame retardants and other polymer additives, water treatment chemicals, performance and fine chemicals, fire extinguishers.

Great Lakes Chemical Japan Ltd., Shimbashi SY Building 4/F, 1-14-2, Nishi-Shimbashi, Minato-ku, Tokyo 105-0003, Japan

Tel: 81-3-5510-7000　　Fax: 81-3-5510-7004

GREY GLOBAL GROUP

777 Third Ave., New York, NY, 10017

Tel: (212) 546-2000　　Fax: (212) 546-1495　　www.grey.com

International advertising agency.

Grey-Daiko Advertising, Grey-Daiko Building, 2-3-20 Motoazabu, Minato-ku, Tokyo 106, Japan

GRIFFITH LABORATORIES INC.

One Griffith Center, Alsip, IL, 60658

Tel: (708) 371-0900　　Fax: (708) 597-3294　　www.griffithlabs.com

Mfr. industrial food ingredients and equipment.

Griffith Laboratories Japan KK, Nissei Bldg., 13-31 Konan 2-chome, Minato-ku, Tokyo 108, Japan

Tel: 81-3-3450-1231　　Fax: 81-3-3450-2608

GUARDIAN INDUSTRIES CORPORATION

2300 Harmon Road, Auburn Hills, MI, 48326-1714

Tel: (248) 340-1800　　Fax: (248) 340-9988　　www.guardian.com

Mfr. and fabricate flat glass products and insulation materials.

Guardian Japan Ltd., Bridgestone Toranomon 802, 25-2, 3-chome,Toranomon, Minato-ku, Tokyo, Japan

Tel: 81-3-3436-5581　　Fax: 81-3-3436-5583

GUAVA TECHNOLOGIES, INC.

25801 Industrial Boulevard, Hayward, CA, 94545-2991

Tel: (510) 576-1412　　Fax: (510) 576-1500　　www.guavatecnologies.com

Engaged in biotechnology research.

Bay Bioscience, Div. Guava Technologies, 5-2, Minatojima Minamimachi, 5-chome, Chuo-ku, Kobe 650-0047, Japan

Contact: Koji Murayama

GUIDANT CORPORATION

111 Monument Circle, 29th Fl., Indianapolis, IN, 46204

Tel: (317) 971-2000　　Fax: (317) 971-2040　　www.guidant.com

Mfr. cardiovascular therapeutic devices.

Guidant Japan KK, Shin Aoyama Bldg East, 4/F, 1-1 Minami-Aoyama, Minato-ku, Tokyo 107, Japan

GUY CARPENTER & COMPANY, INC.

114 West 47th Street, New York, NY, 10036

Tel: (212) 323-1000　　Fax: (212) 345-2494　　www.guycarp.com

Engaged in global reinsurance and risk management.

Guy Carpenter & Company, Inc. Rep Office, 3-20-2 Nishi-Shinjuku, 38/F, Shinjuku-ku, Tokyo 163-1438, Japan

Tel: 81-3-5353-0448　　Fax: 81-3-3320-6131　　Contact: Teisuke Satoh

HAEMONETICS CORPORATION

400 Wood Road, Braintree, MA, 02184-9114

Tel: (781) 848-7100　　Fax: (781) 848-5106　　www.haemonetics.com

Mfr. automated blood processing systems and blood products.

Haemonetics Japan Co., Ltd., Kyodo Building, 16 Ichiban-cho, Chiyoda-ku, Tokyo 102-0082, Japan

Tel: 81-3-3237-7260　　Fax: 81-3-3237-7330

HAGGAR CORPORATION

6113 Lemmon Avenue, Dallas, TX, 75209

Tel: (214) 352-8481   Fax: (214) 956-4367   www.haggarcorp.com

Mfr. apparel.

Haggar Japan Co. Ltd., 11-6 Sarugaku-Cho, Sanroser Daikanyama 201, Shibuya-ku, Tokyo 150-3300, Japan

Tel: 81-3-5457-2093   Contact: Hirotoshi Tashiro

HAHT COMMERCE, INC.

400 Newton Road, Raleigh, NC, 27615

Tel: (919) 786-5100   Fax: (919) 786-5250   www.haht.com

Mfr. e-commerce software.

HAHT Commerce, Shinjuku Park Tower N30F, 3-7-1 Nishi-Shinjuku, Shinjuku-ku, Tokyo 163-1030, Japan

HALL, KINION & ASSOCIATES, INC.

2570 North First Street, Ste. 400, San Jose, CA, 95131

Tel: (408) 895-5200   Fax: (408) 383-0902   www.hallkinion.com

Engaged in placement of information technology professionals on a contract basis.

Hall Kinion TKO Personnel Inc., Koenji-Kinoshita Royal Bldg., Koenji-Minami 4-5-7, Suginami-ku, Tokyo 105, Japan

HALLIBURTON COMPANY

500 North Akard Street, Ste. 3600, Dallas, TX, 75201-3391

Tel: (214) 978-2600   Fax: (214) 978-2685   www.halliburton.com

Engaged in diversified energy services, engineering and construction.

Halliburton Ltd., 2/F, Tokyo Real Iwamotocho Bldg., 12-7 Iwamotocho 2-chome, Chiyoda-ku, Tokyo 101, Japan

Tel: 81-3-5821-2245   Fax: 81-3-5821-2248

HALLMARK CARDS INC.

2501 McGee Street, Kansas City, MO, 64108

Tel: (816) 274-5100   Fax: (816) 274-5061   www.hallmark.com

Mfr. greeting cards and related products.

Nihon Hallmark K.K., 2-6-16 Komazawa, Setagaya-ku, Tokyo, Japan

Tel: 81-3-348-77910

HAMILTON SUNSTRAND

One Hamilton Rd., Windsor Locks, CT, 06096-1010

Tel: (860) 654-6000   Fax: (860) 654-3469   www.hamiltonsunstrandcorp.com

Design/mfr. aerospace systems for commercial, regional, corporate and military aircraft.

Hamilton Sunstrand Corp., Reinazaka Annex, 3F, 11-3 Akasaka 1-chome, Minato-ku, Tokyo 107, Japan

HANDY & HARMAN

555 Theodore Fremd Ave., Rye, NY, 10580

Tel: (914) 921-5200   Fax: (914) 925-4496   www.handyha

Precious and specialty metals for industry, refining, scrap metal; diversified industrial mfr.

Mizuno Handy Harman Ltd., 11-12 Kitaueno 2-chome, Taitoh-ku, Tokyo, Japan

HARCOURT GENERAL, INC.

27 Boylston St., Chestnut Hill, MA, 02467

Tel: (617) 232-8200   Fax: (617) 739-1395   www.harcourt.com

Publisher of educational materials.

Harcourt General Japan, Inc., Ichibancho Central Building, 22-1 Ichibancho, Chiyoda-ku, Tokyo 102, Japan

Tel: 81-3-3234-3911   Fax: 81-3-3265-7186

HARLEY-DAVIDSON INTERNATIONAL

3700 West Juneau Ave., Milwaukee, WI, 53201

Tel: (414) 342-4680   Fax: (414) 343-4621   www.harleydavidson.com

Mfr. motorcycles, recreational and commercial vehicles, parts and accessories.

Harley-Davidson Japan KK, PO Box 39, 718 Shin Nihon Kaikan Bldg., 7-18 Mita 3-chome, Minato-ku, Tokyo, Japan

HARMAN INTERNATIONAL INDUSTRIES, INC.

1101 Pennsylvania Ave. NW, Ste. 1010, Washington, DC, 20004

Tel: (202) 393-1101   Fax: (202) 393-3064   www.harman.com

Mfr. audio and video equipment, loudspeakers and sound reinforcement equipment.

Harman Intl. Japan Co. Ltd., Hinoki Bldg., 3/F, 1-5 Azabudai 3-chome, Minato-ku, Tokyo 106, Japan

THE HARTFORD FINANCIAL SERVICES GROUP, INC.

200 Hopmeadow St., Simsbury, CT, 06089

Tel: (860) 843-8370   Fax: (860) 843-8400   www.thehartford.com

Provides property, casualty and life insurance services.

Hartford Life Insurance K.K., Kamiyacho Mori Building, 4-3-20, Toranomon, Minato-Ku, Tokyo 105-0001, Japan
Tel: 813-5777-8000

HARTFORD LIFE INTERNATIONAL, LTD.

200 Hopmeadow Street, Simsbury, CT, 06089

Tel: (860) 843-8982   Fax: (860) 843-8981   www.the hartford.com

Offers life and health insurance products, pension programs, and related services.

Hartford Re K.K., Kamiyacho Mori Building 3/F, 4-3-20, Toranomon, Minato-Ku, Tokyo 105-0001, Japan
Tel: 81-3-5777-8000   Fax: 81-3-5777-8036   Contact: Timothy P. Schiltz

HARTMARX CORPORATION

101 North Wacker Drive, Chicago, IL, 60606

Tel: (312) 372-6300   Fax: (312) 444-2710   www.hartmarx.com

Mfr. licensing men's and women's apparel.

Hartmarx Japan, 4-2-1 Kyutaromachi, Chuo-ku, Osaka, Japan

HARVARD BIOSCIENCE, INC.

84 October Hill Road, Holliston, MA, 01746-1371

Tel: (508) 893-8999   Fax: (508) 429-5732   www.harvardbioscience.com

Mfr. tools for drug development.

Take-In Inc., Kyosu Bldg., 3-31-11 Amanuma, Suginami, Tokyo 167-0032, Japan
Tel: 81-3-3597-1911   Fax: 81-3-5833-5596

HASBRO INDUSTRIES INC.

1027 Newport Ave., Pawtucket, RI, 02861

Tel: (401) 725-8697   Fax: (401) 727-5099   www.hasbro.com

Mfr. toy products, including games and puzzles, dolls and plush products.

Hasbro Industries, Tokyo, Japan

HAWORTH INC.

1 Haworth Center, Holland, MI, 49423-9576

Tel: (616) 393-3000   Fax: (616) 393-1570   www.haworth.com

Mfr. office furniture.

Haworth Japan, Central Daikanyama 5/F, 14-23 Daikanyamacho, Hibuya-ku, Tokyo, Japan

HEADWAY CORPORATE RESOURCES, INC.

317 Madison Avenue, New York, NY, 10017

Tel: (212) 672-6500   Fax: (212) 672-6699   www.headwaycorp.com

Engaged in operation of temporary staffing centers.

The Whitney Group, Sengokuyama Annex, 5/F, 3-20 Toronoman, 5 Chome, Minato-ku, Tokyo 105, Japan

HEIDRICK & STRUGGLES INTERNATIONAL, INC.

233 South Wacker Drive, Chicago, IL, 60606

Tel: (312) 496-1200   Fax: (312) 496-1290   www.heidrick.com

Executive search firm.

Heidrick & Struggles Intl. Inc., Kasumigaseki Bldg., 31F, 3-2-5 Kasumigaseki, Chiyoda-ku, Tokyo 100, Japan
Tel: 81-3-3500-5310   Fax: 81-3-3500-5350

H.J. HEINZ COMPANY

600 Grant Street, Pittsburgh, PA, 15219

Tel: (412) 456-5700   Fax: (412) 456-6128   www.heinz.com

Processed food products and nutritional services.

Heinz Japan Ltd., Tokyo, Japan

Star-Kist Foods Inc., Tokyo, Japan

HERCULES INC.

Hercules Plaza, 1313 N. Market Street, Wilmington, DE, 19894-0001

Tel: (302) 594-5000   Fax: (302) 594-5400   www.herc.com

Mfr. specialty chemicals, plastics, film and fibers, coatings, resins and food ingredients.

Hercules Japan Ltd., Seiwa Bldg., 9F, 3-4 Minami Aoyama 2-chome, Minato-ku, Tokyo 107, Japan

HERMAN MILLER INC.

855 East Main, Zeeland, MI, 49464

Tel: (616) 654-3000   Fax: (616) 654-5385   www.hermanmiller.com

Mfr. office furnishings.

Herman Miller Japan, Tokyo Design Center, 5F, 25-19 Higashi-Gotanda, Shinagawa-ku, Tokyo 141, Japan

HERSHEY FOODS CORPORATION

100 Crystal A Drive, Hershey, PA, 17033

Tel: (717) 534-6799   Fax: (717) 534-6760   www.hersheys.com

Mfr. chocolate, mints, gum, food and confectionery products.

Fujiya Leaf Japan (JV), Tokyo, Japan

Hershey Japan, Keikyu Nakahara Bldg., 6/F, 30-6 Shinbashi 4-chome, Minato-ku, Tokyo 105, Japan

HEWITT ASSOCIATES LLC

100 Half Day Road, Lincolnshire, IL, 60069

Tel: (847) 295-5000   Fax: (847) 295-7634   www.hewitt.com

Employee benefits consulting firm.

Hewitt Associates, Akasaka Twin Tower Main Tower, 11F, 2-17-22 Akasaka, Minato-ku, Tokyo 107-0052, Japan
Tel: 81-3-5563-1261

HEWLETT-PACKARD COMPANY

3000 Hanover Street, Palo Alto, CA, 94304-1185

Tel: (650) 857-1501   Fax: (650) 857-5518   www.hp.com

Mfr. computing, communications and measurement products and services.

Hewlett-Packard Japan Ltd., 9-1, Takakura-Cho, Hachioji-Shi, Tokyo 192-8510, Japan
Tel: 81-423-52-5663

HEXCEL CORPORATION

281 Tresser Blvd., Stamford, CT, 06901

Tel: (203) 969-0666   Fax: (203) 358-3977   www.hexcel.com

Honeycomb core materials, specialty chemicals, resins and epoxies.

Hexcel, 22-1 Ichiban-cho, Chiyoda-ku, Tokyo 102, Japan

HILLERICH & BRADSBY COMPANY INC

800 West Main St., PO Box 35700, Louisville, KY, 40202

Tel: (502) 585-5226   Fax: (502) 585-1179   www.slugger.com

Golf, baseball and softball equipment.

Hillerich & Bradsby Co. Ltd., Takanawa Annex, 2-20-24 Takanawa, Minato-ku, Tokyo 108, Japan
Tel: 81-3-3280-3911   Fax: 81-3-3280-3918

HILTON HOTELS CORPORATION

9336 Civic Center Drive, Beverly Hills, CA, 90210

Tel: (310) 278-4321   Fax: (310) 205-7880   www.hiltonhotels.com

International hotel chain: Hilton International, Vista Hotels and Hilton National Hotels.

Hilton International Company, 6F Shinjuku Kokusai Bldg., 6-2 Nishi-Shinjuku, 6-chome, Shinjuku-ku, Tokyo 160, Japan

Osaka Hilton, 8-8 Umeda 1-chome, Kita-ku, Osaka 530, Japan

Tokyo Bay Hilton, 1-8 Maihama, Urayasu-City, Chiba 279, Japan

HNC SOFTWARE INC.

5930 Cornerstone Court West, San Diego, CA, 92121

Tel: (858) 546-8877   Fax: (858) 799-8006   www.hnc.com

Mfr. software to manage and detect fraud.

HNC Software KK, Shinjuku Nomura Bldg., 32/F, 1-26-2 Nishi-Shinjuku, Shinjuku-ku, Tokyo 163-05, Japan

Tel: 81-3-5322-2800

HOGAN & HARTSON LLP

555 13th Street NW, Washington, DC, 20004-1109

Tel: (202) 637-5600   Fax: (202) 637-5910   www.hhlaw.com

Engaged in international law.

Hogan & Hartson, Shinjuku Center Bldg., 46th Fl., 25-1 Nishi-Shinjuku 1- chome, Shinjuku-ku, Tokyo 163-0646, Japan

HOLIDAY INN (BASS RESORTS) WORLDWIDE, INC.

3 Ravinia Drive, Ste. 2900, Atlanta, GA, 30346-2149

Tel: (770) 604-2000   Fax: (770) 604-5403   www.holidayinn.com

Hotels, restaurants and casinos.

Holiday Inn (Far East Ltd. Inc.), Kyoto, Japan

Holiday Inn(Far East Ltd. Inc.), Niben Bldg., 5F, 2-8 Muromachii, Nihonbashi, Chuo-ku, Tokyo 103, Japan

HOLLAND & KNIGHT LLP

400 North Ashley Dr., Ste. 2300, Tampa, FL, 33602

Tel: (813) 227-8500   Fax: (813) 229-0134   www.hklaw.com

Engaged in international law.

Holland & Knight, Tokyo Ginko Kyokai Building, 15/F, 1-3-1 Marunouchi, Chiyoda-ku, Tokyo 100-0005, Japan

Tel: 81-3-3216-7206   Fax: 81-3- 3216-7286

HOLLINGSWORTH & VOSE COMPANY

112 Washington Street, East Walpole, MA, 02032

Tel: (508) 668-0295   Fax: (508) 668-3557   www.hollingsworth-vose.com

Mfr. technical and industrial papers and non-woven fabrics.

Hollingsworth & Vose, Japan, You Building, 4/F, 5-7 Nihonbashi-Horidome-Cho 1-Chome Chuo-ku, Tokyo 103, Japan

HONEYWELL INTERNATIONAL INC.

Honeywell Plaza, Minneapolis, MN, 55408

Tel: (612) 951-1000   Fax: (612) 951-8537   www.honeywell.com

Develop/mfr. controls for home and building, industry, space and aviation, burglar and fire alarm systems.

Honeywell Asia Pacific Inc., 1-14-6 Shibaura, Minato-ku, Tokyo 105-0023, Japan

Tel: 81-3-5440-1395   Fax: 81-3-5440-1368

HORWATH INTERNATIONAL ASSOCIATION

420 Lexington Avenue, Suite 526, New York, NY, 10170-0526

Tel: (212) 808-2000   Fax: (212) 808-2020   www.horwath.com

Public accountants and auditors.

Horwath & Showa Co. Ltd. Japan/Showa Audit Corp., Daiko Building, 3-2 Umeda 14-chome, Kita-ku, Osaka 530, Japan

HOUGHTON INTERNATIONAL INC.

PO Box 930, Madison & Van Buren Avenues, Valley Forge, PA, 19482-0930

Tel: (610) 666-4000   Fax: (610) 666-1376   www.houghtonintl.com

Mfr. specialty chemicals, hydraulic fluids and lubricants.

Houghton Japan Co., Ltd., Matsuki Bldg. 1-3-8 Shibakoen, Minato-Ku, Tokyo 105, Japan

Tel: 81-3-3434-4751

Kyodo Yushi Co., Ltd., Dentsu-Kosan-Dai-3 Bldg., 2-16-7 Ginza Chuo-Ku, Tokyo, Japan

Tel: 81-03-543-5813

HOWMEDICA OSTEONICS, INC.

59 Route 17 South, Allendale, NJ, 07401

Tel: (201) 507-7300   Fax: (201) 935-4873   www.howmedica.com

Mfr. of maxillofacial products (orthopedic implants).

Howmedica Japan, Tokyo, Japan

Tel: 81-3-3344-7523

HOWMET CASTINGS

9 Old Kings Hwy. South, Darien, CT, 06820

Tel: (203) 857-3120   Fax: (203) 857-3158   www.howmet.com

Mfr. precision investment castings, alloys, engineering and refurbishment for jet aircraft and industrial gas turbine (IGT) engine components.

Komatsu-Howmet Ltd., 61-1 Acti-Nishi, Terai, Nomi Ishikawa 923-11, Japan

Tel: 81-761-58-6667   Fax: 81-761-58-6668   Contact: Michio Ohta

HQ GLOBAL WORKPLACES INC.

15305 Dallas Parkway, Ste. 1400, Addison, TX, 75001

Tel: (972) 361-8221   Fax: (972) 361-8221   www.hq.com

Provides office outsourcing, officing solutions, including internet access, telecommunications, meeting rooms, furnished offices and team rooms, state-of-the-art videoconferencing, and trained on-site administrative support teams -

HQ Global Workplaces, AIG Bldg., Level 9, 1-1-3 Marunouchi, Chiyoda-Ku, Tokyo 100-0005, Japan

Tel: 81-3-5288-5100

HUCK INTERNATIONAL INC.

3724 East Columbia Street, Tucson, AZ, 85714-3415

Tel: (520) 747-9898   Fax: (520) 750-7420   www.huck.com

Designer and manufacturer of high-performance, proprietary fasteners and fastener installation systems.

Huck International Ltd., Yodogawa-Gobankan, 11/F, 2-1 Toyosaki 3-chome, Kita-ku, Osaka 531, Japan

HUGHES ELECTRONICS CORPORATION

200 N. Sepulveda Blvd., PO Box 956, El Segundo, CA, 90245-0956

Tel: (310) 662-9821   Fax: (310) 647-6213   www.hughes.com

Provides digital television entertainment, satellite services, and satellite-based private business networks.

DirecTV Japan, Inc., 23F, Yebisu Garden Place Tower, 4-20-3 Ebisu, Shibuya-ku, Tokyo, Japan

Tel: 81-3-5424-1900   Fax: 81-3-5424-1901

Hughes Japan, KK, 21F, KDD Otemachi Blvd., 1-8-1 Otemachi, Chiyoda-ku, Tokyo 100-0004, Japan

Tel: 81-3-3243-1093

HUMPHREY PRODUCTS COMPANY

PO Box 2008, Kalamazoo, MI, 49003

Tel: (616) 381-5500   Fax: (616) 381-4113   www.humphrey-products.com

Mfr., sales and services of pneumatic actuators and valves for factory automation, motion control, etc.

Koganei Japan KK, 5F, Tosei Bldg., 3-8-16, Iwamoto-cho, Chiyoda-ku, Tokyo 101-0032, Japan

Tel: 81-03-3863-6521   Contact: Yasuji Tsutsumi, Pres.

HUTCHINSON TECHNOLOGY INC.

40 West Highland Park, Hutchinson, MN, 55350-9784

Tel: (320) 587-1900   Fax: (320) 587-1892   www.htch.com

Mfr. suspension assembly components for rigid disk drives.

Hutchinson Technology Incorporated, Level 32, Nomura Bldg., 1-26-2 Nishi-Shinjuku, Shinjuku-ku, Tokyo 163-05, Japan

Tel: 81-3-5322-1349

HYATT CORPORATION

200 West Madison Street, Chicago, IL, 60606

Tel: (312) 750-1234   Fax: (312) 750-8578   www.hyatt.com

International hotel management.

Grand Hyatt Fukuoka Hotel, 1-2-82 Sumiyoshi, Hakata-ku, Fukuoka 812, Japan

Tel: 81-92-282-1234   Fax: 81-92282-2817

HYPERCOM CORPORATION

2851 West Kathleen Road, Phoenix, AZ, 85053

Tel: (602) 504-5000   Fax: (602) 504-4578   www.hypercom.com

Mfr. point-of-sale systems.

Hypercom Japan, A-105 3-15-2 Asumigaoka, Midori-ku, Chiba 267-0066, Japan

Tel: 81-43-205-6955   Contact: Ryoichi (Roy) Komai

HYPERION SOLUTIONS CORPORATION

1344 Crossman Avenue, Sunnyvale, CA, 94089

Tel: (408) 744-9500   Fax: (408) 744-0400   www.hyperion.com

Mfr. data analysis software tools.

Hyperion KK, 10/F, West Tower Shin-Nikko Bldg., 2-10-1 Toranomon, Minato-ku, Tokyo 105-0001, Japan

Tel: 81-3-5545-9300   Fax: 81-3-5545-9301

i2 TECHNOLOGIES, INC.

11701 Luna Road, Dallas, TX, 75234

Tel: (214) 860-6106   Fax: (214) 860-6060   www.i2.com

Engaged in supply chain management; solutions to help companies collaborate on decision-making processes.

i2 Technologies Japan, Shinagawa Intercity A, 22/F, 2-15-1 Konan, Minato-ku, Tokyo 108-6022, Japan

Tel: 81-3-5783-1212

IBM CORPORATION

1133 Westchester Avenue, White Plains, NY, 10604

Tel: (914) 765-1900   Fax: (914) 765-7382   www.ibm.com

Information products, technology and services.

IBM Japan Ltd., 2-12 Roppongi 3-chome, Minato-ku, Tokyo, Japan

Tel: 81-3-3586-111   Fax: 81-44-200-8600

IBP FOODS COMPANY INC.

PO Box 515, Dakota City, NE, 68731

Tel: (402) 494-2061   Fax: (402) 241-2068   www.ibpinc.com

Produce beef and pork, hides and associated products, animal feeds, pharmaceuticals.

IBP Inc., Akasaka Daiichi Bldg., 10F, 9-17 Akasaka 4-chome, Minato-ku, Tokyo 107, Japan

Tel: 81-33-746-1801   Fax: 81-33-746-1808   Contact: Takamichi Tawara, Mng. Dir.

ICC INDUSTRIES INC.

460 Park Ave., New York, NY, 10022

Tel: (212) 521-1700   Fax: (212) 521-1794   www.iccchem.com

Manufacturing and trading of chemicals, plastics and pharmaceuticals.

Fallek Chemical Japan K.K., 3/F, 11-4 Uchikanda 1 Chome, Chiyoda-Ku, Tokyo 101-0047, Japan

Tel: 81-3-329-12017   Fax: 81-3-323-32978   Contact: Yoshihiro Tadono

ICN PHARMACEUTICALS, INC.

3300 Hyland Ave., Costa Mesa, CA, 92626

Tel: (714) 545-0100   Fax: (714) 641-7268   www.icnpharm.com

Mfr. and distribution of pharmaceuticals.

ICN Pharmaceuticals, Inc., Pineland Bldg. 4/F, 3-11 Nihonbashi Ohdenmacho, Chuo-ku, Tokyo 103-0011, Japan

Tel: 81-3-3808-2102

IDEC PHARMACEUTICALS CORPORATION

3030 Callan Road, San Diego, CA, 92121

Tel: (858) 431-8500   Fax: (858) 431-8750   www.idecpharm.com

Engaged in development of pharmaceuticals for autoimmune diseases.

IDEC Seiyaku KK, 5/F, Kyodo Bldg., Shin-Kyobashi, 4-2-2 Hacchobori Chuo-ku, Tokyo 104, Japan

Tel: 81-3-3552-1721   Fax: 81-3-3552-1820   Contact: Michio Nishida

IDEXX LABORATORIES, INC.

1 IDEXX Dr., Westbrook, ME, 04092-2041

Tel: (207) 856-0300   Fax: (207) 856-0346   www.idexx.com

Mfr. and sales of veterinary products.

IDEXX Laboratories, KK, 3-7 Kitano, 3-chrome MItaka-shi, Tokyo 181, Japan

Tel: 81-4-2271-4951

II-VI INCORPORATED

375 Saxonburg Blvd., Saxonburg, PA, 16056

Tel: (724) 352-4455   Fax: (724) 352-4980   www.ii-vi.com

Mfr. lenses and mirrors.

II-VI Japan, WBG Marive East 17F, 2-6 Nakase, Mihama-Ku, Chiba-Shi, Chiba 261-71, Japan

IKOS SYSTEMS, INC.

79 Great Oaks Blvd., San Jose, CA, 95119

Tel: (408) 284-0400   Fax: (408) 284-0401   www.ikos.com

Mfr. hardware and software.

IKOS KK, KSP R&D Business Park Bldg., D-337, 3-2-1 Sakado, Takatsu-ku, Kawasaki 213, Japan

Tel: 81-44-850-1230   Fax: 81-44-850-1250

ILLINOIS TOOL WORKS (ITW)

3600 West Lake Ave., Glenview, IL, 60025-5811

Tel: (847) 724-7500   Fax: (847) 657-4268   www.itw.com

Mfr. gears, tools, fasteners, sealants, plastic and metal components for industrial, medical, etc.

ITW Dynatec K.K., Daiwashinagawa Bldg., 5/F, 7-15, Konan 3-Chome, Minato-Ku, Tokyo 108-0075, Japan

IMATION CORPORATION

One Imation Place, Oakdale, MN, 55128

Tel: (612) 704-4000   Fax: (612) 704-3444   www.imation.com

Dry laser-imaging film systems.

Imation Japan KK, Setagaya Business Square Hills 1, 3F, 10.2, Yoga, 4.Chome, Setagaya.ku, Tokyo 158 0097, Japan

IMI NORGREN GROUP

5400 South Delaware Street, Littleton, CO, 80120-1663

Tel: (303) 794-2611   Fax: (303) 795-9487   www.usa.norgren.com

Mfr. pneumatic filters, regulators, lubricators, valves, automation systems, dryers, push-in fittings.

IMI Norgren K.K., 14-1 Aobaoka-Kita, Suita City, Osaka 565, Japan

Tel: 81-6-876-8913   Fax: 81-6-876-8929

IMPCO TECHNOLOGIES, INC.

16804 Gridley Place, Cerritos, CA, 90703

Tel: (562) 860-6666   Fax: (562) 809-1240   www.impco.ws

Mfr. fuel control processors.

IMPCO Technologies Japan, 3-9 Morooka 4-Chome, Hakata-Ku, Fukuoka 816-0094, Japan

Tel: 81-9-2592-7270   Fax: 81-9-2592-7280

INCYTE GENOMICS, INC.

3160 Porter Dr., Palo Alto, CA, 94304

Tel: (650) 855-0555   Fax: (650) 855-0572   www.incyte.com

Engaged in development of genetic information for drug development.

Incyte Genomics Asia, Inc., Shinjuku Nomura Building, 1-26-2 Nishi-Shinjuku, Level 32, Shinjuku-ku, Tokyo 163-0532, Japan

Tel: 81-3-5322-2871

INDUCTOTHERM INDUSTRIES

10 Indel Ave., PO Box 157, Rancocas, NJ, 08073-0157

Tel: (609) 267-9000   Fax: (609) 267-5705   www.inductotherm.com

Mfr. induction melting furnaces, induction power supplies, charging and preheating systems, automatic pouring systems and computer control systems.

Inductoheat Japan, No. 1386-1 Kamihirama Nakahara-Ku, Kawasaki City 211 0013, Japan

Inductotherm Japan, 3-10 Minamibefu 1-Chome, Nishi-Ku, Kobe 651-21, Japan

Inductotherm Japan Ltd., 3-10 Minamibefu 1-chome, Nishi-ku, Kobe 651-21, Japan

Tel: 81-78-974-2552   Contact: Tada Yoshinori

INDUS INTERNATIONAL, INC.

3301 Windy Ridge Pkwy., Atlanta, GA, 30339

Tel: (770) 952-8444   Fax: (770) 955-2977   www.indus.com

Mfr. asset management software.

Indus International Japan KK, Kojimachi 3-1-7, 6/F, Chiyoda-ku, Tokyo, Japan

INFONET SERVICES CORPORATION

2160 East Grand Ave., El Segundo, CA, 90245-1022

Tel: (310) 335-2600   Fax: (310) 335-4507   www.infonet.com

Provider of Internet services and electronic messaging services.

Infonet Services Corporation - Japan, KDD Building, 30F, 2-3-2 Nishishinjuku, Shinjuku-ku, Tolyo 163-03, Japan

Tel: 81-3-3347-7663   Fax: 81-3-3342-5530

INFORMATION RESOURCES, INC. (IRI)

150 N. Clinton St., Chicago, IL, 60661

Tel: (312) 726-1221   Fax: (312) 726-0360   www.infores.com

Provides bar code scanner services for retail sales organizations; processes, analyzes and sells data from the huge database created from these services.

Information Resources Japan LTD., Iseki Bldg., 2/F, 2-3-26 Kudan Minami, Chiyoda-ku, Tokyo 102, Japan

Tel: 81-3-5276-5081   Fax: 81-3-5276-5082

INGERSOLL INTERNATIONAL INC.

707 Fulton Ave., Rockford, IL, 61103

Tel: (815) 987-6000   Fax: (815) 987-6725   www.ingersoll.com

Multinational supplier of special machine tools and services for the metalworking industries.

Ingersoll International (Japan) Inc., 48-3 Higashi, Nagane, Nihongi Shinmachi, Anjo City, Aichi 446, Japan

Tel: 81-566-72-1321   Fax: 81-566-72-2603

INGERSOLL-RAND COMPANY

200 Chestnut Ridge Road, Woodcliff Lake, NJ, 07675

Tel: (201) 573-0123   Fax: (201) 573-3172   www.irco.com

Leading innovation and solutions provider for the major global markets of Security and Safety, Climate Control, Industrial Solutions and Infrastructure.

Ingersoll-Rand (Japan) Ltd., Kowa Bldg., 17, 1-2-7 Nishi-Azabu, Minato-ku, Tokyo 106, Japan

INGRAM MICRO INC.

1600 E. St. Andrew Place, Santa Ana, CA, 92799

Tel: (714) 566-1000   Fax: (714) 566-7940   www.ingrammicro.com

Engaged in wholesale distribution of microcomputer products.

Ingram Micro Japan Ltd., 24-1 Nihonbashi-Hakozakicho, Chuo-ku, Tokyo 103-8501, Japan

Tel: 81-3-5642-8487   Fax: 81-3-5641-8311

INKTOMI CORPORATION

4100 East Third Avenue, Foster City, CA, 94404

Tel: (650) 653-2800   Fax: (650) 653-2801   www.iktomi.com

Mfr. software to boost speeds of computer networks.

Inktomi Corporation, Kamiyacho Mori Bldg., 16/F, 4-3-20 Toranomon, Minato-ku, Tokyo 105-0001, Japan

INSTINET

875 Third Ave., New York, NY, 10022

Tel: (212) 310-9500   Fax: (212) 832-5183   www.instinet.com

Online investment brokerage.

Instinet, Tokyo, Japan

INSTRON CORPORATION

100 Royal Street, Canton, MA, 02021-1089

Tel: (781) 575-5000   Fax: (781) 575-5751   www.instron.com

Mfr., markets and services materials testing instruments, systems and accessories.

Instron Japan Co. Ltd., 1-30 Toyotsucho, Shuita-shi, Osaka 584, Japan

Instron Japan Co. Ltd., 1-8-9 Miyamaodaira, Miyamae-ku, Kawaskai-shi, Kanagawa-ken 216, Japan

Instron Japan Co. Ltd., 2-9-30 Sakaa, Naka-ku, Nagoya 460, Japan

INTEGRATED CIRCUIT SYSTEMS, INC. (ICS)

2435 Boulevard of the Generals, Norristown, PA, 19403

Tel: (610) 630-5300   Fax: (610) 630-5399   www.icst.com

Mfr. electronic timing devices.

ICS Japan, 2-10-3-302, Kyara ReHeim, Nishi-Gotanda, Shinagawa-ku, Tokyo 141-0031, Japan

Tel: 81-3-5759-7516   Fax: 81-3-5759-7517

INTEGRATED SILICON SOLUTION, INC.

2231 Lawson Lane, Santa Clara, CA, 95054-3311

Tel: (408) 588-0800   Fax: (408) 588-0805   www.issiusa.com

Mfr. high-speed memory chips and SRAMs.

Integrated Silicon Solution, Inc., Tokyo, Japan

Tel: 81-3-3255-5351   Fax: 81-3-3255-3308

INTEL CORPORATION

2200 Mission College Blvd., Santa Clara, CA, 95052-8119

Tel: (408) 765-8080   Fax: (408) 765-1739   www.intel.com

Mfr. semiconductor, microprocessor and micro-communications components and systems.

Intel (Japan) Kabushki Kaisha, Kokusai Bldg. 5F, 3-1-1 Marunouchi, Chiyoda-ku, Chiyoda-ku, Tokyo 100-0005, Japan

Tel: 81-298-47-8522

INTELLIGROUP, INC.

499 Thornall Street, Edison, NJ, 08837

Tel: (732) 590-1600   Fax: (732) 362-2100   www.intelligroup.com

Provides systems integration, customer software and Internet application development.

Intelligroup Japan Ltd., Sumitomo Irifune Building, 6/F, 2-1-1, Irifune, Chuo-ku, Tokyo 104-0042, Japan

Tel: 81-3-3537-2105   Contact: Sreenivas Unnamatla

INTER-CONTINENTAL HOTELS

3 Ravinia Drive, Suite 2900, Atlanta, GA, 30346-2149

Tel: (770) 604-2000   Fax: (770) 604-5403   www.interconti.com

Worldwide hotel and resort accommodations.

Hotel Inter-Continental Tokyo, 2-1 Nishi-Shinjuku 2-chome, Shinjuku-ku, Tokyo 160-8330, Japan

Tel: 81-3-3344-0111   Fax: 81-3-3345-8269

Inter-Continental Hotels, 9F, 1-16-2 Kaigan, Minato-ku, Tokyo 105-8567, Japan

Tel: 81-3-3578-7272   Fax: 81-3-3578-7273

INTERGRAPH CORPORATION

One Madison Industrial Park, Huntsville, AL, 35894-0001

Tel: (256) 730-2000   Fax: (256) 730-7898   www.intergraph.com

Develop/mfr. interactive computer graphic systems.

Intergraph Japan K.K., Shibuya Tohoseimei Bldg., 26F, 2-15-1 Shibuya, Shibuya-ku, Tokyo 150-0002, Japan

Tel: 81-3-546-77360   Fax: 81-3-546-77061

Intergraph Japan K.K. - Osaka, 12/F, Shin-Osaka 2nd Mori-Bldg., 3-5-36 Miyahara, Yodogawa-ku, Osaka 532-0003, Japan

Tel: 81-6-3947711   Fax: 81-6-3943733

INTERMEC TECHNOLOGIES CORPORATION

6001 36th Avenue West, PO Box 4280, Everett, WA, 98203-9280

Tel: (425) 348-2600   Fax: (425) 355-9551   www.intermec.com

Mfr. and distributor automated data collection systems.

Intermec Corporation, Japan, MKK Building, 5-7-2 Yashio, Shinagawa-ku, Tokyo 140-0003, Japan

Tel: 81-3-5492-7430   Fax: 81-3-3799-5595

INTERNAP NETWORK SERVICES CORPORATION

601 Union Street, Ste. 1000, Seattle, WA, 98101

Tel: (206) 441-8800   Fax: (206) 264-1833   www.internap.com

Mfr. software for data routing.

InterNap Network Services KK, Otemachi Building 8F, 1-6-1 Otemachi, Chiyoda-ku, Tokyo 100-0004, Japan

Tel: 81-3-5222-7577

INTERNATIONAL COMPONENTS CORPORATION

420 N. May Street, Chicago, IL, 60622

Tel: (312) 829-2525   Fax: (312) 829-0213   www.icc-charge.com

Mfr. portable, rechargeable power, control and accessory products.

International Components Corp. (Japan) Ltd., Glory Bldg., 35-13 Nishikamata 6-chome, Ohta-ku, Tokyo 144, Japan

INTERNATIONAL FLAVORS & FRAGRANCES INC.

521 West 57th Street, New York, NY, 10019-2960

Tel: (212) 765-5500   Fax: (212) 708-7132   www.iff.com

Design/mfr. flavors, fragrances and aroma chemicals.

International Flavors & Fragrances KK, Osaka, Japan

International Flavors & Fragrances Ltd., 21-4, Higashi-Ohi, 1-Chome, Shinagawa-ku, Tokyo 140-0011, Japan

Tel: 81-3-5460-1861   Fax: 81-3-5460-0769

International Flavors & Fragrances Ltd., Green Fantasia Bldg., 11-11 Jingumae 1-chome, Shibuya-ku, Tokyo 150, Japan

INTERNATIONAL GAME TECHNOLOGY INC. (IGT)

9295 Prototype Drive, Reno, NV, 89511

Tel: (702) 448-0100   Fax: (702) 448-1488   www.igtonline.com

Mfr. slot machines, video gaming machines and gaming terminals.

Japan K.K., Atago Toyo Bldg., 7F, 1-3-4 Atago, Minato-ku, Tokyo 105, Japan

Tel: 81-3-5403-1760   Fax: 81-3-5403-1765

INTERNATIONAL MANAGEMENT GROUP (IMG)

1360 East Ninth Street, Ste. 100, Cleveland, OH, 44114

Tel: (216) 522-1200   Fax: (216) 522-1145   www.imgworld.com

Manages athletes, sports academies and real estate facilities worldwide.

IMG, Moto-Akasaka Kikutai Building, 4/F, 1-7-18 Moto-Akasaka, Minato-ku, Tokyo 107-0051, Japan

Tel: 81-3-3470-1331   Fax: 81-3-3470-6477

Press Country Club, 4816 Banchi 1, Shimoakima Annaka-shi, Gunma Prefecture 379-01, Japan

Tel: 81-27381-3727   Fax: 81-27392-2277

INTERNATIONAL PAPER COMPANY

400 Atlantic Street, Stamford, CT, 06921

Tel: (203) 541-8000   Fax: (203) 358-6444   www.ipaper.com

Mfr./distributor container board, paper and wood products.

Ilford Anitec Ltd., 4-7 Minamishinagawa 2-chome, Shinagawa-ku, Tokyo 140, Japan

International Paper (Asia) Ltd., 14-11 Ginza 4-chome, Chuo-ku, Tokyo 10, Japan

IPI Corp., 9-6 Nagata-cho 2-chome, Chiyoda-ku, Tokyo, Japan

Rengo Intl. Products Co., 900-5 Kuboki, Soja City, Oklayama, Japan

Veratec Japan Ltd., 14-11 Ginza 4-chome, Chuo-ku, Tokyo 104, Japan

INTERNATIONAL RECTIFIER CORPORATION

233 Kansas Street, El Segundo, CA, 90245

Tel: (310) 322-3331   Fax: (310) 322-3332   www.irf.com

Mfr. power semiconductor components.

International Rectifier Corp., K & H Bldg., 2F, 30-4 Nishi-Ikebukuro 3-chome, Toshima-ku, Tokyo 171-0021, Japan
Tel: 81-33-983-0086   Fax: 81-33-983-0642

INTERNATIONAL SPECIALTY PRODUCTS, INC.

1361 Alps Rd., Wayne, NJ, 07470

Tel: (973) 389-3083   Fax: (973) 628-4117   www.ispcorp.com

Mfr. specialty chemical products.

ISP (Japan) Ltd., Nihonbashi #2 Building, 8F, 41-12 Hakozaki-Cho Nihonbashi, Chuo-ku, Tokyo 103, Japan
Tel: 81-3-3667-0321   Fax: 81-3-3667-4538

ISP (Japan) Ltd., Shin-osaka Coper Bldg., 5F, 4-11-21 Nishinakajima, Yodogawa-ku, Osaka-shi Osaka 532-0011, Japan
Tel: 81-6-6838-5544   Fax: 81-6-838-5752

ISP (Japan) Ltd., Annex, 10F, 16-14 Shinkawa 1-chome, Chou-ku, Tokyo 104-0033, Japan
Tel: 81-3-5566-8661   Fax: 81-3-5566-8682

INTER-TEL INC.

7300 W. Boston Street, Chandler, AZ, 85226

Tel: (480) 961-9000   Fax: (480) 961-1370   www.inter-tel.com

Design and manufacture of business communications systems related call processing software.

Nihon Inter-Tel KK, 18-11 Uchikanda 1-chome, Chioyda-ku, Tokyo, Japan

INTERWORLD CORPORATION

41 E. 11th St., 11th Fl., New York, NY, 10003

Tel: (212) 699-3630   Fax: (212) 699-3645   www.interworld.com

Mfr. commerce software.

InterWorld KK, Level 11 Park West, 6-12 1 Nishi-Shinjuku, Shinjuku 160-0023, Japan

INTERWOVEN, INC.

803 11th Avenue, Sunnyvale, CA, 94089

Tel: (408) 774-2000   Fax: (408) 774-2002   www.interwoven.com

Mfr. web content management software.

Interwoven K.K., 2-2-9 Shinbashi, Minato-ku, 3/F, Tokyo 105-0004, Japan
Tel: 81-3-5251-8551

INTRALOX INC.

Box 50699, New Orleans, LA, 70150-5307

Tel: (504) 733-0463   Fax: (504) 734-0063   www.intralox.com

Mfr. modular conveyor belts and accessories.

Intralox Japan Service Center, 37 Yamano-cho, Funabashi-city, Chiba 273, Japan

INTUIT INC.

2535 Garcia Avenue, Mountain View, CA, 94043

Tel: (650) 944-6000   Fax: (650) 944-3699   www.intuit.com

Mfr. personal finance software.

Intuit KK, Seavans North Bldg., 1-2-1 Shibaura, Minato-ku, Tokyo 105-6791, Japan
Tel: 81-3-5419-3001   Fax: 81-3-5419-3031

Intuit KK, WTC Bldg., 32/F, 1-14-16 Nanko-kita Suminoe-ku, Osaka 559-0034, Japan
Tel: 81-6-6613-7100   Fax: 81-6-6613-7105

INVITROGEN CORPORATION

1600 Faraday Avenue, Carlsbad, CA, 92008

Tel: (760) 603-7200   Fax: (760) 602-6500   www.invitrogen.com

Mfr. products and kits for gene analysis.

Invitrogen Japan KK, Nihonbasi Hama-Cho Park Bldg. 4/F, 2-35-4 Hama-Cho Nihonbashi, Chuo-ku, Tokyo 103-0007, Japan

Tel: 81-3-3663-7974

IOMEGA CORPORATION

4435 Eastgate Mall, 3rd Fl., San Diego, CA, 92121

Tel: (858) 795-7000   Fax: (858) 795-7001   www.iomega.com

Mfr. data storage products.

Iomega Japan KK, Satokura Akebonobashi bld. 4/F, 1-19 Sumiyoshicho Shinjukuku, Tokyo 162-0065, Japan

Tel: 81-3-3341-2900   Fax: 81-3-3341-2920

IONICS INC.

65 Grove Street, Watertown, MA, 02172

Tel: (617) 926-2500   Fax: (617) 926-4304   www.ionics.com

Mfr. desalination equipment.

Yuasa-Ionics Co. Ltd., Tokyo, Japan

IRIDIUM LLC

1600 Wilson Boulevard, Suite 1000, Washington, DC, 20009

Tel: (202) 408-3800   Fax: (202) 408-3801   www.iridium.com

Consortium of companies sharing the construction and implementation of a global satellite communications system.

Nippon Iridium Corporation, Koji-machi Crystal City East Bldg., 8F, 408 Koji-machi, Chiyoda-ku, Tokyo 102-0083, Japan

Tel: 81-3-3221-9577   Fax: 81-3-3221-9576   Contact: Yoshiharu Yasuda, Pres.

ITW DEVCON PLEXUS

30 Endicott Street, Danvers, MA, 01923

Tel: (978) 777-1100   Fax: (978) 774-0516   www.devcon-equip.com

Engaged in technology and products for OEM assembly, and maintenance/repair applications.

ITW Devcon, Tokyo, Japan

Tel: 81-6-6330-7118

ITW RANSBURG FINISHING SYSTEMS

320 Phillips Ave., Toledo, OH, 43612

Tel: (419) 470-2000   Fax: (419) 470-2112   www.itwransburg.com

Engaged in the design, manufacture and marketing of liquid electrostatic paint application equipment.

Ransburg Industrial Finishing KK, 15-5 Fuku-Ura 1 Chome, Kanazawa-Ku, Yokohama 236-0004, Japan

Tel: 81-45-785-6311

J. WALTER THOMPSON COMPANY

466 Lexington Ave., New York, NY, 10017

Tel: (212) 210-7000   Fax: (212) 210-6944   www.jwt.com

International advertising and marketing services.

J. Walter Thompson Japan, Tokyo, Japan

JABIL CIRCUIT, INC.

10560 Ninth St. North, St. Petersburg, FL, 33716

Tel: (727) 557-9749   Fax: (727) 579-8529   www.jabil.com

Mfr. printed circuit boards, electronic components and systems.

Jabil Circuit Japan, 7/F Tamachi Nikko Bldg., 5-29-14 Shiba, Minato-ku, Tokyo 108-0014, Japan

JDA SOFTWARE GROUP, INC.

14400 N. 87th St., Scottsdale, AZ, 85260-3649

Tel: (480) 308-3000   Fax: (480) 308-3001   www.jda.com

Developer of information management software for retail, merchandising, distribution and store management.

JDA Software Japan Ltd., Oxson Building, 6/F, 1-2-13 Shintomi, Chuo-ku, Tokyo 104-0041, Japan
Tel: 81-3-3206-7201 Fax: 81-3-3206-7202

JDA Software Japan Ltd., Shiba Koen Denki Bldg., 7/F, 1-1-12 Shiba Koen, Minato-ku, Tokyo 105-0011, Japan
Tel: 81-3-5402-9750   Fax: 81-3-5402-9759

JEFFERIES GROUP

11100 Santa Monica Boulevard, Los Angeles, CA, 90025

Tel: (310) 445-1199   Fax: (310) 914-1173   www.jefco.com

Real estate, investment banking and research.

Indosuez W.I. Carr Securities, 3-29-1 Kanda-Jimbochi Chi-yoda-ku, Tokyo, Japan

JOHNS MANVILLE CORPORATION

717 17th Street, Denver, CO, 80202

Tel: (303) 978-2000   Fax: (303) 978-2318   www.jm.com

Mfr. fiberglass insulation, roofing products and systems, fiberglass material and reinforcements, filtration mats.

Johns Manville Japan, Neyasu #1 Bldg., 3/F, 1-21 Kanda Nishikicho, Chiyoda-ku, Tokyo 101, Japan

JOHNSON & JOHNSON

One Johnson & Johnson Plaza, New Brunswick, NJ, 08933

Tel: (732) 524-0400   Fax: (732) 214-0334   www.jnj.com

Mfr./distributor/R&D pharmaceutical, health care and cosmetic products.

DePuy Japan, Inc., Tokyo, Japan

Ethicon Endo-Surgery, Tokyo, Japan

Janssen-Kyowa Co. Ltd., Tokyo, Japan

Johnson & Johnson KK, 3-2 Toya 6-chome, Koto-ku, Tokyo 135, Japan

Johnson & Johnson Medical KK, 3-2 Toyo 6-chome, Koto-ku, Tokyo 135, Japan

Ortho-Clinical Diagnostics KK, Tokyo, Japan

Vistakon Japan, Tokyo, Japan

SC JOHNSON

1525 Howe St., Racine, WI, 53403

Tel: (262) 260-2000   Fax: (262) 260-2133   www.scjohnsonwax.com

Home, auto, commercial and personal care products and specialty chemicals.

SC Johnson, PO Box 237, Kanagawa-ken 259-01, Japan

JOHNSON CONTROLS INC.

5757 N. Green Bay Ave., PO Box 591, Milwaukee, WI, 53201-0591

Tel: (414) 228-1200   Fax: (414) 228-2077   www.johnsoncontrols.com

Mfr. facility management and control systems and auto seating.

Yokogawa Johnson Controls Corp, Shin-Hitokuchizaka Bldg.,, 3-9 Kudankita 3-chome, Chiyoda-ku, Tokyo, Japan
Tel: 81-3-3230-7222   Fax: 81-3-3230-7335   Contact: Marshall Grayson, Branch Mgr.

THE JOHNSON CORPORATION

805 Wood Street, Three Rivers, MI, 49093

Tel: (269) 278-1715   Fax: (269) 273-2230   www.joco.com

Mfr. rotary joints and siphon systems.

The Nippon Joint Ltd., 55 Kitaura Ichida, Kumiyama-Cho, Kuse-Gun, Kyoto 613-0022, Japan

JOHNSON OUTDOORS, INC.

555 Main Street, Racine, WI, 53177

Tel: (262) 631-6600   Fax: (262) 631-6601   www.johnsonoutdoors.com

Mfr. diving, fishing, boating and camping sports equipment.

Scubapro Asia Ltd., Marina Plaza 5F, 4-2 Shiraho, Kanazawa-Kv, Yokohama 23G 0007, Japan
Tel: 81-45-775-2288   Fax: 81-45-775-4420

JONES LANG LASALLE

153 East 53rd Street, New York, NY, 10022

Tel: (212) 812-5700 Fax: (212) 421-3544 www.am.joneslanglasalle.com

International marketing consultants, leasing agents and property management advisors.

Jones Lang Wootton, Japan

JONES, DAY, REAVIS & POGUE

North Point, 901 Lakeside Ave., Cleveland, OH, 44114

Tel: (216) 586-3939 Fax: (216) 579-0212 www.jonesday.com

International law firm.

Jones, Day, Reavis & Pogue Gaikokuho Jimu Bengoshi Jimusho, Toranomon 45 Mori Bldg., 3/F, 1-5 Toranomon 5-chome, Minato-ku, Tokyo 105-0001, Japan

Tel: 81-3-3433-3939 Fax: 81-3-5401-2725 Contact: John C. Roebuck, Partner Emp: 4

JUKI UNION SPECIAL CORPORATION

8500 N.W. 17th St., Miami, FL, 33126

Tel: (305) 594-0059 Fax: (305) 594-0720 www.unionspecial.com

Mfr. sewing machines.

Juki Corporation, 8-2-1 Kokuryo-cho,Chofu-shi,, 182-8655, Tokyo 182-8655, Japan

Tel: 81-3-3481-1111

Union Special Japan Ltd., 1-5-17 Mikuni-Honmachi, Yodogawa-ku, Osaka 532, Japan

JUNIPER NETWORKS, INC.

1194 North Mathilda Ave., Sunnyvale, CA, 94089

Tel: (408) 745-2000 Fax: (408) 745-2100 www.juniper.net

Engaged in the design and sales of Internet Protocol routers for access networks.

Juniper Networks Japan KK, Shinjuku Park Tower, 3-7-1 Nishishinjuku, Shinjuki-ku, Tokyo 163-1035, Japan

JUPITER MEDIA METRIX INC.

21 Astor Place, New York, NY, 10003

Tel: (212) 780-6060 Fax: (212) 780-6075 www.jmm.com

Engaged in research services to determine audience measurement.

Jupiter Media Metrix KK, Reinanzaka Annex, 4/F, 1-11-3 Akasaka, Minato-ku, Tokyo 107-0052, Japan

Tel: 81-3-5549-2027

K-2, INC.

4900 South Eastern Ave., Los Angeles, CA, 90040

Tel: (323) 724-2800 Fax: (323) 724-8174 www.k2sports.com

Mfr. sporting goods, recreational and industrial products.

K2 Japan, A-4/F - Nishisando-Yamaki Bldg., 3-28-6 Yoyogi Shibuya-Ku, Tokyo 151-0053, Japan

Tel: 81-3-3320-7822

KANA SOFTWARE, INC.

181 Constitution Drive, Menlo Park, CA, 94025

Tel: (650) 614-8300 Fax: (650) 614-8301 www.kana.com

Mfr. customer relationship management software.

KANA KK, 1-1-1 The Imperial Tower, 15/F, Uchisaiwaicho, Chiyoda-Ky, Tokyo 100-001, Japan

KAYDON CORPORATION

315 E. Eisenhower Pkwy., Ste. 300, Ann Arbor, MI, 48108-3330

Tel: (734) 747-7025 Fax: (734) 747-6565 www.kaydon.com

Design/mfr. custom engineered products: bearings, rings, seals, etc.

Kimura Corporation, Tokyo, Japan

Tel: 81-3-3213-0255

A.T. KEARNEY INC.

5400 Legacy Dr., Plano, TX, 75201

Tel: (972) 604-4600   Fax: (972) 543-7680   www.atkearney.com

Management consultants and executive search.

A. T. Kearney K. K., ARK Mori Bldg., 12-32 Akasaka 1-chome, Minato-ku, Tokyo 107, Japan

Tel: 81-3-5561-9155

KEITHLEY INSTRUMENTS INC.

28775 Aurora Road, Cleveland, OH, 44139

Tel: (440) 248-0400   Fax: (440) 248-6168   www.keithley.com

Mfr. electronic test/measure instruments, PC-based data acquisition hardware/software.

Keithley Instruments/ NF Corporation, 3-20 Tsunashima-Higashi 6-Chome, Kohoku-Ku, Yokohama, Japan

Keithley Instruments/Toyo Corporation, 1-6 Yaesu, 1-chome, Chuo-ku, Tokyo 103-8284, Japan

Tel: 81-3-3279-0771

KELLOGG BROWN & ROOT INC.

PO Box 4557, Houston, TX, 77210-4557

Tel: (713) 676-3011   Fax: (713) 676-8695   www.halliburton.com

Engaged in technology-based engineering and construction.

Kellogg Brown & Root, Kamiyacho Mori Building, 3/F, 3-20 Toranomon 4-Chome, Minato-ku, Tokyo 105-0001, Japan

Kellogg Brown & Root Far East Inc., Kamiyacho Mori Bldg., 3/F, 3-20 Toranomon 4-Chome, Minato-ku, Tokyo 105-0001, Japan

Tel: 81-3-5776-2301   Contact: Peter Hedges, VP

Kellogg Brown & Root KK, Maruyama Bldg., 5F, 3-8 Azabudai 2-chome, Minato-ku, Tokyo 106, Japan

KELLOGG COMPANY

One Kellogg Square, PO Box 3599, Battle Creek, MI, 49016-3599

Tel: (616) 961-2000   Fax: (616) 961-2871   www.kelloggs.com

Mfr. ready-to-eat cereals and convenience foods.

Kellogg KK, Attn: Japanese Office, One Kellogg Square, PO Box 3599, Battle Creek, MI, 49016-3599

THE KENDALL COMPANY TYCO HEALTHCARE

15 Hampshire Street, Mansfield, MA, 02048

Tel: (508) 261-8000   Fax: (508) 261-8542   www.kendallhq.com

Mfr. and markets a broad range of wound care, needles and syringes, electrodes, specialized paper, vascular therapy, urological care, incontinence care, and nursing care products.

Nihon Kendall K.K. (Kendall Japan Ltd.), UK Hongo, 4F, 3-44-2 Hongo, Bunkyo-ku, Tokyo 113, Japan

Tel: 81-3-5684-0451   Fax: 81-3-5684-0450

KENNAMETAL INC.

1600 Technology Way, PO Box 231, Latrobe, PA, 15650

Tel: (724) 539-5000   Fax: (724) 539-4710   www.kennametal.com

Tools, hard carbide and tungsten alloys for metalworking industry.

Kennametal Hertel Japan Ltd., 2-177 Hongo, Meito-kul, Nagoya 465, Japan

Tel: 81-52-776-6581   Fax: 81-52-776-6566

Kennametal Hertel Japan Ltd., Kanehira Bldg., 1-10-7 Itachbori, Nishi-ku, Osaka 550, Japan

Tel: 81-6-536-1314

Kennametal Hertel Japan Ltd., Ma Bldg., 4F, 2-15-12 Kiba, Koto-ku, Tokyo 135, Japan

Tel: 81-3-3820-2888   Fax: 81-3-3820-2800

KEPNER-TREGOE INC.

PO Box 704, Princeton, NJ, 08542-0740

Tel: (609) 921-2806   Fax: (609) 497-0130   www.kepner-tregoe.com

Management consulting; specializing in strategy formulation, problem solving, decision making, project management, and cost reduction.

Kepner-Tregoe (Japan) Inc., Moto-Akasaka Kikutei Bldg., 7-18 Moto-Akasaka 1-chome, Minato-ku, Tokyo 107, Japan

Tel: 81-3-3401-9521 Fax: 81-3-3479-0745

KIDDE-FENWAL, INC.

400 Main Street, Ashland, MA, 01721

Tel: (508) 881-2000   Fax: (508) 881-6729   www.kidde-fenwal.com

Mfr. temperature controls, ignition systems, fire and smoke detection and suppression systems.

Fenwal Controls of Japan Ltd., 3 Mori Bldg., 4-10 Nishi Shinbashi 1-chome, Minato-ku, Tokyo 105, Japan

KIMBERLY-CLARK CORPORATION

351 Phelps Drive, Irving, TX, 75038

Tel: (972) 281-1200   Fax: (972) 281-1435   www.kimberly-clark.com

Mfr./sales/distribution of consumer tissue, household and personal care products.

Kimberly Clark Japan Ltd., Queens Tower A-8F, 20301, Minatorirai, Nishi-ku, Yokohama 220-60, Japan

KINKO'S, INC.

255 W. Stanley Ave., Ventura, CA, 93002-8000

Tel: (805) 652-4000   Fax: (805) 652-4347   www.kinkos.com

Kinko's operates a 24-hour-a-day, global chain of photocopy stores.

Kinko's, SVAX-TS Bldg., 1F, 1-22-12 Toranomon, Minato-ku, Tokyo 105, Japan

Tel: 81-3-3508-2644 Fax: 81-3-3508-2645

Kinko's, 4-6 Chiyogaoka, Chikusa-ku, Nagoya 464, Japan

Tel: 81-52-778-0871 Fax: 81-52-778-0778

Kinko's, 4-1-9 Minamisemba, Dai-Ichi, Toyo Bldg., Chuoh-ku, Osaka 542, Japan

Tel: 81-6-245-1887 Fax: 81-6-258-0291

Kinko's, 2-5-58 Hakata Kaisei Bldg. 1F, Hakata Station Higashi, Hakata-ku, Fukuoka 100, Japan

Tel: 81-92-414-3399 Fax: 81-92-414-3390

KLA-TENCOR CORPORATION

160 Rio Robles, San Jose, CA, 95134

Tel: (408) 875-6000   Fax: (408) 875-3030   www.kia-tencor.ocm

Mfr. software and equipment.

KLA-Tencor, Uemura Nissei Bldg. 10F, 3-3-31 Miyahara, Yodogawa-ku, Osaka 532-0003, Japan

Tel: 81-6-6350-6900 Fax: 81-6-6350-6947

KLA-Tencor Japan, YBP East Tower 7F, 134 Godo-cho, Hodogaya-ku, Yokohama-city, Kanagawa 240-0005, Japan

KNOLL, INC.

1235 Water Street, East Greenville, PA, 18041

Tel: (215) 679-7991   Fax: (215) 679-3904   www.knoll.com

Mfr. and sale of office furnishings.

Knoll International, Inc., 1-20, 4-Chome, Eda Nishi, Aoba-Ku, Yokohama-Shi, Kanagawa-Ken, Yokohama 225-0014, Japan

Tel: 81-45910-2403 Fax: 81-45910-2404

KOCH INDUSTRIES INC.

4111 East 37th Street North, Wichita, KS, 67220-3203

Tel: (316) 828-5500   Fax: (316) 828-5950   www.kochind.com

Oil, financial services, agriculture and Purina Mills animal feed.

Koch International, Div. John Zink, KK, Recruit Shin-Otsuka Building, 22-15 Minami-Otsuka 2 Chrome, Tochima-ku, Tokyo 170, Japan

Tel: 81-3-5978-5580 Fax: 81-3-3947-6551

KOCH-GLITSCH, INC.

4111 E. 37th Street North, Wichita, KS, 67220

Tel: (316) 828-5110   Fax: (316) 828-5263   www.koch-glitsch.com

Engaged in mass transfer, mist elimination, and motionless mixer technology.

Koch-Glitsch Div. of Koch-Asia Pacific, Inc., Kss Gotanda Bldg. 21-8, 7/F, Nishi-Gotanda 1-chome, Shinagawa-Ku, Tokyo 141-8538, Japan

Tel: 81-3-5435-8560   Fax: 81-3-3491-3523   Contact: Akira Yanoma, Pres.

THE KOHLER COMPANY

444 Highland Drive, Kohler, WI, 53044

Tel: (920) 457-4441   Fax: (920) 459-1274   www.kohlerco.com

Plumbing products, ceramic tile and stone, cabinetry, furniture, engines, generators, switch gear and hospitality.

Kohler Engines, North Asia, Azanu Takahashi Bldg., 7F, 4-13-2 Minami-Aabu, Minato-ku, Tokyo 106, Japan

Tel: 81-3-3440-4515   Fax: 81-3-3440-2727

Kohler Japan KK, 4-13-2 Minami Azabu, Minato-ku, Tokyo 106, Japan

Tel: 81-3-3440-4440   Fax: 81-3-3440-2727   Contact: Kakuo Hara, Sales Mgr.

Kohler Power Systems International, Tokyo, Japan

Seidensha Electric Works Ltd., 1-2-23 Haramachida, Machida-Shi, Tokyo 194, Japan

Tel: 81-3-427-242471   Fax: 81-3-427-242478

KORN/FERRY INTERNATIONAL

1800 Century Park East, Los Angeles, CA, 90067

Tel: (310) 843-4100   Fax: (310) 553-6452   www.kornferry.com

Engaged in executive search and management consulting.

Korn/Ferry International Japan, AIG Bldg., 7/F, 1-3 Marunouchi 1-chome, Chiyoda-ku, Tokyo 100, Japan

Tel: 81-3-3211-6851   Fax: 81-3-3216-1300

KPMG CONSULTING INC.

1676 International Dr., McLean, VA, 22102

Tel: (703) 747-3000   Fax: (703) 747-8500   www.kpmg.com

Accounting and audit, tax and management consulting services.

Century Audit Corporation, Aqua Dojima, East Tower, 4-4, Dojimahama 1-chome, Osaka 530, Japan

Tel: 81-6-346-7878   Fax: 81-6-346-7845   Contact: Yasushi Gorokawa, Ptnr.

Century Audit Corporation, The Japan Red Cross Bldg., 1-3, Shiba Daimon 1-chome, Minato-ku, Tokyo 105, Japan

Tel: 81-3-3578-1910   Fax: 81-3-3434-2122   Contact: Osamu Shigeta, Ptnr.

KPMG Century Registar KK, General Bldg. No. 7, 20-1, Shinbashi 6-chome, Minato-ku, Tokyo 105-0004, Japan

KPMG International, The Japan Red Cross Bldg., 1-3 Shiba Daimon 1-chome, Minato-ku, Tokyo 105, Japan

KPMG International, SKF Bldg., 9-1, Shiba Daimon 1-chome, Minato-ku, Tokyo 105, Japan

Tel: 81-3-5400-7300   Fax: 81-3-5400-7373   Contact: Takashi Kuboi, Ptnr.

KPMG International, SKF Bldg., 9-1, Shiba Daimon 1-chome, Minato-ku, Tokyo 105, Japan

Tel: 81-3-5400-7320   Fax: 81-2-5400-7330   Contact: Yoichi Kuze, Ptnr.

KROLL INC.

9023 Columbine Road, Eden Prairie, MN, 55347

Tel: (952) 937-1107   Fax: (952) 937-5815   www.knollworldwide.com

Mfr. of software and engaged in data recovery services.

Kroll Inc., AIG Building 14/F, 1-3, Marunouchi 1-chome, Chiyoda-Ku, Tokyo 100-0005, Japan

Tel: 81-3-3218-4558   Fax: 81-3-3213-7346

KROLL ONTRACK, INC.

9023 Columbine Rd., Eden Prairie, MN, 55347

Tel: (612) 937-1107   Fax: (612) 937-5815   www.krollontrack.com

Computer data evidence services company, rescuing lost or corrupted data, and software sales.

Kroll Ontrack, Inc., 182 Shinkoh, Iruma, Saitama 358-0055, Japan

Tel: 81-42-932-6365   Fax: 81-42-932-6370

K-SWISS INC.

31248 Oak Crest Dr., Westlake Village, CA, 91361

Tel: (818) 706-5100   Fax: (818) 706-5390   www.k-swiss.com

Mfr. casual and athletic shoes, socks and leisure apparel.

K-Swiss KK, Tokyo, Japan

KULICKE & SOFFA INDUSTRIES INC.

2101 Blair Mill Road, Willow Grove, PA, 19090

Tel: (215) 784-6000   Fax: (215) 659-7588   www.kns.com

Semiconductor assembly systems and services.

Kulicke & Soffa (Japan) Ltd., 5 Koike Bldg., 3/F, 1-3-12 Kita-Shinagawa, Shinagawa-ku, Tokyo 140, Japan

Tel: 81-3-5461-1520   Fax: 81-3-5461-1597   Contact: Terry Sawachi, Pres.

KURT SALMON ASSOCIATES (KSA)

1355 Peachtree Street NE, Atlanta, GA, 30309

Tel: (404) 892-0321   Fax: (404) 898-9590   www.kurtsalmon.com

Management consulting: consumer products, retailing.

Kurt Salmon Associates KK, Akasaka Nakagawa Bldg. 5/F, 3-11-3 Akasaka, Minato-ku, Tokyo 107-0052, Japan

Tel: 81-3-3586-6840

KWIK LOK CORPORATION

PO Box 9548, Yakima, WA, 98909

Tel: (509) 248-4770   Fax: (509) 457-6531   www.kwiklok.com

Mfr. bag closing machinery.

Kwik Lok Japan, 4-12 Motogo 2-Chome, Kawaguchi City, Saitama, Japan

Tel: 81-48-224-1666   Fax: 81-48-225-3288

LAM RESEARCH CORPORATION

4650 Cushing Pkwy., Fremont, CA, 94538

Tel: (510) 659-0200   Fax: (510) 572-6454   www.lamrc.com

Mfr. semiconductor processing equipment.

Lam Research Co., Ltd., Yasuda Seimei Fukuyama Bldg., 3/F, Funamachi 7-23, Hiroshima-ken, Fukuyama-shi 720-0043, Japan

Tel: 81-849-28-9870   Fax: 81-849-28-9878

LANDAUER INC.

2 Science Road, Glenwood, IL, 60425-1586

Tel: (708) 755-7000   Fax: (708) 755-7035   www.landauerinc.com

Provider of radiation dosimetry services to hospitals, medical and dental offices, university and national laboratories, nuclear power plants and other industries.

Nagase Landauer Limited, 11-6 Hisamatsu-cho, Nihonbashi Chuo-ku, Tokyo 103-8487, Japan

Tel: 81-3-3666-4300   Fax: 81-3-3662-9518   Contact: T. Iwai, Pres.

LANDOR ASSOCIATES

Klamath House, 1001 Front Street, San Francisco, CA, 94111-1424

Tel: (415) 955-1400   Fax: (415) 365-3190   www.landor.com

International marketing consulting firm, engaged in brand strategy, design, naming, digital branding, print literature design and research services.

Landor Associates, Sogo Hirakawacho Bldg., 6F, 1-4-12 Hirakawacho, Chiyoda-ku, Tokyo 102, Japan

Tel: 81-3-3263-2295   Fax: 81-3-3263-2291   Contact: Kazumoto Kawada, Mng. Dir.

LANDS' END INC.

1 Lands' End Lane, Dodgeville, WI, 53595

Tel: (608) 935-9341   Fax: (608) 935-4260   www.landsend.com

Clothing, home furnishings and mail order catalog company.

Lands' End Japan KK, Sun Hamada Bldg., 4F, 1-19-20 Shinyokohama, Tokyo 222, Japan

Tel: 81-45-476-0830   Fax: 81-45-476-0836   Contact: John Butler, Pres.   Emp: 250

LATHAM & WATKINS

633 West 5th St., Ste. 4000, Los Angeles, CA, 90071-2007

Tel: (213) 485-1234   Fax: (213) 891-8763   www.lw.com

International law firm.

Latham & Watkins, Infini Akasaka, 8-7-15 Akasaka, Minato-ku, Tokyo 107, Japan

Tel: 81-3-3423-3981   Fax: 81-3-3423-3971

LEARNING TREE INTERNATIONAL, INC.

6053 West Century Blvd., Los Angeles, CA, 90045-0028

Tel: (310) 417-9700   Fax: (310) 417-8684   www.learningtree.com

Information technology training services.

Learning Tree International KK (Japan), Tohma Bldg., 6F, 2-1-2 Takadanobaba, Shinjuku-ku, Tokyo 169, Japan

Tel: 81-3-5291-7391   Fax: 81-3-5291-7392   Contact: James Webb   Emp: 2

LECROY CORPORATION

700 Chestnut Ridge Road, Chestnut Ridge, NY, 10977

Tel: (845) 425-2000   Fax: (845) 425-8967   www.lecroy.com

Mfr. signal analyzers and electronic measurement systems.

LeCroy Japan Corporation, Sasazuka Center Bldg., 6/F, 1-6 2 Chome, Sasazuka Shibuya-Ku, Tokyo, Japan

Tel: 81-3--3376-9400

LeCroy Japan Corporation, Nakao Royal Bldg., 4/F, 14-10 2 Chome, Miyahara Yodogawa-Ku, Osaka City Osaka, Japan

Tel: 81-6-6396-0961

LEGATO SYSTEMS, INC.

2350 West El Camino Real, Mountain View, CA, 94040

Tel: (650) 210-7000   Fax: (650) 210-7032   www.legato.com

Mfr. storage management software.

Legato Systems, Level 9, Edobori Centre Bldg., 2-1-1 Edobori, Nishi-ku, Osaka 550-0002, Japan

Legato Systems, 3-30-4 Honcho, Nakano-ku, Tokyo 164-0012, Japan

Tel: 81-353-336-651   Fax: 81-353-336-639

LEHMAN BROTHERS HOLDINGS INC.

*101 Hudson Street, Jersey City, NJ, 07302

Tel: (201) 524-2000   Fax: (201) 524-2000   www.lehman.com

Financial services, securities and merchant banking services.

Lehman Brothers - Asia-Pacific Hdqtrs., Ark Mori Building, 36F, 12-32 Akasaka 1-Chrome, Minato-ku, Tokyo 107, Japan

Tel: 81-3-5571-7000   Fax: 81-3-5571-7900

LEVI STRAUSS & COMPANY

1155 Battery St., San Francisco, CA, 94111-1230

Tel: (415) 544-6000   Fax: (415) 501-3939   www.levistrauss.com

Mfr. and distributor of casual wearing apparel, including jeans and sportswear.

Levi Strauss Japan K.K., 22F, Yebisu Garden Place Tower, 20-3 Yebisu 4-chome, Shibuya-ku, Tokyo 150, Japan

Tel: 81-3-5421-9200   Fax: 81-3-5421-9201

LEXMARK INTERNATIONAL

740 W. New Circle Rd., Lexington, KY, 40550

Tel: (859) 232-2000   Fax: (859) 232-1886   www.lexmark.com

Develop, manufacture, supply of printing solutions and products, including laser, inkjet, and dot matrix printers.

Lexmark International, Co, Ltd., Riverside Yomiuri Bldg., 36-2 Nihonbashi Hakozaki-cho Chuo-ku, Tokyo 103-0015, Japan

Tel: 81-3-5649-0222   Fax: 81-3-5649-0230

LIBERTY MUTUAL GROUP

175 Berkeley Street, Boston, MA, 02117

Tel: (617) 357-9500   Fax: (617) 350-7648   www.libertymutual. com

Provides workers' compensation insurance and operates physical rehabilitation centers and provides risk prevention management.

Liberty International Japan, Kamiyacho Mori Bldg., 5-F, 4-3-20 Toranomon, Minato-ku, Tokyo 105, Japan
Tel: 81-3-3431-5575

ELI LILLY & COMPANY

Lilly Corporate Center, Indianapolis, IN, 46285

Tel: (317) 276-2000   Fax: (317) 277-6579   www.lilly.com

Mfr. pharmaceuticals and animal health products.

Eli Lilly Japan KK, Shin Aoyama Bldg. West, 21F, 1-1 Minaniaoyama 1-chome, Minato-ku, Tokyo 107, Japan
Tel: 81-3-3470-8230   Fax: 81-3-3470-8259

Eli Lilly Japan KK, Sannomiya Plaza Bldg., 7-1-5 Isogami-dori, Chuo-ku, Kobe 651, Japan
Tel: 81-78-242-9000   Fax: 81-78-242-9502

LINCOLN ELECTRIC HOLDINGS

22801 St. Clair Ave., Cleveland, OH, 44117-1199

Tel: (216) 481-8100   Fax: (216) 486-8385   www.lincolnelectric.com

Mfr. arc welding and welding related products, oxy-fuel and thermal cutting equipment and integral AC motors.

Nippon Lincoln Electric K.K., 6/F, Kasuga Bldg., 4-24-5 Hongo, Bunkyo-ku, Tokyo 113, Japan
Tel: 81-3-3813-6410   Fax: 81-3-3818-3208   Contact: Masaaki Suko, Mng. Dir.

Nippon Lincoln Electric KK, 1-45 Aza-Nakamaru, Ohaza-Yamadaoka, Naraha-Machi Futaba-Gun, Fukushima-Ken 979-05, Japan

LINEAR TECHNOLOGY CORPORATION

1630 McCarthy Blvd., Milpitas, CA, 95035

Tel: (408) 432-1900   Fax: (408) 434-6441   www.linear-tech.com

Mfr. linear integrated circuit chips.

Linear Technology KK, 5/F, NAO Building, 1-14 Shin-Ogawa-Machi, Shinjuku-ku, Tokyo 162-0814, Japan
Tel: 81-3-3267-7891   Fax: 81-3-3267-8510

LIONBRIDGE TECHNOLOGIES, INC.

950 Winter St., Waltham, MA, 02451

Tel: (781) 434-6000   Fax: (781) 434-6034   www.lionbridge.com

Provides solutions for worldwide deployment of technology and content.

Lionbridge Japan KK, FT Bldg. 4F, 3-20-6 Minami-Otsuka, Toshima-ku, Tokyo 170-0005, Japan

LITTELFUSE, INC.

800 East Northwest Hwy, Des Plains, IL, 60016

Tel: (847) 824-1188   Fax: (847) 391-0434   www.littelfuse.com

Mfr. fuses and circuit protectors.

Littelfuse KK, Kanekio Daini Bldg. 12/F, 2-6-23 Shin-Yokohama, Kohoku-ku, Yokohama 222-0033, Japan

LOCKHEED MARTIN CORPORATION

6801 Rockledge Drive, Bethesda, MD, 20817

Tel: (301) 897-6000   Fax: (301) 897-6652   www.imco.com

Design/mfr./management systems in fields of space, defense, energy, electronics and technical services.

CalComp, Sumitomo Shoji Nagoya, Marunouchi Bldg., 3-5 1 Marunouchi Naka-ku, Nagoya 460, Japan
Tel: 81-52-853-4011   Fax: 81-52-853-4031

CalComp, Sumitomo Seimei Hakata Building, 3-2-8 Hakata-Ekimae Hakata-ku, Fukuoka 812, Japan
Tel: 81-92-474-5761

CalComp Japan Procurement Office, 3-6-3 Irifune, Chou-ku, Tokyo 104, Japan
Tel: 81-3-3555-8917   Fax: 81-3-3555-8575

Lockheed Fort Worth Intl. Corp., Misawa Air Base, Misawa City, Japan
Tel: 81-3-3117-66-2917 Fax: 81-3117-62-7388   Contact: D. L. Berry, Mgr.

Lockheed Martin Aero & Naval Systems Office, c/o Mitsubishi Heavy Industries Ltd., 101 Akunoura-Machi, Nagasaki 850-91, Japan

Tel: 81-958-28-5753   Fax: 81-958-28-5721   Contact: B. Medina, Office Mgr.

Lockheed Martin Global, Inc., Imperial Tower, 9/F, 1-1-1- Uchisaiwaicho Chiyoda-ku, Tokyo 100-0011, Japan

Tel: 81-3-3412-2210   Fax: 81-3-3419-8557   Contact: Arlo A. Brown VP

Lockheed Martin Intl. Ltd., Akasaka Twin Tower, 15F, 2-17-2 Akasaka, Minato-ku, Tokyo 107, Japan

Tel: 81-33-584-7011   Fax: 81-33-584-7083   Contact: M. Ikehata, Mgr.

Lockheed Martin Intl. Ltd., Haneda Dai-Ichi Sogo Building, 6-6-1 Chome Haneda Kuko, Ota-ku, Tokyo 144, Japan

Tel: 81-33-747-5747   Fax: 81-33-747-1682   Contact: G. R. Racy, Mgr.

Lockheed Martin Intl. Ltd., Kowa Building, 5F, 1-14-14 Akasaka, Minato-ku, Tokyo 107, Japan

Tel: 81-3-3588-5232   Fax: 81-3-3588-5262   Contact: A. A. Brown, VP

NS CalComp Corp., 2-3-1 Shintomi, Chuo Ku, Tokyo 104, Japan

Tel: 81-3-3555-8911   Fax: 81-3-3555-8913

LORD CORPORATION

2000 West Grandview Blvd, Erie, PA, 16514

Tel: (814) 868-0924   Fax: (814) 486-4345   www.lordcorp.com

Mfg. adhesives, coatings, chemicals, film products.

Lord Far East, Inc., 2/F, Yoyogi Center Bldg., 57-1, Yoyogi 1-Chrome Shibuya-ku,, Tokyo 151, Japan

Tel: 81-3-3378-9011   Fax: 81-3-3378-9739

LSI LOGIC CORPORATION

1551 McCarthy Blvd., Milpitas, CA, 95035

Tel: (408) 433-8000   Fax: (408) 954-3220   www.lsilogic.com

Develop and manufacture semiconductors.

LSI Logic KK, Rivage-Shinagawa Building, 14F, 4-1-8 Kounan, Minato-ku, Tokyo 108, Japan

Tel: 81-3-5463-7821   Fax: 81-3-5463-7820

LSI Logic KK, 1-2-27 Shiromi, Chou-ku, Osaka 540, Japan

Tel: 81-6-947-5281   Fax: 81-6-947-5287

LTX CORPORATION

LTX Park, University Ave., Westwood, MA, 02090

Tel: (617) 461-1000   Fax: (617) 326-4883   www.ltx.com

Design/mfr. computer-controlled semiconductor test systems.

LTX Asia International Inc., Kamata K-1 Building, 3/F, 5-8-7 Kamata, Ota-ku, Tokyo 144-0052, Japan

Tel: 81-3-3739-8011   Fax: 81-3-3739-8017

THE LUBRIZOL CORPORATION

29400 Lakeland Blvd., Wickliffe, OH, 44092-2298

Tel: (440) 943-4200   Fax: (440) 943-5337   www.lubrizol.com

Mfr. chemicals additives for lubricants and fuels.

Lubrizol Japan Ltd., Mori Bldg., 5F, 23-7 Toranomon 1-chome, Minato-ku, Tokyo 105, Japan

Tel: 81-3- 5401-4170

LUCENT TECHNOLOGIES, INC.

600 Mountain Ave., Murray Hill, NJ, 07974-0636

Tel: (908) 582-3000   Fax: (908) 582-2576   www.lucent.com

Design/mfr. wide range of public and private networks, communication systems and software, data networking systems, business telephone systems and microelectronics components.

Lucent Technologies Japan Ltd., Mori Bldg., 25, 4-30 Roppongi 1-chome, Minatoku, Tokyo 106, Japan

Tel: 81-3-5561-3000   Fax: 81-3-5561-3113   Contact: Teizo Hotto, PR Mgr.

LYDALL INC.

1 Colonial Road, PO Box 151, Manchester, CT, 06040

Tel: (860) 646-1233   Fax: (860) 646-4917   www.lydall.com

Mfr. converted paper products, paperboard, non-woven specialty media.

Lydall Intl. Inc., Rippongi SK Bldg., 3-15 Rippongi 3-chome, Minato-ku, Tokyo 106, Japan

LYONDELL CHEMICAL COMPANY

1221 McKinney St., Houston, TX, 77010

Tel: (713) 652-7200   Fax: (713) 309-2074   www.lyondell.com

Mfr. polymers and petrochemicals.

Lyondell Chemical Company, Kioicho Building 4F, 3-12 Kioicho, Chiyoda-ku, Tokyo 102-0094, Japan

Nihon Oxirane Company Limited, No. 2 Yanaglya Bldg., 1-12-8 Nihonbashi, Chou-ku Tokyo 103, Japan

Tel: 81-3-3272-0401

M/A-COM INC.

1011 Pawtucket Boulevard, Lowell, MA, 01853-3295

Tel: (978) 442-5000   Fax: (978) 442-5354   www.macom.com

Mfr. radio frequency (RF) and microwave integrated circuits and IP Networks to the wireless telecommunications and defense-related industries.

AMP Japan, Ltd. M/A-COM, 5-8 Hisamoto 3 Chome, Takatsu-Ku, Kawasaki 213-8535, Japan

Tel: 81-44-844-8296   Fax: 81-44-844-8298

AMP Japan, Ltd. M/A-COM, 4-11 Minami Tsukaguchi Cho 2-Chome, Amagasaki City Hyogo-Ken 661-0012, Japan

Tel: 81-6-6423-4351   Fax: 81-6-6423-2526

MacDERMID INC.

245 Freight Street, Waterbury, CT, 06702-0671

Tel: (203) 575-5700   Fax: (203) 575-7900   www.macdermid.com

Chemicals processing for metal industrial, plastics, electronics cleaners, strippers.

Nippon MacDermid Co. Ltd., 35-5 Sakuradai, Midori-ku, Yokohama-Shi, Kanagawa-Kan 227, Japan

Tel: 81-45-984-2262   Fax: 81-45-984-1365

MACROMEDIA, INC.

600 Townsend Street, San Francisco, CA, 94103-4945

Tel: (415) 252-2000   Fax: (415) 626-9603   www.macromedia.com

Engaged in web publishing.

Macromedia Japan, Akasaka Twin Tower, 13/F, 2-17-22 Akasaka, Minato ku, Tokyo 107-0052, Japan

MACROVISION CORPORATION

1341 Orleans Dr., Sunnyvale, CA, 94089

Tel: (408) 743-8600   Fax: (408) 743-8610   www.macrovision.com

Provider of digital rights management technologies for the home video, enterprise software and consumer interactive software markets.

Macrovision Japan K.K., Takaba Bldg. 2F, 6-18-5, Jingumae, Shibuya-ku, Tokyo 150-0001, Japan

Tel: 81-3-5774-6253   Fax: 81-3-5774-6269   Contact: Masao Kumei

MALLINCKRODT PHARMACUTICALS, INC.

675 McDonnell Blvd., Hazelwood, MO, 63042

Tel: (314) 654-2000   Fax: (314) 654-5380   www.mallinckrodt.com

Mfr. products for respiratory care.

Mallinckrodt Japan Co., Ltd, 8-23 Tsunaba-cho, Hakata-ku Fukuoka City, Fukuoka 812-0024, Japan

Tel: 81-92-271-0408   Fax: 81-92-271-0277

MANHATTAN ASSOCIATES, INC.

2300 Windy Ridge Pkwy., Ste. 700, Atlanta, GA, 30339

Tel: (770) 955-7070   Fax: (770) 955-0302   www.manh.com

Mfr. supply chain management software.

Manhattan Associates, Imperial Tower 15/F, 1-1-1- Uchisaiwaicho, Chiyoda-ku, Tokyo 100-0011, Japan

MANPOWER INTERNATIONAL INC.

5301 N. Ironwood Rd., PO Box 2053, Milwaukee, WI, 53201-2053

Tel: (414) 961-1000   Fax: (414) 961-7081   www.manpower.com

Temporary help, contract service, training and testing.

Manpower Japan Co. Ltd., CS Tower, 3/F, 11-30 Akasaka 1-chome, Minato-ku, Tokyo 107, Japan

Tel: 81-3-5570-5139   Fax: 81-3-5570-5148

MAPICS, INC.

1000 Windward Concourse Pkwy., Alpharetta, GA, 30005

Tel: (678) 319-8000   Fax: (678) 319-8000   www.mapics.com

Mfr. software.

MAPICS KK, Toranomon MT Bldg. 2/F, 3-10-3 Toranoman, Minato-ku, Tokyo 105-0001, Japan

MARATHON LE TOURNEAU COMPANY

PO Box 2307, Longview, TX, 75606

Tel: (903) 237-7000   Fax: (903) 236-6533   www.letourneau-inc.com

Mfr. heavy construction and mining machinery equipment.

C. Itoh & Co. Ltd., 5-1 Kita-Aoyama 2-chome, Minato-ku, Tokyo, Japan

MARCONI DATA SYSTEMS INC.

1500 Mittel Blvd., Wood Dale, IL, 60191

Tel: (630) 860-7300   Fax: (630) 616-3657   www.videojet.com

Mfr. computer peripherals and hardware, state-of-the-art industrial ink jet marking and coding products.

Videojet, Div. Marconi Data Systems, 2-2-6 Kito-Bashi, Sumida-ku, Tokyo 130-0022, Japan

Tel: 81-75-256-7288   Fax: 81-75-256-7288   Contact: Takahide Kuwayama

MARK IV INDUSTRIES INC.

501 John James Audubon Pkwy., PO Box 810, Amherst, NY, 14226-0810

Tel: (716) 689-4972   Fax: (716) 689-1529   www.mark-iv.com

Mfr. of engineered systems and components utilizing mechanical and fluid power transmission, fluid transfer, and power systems and components.

Dayco Products, Inc., 502, Sannomiya First Bldg., 3-2-11 Isobe-dori, Chuo-ku, Kobe 651, Japan

Tel: 81-78-251-0170   Fax: 81-78-221-2663

MARKEM CORPORATION

150 Congress Street, Keene, NH, 03431

Tel: (603) 352-1130   Fax: (603) 357-1835   www.markem.com.

Mfr. and sales of industrial marking, print machinery and hot stamping foils.

Markem K.K., 2-19-7 Hatagaya, Shibuya-ku, Tokyo 151, Japan

Tel: 81-3-5350-3051   Fax: 81-3-5350-3148

MARLEY COOLING TOWER COMPANY

7401 West 129th Street, Overland Park, KS, 66213

Tel: (913) 664-7400   Fax: (913) 664-7641   www.marleyct.com

Cooling and heating towers and waste treatment systems.

Marley Japan Kabushiki Kaisha (MJKK), Watanabe Building, 3/F, 2-2 Miyamae-cho Kawasaki-ku, Kawasaki 210-0012, Japan

Tel: 81-44-221-1018   Fax: 81-44-221-2019

MARRIOTT INTERNATIONAL INC.

10400 Fernwood Rd., Bethesda, MD, 20817

Tel: (301) 380-3000   Fax: (301) 380-5181   www.marriott.com

Hotel services.

Hotel New Otani Makuhari, Chiba, Japan

Tel: 81-3-5405-1511

Hotel New Otani Tokyo, Tokyo, Japan

Tel: 81-3-5405-1511

MARSH & McLENNAN COS INC.

1166 Ave. of the Americas, New York, NY, 10036-2774

Tel: (212) 345-5000   Fax: (212) 345-4808   www.marshmac.com

Insurance agents/brokers, pension and investment management consulting services.

Marsh & McLennan Japan Ltd., Captain Bldg., 7F, 3-5-14 Kita-Kyuhoji-machi, Chou-ku, Osaka 541, Japan

Tel: 81-6-243-4002   Fax: 81-6-243-4005   Contact: Phillip A. Grattan

Marsh & McLennan Japan Ltd., Tokyo Opera City, 38F, 3-20-2 Nishi-shinjuku, Shinjuku-ku, Tokyo 163-1438, Japan

Tel: 81-35-334-8200   Fax: 81-35-371-4527   Contact: Phillip A. Grattan

MASTERCARD INTERNATIONAL INC.

200 Purchase Street, Purchase, NY, 10577

Tel: (914) 249-2000   Fax: (914) 249-5475   www.mastercard.com

Provides financial payment systems globally.

MasterCard International Inc., Dai-Tokyo Kasai Shinjuku Bldg., 16F, 25-3 Yoyogi 3-chome, Shibuya-ku, Tokyo 151, Japan

MATRIXONE, INC.

210 Littleton Road, Westford, MA, 01886

Tel: (978) 589-4000   Fax: (978) 589-5700   www.matrixone.com

Mfr. software.

MatrixOne KK, Worldwide Center 3/F, 1-13 Sanbancho, Chiyoda-ku, Tokyo 103-0075, Japan

MAXTOR CORPORATION

500 McCarthy Blvd., Milpitas, CA, 95035

Tel: (408) 894-5000   Fax: (408) 432-4510   www.maxtor.com

Mfr. develops and markets hard disk drives for desktop computer systems.

Maxtor (Japan) Ltd., Shinjuku Monolithk, 21F, PO Box 7013, 3-1 Nishi-Shinjuku 2-chome, Shinjuku-ku, Tokyo 163-09, Japan

Tel: 81-3-3345-6990   Fax: 81-3-3345-6999

MAYFRAN INTERNATIONAL, INC.

PO Box 43038, Cleveland, OH, 44143

Tel: (440) 461-4100   Fax: (440) 461-5565   www.mayfran.com

Mfr. conveying systems, filtration equipment and separators that facilitate material handling and coolant recovery for automobile manufacturers and machine tool builders.

Mayfran Japan KK, Ryokuchi-Eki Building, 4-1 Terauchi 2-chome, Toyonaka Osaka 560, Japan

Mayfran Japan KK, 3-4 Kudankita 3-Chome, Chiyoda-ku, Tokyo 102, Japan

Tsubakimoto Mayfran Inc., 5001 Ohno, Tsuchiyama-cho, Kouga-gun, Shiga 528-02, Japan

Tel: 81-7-486-7-1001   Fax: 81-7-486-7-1097

MBIA INC.

113 King Street, Armonk, NY, 10504

Tel: (914) 273-4545   Fax: (914) 765-3299   www.mbia.com

Provides investment and treasury management services and insurance for municipal bonds.

MBIA-AMBAC International, Shiroyama JT Mori Bldg., 16/F, 4-3-1 Toranomon Minato-ku, Tokyo 105, Japan

Tel: 81-3-5403-4625   Contact: Steve Halpert

McCANN-ERICKSON WORLDGROUP

750 Third Ave., New York, NY, 10017

Tel: (212) 697-6000   Fax: (212) 984-3575   www.mccann.com

International advertising and marketing services.

McCann-Erickson, Inc., Shin Aoyama Building - East Tower, 1-1-1 Minami Aoyama Minato-ku, Tokyo 107-91, Japan

McCORMICK & COMPANY, INC.

18 Loveton Circle, Sparks, MD, 21152-6000

Tel: (410) 771-7301   Fax: (410) 527-8289   www.mccormick.com

Manufactures, markets and distributes spices, seasonings, flavors and other specialty food products.

McCormick-Lion Ltd. (JV), 1-3-7 Honjo, Sumida-ku, Tokyo 130, Japan

Tel: 81-3-3621-6202   Fax: 81-3-3621-6669

Stange (Japan) KK, 5-3 Kayabacho 3-chome, Nihonbashi, Chuo-ku, Tokyo 103, Japan

McDONALD'S CORPORATION

McDonald's Plaza, Oak Brook, IL, 60523

Tel: (630) 623-3000   Fax: (630) 623-7409   www.mcdonalds.com

Fast food chain stores.

McDonald's Corp., Tokyo, Japan

THE McGRAW-HILL COMPANIES

1221 Avenue of the Americas, New York, NY, 10020

Tel: (212) 512-2000   Fax: (212) 512-2703   www.mccgraw-hill.com

Books, magazines, information systems, financial service, publishing and broadcast operations.

McGraw-Hill Book Co., Japan, 20/F, 1-1-7 Uchisaiwaicho Chiyoda-ku, Tokyo 100-0011, Japan

Tel: 81-3-3593-8767

McGraw-Hill Kogakusha Ltd., 77 Bldg., 7/F, 14-11 Ginza 4-chome, Chuo-ku, Tokyo 104, Japan

THE McKENNA GROUP

2350 West El Camino Real, Ste. 200, Mountain View, CA, 94040

Tel: (650) 852-0800   Fax: (650) 494-8660   www.mckenna-group.com

Engaged in strategy consulting services.

The McKenna Group KK, 1-10-1 Yuraku-cho, Yurakucho Bldg., 11/F, Chiyoda-ku, Tokyo 100-0006, Japan

Tel: 81-3-5219-2083

McKINSEY & COMPANY

55 East 52nd Street, New York, NY, 10022

Tel: (212) 446-7000   Fax: (212) 446-8575   www.mckinsey.com

Management and business consulting services.

McKinsey & Company, Roppongi First Bldg., 9F, 9-9 Roppongi 1-chome, Minato-ku, Tokyo 106, Japan

Tel: 81-3-5562-2100   Fax: 81-3-5562-2200

McKinsey & Company, Sakaisujihonmachi Ctr. Bldg., 1-6 Honmachi 2-chome, Chuo-ku, Osaka 541, Japan

Tel: 81-6-267-7400   Fax: 81-6-267-7423

MEADWESTVACO CORPORATION

One High Ridge Park, Stamford, CT, 06905

Tel: (203) 461-7400   Fax: (212) 318-5055   www.meadwestvaco.com

Mfr. paper, packaging, chemicals.

Meadwestvaco Asia KK, Shoyo Kaikan Bldg., 3-3-1 Kasumigaseki, Chiyoda-ku, Tokyo 100, Japan

MECHANICAL DYNAMICS, INC.

2300 Traverwood Drive, Ann Arbor, MI, 48105

Tel: (734) 994-3800   Fax: (734) 994-6418   www.adams.com

Mfr. Adams prototyping software for functional virtual prototyping solutions.

Argo Graphics, Nihonbasi Chuou-Ku, Tokyo 10-0015, Japan

Contact: Massayuki Fukunago

Kozo Deikaku Engineering Inc., 4-5-3 Chuo, Kakano-ku, Tokyo 164-0011, Japan

Mechanical Dynamics Japan, K.K., BABA Bldg., 6/F, 3-8-4 Nishi-Shinjuku, Sinjuku-ku, Tokyo, Japan

Tel: 81-3-5354-7381

Osaka Shipbuiding Co., Ltd., 3-1-202 Fukuzaki Minato-ku, Osaka 552, Japan

MEDIA 100 INC.

450 Donald Lynch Blvd., Marlborough, MA, 01752

Tel: (508) 460-1600   Fax: (508) 481-8627   www.media100.com

Mfr. digital editing software and hardware.

Media 100 KK, Yanaba Bldg., 5/F, 6-7-10 Roppongi, Minato-ku, Tokyo, Japan

MEDICUS GROUP INTERNATIONAL

1675 Broadway, New York, NY, 10019

Tel: (212) 468-3100   Fax: (212) 468-3222   www.medicusgroup.com

Healthcare communications company engaged in professional advertising, sales promotion, global branding and launch planning.

Medicus KK, Shinanomachi Rengakan, 4/F, 35 Shinanomachi, Shinjuku-ku, Tokyo 160-0016, Japan

Tel: 81-3-5361-2750

Medicus KK, Yasui Bldg., 6/F, 6-8 Hiranomachi 1-chome, Chuo-ku, Osaka 541-0046, Japan

Tel: 81-66-208-0020

MEDTRONIC, INC.

7000 Central Ave. N.E., Minneapolis, MN, 55432-5604

Tel: (763) 514-4000   Fax: (763) 514-4879   www.medtronic.com

Mfr., sales and service of electrotherapeutic medical devices, specializing in implantable and invasive therapies.

Medtronic Japan Co. Ltd., Solid Square West Tower 6F, 580 Horikawa-cho, Saiwai-ku, Kanagawa 210-0913, Japan

Tel: 81-44-540-6112   Fax: 81-44-540-6200

MELLON FINANCIAL CORPORATION

One Mellon Bank Center, Pittsburgh, PA, 15258-0001

Tel: (412) 234-5000   Fax: (412) 236-1662   www.mellon.com

Commercial and trade banking and foreign exchange.

Mellon Bank NA, New Yurakucho Bldg., 12-1 Yuraku-cho 1-chome, Chiyoda-ku, Tokyo 100, Japan

Tel: 81-3-3216-5861

MEMC ELECTRONIC MATERIALS, INC.

501 Pearl Drive, St. Peters, MO, 63376

Tel: (636) 474-5500   Fax: (636) 474-5161   www.memc.com

Mfg. and distribution of silicon wafers.

MEMC Japan, Utsunomiya Plant, 11-2 Kiyohara Industrial Plant, Utsunomiya City Tochigi Pref., Japan

Tel: 81-286-67-6333   Fax: 81-286-67-9000

MEMC Japan Ltd., Tokyo Sales Office, 4F Bancho Fifth Building, 5-5 Nibancho Chiyoda-ku, Tokyo 102, Japan

Tel: 81-3-3237-3221   Fax: 81-3-3237-3220

MEMC Japan Ltd. - Osaka Sales Office, 5/F, Higashitenma Building, 1-7-17 Higashi Tenma, Kita-ku Osaka City, Osaka 530, Japan

Tel: 81-6-882-3831   Fax: 81-6-882-3805

MEMOREX CORPORATION

10100 Pioneer Blvd., Ste. 110, Santa Fe Springs, CA, 90670

Tel: (562) 906-2800   Fax: (562) 906-2848   www.memorex.com

Magnetic recording tapes, etc.

Memorex Japan Ltd., Yaesuguchi Kaikan 3, 1-7-20 Yaesu, Chuo-ku, Tokyo, Japan

MENASHA CORPORATION

1645 Bergstrom Road, Neenah, WI, 54957-0367

Tel: (920) 751-1000   Fax: (920) 751-1236   www.menasha.com

Mfr. packaging and paperboard products.

Poly Hi Solidur Japan Ltd., Takanawa-Hikari Bldg. 3F, 3-19-26, Takanawa, Minato-Ku, Tokyo 108-0074, Japan

THE MENTHOLATUM COMPANY, INC.

707 Sterling Drive, Orchard Park, NY, 14127-1587

Tel: (716) 677-2500   Fax: (716) 674-3696   www.mentholatum.com

Mfr. of non-prescription pharmaceuticals, healthcare and cosmeceutical products and medical devices.

Rohto Pharmaceutical Co. Ltd. Intl Div., 1-8-1 Tatsumi-nishi, Sbuno-ku, Osaka 544, Japan

Tel: 81-6-758-9812   Fax: 81-6-758-9820

MERCK & COMPANY, INC.

One Merck Drive, PO Box 100, Whitehouse Station, NJ, 08889-0100

Tel: (908) 423-1000   Fax: (908) 423-2592   www.merck.com

Pharmaceuticals, chemicals and biologicals.

MSD (Japan) Co. Ltd., Kowa Bldg., 7F, 9-20 Akasaka 1-chome, Minato-ku, Tokyo 107, Japan

Tel: 81-3-3586-2711   Fax: 81-3-3587-1176

MERCURY INTERACTIVE CORPORATION

1325 Borregas Ave., Sunnyvale, CA, 94089

Tel: (408) 822-5200   Fax: (408) 822-5300   www.merc-int.com

Mfr. computer software to decipher and eliminate "bugs" from systems.

Mercury Interactive Japan K.K., 5F, TG 115 Bldg., 1-15-7 Toranomon, Minato-ku, Tokyo 105, Japan

Tel: 81-3-3500-5161   Fax: 81-3-3500-5162

MERRILL LYNCH & COMPANY, INC.

World Financial Center, 250 Vesey Street, New York, NY, 10281-1332

Tel: (212) 236-1000   Fax: (212) 449-2892   www.ml.com

Security brokers and dealers, investment and business services.

Merrill Lynch Investment Managers Co., Ltd., Otemachi Financial Center, 1-5-4 Otemachi, Chiyoda-ku Tokyo 100-0004, Tokyo 100-0004, Japan

Tel: 81-3-3213-7000   Fax: 81-3-3213-7001

Merrill Lynch Japan Incorporated, Midosuji Diamodn Building, 6F, 2-1-3 Nishi-Shinsaibashi, Chuo-ku, Osaka 542, Japan

Tel: 81-6-212-3850   Fax: 81-6-212-3874

Merrill Lynch Japan Incorporated, Nagaya Mitsui Building, 12F, 1-24-30 Meieki Minami, Nakamura-ku, Nagoya 450, Japan

Tel: 81-52-561-7940

Merrill Lynch Japan Securities Co., Ltd., Japan Private Client Group Headquarters, Otemachi First Square, 1-5-1 Otemachi, Chiyoda-ku, Tokyo 100-0004, Japan

Tel: 813-5288-5500

META GROUP, INC.

208 Harbor Drive, PO Box 120061, Stamford, CT, 06912-0061

Tel: (203) 973-6700   Fax: (203) 359-8066   www.metagroup.com

Engaged in research and consulting, focusing on information technology and business transformation strategies.

META Group KK, Wako Higashi-Nakano Building 6/F, 4-6-2 Higashi-Nakano, Nakano-ku, Tokyo 164-0003, Japan

Tel: 81-3-5337-8191

METROLOGIC INSTRUMENTS, INC.

90 Coles Road, Blackwood, NJ, 08012

Tel: (856) 225-8100   Fax: (856) 228-6673   www.metrologic.com

Mfr. and sales of hologram based, bar code scanner systems.

Metrologic Japan Co., Ltd., Matsunoya Building, 6/F, 3-14-8 Higashiueno, Taitou-ku, Tokyo 110-0015, Japan

Tel: 81-03- 3839-8511   Fax: 81-03- 3839-8519

METROMEDIA FIBER NETWORK, INC.

360 Hamilton Avenue, White Plains, NY, 10601

Tel: (914) 421-6700   Fax: (914) 421-6777   www.mfn.com

Mfr. urban fiber-optic networks for telecommunications providers.

MFN Japan K.K., 14-1, Nihonbashi Koami-cho, Chuo-ku, Tokyo 103-0016, Japan

Tel: 81-3-5649-2221   Fax: 81-3-5649-2201

MICROCHIP TECHNOLOGY INCORPORATED

2355 West Chandler Boulevard, Chandler, AZ, 85224

Tel: (602) 786-7200   Fax: (602) 899-9210   www.microchip.com

Mfr. electronic subassemblies and components.

Microchip Technology International, Inc., Benex S-1 6/F, 3-18-20 Shinyokohama, Kanagawa 222-0033, Japan

Tel: 81-45-471-6166   Fax: 81-45-471-6122

MICROMUSE INC.

139 Townsend Street, San Francisco, CA, 94107

Tel: (415) 538-9090   Fax: (415) 538-9091   www.micromuse.com

Mfr. software for information technology.

Micromuse Japan KK, Kamiyacho Mori Building 14/F, 4-3-20, Toronomon, Minato-ku, Tokyo 105-0001, Japan

MICRON TECHNOLOGY, INC.

8000 S. Federal Way, Boise, ID, 83707-0006

Tel: (208) 368-4000   Fax: (208) 368-4435   www.micron.com

Mfr. random-access memory chips and semi-conductor memory components.

KMT (JV), 302-2 Hirano-Cho, Nishiwaki-City, Hyogo, Japan

Tel: 81-795-23-6611

Micron Technology Japan, K.K., 4-30, 3 Chome Shiba Koen, #32 Mori Building, 8F, Minato Ku, Tokyo 105, Japan

Tel: 813-34365666   Fax: 813-34361444

MICROSOFT CORPORATION

One Microsoft Way, Redmond, WA, 98052-6399

Tel: (425) 882-8080   Fax: (425) 936-7329   www.microsoft.com

Computer software, peripherals and services.

Microsoft Japan KK, Sasazuka NA Building, 50-1 Sasazuka 1-chome, Shibuyo-ku, Tokyo 151, Japan

Tel: 81-3-5454-8000   Fax: 81-3-5454-7970

MICROSTRATEGY INCORPORATED

1861 International Drive, McLean, VA, 22102

Tel: (703) 848-8600   Fax: (703) 848-8610   www.microstrategy.com

Mfr. business intelligence software.

MicroStrategy KK, 1-8-8-703, Kojimachi, Chiyoda-ku, Tokyo 102-0083, Japan

MIKASA, INC.

1Mikasa Dr., Secaucus, NJ, 07096

Tel: (201) 867-9210   Fax: (201) 867-0457   www.mikasa.com

Dinnerware, crystal and gifts.

American Commercial Inc., 1-1 Shumoku-cho 3 chome, Higashi-ku, Nagoya, Japan

MILACRON INC.

2090 Florence Ave., Cincinnati, OH, 45206

Tel: (513) 487-5000   Fax: (513) 487-5057   www.milacron.com

Metalworking and plastics technologies.

Cincinnati Milacron Japan, 726-4 Unane, Takatsu-ku Kawasaki-shi, Kangawa 213-0031, Japan

Tel: 81-44-811-5746   Fax: 81-44-822-0048

MILBANK, TWEED, HADLEY & McCLOY LLP

1 Chase Manhattan Plaza, New York, NY, 10005-1413

Tel: (212) 530-5000   Fax: (212) 530-5219   www.milbank.com

International law practice.

Milbank, Tweed, Hadley & McCloy, Nippon Press Ctr. Bldg., 2-1 Uchisaiwai-cho 2-chome, Chiyoda-ku, Tokyo 100, Japan

Tel: 81-3-3504-1050   Fax: 81-3-3595-2790

MILLENNIUM PHARMACEUTICALS, INC.

75 Sidney Street, Cambridge, MA, 02139

Tel: (617) 679-7000   Fax: (617) 374-7788   www.mlnm.com

Mfr. pharmaceuticals.

Millennium Pharmaceuticals KK, 1-6-9 Azaudai Minato-ku, Tokyo 106-0041, Japan

Tel: 81-3-3568-3020

MILLIMAN USA, INC.

1301 Fifth Avenue, Ste. 3800, Seattle, WA, 98101

Tel: (206) 624-7940   Fax: (206) 340-1380   www.milliman.com

Engaged in actuarial consulting services.

Milliman Japan KK, Kioicho Hills, 3-32 Kioico, Chioda-ku, Tokyo 102-0094, Japan

Tel: 81-3-5211-7031

MILLIPORE CORPORATION

80 Ashby Road, PO Box 9125, Bedford, MA, 01730

Tel: (781) 533-6000   Fax: (781) 533-3110   www.millipore.com

Mfr. flow and pressure measurement and control components; precision filters, hi-performance liquid chromatography instruments.

Millipore Niho Ltd., Dai 5 Koike Bldg., 3-12 Kitashinagawa 1-chome, Shinagawa-ku, Tokyo 140, Japan

MILTON ROY COMPANY

201 Ivyland Road, Ivylan, PA, 18974

Tel: (215) 441-0800   Fax: (215) 293-0468   www.miltonroy.com

Mfr. medical and industry equipment and process control instruments.

Milton Roy Co., Takanawa Daiichi Bldg., 9F, 1-41-2 Takanawa, Minato-ku, Tokyo 108, Japan

MINE SAFETY APPLIANCES COMPANY

121 Gamma Drive, PO Box 426, Pittsburgh, PA, 15230

Tel: (412) 967-3000   Fax: (412) 967-3452   www.msa.net

Safety equipment, industry filters.

MSA Japan Ltd., Crest Bldg., 12-8 Roppongi 4-chome, Minatoku, Tokyo 106, Japan

MINOLTA-QMS INC.

One Magnum Pass, PO Box 81250, Mobile, AL, 36618

Tel: (205) 633-4300   Fax: (205) 633-4866   www.qms.com

Mfr. of high-performance color and monochrome document printing solutions for office automation, electronic publishing, graphic design, and advanced imaging applications.

Minolta-QMS Inc., Shiba Dai-ichi Bldg., 5-3-2 Shiba, Minato-ku, Tokyo 108, Japan

MINTEQ INTERNATIONAL INC.

395 Grove City Road, Slippery Rock, PA, 16057

Tel: (724) 794-3000   Fax: (724) 794-4455   www.mineralstech.com

Mfr./market specialty refractory and metallurgical products and application systems.

MINTEQ Japan K.K., Higashi-Nihonbashi Sky Bldg., 6/F, 1-7 chome, Chuo-ku, Tokyo 103-0004, Japan

Tel: 81-3-5821-5070   Fax: 81-3-5821-5066   Contact: I. Ohkuma, Mng. Dir.   Emp: 55

MKS INSTRUMENTS INC.

6 Shattuck Road, Andover, MA, 01810-2449

Tel: (978) 975-2350   Fax: (978) 933-0750   www.astex.com

Provider of process infrastructure products and technologies that increase productivity in gas- and vacuum-based manufacturing.

ENI Japan, 1-21-15 Aoyagi Kunitachi, Tokyo 186-0013, Japan

Tel: 81-425-229-011   Fax: 81-425-222-636

MODEM MEDIA, INC.

230 East Avenue, Norwalk, CT, 06855

Tel: (203) 299-7000   Fax: (230) 299-7060   www.modemmedia.com

Provides on-line marketing and consulting services.

Modem Media Tokyo, FIK Minami Aoyama Bldg, 5-13-3 Minami Aoyama, Minato-Ku, Tokyo 107-0062, Japan

Tel: 81-3-54640-0878   Contact: Susan C. MacDermid, Pres.

MODINE MANUFACTURING COMPANY

1500 DeKoven Ave., Racine, WI, 53403

Tel: (262) 636-1200   Fax: (262) 636-1424   www.modine.com

Mfr. heat-transfer products.

Modine Manufacturing Co., Yokohama, Japan

MODUS MEDIA, INC.

690 Canton Street, Westwood, MA, 02090

Tel: (781) 407-2000   Fax: (781) 407-3800   www.modusmedia.com

Engaged in outsourced manufacturing, fulfillment and distribution services.

Modus Media Japan K.K., Ochiai Takayama Building, 2-28-7 Kami-Ochiai, Shinjuku-ku 161-0034, Japan

Tel: 81-3-3227-5211   Fax: 81-3-3227-5212

MOLECULAR DEVICES CORPORATION

1311 Orleans Drive, Sunnyvale, CA, 94089

Tel: (408) 747-1700   Fax: (408) 747-3601   www.moleculardevices.com

Engaged in the development and manufacture of pharmaceuticals.

Nihon Molecular Devices, Sola Shin-Osaka 21, 19/F, 2-Chome,Nishimiyahara, Yodogawa-Ku Osaka, Japan

MOLEX INC.

2222 Wellington Court, Lisle, IL, 60532

Tel: (630) 969-4550   Fax: (630) 969-1352   www.molex.com

Mfr. electronic, electrical and fiber optic interconnection products and systems, switches, application tooling.

Molex Inc., 4-21-1 Minami-Naruse, Machida, Tokyo 196, Japan

Molex Japan Co., Ltd., 1-5-4 Fukami Higashi, Yamato-City, Kanagawa 242-8585, Japan

Tel: 81-462-61-4500   Fax: 81-462-65-2366

MONSANTO

800 N. Lindbergh Boulevard, St. Louis, MO, 63167

Tel: (314) 694-1000   Fax: (314) 694-7625   www.monsanto.com

Life sciences company focusing on agriculture, nutrition, pharmaceuticals, health and wellness and sustainable development.

Monsanto Japan Ltd., Mita 43 Mori Boulevard, 8th Floor, 3-13-16 Mita, Minato-ku, Tokyo 108-0073, Japan

MOODY'S INVESTOR SERVICES, INC.

99 Church St., New York, NY, 10007

Tel: (212) 553-1658   Fax: (212) 553-0462   www.moodys.com

Publishes credit ratings.

Moody's Japan K.K., Imperial Tower, 13F, 1-1 Uchisaiwai-co 1-home, Chiyoda-ku, Tokyo 100, Japan

Tel: 81-3-3593-0921

MOOG INC.

300 Jamison Road, East Aurora, NY, 14052-0018

Tel: (716) 652-2000   Fax: (716) 687-4471   www.moog.com

Mfr. precision control components and systems.

Moog Japan Ltd., 1532 Shindo, Hiratsuka, Kanagawa-ken 254, Japan

MORGAN ADVANCED MATERIALS AND TECHNOLOGY, INC.

441 Hall Ave., Saint Mary's, PA, 15857

Tel: (814) 781-1573   Fax: (814) 781-9262   www.mamat.com

Mfr. carbon graphite and silicon carbide components.

Morganite Carbon K.K., 6-25, Tagawa 3-chome, Yodogawa-Ku, Osaka 532-0027, Japan

J. P. MORGAN CHASE & CO. INC.

270 Park Ave., New York, NY, 10017

Tel: (212) 270-6000   Fax: (212) 622-9030   www.jpmorganchase.com

Provides integrated financial solutions for institutions and individuals worldwide, including asset management, investment banking and commercial banking.

J. P. Morgan Chase & Co., Akasaka Park Bldg., 11F, 5-2-20 Akasaka, Minato-ku, Tokyo 107, Japan

Tel: 81-3-5570-7600   Fax: 81-3-5570-1777

J. P. Morgan Chase & Co., Nichimen Bldg., 8F, 2-2-2 Nakanoshima, Kita-ku, Osaka 530, Japan

Tel: 81-6-229-8281   Fax: 81-6-229-8286

J. P. Morgan Chase & Co., Akasaka Park Bldg., 12F, 5-2-20 Akasaka, Minato-ku, Tokyo 107, Japan

Tel: 81-3-5570-8200   Fax: 81-3-5570-7960

MORGAN STANLEY DEAN WITTER & CO.

1585 Broadway, New York, NY, 10036

Tel: (212) 761-4000   Fax: (212) 761-0086   www.msdw.com

Securities and commodities brokerage, investment banking, money management, personal trusts.

Morgan Stanley Japan Ltd., 20-3 Ebisu 4-chome, Shibuya-ku, Tokyo 150, Japan

Morgan Stanley Japan Ltd., 2F, Nishikawa Mitsui Bldg., 3-14 Kitahama 1-chome, Chuo-ku, Osaka 541, Japan

MORGAN, LEWIS & BOCKIUS LLP

1701 Market St., Philadelphia, PA, 19103-6993

Tel: (215) 963-5000   Fax: (215) 963-5299   www.morganlewis.com

International law firm.

Morgan, Lewis & Bockius LLP, Shin-Tokyo Building, 9/F, 3-1, Marunouchi 3-Chome, Chiyoda-ku, Tokyo 100-0005, Japan

Tel: 81-3-5219-2500   Fax: 81-3-5219-2501   Contact: William R. Huss, Mng. Ptnr.   Emp: 8

MORRISON & FOERSTER

425 Market Street, San Francisco, CA, 94105

Tel: (415) 268-7000   Fax: (415) 268-7522   www.mofo.com

Engaged in international law.

Morrison & Foerster, AIG Bldg., 7/F, 1-1-3 Marunouchi, Chiyoda-ku, Tokyo 100, Japan

MOTIVE COMMUNICATIONS, INC.

12515 Research Blvd., Bldg., Austin, TX, 78759-2220

Tel: (512) 339-8335   Fax: (512) 339-9040   www.motive.com

Mfr. customer service software.

Motive Communications KK, Brodly Nishishinbashi 9/F, 1-9-1 Nishishinbashi, Minato-ku, Tokyo 105-0003, Japan

MOTOROLA, INC.

1303 East Algonquin Road, Schaumburg, IL, 60196

Tel: (847) 576-5000   Fax: (847) 538-5191   www.motorola.com

Mfr. communications equipment, semiconductors and cellular phones.

Nippon Motorola Ltd., Sumitomo Seimei, Shin-Isaka Bldg., North, 4F, 5-5-15 Nishinakajima, Yodogawa-ku Osaka 532, Japan

Tel: 81-6-305-1801   Fax: 81-6-305-0369

Nippon Motorola Ltd., Shiokawa-machi, Yama-gun, Fukushima Ken 969-35, Japan

Tel: 81-241-27-7511

Nippon Motorola Ltd., 3-20-1 Minami-Azabu, Minato-ku, Tokyo 106, Japan

Tel: 81-3-3440-3311   Fax: 81*3-3440-3505

Tegal Intl., Tamahan Bldg., 1-1 Kugenuma-Higashi, Fujisawa-Shi, Kanagawa Prefecture 251, Japan

MPSI SYSTEMS INC.

4343 South 118 East Avenue, Tulsa, OK, 74146

Tel: (918) 877-6774   Fax: (918) 254-8764   www.mpsisys.com

Computer software, information system services.

MPSI Systems K.K., No. 2 Shukaen Bldg., 6F, 11-3 Komazawa 2 Chome, Setagaya-Ku, Tokyo 154-0012, Japan

Tel: 813-5481-8411   Fax: 813-5481-8412

MTS SYSTEMS CORPORATION

14000 Technology Drive, Eden Prairie, MN, 55344-2290

Tel: (612) 937-4000   Fax: (612) 937-4515   www.mts.com

Develop/mfr. mechanical testing and simulation products and services, industry measure and automation instrumentation.

MTS Japan Ltd., Izumikan Gobancho, 12-11 Gobancho, Chiyoda-ku, Tokyo 102, Japan

MTS, INCORPORATED

2500 Del Monte Street, West Sacramento, CA, 95691

Tel: (916) 373-2500   Fax: (916) 373-2535   www.towerrecords.com

Specialty retailer of music and video stores.

Tower Records Shibuya, 1-22-14 Jinnan, Shibuya-ku Tokyo 150, Japan

Tel: 81-3-3496-3661

MULTIGRAPHICS INC.

431 Lakeview Court, Mt. Prospect, IL, 60056

Tel: (847) 375-1700 Fax: (847) 375-1810 www.multigraphics.com

Mfr./sale/service printing and print prod equipment, mailroom/bindery systems, services and supplies for graphics industry.

Multi Graphics Ltd., Yamato Bldg., 3-1 Kojimachie 5-chome, Chiyoda-ku, Tokyo 102, Japan

MYKROLIS CORPORATION

1 Patriots Park, Bedford, MA, 01730

Tel: (781) 695-7654 Fax: (781) 695-7639 www.mykrolis.com

Mfr. filtering equipment for gases and liquids.

Nihon Mykrolis K.K., Mita-Kokusai Bldg., 4-28, 1-Chome Mita Minato-Ku, Tokyo 108-0073, Japan

Tel: 81-3-5442-9718

NACCO INDUSTRIES INC.

5875 Landerbrook Drive, Mayfield Heights, OH, 44124

Tel: (440) 449-9600 Fax: (440) 449-9607 www.nacco.com

Holding company engaged in lift trucks, house wares and lignite coal mining.

NACCO Materials Handling Group, Obu, Japan

NANOMETRICS INCORPORATED

1550 Buckeye Dr., Milpitas, CA, 95035-7418

Tel: (408) 435-9600 Fax: (408) 232-5910 www.nanometrics.com

Mfr. optical measurement and inspection systems for semiconductor industry.

Nanometrics Japan Ltd., Shin-isumi 34, Narita-shi, Chiba Ken 286, Japan

Tel: 81-476-36-1831 Fax: 81-476-36-1866 Contact: Hiroshi Adachi Emp: 40

THE NASH ENGINEERING COMPANY

9 Trefoil Drive, Trumbull, CT, 06611

Tel: (203) 459-3900 Fax: (203) 459-3511 www.nasheng.com

Mfr. air and gas compressors, vacuum pumps.

Elmo Vacuum Technology, Tokyo, Japan

Tel: 81-33-449-0771

NATCO GROUP, INC.

2950 North Loop West, Houston, TX, 77092-8839

Tel: (713) 683-9292 Fax: (713) 683-6787 www.natcogroup.com

Mfr./sale/service oil and gas products.

NATCO Japan Co. Ltd., Kowa Nibancho Bldg., 11-19, Nibancho, Chiyoda-Ku,, Tokyo 101, Japan

Tel: 81-3-3288-1901 Fax: 81-3-3288-1904

NATIONAL GYPSUM COMPANY

2001 Rexford Road, Charlotte, NC, 28211

Tel: (704) 365-7300 Fax: (704) 365-7276 www.national-gypsum.com

Mfr. building products and services.

The Austin Co., Tokyo, Japan

NATIONAL INSTRUMENTS CORPORATION

11550 N. Mopac Expwy., Austin, TX, 78759-3504

Tel: (512) 338-9119 Fax: (512) 794-5794 www.ni.com

Mfr. hardware and graphical software.

National Instruments KK, Shuwa Shiba Park Bldg. A-4F, Shibakoen 2-4-1, Minato-ku, Tokyo 105, Japan

NATIONAL MACHINERY COMPANY

161 Greenfield St., Tiffin, OH, 44883-2471

Tel: (419) 447-5211 Fax: (419) 447-5299 www.nationalmachinery.com

Mfr. high-speed metal parts forming machines.

National Machinery Asia Co., Ltd., No. 102 South Crest, 13-21 2-Chome, Minami-CHO Tanashi-City, Tokyo 188-0012, Japan

Tel: 81-424-50-0571

National Machinery Company, No. 18, Ocean Plaza, 61-6 1-Chome, Shirayama-CHO Kasugai-City, Aichi-Pref 487-0034, Japan

NATIONAL SEMICONDUCTOR CORPORATION

2900 Semiconductor Dr., PO Box 58090, Santa Clara, CA, 95052-8090

Tel: (408) 721-5000   Fax: (408) 739-9803   www.national.com

Engaged in producing computer-on-a-chip solutions for the information highway.

National Semiconductor, daVinci Kiba Building 2-17-16, Kiba Koto-du, Tokyo 135-0042, Japan

Tel: 81-3-5639-7300   Contact: Tatsvo Ishihara, Pres.   Emp: 200

NATIONAL STARCH AND CHEMICAL COMPANY

10 Finderne Ave., Bridgewater, NJ, 08807-3300

Tel: (908) 685-5000   Fax: (908) 685-5005   www.nationalstarch.com

Mfr. adhesives and sealants, resins and specialty chemicals, electronic materials and adhesives, food products, industry starch.

Nippon National Starch & Chemical Co. Ltd., Ginza Wall Building, 3F, 13-16 Ginza 6-chome, Chuo-ku, Tokyo 104, Japan

Tel: 81-3-3542-7731   Fax: 81-3-3542-7794

NATIONWIDE

One Nationwide Plaza, Columbus, OH, 43215-2220

Tel: (614) 249-7111   Fax: (614) 249-7705   www.nationwide.com

Insurance services.

Gartmore Japan Limited, Tokyo, Japan

NCR (NATIONAL CASH REGISTER)

1700 South Patterson Blvd., Dayton, OH, 45479

Tel: (937) 445-5000   Fax: (937) 445-7042   www.ncr.com

Mfr. automated teller machines and high-performance stationary bar code scanners.

NCR Japan, Ltd., 1-2-2 Akasaka, Minato-ku, Tokyo, Japan

Tel: 81-2-5561-5484   Fax: 81-3-5561-8248   Contact: Kiichiro Tanaka, Pres.

NCUBE CORPORATION

1825 NW 167th Place, Beaverton, OR, 97006

Tel: (503) 629-5088   Fax: (503) 645-1737   www.ncube.com

Mfr. computer servers.

nCUBE Japan, 3/F, Paleana Building, 2-2-15, Shin-Yokohama, Kohoku-ku, Yokohama-Shi, Kanagawa 222-0033, Japan

THE NDP GROUP, INC.

900 West Shore Road, Port Washington, NY, 11050

Tel: (516) 625-0700   Fax: (516) 625-2347   www.npd.com

Engaged in consumer buying research.

NDP Group KK GFK Marketing, Nakonasakaue Sunbright Twin15/F, 2-46-1 Honcho, Nakano-Ku, Tokyo 164-0012, Japan

NETIQ CORPORATION

3553 North First Street, San Jose, CA, 95134

Tel: (408) 856-3000   Fax: (408) 273-0578   www.netiq.com

Mfr. performance management software.

NetIQ Japan KK, 6-3-1 NishiShinjuku Shinjuku-ku, 13/F, Tokyo 160-0023, Japan

Tel: 81-3-5909-5400

NETWORK APPLIANCE, INC.

495 E. Java Drive, Sunnyvale, CA, 94089

Tel: (408) 822-6000   Fax: (408) 822-4501   www.netapp.com

Engaged in data storage market equipment.

NetApp Japan, K.K, Shinbashi 2-chome, MT Building 7F, 5-5, Shinbashi 2-chome, Minato-ku, Tokyo 105-0004, Japan

NETWORK ASSOCIATES, INC.

3965 Freedom Circle, Santa Clara, CA, 95054

Tel: (408) 988-3832   Fax: (408) 970-9727   www.networkassociates.com

Designs and produces network security and network management software and hardware.

Network Associates, Shibuya Mark City West, 20/F, 1-12-1 Dougenzaka, Shibuya-ku, Tokyo 150-0043, Japan

Tel: 81-3-5428-1100   Fax: 81-3-5428-1480

Network Associates, 2-5-31 Kutarocho, Chuo-ku, Osaka, Japan

Tel: 81-6-6253-1031   Fax: 81-6-6253-1260

Network Associates, 5F, Yaesu Hakata Bldg., 2-18-30 Hakata eki Higashi, Hakata-ku, Fukuoka 812-0013, Japan

Tel: 81-92-452-3511   Fax: 81-92-452-3515

NEW BALANCE ATHLETIC SHOE, INC.

Brighton Landing, 20 Guest Street, Boston, MA, 02135-2088

Tel: (617) 783-4000   Fax: (617) 787-9355   www.newbalance.com

Mfr. men's and women's athletic shoes.

New Balance Tokyo, Tokyo, Japan

Tel: 81-03-5785-3366

NEW HORIZONS WORLDWIDE, INC.

1900 S. State College Blvd., Anaheim, CA, 92806-6135

Tel: (714) 940-8000   Fax: www.newhorizons.com

Provides customer-focused computer training choices, through computer training centers.

New Horizons Worldwide, Sun Ferista Meguro 8F, 2-27-1 Kamiosaki, Shinagawa-ku, Tokyo 141-0021, Japan

Tel: 81-3-5496-3755   Fax: 81-3-5496-3766

THE NEW YORK TIMES COMPANY

229 West 43rd Street, New York, NY, 10036-3959

Tel: (212) 556-1234   Fax: (212) 556-7389   www.nytimes.com

Diversified media company including newspapers, magazines, television and radio stations, and electronic information and publishing.

International Herald Tribune (IHT), 4 F Mainichi Newspapers, 1-1-1 Hitotsubashi Chiyoda-ku, Tokyo 100, Japan

Tel: 81-3-3201-0210

NEWELL RUBBERMAID

29 East Stephenson Street, Freeport, IL, 61032-0943

Tel: (815) 235-4171   Fax: (815) 489-8212   www.newellco.com

Mfr. hardware, housewares, and office products.

Newell Office Products of Japan Inc., Tenkoh Bldg., 4/F, 220 Sakai, Atsugi City, Kanagawa, Japan

NEWPORT CORPORATION

1791 Deere Ave., PO Box 19607, Irvine, CA, 92606

Tel: (949) 863-3144   Fax: (949) 253-1800   www.newport.com

Engaged in the design, manufacture and marketing of high-precision components, instruments and integrated systems to the fiber optic communications, semiconductor equipment and aerospace and research markets.

KK Newport/Hakato, 1-13 Shinjuku 1-chome, Shinjuku-ku, Tokyo 160, Japan

Tel: 81-3-5379-0261   Fax: 81-3-3225-9012

NEXTEL COMMUNICATIONS

2001 Edmund Halley Dr., Reston, VA, 20191

Tel: (703) 433-4000   Fax: (703) 433-4343   www.nextel.com

Engaged in wireless internet access.

Nexnet, 3-20-1, Minami-Azabu, Minato-ku, Tokyo 106-8573, Japan

AC NIELSEN COMPANY

177 Broad Street, Stamford, CT, 06901

Tel: (203) 961-3000   Fax: (203) 961-3190   www.acnielsen.com

Engaged in market and consumer research.

D&B Marketing Information Services SpA, Nielsen Bldg., 1-1-71 Nakameguro, Meguro-ku, Tokyo 153, Japan

NORDSON CORPORATION

28601 Clemens Road, Westlake, OH, 44145-4551

Tel: (440) 892-1580   Fax: (440) 892-9507   www.nordson.com

Mfr. industry application equipment, sealants and packaging machinery.

Nordson K.K., 3-3-55, Minami-Suita, Suita-shi, Osaka 564-0043, Japan

Tel: 81-6-6338-0981   Fax: 81-6-6338-1949

Nordson K.K., 8F, Toshin Bldg., 5-21 Katsushima 1-chome, Shinagawa-ku, Tokyo 140-0012, Japan

Tel: 81-3-5762-2700   Fax: 81-3-5762-2701   Contact: Shigeru Kobayashi

NORTHWEST AIRLINES CORPORATION

2700 Lone Oak Pkwy., Eagen, MN, 55121

Tel: (612) 726-2111   Fax: (612) 727-7795   www.nwa.com

Airline passenger and cargo carrier.

Northwest Airlines, 12-12 Toranomon 5-chome, Minato-ku 105, Tokyo, Japan

Tel: 81-3-35336000

NOVELL WORLDWIDE

1800 S. Novell Place, Provo, UT, 84606

Tel: (801) 861-7000   Fax: (801) 861-5555   www.novell.com

Develop/mfr. networking software and related equipment.

Novell Japan Ltd., Toei Mishuku Bldg., 1-13-1 Mishuku, Setagaya-Ku, Tokyo 154, Japan

NOVELLUS SYSTEMS INC.

4000 North First Street, San Jose, CA, 95134

Tel: (408) 943-9700   Fax: (408) 943-3422   www.novellus.com

Mfr. chemical vapor deposition (CVD), physical vapor deposition (PVD) and copper electrofill systems.

Nippon Novellus Systems KK, 8-5-75 Yoshizuka, 7/F, Hakata-Ku Fukuoka-shi, Fukuoka-ken 812-0041, Japan

Tel: 81-92-629-1294   Fax: 81-92.611-2293

Nippon Novellus Systems KK, KSP Building R&D C-10/F, 3-2-1 Sakado Takatsu-ku Kawasaki-shi, Kanagawaken 213, Japan

Tel: 81-44-850-1777   Fax: 81-44-850-1778   Contact: M. T. Matsumoto, Pres.

Nippon Novellus Systems KK, Maruya Bldg. Annex, 4/F, 1-21 Betsuin-cho, Ibanaki-shi, Osaka 567-0817, Japan

Tel: 81-72-622-5558   Fax: 81-72-622-5715

OAK TECHNOLOGY, INC.

139 Kifer Court, Sunnyvale, CA, 94086

Tel: (408) 737-0888   Fax: (408) 737-3838   www.oaktech.com

Engaged in the design and manufacture of semiconductors.

Oak Technology, YS Shin-Yokohama Bldg. 5/F, 2-15-10 Shin-Yokohama, Kouhoku-ku, Yokohama City, Kanagawa 222-0033, Japan

OCLI, INC. (OPTICAL COATING LABORATORY, INC.)

2789 Northpoint Pkwy., Santa Rosa, CA, 95407-7397

Tel: (707) 545-6440   Fax: (707) 525-7410   www.ocli.com

Mfr. thin film precision coated optical devices.

OCLI Asia K.K., 1-1-16 Naka-machi, Machida Tokyo 194-0021, Japan

Tel: 81-42-739-3561   Fax: 81-42-720-5211

OCLI Asia K.K. Mfr., 3037-1 Liyama, Atsugi, Kanagawa-ken 243-0213, Japan

OFFICE DEPOT, INC.

2200 Old Germantown Road, Delray Beach, FL, 33445

Tel: (561) 278-4800   Fax: (561) 265-4406   www.officedepot.com

Discount office product retailer with warehouse-style superstores.

Office Depot Japan, TOC Bldg., 3F, 7-22-17 Nishigotanda, Shinagawa-ku, Tokyo 141-0031, Japan

Tel: 81-3-5487-1711   Fax: 81-3-5487-1712   Contact: Shigeru Manabe, Gen. Mgr.

Office Depot Japan, Ishizaki Bldg., 1F, 2-7-6 Otemachi, Naka-ku, Hiroshima 30-0051, Japan

Tel: 81-82-240-9111   Fax: 81-82-240-9123

OFFICEMAX, INC.
3605 Warrensville Center Road, Shaker Heights, OH, 44122-5203

Tel: (216) 921-6900   Fax: (216) 491-4040   www.officemax.com

Office furnishings, printing and copying services and super center office stores.

OfficeMax Japan Company, Ltd./JUSCO Company, Tokyo, Japan

THE O'GARA COMPANY
1250 24th Street, NW, Suite 300, Washington, DC, 20037

Tel: (202) 835-1680   Fax: (202) 835-1685   www.ogara.com

Security and consulting services and vehicles.

Kroll Associates (Asia) Ltd., AIG Bldg., 14F, 1-3 Marunouchi 1-chome, Choyoda-ku, Tokyo 100, Japan

Tel: 81-3-3218-4558   Fax: 81-3-3218-7346

OHAUS CORPORATION
PO Bpx 2033,19a Chapin Road, Pine Brook, NJ, 07058

Tel: (973) 377-9000   Fax: (973) 593-0359   www.ohaus.com

Mfr. balances and scales for laboratories, industry and education.

Ohaus Far East Reg. Office, c/o Mettler-Toledo KK, Crystal Tower Bldg. DF, 1-2-27 Shiromi, Chuo-ku Osaka 540, Japan

Tel: 81-66-949-5922

THE OILGEAR COMPANY
2300 S. 51st Street, Milwaukee, WI, 53219

Tel: (414) 327-1700   Fax: (414) 327-0532   www.oilgear.com

Mfr. hydraulic power transmission machinery.

Oilgear Japan Co., 204 Nishikan, Daini Toyoda Bldg., 4-10-27 Meieki, Nakamara-ku, Nagoya 450, Japan

OLIN CORPORATION
501 Merritt Seven, Norwalk, CT, 06856-4500

Tel: (203) 750-3000   Fax: (203) 750-3292   www.olin.com

Mfr. chemicals, metals, sporting ammunition and copper and copper alloy sheets.

Yamaha - Olin Metal Corp., 2360 Shingai, Iwata-shi, Shizuoka-Ken 438, Japan

Tel: 81-5-383-7-5111   Fax: 81-5-383-7-0147

OM GROUP, INC. (OMG)
3500 Terminal Tower, Cleveland, OH, 44113-2203

Tel: (216) 781-0083   Fax: (216) 781-0902   www.omgi.com

Producer and marketer of metal-based specialty chemicals.

D & O, Inc. (JV with Dainippon Ink & Chemicals (DIC), Tokyo, Japan

O'MELVENY & MYERS LLP
400 South Hope Street, Ste. 1500, Los Angeles, CA, 90017-2801

Tel: (213) 430-6000   Fax: (213) 430-6407   www.omelveny.com

Engaged in international law.

O'Melveny & Myers, Akasaka Twin Tower 14/F, 2-17-22 Akasaka Minato-ku, Tplup 107 0052, Japan

Tel: 81-3-5562-2800   Fax: 81-3-5575-3840

ONESOURCE INFORMATION SERVICES, INC.
300 Baker Avenue, Concord, MA, 01742

Tel: (978) 318-4300   Fax: (978) 318-4690   www.onesource.com

Provides business information services on line.

One Source Information Services Japan KK, Bien Quad, 9-1 Sakuragaoka-Cho, Shibuya-ku, Tokyo 150, Japan

Tel: 81-3-3463-7181   Fax: 81-3-3770-1865

OPEN MARKET, INC.

1 Wayside Road, Burlington, MA, 01803

Tel: (781) 359-3000   Fax: (781) 359-8111   www.openmarket.com

Mfr. catalog management software.

Open Market Japan KK, Nishino Kinryo Bldg., 6/F, 4-9-4 Hacchobori, Chuo-ku, Tokyo 104-0032, Japan
Tel: 81-3-3537-6401   Fax: 81-3-3537-6420

OPENWAVE SYSTEMS INC.

1400 Seaport Blvd., Redwood City, CA, 94063

Tel: (650) 480-8000   Fax: (650) 480-8100   www.openwave.com

Mfr. software for wireless telephones.

Openwave Systems, 17/F Shinjuku Square Tower Bldg., 6-22-1, Nishishinjuku, Shinjuku-ku, Tokyo 163 1117, Japan
Tel: 81-3-5909-6100   Fax: 81-3-5909-6101

OPNEXT, INC.

1 Christopher Way, Eatontown, NJ, 07724

Tel: (732) 544-3400   Fax: (732) 544-3540   www.opnext.com

Mfr. optoelectronic components for fiber optic data and voice communications networks.

OpNext Japan, Inc., 216 Totsuka-cho, Totsuka-ku, Yokohama 244-8567, Japan
Tel: 81-045-865-7089   Fax: 81-045-865-7117

OpNext Japan, Inc., Shinjuku L-Tower 4/F, 1-6-1 Nishi-Shinjuku Shinjuku-ku, Tokyo 163-1504, Japan

ORACLE CORPORATION

500 Oracle Parkway, Redwood Shores, CA, 94065

Tel: (650) 506-7000   Fax: (650) 506-7200   www.oracle.com

Develop/manufacture software.

Oracle Japan, Tokyo, Japan

OSCAR MAYER & COMPANY

PO Box 7188, Madison, WI, 53707

Tel: (608) 241-3311   Fax: (608) 242-6102   www.kraftfoods.com

Meat and food products.

Oscar Mayer & Co. Inc., PO Box 55, Kasumigaseki Bldg., Tokyo 100, Japan

OSG (OUTSOURCING SERVICES GROUP)

25 Commerce Drive, Allendale, NJ, 07401

Tel: (201) 785-1333   Fax: (201) 785-1365   www.osghq.com

Contract manufacturers of cosmetics, household, personal care and healthcare products.

Nihon Kolmar Co., Ltd., Div. OSG, 4-4-1, Fushimimachi, Chuo-ku,, Osaka 541-0044, Japan
Tel: 81-6-6227-5261   Fax: 81-6-6227-5264

OSMONICS INC.

5951 Clearwater Drive, Minnetonka, MN, 55343-8995

Tel: (952) 933-2277   Fax: (952) 933-0141   www.osmonics.com

Mfr. equipment, controls and components for the filtration and water-treatment industries.

Osmonics, Tokyo, Japan

OTIS ELEVATOR COMPANY

One Farm Springs Road, Farmington, CT, 06032

Tel: (860) 676-6000   Fax: (860) 676-5111   www.otis.com

Mfr. elevators and escalators.

Nippon Otis Elevator Co., Shinjuku NS Bldg., 17/F, 4-1 Nishishinjuku 2-chome, Shinjuku-ku, Tokyo 163, Japan

OUTBACK STEAKHOUSE, INC.

2202 N. Westshore Blvd. 5th Fl., Tampa, FL, 33607

Tel: (813) 282-1225   Fax: (813) 282-1209   www.outback.com

Chain of casual steak restaurants.

Outback Steakhouse, Inc., Minami Machida, Grandberry Mall F Tower, 6-3 Tsuruma, Machida-shi, Tokyo 194-8509, Japan

Tel: 81-42-788-3662

PACIFIC ARCHITECTS & ENGINEERS INC. (PAE)

888 South Figueroa Street, 17th Fl., Los Angeles, CA, 90017

Tel: (213) 481-2311   Fax: (213) 481-7189   www.paechl.com

Technical engineering services.

K.K. Halifax Associates, Halifax Shiba Building, 6/7th Floors, 3-10 Shiba Koen 1-chome, Minato-ku 11, Toyko 105-0011, Japan

Tel: 81-3-3436-0591   Fax: 81-3-3436-0889   Contact: Richard van Rooij, Mng. Dir.

PAE International, Halifax Shiba Building, 6/7F, 3-10 Shiba Park 1-chome, Minato-ku, Tokyo 105, Japan

Tel: 81-3-3436-0591   Fax: 81-3-3436-0889   Contact: Mark Griffin, V.P. & Gen. Mgr.

PACIFIC BELL TELEPHONE COMPANY

140 New Montgomery Street, San Francisco, CA, 94105

Tel: (415) 542-9000   Fax: (415) 543-7079   www.pacbell.com

Telecommunications and information systems.

Pacific Bell Japan KK, Toranomon Cntr. Bldg., 1-16-17 Toranomon, Minato-ku, Tokyo 105, Japan

PALL CORPORATION

2200 Northern Boulevard, East Hills, NY, 11548-1289

Tel: (516) 484-5400   Fax: (516) 484-5228   www.pall.com

Specialty materials and engineering; filters and related fluid clarification equipment.

Nihon Pall Ltd., GotandaNomura Shoken Buildin, 1-5-1 Nishi Gotanda, Shinagawa-ku, Tokyo 141, Japan

Tel: 81-3-3495-8380 Fax: 81-3-3495-8369

Pall Gelman Sciences, 1-9-12 Kita-Ueno, Taito-ku, Tokyo 110, Japan

Tel: 81-3-3844-5411   Fax: 81-3-3844-5433

PANAMETRICS

221 Crescent Street, Waltham, MA, 02154

Tel: (781) 899-2719   Fax: (781) 899-1552   www.panametrics.com

Engaged in manufacture and distribution of ultrasonic testing equipment and process control instrumentation.

Panametrics Japan Co., Ltd., 5/F Sumitomo Fudosan Bldg., 5-41-10 Koishikawa Bunkyo-ku, Toyko 112, Japan

Tel: 81-3-5802-8701 Fax: 81-3-5802-8706

PANDUIT CORPORATION

17301 Ridgeland Ave., Tinley Park, IL, 60477-0981

Tel: (708) 532-1800   Fax: (708) 532-1811   www.panduit.com

Mfr. of network connectivity and electrical products.

Panduit Corp. (Japan), 31-5 Omori Kita 6Cchome, Ota-ku, Tokyo 143-0016, Japan

Tel: 81-3-3767-7011   Fax: 81-3-3767-7033

PAPER CONVERTING MACHINE COMPANY

PO Box 19005, 2300 S. Ashland Ave., Green Bay, WI, 54307

Tel: (920) 494-5601   Fax: (920) 494-8865   www.pcmc.com

Mfr. converting machinery for the sanitary tissue, flexible packaging and disposables nonwovens industries.

Paper Converting Machine Co. Far East Inc., Taiso Marine Bldg., 10/F, 23, 4-chome Daigan-Dori, Naku-Ku, Yokohama City, Japan

Tel: 81-45-340-5461 Fax: 81-45-671-5488

PARADYNE NETWORKS, INC.

8545 126 Ave. North, Largo, FL, 33773

Tel: (727) 530-2000   Fax: (727) 530-2875   www.paradyne.com

Engaged in data communications and high-speed network access solutions.

Paradyne Japan, Eitai Bldg., 7&8/F, 1-22-11 Shinkawa, Chuo-ku, Tokyo 104, Japan

Tel: 81-3-5437-5388 Fax: 81-3-5437-5389 Contact: Tom Kojima

PARAMETRIC TECHNOLOGY CORPORATION

140 Kendrick St., Needham, MA, 02494

Tel: (781) 370-5000   Fax: (781) 370-6000   www.ptc.com

Supplier of mechanical design automation and product data management software and services.

Nihon Parametric Technology K.K., Hiroden Mitsuikaijo Building, 9-9 Nishi Tohnkaichi-machi, Hiroshima-shi, Hiroshima-ken 730, Japan

Tel: 81-53-451-0671 Fax: 81-53-451-0672

Nihon Parametric Technology K.K., Hamamatsu Act Tower, 111-2 Itaya-cho, Hamamatsu-shi, Schizuoka-ken, Japan

Tel: 81-39-691-331-1333 Fax: 81-39-562-5232

Nihon Parametric Technology K.K., 1-4-4 Hakata-ekimae, Hakta-ku, Fukuoka-shi Fukuoka-pref, Fukuoka 812, Japan

Tel: 81-92-441-2992 Fax: 81-92-441-2388

Nihon Parametric Technology K.K., 4/F, Benes S-3, 3-20-8 Shin Yokohama, Kohonku-ku Yokohama, Kanagawa 222, Japan

Tel: 81-3-3346-8981 Fax: 81-3-3346-8988

Nihon Parametric Technology K.K., Green Tower Building, 14-1 Nishi Shinjuku 6-chome, Shinjuku-ku, Tokyo 163-09, Japan

Tel: 81-2-2792-7301 Fax: 81-2-2792-7302

Nihon Parametric Technology K.K., Shinjuku Monolith Building, 20F, 2-3-1 Nishi Shin Juku, Tokyo 163-09, Japan

Tel: 81-3-3346-8100 Fax: 81-3-3346-8290

Nihon Parametric Technology K.K., Mihagino Center Building, 5-22 Tzutsujigaoka, Miyagino-ku Sendai-shi, Miyagi-ken 983, Japan

Tel: 81-26-333-3951 Fax: 81-26-333-3915

Nihon Parametric Technology K.K., 6/F, Nagogya Hirokoji Building, 1-3-11 Kosakahonmachi, Toyoda-Shi, Aichi 471, Japan

Tel: 81-92-441-2992 Fax: 81-52-223-3705

Nihon Parametric Technology K.K., Crystal Tower, 27F, 1-2-27 Shiromi, Chuo-ku Osaka-shi, Osaka 540, Japan

Tel: 81-6-946-5071 Fax: 81-6-946-5070

Nihon Parametric Technology K.K., Nagoya Hirokoji Bulding, 2-3-1 Sakae, Naka-ku, Nagoya 460, Japan

Tel: 81-52-223-3701 Fax: 81-52-223-3705

Nihon Parametric Technology K.K., Kenshin Tohon Seimei Building,, 5-2 Fukashi 2-chome, Matsumoto-shi, Nagano 390, Japan

Tel: 81-76-262-1561 Fax: 81-76-2962-1562

Nihon Parmaetric Technology K.K., Rifare, 5-2 Honmachi 1-chome, Kanazawa-shi, Ishikawa-ken, Japan

Tel: 81-82-219-8861 Fax: 81-82-291-8860

PAREXEL INTERNATIONAL CORPORATION

195 West Street, Waltham, MA, 02154

Tel: (781) 487-9900   Fax: (781) 487-0525   www.parexel.com

Provides contract medical, biotechnology, and pharmaceutical research and consulting services.

PAREXEL International Ltd., Urban Ace Sannomiya Bldg., 5F, 4-1-22 Onoe Dori, Chou-ku, Kobe 651, Japan

Tel: 81-782-8026 Fax: 81-782-71-8027

PAREXEL MIRAI, Toko Bldg., Room 102, 10-21 Takata, Toshima-ku, Tokyo 171, Japan

Tel: 81-3-5287-7821 Fax: 81-3-5287-7822

PARKER HANNIFIN CORPORATION

6035 Parkland Blvd., Cleveland, OH, 44124-4141

Tel: (216) 896-3000 Fax: (216) 896-4000 www.parker.com

Mfr. motion-control products.

Parker Hannifin Japan Ltd., 626 Totsuka-cho, Totsuka-ku, Yokohama-shi 244, Japan

Tel: 81-45-861-3811 Fax: 81-45-864-5305

PARSONS BRINCKERHOFF INC.

One Penn Plaza, New York, NY, 10119-0061

Tel: (212) 465-5000 Fax: (212) 465-5096 www.pbworld.com

Provides planning, engineering, construction management and operations and maintenance services.

Parsons Brinckerhoff, Minami Aoyama Bldg., 4/F, 1-10-3 Minami Aoyama, Minato-Ku, Tokyo 107-0062, Japan

Tel: 886-2-8919-3684 Fax: 886-2-8919-3684

PARSONS CORPORATION

100 West Walnut Street, Pasadena, CA, 91124

Tel: (626) 440-2000 Fax: (626) 440-4919 www.parsons.com

Engaged in engineering, procurement, and construction management services.

Parsons Engineering Science Inc., c/o Parsons Polytech Inc., Kyobashi Maruki Bldg., 3/F, 17-9 Kyobashi 2-chome, Chuo-ku, Tokyo 104, Japan

PAUL, HASTINGS, JANOFSKY & WALKER LLP

555 South Flower Street, Los Angeles, CA, 90017-2371

Tel: (213) 683-6000 Fax: (213) 627-0705 www.phjw.com

Engaged in international employment law.

Paul, Hastings, Janofsky & Walker, PO Box 577, 12-32 Akasaka 1-chome, Minato-Ku, Tokyo 107-6027, Japan

PAUL, WEISS, RIFKIND, WHARTON & GARRISON

1285 Ave. of the Americas, New York, NY, 10019-6064

Tel: (212) 373-3000 Fax: (212) 373-2268 www.paulweiss.com

Law firm engaged in American and international law practice.

Paul, Weiss, Rifkind, Wharton & Garrison, 2-2 Uchisaiwaicho 2-chome, Chiyoda-ku, Tokyo 100, Japan

Tel: 81-3-3597-8101 Fax: 81-3-3597-8120

J.C. PENNEY COMPANY, INC.

6501 Legacy Drive, Plano, TX, 75024-3698

Tel: (972) 431-1000 Fax: (972) 431-1977 www.jcpenney.com

Markets family apparel, shoes, home furnishings, jewelry, and offers credit cards.

J. C. Penney Purchasing Corp., Shoho Bldg., 7F, 6-2 Bingo-Machi 3-chome, Chuo-ku, Osaka 541, Japan

PENTAIR, INC.

1500 County Road, B2 West, St. Paul, MN, 55113-3105

Tel: (612) 636-7920 Fax: (612) 636-5508 www.pentair.com

Diversified manufacturer operating in electrical and electronic enclosures, professional tools/equipment and water products.

Pentair Enclosures, Nisso No. 13 Bldg. 4F, 5-1 Shin-yokohama 2-chome, Kohoku-ku, Yokohama 222, Japan

PEOPLESOFT INC.

4460 Hacienda Drive, Pleasanton, CA, 94588-8618

Tel: (925) 225-3000 Fax: (925) 694-4444 www.peoplesoft.com

Mfr. applications to manage business operations across computer networks.

PeopleSoft Japan, Carrot Tower, 22/F, 4-4-1 Taishido, Setagaya-ku, Tokyo 154-0004, Japan

Tel: 81-3-5432-7800 Fax: 81-3-5432-7855

PEPSiCO INC.

700 Anderson Hill Road, Purchase, NY, 10577-1444

Tel: (914) 253-2000 Fax: (914) 253-2070 www.pepsico.com

Beverages and snack foods.

Japan Frito-Lay Ltd., Tokyo, Japan

PEREGRINE SYSTEMS, INC.

3611 Valley Centre Drive, San Diego, CA, 92130

Tel: (858) 481-5000   Fax: (858) 481-1751   www.peregrine.com

Mfr. resource planning software.

Peregrine Systems, K.K., Kamiyacho Mori Bldg., 4-3-20, Toranomon, Minato-ku, Tokyo 105-0001, Japan

Tel: 81-3-5404-5404

PERICOM SEMICONDUCTOR CORPORATION

2380 Bering Drive, San Jose, CA, 95131

Tel: (408) 435-0800   Fax: (408) 321-0933   wwwpericom.com

Mfr. electronic circuits.

Pericom, Nakane Bldg. 8/F, 4-4 Shiba-Daimon2-Chome, Minato-ku, Tokyo 105-0012, Japan

PERKIN ELMER, INC.

45 William Street, Wellesley, MA, 02481

Tel: (781) 237-5100   Fax: (781) 431-4255   www.perkinelmer.com

Mfr. equipment and devices to detect explosives and bombs on airline carriers.

PerkinElmer Life Sciences, 18/F, Parale, Mitsui Building 8, Higashida-Cho, Kawasaki-Ku Shi, Kanagawa-Ken 210-0005, Japan

Tel: 81-44-200-9157   Fax: 81-44-200-9160

PERVASIVE SOFTWARE INC.

12365 Riata Trace Pkwy., Austin, TX, 78727

Tel: (512) 231-6000   Fax: (512) 231-6010   www.pervasive.com

Mfr. software.

AG-Tech Corp., YA-2 Bldg. 3F2-24 Kanda, SakumachoChiyoda-Ki, Tokyo 101-0025, Japan

Tel: 81-3-5835-0891   Fax: 81-3-5835-0889

PFIZER INC.

235 East 42nd Street, New York, NY, 10017-5755

Tel: (212) 573-2323   Fax: (212) 573-7851   www.pfizer.com

Research-based, global health care company.

Pfizer KK, Tokyo, Japan

Pfizer Oral Care Inc., Tokyo, Japan

Pfizer Pharmaceuticals Inc., Tokyo, Japan

Pfizer Shoji Co. Ltd., Tokyo, Japan

Schneider Japan KK, Tokyo, Japan

PHARMACIA CORPORATION

100 Route 206 North, Peapack, NJ, 07977

Tel: (908) 901-8000   Fax: (908) 901-8379   www.pharmacia.com

Mfr. pharmaceuticals, agricultural products, industry chemicals.

Pharmacia & Upjohn Ltd., 3-20-2 Nishi-Shinjuku, Shinjuku-ku, Tokyo 163-1448, Japan

Tel: 81-3-5365-1820   Fax: 81-3-5365-1828

PHELPS DODGE CORPORATION

2600 North Central Ave., Phoenix, AZ, 85004-3089

Tel: (602) 234-8100   Fax: (602) 234-8337   www.phelpsdodge.com

Copper, minerals, metals and special engineered products for transportation and electrical markets.

Columbian Carbon Japan Ltd., 8-12 Nihonbashi Haridomecho 1-chome, Chuo-ku, Tokyo 103, Japan

Cyprus Amax Minerals Japan Corporation, Saisho Bldg., 2F, 8-1-14 Nishi Gotanda, Shinagawa-ku, Tokyo 141, Japan

Tel: 81-3-3491-5651   Fax: 81-3-3491-5670

PHILIP MORRIS COMPANIES, INC.

120 Park Ave., New York, NY, 10017

Tel: (917) 663-5000   Fax: (917) 663-2167   www.philipmorris.com

Mfr. cigarettes and tobacco and consumer food products (Kraft Foods).

Philip Morris Kabushiki Kaisha, Sanno Park Tower, 2-11-1, Nagata-cho, Chiyoda-ku, Tokyo 100-6190, Japan

Tel: 81-3-3506-7716

PHILLIPS PETROLEUM COMPANY

Phillips Building, 411 S. Keeler Ave., Bartlesville, OK, 74004

Tel: (918) 661-6600   Fax: (918) 661-7636   www.phillips66.com

Crude oil, natural gas, liquefied petroleum gas, gasoline and petro-chemicals.

Phillips Petroleum Intl. Ltd., 606 Shin Tokyo Bldg., 3-1 Marunouchi 3-chome, Chiyoda-ku, Tokyo 100, Japan

PHOENIX TECHNOLOGIES LTD.

411 East Plumeria Drive, San Jose, CA, 95134

Tel: (408) 570-1000   Fax: (408) 570-1001   www.phoenix.com

Mfr. BIOS software.

Phoenix Technologies Ltd.-K.K., Tokyo Ginko Kyokai Building, -3-1, Marunouchi Chiyoda-ku, Tokyo 100-0005, Japan

Tel: 81-3-5222-5333   Fax: 81-3-5222-5334

PIC GROUP

2929 Seventh Avenue, Ste. 130, Berkeley, CA, 94710

Tel: (510) 848-8266   Fax: (510) 848-0324   www.pic.com

Engaged in biotechnology.

Iwatani Camborough Co. Ltd., 3-12-8 Kuramae, Taito-ku, Tokyo, Japan

PIER 1 IMPORTS, INC.

301 Commerce St., Ste. 600, Fort Worth, TX, 76102

Tel: (817) 878-8000   Fax: (817) 252-8801   www.pier1.com

Specialty retailer of imported decorative home furnishings.

Pier 1 Imports, Inc., Kobe Fashion Plaza Rink, 5/F, 2-9-1 Naka-Kouyou-cho, Higashinada-ku, Kobe-shi Hyouko 658, Japan

Tel: 81-8846-2580   Contact: Takahiro Yoshida

PIERCE & STEVENS CORPORATION

710 Ohio Street, Buffalo, NY, 14203

Tel: (716) 856-4910   Fax: (716) 856-0942   www.dualite-spheres.com

Mfr. coatings, adhesives and specialty chemical for packaging and graphic arts..

Matsumoto Yushi-Seiyaku Co., Ltd., Shin-Edobashi Bldg., 4F, 8-6 Kobuna-cho Nihonbashi, Chuo-ku, Tokyo, Japan

PILLAR INDUSTRIES INC.

21905 Gateway Road, Brookfield, WI, 53045

Tel: (262) 317-5300   Fax: (262) 317-5353   www.pillar.com

Mfr. induction heating and melting equipment.

Pillar Orient Corp., 1-11-5 Hiroo, 1308, Shibuya-ku, Tokyo 150, Japan

PILLSBURY WINTHROP LLP

50 Fremont Street, San Francisco, CA, 94105

Tel: (415) 983-1000   Fax: (415) 983-1200   www.pillsburylaw.com

International law firm.

Pillsbury Winthrop LLP, Gaikokuho Jimu Bengoshi Jimusho, Fuerte Kojimachi Building, 5/F, 7-25, Kojimachi 1-chome, Chiyoda-ku Tokyo 102-0083, Japan

Tel: 81-3-5226-7260

PINNACLE SYSTEMS

280 North Bernardo Ave., Mountain View, CA, 94043

Tel: (650) 526-1600   Fax: (650) 526-1601   www.pinnaclesys.com

Designs, manufactures, markets and supports a wide range of high-quality digital solutions that enable businesses and consumers to create, store, distribute and view video programs.

Pinnacle Systems Japan KK, Sasazuka Village III, 3/F, 1-30-3 Sasazuka, Shibuya-Ku, Tokyo 151-0073, Japan

PIONEER HI-BRED INTERNATIONAL INC.

400 Locust Street, Ste. 800, Des Moines, IA, 50309

Tel: (515) 248-4800   Fax: (515) 248-4999   www.pioneer.com

Agricultural chemicals, farm supplies, biological products, research.

Pioneer Hi-Bred Japan, Landic Toranomon Bldg., 7/F, 3-7-10 Toranomon, Tokyo 105, Japan

PITNEY BOWES INC.

1 Elmcroft Road, Stamford, CT, 06926-0700

Tel: (203) 356-5000   Fax: (203) 351-6835   www.pitneybowes.com

Mfr. postage meters, mailroom equipment, copiers, bus supplies, bus services, facsimile systems and financial services.

Pitney Bowes Japan, Togoshi Ni Bldg., No. 7-1 Togoshi 1-chome, Shinagawa-ku, Tokyo 142, Japan

Tel: 81-3-5750-4111   Fax: 81-3-5750-4405   Contact: Glynn Brasington, VP Operations   Emp: 142

PLAINS COTTON COOPERATIVE ASSOCIATES

3301 East 50th Street, Lubbock, TX, 79404

Tel: (806) 763-8011   Fax: (806) 762-7333   www.pcca.com

Merchandisers of raw cotton to domestic and foreign textile mills.

Amcot, Tokyo, Japan

PLANTRONICS

345 Encinal Street, Santa Cruz, CA, 95060

Tel: (831) 426-5858   Fax: (831) 425-5198   www.plantronics.com

Mfr. lightweight headsets and communications equipment and electrical and electronic appliances.

Plantronics, Hibiya Central Bldg 14/F, 1-2-9, Nishi-Shinbashi, Minato-ku, Tokyo 105-003, Japan

Tel: 813-5532-7293

PLUMTREE SOFTWARE, INC.

500 Sansome Street, San Francisco, CA, 94111

Tel: (415) 263-8900   Fax: (415) 263-8991   www.plumtree.com

Mfr. organizational software.

Plumtree Software Japan KK, Kudan-Sky Building 2/F, 1-12-11 Kudankita, Chiyodaku, Tokyo, Japan

THE PNC FINANCIAL SERVICES GROUP

249 Fifth Ave., Pittsburgh, PA, 15222

Tel: (412) 762-2000   Fax: (412) 762-7829   www.pncbank.com

Engaged in financial and asset management.

Nomura BlackRock Asset Management Co., Ltd., Div. PNC, Nihonbashi-Muromachi 2-1-1, Chuo-ku, Tokyo 103-0022, Japan

Tel: 81-3-3241-9980   Fax: 81-3-3241-9713

POLAROID CORPORATION

784 Memorial Drive, Cambridge, MA, 02139

Tel: (781) 386-2000   Fax: (781) 386-3924   www.polaroid.com

Photographic equipment and supplies, optical products.

Nippon Polaroid KK, Mori Building No. 30, 3-2-2 Torinomon, Minato-ku, Tokyo 105-8456, Japan

Tel: 813-3-438-8811   Fax: 813-3-433-3537

POLYCOM, INC.

1565 Barber Lane, Milpitas, CA, 95035

Tel: (408) 526-9000   Fax: (408) 526-9100   www.polycom.com

Mfr. video conferencing systems, network bridging and multiplexing products, system peripherals.

Polycom, Inc., URD Building, 5/F, 3-19-6 Shirogane-dai, Minato-ku, Tokyo 108, Japan

Tel: 81-3-5421-3636   Fax: 81-3-5421-3611

POLYONE CORPORATION

200 Public Square, Cleveland, OH, 44114-2304

Tel: (216) 589-4000   Fax: (216) 589-4077   www.polyone.com

Mfr. custom made compounded plastics, including polymer, elastomer, colorant and additive products.

Jikco International PolyOne, 3-6-4-1104, Kanda-Jimbocho, Chiyoda-ku, Tokyo 101-0051, Japan

PORTAL SOFTWARE, INC.

10200 S. De Anza Bolevard, Cupertino, CA, 95014

Tel: (408) 572-2000   Fax: (408) 572-2001   www.portal.com

Mfr. customer management and billing software.

Portal Software KK, 7F East Tower, Kojimachi Crystal City, 4-8 Kojimachi, Chiyoada-ku, Tokyo 102-0083, Japan

Tel: 81-3-3512-6030   Fax: 81-3-3512-6040

POTTERS INDUSTRIES INC.

PO Box 840, Valley Forge, PA, 19482-0840

Tel: (610) 651-4700   Fax: (610) 408-9724   www.pottersbeads.com

Mfr. glass spheres for road marking and industry applications.

Toshiba-Ballotini Co. Ltd., Meguro Suda Bldg., 6/F, 9-1 Meguro-ku, Tokyo 153, Japan

PPG INDUSTRIES

One PPG Place, Pittsburgh, PA, 15272

Tel: (412) 434-3131   Fax: (412) 434-2190   www.ppg.com

Mfr. coatings, flat glass, fiber glass, chemicals.

Asahi-Penn Chemical Co. Ltd., Chiyoda-ku, Tokyo, Japan

PPG-CI Co. Ltd., KRT Aoyama Bldg., 12-5 Kita-Aoyama 2-chome, Minato-ku, Tokyo 107, Japan

PRAXAIR, INC.

39 Old Ridgebury Road, Danbury, CT, 06810-5113

Tel: (203) 837-2000   Fax: (203) 837-2450   www.praxair.com

Produces and distributes industrial and specialty gases.

Iwatani Industrial Gases Corporation, 21-8 Nishi-Shimbasi 3-chome, Minato-ku, Tokyo 105, Japan

Tel: 81-3-3555-5920

Praxair K. K., Minami Aoyama Watanabe Bldg., 1-4-2 Minami Aoyama, Minato-ku, Tokyo 107, Japan

Tel: 81-3-3408-7341   Fax: 81-3-3408-7378

PREMIX INC.

PO Box 281, 3365 E. Center Street, North Kingsville, OH, 44068-0281

Tel: (440) 224-2181   Fax: (440) 224-2766   www.premix.com

Mfr. molded fiber glass, reinforced thermoset molding compounds and plastic parts.

TyH Associates, 29-74, Chigusa-Dai, Aoba-ku, Yokohama, Kanagawa 227, Japan

Tel: 81-45-973-5265   Fax: 81-45-973-5265   Contact: Takashi Hanajima   Emp: 1

PRICEWATERHOUSECOOPERS LLP

1301 Ave. of the Americas, New York, NY, 10019

Tel: (212) 596-7000   Fax: (212) 259-1301   www.pwcglobal.com

Accounting and auditing, tax and management, and human resource consulting services.

PriceWaterhouseCoopers, Daiwa-Hiroshima Bldg., 6F, 2-27 Tatemachi, Naka-ku, Hiroshima 730, Japan

Tel: 81-82-242-0102   Fax: 81-82-242-0166

PriceWaterhouseCoopers, Mainichi Building, 5F, 7-35 Meieki 4-chome, Nakamura-ku, Nagoya 450, Japan

Tel: 81-52-571-6271   Fax: 81-52-571-6273

PriceWaterhouseCoopers, Osaka Centre Building, 10F, 1-3 Kyutaro-machi 4-chome, Chuo-ku, Osaka 541, Japan

Tel: 81-6-252-6791   Fax: 81-6-252-6798

PriceWaterhouseCoopers, Sunmemoria Dai-ichi Seimei Bldg, 6F, 1 Kita-Sanjo Nishi 1-chome Chuo-ku, Sapporo Hokkaido, Japan

Tel: 81-11-232-7530   Fax: 81-11-232-7533

PriceWaterhouseCoopers, Yebisu Garden Place Tower ,14F, 20-3 Ebisu 4-chome Shibuya-ku, PO Box 5034, Tokyo 150, Japan

Tel: 81-3-5424-8500   Fax: 81-3-5425-8423

PriceWaterhouseCoopers, Asahi Seimei Yokohama Honcho Bldg., 36 Honcho 4-chome, Naka-ku, Yokohoma 231, Japan

Tel: 81-45-212-4771   Fax: 81-45-212-4788

PRIMUS KNOWLEDGE SOLUTIONS, INC.

1601 Fifth Avenue, Ste. 1900, Seattle, WA, 98101

Tel: (206) 834-8100   Fax: (206) 834-8125   www.primus.com

Mfr. management software.

Primus Knowledge Solutions KK, Ebisu Prime Square Tower, 1-1-39 Hiroo, Shibuya-ku, Tokyo 150, Japan

PROCTER & GAMBLE COMPANY

One Procter & Gamble Plaza, Cincinnati, OH, 45202

Tel: (513) 983-1100   Fax: (513) 562-4500   www.pg.com

Personal care, food, laundry, cleaning and industry products.

Procter & Gamble Far East Inc., 1-17 Koyo-cho, Naka, Higashi-nada-ku, Kobe 658-0032, Japan

Tel: 81-78-658-0032

Procter & Gamble Paper (Suzhou), Ltd., No. 98 Jinshan Road, New District of Suzhou, Jiangsu, Japan

Tel: 81-512-8258526

PROQUEST COMPANY

300 N. Zeeb Road, Ann Arbor, MI, 48103

Tel: (734) 761-4700   Fax: (734) 997-4040   www.bellhowell.com

Engaged in information management services; publishers of electronic content for the academic, library, automotive and power sports industries.

ProQuest Information and Learning Company, Andoh Fukuyoshi Bldg., Silk Bld. 1017, 1-Bancho Yamashita-Cho Naka-Ku, Yokohama 231-0023, Japan

PROXIM CORPORATION

510 DeGuigne Drive, Sunnyvale, CA, 94089

Tel: (408) 731-2700   Fax: (408) 731-3675   www.proxim.com

Mfr. wireless modems.

Proxim Japan KK, 6/F Yaesu Kyodo Bldg., 2-5-9 Yaesu, Chuo-ku, Tokyo 104-0028, Japan

PRUDENTIAL FINANCIAL

751 Broad Street, Newark, NJ, 07102-3777

Tel: (973) 802-6000   Fax: (973) 802-2804   www.prudential.com

Sale of life insurance, financial services, asset management and brokerage.

Prudential Securities (Japan) Ltd, Yamato Seimei Bldg. 14F, 1-7, Uchisaiwai-cho 1-chome, Chiyodaku, Tokyo 100-0011, Japan

Tel: 81-3-5511-5900   Fax: 81-3-5511-9060

PSC INC.

111 SW Fifth Avenue, Ste. 4100, Portland, OR, 97204-3644

Tel: (503) 553-3920   Fax: (503) 553-3940   www.pscnet.com

Mfr. and sales of bar code scanners.

PSC Japan KK, Gotanda Daiwa Bldg., 7-13-5 Nishigotanda, Shinagawa Tokyo 141-0031, Japan

PSI NET (PERFORMANCE SYSTEMS INTERNATIONAL INC.)

44983 Knoll Square, Ashburn, VA, 20147

Tel: (703) 726-4100   Fax: (703) 726-4200   www.psinet.com

Internet service provider.

PSINet Japan Inc., Plaza Mikado Building, 3F, 2-14-5 Akasaka, Minato-ku, Tokyo 107-0052, Japan

Tel: 81-3-54-89-71-67   Fax: 81-3-55-74-71-73   Contact: Vincent Gebes, Dir.

Rimnet Corporation, Nikko Nanpeidal Building, 2-17 Nanpeidal-cho Shibuya-ku, Tokyo, Japan

Tel: 81-3-54-89-71-67   Fax: 81-3-54-89-56-40   Contact: Chi H. Kwan, SVP, Asia

Tokyo Internet Corporation, Shinjuku Gyoen Building, 5F, 2-3-10 Shinjuku, Shinjuku-ku, Tokyo 160-0022, Japan

Tel: 81-3-33-41-63-01   Fax: 81-3-33-41-28-81   Contact: Chi H. Kwan, SVP, Asia

TWICS Company Ltd., 1-21 Yotsuya, Shinjuku-ku, Tokyo, Japan

Tel: 81-3-33-51-59-77   Fax: 81-3-33-53-60-96   Contact: Chi H. Kwan, SVP, Asia

PUTNAM INVESTMENTS

1 Post Office Square, Boston, MA, 02109

Tel: (617) 292-1000   Fax: (617) 292-1499   www.putnaminv.com

Money management; mutual funds, annuities and retirement plans.

Putnam Advisory Co. Ltd., 18-19 Toranomon Main Bldg., 3-chome, Minato-ku, Tokyo 105, Japan

QAD INC.

6450 Via Real, Carpinteria, CA, 93013

Tel: (805) 684-6614   Fax: (805) 566-4479   www.qad.com

Mfr. software.

QAD Japan KK, Daini Taihei Bldg. 9/F, 720-3 Nishi-Shinjuku, Shinjuku-ku, Tokyo 160-0023, Japan

QUAKER CHEMICAL CORPORATION

1 Quaker Park, 901 Hector St., Conshohocken, PA, 19428-0809

Tel: (610) 832-4000   Fax: (610) 832-8682   www.quakerchem.com

Mfr. developer, producer, and marketer of custom-formulated chemical specialty products.

Nippon Quaker Chemical Ltd. (JV), 1-3 Shibukawa-cho 2-chome, Yao City Osaka, Japan

Tel: 81-729-92-1650   Contact: J. Aida, Pres.

QUANTUM

500 McCarthy Blvd., Milpitas, CA, 95035

Tel: (408) 894-4000   Fax: (408) 894-3218   www.quantum.com

Mfr. computer peripherals.

Quantum Japan Corporation, Shinjuku Square Tower, 4/F, 6-22-1 Nishi, Shinjuku-ku, Tokyo 163-11, Japan

Tel: 81-3-5321-7901

QUARK, INC.

1800 Grant Street, Denver, CO, 80203

Tel: (303) 894-8888   Fax: (303) 894-3398   www.quark.com

Mfr. and sales of desktop publishing software.

Quark Japan KK, 2-4-8 Ebisu-nishi, Shibuya-ku, Tokyo 105-0021, Japan

QUIKSILVER, INC.

15202 Graham Sreet, Huntington Beach, CA, 92649

Tel: (714) 889-2200   Fax: (714) 889-2315   www.quiksilver.com

Mfr. sportswear and activewear.

Quiksilver Japan K.K., 2-11-68 Kowada, Kanagawa Pref, Chigasaki City 253-0012, Japan

QUINTILES TRANSNATIONAL CORPORATION

4709 Creekstone Dr., Durham, NC, 27703

Tel: (919) 998-2000   Fax: (919) 998-9113   www.quintiles.com

Mfr. pharmaceuticals.

Quintiles Transnational Japan K.K., Forefront Tower II, 3-13-1 Kachodoki, Chuo-Ku, Tokyo 104-0054, Japan

QWEST COMMUNICATIONS INTERNATIONAL INC.

1801 California Street, Ste. 5200, Denver, CO, 80202

Tel: (303) 896-2020   Fax: (303) 793-6654   www.uswest.com

Tele-communications provider; integrated communications services.

Chofu Cable Television, Tokyo, Japan

TITUS Communications Corporation, Tokyo, Japan

Tel: 81-3-3499-88-91   Fax: 81-3-3499-89-71   Contact: Rich Metoki, Mgr. Corp. Planning

RADIO SHACK CORPORATION

100 Throckmorton Street, Fort Worth, TX, 76102

Tel: (817) 390-3700   Fax: (817) 415-2647   www.tandy.com

Mfr. electronic and acoustic equipment; Radio Shack retail stores.

A&A Japan Ltd., 1-21-1 Nishi, Shinjuku-ku, Tokyo 160, Japan

InterTAN Radio Shack Japan Ltd., 1-44-1 Tamagawa, Chofu City, Tokyo, Japan

RADISSON HOTELS INTERNATIONAL

Carlson Pkwy., PO Box 59159, Minneapolis, MN, 55459-8204

Tel: (612) 540-5526   Fax: (612) 449-3400   www.radisson.com

Operates, manages and franchises full-service hotels and resorts worldwide.

Radisson Miyako Hotel, 1-50 Shirokanedai 1-chome, Minato-ku, Tokyo 108-8640, Japan

Tel: 81-3-3447-3111   Fax: 81-3-3447-3133

RADISYS CORPORATION

5445 NE Dawson Creek Drive, Hillsboro, OR, 97124

Tel: (503) 615-1100   Fax: (503) 615-1121   www.radisys.com

Mfr. embedded computer systems.

RadiSys Japan KK, TK Bldg. 3F, 3-5-2 Sotokanda, Chiyoda-ku, Tokyo 101-0021, Japan

RAMBUS INC.

4440 El Camino Real, Los Altos, CA, 94022

Tel: (650) 947-5000   Fax: (650) 947-5001   www.rambus.com

Develops and licenses scalable bandwidth, chip connections technologies that enable semiconductor memory devices and ASICs to keep pace with faster generations of processors and controllers.

Rambus KK, World Trade Center Building, 33F, 2-4-1 Hamamatsu-cho, Minato-ku, Tokyo 105, Japan

Tel: 81-3-5425-7321   Fax: 81-3-5425-7326

RATIONAL SOFTWARE CORPORATION

18880 Homestead Road, Cupertino, CA, 95014-0721

Tel: (408) 863-9900   Fax: (408) 863-4120   www.rationale.com

Mfr. application development software.

Nihon Rational Software, Sumitomo Fudosan Hamacho, 3-42-3 Nihonbashi Hamacho Chuo-ku, Tokyo 103-0007, Japan

RAY & BERNDTSON, INC.

301 Commerce, Ste. 2300, Fort Worth, TX, 76102

Tel: (817) 334-0500   Fax: (817) 334-0779   www.prb.com

Executive search, management audit and management consulting firm.

Ray & Berndtson, Sogo Hanzomon Bldg., 9, Fl-7 Kojimachi, Chiyoda-ku, Tokyo 102, Japan

Tel: 81-3-5211-8411   Fax: 81-3-3264-0910   Contact: Roger J. Marshall, Mng. Ptnr.

RAYONIER INC.

50 N. Laura Street, Jacksonville, FL, 32202

Tel: (904) 357-9100   Fax: (904) 357-9155   www.rayonier.com

Engaged in logging and manufacture of paper pulp, chemicals and cellulose.

Rayonier Japan, Tokyo, Japan

RAYTHEON COMPANY

141 Spring Street, Lexington, MA, 02173

Tel: (781) 862-6600   Fax: (781) 860-2172   www.raytheon.com

Mfr. diversified electronics, appliances, energy and environmental products; publishing, industry and construction services.

New Japan Radio Co. Ltd., 5 Mitsuya-Toranomon Bldg., 22-14 Toranomon, Minato-ku, Tokyo 105, Japan

Raytheon International, Tokyo, Japan

Contact: Torkel Patterson, Pres.

RAZORFISH, INC.

32 Mercer Street, New York, NY, 10013

Tel: (212) 966-5960   Fax: (212) 966-6915   www.razorfish.com

Engaged in consulting and web services.

Razorfish Japan KK, Hiroo SK Bldg., 8/F, 2-36-13 Ebisu, Shibuya-ku Tokyo 150-0013, Japan

Tel: 81-3-5475-2011

READ-RITE CORPORATION

44100 Osgood Road, Fremont, CA, 94539

Tel: (510) 683-6100   Fax: (510) 683-7060   www.readrite.com

Mfr. magnetic recording heads for disk drives.

Read-Rite International, Senri Asah-Hankyu Bldg., 1-5-3 Shin Senri Hihashi-machi, Osaka 560-0082, Japan

RECOTON CORPORATION

2950 Lake Emma Road, Lake Mary, FL, 32746

Tel: (407) 333-8900   Fax: (407) 333-8903   www.recoton.com

Mfr. electronic accessories and aftermarket products for computers and office equipment.

Recoton Japan KK, Bldg., 5/F, 1-21-13 Takadanobaba, Shinhka-ka 169, Japan

Tel: 81-33-209-5055   Fax: 81-33-209-5188

RED HAT, INC.

1801 Varsity Drive, Raleigh, NC, 27606

Tel: (919) 754-3700   Fax: (919) 754-3701   www.redhat.com

Mfr. computer hardware and systems.

Red Hat, Inc., 3/F Shinkanda Building, 2-15-2 Sotokanda, Chiyoda-ku, Tokyo 1010021, Japan

REEBOK INTERNATIONAL LTD.

1895 J. W. Foster Blvd., Canton, MA, 02021

Tel: (781) 401-5000   Fax: (781) 401-7402   www.reebok.com

Mfr. athletic shoes including casual, dress golf and walking shoes.

Planet Reebok Japan, Tokyo, Japan

REFAC

115 River Rd., Edgewater, NJ, 07020-1099

Tel: (201) 943-4400   Fax: (201) 943-7400   www.refac.com

Consults to international technology transfer, foreign trade and power supplies firms for brand and trade marking licensing services..

REFAC, 19 Mori Bldg., 2-20 Toranomon 1-chome, Minato-ku, Tokyo 109, Japan

REFLEXITE TECHNOLOGY

120 Darling Drive, Avon, CT, 06001

Tel: (860) 676-7100   Fax: (860) 676-7199   www.reflexite.com

Mfr. plastic film, sheet, materials and shapes, optical lenses.

Reflexite Japan KK, SS Bldg. 7/F, 3-4-2 Nishi-Shimbashi, Minato-ku, Tokyo 105-0003, Japan

Tel: 81-3-3578-8201   Fax: 81-3-3578-8191

REGAL WARE INC.

1675 Reigle Drive, PO Box 395, Kewaskum, WI, 53040-0395

Tel: (414) 626-2121   Fax: (414) 626-8565   www.regalware.com

Mfr. cookware, small electrical appliances, water purification and filtration products for home.

Regal Japan Co. Ltd., Taishoseimei Nishiki Bldg., 18-24 Nishiki 1-chome, Naka-ku, Nagoya 460, Japan

RENAISSANCE HOTELS AND RESORTS

10400 Fernwood Road, Bethesda, MD, 20817

Tel: (301) 380-3000   Fax: (301) 380-5181   www.renaissancehotels.com

upscale, full-service hotel and resort chain under Marriott International, Inc.

Renaissance Gifu Hotel, Tokyo, Japan

Tel: 81-58-295-3100

Renaissance Tokyo Hotel, Tokyo, Japan

Tel: 81-3-3546-0111

RESMED INC.

1440 Danielson Street, Poway, CA, 92064

Tel: (858) 746-2400   Fax: (858) 880-1618   www.resmed.com

Mfr. sleep apnea aids, including nasal masks and accessories.

ResMed Japan, Nihonbashi Hisamatsu Bldg., 4F, 2-28-1 Nihonbashi-Hamacho, Chuo-Ku Tokyo 103-0007, Japan

Tel: 81-33662 5056

RETEK INC.

950 Nicollet Mall, Minneapolis, MN, 55403

Tel: (612) 587-5000   Fax: (612) 587-5100   www.retek.com

Mfr. retail management software.

Retek Tokyo, 11/F, Aoyama Palacio Tower, 3-6-7, Kita Aoyama, Minato-Ku Tokyo 107-0061, Japan

Tel: 81-3-5778-7620   Fax: 81-3-5778-7640

REVLON INC.

625 Madison Ave., New York, NY, 10022

Tel: (212) 527-4000   Fax: (212) 527-4995   www.revlon.com

Mfr. cosmetics, fragrances, toiletries and beauty care products.

Revlon KK, 2-3 Minami-Aoyama 2-chome, Minato-ku, Tokyo 107, Japan

Contact: Thomas Seymour

RHEOMETRIC SCIENTIFIC INC.

1 Possumtown Road, Piscataway, NJ, 08854

Tel: (732) 560-8550   Fax: (732) 560-7451   www.rheosci.com

Design/mfr. rheological instruments and systems.

Rheometric Scientific F.E. Ltd., 19-6 Yanagibashi 2-chome, Taito-ku, Tokyo 111, Japan

RICH PRODUCTS CORPORATION

One Robert Rich Way, Buffalo, NY, 14213

Tel: (716) 878-8000   Fax: (716) 878-8765   www.richs.com

Mfr. non-dairy products and icings, fillings, dry cake mixes, baked goods and desserts, frozen seafood and specialty meat products.

Rich Products Corp., Ginza-Yamamato Bldg., 16-11 Ginza 6-chome, Chuo-ku, Tokyo 104, Japan

RICHARDSON ELECTRONICS, LTD.

40 W 267 Keslinger Road, LaFox, IL, 60147-0393

Tel: (630) 208-2200   Fax: (630) 208-2550   www.rell.com

Mfr. and distribution of electron tubes and related equipment.

Richardson Electronics, Q-Dan 1991 Bldg. 1-12-1 Fujimi, Chiyoda-ku, Tokyo 102-0071, Japan

RICHCO, INC.

5825 N. Tripp Ave., PO Box 804238, Chicago, IL, 60680

Tel: (773) 539-4060   Fax: (773) 539-6770   www.richco.com

Mfr. quality plastic fasteners, wire management devices, circuit board hardware, and custom components.

Richco Japan, 302, Yamadera Building, 12-19 Yutenji 2-Chome, Meguro-ku, Tokyo 153, Japan

Tel: 81-33791-1821

RIDGE TOOL COMPANY

400 Clark Street, Elyria, OH, 44035

Tel: (440) 323-5581   Fax: (440) 329-4853   www.ridgid.com

Mfr. hand and power tools for working pipe, drain cleaning equipment, etc.

Ridge Div. Emerson Japan Ltd., New Pier Takeshiba South Tower, 7F, 1-16-1 Kaigan, Minato-ku, Tokyo 105, Japan

Tel: 81-3-5403-8560   Fax: 81-3-5403-8569

RIGHT MANAGEMENT CONSULTANTS, INC.

1818 Market Street, 33rd Fl., Philadelphia, PA, 19103-3614

Tel: (215) 988-1588   Fax: (215) 988-9112   www.right.com

Out placement and human resources consulting services.

Right Management Consultants, 1-5 Hakozaki-cho Nihonbashi, Chuo-ku, Tokyo 103, Japan

THE RITZ-CARLTON HOTEL COMPANY, L.L.C.

3414 Peachtree Road NE, Ste. 300, Atlanta, GA, 30326

Tel: (404) 237-5500   Fax: (404) 365-9643   www.ritzcarlton.com

5-star hotel and restaurant chain.

The Ritz-Carlton Hotel, 2-2-25 Umeda, Kita-ku, Osaka 530, Japan

Tel: 81-6-347-4784   Fax: 81-6-343-1888

The Ritz-Carlton Hotel Company, Homat Hanzomon, 4F, 12-12 Kojimachi 1-chome, Chiyoda-ku, Tokyo 102, Japan

Tel: 81-3-5210-7511   Fax: 81-3-5210-7524

ROCK OF AGES CORPORATION

369 N. State St., Concord, NH, 03301

Tel: (603) 225-8397   Fax: (603) 225-4801   www.rockofages.com

Quarrier; dimension granite blocks, memorials, and precision industrial granite.

Rock of Ages Asia Corp., 3-8 Uchihonmachi 2-chome, Chuo-ku, Osaka 540, Japan

Tel: 81-6-941-6511   Fax: 816-941-8526   Contact: Takashi Oshio   Emp: 3

ROCKFORD CORPORATION

600 South Rockford Drive, Tempe, AZ, 85281

Tel: (480) 967-3565   Fax: (480) 966-3983   www.rockfordcorp.com

Mfr. of automobile audio systems, amplifiers and speakers.

Rockford Corporation Japan KK, 514-1, Hita, Kannami-Cho Tagata-Gun, Shizuoka-Ken 419-01, Japan

ROCKWELL AUTOMATION, INC.

777 East Wisconsin Ave., Ste. 1400, Milwaukee, WI, 53202

Tel: (414) 212-5200   Fax: (414) 212-5201   www.rockwellautomation.com

Products and service for aerospace and defense, automotive, electronics, graphics and automation industry.

Rockwell Automation Japan Co., Ltd., 8F/9F, Shinkawa Sanko Bldg., 1-3-17 Shinkawa, Chuo-ku, Tokyo 104, Japan

Tel: 81-3-3206-2783   Fax: 81-3-3206-2788

Rockwell Automation Reliance Electric Ltd., Takeda Yakuhin Bldg., 5F, 1-25 Komachi Naka-ku, Hiroshima 730-0041, Japan

Tel: 81-82-242-1201   Fax: 81-82-242-7001

ROFIN-SINAR TECHNOLOGIES, INC.

45701 Mast St., Plymouth, MI, 48170

Tel: (734) 455-5400   Fax: (734) 455-2741   www.rofin-sinar.com

Mfr. industrial lasers.

ROFIN-SINAR KK, Sun Intelligent Bldg., 4/F, 3162 Sakai, Atsugh-shi, Kanagawa-ken 243, Japan

ROGERS CORPORATION

One Technology Drive, PO Box 188, Rogers, CT, 06263-0188

Tel: (860) 774-9605   Fax: (860) 779-5509   www.rogers-corp.com

Mfr. specialty materials including elastomers, circuit laminates and moldable composites.

Rogers INOAC Corp. (JV), No. 2-70, Jinno-cho, Atsuta-ku, Nagoya 456-0068, Japan

Rogers Japan Inc., 10th Floor, Tokiwa Bldg., 3-2-7, Nihonbashi-Hongokucho, Chuo-ku, Tokyo 103-0021, Japan

Tel: 81-33-5200-2700   Contact: William Schunmann, VP

ROHM AND HAAS COMPANY

100 Independence Mall West, Philadelphia, PA, 19106

Tel: (215) 592-3000   Fax: (215) 592-3377   www.rohmhaas.com

Mfr. specialty chemicals.

Kodama (Lab) Morton International, 200-11 Oaza Motohara, Kmikawa-Machi, Kodama-Gun, Saitama 367-0241, Japan

LeaRonal Japan, Sanbancho UF Bldg., 6-3, Sanbancho, Chiyoda-ku, Tokyo 102-0075, Japan
Tel: 81-3-5821-1851

Morton Rohm Haas, 1-64 Funami-cho, Minato-ku, Nagoya Aichi 455-0027, Japan

Nichigo-Morton, Nittobo Bldg. B1, Yaesu 2-chome Chuo-ku, Tokyo 104-0028, Japan

Nichigo-Morton, 200-11 Oaza Motohara, Kamikawa-Machi, Kodama-Gun, Saitama 367-0241, Japan
Tel: 81-4-9577-4581

Nippon Bee Chemical, 2-14-1 Shodai-Ohtani, Hirakata 573-6079, Japan

Rodel Nitta, 172 Ikezawacho, Yamato-Koriyama-Shi, Nara 639-11, Japan

Rodel Nitta, 8-3 Fujigaoka, Fujiwara-Cho, Inabe-Gun, Mie 511-0508, Japan

Rohm and Haas Company, 1-2-3 Koyo, Soma, Fukushima 976-0005, Japan

Rohm and Haas Japan KK, 3-4-26, Moto Azabu, Minato-ku, Tokyo 106-0046, Japan

Shipley Asia Ltd., 300 Aza Kanayahara, Oaza Onnado, Sasagami-Mura Kitakanbara-Gun, Kiigata-Ken 959-21, Japan

Shipley Asia Ltd., Kurosaki Yahatanishi-Ku, Kita Kyushu 806-0004, Japan

Shipley Far East, Nishidai-NC Bldg., 1-83-1 Takashimadaira, Itabashi-ku, Tokyo 175-0082, Japan

Toyo-Morton, Ltd., Forefront Tower II 4F, 3-13-1 Kachidoki Chuo-ku, Tokyo 104-0054, Japan

ROSENBLUTH INTERNATIONAL

2401 Walnut Street, Philadelphia, PA, 19103-4390

Tel: (215) 977-4000   Fax: (215) 977-4028   www.rosenbluth.com

Provides corporate business travel services.

Rosenbluth International, Yamato Bldg., 5-F, 5-3 Koju-Machi, Chiyoda-ku, Tokyo 102-0083, Japan

T. ROWE PRICE ASSOCIATES, INC.

100 East Pratt Street, Baltimore, MD, 21202

Tel: (410) 345-2000   Fax: (410) 345-2394   www.troweprice.com

Investment and portfolio asset management.

Rowe Price-Fleming International, Tokyo, Japan

RUDER FINN INC.

301 East 57th Street, New York, NY, 10022

Tel: (212) 593-6400   Fax: (212) 593-6397   www.ruderfinn.com

Engaged in public relations service and broadcast communications.

Ruder Finn Japan, Akasaka Q Bldg., 207, 9-5 Akasake 7-chome, Minato-ku, Tokyo 107, Japan

RUSSELL REYNOLDS ASSOCIATES INC.

200 Park Avenue, New York, NY, 10166-0002

Tel: (212) 351-2000   Fax: (212) 370-0896   www.russreyn.com

Executive recruiting services.

Russell Reynolds Associates Inc., Taisho Seimei Hibiya Bldg., 5F, 1-9-1 Yurakucho, Chiyoda-ku, Tokyo 100, Japan
Tel: 81-3-3216-1911   Fax: 81-2-3216-5866   Contact: Hirohide Fujii

SALESFORCE.COM

1 Market Street, Ste. 300, San Francisco, CA, 94105

Tel: (415) 901-7000   Fax: (415) 901-7040   www.salesforce.com

Mfr. software to manage customer information.

Salesforce.com, Shibuya Mark City West, 17/F, 1-12-1 Dogenzaka, Shibuya-ku, Tokyo 150-0043, Japan

SALOMON SMITH BARNEY HOLDINGS INC.

388 Greenwich Street, New York, NY, 10013

Tel: (212) 816-6000   Fax: (212) 816-8915   www.smithbarney.com

Securities dealers and underwriters.

Nikko Securities Co., Tokyo, Japan

Salomon Smith Barney Holdings, Fukoku-Seimei Bldg., 2-2 Uchsaiwai-cho 2-chome, Chiyoda-ku, Tokyo, Japan

SANFORD CORPORATION

2711 Washington Boulevard, Bellwood, IL, 60104

Tel: (708) 547-6650   Fax: (708) 547-6719   www.sanfordcorp.com

Mfr. inks, writing, drawing and drafting instruments.

Sanford Japan Ltd., Shibusawa Bldg. 4-28-11, Taito Taito-ku, Tokyo 110-0016, Japan

SAPIENT CORPORATION

1 Memorial Drive, Cambridge, MA, 02142

Tel: (617) 621-0200   Fax: (617) 621-1300   www.sapient.com

Engaged in information technology and consulting services.

Sapient K.K., Toranomon 40 Mori Building, 5-13-1 Toranomon, Minato-ku, Tokyo 105-0001, Japan

SARA LEE CORPORATION

3 First National Plaza, Chicago, IL, 60602-4260

Tel: (312) 726-2600   Fax: (312) 558-4995   www.saralee.com

Mfr./distributor food and consumer packaged goods, intimate apparel and knitwear.

HomCare Japan, Ltd., Tokyo, Japan

SAS INSTITUTE INC.

SAS Campus Drive, Cary, NC, 27513

Tel: (919) 677-8000   Fax: (919) 677-4444   www.sas.com

Mfr. and distribution of decision support software.

SAS Institute (Japan) Ltd., Inui Bldg. Kachidoki 8/F, 1-13-1 Kachidoki, Chuo-ku, Tokyo 104-0054, Japan
Tel: 81-3-3533-3760   Fax: 81-3-3533-6927

SCHAWK, INC.

1695 River Road, Des Plaines, IL, 60018

Tel: (847) 827-9494   Fax: (847) 827-1264   www.schawk.com

Provides graphic arts services for consumer packaging.

Schawk Japan, 9, Koyo-cho Naka 6-chome, 8/F, Higashinada-ku Kobe 658-0032, Japan
Tel: 81-78-842-9160

SCHENECTADY INTERNATIONAL INC.

PO Box 1046, Schenectady, NY, 12301

Tel: (518) 370-4200   Fax: (518) 382-8129   www.siigroup.com

Mfr. electrical insulating varnishes, enamels, phenolic resins, alkylphenols.

Nisshoku Schenectady Kagaku Inc., 5-8 Nishi Otabicho Suita, Osaka 564-0034, Japan
Tel: 81-6-6317-2826   Fax: 81-6-6317-2828   Contact: Hidemitsu Takizawa

SCHENKER USA INC.

150 Albany Ave., Freeport, NY, 11520

Tel: (516) 403-5416   Fax: (516) 377-3092   www.schenkerusa.com

Freight forwarders.

Japan Schenker Co., Kachidoki Sun Square 7-3, Kachidoki 1-chome, Chuo-ku, Tokyo, Japan
Tel: 81-3-5560-8600   Fax: 81-3-5560-8620

Japan Schenker Co., Taiyo Shoji Bldg, 4F5, 11 Nakanoshima 3-chome, Kita-ku, Osaka 530, Japan
Tel: 81-6-444-1191   Fax: 81-6-445-6987

R. P. SCHERER CORPORATION

645 Martinsville Rd., Ste. 200, Basking Ridge, NJ, 07920

Tel: (908) 580-1500   Fax: (908) 580-9220   www.rpscherer.com

Mfr. pharmaceuticals; soft gelatin and two-piece hard shell capsules.

P.R. Scherer KK, Shin Tokyo Akasaka Bldg., 4-9-25 Akasaka, Minato-ku, Tokyo 107-0052, Japan

Tel: 81-3-3470-2311 Fax: 81-3-3408-5554 Contact: Shusuke Kato, President Emp: 144

SCHERING-PLOUGH CORPORATION

One Giralda Farms, Madison, NJ, 07940-1000

Tel: (973) 822-7000   Fax: (973) 822-7048   www.sch-plough.com

Proprietary drug and cosmetic products.

Coppertone (Japan) Ltd., PO Box 36, Akasaka, Tokyo, Japan

Essex Nippon KK (Schering Corp.), CPO Box 1235, Osaka 530-91, Japan

Japan Schering-Plough K.K., Ichiban-cho, 2/F, 10-2 Ichiban-cho Chiyoda-ku, Tokyo 102-0082, Japan

SCHLEGEL SYSTEMS

1555 Jefferson Road, PO Box 23197, Rochester, NY, 14692-3197

Tel: (716) 427-7200   Fax: (716) 427-9993   www.schlegel.com

Mfr. engineered perimeter sealing systems for residential and commercial construction; fibers; rubber product.

Schlegel Engineering KK Japan, 4/F, Iwanami Shoten Annex, 3-1 Kanda Jinbocho 2-chome, Chiyoda-ku, Tokyo 101, Japan

Tel: 81-332-639621 Fax: 81-332-345370

SCHLUMBERGER LIMITED

153 East 53rd St., 57th Fl., New York, NY, 10022-4624

Tel: (212) 350-9400   Fax: (212) 350-9457   www.slb.com

Engaged in oil and gas services, metering and payment systems, and produces semiconductor testing equipment and smart cards.

Schlumberger K.K., Sumitomohamamatsucho Building, 5F, 1-18-16 Hamamatsucho, Minato-ku, Tokyo 105-0013, Japan

SCHNITZER STEEL INDUSTRIES, INC.

3200 NW Yeoan Avenue, Portland, OR, 97296-0047

Tel: (503) 224-9900   Fax: (503) 321-2648   www.schn.com

Engaged in processing and recycling steel and iron scrap.

Lasco Shipping Japan K, Marubun Tamura Bldg., 9/F, 6-4-3 Chome, Nihonbashi Kayabacho, Chuo-ku Tokyo 104, Japan

Tel: 81-3-3665-0611 Fax: 81-3-3665-0612

THE CHARLES SCHWAB CORPORATION

101 Montgomery Street, San Francisco, CA, 94104

Tel: (415) 627-7000   Fax: (415) 627-8840   www.schawb.com

Financial services; discount brokerage, retirement accounts.

Charles Schwab Tokio Marine Securities Co., Ltd., Tokyo, Japan

SCIENCE APPLICATIONS INTL. CORPORATION (SAIC)

10260 Campus Point Dr., San Diego, CA, 92121

Tel: (858) 826-6000   Fax: (858) 535-7589   www.saic.com

Engaged in research and engineering.

SAIC Japan, Samon Eleven Building, 4/F, 3-1 Samon-Cho, Shinjuku-Ku, Tokyo 160, Japan

Tel: 81-3-33578057 Fax: 81-3-3357-8176

SCIENTIFIC-ATLANTA, INC.

5030 Sugarloaf Pkwy., Lawrenceville, GA, 30044

Tel: (770) 903-5000   Fax: (770) 236-6777   www.sciatl.com

Mfr. cable set-top boxes, modems, transmission and distribution equipment.

Scientific-Atlanta Japan, KK, Level 5, Shinjuku 1-Land Tower, Nishi-Shinjuku, Shinjuku-ku, Tokyo 163-1305, Japan

Tel: 81-3-5908-2153 Fax: 81-3-5908-2155 Contact: Peter Schalkwijk

SCM MICROSYSTEMS, INC.

47211 Bayside Pkwy., Fremont, CA, 94538

Tel: (510) 360-2300   Fax: (510) 360-0211   www.scmmicro.com

Mfr. computer hardware for digital cameras.

SCM Microsystems, 2/F, Royal Building, 12-8, Niban-cho, Chiyoda-ku, Tokyo 102-0084, Japan

SDI TECHNOLOGIES

1299 Main St., Rahway, NJ, 07065

Tel: (732) 574-9000   Fax: (732) 574-3797   www.sdidirect.com

Mfr. clock radios and electronic products.

SDI Technologies, 9-14 Nihonbashi 2-chome, Chuo-ku, Tokyo, Japan

SEAGATE TECHNOLOGY, INC.

920 Disc Dr., Scotts Valley, CA, 95066

Tel: (408) 438-6550   Fax: (408) 438-7205   www.seagate.com

Develop computer technology, software and hardware.

Nipon Seagate, Inc., Tennoz Parkside Bldg., 3F, 2-5-8 Higashi-Shinagawa, Shinagawa-ku, Tokyo 140, Japan

Tel: 81-3-5462-2901   Fax: 81-3-5462-2978   Contact: Tsuyoshi Kobayashi, Dir.   Emp: 50

SEALED AIR CORPORATION

Park 80 East, Saddle Brook, NJ, 07663

Tel: (201) 791-7600   Fax: (201) 703-4205   www.sealedaircorp.com

Mfr. protective and specialty packaging solutions for industrial, food and consumer products.

Instapak Ltd., Kano Bldg., 2-5-14 Nanbanaka, Naniwa-ku, Osaka, Japan

Instapak Ltd., 2-53 Kamioka-cho, Meito-ku, Nagoya, Japan

Instapak Ltd., 3-20-5 Shiba, Minato-ku, Tokyo 105, Japan

Sealed Air Japan Ltd., 1-14-2 Saga, Koto-ku, Tokyo 135, Japan

Tel: 81-3-5245-1635   Fax: 81-3-5245-1636

G.D. SEARLE & COMPANY

5200 Old Orchard Road, Skokie, IL, 60077

Tel: (847) 982-7000   Fax: (847) 470-1480   www.searlehealthnet.com

Mfr. pharmaceuticals, health care, optical products and specialty chemicals.

Searle, Division of Monsanto Japan Ltd., 730 Oaza-Noharu Yamaga-Cho, Hayami-Gun Oita-Ken 879-13, Japan

Tel: 81-977-75-1311   Fax: 81-977-75-1576

SECURE COMPUTING CORPORATION

4810 Harwood Rd., San Jose, CA, 95124

Tel: (408) 979-6000   Fax: (408) 979-6101   www.sctc.com

Mfr. software.

Secure Computing Japan KK, Level 11, Aoyama Palacio Tower, 3-6-7 Kita Aoyama, Minato-Ku, Tokyo 107-0061, Japan

Tel: 813-5778-7687

SELAS CORPORATION OF AMERICA

2034 S. Limekiln Pike, Dresher, PA, 19025

Tel: (215) 646-6600   Fax: (215) 646-3536   www.selas.com

Mfr. heat treating equipment for metal, glass, ceramic and chemical industry.

Nippon Selas Co. Ltd., 4-3 Arakawa 7-chome, Arakawa-ku, Tokyo 116, Japan

SEMINIS, INC.

2700 Camino del Sol, Oxnard, CA, 93030-7967

Tel: (805) 647-1572   Fax: (805) 918-2545   www.seminis.com

Produces fruit and vegetable seeds.

Seminis Japan KK, Yoshida Bldg. 3/F, 2-8-9 Teramae, Kanazawa-ku, Yokohama 236-0014, Japan

SEMITOOL, INC.

655 West Reserve Drive, Kalispell, MT, 59901

Tel: (406) 752-2107   Fax: (406) 752-5522   www.semitool.com

Mfr. semiconductor manufacturing equipment.

Semitool Japan, KK, 2-15-10 Shin-Yokohama, Kouhoku-ku, Yokohama-shi, Kanagawa 222-0033, Japan

SEMTECH CORPORATION

200 Flynn Road, Camarillo, CA, 93012-8790

Tel: (805) 498-2111   Fax: (805) 498-3804   www.semtech.com

Mfr. silicon rectifiers, rectifier assemblies, capacitors, switching regulators, AC/DC converters.

Semtech Ltd. Japan, 1-22-6 Higashigotanda, 8/F, Tsuzuki-ku, Shinagawa, Tokyo 141-0022, Japan

Tel: 81-3-6408-0950   Fax: 81-3-6408-0951   Contact: Yuji Yoshimura

SENCO PRODUCTS INC.

8485 Broadwell Road, Cincinnati, OH, 45244

Tel: (513) 388-2000   Fax: (513) 388-2026   www.senco.com

Mfr. industry nailers, staplers, fasteners and accessories.

Senco Products (Japan) Ltd., Wakasugi Grand Bldg., 11-D, 25-5 Tenjinbashi 2-chome, Kita-ku, Osaka 530, Japan

SENSIENT TECHNOLOGIES CORPORATION

777 E. Wisconsin Ave., Milwaukee, WI, 53202

Tel: (414) 271-6755   Fax: (414) 347-4783   www.sensient.com

Mfr. flavor applications for the beverage, bakery, confection, dairy, snack and savory markets.

Sensient Asia Pacific, Tokyo, Japan

THE SERVICEMASTER COMPANY

2300 Warrenville Road, Downers Grove, IL, 60515-1700

Tel: (630) 271-1300   Fax: (630) 271-2710   www.svm.com

Provides residential consumer services, including lawn care and landscape maintenance, termite and pest control, plumbing, heating and air conditioning maintenance and repair.

ServiceMaster Japan Inc., PJ Bldg., 22 Kaikyo-cho, Shinjuku-ku, Tokyo 160, Japan

SHAKESPEARE FISHING TACKLE GROUP

3801 Westmore Drive, Columbia, SC, 29223

Tel: (803) 754-7000   Fax: (803) 754-7342   www.shakespeare-fishing.com

Mfr. fishing tackle.

Shakespeare Japan Ltd., Nishiwaki Bldg., 1 Kohjimachi 4-chome, Chiyoda ku, Tokyo, Japan

THE SHARPER IMAGE CORPORATION

650 Davis Street, San Francisco, CA, 94111

Tel: (415) 445-6000   Fax: (415) 445-1588   www.sharperimage.com

Specialty retailer of innovative products.

The Sharper Image, Shinkobe Oriental City, 1 Kitano-cho, chul-ku, Kobe, Japan

SHEARMAN & STERLING

599 Lexington Ave., New York, NY, 10022-6069

Tel: (212) 848-4000   Fax: (212) 848-7179   www.shearman.com

Law firm engaged in general American and international financial and commercial practice.

Shearman & Sterling, Fukoku Seimei Bldg., 5/F, 2-2-2 Uchisaiwaicho, Chiyoda-ku, Tokyo 100, Japan

Tel: 81-3-5251-1601   Fax: 81-3-5251-1602   Contact: William M. Burke, Mng. Ptnr.

SHELDAHL, INC.

1150 Sheldahl Rd., Northfield, MN, 55057-9444

Tel: (507) 663-8000   Fax: (507) 663-8545   www.sheldahl.com

Mfr. electrical and electronic components and laminated plastic products/adhesive-based tapes and materials and adhesiveless Novaclad®.

Shinko Electric Industrial Co., Ltd., Nagano, Japan

SHIPLEY COMPANY, LLC

455 Forest Street, Marlborough, MA, 01752

Tel: (508) 481-7950   Fax: (508) 485-9113   www.shipley.com

Supplier of materials and processes technology to the microelectronics and printed wiring board industries.

Shipley Far East Ltd., Nishidai NC Bldg., 1-83-1 Takashimadaira, Itabashi-ku, Tokyo 175, Japan

Tel: 81-35-920-5300   Fax: 81-35-920-5471   Contact: T. Suzuki, Pres.

SIDLEY AUSTIN BROWN & WOOD, LLP

10 South Dearborn, Bank One Plaze, Chicago, IL, 60603

Tel: (312) 853-7000   Fax: (312) 853-7036   www.sidley.com

Engaged in international law.

Sidley Austin Brown & Wood LLP, 9-1 Yurakucho 1-chome, Chiyoda-ku, Tokyo 100, Japan

Tel: 81-3-3218-5900   Fax: 81-3-3218-5922   Contact: Shuichi Suzuki, Ptnr.

SIGNODE PACKAGING SYSTEMS

3610 West Lake Ave., Glenview, IL, 60025

Tel: (847) 724-6100   Fax: (847) 657-4392   www.signode.com

Mfr. industrial tools and machinery for packaging and strapping.

Signode KK, Sannomiya Intl. Bldg., 1-30 Hamabe-dori 2-chome, Chuo-ku, Kobe 651, Japan

SILICON GRAPHICS INC.

1600 Amphitheatre Pkwy., Mountain View, CA, 94043-1351

Tel: (650) 960-1980   Fax: (650) 932-0661   www.sgi.com

Design/mfr. special-effects computer graphic systems and software.

Silicon Graphics, Japan

SILICON STORAGE TECHNOLOGY, INC.

1171 Sonora Court, Sunnyvale, CA, 94086

Tel: (408) 735-9110   Fax: (408) 735-9036   www.ssti.com

Mfr./sale single power supply small ease-block flash memory components, and two-power supply MTP flash products.

Silicon Storage Technology Ltd., 5F, Kose #2, 1-14-20 Shin-Yokohama, Kohoku-ku, Yokohama 222-0033, Japan

Tel: 81-45-471-1851 Fax: 81-45-471-3285   Contact: Masami Goto

Silicon Storage Technology Ltd., 2-2-16 YK Bld., Sangenjaya, Setagaya-ku, Tokyo 154, Japan

Tel: 81-3-3795-6461 Fax: 81-3-3795-2425

SIMON & SCHUSTER INC.

1230 Avenue of the Americas, New York, NY, 10020

Tel: (212) 698-7000   Fax: (212) 698-7007   www.simonandschuster.com

Publishes and distributes hardcover and paperback books, audiobooks and software.

Prentice-Hall of Japan Inc., Jochi Kojimachi Bldg., 3/F, 1-25 Kojimachi 6 chome, Chigoda-ku, Tokyo 102, Japan

SIMPSON INVESTMENT COMPANY, INC.

1301 Fifth Ave., Ste. 2800, Seattle, WA, 98101

Tel: (206) 224-5000   Fax: (206) 224-5060   www.simpson.com

Paper, pulp and saw mills, wood products.

Simpson Far East KK, 2 Onishi Bldg., 1-6 Toranomon 4-chome, Minato-ku, Tokyo 105, Japan

SIMPSON THACHER & BARTLETT

425 Lexington Ave., New York, NY, 10017

Tel: (212) 455-2000   Fax: (212) 455-2502   www.simpsonthacher.com

Engaged in international law.

Simpson Thacher & Bartlett, Ark Mori Bldg., 30/F, 12-32 Akasaka 1-chome, Minato-ku, Tokyo 107, Japan

Tel: 81-3-5562-8601 Fax: 81-3-5562-8606   Contact: David A. Sneider, Ptnr.

SKADDEN, ARPS, SLATE, MEAGHER & FLOM LLP

4 Times Square, New York, NY, 10036

Tel: (212) 735-3000   Fax: (212) 735-2000   www.sasmf.com

American/International law practice.

Skadden, Arps, Slate, Meagher & Flom LLP, Shiroyama JT Mori Bldg., 16/F, 4-3-1 Toranomon, Minato-ku, Tokyo 105, Japan

Tel: 81-3-5403-4730   Fax: 81-3-5403-4731   Contact: E. Anthony Zaloom, Partner

SKYWORKS SOLUTIONS, INC.

20 Sylvan Road, Woburn, MA, 01801

Tel: (781) 935-5150   Fax: (781) 824-4579   www.skyworksinc.com

Mfr. electronic and microwave components.

Skyworks Solutions, Shimomoto Bldg.,, -46-3 Hatsudai, Shibuya-Ku, Tokyo 151-0061, Japan

SMURFIT-STONE CONTAINER CORPORATION

150 N. Michigan Ave., Chicago, IL, 60601-7568

Tel: (312) 346-6600   Fax: (312) 580-3486   www.smurfit-stone.net

Mfr. paper and paper packaging.

Smurfit-Stone Container Corporation, Tokyo, Japan

SNAP-ON INCORPORATED

10801 Corporate Dr., Pleasant Prairie, WI, 53158-1603

Tel: (262) 656-5200   Fax: (262) 656-5577   www.snapon.com

Mfr. auto maintenance, diagnostic and emission testing equipment, hand tools, hydraulic lifts and tire changers.

Snap-On Tools Japan KK (SOJ), 8-10 Shinkiba 1-chome, Kotoh-ku, Tokyo 136, Japan

SOLA INTERNATIONAL INC.

10690 W. Ocean Air Drive, Ste. 300, San Diego, CA, 92130

Tel: (858) 509-9899   Fax: (858) 509-9898   www.sola.com

Mfr. and sales of plastic and glass eyeglasses.

SOLA International KK, Nissei Fushimi-machi Bldg., 4/F, 4-4-1 Fushimi-machi, Chuo-Ku, Osaka 541, Japan

SOLECTRON CORPORATION

777 Gibraltar Drive, Milpitas, CA, 95035

Tel: (408) 957-8500   Fax: (408) 956-6075   www.solectron.com

Provides contract manufacturing services to equipment manufacturers.

Force Computers, Inc., Yurakucho Denki Building, South Tower ,13F, 1-7-1 Yurakucho Chiyoda-ku, Tokyo 100-0006, Japan

Tel: 81-3-3287-2031   Fax: 81-3-3287-2032

Force Computers, Japan K.K., Shibadaimon MF Building, 2-1-16 Shiba Daimon, Minato-ku, Tokyo 105, Japan

Tel: 81-3-3437-3948   Fax: 81-3-3437-3968

SOLUTIA INC.

575 Maryville Center Dr, St. Louis, MO, 63141

Tel: (314) 674-1000   Fax: (314) 694-8686   www.solutia.com

Mfr. specialty chemical based products.

Solutia Japan Ltd., Shinkawa Sanko Building, 1-3-17 Shinkawa, Chuo-Ku, Tokyo 104-0033, Japan

Tel: 81-3-56441638

SONOCO PRODUCTS COMPANY

North Second Street, PO Box 160, Hartsville, SC, 29550

Tel: (843) 383-7000   Fax: (843) 383-7008   www.sonoco.com

Mfr. packaging for consumer and industrial market and recycled paperboard.

Hiyoshimaru Shiko Co., Ltd., 10-2 Nanso-Cho, Higashi-Osaka 579, Japan

Tel: 81-729-84-5231

Showa Products Co. Ltd., 8/F, Nittochi Dojima Hama, 4-19 Dojima-Hama 1-chome, Kita-ku, Osaka 530, Japan

Tel: 81-6-345-3751

Showa Products Co., Ltd. (Tokyo Office), Sengoku Building, 8F, 2-4-15 Nihinbashi, Muromachi, Chou-ku, Tokyo 103, Japan

Tel: 81-3-3242-2751

SOTHEBY'S HOLDINGS, INC.

1334 York Avenue, New York, NY, 10021

Tel: (212) 606-7000   Fax: (212) 606-7027   www.sothebys.com

Auction house specializing in fine art and jewelry.

Sotheby's Holdings, Inc., Fuerte Kojimachi Bldge., 3/F, 1-7 Kojimachi Chiyoda-ku, Tokyo 102, Japan

Tel: 81-3-3230-2755

SPARKLER FILTERS INC.

PO Box 19, Conroe, TX, 77305-0019

Tel: (936) 756-4471   Fax: (936) 539-1165   www.sparklerfilters.com

Mfr. chemical process filtration industry.

Sparkler Filters Japan KK, No. 6-9-35 Zaimokuza, Kamakura 248, Japan

Tel: 81-46722-7447

SPARTECH CORPORATION

120 S. Central, Ste. 1700, Clayton, MO, 63105-1705

Tel: (314) 721-4242   Fax: (314) 721-1447   www.spartech.com

Mfr. and sales of engineered thermoplastic materials and polymeric compounds.

Takiron Co. (JV), Osaka, Japan

SPECTRA-PHYSICS, INC.

1335 Terra Bella Avenue, Bldg. 7, Mountain View, CA, 94043

Tel: (650) 961-2550   Fax: (650) 968-5215   www.spectra-physics.com

Mfr. lasers.

Spectra-Physics KK, Daiwa-Nakameguro Bldg., 4-6-1 Nakameguro Meguro-ku, Tokyo 153, Japan

Tel: 81-3-3794-5511   Fax: 81-3-3794-5510

SPEEDFAM-IPEC INC.

305 N. 54th Street, Chandler, AZ, 85226-2416

Tel: (480) 961-1600   Fax: (480) 705-2793   www.sfamipec.com

Mfr. semiconductors.

SpeedFam-IPEC Japan, 2754-8, Hayakawa, Ayase-City, Kanagawa-pref., Tokyo 252-1123, Japan

SPENCER STUART MANAGEMENT CONSULTANTS

401 North Michigan Ave., Ste. 3400, Chicago, IL, 60611

Tel: (312) 822-0080   Fax: (312) 822-0116   www.spencerstuart.com

Executive recruitment firm.

Spencer Stuart & Associates Inc., Kawakita Memorial Building, 8F, 18 Ichibancho, Chiyoda-ku, Tokyo 102-0082, Japan

Tel: 81-3-3238-8901   Fax: 81-3-3238-8902   Contact: Joji Hara

SPRAYING SYSTEMS COMPANY

PO Box 7900, Wheaton, IL, 60189-7900

Tel: (630) 665-5000   Fax: (630) 260-0842   www.spray.com

Designs and manufactures industrial spray products.

Spraying Systems Co. Japan, 5-10-18 Higashi-Gotanda, Shinagawa-ku, Tokyo 141, Japan

Spraying Systems Japan, Park Side Bldg., 5/F, 1-1 Sakae 5-chrome, Naka-ku, Nagoya 460, Japan

SPRINT CORPORATION

2330 Shawnee Mission Parkway, Westwood, KS, 66205

Tel: (913) 624-3000   Fax: (913) 624-3281   www.sprint.com

Telecommunications equipment and services.

Sprint Corporation, 21-13 Himonya 4-chome, Meguro-ku, Tokyo 152, Japan

SPS TECHNOLOGIES INC.

165 Township Line Rd., Two Pitcairn Place, Jenkintown, PA, 19046

Tel: (215) 517-2000   Fax: (215) 517-2032   www.spstech.com

Mfr. aerospace and industry fasteners, tightening systems, magnetic materials, super alloys.

SPS/Unbrako KK, 2-25-5 Ogawa, Machida, Tokyo 194, Japan

Tel: 81-427-99-5991   Fax: 81-427-99-5442   Contact: Kazutaka Mori, Pres.

SPSS INC.

233 S. Wacker Dr., 11th Fl., Chicago, IL, 60606

Tel: (312) 651-6000   Fax: (312) 329-3668   www.spss.com

Mfr. statistical software.

SPSS Japan Inc., AY Bldg., 3-2-2 Kitaaoyama, Minato-ku, Tokyo 107, Japan

SPX CORPORATION

700 Terrace Point Drive, PO Box 3301, Muskegon, MI, 49443-3301

Tel: (231) 724-5000   Fax: (231) 724-5720   www.spx.com

Mfr. auto parts, special service tools, engine and drive-train parts.

Kent-Moore Japan (JATEK), Dai-Ni Maruzen Building, 8/F, 9-2 Nihonbashi 3-chome, Chuo-ku, Tokyo 103, Japan

Robinair Japan, c/o JATEK Ltd.,, Dai-Ni Maruzen Building, 9/2 Nihonbashi 3-chome, Chuo-ku, Tokyo 103, Japan

RSV Corp., 4-38 Hokuto-cho, Kashiwazaki, Nigata 945, Japan

SQUIRE, SANDERS & DEMPSEY

4900 Key Tower, 127 Public Square, Cleveland, OH, 44114-1304

Tel: (216) 479-8500   Fax: (216) 479-8780   www.ssd.com

Engaged in international law.

Squire, Sanders & Dempsey L.L.P., Gaikokuho Jimu Bengoshi Jimusho, Ebisu Prime Square Tower, 16/F, 1-1-39 Hiroo, Shibuya-ku, Tokyo 150-0012, Japan

Tel: 81-3-5774-1800

SRI INTERNATIONAL

333 Ravenswood Ave., Menlo Park, CA, 94025-3493

Tel: (650) 859-2000   Fax: (650) 326-5512   www.sri.com

Engaged in international consulting and research.

SRI East Asia, Shin-Nikko Bldg., East Wing, 15/F, 10-1 Toranoman 2-chome, Minato-ku, Tokyo 105, Japan

SRI International, Daito Building, 2/F, 7-1 Kasumigaseki 3-chome Chiyoda-ku, Tokyo 100-0013, Japan

Tel: 81-3-5251-1761   Fax: 81-3-5251-1766

SS&C TECHNOLOGIES, INC.

80 Lamberton Road, Windsor, CT, 06095

Tel: (860) 298-4500   Fax: (860) 298-4900   www.ssctech.com

Mfr. tracking software.

SS&C Technologies KK, Hiramori Bldg., 4/F, Nishi-Gotanda, 8-1-2, Shinagawa-ku, Tokyo 141-0031, Japan

Tel: 81-3-5740-6121

THE ST. PAUL COMPANIES, INC.

385 Washington Street, St. Paul, MN, 55102

Tel: (651) 310-7911   Fax: (651) 310-8294   www.stpaul.com

Provides investment, insurance and reinsurance services.

Taisei Fire & Marine Insurance Company Ltd., 2-1 Kudan Kita 4-chome, Chiyoda-ku, Tokyo 102, Japan

STANDARD & POOR'S SECURITIES, INC.

25 Broadway, New York, NY, 10004

Tel: (212) 208-8000   Fax: (212) 410-0200   www.standardandpoors.com

Investment, finance, economic, mutual funds data and marketing information.

Standard & Poor's Corp., Nihon Keisa Shambun, 5 Otemachi 1-chome, Chiyoda-ku, Tokyo, Japan

STAR TELECOMMUNICATIONS, INC.

223 East De La Guerra Street, Santa Barbara, CA, 93101

Tel: (805) 899-1962   Fax: (805) 899-2972   www.startel.com

Provides long-distance telecommunications services.

Star Japan KK, Toushin Takanawa Bldg., 9/F, 11-3 Takanawa 3-Chome, Minato-ku, Tokyo 108-0074, Japan

Tel: 81-3-3448-0482   Fax: 81-3-3448-0490

STARBUCKS CORPORATION

2401 Utah Ave. South, Seattle, WA, 98134

Tel: (206) 447-1575   Fax: (206) 447-0828   www.starbucks.com

Coffee bean retail store and coffee bars.

Starbucks Coffee Japan, 4-22-5 Minomi-Aoyama, Minato-ku, Tokyo 107-0062, Japan

Tel: 81-3-5412-7031   Fax: 81-3-5412-7564

STARKEY LABORATORIES, INC.

6700 Washington Avenue South, Eden Prairie, MN, 55344

Tel: (952) 941-6401   Fax: (952) 947-4787   www.starkey.com

Mfr. custom in-the-ear hearing aids.

Starkey Japan KK, 5-2-20 Nakamachidai, Tsuzuki-ku, Yokohama 224, Japan

Tel: 81-45-942-7226

STARWOOD HOTELS & RESORTS WORLDWIDE

777 Westchester Avenue, White Plains, NY, 10604

Tel: (914) 640-8100   Fax: (914) 640-8316   www.starwoodhotels.com

Hotel operations including Sheraton, Westin, St. Regis, Four Points and Caesars.

Sheraton Grande Tokyo Bay Hotel & Towers, 1-9 Maihama Uraysau, Chiba Tokyo 279, Japan

Tel: 81-473-55-5555   Fax: 81-473-55-5566

Sheraton Intl. Sales & Reservations, Sumitomo Seimei Midosuji Bldg., 4-4-3 Nishi Tenma, Kita-ku, Osaka 530, Japan

Sheraton Intl. Sales & Reservations, Hotel New Otami, 4 Kioi-cho, Chiyoda-ku, Tokyo 102, Japan

Westin Tokyo, 1-4-1 Mita, Meguro-ku, Tokyo 153, Japan

Tel: 81-3-5423-7000   Fax: 81-3-5423-7600

STATE STREET CORPORATION

225 Franklin Street, Boston, MA, 02101

Tel: (617) 786-3000   Fax: (617) 654-3386   www.statestreet.com

Engaged in investment management and institutional investor services.

State Street Trust & Banking, Shiroyama JT Mori Building 14/F, 4-3-1 Toranomon, Minato-ku, Tokyo 105-6014, Japan

State Street Trust & Banking, Fuji Building, Ste. 227, 3-2-3 Marunouchi Chiyoda-ku, Tokyo 100-0005, Japan

STEELCASE INC.

901 44th Street SE, Grand Rapids, MI, 49508

Tel: (616) 247-2710   Fax: (616) 248-7010   www.steelcase.com

Mfr. office, computer-support and systems furniture.

Steelcase Japan Ltd., 32 Kowa Bldg., 5-2-32 Minami-Azabu, Minato-ku, Tokyo 106, Japan

STEINWAY MUSICAL INSTRUMENTS, INC.

800 South St., Ste.305, Waltham, MA, 02453

Tel: (781) 894-9770   Fax: (781) 894-9803   www.steinway.com

Manufacture and marketing of pianos.

Steinway & Sons Japan Ltd., Room 1305, Onarimon Yusen Bldg., No. 23-5 Nishi Shimbashi 3-chome, Minato-ku, Toyko 105, Japan

Tel: 81-3-3432-1611   Fax: 81-3-3432-1640   Contact: Peter Suzuki, Pres.

STERIS CORPORATION
5960 Heisley Road, Mentor, OH, 44060

Tel: (440) 354-2600   Fax: (440) 639-4459   www.steris.com

Mfr. sterilization and infection control equipment, surgical tables, lighting systems for health, pharmaceutical and scientific industries.

Steris Corporation, Koji Kazuma, 6-11 Sakushindai 1-chome, Hanamigawa-ku, Chiba City 262, Japan

STIEFEL LABORATORIES INC.
255 Alhambra Circle, Ste. 1000, Coral Gables, FL, 33134

Tel: (305) 443-3807   Fax: (305) 443-3467   www.stiefel.com

Mfr. pharmaceuticals, dermatological specialties.

Stiefel Laboratories Japan, 704, Ichibancho Central Bldg., 22-1 Ichiban-cho, Chiyoda-ku, Tokyo 102, Japan

STORAGE NETWORKS, INC.
255 Wyman Street, Waltham, MA, 02451

Tel: (781) 622-6700   Fax: (781) 622-6799   www.storagenetworks.com

Mfr. software to store and access data.

StorageNetworks KK, Imperial Tower, 15th Fl., 1-1-1 Uchisaiwaicho Chiyoda-ku, Tokyo 100-0011, Japan
Tel: 81-3-3507-5650 Fax: 81-3-3507-5601

STORAGE TECHNOLOGY CORPORATION
One Storagetech Dr., Louisville, CO, 80028-4377

Tel: (303) 673-5151   Fax: (303) 673-5019   www.stortek.com

Mfr., market, service information, storage and retrieval systems.

StorageTek Ltd., 4-11 Jingumae 2-chome, Shibuya-ku, Tokyo 150-0001, Japan
Tel: 81-3-3746-9812 Contact: Taizo Yamagiwa

STREAM INTERNATIONAL
85 Dan Road, Canton, MA, 02021

Tel: (781) 575-6800   Fax: (781) 575-6999   www.stream.com

Provider of outsourced technical support for major computer industry companies.

Corporate Software Ltd. K.K. (JV), Tennozu Parkside Building, 2-5-8 Higashi Shinagawa, Shinagawa ku, Tokyo 140-0002, Japan
Tel: 81-3-5462-2800 Fax: 81-3-5462-3830

SUDLER & HENNESSEY
230 Park Avenue South, New York, NY, 10003-1566

Tel: (212) 614-4100   Fax: (212) 598-6933   www.sudler.com

Engaged in healthcare products advertising.

Dentsu Sudler & Hennessey Havas KK, Tsukiji MK Bldg., 2-11-26 Tsukiji, Chuo-ku, Tokyo 104-0045, Japan
Tel: 81-3-3546-0451 Fax: 81-3-3546-0455 Contact: Shinzo Ueno

SUGHRUE, MION PLLC
2100 Pennsylvania Ave., NW Ste. 800, Washington, DC, 20037-3202

Tel: (202) 293-7060   Fax: (202) 293-7860   www.sughrue.com

International law firm.

Sughrue, Mion, Toei Nishi Shimbashi Bldg., 4F, 13-5 Nishi Shinbashi 1-Chome, Minato-ku, Tokyo 105, Japan
Tel: 81-3-3503-3760 Fax: 81-3-3503-3756 Contact: John Inge & Abraham Rosner, Partners Emp: 2

SULLIVAN & CROMWELL
125 Broad Street, New York, NY, 10004-2498

Tel: (212) 558-4000   Fax: (212) 558-3588   www.sullcrom.com

Engaged in international law.

Sullivan & Cromwell, Otemachi First Square East Tower 16/F, 5-1, Otemachi 1-chome Chiyoda-ku, Tokyo 100-0004, Japan

SUNKIST GROWERS INC.

14130 Riverside Drive, Van Nuys, CA, 91423

Tel: (818) 986-4800   Fax: (818) 379-7405   www.sunkist.com

Citrus marketing cooperative; fruits and vegetables.

Sunkist Pacific Ltd., 5-19 Akasaka 4-chome, Minato-ku, Tokyo, Japan

SUNRISE MEDICAL INC.

7477 East Dry Creek Parkway, Longmont, CO, 80503

Tel: (303) 218-4500   Fax: (303) 218-4590   www.sunrisemedical.com

Designs, manufactures and markets rehabilitation products and assistive technology devices for people with disabilities, and patient care products used in nursing homes, hospitals and homecare settings.

Sunrise Medical Japan, Higashi-Nakano Green 202, 32-8 Higashi-Nikano 1-chrome, Nakano-ku, Tokyo, Japan

SWECO INC.

PO Box 1509, 8029 U.S. Highway 25, Florence, KY, 41042-1509

Tel: (859) 283-8400   Fax: (859) 283-8469   www.sweco.com

Engaged in separation technology and manufacture of vibratory process and solids control equipment.

Shinko Pantec Co. Ltd., 19 Niijima, Harima-Cyo, Kako-Gun, Hyougo-Ken T675-0, Japan

SYBASE, INC.

5000 Hacienda Dr., Dublin, CA, 94568

Tel: (925) 236-5000   Fax: (925) 236-4321   www.sybase.com

Design/mfg/distribution of database management systems, software development tools, connectivity products, consulting and technical support services..

Powersoft K.K., Chichibuya Building, 6F, 3-7-4 Kojimachi, Chiyoda-ku, Tokyo 102, Japan

Tel: 81-3-5214-0850 Fax: 81-3-5214-0888

Sybase K.K., Kioi-cho Building, 12F, 3-12 Kioi-cho, Chiyoda-ku, Tokyo 102, Japan

Tel: 81-3-5210-6000 Fax: 81-3-5210-6300

SYBRON DENTAL SPECIALTIES, INC.

1717 West Collins, Orange, CA, 92867

Tel: (714) 516-7400   Fax: (714) 516-7904   www.sybrondental.com

Mfr. consumable dental products, light curing instruments and plastics for dental use.

Sybron Dental Specialties, Kitamura Bldg., #29-24, Honkomagome 2-chome, Bunkyo-ku, Tokyo 113-0021, Japan

Tel: 81-3-5977-3126 Fax: 81-3-3941-3126 Contact: Teddy Tsuneda

SYMANTEC CORPORATION

20330 Stevens Creek Blvd., Cupertino, CA, 95014-2132

Tel: (408) 253-9600   Fax: (408) 253-3968   www.symantec.com

Designs and produces PC network security and network management software and hardware.

Symantec Japan Ltd., Shibuya Infoss Tower, 16F, 20-1 Sakuragaoka-cho, Shibuya-ku, Tokyo 150, Japan

Tel: 81-3-5457-5300 Fax: 81-2-3498-0520

SYMBOL TECHNOLOGIES, INC.

One Symbol Plaza, Holtsville, NY, 11742-1300

Tel: (631) 738-2400   Fax: (631) 738-5990   www.symbol.com

Mfr. Bar code-driven data management systems, wireless LAN's, and Portable Shopping System™.

Olympus Symbol Inc., San-Ei Bldg., 4F, 22-2 Nishi-Shinjuku 1-chome, Shinjuku-ku, Tokyo 160, Japan

Tel: 81-3-3348-0212 Fax: 81-3-3348-0216

SYNAPTICS INCORPORATED

2381 Bering Drive, San Jose, CA, 95131

Tel: (408) 434-0110   Fax: (408) 434-9819   www.synaptics.com

Designs and sells interfaces for portable electronic devices.

Synaptics Japan, 2-8, 1-Chome Yotsuya, Shinjuku-ku, Tokyo 160-0004, Japan

SYNAVANT INC.

3445 Peachtree Road NE, Ste. 1400, Atlanta, GA, 30326

Tel: (404) 841-4000   Fax: (404) 841-4115   www.synavant.com

Mfr. support software for pharmaceutical industry.

Synavant, Landic Toranomon Building II, 3-7-8 Toranomon Minato-ku, Tokyo 105-0001, Japan

SYNCHRONICITY SOFTWARE, INC.

201 Forest Street, Marlboro, MA, 01752

Tel: (508) 485-4122   Fax: (508) 485-7514   www.synchronicity.com

Mfr. communications software.

Itochu Techno-Science Corp., 11-5, Fujimi 1-chome Chiyoda-ku, Tokyo 102-0071, Japan

SYNOPSYS, INC.

700 East Middlefield Road, Mountain View, CA, 94043

Tel: (650) 962-5000   Fax: (650) 965-8637   www.synopsys.com

Mfr. electronic design automation software.

Nihon Synopsys Co. KK, 19F/20F, Shinjuku Mitsui Building, 2-1-1 Nishi Shinjuku, Shinjuku-ku, Tokyo 163-0420, Japan

Tel: 81-3-3346-7030 Fax: 81-3-3346-7050

Nihon Synopsys Co. KK, Pias Tower 13F, 3-19-3 Toyosaki, Kita-ku Osaka-shi, Osaka 531-0072, Japan

Tel: 81-6-6359-8139 Fax: 81-6-6359-8149

SYNPLICITY, INC.

935 Stewart Drive, Sunnyvale, CA, 94085

Tel: (408) 215-6000   Fax: (408) 990-0290   www.synplicity.com

Mfr. software.

Synplicity KK, K.I. Shinjuku Bldg. 6F, 2-10-8 Yoyogi, Shinjuku-ku, Tokyo 151-0053, Japan

Tel: 81-3-5358-3311 Fax: 81-3-5358-3321

SYNTEGRA

4201 Lexington Avenue North, Arden Hills, MN, 55126-6198

Tel: (651) 415-2999   Fax: (651) 415-4891   www.cdc.com

Engaged in consulting and systems integration.

Syntegra Japan, Tokyo, Japan

SYSTEMSOFT CORPORATION

2 Apple Hill, Natick, MA, 01760

Tel: (508) 651-0088   Fax: (508) 651-8188   www.systemsoft.com

Mfr. computer utility software.

Pacific SystemSoft KK, 20/F, #4 Ohsaki New City, 1-6-4, Ohsaki, Shinagawa-ku, Tokyo 141-0032, Japan

THE TCW GROUP

865 S. Figueroa St., Ste. 1800, Los Angeles, CA, 90017

Tel: (213) 244-0000   Fax: (213) 244-0000   www.tcwgroup.com

Engaged in managing pension and profit sharing funds, retirement/health and welfare funds, insurance company funds, endowments and foundations.

TCW Group (JV), Tokyo, Japan

TECA CORPORATION (THERMO ELECTRIC COOLING AMERICA

4048 West Schubert, Chicago, IL, 60639

Tel: (773) 342-4900   Fax: (773) 342-0191   www.thermoelectric.com

Mfr. solid state cooling products, including air-conditioners, cold plates and liquid chillers.

Tel-Thermco Engineering Co. Inc., 32-10 Kawajiri Shiroyama 1-chome, Tsukui, Kanakawa Pref. 220-01, Japan

TECH/OPS SEVCON INC.

40 North Avenue, Burlington, MA, 01803

Tel: (781) 229-7896   Fax: (781) 229-8603   www.sevcon.com

Design, manufacture, and marketing of microprocessor based control systems for battery powered vehicles.

Sevcon Japan., 1-22-10-303, Setagaya Daita, Setagaya-Ku, Tokyo 155-0022, Japan

TEKELEC

26580 West Agoura Road, Calabasas, CA, 91302

Tel: (818) 880-5656   Fax: (818) 880-6993   www.tekelec.com

Mfr. telecommunications testing equipment.

Tekelec Ltd., Daiichi Ogikubo Bldg., 27-8 Ogikubo 5-chome, Suginami-ku, Tokyo 167, Japan

Contact: Akira Ohsone, Pres.   Emp: 34

TEKTRONIX INC.

14200 SW Karl Braun Dr., PO Box 500, Beaverton, OR, 97077

Tel: (503) 627-7111   Fax: (503) 627-2406   www.tek.com

Mfr. test and measure, visual systems/color printing and communications/video and networking products.

Sony/Tektronix Corp. (JV), Tokyo International, 5-9-31 Kitashinagawa, Shinagawa-ku, Tokyo 141-0001, Japan

Tel: 81-3-3448-3111   Fax: 81-3-3444-3663

TELEFLEX INC.

630 W. Germantown Pike, Ste. 450, Plymouth Meeting, PA, 19462

Tel: (610) 834-6301   Fax: (610) 834-8307   www.teleflex.com

Design, manufacture and marketing of mechanical and electro-mechanical systems, control systems and surgical devices.

Rüsch Asia Pacific Sdn. Bhd., Tokyo, Japan

TELEX COMMUNICATIONS INC.

12000 Portland Ave. South, Burnsville, MN, 55337

Tel: (952) 884-4051   Fax: (952) 884-0043   www.telexcommunications.com

Mfr. communications, audio-visual and professional audio products.

EVI Audio Japan, Ltd., 3-29-10 1F Chiyoda, Naka-Ku Nagoya-shi, Aichi 460-001, Japan

TELLABS INC.

1415 W. Diehl Rd., Naperville, IL, 60563

Tel: (630) 378-8800   Fax: (630) 852-7346   www.tellabs.com

Design/mfr./service voice/data transport and network access systems.

Tellabs, Toranomon 40 - Mori Building, 9/F, Toranomon 5-13-1, Minato-ku, Tokyo 105-0001, Japan

TENNANT COMPANY

701 North Lilac Drive, Minneapolis, MN, 55440

Tel: (763) 540-1208   Fax: (763) 540-1437   www.tennantco.com

Mfr. industry floor maintenance sweepers and scrubbers and floor coatings.

Tennant Japan, Sanka Bldg., 5/F, 2-9 Minami Saiwai-cho, Saiwai-ku, Kawasaki 210, Japan

Tel: 81-44-556-1201   Fax: 81-44-556-1202   Contact: Sheila LeGeros, Mng. Dir.

TENNECO AUTOMOTIVE INC.

500 North Field Drive, Lake Forest, IL, 60045

Tel: (847) 482-5241   Fax: (847) 482-5295   www.tenneco-automotive.com

Mfr. automotive parts, exhaust systems and service equipment.

Tenneco Automotive Japan Ltd., 20-20 Hiradai, Tsuzuke-ku, Yokohama-shi, Kanagawa Prefecture 224, Japan

Tel: 81-45-942-5211   Fax: 81-45-942-5228   Contact: Kan Shishikura, Mgr.   Emp: 23

TERADYNE INC.

321 Harrison Ave., Boston, MA, 02118

Tel: (617) 482-2700   Fax: (617) 422-2910   www.teradyne.com

Mfr. electronic test equipment and blackplane connection systems.

Teradyne K.K. - Far East Sales Office, Teradyne Bldg., 1-5-4 Higashiyama, Meguro-ku, Tokyo 153, Japan

Tel: 81-3-3719-0180   Contact: Akira Kasai, Reg. Mgr.

TEXAS INSTRUMENTS INC.

12500 TI Blvd., Dallas, TX, 75266

Tel: (972) 995-3773   Fax: (972) 995-4360   www.ti.com

Mfr. semiconductor devices, electronic electro-mechanical systems, instruments and controls.

Texas Instruments Japan Ltd., 305 Tangashira, Oyama-cho Suntoh-gun, Shizuoka-ken, Oyama Plant 410-13, Japan

Tel: 81-550-781211

Texas Instruments Japan Ltd., 4260 Aza-Takao, Oaza-Kawasaki, Hayami-gun, Hiji-machi 879-15, Japan

Texas Instruments Japan Ltd., 18-36 Minami 3-chome, Hatagoya City 334, Japan

Tel: 81-48-282-2211

Texas Instruments Japan Ltd., 2355 Kihara Miho-mura, Inashiki-gun, Ibaragi-ken, Miho Plant 300-04, Japan

Tel: 81-298-40-4435

TEXTRON INC.

40 Westminster Street, Providence, RI, 02903

Tel: (401) 421-2800   Fax: (401) 421-2878   www.textron.com

Mfr. Aerospace (Bell Helicopter and Cessna Aircraft), industry and consumer products, fasteners and financial services.

Japan Avdel KK, Takahashi Building, 9-3, 5-Chome, Nishitenma, Kita-Ku, Osaka 530, Japan

Tel: 81-6-3631876   Fax: 81-6-3651620   Contact: Akira Rai

THE MARMON GROUP, INC.

200 West Adams, Ste. 2211, Chicago, IL, 60606

Tel: (312) 372-9500   Fax: (312) 845-5305   www.marmon.com

Holding company for diversified manufacturing and service firms.

Getz Bros. & Co. Ltd., Sumitomo Seimei Aoyama Bldg., 3-1-30 Minami-Aoyama, Minato-ku, Tokyo 107, Japan

Tel: 81-3-3423-1302   Fax: 81-3-3402-5979   Contact: Paul Bond, Gen. Mgr.   Emp: 330

THERMADYNE HOLDINGS CORPORATION

101 South Hanley Road, Suite 300, St. Louis, MO, 63105

Tel: (314) 746-2197   Fax: (314) 746-2349   www.thermadyne.com

Mfr. welding, cutting, and safety products.

Thermadyne Japan Ltd., 4-3-18-201, Zuiko, Higashi-yodogawa-ku, Osaka 533-0005, Japan

THERMO ELECTRON CORPORATION

81 Wyman Street, Waltham, MA, 02454-9046

Tel: (781) 622-1000   Fax: (781) 622-1207   www.thermo.com

Develop, mfr., sale of process equipment &instruments for energy intensive and healthcare industries.

Nicolet Biomedical Japan Inc., Ryokuci-eki Bldg., 6F, 4-1-Terauchi 2 chome, Toyonaka City Osaka Pref. 560, Japan

Tel: 81-6-866-3500

Nicolet Biomedical Japan Inc., Nish-Shinjuku Forest Bldg., 3F, 32-12 Nishi 4 chome, Shinjuku-ku, Tokyo 160, Japan

Tel: 81-3-332-0661

Thermo Electron Nippon Co. Ltd., 3-5-11 Minami-Nakaburi, Hiakaba, Osaka, Japan

THERMO FINNIGAN CORPORATION

355 River Oaks Parkway, San Jose, CA, 95134-1991

Tel: (408) 433-4800   Fax: (408) 433-4823   www.thermo.com

Mfr. mass spectrometers.

Thermo Finnigan, Nishi-Shinjuku Toyokuni Bldg., Hatsudai 2-5-8, Shibuya-Ku, Tokyo 151151, Japan

THERMO NICOLET CORPORATION

5225 Verona Road, Madison, WI, 53711-4495

Tel: (608) 276-6100   Fax: (608) 276-6222   www.nicolet.com

Mfr. infrared spectrometers and oscilloscopes and medical electro-diagnostic equipment.

Nicolet Japan Corp., 7-1 Hirakawa-cho 2-chome, Chiyoda-ku, Tokyo 102, Japan

Nicolet Japan Corp., Ryokuchi-Eki Bldg., 6F, 4-1 Terauchi 2-chome, Toyonaka, Osaka 560, Japan

Nicolet Japan Corp., 17-10 Uchiyama 3-chome, Chikusa-ku, Nagoya 464, Japan

THERM-O-DISC, INC.

1320 S. Main Street, Mansfield, OH, 44907-0538

Tel: (419) 525-8300   Fax: (419) 525-8344   www.thermodisc.com

Mfr. thermostats, controls, sensor and thermal cutoffs, switches.

Therm-O-Disc, 102 Takasago Bldg., 100 Edo-Machi, Chuo-ku, Kobe 650, Japan

THERMON MANUFACTURING COMPANY

100 Thermon Drive, PO Box 609, San Marcos, TX, 78667-0609

Tel: (512) 396-5801   Fax: (512) 396-3627   www.thermon.com

Mfr. steam and electric heat tracing systems, components and accessories.

Thermon Far East, 3F, Recruit Yokohama Building, 6-3 Kin Koa-Cho, Kanagawa-ku, Yokohama 221, Japan

THOMAS & BETTS CORPORATION

8155 T&B Blvd., Memphis, TN, 38125

Tel: (901) 252-5000   Fax: (901) 685-1988   www.tnb.com

Mfr. elect/electronic connectors and accessories.

Thomas & Betts Japan Ltd., 44 Kowa Bldg., 2-7 Higashiyama 1-chome, Meguru-ku, Tokyo 153, Japan

THOMAS PUBLISHING COMPANY

5 Penn Plaza, New York, NY, 10007

Tel: (212) 695-0500   Fax: (212) 290-7362   www.thomaspublishing.com

Publishing magazines and directories.

Incom Co. Ltd., Plaza Edo Gawabashi, 1-23-6 Sekiguchi, Bunkyo-ku, Tokyo 112, Japan

TIBCO SOFTWARE INC.

3165 Porter Drive, Palo Alto, CA, 94304

Tel: (650) 846-5000   Fax: (650) 846-1005   www.tibco.com

Mfr. software and provides e-commerce, consulting, and support services. (JV of Reuters UK)

TIBCO Software Inc., 11/F Atago Toyo Building, 1-3-4 Atago, Minato-ku, Tokyo 105-0002, Japan

Tel: 81-3-5425-6060

TIFFANY & COMPANY

727 Fifth Ave., New York, NY, 10022

Tel: (212) 755-8000   Fax: (212) 605-4465   www.tiffany.com

Mfr./retail fine jewelry, silverware, china, crystal, leather goods, etc.

Tiffany & Co. Japan, 6-16 Ginza 4-chome, Chuo-ku, Tokyo 104, Japan

TMP WORLDWIDE, INC.

622 Third Ave., New York, NY, 10017

Tel: (212) 351-7000   Fax: (212) 658-0540   www.tmpw.com

#1 Yellow Pages agency and a leader in the recruitment and interactive advertising fields.

TMP Worldwide/JDAC, #303, Yotsuya Mansion, 1-22 Arakicho, Shinjuku-ku, Tokyo 160, Japan

Tel: 81-33-358-24-41

TOGETHERSOFT CORPORATION

900 Main Campus Drive, Ste. 500, Raleigh, NC, 27606

Tel: (919) 833-5550   Fax: (919) 833-5533   www.togethersoft.com

Mfr. software.

TogetherSoft Japan KK, Level 18, Yebisu Garden Place Tower, 4-20-3, Ebisu Shibuya-ku, Tokyo 150-6018, Japan

TOMMY HILFIGER CORPORATION

25 West 39th Street, 13th Fl., New York, NY, 10018

Tel: (212) 840-8888   Fax: (212) 302-8718   www.tommy.com

Clothing manufacturer and chain stores. (JV with Tommy Hilfiger Corp., Hong Kong)

Tommy Hilfiger Sportswear, Inc., Tokyo, Japan

THE TORRINGTON COMPANY

59 Field St., PO Box 1008, Torrington, CT, 06790

Tel: (860) 626-2000   Fax: (860) 496-3625   www.torrington.com

Mfr. precision bearings, motion control components and automotive steering assemblies.

NSK Torrington Company Ltd. (JV), Tokyo, Japan

TOWERS PERRIN

335 Madison Ave., New York, NY, 10017-4605

Tel: (212) 309-3400   Fax: (212) 309-0975   www.towers.com

Management consulting services.

Towers Perrin KK, Imperial Tower, 1-1 Uchisaiwai-cho 1-chome, Chiyoda-ku, Tokyo 100, Japan

Tel: 81-3-3581-5731   Fax: 81-3-3581-5719

TOYS R US INC.

461 From Road, Paramus, NJ, 07652

Tel: (201) 262-7800   Fax: (201) 845-0973   www.toysrus.com

Retail stores: toys and games, sporting goods, computer software, books, records.

Toys R Us Japan Ltd., 3-1 Ekimae Honcho, Kawasaki, Kanagawa 0210, Japan

THE TRANE COMPANY

3600 Pammel Creek Road, La Crosse, WI, 54601

Tel: (608) 787-2000   Fax: (608) 787-4990   www.trane.com

Mfr. distribution and service of A/C systems and equipment.

Trane Japan, Tokyodo Nishi-Cho Bldg., 5/F, 3-7-2 Kanda Nishi-cho, Chiyoda-ku, Tokyo, Japan

TRANSATLANTIC HOLDINGS, INC.

80 Pine Street, New York, NY, 10005

Tel: (212) 770-2000   Fax: (212) 289-6801   www.transre.com

Engaged in reinsurance.

TRC Reinsurance, Hibaya Park Bldg., 9/F, 8-1 Yurakucho, 1-Chome Chiyoda-Ku, Tokyo 100-0006, Japan

TREDEGAR CORPORATION

1100 Boulders Pkwy., Richmond, VA, 23225

Tel: (804) 330-1000   Fax: (804) 330-1177   www.tredegar.com

Engaged in oil and gas production and manufacture of plastics and aluminum products.

Tredegar Film Products, Kobe, Japan

TREIBACHER SCHLEIFMITTEL CORPORATION

2000 College Ave., Niagara Falls, NY, 14305

Tel: (716) 286-1234   Fax: (716) 286-1224   www.treibacher-schleifm.com

Mfr. abrasives.

Treibacher Schleifmittel KK, SBS Hills II Room 44, 4-10-3 Yoga Setagaya-ku, Tokyo 158, Japan

TRIMBLE NAVIGATION LIMITED

645 N. Mary Ave., Sunnyvale, CA, 94086

Tel: (408) 481-8000   Fax: (408) 481-2000   www.trimble.com

Design/mfr. electronic geographic instrumentation.

Trimble Japan K.K., Shin-ohashi Riverside, Bldg. 101, Tokyo 135-0007, Japan

Tel: 81-3-5638-5015

TROPICANA PRODUCTS, INC.

1001 13th Avenue East, Bradenton, FL, 34208

Tel: (941) 747-4461   Fax: (941) 665-5330   www.tropicana.com

Marketer and producer of branded juices, including Tropicana, Dole, Looza and Copella.

Kirin-Tropicana, Inc., Kanda Izumicho Bldg., 11/F, 1 Kanda Izumicho, Chiyoda-ku, Tokyo, Japan

Tel: 81-3-5821-4080   Fax: 81-3-5821-4144

TRW INC.

1900 Richmond Road, Cleveland, OH, 44124-2760

Tel: (216) 291-7000   Fax: (216) 291-7932   www.trw.com

Electric and energy-related products, automotive and aerospace products, tools and fasteners.

TRW Automotive-Electronics Asia Inc., Tameike Meisan Bldg., 8F, 1-12 Akasaka 1-chome, Minato-ku, Tokyo 107, Japan

TW METALS INC.

760 Constitution Drive, Ste. 204, Exton, PA, 19341

Tel: (610) 458-1300   Fax: (610) 458-1399   www.twmetals.com

Engaged in metals distribution and processing.

TW Metals Japan KK, 3-15-1-513 Higashi-Asahina, Kanazawa-ku, Yokohama, Kanagawa 236-0033, Japan

TWIN DISC INCORPORATED

1328 Racine Street, Racine, WI, 53403-1758

Tel: (262) 638-4000   Fax: (262) 638-4482   www.twindisc.com

Mfr. industry clutches, reduction gears and transmissions.

Twin Disc Nico Transmission Co., Inc., 405-3, Yoshinocho 1-chome, Saitama-Shi, Saitama-Ken 330-8646, Japan

Tel: 81-3-3354-6931   Fax: 81-3-3341-5365

TYSON FOODS INC.

2210 W. Oaklawn Dr., Springdale, AR, 72762-6999

Tel: (501) 290-4000   Fax: (501) 290-4061   www.tyson.com

Production/mfr./distributor poultry, beef, pork and seafood products.

Tyson Japan, Market Makers, Seibunkin Bldg., 5F, 1-5-9 Iidabashi, Chiyoda-ku, Tokyo 102, Japan

Tel: 81-3-3221-5852   Fax: 81-3-3221-5960   Contact: Jeff McNeill, Managing Director

U.S. WHEAT ASSOCIATES

1620 "I" Street NW, Ste. 801, Washington, DC, 20006-4005

Tel: (202) 463-0999   Fax: (202) 785-1052   www.uswheat.org

Market development for wheat products.

U.S. Wheat Associates Inc., 1-14 Akasaka 1-chome, Minato-ku, Tokyo 107, Japan

Tel: 81-3-3582-7911

UAL CORPORATION

1200 E. Algonquin Rd., Chicago, IL, 60007

Tel: (847) 700-4000   Fax: (847) 700-4081   www.ual.com

Air transportation, passenger and freight services.

United Airlines, Tokyo, Japan

United Airlines, Honmachi Nomura Bldg., 3-4-10 Honmachi, Chuo-ku, Osaka 541, Japan

Tel: 81-3-3817-4411

UBS PAINEWEBBER

1285 Ave. of the Americas, New York, NY, 10019

Tel: (212) 713-2000   Fax: (212) 713-4889   www.ubspainewebber.com

Engaged in stock brokerage and investment services.

UBS PaineWebber Intl., Asahi Seimei Hibiya, Bldg., 3F, 1-5-1 Yorako-cho, Chiyoda-ku, Tokyo 100, Japan

Tel: 81-3-3593-5200

UNION CARBIDE CORPORATION

39 Old Ridgebury Road, Danbury, CT, 06817

Tel: (203) 794-2000   Fax: (203) 794-6269   www.unioncarbide.com

Mfr. industrial chemicals, plastics and resins.

Nippon Uninar Co., Asahi Bldg., 16-17/F, 6-1 Ohtemachi 2-chome, Minato-ku, Tokyo 100, Japan

UNION PACIFIC CORPORATION

1416 Dodge St., Room 1230, Omaha, NE, 68179

Tel: (402) 271-5777   Fax: (402) 271-6408   www.up.com

Holding company: railroad, crude oil, natural gas, petroleum refining, metal mining service, real estate.

Union Pacific Railroad, Satoh Bldg., 4F, 1-19-4 Hamamatsu-cho, Minato-ku, Tokyo 105, Japan

UNISYS CORPORATION.

PO Box 500, Union Meeting Road, Blue Bell, PA, 19424

Tel: (215) 986-4011   Fax: (215) 986-6850   www.unisys.com

Mfr./marketing/servicing electronic information systems.

Nihon Unisys/Univac Ltd., 17-15 Akasaka 2-chome, Minato-ku, Tokyo 107, Japan

Unisys Japan Ltd., Mori Bldg. 31, Tokyo 102, Japan

UNITED ASSET MANAGEMENT CORPORATION

One International Place, 44th Fl., Boston, MA, 02110

Tel: (617) 330-8900   Fax: (617) 330-1133   www.uam.com

Holding company for investment management services.

UAM Japan, Imperial Tower 14F, 1-1-1, Uchisaiwaicho, Chiyoda-ku, Tokyo 105-0011, Japan

Tel: 81-3-3519-4080   Fax: 81-3-3519-4155   Contact: Masaharu Izumi, Pres.

UNITED PARCEL SERVICE, INC.

55 Glenlake Parkway, NE, Atlanta, GA, 30328

Tel: (404) 828-6000   Fax: (404) 828-6593   www.ups.com

International package-delivery service.

UPS - Yamato Co. Ltd., 1-6 Ariake, Koto-ku, Tokyo 135-1163, Japan

Tel: 81-3-3520-0090   Fax: 81-3-3520-0091

UNITED TECHNOLOGIES CORPORATION

One Financial Plaza, Hartford, CT, 06103

Tel: (860) 728-7000   Fax: (860) 728-7979   www.utc.com

Mfr. aircraft engines, elevators, A/C, auto equipment, space and military electronic and rocket propulsion systems. Products include Pratt and Whitney, Otis elevators, Carrier heating and air conditioning and Sikorsky helicopters.

United Technologies Intl. Operations Inc., Uchisaiwaicho Dai Building, 7F, 3-3 Uchisaiwaicho 1-chome, Chiyoda-k, Tokyo 100, Japan

Tel: 81-3-358-13221   Fax: 81-3-358-13226   Contact: Randall Green

UNIVERSAL SECURITY INSTRUMENTS, INC.

PO Box 825, Binghamton, NY, 13902-0825

Tel: (607) 779-7689   Fax: (607) 779-7301   www.uic.com

Provider of innovative electronic circuit assembly technology and equipment, integrated system solutions, and process expertise.

Universal Instruments Japan Ltd., Tokyo, Japan

Tel: 81-3-3861-9701   Fax: 81-3-3861-9500

UNIVERSAL WEATHER & AVIATION INC.

8787 Tallyho Road, Houston, TX, 77061

Tel: (713) 944-1622   Fax: (713) 943-4650   www.univ-wea.com

Provides service management, and worldwide weather and communications to the corporate aviation community.

Universal Weather & Aviation, Japan Airlines Bldg., Narita International Airport, Tokyo, Japan

Tel: 81-476-34-3957   Fax: 81-476-34-6575   Contact: Hiroshi Higashiyama

UNUM PROVIDENT

2211 Congress Street, Portland, ME, 04122

Tel: (207) 770-2211   Fax: (207) 770-4510   www.unum.com

Disability and special risk insurance.

Unum Japan Accident Insurance Co. Ltd., Sanbancho UF Building, 2F, 6-3 Sanban-cho, Chiyada-ku, Tokyo 102-0075, Japan

Tel: 81-3-5276-1391   Fax: 81-3-5276-0098   Contact: Kevin McCarthy, Pres.

UOP LLC

25 East Algonquin Road, Des Plaines, IL, 60017

Tel: (847) 391-2000   Fax: (847) 391-2253   www.uop.com

Engaged in developing and commercializing technology for license to the oil refining, petrochemical and gas processing industries.

Nikki Universal Co., 2-4 Ohtemachi, Chiyoda-ku, Tokyo, Japan

Nikki-Universal Co. Ltd., Nissei Bldg., 6-3 Ohsaki 1-chome, Shinagawa-ku, Tokyo 141, Japan

Tel: 81-3-5436-8446   Fax: 81-3-5436-8388

Union Showa K.K., Molecular Sieves, 27-17 Hamamatsu-cho 1-chome, Minato-ku, Tokyo 105, Japan

UOP KK, NK Bldg. Ohsaki City, 6/F, 6-28 Kitashinagawa 5-chome, Shinagawa-ku, Tokyo 141-001, Japan

Tel: 81-3-5421-2560   Fax: 81-3-5421-2788

URS CORPORATION

100 California Street, Ste. 500, San Francisco, CA, 94111

Tel: (415) 774-2700   Fax: (415) 398-1905   www.urscorp.com

Engineering, environmental and construction management services.

Dames & Moore Ltd., Asahi Bldg., 7F, 38-3 Kamata 5-chome, Ota-ku, Tokyo 144, Japan

URSCHEL LABORATORIES INC.

2503 Calumet Ave., PO Box 2200, Valparaiso, IN, 46384-2200

Tel: (219) 464-4811   Fax: (219) 462-3879   www.urschel.com

Design/mfr. precision food processing equipment.

Urschel Japan, 2-18-9 Ningyoch, Nihonbashi, Chuo-ku, Tokyo, Japan

UTSTARCOM, INC.

1275 Harbor Bay Pkwy., Alameda, CA, 94502

Tel: (510) 864-8800   Fax: (510) 864-8802   www.utstar.com

Mfr. and sales of wireless telecommunications access systems and software products.

UTStarcom Inc., TT-2 Building, 8/F, 3-8-1 Nihonbashi Ningyocho Chuo-ku, Tokyo 103-0013, Japan

UUNET

22001 Loudoun County Pkwy., Ashburn, VA, 20147

Tel: (703) 206-5600   Fax: (703) 206-5601   www.uu.net

World's largest Internet service provider; World Wide Web hosting services, security products and consulting services to businesses, professionals, and on-line service providers.

UUNET KK, Odakyu Southern Tower, 2-2-1 Yoyogi, Shibuya-ku, Tokyo 151-8583, Japan

VALSPAR CORPORATION

1101 South Third Street, Minneapolis, MN, 55415-1259

Tel: (612) 332-7371   Fax: (612) 375-7723   www.valspar.com

Mfr. paints and coatings.

Valspar Rock Co., Ltd., 37-2 2-chome Minamisuna, Koto-ku Tokyo 136-0076, Japan

VARIAN MEDICAL SYSTEMS, INC.

3050 Hansen Way, Palo Alto, CA, 94304-100

Tel: (650) 493-4000   Fax: (650) 424-5358   www.varian.com

Mfr. microwave tubes and devices, analytical instruments, semiconductor process and medical equipment, vacuum systems.

Nippon Oncology Systems, Ltd. (JV), Keio Chofu Kojimacho Building, 32-2 Kojimacho 1-Chome, Chofu-shi, Tokyo 182, Japan

Nippon Oncology Systems, Ltd. (JV), Sumitomo Shoji Yodogawa Building, 11-1, Nishinakajima 1-Chome, Yodogawa-ku Osaka-shi, Osaka 532, Japan

VARIAN SEMICONDUCTOR EQUIPMENT ASSOCIATES, INC. (VSEA)

35 Dory Road, Gloucester, MA, 01930

Tel: (978) 281-2000   Fax: (978) 283-5391   www.vsea.com

Mfr. semiconductors and ion implantation systems.

Varian Semiconductor Equipment Assocates, 3-17-2 Shin-Yokohama Kouhoku-ku, Yokohama-shi, Kanagawa 222-0033, Japan

VASTERA, INC.

45025 Aviation Drive, Ste. 300, Dulles, VA, 20166

Tel: (703) 661-9006   Fax: (703) 742-4580   www.vastera.com

Helps companies to define and deploy best business processes for trade and manages their global trade operations.

Vastera Japan, Tokyo Ginko Kyokai 15/F, 1-3-1 Marunouchi Chiyoda-ku, Tokyo, Japan

Tel: 81-3-3216-7188

VEECO INSTRUMENTS INC.

100 Sunnyside Blvd., Woodbury, NY, 11797

Tel: (516) 677-0200   Fax: (516) 677-9125   www.veeco.com

Mfr. surface profiler, atomic force microscopes, leak and plating thickness detectors and semiconductor products.

Nihon Veeco K.K., Japan Headquarters, 13-7 Rokuban-cho, Chiyoda-ku, Tokyo 102, Japan

Tel: 81-3-3262-6151   Fax: 81-3-3262-6155

VELCRO USA INC.

406 Brown Avenue, Manchester, NH, 03108

Tel: (603) 669-4892   Fax: (603) 669-9271   www.velcro.com

Mfr./sales of Velcro brand hook and loop fasteners, plastic buckles and metal hardware and cable control straps.

Kuraray Co., Ltd., 12-39 Umeda, 1 Chrome, Kita-Ku, Osaka 530, Japan

Tel: 81-6-348-2111   Fax: 81-6-348-2106

VENTURE MEASUREMENT COMPANY

150 Venture Blvd., Spartanburg, SC, 29306

Tel: (864) 574-8960   Fax: (864) 578-7308   www.bindicator.com

Mfr. level control instruments for measuring solids and liquids.

Kinsho - Mataichi (Bindicator), 1-24-1 Shinkawa Chuo-Ku, Toyko, Japan

Tel: 81-33-2977111   Fax: 81-33-2977393

VERINT SYSTEMS INC.

234 Crossways Park Drive, Woodbury, NY, 11797

Tel: (516) 677-7300   Fax: (516) 677-7197   www.verintsystems.com

Mfr. and sales of analytic software.

Verint Systems Japan KK, Meiho Bldg., 8/F, 1-21-1 Nishi-shinjuku Shinjuku-ku, Tokyo 160-0023, Japan

Tel: 81-3-5324-9171   Fax: 81-3-5324-9121

VERITAS SOFTWARE INC.

350 Ellis Street, Mountain View, CA, 94043

Tel: (650) 527-8000   Fax: (650) 527-8050   www.veritas.com

Mfr. of storage management software for data protection, application availability, and disaster recovery.

VERITAS Software K.K., Fukoku-Seimei Building, 22F, 2-2-2 Uchisaiwai-cho, Chiyoda-ku, Tokyo 100-0011, Japan

VERIZON COMMUNICATIONS INC.

1095 Ave. of the Americas, New York, NY, 10036

Tel: (212) 395-2121   Fax: (212) 395-1285   www.verizon.com

Telecommunications.

PSINet Japan Inc., Gate City Ohsaki, East Tower 11F, 1-11-2 Ohsaki, Shinagawa-ku, Tokyo 141-0032, Japan

Fax: 81-3-5437-5278

TU-KA Cellular Tokyo Inc., 1-10-11 Shiba Daimon, Minato-ku, Tokyo 105-8540, Japan

Tel: 81-3-5400-6100   Fax: 81-3-5400-6150   Contact: Hajime Nakayama, Pres.

VERIZON WIRELESS, INC.

180 Washington Valley Rd., Bedminster, NJ, 07921

Tel: (908) 306-7000   Fax: (908) 306-6927   www.verizonwireless.com

Engaged in mobile phone operations.

Japan Telecom Co. Ltd., 4-7-1 Hatcho-Bori Chuo-Ku, Tokyo 104-8508, Japan

VERNAY LABORATORIES INC.

120 East South College St., Box 310, Yellow Springs, OH, 45387

Tel: (937) 767-7261   Fax: (937) 767-1208   www.vernay.com

Mfr. precision fluid handling products.

Vernay Japan, Chai Building, 1st Floor, 1006, 1-Chome, Hirabari, Tanpaku-ku, Nagoya 468-0011, Japan

VIACOM INC.

1515 Broadway, 28th Fl., New York, NY, 10036-5794

Tel: (212) 258-6000   Fax: (212) 258-6358   www.viacom.com

Communications, publishing and entertainment.

Viacom Japan Inc., Mitsuwa Bldg., 7-2 Ginza 6-chome, Chuo-ku, Tokyo 104, Japan

VIEWSONIC CORPORATION
381 Brea Canyon Road, Walnut, CA, 91789

Tel: (909) 444-8888   Fax: (909) 869-7958   www.viewsonic.com

Mfr. displays.

ViewSonic Japan KK, WBG Marive West 30F, 2-6 Nakase, Mihama-Ku,, Chiba-Shi Chiba 261, Japan

Tel: 81-43-297-1006   Fax: 81-43-297-1007

VIGNETTE CORPORATION
1601 South Mopac Expwy., Bldg. 3, Austin, TX, 78746-5776

Tel: (512) 741-4300   Fax: (512) 741-4500   www.vignette.com

Mfr. software.

Vignette KK, Level 15, JT Bldg., 2-2-1 Toranomon, Minato-ku, Tokyo 105 001, Japan

THE VIKING CORPORATION
210 N. Industrial Park Rd., Hastings, MI, 49058

Tel: (616) 945-9501   Fax: (616) 945-9599   www.vikingcorp.com

Mfr. fire extinguishing equipment.

The Viking Corporation (Japan), 507 AIOS Hiroo Building, 1-11-2 Hiroo, Shibuya-Ku, Tokyo 150-0012, Japan

Tel: 81-3-3440-8711

VIRAGE LOGIC CORPORATION
46501 Landing Pkwy., Fremont, CA, 94538

Tel: (510) 360-8000   Fax: (510) 360-8099   www.viragelogic.com

Mfr. software.

Virage Logic Corporation, SII Kameido Bldg., West 2F, 41-6, Kameido 6, Koto-ku, Tokyo 136-8512, Japan

Tel: 81-3-5626-8271   Fax: 81-3-5626-8286

VISHAY INTERTECHNOLOGY INC.
63 Lincoln Hwy., Malvern, PA, 19355

Tel: (610) 644-1300   Fax: (610) 296-0657   www.vishay.com

Mfr. resistors, strain gages, capacitors, inductors, printed circuit boards.

Vishay Japan, KK, Shibuya No. 2 Toho Seimei Bldg, 3-5-16 Shibuya, Shibuya-ku, Tokyo 150-0002, Japan

Tel: 81-3-5464-6411   Fax: 81-3-5464-6433

Vishay Japan, KK, Shin Osaka Nishiura Bldg. 7F, 2-7-38, Nishi Miyahara, Yodogawa-Ku, Osaka 532-0004, Japan

VISHAY SILICONIX INC.
2201 Laurelwood Drive, Santa Clara, CA, 95054

Tel: (408) 988-8000   Fax: (408) 970-3950   www.siliconix.com

Mfr. power IC's and analog signal processing devices for computers, cell phones, fixed communications networks, automobiles, and other electronic systems.

Vishay Siliconix Japan KK, 3-5-16 Shibuya, Shibuya-Ku, hibuya 3/F, GE Edison Bldg., Tokyo 150-0002, Japan

VITESSE SEMICONDUCTOR CORPORATION
741 Calle Plano, Camarillo, CA, 93012

Tel: (805) 388-3700   Fax: (805) 389-7188   www.vitesse.com

Mfr. integrated circuits.

Vitesse Semiconductor Japan, 2-9-21-201 Honcho, Kokubunji, Tokyo 185-0012, Japan

Tel: 81-42-326-6667   Fax: 81-42-320-5020

VIVITAR CORPORATION
1280 Rancho Conejo Blvd, Newbury Park, CA, 91320

Tel: (805) 498-7008   Fax: (805) 498-5086   www.vivitar.com

Mfr. photographic equipment, electronic supplies.

Vivitar Japan Ltd., Marusho Bldg., 6F, 12 Yotsuya 3-chome, Shinjuku-ku, Tokyo 160, Japan

VSOURCE, INC.

16875 w. Bernardo Drive, Ste. 250, San Diego, CA, 92127

Tel: (858) 618-5884   Fax: (858) 618-5904   www.vsource.com

Engaged in outsourcing services.

Vsource, Kintetsu Shin-namba Bldg., 10/F Naniwa-ku, Osaka-City, Osaka 556-0017, Japan

WACHOVIA CORPORATION

301 South College Street, Ste. 4000, Charlotte, NC, 28288-0013

Tel: (704) 374-6161   Fax: (704) 383-1240   www.wachovia.com

Engaged in commercial and retail banking services.

Wachovia Corporation, Toranomon ACT Bldg., 21-1 Toranomon 5-chome, Minato-ku, Tokyo, Japan

THE WACKENHUT CORPORATION

4200 Wackenhut Dr., Ste. 100, Palm Beach Gardens, FL, 33410

Tel: (561) 622-5656   Fax: (561) 691-6736   www.wackenhut.com

Security systems and services.

Wackenhut Keibi Co., Ginza-Matsuyoshi Bldg., 7-17-8 Ginza, Chuo-ku, Tokyo 104, Japan
Tel: 81-3-3542-3213   Fax: 81-3-3542-3214

WAHL CLIPPER CORPORATION

2902 N. Locust Street, Sterling, IL, 61081

Tel: (815) 625-6525   Fax: (815) 625-1193   www.wahlclipper.com

Mfr. hair clippers, beard and mustache trimmers, shavers, pet clippers and soldering irons.

Nippon Wahl K.K., 2-17-18 Shimo-yugi, Hachioji-shi, Tokyo 192-08, Japan

WALBRO ENGINE MANAGEMENT

7400 N. Oracle Road, Ste. 310, Tucson, AZ, 85704

Tel: (520) 877-3000   Fax: (520) 877-3006   www.walbro.com

Mfr. motor vehicle accessories and parts, automotive fluid carrying systems.

TI Group Automotive Systems/Walbro, 23-1 Sanbyakukoku, Kunisada Azuma-mura, Sawa-gun, Kiryu City Gunma-ken 379-2221, Japan

Walbro Engine Management, Terada Building, 4F, 2-3-3 Shiba Kouen, Minato-ku, Tokyo 105-0011, Japan
Tel: 81-3-5401-4511

Walbro Japan, Terada Building 4/F, 2-3-3 Shiba Kouen, Minato Ku, Minato - Ku, Tokyo 105-0011, Japan

WARNER BROS.

4000 Warner Boulevard, Bldg.170, 3rd Fl., Burbank, CA, 91522

Tel: (818) 954-6000   Fax: (818) 977-4040   www.wbitv.com

Distributor TV programming and theatrical features.

Warner Bros., 1-2-4 Hamamatsu-Cho, Minato-ku, Tokyo 105, Japan
Tel: 81-3-5472-8341   Fax: 81-3-5472-6343   Contact: Teruji Mochimaru, Mng. Dir.

THE WASHINGTON POST COMPANY

1150 15th St. NW, Washington, DC, 20071

Tel: (202) 334-6000   Fax: (202) 334-4536   www.washpostco.com

Engaged in magazine publishing, cable and television broadcasting, educational services and the Internet.

Mainichi Newspapers, 1-1-1 Hitotsubashi, 4/F, Chiyoda-ku, Tokyo 100, Japan
Tel: 81-3-3201-0210

Newsweek Japan Nihon Ban, Sumitomo Seimei Aoyama Bldg., 3F, 3-1-30 Minami-Aoyama, Minato-ku, Tokyo 107, Japan

TD WATERHOUSE GROUP, INC.

100 Wall Street, New York, NY, 10005

Tel: (212) 806-3500   Fax: (212) 361-6656   www.tdwaterhousegroup.com

Engaged in online brokerage.

Waterhouse/Bank of Mitsubishi (JV), 2-7-1 Marunouchi 2-chome, Chiyoda-ku, Tokyo 100, Japan

WATERS CORPORATION

34 Maple Street, Milford, MA, 01757

Tel: (508) 478-2000   Fax: (508) 872-1990   www.waters.com

Mfr./distribute liquid chromatographic instruments and test and measurement equipment.

Nihon Waters Ltd., Shuwa Kioicho Park Bldg., 3 Kioi-cho, Chiyoda-ku, Tokyo 102, Japan

WATSON WYATT & COMPANY HOLDINGS

1717 H Street NW, Washington, DC, 20006-3807

Tel: (202) 715-7000   Fax: (202) 715-7700   www.watsonwyatt.com

Creates compensation and benefits programs for major corporations.

Watson Wyatt & Co., Emina Building, 1-8-7 Kojimachi Chiyoda-Ku, Tokyo 102-0083, Japan

Tel: 81-3-3556-9800   Fax: 81-3-3262-7055   Contact: Konomi Uno

WEBER MARKING SYSTEMS INC.

711 West Algonquin Road, Arlington Heights, IL, 60005-4457

Tel: (847) 364-8500   Fax: (847) 364-8575   www.webermarking.com

Mfr. label printing systems and custom labels.

Weber Marking Systems Far East Co. Ltd., 3-6 Tsukiji 1-chome, Chuo-ku, Tokyo 104, Japan

WEBMETHODS, INC.

3930 Pender Drive, Fairfax, VA, 22030

Tel: (703) 460-2500   Fax: (703) 460-2599   www.webmethods.com

Mfr. automated business software.

WebMethods Japan KK, 2-6-1 Nishi Shinjuku, Shinjuki-ku, Tokyo 163-0209, Japan

WEBRIDGE, INC.

1925 NW Amber Glen Pkwy., Ste. 400, Beaverton, OR, 97006

Tel: (503) 601-4000   Fax: (503) 601-4001   www.webridge.com

Mfr. software to manage online transactions.

Webridge Asia Pacific Headquarters, #4 NS Building, 7/F, 1-10-5 Kudankita, Chiyoda-Ku, Tokyo 102-0073, Japan

Tel: 81-3-5210-1184

WEBSENSE, INC.

10240 Sorrento Valley Road, San Diego, CA, 92121

Tel: (858) 320-8000   Fax: (858) 458-2950   www.websense.com

Mfr. software.

Websense Japan KK, Level 32, Shinjuku Nomura Bldg., 1-26-2 Nishi-Shinjuku, Shinjuku-ku, Tokyo 163-0532, Japan

WELCH ALLYN INC.

4341 State Street Road, Skaneateles Falls, NY, 13153

Tel: (315) 685-4100   Fax: (315) 685-4091   www.welchallyn.com

Mfr. fiber optic products and medical diagnostic equipment.

Welch Allyn Japan K.K., Bon Marrusan, 8/F, 3-5-1 Kanda Jinbo-cho, Chiyoda-ku, Tokyo 101, Japan

Tel: 81-5212-7391

WENDY'S INTERNATIONAL, INC.

4288 West Dublin Granville Roads, Dublin, OH, 43017-0256

Tel: (614) 764-3100   Fax: (614) 764-3459   www.wendysintl.com

Fast food restaurant chain.

Wendy's International, Tokyo, Japan

WESTERN DIGITAL CORPORATION

20511 Lake Forest Dr., Lake Forest, CA, 92630-7741

Tel: (949) 672-7000   Fax: (949) 672-5408   www.westerndigital.com

Mfr. hard disk drives, video graphics boards, VLSI.

Western Digital Japan Ltd., 44 Kowa Bldg., 8/F, 1-2-7 Higashiyama, Megoro-ku, Tokyo, Japan

WEYERHAEUSER COMPANY

33663 Weyerhaeuser Way South, Federal Way, WA, 98003

Tel: (253) 924-2345   Fax: (253) 924-2685   www.weyerhaeuser.com

Wood and wood fiber products.

Weyerhaeuser Japan Ltd., PO Box 18, Tokyo 107, Japan

WHIRLPOOL CORPORATION

2000 N. M-63, Benton Harbor, MI, 49022-2692

Tel: (616) 923-5000   Fax: (616) 923-5443   www.whirlpoolcorp.com

Mfr., market home appliances: Whirlpool, Roper, KitchenAid, Estate, and Inglis.

Whirlpool Corporation, Tokyo, Japan

WHITE & CASE LLP

1155 Ave. of the Americas, New York, NY, 10036-2767

Tel: (212) 819-8200   Fax: (212) 354-8113   www.whitecase.com

Engaged in international law.

White & Case LLP, Kandabashi Law Offices, Kandabashi Park Bldg., 19-1 Kanda-nishikicho 1-chome, Chiyoda-ku Tokyo 101-0054, Japan

Tel: 81-3-3259-0200   Fax: 81-3-3259-0150   Contact: Christopher P. Wells

WIDIA VALENITE INC

31700 Research Park Dr., Madison Heights, MI, 48071-4627

Tel: (248) 589-1000   Fax: (248) 597-4820   www.valenite.com

Cemented carbide, high speed steel, ceramic and diamond cutting tool products, etc.

Valenite-WIDIA Japan Inc., 21-10 Kita-Kohjiya 1-chome, Ohta-ku, Tokyo 144-0032, Japan

WILBUR-ELLIS COMPANY

345 California St., 27th Fl., San Francisco, CA, 94120

Tel: (415) 772-4000   Fax: (415) 772-4011   www.wilburellis.com

Marketing, distribution, formulation of agricultural products and industrial specialty chemicals and raw materials.

Connell Bros. Co. Ltd., 2-12-18 Minato-Machi, Naha, Okinawa 900, Japan

Tel: 8198-863-3991

Connell Bros. Co. Ltd., Sanshin Building, 4-1 Yurakucho 1-Chome, Chiyoda-Ku, Tokyo 100-0006, Japan

Tel: 813-3591-3221   Fax: 813-3591-3415   Contact: Ken Kanai, Pres.

WINCHESTER/RETCONN ELECTRONICS

400 Park Road, Watertown, CT, 06795-0500

Tel: (860) 945-5000   Fax: (860) 945-5191   www.litton-wed.com

Mfr. electrical and electronic connectors, PCB assemblies and hardware.

Litton Winchester Electronics Japan, c/o Litton Westrex Co., Chiyoda Bldg., 2-1-2 Marunochi, Chiyoda-ku, Tokyo 100, Japan

WIND RIVER SYSTEMS, INC.

500 Wind River Way, Alameda, CA, 94501

Tel: (510) 748-4100   Fax: (510) 749-2010   www.isi.com

Develops and markets computer software products and services.

Wind River Systems Japan/Asia-Pacific., Pola Ebisu Building, 11/F, 3-9-19 Higashi, Shibuya-ku, Tokyo 150, Japan

Tel: 81-03-5467-5900   Fax: 81-03-5467-5877

HARRY WINSTON INC.

718 Fifth Ave., New York, NY, 10019

Tel: (212) 245-2000   Fax: (212) 245-2000   www.harry-winston.com

Diamonds and lapidary work.

Harry Winston Far East, Yomiko Building, 1/2F, 1-8-14 Ginza, Osaka, Japan

Tel: 81-6-6448-3311

Harry Winston Far East, 1-8-14 Ginza, Chuo-ku, Tokyo, Japan

Tel: 81-3-3535-6441

WIT SOUNDVIEW GROUP, INC.

826 Broadway, 6th Fl., New York, NY, 10003

Tel: (212) 253-4400   Fax: (212) 253-4428   www.witsoundview.com

Internet-based investment bank.

Wit Soundview Group Japan, Shin Aoyama Bldg., 12/F, 1-1-1 Minami Aoyama, Minato-ku, Tokyo 1070062, Japan

WITNESS SYSTEMS, INC.

300 Colonial Center Pkwy., Roswell, GA, 30076

Tel: (770) 754-1900   Fax: (707) 541-8888   www.witsys.com

Mfr. multimedia software.

Witness Japan KK, 1-1 Ichigaya Honmura-cho, Shinjuku-ku, Tokyo 162-0845, Japan

Tel: 81-3-5225-1290

WOMETCO ENTERPRISES INC.

3195 Ponce de Leon Blvd., Coral Gables, FL, 33134

Tel: (305) 529-1400   Fax: (305) 529-1499

Television broadcasting, film distribution, bottling, vending machines and proprietor of Miami Seaquarium.

Intl. Leisure Corp., Tokyo Tower Wax Museum, 20-1 Shiba Park, Minato-ku, Tokyo, Japan

WOODHEAD INDUSTRIES INC.

Three Parkway North, Ste. 550, Deerfield, IL, 60015

Tel: (847) 236-9300   Fax: (847) 236-0503   www.woodhead.com

Develop/mfr./sale/distributor elect/electronic, fiber optic and ergonomic special-function, non-commodity products.

Woodhead Japan Corporation, Unit 4309, Yokohama Landmark Tower, 2-2-1 Minato Mirai, Nishi-ku Yokohama-shi, Kanagawa-ken 220-8143, Japan

Contact: Bela J. Horvath

WOODWARD GOVERNOR COMPANY

5001 N. Second Street, PO Box 7001, Rockford, IL, 61125-7001

Tel: (815) 877-7441   Fax: (815) 639-6033   www.woodward.com

Mfr./service speed control devices and systems for aircraft turbines, industrial engines and turbines.

Woodward Governor Japan Ltd., Tomisato, PO Box 1, 251-1 Nakazawa Tomisato-Machi Inba-Gun, Chiba-Ken 286--02, Japan

Tel: 81-476-93-4661   Fax: 81-476-93-7939   Contact: John Sundstedt   Emp: 150

Woodward Governor Japan Ltd. (Kansai Branch), 105 Moritomo, Nishi-ku, Kobe-shi, Hyogoken 651-21, Japan

Tel: 81-78-928-8500   Fax: 81-78-928-8322   Contact: Nikki Hayashi   Emp: 20

WORLD AIRWAYS, INC.

HLH Building, 101 World Drive, Peachtree City, GA, 30269

Tel: (770) 632-8000   Fax: (770) 632-8075   www.worldair.com

Engaged in air transport leasing.

World Airways Japan KK, Noriko Sisneros, Tokyo, Japan

WORLD COURIER INC.

45 Southfield Avenue, Ste. 3450, Stamford, CT, 06902-7210

Tel: (203) 975-9333   Fax: (203) 316-9455   www.worldcourier.com

International courier service.

World Courier Japan, Ginza Chuo Bldg., 7/F, 3-10 Ginza 4-chome, Chuo-ku, Tokyo 104, Japan

WORLD FUEL SERVICES CORPORATION

700 S. Royal Poinciana Blvd., Ste. 800, Miami Springs, FL, 33166

Tel: (305) 883-8554   Fax: (305) 887-2642   www.wfscorp.com

Provides airport services to aircraft.

Trans-Tec Services KK, 6th Floor, Tozan Building, 4-4-2, Nihonbashi Hon-Cho, Choo-Ku 103-0023, Japan

WORLDCOM, INC.

500 Clinton Center Drive, Clinton, MS, 39060

Tel: (601) 360-8600   Fax: (601) 360-8616   www.wcom.com

Telecommunications; serving local, long distance and Internet customers domestically and internationally. **Corporation under worldwide reorganization under Chapter 11 Bankruptcy; new data unavailable for this edition.*

WorldCom International, PO Box 17, 3-2 Nishi Shinjuku 2-chome, Shinjuku-ku, Tokyo 163-03, Japan

WORLDXCHANGE COMMUNICATIONS

9999 Willow Creek Road, San Diego, CA, 92131

Tel: (858) 547-4933   Fax: (800) 995-4502   www.worldxchange.com

Provides international, long distance telecommunications services worldwide.

WorldxChange Communications S.A., Tokyo, Japan

WRIGHT MEDICAL GROUP, INC.

5677 Airline Road, Arlington, TN, 38002

Tel: (901) 867-9971   Fax: (901) 867-9534   www.wmt.com

Mfr. orthopedic reconstructive implants.

Wright Medical Japan, KK, Kyobashi Toei Building BF, Kyobashi 1-Chome, 14-4, Chuo-Ku, Tokyo 104, Japan

WM WRIGLEY JR. COMPANY

410 N. Michigan Ave., Chicago, IL, 60611-4287

Tel: (312) 644-2121   Fax: (312) 644-0353   www.wrigley.com

Mfr. chewing gum.

Wrigley & Company Ltd. Japan, Tokyo, Japan

WYETH PHARMACEUTICALS

555 E. Lancaster Ave., Wayne, PA, 19087-5109

Tel: (610) 971-5400   Fax: (610) 995-4668   www.wyeth.com

Mfr. antibiotics and pharmaceutical products.

Wyeth-Lederle (Japan) Limited, Hattori Bldg., 5/F, 1-10-3 Kyobashi Chuo-Ku, Tokyo 104-0311, Japan
Tel: 81-3-3561-8781   Fax: 81-3-3561-0267

XEROX CORPORATION

800 Long Ridge Road, PO Box 1600, Stamford, CT, 06904

Tel: (203) 968-3000   Fax: (203) 968-4312   www.xerox.com

Mfr. document processing equipment, systems and supplies.

Akita Xerox Co., Ltd., 170-92 Aza Ookawa-bata, Kawajiri-machi, Akita-shi 100, Japan
Tel: 81-188-23-4645   Fax: 81-188-23-7559

Fuji Xerox Co. Ltd., 3-5 Akasaka 3-chome, Minato-ku, Tokyo 107, Japan

Hokkaido Xerox Co., Ltd., No. 3 Yuuraku-terashima Bldg., 7F, 4-133 Odori-Nishi 10-chome, Chuo-ku, Sapporo 060, Japan
Tel: 81-271-4533

Xerox Co., Ltd., 17-48 Teppo-cho 1 chome, Yamagata-shi 990, Japan
Tel: 81-2-3624-2468

XILINX INC.

2100 Logic Drive, San Jose, CA, 95124-3400

Tel: (408) 559-7778   Fax: (408) 559-7114   www.xilinx.com

Programmable logic and related development systems software.

Xilinx Japan KK, Shinjuku Square Towerk 18F, 22-1 Nishi-Shinjuku 6 chome, Shinjuku-ku, Tokyo 163-1118, Japan
Tel: 81-3-5321-7711   Contact: Hiroyuki Takasaki, Pres.

XIRCOM, INC.

2300 Corporate Center Drive, Thousand Oaks, CA, 91320

Tel: (805) 376-9300   Fax: (805) 376-9311   www.xircom.com

Mfr. PC card network adapters and modems.

Xircom Japan KK, 3-10-5 Shibuya, Shibuya-Ku, Tokyo 105-0002, Japan
Tel: 81-3-3407-0056   Fax: 81-3-3407-0218

X-RITE, INC.

3100 44th Street SW, Grandville, MI, 49418

Tel: (616) 534-7663   Fax: (616) 534-9215   www.xrite.com

Mfr. precision measurement devices, systems and processes that enhance the measurement of color, light and shape.

X-Rite Asia Pacific Ltd., 7F, IMAS Hamamatsu-cho Bldg., 2-10-4, Hamamatsu-cho, Minato-ku, Tokyo 105-0013, Japan

Tel: 81-3-5777-5488

XTRA CORPORATION

200 Nyala Farms Rd., Westport, CT, 06880

Tel: (203) 221-1005   Fax: (203) 221-9024   www.xtracorp.com

Holding company: leasing.

XTRA International, Tokyo, Japan

YAHOO! INC.

701 First Avenue, Sunnyvale, CA, 94089

Tel: (408) 439-3300   Fax: (408) 439-3301   www.yahoo-inc.com

Internet media company providing specialized content, free electronic mail and community offerings and commerce.

Yahoo! Inc., 24-1 Nihonbashi-Hakozaki Cho, Chuo-ku, Tokyo, Japan

Tel: 81-3-5642-8028   Fax: 81-3-5641-3680

YELLOW CORPORATION

10990 Roe Ave., PO Box 7270, Overland Park, KS, 66207

Tel: (913) 696-6100   Fax: (913) 696-6116   www.yellowcorp.com

Commodity transportation.

Trans-Atlantic (Japan) Ltd., Osakan Sakuragaoka Bldg., 5/F, 31-14 Sakuragaoka-cho, Shibuya-ku, Tokyo 150-0031, Japan

YORK INTERNATIONAL CORPORATION

631 South Richland Ave., York, PA, 17403

Tel: (717) 771-7890   Fax: (717) 771-6212   www.york.com

Mfr. heating, ventilating, air conditioning and refrigeration equipment.

York International Corporation, 2-21-11 Sanno, Ota-Ku, Tokyo 143, Japan

Tel: 81-3-57009-1310

YOUNG & RUBICAM INC.

285 Madison Ave., New York, NY, 10017

Tel: (212) 210-3000   Fax: (212) 370-3796   www.yr.com

Advertising, public relations, direct marketing and sales promotion, corporate and product ID management.

Dentsu Young & Rubicam (Pvt.) Ltd., Kyobashi K-1 Bldg., 2-7-12 Yaesu, Chuo-ku, Tokyo 104-8477, Japan

Tel: 81-3-3278-4811   Fax: 81-3-3278-4851

YSI INC.

1700-1725 Brannum Lane, Yellow Springs, OH, 45387

Tel: (937) 767-7241   Fax: (937) 767-9353   www.ysi.com

Mfr. analyzers, measure instruments and electrical components.

YSI Japan KK, Sakura Bldg., 5-6-13 Shinjuka, Shinjuku-ku, Tokyo 160-427, Japan

ZEBRA TECHNOLOGIES CORPORATION

333 Corporate Woods Pkwy., Vernon Hills, IL, 60061-3109

Tel: (847) 634-6700   Fax: (847) 913-8766   www.zebracorporation.com

Mfr. bar code systems.

Zebra Technologies Japan, Level 15/F East Tower, Yokohama Business Park, 134 Godo-cho, Hodogaya-ku, Yokohama 240-0005, Japan

Tel: 81-45-340-2055   Fax: 81-45-340-2056

ZIEBART INTERNATIONAL CORPORATION

1290 East Maple Road, Troy, MI, 48083

Tel: (248) 588-4100   Fax: (248) 588-0718   www.ziebart.com

Automotive aftermarket services.

Ziebart Japan Ltd., 5-1 Kita-Aoyama-a-chome, Minato-ku, Tokyo 107-77, Japan
Tel: 81-3-3497-2554   Fax: 81-3-3497-4115

ZILOG, INC.

532 Race Street, San Jose, CA, 95126

Tel: (408) 558-8500   Fax: (408) 558-8300   www.zilog.com

Mfr. integrated circuits.

ZILOG Japan KK, 5-1-15 Nishishinjuku, Shinjuku-ku, Tokyo 160-0023, Japan

ZIMMER HOLDINGS, INC.

345 East Main St., Warsaw, IN, 46580

Tel: (574) 267-6131   Fax: (574) 372-4988   www.zimmer.com

Engaged in design and manufacture of orthopedic products.

Zimmer Japan KK, 1-17, Toranomon 4 Chome, Minato-Ku, Tokyo 105-0001, Japan
Tel: 81-3-6402-6600   Fax: 81-3-6402-6620

JOHN ZINK COMPANY

11920 East Apache, Tulsa, OK, 74121-1220

Tel: (918) 234-1800   Fax: (918) 234-2700   www.johnzink.com

Engaged in the development and manufacture of next-generation combustion products, technologies and clean-air solutions that power global industry.

John Zink Asia-Pacific, Div. Koch Asia-Pacific, KSS Gotanda Bldg., 7/F, 21-8 Nishi-Gotanda 1-chrome, Shinagawa-ku, Tokyo 141-8538, Japan

ZIPPERTUBING COMPANY

13000 S. Broadway, PO Box 61129, Los Angeles, CA, 90061

Tel: (310) 527-0488   Fax: (310) 767-1714   www.zippertubing.com

Mfr. zip-on plastic tubing, wire markers, pipe insulation, EMI shielding.

Zippertubing (Japan) Ltd., 3-2-56 Takatsukadai, Nishi-ku, Kobe 651-22, Japan

ZOLL MEDICAL CORPORATION

32 Second Avenue, Burlington, MA, 01803

Tel: (781) 229-0020   Fax: (781) 272-5578   www.zoll.com

Mfr. electrical resuscitation devices and equipment.

ZOLL Medical Japan KK, 4-20-14 Meguro, Megura- Ku, Tokyo 153-0063, Japan

ZORAN CORPORATION

3112 Scott Boulevard, Santa Clara, CA, 95054

Tel: (408) 919-4111   Fax: (408) 919-4122   www.zoran.com

Mfr. specialized integrated circuits and software.

Zoran Japan, 2-2-8 Roppongi, Minato-ku, Tokyo 106-0032, Japan
Tel: 81-3-5574-7081

ZYGO CORPORATION

Laurel Brook Road, Middlefield, CT, 06455

Tel: (860) 347-8506   Fax: (860) 347-8372   www.zygo.com

Mfr. high-precision, electro-optical measuring equipment.

Zygo KK, Ueno Sanwa Bldg., 1-14-4 Higashiueno, Taitou-ku, Tokyo 110-0015, Japan
Tel: 81-3-5812-6051   Fax: 81-3-5812-6055   Contact: Hideki Ogawa

Jordan

ANDERSEN

33 West Monroe Street, Chicago, IL, 60603

Tel: (312) 580-0033 Fax: (312) 507-6748 www.andersen.com

*Accounting and audit, tax and management consulting services. **Firm under worldwide reorganization; new data unavailable for this edition.*

Allied Accountants/Shair, Dajani, Alaeddin & Co., Mecca St., Wadi Saqra, Jabal Amman, PO Box 5552, Amman 11183, Jordan

Tel: 962-6-686111

BATES WORLDWIDE INC.

498 Seventh Avenue, New York, NY, 10018

Tel: (212) 297-7000 Fax: (212) 986-0270 www.batesww.com

Advertising, marketing, public relations and media consulting.

Bates Jordon, PO Box 3371, Amman 11181, Jordan

Tel: 962-5-680-507 Fax: 962-5-687-451 Contact: R.G. Naljar, CEO

BDO SEIDMAN, LLP BELGIUM

130 East Randolph Street, Chicago, IL, 60601

Tel: (312) 856-9100 Fax: (312) 856-1379 www.bdo.com

International accounting and financial consulting firm.

BDO National Brothers, Al-Youbeel Circle, Shukri Elaian Ctr., 3rd Fl., Office No 306, Amman, Jordan

Tel: 962-6-5538-618 Fax: 962-6-5538-618 Contact: Mohammed Al-Nobani

BECHTEL GROUP INC.

50 Beale Street, PO Box 3965, San Francisco, CA, 94105-1895

Tel: (415) 768-1234 Fax: (415) 768-9038 www.bechtel.com

General contractors in engineering, construction and project management.

Bechtel Corp., PO Box 5226, Amman, Jordan

BRISTOL-MYERS SQUIBB COMPANY

345 Park Ave., New York, NY, 10154-0037

Tel: (212) 546-4000 Fax: (212) 546-4020 www.bms.com

Pharmaceutical and food preparations, medical and surgical instruments.

Kawar Drug Stores, PO Box 922025, Amman, Jordan

CDM INTERNATIONAL INC.

50 Hampshire Street, Cambridge, MA, 02139

Tel: (617) 452-6000 Fax: (617) 452-8000 www.cdm.com

Consulting engineers.

Camp Dresser & McKee Intl. Inc., 1 Queen Alia International Airport Road 4/F, PO Box 941895, Amman 11194, Jordan

Tel: 9-6-585-5267

THE CHRISTIAN SCIENCE PUBLISHING SOCIETY

1 Norway Street, Boston, MA, 02115

Tel: (617) 450-2000 Fax: (617) 450-7575 www.christianscience.com

Publishing company.

The Christian Science Monitor Publication, Box 2604, Amman 11181, Jordan

Contact: Scott Peterson Emp: 1

CITIGROUP, INC.

399 Park Avenue, New York, NY, 10022

Tel: (212) 559-1000   Fax: (212) 559-3646   www.citigroup.com

Provides insurance and financial services worldwide.

Citigroup, Country Corporate Officer, PO Box 5055, Amman 11183, Jordan

Contact: Suhair Al-Ali

CUNO INCORPORATED

400 Research Pkwy., Meriden, CT, 06450

Tel: (203) 237-5541   Fax: (203) 238-8977   www.cuno.com

Mfr. water filtration products.

CUNO Middle East, PO Box 2456, Amman 11181, Jordan

CUTLER-HAMMER, DIV. EATON CORP.

173 Heatherdown Drive, Westerville, OH, 43082

Tel: (614) 882-3282   Fax: (614) 895-7111   www.cutlerhammer.com

Mfr. electrical control products and power distribution equipment.

Cutler-Hammer, Farraj Centre, PO Box 510449, Amman 11151, Jordan

DANZAS AEI, INC.

120 Tokeneke Road, PO Box 1231, Darien, CT, 06820

Tel: (203) 655-7900   Fax: (203) 655-5779   www.aeilogistics.com

International air freight forwarder.

Danzas AEI Amman Eastern Services, Peace Bldg. Jabal Lweidbeh, PO Box 815408, Amman 11180, Jordan

Tel: 962-6-621-775 Fax: 962-6-656-270

DELOITTE TOUCHE TOHMATSU INTERNATIONAL

1633 Broadway, New York, NY, 10019

Tel: (212) 492-4000   Fax: (212) 392-4154   www.deloitte.com

Accounting, audit, tax and management consulting services.

Saba & Co., Jordan Ins. Co. Bldg., Third Circle, Jabal Amman, PO Box 248, Amman 11118, Jordan

DHL WORLDWIDE EXPRESS

50 California Avenue, San Francisco, CA, 94111

Tel: (415) 677-6100   Fax: (415) 824-9700   www.dhl.com

Worldwide air express carrier.

DHL Worldwide Express, 7th, Circle Jabal Amman, PO Box 927111, Amman, Jordan

Tel: 962-6-858514

EGL INC. (EAGLE GLOBAL LOGISTICS)

15350 Vickery Drive, Houston, TX, 77032

Tel: (281) 618-3100   Fax: (281) 618-3223   www.eagleusa.com

Ocean/air freight forwarding, customs brokerage, packing and wholesale, logistics management and insurance.

EGL Eagle Global Logistics, PO Box 2143, Amman 11181, Jordan

Tel: 962-6-662-722 Fax: 962-6-601-507

ERNST & YOUNG INTERNATIONAL

5 Times Square, New York, NY, 10036

Tel: (212) 773-3000   Fax: (212) 773-6350   www.eyi.com

Engaged in assurance and advisory business services, tax, law and corporate finance.

Ernst & Young/Whinney, Murray & Company, PO Box 1140, 4F, Haddad Commercial Centre, Wasfi Al-Tai St. Gardens, Amman 11118, Jordan

Tel: 962-6-681885 Fax: 962-6-681885 Contact: Mohamed A.K. Saadeh

FMC CORPORATION

1735 Market St., Philadelphia, PA, 19103

Tel: (215) 299-6000   Fax: (215) 299-6618   www.fmc.com

Mfr. specialty chemicals, including alginate, carrageenan and microcrystalline cellulose.

FMC Jordan, Sharea's College Street, PO Box 911660, Amman 11191, Jordan

Tel: 962-6-461-8150

FRITZ COMPANIES, INC., DIV. UPS

706 Mission Street, Ste. 900, San Francisco, CA, 94103

Tel: (415) 904-8360   Fax: (415) 904-8661   www.fritz.com

Integrated transportation, sourcing, distribution and customs brokerage services.

Fritz Companies Inc., Amman, Jordan

GENZYME CORPORATION

1 Kendall Square, Cambridge, MA, 02139-1562

Tel: (617) 252-7500   Fax: (617) 252-7600   www.genzyme.com

Mfr. healthcare products for enzyme deficient diseases.

Genzyme Jordan, PO Box 911821, Amman 11191, Jordan

Tel: 962-6-585-4444

HOLIDAY INN (BASS RESORTS) WORLDWIDE, INC.

3 Ravinia Drive, Ste. 2900, Atlanta, GA, 30346-2149

Tel: (770) 604-2000   Fax: (770) 604-5403   www.holidayinn.com

Hotels, restaurants and casinos.

Holiday Inn, PO Box 6399, Amman, Jordan

HORWATH INTERNATIONAL ASSOCIATION

420 Lexington Avenue, Suite 526, New York, NY, 10170-0526

Tel: (212) 808-2000   Fax: (212) 808-2020   www.horwath.com

Public accountants and auditors.

Sawalha & Qunsol & Partners, PO Box 940578, Amman 11194, Jordan

HYATT CORPORATION

200 West Madison Street, Chicago, IL, 60606

Tel: (312) 750-1234   Fax: (312) 750-8578   www.hyatt.com

International hotel management.

Grand Hyatt Amman, Amman, Jordan

IBM CORPORATION

1133 Westchester Avenue, White Plains, NY, 10604

Tel: (914) 765-1900   Fax: (914) 765-7382   www.ibm.com

Information products, technology and services.

IBM Jordan - United Business Machines, Shmeisani, PO Box 6410, Amman 11118, Jordan

Tel: 962-6-567-0171   Fax: 962-6-567-0173

IDEX CORPORATION

630 Dundee Road, Ste. 400, Northbrook, IL, 60062

Tel: (847) 498-7070   Fax: (847) 498-3940   www.idexcorp.com

Mfr. industrial pumps, lubrication systems, metal fabrication equipment, bending and clamping devices.

Viking Pump, Shahatit Bureau Razan Hotel Building, Third Circle, PO Box 2674, Amman 11181, Jordan

INTER-CONTINENTAL HOTELS

3 Ravinia Drive, Suite 2900, Atlanta, GA, 30346-2149

Tel: (770) 604-2000   Fax: (770) 604-5403   www.interconti.com

Worldwide hotel and resort accommodations.

Petra Forum Hotel, PO Box 30, Wadi Mousa, Jordan

Tel: 962-3-215-6266   Fax: 962-3-215-6977

IRRIDELCO INTERNATIONAL CORPORATION

440 Sylvan Ave., Englewood Cliffs, NJ, 07632

Tel: (201) 569-3030   Fax: (201) 569-9237   www.irridelco.com

Mfr. and distributor of the most comprehensive lines of mechanical and micro irrigation; pumps and irrigation systems.

IDC Jordan, PO Box 5474, Amman, Jordan

Tel: 962-683-2424   Fax: 962-683-2424   Contact: Marwan Hurani

KPMG CONSULTING INC.

1676 International Dr., McLean, VA, 22102

Tel: (703) 747-3000   Fax: (703) 747-8500   www.kpmg.com

Accounting and audit, tax and management consulting services.

Khleif & Co., Amman Commercial Centre, Abdali, 2F, Amman, Jordan

Tel: 962-6-681798   Fax: 962-6-681798   Contact: Adnan Khleif, Sr. Ptnr.

THE KULJIAN CORPORATION

3700 Science Center, Philadelphia, PA, 19104

Tel: (215) 243-1900   Fax: (215) 243-1909

Studies, design, engineering, construction management and site supervision.

The Kuljian Corp., PO Box 2749, Amman, Jordan

LOCKHEED MARTIN CORPORATION

6801 Rockledge Drive, Bethesda, MD, 20817

Tel: (301) 897-6000   Fax: (301) 897-6652   www.imco.com

Design/mfr./management systems in fields of space, defense, energy, electronics and technical services.

Lockheed Aeronautical Systems, Q.A.I. Airport, 41 Tabouk Street, Um Uthaina, Amman, Jordan

Tel: 962-8-51821   Fax: 962-8-53337   Contact: N. D. Bowler, Mgr.

MARRIOTT INTERNATIONAL INC.

10400 Fernwood Rd., Bethesda, MD, 20817

Tel: (301) 380-3000   Fax: (301) 380-5181   www.marriott.com

Hotel services.

Amman Marriott Hotel, Amman, Jordan

Tel: 962-6-569-7756

MERCK & COMPANY, INC.

One Merck Drive, PO Box 100, Whitehouse Station, NJ, 08889-0100

Tel: (908) 423-1000   Fax: (908) 423-2592   www.merck.com

Pharmaceuticals, chemicals and biologicals.

Merck/Charles E. Frost & Co., PO Box 20604, Amman, Jordan

J. P. MORGAN CHASE & CO. INC.

270 Park Ave., New York, NY, 10017

Tel: (212) 270-6000   Fax: (212) 622-9030   www.jpmorganchase.com

Provides integrated financial solutions for institutions and individuals worldwide, including asset management, investment banking and commercial banking.

J. P. Morgan Chase & Co., First Circle, PO Box 20191, Jebal Amman, Jordan

AC NIELSEN COMPANY

177 Broad Street, Stamford, CT, 06901

Tel: (203) 961-3000   Fax: (203) 961-3190   www.acnielsen.com

Engaged in market and consumer research.

ACNielsen, Shmesani Suheib ben Sinan St., PO Box 5141, Amman 11183, Jordan

OTIS ELEVATOR COMPANY

One Farm Springs Road, Farmington, CT, 06032

Tel: (860) 676-6000   Fax: (860) 676-5111   www.otis.com

Mfr. elevators and escalators.

Otis/Jordan Elevator Overseas Ltd., PO Box 7490, Amman, Jordan

RAYTHEON COMPANY

141 Spring Street, Lexington, MA, 02173

Tel: (781) 862-6600   Fax: (781) 860-2172   www.raytheon.com

Mfr. diversified electronics, appliances, energy and environmental products; publishing, industry and construction services.

Raytheon Technical Assistance Co., PO Box 3414, Jebal, Amman, Jordan

THE SERVICEMASTER COMPANY

2300 Warrenville Road, Downers Grove, IL, 60515-1700

Tel: (630) 271-1300   Fax: (630) 271-2710   www.svm.com

Provides residential consumer services, including lawn care and landscape maintenance, termite and pest control, plumbing, heating and air conditioning maintenance and repair.

ServiceMaster, Amman, Jordan

STANLEY CONSULTANTS, INC.

Stanley Building, 225 Iowa Ave., Muscatine, IA, 52761-3764

Tel: (563) 264-6600   Fax: (563) 264-6658   www.stanleygroup.com

Engaged in engineering, architectural, planning and management services.

Stanley Consultants, Inc., PO Box 830746, Fourth Circle, 73 Almutanabi St., Amman 11183, Jordan

Tel: 9626-4-612-377

UNION CARBIDE CORPORATION

39 Old Ridgebury Road, Danbury, CT, 06817

Tel: (203) 794-2000   Fax: (203) 794-6269   www.unioncarbide.com

Mfr. industrial chemicals, plastics and resins.

Union Carbide Europe SA, PO Box 927277, Amman, Jordan

THE WACKENHUT CORPORATION

4200 Wackenhut Dr., Ste. 100, Palm Beach Gardens, FL, 33410

Tel: (561) 622-5656   Fax: (561) 691-6736   www.wackenhut.com

Security systems and services.

WII/Sound & Security Eng. Co., PO Box 9881, Amman, Jordan

Tel: 962-6-642407   Fax: 962-6-656899

WYETH PHARMACEUTICALS

555 E. Lancaster Ave., Wayne, PA, 19087-5109

Tel: (610) 971-5400   Fax: (610) 995-4668   www.wyeth.com

Mfr. antibiotics and pharmaceutical products.

Wyeth-Ayerst International, Inc., Yousef Al Aseer St. No. 10, Rajab Commercial Bldg., 2/F, Amman, Jordan

XEROX CORPORATION

800 Long Ridge Road, PO Box 1600, Stamford, CT, 06904

Tel: (203) 968-3000   Fax: (203) 968-4312   www.xerox.com

Mfr. document processing equipment, systems and supplies.

Arabian Office Automation WLL, Amman Commercial Complex, Mezanin 1, Al-Abdaly-Amman, Jordan

Tel: 962-6-698804   Fax: 962-6-698806

Kazakhstan

THE AES CORPORATION

1001 North 19th Street, Arlington, VA, 22209

Tel: (703) 522-1315   Fax: (703) 528-4510   www.aesc.com

Gas and electric utility.

AES Sogrinsk TETS, Almaty, Kazakhstan

AIG AMERICAN INTERNATIONAL GROUP INC.

70 Pine Street, New York, NY, 10270

Tel: (212) 770-7000   Fax: (212) 509-9705   www.aig.com

Worldwide insurance and financial services.

AIG Kaz. Ins. Co., 64 Almangeldy Street, 480012 Almtaz, Kazakhstan

AMERICAN INTERNATIONAL PETROLEUM CORP.

2950 North Loop West, Suite 1000, Houston, TX, 77092

Tel: (713) 802-0087   Fax: (713) 802-9515   www.aipcorp.com

Engaged in oil and gas exploration.

American International Petroleum Kazakhstan (AIPK), Almaty, Kazakhstan

ANDERSEN

33 West Monroe Street, Chicago, IL, 60603

Tel: (312) 580-0033   Fax: (312) 507-6748   www.andersen.com

*Accounting and audit, tax and management consulting services. **Firm under worldwide reorganization; new data unavailable for this edition.*

Andersen Worldwide, 69 Tole Bi St., 480091 Almaty, Kazakhstan

Tel: 7-327-269-1619

AON CORPORATION

200 East Randolph, Chicago, IL, 60601

Tel: (312) 381-1000   Fax: (312) 381-6032   www.aon.com

Insurance brokers worldwide; underwrites accident and health insurance, specialty and professional insurance; and provides risk management consultation.

Alexander Howden Group Kazakhstan Office Ltd., Ministry of Rd., 7th Fl., Construction UL Gogolya 86, Almaty, Kazakhstan

Tel: 7-327-232-2549   Fax: 7-327-581-1475   Contact: Jack Murphy

BAKER & McKENZIE

130 East Randolph Drive, Ste. 2500, Chicago, IL, 60601

Tel: (312) 861-8000   Fax: (312) 861-2899   www.bakerinfo.com

International legal services.

Baker & McKenzie - CIS Ltd., 155 Abai Ave., 29/30, 480009 Almaty, Kazakhstan

Tel: 7-327-509945   Fax: 7-327-2509579

LOUIS BERGER INTERNATIONAL INC.

100 Halsted Street, East Orange, NJ, 07019

Tel: (201) 678-1960   Fax: (201) 672-4284   www.louisberger.com

Consulting engineers, engaged in architecture, environmental and advisory services.

Louis Berger International Inc., c/o NIIAT, PK631, Prospekt ABAY 76, 109, 480057 Almaty, Kazakhstan

BRACEWELL & PATTERSON LLP

711 Louisiana Street, Ste. 2900, Houston, TX, 77002-2721

Tel: (713) 223-2900   Fax: (713) 223-2900   www.bracepatt.com

Engaged in international law.

Bracewell & Patterson LLP, 65 Kazybek Bi Street, Ste. 410, 480091 Almaty, Kazakhstan

BRISTOL-MYERS SQUIBB COMPANY

345 Park Ave., New York, NY, 10154-0037

Tel: (212) 546-4000   Fax: (212) 546-4020   www.bms.com

Pharmaceutical and food preparations, medical and surgical instruments.

Bristol-Myer Squibb Company, 83 Ulitsa Zhectoksan, 480091 Almaty, Kazakhstan

LEO BURNETT, DIV. B-COM 3 GROUP

35 West Wacker Drive, Chicago, IL, 60601

Tel: (312) 220-5959   Fax: (312) 220-6533   www.leoburnett.com

Engaged in advertising, marketing, media buying and planning, and public relations.

Styx & Leo Burnett, Almaty, Kazakhstan

CARANA CORPORATION

4350 N. Fairfax Drive, Ste. 500, Arlington, VA, 22203

Tel: (703) 243-1700   Fax: (703) 243-0471   www.carana.com

Foreign trade consulting.

CARANA Corp., ul. Ablai-Khan 93/95, Ste. 528, Almaty, Kazakhstan

CARGILL, INC.

15407 McGinty Road West, Minnetonka, MN, 55440-5625

Tel: (612) 742-7575   Fax: (612) 742-7393   www.cargill.com

Food products, feeds, animal products.

DAN (JV), Dostyk 38, Rm. 716, 480100 Almaty, Kazakhstan

CATERPILLAR INC.

100 NE Adams Street, Peoria, IL, 61629-6105

Tel: (309) 675-1000   Fax: (309) 675-1182   www.cat.com

Mfr. earth/material-handling and construction machinery and equipment and engines.

Caterpillar, Inc., Kazakhstan

CHADBOURNE & PARKE LLP

30 Rockefeller Plaza, New York, NY, 10112-0127

Tel: (212) 408-5100   Fax: (212) 541-5369   www.chadbourne.com

Engaged in international law.

The Zanger Law Firm, 157 Abaya Street, Suite 26/27, 480124 Almaty, Kazakhstan
Tel: 7-327-250-9473   Contact: Maidan K. Suleimenov

CHEVRON TEXACO CORPORATION

575 Market Street, San Francisco, CA, 94105-2856

Tel: (415) 894-7700   Fax: (415) 894-2248   www.chevrontexaco.com

Oil exploration, production and petroleum products.

ChevronTexaco, Tengiz, Kazakhstan

CITIGROUP, INC.

399 Park Avenue, New York, NY, 10022

Tel: (212) 559-1000   Fax: (212) 559-3646   www.citigroup.com

Provides insurance and financial services worldwide.

Citigroup, 155 Abai St., 11th Fl., 480009 Almaty, Kazakhstan
Contact: Reza Ghaffari

COUDERT BROTHERS LLP

1114 Ave. of the Americas, New York, NY, 10036-7794

Tel: (212) 626-4400   Fax: (212) 626-4120   www.coudert.com

Engaged in international law.

Coudert Brothers, Samal 1., Bldg. 36, Third Fl., 480099 Almaty, Kazakhstan
Tel: 7-327-253-3370   Fax: 7-327-253-3372

DELOITTE TOUCHE TOHMATSU INTERNATIONAL

1633 Broadway, New York, NY, 10019

Tel: (212) 492-4000   Fax: (212) 392-4154   www.deloitte.com

Accounting, audit, tax and management consulting services.

Deloitte & Touche CIS, 29 Kurmangazy St., Rooms 117-119, 480021 Almaty, Kazakhstan

DHL WORLDWIDE EXPRESS

50 California Avenue, San Francisco, CA, 94111

Tel: (415) 677-6100   Fax: (415) 824-9700   www.dhl.com

Worldwide air express carrier.

DHL Worldwide Express, Offices 1-4, 157 Abaya St., 480009 Almaty, Kazakhstan

Tel: 7-327-250-9416

EMERSON PROCESS MANAGEMENT

8301Cameron Road, Austin, TX, 78754

Tel: (512) 834-7689   Fax: (512) 832-3232   www.frco.com

Mfr. industrial process control equipment.

Emerson Process Management, 42 Timiriyazev Str. Pavilion 17, Business Center "Atakent", 480057 Almaty, Kazakhstan

ERNST & YOUNG INTERNATIONAL

5 Times Square, New York, NY, 10036

Tel: (212) 773-3000   Fax: (212) 773-6350   www.eyi.com

Engaged in assurance and advisory business services, tax, law and corporate finance.

Ernst & Young Kazakhstan, Prospect Lenina 212a, 480051 Almaty, Kazakhstan

Tel: 7-327-250-9423   Fax: 7-327-241-4800   Contact: Robert Langham

EXXON MOBIL CORPORATION

5959 Las Colinas Blvd., Irving, TX, 75039-2298

Tel: (972) 444-1000   Fax: (972) 444-1882   www.exxonmobil.com

Petroleum exploration, production, refining; mfr. petroleum and chemicals products; coal and minerals.

Exxon Mobil, Inc., Almaty, Kazakhstan

FRITZ COMPANIES, INC., DIV. UPS

706 Mission Street, Ste. 900, San Francisco, CA, 94103

Tel: (415) 904-8360   Fax: (415) 904-8661   www.fritz.com

Integrated transportation, sourcing, distribution and customs brokerage services.

Kaz-Fritz Transportation (Ltd.), 127 Furmanov St., Almaty, Kazakhstan

GENERAL ELECTRIC COMPANY

3135 Easton Turnpike, Fairfield, CT, 06431

Tel: (203) 373-2211   Fax: (203) 373-3131   www.ge.com

Diversified manufacturing, technology and services.

GE International, 153 Abai Avenue, Apt. 13-14, Almatzy, Kazakhstan

Tel: 7-327-260-8528   Fax: 7-327-240-0558

HEWLETT-PACKARD COMPANY

3000 Hanover Street, Palo Alto, CA, 94304-1185

Tel: (650) 857-1501   Fax: (650) 857-5518   www.hp.com

Mfr. computing, communications and measurement products and services.

Hewlett Packard SA, Ablay Khan Avenue 135, 480091 Almaty, Kazakhstan

Tel: 32-72-608-0625

HONEYWELL INTERNATIONAL INC.

Honeywell Plaza, Minneapolis, MN, 55408

Tel: (612) 951-1000   Fax: (612) 951-8537   www.honeywell.com

Develop/mfr. controls for home and building, industry, space and aviation, burglar and fire alarm systems.

Honeywell Automation Controls LLP, Temirjazeva 42, Atakent Business Center, 5/F, 480057 Almaty, Kazakhstan

Tel: 7-327-2-447747   Fax: 7-327-2-473290

HYATT CORPORATION

200 West Madison Street, Chicago, IL, 60606

Tel: (312) 750-1234   Fax: (312) 750-8578   www.hyatt.com

International hotel management.

Hyatt Regency Almaty Hotel, Akademik Satpaev Ave. 29/6, 480004 Almaty, Kazakhstan

Tel: 7-327-581-1234   Fax: 7-327-581-1635

KELLOGG BROWN & ROOT INC.

PO Box 4557, Houston, TX, 77210-4557

Tel: (713) 676-3011   Fax: (713) 676-8695   www.halliburton.com

Engaged in technology-based engineering and construction.

Kellogg Brown & Root, #4 Mornyshully St., 465002 Atyrau, Kazakhstan

KPMG CONSULTING INC.

1676 International Dr., McLean, VA, 22102

Tel: (703) 747-3000   Fax: (703) 747-8500   www.kpmg.com

Accounting and audit, tax and management consulting services.

KPMG Janat, 105 Ave. Abylai Khan, 480091 Almaty, Kazakhstan

Tel: 7-327-262-2694   Fax: 7-327-269-5927   Contact: Michael Roberts, Ptnr.

LeBOEUF, LAMB, GREENE & MacRAE LLP

125 West 55th Street, 12th Fl., New York, NY, 10019

Tel: (212) 424-8000   Fax: (212) 424-8500   www.llgm.com

International law firm.

LeBoeuf, Lamb, Greene & MacRae LLP, Prospect Seyfullina 531, 480083 Almaty, Kazakhstan

Tel: 7-327-250-7575   Fax: 7-327-261-7576   Contact: John I. Huhs

ELI LILLY & COMPANY

Lilly Corporate Center, Indianapolis, IN, 46285

Tel: (317) 276-2000   Fax: (317) 277-6579   www.lilly.com

Mfr. pharmaceuticals and animal health products.

Eli Lilly (Suisse) S.A., c/o Republican Centre of Modern Medicine, Ul. Bazaikova 299, 480070 Almaty, Kazakhstan

Tel: 7-327-244-2477   Fax: 7-327-250-9247

MARSH & McLENNAN COS INC.

1166 Ave. of the Americas, New York, NY, 10036-2774

Tel: (212) 345-5000   Fax: (212) 345-4808   www.marshmac.com

Insurance agents/brokers, pension and investment management consulting services.

J&H Unison, 5th Fl., 69 Tole Bi St., 480091 Almaty, Kazakhstan

Tel: 7-327-269-4906   Fax: 7-327-269-4089   Contact: Laila Dosbaeva

MARY KAY COSMETICS INC.

16251 No. Dallas Pkwy, Dallas, TX, 75248

Tel: (972) 687-6300   Fax: (972) 687-1609   www.marykay-cosmetic.com

Mfr. and direct sales of cosmetics and toiletries.

Mary Kay, Inc., 85a Dostyk Ave. #114, Almaty, Kazakhstan

MAYER, BROWN, ROWE & MAW

190 S. LaSalle Street, Chicago, IL, 60603

Tel: (312) 782-0600   Fax: (312) 701-7711   www.mayerbrown.com

Engaged in international law.

Mayer, Brown, Rowe & Maw, 162 Tulabaev St., # 32, Almaty, Kazakhstan

Tel: 7-327-263-6388   Fax: 7-327-250-7828

McCANN-ERICKSON WORLDGROUP

750 Third Ave., New York, NY, 10017

Tel: (212) 697-6000   Fax: (212) 984-3575   www.mccann.com

International advertising and marketing services.

McCann-Erickson Kazakhstan, Almaty, Kazakhstan

McGUIRE, WOODS LLP

One James Center, 901 E. Cary Street, Richmond, VA, 23219

Tel: (804) 775-1000   Fax: (804) 775-1061   www.mwbb.com

Engaged in international law.

McGuire, Woods, Park Place 41, Kazibek Bi St., 2nd Fl., 480100 Almaty, Kazakhstan

Tel: 7-327-2608-3000   Fax: 7-327-260-8305

MOTOROLA, INC.

1303 East Algonquin Road, Schaumburg, IL, 60196

Tel: (847) 576-5000   Fax: (847) 538-5191   www.motorola.com

Mfr. communications equipment, semiconductors and cellular phones.

Motorola Kazakhstan, Samal 1, Bldg. 36, Fl. 2, 480099 Almaty, Kazakhstan

Tel: 7-327-581-1571   Fax: 7-327-581-1572

AC NIELSEN COMPANY

177 Broad Street, Stamford, CT, 06901

Tel: (203) 961-3000   Fax: (203) 961-3190   www.acnielsen.com

Engaged in market and consumer research.

ACNielsen, 65 Kazbek bi Street, 705-706, 480091 Almaty, Kazakhstan

OFFSHORE LOGISTICS, INC.

224 Rue de Jean, Lafayette, LA, 70505

Tel: (337) 233-1221   Fax: (337) 235-6678   www.olog.com

Engaged in helicopter transportation services for offshore oil and gas companies.

ABAS, Atyrau Airport, 465050 Atyrau, Kazakhstan

PALMS & COMPANY, INC. (U.S. FUR EXCHANGE)

515 Lake Street South, Bldg., Ste. 103, Kirkland, WA, 98033

Tel: (425) 828-6774   Fax: (425) 827-5528   www.peterpalms.com

Engaged in general import and export and web-design, web-promotion and e-commerce.

Palms & Co. Inc., Pr. Asddirova 46/2, Kv. 66, 470055 Karaganda, Kazakhstan

Tel: 7-3212-580773   Contact: Sergei Voronov   Emp: 5

PARKER DRILLING COMPANY

1401 Enclave Pkwy., Ste. 600, Houston, TX, 77077

Tel: (281) 406-2000   Fax: (281) 406-2001   www.parkerdrilling.com

Provides land contract drilling services to firms in the oil and gas industry.

Parker Drilling, 11 Bukhar Zhrau Street, 480013 Almaty, Kazakhstan

PRICEWATERHOUSECOOPERS LLP

1301 Ave. of the Americas, New York, NY, 10019

Tel: (212) 596-7000   Fax: (212) 259-1301   www.pwcglobal.com

Accounting and auditing, tax and management, and human resource consulting services.

PriceWaterhouseCoopers, 105 Ablai Khan Prospect, 480091 Almaty, Kazakhstan

Tel: 7-327-262-7635   Fax: 7-327-250-6102

PROCTER & GAMBLE COMPANY

One Procter & Gamble Plaza, Cincinnati, OH, 45202

Tel: (513) 983-1100   Fax: (513) 562-4500   www.pg.com

Personal care, food, laundry, cleaning and industry products.

Procter & Gamble Almaty, 155 Abaya Ave., Apt 31/32 Alma-Ata, Almaty, Kazakhstan

SALANS HERTZFELD HEILBRONN CHRISTY & VIENER

620 Fifth Avenue, New York, NY, 10020-2457

Tel: (212) 632-5500   Fax: (212) 632-5555   www.salans.com

International law firm.

Salans Hertzfeld & Heilbronn, Ulitsa Gogolya 86, 480091 Almaty, Kazakhstan

SCHLUMBERGER LIMITED

153 East 53rd St., 57th Fl., New York, NY, 10022-4624

Tel: (212) 350-9400   Fax: (212) 350-9457   www.slb.com

Engaged in oil and gas services, metering and payment systems, and produces semiconductor testing equipment and smart cards.

Schlumberger, 86 Gogolya St., 480091 Almaty, Kazakhstan

SCIENTECH, INC.

2650 McCormick Drive, Suite 300, Clearwater, FL, 33759

Tel: (727) 669-3003   Fax: (727) 669-3100   www.scientech.com

worldwide provider of expert services to the energy and telecommunication markets

Scientech, Inc., Almaty, Kazakhstan

SQUIRE, SANDERS & DEMPSEY

4900 Key Tower, 127 Public Square, Cleveland, OH, 44114-1304

Tel: (216) 479-8500   Fax: (216) 479-8780   www.ssd.com

Engaged in international law.

Squire, Sanders & Dempsey, 84 Gogol St., Ste. 213, 48091 Almaty, Kazakhstan

Tel: 7-327-250-1125   Fax: 7-327-2322-539

WHITE & CASE LLP

1155 Ave. of the Americas, New York, NY, 10036-2767

Tel: (212) 819-8200   Fax: (212) 354-8113   www.whitecase.com

Engaged in international law.

White & Case LLP, 64 Amangeldy St., 480012 Almaty, Kazakhstan

Tel: 7-327-250-7491   Fax: 7-327-20-7493   Contact: Witold Danilowicz

Kenya

3M (MINNESOTA MINING & MFG.)

3M Center, St. Paul, MN, 55144-1000

Tel: (651) 733-1110   Fax: (651) 733-9973   www.mmm.com

Mfr. diversified products for industry, consumer, health care, imaging, communications, transport, safety, etc.

3M Kenya Ltd., 3M House, Ngong Rd., PO Box 48567, Nairobi, Kenya

Tel: 254-2-560-100   Fax: 254-2-560-712

AIG AMERICAN INTERNATIONAL GROUP INC.

70 Pine Street, New York, NY, 10270

Tel: (212) 770-7000   Fax: (212) 509-9705   www.aig.com

Worldwide insurance and financial services.

Alico Kenya, PO Box 49460, Nairobi, Kenya

AON CORPORATION

200 East Randolph, Chicago, IL, 60601

Tel: (312) 381-1000   Fax: (312) 381-6032   www.aon.com

Insurance brokers worldwide; underwrites accident and health insurance, specialty and professional insurance; and provides risk management consultation.

AON Worldwide/ Bain Hogg Insurance Brokers Kenya Ltd., Chester House, Koinange St., Nairobi, Kenya

Tel: 254-2-335-766   Fax: 254-2-225476   Contact: Peter Hood

ARMOR HOLDINGS, INC.

1400 Marsh Landing Parkway, Ste. 112, Jacksonville, FL, 32250

Tel: (904) 741-5400   Fax: (904) 741-5403   www.armorholdings.com

Holding company engaged in security products and services.

Armor Group Kenya, Armor House, Lenara Road, Nairobi, Kenya

Tel: 254-2-710-042   Contact: Sam Gakunga

ASSOCIATED PRESS INC.

50 Rockefeller Plaza, New York, NY, 10020-1605

Tel: (212) 621-1500   Fax: (212) 621-5447   www.ap.com

News gathering agency.

The Associated Press (JV), PO Box 47590, Nairobi, Kenya

Tel: 254-2-223-143

LOUIS BERGER INTERNATIONAL INC.

100 Halsted Street, East Orange, NJ, 07019

Tel: (201) 678-1960   Fax: (201) 672-4284   www.louisberger.com

Consulting engineers, engaged in architecture, environmental and advisory services.

Louis Berger International Inc., Esteer Wahome Bureau, Jubilee Insurance House, Wabera Street, Nairobi, Kenya

Tel: 254-2-228178   Fax: 254-2-333448

Louis Berger International Inc., c/o USAID, PO Box 30261, 10th Floor, Union Towers, Nairobi, Kenya

SAMUEL BINGHAM ENTERPRISES INC.

9529 South Main Street, Jonesboro, GA, 30236

Tel: (770) 477-7503   Fax: (770) 477-9532   www.binghamrollers.com

Mfr. rubber covered rolls, chemicals and supplies for the printing industry.

Coates Bros. (East Africa) Ltd., PO Box 30607, Addis Ababa Rd., Industrial Area, Nairobi, Kenya

BUDGET GROUP, INC.

125 Basin St., Ste. 210, Daytona Beach, FL, 32114

Tel: (904) 238-7035   Fax: (904) 238-7461   www.budgetrentacar.com

Car and truck rental system.

Budget Rent A Car, La Piazetta, Italian Complex, Lamu Rd., Malindi, Kenya

Tel: 254-2-223-581

Budget Rent A Car, Saroya House, Moi Ave., Mombasa, Kenya

Tel: 254-11-22629

Budget Rent A Car, Jomo Kenyatta Intl Airport, Arrivals Terminal, Nairobi, Kenya

CALTEX CORPORATION

PO Box 619500, Dallas, TX, 75261-9500

Tel: (972) 830-1000   Fax: (972) 830-1081   www.caltex.com

Petroleum products.

Caltex Oil Kenya Ltd., Caltex House, Koinange St., Nairobi, Kenya

Kenya Petroleum Refinery, Ltd., Caltex House, Koinange St., Nairobi, Kenya

CITIGROUP, INC.

399 Park Avenue, New York, NY, 10022

Tel: (212) 559-1000   Fax: (212) 559-3646   www.citigroup.com

Provides insurance and financial services worldwide.

Citigroup, PO Box 30711, Nairobi, Kenya

Contact: Peter H. Harris

THE COCA-COLA COMPANY

1 Coca Cola Plaza, Atlanta, GA, 30313

Tel: (404) 676-2121   Fax: (404) 676-6792   www.coca-cola.com

Mfr./marketing/distributor soft drinks, syrups and concentrates, juice and juice-drink products.

The Coca-Cola Co. Kenya, Nairobi, Kenya

COLGATE-PALMOLIVE COMPANY

300 Park Ave., New York, NY, 10022

Tel: (212) 310-2000   Fax: (212) 310-2919   www.colgate.com

Mfr. pharmaceuticals, cosmetics, toiletries and detergents.

Colgate-Palmolive (E.A.) Ltd., PO Box 30264, Nairobi, Kenya

CORN PRODUCTS INTERNATIONAL, INC.

6500 South Archer Ave., Bedford Park, IL, 60501-1933

Tel: (708) 563-2400   Fax: (708) 563-6852   www.cornproducts.com

Produces corn products for ingredients corn starch corn oil and corn syrups.

Corn Products Kenya Ltd., Outer Ring Road, Ruaraka, PO Box 11889, Nairobi, Kenya

Tel: 254-2-861537   Fax: 254-2-861754

CROWN CORK & SEAL COMPANY, INC.

One Crown Way, Philadelphia, PA, 19154-4599

Tel: (215) 698-5100   Fax: (215) 698-5201   www.crowncork.com

Mfr. metal and plastic packaging, including steel and aluminum cans for food, beverage and household products.

Crown Cork E.A. Ltd., PO Box 46408, Nairobi, Kenya

DANZAS AEI, INC.

120 Tokeneke Road, PO Box 1231, Darien, CT, 06820

Tel: (203) 655-7900   Fax: (203) 655-5779   www.aeilogistics.com

International air freight forwarder.

Danzas AEI, Rahimtulla Trust Bldg., Moi Ave., PO Box 44469, Nairobi, Kenya

D'ARCY MASIUS BENTON & BOWLES INC. (DMB&B)

1675 Broadway, New York, NY, 10019

Tel: (212) 468-3622   Fax: (212) 468-2987   www.darcyww.com

Full service international advertising and communications group.

DMB&B Mid East-Africa, Bishop's Garden Towers, 6/F, PO Box 42379, Nairobi, Kenya

Tel: 254-2-71-9501

DELOITTE TOUCHE TOHMATSU INTERNATIONAL

1633 Broadway, New York, NY, 10019

Tel: (212) 492-4000   Fax: (212) 392-4154   www.deloitte.com

Accounting, audit, tax and management consulting services.

Deloitte & Touche, "Kirungii" King Rd., Westlands, PO Box 40092, Nairobi, Kenya

Deloitte & Touche, 8th Fl., Kenya Reinsurance Plaza, Moi Ave., PO Box 84712, Mombasa, Kenya

DELTA AIR LINES INC.

Hartsfield International Airport, 1030 Delta Blvd., Atlanta, GA, 30320-6001

Tel: (404) 715-2600   Fax: (404) 715-5494   www.delta-air.com

Major worldwide airline; international air transport services.

Delta Air Lines Inc., Nairobi, Kenya

DHL WORLDWIDE EXPRESS

50 California Avenue, San Francisco, CA, 94111

Tel: (415) 677-6100   Fax: (415) 824-9700   www.dhl.com

Worldwide air express carrier.

DHL Worldwide Express, Longonot Place, Kijabe St., PO Box 67577, Nairobi, Kenya

Tel: 254-2-225063

EASTMAN KODAK COMPANY

343 State Street, Rochester, NY, 14650

Tel: (716) 724-4000   Fax: (716) 724-1089   www.kodak.com

Develop/mfr. photo and chemicals products, information management/video/copier systems, fibers/plastics for various industry.

Kodak Kenya Ltd., Funzi Rd., PO Box 18210, Nairobi, Kenya

ECOLAB INC.

370 N. Wabasha Street, St. Paul, MN, 55102

Tel: (651) 293-2233   Fax: (651) 293-2379   www.ecolab.com

Develop/mfr. premium cleaning, sanitizing and maintenance products and services for the hospitality, institutional, and residential markets.

Ecolab Ltd., Nairobi, Kenya

Tel: 254-2-860746

EGL INC. (EAGLE GLOBAL LOGISTICS)

15350 Vickery Drive, Houston, TX, 77032

Tel: (281) 618-3100   Fax: (281) 618-3223   www.eagleusa.com

Ocean/air freight forwarding, customs brokerage, packing and wholesale, logistics management and insurance.

EGL Eagle Global Logistics, Cannon Tower Bldg., 1st Fl., Moi Ave., PO Box 86466, Mombasa, Kenya

Tel: 254-11-227-338   Fax: 254-11-227-338

EGL Eagle Global Logistics, 4th Fl., St. Georges House, Parliament Rd., Nairobi, Kenya

Tel: 254-2-217997   Fax: 254-2-218052

ERNST & YOUNG INTERNATIONAL

5 Times Square, New York, NY, 10036

Tel: (212) 773-3000   Fax: (212) 773-6350   www.eyi.com

Engaged in assurance and advisory business services, tax, law and corporate finance.

Bellhouse Mwangi / Ernat & Young, PO Box 44286, Nairobi, Kenya

Tel: 254-2-727640   Fax: 254-2-716271   Contact: Geoffrey Karuu

Ernst & Young International, PO Box 43, Eldoret, Kenya

Ernst & Young International, PO Box 45, Nakuru, Kenya

Ernst & Young International, PO Box 99361, Mombasa, Kenya

Ernst & Young International, PO Box 60, Nyeri, Kenya

FRITZ COMPANIES, INC., DIV. UPS

706 Mission Street, Ste. 900, San Francisco, CA, 94103

Tel: (415) 904-8360   Fax: (415) 904-8661   www.fritz.com

Integrated transportation, sourcing, distribution and customs brokerage services.

Fritz Companies Inc., Mombasa, Kenya

GENERAL MOTORS CORPORATION

300 Renaissance Center, Detroit, MI, 48285

Tel: (313) 556-5000   Fax: (313) 556-5108   www.gm.com

Mfr. full line vehicles, automotive electronics, commercial technologies, telecommunications, space, finance.

General Motors Corp., PO Box 30527, Nairobi, Kenya

THE GILLETTE COMPANY

Prudential Tower Building, Boston, MA, 02199

Tel: (617) 421-7000   Fax: (617) 421-7123   www.gillette.com

Develop/mfr. personal care/use products: blades and razors, toiletries, cosmetics, stationery.

Gillette Interproducts Ltd., Nairobi, Kenya

GREY GLOBAL GROUP

777 Third Ave., New York, NY, 10017

Tel: (212) 546-2000   Fax: (212) 546-1495   www.grey.com

International advertising agency.

Century Advertising, Nairobi, Kenya

HILTON HOTELS CORPORATION

9336 Civic Center Drive, Beverly Hills, CA, 90210

Tel: (310) 278-4321   Fax: (310) 205-7880   www.hiltonhotels.com

International hotel chain: Hilton International, Vista Hotels and Hilton National Hotels.

Nairobi Hilton, Mama Ngina St., PO Box 30624, Nairobi, Kenya

HORWATH INTERNATIONAL ASSOCIATION

420 Lexington Avenue, Suite 526, New York, NY, 10170-0526

Tel: (212) 808-2000   Fax: (212) 808-2020   www.horwath.com

Public accountants and auditors.

Muchekehu & Co., 5th Floor, Nationwide House, Koinange St., Nairobi, Kenya

IBM CORPORATION

1133 Westchester Avenue, White Plains, NY, 10604

Tel: (914) 765-1900   Fax: (914) 765-7382   www.ibm.com

Information products, technology and services.

IBM East Africa Ltd., Unga House Ltd., Westlands, PO Box 35475, Nairobi, Kenya

Tel: 254-2-446910 Fax: 254-2-447012

INTER-CONTINENTAL HOTELS

3 Ravinia Drive, Suite 2900, Atlanta, GA, 30346-2149

Tel: (770) 604-2000   Fax: (770) 604-5403   www.interconti.com

Worldwide hotel and resort accommodations.

Hotel Inter-Continental Nairobi, City Hall Way, PO Box 30353, Nairobi, Kenya

Tel: 254-2-224302 Fax: 254-2-214617

INTERNATIONAL FLAVORS & FRAGRANCES INC.

521 West 57th Street, New York, NY, 10019-2960

Tel: (212) 765-5500   Fax: (212) 708-7132   www.iff.com

Design/mfr. flavors, fragrances and aroma chemicals.

International Flavors & Fragrances, P O Box 13526, Nairobi, Kenya

JOHNSON & JOHNSON

One Johnson & Johnson Plaza, New Brunswick, NJ, 08933

Tel: (732) 524-0400   Fax: (732) 214-0334   www.jnj.com

Mfr./distributor/R&D pharmaceutical, health care and cosmetic products.

Johnson & Johnson (Kenya) Ltd., PO Box 47591, Nairobi, Kenya

SC JOHNSON

1525 Howe St., Racine, WI, 53403

Tel: (262) 260-2000   Fax: (262) 260-2133   www.scjohnsonwax.com

Home, auto, commercial and personal care products and specialty chemicals.

SC Johnson, Lunga Rd., PO Box 18373, Nairobi, Kenya

KPMG CONSULTING INC.

1676 International Dr., McLean, VA, 22102

Tel: (703) 747-3000   Fax: (703) 747-8500   www.kpmg.com

Accounting and audit, tax and management consulting services.

KPMG International, Jubilee Insurance Exchange, Mama Ngina St., Nairobi, Kenya
Tel: 254-2-222862   Fax: 254-2-215695   Contact: Robin D. Cahill, Sr. Ptnr.

THE KULJIAN CORPORATION

3700 Science Center, Philadelphia, PA, 19104

Tel: (215) 243-1900   Fax: (215) 243-1909

Studies, design, engineering, construction management and site supervision.

The Kuljian Corp., PO Box 53295, Nairobi, Kenya

ELI LILLY & COMPANY

Lilly Corporate Center, Indianapolis, IN, 46285

Tel: (317) 276-2000   Fax: (317) 277-6579   www.lilly.com

Mfr. pharmaceuticals and animal health products.

Eli Lilly (Suisse) S.A., Chiromo Court, 2nd Fl., Chiromo Rd., Westlands, Nairobi, Kenya
Tel: 254-2-74-7054   Fax: 254-2-74-7070

MARSH & McLENNAN COS INC.

1166 Ave. of the Americas, New York, NY, 10036-2774

Tel: (212) 345-5000   Fax: (212) 345-4808   www.marshmac.com

Insurance agents/brokers, pension and investment management consulting services.

Bain Hogg Insurance Brokers Kenya Ltd., Chester House, Koinange St., Nairobi, Kenya
Tel: 254-233-5766   Fax: 254-222-5476   Contact: Peter Hood

McCANN-ERICKSON WORLDGROUP

750 Third Ave., New York, NY, 10017

Tel: (212) 697-6000   Fax: (212) 984-3575   www.mccann.com

International advertising and marketing services.

McCann-Erickson (Kenya) Ltd., PO Box 48541, Nairobi, Kenya

MERCK & COMPANY, INC.

One Merck Drive, PO Box 100, Whitehouse Station, NJ, 08889-0100

Tel: (908) 423-1000   Fax: (908) 423-2592   www.merck.com

Pharmaceuticals, chemicals and biologicals.

Merck, Sharp & Dohme Intl., PO Box 30676, Arwings-Kodhek Road, Nairobi, Kenya

MONSANTO

800 N. Lindbergh Boulevard, St. Louis, MO, 63167

Tel: (314) 694-1000   Fax: (314) 694-7625   www.monsanto.com

Life sciences company focusing on agriculture, nutrition, pharmaceuticals, health and wellness and sustainable development.

Monsanto Nairobi, I&M Building, 6th Floor, 2nd Ngong Avenue Ngong Road, Nairobi, Kenya

J. P. MORGAN CHASE & CO. INC.

270 Park Ave., New York, NY, 10017

Tel: (212) 270-6000   Fax: (212) 622-9030   www.jpmorganchase.com

Provides integrated financial solutions for institutions and individuals worldwide, including asset management, investment banking and commercial banking.

J. P. Morgan Chase & Co., Kencom House, 7th Fl., PO Box 57051, Nairobi, Kenya

J. P. Morgan Chase & Co., International House, 13/F, Mama Ngina St., Nairobi, Kenya

AC NIELSEN COMPANY

177 Broad Street, Stamford, CT, 06901

Tel: (203) 961-3000   Fax: (203) 961-3190   www.acnielsen.com

Engaged in market and consumer research.

ACNielsen, PO Box 60680, Nairobi, Kenya

OGILVY & MATHER WORLDWIDE

309 West 49th Street, New York, NY, 10017-7399

Tel: (212) 237-4000   Fax: (212) 237-5123   www.ogilvypr.com

Engaged in public relations and communications.

Ogilvy Public Relations Worldwide, Nairobi, Kenya

OTIS ELEVATOR COMPANY

One Farm Springs Road, Farmington, CT, 06032

Tel: (860) 676-6000   Fax: (860) 676-5111   www.otis.com

Mfr. elevators and escalators.

East African Elevator Co. Ltd., Finance House, 9th Fl., Bondo Rd., Industrial Area, PO Box 20014, Nairobi, Kenya

PFIZER INC.

235 East 42nd Street, New York, NY, 10017-5755

Tel: (212) 573-2323   Fax: (212) 573-7851   www.pfizer.com

Research-based, global health care company.

Pfizer Laboratories Ltd., Nairobi, Kenya

PIONEER HI-BRED INTERNATIONAL INC.

400 Locust Street, Ste. 800, Des Moines, IA, 50309

Tel: (515) 248-4800   Fax: (515) 248-4999   www.pioneer.com

Agricultural chemicals, farm supplies, biological products, research.

Freshco International Ltd., PO Box 65082, Nairobi, Kenya

PRICEWATERHOUSECOOPERS LLP

1301 Ave. of the Americas, New York, NY, 10019

Tel: (212) 596-7000   Fax: (212) 259-1301   www.pwcglobal.com

Accounting and auditing, tax and management, and human resource consulting services.

PriceWaterhouseCoopers, Rattansi Educational Trust Building, Koinange Street, PO Box 41968, Nairobi, Kenya
Tel: 254-2-221244 Fax: 254-2-335937

PriceWaterhouseCoopers, Ralli House, Nyerere Avenue, PO Box 81824, Mombasa, Kenya
Tel: 254-11-312394

PROCTER & GAMBLE COMPANY

One Procter & Gamble Plaza, Cincinnati, OH, 45202

Tel: (513) 983-1100   Fax: (513) 562-4500   www.pg.com

Personal care, food, laundry, cleaning and industry products.

Procter & Gamble, PO BOX 30453, Nairobi, Kenya
Tel: 254-2-540650

ROCKWELL AUTOMATION, INC.

777 East Wisconsin Ave., Ste. 1400, Milwaukee, WI, 53202

Tel: (414) 212-5200   Fax: (414) 212-5201   www.rockwellautomation.com

Products and service for aerospace and defense, automotive, electronics, graphics and automation industry.

Rockwell Automation (Proprietary) Ltd., Lonrho House, 6th Fl., Standard St., Nairobi, Kenya

Tel: 254-2-223-961   Fax: 254-2-230-331

SCHENKER USA INC.

150 Albany Ave., Freeport, NY, 11520

Tel: (516) 403-5416   Fax: (516) 377-3092   www.schenkerusa.com

Freight forwarders.

Schenker & Co Ltd., Schenker House Cargo, Kenyatta Intl Airport, PO Box 46757, Nairobi, Kenya

Tel: 254-2-822-828   Fax: 254-2-823-269

Schenker & Co. Ltd., Freed House, Kwashibu Rd., PO Box 84361, Mombasa, Kenya

Tel: 254-11-311-620   Fax: 254-11-314-083

SCHERING-PLOUGH CORPORATION

One Giralda Farms, Madison, NJ, 07940-1000

Tel: (973) 822-7000   Fax: (973) 822-7048   www.sch-plough.com

Proprietary drug and cosmetic products.

Essex East Africa Ltd., PO Box 30409, Nairobi, Kenya

SIGNODE PACKAGING SYSTEMS

3610 West Lake Ave., Glenview, IL, 60025

Tel: (847) 724-6100   Fax: (847) 657-4392   www.signode.com

Mfr. industrial tools and machinery for packaging and strapping.

Signode Packaging Systems Ltd., Mombasa Rd., PO Box 78160, Nairobi, Kenya

SPSS INC.

233 S. Wacker Dr., 11th Fl., Chicago, IL, 60606

Tel: (312) 651-6000   Fax: (312) 329-3668   www.spss.com

Mfr. statistical software.

SPSS East Africa, NorthStar Complex, Lenana Road, PO Box 66405, Nairobi, Kenya

THE ST. PAUL COMPANIES, INC.

385 Washington Street, St. Paul, MN, 55102

Tel: (651) 310-7911   Fax: (651) 310-8294   www.stpaul.com

Provides investment, insurance and reinsurance services.

Insurance Company of East Africa Ltd., ICEA Building, Kenyatta Ave., PO Box 46142, Nairobi, Kenya

UNITED PARCEL SERVICE, INC.

55 Glenlake Parkway, NE, Atlanta, GA, 30328

Tel: (404) 828-6000   Fax: (404) 828-6593   www.ups.com

International package-delivery service.

UPS Kenya, PO Box 46586, Nairobi, Kenya

Tel: 254-2-820-804   Fax: 254-2-823-124

WM WRIGLEY JR. COMPANY

410 N. Michigan Ave., Chicago, IL, 60611-4287

Tel: (312) 644-2121   Fax: (312) 644-0353   www.wrigley.com

Mfr. chewing gum.

Wrigley Company Ltd., PO Box 30767, Nairobi, Kenya

WYETH PHARMACEUTICALS

555 E. Lancaster Ave., Wayne, PA, 19087-5109

Tel: (610) 971-5400   Fax: (610) 995-4668   www.wyeth.com

Mfr. antibiotics and pharmaceutical products.

Lederle Labs., Div. American Cyanamid, PO Box 47341, Nairobi, Kenya

XEROX CORPORATION

800 Long Ridge Road, PO Box 1600, Stamford, CT, 06904

Tel: (203) 968-3000   Fax: (203) 968-4312   www.xerox.com

Mfr. document processing equipment, systems and supplies.

Rank Xerox Kenya Ltd., PO Box 20410, Parklands Rd., Westlands, Nairobi, Kenya

YOUNG & RUBICAM INC.

285 Madison Ave., New York, NY, 10017

Tel: (212) 210-3000   Fax: (212) 370-3796   www.yr.com

Advertising, public relations, direct marketing and sales promotion, corporate and product ID management.

Ayton Young & Rubicam, Nairobi, Kenya

Kirghizia

LeBOEUF, LAMB, GREENE & MacRAE LLP

125 West 55th Street, 12th Fl., New York, NY, 10019

Tel: (212) 424-8000   Fax: (212) 424-8500   www.llgm.com

International law firm.

LeBoeuf, Lamb, Greene & MacRae LLP, Ul. Panfilova 205, Bishkek, Kirghizia

Tel: 7-3312-22-2994   Fax: 7-3312-62-0393

MAYER, BROWN, ROWE & MAW

190 S. LaSalle Street, Chicago, IL, 60603

Tel: (312) 782-0600   Fax: (312) 701-7711   www.mayerbrown.com

Engaged in international law.

Mayer, Brown, Rowe & Maw, 66 Kalykh Akieva St., Bishkek 72000, Kirghizia

Tel: 996-3312-620980   Fax: 996-3312-620980

Kuwait

ANC RENTAL CORPORATION

200 S. Andrews Ave., Ft. Lauderdale, FL, 33301

Tel: (954) 320-4000   Fax: (954) 320-4077   www.ancrental.com

Engaged in car rental services, including National Car Rental and Alamo Rent A Car.

National Car Rental, PO Box 81, Safat, Kuwait

ANDERSEN

33 West Monroe Street, Chicago, IL, 60603

Tel: (312) 580-0033   Fax: (312) 507-6748   www.andersen.com

Accounting and audit, tax and management consulting services. **Firm under worldwide reorganization; new data unavailable for this edition.

Arthur Andersen/Al-Bazie & Co., Kuwait Airways Bldg., 7th Fl., Shuhada St., PO Box 2115, Safat 13022, Kuwait

Tel: 965-241-0010

AON CORPORATION

200 East Randolph, Chicago, IL, 60601

Tel: (312) 381-1000   Fax: (312) 381-6032   www.aon.com

Insurance brokers worldwide; underwrites accident and health insurance, specialty and professional insurance; and provides risk management consultation.

AON Worldwide/ Insurance Management Bureau, PO Box 25483, Safat Kuwait City 13115, Kuwait

Tel: 965-241-4124   Fax: 965-245-7976   Contact: Sami Bekhazi

BBDO WORLDWIDE

1285 Ave. of the Americas, New York, NY, 10019

Tel: (212) 459-5000   Fax: (212) 459-6645   www.bbdo.com

Multinational group of advertising agencies.

Impact & Echo Advertising, Kuwait City, Kuwait

BDO SEIDMAN, LLP   BELGIUM

130 East Randolph Street, Chicago, IL, 60601

Tel: (312) 856-9100   Fax: (312) 856-1379   www.bdo.com

International accounting and financial consulting firm.

BDO Burgan Auditing Office, Dasman Complex, Block 1, 4th Fl., Ahmad Al Jaber St., Sharq Kuwait City, Kuwait

Tel: 965-242-6862   Fax: 965-241-4956   Contact: Hokmat Mukhaimer

BECHTEL GROUP INC.

50 Beale Street, PO Box 3965, San Francisco, CA, 94105-1895

Tel: (415) 768-1234   Fax: (415) 768-9038   www.bechtel.com

General contractors in engineering, construction and project management.

Eastern Bechtel Corp., PO Box 29396, Salhia Commercial Complex, Gate #1, First Fl., Safat 13020, Kuwait

Tel: 965-244-4300   Fax: 965-245-5301

BENTLY NEVADA CORPORATION

1631 Bently Parkway South, Minden, NV, 89423

Tel: (775) 782-3611   Fax: (775) 782-9259   www.bently.com

Provides hardware, software, and services for machinery information and management systems.

A.Z. Trading Co. WWL, PO Box 25752, Safat, Kuwait

BLACK & VEATCH LLP

8400 Ward Pkwy., PO Box 8405, Kansas City, MO, 64114

Tel: (816) 339-2000   Fax: (816) 339-2934   www.bv.com

Engaged in engineering, construction and consulting, specializing in infrastructure development in the fields of energy, water and information.

Black & Veatch International, Plot 110, Block 6, East Ahmadi, Kuwait

Tel: 965-398-1765   Fax: 965-398-6297

BOZELL GROUP

40 West 23rd Street, New York, NY, 10010

Tel: (212) 727-5000   Fax: (212) 645-9173   www.bozell.com

Advertising, marketing, public relations and media consulting.

Bozell Prime New Media, PO Box 17958, Khaldia 72460, Kuwait

Tel: 965-533-0046 Fax: 965-533-0048   Contact: Bader Al Duwaisan, Chmn.

BRISTOL-MYERS SQUIBB COMPANY

345 Park Ave., New York, NY, 10154-0037

Tel: (212) 546-4000   Fax: (212) 546-4020   www.bms.com

Pharmaceutical and food preparations, medical and surgical instruments.

Yusuf Ibrahim Al Ghanim & Sons, PO Box 435, Safat 13005, Kuwait

BRYAN CAVE LLP

211 North Broadway, St. Louis, MO, 63102

Tel: (314) 259-2000   Fax: (314) 259-2020   www.bryancave.com

International law firm.

Bryan Cave LLP, Sheraton Towers 2/F, PO Box 5902, Safat 13060, Kuwait

Tel: 965-240-4470   Contact: John V. Lonsberg

LEO BURNETT, DIV. B-COM 3 GROUP

35 West Wacker Drive, Chicago, IL, 60601

Tel: (312) 220-5959   Fax: (312) 220-6533   www.leoburnett.com

Engaged in advertising, marketing, media buying and planning, and public relations.

Radius/Leo Burnett Advertising, Al Khalcejia Bldg., PO Box 26100, Safat 13121, Kuwait

CARRIER CORPORATION

One Carrier Place, Farmington, CT, 06034-4015

Tel: (860) 674-3000   Fax: (860) 679-3010   www.carrier.com

Mfr./distributor/services A/C, heating and refrigeration equipment.

Kuwait American Airconditioning Co., PO Box 146, Safat 13002, Kuwait

Tel: 965-481-9733   Fax: 98-65-483-3882

DANZAS AEI, INC.

120 Tokeneke Road, PO Box 1231, Darien, CT, 06820

Tel: (203) 655-7900   Fax: (203) 655-5779   www.aeilogistics.com

International air freight forwarder.

Kuwait Maritime & Mercantile Co. KSC, PO Box 78, Safat Kuwait City 13001, Kuwait

Tel: 965-243-4752   Fax: 965-243-7956

D'ARCY MASIUS BENTON & BOWLES INC. (DMB&B)

1675 Broadway, New York, NY, 10019

Tel: (212) 468-3622   Fax: (212) 468-2987   www.darcyww.com

Full service international advertising and communications group.

DMB&B Mid East-Africa, Kuwait City, Kuwait

DELOITTE TOUCHE TOHMATSU INTERNATIONAL

1633 Broadway, New York, NY, 10019

Tel: (212) 492-4000   Fax: (212) 392-4154   www.deloitte.com

Accounting, audit, tax and management consulting services.

Al-Fahad Al-Marzook Deloitte & Touche, Fahad Al-Salem St., Salhia Complex E-2, 4th Fl., PO Box 23049, Safat 13091, Kuwait City, Kuwait

DHL WORLDWIDE EXPRESS

50 California Avenue, San Francisco, CA, 94111

Tel: (415) 677-6100   Fax: (415) 824-9700   www.dhl.com

Worldwide air express carrier.

DHL Worldwide Express, Old TV Centre, Arabian Gulf St., Dasman PO Box 26523, Safat 13126, Kuwait

Tel: 965-244-2375

DIONEX CORPORATION

1228 Titan Way, PO Box 3603, Sunnyvale, CA, 94086-3603

Tel: (408) 737-0700   Fax: (408) 730-9403   www.dionex.com

Develop/mfr./market chromatography systems and related products.

Tareq Company, PO Box 20506 Safat, 13066 Safat, Area 1, Block #103, Ardiya, Kuwait

Tel: 965-4313729 2063

DYN CORPORATION

11710 Plaza America Drive, Reston, VA, 20190

Tel: (703) 261-5000   Fax: (703) 261-5090   www.dyncorp.com

Engaged in diversified technical services.

DYN Corp., Spanish Villas Area 11, Street 4, Building 10, STE 3, Saiwa, Kuwait

EGL INC. (EAGLE GLOBAL LOGISTICS)

15350 Vickery Drive, Houston, TX, 77032

Tel: (281) 618-3100   Fax: (281) 618-3223   www.eagleusa.com

Ocean/air freight forwarding, customs brokerage, packing and wholesale, logistics management and insurance.

EGL Eagle Global Logistics, PO Box 42491, Pin Kuwait City 70655, Kuwait

Tel: 965-473-8323   Fax: 965-473-5558

EMERY FORWARDING

One Lagoon Drive, Ste. 400, Redwood City, CA, 94065

Tel: (650) 596-9600   Fax: (650) 596-7901   www.emeryworld.com

Freight transport, global logistics and air cargo.

Emery Forwarding, PO Box 5133, Sufat 13052, Kuwait

ERNST & YOUNG INTERNATIONAL

5 Times Square, New York, NY, 10036

Tel: (212) 773-3000   Fax: (212) 773-6350   www.eyi.com

Engaged in assurance and advisory business services, tax, law and corporate finance.

Ernst & Young (Al Aiban, Al Osaimi & Partners), PO Box 72, Safat, Souk Al Maseel, 4th Fl., Abdullah Mubarak St., Safat Kuwait City 13001, Kuwait

Tel: 965-245-2880   Fax: 965-245-6419   Contact: Michael L. Hunter

ETHAN ALLEN INTERIORS INC.

Ethan Allen Drive, Danbury, CT, 06811

Tel: (203) 743-8000   Fax: (203) 743-8298   www.ethanallen.com

Mfr. and sale of premium-priced furniture and home furnishings.

Ethan Allen Home Interiors, Hassawi Street, Al Rai, Kuwait City, Kuwait

Tel: 965-471-0020

EXPEDITORS INTERNATIONAL OF WASHINGTON INC.

1015 Third Avenue, 12th Fl., Seattle, WA, 98104-1182

Tel: (206) 674-3400   Fax: (206) 682-9777   www.expd.com

Air/ocean freight forwarding, customs brokerage, international logistics solutions.

Expeditors International, Block 125, J Shuwaikh, PO Box 27063, Safat 13131, Kuwait

Tel: 965-482-2805   Fax: 965-482-2802

FRITZ COMPANIES, INC., DIV. UPS

706 Mission Street, Ste. 900, San Francisco, CA, 94103

Tel: (415) 904-8360   Fax: (415) 904-8661   www.fritz.com

Integrated transportation, sourcing, distribution and customs brokerage services.

Fritz Companies Inc., Safat, Kuwait

GLOBAL SILVERHAWK INTERNATIONAL MOVING

1000 Burnett Avenue, Concord, CA, 94520

Tel: (510) 609-7080   Fax: (510) 609-7081   www.globalsilverhawk.com

International moving and forwarding.

Global Silverhawk, PO Box 42065, Shuwaikh 70651, Kuwait

Tel: 965-245-7406

GRANT THORNTON INTERNATIONAL

800 One Prudential Plaza, 130 E. Randolph Drive, Chicago, IL, 60601-6050

Tel: (312) 856-0001   Fax: (312) 616-7052   www.grantthornton.com

Accounting, audit, tax and management consulting services.

Grant Thornton Anwar Al-Qatami & Co., Souq Al-Kabeer Bldg., Block A - 9/F, Kuwait City 13030, Kuwait

Contact: Anwar Al-Qatami

GREY GLOBAL GROUP

777 Third Ave., New York, NY, 10017

Tel: (212) 546-2000   Fax: (212) 546-1495   www.grey.com

International advertising agency.

CSS & Grey, Fisheries Building, 4/F, Al Hilali Street, Safat 13103, Kuwait

HALLIBURTON COMPANY

500 North Akard Street, Ste. 3600, Dallas, TX, 75201-3391

Tel: (214) 978-2600   Fax: (214) 978-2685   www.halliburton.com

Engaged in diversified energy services, engineering and construction.

Halliburton Ltd., PO Box 9022, Ahmadi 61001, Kuwait

Tel: 965-398-4801   Fax: 965-398-9145

HONEYWELL INTERNATIONAL INC.

Honeywell Plaza, Minneapolis, MN, 55408

Tel: (612) 951-1000   Fax: (612) 951-8537   www.honeywell.com

Develop/mfr. controls for home and building, industry, space and aviation, burglar and fire alarm systems.

Honeywell Kuwait KSC, PO Box 20825, Safat 13069, Kuwait

Tel: 965-242-1327   Fax: 965-242-8315

IBM CORPORATION

1133 Westchester Avenue, White Plains, NY, 10604

Tel: (914) 765-1900   Fax: (914) 765-7382   www.ibm.com

Information products, technology and services.

IBM Kuwait - Khorafi Business Machines, PO Box 4175, Safat, Kuwait

Tel: 965-243-9900   Fax: 965-242-4577

IDEX CORPORATION

630 Dundee Road, Ste. 400, Northbrook, IL, 60062

Tel: (847) 498-7070   Fax: (847) 498-3940   www.idexcorp.com

Mfr. industrial pumps, lubrication systems, metal fabrication equipment, bending and clamping devices.

Al Sultan & Khalaf Trading Co., Shuwaikh-Al-Mouasalet St., PO Box 42130, Shuwaikh, Kuwait

INTERGRAPH CORPORATION

One Madison Industrial Park, Huntsville, AL, 35894-0001

Tel: (256) 730-2000 Fax: (256) 730-7898 www.intergraph.com

Develop/mfr. interactive computer graphic systems.

Intergraph Technical Services Middle East Ltd., c/o M.A.. Kharafi, PO Box 886, Safat 13009, Kuwait

Tel: 965-5623571 Fax: 965-5623496

KPMG CONSULTING INC.

1676 International Dr., McLean, VA, 22102

Tel: (703) 747-3000 Fax: (703) 747-8500 www.kpmg.com

Accounting and audit, tax and management consulting services.

KPMG Masoud & Co., Sahab Tower, 6th Fl., Mohammed Thunian al Ghanim St., Al Salhia Area, Kuwait

Tel: 965-240-0121 Fax: 965-240-0120 Contact: Masoud Sorkhou, Sr. Ptnr.

LOCKHEED MARTIN CORPORATION

6801 Rockledge Drive, Bethesda, MD, 20817

Tel: (301) 897-6000 Fax: (301) 897-6652 www.imco.com

Design/mfr./management systems in fields of space, defense, energy, electronics and technical services.

Lockheed Aeronautical Systems Support Company, Lockheed Rep., Mangaf Complex, Kuwait

Tel: 965-431-1588 Fax: 965-372-4910 Contact: E. J. Wisner, Mgr.

M-I

PO Box 48242, Houston, TX, 77242-2842

Tel: (713) 739-0222 Fax: (713) 308-9503 www.midf.com

Developer, manufacturer and marketer of drilling and completion fluids and services.

Kuwait Drilling, Shuaiba Industrial Area 13046, Kuwait

Tel: 965-326-2455 Fax: 965-326-2269

MOTOROLA, INC.

1303 East Algonquin Road, Schaumburg, IL, 60196

Tel: (847) 576-5000 Fax: (847) 538-5191 www.motorola.com

Mfr. communications equipment, semiconductors and cellular phones.

Motorola S.A., PO Box 3301, Salmiya 22004, Kuwait

Tel: 965-534-2365 Fax: 965-534-2361

AC NIELSEN COMPANY

177 Broad Street, Stamford, CT, 06901

Tel: (203) 961-3000 Fax: (203) 961-3190 www.acnielsen.com

Engaged in market and consumer research.

ACNielsen, PO Box 11743A1, Dasmah 35158, Kuwait

OTIS ELEVATOR COMPANY

One Farm Springs Road, Farmington, CT, 06032

Tel: (860) 676-6000 Fax: (860) 676-5111 www.otis.com

Mfr. elevators and escalators.

Otis Elevator Co. (Kuwait), PO Box 11169, Dasma 35152, Kuwait

PANAMETRICS

221 Crescent Street, Waltham, MA, 02154

Tel: (781) 899-2719 Fax: (781) 899-1552 www.panametrics.com

Engaged in manufacture and distribution of ultrasonic testing equipment and process control instrumentation.

Al Siyahead Mechanical Contracting Est., PO Box 12309, Shamiya 71654, Kuwait

Tel: 965-240-1188 Fax: 965-240-1088

PARKER DRILLING COMPANY

1401 Enclave Pkwy., Ste. 600, Houston, TX, 77077

Tel: (281) 406-2000 Fax: (281) 406-2001 www.parkerdrilling.com

Provides land contract drilling services to firms in the oil and gas industry.

Parker Drilling Co., East Ahmadi-Ahmadi, Block No. 8, Plot No. 142, PO Box 9066, Kuwait City 61001, Kuwait

PARSONS CORPORATION

100 West Walnut Street, Pasadena, CA, 91124

Tel: (626) 440-2000 Fax: (626) 440-4919 www.parsons.com

Engaged in engineering, procurement, and construction management services.

Parsons Engineering Science Inc., PO Box 36781, Raas Salmiyah 24758, Kuwait

POLARIS INDUSTRIES INC.

2100 Highway 55, Medina, MN, 55440

Tel: (612) 542-0500 Fax: (612) 542-0599 www.polarisindustries.com

Mfr. snowmobiles and all-terrain recreational and utility vehicles.

Amiry International Marine, PO Box 110, Safat l3002, Kuwait

Tel: 965-484-5346

RAYTHEON COMPANY

141 Spring Street, Lexington, MA, 02173

Tel: (781) 862-6600 Fax: (781) 860-2172 www.raytheon.com

Mfr. diversified electronics, appliances, energy and environmental products; publishing, industry and construction services.

Raytheon Gulf Systems Co., PO Box 33147, Rawda, Kuwait

THE RENDON GROUP INC.

1875 Connecticut Ave., NE, Washington, DC, 20009

Tel: (202) 745-4900 Fax: (202) 745-0215 www.rendon.com

Public relations, print and video production, strategic communications.

The Rendon Group Inc., Flat 802, Tower 8, Floor 3, Bneid Al Ghar, Kuwait City, Kuwait

STANLEY CONSULTANTS, INC.

Stanley Building, 225 Iowa Ave., Muscatine, IA, 52761-3764

Tel: (563) 264-6600 Fax: (563) 264-6658 www.stanleygroup.com

Engaged in engineering, architectural, planning and management services.

Stanley Consultants, Inc., PO Box 22448, Safat Kuwait City 13085, Kuwait

Tel: 965-242-4146 Fax: 965-242-6350

STARWOOD HOTELS & RESORTS WORLDWIDE

777 Westchester Avenue, White Plains, NY, 10604

Tel: (914) 640-8100 Fax: (914) 640-8316 www.starwoodhotels.com

Hotel operations including Sheraton, Westin, St. Regis, Four Points and Caesars.

Kuwait Sheraton Hotel, PO Box 5902, Fahd al Salem St., Kuwait

TURNER INTERNATIONAL, DIV. THE TURNER CORPORATION

901 Main St., Ste. 4900, Dallas, TX, 75202

Tel: (214) 915-9600 Fax: (214) 915-9700 www.turnerconstruction.com

Engaged in general construction and construction management.

Turner Steiner International SA, Kuwait City, Kuwait

UNION CARBIDE CORPORATION

39 Old Ridgebury Road, Danbury, CT, 06817

Tel: (203) 794-2000 Fax: (203) 794-6269 www.unioncarbide.com

Mfr. industrial chemicals, plastics and resins.

Union Carbide (JV), Al-Shuaiba, Kuwait

UNITED PARCEL SERVICE, INC.

55 Glenlake Parkway, NE, Atlanta, GA, 30328

Tel: (404) 828-6000 Fax: (404) 828-6593 www.ups.com

International package-delivery service.

UPS Kuwait, PO Box 20637, Safat 13067, Kuwait

Tel: 965-434-4822 Fax: 965-434-4622

THE WASHINGTON POST COMPANY

1150 15th St. NW, Washington, DC, 20071

Tel: (202) 334-6000   Fax: (202) 334-4536   www.washpostco.com

Engaged in magazine publishing, cable and television broadcasting, educational services and the Internet.

Dar Al-Watan Publishing Group (Newsweek Bil-Logha Al-Arabia), Kuwait

WEATHERFORD INTERNATIONAL, INC.

515 Post Oak Blvd. Ste. 600, Houston, TX, 77027-3415

Tel: (713) 287-8400   Fax: (713) 963-9785   www.weatherford.com

Oilfield services, products and equipment; mfr. marine cranes for oil and gas industry.

Weatherford Intl. Inc., c/o Ajal Contracting & General Trading Co., PO Box 26256, Safat, Kuwait

Tel: 965-242-7773   Fax: 965-240-5124

WENDY'S INTERNATIONAL, INC.

4288 West Dublin Granville Roads, Dublin, OH, 43017-0256

Tel: (614) 764-3100   Fax: (614) 764-3459   www.wendysintl.com

Fast food restaurant chain.

Wendy's International, Kuwait

XEROX CORPORATION

800 Long Ridge Road, PO Box 1600, Stamford, CT, 06904

Tel: (203) 968-3000   Fax: (203) 968-4312   www.xerox.com

Mfr. document processing equipment, systems and supplies.

Alamana Industries Co., SAK, POBox 20244, Safat 13063, Kuwait

Tel: 965-242 4950   Fax: 965-243 6134

YORK INTERNATIONAL CORPORATION

631 South Richland Ave., York, PA, 17403

Tel: (717) 771-7890   Fax: (717) 771-6212   www.york.com

Mfr. heating, ventilating, air conditioning and refrigeration equipment.

York Air Conditioning & Refrigeration, Inc., Salhia Complex, Gate No. 1, Mez. 2, PO Box 29034 Safat, Kuwait City, Kuwait

Tel: 965-245-1599

Laos

BATES WORLDWIDE INC.
498 Seventh Avenue, New York, NY, 10018

Tel: (212) 297-7000   Fax: (212) 986-0270   www.batesww.com

Advertising, marketing, public relations and media consulting.

Bates Laos, c/o Adena Mahavong, PO Box 1421, Vientiane, Laos

Tel: 856-21-313-868-069   Fax: 856-21-313-868   Contact: Herve Deville, CEO Indochine

DHL WORLDWIDE EXPRESS
50 California Avenue, San Francisco, CA, 94111

Tel: (415) 677-6100   Fax: (415) 824-9700   www.dhl.com

Worldwide air express carrier.

DHL Worldwide Express, 27 Nongno St., Ban Wattay Noy Thong, PO Box 7083, Vientiane, Laos

Tel: 856-21-216830

McCANN-ERICKSON WORLDGROUP
750 Third Ave., New York, NY, 10017

Tel: (212) 697-6000   Fax: (212) 984-3575   www.mccann.com

International advertising and marketing services.

Exprim McCann-Erickson (Laos), Vientiane, Laos

Latvia

AIG AMERICAN INTERNATIONAL GROUP INC.
70 Pine Street, New York, NY, 10270

Tel: (212) 770-7000   Fax: (212) 509-9705   www.aig.com

Worldwide insurance and financial services.

Seesam Latvia Ins. Co., Jekaba Kaz. Toma 4, 18-201, LV-1050 Riga, Latvia

ANDERSEN
33 West Monroe Street, Chicago, IL, 60603

Tel: (312) 580-0033   Fax: (312) 507-6748   www.andersen.com

Accounting and audit, tax and management consulting services. ****Firm under worldwide reorganization; new data unavailable for this edition.**

Andersen Worldwide, Pulkveza Brieza Iela 15, LV-1010 Riga, Latvia

Tel: 371-732-1140

APPLERA CORPORATION
301 Merritt 7, Norwalk, CT, 06851

Tel: (203) 840-2000   Fax: (203) 840-2312   www.applera.com

Leading supplier of systems for life science research and related applications.

Ameto Ltd., Struktoru 14/A, 312, LV-1039 Riga, Latvia

BATES WORLDWIDE INC.
498 Seventh Avenue, New York, NY, 10018

Tel: (212) 297-7000   Fax: (212) 986-0270   www.batesww.com

Advertising, marketing, public relations and media consulting.

Bates Latvia, 9/11 Perses St., LV-1010 Riga, Latvia

Tel: 371-7-770-585   Fax: 371-1-770-588   Contact: R. Plakajia, Dir.

DDB WORLDWIDE COMMUNICATIONS GROUP
437 Madison Ave., New York, NY, 10022

Tel: (212) 415-2000   Fax: (212) 415-3417   www.ddbn.com

Advertising agency.

Brand Sellers DDB Baltics, Riga, Latvia

DELOITTE TOUCHE TOHMATSU INTERNATIONAL
1633 Broadway, New York, NY, 10019

Tel: (212) 492-4000   Fax: (212) 392-4154   www.deloitte.com

Accounting, audit, tax and management consulting services.

Deloitte & Touche, Kr. Barona 64-3, LV-1001 Riga, Latvia

DHL WORLDWIDE EXPRESS
50 California Avenue, San Francisco, CA, 94111

Tel: (415) 677-6100   Fax: (415) 824-9700   www.dhl.com

Worldwide air express carrier.

DHL Worldwide Express, Dzintaru 22, LV-3602 Ventsplis, Latvia

Tel: 371-701-3292

DIAGNOSTIC PRODUCTS CORPORATION
5700 West 96th Street, Los Angeles, CA, 90045

Tel: (310) 645-8200   Fax: (310) 645-9999   www.dpcweb.com

Mfr. diagnostic products.

DPC Baltic SIÀ, Brivibas Iela 226/2, LV-1039 Riga, Latvia

Tel: 371-780-1187   Fax: 371-754-1477

J.D. EDWARDS & COMPANY

One Technology Way, Denver, CO, 80237

Tel: (303) 334-4000   Fax: (303) 334-4970   www.jdedwards.com

Computer software products.

Robertson & Blums - Riga CIBS, 12 Miesnieku iela, LV-1050 Riga, Latvia

Tel: 371-721-1101   Fax: 371-782-0379

EMERSON PROCESS MANAGEMENT

8301Cameron Road, Austin, TX, 78754

Tel: (512) 834-7689   Fax: (512) 832-3232   www.frco.com

Mfr. industrial process control equipment.

SIA Rino, Tallinas 51-8, LV-1012 Riga, Latvia

Tel: 371-731-5087

ERNST & YOUNG INTERNATIONAL

5 Times Square, New York, NY, 10036

Tel: (212) 773-3000   Fax: (212) 773-6350   www.eyi.com

Engaged in assurance and advisory business services, tax, law and corporate finance.

Ernst & Young Latvia, Kalku St. 11, LV-1050 Riga, Latvia

Tel: 371-2-225700   Fax: 371-2-227753   Contact: Monty Akesson

FRITZ COMPANIES, INC., DIV. UPS

706 Mission Street, Ste. 900, San Francisco, CA, 94103

Tel: (415) 904-8360   Fax: (415) 904-8661   www.fritz.com

Integrated transportation, sourcing, distribution and customs brokerage services.

Fritz Companies Inc., Riga, Latvia

GEN RE INTERMEDIARIES CORPORATION

PO Box 10216, Stamford, CT, 06904-2216

Tel: (203) 357-8883   Fax: (203) 328-6408   www.genre.com

Provides reinsurance services worldwide.

Die Kölnische Rück Riga GmbH, Elizabetes Iela 11-1, LV-1010 Riga, Latvia

Tel: 371-783-0107   Fax: 371-783-0127   Contact: Michail Kuharenok

GREY GLOBAL GROUP

777 Third Ave., New York, NY, 10017

Tel: (212) 546-2000   Fax: (212) 546-1495   www.grey.com

International advertising agency.

Grey Advertising, Riga, Latvia

IBM CORPORATION

1133 Westchester Avenue, White Plains, NY, 10604

Tel: (914) 765-1900   Fax: (914) 765-7382   www.ibm.com

Information products, technology and services.

IBM Latvia, Elizabetes Str. 65, LV-1050 Riga, Latvia

Tel: 371-724-2330   Fax: 371-782-8111

KELLOGG COMPANY

One Kellogg Square, PO Box 3599, Battle Creek, MI, 49016-3599

Tel: (616) 961-2000   Fax: (616) 961-2871   www.kelloggs.com

Mfr. ready-to-eat cereals and convenience foods.

Kellogg Latvia Inc., Attn: Latvian Office, One Kellogg Square, PO Box 3599, Battle Creek, MI, 49016-3599

KPMG CONSULTING INC.

1676 International Dr., McLean, VA, 22102

Tel: (703) 747-3000   Fax: (703) 747-8500   www.kpmg.com

Accounting and audit, tax and management consulting services.

KPMG International, Kr. Valdemara Iela 33-4, LV-1010 Riga, Latvia

Tel: 371-733-3023   Fax: 371-733-3023   Contact: Daina Eiche, Sr. Ptnr.

ELI LILLY & COMPANY

Lilly Corporate Center, Indianapolis, IN, 46285

Tel: (317) 276-2000   Fax: (317) 277-6579   www.lilly.com

Mfr. pharmaceuticals and animal health products.

Eli Lilly (Suisse) S.A., Rep Office, Elizabetes 85a, LV-1011 Riga, Latvia

Tel: 371-7-282-001 Fax: 371-7-288-078

McCANN-ERICKSON WORLDGROUP

750 Third Ave., New York, NY, 10017

Tel: (212) 697-6000   Fax: (212) 984-3575   www.mccann.com

International advertising and marketing services.

Division McCann-Erickson Latvia, Riga, Latvia

McDONALD'S CORPORATION

McDonald's Plaza, Oak Brook, IL, 60523

Tel: (630) 623-3000   Fax: (630) 623-7409   www.mcdonalds.com

Fast food chain stores.

McDonald's Corp., Latvia

MOTOROLA, INC.

1303 East Algonquin Road, Schaumburg, IL, 60196

Tel: (847) 576-5000   Fax: (847) 538-5191   www.motorola.com

Mfr. communications equipment, semiconductors and cellular phones.

Motorola Latvia, 15 Kalku Iela, LV-1050 Riga, Latvia

Tel: 371-2-722-7285   Fax: 371-2-782-0322

PHARMACIA CORPORATION

100 Route 206 North, Peapack, NJ, 07977

Tel: (908) 901-8000   Fax: (908) 901-8379   www.pharmacia.com

Mfr. pharmaceuticals, agricultural products, industry chemicals.

Pharmacia, 4 Meza Str., LV-1048 Riga, Latvia

Tel: 371-7-616-900   Fax: 371-7-805-680

PROCTER & GAMBLE COMPANY

One Procter & Gamble Plaza, Cincinnati, OH, 45202

Tel: (513) 983-1100   Fax: (513) 562-4500   www.pg.com

Personal care, food, laundry, cleaning and industry products.

Procter & Gamble, Vilandes 6, LV-1010 Riga, Latvia

Tel: 371-800-3000

THE ST. PAUL COMPANIES, INC.

385 Washington Street, St. Paul, MN, 55102

Tel: (651) 310-7911   Fax: (651) 310-8294   www.stpaul.com

Provides investment, insurance and reinsurance services.

Balva Joint Stock Insurance Company, 36 Kr Valdemara, LV-1010 Riga, Latvia

THE MARMON GROUP, INC.

200 West Adams, Ste. 2211, Chicago, IL, 60606

Tel: (312) 372-9500   Fax: (312) 845-5305   www.marmon.com

Holding company for diversified manufacturing and service firms.

Getz Bros. & Co. (Latvia) SIA, Kugu Strasse 11, 3rd Floor, LV-108 Riga, Latvia

Tel: 371-2-612345 Fax: 371-7-222356   Contact: Simons Kozlinskis, Gen. Mgr.   Emp: 12

UNITED PARCEL SERVICE, INC.

55 Glenlake Parkway, NE, Atlanta, GA, 30328

Tel: (404) 828-6000   Fax: (404) 828-6593   www.ups.com

International package-delivery service.

UPS Latvia, 33 13th January Str., LV-1050 Riga, Latvia

Tel: 371-7222247 Fax: 371-7211509

XEROX CORPORATION

800 Long Ridge Road, PO Box 1600, Stamford, CT, 06904

Tel: (203) 968-3000   Fax: (203) 968-4312   www.xerox.com

Mfr. document processing equipment, systems and supplies.

Xerox Corp., Riga, Latvia

YORK INTERNATIONAL CORPORATION

631 South Richland Ave., York, PA, 17403

Tel: (717) 771-7890   Fax: (717) 771-6212   www.york.com

Mfr. heating, ventilating, air conditioning and refrigeration equipment.

York International, Krustpils Iela 1, LV-1073 Riga, Latvia

Tel: 371-711-3068

Lebanon

3M (MINNESOTA MINING & MFG.)

3M Center, St. Paul, MN, 55144-1000

Tel: (651) 733-1110   Fax: (651) 733-9973   www.mmm.com

Mfr. diversified products for industry, consumer, health care, imaging, communications, transport, safety, etc.

3M Gulf Ltd Lebanon, Saint Charles City Center Omar Al Daouk St., Box 11-5025, Riad el Solh, Beirut 1107 2180, Lebanon

Tel: 961-1-373771

ABC, INC.

77 West 66th Street, 13th Fl., New York, NY, 10023

Tel: (212) 456-7777   Fax: (212) 456-6384   www.abc.com

Radio/TV production and broadcasting.

American Broadcasting Co., Gefinar Center, Block B, Rm. 1602, Beirut, Lebanon

ANC RENTAL CORPORATION

200 S. Andrews Ave., Ft. Lauderdale, FL, 33301

Tel: (954) 320-4000   Fax: (954) 320-4077   www.ancrental.com

Engaged in car rental services, including National Car Rental and Alamo Rent A Car.

National Car Rental, PO Box 5965, Ain-Al-Mraisse St. Nsouli Building, Beirut, Lebanon

ANDERSEN

33 West Monroe Street, Chicago, IL, 60603

Tel: (312) 580-0033   Fax: (312) 507-6748   www.andersen.com

Accounting and audit, tax and management consulting services. **Firm under worldwide reorganization; new data unavailable for this edition.

Andersen Worldwide, Ashrafieh, Sassin Square, Asco Centre, 10th Fl., PO Box 113-5309, Beirut, Lebanon

Tel: 961-1-602602

AON CORPORATION

200 East Randolph, Chicago, IL, 60601

Tel: (312) 381-1000   Fax: (312) 381-6032   www.aon.com

Insurance brokers worldwide; underwrites accident and health insurance, specialty and professional insurance; and provides risk management consultation.

AON Worldwide / Care Middle East S.A.L., c/o Santa Maria Bldg., PO Box 2119, Jounieh, Lebanon

Tel: 961-9-912344 Fax: 961-9-936491   Contact: Antoine Khoury

Care Middle East S.A.L., 8th Fl., Mardini Centre Mirna Chalouhi, Highway Sin-el-Fil, Beirut, Lebanon

Tel: 961-1-480320 Fax: 961-1-502279   Contact: Antoine Khoury

ASSOCIATED PRESS INC.

50 Rockefeller Plaza, New York, NY, 10020-1605

Tel: (212) 621-1500   Fax: (212) 621-5447   www.ap.com

News gathering agency.

The Associated Press, 121 rue Clemenceau, PO Box 3780, Beirut, Lebanon

Tel: 961-1-602146

THE BANK OF NEW YORK

One Wall Street, New York, NY, 10286

Tel: (212) 495-1784   Fax: (212) 495-2546   www.bankofny.com

Banking services.

The Bank of New York, Avco Center, 2nd Fl, Autostrade Jdeideh, Beirut, Lebanon

Tel: 961-1-898026

BATES WORLDWIDE INC.

498 Seventh Avenue, New York, NY, 10018

Tel: (212) 297-7000   Fax: (212) 986-0270   www.batesww.com

Advertising, marketing, public relations and media consulting.

Bates Lebanon, Asco Centre, Achralish, Beirut, Lebanon

Tel: 961-1-602-613 Fax: 961-1-602-612   Contact: R. Najjar, CEO

BBDO WORLDWIDE

1285 Ave. of the Americas, New York, NY, 10019

Tel: (212) 459-5000   Fax: (212) 459-6645   www.bbdo.com

Multinational group of advertising agencies.

Impact/BBDO Sal, Beirut, Lebanon

Strategies Sal, Beirut, Lebanon

BDO SEIDMAN, LLP   BELGIUM

130 East Randolph Street, Chicago, IL, 60601

Tel: (312) 856-9100   Fax: (312) 856-1379   www.bdo.com

International accounting and financial consulting firm.

Fiduciaire de Moyen Orient SARL, Geahchan Bldg., 2nd Fl., blvd Fouad Chehab, Sin El Fil-Mekalles, Beirut, Lebanon

Tel: 961-1-480-917 Fax: 961-1-496-682   Contact: Gérard Zovighoan

LOUIS BERGER INTERNATIONAL INC.

100 Halsted Street, East Orange, NJ, 07019

Tel: (201) 678-1960   Fax: (201) 672-4284   www.louisberger.com

Consulting engineers, engaged in architecture, environmental and advisory services.

Louis Berger International Inc., PO Box 11-8484, Weavers Center, 5th Floor, Clemenceau Street, Beirut, Lebanon

Tel: 961-1-379-067 Fax: 961-1-379-065

BRISTOL-MYERS SQUIBB COMPANY

345 Park Ave., New York, NY, 10154-0037

Tel: (212) 546-4000   Fax: (212) 546-4020   www.bms.com

Pharmaceutical and food preparations, medical and surgical instruments.

Khalil Fattal & Fills SAL, PO Box 773, Sin El Fil Jisr El Wati, Beirut, Lebanon

LEO BURNETT, DIV. B-COM 3 GROUP

35 West Wacker Drive, Chicago, IL, 60601

Tel: (312) 220-5959   Fax: (312) 220-6533   www.leoburnett.com

Engaged in advertising, marketing, media buying and planning, and public relations.

H&C Leo Burnett, Sofil Center, PO Box 55369, Beirut, Lebanon

CARLISLE SYNTEC SYSTEMS

PO Box 7000, Carlisle, PA, 17013

Tel: (717) 245-7000   Fax: (717) 245-9107   www.carlisle-syntec.com

Mfr. electrometric roofing and waterproofing systems.

BMC Lebanon, Sabbah Building, 4/F, Memari Street, Hamra Beirut, Lebanon

Tel: 961-1-353-171 Fax: 961-1-738-731

CARRIER CORPORATION

One Carrier Place, Farmington, CT, 06034-4015

Tel: (860) 674-3000   Fax: (860) 679-3010   www.carrier.com

Mfr./distributor/services A/C, heating and refrigeration equipment.

NTC Carrier, PO Box 11-8680, Beirut, Lebanon

Tel: 961-1-575555

CIGNA COMPANIES

One Liberty Place, Philadelphia, PA, 19192

Tel: (215) 761-1000   Fax: (215) 761-5511   www.cigna.com

Insurance, invest, health care and other financial services.

Insurance Co. of North America, c/o Joseph E. Zakhour & Co. SARL, Ashrafieh Rmeil, Liberty Bldg., Beirut, Lebanon

CISCO SYSTEMS, INC.

170 West Tasman Drive, San Jose, CA, 95134-1706

Tel: (408) 526-4000   Fax: (408) 526-4100   www.cisco.com

Develop/mfr./market computer hardware and software networking systems.

Cisco Systems Lebanon, Sodeco Square, Block C, 11th Fl., PO Box 16-5480, Beirut, Lebanon

Tel: 961-1-611-081   Fax: 961-1-611-083

CITIGROUP, INC.

399 Park Avenue, New York, NY, 10022

Tel: (212) 559-1000   Fax: (212) 559-3646   www.citigroup.com

Provides insurance and financial services worldwide.

Citigroup, Beirut, Lebanon

Contact: Elia S. Smaha

DANZAS AEI, INC.

120 Tokeneke Road, PO Box 1231, Darien, CT, 06820

Tel: (203) 655-7900   Fax: (203) 655-5779   www.aeilogistics.com

International air freight forwarder.

Danzas AEI, Pasteur St., Zoughbi Ctr., 1st Fl., PO Box 175772, Achrafich Beirut, Lebanon

Tel: 961-1-564-78992   Fax: 961-1-564-793

D'ARCY MASIUS BENTON & BOWLES INC. (DMB&B)

1675 Broadway, New York, NY, 10019

Tel: (212) 468-3622   Fax: (212) 468-2987   www.darcyww.com

Full service international advertising and communications group.

DMB&B Mid East-Africa, Palm Center Rond Point Chev., Damascus Road, Beirut, Lebanon

DDB WORLDWIDE COMMUNICATIONS GROUP

437 Madison Ave., New York, NY, 10022

Tel: (212) 415-2000   Fax: (212) 415-3417   www.ddbn.com

Advertising agency.

Idees & Communications DDB, Beirut, Lebanon

DELOITTE TOUCHE TOHMATSU INTERNATIONAL

1633 Broadway, New York, NY, 10019

Tel: (212) 492-4000   Fax: (212) 392-4154   www.deloitte.com

Accounting, audit, tax and management consulting services.

Deloitte & Touche/Saba & Co., Arabia House, 131 Phoenicia St., PO Box 961, Beirut, Lebanon

DHL WORLDWIDE EXPRESS

50 California Avenue, San Francisco, CA, 94111

Tel: (415) 677-6100   Fax: (415) 824-9700   www.dhl.com

Worldwide air express carrier.

SNAS DHL Worldwide, Park Bldg., Ground Fl., Sami El Solh Ave., PO Box 166/439, Beirut, Lebanon

Tel: 961-1-390900

EASTMAN KODAK COMPANY

343 State Street, Rochester, NY, 14650

Tel: (716) 724-4000   Fax: (716) 724-1089   www.kodak.com

Develop/mfr. photo and chemicals products, information management/video/copier systems, fibers/plastics for various industry.

Kodak (Near East) Inc., Beirut Lebanon, c/o Kodak (Near East) Inc., PO Box 11460, Dubai UAE

EGL INC. (EAGLE GLOBAL LOGISTICS)

15350 Vickery Drive, Houston, TX, 77032

Tel: (281) 618-3100   Fax: (281) 618-3223   www.eagleusa.com

Ocean/air freight forwarding, customs brokerage, packing and wholesale, logistics management and insurance.

EGL Eagle Global Logistics, Beirut Cargo Ctr. Sarl, Charles Helou Ave., Sehnaoui Bldg., Fourth Fl., Ste. 41, PO Box 17-5040, Beirut, Lebanon

Tel: 961-1-585-164 Fax: 961-1-585-580

ERNST & YOUNG INTERNATIONAL

5 Times Square, New York, NY, 10036

Tel: (212) 773-3000   Fax: (212) 773-6350   www.eyi.com

Engaged in assurance and advisory business services, tax, law and corporate finance.

Ernst & Young S.A.R.L., PO Box 11-1639, Sabbagh Ctr., Hamra St., Beirut, Lebanon

Tel: 961-1-353420 Fax: 961-1-346203   Contact: Yacoub Khoury

ESCO ENGINEERING INC.

40 Robbie Road, Avon Industrial Park, Avon, MA, 02322

Tel: (508) 588-1500   Fax: (508) 588-0135   www.escogroup.com

Water purification and sewage treatment.

Esco Group, PO Box 113-5993, Beirut, Lebanon

EXPEDITORS INTERNATIONAL OF WASHINGTON INC.

1015 Third Avenue, 12th Fl., Seattle, WA, 98104-1182

Tel: (206) 674-3400   Fax: (206) 682-9777   www.expd.com

Air/ocean freight forwarding, customs brokerage, international logistics solutions.

Expeditors International Service Center, PO Box 50252, Furn El Chebback, Lebanon

JOHN FABICK TRACTOR COMPANY

1 Fabick Drive, Fenton, MO, 63026

Tel: (314) 343-5900   Fax: (314) 343-4910   www.johnfabick.com

Wheel tractors, excavating and road building equipment.

A.K. Zarby & Associates, Ardeti Building, Bliss St., Manara Beirut, Lebanon

FRITZ COMPANIES, INC., DIV. UPS

706 Mission Street, Ste. 900, San Francisco, CA, 94103

Tel: (415) 904-8360   Fax: (415) 904-8661   www.fritz.com

Integrated transportation, sourcing, distribution and customs brokerage services.

Fritz Companies Inc., Beirut, Lebanon

GEN RE INTERMEDIARIES CORPORATION

PO Box 10216, Stamford, CT, 06904-2216

Tel: (203) 357-8883   Fax: (203) 328-6408   www.genre.com

Provides reinsurance services worldwide.

Cologne Re of Beirut S.A.L., Sami Solh St., Badaro Trade Centre, 7th Fl., PO Box 116-5096, Museum Beirut, Lebanon

Tel: 961-1-399-000 Fax: 961-1-399-009   Contact: Nouhad Taleb, SVP

GeneralCologne Re Beirut s.a.l., Sami Solh Street, Badaro Trade Centre, Box 116-5096 Museum, Beirut, Lebanon

GENERAL ELECTRIC CAPITAL CORPORATION

260 Long Ridge Road, Stamford, CT, 06927

Tel: (203) 357-4000   Fax: (203) 357-6489   www.gecapital.com

Financial, property, casualty insurance, computer sales and trailer leasing services.

ERC Group, Div. GE Capital, SNA Bldg., 4th Fl., Tabais Square, Beirut, Lebanon

Tel: 961-1-333-199 Fax: 961-1-329-812

GRACO INC.
88 - 11th Avenue NE, PO Box 1441, Minneapolis, MN, 55440-1441

Tel: (612) 623-6000   Fax: (612) 623-6777   www.graco.com

Mfr. systems and equipment to service fluid handling systems and automotive equipment.

Duratrade Ltd., Kfan Rbab, Ghazir, Green Zone, V 7 St., Bldg. 1774, Jounieh, Lebanon

Tel: 961-991-8582   Fax: 961-140-2237   Contact: Samir Dibeh

GRANT THORNTON INTERNATIONAL
800 One Prudential Plaza, 130 E. Randolph Drive, Chicago, IL, 60601-6050

Tel: (312) 856-0001   Fax: (312) 616-7052   www.grantthornton.com

Accounting, audit, tax and management consulting services.

Grant Thornton Yafi & Co., PO Box 11, Beirut, Lebanon

Contact: Mowafak El Yafi

GREY GLOBAL GROUP
777 Third Ave., New York, NY, 10017

Tel: (212) 546-2000   Fax: (212) 546-1495   www.grey.com

International advertising agency.

CSS & Grey, Beitmery Roundabout, Beitmery, Beirut, Lebanon

HORWATH INTERNATIONAL ASSOCIATION
420 Lexington Avenue, Suite 526, New York, NY, 10170-0526

Tel: (212) 808-2000   Fax: (212) 808-2020   www.horwath.com

Public accountants and auditors.

Horwath Abou Chakra Co., Minkara Bldg., Clemenceau St., Beirut, Lebanon

Contact: Wael Abou Chakra

IDEX CORPORATION
630 Dundee Road, Ste. 400, Northbrook, IL, 60062

Tel: (847) 498-7070   Fax: (847) 498-3940   www.idexcorp.com

Mfr. industrial pumps, lubrication systems, metal fabrication equipment, bending and clamping devices.

Bardawil & Co. S.A.R.L., PO Box 110967 Dora Blvd., Beirut, Lebanon

INTERGRAPH CORPORATION
One Madison Industrial Park, Huntsville, AL, 35894-0001

Tel: (256) 730-2000   Fax: (256) 730-7898   www.intergraph.com

Develop/mfr. interactive computer graphic systems.

Integraph Middle East LLC, Dora Highway, Cite Dora 3 Bldg., 10th Fl., PO Box 90-710, Beirut, Lebanon

Tel: 961-1-881-322   Fax: 961-1-915-575

INTRACO CORPORATION
530 Stephenson Hwy., Troy, MI, 48083

Tel: (248) 585-6900   Fax: (248) 585-6920   www.intracousa.com

Export management and marketing consultants.

INTRACO Corp., PO Box 135714, Shouran, Beirut, Lebanon

KPMG CONSULTING INC.
1676 International Dr., McLean, VA, 22102

Tel: (703) 747-3000   Fax: (703) 747-8500   www.kpmg.com

Accounting and audit, tax and management consulting services.

KPMG International, Hamra Square Bldg., KPMG Level, Hamra St., Beirut Ras, Lebanon

Tel: 961-1-350518   Fax: 961-1-350238   Contact: Riad A. Mansour, Sr. Ptnr.

ELI LILLY & COMPANY
Lilly Corporate Center, Indianapolis, IN, 46285

Tel: (317) 276-2000   Fax: (317) 277-6579   www.lilly.com

Mfr. pharmaceuticals and animal health products.

Eli Lilly S.A., Spinnes Area, Yousif Hitti St., Kassar Bldg., 1st Fl., Beirut, Lebanon

Tel: 961-1-825-931   Fax: 961-1-823-570

MARRIOTT INTERNATIONAL INC.

10400 Fernwood Rd., Bethesda, MD, 20817

Tel: (301) 380-3000   Fax: (301) 380-5181   www.marriott.com

Hotel services.

Beirut Mrriott Hotel, Beirut, Lebanon

MERCK & COMPANY, INC.

One Merck Drive, PO Box 100, Whitehouse Station, NJ, 08889-0100

Tel: (908) 423-1000   Fax: (908) 423-2592   www.merck.com

Pharmaceuticals, chemicals and biologicals.

Merck, Sharp & Dohme Intl. Middle East, Naji Itani Bldg., Jeanne d'Arc St., Ras Beirut, Lebanon

MERRILL LYNCH & COMPANY, INC.

World Financial Center, 250 Vesey Street, New York, NY, 10281-1332

Tel: (212) 236-1000   Fax: (212) 449-2892   www.ml.com

Security brokers and dealers, investment and business services.

Merrill Lynch Pierce Fenner & Smith Middle East S.A.L., Maarad Street, PO Box 11-5316, 1107 2190, Beirut, Lebanon

Tel: 961-1-602120   Fax: 961-1-602123

J. P. MORGAN CHASE & CO. INC.

270 Park Ave., New York, NY, 10017

Tel: (212) 270-6000   Fax: (212) 622-9030   www.jpmorganchase.com

Provides integrated financial solutions for institutions and individuals worldwide, including asset management, investment banking and commercial banking.

J. P. Morgan Chase & Co., Gefinor Center, Block C, Clemenceau St., 2nd. Fl., Beirut, Lebanon

Tel: 961-1-351065   Fax: 961-1-739581

AC NIELSEN COMPANY

177 Broad Street, Stamford, CT, 06901

Tel: (203) 961-3000   Fax: (203) 961-3190   www.acnielsen.com

Engaged in market and consumer research.

ACNielsen, Geoco Center 3 (GGF), Bloc C, 2/F, Sin El Fil Horch Tabet, Beirut, Lebanon

OMNICOM GROUP INC.

437 Madison Ave., New York, NY, 10022

Tel: (212) 415-3600   Fax: (212) 415-3530   www.omnicomgroup.com

International network of advertising, marketing, direct mail, public relations and consulting services.

Intermarkets Advertising, Chalouhi Canter, PO Box 55434, Sin El Fil, Beirut, Lebanon

Tel: 961-1-480477 Fax: 961-1-502121   Contact: Erwin Guerrovich, CEO   Emp: 287

OTIS ELEVATOR COMPANY

One Farm Springs Road, Farmington, CT, 06032

Tel: (860) 676-6000   Fax: (860) 676-5111   www.otis.com

Mfr. elevators and escalators.

Otis Elevator Co. SAL, Drab Building, Mekalles, PO Box 11-7968, Beirut, Lebanon

PARSONS BRINCKERHOFF INC.

One Penn Plaza, New York, NY, 10119-0061

Tel: (212) 465-5000   Fax: (212) 465-5096   www.pbworld.com

Provides planning, engineering, construction management and operations and maintenance services.

Parsons Brinckerhoff, PO Box 14-6565, Beirut, Lebanon

PHILLIPS PETROLEUM COMPANY

Phillips Building, 411 S. Keeler Ave., Bartlesville, OK, 74004

Tel: (918) 661-6600   Fax: (918) 661-7636   www.phillips66.com

Crude oil, natural gas, liquefied petroleum gas, gasoline and petro-chemicals.

Phillips Petroleum Intl. Corp., Shell Building, 14th Fl., 8 Raouche, PO Box 6106, Beirut, Lebanon

POLARIS INDUSTRIES INC.

2100 Highway 55, Medina, MN, 55440

Tel: (612) 542-0500   Fax: (612) 542-0599   www.polarisindustries.com

Mfr. snowmobiles and all-terrain recreational and utility vehicles.

Empty Helmets S.A.R.L., PO Box 255 Zouk Mikael, Elias Nakhoul Bldg. St. Charbel Street, Sarba Jounich, Lebanon

Tel: 961-963-6046

PROCTER & GAMBLE COMPANY

One Procter & Gamble Plaza, Cincinnati, OH, 45202

Tel: (513) 983-1100   Fax: (513) 562-4500   www.pg.com

Personal care, food, laundry, cleaning and industry products.

Procter & Gamble Mfg. Co. of Lebanon SAL, PO Box 4992, Beirut, Lebanon

THE SERVICEMASTER COMPANY

2300 Warrenville Road, Downers Grove, IL, 60515-1700

Tel: (630) 271-1300   Fax: (630) 271-2710   www.svm.com

Provides residential consumer services, including lawn care and landscape maintenance, termite and pest control, plumbing, heating and air conditioning maintenance and repair.

ServiceMaster, Beirut, Lebanon

TELLABS INC.

1415 W. Diehl Rd., Naperville, IL, 60563

Tel: (630) 378-8800   Fax: (630) 852-7346   www.tellabs.com

Design/mfr./service voice/data transport and network access systems.

Tellabs, Dbayeh Highway, Victoria Center, 5/F, Dbayeh, Lebanon

TEREX CORPORATION

500 Post Road East, Ste. 320, Westport, CT, 06880

Tel: (203) 222-7170   Fax: (203) 222-7976   www.terex.com

Mfr. lifting and earthmoving equipment.

Terex Mining Middle East, Highway Road, Zalka Tower 686, Beirut, Lebanon

UNITED PARCEL SERVICE, INC.

55 Glenlake Parkway, NE, Atlanta, GA, 30328

Tel: (404) 828-6000   Fax: (404) 828-6593   www.ups.com

International package-delivery service.

UPS Lebanon, Achrafieh Sassine Square, Le Doyen Bldg., Beirut, Lebanon

Tel: 961-1-218575

URS CORPORATION

100 California Street, Ste. 500, San Francisco, CA, 94111

Tel: (415) 774-2700   Fax: (415) 398-1905   www.urscorp.com

Engineering, environmental and construction management services.

Dames & Moore, PO Box 116-5249 Museum, Achrafieh-Beirut, Lebanon

XEROX CORPORATION

800 Long Ridge Road, PO Box 1600, Stamford, CT, 06904

Tel: (203) 968-3000   Fax: (203) 968-4312   www.xerox.com

Mfr. document processing equipment, systems and supplies.

Te Vega (Xerox), Sin El Fil, PO Box 110-773, Immeuble Fattal, Beirut, Lebanon

Tel: 961-1-425 450   Fax: 961-1-494 820

YOUNG & RUBICAM INC.

285 Madison Ave., New York, NY, 10017

Tel: (212) 210-3000   Fax: (212) 370-3796   www.yr.com

Advertising, public relations, direct marketing and sales promotion, corporate and product ID management.

TEAM/Y&R Beirut, Beirut, Lebanon

Lesotho

AON CORPORATION

200 East Randolph, Chicago, IL, 60601

Tel: (312) 381-1000   Fax: (312) 381-6032   www.aon.com

Insurance brokers worldwide; underwrites accident and health insurance, specialty and professional insurance; and provides risk management consultation.

AON Worldwide/ Minet Kingsway (Lesotho) (Pty.) Ltd., 1/F, Carlton Centre, Kingsway, Maseru, Lesotho

Tel: 266-313540   Fax: 266-310033   Contact: Bonang Malebo

DHL WORLDWIDE EXPRESS

50 California Avenue, San Francisco, CA, 94111

Tel: (415) 677-6100   Fax: (415) 824-9700   www.dhl.com

Worldwide air express carrier.

DHL Worldwide Express, Options Bldg., 1st Fl., Pioneer Road, Maseru, Lesotho

Tel: 266-311082

ERNST & YOUNG INTERNATIONAL

5 Times Square, New York, NY, 10036

Tel: (212) 773-3000   Fax: (212) 773-6350   www.eyi.com

Engaged in assurance and advisory business services, tax, law and corporate finance.

Ernst & Young International, Private Bag A169, LNDC, 2ND Fl., Maseru, Lesotho

SEABOARD CORPORATION

9000 West 67th St., Shawnee Mission, KS, 66002

Tel: (913) 676-8800   Fax: (913) 676-8872   www.seaboardcorp.com

Engaged in diversified agribusiness and transportation businesses, including wine, sugar and citrus.

Lesotho Flour Mills Ltd., Div. Seaboard, Lesotho

THE ST. PAUL COMPANIES, INC.

385 Washington Street, St. Paul, MN, 55102

Tel: (651) 310-7911   Fax: (651) 310-8294   www.stpaul.com

Provides investment, insurance and reinsurance services.

Lesotho National Insurnace Group, LNIC House, Constitution Roa, Private Bag A65, Maseru 100, Lesotho

Tel: 266-313-031   Fax: 266-310-007

XEROX CORPORATION

800 Long Ridge Road, PO Box 1600, Stamford, CT, 06904

Tel: (203) 968-3000   Fax: (203) 968-4312   www.xerox.com

Mfr. document processing equipment, systems and supplies.

Maseru Business Machines, BNP Centre Parliament Road, Pvt Bag 80, Maseru, Lesotho

Tel: 266-324427   Fax: 266-310119

Liberia

CIGNA COMPANIES

One Liberty Place, Philadelphia, PA, 19192

Tel: (215) 761-1000 Fax: (215) 761-5511 www.cigna.com

Insurance, invest, health care and other financial services.

CIGNA Worldwide Insurance Co., c/o Lone Star Insurances Inc., 51 Broad St., PO Box 1142, Monrovia, Liberia

DANZAS AEI, INC.

120 Tokeneke Road, PO Box 1231, Darien, CT, 06820

Tel: (203) 655-7900 Fax: (203) 655-5779 www.aeilogistics.com

International air freight forwarder.

Danzas AEI, PO Box 209, Monrovia, Liberia

DHL WORLDWIDE EXPRESS

50 California Avenue, San Francisco, CA, 94111

Tel: (415) 677-6100 Fax: (415) 824-9700 www.dhl.com

Worldwide air express carrier.

DHL Worldwide Express, 58 Broad St., Monrovia, Liberia

Tel: 231-226986

THE DOW CHEMICAL COMPANY

2030 Dow Center, Midland, MI, 48674

Tel: (989) 636-1000 Fax: (989) 636-3228 www.dow.com

Mfr. chemicals, plastics, pharmaceuticals, agricultural products, consumer products.

Chief Shipping Co., Liberia

IBM CORPORATION

1133 Westchester Avenue, White Plains, NY, 10604

Tel: (914) 765-1900 Fax: (914) 765-7382 www.ibm.com

Information products, technology and services.

IBM Liberia, c/o Liberia Business Machines, Mid Town Plaza, Carey St., PO Box 1536, Monrovia, Liberia

J. P. MORGAN CHASE & CO. INC.

270 Park Ave., New York, NY, 10017

Tel: (212) 270-6000 Fax: (212) 622-9030 www.jpmorganchase.com

Provides integrated financial solutions for institutions and individuals worldwide, including asset management, investment banking and commercial banking.

J. P. Morgan Chase & Co., PO Box 181, Ashmun & Randall Sts., Monrovia, Liberia

J. P. Morgan Chase & Co., PO Box 46, Harbel, Monrovia, Liberia

Libya

DHL WORLDWIDE EXPRESS

50 California Avenue, San Francisco, CA, 94111

Tel: (415) 677-6100   Fax: (415) 824-9700   www.dhl.com

Worldwide air express carrier.

DHL Worldwide Express, Ahmed Swaihly St., Mahri House, PO Box 12499, Tripoli, Libya

Tel: 218-21-444-3782

ERNST & YOUNG INTERNATIONAL

5 Times Square, New York, NY, 10036

Tel: (212) 773-3000   Fax: (212) 773-6350   www.eyi.com

Engaged in assurance and advisory business services, tax, law and corporate finance.

Ernst & Young International, PO Box 91873, That El Emad Towers, Tripoli, Libya

Tel: 218-21-75889   Fax: 218-21-360-0046   Contact: John Kirkpatrick

KPMG CONSULTING INC.

1676 International Dr., McLean, VA, 22102

Tel: (703) 747-3000   Fax: (703) 747-8500   www.kpmg.com

Accounting and audit, tax and management consulting services.

Ibrahim Al-Baruni & Company, 11 Omar Abdel Aziz, Tripoli, Libya

Tel: 218-21-333-2225   Fax: 218-21-333-2225   Contact: Ibrahim Al-Baruni, Sr. Ptnr.

Liechtenstein

BLACK & DECKER CORPORATION

701 E. Joppa Road, Towson, MD, 21286

Tel: (410) 716-3900   Fax: (410) 716-2933   www.blackanddecker.com

Mfr. power tools and accessories, security hardware, small appliances, fasteners, information systems and services.

Black & Decker Lichtenstein, Liechtenstein Office, 701 East Joppa Road, Towson, MD, 21286

CARRIER CORPORATION

One Carrier Place, Farmington, CT, 06034-4015

Tel: (860) 674-3000   Fax: (860) 679-3010   www.carrier.com

Mfr./distributor/services A/C, heating and refrigeration equipment.

Clymalynx AG, Vaduz, Liechtenstein

DHL WORLDWIDE EXPRESS

50 California Avenue, San Francisco, CA, 94111

Tel: (415) 677-6100   Fax: (415) 824-9700   www.dhl.com

Worldwide air express carrier.

DHL Worldwide Express, Liechtenstein

Tel: 41-1-734-5757

ERNST & YOUNG INTERNATIONAL

5 Times Square, New York, NY, 10036

Tel: (212) 773-3000   Fax: (212) 773-6350   www.eyi.com

Engaged in assurance and advisory business services, tax, law and corporate finance.

Revikon, Revisions & Beratungs AG, Aeulstresse 60, PO Box 651, FL-9490 Vaduz, Liechtenstein

Tel: 41-756-70-70   Fax: 41-756-16-32   Contact: Dr. M. Oertli

INFICON HOLDING

Two Technology Place, Syracuse, NY, 13057

Tel: (315) 434-1100   Fax: (315) 437-3803   www.inficon.com

Provides instrumentation for monitoring, analysis, control, leak detection and plasma cleaning in the semiconductor, vacuum coatings, air conditioning and refrigeration markets.

Inficon GmbH, PO Box 1000, FL-9496 Balzers, Liechtenstein

Tel: 423-388-3346

Lithuania

AIG AMERICAN INTERNATIONAL GROUP INC.
70 Pine Street, New York, NY, 10270
Tel: (212) 770-7000   Fax: (212) 509-9705   www.aig.com
Worldwide insurance and financial services.
Seesam Ins. Co. Ltd., Sermukaniu 1/13-24, LT-2001 Vilnius, Lithuania

ANDERSEN
33 West Monroe Street, Chicago, IL, 60603
Tel: (312) 580-0033   Fax: (312) 507-6748   www.andersen.com
*Accounting and audit, tax and management consulting services. **Firm under worldwide reorganization; new data unavailable for this edition.*
Andersen Worldwide, PO Box 2849, Aludariu 2, LT-2000 Vilnius, Lithuania
Tel: 370-2-624-281

APPLERA CORPORATION
301 Merritt 7, Norwalk, CT, 06851
Tel: (203) 840-2000   Fax: (203) 840-2312   www.applera.com
Leading supplier of systems for life science research and related applications.
Applied Biosystems, Linea Libera, Mokslininku 12A, LT-2021 Vilnius, Lithuania

BATES WORLDWIDE INC.
498 Seventh Avenue, New York, NY, 10018
Tel: (212) 297-7000   Fax: (212) 986-0270   www.batesww.com
Advertising, marketing, public relations and media consulting.
Bates Adell Saatchi & Saatchi, Trak g. 3/2, LT-2001 Vilnius, Lithuania
Tel: 370-2-615-114   Fax: 370-2-626-048   Contact: V. Varlavicluz

LEO BURNETT, DIV. B-COM 3 GROUP
35 West Wacker Drive, Chicago, IL, 60601
Tel: (312) 220-5959   Fax: (312) 220-6533   www.leoburnett.com
Engaged in advertising, marketing, media buying and planning, and public relations.
Dvyniu Ratas & Leo Burnett, Vilnius, Lithuania

CHECKPOINT SYSTEMS, INC.
101 Wolf Drive, Thorofare, NJ, 08086
Tel: (856) 848-1800   Fax: (856) 848-0937   www.checkpointsystems.com
Mfr. test, measurement and closed-circuit television systems.
Checkpoint Systems Vilnius, Rudninku 8-3, LT-2024 Vilnius, Lithuania
Tel: 370-2-314-020   Fax: 370-2-22-7087   Contact: Andrius Vidas Gen. Mgr.

DELOITTE TOUCHE TOHMATSU INTERNATIONAL
1633 Broadway, New York, NY, 10019
Tel: (212) 492-4000   Fax: (212) 392-4154   www.deloitte.com
Accounting, audit, tax and management consulting services.
Deloitte & Touche, Didziojii 25-6, PO Box 1024, LT-2001 Vilnius, Lithuania

DHL WORLDWIDE EXPRESS
50 California Avenue, San Francisco, CA, 94111
Tel: (415) 677-6100   Fax: (415) 824-9700   www.dhl.com
Worldwide air express carrier.
DHL Worldwide Express, Dariaus Ir Gireno Str. 42, LT-2600 Vilnius, Lithuania
Tel: 370-2-267-722

EMERSON PROCESS MANAGEMENT

8301Cameron Road, Austin, TX, 78754

Tel: (512) 834-7689 Fax: (512) 832-3232 www.frco.com

Mfr. industrial process control equipment.

LA-KAMA, Paneriu 45, LT-2006 Vilnius, Lithuania

Tel: 370-5-213-4984

GREY GLOBAL GROUP

777 Third Ave., New York, NY, 10017

Tel: (212) 546-2000 Fax: (212) 546-1495 www.grey.com

International advertising agency.

Grey Advertising, Vilnius, Lithuania

KPMG CONSULTING INC.

1676 International Dr., McLean, VA, 22102

Tel: (703) 747-3000 Fax: (703) 747-8500 www.kpmg.com

Accounting and audit, tax and management consulting services.

KPMG International, Stulginskio 4, 4/F, LT-2600 Vilnius, Lithuania

Tel: 370-2-611-803 Fax: 370-2-620-851 Contact: Leif René Hansen, Sr. Ptnr.

ELI LILLY & COMPANY

Lilly Corporate Center, Indianapolis, IN, 46285

Tel: (317) 276-2000 Fax: (317) 277-6579 www.lilly.com

Mfr. pharmaceuticals and animal health products.

Eli Lilly (Suisse) S.A., Rep. Office, Rudninku 18/2-8, LT-2001 Vilnius, Lithuania

Tel: 370-2-220-265 Fax: 370-2-220-235

LUCENT TECHNOLOGIES, INC.

600 Mountain Ave., Murray Hill, NJ, 07974-0636

Tel: (908) 582-3000 Fax: (908) 582-2576 www.lucent.com

Design/mfr. wide range of public and private networks, communication systems and software, data networking systems, business telephone systems and microelectronics components.

Lucent Technologies, Gedimino pr. 64-61, LT-2001 Vilnius, Lithuania

McCANN-ERICKSON WORLDGROUP

750 Third Ave., New York, NY, 10017

Tel: (212) 697-6000 Fax: (212) 984-3575 www.mccann.com

International advertising and marketing services.

Asta Dizainas McCann-Erickson, Vilnius, Lithuania

McDONALD'S CORPORATION

McDonald's Plaza, Oak Brook, IL, 60523

Tel: (630) 623-3000 Fax: (630) 623-7409 www.mcdonalds.com

Fast food chain stores.

McDonald's Corp., Vilnius, Lithuania

MECHANICAL DYNAMICS, INC.

2300 Traverwood Drive, Ann Arbor, MI, 48105

Tel: (734) 994-3800 Fax: (734) 994-6418 www.adams.com

Mfr. Adams prototyping software for functional virtual prototyping solutions.

IN RE Ltd., Gostauto 8, Room 216, LT-2600 Vilnius, Lithuania

Tel: 370-2-224-660 Fax: 370-2-22-4660

MULTILINK TECHOLOGY CORPORATION

300 Atrium Drive, 2nd Fl., Somerset, NJ, 08873-4105

Tel: (732) 537-3700 Fax: (732) 805-9177 www.mltc.com

Mfr. high-band, mixed-signal integrated circuits.

Multilink Technology, Ozeskienes Str. 15, LT-3000 Kaunas Lithuania, Lithuania

NIBCO INC.

1516 Middlebury St., PO Box 1167, Elkhart, IN, 46515-1167

Tel: (219) 295-3000   Fax: (219) 295-3307   www.nibco.com

Mfr. fluid handling products for residential, commercial, industrial and fire protection markets.

UAB Nibco, Linkmenu 37, LT-2042 Vilnius, Lithuania

AC NIELSEN COMPANY

177 Broad Street, Stamford, CT, 06901

Tel: (203) 961-3000   Fax: (203) 961-3190   www.acnielsen.com

Engaged in market and consumer research.

ACNielsen, A. Juozapaviciaus Street 6/2, LT-2600 Vilnius, Lithuania

PALMS & COMPANY, INC. (U.S. FUR EXCHANGE)

515 Lake Street South, Bldg., Ste. 103, Kirkland, WA, 98033

Tel: (425) 828-6774   Fax: (425) 827-5528   www.peterpalms.com

Engaged in general import and export and web-design, web-promotion and e-commerce.

Palms & Co. (Latvia) Inc., Verkiu str. 32/70, LT-3035 Kaunas, Lithuania

Tel: 370-7-742-385   Fax: 370-7-799-786   Contact: Arunas Sialuys

Palms & Co. Inc., Zirmunu 58-41, Vilnius, Lithuania

Tel: 370-2-525-440   Fax: 370-2-721-134   Contact: Grigorij Kolesnikov   Emp: 2

PAREXEL INTERNATIONAL CORPORATION

195 West Street, Waltham, MA, 02154

Tel: (781) 487-9900   Fax: (781) 487-0525   www.parexel.com

Provides contract medical, biotechnology, and pharmaceutical research and consulting services.

PAREXEL MEDSTAT, Kalinausko 10-11, LT-2009 Vilnius, Lithuania

Tel: 370-2-313-725   Fax: 370-2-623-603

PHARMACIA CORPORATION

100 Route 206 North, Peapack, NJ, 07977

Tel: (908) 901-8000   Fax: (908) 901-8379   www.pharmacia.com

Mfr. pharmaceuticals, agricultural products, industry chemicals.

Pharmacia & Upjohn S.A., Lukiskiu 5-303, LT-2600 Linius, Lithuania

Tel: 370-2-251026   Fax: 370-2-251023

PRICEWATERHOUSECOOPERS LLP

1301 Ave. of the Americas, New York, NY, 10019

Tel: (212) 596-7000   Fax: (212) 259-1301   www.pwcglobal.com

Accounting and auditing, tax and management, and human resource consulting services.

PriceWaterhouseCoopers, Seimynskiu 16, LT-2005 Vilnius, Lithuania

Tel: 370-2-726-902   Fax: 370-2-726-903

PROCTER & GAMBLE COMPANY

One Procter & Gamble Plaza, Cincinnati, OH, 45202

Tel: (513) 983-1100   Fax: (513) 562-4500   www.pg.com

Personal care, food, laundry, cleaning and industry products.

Sanitex (JV), P.d. Nr. 705, LT-3035 Kaunas, Lithuania

Tel: 370-7-800-300

SCIENTECH, INC.

2650 McCormick Drive, Suite 300, Clearwater, FL, 33759

Tel: (727) 669-3003   Fax: (727) 669-3100   www.scientech.com

worldwide provider of expert services to the energy and telecommunication markets

UAB Scientech Baltic, Kalvariju g. 126-629, LT-2600 Vilnius, Lithuania

SICOR INC.

19 Hughes, Irvine, CA, 92618

Tel: (949) 455-4700   Fax: (949) 855-8210   www.gensiasicor.com

Mfr. and sales oncology drugs.

Biotechna, V. Graiciuno 8, LT2028 Vilnius, Lithuania

UNITED PARCEL SERVICE, INC.

55 Glenlake Parkway, NE, Atlanta, GA, 30328

Tel: (404) 828-6000   Fax: (404) 828-6593   www.ups.com

International package-delivery service.

UPS Lithuania, Laisvëa al. 99-3, LT-3000 Kaunas, Lithuania

Tel: 370-7-209-194   Fax: 370-7-201-994

YORK INTERNATIONAL CORPORATION

631 South Richland Ave., York, PA, 17403

Tel: (717) 771-7890   Fax: (717) 771-6212   www.york.com

Mfr. heating, ventilating, air conditioning and refrigeration equipment.

York International GmbH, Verkiu 37, Room 210-212, LT-2600 Vilnius, Lithuania

Tel: 370-2-724-758

Luxembourg

ACCENTURE LTD.

1345 Avenue of the Americas, New York, NY, 10105

Tel: (917) 452-4400   Fax: (917) 527-9915   www.accenture.com

Provides management and technology consulting services.

Accenture, 6, rue Jean Monnet, L-2180 Luxembourg City, Luxembourg

Tel: 352-43-27-171   Fax: 352-43-27-233

AETNA INC.

151 Farmington Avenue, Hartford, CT, 06156

Tel: (860) 273-0123   Fax: (860) 275-2677   www.aetna.com

Managed health care, annuities, individual retirement and group pension services, and asset management products worldwide.

Aetna International Funds, Luxembourg

AIG AMERICAN INTERNATIONAL GROUP INC.

70 Pine Street, New York, NY, 10270

Tel: (212) 770-7000   Fax: (212) 509-9705   www.aig.com

Worldwide insurance and financial services.

AIG Europe S.A., 11, Avenue Guillaume, L-1651 Luxembourg City, Luxembourg

ALLIANCE CAPITAL MANAGEMENT HOLDING LP

1345 Ave. of the Americas, New York, NY, 10105

Tel: (212) 969-1000   Fax: (212) 969-2229   www.alliancecapital.com

Engaged in fund management for large corporations.

ACM Global Investor Services, S.A., 18-20 Rue Eugene Ruppert, L-2453 Luxembourg, Luxembourg

Tel: 352-22-6693

AMPACET CORPORATION

660 White Plains Road, Tarrytown, NY, 10591-5130

Tel: (914) 631-6600   Fax: (914) 631-7197   www.ampacet.com

Mfr. color and additive concentrates for the plastics industry.

Ampacet Luxembourg S.A., Rue des Scillas 45, L-2529 Howald, Luxembourg

Tel: 352-2920-991   Fax: 352-2920-99594

ANC RENTAL CORPORATION

200 S. Andrews Ave., Ft. Lauderdale, FL, 33301

Tel: (954) 320-4000   Fax: (954) 320-4077   www.ancrental.com

Engaged in car rental services, including National Car Rental and Alamo Rent A Car.

National Car Rental, 33, blvd Prince Henri, Luxembourg City, Luxembourg

ANDERSEN

33 West Monroe Street, Chicago, IL, 60603

Tel: (312) 580-0033   Fax: (312) 507-6748   www.andersen.com

*Accounting and audit, tax and management consulting services. **Firm under worldwide reorganization; new data unavailable for this edition.*

Andersen Worldwide, 6, rue Jean Monnet, PO Box 2381, L-2180, Luxembourg

Tel: 352-42-22-331

AON CORPORATION

200 East Randolph, Chicago, IL, 60601

Tel: (312) 381-1000   Fax: (312) 381-6032   www.aon.com

Insurance brokers worldwide; underwrites accident and health insurance, specialty and professional insurance; and provides risk management consultation.

AON Risk Services Europe SA, 283, Route d'Arion, L-8011 Strassen, Luxembourg

Tel: 352-317-171   Fax: 352-317-174   Contact: Lambert Schroeder

AVERY DENNISON CORPORATION

150 N. Orange Grove Blvd., Pasadena, CA, 91103

Tel: (626) 304-2000   Fax: (626) 792-7312   www.averydennison.com

Mfr. pressure-sensitive adhesives and materials, office products, labels, tags, retail systems, Carter's Ink and specialty chemicals.

Fasson Roll Europe, Zone Industrielle PED, BP 38, L-4801 Rodange, Luxembourg

Tel: 352-50-46-501   Fax: 352-50-46-50277

THE BANK OF NEW YORK

One Wall Street, New York, NY, 10286

Tel: (212) 495-1784   Fax: (212) 495-2546   www.bankofny.com

Banking services.

Bank of New York Luxembourg, S.A., 13, rue Beaumont, 4th Fl., L-1219 Luxembourg City, Luxembourg

BDO SEIDMAN, LLP   BELGIUM

130 East Randolph Street, Chicago, IL, 60601

Tel: (312) 856-9100   Fax: (312) 856-1379   www.bdo.com

International accounting and financial consulting firm.

BDO Binder (Luxembourg) s.a.r.l., 17, rue des Pommiers, L-2343 Luxembourg City, Luxembourg

Tel: 352-42-3042   Fax: 352-42-3040   Contact: Georg Peter Rockel

BROWN BROTHERS HARRIMAN & COMPANY

140 Broadway, New York, NY, 10005

Tel: (212) 483-1818   Fax: (212) 493-8526   www.bbh.com

Leading provider of mergers and acquisition advisory services and private equity capital to private and closely held public companies.

Brown Brothers Harriman (Luxembourg) SA, 33 Boulevard Prince Henri, BP 403, L-2014 Luxembourg, Luxembourg

THE CHERRY CORPORATION

3600 Sunset Ave., PO Box 718, Waukegan, IL, 60087

Tel: (847) 662-9200   Fax: (847) 662-2990   www.cherrycorp.com

Mfr. electrical switches, electronic keyboards, controls and displays.

Multiprox NV, Lion d'Orweg 12, L-9300 Aalst, Luxembourg

Tel: 352-53-766566   Fax: 352-53-783977

CISCO SYSTEMS, INC.

170 West Tasman Drive, San Jose, CA, 95134-1706

Tel: (408) 526-4000   Fax: (408) 526-4100   www.cisco.com

Develop/mfr./market computer hardware and software networking systems.

Cisco Systems Luxembourg, 26, Bd Royal, 6th Floor, L-2449 Luxembourg City, Luxembourg

Tel: 352-22-9999-5262   Fax: 352-22-9999-5499

CITIGROUP, INC.

399 Park Avenue, New York, NY, 10022

Tel: (212) 559-1000   Fax: (212) 559-3646   www.citigroup.com

Provides insurance and financial services worldwide.

Citigroup, Luxembourg

Contact: William M. O'Dea

COMPUTER TASK GROUP, INC.

800 Delaware Avenue, Buffalo, NY, 14209-2094

Tel: (716) 882-8000   Fax: (716) 887-7456   www.ctg.com

Provides data processing information through information technology.

Computer Task Group, 3, Rue Jean Piret, L-2350 Luxembourg, Luxembourg

DANZAS AEI, INC.

120 Tokeneke Road, PO Box 1231, Darien, CT, 06820

Tel: (203) 655-7900   Fax: (203) 655-5779   www.aeilogistics.com

International air freight forwarder.

Danzas AEI, Room F2036-2038, New Cargocenter, L-1360 Luxembourg Airport, Luxembourg

Tel: 352-34-640-9450   Fax: 352-34-640-9457

DELOITTE TOUCHE TOHMATSU INTERNATIONAL

1633 Broadway, New York, NY, 10019

Tel: (212) 492-4000   Fax: (212) 392-4154   www.deloitte.com

Accounting, audit, tax and management consulting services.

Fiduciaire Generale de Luxembourg, 3, Route d'Arlon, L-8009 Strassen, Luxembourg

DELTA AIR LINES INC.

Hartsfield International Airport, 1030 Delta Blvd., Atlanta, GA, 30320-6001

Tel: (404) 715-2600   Fax: (404) 715-5494   www.delta-air.com

Major worldwide airline; international air transport services.

Delta Air Lines Inc., Luxembourg City, Luxembourg

DHL WORLDWIDE EXPRESS

50 California Avenue, San Francisco, CA, 94111

Tel: (415) 677-6100   Fax: (415) 824-9700   www.dhl.com

Worldwide air express carrier.

DHL Worldwide Express, 7, Ruede Bitbourg, Zone Industrielle Hamm, L-1273, Luxembourg

Tel: 352-422542

R.R. DONNELLEY & SONS COMPANY

77 West Wacker Drive, Chicago, IL, 60601-1696

Tel: (312) 326-8000   Fax: (312) 326-8543   www.rrdonnelley.com

Engaged in commercial printing and allied communication services.

R. R. Donnelley Financial, European Bank & Business Centre, 6D, Route de Treves, L-2633 Senningerberg, Luxembourg

Tel: 352-34-14341

THE DOW CHEMICAL COMPANY

2030 Dow Center, Midland, MI, 48674

Tel: (989) 636-1000   Fax: (989) 636-3228   www.dow.com

Mfr. chemicals, plastics, pharmaceuticals, agricultural products, consumer products.

Administration de Participations Etrangeres SA, 13, blvd Royal, L-2449 Luxembourg City, Luxembourg

E.I. DUPONT DE NEMOURS & COMPANY

1007 Market Street, Wilmington, DE, 19898

Tel: (302) 774-1000   Fax: (302) 774-7321   www.dupont.com

Mfr. and sales of diversified chemicals, plastics, specialty products and fibers.

DuPont Teijin Films Luxembourg S.A., PO Box 1681, L-1061, Luxembourg

ERNST & YOUNG INTERNATIONAL

5 Times Square, New York, NY, 10036

Tel: (212) 773-3000   Fax: (212) 773-6350   www.eyi.com

Engaged in assurance and advisory business services, tax, law and corporate finance.

Campagnie Fiduciare, 5, blvd de la Foire, PO Box 351, L-2013 Luxembourg City, Luxembourg

Tel: 352-45-123-224   Fax: 352-45-123-204   Contact: Armand Haas

FMR (FIDELITY INVESTMENTS)

82 Devonshire Street, Boston, MA, 02109

Tel: (617) 563-7000   Fax: (617) 476-6105   www.fidelity.com

Diversified financial services company offering investment management, retirement, brokerage, and shareholder services directly to individuals and institutions and through financial intermediaries.

Fidelity Investments Luxembourg SA, Kanasallis House, Place de l'Etolie, BP 2174, L-1021, Luxembourg

Tel: 352-250340

FOOT LOCKER INC.

112 West 34th Street, New York, NY, 10020

Tel: (212) 720-3700   Fax: (212) 553-2042   www.venatorgroup.com

Mfr./sales shoes and sneakers.

Foot Locker International, 43, Ave. De La Gare, L1611 Luxembourg City, Luxembourg

Tel: 352-491214

Foot Locker International, 18, rue De L'Alzette, L-4010 Esch-Zur-Alzette, Luxembourg

Tel: 352-542825

FRANKLIN RESOURCES, INC.

1 Franklin Pkwy., Bldg. 970, 1st Fl., San Mateo, CA, 94404

Tel: (415) 312-2000   Fax: (415) 312-5606   www.frk.com

Global and domestic investment advisory and portfolio management.

Templeton Global Strategic Services, S.A., 26, Boulevard Royal, L-2449 Luxembourg City, Luxembourg

Tel: 352-46-66-67-212   Fax: 352-46-66-76

GENERAL ELECTRIC CAPITAL CORPORATION

260 Long Ridge Road, Stamford, CT, 06927

Tel: (203) 357-4000   Fax: (203) 357-6489   www.gecapital.com

Financial, property, casualty insurance, computer sales and trailer leasing services.

ERC Group, Div. GE Capital, 4, rue de l'Eau, L-1449 Luxembourg City, Luxembourg

Tel: 352-467-250   Fax: 352-467-230

GENERAL ELECTRIC COMPANY

3135 Easton Turnpike, Fairfield, CT, 06431

Tel: (203) 373-2211   Fax: (203) 373-3131   www.ge.com

Diversified manufacturing, technology and services.

GE Fanuc Automation, Zone Industrielle, L-6468 Echternach, Luxembourg

Tel: 352-72797-9324   Fax: 352-72797-9351

GENERAL MOTORS CORPORATION

300 Renaissance Center, Detroit, MI, 48285

Tel: (313) 556-5000   Fax: (313) 556-5108   www.gm.com

Mfr. full line vehicles, automotive electronics, commercial technologies, telecommunications, space, finance.

General Motors Luxembourg Operations SA, Route de Luxembourg, BP 29, L-4901 Bascharage, Luxembourg

THE GOODYEAR TIRE & RUBBER COMPANY

1144 East Market Street, Akron, OH, 44316

Tel: (330) 796-2121   Fax: (330) 796-1817   www.goodyear.com

Mfr. tires, automotive belts and hose, conveyor belts, chemicals; oil pipeline transmission.

Goodyear SA, Ave. Gordon Smith, L-7750 Colmar-Berg, Luxembourg

GRANT THORNTON INTERNATIONAL

800 One Prudential Plaza, 130 E. Randolph Drive, Chicago, IL, 60601-6050

Tel: (312) 856-0001   Fax: (312) 616-7052   www.grantthornton.com

Accounting, audit, tax and management consulting services.

Grant Thornton Revision et Conseils SA, 2, Blvd. Grande Duchesse, L-1330 Charlotte, Luxembourg

GUARDIAN INDUSTRIES CORPORATION

2300 Harmon Road, Auburn Hills, MI, 48326-1714

Tel: (248) 340-1800   Fax: (248) 340-9988   www.guardian.com

Mfr. and fabricate flat glass products and insulation materials.

Guardian Luxguard S.A., Route de Luxembourg, L-4940 Bascharage, Luxembourg

Tel: 352-50-301

HOLIDAY INN (BASS RESORTS) WORLDWIDE, INC.

3 Ravinia Drive, Ste. 2900, Atlanta, GA, 30346-2149

Tel: (770) 604-2000   Fax: (770) 604-5403   www.holidayinn.com

Hotels, restaurants and casinos.

Holiday Inn, BP 512, Luxembourg City, Luxembourg

HORWATH INTERNATIONAL ASSOCIATION

420 Lexington Avenue, Suite 526, New York, NY, 10170-0526

Tel: (212) 808-2000   Fax: (212) 808-2020   www.horwath.com

Public accountants and auditors.

Hoogewerf & Co., 19, rue Aldringen, L-1118 Luxembourg City, Luxembourg

IBM CORPORATION

1133 Westchester Avenue, White Plains, NY, 10604

Tel: (914) 765-1900   Fax: (914) 765-7382   www.ibm.com

Information products, technology and services.

IBM World Trade Corporation, Ceinture "Um Schlass" 1, L-5880 Hesperange, Luxembourg

INFONET SERVICES CORPORATION

2160 East Grand Ave., El Segundo, CA, 90245-1022

Tel: (310) 335-2600   Fax: (310) 335-4507   www.infonet.com

Provider of Internet services and electronic messaging services.

Infonet Luxembourg, 55 rue des Bruyeres, L-1274 Howald, Luxembourg

Tel: 352-405-6371   Fax: 352-405-639

JONES LANG LASALLE

153 East 53rd Street, New York, NY, 10022

Tel: (212) 812-5700   Fax: (212) 421-3544   www.am.joneslanglasalle.com

International marketing consultants, leasing agents and property management advisors.

Jones Lang Wootton, Luxembourg

KELLY SERVICES, INC.

999 W. Big Beaver Road, Troy, MI, 48084

Tel: (248) 362-4444   Fax: (248) 244-4154   www.kellyservices.com

Temporary help placement.

Kelly Services Luxembourg S.A.R.L., 19-25, rue des Capucins, L-1313 Luxembourg City, Luxembourg

Tel: 352-466266   Fax: 352-466267

KOCH INDUSTRIES INC.

4111 East 37th Street North, Wichita, KS, 67220-3203

Tel: (316) 828-5500   Fax: (316) 828-5950   www.kochind.com

Oil, financial services, agriculture and Purina Mills animal feed.

Koch Membrane Systems, Inc., PO Box 83, L-3400 Dudelange, Luxembourg

KORN/FERRY INTERNATIONAL

1800 Century Park East, Los Angeles, CA, 90067

Tel: (310) 843-4100   Fax: (310) 553-6452   www.kornferry.com

Engaged in executive search and management consulting.

Korn/Ferry International, 19, Cote d'Eich, L-1450 Luxembourg City, Luxembourg

Tel: 352-4643-421   Fax: 352-4643-45/60

KPMG CONSULTING INC.

1676 International Dr., McLean, VA, 22102

Tel: (703) 747-3000   Fax: (703) 747-8500   www.kpmg.com

Accounting and audit, tax and management consulting services.

KPMG International, 31, Allée Scheffer, L-2520, Luxembourg

Tel: 352-2251511   Fax: 352-225171   Contact: Dennis Robertson, Ptnr.

KPMG International, 121, Ave. de la Faïencerie, L-1511 Luxembourg City, Luxembourg

Tel: 352-47-68-471   Fax: 352-47-0761   Contact: Bob Bernard, Sr. Ptnr.

MANPOWER INTERNATIONAL INC.

5301 N. Ironwood Rd., PO Box 2053, Milwaukee, WI, 53201-2053

Tel: (414) 961-1000   Fax: (414) 961-7081   www.manpower.com

Temporary help, contract service, training and testing.

Manpower SARL, 19, rue Glesener, Luxembourg City, Luxembourg

Tel: 352-482-323

MARSH & McLENNAN COS INC.

1166 Ave. of the Americas, New York, NY, 10036-2774

Tel: (212) 345-5000   Fax: (212) 345-4808   www.marshmac.com

Insurance agents/brokers, pension and investment management consulting services.

J&H Marsh & McLennan Management Services S.A., 65, Ave. de la Gare, L-1611 Luxembourg City, Luxembourg

Tel: 352-49-6951   Fax: 352-49-6936   Contact: Claude Weber

MASS MUTUAL FINANCIAL GROUP

1295 State Street, Springfield, MA, 01111

Tel: (413) 788-8411   Fax: (413) 744-6005   www.massmutual.com

Individual insurance, personal accident insurance, credit and group life insurance.

MassMutual Luxembourg, Luxembourg

MERCURY INTERACTIVE CORPORATION

1325 Borregas Ave., Sunnyvale, CA, 94089

Tel: (408) 822-5200   Fax: (408) 822-5300   www.merc-int.com

Mfr. computer software to decipher and eliminate "bugs" from systems.

Mercury Interactive, Rue de Kehlen, L-8295 Keispelt, Luxembourg

MERRILL LYNCH & COMPANY, INC.

World Financial Center, 250 Vesey Street, New York, NY, 10281-1332

Tel: (212) 236-1000   Fax: (212) 449-2892   www.ml.com

Security brokers and dealers, investment and business services.

Merrill Lynch International Bank, 68-70, blvd de la Petrusse, L-2320 Luxembourg City, Luxembourg

Tel: 352-49-5156-1   Fax: 352-48-1271

MOOG INC.

300 Jamison Road, East Aurora, NY, 14052-0018

Tel: (716) 652-2000   Fax: (716) 687-4471   www.moog.com

Mfr. precision control components and systems.

Moog Hydrolux Luxembourg Sarl, PO Box 1963, 1, rue de l'Aciérie, L-1019, Luxembourg

MORGAN ADVANCED MATERIALS AND TECHNOLOGY, INC.

441 Hall Ave., Saint Mary's, PA, 15857

Tel: (814) 781-1573   Fax: (814) 781-9262   www.mamat.com

Mfr. carbon graphite and silicon carbide components.

Morganite Luxembourg S.A., PO Box 15, L-8301 Capellen, Luxembourg

J. P. MORGAN CHASE & CO. INC.

270 Park Ave., New York, NY, 10017

Tel: (212) 270-6000   Fax: (212) 622-9030   www.jpmorganchase.com

Provides integrated financial solutions for institutions and individuals worldwide, including asset management, investment banking and commercial banking.

J. P. Morgan Chase & Co., 37, rue Notre Dame, Luxembourg City, Luxembourg

J. P. Morgan Chase & Co., 5, rue Plaetis, BP 240, L-2012, Luxembourg

Tel: 352-46-26-851   Fax: 352-46-224590

MORGAN STANLEY DEAN WITTER & CO.

1585 Broadway, New York, NY, 10036

Tel: (212) 761-4000   Fax: (212) 761-0086   www.msdw.com

Securities and commodities brokerage, investment banking, money management, personal trusts.

Morgan Stanley Bank Luxembourg S.A., 6C Route de Treves, L-2633 Senningerberg, Luxembourg

NATIONWIDE

One Nationwide Plaza, Columbus, OH, 43215-2220

Tel: (614) 249-7111   Fax: (614) 249-7705   www.nationwide.com

Insurance services.

PanEuroLife, 291, route d'Arlon, BP 2408, L- 1024, Luxembourg

NORTON ABRASIVES COMPANY

1 New Bond Street, Worcester, MA, 01606

Tel: (508) 795-5000   Fax: (508) 795-5741   www.nortonabrasives.com

Mfr. abrasives for industrial manufacturing.

Norton SA, Chemin Rouge Belvaux, Luxembourg City, Luxembourg

OTIS ELEVATOR COMPANY

One Farm Springs Road, Farmington, CT, 06032

Tel: (860) 676-6000   Fax: (860) 676-5111   www.otis.com

Mfr. elevators and escalators.

General Technic-Otis SARL, 44, rue des Bruyeres, BP 1056, L-1274 Howald, Luxembourg

THE PHOENIX COMPANIES

1 American Row, Hartford, CT, 06102-5056

Tel: (860) 403-5000   Fax: (860) 403-5855   www.phoenixwm.com

Engaged in life insurance, annuity and investment management products and services.

Lombard International Assurance S.A. (JV), Luxembourg

PRICEWATERHOUSECOOPERS LLP

1301 Ave. of the Americas, New York, NY, 10019

Tel: (212) 596-7000   Fax: (212) 259-1301   www.pwcglobal.com

Accounting and auditing, tax and management, and human resource consulting services.

PriceWaterhouseCoopers, 24-26, Ave. de la Liberte, PO Box 1443, L-1014 Luxembourg City, Luxembourg

Tel: 352-402455-1   Fax: 352-402455-600

PRUDENTIAL FINANCIAL

751 Broad Street, Newark, NJ, 07102-3777

Tel: (973) 802-6000   Fax: (973) 802-2804   www.prudential.com

Sale of life insurance, financial services, asset management and brokerage.

Prudential-Bache International Limited, 8 rue Beck, L-1222 Grand Duche De Luxembourg, Luxembourg

Tel: 352-463-6661   Fax: 352-463-666-500   Contact: Helmer Moller

RAYMOND JAMES FINANCIAL, INC.

880 Carillon Parkway, St. Petersburg, FL, 33716

Tel: (813) 573-3800   Fax: (813) 573-8244   www.rjf.com

Financial services; securities brokerage, asset management, and investment banking services.

Raymond James Benelux, 25, rue Notre Dame, L-2240 Luxembourg City, Luxembourg

Tel: 352-229-666   Fax: 352-221-044

RPM INC.

PO Box 777, 2628 Pearl Road, Medina, OH, 44258

Tel: (330) 273-5090   Fax: (330) 225-8743   www.rpminc.com

Mfr. protective coatings and paints.

Akron SARL, 3, rue de la Sapiniere, Bridel, Luxembourg

S1 CORPORATION

3500 Lenox Road, Ste. 200, Atlanta, GA, 30326-1108

Tel: (404) 923-3500   Fax: (404) 923-6727   www.s1.com

Mfr. on-line banking software.

S1 Luxembourg, 26, rue Michel Rodange, L-2430 Luxembourg, Luxembourg

SILICON GRAPHICS INC.

1600 Amphitheatre Pkwy., Mountain View, CA, 94043-1351

Tel: (650) 960-1980   Fax: (650) 932-0661   www.sgi.com

Design/mfr. special-effects computer graphic systems and software.

Silicon Graphics, Luxembourg

SOTHEBY'S HOLDINGS, INC.

1334 York Avenue, New York, NY, 10021

Tel: (212) 606-7000   Fax: (212) 606-7027   www.sothebys.com

Auction house specializing in fine art and jewelry.

Sotheby's Holdings, Inc., 156A, Route de Luxembourg, L-7374 Bofferdange, Luxembourg

Tel: 352-33-9747   Contact: Nadia Meyer-Quiring

THE ST. PAUL COMPANIES, INC.

385 Washington Street, St. Paul, MN, 55102

Tel: (651) 310-7911   Fax: (651) 310-8294   www.stpaul.com

Provides investment, insurance and reinsurance services.

Fortis Luxembourg Assurances, 74, Grand'rue, L-1660 Luxembourg City, Luxembourg

STARWOOD HOTELS & RESORTS WORLDWIDE

777 Westchester Avenue, White Plains, NY, 10604

Tel: (914) 640-8100   Fax: (914) 640-8316   www.starwoodhotels.com

Hotel operations including Sheraton, Westin, St. Regis, Four Points and Caesars.

Aerogulf Sheraton Hotel, BP 1793, Luxembourg City, Luxembourg

STATE STREET CORPORATION

225 Franklin Street, Boston, MA, 02101

Tel: (617) 786-3000   Fax: (617) 654-3386   www.statestreet.com

Engaged in investment management and institutional investor services.

State Street Bank SA, 47 Blvd. Royal, L-2449 Luxembourg City, Luxembourg

TEREX CORPORATION

500 Post Road East, Ste. 320, Westport, CT, 06880

Tel: (203) 222-7170   Fax: (203) 222-7976   www.terex.com

Mfr. lifting and earthmoving equipment.

Parc Material, Div. Terex, 295 Route d'Arlon, L-8011 Strassen, Luxembourg

TEXAS REFINERY CORPORATION

840 North Main Street, Fort Worth, TX, 76101

Tel: (817) 332-1161   Fax: (817) 332-2340   www.texasrefinery.com

Mfr. lubricants and specialty coatings.

Texas Refinery Corp. Inter-Continental SA, BP 4, Zone Industrielle Echternach, L-640 1 Echternach, Luxembourg

THOMAS & BETTS CORPORATION

8155 T&B Blvd., Memphis, TN, 38125

Tel: (901) 252-5000   Fax: (901) 685-1988   www.tnb.com

Mfr. elect/electronic connectors and accessories.

Thomas & Betts (Luxembourg) SA, rue de l'Industrie, Zone Industrielle, L-2895 Fuetz, Luxembourg

UUNET

22001 Loudoun County Pkwy., Ashburn, VA, 20147

Tel: (703) 206-5600   Fax: (703) 206-5601   www.uu.net

World's largest Internet service provider; World Wide Web hosting services, security products and consulting services to businesses, professionals, and on-line service providers.

UUNET Luxembourg, 39, Ual Saint André, L-1128 Luxembourg City, Luxembourg

Tel: 352-44-0291   Fax: 352-25-4404   Contact: Luc Dierckx

THE VIKING CORPORATION

210 N. Industrial Park Rd., Hastings, MI, 49058

Tel: (616) 945-9501   Fax: (616) 945-9599   www.vikingcorp.com

Mfr. fire extinguishing equipment.

Viking SA, Zone Industrielle Haneboesch, L-4562 Differdange Niedercorn, Luxembourg

JOHN ZINK COMPANY

11920 East Apache, Tulsa, OK, 74121-1220

Tel: (918) 234-1800   Fax: (918) 234-2700   www.johnzink.com

Engaged in the development and manufacture of next-generation combustion products, technologies and clean-air solutions that power global industry.

John Zink Luxembourg, Zone Industrielle Riedgen, L-3401 Dudelange, Luxembourg

Tel: 352-51899206   Contact: Manuel Martinez

Macau

AIG AMERICAN INTERNATIONAL GROUP INC.

70 Pine Street, New York, NY, 10270

Tel: (212) 770-7000   Fax: (212) 509-9705   www.aig.com

Worldwide insurance and financial services.

American Home Assurance Co., #61 Av da Almeida, Central Plaza, Blk G15, Macau

AMWAY CORPORATION

7575 Fulton Street East, Ada, MI, 49355-0001

Tel: (616) 787-6000   Fax: (616) 787-6177   www.amway.com

Mfr./sale home care, personal care, nutrition and houseware products.

Amway Macau Lda., Rua de Pedro Coutinbo, Np. 52 Edif. Hio Fai, Bloco D, R/C, Macau

BANK OF AMERICA CORPORATION

Bank of America Corporate Center, Charlotte, NC, 28255

Tel: (415) 622-3530   Fax: (704) 386-6699   www.bankofamerica.com

Financial services.

Bank of America NT & SA, 2F-G Av. de Almeida, Ribeiro, Macau

Tel: 853-568821   Fax: 853-570386

BEL FUSE INC.

198 Van Vorst Street, Jersey City, NJ, 07302

Tel: (201) 432-0463   Fax: (201) 432-9542   www.belfuse.com

Mfr. electronic components for networking, fuses, delay lines, hybrids and magnetic products.

Bel Fuse Macau Lda., 218 Largo do Pac On, Taipa, Macau

CITIGROUP, INC.

399 Park Avenue, New York, NY, 10022

Tel: (212) 559-1000   Fax: (212) 559-3646   www.citigroup.com

Provides insurance and financial services worldwide.

Citigroup, Macau

Contact: Stephen H. Long

DELOITTE TOUCHE TOHMATSU INTERNATIONAL

1633 Broadway, New York, NY, 10019

Tel: (212) 492-4000   Fax: (212) 392-4154   www.deloitte.com

Accounting, audit, tax and management consulting services.

Deloitte Touche Tohmatsu, 223-225 Av Dr. Rodrigo Rodrigues, 14/F, Nam Kwong Bldg., Apt.1, PO Box 746, Macau

DHL WORLDWIDE EXPRESS

50 California Avenue, San Francisco, CA, 94111

Tel: (415) 677-6100   Fax: (415) 824-9700   www.dhl.com

Worldwide air express carrier.

DHL Worldwide Express, 14-16 Beco do Praia Grande, Edidicio Hoi Tin R/C, Macau

Tel: 853-372828

IBM CORPORATION

1133 Westchester Avenue, White Plains, NY, 10604

Tel: (914) 765-1900   Fax: (914) 765-7382   www.ibm.com

Information products, technology and services.

IBM World Trade Corporation, Av. Dr. Mario Soraes, Edif. Banco da China, Macau

Tel: 853-786687   Fax: 853-782136

INTERNATIONAL GAME TECHNOLOGY INC. (IGT)

9295 Prototype Drive, Reno, NV, 89511

Tel: (702) 448-0100   Fax: (702) 448-1488   www.igtonline.com

Mfr. slot machines, video gaming machines and gaming terminals.

IGT Macau, Box 1024, Macau

Tel: 853-375111   Fax: 853-510239

KPMG CONSULTING INC.

1676 International Dr., McLean, VA, 22102

Tel: (703) 747-3000   Fax: (703) 747-8500   www.kpmg.com

Accounting and audit, tax and management consulting services.

KPMG International, Bank of China Bldg., Av. Doutor Mario Soares, Macau

PRICEWATERHOUSECOOPERS LLP

1301 Ave. of the Americas, New York, NY, 10019

Tel: (212) 596-7000   Fax: (212) 259-1301   www.pwcglobal.com

Accounting and auditing, tax and management, and human resource consulting services.

PriceWaterhouseCoopers, Edif. Banco Luso Internacional, rua Dr. Pedro Jose Lobo Nos 1-3, andar 27, Macau

Tel: 853-589589   Fax: 853-558861

SCHENKER USA INC.

150 Albany Ave., Freeport, NY, 11520

Tel: (516) 403-5416   Fax: (516) 377-3092   www.schenkerusa.com

Freight forwarders.

Schenker (H. K.) Ltd., Praia Grande Commercial Ctr., Rm. 1206429, Av. De Praia, Macau

Tel: 853-712687   Fax: 853-712676

STARWOOD HOTELS & RESORTS WORLDWIDE

777 Westchester Avenue, White Plains, NY, 10604

Tel: (914) 640-8100   Fax: (914) 640-8316   www.starwoodhotels.com

Hotel operations including Sheraton, Westin, St. Regis, Four Points and Caesars.

Westin Resort, Estrada de Hac Sa, Ilha de Coloane, Coloane, Macau

Tel: 853-871-111   Fax: 853-871-122

VOLUME 2

PUBLISHER'S NOTES

Related publications

11th Edition

DIRECTORY OF FOREIGN FIRMS OPERATING IN THE UNITED STATES

EDITED & PUBLISHED BY
UNIWORLD BUSINESS PUBLICATIONS, INC.
Published January 2002

ONE VOLUME • 1480 PAGES • PRICE: $250.00 • ISBN: 0-8360-0046-3

VOLUME   PRICE: $250.00
PAGES   ISBN: 0-8360-0046-3

OM one year subscription $ 675.00
OM two year subscription $1000.00
    (see insert for details)

REHENSIVE LISTINGS

,800 Foreign Firms
,200 U.S. Affiliates
9 Countries

AND FLEXIBLE ACCESS

irm(s) you are looking for can
nd:
y country --(Part I)
y name------the name of the parent
ompany (Part II)
y affiliate---the name of the
American based affiliate (Part III)

KEY CONTACT AND LOCATION INFORMATION

Name of Parent Foreign Firm and Address   *Revenue*

Italy

● **LUXOTTICA GROUP, S.p.A.**   *Telephone/Fax Number*
Via Vacozzena, 10, I-32021 Agordo Belluno, Italy
CEO — CEO: Leonardo Del Vecchio, Pres.   Tel: 39-0437-63746   Rev: $2,275
Bus: *Mfr. eyeglass frames, retail eyecare and*   Fax: 39-0437-63840   Emp: 19,400
clothing stores.   www.luxottica.it ●— *Web*

Number of Employees

AVANT GARDE OPTICS INC.
44 Harbor Park Drive, Port Washington, NY   11050
CEO — CEO: Claudio Del Vecchio, Pres.   Tel: (516) 484-3800   %FO: 100
Bus: *Distribution, eyeglass frames.*   Fax: (516) 484-4481   Emp: 326

LENSCRAFTERS INC.
8650 Governor's Hill Drive, Cincinnati, OH   43068   *Telephone/Fax Number*
CEO: Cliff Bartow, COO   Tel: (513) 583-6000   ● %FO: 100
Bus: *Eyeglass frames, eyecare retail*   Fax: (513) 583-6388   Emp: 12,800
stores.

Principal Product   *Principal Product*   *% Foreign Owned*
or Service   *or Service*   *Number of Employees*

TIAL BUYERS LIST

gfield Library
ard University Office of Career Services
Waterhouse
ternational Trade Commission
nk
ick & Struggles
dian Embassy

y University Career Services

Executive Office of the President
US Chamber of Commerce
Rochester Public Library
LA Chamber of Commerce
Merrill Lynch
Hitachi Foundation
John Hopkins Hospital
Columbia University
CBS

IBM
New York Public Library
University of Texas
MCI WorldCom
Notre Dame University
Stentor International
The Washington Opera
Zagat
Liberty Mutual

NEW 17ᵗʰ Edition

DIRECTORY OF AMERICAN FIRMS OPERATING IN FOREIGN COUNTRIES

REVISED & EXPANDED
20% more listings
NAICS NOW INCLUDED
(North American Industry Classification System)

EDITED & PUBLISHED BY UNIWORLD BUSINESS PUBLICATIONS, INC.
Published January 2003

THREE VOLUMES   PRICE: $355.00
4200 PAGES   ISBN: 0-8360-0047-1

CD ROM one year subscription $ 975.00
CD ROM two year subscription $1500.00
(See insert for details)

Name of Firm and Address

__KEY CONTACT AND LOCATION INFORMATION__

PART 1
US listings by Name

ALLEGIANCE HEALTHCARE CORPORATION
Website www.allegiance.net
1430 Waukegan Road
McGaw Park, IL 60085
Tel: (847) 689-8410   Fax: (847) 578-4437
CEO: Ronald K. Labrum, Pres. & CEO
Number of Employees
IO: Roger L. Sisterman, SVP
HR: Robert B. DeBaun, SVP
Emp: 19500   Rev: $4,400 mil.
NAICS NAICS: 339111, 339112, 339113
Manufactures and distributes medical, surgical, respiratory therapy and laboratory products.
Principal product or service Belgium, Canada, England, U.K., France, Germany, Italy, Japan, Netherlands, Spain, Switzerland

Phone/Fax numbe of US Headquar
CEO
International Officer
Human Resources C
Revenues
Countries where fore affiliates are located

PART 2
Listings by Foreign Country

ALLEGIANCE HEALTHCARE CORPORATION
1430 Waukegan Road, McGaw Park, IL, 60085
Tel: (847) 689-8410   Fax: (847) 578-4437   www.allegiance.net
Manufactures and distributes medical, surgical, respiratory therapy and laboratory products.
Allegiance Medica srl, Viale Tiziano 25, I-00196 Rome, Italy
Tel: 39-06-32-4911 Fax: 39-06-32-491204   Contact: Sandro Lombardi, Bus. Dir.

Name of Fir Address in U

Principal Product or service
Names and address of subsidiary, affiliate or branch
Where available, telephone, fax and local contacts for foreign subsidiaries

CD Rom Versions

American Firms Operating in Foreign Countries 17th edition
Foreign Firms Operating in The United States 11th edition
are available.

The marketing and research tool that is necessary to expand your business in the 21st century.
Libraries put it on your server for multiple viewing.

bscription information:

erican Firms **$ 975.00** one-year subscription includes original and one semi-annual update.
erican Firms **$1500.00** two-year subscription includes original and three semi-annual updates.
eign Firms **$ 675.00** one-year subscription includes original and one semi-annual update.
eign Firms **$1000.00** two-year subscription includes original and three semi-annual updates.
tomatic renewal subscriptions receive a **5%** discount starting with the next edition.

atures:

American Firms Directory	Foreign Firms Directory
Over 3,000 American Parent Companies	2,800 Foreign Parent Companies
Over 36,300 Foreign Subsidiaries	7,200 American Subsidiaries
6 PDF formats	4 PDF formats

Mailing Labels
Merge Letters
Print Reports
Search Ability

stom editions of the CD Rom are available for country, regional and state ctions of the book at special pricing with all the same features as the world ition CD.

closed price list has pricing for CD Rom as well as print versions of Country or gional editions. Please call 212-496-2448, Fax 212-769-0413 or Email: iworldbp@aol.com for pricing of state and customized editions of the CD Rom. **ALL** **) ROM SALES ARE FINAL**

Country, Regiona
State Editions &
Mailing Lists

Directory of American Firms Operating in Foreign Countries and the
Directory of Foreign Firms Operating in The United States
Country, **Regional** or **State** editions with all the same information that is in the library set.

- **Country and Regional Editions** ~ list the companies alphabetically within each country.

- **State Editions** ~ *Directory of American Firms Operating in Foreign Countries*
  lists by State the American firms (alphabetically) at the headqua
  location within the state.

  ~ *Directory of Foreign Firms Operating in The United States*
  lists by State the Foreign Firms (alphabetically) at each America
  Affiliate headquarters location within the state.

- **Mail Lists-Labels** ~ available for all directories, **Country**, **Regional** or the complete
  World List: *Name and American Address of the Parent Comp*
  with a corporate officer: ***CEO, International Operations Office***
  Human Resources Director (where available) or any title you w
  with telemarketing list.

- **Custom Order** ~ Create your own regions or country groupings to suit your project nee

To place an order, please call (212)-496-2448 or send the attached **Order Form** by FAX (212) 769
Orders for Country, Regional, State editions and Mailing lists require pre-payment by credit card, c
or money order in U.S. dollars, drawn on a U.S. Bank. **ALL SALES ARE FINAL**

Please see reverse side for title and pricing information.

...ion Directory of ...n Firms Operating ...n Countries

	Print/CD Rom
...ola, Benin, Botswana, Burkina ...i, Cameroon, Cent. African ...congo, Dem. Rep. Of Congo, ...ypt, Ethiopia, Gabon, Ghana, ...y Coast, Kenya, Lesotho, ...a, Madagascar, Malawi, Mali, ...orocco, Mozambique, ...er, Nigeria, Reunion, Senegal, ...ierra Leone, South Africa, ...land, Tanzania, Tunisia, ...bia & Zimbabwe	$ 79.00/$200.00
...Brunei, Cambodia, China, ...India, Indonesia, Japan, ...Kirgnizia, Laos, Macau, ...ongolia, Myanmar, Nepal, ...lippines, Singapore, South ...anka, Taiwan, Tajikistan, ...bekistan & Vietnam	$189.00/$420.00
...a ...India, Myanmar, Pakistan &	$ 59.00/$150.00
...st Asia ...bodia, Indonesia, India, Laos, ...ilippines, Singapore, Thailand	$109.00/$265.00
...South Korea	$ 99.00/$250.00
...oup ...Kong, Macau, Singapore &	$129.00/$325.00
...MIDDLE EAST ...rus, Iran, Israel, Jordan, ...anon, Oman, Palestine, Qatar, ...a, Syria, Turkey, United Arab ...Yemen	$ 79.00/$200.00
...ic Countries ...rain, Egypt, Iran, Jordan, ...anon, Libya, Morocco, Oman, ...atar, Saudi Arabia, Sudan, ...a, United Arab Emirates &	$ 69.00/$175.00
...Middle East & Arabic ...s Combined	$ 89.00/$225.00
...ALIA GROUP ...ew Zealand, Fiji, French ...uam, New Caledonia, No. ...Palau, Papua New Guinea, ...olomon Isl. & Vanuatu	$ 89.00/ $225.00
...e	$239.00/$600.00
...Western ...gium, Channel Isl., Denmark, ...land, France, Germany, ...reece, Iceland, Ireland, Isle of ...iechtenstein, Luxembourg, ...alta, Monaco, Netherlands, No. ...way, Portugal, San Marino, ...ain, Sweden, Switzerland &	$209.00/$525.00

	Print/CD Rom
British Isles Channel Is., England, Gibraltar, Ireland, Isle of Man, No. Ireland, Scotland & Wales	$129.00/$325.00
Europe West. Excl. British Isles	$189.00/$465.00
Belgium	$ 59.00/$150.00
France	$ 79.00/$200.00
Germany	$ 89.00/$225.00
Italy	$ 69.00/$175.00
Netherlands	$ 69.00/$175.00
Spain	$ 59.00/$150.00
Sweden	$ 49.00/$125.00
Switzerland	$ 49.00/$125.00
Scandinavia (Denmark, Finalnd, Iceland, Norway & Sweden)	$ 89.00/$225.00
Europe Eastern Albania, Armenia, Azerbaijan, Belarus, Bosnia-Herzegovina, Bulgaria, Croatia, Czech Rep., Estonia, Georgia, Hungary, Kazabhstan, Kirgnizia, Latvia, Lithuania, Macedonia, Poland, Romania, Russia, Slovakia, Slovenia, Tajikistan, Turkmenistan, Ukraine, Uzbekistan & Yugoslavia	$ 99.00/$250.00
NORTH AMERICA Canada, Greenalnd & Mexico	$119.00/$350.00
Canada	$ 99.00/$250.00
Mexico	$ 69.00/$175.00
Central America Belize, Costa Rica, El Salvador, Guatemala, Honduras, Nicaragua & Panama	$ 49.00/$125.00
Caribbean Islands Anguilla, Antigua, Aruba, Bahamas, Barbados, Bermuda, British Virgin Is., Cayman Isl., Dominican Rep., French Antilles, Grenada, Haiti, Jamaica, Neth. Antilles, Trinidad/Tobago & Turks/Caicos	$ 49.00/$125.00
South America Argentina, Bolivia, Brazil, Chile, Colombia, Ecuador, French Guiana, Guyana, Paraguay, Peru, Surinam, Uruguay, Venezuela	$119.00/$350.00
Argentina	$ 49.00/$125.00
Argentina, Brazil & Chile	$ 89.00/$225.00
Brazil	$ 69.00/$175.00
Venezuela	$ 39.00/$100.00

11th Edition Directory of Foreign Firms Operating in The United States

AFRICA Burkina Faso, Egypt, Ivory Coast, Nigeria, & South Africa	$ 29.00/$ 75.00
ASIA China, Hong Kong, India, Indonesia, Japan, Malaysia, Pakistan, Philippines, Singapore, South Korea, Taiwan & Thailand	$ 89.00/$225.00
Japan & South Korea	$ 79.00/$200.00
China Group China, Hong Kong, Singapore & Taiwan	$ 39.00/$100.00

	Print/CD Rom
NEAR & MIDDLE EAST Bahrain, Cyprus, Egypt, Iran, Israel, Jordan, Kuwait, Lebanon, Saudi Arabia, Turkey & United Arab Emirates	$39.00/$100.00
AUSTRALIA GROUP Australia & New Zealand	$ 29.00/$ 75.00
NORTH AMERICA Canada Mexico	$49.00/$125.00
LATIN AMERICA Argentina, Bahamas, Barbados, Bermuda, Bolivia, Brazil, British Virgin Is., Cayman Isl., Chile, Colombia, Costa Rica, Dominican Rep., El Salvador, Guatemala, Guyana, Mexico, Panama, Peru, Uruguay & Venezuela	$ 39.00/$100.00
EUROPE Austria, Belgium, Czech Rep., Denmark, England, Finland, France, Germany, Greece, Hungary, Iceland, Ireland, Italy, Liechtenstein, Luxembourg, Monaco, Netherlands, Norway, Poland, Portugal, Romania, Russia, Scotland, Slovenia, Spain, Sweden, Switzerland & Wales	$149.00/$375.00
British Isles Channel Is., England, Ireland Scotland & Wales	$ 69.00/$175.00
Europe West. Excl. British Isles	$119.00/$300.00
France	$ 49.00/$125.00
Germany	$ 59.00/$150.00
Italy	$ 39.00/$100.00
Netherlands	$ 39.00/$100.00
Scandinavia	$ 59.00/$175.00
Sweden	$ 39.00/$100.00
Switzerland	$ 49.00/$125.00
Europe Eastern Czech Rep., Hungary, Poland, Russia & Slovenia	$ 29.00/$ 75.00

Uniworld Business Publications, Inc.
257 Central Park West, Suite 10A
New York, New York 10024
Tel: (212) 496-2448
Fax: (212) 769-0413
E-mail: uniworldbp@aol.com
Website: http://uniworldbp.com

ALL SALES ARE FINAL
Prices subject to change without notice

11/15/02

ORDER FORM

UNIWORLD BUSINESS PUBLICATIONS, I

257 Central Park West, Suite 10A, New York, New York 10024-
Tel: 212-496-2448   Fax: 212-769-
E-mail: uniworldbp@aol.com   WEBsite: http://www.uniworldbp

Order by Title	Standing Order*	Quantity	Price	Subtota
Directory of American Firms Operating in Foreign Countries			$ 355.00	
CD ROM Directory of American Firms Operating in Foreign Countries **1 year subscription**			$ 975.00	
CDROM Directory of American Firms Operating in Foreign Countries **2 year subscription**			$ 1500.00	
Directory of Foreign Firms Operating in the United States			$ 250.00	
CD Rom Directory of Foreign Firms Operating in the United States **1 year subscription**			$ 675.00	
CD Rom Directory of Foreign Firms Operating in the United States **2 year subscription**			$ 1000.00	

PAYMENT INFORMATION

☐ Check or money order enclosed for $_____ payable to:

Uniworld Business Publications, Inc. (in U.S. dollars drawn on a U.S. bank)

☐ Charge to
  ☐ American Express ☐ MasterCard ☐ VISA

Credit card holder:_____

Card number:_____

Expiration Date:__/__/__ Signature:_____

Subtotal _____

Shipping & Handling _____

NY & CT buyers and
sales tax _____

Total _____

☐ Bill me (Public Libraries and Educational Institutions only)

P.O.#:_____Name:_____

Signature:_____

MAILING ADDRESS

Name:_____

Title/Dept.:_____

Firm/Org.:_____

Address:_____

City:_____State:____Zip:_____ -

Tel. #:_____Fax #:_____

E-mail:_____

Website:_____

BILLING ADDRESS (if different than mailing address)

Name:_____

Title/Dept.:_____

Firm/Org.:_____

Address:_____

City:_____State:____Zip:_____

Tel. #:_____Fax #:_____

E-mail:_____

Website:_____

SHIPPING AND HANDLING

Via UPS: Directory of American Firms Operating in Foreign Countries **$15.50**
Directory of Foreign Firms Operating in the United States **$8.50.**
Via US Mail: CD Rom one year $15.00, two year $30.00
Shipping outside the United States or next day delivery rates
please call **212-496-2448**.

TAX EXEMPTION STATUS

Purchasers whose organizations are tax-exempt must include the tax-exemption
number below or enclose a copy of the tax-exemption certificate.

#_____

FEDERAL TAX ID NUMBER

Uniworld Business Publications, Inc. **Federal Tax ID# is 13-2897346**

*STANDING ORDERS

All publications in this brochure are available on a continuation basis
ensuring immediate receipt upon publication of the new editions.
Mark "Y" in Standing Order column above.

SATISFACTION GUARANTEED

Hardbound directories may be returned in salable condition within 10 days
for a refund of the purchase price, excluding shipping and handling.
CDRoms and soft bound Regional and Country Editions are "Final Sale."

Office Use Only
Received_____Amount $_____

Check #_____Order #_____